RHS Plant Finder 2015

Devised by Chris Philip
and Realised by Tony Lord

Editor-in-Chief
Janet Cubey

RHS Editors
James Armitage Dawn Edwards
Kálmán Könyves Neil Lancaster

Compiler
Judith Merrick

Royal Horticultural Society

Royal Horticultural Society

Published and compiled by
The Royal Horticultural Society
80 Vincent Square
London SW1P 2PE

Reg charity no: 222879/SC038262

First edition 1987
Twenty-ninth edition 2015

British Library Cataloguing Publication Data
A catalogue record for this book is available from the British Library

ISBN 978-1-907057-57-1

Publisher – Rae Spencer-Jones

RHS Editor – Simon Maughan

Designer – Peter Cooling

Illustrations – Sarah Young

Maps – Alan Cooper

Printed and bound by CPI Group (UK) Ltd, Croydon, CR0 4YY

The compiler and the editors of the *RHS Plant Finder* have taken every care, in the time available, to check all the information supplied to them by the nurseries concerned. Nevertheless, in a work of this kind, containing as it does hundreds of thousands of separate computer encodings, errors and omissions will inevitably occur. The RHS, the Publisher and the Editors cannot accept responsibility for any consequences that may arise from such errors.

If you find any mistakes we hope that you will let us know so that the matter can be corrected in the next edition.

Front cover photograph: *Scilla peruviana* (RHS/Neil Hepworth)
Back cover: Nursery image (RHS/Tim Sandall)
Plant portraits from left to right: *Lobelia* × *speciosa* 'Vedrariensis' (RHS/Carol Sheppard)
Crocus tommasinianus 'Whitewell Purple' (RHS/Wendy Wesley)
Clematis 'Venosa Violacea' AGM (RHS/Barry Phillips)
Iris ensata 'Katy Mendez' AGM (RHS/Carol Sheppard)

The Royal Horticultural Society is the UK's leading gardening charity dedicated to advancing horticulture and promoting good gardening. Its charitable work includes providing expert advice and information, training the next generation of gardeners, creating hands-on opportunities for children to grow plants and conducting research into plants, pests and environmental issues affecting gardeners.

For more information visit www.rhs.org.uk or call 0845 130 4646

Contents

Introduction

The *RHS Plant Finder* exists to put enthusiastic gardeners in touch with suppliers of plants. It is comprehensively updated every year.

The book is divided into two related sections, **Plants** and **Nurseries.**

Plants includes an A–Z Directory of around 70,000 plant names, against which are listed a series of nursery codes. These codes point the reader to the full nursery details contained in the **Nurseries** section towards the back of the book.

It is important to remember when ordering plants that many of the nurseries listed in the book are small, family-run businesses that propagate their own material. They cannot, therefore, guarantee to hold large stocks of the plants they list. Some will, however, propagate to order.

Nurseries appearing in the *RHS Plant Finder* for the first time or re-entering after an absence are printed in bold type in the **Nursery Index by Name** (pp.927-932).

New in this edition

The 2015 edition reflects the decisions made by the RHS Nomenclature and Taxonomy Advisory Group (NATAG) during 2014. The **Nomenclatural Notes** section (p.24) gives a brief overview of these changes made since the compilation of the previous edition of the book.

This year's essay on *Plant Health in the Garden* is by Dr Gerard Clover, RHS Head of Plant Health (pp.8-10).

Lists of Nurseries for Plants with more than 30 Suppliers

To prevent the book from becoming too big, we do not print nursery codes where more than 30 nurseries offer the same plant. The plant is then listed as being "widely available". See **How to Use the Plant Directory** (p.18).

A full list of all the nurseries held on file as current suppliers can be found by searching the RHS website Find-a-Plant facility or can be made available in printed form by post from the Compiler at the address below. For the latter, please ensure you include the full name of the plant (as given in the *RHS Plant Finder*) and enclose a stamped addressed envelope.

Plants Last Listed in Earlier Editions

Plants cease to be listed for a variety of reasons. For more information, turn to **How to Use the Plant Directory** (p.18). A listing of more than 60,000 plants listed in earlier editions but for which we have no current suppliers will be made available on the RHS website.

RHS Online

The plant data from the *RHS Plant Finder* is available on the Royal Horticultural Society's website at www.rhs.org.uk/plants under the Find-a-Plant section.

Application for Entry

If you would like your nursery to be considered for inclusion in the next edition of the *RHS Plant Finder*, please contact the Compiler. Entries to the book are free.

Contact details

The Compiler, RHS Plant Finder
RHS Garden Wisley
Woking
Surrey
GU23 6QB
Ⓣ (01483) 224234
Ⓔ plantfinder@rhs.org.uk

ACKNOWLEDGEMENTS

This edition was compiled by Judith Merrick, assisted by June Skinner, Vicky Turner, and Deborah Chubb. Richard Sanford managed the editing of the plant names in the database and Rupert Wilson administered the RHS Horticultural Database using the BG-BaseTM Collection Management Software.

RHS botanists James Armitage, Dawn Edwards, Kálmán Könyves and Neil Lancaster undertook the task of editing the new plant names for this edition of the book.

We also acknowledge the contribution of Sharon McDonald, Melanie Underwood and Gill Skilton (RHS Science), Louise Bowering, Diana Levy, Simon Maughan, Rae Spencer-Jones and Mark Timothy (RHS Media).

As ever, we are grateful to Kerry Walter of BG-Base (UK) Ltd., Max Phillips of Strange Software Ltd. and Alan Cooper, without whose professional assistance we would be unable to produce the book. Finally, we are indebted to Peter Cooling for his consummate skill in turning our mass of raw data into a publishable form.

Our colleagues on the RHS Nomenclature and Taxonomy Advisory Group, along with the RHS International Cultivar Registrars, have all provided valuable guidance and information. Many nurseries have supplied useful details on new plants and have suggested corrections to existing entries. Some of these remain to be checked and will be entered in the next edition, although those that contravene the Codes of Nomenclature may have to be rejected. We appreciate your patience while these checks are made. We are also grateful to our regular correspondents and to all those readers who have made helpful comments.

Clematis	D.R. Donald, Int. Cultivar Registrar, RHS
Chrysanthemum	J. Barker
Conifers	S. McDonald, Int. Cultivar Registrar, RHS
Dahlia	R. Hedge, Hon. Asst. Cultivar Registrar, RHS S. McDonald, Int. Cultivar Registrar, RHS
Dianthus	Dr A.C. Leslie, Int. Cultivar Registrar, RHS
Delphinium	M.R. Underwood, Int. Cultivar Registrar, RHS
Heathers	Dr E.C. Nelson, Int. Cultivar Registrar
Ilex	S. Andrews
Lilium	D.R. Donald, Int. Cultivar Registrar, RHS
Narcissus	M.R. Underwood, Int. Cultivar Registrar, RHS
Nerine	Dr J.C. David
Orchids	J.M.H. Shaw, Int. Cultivar Registrar, RHS
Rhododendron	Dr A.C. Leslie, Int. Cultivar Registrar, RHS
Sorbus	Dr H. McAllister
Thymus	M. Easter, Int. Cultivar Registrar

Janet Cubey
RHS Editor in Chief
February 2015

Conservation and the Environment

Invasive Plants
As the *RHS Plant Finder* demonstrates, gardens in Britain have been greatly enriched by the diversity of plants introduced to cultivation from abroad. While the vast majority of those introduced have enhanced our gardens, a few have proved to be highly invasive and to threaten native habitats. Once such plants are established it is very difficult, costly and potentially damaging to native ecosystems to eradicate or control the invasive "alien" species. Gardeners can help by choosing not to buy or distribute non-native invasive plants and by taking steps to prevent them escaping into the wild and by disposing of them in a responsible way.

Ten of the most serious invasive non-native species are no longer listed in the *RHS Plant Finder*. Any cultivars or varieties of them that are listed are believed to be less invasive than the species themselves. These 10 plants are:

Azolla filiculoides – fairy fern
Crassula helmsii – New Zealand pygmy weed
Elodea nuttalli – Nuttall's waterweed
Fallopia japonica – Japanese knotweed
Heracleum mantegazzianum – giant hogweed
Hydrocotyle ranunculoides – floating pennywort
Impatiens glandulifera – Himalayan balsam
Lagarosiphon major – curly waterweed
Ludwigia grandiflora – water primrose
Myriophyllum aquaticum – parrot's feather

From April 2014 the five aquatic species indicated by * above will be banned from sale. After that point anyone trading in these species will be liable to up to a £5000 fine or a six months prison sentence.

Further species are considered to present a threat to UK habitats and gardeners are encouraged to grow alternative plants. Guidance on this can be found in three booklets:

Gardening without harmful invasive plants
Landscaping without harmful invasive plants
Keeping ponds and aquaria without harmful invasive plants

These are available on the Plantlife website www.plantlife.org.uk. For further information on non-native invasive species:
Ⓦ www.nonnativespecies.org
Ⓦ www.rhs.org.uk/advicesearch/Profile.aspx?pid=530.

Bringing plants back from abroad
Travelling can be a great source of inspiration for gardeners and often provides an opportunity to encounter new and interesting plants. Anyone wishing to bring plants back into Britain from overseas must realise, however, that this is a complex matter. Various regulations are in force that apply to amateur gardeners as well as to commercial nurseries. The penalties for breaking these can be serious.

Some of the most important regulatory instruments are listed below.

Plant Health regulations are in place to control the spread of pests and diseases. Plants are divided into the categories of prohibited, controlled and unrestricted, but there are also limits that vary according to the part of the world you are travelling from.
Ⓦ https://www.gov.uk/bringing-food-animals-plants-into-uk/plants

The Convention on International Trade in Endangered Species (CITES) affects the transport of animal and plant material across international boundaries. Its aim is to prevent exploitative trade and thereby to prevent harm and the ultimate extinction of wild populations. A tighter regime on trade in species of wild fauna and flora exists in the EU that requires export permits for any plants listed in Appendices A, B & C and import permits for Appendices A & B. There is a further Appendix D for non-CITES listed species that the EU consider to be endangered. A broad range of plants is covered in these Appendices, including *Cactaceae* and *Orchidaceae* and, although species are mentioned in the convention title, the restrictions cover all cultivars and hybrids of listed species too, except for specific exclusions, where there are annotations in the Appendices.
Ⓦ https://www.gov.uk/cites-imports-and-exports#cites-species

The Convention on Biological Diversity (CBD or the "Rio Convention") recognises the sovereign rights of individual countries in relation to their own biodiversity. One provision of the CBD is to enable access to that biodiversity, but equally to ensure the sharing of any benefit derived from it. Subject to national legislation it is possible to collect plant material from other countries that have asserted their rights under the CBD, by ensuring that you have obtained documentary evidence of prior informed consent on the basis of mutually agreed terms for any uses that the material will be put to in the future. Since the legal requirements for collecting plant material varies from country to country and it is advisable to contact the National Focal Point for further information.
Ⓦ www.cbd.int.

The **Nagoya Protocol**, is a supplementary agreement of the CBD which entered into force late last year, and provides a framework for Access and Benefit Sharing. In the UK this is implemented by

the European Union Regulation which is effective from 12 October 2014, and requires anyone utilising genetic resources from another country which is a signatory of the Nagoya Protocol, collected after 12 October 2014, to carry out due diligence to ensure that the material was collected in accordance with the Protocol and the CBD. While the most likely examples of utilisation are the development of new products or medicines from plants, breeding programmes to raise new plants for horticulture would also be covered. While the burden to prove legitimate use of the genetic resource lies with the person or organisation utilising the genetic resource, anyone providing the source of the genetic resource (such as wild collected plants) will need to be able to provide the relevant paperwork, such as a Material Transfer Agreement and Prior Informed Consent.
Ⓦ https://www.cbd.int/abs/about/

European Habitats Directive. The full implementation of this Directive into UK law in 2007 extended protection to all of the European Protected Species (EPS) listed in the Appendices of that Directive (these are Appendices II(b) and IV(b) for plants) whether they are native to the UK or not. This requires a licence for material of any of these species collected in the wild after 1994. These are issued by Natural England (for England), the Countryside Council for Wales (in Wales) and Scottish Natural Heritage (for Scotland).
Ⓦ www.jncc.gov.uk/page-1374.defra.

The UK authorities issue licences for UK plants. For other EU states a collector would need to contact the relevant national authorities.

Contact addresses:

Plantlife
14 Rollestone Street
Salisbury
Wiltshire
SP1 1DX
Ⓣ (01722) 342730

Animal and Plant Health Agency (APHA)
Centre for International Trade – Bristol
1/17 Temple Quay House
2 The Square
Temple Quay
Bristol
BS1 6EB
Ⓣ 0117 372 3700
Ⓕ 0117 372 8206
Ⓔ wildlife.licensing@apha.gsi.gov.uk

Plant Health is now covered by the Plant Health and Seeds Inspectorate (PHSI) which is part of the Animal and Plant Health Agency.
Ⓦ https://www.gov.uk/plant-health-controls

Natural England Wildlife Management and Licensing
Wildlife Licensing
Natural England
First Floor
Temple Quay House
2 The Square
Bristol
BS1 6EB
For general queries and wildlife management licensing contact:
Ⓔ wildlife@naturalengland.org.uk
Ⓣ 0845 601 4523

Department for Environment, Food & Rural Affairs (Defra)
Nobel House
17 Smith Square
London
SW1P 3JR
For general biodiversity queries:
Ⓔ biodiversity@defra.gsi.gov.uk

Non-Native Species Secretariat
Animal and Plant Health Agency
Sand Hutton
York
YO41 1LZ
Ⓦ www.nonnativespecies.org

PLANT HEALTH IN THE GARDEN

The fact that gardeners value plants that have been introduced from abroad is reflected in the diversity of garden plants grown in the British Isles, approximately 14,000 species (at least 70,000 taxa) compared with around 1,400 native vascular species and a similar number of naturalised species. Many of these introduced plants are of course desirable additions to our garden flora and *RHS Plant Finder* provides a valuable resource to identify suppliers of new and unusual plants. However, some plants have proved to be less welcome guests. Familiar examples are Japanese knotweed and Himalayan balsam, both of which were introduced as ornamental plants but have become serious weeds in the British countryside.

As with native plants, garden plants are not only subject to competition from weeds for water, light and nutrients, they must also contend with the depredations of pests and diseases. These include invertebrates (for example aphids, mites, beetles, slugs and snails), mammals such as mice and squirrels, and diseases caused by bacteria, fungi and viruses. Many of these pests and diseases are only too familiar and may be commonly found in the garden, for example chafer grubs, vine weevils, powdery mildew and rose black spot. In recent years, however, there has been an increase in the number of new pests and diseases arriving from abroad (Figure 1).

New pests and diseases
Such pests and diseases may cause economic, environmental or sociocultural damage to natural habitats, crops or gardens. Trees have been particularly badly affected by new pests and diseases; one of the best-publicised examples being ash dieback. This disease was first detected in the UK in 2012 when it was found in a Buckinghamshire nursery on ash trees imported from the Netherlands. Later that year it was found in woodland in East Anglia and has since been confirmed on more than 900 sites in England, Scotland and Wales. The disease causes bark lesions, leaf loss and dieback and is usually fatal. Ash is the third most prevalent broad-leaved species in the UK and comprises around 5% of our woodlands. It is likely that most trees will succumb to the disease over time, with consequent impacts on the estimated 950 species which use the tree as a food source or habitat. Another new threat, oak processionary moth, was originally identified in the UK in 2006 in south-west London. The caterpillars can defoliate mature oaks and are covered with hairs containing an irritating substance which can cause skin rashes and eye and throat irritation in people and animals. The moth is thought to have been introduced on large specimen oaks imported from the continent. Such specimen trees provide an instant impact but have inherent risks since they are very difficult to inspect, meaning pest infestation may go undetected. A new pest facing UK gardeners is fuchsia gall mite, which infests the shoot tips, causing the foliage to become increasingly distorted until the plants no longer produce normal

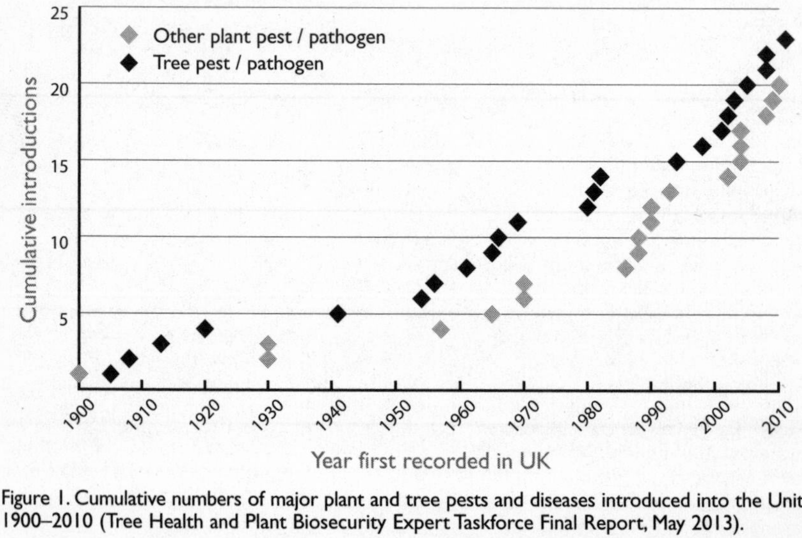

Figure 1. Cumulative numbers of major plant and tree pests and diseases introduced into the United Kingdom 1900–2010 (Tree Health and Plant Biosecurity Expert Taskforce Final Report, May 2013).

leaves or flowers. The RHS first identified the gall mite in Britain in 2007 when infected material from a private garden in Hampshire was submitted to RHS Gardening Advice. The mite was probably introduced either via the nursery trade on imported pot plants or on cuttings imported privately.

This increase in threats from new pests and diseases is primarily due to the rise in the volume and diversity of plants and plant products imported into the UK from an increasingly diverse range of sources. For example, the value of imported plants increased by 83% (in real terms) from 1996 to £287 million in 2011. The reasons for this rise in imports are complex and include globalisation in trade and travel, growing affluence and reduced trade barriers. Despite the best efforts of those involved, imported plants and plant products may inadvertently harbour new pests and diseases. Predicted climate change, such as warmer winters and changes in rainfall and storm patterns, and subsequent phenological changes may also increase the risk of pest establishment, transmission and impact.

Prevention and control

Despite the increasing threat from pests and diseases, the availability of pesticides has decreased as products are reviewed and those no longer deemed effective or safe are withdrawn from the market. For example, the use of some neonicotinoid insecticides has been restricted in Europe. There are of course other ways that home gardeners can manage pests and diseases, including cultural practices and physical and biological controls.

As with human ailments, prevention is better than cure, and the most important way to reduce pest and disease threats is therefore to take measures to prevent their entry or establishment. Once pests and diseases become established they may be impossible to eradicate, and control is costly both economically and environmentally. Preventing the entry and establishment of pests and diseases is the role of government, industry, farmers, landowners and the public, especially gardeners.

International and national legislation has been developed to prevent the movement of harmful plant pests and diseases. This legislation is generally implemented by governments who may certify that imported plants and plant products are pest- and disease-free and undertake surveillance to assess plant health. Should a new pest or disease be found, an assessment of its risk is completed and an eradication campaign may be attempted, provided that the pest or disease is not well established

The horticultural industry clearly has a key role in ensuring that gardeners are supplied with healthy planting material, free from pests and diseases. In some instances there is specific legislation restricting plant movement which aims to reduce the spread of pests and diseases. For example, some rosaceous plants such as apple, cotoneaster and pear moved within the European Union must be accompanied by a "plant passport", stating that the material has been produced in a place free from fireblight. Certification schemes have also been developed for propagation material of various crops such as seed potatoes. In these schemes the parent material is inspected during the growing season and specified levels for certain pests and diseases must not be exceeded. The resulting progeny may be sold to commercial growers as well as private gardeners. There are also certification schemes for producers of ornamental plants and the UK government has produced best practice protocols for the industry to help prevent pest and disease outbreaks.

The role of gardeners

There is increasing recognition that the public, and in particular gardeners, have an important part to play in preventing new pests and diseases from entering or establishing in the UK. Gardeners should consider purchasing plants that are grown in the UK. Although many garden plants have their origins overseas, they are often available from UK nurseries and *RHS Plant Finder* provides a comprehensive listing of these. Gardeners should also consider checking that their supplier has effective quarantine measures to ensure imported plants are healthy. For example, some nurseries grow imported trees for at least one year in their UK nursery before selling them in the retail market. Purchasing large semi-mature specimen trees directly from abroad without quarantining should be avoided because of the associated risk of introducing pests and diseases. Gardeners should also avoid privately importing plants, cuttings or seeds. The health of new plants should be monitored once planted in the garden. If new or unusual symptoms are observed members are encouraged to contact RHS Gardening Advice to assist with identification. It is also wise to follow basic hygiene measures, such as keeping garden equipment and footwear clean, and disposing of garden waste by composting or via local council green waste collection.

The RHS has made a long-term commitment to addressing threats to plant health in gardens and the wider environment, and "Plant Health in Gardens" is one of four themes in the charity's science strategy. As part of this theme the RHS will undertake research on prevention, surveillance, detection and identification, and control and management of pests and diseases in gardens and the wider environment, for the benefit of members, industry, policy-makers and society at large.

Gerard Clover
Head of Plant Health

Extended Glossary

This glossary combines some of the helpful introductory sections from older editions in an alphabetical listing. A fuller, more discursive account of plant names, *Guide to Plant Names*, and a detailed guide to the typography of plant names, *Recommended Style for Printing Plant Names*, are both available as leaflets. To request a copy of either please send an A4 sae to The Compiler at the contact address given on page 4.

Advisory Committee on Nomenclature and Taxonomy

See **Nomenclature and Taxonomy Advisory Group**

Authorities

In order that plant names can be used with precision throughout the scientific world, the name of the person who coined the name of a plant species (its author, or authority) is added to the plant name. Usually this information is of little consequence to gardeners, except in cases where the same name has been given to two different plants or a name is commonly misapplied. Although only one usage is correct, both may be encountered in books, so indicating the author is the only way to be certain about which plant is being referred to. This can happen equally with cultivars. Authors' names, where it is appropriate to cite them, appear in a smaller typeface after the species or cultivar name to which they refer and are abbreviated following Brummitt and Powell's *Authors of Plant Names*.

🏆 Award Of Garden Merit

The Award of Garden Merit (AGM) is intended as a practical guide for the gardener and is therefore awarded only after a period of assessment by the RHS Standing and Joint Committees. The AGM is awarded only to plants that are:

- excellent for ordinary use in appropriate conditions
- available
- of good constitution
- essentially stable in form and colour
- reasonably resistant to pests and diseases

The AGM symbol is cited in conjunction with the **hardiness** rating. A full list of AGM plants may be found on the RHS website at www.rhs.org.uk/agmplants.

The AGM list was originally reviewed every ten years, to ensure that every plant still merited the award. The last review took place in 2012; since 2013, the list has been subject to a "rolling review", and AGMs may now be rescinded at any time.

Botanical Names

The aim of the botanical naming system is to provide each different plant with a single, unique, universal name. The basic unit of plant classification is the species. Species that share a number of significant characteristics are grouped together to form a genus (plural **genera**). The name of a species is made up of two elements; the name of the genus followed by the specific epithet, for example, *Narcissus romieuxii.*

Variation within a species can be recognised by division into subspecies (usually abbreviated to subsp.), varietas (or variety abbreviated to var.) and forma (or form abbreviated to f.). Whilst it is unusual for a plant to have all of these, it is possible, as in this example, *Narcissus romieuxii* subsp. *albidus* var. *zaianicus* f. *lutescens.*

The botanical elements are always given in italics, with only the genus taking an initial capital letter. The rank indications are never in italics. In instances where the rank is not known it is necessary to form an invalid construction by quoting a second epithet without a rank. This is an unsatisfactory situation, but requires considerable research to resolve.

In some genera, such as *Hosta*, we list the cultivar names alphabetically with the species or **hybrid** to which they are attributed afterwards in parentheses. For example, *Hosta* 'Reversed' (*sieboldiana*). In other situations where the aim is not to create a list alphabetically by cultivar name we would recommend styling this as *Hosta sieboldiana* 'Reversed'.

Classification of Genera

Genera that include a large number of species or with many cultivars are often subdivided into informal horticultural classifications or more formal Cultivar Groups, each based on a particular characteristic or combination of characteristics. Colour of flower or fruit and shape of flower are common examples and, with fruit, whether a cultivar is grown for culinary or dessert purposes. How such groups are named differs from genus to genus.

To help users of the *RHS Plant Finder* find the plants they want, the classifications used within cultivated genera are listed using codes and plants are marked with the appropriate code in brackets after its name in the Plant Directory. To find the explanation of each code, simply look it up under the genus concerned in the **Classification of Genera** starting on p.25. The codes relating to edible fruits are also listed here, but these apply across several genera.

COLLECTORS' REFERENCES

Abbreviations (usually with numbers) following a plant name refer to the collector(s) of the plant. These abbreviations are expanded, with a collector's name or expedition title, in the section **Collectors' References** starting on p.20.

A collector's reference may indicate a new, as yet unnamed range of variation within a species. The inclusion of collectors' references in the *RHS Plant Finder* supports the book's role in sourcing unusual plants.

The Convention on Biological Diversity calls for conservation of biodiversity, its sustainable use and the fair and equitable sharing of any derived benefits. Since its adoption in 1993, collectors are required to have prior informed consent from the country of origin for the acquisition and commercialisation of collected material.

COMMON NAMES

In a work such as this, it is necessary to refer to plants by their botanical names for the sake of universal comprehension and clarity. However, at the same time we recognise that with fruit and vegetables most people are more familiar with their common names than their botanical ones. Cross-references are therefore given from common to botanical names for fruit, vegetables and the commoner culinary herbs throughout the Plant Directory.

CULTIVAR

Literally meaning cultivated variety, cultivar names are given to denote variation within species and that generated by hybridisation, in cultivation. To make them easily distinguishable from botanical names, they are not printed in italics and are enclosed in single quotation marks. Cultivar names coined since 1959 should follow the rules of the International Code of Nomenclature for Cultivated Plants (**ICNCP**).

DESCRIPTIVE TERMS

Terms that appear after the main part of the plant name are shown in a smaller font to distinguish them. These descriptive elements give extra information about the plant and may include the **collector's reference**, **authority**, or what colour it is. For example, *Clematis henryi* B&SWJ 3402, *Penstemon* 'Sour Grapes' M. Fish, *Akebia quinata* cream-flowered.

FAMILIES

Genera are grouped into larger groups of related plants called families. Most family names, with the exception of eight familiar names, end with the same group of letters, *-aceae*. While it is still acceptable to use these eight exceptions, the modern trend adopted in the *RHS Plant Finder* is to use alternative names with *–aceae* endings. The families concerned are *Compositae* (*Asteraceae*), *Cruciferae* (*Brassicaceae*), *Gramineae* (*Poaceae*), *Guttiferae* (*Clusiaceae*), *Labiatae* (*Lamiaceae*), *Leguminosae* (split here into *Caesalpiniaceae*, *Mimosaceae* and *Papilionaceae*), *Palmae* (*Arecaceae*) and *Umbelliferae* (*Apiaceae*).

Apart from these exceptions we now follow (from 2010) *Mabberley's Plant Book* (3rd edition).

GENUS (plural – GENERA)

Genera used in the *RHS Plant Finder* were originally based on Brummitt's *Vascular Plant Families and Genera* but are now based on a range of sources. For spellings and genders of generic names, Greuter's *Names in Current Use for Extant Plant Genera* has also been consulted. See **Botanical Names**.

GREX

Within orchids, hybrids of the same parentage, regardless of how alike they are, are given a grex name. Individuals can be selected, given cultivar names and propagated vegetatively. For example, *Pleione* Versailles gx 'Bucklebury', where Versailles is the grex name and 'Bucklebury' is a selected **cultivar**.

GROUP

This is a collective name for a group of cultivars within a genus with similar characteristics. The word Group is always included and, where cited with a cultivar name, it is enclosed in brackets, for example, *Actaea simplex* (Atropurpurea Group) 'Brunette', where 'Brunette' is a distinct cultivar in a group of purple-leaved cultivars.

Another example of a Group is *Rhododendron polycladum* Scintillans Group. In this case *Rhododendron scintillans* was a species that is now botanically 'sunk' within *R. polycladum*, but it is still recognised horticulturally as a Group.

Group names are also used for swarms of hybrids with the same parentage, for example, *Rhododendron* Polar Bear Group. These were formerly treated as

grex names, a term now used only for orchids. A single clone from the Group may be given the same cultivar name, for example, *Rhododendron* 'Polar Bear'.

Hardiness

Hardiness ratings are shown for **Award of Garden Merit** plants. To assist gardeners to determine more clearly which plants are hardy in their local area, the RHS introduced a new, enhanced, hardiness rating scheme in 2013, to coincide with the publication of the new **Award of Garden Merit** plant list. The categories now used are as follows:
Temperature ranges given are intended to be absolute minimum winter temperatures (°C).
H1a = Heated greenhouse – tropical >15
H1b = Heated greenhouse – subtropical 10 to 15
H1c = Heated greenhouse – warm temperate 5 to 10
H2 = Tender – cool or frost-free greenhouse 1 to 5
H3 = Half-hardy – unheated greenhouse/mild winter -5 to 1
H4 = Hardy – average winter -10 to -5
H5 = Hardy – cold winter -15 to -10
H6 = Hardy – very cold winter -20 to -15
H7 = Very hardy <-20

Further definition of these categories can be found on the RHS website, in the Feb 2013 edition of *The Garden* and in the *RHS Plant Finder 2013* essay.

Hybrids

Some species, when grown together, in the wild or in cultivation, are found to interbreed and form hybrids. In some instances a hybrid name is coined, for example hybrids between *Primula hirsuta* and *P. minima* are given the name *Primula* × *forsteri*, the multiplication sign indicating hybrid origin. Hybrid formulae that quote the parentage of the hybrid are used where a unique name has not been coined, for example *Rhododendron calophytum* × *R. praevernum*. In hybrid formulae you will find parents in alphabetical order, with the male (m) and female (f) parent indicated where known. Hybrids between different genera are also possible, for example × *Mahoberberis* is the name given to hybrids between *Mahonia* and *Berberis*.

There are also a few special-case hybrids called graft hybrids, where the tissues of two plants are physically rather than genetically mixed. These are indicated by an addition rather than a multiplication sign, so *Laburnum* + *Cytisus* becomes + *Laburnocytisus*.

ICNCP

The ICNCP is the International Code of Nomenclature for Cultivated Plants. First published in 1959, the 8th edition was published in 2009 and the 9th edition is due for publication during 2015.

Cultivar names that do not conform to this Code, and for which there is no valid alternative, are flagged I (for invalid). This code states that the minimum requirement is for a cultivar name to be given in conjunction with the name of the genus. However, in the *RHS Plant Finder* we choose to give as full a name as possible to give the gardener and botanist more information about the plant, following the Recommendation in the Code.

Nomenclature and Taxonomy Advisory Group

This Group advises the RHS on individual problems of nomenclature regarding plants in cultivation and, in particular, use of names in the *RHS Horticultural Database*, reflected in the annual publication of the *RHS Plant Finder*.

The aim is always to make the plant names in the *RHS Plant Finder* as consistent, reliable and stable as possible and acceptable to gardeners and botanists alike, not only in the British Isles but around the world. Recent proposals to change or correct names are examined with the aim of creating a balance between the stability of well-known names and botanical and taxonomic correctness. In some cases the conflicting views on the names of some groups of plants will not easily be resolved. The Group's policy is then to wait and review the situation once a more obvious consensus is reached, rather than rush to rename plants only to have to change them again when opinions have shifted.

In 2015 the Group is chaired by Dr John Grimshaw and includes: Dr Crinan Alexander, Susyn Andrews, Chris Brickell, Dr James Compton, Dr Janet Cubey, Mike Grant, Dr Stephen Jury, Dr Alan Leslie, Dr Tony Lord, Chris Sanders, with Prof David Mabberley, Dr Charles Nelson and Julian Sutton (corresponding members), James Armitage and Dr John David (attending RHS staff) and Julian Shaw as Secretary.

Notes on Nomenclature and Identification

The **Notes on Nomenclature and Identification**, p.24, give further information for names that are complex or may be confusing. See also **Nomenclature and Taxonomy Advisory Group**.

Plant Breeders' Rights

Plants covered by an *active* grant of Plant Breeders' Rights (PBR) are indicated throughout the Plant Directory. Grants indicated are those awarded by both UK and EU Plant Variety Rights offices. Because grants can both come into force and lapse at any time, this book can only aim to represent the situation at one point in time, but it is hoped that this will act as a useful guide to growers and gardeners. UK and EU grants represent the published position as of the end of December 2014. We do not give any indication where PBR grants may be pending.

To obtain PBR protection, a new plant must be registered and pass tests for distinctness, uniformity and stability under an approved name. This approved name, under the rules of the **ICNCP**, established by a legal process, has to be regarded as the cultivar name. Increasingly however, these approved names are a code or "nonsense" name and are therefore often unpronounceable and meaningless, so the plants are given other names designed to attract sales when they are released. These secondary names are often referred to as selling names but are officially termed **trade designations**.

For further information on UK PBR contact:
Plant Variety Rights Office,
Animal and Plant Health Agency,
Eastbrook,
Shaftesbury Road,
Cambridge CB2 8DR
Ⓣ **(0300) 060 0740**
Ⓦ **www.gov.uk/plant-breeders-rights**

For details of plants covered by EU Community Rights contact:
Community Plant Variety Office (CPVO),
3 Boulevard Maréchal Foch, BP 10121,
FR-49101 Angers Cedex 02, France
Ⓣ **00 33 (02) 41 25 64 00**
Ⓕ **00 33 (02) 41 25 64 10**
Ⓦ **www.cpvo.europa.eu**

The *RHS Plant Finder* takes no responsibility for ensuring that nurseries selling plants with PBR are licensed to do so.

Reverse Synonyms

It is likely that users of this book will come across names in certain genera that they did not expect to find. This may be because species have been transferred from another genus (or **genera**).

Selling Names

See **Trade Designations**

Series

With seed-raised plants and some popular vegetatively-propagated plants, especially bedding plants and pot plants such as *Petunia* or *Verbena*, Series have become increasingly popular. A Series contains a number of similar cultivars, but differs from a **Group** in that it is a marketing device, with cultivars added to create a range of flower colours in plants of similar habit. Individual colour elements within a Series may be represented by slightly different cultivars over the years.

The word Series is always included and, where cited with a cultivar name it is enclosed in brackets, for example *Aquilegia* 'Robin' (Songbird Series). The Series name usually follows the rest of the plant name, but sometimes in this book we list it before the cultivar name in order to group members of a Series together when they occur next to one another on the page.

Species

See under **Botanical Names**

Subspecies

See under **Botanical Names**

Synonyms

Although the ideal is for each species or cultivar to have only one name, anyone dealing with plants soon comes across a situation where one plant has received two or more names, or two plants have received the same name. In each case, only one name and application, for reasons of precision and stability, can be regarded as correct. Additional names are known as synonyms. Further information on synonyms and why plants change names is available in *Guide to Plant Names*. See the introduction to this glossary for details of how to request a copy.

See also **Reverse Synonyms**.

Trade Designations

A **trade designation** is the name used to market a plant when the cultivar name is considered unsuitable for selling purposes. It is styled in a different typeface and without single quotation marks.

In the case of **Plant Breeders' Rights** it is a legal requirement for the cultivar name to appear with the trade designation on a label at the point of sale. Most plants are sold under only one trade designation, but some, especially roses, are sold under a number of names, particularly when cultivars are introduced from other countries. Usually, the correct cultivar name is the only way to ensure that the same plant is not bought unwittingly under two or more different trade designations. The *RHS Plant Finder* follows the recommendations of the **ICNCP** when dealing with trade designations and PBR. These are always to quote the cultivar name and trade designation together and to style the trade designation in a different typeface, without single quotation marks, for example *Choisya* × *dewitteana* Goldfingers = 'Limo'PBR. Here Goldfingers is the trade designation and 'Limo' is the cultivar name that has been granted **Plant Breeders' Rights**. This may also be styled in other ways, such as *Choisya* × *dewitteana* GOLDFINGERS ('Limo')PBR.

TRANSLATIONS

When a cultivar name is translated from the language of first publication, the translation is regarded as a **trade designation** and styled accordingly. We endeavour to recognise the original cultivar name in every case and to give an English translation where it is in general use.

VARIEGATED PLANTS

Following a suggestion from the Variegated Plant Group of the Hardy Plant Society, a (v) is cited after those plants which are "variegated". The dividing line between variegation and less distinct colour marking is necessarily arbitrary and plants with light veins, pale, silver or dark zones, or leaves flushed in paler colours, are not shown as being variegated unless there is an absolutely sharp distinction between paler and darker zones.

For further details of the Variegated Plant Group, please write to:

Brian Dockerill
19 Westfield Road
Glyncoch
Pontypridd
Mid-Glamorgan
CF37 3AG

VARIETY

See under **Botanical Names** and **Cultivar**

Symbols and Abbreviations

Symbols Appearing to the Left of the Name

*	Name not validated. Not listed in the appropriate International Registration Authority checklist nor in works cited in the Bibliography. For fuller discussion see p.11
I	Invalid name. See *International Code of Botanical Nomenclature 2012* and *International Code of Nomenclature for Cultivated Plants 2009*. For fuller discussion see p.11
§	Plant listed elsewhere in the Plant Directory under a synonym
×	Hybrid genus
+	Graft hybrid genus

Symbols Appearing to the Right of the Name

✿	Plant Heritage National Plant Collection® exists for all or part of this genus. Further details can be found in the *2015 National Plant Collections® Directory* available from: www.plantheritage.com or Plant Heritage, 12 Home Farm, Loseley Park, Guildford, Surrey GU3 1HS
♀H4	The Royal Horticultural Society's Award of Garden Merit, see p.11
(d)	double-flowered
(F)	Fruit
(f)	female
(m)	male
(v)	variegated plant, see p.15
PBR	Plant Breeders Rights see p.13
new	New plant entry in this edition

For abbreviations relating to individual genera see **Classification of Genera** p.25

For **Collectors' References** see p.20

For symbols used in the **Nurseries** section see p.829

Symbols and Abbreviations used as Part of the Name

×	hybrid species
aff.	affinis (akin to)
agg.	aggregate, a single name used to cover a group of very similar plants, regarded by some as separate species
ambig.	ambiguous, a name used by two authors for different plants and where it is unclear which is being offered
cf.	compare to
cl.	clone
f.	forma (botanical form)
gx	grex
sensu lato	in the broadest sense
sp.	species
subsp.	subspecies
subvar.	subvarietas (botanical subvariety)
var.	varietas (botanical variety)

It is not within the remit of this book to check that nurseries are applying the right names to the right plants or to ensure nurseries selling plants with Plant Breeders' Rights are licensed to do so.

Please, never use an out of date edition

PLANTS

WHATEVER PLANT YOU ARE LOOKING FOR, MAYBE AN OLD FAVOURITE OR A MORE UNUSUAL CULTIVAR, SEARCH HERE FOR A LIST OF THE SUPPLIERS THAT ARE CLOSEST TO YOU.

How to Use the Plant Directory

Nursery Codes

Look up the plant you require in the alphabetical Plant Directory. Against each plant you will find one or more four-letter codes, for example WCru, each code represents one nursery offering that plant. The first letter of each code indicates the main area of the country in which the nursery is situated. For this geographical key, refer to the **Nursery Codes and Symbols** on p.828.

Turn to the **Nursery Details by Code** starting on p.832 where, in alphabetical order of codes, you will find details of each nursery which offers the plant in question. If you wish to visit any nursery, you may find its location on one of the maps (following p.933). Please note that not all nurseries choose to be shown on the maps. For a fuller explanation of how to use the nursery listings please turn to p.829. **Always check that the nursery you select has the plant in stock before you set out.**

Plants with more than 30 Suppliers

In some cases, against the plant name you will see the term 'Widely available' instead of a nursery code. If we were to include every plant listed by all nurseries, the *RHS Plant Finder* would become unmanageably bulky. We therefore ask nurseries to restrict their entries to those plants that are not already well represented. As a result, if more than 30 nurseries offer any plant the Directory gives no nursery codes and the plant is listed instead as being 'Widely available'.

You should not have difficulty in locating these in local nurseries or garden centres. If, however, you are unable to find such plants, a list of all the current suppliers we have on file is available by post or online. See the Introduction (p.4).

Finding Fruit, Vegetables and Herbs

You will need to search for these by their botanical names. Common names are cross-referenced to their botanical names in the Plant Directory.

If you have Difficulty Finding your Plant

If you cannot immediately find the plant you seek, look through the various species of the genus. You may be using an incomplete name. The problem is most likely to arise in very large genera such as *Phlox* where there are a number of possible species, each with a large number of cultivars. A search through the whole genus may well bring success. For space reasons, we are not able to list in the Plant Directory annuals, orchids or cacti (except hardy terrestrial orchids and hardy cacti), or non-ornamental vegetables.

Cross-references

It may be that the plant name you seek is a synonym. Our intention is to list nursery codes only against the correct botanical name. Where you find a synonym you will be cross-referred to the correct name.

Plants Last Listed in Earlier Editions

It may be that the plant you are seeking has no known suppliers and is thus not listed.

The loss of a plant name from the Directory may arise for a number of reasons – the supplier may have gone out of business, or may not have responded to our latest questionnaire and has therefore been removed from the book. Such plants may well be available but we have no knowledge of current suppliers. Alternatively, some plants may have been misnamed by nurseries in previous editions, but are now appearing under their correct name.

For further information on plants last listed in earlier editions please see the Introduction (p.4).

Please, never use an out of date edition

USING THE PLANT DIRECTORY

The purpose of the Plant Directory is to help the reader correctly identify the plant they seek and find stockists. Each nursery has a unique code which appears to the right of the plant name. **Nursery Details by Code** (p.832) gives details about each nursery. The first letter in each code denotes its geographical region. Turn to the **Map Index** (p.933) to find the correct code for an area.

The Plant Directory provides information about plants through symbols and notes. For example: if a plant has an alternative name; is new to the book; or has received the RHS Award of Garden Merit.

Abelia ✿ (*Caprifoliaceae*)

	Auderose = 'Minaud'PBR	LAst
	biflora	see *Zabelia biflora*
	chinensis misapplied	see *A.* × *grandiflora* 'Lake Maggiore'
§	***chinensis*** R. Br.	CBcs CExl CMCN CMac ELan EPfP EWTr LRHS MAsh MMuc SEND SHil SKHP SPer SRms WCot WFar WGrn WPat
	- 'China Rose' ♀H5 **new**	LPfy SKHP
§	***dielsii***	CBot
	'Edward Goucher' ♀H5	Widely available
	engleriana	CExl EPfP LHop LRHS MAsh MBlu NLar SEND SLon SSpi
	floribunda ♀H5	CBcs CBot CDul CExl CMac CSam CSde CWib ECre ELan ELon EPfP LHop LRHS MRav NLar SAko SBrt SEND SGbt SGol SKHP SPer SPoG SRms SSpi WPat
	× ***grandiflora*** common clone	see *A.* × *grandiflora* 'Lake Maggiore'
	- 'Aurea'	see *A.* × *grandiflora* 'Gold Spot'
	- 'Brockhill Allgold'	EMil EPfP LRHS
	- 'Compacta'	LRHS WFar
	- Confetti = 'Conti'PBR (v)	CBcs CDoC CLet CMac CSBt ECrN ELan EMil EPfP LAst LRHS LSRN MAsh MBri MGos MRav NLar SCob SGol SLim SPer SPoG SWvt WFar
§	- 'Francis Mason' (v)	Widely available
§	- 'Gold Spot' (v)	CBot EPfP LRHS MGos NLar SPer WPat
	- 'Gold Strike'	see *A.* × *grandiflora* 'Gold Spot'
	- Golden Panache = 'Minpan'	MRav
	- 'Goldsport'	see *A.* × *grandiflora* 'Gold Spot'
	- 'Hopleys'PBR (v) ♀H5	CBcs CDoC CMac CSBt CTri CWib ELan EMil EPfP LHop LRHS MAsh MBri MGos NLar SCob SEND SEle SLon SPoG SRms SWvt WGrn WHar
	- 'Kaleidoscope'PBR (v)	Widely available
	- Lady Liberty = 'Keylib' **new**	MGos
	- 'Lady Summerdream' **new**	EBee
§	- 'Lake Maggiore' ♀H5	Widely available
	- Lucky Lots = 'Wevo2' (v)	EBee LLHF NLar SCob
	- 'Panache' (v)	LLHF WCot
	- 'Prostrate White'	EBee ECrN LRHS NLar
	- 'Semperflorens'	LRHS
	- 'Sherwoodii'	CDoC EBee ECrN EHoe EPfP LRHS MAsh MGos SLim WRHF
	- 'Sunrise' (v)	NLar
	- Sunshine Daydream = 'Abelops'PBR (v)	CTsd LAst LLHF LRHS MPkF NLar SCob

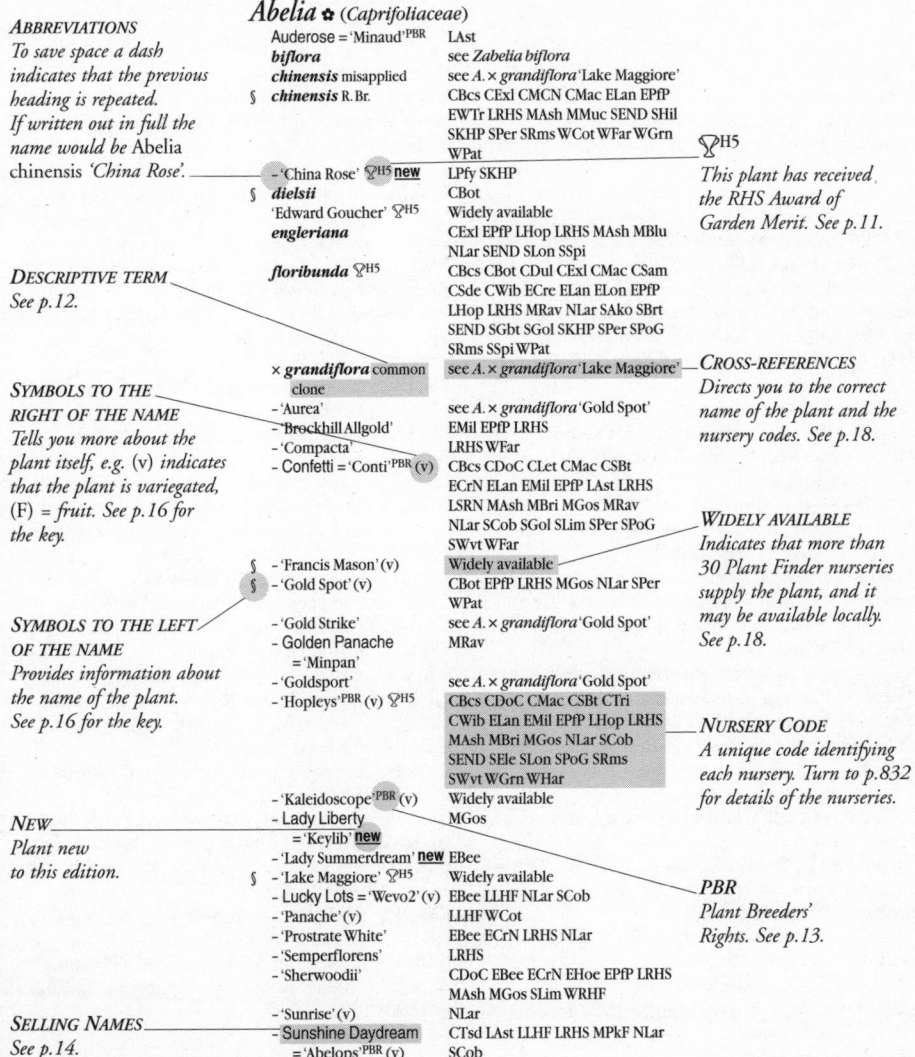

ABBREVIATIONS
To save space a dash indicates that the previous heading is repeated. If written out in full the name would be Abelia chinensis *'China Rose'.*

♀H5
This plant has received the RHS Award of Garden Merit. See p.11.

DESCRIPTIVE TERM
See p.12.

CROSS-REFERENCES
Directs you to the correct name of the plant and the nursery codes. See p.18.

SYMBOLS TO THE RIGHT OF THE NAME
Tells you more about the plant itself, e.g. (v) *indicates that the plant is variegated,* (F) *= fruit. See p.16 for the key.*

WIDELY AVAILABLE
Indicates that more than 30 Plant Finder nurseries supply the plant, and it may be available locally. See p.18.

SYMBOLS TO THE LEFT OF THE NAME
Provides information about the name of the plant. See p.16 for the key.

NURSERY CODE
A unique code identifying each nursery. Turn to p.832 for details of the nurseries.

NEW
Plant new to this edition.

PBR
Plant Breeders' Rights. See p.13.

SELLING NAMES
See p.14.

SUPPLEMENTARY KEYS TO THE DIRECTORY

COLLECTORS' REFERENCES

Abbreviations following a plant name, refer to the collector(s) of the plant. These abbreviations are expanded below, with a collector's name or expedition title. For a fuller explanation, see p.12.

A&JW	Watson, A. & J.
A&L	Ala, A. & Lancaster, Roy
AB&S	Archibald, James; Blanchard, John W. & Salmon, M.
AC	Clark, Alan J.
AC&H	Apold, J.; Cox, Peter & Hutchison, Peter
AC&W	Albury; Cheese, M. & Watson, J.M.
ACE	AGS Expedition to China (1994)
ACL	Leslie, Alan C.
AER	Robinson, Allan
AGS/ES	AGS Expedition to Sikkim (1983)
AGSJ	AGS Expedition to Japan (1988)
AH	Hoog, A.
AIM	Avent, Tony Mexico (1994)
Airth	Airth, Murray
Akagi	Akagi Botanical Garden
AL&JS	Sharman, Joseph L. & Leslie, Alan C.
APA	Cox, K.; Hootman, S.; Hudson, T.; et al, Expedition to Arunchal Pradesh (2005)
ARG	Argent, G.C.G.
ARGS	Alaska Rock Garden Society trip to China
ARJA	Ruksans, J. & Siesums, A.
B	Blanchard, John
B&F MA	Brown, Robert & Fisher, Rif & Middle Atlas (2007)
B L.	Beer, Len
B&L	Brickell, Christopher D. & Leslie, Alan C.
B&M & BM	Brickell, Christopher D. & Mathew, Brian
B&S	Bird P. & Salmon M.
B&SWJ	Wynn-Jones, Bleddyn & Susan
B&V	Burras, K. & Vosa, C.G.
BB	Bartholomew, B.
BBJMT	Boland, Brownless, Jamieson & McNamara
BC	Chudziak, W.
BC&W	Beckett; Cheese, M. & Watson, J.M.
Beavis	Beavis, Derek S.
Berry	Berry, P.
Berry & Brako	Berry, P. & Brako, Lois
BKBlount	Blount, B.K.
BKN	Bis, J., Kupčák, P. & Novak, H.
BL&M	University of Bangor Expedition to NE Nepal
BM	Mathew, Brian F.
BM&W	Binns, David L.; Mason, M. & Wright, A.
BOA	Boardman, P.
Breedlove	Breedlove, D.
BR	Rushbrooke, Ben
BS	Smith, Basil
BSBE	Bowles Scholarship Botanical Expedition (1963)
BSSS	Crûg Expedition, Jordan (1991)
Bu	Bubert, S.
Burtt	Burtt, Brian L.
BWJ	Wynn-Jones, Bleddyn
C	Cole, Desmond T.
C&C	Cox, P.A. & Cox, K.N.E.
C&Cu	Cox, K.N.E. & Cubey, J.
C&H	Cox, Peter & Hutchison, Peter
C&K	Chamberlain & Knott
C&R	Christian & Roderick
C&S	Clark, Alan & Sinclair, Ian W.J.
C&V	K.N.E. Cox & Vergera, S.
C&W	Cheese, M. & Watson, J.M.
CC	Chadwell, Christopher
CC&H	Chamberlain, David F.; Cox, Peter & Hutchison, P.
CC&McK	Chadwell, Christopher & McKelvie, A.
CC&MR	Chadwell, Christopher & Ramsay
CCH&H	Chamberlain, D.F.; Cox, P.; Hutchison, P. & Hootman, S.
CD&R	Compton, J.; D'Arcy, J. & Rix, E.M.
CDB	Brickell, Christopher D.
CDC	Coode, Mark J.E.; Dockrill, Alexander
CDC&C	Compton; D'Arcy; Christopher & Coke
CDPR	Compton; D'Arcy; Pope & Rix
CE&H	Christian, P.J.; Elliott & Hoog
CEE	Chengdu Edinburgh Expedition China (1991)

CGG	Glendoick Gardens Expedition to Guizou (2009)
CGV	Vosa, Canio
CGW	Grey-Wilson, Christopher
CH	Christian, P. & Hoog, A.
CH&M	Cox, P.; Hutchison, P. & Maxwell-MacDonald, D.
CHP&W	Kashmir Botanical Expedition
CL	Lovell, Chris
CLD	Chungtien, Lijiang & Dali Exped. China (1990)
CM&W	Cheese M.; Mitchel J. & Watson, J.
CN&W	Clark; Neilson & Wilson
CNDS	Nelson, C. & Sayers D.
COLA	Costin, J.J. & Lancaster, R., Japan (1990)
Cooper	Cooper, R.E.
Cox	Cox, Peter A.
CPC	Cobblewood Plant Collection
CPN	Compton, James
CS	Stapleton, Christopher
CSE	Cyclamen Society Expedition (1990)
CT	Teune, Carla
CW&T	Clark, A., Wilson, H. & Taggart, J., North Vietnam
CWJ	Colley, Finlay; Wynn-Jones, Bleddyn, Taiwan (2007)
Dahl	Dahl, Sally
DBG	Denver Botanic Garden, Colorado
DC	Cheshire, David
DF	Fox, D.
DG	Green, D.
DHTU	Hinkley, D., Turkey (2000)
DJF	Ferguson, Dave
DJH	Hinkley, Dan
DJHC	Hinkley D., China
DJHS	Hinkley, D., Sichuan
DJHV	Hinkley, D., Vietnam
DM	Millais, David
Doleshy	Doleshy, F.L.
DS&T	Drake, Sharman J. & Thompson
DWD	Rose, D.
DZ	Zummell, D.
ECN	Nelson, E. Charles
EDHCH	Hammond, Eric D.
EGM	Millais, T.
EKB	Balls, Edward K.
EM	East Malling Research Station
EMAK	Edinburgh Makalu Expedition (1991)
EMR	Rix, E.Martyn
EN	Needham, Edward F.
ENF	Fuller, E. Nigel
ETE	Edinburgh Taiwan Expedition (1993)
ETOT	Kirkham, T.S.; Flanagan, Mark
F	Forrest, G.
F&M	Fernandez & Mendoza, Mexico
F&W	Watson, J. & Flores, A.
Farrer	Farrer, Reginald
FK	Kinmonth, Fergus W.
FMB	Bailey, F.M.
G	Gardner, Martin F.
G&K	Gardner, Martin F. & Knees, Sabina G.
G&P	Gardner, Martin F. & Page, Christopher N.
GDJ	Dumont, Gerard
GG	Gusman, G.
GS	Sherriff, George
Green	Green, D.
Guitt	Guittoneau, G.G.
Guiz	Guizhou Expedition (1985)
GWJ	Goddard, Sally; Wynne-Jones, Bleddyn & Susan
G-W&P	Grey-Wilson, Christopher & Phillips
H	Huggins, Paul
H&B	Hilliard, Olive M. & Burtt, Brian L.
H&D	Howick, C. & Darby
H&M	Howick, Charles & McNamara, William A.
H&W	Hedge, Ian C. & Wendelbo, Per W.
Harry Smith	Smith, K.A.Harry
Hartside	Hartside Nursery
HCM	Heronswood Expedition to Chile (1998)
HECC	Hutchison; Evans; Cox, P.; Cox, K.
HEHEHE	Zetterlund, H. et al, Gothenburg Botanic Gardens Expedition to northern China
Hird	Hird
HH&K	Hannay, S & S & Kingsbury, N.
HK	Kuenzler, Horst
HLMS	Springate, L.S.
HM&S	Halliwell, B.; Mason, D. & Smallcombe
HOA	Hoog, Anton
HOLUB	Holubec, V.
HRS	Hers, J.
Hummel	Hummel, D.
HW&E	Wendelbo, Per; Hedge, I. & Ekberg, L.
HWEL	Hirst, J.Michael; Webster, D.
HWJ	Crûg Heronswood Joint Expedition
HWJCM	Crûg Heronswood Expedition
HWJK	Crûg Heronswood Expedition, East Nepal (2002)
HZ	Zetterlund, Henrik
ICE	Instituto de Investigaciónes Ecológicas Chiloé & RBGE
IDS	International Dendrological Society
ISI	Int. Succulent Introductions
J&JA	Archibald, James & Jennifer
J. Jurasek	Jurasek, J.
JCA	Archibald, James
JE	Jack Elliott
JJ	Jackson, J.
JJ&JH	Halda, J. & Halda, J.
JJH	Halda, Joseph J.
JL	Lode, Joel
JLS	Sharman, J.L.
JM-MK	Mahr, J.; Kammerlander, M.
JMT	Mann Taylor, J.

JN	Nielson, Jens
JR	Russell, J.
JRM	Marr, John
JW	Watson, J.M.
K	Kirkpatrick, George
K&LG	Gillanders, Kenneth & Gillanders, L.
K&Mc	Kirkpatrick, George & McBeath, Ronald J.D.
K&P	Josef Kopec & Milan Prasil
K&T	Kurashige, Y. & Tsukie, S.
KC	Cox, Kenneth
KEKE	Kew/Edinburgh Kanchenjunga Expedition (1989)
KGB	Kunming/Gothenburg Botanical Expedition (1993)
KM	Marsh, K.
KMR	Kupčák, M.
KR	Rushforth, K.D.
KRW	Wooster, K.R. (distributed after his death by Kath Dryden)
KW	Kingdon-Ward, F.
KWJ	Crûg-World of Ferns Joint Expedition, Vietnam (2007)
L	Lancaster, C. Roy
L&S	Ludlow, Francis & Sherriff, George
LA	Long Ashton Research Station clonal selection scheme
LB	Bercht, L. (*Cactaceae*)
LB	Bird P.; Salmon, M.
LEG	Lesotho Edinburgh/Gothenburg Expedition (1997)
Lismore	Lismore Nursery, Breeder's Number
LM&S	Leslie, Mattern & Sharman
LP	Palmer, W.J.L.
LS&E	Ludlow, Frank; Sherriff, George & Elliott, E. E.
LS&H	Ludlow, Frank; Sherriff, George & Hicks, J. H.
LS&T	Ludlow, Frank; Sherriff, George & Taylor, George
LZ	Lutz, Eberhard
M&PS	Mike & Polly Stone
M&T	Mathew & Tomlinson
Mac&W	McPhail & Watson
McB	McBeath, R.J.D.
McLaren	McLaren, H.D.
MDM	Myers, Michael D.
MECC	Scottish Rock Garden Club, Nepal (1997)
MESE	Alpine Garden Society Expedition, Greece (1999)
MF	Foster, Maurice
MH	Heasman, Matthew T.
MK	Kammerlander, Michael
MP	Pavelka, Mojmir
MPF	Frankis, M.P.
MS	Salmon, M.
MS&CL	Salmon, M. & Lovell, C.
MSF	Fillan, M.S.
MUG	Uhlig, M.
NAPE	Hootman, S.; et al, Expedition to Naglaland and Arunachal Pradesh (2003)
NICE	North India Expedition (1997)
NJM	Macer, N.J.
NN	Nielsen & Nielsen (2009)
NNS	Ratko, Ron
NS	Turland, Nick
NVD	Expedition to Vietnam
NVFDE	Northern Vietnam First Darwin Expedition
Og	Ogisu, Mikinori
ORO	Oron, Peri
OS	Sonderhousen, O.
P. Bon	Bonavia, P.
P&C	Paterson, David S. & Clarke, Sidney
P&W	Polastri & Watson, J. M.
PAB	Barney, P.A.
PB	Bird, Peter
PC&H	Pattison, G.; Catt, P. & Hickson, M.
PD	Davis, Peter H.
PDM	Purdom, William
PF	Furse, Paul
PG	Pichler, G.
PJC	Christian, Paul J.
PJC&AH	P.J. Christian & A. Hogg
PNMK	Nicholls, P.; Kammerlander, M.
Polunin	Polunin, Oleg
Pras	Prasil, M.
PS&W	Polunin, Oleg; Sykes, William & Williams, John
PW	Wharton, Peter
R	Rock, J.F.C.
RB	Brown, R.
RBS	Brown, Ray, Sakharin Island
RCB AM	Brown, Robert, Expedition to Armenia
RCB/Arg	Brown, Robert, Argentina, (2002)
RCB E	Brown, Robert, Expedition to Spain (Andalucia)
RCB/Eq	Brown, Robert, Ecuador, (1988)
RCB RA	Brown, Robert
RCB RL	Brown, Robert, Expedition to Lebanon
RCB/TQ	Brown, Robert, Turkey (2001)
RE	Evans, Ron
RH	Hancock, R.
RKMP	Ruksans, J.; Krumins, A.; Kitts, M.; Paivel, A.
RM	Ruksans, J. & Kitts, M.
RMRP	Rocky Mountain Rare Plants, Denver, Colorado
RS	Suckow, Reinhart
RSC	Richard Somer Cocks
RV	Richard Valder
RWJ	Crûg Farm-Rickards Ferns Expedition to Taiwan (2003)
S&B	Blanchard, J.W. & Salmon, M.
S&F	Salmon, M. & Fillan, M.
S&L	Sinclair, Ian W.J. & Long, David G.
S&SH	Sheilah & Spencer Hannay

Sandham	Sandham, John
SB	Brack, Steven
SB&L	Salmon, Bird & Lovell
SBEC	Sino-British Expedition to Cangshan
SBEL	Sino-British Lijiang Expedition
SBQE	Sino-British Expedition to Quinghai
Sch	Schilling, Anthony D.
SD	Sashal Dayal
SDR	Rankin, Stella & David
SEH	Hootman, Steve
SEP	Swedish Expedition to Pakistan
SF	Forde, P.
SG	Salmon, M. & Guy, P.
SH	Hannay, Spencer
Sich	Simmons, Erskine, Howick & Mcnamara
SJ	Johansson, Stellan
SLIZE	Swedish-Latvian-Iranian Zagros Expedition to Iran (May 1988)
SOJA	Kew/Quarryhill Expedition to Southern Japan
SS&W	Stainton, J.D. Adam; Sykes, William & Williams, John
SSNY	Sino-Scottish Expedition to NW Yunnan (1992)
T	Taylor, Nigel P.

T&K	Taylor, Nigel P. & Knees, Sabina
TCM	Mitchell, Thomas Carly
TG	Thomas, H-P. & Gilmer, K.
TH	Hudson, T.
TJR	Roberts, Tim
TS&BC	Smythe, T. & Cherry, B.
TSS	Spring Smyth, T.L.M.
TW	Weston, Tony
USDAPI	US Department of Agriculture Plant Index Number
USDAPQ	US Dept. of Agriculture Plant Quarantine Number
USNA	United States National Arboretum
VHH	Vernon H. Heywood
VV	Victor, David
W	Wilson, Ernest H.
W&B	Watkins, D. & Brown, R., Bulgaria (2012)
WJC	Wynn-Jones, B. & S. & Colley, F.
WM	McLewin, William
Woods	Woods, Patrick J.B.
Wr	Wraight, David & Anke
WWJ	Wharton, Peter; Wynn-Jones, Bleddyn & Susan
Yu	Yu, Tse-tsun

NOMENCLATURAL NOTES

The following changes have been made during 2014 to the names used by the *RHS Plant Finder* based upon decisions of the RHS Nomenclature and Taxonomy Advisory Group (NATAG). If you have any suggestions for other plant name changes within the *RHS Plant Finder*, then please write, stating your reasons in full, to:

The Chairman & Vice-Chairman
Dr John Grimshaw & Dr Janet Cubey
Nomenclature and Taxonomy Advisory Group
Royal Horticultural Society
RHS Garden Wisley
Woking
Surrey
GU23 6QB

- *Acacia karroo* and *A. caven* should be transferred to *Vachellia karroo* and *V. caven* respectively.
- Plants sold as *Acalypha reptans* and *A. pendula* should be listed as *A. herzogiana.*
- The cultivar 'Hilo Beauty' variously recorded as an *Alocasia/Caladium/Colocasia* should be listed as *Caladium praetermissum* 'Hilo Beauty'.
- North American members of *Aster* should be separated into distinct genera, including *Symphyotrichum, Eurybia, Galatella, Ampelaster* and *Doellingeria.*
- Add a new cross-reference from *Beesia deltophylla* misapplied to *Beesia calthifolia.*
- *Delosperma congestum* is misapplied in cultivation, and plants previously listed under this name should move to *Malotigena frantiskae-niederlovae*. Within this species, plants listed as 'Album' and "white-flowered" should be included in 'White Nugget'.
- *Delosperma alpina* should be listed as *Ectotropis alpina* and the *Delosperma* collection "from Sani Pass" should be listed as *Ectotropis seanii-hoganii.*
- New splits of *L. aloides* proposed in the *Lachenalia* monograph should be adopted.
- *Parochetus africanus* should be treated as a subspecies of *P. communis.*
- *Persicaria* 'Johanniswolke' should be listed as a cultivar of *P.* × *fennica.*
- *Plectranthus excisus* should be moved to *Isodon excisus.*
- *Rhodohypoxis* 'Pictus' should be changed to *R.* 'Picta'.
- *Salvia meyeri* should be included within *S. atrocyanea.*
- *Washingtonia* 'Filibusta' should become *W.* × *filibusta.*
- Replace *Watsonia meriania* with *W. meriana.*
- *Wedelia trilobata* should be moved to *Sphagneticola trilobata.*

This is not an exhaustive list of the changes made to the RHS Horticultural Database; many more changes are made during the year by the RHS botanical team. This list is to highlight some of the NATAG changes.

Changes already proposed for the 2016 edition of this book, include:

- Adopting *Chaenostoma* for splits from *Sutera*, including *Sutera cordata.*
- Adopting the splitting of *Vesalea* and *Diabelia* from *Abelia.*
- Separating *Charybdis* from *Urginea.*
- Separating *Clinanthus* from *Stenomesson.*
- Separating *Ismene* and *Hymenocallis.*
- Incorporating *Spiloxene* within *Pauridia.*
- Incorporating *Stemmacantha* within *Rhaponticum.*

CLASSIFICATION OF GENERA

Genera including a large number of species, or with many cultivars, are often subdivided into informal horticultural classifications, or formal cultivar groups in the case of *Clematis* and *Tulipa*. The breeding of new cultivars is sometimes limited to hybrids between closely-related species, thus for *Saxifraga* and *Primula*, the cultivars are allocated to the sections given in the infrageneric treatments cited. Please turn to p.11 for a fuller explanation.

ACER

(A) Amoenum Group
(D) Dissectum Group
(Dw) Dwarf Group
(L) Linearilobum Group
(M) Matsumurae Group
(P) Palmatum Group

ACTINIDIA

(s-p) Self-pollinating

BEGONIA

(C) Cane-like
(R) Rex Cultorum
(S) Semperflorens Cultorum
(T) × *tuberhybrida* (Tuberous)

CHRYSANTHEMUM

(By the National Chrysanthemum Society)
(1) Indoor Large (Exhibition)
(2) Indoor Medium (Exhibition)
(3a) Indoor Incurved: Large-flowered
(3b) Indoor Incurved: Medium-flowered
(3c) Indoor Incurved: Small-flowered
(4a) Indoor Reflexed: Large-flowered
(4b) Indoor Reflexed: Medium-flowered
(4c) Indoor Reflexed: Small-flowered
(5a) Indoor Intermediate: Large-flowered
(5b) Indoor Intermediate: Medium-flowered
(5c) Indoor Intermediate: Small-flowered
(6a) Indoor Anemone: Large-flowered
(6b) Indoor Anemone: Medium-flowered
(6c) Indoor Anemone: Small-flowered
(7a) Indoor Single: Large-flowered
(7b) Indoor Single: Medium-flowered
(7c) Indoor Single: Small-flowered
(8a) Indoor True Pompon
(8b) Indoor Semi-pompon
(9a) Indoor Spray: Anemone
(9b) Indoor Spray: Pompon
(9c) Indoor Spray: Reflexed
(9d) Indoor Spray: Single
(9e) Indoor Spray: Intermediate
(9f) Indoor Spray: Spider, Quill, Spoon or Any Other Type
(10a) Indoor, Spider
(10b) Indoor, Quill
(10c) Indoor, Spoon
(11) Any Other Indoor Type
(12a) Indoor, Charm
(12b) Indoor, Cascade
(13a) October-flowering Incurved: Large-flowered
(13b) October-flowering Incurved: Medium-flowered
(13c) October-flowering Incurved: Small-flowered
(14a) October-flowering Reflexed: Large-flowered
(14b) October-flowering Reflexed: Medium-flowered
(14c) October-flowering Reflexed: Small-flowered
(15a) October-flowering Intermediate: Large-flowered
(15b) October-flowering Intermediate: Medium-flowered
(15c) October-flowered Intermediate: Small-flowered
(16) October-flowering Large
(17a) October-flowering Single: Large-flowered
(17b) October-flowering Single: Medium-flowered
(17c) October-flowering Single: Small-flowered
(18a) October-flowering Pompon: True Pompon
(18b) October-flowering Pompon: Semi-pompon
(19a) October-flowering Spray: Anemone
(19b) October-flowering Spray: Pompon
(19c) October-flowering Spray: Reflexed
(19d) October-flowering Spray: Single
(19e) October-flowering Spray: Intermediate
(19f) October-flowering Spray: Spider, Quill, Spoon or Any Other Type
(20) Any Other October-flowering Type
(21a) Korean: Anemone
(21b) Korean: Pompon
(21c) Korean: Reflexed
(21d) Korean: Single
(21e) Korean: Intermediate
(21f) Korean: Spider, Quill, Spoon, or any other type
(22a) Charm: Anemone

(22b)	Charm: Pompon
(22c)	Charm: Reflexed
(22d)	Charm: Single
(22e)	Charm: Intermediate
(22f)	Charm: Spider, Quill, Spoon or Any Other Type
(23a)	Early-flowering Outdoor Incurved: Large-flowered
(23b)	Early-flowering Outdoor Incurved: Medium-flowered
(23c)	Early-flowering Outdoor Incurved: Small-flowered
(24a)	Early-flowering Outdoor Reflexed: Large-flowered
(24b)	Early-flowering Outdoor Reflexed: Medium-flowered
(24c)	Early-flowering Outdoor Reflexed: Small-flowered
(25a)	Early-flowering Outdoor Intermediate: Large-flowered
(25b)	Early-flowering Outdoor Intermediate: Medium-flowered
(25c)	Early-flowering Outdoor Intermediate: Small-flowered
(26a)	Early-flowering Outdoor Anemone: Large-flowered
(26b)	Early-flowering Outdoor Anemone: Medium-flowered
(27a)	Early-flowering Outdoor Single: Large-flowered
(27b)	Early-flowering Outdoor Single:Medium-flowered
(28a)	Early-flowering Outdoor Pompon: True Pompon
(28b)	Early-flowering Outdoor Pompon: Semi-pompon
(29a)	Early-flowering Outdoor Spray: Anemone
(29b)	Early-flowering Outdoor Spray: Pompon
(29c)	Early-flowering Outdoor Spray: Reflexed
(29d)	Early-flowering Outdoor Spray: Single
(29e)	Early-flowering Outdoor Spray: Intermediate
(29f)	Early-flowering Outdoor Spray: Spider, Quill, Spoon or Any Other Type
(29Rub)	Early-flowering Outdoor Spray: Rubellum
(30)	Any Other Early-flowering Outdoor Type

Clematis

(Cultivar Groups as per Matthews, V. (2002) *The International Clematis Register & Checklist 2002*, RHS, London.)

(A)	Atragene Group
(Ar)	Armandii Group
(C)	Cirrhosa Group
(EL)	Early Large-flowered Group
(F)	Flammula Group
(Fo)	Forsteri Group
(H)	Heracleifolia Group
(I)	Integrifolia Group
(LL)	Late Large-flowered Group
(M)	Montana Group
(T)	Texensis Group
(Ta)	Tangutica Group
(V)	Viorna Group
(Vb)	Vitalba Group
(Vt)	Viticella Group

Dahlia

(Classification according to The International Dahlia Register (1969), 22nd Supp. (2012) formed through consultation with national dahlia societies.)

(Sin)	1 Single
(Anem)	2 Anemone-flowered
(Col)	3 Collerette
(WL)	4 Waterlily
(D)	5 Decorative
(Ba)	6 Ball
(Pom)	7 Pompon
(C)	8 Cactus
(S-c)	9 Semi-cactus
(Misc)	10 Miscellaneous
(Fim)	11 Fimbriated
(SinO)	12 Single Orchid (Star)
(DblO)	13 Double Orchid
(P)	14 Peony-flowered
(B)	Botanical
(DwB)	Dwarf Bedding
(Lil)	Lilliput

Dianthus

(By the RHS)

(b)	Carnation, border
(M)	Carnation, Malmaison
(p)	Pink
(p,a)	Pink, annual
(pf)	Carnation, perpetual-flowering
(pt)	Carnation, pot

Fruit

(B)	Black (*Vitis*), Blackberry (*Rubus*), Blackcurrant (*Ribes*)
(Ball)	Ballerina (*Malus*)
(C)	Culinary (*Malus, Prunus, Pyrus, Ribes*)
(Cider)	Cider (*Malus*)
(D)	Dessert (*Malus, Prunus, Pyrus, Ribes*)
(F)	Fruit
(G)	Glasshouse (*Vitis*)
(O)	Outdoor (*Vitis*)
(P)	Pinkcurrant (*Ribes*)
(Perry)	Perry (*Pyrus*)
(R)	Red (*Vitis*), Redcurrant (*Ribes*)
(S)	Seedless (*Citrus, Vitis*)
(W)	White (*Vitis*), Whitecurrant (*Ribes*)

FUCHSIA

(E) Encliandra
(T) Variants and hybrids of *F. triphylla*

GLADIOLUS

(B) Butterfly
(E) Exotic
(G) Giant
(L) Large
(M) Medium
(Min) Miniature
(N) Nanus
(P) Primulinus
(S) Small
(Tub) Tubergenii

HEPATICA NOBILIS

(Adapted from the International Hepatica Society classification for *Hepatica nobilis*)
(1) Hyoujun (normal)
(2) (degenerated anther)
(3) Otome (degenerated stamen)
(4) Henka (petal deformity)
(5/d) Herashibe (semi-double, primitive)
(5A/d) Choji (semi-double, primitive)
(6/d) Nidan (semi-double, advanced)
(7/d) Sandan (double, primitive)
(8/d) Karako (double, advanced)
(9/d) Sene-e (double, completed)

HYDRANGEA MACROPHYLLA

(H) Hortensia
(L) Lacecap

IMPATIENS

(NG) New Guinea Group

IRIS

(Adapted from the American Iris Society Classification)
(AB) Arilbred
(BB) Border Bearded
(Cal-Sib) Series *Californicae* × Series *Sibiricae*
(CH) Californian Hybrid
(DB) Dwarf Bearded (not assigned)
(Dut) Dutch
(IB) Intermediate Bearded
(J) Juno (subgenus *Scorpiris*)
(La) Louisiana Hybrid
(MDB) Miniature Dwarf Bearded
(MTB) Miniature Tall Bearded
(Rc) Regeliocyclus (Section *Regelia* × Section *Oncocyclus*)
(SDB) Standard Dwarf Bearded
(Sib) Siberian
(Sino-Sib) Series *Sibiricae*, chromosome number 2n=40
(SpH) Species Hybrid
(Spuria) Spuria
(TB) Tall Bearded

LILIUM

(Classification according to *The International Lily Register* (ed. 4, 2007))
(I) Asiatic hybrids derived from *L. amabile, L. bulbiferum, L. callosum, L. cernuum, L. concolor, L. dauricum, L. davidii, L. × hollandicum, L. lancifolium, L. lankongense, L. leichtlinii, L. × maculatum* and *L. pumilum, L. × scottiae, L. wardii* and *L. wilsonii.*
(II) Martagon hybrids derived from *L. dalhansonii, L. hansonii, L. martagon, L. medeoloides and L. tsingtauense*
(III) Euro-Caucasian hybrids derived from *L. candidum, L. chalcedonicum, L. kesselringianum, L. monadelphum, L. pomponium, L. pyrenaicum* and *L. × testaceum.*
(IV) American hybrids derived from *L. bolanderi, L. × burbankii, L. canadense, L. columbianum, L. grayi, L. humboldtii, L. kelleyanum, L. kelloggii, L. maritimum, L. michauxii, L. michiganense, L. occidentale, L. × pardaboldtii, L. pardalinum, L. parryi, L. parvum, L. philadelphicum, L. pitkinense, L. superbum, L. vollmeri, L. washingtonianum* and *L. wigginsii.*
(V) Longiflorum lilies derived from *L. formosanum, L. longiflorum, L. philippinense and L. wallichianum.*
(VI) Trumpet and Aurelian hybrids derived from *L. × aurelianense, L. brownii, L. × centigale, L. henryi, L. × imperiale, L. × kewense, L. leucantheum, L. regale, L. rosthornii, L. sargentiae, L. sulphureum* and *L. sulphurgale* (but excluding hybrids of *L. henryi* with all species listed in Division VII).
(VII) Oriental hybrids derived from *L. auratum, L. japonicum, L. nobilissimum, L. × parkmanii, L rubellum* and *L. speciosum* (but excl. all hybrids of these with *L. henryi*).
(VIII) Other hybrids not covered by any of the previous divisions (I-VII)
(IX) Species and cultivars of species
a/ upward-facing flowers
b/ outward-facing flowers
c/ downward-facing flowers
/a trumpet-shaped flowers
/b bowl-shaped flowers
/c flat flowers (or with only tepal tips recurved)
/d recurved flowers

Malus *see* Fruit

Narcissus

(By the RHS, revised 1998)

(1)	Trumpet
(2)	Large-cupped
(3)	Small-cupped
(4)	Double
(5)	Triandrus
(6)	Cyclamineus
(7)	Jonquilla and Apodanthus
(8)	Tazetta
(9)	Poeticus
(10)	Bulbocodium
(11a)	Split-corona: Collar
(11b)	Split-corona: Papillon
(12)	Miscellaneous
(13)	Species

Nymphaea

(H)	Hardy
(D)	Day-blooming
(N)	Night-blooming
(T)	Tropical

Papaver

(Not a horticultural classification, used to save space in this publication)

(SPS)	Super Poppy Series

Paeonia

(S)	Shrubby

Pelargonium

(A)	Angel
(C)	Coloured Foliage (in combination)
(Ca)	Cactus (in combination)
(d)	Double (in combination)
(Dec)	Decorative
(Dw)	Dwarf
(DwI)	Dwarf Ivy-leaved
(Fr)	Frutetorum
(I)	Ivy-leaved
(Min)	Miniature
(MinI)	Miniature Ivy-leaved
(R)	Regal
(Sc)	Scented-leaved
(St)	Stellar (in combination)
(T)	Tulip (in combination)
(U)	Unique
(Z)	Zonal

Primula

(Classification by Section as per Richards. J. (2002) *Primula* (2nd edition). Batsford, London)

(Ag)	*Auganthus*
(Al)	*Aleuritia*
(Am)	*Amethystinae*
(Ar)	*Armerina*
(Au)	*Auricula*
(A)	Alpine Auricula
(B)	Border Auricula
(S)	Show Auricula
(St)	Striped Auricula
(Bu)	*Bullatae*
(Ca)	*Capitatae*
(Cf)	*Cordifoliae*
(Ch)	*Chartaceae*
(Co)	*Cortusoides*
(Cr)	*Carolinella*
(Cu)	*Cuneifoliae*
(Cy)	*Crystallophlomis*
(Da)	*Davidii*
(De)	*Denticulatae*
(Dr)	*Dryadifoliae*
(F)	*Fedtschenkoanae*
(G)	*Glabrae*
(Ma)	*Malvaceae*
(Mi)	*Minutissimae*
(Mo)	*Monocarpicae*
(Mu)	*Muscarioides*
(Ob)	*Obconicolisteri*
(Or)	*Oreophlomis*
(Pa)	*Parryi*
(Pe)	*Petiolares*
(Pf)	*Proliferae*
(Pi)	*Pinnatae*
(Pr)	*Primula*
(Poly)	Polyanthus
(Prim)	Primrose
(Pu)	*Pulchellae*
(Py)	*Pycnoloba*
(R)	*Reinii*
(Si)	*Sikkimenses*
(So)	*Soldanelloides*
(Sp)	*Sphondylia*
(Sr)	*Sredinskya*
(Su)	*Suffrutescentes*
(Y)	*Yunnannenses*

Prunus *see* Fruit

Pyrus *see* Fruit

Rhododendron

(A)	Azalea (deciduous, species or unclassified hybrid)
(Ad)	Azaleodendron
(EA)	Evergreen azalea
(G)	Ghent azalea (deciduous)
(K)	Knap Hill or Exbury azalea (deciduous)
(M)	Mollis azalea (deciduous)
(O)	Occidentalis azalea (deciduous)
(R)	Rustica azalea (deciduous)
(V)	Vireya rhododendron
(Vs)	Viscosa azalea (deciduous)

RIBES *SEE* FRUIT

ROSA

(A)	Alba
(Bb)	Bourbon
(Bs)	Boursault
(Ce)	Centifolia
(Ch)	China
(Cl)	Climbing (in combination)
(D)	Damask
(DPo)	Damask Portland
(F)	Floribunda or Cluster-flowered
(G)	Gallica
(Ga)	Garnette
(GC)	Ground Cover
(HM)	Hybrid Musk
(HP)	Hybrid Perpetual
(HT)	Hybrid Tea or Large-flowered
(Min)	Miniature
(Mo)	Moss (in combination)
(N)	Noisette
(Patio)	Patio, Miniature Floribunda or Dwarf Cluster-flowered
(Poly)	Polyantha
(Ra)	Rambler
(RH)	Rubiginosa hybrid (Hybrid Sweet Briar)
(Ru)	Rugosa
(S)	Shrub
(SpH)	Spinosissima Hybrid
(T)	Tea

RUBUS *SEE* FRUIT

SAXIFRAGA

(Classification by Section from Gornall, R.J. (1987). *Botanical Journal of the Linnean Society,* 95(4): 273-292)

(1)	*Ciliatae*
(2)	*Cymbalaria*
(3)	*Merkianae*
(4)	*Micranthes*
(5)	*Irregulares*
(6)	*Heterisia*
(7)	*Porphyrion*
(8)	*Ligulatae*
(9)	*Xanthizoon*
(10)	*Trachyphyllum*
(11)	*Gymnopera*
(12)	*Cotylea*
(13)	*Odontophyllae*
(14)	*Mesogyne*
(15)	*Saxifraga*

TULIPA

(Classification by Cultivar Group from *Classified List and International Register of Tulip Names* by Koninklijke Algemeene Vereniging voor Bloembollencultuur 1996)

(1)	Single Early Group
(2)	Double Early Group
(3)	Triumph Group
(4)	Darwin Hybrid Group
(5)	Single Late Group (including Darwin Group and Cottage Group)
(6)	Lily-flowered Group
(7)	Fringed Group
(8)	Viridiflora Group
(9)	Rembrandt Group
(10)	Parrot Group
(11)	Double Late Group
(12)	Kaufmanniana Group
(13)	Fosteriana Group
(14)	Greigii Group
(15)	Miscellaneous

VERBENA

(G)	Species and hybrids considered by some botanists to belong to the separate genus *Glandularia*.

VIOLA

(C)	Cornuta Hybrid
(dVt)	Double Violet
(ExVa)	Exhibition Viola
(FP)	Fancy Pansy
(PVt)	Parma Violet
(SP)	Show Pansy
(T)	Tricolor
(Va)	Viola
(Vt)	Violet
(Vtta)	Violetta

VITIS *SEE* FRUIT

THE PLANT DIRECTORY

A

Abelia ✿ (*Caprifoliaceae*)

	chinensis misapplied	see *A.* × *grandiflora* 'Lake Maggiore'
§	***chinensis*** R. Br.	CBcs CMCN CMac CRos EHyd ELan EPfP EWTr LRHS MAsh MMuc SEND SHil SKHP SPer SRms WFar WGrn WPat
	- 'China Rose' ♀H5	SKHP
§	***dielsii***	CBot
	'Edward Goucher' ♀H5	Widely available
	engleriana	CRos EHyd EPfP LHop LRHS MAsh MBlu NLar SEND SLon
	floribunda ♀H5	CBcs CBot CDul CMac CWib ECre EHyd ELan ELon EPfP LHop LRHS MAsh MRav NLar SAko SBrt SGbt SGol SKHP SPer SPoG SRms WPat
	× ***grandiflora*** common clone	see *A.* × *grandiflora* 'Lake Maggiore'
	- 'Aurea'	see *A.* × *grandiflora* 'Gold Spot'
	- 'Brockhill Allgold'	EMil EPfP
	- 'Compacta'	LRHS WFar
	- Confetti = 'Conti'PBR (v)	CBcs CLet CMac CSBt ECrN EHyd ELan EMOT EMil EPfP GMcL LRHS LSRN MAsh MGos MRav NLar SCob SEle SGol SLim SPer SPoG SWvt WFar
§	- 'Francis Mason' (v)	Widely available
§	- 'Gold Spot' (v)	CBot EPfP LRHS MNHC NLar SPer WPat
	- 'Gold Strike'	see *A.* × *grandiflora* 'Gold Spot'
	- Golden Panache = 'Minpan'	MRav
	- 'Goldsport'	see *A.* × *grandiflora* 'Gold Spot'
	- 'Hopleys'PBR (v) ♀H5	CBcs CMac CRos CSBt CTri CWib EHyd ELan EMil EPfP EWTr LHop LRHS MAsh MGos NLar SCob SEND SEle SLon SPoG SRms SWvt WGrn WHar
	- 'Kaleidoscope'PBR (v)	Widely available
	- Lady Liberty = 'Keylib'	SPoG
	- 'Lady Summerdream'	EBee
§	- 'Lake Maggiore' ♀H5	Widely available
	- Lucky Lots = 'Wevo2' (v)	LLHF NLar SCob
	- 'Panache' (v)	LLHF WCot
	- 'Prostrate White'	EBee ECrN LRHS NLar
	- 'Semperflorens'	LRHS
	- 'Sherwoodii'	EBee ECrN EHoe EPfP LRHS MAsh MGos WRHF
	- 'Sparkling Silver' (v) **new**	EBee LRHS
	- Sunny Charms = 'Mindu01'PBR **new**	LCro
	- 'Sunrise' (v)	NLar
	- Sunshine Daydream = 'Abelops'PBR (v)	CEnd CTsd LLHF MMrt MPkF NLar SCob SGbt SRms
	- 'Variegata'	see *A.* × *grandiflora* 'Francis Mason'
§	'Lynn'	EBee LLHF LPre MPkF SCob
	mosanensis	CAbP CBot CMCN EHyd ELan EPfP LLHF LRHS MBlu MGil NLar SLon SPoG WSHC
	- Bridal Bouquet = 'Monia' **new**	LRHS
	parvifolia	CAbP CBcs CBot CMCN CMac CSBt CTri EHyd EPfP LHop LRHS MMuc MRav NLar NRHS SGbt SKHP SLim SLon SPer SWvt WBod WGrn WPat
	- 'Bumblebee' **new**	LCro MAsh MPkF NLar SHil SPoG
	Pastel Charm = 'Minduo2' **new**	LRHS
	Petite Garden = 'Minedward'PBR	LLHF LRHS
	Pinky Bells	see *A.* 'Lynn'
	rupestris misapplied	see *A.* × *grandiflora*
	rupestris Lindl.	see *A. chinensis* R. Br.
	triflora	see *Zabelia triflora*
	zanderi	see *A. dielsii*

Abeliophyllum (*Oleaceae*)

distichum	CBcs CDul CEnd CRos CWib ECrN EHyd ELan ELon EPfP EWld IDee LBMP LRHS MAsh MBlu NRHS SGol SWvt WBod WCFE WSHC
- Roseum Group	CBcs CRos EHyd ELan ELon EPfP LCro LHop LRHS MAsh MMuc MRav SKHP SLon SPer SPoG

Abelmoschus (*Malvaceae*)

esculentus	SVic

Abies ✿ (*Pinaceae*)

alba	CAco CDul MMuc NWea
- 'Bystricka'	MAsh NLar
- 'Compacta'	CKen
- 'Green Spiral'	NLar
- 'King's Dwarf'	CKen
- 'Microphylla'	CKen
- 'Münsterland'	CKen
- 'Nana' misapplied	see *Picea glauca* 'Nana'
- 'Nana' ambig.	CKen
- 'Pendula'	CKen
- 'Pyramidalis'	NLar
amabilis 'Spreading Star'	SLim
arizonica	see *A. lasiocarpa* var. *arizonica*
arnoldiana 'Cyrille'	IArd
balsamea	MAsh
- 'Cook's Blue'	CKen
- 'Eugene Gold' **new**	NLar
- Hudsonia Group	CKen CMac LRHS SLim WIce
- - 'Hudsonia' ♀H7 **new**	GMcL
- - 'Nana'	CKen ELan LRHS MJak NEgg NWad
- 'Jamie'	CKen
- 'Kiwi' **new**	NLar
- 'Le Feber'	CKen
- 'Little Carleigh' **new**	NLar
- var. ***phanerolepis*** 'Bear Swamp'	CKen NHol

	- 'Piccolo'	CKen LRHS NLar SBod
	- 'Renswoude'	CKen
	- 'Tyler Blue'	CKen NLar
	- 'Verkade's Prostrate'	CKen
*	***borisii-regis*** 'Pendula'	CKen
	- 'Spring Delight'	LRHS
	brachyphylla dwarf	see *A. homolepis* 'Prostrata'
	cephalonica	CDul CKen NWea
	- 'Greg's Broom'	CKen NLar
§	- 'Meyer's Dwarf'	CMac NEgg NLar SLim
	- 'Nana'	see *A. cephalonica* 'Meyer's Dwarf'
	cephalonica* × *nordmanniana	MHtn
	chensiensis	CDul
	cilicica 'Spring Grove'	CKen
	concolor	CAco CBcs CDul CTho LPar LRHS NWea SEND WMou
	- 'Archer's Dwarf'	CKen NEgg NLar SLim
	- 'Aurea'	NLar
	- 'Birthday Broom'	CKen
	- 'Blue Cloak'	CKen
	- 'Blue Sapphire'	CKen
	- 'Bryce Canyon' **new**	NLar
§	- 'Compacta' ♀H7	CKen LRHS MGos NEgg NHol NLar SLim
	- 'Fagerhult'	CKen
	- 'Gable's Weeping'	CKen
	- 'Glauca'	see *A. concolor* (Violacea Group) 'Violacea'
	- 'Glauca Compacta'	see *A. concolor* 'Compacta'
	- 'Hillier Broom'	see *A. concolor* 'Hillier's Dwarf'
§	- 'Hillier's Dwarf'	CKen
	- 'Husky Pup'	CKen
	- 'La Veta' **new**	CKen
	- (Lowiana Group) 'Creamy'	CKen NEgg NLar
	- 'Masonic Broom'	CKen
	- 'Mike Stearn'	CKen
	- 'Mora'	CKen
	- 'Ostrov nad Ohri'	CKen
	- 'Piggelmee'	CKen MAsh NLar
	- 'Pygmy'	CKen
	- 'Scooter'	CKen NLar
	- 'Sherwood's Blue'	NEgg
	- Violacea Group	CKen SLim
§	- - 'Violacea' ♀H7	WMat
	- - 'Violacea Prostrate' ♀H7	NHol NLar
	- 'Viona' **new**	NLar
	- 'Wattezii'	CKen
	- 'Wintergold'	CKen LRHS MBlu NEgg NHol NLar SLim
	delavayi	CDul EPfP LRHS NWea
	- 'Buchanan' **new**	NLar
	- var. ***delavayi*** Fabri Group	see *A. fabri*
	- 'Major Neishe'	CKen
§	***fabri***	CDul CKen
	fargesii	CKen
	firma	NWea
	forrestii	CKen
	- var. ***georgei***	NWea
	fraseri	CDul CTho MMuc NWea WMou WTSh
	- 'Blue Bonnet'	CKen NLar
	- 'Kline's Nest'	SLim
	- 'Raul's Dwarf'	CKen
	grandis	CBcs CDul CJun CMCN ELan EPfP MMuc NWea WTSh
	- 'Compacta'	CKen
	- 'Van Dedem's Dwarf'	CKen NLar NWad SLim
	holophylla	NWea
	homolepis	CDul CKen NWea
§	- 'Prostrata'	CKen
	koreana ♀H7	Widely available
	- 'Alpin Star'	CKen MAsh NEgg NLar
	- 'Blaue Zwo'	CKen LRHS
	- 'Blauer Eskimo' ♀H7	CKen MAsh SLim
	- 'Blauer Pfiff'	CKen
	- 'Blinsham Gold'	CKen
	- 'Blue Emperor'	MBlu
	- 'Blue Magic'	CKen NLar
	- 'Blue 'n' Silver'	NLar
	- 'Brilliant'	CKen
	- 'Cis' ♀H7	CKen NHol NLar NWad SLim
	- Crystal Globe	see *A. koreana* 'Kristallkugel'
	- 'Dark Hill'	NLar
	- 'Doni-tajuso'	CKen
	- 'Eisregen'	CKen
	- 'Festival'	NEgg NHol
	- 'Frosty'	SLim
	- 'Gait'	CKen NLar
	- 'Golden Glow'	NLar SLim
	- 'Goldener Traum'	CKen NLar
	- 'Green Carpet'	CKen NLar
	- 'Horstmann'	CKen
	- 'Inge' **new**	NLar
	- 'Inverleith'	CKen
	- 'Kleiner Prinz'	NLar
	- 'Kohout'	CKen
	- 'Kohout's Ice Breaker' PBR ♀H7	CKen MAsh NLar SLim
§	- 'Kristallkugel'	CKen MAsh NEgg NLar
	- 'Lippetal'	CKen
	- 'Luminetta'	CKen NHol
	- 'Nadelkissen'	CKen NHol
	- 'Nisbet'	NEgg NHol SCoo
	- 'Oberon'	CKen MAsh NHol NLar
	- 'Piccolo'	CKen
	- 'Pinocchio'	CKen NHol NWad
	- 'Ry'	NLar
	- 'Schneestern'	NLar
	- 'Sherwood Compact'	CKen
	- 'Shorty'	CKen NLar
	- 'Silberkugel'	CKen CMen MAsh NLar NWad SLim
	- 'Silberlocke' ♀H7	CCVT CDul CKen LRHS MAsh MBlu MGos NLar NOra SCoo SLim WHar WMat
	- 'Silbermavers'	CKen
	- 'Silberperl'	CKen CMen NLar SAko SLim
	- 'Silberschmelze'	NLar
	- 'Silberzwerg'	NLar
	- 'Silver Show'	CDul LRHS NHol NLar SLim
	- 'Threave'	CKen NHol
	- 'Tundra'	NEgg NLar
	- 'Wellenseind'	CKen
	lasiocarpa 'Alpine Beauty'	CKen NLar
§	- var. ***arizonica***	CAco
	- - 'Compacta' Hornibr. ♀H7	CKen CMac LRHS MAsh MGos NHol SLim SPoG WMat
	- - 'Kenwith Blue'	CKen NEgg SLim
	- 'Beano Broom'	CKen
	- 'Chikov'	CKen
	- 'Day Creek'	CKen NLar
	- 'Duflon'	CKen MAsh
	- 'Elaine'	CKen
	- 'Green Globe'	CKen NLar SLim
	- 'Joe's Alpine'	CKen
	- 'Kyle's Alpine'	CKen NLar
	- 'Logan Pass'	CKen
	- 'Lopalpun'	CKen
	- 'Mulligan's Dwarf'	CKen

	- 'Prickly Pete'	CKen NLar
I	- 'Prostrata'	CMac
	- 'Stevens Blue'	CKen MAsh NLar
	- 'Toenisvorst'	CKen
	- 'Utah'	CKen
	magnifica 'Mount Si' **new**	CKen NLar
I	- 'Nana'	CKen
	- witches' broom	CKen
	nebrodensis	CKen
	- 'Sicilian Gold'	NLar
	nobilis	see *A. procera*
	nordmanniana	CAco CCVT CDul CJun CMCN CMac CTho ELan EPfP EWTr GMcL IBoy LBuc LPar MJak MMuc NWea SEND SLim SPoG WHar WMou WTSh
	- 'Arne's Dwarf'	CKen
	- 'Barabits' Compact'	NLar
	- 'Barabits' Spreader'	CKen
	- 'Dahlheim'	MAsh
	- 'Dobřichovice'	NLar
	- subsp. ***equi-trojani***	CDul NWea
	- - 'Archer'	CKen
	- 'Golden Spreader' ♀H7	CKen CMac LRHS MAsh MBlu MGos NEgg NLar SCoo SLim
	- 'Hasselt'	see *A. nordmanniana* 'Peve Hasselt'
	- 'Jakobsen'	CKen
	- 'Kbng' **new**	NLar
	- 'Midwinter Gold'	NLar
	- 'Münsterland' **new**	NLar
	- 'Peli' **new**	NLar
	- 'Pendula'	MBlu SMad
§	- 'Peve Hasselt' **new**	CKen NLar
	- 'Silberspitze'	CKen
	numidica	CKen
	- 'Glauca'	CKen
	- 'Lawrenceville'	NEgg
	pindrow	CDul NWea
	pinsapo	CDul WThu
	- 'Atlas'	MAsh NLar
	- 'Aurea' ♀H5	CKen ELan MPkF NHol SLim
I	- 'Aurea Nana'	CKen
	- 'Fastigiata'	MPkF SGol
	- 'Glauca' ♀H5	CAco CCVT CDul CKen ELan MBlu NLar SLim
	- 'Hamondii'	CKen
I	- 'Horstmann'	CKen NEgg NHol NLar SLim
	- 'Marokko'	NLar
	- 'Pendula'	CKen LRHS
	- 'Quicksilver'	CKen
	- 'Ronda Mountain' **new**	NLar
	- 'San Pedro'	CKen NLar
§	***procera***	CBcs CDul CMCN EPfP EWTr NWea WTSh
	- 'Bizarro'	NEgg
	- 'Blaue Hexe'	CKen LRHS MAsh NEgg SLim
	- 'Delbar Cascade'	CKen
	- Glauca Group	CAco CDul EPfP GKin LRHS MAsh MBlu NHol NLar SLim
	- - 'Glauca Prostrata' ♀H6	SLim
	- 'Hupp's Dwarf' **new**	CKen
	- 'La Graciosa'	NLar
	- 'Noble's Dwarf'	SLim
	- 'Prostrata'	MAsh
	- 'Rat Tail'	NLar
	- 'Seattle Mount'	CKen
	- 'Sherwoodii'	CKen SLim
	Rosemoor hybrid	CKen
	sachalinensis	CKen
	sibirica	EPfP NWea
	spectabilis	EPfP
	veitchii	NEgg NWea WTSh
	- 'Heddergott'	CKen NEgg NHol NLar SLim
	- 'Heine'	CKen
	- 'Kramer'	CKen
	- 'Otovenack'	NLar
I	- 'Pendula'	CKen
	- 'Rumburk'	CKen NLar SLim
	- 'Syców'	CKen
	vejarii	SLim

Abromeitiella see *Deuterocohnia*

Abutilon ✿ (*Malvaceae*)

	'Amiti'	GFai WTcb
	'Aphrodite' **new**	WTcb
	'Apricot Belle'	GFai WTcb
	'Ashford Red'	CBcs CCCN ELan LRHS SKHP WCot WFar WKif WTcb
	'Bartley Schwarz'	WTcb
	'Bella Red' (Bella Series)	WTcb
	'Boule de Neige'	CBot GFai
	'Canary Bird' misapplied	see *A.* 'Golden Fleece'
	'Canary Bird' ♀H1b	CBcs CCCN CHll ELan WKif WTcb
	'Cannington Carol' (v) ♀H1b	CCCN CLet ELan EMil LLHF LSRN SEND SLim WTcb
	'Cannington Peter' (v) ♀H1b	CCCN GFai LSRN WTcb
	'Cannington Sally' (v)	GFai WTcb
	'Cannington Sonia' (v)	WTcb
	'Cloth of Gold'	CMac GFai WTcb
	'Cynthia Pike' (v)	CRos EHyd GFai LRHS NRHS
	'Eric's Wotsit'	WTcb
	'Fanta' **new**	WTcb
§	'Feuerglocke'	GFai
	Firebell	see *A.* 'Feuerglocke'
	'Flamenco'	CCCN CWGN WTcb
	'Fool's Gold'	GFai WTcb
	'Gloucestershire Belle'	WTcb
§	'Golden Fleece'	GFai
	'Heather Bennington'	GFai WTcb
	'Henry Makepeace'	GFai WTcb
	'Herefordshire Belle'	WTcb
	'Hinton Seedling'	CCCN CRHN GFai WTcb
	× ***hybridum*** Voss apricot-flowered	WTcb
	- red-flowered	WTcb
	indicum	WTcb
	'Jacqueline Morris'	LRHS
	'John Thompson'	CCCN CWGN LSRN WCot WTcb
	'Julia'	GFai WTcb
	'Juliet'	WTcb
	'Kentish Belle' ♀H3	Widely available
	'Kreutzberger'	WTcb
	'Leila Jackson' **new**	WTcb
	'Lemon Queen'	WTcb
	'Linda Vista Peach' ♀H1b	GFai WTcb
	'Louis Marignac'	GFai WTcb
	Lucky Lantern Tangerine = 'Nuabtang'	SPad
	'Marion' ♀H1b	CRHN EHyd LRHS LSRN NRHS SPlb WTcb
	'Master Michael'	CMac GFai WTcb
	megapotamicum ♀H3	Widely available
	- 'Big Bell' **new**	WGob
	- 'Big Bud' **new**	WTcb
	- 'Compactum'	WTcb
	- 'Ines'	EBee GFai SAko SChF WPGP WTcb
	- 'Joy Bells'	GFai
	- 'Pink Charm'	WTcb

- 'Variegatum' (v) ♀H3	CBcs CBot CCCN CMac ELon EPfP LRHS SEle SKHP SLim SLon SNig SPer SPoG SWvt WGrn WTcb XLum
- 'Wisley Red'	CRHN CTsd LRHS SKHP
× ***milleri*** hort. ♀H3	CCCN CMac CRHN GFai WCot WTcb
- 'Variegatum' (v)	CCCN CMac LRHS WCot WTcb
'Millie Houghton'	WTcb
'Moonchimes'	WTcb
'Nabob' ♀H1b	CBcs CBot CCCN CRHN EMOT EUJe LSou SAko SEND WTcb
'Old Rose Belle'	GFai WTcb
'Orange Glow' (v) ♀H1b	GFai
'Orange Hot Lava'	CBcs CBct EBee GFai SAko SChF SMad WPGP WTcb
'Orange Vein'	GFai WTcb
'Paddy's Nephew'	WTcb
'Patrick Synge'	CBcs CCCN CHGN CHll CMHG EBee SPhx WPGP WTcb
'Patrick's Peach' **new**	WTcb
'Peach Perfect' **new**	WTcb
pictum	WTcb
- 'Thompsonii' (v) ♀H1b	CCCN GFai SEND WTcb
pink-flowered **new**	WTcb
'Pink Lady'	CCCN WTcb
'Pink Lipstick'	WTcb
'Red Bells'	GFai
'Red Goblin'	GFai WTcb
'Red Queen'	WTcb
Red Trumpet = 'Oostredtrump'PBR	GFai WTcb
'Redisch'	GFai WTcb
'Rose Glow'	WTcb
'Roseum' **new**	WTcb
'Rotterdam'	WTcb
'Russels Dwarf'	CCCN WTcb
'Satin Pink Belle'	GFai WTcb
'Savitzii' (v) ♀H1b	GFai MSCN WTcb
'Silver Belle'	CCCN
'Simcox White'	CCCN WTcb
'Snowfall'	GFai WTcb
'Sophia Jackson'	WTcb
'Souvenir de Bonn' (v) ♀H1b	CCCN CHll WTcb
'Sunflower Cream'	WTcb
× ***suntense***	CBcs CCCN CMHG CSBt CWld EBee EHyd EPfP EWld GKev LRHS MSCN NPer NRHS SChF WTcb
- 'Jermyns' ♀H4	CAbP EPfP LSRN MGos SAko SCoo SKHP SWvt
- 'Violetta'	CBot WSHC
'Sydney Belle' **new**	WTcb
'Tango'	CBot CCCN CKel CWGN EUJe SEND WTcb
'Teri Turner'	WTcb
'Thomas Jackson' **new**	WTcb
Tricolour **new**	WTcb
variegated, salmon-flowered (v)	GFai WTcb
'Victorian Lady'	WTcb
'Victory'	CCCN CWGN SKHP WTcb
vitifolium	CBcs CBot CCCN CDTJ CWib EPfP NEgg SEND SPad SPer SPtp WCot WFar WKif
- 'Album'	CBcs CCCN ELan SPer WSHC
- 'Tennant's White' ♀H4	CAbP CBot CCCN EHyd EPfP LRHS NRHS SAko SKHP
- 'Veronica Tennant' ♀H4	EBee EPfP LRHS SChF
'Voodoo'	WTcb
'Wakehurst'	GFai
'Waltz'	CCCN CWGN EMOT EUJe LLHF SBod SEND WCot WTcb
'Westfield Bronze' (v)	CRHN WTcb
'White Dove' **new**	WTcb
'White King'	WTcb
White Trumpet = 'Oostwhitru'PBR	WTcb
'Will's Scarlet' **new**	WTcb
'Worcestershire Belle'	WTcb
Yellow Trumpet = 'Oosttrump'PBR	CBot GFai WTcb

Acacia (*Mimosaceae*)

sp.	LSRN
acinacea	IDee SPlb
adunca	SPlb
alata	WBod
angustissima	SPlb
armata	see *A. paradoxa*
axillaris	SPlb
baileyana ♀H2	CBcs CCCN CEnd CLet CMac CSBt EHoe ELan EPfP LRHS LSRN LTro MGos SBig SCoo SPer SPlb SWvt WBod WFar WPat
- var. ***aurea***	SPlb
- 'Purpurea' ♀H3	CBcs CBod CCCN CDul CEnd CLet CMHG CMac CSBt CSpe CTri CTsd EBee ELan EPfP LHop LSRN MGos NOra SBig SCoo SMad SPlb SPoG SWvt WCot WFar WPGP WPat
- 'Songlines'	LRHS MGos NRHS SHil
boormanii	CAbb GBin SPlb WPGP
covenyi	WPGP
cultriformis	CCCN CTsd ESwi
dealbata ♀H2	Widely available
- 'Gaulois Astier'	CSBt LRHS LSRN MGos SHil SPoG SWvt
- subsp. ***subalpina***	WPGP
'Exeter Hybrid'	CSBt
fimbriata	CRHN
glaucoptera	SPlb
gregorii	SPlb
jibberdingensis	SPlb
julibrissin	see *Albizia julibrissin*
karroo	see *Vachellia karroo*
longifolia	CCCN CDTJ
- subsp. ***sophorae***	CCCN
macradenia	SPlb
melanoxylon	CBcs CDTJ CMCN ESwi MTPN SPlb
nanodealbata	SPad
§ ***paradoxa***	IDee
pataczekii	CSBt EPfP WPGP
pendula	SPlb
podalyriifolia	CCCN SPlb
pravissima ♀H3	CAbb CBcs CChe CDul CHll CLet CMac CTri CTsd EBee ELan EPfP EUJe GBin IDee ILea LHop LRHS LSRN SAko SArc SDix SLim SMad SPlb SPoG SWvt WSHC
retinodes	CBcs CCCN CDTJ CTsd LRHS MTPN SEND SPad SWvt
- 'Lisette'	LRHS MGos
riceana	CTsd SVen
rubida	CTsd SPlb
sentis	see *A. victoriae*
spectabilis	SPlb
suaveolens	SPlb
truncata	SPlb
verticillata	CBcs CCCN CDTJ CHGN CHll EPfP MTPN

– riverine form	CCCN EPfP LRHS SAko SEND
§ ***victoriae***	SPlb

Acaena (*Rosaceae*)

adscendens misapplied	see *A. affinis*, *A. saccaticupula* 'Blue Haze'
adscendens ambig. 'Glauca'	EHoe NBir
§ ***affinis***	EBee ECha MCot
anserinifolia misapplied	see *A. novae-zelandiae*
argentea new	GJos
buchananii	CTri EBee EHoe EPPr GAbr GBin GCrg GEdr MBrN MMuc NLar SCob SRms
caerulea hort.	see *A. caesiiglauca*
§ ***caesiiglauca***	CTri GAbr GMaP
inermis	SPlb
– 'Purpurea'	CSam EBee ECha ECtt EHoe EWes GAbr GMaP GQue MMuc NDov NHol NHpl NLar NWad SPlb WMoo XLum
magellanica	GCal GKev
microphylla 🏆H5	CSam CTri MBel MBrN NLar SPlb SRms WMoo
– Copper Carpet	see *A. microphylla* 'Kupferteppich'
– 'Glauca'	see *A. caesiiglauca*
– 'Grüner Zwerg'	NLar
§ – 'Kupferteppich'	CSam ECtt EHoe ELan EPPr GAbr GBin GCal GCrg GKev GLog GMaP GQue LHop MHol MRav NBir NBro NChi NLar SCob SRms WMoo XLum
minor var. ***antarctica***	GBin
§ ***novae-zelandiae***	CTri EBee GKev SDix WMoo XLum
ovalifolia	GAbr GKev
'Pewter'	see *A. saccaticupula* 'Blue Haze'
'Purple Carpet'	see *A. microphylla* 'Kupferteppich'
'Purple Haze'	CSpe SCob
saccaticupula	GKev
§ – 'Blue Haze'	CRos EBee ECha ECho EDAr EHyd LHop LRHS MBrN MRav NRHS SPlb SRms WMoo
sericea	GJos
tesca	GBin

Acalypha (*Euphorbiaceae*)

§ ***herzogiana***	CCCN EShb
pendula misapplied	see *A. herzogiana*
reptans misapplied	see *A. herzogiana*

Acanthocalyx see *Morina*

Acantholimon (*Plumbaginaceae*)

acerosum	GKev
androsaceum	see *A. ulicinum*
armenum	XSen
glumaceum	LLHF
§ ***ulicinum***	XEll
venustum new	LLHF

Acanthopanax see *Eleutherococcus*

ricinifolius	see *Kalopanax septemlobus*

Acanthus ✿ (*Acanthaceae*)

arboreus	XLum
balcanicus misapplied	see *A. hungaricus*
'Candelabra'	MAvo
caroli-alexandri	see *A. spinosus* L.
dioscoridis	GCal SMHy
– var. ***perringii***	CDor ECha GBin MNrw NLar WCot WFar XLum
eminens	WCot
hirsutus	CDor CFis EPri IFoB WCot
– subsp. ***syriacus***	ECha EHrv GCal SIgm
'Hollande du Nort'	XLum
§ ***hungaricus***	CDor CHid CMHG CMac EBee ELan ILea LCro LOPS LRHS MBel MMuc MRav NLar SCob SDix SWat WCot WFar XLum
– MESE 561	EPPr
– 'White Lips'	EBee MAvo MNrw NLar WCot WHlf
longifolius Host	see *A. hungaricus*
mollis	Widely available
– 'Fielding Gold'	see *A. mollis* 'Hollard's Gold'
– free-flowering	ESwi GCal MAvo XLum
§ – 'Hollard's Gold'	CBct CMac EAEE EBee ECha ECtt EHoe ELan EPPr EPfP GBuc GCal GKin GMaP LHop LRHS LSou MAvo MNrw NGdn NLar SDix SPoG SRms SWat WCot WFar WSHC
– 'Jefalba'	see *A. mollis* (Latifolius Group) 'Rue Ledan'
– Latifolius Group	CDor MRav SRms WHil WHoo
§ – – 'Rue Ledan'	EBee ECtt EPPr EWTr GBin LHop LRHS MAvo MNrw NGdn NLar NPnk NSti SCob SMHy SPhx WCot XLum
– – 'Sjaak'	MAvo
– 'Long Spike'	GCal
– 'Tasmanian Angel' (v)	CAbb CBct CBod CWGN EBee ECtt EHyd ESwi IBoy LHop LPre LRHS MHol NRHS SBig SCob SMad SPoG WCot WFar XLum
'Morning's Candle'	CBct EBee ECtt MNrw NGdn NLar XLum
sennii	CAby IMou LTro SPhx WHil WSHC XLum
spinosus misapplied	see *A. spinosus* Spinosissimus Group
§ ***spinosus*** L.	Widely available
– Ferguson's form	EBee MAvo WCot WFar XLum
– 'Lady Moore' (v)	CDor NLar XLum
– 'Royal Haughty'	MAvo XLum
§ – Spinosissimus Group	CBct CBod CMHG CTsd ECha ELan GBin GCal GCra IBoy LEdu MGos MRav NPnk SMad SWat WCot WFar WHar
'Summer Beauty'	ECtt EWes LHop LRHS MAvo MRav WCot WFar XLum
'Whitewater' (v)	CWGN EBee ECtt GEdr LHop LPre MHol NLar NSti NWad SBig SCob SMad SPad SPoG SRms WCot WHil

Acca (*Myrtaceae*)

sellowiana (F)	CAgr CBcs CCCN CCht CDTJ CDul CHll CMac CTsd CWib ELan EMil EPfP EShb LHop LPar LRHS LSou MGos MHtn NPla SCob SEle SLim SPer SPlb SPoG SVic SWvt XSen
– 'Apollo' (F)	EUJe
– 'Mammoth' (F)	CBcs CCCN
– 'Triumph' (F)	CBcs CCCN
– 'Unique' (F)	ERea EUJe
– 'Variegata' (F/v)	CCCN

Acer ✿ (*Sapindaceae*)

amoenum B&SWJ 10916	WCru
– B&SWJ 10977	WCru
– 'Firecracker'	see *A. palmatum* 'Firecracker'
'Ample Surprise'	MBlu
buergerianum	CAco CDul CJun CMCN CMen CTho ECrN MMuc MPkF NLar SBrt SGol WMou

- B&SWJ 12676 from South Korea	WCru
- var. ***formosanum*** CWJ 12477	WCru
- 'Marubato-kaede' **new**	CMCN
- 'Mino-yatsubusa'	MPkF
- 'Miyasama-yatsubusa'	MPkF
- 'Naruto'	CMCN MPkF
campbellii	MBlu
- subsp. ***campbellii*** GWJ 9360	WCru
- - NJM 12.069	WPGP
- - PAB 13.071 **new**	LEdu
- 'Exuberance'	CJun
* - var. ***fansipanense***	WPGP
campestre 🏆H6	Widely available
- 'Anny's Globe' **new**	MBlu
- 'Carnival' (v) 🏆H6	CCVT CEnd EBee ECrN ELon EMOT MAsh MBlu NOrn SCob SGol SMad SPer SPoG SWvt WHar
- 'Eco Sentry' PBR	EBee
- 'Elsrijk'	CCVT CLnd EMOT SCoo SGol
- 'Evelyn'	see *A. campestre* 'Queen Elizabeth'
- 'Evenley Red'	MBlu WPGP
- 'Green Column' **new**	EMOT
- 'Pendulum'	CEnd
- 'Postelense'	MBlu
- 'Pulverulentum' (v)	NEgg
§ - 'Queen Elizabeth'	CDul MGos SGol
- 'Red Shine'	EBar EMOT SGol
- 'Royal Ruby'	MGos
- 'Ruby Glow' 🏆H6	CEnd
I - 'Silver Celebration' (v)	CJun
- 'William Caldwell'	CEnd CTho MBlu
capillipes	CBcs CDul CMCN CTho CWib ELan MJak MMuc NOrn NWea SCob SPlb WHCr WHar WMat WPGP WTSh
- 'Antoine'	MBlu
- 'Candy Stripe'	see *A. × conspicuum* 'Candy Stripe'
- 'Honey Dew'	CJun SSta
cappadocicum	CCVT CDul CEnd CMCN ECrN MHid NWea WMou
- 'Aureum' 🏆H6	CBcs CDul CEnd CMCN CNWT CTho EBee ECrN ELan EPfP GKin IArd LPar MAsh MBlu MRav NLar NOra NOrn SCob SGol SMad SPer SWvt WFar WHar WHor WMat WTSh
- var. ***mono***	see *A. pictum*
- 'Rubrum' 🏆H6	CArg CBcs CDul CLnd CMCN EBee ECrN EPfP GKin IDee MBlu MMuc MRav NOra NOrn SCob SEND SGol SPer WFar WHar WHer WHor WMat
carpinifolium	CDul CMCN EBee EBtc EPfP IArd MBlu MPkF NLar WPGP
- B&SWJ 10955	WCru
- B&SWJ 11124	WCru
§ ***caudatifolium***	CMCN WPat
- CWJ 12403	WCru
- RWJ 9843	WCru
§ ***caudatum*** GWJ 9279	WCru
- GWJ 9317	WCru
- HWJK 2240	WCru
- HWJK 2338	WCru
- subsp. ***ukurunduense***	MPkF
- - B&SWJ 8658	WCru
circinatum	CAco CBcs CCVT CDul CJun CMCN ECrN IVic MBlu MHid MMuc NEgg NLar NWea SEND SPlb WMou
- B&SWJ 9565	WCru

- 'Burgundy Jewel'	CJun
- 'Monroe'	CJun CMCN SGol
- 'Pacific Fire'	CJun
- 'Sunny Sister'	LRHS
circinatum × palmatum	SBig
cissifolium	CMCN EPfP NLar
- B&SWJ 10801	WCru
§ × ***conspicuum*** 'Candy Stripe'	CJun NLar WPGP
- 'Elephant's Ear'	CJun MBlu NLar
- 'Phoenix'	CEnd CJun CMCN CRos EPfP GKin IVic LRHS MBlu NLar SPoG SSta WHar WPGP WPat
- 'Silver Ghost'	SWvt
§ - 'Silver Vein'	CEnd CJun CMCN EPfP NLar SSta SWvt WPGP
crataegifolium	SSta
- B&SWJ 11036	WCru
- B&SWJ 11355	WCru
- 'Ittai-san-nishiki'	SSta
- 'Meuri-keade-no-fuiri' (v)	MPkF
- 'Meuri-no-ōfu' (v)	MPkF SSta
- 'Veitchii' (v)	CJun CMCN EBee EPfP MBlu MPkF SBig SSta
creticum misapplied	see *A. sempervirens*
dasycarpum	see *A. saccharinum*
davidii	CBcs CDul CTsd ECrN LCro MBlu MGos MMuc MRav NOrn SCob SGol SSta WHar WPat
- AC 1471	MHid
§ - 'Canton'	CJun SSta
- 'Cantonspark'	see *A. davidii* 'Canton'
- 'Cascade'	CJun MBlu SSta WHor
- 'Ernest Wilson'	SSta
- 'George Forrest' 🏆H5	CAco CBcs CDul CJun CMCN CMac CTho EBee ELan EPfP GBin MMuc NLar NOra NOrn NWea SCob SPoG SSta SWvt WHar WMat WMou
- 'Hagelunie'	SBir SSta
- 'Hansu-suru' (v)	SSta
- 'Karmen'	CBcs CDul CJun EPfP SSta WPGP
- 'Madeline Spitta'	LRHS
- 'Purple Bark'	CJun NLar SBir SSta
- 'Rosalie'	CBcs CJun EPfP MBlu NLar SBir SSta WHor
- 'Sekka'	SSta
- 'Serpentine'	CBcs CDul CJun CMCN CNWT ELan EPfP IDee MBlu NEgg NLar SSta WHor
- 'Silver Vein'	see *A. × conspicuum* 'Silver Vein'
- Viper = 'Mindavi'	CDul EBee EPfP GQue LPre LRHS NLar NOra NWea SPer SPoG WMat
diabolicum	CMCN
elegantulum	CJun GBin WPGP
erianthum	CMCN
erythranthum B&SWJ 11733	WCru
- DJHV 06147	WCru
fabri	CDul
- WWJ 11614	WCru
flabellatum	CJun CMCN WPat
- NJM 11.017	WPGP
- PAB 9865	LEdu
- var. ***yunnanense***	CMCN MHid MMuc WPat
forrestii	CMCN MMuc NEgg WPat
- BWJ 7515	WCru
- 'Alice'	CEnd CJun SSta
- 'Inoense'	SSta
- 'Sirene'	CJun SSta
- 'Sparkling'	CJun

× ***freemanii***	CMCN
- 'Armstrong'	CCVT EMOT SGol
- Autumn Blaze = 'Jeffersred' ♀H6	CBcs CCVT CDul CLnd CMCN CTho EMOT EPfP IArd MBlu MGos MMuc NLar NOra NOrn SBir SCoo SEND SGol SPer SPoG WHar WMat WMou
- Celebration = 'Celzam'	CArg CCVT CDul CTho EBee MGos
- 'Indian Summer'	see *A.* × *freemanii* 'Morgan'
§ - 'Morgan'	CJun NLar
ginnala	see *A. tataricum* subsp. *ginnala*
globosum	see *A. platanoides* 'Globosum'
grandidentatum	see *A. saccharum* subsp. *grandidentatum*
griseum ♀H5	Widely available
- 'Golden Lucky'	NLar
grosseri	CDul CMCN CTri SGol
- var. ***hersii***	CBcs CDul CMac CWib EBee ECrN ELan EPfP ESps LSRN MMuc MRav NOra NOrn NWea SCob SPoG SSta SWvt WHar WMat
- 'Leiden'	EPfP
heldreichii	CMCN
henryi	CBcs CDul EPfP NEgg NLar
heptaphlebium B&SWJ 11695	WCru
- B&SWJ 11713	WCru
- DJHV 06063	WCru
- FMWJ 13369	WCru
hyrcanum	LRHS
japonicum	CMCN LPar MMuc SEWo
- B&SWJ 8417	WCru
- B&SWJ 12847	WCru
§ - 'Aconitifolium' ♀H6	Widely available
- 'Aki-hi'	NLar
- 'Ao-jutan'	CJun
- 'Attaryi'	CMen MPkF NEgg
- 'Aureum'	see *A. shirasawanum* 'Aureum'
- 'Emmit's Pumpkins'	CJun
- 'Ezo-no-momiji'	see *A. shirasawanum* 'Ezo-no-momiji'
- 'Fairy Lights'	NLar
- 'Filicifolium'	see *A. japonicum* 'Aconitifolium'
- 'Green Cascade' ♀H6	CAco CEnd CJun CMCN CMac CMen IVic LRHS MGos MPkF NEgg NLar NRHS SBig SGol WPat
- 'King's Copse'	CJun LRHS NRHS
- 'Laciniatum'	see *A. japonicum* 'Aconitifolium'
- f. ***microphyllum***	see *A. shirasawanum* 'Microphyllum'
- 'Ogurayama'	see *A. shirasawanum* 'Ogurayama'
- 'Ō-isami'	MPkF SBig
- 'Ō-taki'	CJun
- 'Vitifolium' ♀H6	CEnd CJun CMCN CMac CTho ELan EPfP GBin LPar LRHS MBlu MGos MPkF NEgg NLar NRHS SBig SGol SPer SSta WCFE WPGP WPat WTSh
kawakamii	see *A. caudatifolium*
laevigatum B&SWJ 11684	WCru
- FMWJ 13378	WCru
- NJM 10.049	WPGP
§ - var. ***reticulatum*** B&SWJ 11698	WCru
laurinum NJM 10.048	WPGP
- NJM 10.087	WPGP
- NJM 10.111	WPGP
- NJM 10.112	WPGP
laxiflorum	SSta
macrophyllum	CDul CMCN EPfP MBlu
mandshuricum	CDul CMCN
- B&SWJ 12592	WCru
§ ***maximowiczianum***	CBcs CMCN MMuc MPkF SGol SSta
maximowiczii	MPkF WHCr
metcalfii	CFil
micranthum ♀H6	CDul CMCN EBee EPfP MBlu NLar WHar WPGP WPat
miyabei	MPkF
mono	see *A. pictum*
monspessulanum	CDul CMCN MMuc SEND
- subsp. ***oksalianum***	LRHS WMat
morifolium B&SWJ 11473	WCru
morrisonense Hayata	see *A. caudatifolium*
negundo	CAco CDul CMCN CWib ECrN EMOT ESps NWea SCob SWvt
- 'Auratum'	CMCN SGol
- 'Aureomarginatum' (v)	CCVT ECrN SGol
- 'Aureovariegatum' (v)	CBcs
§ - 'Elegans' (v)	CDul CEnd CMCN EMOT ESps SCoo WHar
- 'Elegantissimum'	see *A. negundo* 'Elegans'
- 'Flamingo' (v)	CAco CBcs CCVT CDul CEnd CMCN CMac CWib ECrN ELan ELon EMOT EPfP ESps LHop MAsh NLar NOra NWea SCob SGol SHil SPer SPoG SWvt WFar WHar WMat
- 'Kelly's Gold'	CBcs CCVT CMCN EMOT ESps NLar NOrn NWea SCob SGol WHar WMat
- subsp. ***mexicanum***	CFil
- 'Sensation'	NLar
- 'Variegatum' (v)	CBcs ECrN SGol
- var. ***violaceum*** ♀H6	CEnd CMCN SVen
- 'Winter Lightning' ♀H6	NLar
nikoense misapplied	see *A. maximowiczianum*
nipponicum	CDul CMCN
'Norwegian Sunset'	CCVT EMOT
oblongum	CMCN
- FMWJ 13412 new	WCru
- KWJ 12232	WCru
oliverianum	CDul CMCN IArd MBlu
- subsp. ***formosanum*** CWJ 12437	WCru
opalus	CMCN SEND
orientale misapplied	see *A. sempervirens*
orizabense	EBee
Pacific Sunset = 'Warrenred'	NLar
palmatum	CBcs CCVT CDul CMCN CMHG CMen CSBt CTri CWib EMOT EPfP ESps ETod GKin LCro LPar MBlu MGos NEgg NWea SArc SCob SEWo SGol SPlb SWvt WFar WHar WPat WTSh
- 'Akane' (P)	CMen
§ - 'Aka-shigitatsu-sawa' (M)	CBcs CJun CMCN CMen ESMi MGos MJak MPkF NLar SAko SGol SPer
- 'Akegarasu' (M)	CMCN CMen NLar
- 'Alpenweiss' (P)	CJun
- 'Amagi-shigure' (M)	CJun MPkF
- 'Amber Ghost' (M)	CJun
- 'Boskoop Glory' (A)	GKin
- 'Anne-Irene' (P)	MPkF
- 'Aoba-jo' (Dw)	CJun CMen MPkF NEgg
- 'Ao-kanzashi' (P/v)	MPkF NLar
- 'Ao-shidare' (D)	CJun
- 'Aoshime-no-uchi'	see *A. palmatum* 'Shinobuga-oka'
- 'Aoyagi' (P)	CEnd CJun CMCN CMen ELon ESMi LRHS MGos MPkF NEgg NLar NRHS WPat

– 'Aoyagi-gawa'	CJun
§ – 'Arakawa' (P)	CEnd CMCN CMac CMen ESMi MPkF NEgg SBod
– 'Arakawa-ukon'	CJun NLar
– 'Aratama' (Dw)	CJun CMCN CMen ESMi MJak MPkF
– 'Ariadne' (M/v) ♀H6	CEnd CJun LRHS MGos MPkF NLar SBig SCoo SPoG WMou WPat
– 'Ariake-nomura' (A)	CMen MPkF
– 'Asahi-zuru' (P/v)	CBcs CJun CMCN CMen CRos LRHS MGos NLar NRHS SBod SHil SPer WMat
– 'Ashurst Wood'	SBig
– 'Atrolineare' (L)	CMen MPkF NEgg NLar SPoG
– 'Atropurpureum' (A)	Widely available
– 'Atropurpureum Novum'	MPkF NLar SGol
– 'Attraction' (P)	CMen NEgg
– 'Aureum' (P)	CAco CMCN CMen CRos CTri CWib ELan EPfP GMcL IBoy LMil LPar LRHS MAsh MBlu MGos MPkF NEgg NLar NRHS SBod SPoG WCFE WFar
– 'Autumn Fire' (D)	CJun
– 'Autumn Glory' (M)	CAco CEnd CJun CMac CMen WPat
– 'Autumn Red' (M)	CMen ESMi LRHS NEgg
* – 'Autumn Showers'	CEnd CJun
– 'Azuma-murasaki' (M)	CJun CMen MPkF NEgg NLar
– 'Baby Lace' (Dw)	CWGN IVic SAko
– 'Balcombe Green' (D)	SBig
– 'Baldsmith' (D)	CJun EUJe LRHS MPkF SBod WPat
– 'Barrie Bergman' (D)	CJun
– 'Beni-chidori' (P)	CMen SBod
– 'Beni-fushigi' (P)	MPkF
– 'Beni-gasa' (M)	CJun MPkF WPat
– 'Beni-hime' (Dw)	MPkF SAko WPat
– 'Beni-hoshi' (Dw)	MPkF
– 'Beni-kagami' (M)	CEnd CJun CMCN LRHS MPkF NLar SGol
– 'Beni-kawa' (P)	CJun CMCN CMen MPkF SBig SGol WPat
– 'Beni-komachi' (P)	CAco CEnd CJun CMCN CMen CRos EPfP ESMi LRHS MGos MPkF NLar NRHS SCob SHil SSta
– 'Beni-kosode' (v) **new**	MPkF NLar
– 'Beni-maiko' (P) ♀H6	CEnd CJun CMCN CMen CRos CWib EPfP ESMi EUJe LRHS MGos MJak MPkF NBes NLar NOrn NRHS SBig SCob SCoo SHil SWvt WPat
– 'Beni-musume'	MPkF
– 'Beni-otake' (L)	CBcs CJun CMen ELan EPfP ESMi EUJe IVic LRHS MGos MPkF NEgg NLar SAko SBig SBod SCob SWeb WPat
– 'Beni-otome'	MPkF
– 'Beni-schichi-henge' (P/v)	CBcs CEnd CJun CMCN CMen CRos CWGN EBee ELon ESMi LRHS MAsh MGos MJak MPkF NEgg NHol NLar NOra NRHS SAko SBig SBod SCob SCoo SGol SHil SSta WMat WPat
– 'Beni-shidare' (D)	LPar NLar SCob
– 'Beni-shidare Tricolor'	see *A. palmatum* 'Toyama-nishiki'
– 'Beni-shidare Variegated'	see *A. palmatum* 'Toyama-nishiki'
– 'Beni-shi-en' (P)	CJun MPkF NLar WPat
– 'Beni-shigitatsu-sawa'	see *A. palmatum* 'Aka-shigitatsu-sawa'
– 'Beni-tsukasa' (P/v) ♀H6	CEnd CJun CMCN CMen ESMi LRHS MAsh MPkF NLar NRHS SSta
– 'Beni-tsuru'	MPkF
– 'Beni-yubi-gohon' (P)	CBcs CJun MJak MPkF NLar
– 'Beni-zuru' (P)	WPat
– 'Berrima Bridge' (D)	CJun
– 'Berry Broom'	MPkF NLar SBod
– 'Berry Dwarf' (Dw)	CJun MPkF
– 'Bewley's Red' (D)	CJun
– 'Bi Hō' (P)	CJun IVic LCro LRHS NLar SAko SGol WPat
– 'Black Lace' (M)	LRHS MPkF NLar NRHS SHil
– 'Bloodgood' (A) ♀H6	Widely available
– 'Bonfire' misapplied	see *A. palmatum* 'Seigai'
– 'Bonfire' ambig.	CJun
– 'Bonnie Bergman'	CJun
– 'Brandt's Dwarf' (Dw)	NLar WPat
– 'Brocade' (D)	CJun IVic MPkF WPat
– 'Bronzewing' (D)	CJun
– 'Burgundy Lace' (M) ♀H6	CAco CBcs CEnd CJun CMCN CMen CWib ELan EPfP ESMi EUJe GKin IBoy LMil LRHS LSRN MAsh MGos MJak MPkF NEgg NRHS SBig SBod SCoo SGol SPer SPoG SSta WPat
– 'Butterfly' (P/v)	Widely available
– 'Calico' (P)	CJun
– 'Caperci Dwarf' (Dw)	MPkF
– 'Carlis Corner' (Dw)	CJun MPkF
– 'Carminium'	see *A. palmatum* 'Corallinum'
– 'Chantilly Lace' (D)	CJun IBoy MPkF
– 'Chikuma-no' (A)	CMen MPkF NLar
– 'Chirimen-nishiki' (P/v)	MPkF
– 'Chishio' (P)	CMCN CMen ESMi LMil MPkF SBig SBod WPat
– 'Chishio Improved' (P)	CEnd CJun CMCN CMac CMen CTho EPfP LRHS MAsh MGos MPkF NHol NLar NOrn NRHS SBig SWvt
– 'Chitose-yama' (M) ♀H6	CDul CEnd CJun CMCN CMen EPfP GKin LPar LRHS MAsh MGos MPkF NEgg NLar NRHS SBod SGol SLim SSta WPat
§ – 'Chiyo-hime'	CRos ELan EPfP LCro LOPS LPar NEgg NLar NPri
– 'Collingwood Ingram'	SGol
– 'Coonara Pygmy' (Dw)	CJun CMCN CMac CMen ESMi GKin MPkF SBod SCoo
– 'Coral Pink' (Dw)	CJun CMen MPkF SGol SSta
§ – 'Corallinum' (P) ♀H6	CAco CEnd CJun CMCN CMen MPkF NLar SAko SBod WCFE WPat
– var. ***coreanum*** B&SWJ 8606	WCru
– 'Crimson Carol' (M)	CJun
– 'Crimson Prince'	CJun MPkF SCoo
– 'Crimson Princess' (D)	CBcs EPfP EUJe LRHS MJak MPkF NRHS SBod SWeb WMat
– 'Crimson Queen' (D) ♀H6	Widely available
– 'Crippsii' (D)	CBcs CMac CMen MPkF SBod SCoo SGol
– 'Deshōjō' (P)	CMCN CMen CWib ESMi LPar MBlu MGos MPkF NLar SCoo SGol WMat
– 'Diana' (Dw)	CJun CMen MPkF NLar SGol
– 'Diane Verkade'	MPkF
– 'Dissectum' (D)	CAco CTho EMOT LBrs LPar NOra NWea WHar WTSh
– 'Dissectum Flavescens' (D)	CAco CEnd CJun CMac CMen LRHS MBlu MGos MPkF NEgg NRHS SBod SWeb WMat
– Dissectum Group (D)	Widely available
§ – 'Dissectum Nigrum' (D)	CAco CJun CMac CMen LRHS MAsh MPkF NEgg NLar NRHS SWeb WPat
– 'Dissectum Palmatifidum' (D)	CAco CMen EUJe LRHS MPkF NEgg NRHS SBod SCoo SGol SPer

	– 'Dissectum Rubrifolium' (D)	MPkF
§	– 'Dissectum Variegatum' (Dw/v)	CJun ESps LRHS MPkF NRHS
	– Dissectum Viride Group	Widely available
	– 'Donzuru-bo'	CJun
	– 'Dormansland'	SBig
	– 'Dragon's Fire'	CJun
	– 'Earthfire'	MJak MPkF WPat
I	– 'Ebbingei'	CMac
	– 'Eddisbury' (P) ♀H6	CEnd CJun CMen CSBt EPfP MBlu NLar SSta WPGP WPat
	– 'Edna Bergman' (M)	CJun
	– 'Effegi'	see *A. palmatum* 'Fireglow'
§	– 'Elegans' (M) ♀H6	CMen EPfP LRHS MPkF NEgg NLar NRHS
	– 'Elizabeth' (Dw)	CJun
	– 'Ellen' (D)	CJun LBuc MPkF NLar WPat
	– 'Emerald Lace' (D) ♀H6	CJun CRos EBee EUJe GKin LBuc LCro LOPS LRHS MGos MPkF NEgg NLar NRHS SBod SHil SPoG SSta WCFE WPat
	– 'Emma' (D)	LBuc NLar
	– 'Englishtown' (Dw)	NLar WPat
	– 'Enkan' (L)	CEnd CJun CMen CWGN EBee ESMi LRHS MGos MPkF NLar NOra NPri NRHS SGol SPoG WMat WPat
	– 'Eono-momiji'	CMen
	– 'Ever Red'	see *A. palmatum* 'Dissectum Nigrum'
	– 'Fairy Hair' (L)	CJun NLar
	– 'Fall's Fire' (P)	CJun NLar
	– 'Fascination' (M)	CJun
	– 'Felice' (D)	CJun MPkF WPat
	– 'Filigree' (Dw/v)	CAco CJun CMCN CMen EPfP LRHS MAsh MGos MPkF NLar NRHS SBig SBod SSta WCFE WPat
	– 'Fior d'Arancio' (M)	CJun IVic MPkF NLar WPat
	– 'Fireball'	CJun
§	– 'Firecracker'^{PBR} (D)	LBuc MPkF NEgg NLar
§	– 'Fireglow' (A)	CBcs CEnd CJun CMCN CMen CSBt ESMi LBrs LMil LPar LRHS LSRN MGos MJak MPkF NEgg NLar NRHS SAko SBod SCob SCoo SGol SPer SWeb WCFE WPat
	– 'First Ghost' (M/v)	CJun
	– 'Fransman'	NLar
	– 'Frederici Guglielmi'	see *A. palmatum* 'Dissectum Variegatum'
	– 'Garnet' (D) ♀H6	Widely available
	– 'Garyū' (Dw)	MPkF
	– 'Geisha' (Dw)	MPkF
	– 'Geisha Gone Wild' (P/v)	CJun
	– 'Gentaku'	CJun
	– 'Germaine's Gyration' (D)	CJun
	– 'Gibbsii'	CMen
	– 'Ginko-san' **new**	WPat
I	– 'Globosum' (Dw)	IBoy MPkF
	– 'Glowing Embers' (P)	CJun MPkF WPat
	– 'Golden Pond' (A)	CJun
	– 'Goshiki-kotohime' (Dw/v)	CJun CMCN NLar
	– 'Goshiki-shidare'	see *A. palmatum* 'Toyama-nishiki'
	– 'Goten-nomura'	NLar
	– 'Grace'	CJun
	– 'Grandma Ghost' (M)	CJun
	– 'Green Flag'	CJun
	– 'Green Globe' (D)	CJun
	– 'Green Hornet' (D)	CJun
	– 'Green Lace' (D)	CMen MPkF
	– 'Green Mist' (D)	CJun LRHS NRHS WPat
	– 'Green Star' (A)	WPat
	– 'Green Trompenburg' (M)	CJun CMen GBin GMcL MPkF NEgg NLar
	– 'Groundcover' (Dw)	MPkF
§	– 'Hagoromo'	CMac CMen ESMi MPkF NEgg SCoo
	– 'Hana-matoi'^{PBR} (v)	CMCN
	– 'Hanami-nishiki' (Dw)	CMen MPkF WPat
	– 'Hanzel' (D)	WPat
	– 'Happy Corallinum' (A) **new**	CJun
	– 'Haru-iro'	CJun
	– 'Harusame' (P/v)	MPkF NLar WPat
	– 'Hazeroino' (v)	CMen MPkF
	– 'Heartbeat' (D)	CJun LRHS MPkF SBod WPat
	– 'Heffner's Red'	CJun
	– 'Helena'	see *A. shirasawanum* 'Helena'
	– var. ***heptalobum***	CMCN
	– 'Heptalobum Elegans Purpureum'	see *A. palmatum* 'Hessei'
	– 'Herbstfeuer' (P)	CJun MPkF WPat
§	– 'Hessei' (M)	CEnd CMen MPkF NLar
	– 'Higasa-yama' (P/v)	CAco CBcs CEnd CJun CMCN CMen CWGN ESMi IVic LRHS MPkF NLar SBod SGol WPat
	– 'Hino-tori-nishiki'	CMen NLar SBod SGol
	– 'Hōgyoku' (A)	CBcs CJun CMCN CMen MPkF SBod
	– 'Hondoshi' (A)	LPar NLar
	– 'Hōno-o'	MPkF
	– 'Hoshi-kuzu' (Dw)	MPkF
	– 'Hupp's Dwarf' (Dw)	CJun MPkF
	– 'Hupp's Red Willow'	NLar WMat
	– 'Ibo-nishiki' (P)	CMen ESMi MPkF NEgg
	– 'Ichigyōji' (A)	CEnd CJun CMen IVic MAsh NEgg NLar SBig WPGP WPat
	– 'Ightham Gold'	SSta
	– 'Iijima-sunago' (M)	CMen MPkF
	– 'Inaba-shidare' (D) ♀H6	Widely available
	– 'Inazuma' (M)	CAco CBcs CJun CMCN CMen LRHS MPkF NLar NRHS SBod SCoo SGol SLau WPat
	– 'Irish Lace'	CJun
	– 'Irish Lace' × ***palmatum*** 'Yasemin' **new**	CJun
	– 'Iso-chidori' (Dw)	MPkF
	– 'Issai-nishiki'	CMen MPkF
*	– 'Issai-nishiki-kawazu'	MPkF
	– 'Jane'	CJun MPkF
	– 'Japanese Sunrise' (P)	CBcs CJun SBod WMat WPat
	– 'Jerre Schwartz' (Dw)	CRos EPfP LCro LRHS MGos MPkF NLar NRHS SBod SHil WPat
	– 'Jirō-shidare' (P)	CJun EPfP LRHS MPkF NLar SBig
	– 'JJ'	CJun
	– 'Julia D.'	CJun
	– 'Kaba' (Dw)	CMen IVic MPkF SPoG
	– 'Kagero' (A/v)	MPkF
§	– 'Kagiri-nishiki' (P/v)	CBcs CJun CMCN CMac CMen CWGN IVic MPkF NEgg NLar SBod SPer SWeb
	– 'Kamagata' (Dw)	CAco CEnd CJun CMCN CMen ESMi IVic LRHS MAsh MGos MPkF NLar NRHS SCoo WPat
	– 'Kandy Kitchen' (Dw)	CJun CMen LRHS
	– 'Karaori-nishiki' (P/v)	CMen MPkF NLar
	– 'Karasu-gawa' (P/v)	CJun CMen CWGN MPkF
	– 'Kasagiyama' (M)	CEnd CJun CMen LRHS MPkF NLar NRHS
	– 'Kasen-nishiki' (P)	CMen MPkF
	– 'Kashima' (Dw)	CEnd CJun CMCN CMen EBee LRHS MPkF NEgg NLar NRHS SBod WPat

	– 'Kashima-yatsubusa'	MPkF
	– 'Katja'	CJun CMen MPkF
	– 'Katsura' (P) ♀H6	Widely available
	– 'Katsura-nishiki'	MPkF
	– 'Kawahara Rose'	MPkF
I	– 'Kawaii' (D)	CJun
	– 'Ki-hachijō' (M)	CJun CMCN CMen GMcL MPkF NLar SBod WPat
	– 'Killarney' (M)	CJun
	– 'Kingsville Variegated' (P/v)	MPkF
	– 'Kinky Krinkle' (P)	CJun
	– 'Kinran' (M)	CAco CMen ESMi LRHS MPkF NEgg NRHS
	– 'Kinshii' (L) ♀H6	CEnd CJun CMCN CMen EPfP GBin IVic LRHS MPkF NEgg NLar NOra NRHS SAko WMat WPat
	– 'Kiri-nishiki' (D)	CJun CMen LRHS MPkF NLar NRHS
	– 'Ki-shuzan' (M)	CJun
	– 'Kiyohime' (Dw) ♀H6	CMCN CMen MPkF NEgg SBod WPat
	– 'Koba-shōjō' (M)	MPkF
	– 'Kogane-nishiki' (P)	CMen LPar NLar SGol
	– 'Kogane-sakae' (A)	CJun MPkF
	– 'Kokobunji-nishiki' (v)	MPkF
	– 'Komachi-hime' (Dw)	CJun CMen MPkF SBod WPat
	– 'Komon-nishiki' (P/v)	CJun CMen MPkF NEgg
	– 'Korean Gem' (M)	CAco CJun CMen MPkF NEgg
	– 'Koriba' (P)	CJun MPkF NLar
	– 'Koshibori-nishiki' (P)	MPkF
	– 'Kotohime' (Dw)	CJun CMCN CMen CRos IVic MGos MPkF NLar SBig SCoo SHil SPoG
	– 'Koto-ito-komachi' (Dw)	CJun CMen ESMi LRHS MPkF NEgg NRHS SBod
	– 'Koto-maru' (Dw)	NLar SBod SGol
	– 'Koto-no-ito' (L)	CMCN LRHS MBlu MGos MPkF NLar NRHS SAko SBod SGol SPoG WPat
	– 'Koya-san' (Dw)	CMen MPkF NLar
	– 'Kurabu-yama' (M)	CMen MPkF
	– 'Kuro-hime' (Dw)	WPat
	– 'Kurui-jishi' (Dw)	MPkF
	– 'Kyōryū'	MPkF
	– 'Kyra'	CMen MPkF
	– 'Lace Lady' (D)	LRHS
	– 'Leather Leaf'	MPkF
	– 'Limelight' (P)	SBod
§	– 'Linearilobum' (L)	CBcs CMen EPfP IVic LRHS MGos MPkF NEgg NLar NOra SBod SCoo SLau WMat
*	– 'Lionheart' (D)	CJun CMen CWGN ESMi LRHS MGos MPkF NLar NRHS SBod SCoo
	– 'Little Princess'	see *A. palmatum* 'Chiyo-hime'
	– 'Lozita' (P)	NLar WPat
	– 'Lutescens' (A)	CMen MPkF NEgg
	– 'Lydia'	MPkF
	– 'Maiko' (P)	CMen MPkF
	– 'Mama' (P)	CMen
	– 'Mapi-no-machi-hime' (Dw)	CEnd CJun CMCN CMen LRHS MAsh MPkF NHol NRHS WPat
	– 'Marakumo' (P)	MPkF
	– 'Marasaki-yama'	MPkF
	– 'Mardi Gras'	CJun
	– 'Margaret'	MPkF
	– 'Margaret Bee' (A)	CJun NLar
	– 'Marjan' (M)	CJun MPkF SBod
	– 'Marlo' PBR (D)	CRos LCro LOPS LRHS MAsh MGos NLar NRHS SHil
	– 'Masamurasaki'	CMen MPkF
	– 'Masukagami' (P/v)	CEnd CJun MPkF NLar
	– 'Matsu-ga-e' (P/v)	CMen MPkF
	– 'Matsukaze'	CJun CMCN CMen
	– var. ***matsumurae*** B&SWJ 11100	WCru
	– – B&SWJ 11195	WCru
	– 'Matsuyoi' (A)	CJun MPkF NLar
	– 'Meihō-nishiki'	CJun
	– 'Melanie'	CJun SBig
	– 'Meoto'	CJun
	– 'Midori-no-teiboku' (Dw)	CJun
	– 'Mikasa-nishiki' (v) **new**	MPkF
	– 'Mikawa-yatsubusa' (Dw)	CJun CMCN CMac CMen IVic MGos MPkF NEgg NLar SAko SBod SGol WPat
	– 'Mikazuki' (M/v)	CJun MPkF
	– 'Mimaye'	CJun
	– 'Mini Mondo'	MPkF
	– 'Mirte' (M)	CJun CMen MPkF NLar SBig SGol
	– 'Mizuho-beni' (P)	CJun CMen NLar
	– 'Mizu-kuguri' (A)	MPkF NLar
	– 'Momoiro-koya-san' (Dw)	CJun MPkF NLar SGol WPat
	– 'Mon Papa' (M)	CJun CMen NLar
	– 'Monzukushi' (A)	CJun MPkF
	– 'Moonfire' (M)	CJun CMCN EPfP MAsh MPkF SGol WPat
*	– 'Muncaster'	SBig
	– 'Murasaki-hime' (Dw)	MPkF
	– 'Murasaki-kiyohime' (Dw)	CAco CEnd CJun CMCN CMen ESMi LRHS MPkF NRHS SBod WPat
	– 'Mure-hibari' (M)	CJun CMen MPkF
	– 'Murogawa' (A)	CJun CMen
	– 'Musashino' (M)	CJun SGol
	– 'Nakata'	NLar
	– 'Nanase-gawa' (A)	MPkF
	– 'Nicholsonii' (M)	CMen IVic MPkF NEgg NLar WPat
	– 'Nigrum' (A)	CMCN CTri SWeb WPat
	– 'Nishiki-gasane' (P/v)	CMen MPkF
§	– 'Nishiki-gawa' (P)	CEnd CJun CMen ESMi LRHS MPkF NEgg NRHS SBod
	– 'Nishiki-momiji' (P)	CMen
	– 'Nishiki-yamato'	NLar
	– 'Nomura'	CJun CMen
	– 'Nomura-nishiki' (Dw/v)	CMen
	– 'Nomurishidare' misapplied	see *A. palmatum* 'Shōjō-shidare'
	– 'Nuresagi' (M)	CEnd CJun MPkF SBod WPat
	– 'Octopus' (D)	CJun NLar
	– 'Ōgi-nagashi' (P/v)	MPkF NLar
	– 'Ōgi-no-sen'	MPkF
	– 'Ōgon-sarasa' (A)	CJun MPkF
	– 'Ojishi' (Dw)	CMen MPkF
	– 'Ō-kagami' (P)	CAco CBcs CEnd CJun CMac CMen CSBt ELon EPfP ESMi EUJe LRHS MAsh MGos MPkF NLar NRHS SBod SCoo WCFE WPat
	– 'Okina'	NLar
	– 'Okukuji-nishiki' (P)	CJun
	– 'Okushimo' (P)	CEnd CJun CMCN CMen ETod IVic LRHS MPkF NEgg NLar NRHS SSta WPat
	– 'Omato' (A)	CJun MAsh MPkF SBig
	– 'Omure-yama' (M)	CAco CBcs CEnd CJun CMCN CMen EPfP ESMi LRHS MGos MPkF NEgg NLar NRHS SBod SCob SCoo SGol SPer SSta
	– 'Orange Dream' (P) ♀H6	Widely available
	– 'Orangeola' (D) ♀H6	CJun CMen CSBt CTri ESMi EUJe IBoy IVic LRHS MAsh MGos MJak MPkF NEgg NHol NLar NOrn NRHS SBig SBod SCob SCoo SGol SPer SPoG SSta WMat WPat

- 'Oranges and Lemons' CJun SGol
- 'Oregon Sunset' (M) CJun LRHS MJak MPkF NLar WMat WPat
- 'Oridono-nishiki' (P/v) CEnd CJun CMCN CMac CMen CWGN ELan ELon EPfP ESMi LPar LRHS MAsh MBlu MGos MPkF NEgg NLar NRHS SBod SLim SPoG SSta
- 'Oriental Mystery' CJun
- 'Ornatum' (D) ♀H6 CMCN CMen CWib EPfP ESMi ESps GMcL LPar LSRN MGos MPkF MRav NEgg NLar NPri SBod SCob SCoo WCFE
- 'Ōsakazuki' (A) ♀H6 Widely available
- 'Ōshio-beni' (A) CJun CMen NEgg
- 'Ōshū-shidare' (M) CJun CMen IBoy MPkF
- 'Oto-hime' (Dw) CJun CMen LRHS MPkF NRHS SBod
- 'Otome-zakura' (P) CJun CMen LRHS MPkF NRHS
- 'Otto's Dissectum' (D) CJun
- 'Peaches and Cream' (M/v) CAco CBcs CJun CMen ELon MPkF NLar SGol SPer
- 'Pendulum Julian' (D) CMCN MPkF SPer
- 'Peve Chameleon' MPkF
- 'Peve Dave' MPkF NLar WPat
- 'Peve Multicolor' CJun MPkF NLar
- 'Peve Ollie'PBR MPkF NLar
- 'Peve Stanley' MPkF NLar
- 'Phoenix' (P) CJun CRos EBee EUJe LRHS MAsh MGos MPkF NLar SBod SHil
- 'Pine Bark Maple' see *A. palmatum* 'Nishiki-gawa'
- 'Pink Ballerina' (Dw/v) CJun NLar
- 'Pink Filigree' (D) CJun CMen EPfP NLar
- 'Pink Passion' (v) LBrs LPar LSRN NLar
- 'Pixie' (Dw) CJun CMen CSBt IVic LRHS MGos MPkF NLar NOra SAko SBod SCob WMat WPat
- 'Princetown Gold' EUJe NLar
- 'Pung-kil' IVic LBuc LRHS MPkF SAko
- 'Purple Ghost' (M) CJun EBee NLar
- 'Purpureum' (P) LPar
- 'Raraflora' (D) CJun
- 'Red Autumn Lace' (D) CJun WPat
- 'Red Baron' (A) CJun IBoy WPat
- 'Red Cloud' (L) CJun MPkF
- 'Red Dragon' (D) CJun CMen CWGN ESMi EUJe LRHS MAsh MJak MPkF NLar NRHS SAko SBig SBod
- Red Emperor = 'Emperor 1' (A) CBcs ELan EUJe IBoy LMil LRHS MPkF NLar SBod SCob SWeb WMat WPat
- 'Red Feather' (D) CJun
- 'Red Filigree Lace' (D) CEnd CJun CMCN CMen CWGN LRHS MPkF NRHS SBig WPat
- 'Red Flame' NLar
- 'Red Flash' (A) CJun CMen MPkF
- 'Red Jonas' MPkF
- 'Red Pygmy' (L) ♀H6 Widely available
- 'Red Select' (D) MPkF
- 'Red Spider' (L) CJun
- 'Red Wood' (P) CJun SGol SLau
- 'Redwine'PBR (P) CRos EPfP LRHS MPkF NLar NRHS SHil
- 'Renjaku-maru' MPkF
- 'Reticulatum' see *A. palmatum* 'Shigi-tatsu-sawa'
- 'Ribesifolium' see *A. palmatum* 'Shishi-gashira'
- 'Rising Sun' CJun NLar
- 'Rokugatsu-en-nishiki' (P) WPat
- 'Roseomarginatum' see *A. palmatum* 'Kagiri-nishiki'
- 'Rough Bark Maple' see *A. palmatum* 'Arakawa'
- 'Rubrum' (A) CMen

I - 'Rubrum Kaiser' CJun

- 'Ruby Ridge' (M) CJun
- 'Ruby Star' CJun MPkF
- 'Rufescens' (P) MPkF WPat
- 'Ryokū-ryū' (P) CMen MPkF
- 'Ryusen' CJun LCro NLar
- 'Ryuzu' (Dw) CJun MPkF
- 'Sagara-nishiki' (v) CAco CEnd CMen LRHS MPkF NEgg NRHS
- 'Sai-ho' MPkF
- 'Saint Jean' MPkF
- 'Samidare' (A) CJun MPkF NLar
- 'Sandra' (Dw) CMen MPkF

§ - 'Sango-kaku' (P) ♀H6 Widely available

- 'Saoshika' (A) CJun CMen MPkF NLar
- 'Sa-otome' (P) CMen MPkF
- 'Satsuki-beni' (M) CJun CMen ELon ESMi MPkF NEgg
- 'Sazanami' (M) CEnd CJun CMen MPkF NEgg NLar WPat
- 'Scolopendriifolium' see *A. palmatum* 'Linearilobum'

§ - 'Seigai' (M) CJun

- 'Seigen' (Dw) CEnd CJun CMCN CMen LRHS MBlu MPkF NRHS
- 'Seiryū' (D) ♀H6 Widely available
- 'Seiun-kaku' (P) CJun CMen MPkF NLar WPat
- 'Sekimori' (D) CJun NLar SBig
- 'Sekka-yatsubusa' (P) CMCN CMen MPkF NLar
- 'Semi-no-hane' (M) CJun NLar
- 'Senkaki' see *A. palmatum* 'Sango-kaku'
- 'Septemlobum Elegans' see *A. palmatum* 'Elegans'
- 'Septemlobum Purpureum' see *A. palmatum* 'Hessei'
- 'Sessilifolium' dwarf see *A. palmatum* 'Hagoromo'
- 'Shaina' (P) CBcs CEnd CJun CMen CRos CSBt CWGN CWib EPfP IVic LBuc LCro LRHS MBlu MGos MJak MPkF NLar NRHS SAko SCob SCoo SGol SHil SLim SPoG
- 'Sharon' WPat
- 'Sharp's Pygmy' (P) CJun CMen MPkF SGol
- 'Sherwood Flame' (M) CJun CMen LRHS MAsh MBlu MGos MPkF NEgg NLar NRHS SCoo SGol
- 'Shichigosan' CMen
- 'Shichihenge' (P) NLar
- 'Shidava Gold' (Dw) CJun MPkF SBod WPat
- 'Shigarami' (P) CJun CMen MPkF

§ - 'Shigi-tatsu-sawa' (A/v) CEnd CJun CMCN CMac CMen LRHS MGos MPkF NEgg NLar NRHS SBig SWeb

- 'Shigure-bato' (M) CJun MPkF
- 'Shigurezome' (M) MPkF NLar
- 'Shikageori-nishiki' (P) CJun CMen MPkF
- 'Shime-no-uchi' (L) CJun MPkF SBig
- 'Shimofuri-nishiki' MPkF
- 'Shin-chishio' (P) CJun
- 'Shin-deshōjō' (P) ♀H6 Widely available
- 'Shin-nyo' MBlu

§ - 'Shinobuga-oka' (L) CBcs CJun CMCN CMen LRHS MPkF SBod SGol SLau SWeb

- 'Shinonome' (M) CJun CMen MPkF NLar
- 'Shin-seyu' LPar
- 'Shirazz' (P/v) CWGN ESMi IBoy LRHS LSRN MGos MJak MPkF NLar NOra NRHS SBod SCob SPer SWeb SWvt WMat

§ - 'Shishi-gashira' (P) ♀H6 CJun CMCN CMac CMen EBee ESMi GMcL IVic LPar LRHS MBlu MGos MPkF NEgg NLar NRHS SBod SCoo SGol SHil SPoG WPat

- 'Shishio-hime' (Dw) MPkF
- 'Shishi-yatsubusa' CJun MPkF

	- 'Shōjō' (A)	CJun CMCN NLar
	- 'Shōjō-no-mai' (P)	CJun
	- 'Shōjō-nomura' (A)	CEnd CMen MPkF NLar SHil SWeb WPat
§	- 'Shōjō-shidare' (D)	CEnd CJun CMen LRHS MPkF NLar NOra NRHS WMat
	- 'Shu-shidare' (D)	CJun
	- 'Sister Ghost' (M)	CJun
	- 'Skeeter's Broom' (Dw)	CAco CBcs CJun CMen CSBt ELan EPfP ESMi EUJe IArd IBoy LMil LRHS MGos MPkF NEgg NLar NRHS SBig SBod SCoo SPoG WPat
*	- 'Sode-nishiki' (P)	CJun MPkF NLar
	- 'Spring Delight' (D)	CJun MPkF
	- 'Starfish'[PBR]	MPkF
	- 'Stella Rossa' (D)	CEnd CJun LRHS MJak MPkF NLar NPri SBod
	- 'Suisei' (Dw/v)	MPkF
	- 'Sumi-nagashi' (M)	CBcs CCVT CMen ESMi LRHS MGos MJak MPkF NEgg NLar NOra NRHS SBod SCoo SGol SLau WMat WPat
I	- 'Summer Gold' (P)	CJun EBee MPkF NLar SAko SWvt
	- 'Sunset' (D)	CJun MPkF
	- 'Sunshine' (D)	MPkF
	- 'Susan'	MPkF
	- 'Taiyō-nishiki' (P)	CJun MPkF
	- 'Takao' (P)	CMen
	- 'Tama-hime' (Dw)	CJun CMen ESMi LRHS MPkF NEgg NRHS SBod
	- 'Tamukeyama' (D)	CAco CJun CMCN CMen ELan ELon ESMi EUJe LRHS MGos MJak MPkF NEgg NLar NOra NRHS SAko SCob SCoo SGol SLau SWeb WHor WMat WPat
	- 'Tana' (A)	CJun CMCN CMen EPfP MPkF NLar WPat
	- 'Tarō-yama' (Dw)	CJun MPkF WPat
	- 'Tatsuta'	CMen MPkF
	- 'Taylor'[PBR] (P/v)	CEnd CRos CWGN EPfP EUJe IVic LCro LRHS LSRN MAsh MGos MPkF NEgg NLar NPri NRHS SCoo SHil
	- 'Tennyo-no-hoshi' (P)	CMen MPkF NLar
	- 'Tiger Rose' (M)	CJun
	- 'Tiny Tim'	CJun MPkF
	- 'Tobiosho' (P)	CJun
§	- 'Toyama-nishiki' (Dw/v)	CJun CMCN CMen CWGN ESMi LPar LRHS MPkF NLar
	- 'Trompenburg' (M) ♀H6	Widely available
	- 'Tsuchigumo' (P)	CJun CMen MPkF NLar SBod
	- 'Tsukasa Silhouette'	CJun LCro MPkF WPat
	- 'Tsukubane' (A)	WPat
	- 'Tsukuma-no'	MPkF
	- 'Tsukushigata' (A)	MPkF SBod SGol WPat
	- 'Tsuma-gaki' (A)	CAco CJun CMCN CMen EPfP ESMi LPar LRHS MGos MPkF NEgg NLar NRHS WPat
	- 'Tsuri-nishiki' (M)	CJun CMen MPkF
	- 'Twombly's Red Sentinel'	CJun MPkF
	- 'Ueno-homare' (P)	CMen EUJe MPkF
	- 'Ueno-yama'	CBcs CJun EUJe MPkF NEgg NLar SBod SGol SPer WPat
	- 'Uki-gumo' (P/v)	CAco CBcs CEnd CJun CMCN CMac CMen EBee ELan ESMi LRHS MGos MJak NHol NLar NRHS SBig SCoo SPer SPoG SSta
	- 'Ukon'	CJun CMen CTho ESMi LMil LRHS MJak MPkF NEgg NRHS SBod SCoo
	- 'Umegae' (A)	CJun
	- 'Uncle Ghost' (M)	CJun
	- 'Usu-midori'	CJun
	- 'Utsu-semi' (A)	CJun MPkF
	- 'Van der Akker'	CJun
	- 'Van der Maat' (D) **new**	SBod
	- 'Versicolor' (P/v)	CMCN MPkF
	- 'Vic Pink' (D)	CJun
	- 'Victoria'	SGol
	- 'Villa Taranto' (L) ♀H6	CEnd CJun CMCN CMen EPfP ESMi EUJe IVic LRHS MBlu MGos MPkF NEgg NLar NOra NRHS SBod SCoo SGol WMat WPGP WPat
	- 'Volubile' (P)	CMCN CMen MPkF NEgg SBod WPat
	- 'Wabito' (P)	CJun CMen MPkF
	- 'Waka-midori'	CMen
	- 'Waka-momiji' (P/v)	CJun
	- 'Wakehurst Pink' (M/v)	CMCN MPkF NOrn WPat
	- 'Waterfall' (D)	CJun CMCN
	- 'Watnong' (D)	CJun EUJe LRHS MPkF
	- 'Wendy' (P)	CJun CMen IVic MPkF NLar SGol
	- 'Wetumpka Red'	CJun
	- 'Whitney Red' (A)	CMen
	- 'Wild Goose' (P)	MPkF
	- 'Will's Devine'	CJun
	- 'Wilson's Pink Dwarf' (Dw)	CAco CEnd CJun CMen CWib EUJe IVic LRHS MGos MJak MPkF NLar NRHS SAko SCoo SPoG WPat
	- 'Winter Flame' (P)	CJun LRHS MPkF NHol NOrn NRHS SBod SPer WPat
	- 'Wou-nishiki'	CMCN CMen MPkF
	- 'Yana-gawa'	CMen
	- 'Yasemin' (M)	CJun CMen CWGN IVic LRHS MJak MPkF NEgg NLar SBig SBod
	- 'Yatsubusa' (Dw)	MPkF
	- 'Yezo-nishiki' (A/v)	CMen MBlu MPkF NLar SHil
	- 'Yūba-e' (M)	MPkF
	- 'Yūgure' (M)	IVic MPkF
	- 'Yuri-hime' (Dw)	MPkF
	- 'Zaaling' (D)	CAco CMen CTho NEgg
	papilio	see *A. caudatum*
	pauciflorum 'Blaze Away'	CJun LRHS NRHS
	pectinatum	MMuc WPat
	- GWJ 9354	WCru
	- 'Mozart'	CBcs CJun MBlu NLar SSta
	- subsp. ***pectinatum*** HWJ 569	WCru
	- - HWJ 944	WCru
	pensylvanicum	CBcs CDul CMCN CTho ELan EPfP MGos MJak MMuc MRav NEgg NWea SCob SSta WHor
	- 'Erythrocladum'	CBcs CEnd CJun CMCN EPfP IArd MAsh MGos NHol NLar NOrn WPGP
	pentaphyllum	SBig WPGP
§	***pictum***	CMCN
	- subsp. ***okamotoanum***	CMCN
	- - B&SWJ 12623	WCru
	- subsp. ***pictum*** f. ***ambiguum*** B&SWJ 8806	WCru
	- 'Shufu-nishiki'	CMCN
	- 'Usugomo'	WPat
	platanoides	CAco CBcs CCVT CDul CLnd CMCN CSBt CTri CWib ECrN ELan EMOT EPfP MGos MMuc MSwo NOrn NWea SEND SEWo SGol SPer WHar WMat WMou WTSh
	- 'Cleveland'	CBcs
	- 'Columnare'	CLnd CMCN SCoo
	- 'Crimson King' ♀H6	Widely available
	- 'Crimson Sentry'	CArg CCVT CDul CEnd CLet CLnd CTri EBee ECrN ELan EMOT EPfP

		ESps EUJe IVic LCro LSRN MAsh MGos MRav NOrn SGol SPer SPoG SWvt WHar WPat
	- 'Deborah'	CBcs CDul CLnd CTho EPfP EWTr SGol SPer
	- 'Dissectum'	CAco CTho WPat
	- 'Drummondii' (v)	Widely available
	- 'Emerald Queen'	CDul ECrN ESps
	- 'Faassen's Black'	CDul
§	- 'Globosum'	CDul CLnd CMCN ECrN NLar SWvt
	- 'Goldsworth Purple'	CLnd
	- 'Jules' (v) **new**	EMOT
	- 'Laciniatum'	CMCN EBtc GBin WPat
	- 'Marit'	WPat
	- Princeton Gold = 'Prigo'PBR ♀H6	CBcs CDul CTho EBee ECrN ELan EMOT ESps EUJe GQue LBuc LRHS MAsh MGos NEgg NOra NOrn NWea SCoo SEWo SLim SPer SPoG SWvt WHar WMat
	- 'Reitenbachii'	CDul
	- 'Royal Red'	CDul ECrN EPfP MRav NLar SCoo SEWo
	- 'Schwedleri' ♀H6	CMCN WTSh
	- 'Stollii'	WPat
	- subsp. ***turkestanicum***	CMCN SSta
	- 'Ulmers Select'	WMat
	pseudoplatanus	CAco CBcs CCVT CDul CLnd CMCN CTri ECrN ELan EMOT LBuc MGos NWea SGol SPer WHar WHed WMou WTSh
§	- 'Atropurpureum'	CDul ECrN ESps NWea SEWo WHar
	- 'Brilliantissimum' ♀H6	Widely available
	- 'Corstorphinense'	CDul
	- f. ***erythrocarpum*** 'Erythrocarpum'	CMac
	- 'Gadsby'	CDul
	- 'Negenia'	CDul
	- 'Prinz Handjéry'	CBcs CDul CEnd CMCN CTri CWib ESps MGos NHol NLar NOra NOrn NWea SGol WHar WMat
	- 'Spaethii' misapplied	see *A. pseudoplatanus* 'Atropurpureum'
	- f. ***variegatum*** 'Esk Sunset' (v)	CLnd EBee ELan LSRN MGos MPkF NLar SPoG WHar
	- - 'Leopoldii' ambig. (v)	CBcs CCVT CDul CLnd CMCN ECrN EMOT ESps SWvt
	- - 'Leopoldii' Vervaene (v)	SPer
	- - 'Simon-Louis Frères' (v)	CBcs CCVT CDul CLnd CMCN CWib ECrN EMOT ESps MAsh MGos NLar NOrn SGol SPer SWvt WHar WMat
	- 'Worley'	CBcs CDul CLnd CMCN CMac ECrN EMOT ESps MRav NWea SGol SLim SPer
	pseudosieboldianum	CMCN MBlu MPkF
	- B&SWJ 8468	WCru
	- B&SWJ 8746	WCru
	- B&SWJ 8769	WCru
	- var. ***microsieboldianum*** B&SWJ 8766	WCru
	- subsp. ***takesimense*** B&SWJ 8500	WCru
	- - B&SWJ 8540	WCru
	pubipalmatum	LRHS NRHS
	pycnanthum	EPfP
	'Red Flamingo' (v)	CJun CRos EBee EPfP LRHS MBlu MGos NLar NOra SGol SHil SMad SPoG WMat
	'Red Wings' (*A. palmatum* hybrid)	CJun
	reticulatum	see *A. laevigatum* var. *reticulatum*
	rubescens CWJ 12438	WCru
	rubrum	CAco CAgr CBcs CDul CLnd CMCN CSBt CTri EBee ECrN ELan EMOT EPfP LCro LOPS MGos MMuc NEgg NWea SCoo SEWo SGol WCFE WHar WMat WTSh
	- Autumn Flame	see *A. rubrum* 'Pete's Red'
	- 'Autumn Spire'	CJun
	- 'Brandywine'	CDul CJun CTho EBee EMOT EPfP LRHS LSRN MAsh MBlu NLar NOra NWea SBir SCoo WHar WMat
	- 'Embers'	CJun
	- Fairview Flame	see *A. rubrum* 'Pete's Fairview'
	- 'Firedance'	CJun
	- 'Joseph'	NLar
	- 'New World'	SCoo
	- 'October Glory' ♀H6	Widely available
§	- 'Pete's Fairview'	CJun MMuc SEND SPer
§	- 'Pete's Red'	CLnd MPkF
	- 'Red King'	CJun
	- Red Sunset = 'Franksred' ♀H6	CAco CDul CEnd CMCN CTho EBee ELan EMOT EPfP LHop NLar SBir SCoo SGol SLim SPer WMou
	- 'Scanlon'	CBcs CDul CEnd CJun CMCN CTho ELan EPfP LRHS NOra SLim SPer
	- 'Schlesingeri'	CEnd CJun CLnd CMac EPfP
I	- 'Sekka'	MBlu
	- 'Somerset'	CDul CJun CTho CTri EBee SCoo WHar WMat
	- Summer Red = 'Hosr'	EMOT EPfP SCoo WMat
	- 'Sun Valley'	CJun EBee NOra NOrn NWea WHar WMat
	- 'Tilford'	CJun SSta
§	***rufinerve***	CAco CBcs CDul CLnd CMCN CTho CTri EBee ELan EPfP ESps EWTr MMuc NEgg NLar NOra NWea SCoo SGol SPer SSta SWvt WHar WMat WTSh
	- B&SWJ 10845	WCru
	- B&SWJ 10924	WCru
	- B&SWJ 10959	WCru
	- B&SWJ 11571	WCru
	- 'Albolimbatum' (v)	CEnd CJun CMCN EBee SBig SSta
	- 'Erythrocladum'	CJun MBlu SKHP
	- 'Ko-fuji-nishiki'	SSta
I	- 'Sunshine'	SSta
	- 'Winter Gold'	CJun EPfP NLar SSta
	- 'Yellow Ribbon'	WHor
§	***saccharinum***	CAco CBcs CCVT CDul CLnd CMCN CTri CWib ECrN ELan EPfP ESps LRHS MGos MHid MMuc NLar NOra NWea SCoo SGol SPer WHar WMat WTSh
	- 'Born's Gracious'	CJun
	- 'Fastigiatum'	see *A. saccharinum* 'Pyramidale'
	- f. ***laciniatum***	MBlu MMuc SGol SPer
	- - 'Laciniatum Wieri'	CDul CMCN NLar SGol
	- 'Lutescens'	CTho
§	- 'Pyramidale'	ECrN NWea SPer
	saccharum	CAco CAgr CBcs CDul CLnd CMCN CTho ECrN EPfP MBlu NEgg NWea WTSh
	- 'Brocade'	CJun
	- 'Fiddlers Creek'	CJun
§	- subsp. ***grandidentatum***	CMCN EPfP
§	***sempervirens***	EBee EPfP LEdu WCot
	'Sensu'	CJun
	'Serendipity'	SSta
	serrulatum	CMCN

- CWJ 12437	WCru
shirasawanum	CMCN
§ - 'Aureum' ♀H6	Widely available
- 'Autumn Moon'	CBcs CJun CMCN CMen CWGN EPfP LPar LRHS MPkF NEgg NLar NOra NRHS SBod SCob SCoo SGol SPer SPoG WMat WPat
§ - 'Ezo-no-momiji'	CJun CMen MPkF NEgg
- 'Gloria'	MPkF SGol
§ - 'Helena'	WPat
- 'Jordan'PBR	CDul CEnd CLet CRos CWGN LRHS LSRN MGos MPkF NRHS SHil SPoG SWvt WPat
- 'Kakure-gasa' **new**	CJun EBee
- 'Lovett'	CJun
§ - 'Microphyllum'	MPkF NEgg
- 'Mr Sun'	CJun
§ - 'Ogurayama'	CAco CJun CMen
- 'Palmatifolium'	CJun
- 'Red Dawn'	CJun
- 'Susanne'	CJun CMen MPkF SGol
- var. ***tenuifolium*** B&SWJ 11073	WCru
sieboldianum ♀H6	CDul CMen CTho CTri ECrN LRHS MAsh MBlu MMuc SEND SGol WHCr WHar WMou WPGP WPat
- B&SWJ 10849	WCru
- B&SWJ 11049	WCru
- B&SWJ 11090	WCru
- 'Sode-no-uchi'	CJun CMen MPkF
- var. ***tsushimense*** B&SWJ 10962	WCru
sikkimense B&SWJ 11689	WCru
- B&SWJ 11703	WCru
- FMWJ 13166	WCru
- NJM 10.134 **new**	WPGP
- WWJ 11601	WCru
- WWJ 11613	WCru
- WWJ 11853	WCru
'Silver Cardinal' (v)	CBcs CEnd CJun CMCN EPfP MBlu MGos MPkF NLar SSta WHar
'Silver Vein'	see *A.* × *conspicuum* 'Silver Vein'
sinense	CMCN
spicatum	CMCN NLar
§ ***stachyophyllum***	GQui
§ ***sterculiaceum***	EBee
- PAB 13.135 **new**	LEdu
- subsp. ***franchetii***	CMCN NLar
- subsp. ***sterculiaceum*** NJM 13.087 **new**	WPGP
tataricum	CMCN
§ - subsp. ***ginnala***	CAco CArg CBcs CDul CLnd CMCN CNWT CTri ECrN MBlu MGos NLar NWea SGol SPer
- - 'Flame'	CCVT CDul CJun EBee ECrN EPfP MGos MHid MMuc NLar WPat
- Hot Wings = 'Gar Ann' **new**	LRHS
tegmentosum ♀H5	CJun CMCN EPfP IArd MBlu NLar SMad SSta WHor
- subsp. ***glaucorufinerve***	see *A. rufinerve*
- 'Joe Witt'	NLar
tetramerum	see *A. stachyophyllum*
tonkinense subsp. ***liquidambarifolium*** DJHV 06173	WCru
trautvetteri	CMCN
triflorum ♀H6	CBcs CCVT CDul CJun CMCN EBee EPfP MBlu NLar NOra WMat
truncatum	CDul MPkF
- 'Akikaze-nishiki' (v)	CJun MPkF
tschonoskii	MPkF
subsp. ***koreanum***	
- - B&SWJ 12596	WCru
- - B&SWJ 12603 **new**	WCru
'Valley Phantom'	SSta
velutinum	CMCN
villosum	see *A. sterculiaceum*
'White Tigress'	CBcs CJun CTho EPfP GQue NLar NWea SSta WHar WMat WPGP WPat
× ***zoeschense***	CMCN MPkF
- 'Annae'	MMuc SEND SGol

Aceriphyllum see *Mukdenia*

Achillea (*Asteraceae*)

ageratifolia ♀H5	CMea ECha ECho ECtt EDAr GWyn NGdn SRms XLum XSen
§ ***ageratum***	CArn CLau ENfk GPSL GPoy LEdu MHer MNHC SIde SRms WFar WGwG WHer WJek WTre XLum
'Alabaster'	LRHS SPhx
Anthea = 'Anblo'PBR	CKno EBee ECtt IBoy LRHS LSRN MCot MRav MSpe SHar SRms SWvt WCAu
§ 'Apfelblüte' (Galaxy Series)	CAby CWld EAEE EBee ECha ECtt ELan EPed GKin LRHS LSRN MRav NGdn NHol NQui NSti SBod SCob SEND SPer SRms XSen
Appleblossom	see *A.* 'Apfelblüte'
'Apricot Beauty'	ECtt ELan EWTr SBod
'Apricot Delight' (Tutti Frutti Series)	MNrw NAst NLar
argentea misapplied	see *A. clavennae*, *A. umbellata*
argentea Lamarck	see *Tanacetum argenteum*
aurea	see *A. chrysocoma*
'Bahama'	GBin GQue
'Belle Epoque'	XSen
biebersteinii	XLum
brachyphylla	EPot
'Breckland Bouquet'	EWes
'Breckland Cream'	EBee EPed
'Breckland Ruby'	EWes
'Carmina Burana'	CMea
cartilaginea	see *A. salicifolia*
'Christine's Pink'	MSpe
§ ***chrysocoma***	ECho WMoo
- 'Grandiflora'	ECha MMuc NGdn WBrk
§ ***clavennae***	GKev SRms WAbe WIce
clypeolata Sibth. & Sm.	CRos EBee EHyd LRHS NRHS SPlb SRms XLum
coarctata	NBir XSen
Colorado Group	CBod CNec CRos EHyd LRHS NRHS WHar
'Coronation Gold' ♀H7	CWCL EBee ECtt ELan EPed EPfP GBuc IBoy LRHS MAsh MRav MWat NChi NDov SCob SPer SRms SWvt WBod WCAu WCot XLum XSen
'Credo' ♀H7	CAby CDor CWld EAEE EAJP ECha ECtt EPed EPfP EWTr EWoo GBin IBoy LCro LOPS LRHS MBel MRav MSpe NBir NDov NGdn NHol NLar NSti SDix SMad SPer WCAu XSen
crithmifolia	XLum XSen
decolorans	see *A. ageratum*
(Desert Eve Series) Desert Eve Cream = 'Deseve'	CRos EBee EHyd LRHS NRHS
- Desert Eve Deep Rose = 'Desderos'	CRos EBee EHyd LRHS MAsh MTis NRHS
- Desert Eve Light Yellow	LRHS NRHS SRms

	- Desert Eve Red = 'Desred'PBR	CWld EBee LRHS MAsh NRHS
	- Desert Eve Yellow = 'Desyel'PBR	EBee
	erba-rotta subsp. ***moschata***	NBro
	falcata **new**	GKev
§	'Fanal'	CAby CLet CWCL EAEE EBee ECha ECtt ELan EPed EPfP GBuc GKin GWyn IBoy LRHS MCot MRav MSpe MTis NBir NEgg NHol NLar NPri SPer SWvt WCAu WCot
	'Faust'	CDor ELon
	'Federsee'	MArl
	'Feuerland'	CMac CSam EBee ECha ECtt ELon EPfP GKin GQue LRHS MRav NBir NDov NGdn SAko SMad SPer SPoG WFar XSen
	filipendulina 'Cloth of Gold' ♀H7	Widely available
	- 'Gold Plate' ♀H7	Widely available
	- 'Hymne' **new**	EBee
	- 'Parker's Variety' ♀H7	CBod EBee GQue NBre WFar WMoo XLum XSen
	'Fleur van Zonneveld'	NDov
	Flowers of Sulphur	see *A.* 'Schwefelblüte'
	(Forncett Series) 'Forncett Beauty'	LHop SWvt
	- 'Forncett Bride'	EBee
	- 'Forncett Citrus'	MAvo
	- 'Forncett Fletton'	CWCL CWld ECtt EHrv ELon EPed EPfP GBin GKin LHop MBel MNrw MRav MSpe NGdn NHol WCAu
	- 'Forncett Ivory'	MAvo
	fraasii	XSen
	'Gloria Jean'	SHar
	'Golden Fleece'	GWyn
	grandifolia misapplied	see *Tanacetum macrophyllum* (Waldst. & Kit.) Sch.Bip.
§	***grandifolia*** Friv.	CSam GBin NBro WFar WMoo WOld WOut
	'Great Expectations'	see *A.* 'Hoffnung'
	'Heidi' ♀H7	CCVN MRav NPnk
	'Heinrich Vogeler'	EBee WCot
	'Hella Glashoff' ♀H7	CWCL EBee ELon LRHS MAsh NDov
§	'Hoffnung'	CWCL WBod
	× ***huteri***	ECho ECtt EDAr GCrg MMuc MRav NGdn NHpl SEND SIgm SRms SWvt
	'Inca Gold'	CSam CWCL EAEE ECha ECtt EHoe EHrv EPed GBuc LRHS MRav MSpe NCGa NDov NHol NSti SPer SRms SWvt WFar WGwG WHoo WWtn
	'Jacqueline'	MTis
	'Judity'	WOut
	× ***kellereri***	XLum XSen
	'King Alfred'	CMea NHpl SRms
	× ***kolbiana***	SRms XSen
§	'Lachsschönheit' (Galaxy Series) ♀H7	CAby CBWd CKno CWCL EBee ECha ECtt ELan EPed EPfP GBin GMaP LBMP LHop LRHS MBNS MCot MRav NBir NDov NHol NLar NSti SCob SPer SRms
	× ***lewisii*** 'King Edward' ♀H5	ECho EDAr GCrg GMaP NBir SRms WAbe WFar WIce
	'Lucky Break' ♀H7	EBee ECha ECtt LEdu MHol NSti WBrk WCot WRHF
	macrophylla	MBNS
	'Marie Ann'	CWCL GQue LSRN NLar NPnk
	'Marmalade'	CDor MRav NDov
	'Martina' ♀H7	CAby CSam ECtt EWoo GBin GBuc GKin GQue LHop LRHS MAsh MBNS MBel MCot MRav NDov NGdn NHol SRGP WCAu WCot WHea WHoo
	'McVities'	CWCL ECtt MSpe
	millefolium	CArn CHab CLau ENfk GPoy MNHC NMir SRms WHer WJek WOut WSFF XLum
	- 'Bloodstone'	ECtt EWes MRav
	- 'Carla Hussey'	WFar
	- 'Cassis'	CBod CRos CSam CSpe EHyd GQue LRHS MCot NGBl NLar NRHS SPtp WBor WMoo WOut
§	- 'Cerise Queen'	Widely available
	- 'Chamois'	MNrw
	- 'Cherry King'	NBir
	- 'Christel'	CCVN EWes
	- 'Circus'	XLum
	- 'Dark Lilac Beauty'	CWCL
	- Kirschkönigin	see *A. millefolium* 'Cerise Queen'
	- 'Lansdorferglut' ♀H7	EBee IRob LRHS MTis NDov SPhx
	- 'Laura'	CSam CWGN EBee EPfP LSou MBel MNrw
	- 'Lavender Beauty'	see *A. millefolium* 'Lilac Beauty'
§	- 'Lilac Beauty'	CRos ECha EHrv ELon EPfP GBuc GMaP IBoy IPot LCro LOPS LRHS LSRN MMuc MRav NBir NEgg NLar SCob SEND SHil SRms WCAu WFar WHar XLum
*	- 'Lilac Queen'	MArl
	- 'Little Suzie'	CWGN
	- 'Maskerade' **new**	EBee
	- (New Vintage Series) New Vintage Red = 'Balvinred' **new**	WHil
	- - New Vintage Rose = 'Balvinrose' **new**	WHil
	- 'Old Brocade'	EShb NDov
	- Pastel Shades	IFoB IFro WFar
	- 'Peggy Sue'	CWGN EBee ECtt WFar
	- 'Pomegranate' (Tutti Frutti Series)	CMos CWGN IPot LCro MNrw SCob SHar WTor XLum
	- 'Pretty Woman'	CBWd CSam CWGN EBee SPoG
	- 'Raspberry Ripple'	GBin GWyn
	- 'Red Beauty'	CWCL ELan EPfP EWTr MBNS SRms XLum XSen
	- 'Red Salmon'	EWes
	- 'Red Velvet'	Widely available
	- 'Rose Madder'	Widely available
	- 'Salmon Pink'	IBoy
	- 'Salmon Queen'	NHol WFar WHar
	- 'Sammetriese'	ELon MNrw SMad SPhx
	- 'Serenade'	ECtt MSpe
	- 'Sonoma Coast' **new**	CSpe
	- 'Sue's Pink'	CSam
	- (Summer Fruits Series) 'Summer Fruits Carmine'	EBee LRHS MTis WHar
	- - 'Summer Fruits Lemon'	EBee LRHS WHar
	- - 'Summer Fruits Salmon'	EBee LRHS WHar
	- 'Summertime'	WFar
	- 'White Beauty'	EWTr
	- 'White Queen'	EBee
	- 'Wonderful Wampee'	CRos EBee EHyd EWTr LRHS MNrw NAst NRHS SCob WCot
	'Mondpagode' ♀H7	CAby EPfP EWTr LRHS MBNS MCot MRav NDov NGdn NHol SPhx SWvt WHoo
*	'Moonbeam'	GKin SEND
	'Moonshine' ♀H7	Widely available
	'Moonwalker'	CAbP CBod EPfP SPav WCot XLum

	nana	WFar
	nobilis	XSen
	- subsp. ***neilreichii***	ECGP EHoe EHrv EWTr GQue IKil MMuc NDov NSti SEND SPer SWvt WGwG
*	***odilis***	EWTr
	'Paprika' (Galaxy Series)	Widely available
	'Petra'	EBee ILea MNrw XLum
	pindicola subsp. ***integrifolia***	EWes
	'Pineapple Mango'[PBR]	SCob
	pink-flowered from Santa Cruz Island	CWCL
	'Pink Grapefruit' (Tutti Frutti Series)	GWyn IPot MAsh MAvo MNrw MTis NLar SCob WCAu
	'Pretty Belinda'	CDor CRos EBee ECtt EHyd EPfP GWyn ILea IPot LRHS LSRN LSou MAvo MBel MCot MSpe NDov NPri NRHS NSti SAko SKHP SPoG SRms WCAu WFar
	'Prospero'	WCot
	ptarmica	CArn CBod CBre CLau MArt MHer NMir SCob SDix SRms WWtn XLum
*	- 'Ballerina'	MBNS NBre NDov NLar
	- 'Double Diamond' (d) **new**	CRos EHyd LRHS NRHS
	- 'Nana Compacta'	CRos EHyd IBoy LRHS NBir NRHS SPlb WCFE WCot WFar
	- 'Noblessa'	MHol
	- 'Perry's White' (d)	CBcs CBre ECha MNrw SRGP WCot
	- 'Stephanie Cohen'	see *A. sibirica* 'Stephanie Cohen'
	- The Pearl Group seed-raised (d)	CTri CWld ELan GWyn MMuc SGbt SPlb WBod WFar WMoo
	- - 'Boule de Neige' (clonal) (d)	GKin IBoy MRav MSpe NPer NSti SPer WFar XLum
	- - 'The Pearl' (clonal) (d)	Widely available
	pyrenaica	XLum
	'Rougham Salmon'	CDor
	'Ruby Wine'	WFar
	'Safran'	EBee LRHS NDov XLum
§	***salicifolia***	WFar
	- 'Silver Spray'	IPot NLar SDix SPav WOut
	Salmon Beauty	see *A.* 'Lachsschönheit'
	'Sandra Wagg'	ECtt
	'Sandstone'	see *A.* 'Wesersandstein'
	'Saucy Seduction' (Seduction Series)	CWCL ELon MHol MTis NBid
§	'Schwefelblüte'	MRav NBir
	'Schwellenburg'	NBre WCot WFar
	sibirica subsp. ***camschatica*** 'Love Parade'	CBod CHid EBee LHop MArt MHol MMuc MNrw SGbt SPer SPtp XLum
§	- 'Stephanie Cohen'	GBin LHop WFar
	sipikorensis	SIgm
	'Stephanie'	EWes LSRN
	Summer Berries Group	CBod CRos EHyd LRHS NFav NRHS WHil
	Summer Pastels Group	CBod CRos EHyd EPfP GMcL IBoy LRHS NLar NRHS SRms WFar WHar WWtn XLum
	- (Seduction Series) 'Peachy Seduction'[PBR]	NLar
	- - 'Strawberry Seduction'	ECtt
	'Summerwine' 🏆H7	Widely available
	'Sunbeam'	SHar
	'Sunny Seduction' (Seduction Series)	ECtt ELon IKil MAsh MTis NAst
I	'Taygetea'	ELan EPfP LCro LOPS MBNS SCob SPer SPoG SRkn WCAu WCot XLum
	'Terracotta'	Widely available
	'The Beacon'	see *A.* 'Fanal'
	'Tissington Old Rose'	MNrw
	tomentosa 🏆H5	CTri ECha ECho ECtt GPSL XSen
§	- 'Aurea'	NBro XLum
	- 'Goldie'	CRos EHyd LRHS NRHS SWvt
	- 'Maynard's Gold'	see *A. tomentosa* 'Aurea'
	'Tri-colour'	LCro NGdn
§	***umbellata***	EPot NSla SIgm XSen
	'Velour'	GBin
	'W.B. Childs'	ELan MNrw MRav NDov SHar
	'Walther Funcke'	Widely available
§	'Wesersandstein'	CWCL GMaP MNrw NBir SCob SGbt
	'Wilczekii'	SRms
	'Yellowstone'	EWes

× *Achimenantha* (*Gesneriaceae*)

'Aries'	WDib
'Cool Inferno'	WDib
'Golden Jubilee'	WDib
'Himalayan Sunrise'	LAma WDib
'Inferno' 🏆H1c	WDib
'Pisces'	WDib
'Texas Blue Bayou'	WDib

Achimenes (*Gesneriaceae*)

'Addano'	WDib
admirabilis	WDib
'Ambroise Verschaffelt' 🏆H1c	EShb LAma SDir WDib
'Ami Van Houtte'	WDib
'Apricot Glow'	WDib
'Aquamarine'	WDib
'Aurora Charm'	WDib
'Ballerina'	WDib
'Beautiful Fire'	WDib
'Big Weiss'	WDib
'Blue Sparkles'	SDeJ
'Caligula'	WDib
'Cameo Rose'	WDib
'Candy Shop'	WDib
'Cascade Fairy Pink'	WDib
'Cascade Fashionable Pink'	WDib
'Cascade Rose Red'	WDib
'Cascade Violet Night'	WDib
'Cattleya'	LAma SDir
cettoana	WDib
'Charity'	WDib
'Charm'	LAma SDeJ WDib
'Claret'	WDib
'Crackerjack'	WDib
'Crummock Water'	WDib
'Double Picotee Rose' (d)	WDib
'Double Pink Rose' (d)	WDib
erecta	WDib
'Erlkönig'	WDib
'Escheriana'	LAma
'Extravaganza'	WDib
'Firefly'	WDib
'Flamenco'	WDib
'Glory'	WDib
'Golden Butterfly'	WDib
'Harry Williams'	EShb LAma SDir WDib
'Hilda Michelssen' 🏆H1c	WDib
'Himalayan Angel'	LAma
'Himalayan Double'	LAma
'Himalayan Mandarin'	LAma
'Hugues Aufray'	WDib
'Ice Tea'	WDib
'India'	EShb
'Jay Dee Coral'	WDib
'Jay Dee Large White'	WDib
'Jay Dee Pink'	WDib

'Jay Dee Purple'	WDib
'Jennifer Goode'	WDib
'Johanna Michelssen'	WDib
'Just Divine'	WDib
'Kim Blue'	WDib
'Lady in Black'	WDib
'Light Lilac'	WDib
'Little Beauty'	WDib
longiflora 'Major'	WDib
'Maxima'	LAma
'Melon Ice Cream'	WDib
'Menuett'	WDib
mexicana	LAma SDeJ
misera	WDib
'Opal'	WDib
'Orange Delight'	WDib
'Pally'	WDib
'Patens Major'	WDib
'Peach Blossom'	EShb LAma SDeJ WDib
'Peach Glow'	WDib
pedunculata	WDib
'Petite Fadette'	WDib
'Primadonna'	SDeJ WDib
'Pulcherrima'	SDeJ
'Purple King'	WDib
'Purple Queen'	WDib
'Purple Triumph'	WDib
'Queen of Queens'	WDib
'Rai'	WDib
'Rainbow'	WDib
'Rainbow Warrior'	WDib
'Red Hilda Michelssen'	WDib
'Rozi Roza'	WDib
'Santa Claus'	WDib
'Schneewittchen'	WDib
'Serge Saliba'	WDib
'Serge's Fantasy'	WDib
'Show-off'	WDib
'Shy Sun'	WDib
skinneri	WDib
'Snow Princess'	EShb SDeJ
'Stan's Delight' (d) ♀H1c	WDib
'Sterntaler'	WDib
'Sugarland'	WDib
'Sun Wind'	WDib
'Sweet and Sour'	WDib
'Tango'	WDib
'Tarantella'	WDib
(Tetra Series) 'Tetra Himalayan Purple'	LAma SDir WDib
- 'Tetra Purple' **new**	SDir
'Tiger Eye'	WDib
'Valse Bleu'	WDib
'Violacea Semiplena' (d)	WDib
'Vivid'	LAma WDib
'Weinrot Elfe'	WDib
'Wetterlow's Triumph'	WDib
'Yellow Beauty'	WDib

Achlys (*Berberidaceae*)

japonica	WCru
triphylla	IMou WCru

Achnatherum see *Stipa*

Achyranthes (*Amaranthaceae*)

bidentata var. ***longifolia*** PAB 8037	LEdu

Acidanthera see *Gladiolus*

Acinos (*Lamiaceae*)

§ ***alpinus***	EBee EDAr GJos LLHF MArt NHpl SBch SRms WJek XLum
§ ***corsicus***	WHoo WKif

Aciphylla (*Apiaceae*)

aurea	GCal SPlb
congesta	CMen
dieffenbachii	EUJe SPoG
glaucescens	EBee EUJe GCal GKev SPlb
hectorii	CMen
montana	CMen
pinnatifida	CMen
simplex	CMen
spedenii	CMen

Acis (*Amaryllidaceae*)

§ ***autumnalis*** ♀H5	Widely available
- var. ***oporantha***	CWCL EPri LAma NRog
- - f. ***dispathacea***	GEdr NRog
- var. ***pulchella***	ECho NRog
- 'September Snow'	ELan EPri GKev LAma NRog
ionica	NRog
nicaeensis	CTal ECho EHyd EPot GCal LLHF LRHS NRHS NWad WAbe WCot WThu
§ ***rosea***	CTal NRog WAbe
§ ***tingitana***	CBro
§ ***trichophylla***	EPot
- pink-flowered **new**	EPri
- f. ***purpurascens***	WCot
§ ***valentina***	NRog SRot WCot

Acnistus (*Solanaceae*)

australis	see *Iochroma australe*

Aconitum (*Ranunculaceae*)

CNDS 036 from Burma	WCru
alboviolaceum	WCot
- var. ***alboviolaceum*** f. ***albiflorum*** B&SWJ 8444	WCru
- var. ***purpurascens*** B&SWJ 8477	WCru
altissimum	see *A. lycoctonum* subsp. *vulparia*
anglicum	see *A. napellus* subsp. *napellus* Anglicum Group
* ***angulosum***	EWld
§ ***anthora***	CArn EPfP IKil MHol
arcuatum	see *A. fischeri* var. *arcuatum*
austroyunnanense	CMea WHal WSHC
- BWJ 7902	WCru
autumnale misapplied	see *A. carmichaelii* Wilsonii Group
autumnale Rchb.	see *A. fischeri* Rchb.
× ***bicolor***	see *A.* × *cammarum* 'Bicolor'
'Blue Lagoon'PBR	CWGN EBee EWTr GMcL WHil
'Blue Opal'	EBee ECtt EWes MAvo
'Blue Sceptre'	SRms
'Bressingham Spire' ♀H7	Widely available
bulbilliferum HWJK 2120	WCru WSHC
§ × ***cammarum*** 'Bicolor' ♀H7	Widely available
- 'Eleanora'	ECtt EPPr EPfP EWes EWld GBuc GCra GMaP LHop LSou SRms WCAu
- 'Grandiflorum Album'	CAby MNrw
- 'Pink Sensation'PBR	CAby GQue NLar NPnk
§ ***carmichaelii***	CMea CRos CSam EHyd ELan EPfP GAbr GBuc GCra GKin IFoB IFro LRHS LSou MMuc MNrw NBro

		NChi NEgg NGdn NRHS SEND SRms WBod WCot WFar WHar WHil WHoo WWtn
	- Arendsii Group	ECtt LEdu SRot WCAu
	- - 'Arendsii' ♀H7	Widely available
	- - 'Cloudy' [PBR]	EWTr LHop MAvo NLar WHil
	- 'Moody Blues'	EBee
	- 'Redleaf'	see *A. carmichaelii* 'Royal Flush'
	- 'River Finn'	WCot
	- 'River Lugg'	WCot
	- 'River Medway'	WCot
	- 'River Nene'	WCot
	- 'River Ouse'	ECtt WCot
	- 'River Spey'	WCot
	- 'River Tees'	WCot
	- 'River Teifi'	WCot
	- 'River Trent'	WCot
	- 'River Welland'	WCot
§	- 'Royal Flush' [PBR]	CDor CWGN EBee ECtt IBoy LSun MBNS MHol MNrw NEgg NLar SPad SPer SPoG WCot
	- var. ***truppelianum***	WCot
	- - HWJ 732	EBee WCot
§	- Wilsonii Group	EBee EWoo GMaP MCot MRav MWat NDov NEgg WHoo XLum
	- - 'Barker's Variety'	CKno ELon GBuc GCal GQue LHop LPot LRHS NGdn NLar NSti SRms WCot
	- - 'Kelmscott' ♀H7	EWes MCot MRav SDix SMHy WFar WRHF
	- - 'Spätlese'	CSam CWGN EBee ECtt ELon GBin GCal LEdu LRHS LSou LSun MCot MHol NBir NGdn NLar SGbt SPer WCot WRHF
§	***chasmanthum***	LRHS
	- GWJ 9393	WCru
	chiisanense B&SWJ 4446	WCru
	cilicicum	see *Eranthis hyemalis* Cilicica Group
	'Cloudy'	CWGN EBee ECtt LEdu NGdn SPer WCot
	compactum	see *A. napellus* subsp. *vulgare*
	confertiflorum	see *A. anthora*
	elliotii	EBee
	elwesii	EBee LEdu
	episcopale	WCot WCru
	aff. ***episcopale*** CLD 1426	GBuc
	excelsum	see *A. lycoctonum* subsp. *lycoctonum*
	ferox	EBee EWes LLHF
	- GWJ 9333 from Sikkim	WCru
	- GWJ 9403 **new**	WCru
	fischeri misapplied	see *A. carmichaelii*
§	***fischeri*** Rchb.	EBee LRHS NBid NLar WCot
	- B&SWJ 8809	WCru
§	- var. ***arcuatum*** B&SWJ 774	WCru
	formosanum B&SWJ 3057	WCru
	fukutomei B&SWJ 337	LEdu MRav WCru
	gammiei GWJ 9418	WCru
	gmelinii	see *A. lycoctonum* subsp. *lycoctonum*
	grossedentatum	NLar
§	***hemsleyanum***	CAby CRHN CTal CWGN ECtt EWld GCra GKev GLog MBel NBid WCot WCru WHea WOld
	- 'Red Wine'	WCot
	hyemale	see *Eranthis hyemalis*
	'Ivorine'	CLet CRos CSam CTri EBee ECha EHyd ELan EPfP GBuc GCra GMaP IBoy ILea LEdu LHop LRHS MCot MHol NEgg NGdn NLar NPnk NRHS SCob SPer WFar WPnP WWtn
	jaluense B&SWJ 8741	WCru
	japonicum	EBee GCal NLar WCot
	- var. ***montanum*** B&SWJ 5507	WCru
§	- subsp. ***napiforme***	EWes WCot
	- - B&SWJ 943	EBee ELon WCru
§	- subsp. ***subcuneatum*** B&SWJ 6228	WCru
	kitadakense B&SWJ 11173	WCru
	krylovii	WCot
	kusnezoffii	WCot
	laciniatum GWJ 9254	WCru
	- GWJ 9324	WCru
	lamarckii	see *A. lycoctonum* subsp. *neapolitanum*
	lasianthum	see *A. lycoctonum* subsp. *vulparia*
	leucostomum	EBee GCal
	loczyanum B&SWJ 11529	WCru WSHC
	longecassidatum B&SWJ 4277	WCru
	- B&SWJ 8486	WCru
	lycoctonum	CTal NLar
	- 'Darkeyes'	WCot
§	- subsp. ***lycoctonum***	SRms WCot
§	- subsp. ***moldavicum***	WCot
§	- subsp. ***neapolitanum***	CDor EBee GCal GMaP IMou MMuc NLar SEND
	- 'Russian Yellow'	EWld GCal
§	- subsp. ***vulparia***	CArn CMac GPoy MRav NEgg NGdn SRms WCot WWtn
	mairei	see *A. vilmorinianum*
	moldavicum	see *A. lycoctonum* subsp. *moldavicum*
	nagarum	WCot
	- KR 7589	EBee WPGP
	napellus	CAby CArn CBod CMHG ECtt EPfP EWTr GAbr GBin GPoy LCro LEdu LOPS LRHS MBel MCot MMuc MNHC MWat SEND SPoG SRms SWat WFar WHar WHoo WPnP WShi XLum
	- 'Bergfürst'	CAby CMea EBee NDov
	- 'Blue Valley'	EBee ELan EPfP EWes
	- 'Gletschereis'	EBee LRHS
§	- subsp. ***napellus*** Anglicum Group	MCot MHol MMuc SEND WCot
	- - - 'Spring Yellow' **new**	WCot
	- 'Rubellum'	ELan EWTr IBoy IMou LRHS NBir NBro NLar SPoG
	- 'Schneewittchen'	CSpe EBee EWes SAko
§	- subsp. ***vulgare***	CTal
	- - 'Albidum'	CAby CBod CMea EHrv ELan ELon EPfP EWTr EWoo GAbr GMaP LEdu LRHS MBel NBid NCGa NHol NLar SPer SPoG WBor WWtn
	- - 'Carneum'	GCra WHer
	napiforme	see *A. japonicum* subsp. *napiforme*
	nasutum	WCot
	neapolitanum	see *A. lycoctonum* subsp. *neapolitanum*
	'Newry Blue'	EBee ECtt GBuc GMcL IMou LRHS MRav NBir NWad SPoG SRms
	orientale misapplied	see *A. lycoctonum* subsp. *vulparia*
	paniculatum misapplied	see *A. variegatum* subsp. *paniculatum*
	piepunense	EBee GKev
	proliferum	WCot

- B&SWJ 4107	WCru
pseudolaeve B&SWJ 8663	WCru
- var. ***erectum*** B&SWJ 8466	WCru
pubiceps white-flowered	GCal
pyramidale	see *A. napellus* subsp. *vulgare*
pyrenaicum misapplied	see *A. lycoctonum* subsp. *neapolitanum*
ranunculifolium	see *A. lycoctonum* subsp. *neapolitanum*
sachalinense	WCot
- subsp. ***yezoense***	EBee LPla NLar WCot
senanense var. ***incisum*** B&SWJ 11032	WCru
- subsp. ***paludicola*** B&SWJ 10866	WCru
seoulense	EBee
- B&SWJ 694	WCru
- B&SWJ 864	WCru
- BWJ 4107	IMou
septentrionale	see *A. lycoctonum* subsp. *lycoctonum*
'Shirui Blue'	LEdu
'Spark's Variety' 🏆H7	Widely available
spicatum GWJ 9394	WCru
'Stainless Steel' 🏆H7	Widely available
subcuneatum	see *A. japonicum* subsp. *subcuneatum*
'Surprise' **new**	WCot
× ***tubergenii***	see *Eranthis hyemalis* Tubergenii Group
uchiyamae B&SWJ 1005	WCru
- B&SWJ 1216	ELon EPPr WCru
- B&SWJ 4446	NLar
variegatum	EBee GCal
§ - subsp. ***paniculatum***	CBod GCal WCot
§ ***vilmorinianum*** BWJ 8055	WCru
violaceum var. ***robustum***	see *A. chasmanthum*
volubile misapplied	see *A. hemsleyanum*
volubile Pall.	EBee
vulparia	see *A. lycoctonum* subsp. *vulparia*
yamazakii	WCru
zigzag var. ***ryohakuense*** B&SWJ 8906	WCru

Aconogonon see *Persicaria*

Acorus ✿ (*Acoraceae*)

calamus	CArn CBen CKno CWat GPoy MNHC MSKA MWLS NPer SWat WHer WMAq
- subsp. ***angustatus***	GPoy
- 'Argenteostriatus' (v)	CBen CWat ECha MCot MMuc SCob SEND SRms SWat WMAq
* ***christophii***	ELon EPPr
gramineus	GPoy LPar MSKA NPer SWat WBod WHer
- 'Golden Delight'	SCob
- 'Golden Edge' (v)	ELon NWad
- 'Hakuro-nishiki' (v)	ESps GBin GMcL LRHS NBid NRHS NWad SCob SRms SWvt WMoo XLum
- 'Kinchinjunga' (v)	IFro
- 'Licorice'	GBin GCal WGrn
- 'Masamune' (v)	EWes GBin GCal
- 'Minimus Aureus'	CBre GCal
- 'Oborozuki' misapplied	see *A. gramineus* 'Ōgon'
- 'Oborozuki' (v)	EHoe
§ - 'Ōgon' (v)	Widely available
- var. ***pusillus***	NBro
- 'Variegatus' (v)	Widely available
'Intermedius'	NPer

Acradenia (*Rutaceae*)

frankliniae	CBcs CCCN CMHG CMac EBee EPfP LRHS MBlu SAko SEND SKHP SPlb WHor WPGP

Actaea (*Ranunculaceae*)

alba misapplied	see *A. pachypoda*, *A. rubra* f. *neglecta*
arizonica	EBee LRHS NLar SPhx WCru
asiatica B&SWJ 616	WCru
- B&SWJ 6351 from Japan	WCru
- B&SWJ 8694 from Korea	WCru
- BWJ 8174 from China	WCru
biternata B&SWJ 8917	NLar WCru
- B&SWJ 11190	WCru
'Chocoholic'	CBWd CLAP CMos CWGN EBee ECtt ELan GBin GEdr IKil IPot LRHS MAsh MAvo NCGa
§ ***cimicifuga***	ECha GCal GPoy
§ ***cordifolia***	EBee GBin GMaP LHop LRHS NGdn NLar SWvt
- variegated (v)	EBee
dahurica	EWTr GBin GQue
- B&SWJ 8426	WCru
- B&SWJ 8573	WCru
- tall	GBin NBid
elata	IMou
erythrocarpa	see *A. rubra*
frigida B&SWJ 2966	WCru
heracleifolia B&SWJ 8843	WCru
§ ***japonica***	GCal NLar
- B&SWJ 5828	WCru
- B&SWJ 11136	WCru
- B&SWJ 11526	WCru
- from Jejudo, South Korea	EBee IMou LEdu MNrw NDov NLar WPGP
- var. ***acutiloba*** B&SWJ 6257	WCru
- compact B&SWJ 8758A	WCot WCru
mairei	IMou LRHS
- BWJ 7635	WCru
- BWJ 7939	WCru
§ ***matsumurae*** B&SWJ 11187	WCru
- B&SWJ 11528	WCru
- 'Elstead Variety' 🏆H7	GCal MRav
- 'White Pearl'	Widely available
§ ***pachypoda***	CBro CTal EBee EPfP EWTr GCal GLog GPoy MBel NBid NSti SMad WCru
- 'Misty Blue'	CBct CBro CLAP CSpe CWGN EBee ECtt ESwi GEdr GMcL MAvo MHol SCob SMad SPoG WCot
- f. ***rubrocarpa***	GCal
§ ***podocarpa***	EBee SPlb SRms WCru
'Queen of Sheba'	EBee NDov
racemosa 🏆H7	CBod CMac EBee ELan EPfP GCal GPoy LSun NBid NGdn NLar NSti SCob SPer SWvt WFar XLum
§ ***rubra***	CBod CBro CLAP CTal EBee ECha ELan GCal MBel MMrt MNrw NBid NLar SMad SPoG WCru
- B&SWJ 9555	WCru
- ***alba***	see *A. pachypoda*, *A. rubra* f. *neglecta*
§ - f. ***neglecta***	GLog GQue SKHP WCot WCru
simplex	EBee GCra GLog NEgg SWat WCot
- B&SWJ 8653	WCru
- B&SWJ 8664	WCru

- B&SWJ 10957	WCru
- B&SWJ 11133	WCru
§ - Atropurpurea Group	EBee ECha ELan ELon EPfP GMaP IBoy LCro LRHS MGos MJak MRav NAst NBir NGdn NLar NSti SPer SRkn SRms SWat SWvt WFar WHar WMoo WPGP WPnP
- - 'Black Negligee'	Widely available
- - 'Brunette' 🏆^{H7}	Widely available
- - 'Carbonella'	EBee ECtt GBin NCGa
- - 'Hillside Black Beauty'	CCVN CDor CLAP ECtt GEdr GKin GMaP LRHS MAsh MNrw MTis NBir NLar NPnk SCob WCot
- - 'James Compton' 🏆^{H7}	Widely available
- - 'Mountain Wave'	ECtt MAsh NDov WPGP
- 'Pink Spike'	Widely available
§ - 'Prichard's Giant'	CLAP EBee GCal MRav NLar WFar
- ***ramosa***	see *A. simplex* 'Prichard's Giant'
- 'Silver Axe'	GCal NGdn
- variegated (v)	WCot
spicata	EPPr GBin GCra GPoy LEdu WCru WPGP
- PAB 8131	LEdu
- from England	WCru
taiwanensis B&SWJ 3413	WCru
- RWJ 9996	WCru
yesoensis B&SWJ 6355	WCru
- B&SWJ 10860	WCru
yunnanensis	GCal

Actinella see *Tetraneuris*

Actinidia (*Actinidiaceae*)

BWJ 8161 from China	WCru
arguta	CPne CRHN EBee
- (f/F)	CAgr
- B&SWJ 4455 from Jejudo, South Korea	WCru
- B&SWJ 4823 from Japan	WCru
- B&SWJ 8529 from Ulleungdo, South Korea	WCru
- 'Ambrosia' (f/F)	LRHS WMat
- 'Ambrosia Grande'	NLar
- 'Ananasnaya' (f/F)	CAgr
- 'Bayern' (F)	CAgr CCCN
- 'Geneva 2' (f/F)	CAgr
- 'Honigbeere'	NLar
- 'Issai' (s-p/F)	CAgr CBcs CCCN EHyd EPfP EPom LBuc LCro LRHS NRHS SVic WCot
- 'Jumbo' (f/F)	CAgr LEdu SVic
- 'Ken's Red' (F)	CAgr CCCN CFGn SVic
- 'Meader' (m)	CAgr
- 'MSU' (F)	CAgr
- 'Purpurna Sadowa' (f/F)	NLar
- 'Shoko' (f)	WCru
- 'Unchae' (m)	WCru
- 'Weiki' (m)	CAgr CCCN LRHS SVic
chinensis misapplied	see *A. deliciosa*
chinensis Planch. var. ***setosa*** H.L. Li B&SWJ 3563	WCru
§ ***deliciosa***	ESps MRav SPlb WFar WSHC
- 'Atlas' (m)	CAgr NLar SDea
- 'Golden Delight' (F) new	CBcs CFGn
- 'Hayward' (f/F)	CAgr CBcs CCCN CMac EPfP LSRN SCob SDea SWvt WFar
- 'Jenny' (s-p/F)	CAgr CEnd CMac CRos CSut CTri EHyd ELan EMOT EPfP EPom LBuc LCro LRHS MGos MJak NRHS SCob SDea SPoG SPre SVic WFar
- 'Oriental Delight' (s-p/F) new	CRHN
- Solissimo = 'Renact' (s-p/F)	EHyd LRHS MCoo NRHS SPoG WMat
- 'Solo' (s-p/F)	CBar CBcs CCCN CMac CRHN CSBt ECrN EPfP LRHS LSRN NLar NPri SLim SPer SWvt WPGP
- 'Tomuri' (m)	CBcs CCCN CMac EBee EPfP LSRN SWvt
hypoleuca B&SWJ 5942	WCru
'Kiwai Bee' new	CCCN
kolomikta 🏆^{H5}	Widely available
- (m)	MBlu NPla SDix
- B&SWJ 4243	LSRN WCru
- 'Adam' (m) new	ETho
- 'Doctor Szymanowski'	WPGP
- 'Sentyabraskaya' (f/F)	NLar
- 'Tomoko' (f/F)	WCru
- 'Yazuaki' (m)	WCru
melanandra	SPlb WPGP
petelotii FMWJ 13137	WCru
- HWJ 628	WCru
pilosula misapplied	see *A. tetramera* var. *maloides*
pilosula (Finet & Gagnep.) Stapf ex Hand.-Mazz.	CKel EHyd ELan IArd LRHS NRHS SHil SPoG SRms WKif
polygama	CMen GCal
- B&SWJ 5444	WCru
- B&SWJ 8525 from Korea	WCru
- B&SWJ 8923 from Japan	WCru
- B&SWJ 12564 from Korea	WCru
rufa B&SWJ 3525	WCru
strigosa WJC 13662 new	WCru
- WJC 13807 new	WCru
aff. ***strigosa*** HWJK 2367	WCru
tetramera B&SWJ 3564	WCru
§ - var. ***maloides*** 🏆^{H5}	CBcs CBot CRos CWGN EBee EUJe GCal LHop MGil NLar SBrt SCoo SDix SKHP WBor WCru WPGP WSHC

Adansonia (*Malvaceae*)

grandidieri	SPlb
madagascariensis	SPlb
rubrostipa	SPlb
za	SPlb

Adelocaryum see *Lindelofia*

Adenanthos (*Proteaceae*)

sericeus	SPlb

Adenia (*Passifloraceae*)

glauca	LToo
keramanthus new	LToo

Adenium (*Apocynaceae*)

obesum 🏆^{H1a}	CCCN LToo
- subsp. ***socotranum***	LToo

Adenocarpus (*Papilionaceae*)

decorticans	SPlb

Adenophora (*Campanulaceae*)

sp.	MHol
'Afterglow'	see *Campanula rapunculoides* 'Afterglow'
asiatica	see *Hanabusaya asiatica*
bulleyana	CHVG ELan LRHS NBid NGdn NLar SPav SPlb WCot
capillaris subsp. ***leptosepala***	EWld WCot

- - BWJ 7986	WCru
coelestis	EBee NBid
- B&SWJ 7998	WCru
confusa	WHer WSHC
* ***cymerae***	GJos WTcb
divaricata B&SWJ 11018	WCru
'Gaudi Violet'	SPoG
grandiflora B&SWJ 8555	WCru
jasionifolia	LLHF
khasiana	LLHF NLar XLum
lamarkii B&SWJ 8738	WCru
latifolia misapplied	see *A. pereskiifolia*
latifolia ambig. white-flowered	MMuc
liliifolia	CMea ELan EPfP GCal GKev LHop NLar NPer WFar
maximowicziana B&SWJ 11008	WCru
morrisonensis RWJ 10008	WCru
§ ***nikoensis***	GEdr NBid
§ ***pereskiifolia***	EWes SHar SPlb WCot
polyantha	EWTr NLar SRms
polymorpha	see *A. nikoensis*
potaninii	EBee ELan MMuc SEND WHal
- pale-flowered	MAvo WHal
remotiflora B&SWJ 8714	WCru
- B&SWJ 11016	WCru
stricta subsp. ***confusa*** new	GKev
takedae	EBee SBrt
- B&SWJ 11424	WCru
taquetii	GEdr WAbe
tashiroi	GKev XLum
triphylla B&SWJ 8608	WCru
- B&SWJ 10916	WCru
- var. ***hakusanensis***	LLHF
- var. ***japonica***	GJos
- - B&SWJ 10933	WCru
uehatae	GEdr
- B&SWJ 126	SKHP WCru

Adenostyles (*Asteraceae*)

alpina new	SBrt

Adesmia (*Papilionaceae*)

longipes	SPlb

Adiantum ✿ (*Pteridaceae*)

sp.	CMac
aethiopicum	NLos XBlo
§ ***aleuticum*** ♀H6	CLAP NBro NLar SPlb WFib WPGP
- 'Imbricatum'	CElw CLAP EBee ECha ELon EShb EUJe GBin GEdr IKil ISha IVic LPla LPre LRHS MAvo MGos NBid NBro NLar NLos SRms WCot WFar WFib XLum
§ - 'Japonicum'	WFar WPGP
- 'Miss Sharples'	CAby CBod CDTJ CHVG CLAP ECha ELon GBin GEdr LPla LRHS MGos NBid NLar SPoG SRms WCot WFar WPGP WRHF
§ - 'Subpumilum' ♀H5	CLAP NBid WCot WFib
- 'Tasselatum'	WCot
andicola B&SWJ 10448	WCru
capillus-veneris	EBee ISha WFib
- 'Mairisii'	see *A.* × *mairisii*
caudatum new	ISha
chilense	NLos
hispidulum	CCCN EBee ISha LLHF LRHS NLos
- 'Bronze Venus'	CCCN ISha LRHS SRms
§ × ***mairisii*** ♀H5	EBee ISha LCro LRHS NLos
pedatum misapplied	see *A. aleuticum*
pedatum ambig.	ISha NLos SPer
pedatum L.	CBcs CDor CLAP ECha EFer ELan ELon EShb GMaP LLWG LPot LRHS SWat WFar WPGP
- Asiatic form	see *A. aleuticum* 'Japonicum'
- 'Japonicum'	see *A. aleuticum* 'Japonicum'
- 'Roseum'	see *A. aleuticum* 'Japonicum'
- var. ***subpumilum***	see *A. aleuticum* 'Subpumilum'
poiretii	WCot
pubescens	ISha
raddianum 'Fragrans'	see *A. raddianum* 'Fragrantissimum'
§ - 'Fragrantissimum'	EShb ISha NLos
- 'Fritz Lüthi' ♀H1c	NLos
- 'Lady Geneva'	WCot
- 'Legrand Morgan'	NLos
- 'Monocolor'	ISha
reniforme	NLos WAbe
tenerum 'Bicolor'	ISha
× ***tracyi*** new	ISha
venustum ♀H7	CFil CHVG CLAP CSpe CTsd EBee EFer EUJe GCal ISha IVic LLWG LRHS MCot MHol NBid NBro NCGa SBrt SChr SDix SKHP SPlb SRms SWat WCot WFar WFib WHal WPGP

Adina (*Rubiaceae*)

rubella	NLar

Adlumia (*Papaveraceae*)

fungosa	CSpe LRHS

Adonis (*Ranunculaceae*)

amurensis misapplied	see *A.* 'Fukujukai', *A. multiflora*
amurensis ambig.	CMea EBee ECGP GEdr LEdu LRHS NHpl WCot
amurensis Regel & Radde	GKev
- 'Pleniflora'	see *A. multiflora* 'Sandanzaki'
- 'Sakhalin'	EBee
brevistyla	GBuc GEdr
'Chichibu-beni'	GEdr
§ 'Fukujukai'	ECha GEdr GKev XEll
§ ***multiflora***	EHrv SRot
- 'Beni-nadeshiko'	GEdr
- 'Hakuju'	GEdr
- 'Hanazono' (d)	GEdr
§ - 'Sandanzaki' (d)	EBee EPot GEdr GKev MMrt NLar
ramosa	GEdr
'Sado-no-maboroshi' (d) new	GEdr
vernalis	EBee GPoy NLar WCot

Adoxa (*Adoxaceae*)

moschatellina	CBre EBee ECho EWld LEdu MNrw NMir NRya WHer WSFF WShi

Adromischus (*Crassulaceae*)

maculatus ♀H2	LToo

Aechmea ✿ (*Bromeliaceae*)

sp.	XBlo
caudata	NLos
- var. ***variegata***	NLos
cylindrata 'Blue Cone'	WCot
'Echidna'	SPlb
fasciata ♀H1a	XBlo
gamosepala	NLos
nudicaulis ♀H1a	NLos
- var. ***capitata***	NLos

I	– – f. ***albomarginata***	NLos
	ramosa	XBlo
	recurvata	CBlu NLos
	– 'Paraguay'	NLos
	– var. ***recurvata***	NLos
	victoriana	XBlo
	– var. ***discolor***	NLos

Aegle (*Rutaceae*)

	sepiaria	see *Citrus trifoliata*

Aegopodium (*Apiaceae*)

	podagraria 'Dangerous' (v)	CHid
	– gold-margined (v)	EPPr
	– 'Variegatum' (v)	CBod CLet EBee ECha EHoe EHrv EPPr EShb GMaP GMcL LHop LRHS LSou MBel MRav NBid NEgg NSti SEND SPer SPoG WCFE WCot WMoo WSHC XLum

Aeonium (*Crassulaceae*)

	sp.	CArn
	arboreum	CDTJ CKno CTre ELan EShb GCal SEND
	– 'Atropurpureum'	CAbb CCCN CDTJ CRos ELan EShb NPer SEND SPer
I	– 'Magnificum'	EShb ESwi ETod GBin SArc
	– 'Variegatum' (v)	CTre NPer
	balsamiferum	CCCN CDTJ CTre
	'Black Cap'	CCCN
	'Blush'	CKno
	canariense	CCCN CDTJ SVen
	– var. ***palmense***	SVen
	castello-paivae	SChr
	ciliatum	SPlb
	'Cornish Tribute'	CCCN CTre
	'Cristata Sunburst'	CDTJ CTre WCot
	cuneatum	CDTJ CTre SEND
*	***decorum*** 'Variegatum' (v)	WCot
	'Dinner Plate'	CDTJ CTre
	× ***domesticum***	see *Aichryson* × *aizoides* var. *domesticum*
	'Du Rozzen' **new**	CTre
*	***escobarii***	SPlb
	glandulosum	SVen
	goochiae	SBch
	haworthii ♀H1c	CDTJ LAll NHpl SEND SVen
	– 'Kiwi' **new**	CCCN
	– 'Variegatum' (v) ♀H1c	CDTJ CTre EShb LAll SVen
	hierrense	CTre SPlb
	holochrysum Webb & Berth.	CAbb
	'Lemon-Lime' (v)	WCot
	lindleyi	SChr
	'Logan Rock'	CTre
	'Merry Maiden' **new**	CTre
*	***multiflorum*** 'Variegatum' (v)	CDTJ
	nobile	CBrP
	'Poldark'	CCCN CTre
	sedifolium	CTre LAll
	simsii	CDTJ CTre
	simsii × 'Zwartkop'	CCCN CTre ELan ETod MHer SChr
	spathulatum	CTre WCot
	'Sunburst' (v) ♀H1c	CTre WCot
	tabuliforme ♀H1c	CCCN CDTJ CSpe CTre SMad SPlb WCot
	– 'Cristatum'	WCot
	undulatum	SPlb
	urbicum	EShb
	'Velour'	CCCN
	'Voodoo'	ESwi ETod GCal WCot
	'Zwartkop' ♀H1c	CAbb CBcs CCCN CCht CHVG CHil CKno CSpe CTre ECtt EShb EUJe GBin LSou MCot MSCN NLos NPer NPla SArc SChr SDix SEND SEle SMad SPlb SRot SWvt WCot WWFP

Aeschynanthus ✿ (*Gesneriaceae*)

	Black Pagoda Group	WDib
	buxifolius KR 7798	WAbe WCot
	'Fire Wheel'	WDib
	hildebrandii	WDib
	'Hot Flash'	WDib
	'Little Tiger'	WDib
	longicalyx	WDib
§	***longicaulis*** ♀H1c	WDib
	marmoratus	see *A. longicaulis*
	radicans ♀H1c	WDib
	'Scooby Doo'	WDib
	speciosus ♀H1c	WDib

Aesculus ✿ (*Sapindaceae*)

	arguta	see *A. glabra* var. *arguta*
	× ***arnoldiana***	CDul
	assamica NJM 10.030	WPGP
	– WWJ 11886	WCru
	'Autumn Splendor'	EPfP
§	× ***bushii***	CDul CMCN
	californica	CBcs CDul CMCN CMac EPfP ERod SBrt SKHP WPGP
	– 'Blue Haze'	WMat
	– 'Canyon Pink'	CMCN
	× ***carnea***	CDul SGol WHar
	– 'Aureomarginata' (v)	ERod LLHF WHar
	– 'Briotii'	CAco CBcs CCVT CDul CEnd CLnd CMac CSBt CWib EBee ECrN ELan EMOT EPfP ESps EWTr LRHS MGos MMuc NLar NOrn NWea SCob SEND SEWo SPer WFar WHar WMat WTSh
	– 'Plantierensis'	CDul
*	– 'Variegata' (v)	CDul CMCN
	chinensis	CBcs CMCN
	'Dallimorei' (graft-chimaera)	WPat
	flava ♀H5	CDul CMCN ELan EPfP EWTr MMuc SEND
	– f. ***vestita***	CDul MBlu
	georgiana	see *A. sylvatica*
	glabra	CDul CMCN
§	– var. ***arguta***	CMCN NLar WPat
	– 'Autumn Blaze'	EPfP
	– 'October Red'	EPfP
	glaucescens	see *A.* × *neglecta*
	hippocastanum	CAco CBcs CCVT CDul CMac CSBt CTri CWib ECrN ELan EMOT ESps MGos MMuc MSwo NLar NOra NWea SCob SEND SEWo SGol SPer WFar WHar WHed WMat WTSh
	– 'Aureomarginata' (v)	CMac
§	– 'Baumannii' (d)	CDul CLnd CMCN ECrN ELan ESps MGos MSwo NWea SCob SPer
	– 'Digitata'	CDul CMCN WCot WPat
	– 'Flore Pleno'	see *A. hippocastanum* 'Baumannii'
	– 'Hampton Court Gold'	CDul CMCN CMac
	– f. ***laciniata***	CDul CMCN NLar SMad WPat
	– 'Monstrosa'	WPat
	– 'Wisselink'	CDul CMCN ECrN WCot WPat
	indica	CDul CLnd CMCN ECrN ELan EPfP EWTr LEdu SEND SGol WTSh
	– 'Sydney Pearce' ♀H5	CBcs CDul CEnd CJun CMCN EPfP ERod MBlu MGos NLar NOra SLim WMat WPat

	× ***marylandica***	CDul
	× ***mississippiensis***	see *A.* × *bushii*
	× ***mutabilis*** 'Harbisonii'	WPat
	- 'Induta'	CDul CLnd CMCN EPfP NOra SKHP WMat
§	- 'Penduliflora'	CDul
§	× ***neglecta***	CMCN
	- 'Autumn Fire'	EPfP NOrn SLim SPoG WMat WPat
	- 'Erythroblastos' ♀H5	CBcs CDul CEnd CJun CMCN EPfP ERod EUJe MBlu SCoo SMad SPer SPoG WCot WMat WPat
	parviflora ♀H5	CBcs CDul CMCN CMac CTri EBee ELan EPfP ESps EWTr GKin GMcL IDee MBlu MGos MMuc MPkF MRav NLar NOra NWea SEND SGol SMad SPer SWvt WHar WMat
	pavia	CBcs CDul CMCN EPfP
	- 'Atrosanguinea'	CEnd CMCN EPfP ERod SKHP
	- var. ***discolor*** 'Koehnei'	CMCN EPfP MMrt NLar NOra WMat
	- 'Penduliflora'	see *A.* × *mutabilis* 'Penduliflora'
	- 'Purple Spring'	WPat
	- 'Rosea Nana'	CMCN WPat
§	- Splendens Group	CMCN EPfP
	splendens	see *A. pavia* Splendens Group
§	***sylvatica***	CMCN
	turbinata	CBcs CDul CMCN
	wilsonii	CBcs

Aethionema (*Brassicaceae*)

	armenum	GKev
	capitatum	CPBP GKev SIgm
	coridifolium	GJos
§	***grandiflorum*** ♀H5	ECho ELan GJos GKev NBro SRms XSen
	- Pulchellum Group ♀H5	CSpe GJos MMuc SEND
*	***kotschyi*** hort.	EDAr GJos WAbe
	membranaceum	GJos
	oppositifolium	LLHF
	pulchellum	see *A. grandiflorum*
	saxatile	GJos GKev
	schistosum	GJos LLHF
	subulatum	GEdr LLHF
	'Warley Rose' ♀H5	CRos ECho EHyd ELan EPot GCrg GKev ITim LHop LRHS NBir NRHS NSla SBch SRms WIce WThu WTor XSen
	'Warley Ruber'	CMea EPot

Afrocarpus (*Podocarpaceae*)

	falcatus	CBcs

Agapanthus ✿ (*Agapanthaceae*)

	'Aberdeen'	IBal
	'Adonis'	CPrp IBlr
	'African Moon'	CPen CPne CPrp IBal MAvo
	'African Skies'	CAbb CPen CPne CPrp CTal IBal LRHS SFai
	africanus misapplied	CBlu CElw CLet CTsd CWCL CWib EBee EHrv ELan EPfP EPot ESps ETod EUJe GKev ILea ITim LCro LPar LRHS MJak SArc SChr SCob SPer SRot SVic WBor XLum XSen
	- 'Albus' misapplied	CBcs CRos CWCL EBee EHyd ELan EPfP EPot ESps ETod ILea LPar LRHS LSRN MGos MJak NRHS SCob SDeJ SEND SPer SRms XLum XSen
	- hybrid **new**	IBoy
	'Aimee'	CBro IBal
	'Alan Street'	CAvo IBal
	'Albus' ambig.	GMaP MHer
I	'Albus Nanus'	IBal
I	'Albus Roseus'	IBal
	'Alice Gloucester'	CPrp
	'Allisio' **new**	IBal
	'Amsterdam'	CPen EBee EWTr IBal IMou
	'Ancona' **new**	IBal
	'Angela'	CPen CPrp IBal MAvo
	'Ankara' **new**	IBal
	'Anneke' **new**	IBal
	'Antibe' **new**	IBal
	'Aphrodite'	IBlr
	'Apple Court'	LRHS
	'Aquamarine'	CAvo EPri IBal
	'Arctic Star'	CAvo CCCN CKno CMac CPen CPne CPou CPrp CSpe CWCL EBee ELon EWoo IBal LRHS LSRN LSou MAvo NLar SDys SFai SPoG
	'Ardernei Hybrid'	CAvo ECha ECtt EWes GAbr GCal IBal IBlr LSou MAvo WCot WGwG WPGP
§	'Argenteus Vittatus' (v) ♀H2	CPen
	'Arosa'	IMou
	'Atlas'	IBlr
	'Aureovittatus' (v)	IBal
	'Autumn Mist'	IBal
	'Avalanche' **new**	EBee IBal SFai
	'Baby Blue'	see *A.* 'Blue Baby' Rom.
	'Baby Pete' PBR	CPen EBee IBal
	Back in Black = 'B in B' PBR	CBro CCCN CWCL ELan EPfP EWes IBal MBNS MRav NBid SCob SHyH SMad SPer WCot WFar
	'Ballerina'	CPne IBal LRHS
	'Ballyrogan'	IBal IBlr
	'Bangor Blue'	IBlr
	'Barley Blue'	IBal
	'Barnfield Blue'	CPne CPrp EBee IBal SFai
	'Basutoland'	LRHS
	'Becky'	IBal
	'Beeches Dwarf'	IBal
	'Ben Hope'	CBro ESps IBal IBlr WCot
	'Berlin' **new**	IBal
	'Best Barn Blue'	SMHy
	'Beth Chatto'	see *A. campanulatus* 'Albovittatus'
	'Bethlehem Star'	EPri
	'Bicton Bell'	IBlr
	'Bicton Bride'	CPne IBal
	'Big Ben'	IBal
	'Big Blue'	CBod CCCN CMac CPrp CWCL EBee LSou SEND SLdr SRkn
	'Black Beauty'	IBal LRHS
	'Black Buddhist'	CBod CCCN CPen CWCL EBee ECtt EPfP EPri EUJe GBuc GMcL IBal LRHS NGdn SAko SFai SPer XSen
	'Black Magic'	CAbb CPne CPrp EBee IBal LCro LOPS LSou NSti SFai SPoG
	'Black Pantha' PBR	Widely available
§	'Blauwe Valk'	EPfP
	'Bloemfontein' **new**	IBal
§	'Blue Baby' Rom.	CCCN CChe CPen CRos EHyd ELan ELon IBal LRHS MJak NRHS XTur
	'Blue Bayou'	IBal
	'Blue Beauty'	LRHS
	Blue Bird	see *A.* 'Blauwe Valk'
	'Blue Bird'	CRos LRHS SHil
	'Blue Brush'	CPrp CRos EHyd EPfP IBal LRHS NRHS SCoo WCot
	'Blue Cascade'	IBlr
	'Blue Companion'	CPrp IBlr
	'Blue Diamond' ambig.	CMac
	'Blue Dot'	CPrp ECtt EPfP LLHF LRHS LSou SDys

	'Blue Flare'	IBal
	'Blue Flash'	IBal
	'Blue Formality'	IBal IBlr
	'Blue Giant'	CBro CCCN CChe CDor CKno CPrp EBee IBal LRHS MGos SCob SWat WPGP
	'Blue Globe'	CHid EBee EPri GMaP LRHS
	'Blue Gown'	CSam
	'Blue Heaven'PBR	CPne CWGN EWoo IBal LHop SCob
	'Blue Horizons'PBR (v)	CCCN IBal LRHS
	'Blue Ice'	CAbb CPen CPne CPou CPrp EBee EWoo IBal LRHS SAko
	'Blue Imp'	CBro IBal IBlr
	'Blue Jay'	CPen IBal
	'Blue Magic'	EBee IBal
	'Blue Moon'	CAbP CBro CPen CPrp EBee ECha ECtt EPri EWoo GMcL IBal IBlr ILea LLWG LRHS MHol NLar SEND SHyH SLdr WCot
	'Blue Nile'	CPne IBal
	'Blue Pixie'	IBal
	'Blue Prince'	CPen EBee
	'Blue Rinse'	CAvo IBal
	'Blue Skies' ambig.	LRHS NCGa
I	'Blue Skies' Dunlop	IBlr
	'Blue Spear'	CPen
	'Blue Steel' **new**	IBal
	'Blue Triumphator'	CDor EPfP GBin GKev GMaP IBal LRHS MHer MNHC SCob
	'Blue Umbrella'	CDor GMcL SRkn WHar
	'Blue Yonder'	EBee
	blue-flowered	WCFE
	Bluestorm = 'Atiblu'PBR	CPrp CRos EHyd EPfP IBal LBuc LRHS NRHS SArc SCob SEND
	'Bluety'PBR	CPen IBal
	'Bray Valley'	CPne CPrp
	'Bressingham Blue'	CAbb CBro CPrp CSam CTri EAEE ESps EWes GCal IBal IBlr LRHS MRav SFai
	'Bressingham Bounty'	EAEE IBal LRHS
	'Bressingham White'	ESps LRHS MRav
	'Bridal Bouquet'	EBee IBal LCro LSRN SFai
	'Bright Blue' **new**	IBal
	'Brilliant Blue'	EBee IBal LRHS SFai
	'Bristol'	IBal
	'Buckingham Palace'	CBro CPne EBee EWes GAbr IBal IBlr MAvo NChi WCot WPGP
	'Calimero' **new**	IBal
	'Cally Blue'	GAbr GCal IBal
	'Cally Longstem'	EBee EPri GCal
	'Cally Pale Blue'	IBal
	campanulatus	CBlu CMac CPrp CTre ELan EPfP GKin IBal IBlr LRHS MRav NEgg SWat WFar WPGP
	- var. ***albidus***	CBWd CPrp ECha ELan EPfP GKin IBlr LHop LRHS MMuc NBid NGdn SEND SPer WGwG WHoo WPGP
§	- 'Albovittatus' (v)	ECho IBal LSou
	- bright blue-flowered	GCal IBal
	- 'Cobalt Blue'	CPrp EPri GBin GKin IBal LRHS LSou MAsh MAvo NEgg NGdn
	- 'Oxford Blue'	IBlr
	- subsp. ***patens*** ♀H4	CLet EAEE EPfP IBal LRHS MRav SWat WPGP
	- - deep-blue-flowered	IBlr LRHS
	- 'Profusion'	CBro CPrp ECha EPri IBal IBlr LRHS
	- 'Ultramarine'	IBal
	- variegated (v)	EBee ECha NPer
	- 'Wedgwood Blue'	EBee IBal IBlr LRHS
	- 'Wendy'	CPne EBee IBal IBlr LRHS
	- 'White Hope'	IBal IBlr
	'Carefree'	IBal
	'Castle of Mey'	CAvo CBod CBro CFil CPrp EBee GAbr GCal IBal IBlr LCro LRHS LSou MAvo SFai WPGP
	'Catharina'	IBal
§	***caulescens*** ♀H2	CPrp IBal IBlr LRHS WPGP
	- subsp. ***angustifolius***	CHid ELon IBal IBlr MHol SEND WCot WPGP
	- subsp. ***caulescens***	IBlr SWat
	'Cedric Morris'	CPen EPri IBal IBlr
	'Celebration'	IBal
	'Chandra'	IBal IBlr
	'Charlotte'PBR	CMac CPen EBee EPfP IBal LRHS SHil SPoG
	'Cherbours' **new**	IBal
	'Cherry Holley'	ELon IBal
	'Chika's Blue'	IBal MAvo
	'Clarence House'	CBro CPen CPrp IBal
	coddii	CTal EPri EWes IBal IBlr MHer WCot
	'Columba'	CPen CPrp EBee ELon IBal LAma NBid XSen
	comptonii	see *A. praecox* subsp. *minimus*
	'Cool Blue'	IBal MAvo
	'Corina'	EBee
	'Crystal'	GCal
	'Crystal Drop'	CPen CPne CPou CPrp EBee EPri EWoo IBal LRHS SFai SWat WPGP
	Danube	see *A.* 'Donau'
	'Dart Valley'	CPne CPrp IBal
	'Dartmoor'	CPne
	'Debbie'	IBal
	'Delft'	CPrp EBee IBal IBlr
	'Delft Blue'	IBal LRHS
	'Density'	IBlr
	'Devon Dawn'	IMou
	'Dnjepr'	CBro EBee IBal
	'Dokkum' **new**	IBal
	'Dokter Brouwer'	CKno EWTr GKev IBoy IKil ILea LRHS LSRN MCot SHyH
§	'Donau'	CBro CPen CPrp EBee EPri IBal NBir SWat WCot
	Double Diamond = 'Rfdd'PBR	CPen CPne CRos EBee EHyd EPfP EPri EWes IBal LRHS LSRN LSou NRHS SAko SCob SFai SPoG XEll
	'Dublin'	IBal
	'Duivenbrugge Blue'	IBal
	'Duivenbrugge White'	IBal
	'Durban' **new**	IBal
	dyeri	see *A. inapertus* subsp. *intermedius*
	'Early Blue'	EBee EWTr EWoo IPot
	'Ed Carman' (v)	LSou
	'Eggesford Sky'	CPne CPrp EBee IBal
	'Elaine'	IBal
	'Elisa' **new**	IBal
	'Elisabeth'	LRHS
	'Elizabeth Salisbury'	CPne IBal
	'Ellamae'	IBal
	'Enigma'	Widely available
	'Enigma Variations'	EBee
	'Essence of Summer'	WCot
	'Ethel's Joy'	CPen EPri IBal
	'Eve'	IBlr
	'Evening Eclipse'	IBal
	'Evening Star'	CPne EPri
	'Exmoor'	CPne IBal LRHS
	'Findlay's Blue'	LRHS MAvo SMHy
	'Finnline' (v)	CPen SRms

	'Flore Pleno' (d)	CAby CBcs CMac CPen CPrp EBee ECha ECtt EHrv ELan GKin IBal IBlr LSou MHer MHol NEgg NGdn WCot WFar WPGP WSHC
	'Gayle's Lilac'	CBcs CCCN CElw CPen CPrp ECtt ELan ELon EPfP EWTr GKin LHop LRHS MRav NGdn WGwG XTur
	'Gem'	CPrp ELon LRHS MAvo
	'Genua' **new**	IBal
	'Getty White'	LRHS
	'Glacier'	IBal
	'Glacier Stream'	CBro CDor CPen EPri GBuc IBal IKil XSen XTur
	'Glen Avon'	CAbb CCCN CPen CPrp CRos EBee EHyd EPfP GBin IBal LRHS NLar SCoo SFai SLon
	'Gold Strike'[PBR] (v)	IBal SFai
	'Golden Drop'[PBR] (v)	CRos EHyd LRHS NPri NRHS SFai SRms
	'Golden Rule' (v)	EHoe GBuc IBlr
	'Gothenburg' **new**	IBal
	'Greenfield' **new**	IBal
	'Hamar' **new**	IBal
	'Hanneke'	CPen IBal
	'Hannover' **new**	IBal
	'Happy Blue' **new**	IBal
	'Harvest Blue'	IBal
§	Headbourne hybrids	Widely available
	Headbourne hybrids dark blue-flowered	GBuc LRHS
	Headbourne hybrids dwarf	GBuc
	'Headbourne White'	CAvo EPri
	'Heavenly Blue'	CCCN
	'Helen'	IBlr
	'Helsinki' **new**	IBal
	'Holbeach'	CPen
	'Holbrook'	CSam
	'Hoyland Blue'	IBal
	'Ice Blue Star'	CBro
	'Ice Lolly'	CBro CPen IBal IKil
	inapertus	CAvo CBod CBro CFil CPrp CTre EWes SMHy SWat WPGP
	- dwarf	IBlr
	- subsp. ***hollandii***	IBal IBlr SWat
	- - 'Zealot'	IBlr
	- 'Ice Cascade'	CCCN CPen EBee IBal LRHS SWat
	- 'Icicle'	GCal
	- subsp. ***inapertus***	IBlr SWat
I	- - 'Albus'	IBlr
	- - 'Cyan'	IBlr
	- - 'White'	CPrp IBal
§	- subsp. ***intermedius***	CPrp EPfP IBlr
	- - 'Long Tom'	CPne CPrp CSpe EBee EPri IBal LRHS WPGP
	- - white-flowered	CPen CPou
	- large	IBal
	- 'Little Black Number'	CPen
	- 'Margaret'	CCCN
	- 'Midnight Cascade'	CCCN CPar CPen EBee ECtt ELan GBin IBal IPot LEdu NBid SCob SFai SRms SWat
I	- 'Nigrescens'	CPen IPot
	- subsp. ***parviflorus***	IBlr
	- subsp. ***pendulus***	IBal IBlr LRHS WPGP
	- - 'Black Magic'	IBal
	- - 'Graskop'	CAvo CBcs CCCN CPen CPrp CRos CSam CSpe EBee EHyd EPfP EPri EWoo GBin IBal IBlr IMou LRHS LSou MNrw NRHS NSti SFai SKHP SMHy SRms WPGP
	- - 'Violet Dusk'	IBlr
	- 'Sapphire Cascade'	CPen IBal SWat
	'Indigo Dreams'	CPen CPne CPrp CTal EBee IBal LLHF LPla SFai
	'Inkspots'	CCCN CMac CPen CRos EHyd EPfP IBal LRHS LSou NRHS SFai SPoG
	'Intermedius' Leichtlin	CWCL IBal
I	'Intermedius' van Tubergen	EBee IBal NBid
	'Isis'	CAvo CBro CPrp CSam CTri EAEE ECha EPri GBuc IBal IBlr LRHS MAvo
	'Jacaranda'	CMac EBee IBal LRHS SFai
	'Jack Elliott'	MAvo
	'Jack's Blue'	Widely available
	'Jersey Giant'	IBal
	'Jodie'	CPne ELon MAvo
	'Johanna'	CPen IBal
	'Johannesburg' **new**	IBal
	Johannesburg hybrids	ECha EPfP
	'Jolanda'	CPrp ELon IBal LAma
	'Jonie'	IBal
	'Jonny's White' **new**	IBal
	'Kalmthout Blue'	IBal
	'Kilmurry Blue'	IBal IKil
	'Kilmurry White'	IBal IKil
	'Kingston Blue'	IBal IBlr LRHS NBid
	'Kobold'	CBro IBal WFar
	'Lady Edith'	IBlr
§	'Lady Grey'	IBlr
	'Lady Moore'	IBlr SMHy
	'Lady Thumb' **new**	SFai
	'Lapis'	CAvo CBod CHid CMac CPne CPrp EBee EPri IBal LRHS SFai SHyH SLdr
	'Latent Blue'	IBlr
	'Lavender Haze'	CCCN CMac CPen CRos EHyd EPfP IBal LRHS NRHS SFai
	'Leanne'	IBal LRHS
	'Leicester'	CPen IBal
	'Liam's Lilac'	CCCN CKno CPar CPen CPne CPou CPrp CRos EHyd ELon EWoo IBal LCro LOPS LRHS MAvo NLar NRHS SFai
	'Lilac Flash'	CPen IBal LRHS
	'Lilac Time'	CPne CPrp IBlr WCot
	'Lilliput'	CBcs CBro CCCN CMac CMea CPrp CSpe ECha ECtt ELan EPfP EShb EWTr GBuc GKev GMaP IBal LHop LRHS MRav NGdn SPer SRms WCFE WFar XEll XSen
	'Lissabon' **new**	IBal
	'Lisse' **new**	IBal
	'Little Dutch Blue' **new**	IBal
	'Little Dutch White'[PBR] **new**	IBal
	'Little White'	CPen IBal
	'Littlecourt'	CBro IBal
	'Loch Hope' ♀H6	CAvo CBro CPrp CSam ECtt ELon EPfP EWoo GCal IBal LRHS MAvo MHol MRav SDix SLdr SPer WCot WHoo
	'Los Angeles' **new**	IBal
	'Luly'	CPen CPne CPrp CRos CTal EPfP IBal LRHS MAvo MGos SHil SWat
	'Luna'	EBee IBal
	'Lydenburg'	CPen CPne EBee EPri IBal IBlr
	'Lyn Valley'	CPrp EBee IBal SFai
	'Mabel Grey'	see *A.* 'Lady Grey'
	'Madurodam' **new**	IBal
	'Magnifico'	IBal IBlr
	'Malaga'	IBal
	'Malmo' **new**	IBal
	'Marchants Cobalt Cracker'	SMHy

	'Marchant's Midnight Blue'	SMHy
	'Marcus'	IBal SDir
	'Margaret'	GCal IBal LRHS LSRN
	'Marianne'	IBal
	'Mariètte'	CPen EBee
	'Marijke'	IBal
	'Marjorie'	LRHS
	'Marnie'	CPne
	'Martine'	CPen EBee IBal MAvo
	'Maureen'	CPne CPrp EBee IBal LSRN
	'Maurice'	IBal
	'May Snow' (v)	LRHS WCot
	'Medan' **new**	IBal
	'Medusa'	IBal
	'Megan's Mauve'	CKno CPne CPou CPrp EBee ELon EPri IBal LCro LOPS LRHS LSRN LSou NSti SFai SHyH
	'Meibont' (v)	IBal WCot
	'Mercury'	IBlr
	'Messina' **new**	IBal
	'Michelle'	IBal
	'Middleburg'	IBal
	Midknight Blue = 'Monmid'	NNys WSHC XTur
	'Midnight'	CPen EWes IBal MAvo
	'Midnight Blue' ambig.	CAby CPen ELan EPfP EShb IBal WFar
	'Midnight Blue' P.Wood	GCal IBlr LRHS
	'Midnight Dream'	CPen EBee ECtt IBal STPC
§	'Midnight Star'	Widely available
	'Miniature Blue'	SWat
	'Misty Dawn' (v)	CWGN EBee ECtt IBal MHol SEND SHyH SLdr WCot
	mixed seedlings	IBal
	mixed white-flowered	WCFE
	'Mole Valley'	CPne IBal
	'Molly Howick'	EBee LRHS
	'Monique' **new**	IBal
	'Montreal'	IBal
	'Mood Indigo'	CAbb CPen CPne EBee IBal
	'Moonlight Star'	EBee IBal
	'Moonshine'	CPen IBal
I	'Mooreanus' misapplied	EBee EPfP IBal NBid
	'Mooreanus' H.R.Wehrh.	GCal MAvo
	'Morning Star'	IBal
	'Mount Stewart'	IBal IBlr
	'Nana Blue'	SHyH
	'Nancy' **new**	IBal
	'Napoli' **new**	IBal
	'Navy Blue'	see *A.* 'Midnight Star'
	'Newcastle' **new**	IBal
	'Newa'	EBee
	'Nikki'	CMea CPne IBal
	'Norman Hadden'	IBlr
	'Northern Light'	CPen IBal LLHF
	'Northern Star'^{PBR}	CAbb CAvo CKno CPen CPne CPrp CRos CTal CWGN EAEE EBee EHyd ELon EPri EWes EWoo IBal LOPS LRHS LSRN LSou NLos NPri NRHS NSti SCob SFai SLon SPoG WPGP
	nutans	see *A. caulescens*
	'Nyx'	IBlr
	'Odessa' **new**	IBal
	'Oslo'	IBal
	'Oxbridge'	IBlr
	'Oxford' **new**	IBal
	'Pacific Blue'^{PBR}	CRos CWCL EBee EHyd EWTr IBal LRHS NRHS SHyH SLdr
	Palmer's hybrids	see *A.* Headbourne hybrids
	'Paris'	CPen
	'Patent Blue'	CPrp IBal IBlr
	'Patriot'	EPfP LRHS
	'Pavlova' **new**	IBal
	'Penelope Palmer'	CPrp IBlr
	'Peter Franklin'	CPne CPrp EBee IBal
	'Peter Pan' ambig.	Widely available
	'Peter Pan' Giridlion	LLWG
	'Phantom'	CAbb CPne CPrp EBee EWoo IBal IBlr IMou LCro LRHS SFai SWeb WPGP
	'Picton Blue' **new**	ETho
	Pine Cottage hybrids	CPne
	'Pino' **new**	LRHS
	'Pinocchio'	CPen GKev IMou SDeJ
	'Pirame' **new**	IBal
	'Plas Merdyn Blue'	IBlr
	'Plas Merdyn White'	IBal IBlr
	'Podge Mill'	IBal IBlr
	'Polar Ice'	CPen EBee ELon EPri EWoo GKev IBal IBoy IPot LAma LRHS LSRN MAvo MNrw NNys WCAu XTur
	'Polar Star' **new**	IBal
	'Porcelain'	IBal IBlr
	praecox ♀^{H2}	CPrp ESps IBlr LRHS
	- 'Albiflorus' ♀^{H2}	CBcs CBro CPou CPrp CTri EPri ESps LRHS NEgg SEND
	- 'Floribundus'	SWat
	- 'Maximus Albus'	CPne CPou IBal IBlr
§	- subsp. ***minimus***	CElw CPou IBal IBlr SEND SWat
	- - 'Adelaide'	CPrp IBal
	- - blue-flowered	SWat
	- - white-flowered	SWat
	- 'Neptune'	IBlr
§	- subsp. ***orientalis***	CBro CCCN IBlr SWat
	- - 'Full Moon' **new**	IBal
	- - 'Mount Thomas'	CPrp
	- - 'Silver Star' (v)	CPen
	- subsp. ***praecox***	IBlr
	- - azure-flowered	CPrp SWat
	- - 'Variegatus'	see *A.* 'Argenteus Vittatus'
	- 'Saturn'	IBlr
	- Slieve Donard form	IBlr
	- 'Storms River'	IBal
	- 'Uranus'	IBlr
	- 'Venus'	IBlr
	'Premier'	CPrp IBlr LRHS
	'Pretty Wendy' **new**	IBal
	'Princess Margaret'	IBal
§	'Purple Cloud'	Widely available
	'Purple Delight'	CPne CPrp EBee IBal LCro LRHS SAko SFai
	'Purple Emperor'	CPne SFai
	'Purple Fountain'	CPne CPrp IBal SFai SRms
	'Purple Haze'	CPen IBal
	'Purple Magic' **new**	IBal
	'Purple Ripple'	CPne IBal
	'Purple Star'	CCCN CKno
	'Queen Anne'	IBal
	'Queen Mother'	CHid IBal LRHS
	Queen Mum = 'Pmn06'^{PBR}	Widely available
	'Queen of the Ocean'	IBal
	'Quink Drops'	SMHy
	'Radiant Star'	IBal LRHS
	'Regal Beauty'	CBro CPen CPrp CSBt EBee EWoo IBal LRHS LSRN NBid SFai
	'Rhone'	CBro IBal IBlr
	'Robin' **new**	IBal
	'Rosewarne'	CBcs CBod CCCN CPrp IBal IBlr NLar
	'Rotterdam'	CPen IBal XSen
	'Roxanne' **new**	IBal
	'Royal Blue'	CBro GMaP IBal

'Royal Knight'	IBal
'Ruan Vean'	CPrp
'Sabang' **new**	IBal
'Sally Anne'	CPne
'San Gabriel' (v)	CPne
'San Remo' **new**	IBal
'Sandringham'	CPen CPne CPrp CSpe EBee ELon EPfP EPri EWes IBal LRHS LSou MMuc SFai WPGP
'Sandy' **new**	IBal
'Sapphire'	CPrp IBlr
'Sarah' PBR	CCCN CPen EBee IBal LSRN SEND SFai SHyH SLdr
'Sea Coral'	CCCN CMac CPrp EBee EPri LRHS MAvo NSti
'Sea Foam'	CMac CPen CPne NLar XLum
'Sea Mist'	CCCN CPne EBee
'Sea Spray'	CCCN CSBt EBee EPri IBal WFar
'Selma Bock'	CPen IBal
'Semarang' **new**	IBal
'Senna' PBR	CCCN EBee IBal LSou WCot
'Septemberhemel'	CPen IBal
'Silberpfeil' **new**	IBal
'Silver Anniversary'	IBal
'Silver Baby'	CAbb CKno CPen CPne CPrp CRos CWGN EBee EHyd ELon EPfP EPri ETod EWoo IBal LEdu LRHS LSou MAvo NRHS SFai SRms
'Silver Jubilee'	IBal
'Silver Lining'	ECtt IBal LRHS
'Silver Mist'	CPen CPne IBal IBlr SWat
Silver Moon = 'Notfred' PBR (v)	CAbb CCCN CPen CRos EBee EHyd ELan EPfP EWes EWoo GKev IBal LBMP LRHS LSou MGos MJak NLar NRHS NSti SCob SFai SPoG WCot XTur
'Silver Sceptre'	IBlr
'Silver Suzy'	IBal
'Sky'	CAbb CPne CRos CSBt EHyd EPfP EPri EWTr EWoo IBal IBlr LCro LRHS LSRN NBid NRHS SFai SKHP SRkn SRms SWat
'Sky Pendulous'	CBcs
'Sky Rocket'	CPrp IBal IBlr
'Sky Star'	IBal
'Skyscraper' **new**	IBal
'Slieve Donard'	IBlr
'Snow Cloud'	CAbb CBro CPen CRos CSBt EBee EHyd EPfP LCro LOPS LRHS NLar NRHS SEND SFai SLdr SLon
'Snow Pixie'	CSpe EBee IBal LRHS LSRN LSou SFai SHyH SLdr
'Snow Princess'	CPen ELon EPfP IBal
'Snow Shadows'	CBro IBal
'Snowball'	CBcs CChe CPen LSou NLos
'Snowdrops'	CCCN EBee ELan LHop SKHP WFar
'Snowstorm' PBR	EBee EPfP IBal LBuc LRHS
'Sofie' PBR	CBod CPen EBee SCob STPC XTur
'Sorento' **new**	IBal
'Southern Cross'	CRos EBee EHyd IBal LRHS NRHS SFai
'Southern Star'	IBal
'Spokes'	IBlr
'Star Quality'	IBal LBuc LRHS MNrw SFai
'Starburst'	IBlr
'Stardust'	CRos IBal LBuc LRHS SHil
'Stargazer'	EBee LBuc LRHS
'Stars and Stripes'	IBal
'Stéphanie Charm'	CPen IBal
'Stockholm'	IBal
'Storm Cloud' Reads	see *A.* 'Purple Cloud'
'Storm Cloud' (d)	CBro IBal
'Strawberry Ice'	CPen EBee IBal SFai
'Stream Cottage' **new**	SDix
'Streamline'	CBcs CBod CElw CKno CMea EBee ECtt EHyd ELon EPfP EShb ETod GAbr GKin GMaP GMcL IBal LRHS LSou MRav SDys SEND SFai
'Summer Blue'	IBal
'Summer Clouds'	ELan
'Summer Days'	CPne CPrp EBee IBal SFai
'Summer Delight'	IBal
'Summer Skies'	IBal
'Sunfield'	CDor CKno CPrp CRos EPfP IBal ILea IPot LAma LRHS MNrw NLar NPer NRHS
'Super Star'	CBro CPrp IBal
'Sweet Surprise'	EBee IBal SFai
'Sylvia' PBR	IBal
'Sylvine'	CPen IBal
'Tall Boy'	IBal IBlr
'Tarka'	CPen CPne CPrp CRos ELon EPfP EPri EWoo IBal LRHS LSou NLar SDys SFai SHil
'Taw Valley'	CAbb CAvo CKno CPen CPne CPrp CTal EBee ELon EWoo IBal LCro LRHS MGos SFai SHil SHyH SLon SPoG WHil WPGP
'Thorn'	IBal
'Thumbelina'	CBro CMac EBee IBal LRHS LSou NLar SFai XLum
'Timaru'	CBro CCVN CElw CPen CPrp ECtt ELan ELon EPfP EWoo GAbr GMaP GMcL IBal MHol NGdn NLar SFai SHyH SLdr WCot
'Tinkerbell' (v)	CBcs CBro CCCN CLet CPne CPrp EBee EHoe ELan EPfP EPri EShb IBal LEdu LHop LRHS LSou MGos MRav NPer SPoG SRms SWvt
'Tiny White'	EPri
'Titan'	IBlr
'Titch'	CPne IBal
'Tom Thumb'	CAvo CPrp CRos ECtt EHyd EPfP GBin IBal LRHS LSou MAsh NCou NRHS SFai SRkn SRot
'Torbay'	CElw CPrp EAEE ECtt ELon EPfP EShb EWTr GAbr GCal GKin IBal LRHS MAvo MMuc MNrw NCGa NEgg NHol SBod WHoo
'Tornado'	CBod CPen EBee ECtt ELon GBin IBal ILea LRHS SEND SFai STPC WCot
'Triangle'	CPen
'Tsolo'	CPne IBal
'Twilight'	IBlr
'Twilight Zone'	IBal
'Twister'	SFai
umbellatus Redouté	see *A. praecox* subsp. *orientalis*
'Underway'	EWes GCal GKev IBal IBlr
'Vallée Blanche'	MNHC XTur
'Vallée Bleue'	XTur
'Vallée de la Belle'	XTur
'Vallée de la Loire'	XTur
'Vallée de la Sarthe'	XTur
'Vallée de l'Authion'	XTur
'Vallée du Cap'	XTur
'Vallée du Lathan'	XTur
'Velvet Night'	CPen
'Volendam'	IBal
'Washington' **new**	IBal
'Wavy Navy'	CPen IBal

	'Wedding Day'	EBee IBal SFai
	'Wembworthy'	CPne CPrp EBee IBal SFai
	'White Avon'	CPen
	'White Baby'	XTur
	'White Cloud'	IBal
	'White Dwarf'	see *A.* white-flowered, dwarf
	'White Flash'	IBal
	'White Heaven' PBR	Widely available
	'White Ice'	CBcs CPen
	'White Pixie'	IBal
	'White Smile'	EPri
	'White Superior'	CPen EBee EPfP GMaP
	'White Swan'	SCob
	'White Triumphator'	CBWd
	'White Umbrella'	CRos EHyd GMcL LRHS NRHS WHar
	'White Wings'	IBal
§	white-flowered, dwarf	CBro CKno CPen EBee ECha ECtt EPfP EShb GBuc IBal LRHS NBir NGdn NHol
	'Whitestorm'	SCob
	'Whitney' PBR	CPen IBal IBlr LRHS
	'Windlebrooke'	CCCN EAJP EPri IBal
	'Windsor Castle'	CPen CPrp IBal IBlr
	'Windsor Grey'	Widely available
	'Winsome'	IBlr
	'Winter Sky'	IBal
	'Wolga'	CBro EBee IBal
	'Wolkberg' Kirstenbosch	IBal IBlr
	'Yves Klein'	IBlr
	'Zachary'	CPen CPne CPou CPrp EBee ELon
	'Zeal Thomas'	IBal
	'Zigzag White' **new**	WCot

Agapetes (*Ericaceae*)

	'Ludgvan Cross' ♀H2	CBcs CCCN CTsd EShb SEle SPad
	serpens ♀H2	CBcs CCCN CHll CWib SLon
	- 'Scarlet Elf'	CCCN CTsd LRHS
	smithiana var. ***major***	GGGa

Agastache (*Lamiaceae*)

	'After Eight'	EBee ECtt IBoy LCro LRHS MAvo NCGa
	anethiodora	see *A. foeniculum* (Pursh) Kuntze
	anisata	see *A. foeniculum* (Pursh) Kuntze
	aurantiaca	NGBl SPhx WMoo
	- 'Apricot Sprite'	CWld EPfP ESps LRHS NGdn SRkn WHar
	- 'Raspberry Daiquiri' (Cocktail Series)	MAvo
	'Ayala' **new**	SAko
	'Blackadder'	Widely available
	'Blaue Sangria'	LPla MAvo NDov
	'Blue Boa' PBR	CBod CWGN ECtt LCro LRHS MAvo MHol NCGa NDov NLar SHil
	'Blue Delight'	SBch
	'Blue Fortune' ♀H6	CBWd CBcs CBod CRos ECha EHyd LCro LHop LOPS LRHS MAvo MCot MRav NDov NLar NRHS SAko SCob SHil SMad SPer SPhx SRms SWvt WCAu
	'Bolero'	CSpe EBee IBoy LRHS MHol MSpe SPhx WCot WHoo
§	***cana***	SBee SPhx
	- 'Heatwave' PBR	EAEE EPfP LRHS NDov
	- 'Purple Pygmy'	EPfP LHop
	'Cotton Candy' PBR	IBoy LCro
	cusickii	EBee SPhx
	'Firebird'	EAEE EBee ECtt ELan EPfP LHop LSou SAko SPer SRms SWvt
	foeniculum misapplied	see *A. rugosa*
§	***foeniculum*** (Pursh) Kuntze	EBee ELan ENfk GMaP GPoy MCot MHer MNHC SPav SPhx SRms WJek WTre
	- 'Alabaster'	CBcs EBee LCro NLar
	- 'Alba'	NBre SHDw SPav
	- 'Blaustrahl' **new**	SAko
	'Globetrotter'	ELan MArt SPhx WSHC
	'Grapefruit Nectar' (Nectar Series)	SCob
	'Kolibri'	ECtt ILea LHop LRHS
	(Kudos Series) 'Kudos Ambrosia' **new**	LRHS
	- 'Kudos Coral' **new**	LRHS
	- 'Kudos Gold' **new**	CMea LRHS
	- 'Kudos Mandarin' **new**	CMea IPot LRHS SPad WHil
	- 'Kudos Silver Blue' **new**	IPot
	'Linda'	NDov WCot
§	***mexicana***	SPav
	- 'Champagne'	NWad
	- 'Red Fortune' PBR	CAbP CHVG CRos CWGN CWld EAEE ECtt EHyd IKil ILea LCro LHop LRHS MCot MHol MHtn MPie NEgg NLar NRHS SCob SPad WCot
	- 'Rosea'	see *A. cana*
	- 'Sangria'	LHop LRHS NGdn SPad SPhx SRms XLum
	micrantha	SPhx
	nepetoides	EPPr NDov SPav
	occidentalis	EBee SPhx
	Orange Nectar (Nectar Series)	MHol WCot
	'Painted Lady'	CSpe ECtt WHea WTcb
	pallidiflora var. ***neomexicana***	SPhx
	- - 'Rose Mint'	CSpe EBee
	'Pink Beauty'	NLar
	'Pink Panther'	WSHC
	'Pink Pop'	EPfP SPad
	'Purple Flame'	EAEE
	'Purple Haze'	LRHS NDov SAko
	'Raspberry Summer' PBR	CWGN ECtt EPfP LHop LRHS LSou NCGa NLar SCob SPad WAul
§	***rugosa***	CAby CBod CLau ECha GPoy LEdu LHop MNHC SPav SPhx SPlb SRms SWat WJek WMoo
	- B&SWJ 4187 from Korea	WCru
	- f. ***albiflora***	NBre WCAu
	- - 'Alabaster'	NDov
	- - 'Liquorice White'	CBWd CBod EBee ELan EPed EPfP GWyn MBel NGBl NLar SPer SPlb SRms
	- 'Golden Jubilee'	CAby CBct CSpe EAEE EBee ECha ECtt ELan EPfP IBoy LRHS MAvo MHer MHtn MSpe NLar NSti SCob SHil SRms SWvt WJek WMoo WTre XLum
	- 'Heronswood Mist'	EBee
	- 'Korean Zest'	WCru
	- 'Liquorice Blue'	CKno CTsd ELan EPed EPfP LRHS MBel MSpe NEgg NGBl NGdn SPoG SRms SSut SWvt WMoo
	rupestris	CSpe CWld SPhx XSen
	- 'Apache Sunset'	SPlb
	'Serpentine'	ECtt MAvo NDov SPhx
	'Spicy'	NDov
	'Summer Fiesta' PBR	EBee ECtt IBoy LSou MAvo MNrw NDov
	'Summer Glow' PBR	CDor CKno CWGN EBee ECtt LHop LLHF LRHS LSou MNrw

	NCGa NDov SCob SDys SPoG WBod WHil
'Summer Love'PBR	ECtt LRHS LSou MNrw NCGa NDov NLar WTor
'Summer Sky'PBR	EBee ECtt LRHS NCGa NDov SPoG
'Summer Sunset'PBR	CDor CSpe CWGN EAEE EBee ELan LBMP LHop LPla LRHS LSou MHol MPie NCGa SCob SPoG WCot WTor
'Tangerine Dreams'	ECtt ELan EPfP LHop NCGa NEgg SCoo
'Tango'	EBee LRHS SGbt WKif
'Tutti-frutti'	EAEE ECtt LRHS
urticifolia	MArt

Agathaea see *Felicia*

Agathosma (*Rutaceae*)

ovata	CCCN

Agave ✿ (*Asparagaceae*)

albomarginata	CDTJ
americana ♀H2	CAbb CBcs CBen CBot ELan EPfP EShb ESps EUJe IDee LPar LRHS LSun LTro NLos SArc SChr SCob SEND SMad SPlb SPre SVen SWvt WCot WGrn
§ - subsp. *americana* JL 2007-01	CCac
- 'Marginata' (v) ♀H2	CBot CBrP CDTJ CFil CHll GMcL LTro NQui SEND SVen WCot WSFF
- 'Mediopicta' misapplied	see *A. americana* 'Mediopicta Alba'
- 'Mediopicta' (v) ♀H2	CDTJ CFil SArc SBig WGrn
§ - 'Mediopicta Alba' (v) ♀H2	CBrP CDTJ CFil CJun CTre ELan ESwi LTro SPlb WCot WGrn
- 'Mediopicta Aurea' (v)	CFil WCot
- var. *oaxacensis*	WPGP
- subsp. *protamericana*	CDTJ
- subsp. *protamericana* × *scabra* F&M 310	WPGP
- 'Striata' (v)	CDTJ EShb WCot
- 'Variegata' (v) ♀H2	CAbb CBcs CBen CFil CLet CTre ELan EPfP EShb ESps EUJe LRHS LSun MGos NPer NPla SArc SChr SCob SPlb SWvt WCot
angustifolia	see *A. vivipara* var. *vivipara*
- var. *marginata* hort.	SBig WCot
applanata	CFil CJun WPGP
asperrima	CDTJ
§ - subsp. *maderensis*	SPlb
asperrima × *lechuguilla*	CCac
atrovirens	WCot
- from Carneros, Coah, Mexico	CCac
- from Concepción del Oro, Mexico	CCac
- var. *mirabilis*	CDTJ CFil
- - F&M 245	WPGP
attenuata	CAbb CDTJ NLos SBig SPlb WCot WPGP
'Bloodspot'	WCot
boldinghiana	WCot
bovicornuta	WCot
bracteosa	CBlu CCCN CDTJ WCot
celsii	see *A. mitis* var. *mitis*
cerulata subsp. *nelsonii*	CDTJ
chrysantha	CCCN CDTJ CTre EBee WCot WGrn
- 'Black Canyon'	WCot
colimana	see *A. ortgiesiana*
colorata	CCCN CDTJ CJun WCot
cordillerensis	see *A. americana* subsp. *americana*
'Cornelius'	WCot WGrn
cupreata	CDTJ LTro
deserti	CDTJ CJun CTre LRHS WCot
- var. *deserti*	LTro
- var. *simplex*	LTro WCot
difformis	CDTJ
- NJM 05.034	WPGP
durangensis	SPlb
elongata	see *A. vivipara* var. *vivipara*
ensifera	CJun
felgeri	CDTJ
ferdinandi-regis	see *A. victoriae-reginae*
ferox	see *A. salmiana* var. *ferox*
filifera ♀H2	CCCN CDTJ CJun CTre LTro SChr SMad SPlb WCot
flexispina	SPlb
- from Parral, Chihuahua, Mexico	CCac
garciae-mendozae	CDTJ
geminiflora	CCCN CDTJ CFil CJun CTre EShb
gentryi	CDTJ CFil LTro SPlb WCot
- F&M 213A	WPGP
ghiesbreghtii	CTre
gigantea	see *Furcraea foetida*
× *gracilipes*	WPGP
guadalajarana	CDTJ CTre
guttata	WCot
havardiana	CFil CTre LTro WCot XSen
- DJF 1326 from Davis Mountains, Texas	CCac
horrida	CDTJ CFil CJun SBig
- subsp. *horrida*	LTro SPlb
- 'Perotensis'	EShb
hurteri	CDTJ
impressa	WCot
kerchovei	WCot
lechuguilla	CDTJ LTro WCot XSen
lophantha	see *A. univittata*
- var. *caerulescens*	see *A. univittata*
§ 'Macha Mocha'	WCot
macroacantha ♀H1c	CDTJ NLos
§ *maculosa*	WCot
marmorata	CJun WCot
maximilliana	SPlb
mckelveyana	WCot
- DJF 1575 from Bagdad, Arizona	CCac WCot
- from Hillside, Arizona	CCac
§ *mitis* var. *mitis*	CDTJ SPlb
- var. *mitis* × *variegata*	WCot
montana	CBlu CCac CDTJ CFil ETod EUJe LTro NLos SChr SPlb
- F&M 221	WPGP
- F&M 289	WPGP
§ *obscura*	CDTJ WCot
oroensis	WCot
- from Estanción Margarita, Zacatecas, Mexico	CCac
§ *ortgiesiana*	WCot
ovatifolia	CBlu CDTJ CFil CJun SKHP SPlb WCot
- NJM 09.002	WPGP
palmeri	CCCN CCac CFil EBee LTro SPlb WCot
panamana	see *A. vivipara* var. *vivipara*
parrasana ♀H2	CDTJ WCot WPGP
- from Sierra Parras, Mexico	CCac
parryi ♀H2	CDTJ CTre ETod SPlb WCot WPGP XSen

- DJF 138	CCac
- HK 1684	CCac
- var. ***couesii***	CCac LTro SKHP XSen
- 'Cream Spike' (v)	CBcs CFil EMFm ESwi MArt SMad SPad WCot WGrn
- var. ***huachucensis***	CBlu CCac CDTJ LTro WCot
- subsp. ***neomexicana***	CCCN CDTJ CFil LTro SPlb XSen
- - SB 948 from W of Artesia, New Mexico	CCac WCot
- 'Ohi-kissho-ten-nishiki' (v)	WCot
- subsp. ***parryi***	CBlu CDTJ LTro WCot WPGP
- small	ETod
- var. ***truncata***	CBlu CCac ETod SPlb
- - variegated (v)	WCot
parviflora ♀H2	WCot
polianthiflora	LTro
polyacantha var. ***xalapensis***	see *A. obscura*
potatorum 'Gary Fisher'	WCot
- 'Shoji-rasin' **new**	LToo
salmiana	CCac CDTJ CFil SBig SPlb
- F&M 290	WPGP
- subsp. ***crassispina***	SPlb
§ - var. ***ferox***	CCac CDTJ CTre SArc SBig SChr SPlb
- - from Tlacotepec, Pue, Mexico	CCac
scabra	CCCN CTre WCot
- subsp. ***maderensis***	see *A. asperrima* subsp. *maderensis*
schidigera 'Shira-ito-no-ohi' (v)	WCot
schottii	CDTJ WCot
'Sharkskin Shoes'	NLos WCot
shrevei subsp. ***magna***	SPlb
§ ***sileri***	WCot
stictata	WCot
striata subsp. ***falcata***	LTro WCot
* - 'Rubra'	CDTJ LTro SPlb WCot
- subsp. ***striata***	LTro
stricta ♀H2	CCCN CDTJ LTro WCot
- 'Nana'	CDTJ LToo
aff. ***stricta***	WCot
toumeyana ♀H2	CTre LTro WCot
- from Globe, Arizona	CCac
- var. ***bella***	CDTJ XSen
triangularis	CDTJ
§ ***undulata***	WCot
- 'Chocolate Chips'	WCot
§ ***univittata***	CDTJ CJun NLos WCot
- 'Quadricolor' (v)	CDTJ NLos SMad SPlb WCot
utahensis ♀H3	CCac LTro SEND SPlb WCot XSen
- DJF 1521 from Peach Springs, Arizona	CCac WCot
- LZ 2042 from Beaver Dam Mountains, Utah	CCac
- from Kingman, Arizona	CCac
- var. ***eborispina***	CCac WCot XSen
- subsp. ***kaibabensis***	CCac WCot XSen
- subsp. ***utahensis***	LTro
§ ***variegata***	WCot
- B&SWJ 10234	WCru
§ ***victoriae-reginae*** ♀H2	CCCN CDTJ CJun CTre IDee NLos SChr WCot
- dwarf	WCot
- 'Huasteca Canyon' **new**	LTro
§ ***virginica***	GKev WCot
§ ***vivipara*** var. ***vivipara***	EBee WCot
wocomahi	WCot
xylonacantha	SChr SPlb WCot

Ageratina (*Asteraceae*)

§ ***altissima***	CHid CMac EBee
- 'Braunlaub'	NBir NLar SAko SHar SWat WPtf WWtn
- 'Chocolate'	Widely available
§ ***aromatica***	MRav SHar SWat
§ ***ligustrina***	CLet CMHG CRHN CRos CTri EBee ECha EHoe ELan EWTr EWoo LHop LRHS MBlu SBrt SEND SPer SPoG SRkn SRms WPGP WPat WSFF WSHC

Ageratum (*Asteraceae*)

'Blue Champion'	NPri
corymbosum	CHll CSpe
houstonianum 'Blue Danube'	CWCL
- 'High Tide Blue'	NPri
petiolatum	LRHS

Agrimonia (*Rosaceae*)

eupatoria	CArn CBod CHab CWld ENfk GPoy MHer MNHC NMir SRms SWat WHer
* - var. ***alba***	NLar
odorata misapplied	see *A. procera*
odorata (L.) Mill.	see *A. repens*
pilosa	EBee
§ ***procera***	EBee
§ ***repens***	WMoo

Agropyron (*Poaceae*)

glaucum	see *Elymus hispidus*
magellanicum	see *Elymus magellanicus*
pubiflorum	see *Elymus magellanicus*

Agrostemma (*Caryophyllaceae*)

coronaria	see *Lychnis coronaria*
githago	CHab CWld MNHC SRms WTre
- 'Ocean Pearl'	CSpe MCot SPhx

Agrostis (*Poaceae*)

calamagrostis	see *Stipa calamagrostis*
capillaris	CHab
§ ***montevidensis***	SMad
nebulosa	SPhx
- 'Fibre Optics'	see *Panicum* 'Fibre Optics'
stolonifera 'Julia Ann' (v)	WCot

Aichryson (*Crassulaceae*)

§ × ***aizoides*** var. ***domesticum***	LAll
- - 'Variegatum' (v) ♀H1c	CDTJ CTre EBak WCot

Ailanthus (*Simaroubaceae*)

§ ***altissima***	CBcs CCVT CDul CMac EBee EPfP EUJe LEdu NWea SPer SPlb SWvt
- 'Purple Dragon' **new**	MBlu
- var. ***tanakae*** CWJ 12452	WCru
- - RWJ 9906	WCru
glandulosa	see *A. altissima*

Ainsliaea (*Asteraceae*)

acerifolia B&SWJ 4795	WCru
- var. ***subapoda*** B&SWJ 11537	WCru
apiculata B&SWJ 11397	WCru
- var. ***acerifolia*** B&SWJ 6059	WCru
chapaensis B&SWJ 11720	WCru
- B&SWJ 11732	WCru
latifolia FMWJ 13426	WCru

nervosa B&SWJ 11344	WCru
petelotii FMWJ 13427	WCru
tonkinensis B&SWJ 11819	WCru
uniflora	GEdr

Ajania (*Asteraceae*)

pacifica 'Silver Edge'	XLum

Ajuga (*Lamiaceae*)

ciliata var. ***villosior***	GBin
genevensis	GWyn SIgm SPhx WOut
incisa	EBee EPPr EWld GCal
- 'Bikun' (v)	EBee SRGP WCot
- 'Blue Enigma'	CLAP ELon IMou NLar
- 'Blue Ensign'	WSHC
'Little Court Pink'	see *A. reptans* 'Purple Torch'
metallica hort.	see *A. pyramidalis*
'Pink Lightning' (v)	EBee LSou NHpl WHil
'Pink Spires'	WFar
§ ***pyramidalis***	CArn
- 'Metallica Crispa'	CBre EBee ECho ELan EPri EWes NBir NEoE NHol NHpl NLar NPnk SRms SWvt WTor
reptans	CArn CHab CRos CTri ECtt EHyd ENfk EPed GKev GPoy LRHS MBel MHer MNHC NMir NRHS SRms WJek WOut XLum
- f. ***albiflora*** 'Alba'	CArn CBre EBee ELon MBel MRav NBro SRms WMoo
- 'Arctic Fox' (v)	GEdr LSou MRav SWvt
- 'Argentea'	see *A. reptans* 'Variegata'
§ - 'Atropurpurea'	CBar CRos ECha ECho EHyd ELan EPfP ESps GAbr GBin LCro LRHS MGos MMuc NRHS NWad SEND SGol SPer SPlb SRms SWvt WBrk WJek WTcb XLum
- Black Scallop = 'Binblasca' PBR	Widely available
- 'Blueberry Muffin'	NHpl
- 'Braunherz'	CCVN CRos CTri EAEE ECho ECtt EHoe EHyd ELan EPfP GMaP IBoy LHop LRHS MWat NBir NHpl NLar NPri NRHS SCob SGol SPer SRms SWvt WFar WHar WMoo
- 'Burgundy Glow' (v)	Widely available
§ - 'Catlin's Giant' 🏆H7	Widely available
- 'Choc Ice'	EPPr
- 'Chocolate Chip'	see *A. reptans* 'Valfredda'
- 'Delight' (v)	ECho
- 'Ebony'	LSRN
- 'Evening Glow'	CBod WIce WMoo
- 'Flisteridge'	CNat
- 'Golden Beauty'	SRms
- 'Grey Lady'	GBuc
- 'Harlequin' (v)	SWvt
- 'John Pierpoint'	SHar
- 'Jumbo'	see *A. reptans* 'Jungle Beauty'
§ - 'Jungle Beauty'	EPfP MRav XLum
- 'Kerichen' **new**	SAko
- 'Macrophylla'	see *A. reptans* 'Catlin's Giant'
- 'Mahogany'	CBod SRms
§ - 'Multicolor' (v)	CBcs ECho ELan LRHS MRav NPri SPer SPlb SPoG SRms SWvt WMoo
- Party Colors = 'Binparcol' PBR	CLAP SCob
- 'Pink Elf'	CDor CMHG ECho GCra MRav NBro SWat WOut
- 'Pink Surprise'	EHoe EPri MHer NRya
- 'Purple Brocade'	EHoe
§ - 'Purple Torch'	MPie NLar SRms WCAu
- 'Purpurea'	see *A. reptans* 'Atropurpurea'
- 'Rainbow'	see *A. reptans* 'Multicolor'
- 'Rosea'	ELon WMoo XLum
- 'Rowden Amethyst'	MHCG
- 'Rowden Royal Purple'	EBee ELon
- 'Toffee Chip' PBR (v)	LSou
- 'Tricolor'	see *A. reptans* 'Multicolor'
§ - 'Valfredda'	CBod CRos EAEE ECrN ECtt EHyd EPfP GAbr GBin GKev GWyn LBMP LRHS MHCG NHpl NLar NRHS SRms SWvt WBrk WHar WMoo
§ - 'Variegata' (v)	ECho ECtt EPfP LBMP MMuc NHpl SPer SPoG SRms SWat WFar WTor
'Rose Glow'	NHpl
'Sparkler' (v) **new**	EBee NHpl

Akebia ✿ (*Lardizabalaceae*)

longeracemosa	CRHN EBee SBrt SChF
- B&SWJ 3606	LEdu WCot WCru WPGP
× ***pentaphylla***	CBcs CRHN CWld EBee EHyd ELan EPfP LRHS MAsh MRav NLar SPer
- B&SWJ 2829	WCru
quinata	Widely available
- B&SWJ 4425	WCru
- 'Amethyst Glow'	CRos CWCL EBee EHyd EMil EPfP LHop LRHS NLar SKHP SPer SPoG
- cream-flowered	CBot CCCN CKel CRHN CWld EBee EHyd EMil EPfP EWld LCro LOPS LPar LRHS MGos MRav NLar SKHP SPer SRms SSta SWvt WBor WCru WPGP
- 'Shirobana'	CBcs CHll CMen CWGN MBlu MGil SMDP
- 'Silver Bells' **new**	LRHS
- variegated (v)	CBcs LLHF SMad
- 'White Chocolate' 🏆H5	ESwi NLar SBrt WCru WSHC
trifoliata	CBcs CRHN EHyd ELan EPfP EWld LRHS MGil MGos SEND SLon WOld
- B&SWJ 2829	WCru
- B&SWJ 5063	WCru
- 'Amethyst'	CBot

Alangium (*Cornaceae*)

platanifolium	CAbP CBcs CBot ESwi WPGP WPat
- var. ***macrophyllum***	EBee EPfP MMrt WBor

Albizia (*Mimosaceae*)

chinensis	EPfP LRHS
distachya	see *Paraserianthes lophantha*
§ ***julibrissin***	CArn CDTJ CWib EBee EPfP IDee LTro MGil NEgg NLos
- 'Ernest Wilson'	MTPN
- 'Evy's Purple'	ERea
- Ombrella = 'Boubri' PBR	CBcs EBee ELan EPfP ERea NOra WHar WMat WPGP
- f. ***rosea*** 🏆H2	CAco CBcs CLet CLnd CMCN CWGN EBee ELan ELon EPfP LEdu LHop LRHS SArc SEND SHil SLim SPad SPlb SPoG SPtp WPGP WSHC
I - 'Rouge Selection'	EPfP LRHS SPoG
- 'Shidare'	NOra WMat
- 'Summer Chocolate' PBR 🏆H2	CBcs CRos CWGN EBee EHyd ELan EPfP ERea IDee LRHS NOra NRHS SCoo SHil SPer SPoG WHar WMat WPGP
kalkora	SPlb
lophantha	see *Paraserianthes lophantha*

Albuca ✿ (*Asparagaceae*)

JCA 15856	CTca

from Namibia **new**	LToo
angolensis	CPou
aurea	CTca
* ***batliana***	ECho
batteniana	ECho
canadensis	CPou WHil
cooperi	ECho
fragrans	EBee
glauca	EBee
humilis	ECho LLHF WAbe WHil
nelsonii	CAvo CPne CPrp CTca EBee ECho LAma
setosa	CTca EBee
shawii	CAvo CBod CMos CPne CPou CTca EAJP EBee ECho EHoe EHrv EPot EPri ERCP EWld GKev MHer NCGa NPnk SPoG WAbe WGwG WHil
spiralis	GKev
wakefieldii	WHil

× *Alcalthaea* (*Malvaceae*)

suffrutescens 'Freedom' **new**	ELan
- 'Parkallee' (d)	CAbP EBee ECha ECtt ELan ELon GMaP LHop LRHS MAvo MHol MNrw NGdn NLar SEND SHil SPad SPhx WBrk WCot XLum
- 'Parkfrieden' (d)	CSpe ECtt ELon LRHS MAvo MNrw SPhx XLum
- 'Parkrondell' (d)	CBod ECha ECtt ELan ELon LHop LRHS MAvo MNrw SHar SHil SPad SPhx WCot XLum
- 'Poetry'	EBee ECtt ELan LRHS
- white-flowered	IFro

Alcea (*Malvaceae*)

'Apple Blossom' (d)	EPfP
'Arabian Nights'	SPav
'Blackcurrant Whirl'	SPav
'Burgundy Towers'	SEND WCAu
ficifolia	NChi SPav WMoo
'Happy Lights'	ELon
kurdica	CBot
'Las Vegas'	ECtt LSun
nudiflora **new**	GCal
pallida	XSen
'Peaches 'n' Dreams'	CBot EPfP LHop NGBl
§ ***rosea***	ESps SVic
- 'Blacknight' (Spotlight Series)	CBot EPfP GKev MHer
- Chater's Double Group (d)	EPfP GMcL IBoy SPoG SRms WBor WHar WRHF
- - chamois (d)	EPfP
- - chestnut-brown-flowered (d)	EPfP
- - maroon-flowered (d)	EPfP ESps SPoG
- - pink-flowered (d)	ELan EPfP ESps
- - red-flowered (d)	ELan EPfP GMcL SPoG
- - salmon-pink-flowered (d)	EPfP
- - scarlet-flowered (d)	EPfP IBoy SPoG
- - violet-flowered (d)	EPfP
- - white-flowered (d)	ELan EPfP GMcL SPoG
- - yellow-flowered (d)	EPfP GMcL SPoG SRms
- 'Crème de Cassis'	CBot ELan EPfP LRHS NGBl SPav
- 'Fiesta Time' (d)	CBot EBee
- (Halo Series) 'Halo Apricot'	CBod CBot CRos EHyd EPfP LRHS NRHS SPoG WHoo
- - 'Halo Blush'	CBot CRos EHyd EPfP LRHS NRHS SPoG
- - 'Halo Cerise'	CBot CRos EHyd LRHS NRHS SPoG
- - 'Halo Cream'	CBot CRos EHyd LRHS NRHS SPoG
- - 'Halo Red'	CBod CBot EPfP LRHS NRHS SPoG
- - 'Halo White'	CBot CRos EHyd LRHS SPoG
- 'Mars Magic' (Spotlight Series)	CBod EPfP EWTr LRHS MHer
- 'Nigra'	CBod CBot CSpe ECtt ELan EPfP ESps GMcL IBoy LCro LHop LOPS LRHS LSRN MNHC NGBl NGdn SPer SPhx SRms WCAu WHar XEll
- 'Polarstar' (Spotlight Series)	CBod EWTr LRHS
- 'Radiant Rose' (Spotlight Series) **new**	CBod LRHS
- single pink-flowered	EWoo
- single-flowered	MMuc SEND SRms
- (Spring Celebrities Series) 'Spring Celebrities Crimson' (d) **new**	LRHS SHil
- - 'Spring Celebrities Lemon' (d) **new**	LRHS NRHS SHil
- - 'Spring Celebrities Pink' (d) **new**	LRHS NRHS SHil
- - 'Spring Celebrities White' (d) **new**	LRHS NRHS SHil
- Summer Carnival Group	SRms
- 'Sunshine' (Spotlight Series)	CBod EPfP LRHS
§ ***rugosa***	CBot LEdu MSpe SHar SPav XSen

Alcea × *Althaea* see × *Alcalthaea*

Alchemilla ✿ (*Rosaceae*)

abyssinica	EBee
alpina misapplied	see *A. conjuncta*, *A. plicatula*
alpina ambig.	MCot SCob
alpina L.	EBee ECho EHoe ELan EPfP EWTr GPoy LEdu LHop LRHS MMuc MRav NChi SBch SEND SRms SWat WMoo WPGP WSHC
§ ***conjuncta***	CDor CMac CSam CSpe EBee ECha EHrv ELan EPfP GAbr GMaP GMcL LHop MHer MRav NBid NChi NRya NSti SPer SPlb SRms WHoo WJek
ellenbeckii	ECho GAbr IMou NChi WTor WWFP
epipsila	EBee ELan EPfP EShb GCal LRHS LSun NLar SPhx WSHC
erythropoda ♀H5	Widely available
- Turkish form	ECha
faeroensis	WMoo WPtf XLum
- var. ***pumila***	EBee GEdr GKev
fissa	EBee EPPr
glaucescens	CNat
hoppeana misapplied	see *A. plicatula*
hoppeana (Reichenb.) Dalla Torre	EBee
iniquiformis	EBee
lapeyrousei	NChi
mollis ♀H7	Widely available
I - 'Auslese'	SWvt
- 'Robustica'	MMuc SEND SPlb SWat WFar WMoo WPnP
- 'Thriller'	CBod CRos EHyd EPfP LRHS NRHS WFar
- 'Variegata' (v)	CNat
'Mr Poland's Variety'	see *A. venosa*
pedata	CHid EBee NChi
peristerica	EBee
§ ***plicatula***	NLar
saxatilis	EBee NLar

sericata 'Gold Strike'	EBee ECtt ELan EPfP GLog IMou LBMP SHar SWvt
straminea	MRav
valdehirsuta	EBee
§ ***venosa***	EBee SHar SMHy
vetteri	EBee LRHS WHrl
vulgaris misapplied	see *A. xanthochlora*
§ ***xanthochlora***	CArn GPoy NLar SRms WFar WHer

Aldrovanda (*Droseraceae*)

vesiculosa	EFEx

alecost see *Tanacetum balsamita*

Alectorurus (*Liliaceae*)

yedoensis var. ***platypetalus***	EBee GEdr

Alectryon (*Sapindaceae*)

excelsus	CBcs

Alisma (*Alismataceae*)

lanceolatum	MSKA XBlo
plantago-aquatica	CBen CHab MSKA MWLS MWts NPer SWat WMAq WWtn XBlo
- var. ***parviflorum***	MSKA SPlb SWat

Allamanda (*Apocynaceae*)

cathartica	CCCN

Alliaria (*Brassicaceae*)

petiolata	GPoy WHer WOut WSFF

Allium ✿ (*Alliaceae*)

RCBAM 21	WCot
SSSE 250	GEdr
§ ***acuminatum***	ECho NBir NRog
I - 'Album'	ECho LRHS
acutiflorum	GKev LAma NRog
aflatunense misapplied	see *A. hollandicum*
aflatunense ambig.	GKev GMcL LCro LRHS LSRN SCob SDeJ SEND
akaka	NRog
'Akbulak'	EBee LAma
albopilosum	see *A. cristophii*
alexeianum	NRog
altissimum	GKev LAma NRog
- 'Goliath'	CTca GKev NRog WCot
amabile	see *A. mairei* var. *amabile*
'Ambassador'	CAvo CBro CMea CTca CWCL ERCP GKev ILea LAma LRHS NRog SDir SDix SPhx WCot
amethystinum 'Red Mohican'	CMea EBee ERCP GKev IPot LAma LOPS WCot
ampeloprasum	EBee ECha ECho GKev LAma NRog SPlb WHer WShi
- var. ***babingtonii***	CAgr CArn CTca GKev GPoy LEdu NRog SRms WHer WPGP WShi
§ - 'Elephant'	LCro LEdu LOPS
amphibolum	EBee ECho EPot GKev LAma NRog
amplectens	LAma LLHF NRog
- 'Graceful Beauty'	EBee EPfP EPot ERCP GKev LAma LCro LOPS NNys NRog SCob SDeJ SHil SPer WCot XEll
anceps	NRog
§ ***angulosum***	CAvo CTca ECho EWld GKev LAma LEdu NHpl NRog WCot
aschersonianum	EBee GKev SDeJ WCot
atropurpureum	EAJP EBee ECha EHrv ELan EPfP EPot ERCP GBin GKev LAma LCro LOPS LRHS MCot NRog SDeJ SDir SPer SPhx
atropurpureum × ***schubertii***	LSRN
auctum	EBee
azureum	see *A. caeruleum*
backhousianum	GKev LAma NRog
barszczewskii	NRog
'Beau Regard' ♀H7	CTca CWCL EBee ELan ERCP GKev ILea LAma LRHS NLar NRog
beesianum misapplied	see *A. cyaneum*
beesianum W.W.Sm. ♀	EBee LLHF NBir NHpl NRya
bisceptrum	GKev NRog
'Bizar'	LAma
blandum	see *A. carolinianum*
bodeanum	see *A. cristophii*
'Bolero'	EBee LAma LRHS NRog
bulgaricum	see *Nectaroscordum siculum* subsp. *bulgaricum*
§ ***caeruleum*** ♀H5	CAvo CBro CTca CTri CWld EAJP EBee ECho EPfP EPot ERCP GKev LAma LCro LHop LPot LRHS MGos MNrw NBir NLar NPer NRog NRya SCob SDeJ SPer SPhx
- ***azureum***	see *A. caeruleum*
caesium ♀H5	CAvo EBee ECho ERCP GKev NRog WCot
- 'Pskem's Beauty' new	GKev
caespitosum	ECho
callimischon subsp. ***callimischon***	ECho EPot NRog
- subsp. ***haemostictum***	ECho NRog WAbe WCot
'Cameleon'	EBee ECho ERCP GKev LAma LCro LOPS LRHS NPnk NRog SCob
campanulatum	NRog
canadense	CArn SHar
§ ***carinatum***	ECho GKev MBel WHer
§ - subsp. ***pulchellum*** ♀H5	CBro CSpe EBee ECha ECho EPot GKev LAma LHop LLWP LRHS MArt MHer MMuc MNrw NRog SPhx WThu
- - f. ***album*** ♀H5	CBro EBee ECha ECho GKev LEdu LLWP LSun MNrw NRog SPhx WPtf
- - 'Bill Baker'	LEdu
§ ***carolinianum***	GKev LAma NRog
cepa	CBod SVic
- Aggregatum Group	CLau GPoy SRms
- - 'Golden Gourmet' ♀H3	LCro LOPS SVic
- - 'Longor'PBR ♀H3	LCro LOPS
- - 'Matador' ♀H3	SVic
- - 'Pikant'	SVic
- - 'Red Sun'PBR	LCro
- 'Electric'PBR	LCro
- 'Kew White'	WCot
- 'Perutile'	CArn CHby GPoy LEdu MHer SHDw
- Proliferum Group	CAgr CArn GPoy LEdu MHer MNHC SIde SRms WGwG WHer WJek XLum
- 'Red Brunswick'	SVic
- var. ***viviparum***	ECho GKev LAma NRog
- 'White Lisbon' ♀H4	LCro SVic
cernuum	Widely available
§ - 'Hidcote' ♀H5	CSam EBee MArt WKif
- 'Major'	see *A. cernuum* 'Hidcote'
- pink-flowered	NBir
- 'White Dwarf'	CMea EBee ECho GKev LAma NRog
- 'White Max' new	GKev
chinense	CAgr GPoy LEdu
- 'October Mist' new	LEdu

	cirrhosum	see *A. carinatum* subsp. *pulchellum*
*	***cneorum***	LAma
	colchicifolium	NRog
	convallariodes	GKev LAma
	- pink-flowered **new**	GKev
	cowanii	see *A. neapolitanum* Cowanii Group
	crenulatum	GKev LAma NRog
	- pink-flowered **new**	GKev
	crispum	NRog
§	***cristophii*** 🏆^{H7}	Widely available
	cupanii	ECho GKev
	cupuliferum	GKev NRog
	curtum RCB RL 13	WCot
§	***cyaneum*** 🏆^{H5}	CPBP ECho GEdr GKev LAma LBee LRHS MHer NHpl NRog NRya WCot
	cyathophorum	ECho
§	- var. ***farreri***	CArn CAvo CBro CElw ECho EPot GKev LAma LEdu LLWP LRHS MHer MNrw MRav NHpl NRya WCot WPtf WThu
	cyrilli **new**	GKev
	decipiens	GKev LAma NRog
	diabaloense	NRog
	dichlamydeum	NRog
	douglasii	NRog
§	***drummondii***	EBee LRHS
	'Early Emperor'	CWCL EBee EPfP ERCP GKev LAma LRHS NRog SCob
	elatum	see *A. macleanii*
	elburzense	NRog
	'Emir'	GKev NRog
	ericetorum	GKev NRog WCot
	- PAB 1009	LEdu
	'Eros'	EBee GKev LAma LCro LOPS
	falcifolium	CTal ECho GKev LAma LLHF NRog WCot
	farreri	see *A. cyathophorum* var. *farreri*
	fasciculatum	LAma
	fimbriatum	ECho NRog
	- var. ***purdyi***	NRog
	'Firmament'	CBro CWCL ECha ERCP GKev LAma LRHS NRog SDeJ SPhx WCot XEll
	fistulosum	CAgr CArn CHby CLau ECho ENfk GKev GPoy LAma LEdu MHer MNHC NPri SEND SIde SRms SVic WCot WGwG WJek XLum
	- 'Red Welsh'	SRms WJek
	flavum 🏆^{H4}	CBro CMea CTca ECGP ECha ECho EPot ERCP GKev LAma LRHS NHpl NSla SDeJ SDir WGwG WPtf WThu
§	- 'Blue Leaf'	ECho NBir
	- subsp. ***flavum***	EBee ECho GKev NRog
	- - var. ***minus***	ECho MMuc NRog SEND
	- 'Glaucum'	see *A. flavum* 'Blue Leaf'
	- var. ***nanum***	ECho EPot NRog
	- subsp. ***tauricum***	CSpe ECho GKev NRog SPhx WCot
	'Forelock'	CTca EBee EPfP ERCP GKev LAma MNrw NRog SCob SDir WCot XEll
	forrestii	GKev WCot
	geyeri	EBee ECho GBin
	giganteum	Widely available
	- 'Twinkling Stars'	GKev LAma
	'Gladiator' 🏆^{H7}	CAvo CTca CWCL EBee EPfP ERCP GKev GMaP LAma LCro LOPS LRHS NRog SCob SDeJ SDix
	glaucum	see *A. senescens* subsp. *glaucum*
	'Globemaster' 🏆^{H7}	Widely available
	'Globus'	CBro EBee GKev LAma NRog
	guttatum subsp. ***dalmaticum***	GKev NRog
	- subsp. ***sardoum***	GKev NRog
	gypsaceum	NRog
	'Haarlem Superglobe'	CPne
	haemanthoides	WCot
	haematochiton	ECho NRog
	'Hair'	see *A. vineale* 'Hair'
	heldreichii	EBee ECho NRog
*	***hirtifolium*** var. ***album***	EBee GKev LAma NRog
	'His Excellency'	CWCL EBee ERCP GBin GKev LAma LRHS NRog SCob
§	***hollandicum*** 🏆^{H7}	CAvo CBro ECGP ECha EPfP GKev LAma LCro LOPS NNys NRog SPer SPlb WFar
	- 'Purple Sensation' 🏆^{H7}	Widely available
	- 'Purple Surprise' 🏆^{H7}	NBir WCot
	hookeri	LEdu
	- ACE 2430	LEdu WCot
	- var. ***muliense***	GEdr LEdu
	- 'Zorami'	CAgr ELan LEdu WPGP
	howellii var. ***clokeyi***	NRog
	huber-morathii	EBee GKev
	humile	GEdr
	hyalinum	NRog
	- pink-flowered	EBee
	inconspicuum	GKev LAma NRog
§	***insubricum*** 🏆^{H5}	CSpe EPot GEdr GKev MNrw NBir NHpl NRog NRya NSla SChF WAbe
	'Jackpot'	CWCL EBee ERCP GKev ILea LAma NRog
	jajlae	see *A. rotundum* subsp. *jajlae*
	jesdianum 'Michael Hoog'	see *A. rosenorum* 'Michael H. Hoog'
	- 'Purple King'	GKev LAma LRHS NRog
	- 'White Empress'^{PBR}	CAvo EBee LRHS NRog SPhx
	kansuense	see *A. sikkimense*
	karataviense 🏆^{H5}	CAby CAvo EBee ECha ELan EPot GAbr GKev LAma LCro LHop LOPS LRHS LSun MCot NBir NHpl NLar NRog SCob SDeJ SWvt
	- subsp. ***henrikii***	GKev LAma NRog WCot
	- 'Ivory Queen'	CAby CAvo CBro CTca EBee ECha EPfP ERCP GKev LAma LCro LOPS LRHS LSRN NHpl NLar NRog SCob SDeJ SDir SPlb WWFP
	kharputense	NRog
	komarovianum	see *A. thunbergii*
	komarovii	GKev LAma NRog
	lacunosum	NRog
	- var. ***lacunosum***	NRog
	ledebourianum	GKev LAma NRog
	lemmonii	NRog
	lenkoranicum	ECho GKev LAma NRog WCot
	litvinovii	EBee GKev LAma NRog WCot
	loratum	EBee GKev LAma NRog
	'Lucy Ball'	CBro EPfP ERCP GKev LAma LRHS NBir NLar NRog SDeJ SDix
§	***lusitanicum***	CBro CSpe ECha ECho ERCP GKev LEdu NBre NDov NRog SRms
§	***macleanii***	EBee ECho EPfP GKev LAma LRHS NRog
	macranthum	CSpe EBee ECho GKev LAma NHpl NRog WCot
	mairei	CRos ECho EHyd LAma LHop LRHS MMuc NRHS NRya
§	- var. ***amabile***	ECho GEdr NRya NSla WThu
	- - pink-flowered	ECho
	- - red-flowered	ECho
	maximowiczii	ECho GKev NHpl
	- white-flowered	ECho LAma
	'Mercurius'^{PBR}	EBee GKev LAma NRog SPhx WCot
	meteoricum	GKev NRog WCot

'Miami'	EBee ERCP GKev LAma LRHS NRog SDix
'Millennium'	SHar WCot
moly	CWCL EBee ECho GKev LAma LCro MRav NRog NRya SCob SDeJ SRms WCot XLum
- 'Jeannine' ♀H5	CBro EBee ECho EPot GKev LAma LRHS NRog
'Mont Blanc'	CMea EBee ELan ERCP GBin GKev ILea LAma LRHS NLar NRog SCob SHil
multibulbosum	see *A. nigrum*
murrayanum misapplied	see *A. unifolium*
murrayanum Regel	see *A. acuminatum*
myrianthum	NRog
- KMT-19-04	EBee
narcissiflorum misapplied	see *A. insubricum*
§ ***narcissiflorum*** Vill.	CSpe ECho GCal LEdu MNrw NWad
neapolitanum	CAgr ECGP ECho EPot GKev LAma LRHS MCot NRog SEND SPer SRms WGwG
§ - Cowanii Group	ECGP ECho GKev LCro LOPS LRHS NRog SDeJ WCot
- 'Grandiflorum'	ECho
§ ***neriniflorum***	WAbe
nevii	NRog
nevskianum	GKev LAma NRog SKHP
§ ***nigrum***	CAvo CBWd CBro ECha EHrv EPfP EPot ERCP GKev IBoy LAma LCro LOPS LRHS MCot NBir NPer NRog SCob SDeJ SDir SPhx WCot WRHF
- f. ***roseum*** new	CBro
nutans	GKev LAma LEdu MHer NRog SHDw SMHy SRms WHal WHil WJek
nuttallii	see *A. drummondii*
§ ***obliquum***	CAvo CBro CSpe ECha EPri ERCP GEdr GKev NRog SDeJ SPhx WCot
ochotense	WCot
odorum L.	see *A. ramosum* L.
oleraceum	WHer
olympicum	GKev NRog
§ ***oreophilum***	CSam ECha ECho GKev LAma LCro LOPS LRHS NRog SPer SRms WCot
- 'Agalik Giant'	NRog
- 'Samur'	WCot
- 'Zwanenburg' ♀H5	ECho EPot
orientale	GKev NRog
oschaninii	LAma NRog
'Ostara' new	ERCP
ostrowskianum	see *A. oreophilum*
ovalifolium var. ***leuconeurum***	GEdr WCot
pallasii	NRog
pallens	CBre NBir
§ ***paniculatum***	GKev LAma NRog
- AH 8673 new	GKev
* - var. ***minor***	GKev LAma NRog
paradoxum	ECho LEdu NBir
- var. ***normale***	CBro ECho EPot EWld GKev NBir NRog WCot
parciflorum	GKev NRog
parvum	NRog
pedemontanum	see *A. narcissiflorum* Vill.
pendulinum	GKev NRog
'Pinball Wizard'	CAvo CBro CRos CTca CWCL EHyd ERCP GKev LAma LRHS NRHS NRog SDix
'Ping Pong' new	EBee
'Pink Jewel'	EBee ERCP GKev LAma NRog WCot
platycaule	GKev LAma NRog SKHP WCot
plummerae	EBee GKev NRog SKHP
plurifoliatum	ECho LAma
polyphyllum	see *A. carolinianum*
porrum 'Musselburgh'	NPri SVic
'Powder Puff'	CBro EBee GKev LAma
prattii	EBee
protensum	NRog
przewalskianum	LAma LEdu NRog
pskemense	LAma NRog WCot
pulchellum	see *A. carinatum* subsp. *pulchellum*
'Purple Rain'	CBro CWCL ELan ERCP GKev LAma LRHS NRog WCot WRHF
'Purple Suze'	LAma
pyrenaicum misapplied	see *A. angulosum*
pyrenaicum ambig.	SEND
ramosum Jacq.	see *A. obliquum*
§ ***ramosum*** L.	ECho GKev LAma LEdu NRog
'Red Eye'	EBee SDir
'Rien Poortvliet'	LAma
roborowskianum	GKev
robustum	NRog
rosenbachianum misapplied	see *A. stipitatum*
rosenbachianum Regel	CBro LRHS
- 'Akbulak'	GKev LRHS
- 'Album'	EPfP GKev LAma NRog WCot
- 'Michael Hoog'	see *A. rosenorum* 'Michael H. Hoog'
- 'Shing'	GKev IBal LAma
§ ***rosenorum*** 'Michael H. Hoog'	ECho EPot GKev LAma NRog
roseum	CMea EPfP GKev LAma LCro LOPS LRHS NRog SCob SDeJ XLum
- ***albiflorum***	GMcL
§ ***rotundum*** subsp. ***jajlae***	LAma NRog WCot
'Round and Purple'	CAby CAvo ERCP GKev LAma LRHS NRog
rupestre new	GKev
sarawschanicum	GKev NRog
sativum	ENfk LBMP NPri SIde SPoG SRms
- 'Elephant'	see *A. ampeloprasum* 'Elephant'
- var. ***ophioscorodon***	GKev GPoy LAma SPlb
- - 'Purple Wight'	LOPS
saxatile	GKev NRog
- pink-flowered new	GKev
schoenoprasum	Widely available
- f. ***albiflorum***	CPbn ECha ECho GKev LEdu MHer NBir NCGa SIde
- 'Black Isle Blush'	CPbn EBee GPoy LEdu MHer WPGP
- 'Colesbourne Giant'	EBee
- 'Corsican White'	LEdu
- 'Elbe' new	LEdu
- fine-leaved	CLau NDov
- 'Forescate'	CAvo CTca ECha GKev LAma LEdu LHop LRHS MHer MRav NBir SIde SRms WAul XLum
- medium-leaved	CLau NPri
- 'Pink Perfection'	GPoy LEdu MHer NDov
- 'Polyphant'	CBre
- 'Shining Silver'	LEdu
- var. ***sibiricum***	SDix WShi
- 'Silver Chimes'	EBee MRav
- thick-leaved	CLau SRms
- 'Wallington White'	LEdu
schubertii ♀H4	CAvo CBod CBro CRos CSpe CTca CWCL EHyd ELan EPfP EPot ERCP GKev GMcL LAma LCro LOPS LRHS NFav NRHS NRog SCob SDeJ SPer SPhx WCot WFar WWFP
scorodoprasum	ECho LAma SIde
- 'Art'	ERCP GKev LAma NRog
- subsp. ***jajlae***	see *A. rotundum* subsp. *jajlae*

	- 'Passion'	ERCP GKev LAma NRog WRHF
	- 'Purple Caila' new	GKev
	- subsp. ***scorodoprasum***	ECho NRog
	senescens	CBro CTca CTri ECGP EDAr EPot GJos GNew IMou LAma LEdu LRHS MBel MRav SBch SRms WBrk XLum XSen
§	- subsp. ***glaucum***	CArn CAvo CMea CPBP CSpe CTal EAEE EBee ECha ECho EWTr GKev LEdu LRHS NDov NGdn NLar NRog NRya SEND SWat WCot WHoo XSen
	- subsp. ***senescens***	ECho GKev LEdu NRog WPGP
	serra	WCot
	sewerzowii	NRog
	shelkovnikovii	CTal
	sibthorpianum	see *A. paniculatum*
	siculum	see *Nectaroscordum siculum*
§	***sikkimense***	EBee ECho EWTr GEdr LRHS MHer MMuc NHpl NSla WCot
	'Silver Spring'	EPot ERCP MNrw NRog SDeJ
	sphaerocephalon	Widely available
	- subsp. ***arvense***	NRog WCot
	'Spider'	CWCL EBee EPot ERCP ESwi GBin GKev LAma LRHS NRog SPhx WCot
I	***splendens*** var. ***kurilense***	GEdr
	stamineum W&B BGF-2	WCot
	'Statos'	EBee GKev LAma WCot
	stellatum	LRHS NRog WGwG
	stellerianum var. ***kurilense***	WAbe WThu
§	***stipitatum***	GKev LAma NRog SPhx WCot
	- 'Album'	NRog
	- 'Mars'	EBee EPfP ERCP GKev GMcL LAma LRHS NRog SDix
	- 'Mount Everest'	CAvo CBro CHid CTca CWCL EPfP EPot ERCP GKev GMaP ILea LAma LCro LOPS LRHS LSRN MHtn NRog SDeJ SDir SPer SPhx
	- 'Violet Beauty'	CCse CWCL GKev LAma LCro LOPS LRHS MHtn NNys SDix SHil WCot WRHF
	- 'White Giant'	CTca CWCL EBee ERCP GKev LAma LRHS NRog
	stracheyi	WCot
	suaveolens	MMuc
	subhirsutum	GKev NRog XLum
	subvillosum	EPot GKev NRog
	'Summer Beauty'	see *A. lusitanicum*
	'Summer Drummer'	CTca EBee EPfP ERCP GKev LEdu LRHS NRog SDeJ SDir SDix SPer SPhx
	suworowii	GKev NRog
	'Sweet Discovery'	LAma NRog
	taquetii	see *A. thunbergii*
	tauricola	GKev NRog
	texanum	GKev LAma NRog
§	***thunbergii*** ♀H5	EBee ECho EPot LAma LHop MHer NBir NRog NRya SPhx WAbe
	- PAB 3821	LEdu
	- 'Album'	ECho WAbe
	- 'Ozawa'	EBee ECho GEdr SMHy SRms WAbe WCot
	tibeticum	see *A. sikkimense*
	tolmiei var. ***platyphyllum***	NRog
	- - NNS 01-20 new	GKev
	- var. ***tolmiei***	NRog
*	***tournefortii***	ECho
	triquetrum	ELan EPot GKev LAma LEdu NBir SEND WCot WHer WMoo WPnP XLum
	tschimganicum	EBee LAma NRog SKHP
	tuberosum	Widely available
	- B&SWJ 8881	WCru
	- purple/mauve-flowered	CHby CLau
	- 'White Dwarf' new	GKev
	umbilicatum	GKev NRog
§	***unifolium*** ♀H4	CAvo CMea EBee ECho EPfP EPot ERCP GKev LAma LCro LOPS MRav NBir NPer NQui NRog SDeJ SEND SRms WCot
	ursinum	CArn CHab CHby CWld ECho ENfk GJos GKev GPoy LAma LEdu MHer MMuc NPri NRog SRms WJek WSFF WShi XLum
	validum NNS 06-41	WCot
	victorialis	ECho
	- 'Cantabria'	EBee GKev NRog WCot
	vineale	NMir WHer WJek
	- PAB 2763	LEdu
	- 'Dready'	ECho ERCP GKev LAma NRog
§	- 'Hair'	CAby EPfP ERCP GKev LAma MCot NBir NPer NRog SCob WTor
	violaceum	see *A. carinatum*
	virgunculae	CMea GEdr WAbe
	wallichii	EBee EPot EWes GKev LEdu LLHF MBNS NBir NChi SKHP XLum
	- CC 2643	WCot
	- CLD 1500	NBid
	- PAB 2976	LEdu WPGP
	- PAB 9191 new	LEdu
	- dark-flowered	LPla WCot
	'White Cloud'	EBee GKev XEll
	'World Cup'	LAma
	woronowii	NRog SDir
	zaprjagajevii	WCot
	zebdanense	EBee ECho GKev LAma NRog

almond see *Prunus dulcis*

Alniphyllum (*Styracaceae*)

eberhardtii FMWJ 13121	WCru
fortunei FMWJ 13013 new	WCru

Alnus ✿ (*Betulaceae*)

cordata ♀H5	Widely available
cremastogyne	EBtc
fauriei from Niigata, Japan	CSto
firma	CSto
formosana	IArd
glutinosa	Widely available
- 'Aurea'	CDul CEnd CWib MGos
- var. ***barbata***	CSto
- 'Imperialis' ♀H6	CCVT CDul CEnd CLnd CTho EBee ECrN ELan EMOT EPfP ESps EWTr IDee LHop MBlu MMuc MPkF NBro NLar NOra NOrn NWea SCob SEND SGol SKHP SPer WHar WMat WTSh
- 'Laciniata'	CCVT CDul CLnd CMac CTho ECrN MGos NLar NWea WMou
- 'Pyramidalis'	CDul
hirsuta	CSto
incana	CBcs CCVT CDul CLnd CMCN CSto CTho CWib ECrN EMOT ESps LBuc MGos NLar NWea SCob SGol SPer WHar WHed WMat WMou WTSh
- 'Aurea' ♀H6	CBcs CCVT CDul CEnd CLnd CMac CTho EBee ECrN ELan EMOT EPfP ESps GBin IArd MBlu MGos MRav NBro NEgg NLar NOra NOrn NWea SEWo SGol SPer WFar WHar WMat
- 'Laciniata'	CTho ELan ESps NLar SCoo WFar WMou

- 'Pendula'	CDul CTho
japonica	MBlu
maximowiczii	CSto
- from Ulleungdo	WCru
nitida	EBtc
oregana	see *A. rubra*
pendula B&SWJ 10895	WCru
rhombifolia	EBtc
§ ***rubra***	CDul CMCN CTho ELan MCoo NWea WMat WTSh
- f. ***pinnatisecta***	CDul CMCN MBlu
sieboldiana	CSto GKev WCru
× ***spaethii***	EWTr MBlu
subcordata	CSto
- NJM 13.009 **new**	WPGP
viridis	CAgr CSto EBtc MCoo NWea WTSh
- subsp. ***sinuata***	CAgr CSto

Alocasia (*Araceae*)

× ***amazonica*** 🏆^{H1a}	XBlo
- 'Polly'	NLos
'Bambino' (Bambino Series) **new**	NLos
'Black Velvet'	NLos
'Calidora'	CDTJ NLos
cucullata	NLos XBlo
gageana	CDTJ
macrorrhiza	CDTJ EUJe LTro NLos SBig
odora	CAbb CDTJ EUJe XBlo
plumbea	XBlo
'Portodora'	NLos
wentii	NLos
zebrina	NLos

Aloe ✿ (*Asphodelaceae*)

africana	CAbb
antandroi	LToo
arborescens	CDTJ CTre EShb EUJe NLos SEND
- 'Variegata' (v) 🏆^{H1c} **new**	SRms
aristata 🏆^{H3}	CCac EUJe LTro NLos SArc SChr SEND SPad SPlb XLum
- 'Cathedral Peak'	SChr
- 'Green Pearl'^{PBR}	SMad
aristata × striatula	CCac
barbadensis	see *A. vera*
barberae	CCCN CTre
boylei	CTre
brevifolia 🏆^{H2}	CAbb CTre EShb SArc
broomii	CAbb CCCN CTre LToo SPlb
camperi 'Maculata'	SEND
ciliaris	CCac CHll EShb SChr
'Cleopatra' **new**	WCot
comptonii	CAbb
cooperi	CCCN CDTJ
descoingsii 🏆^{H1b}	LToo
dichotoma	CAbb CTre SPlb
'Doran Black'	LToo
ecklonis	CBlu CCCN SPlb
erinacea	LToo
ferox	CAbb CBod CCCN CDTJ CTre SBig
fosteri	CDTJ
greatheadii var. ***davyana***	SChr SPlb
humilis	SChr SEND
juvenna	SRms
kedongensis	SEND
krapohliana	CAbb
'Lime Fizz'	LToo
lineata	CAbb
littoralis	CAbb
maculata	CDTJ
marlothii	CAbb CCCN LTro SPlb
melanacantha	CAbb
microstigma	CCCN CTre
millotii	LToo
mitriformis	NGBl SEND
mutabilis	SChr SEND
peglerae	SRms
petricola	CAbb
plicatilis 🏆^{H2}	CBlu CCCN CDTJ EShb
pluridens	CAbb
polyphylla 🏆^{H3}	CBlu CCCN CCac CTre WPGP
pratensis	CCCN CDTJ
rauhii 🏆^{H1b}	CTre LToo
reitzii	CAbb CBlu CTre SPlb
'Snowflake'	NLos
somaliensis 🏆^{H1b}	LToo NLos
speciosa	CAbb
spicata	CAbb
× ***spinosissima***	SChr SMad
striata	CAbb CBlu CCCN CTre EShb LToo SPlb
striatula 🏆^{H3}	CAbb CBrP CCac CDTJ CSam CTca CTre ETod EUJe IBlr LEdu LTro SArc SBig SChr SEND SKHP SMad SPlb SVen WCot WPGP
succotrina	CAbb
suprafoliata	CAbb CBlu
thraskii	CAbb
variegata (v) 🏆^{H1b}	EShb LSun NLos
§ ***vera*** 🏆^{H1b}	CArn CCCN CSpe ELan ESps GPoy MHer MNHC NPer NPla NPri SChr SEND SIde SMad SPlb SPre SRms SVic WJek
wickensii	SPlb
yavellana	SPlb

Alonsoa (*Scrophulariaceae*)

'Bright Spark'	CSpe
incisifolia	CCCN CSpe
meridionalis	CCCN
- 'Rebel'	CMos ECtt SRkn
- 'Salmon Beauty'	CRos EHyd LRHS NRHS
'Pink Beauty'	CSpe ELan
'Scarlet Lucky Lips' (v)	LSou
warscewiczii	CCCN ELan MSCN
- 'Peachy-keen'	CSpe

Alopecurus (*Poaceae*)

alpinus	see *A. magellanicus*
§ ***magellanicus***	ELan EPPr GBin LPot
pratensis	CHab
- 'Aureovariegatus' (v)	EHoe EPPr EShb GMaP GMcL NBid SPer SRms
- 'Aureus'	NBro SPlb
- 'No Overtaking' (v)	EPPr

Alophia (*Iridaceae*)

lahue	see *Herbertia lahue*

Aloysia (*Verbenaceae*)

chamaedryfolia	EPfP LRHS
citriodora	see *A. citrodora*
§ ***citrodora*** 🏆^{H3}	Widely available
- 'Spilsbury Mint' **new**	ELan
gratissima	WJek
triphylla	see *A. citrodora*

Alpinia (*Zingiberaceae*)

formosana	LEdu
galanga	CArn

japonica LEdu
- B&SWJ 8889 WCru
- PAB 6441 LEdu
zerumbet 'Variegata' (v) MPkF NLos XBlo

Alsobia see *Episcia*

Alstroemeria ✿ (*Alstroemeriaceae*)

'Adonis' PBR SPer WViv
'Aimi' ELan MNrw SPer SWvt WViv
'Alexis' PBR WViv
'Aliénor' (Midi Series) XTur
'Amarillo' WViv
'Andez Red' EWTr
'Andigné' (Garden Series) XTur
'Angelina' SWvt
'Anne' (Midi Series) XTur
'Antoine' (Maxi Series) LSou XTur
'Apollo' ♀H4 CTsd ELan LRHS MBNS MNrw NBre SPer SWvt WViv
'Arthur' (Maxi Series) XTur
'Athena' WViv
'Aubance' (Garden Series) XTur
aurantiaca see *A. aurea*
§ ***aurea*** GWyn MRav SRms XLum
- 'Apricot' GCal
- 'Lutea' GKev NLar SDeJ SPlb
- 'Orange King' CTsd ELan EPfP EWTr GKev NLar SDeJ
'Authion' (Garden Series) XTur
'Avanti' ELan LRHS WViv
'Avrillé' (Garden Series) XTur
'Baracé' (Garden Series) WHlf XTur
'Baugé' (Garden Series) XTur
'Béatrice' (Midi Series) XTur
'Blushing Bride' MBNS SWvt WViv
'Bodega' PBR WViv
'Bolero' WViv
'Bonanza' SPer WViv
brasiliensis CTsd GCal SBrt WCot WRHF WSHC WViv XLum
- 'Cally Star' (v) EBee GCal NLar
'Brezé' (Garden Series) XTur
'Briançon' (Garden Series) WHlf XTur
'Cahors' (Planet Series) ♀H4 LCro LOPS
'Camille' (Mini Series) SHil XTur
'Candé' (Garden Series) XTur
'Candy' WViv
'Candy Floss' ELan EPfP
'Caroline' (Midi Series) XTur
'Charles' (Maxi Series) LSou XTur
'Charm' CTsd SPer WViv
'Chartrené' (Garden Series) XTur
'Chi Chi' WCot
'Chinon' (Garden Series) XTur
'Chloé' (Mini Series) XTur
§ 'Christina' PBR MBNS SWvt WViv
'Christine' (Midi Series) SHil XTur
'Christine Marsh' WViv
'Cindy' WViv
'Coronet' ♀H4 MBNS WViv
'Dandy Candy' CBod EBee ECGP ECtt GKev LLWG LRHS MHol NGdn NLar WBrk WCot
'Davina' PBR NLar
'Dayspring Delight' (v) GCal MNrw
§ Diana, Princess of Wales = 'Stablaco' CBcs CRos LRHS NRHS
'Diane' (Midi Series) XTur
diluta subsp. ***chrysantha*** F&W 8700 WCot
Doctor Salter's hybrids SRms
'Dorothée' (Midi Series) XTur
'Eleanor' **new** SHil WViv
'Elvira' ELan MNrw SPer WViv
'Etna' PBR SPer WViv
'Evening Song' LRHS MBNS MNrw SPer SWvt
exserens WCot
'Flaming Star' WViv
'Fougeré' (Garden Series) XTur
'Frances' (v) CAvo CBro WCot
'François' (Maxi Series) XTur
'Freedom' CBod CWGN ECtt ELon EWoo LSou MBNS MHol NEgg NLar NSti SCob SPoG WCot
'Friendship' ♀H5 CTsd ELan EWoo LRHS NBre SWvt WViv
'Gaspard' (Mini Series) XTur
'Georges' (Maxi Series) XTur
'Gloria' LRHS MBNS SWvt WViv
'Glory of the Andes' (v) CWGN NLar
'Golden Delight' ELan LRHS MNrw SPer WViv
haemantha GKev
I 'Hatch Hybrid' GCal
'Hawera' GBin GCal
'Héloïse' (Mini Series) XTur
'Henri' (Maxi Series) XTur
hookeri GKev
subsp. ***cummingiana***
Inca Adore = 'Koadore' SPoG
Inca Avanti = 'Koncavanti' PBR CWGN LBuc SCob WViv
Inca Azure = 'Konazur' PBR GBin WViv
Inca Classic = 'Konclassic' WViv
Inca Coral = 'Konocoral' IBoy WViv
Inca Devotion = 'Konevotio' PBR EBee LHop NLar
Inca Dream = 'Kodream' WViv
Inca Exotica = 'Koexotica' EBee SPoG WViv
Inca Glow = 'Koglow' CBcs CBod CWGN EBee ELon GBin GKev LRHS LSou MHol NLar SDeJ SPoG SRms WViv
Inca Goal = 'Koncagoal' WViv
Inca Husky = 'Konhusky' CBcs CBod CWGN EBee MHol SCob SPoG WViv
Inca Ice = 'Koice' CWGN NLar SPoG WViv
Inca Joli = 'Koncajoli' PBR LBuc WViv
Inca Lake = 'Koncalake' CWGN LBuc SCob WViv
Inca Lolly = 'Koncalolly' PBR WViv
Inca Mambo = 'Koncamambo' PBR WViv
Inca Milk = 'Koncamilk' WViv
Inca Noble = 'Koncanoble' WViv
Inca Obsession = 'Koobsion' WViv
Inca Pulse = 'Konpulse' PBR CWGN EBee ELon GBin GKev LSou NLar SDeJ SPoG WViv
Inca Serin = 'Koserin' PBR CWGN LHop WViv
Inca Smile = 'Koncasmile' SCob WViv
Inca Sweety = 'Koncasweet' PBR EBee WViv
Inca Toto = 'Koncatoto' PBR EBee WViv
Inca Tropic = 'Kotrop' CWGN WViv
Inca Vito = 'Koncavito' PBR CBcs CBod CWGN LSou MHol NLar SCob SHil SPoG WViv
Inca Yuko = 'Koncayuko' PBR CBcs CBod CWGN LBuc LSou MHol SHil SPoG WViv
Indian Summer = 'Tesronto' PBR CBod CRos CWGN LRHS NRHS SPoG WViv
Inticancha Antarctica = 'Tesantara' **new** WViv

Inticancha Bryce = 'Tesbryce'PBR	WFar WViv
Inticancha Creamy Dark Pink = 'Tescreda'	SDeJ WViv
Inticancha Dark Purple = 'Tesdarklin'PBR	IBoy LSou SPoG WFar WViv
Inticancha Machu = 'Tesmach'PBR	WFar WViv
Inticancha Maya = 'Tesmaya'PBR	CWGN GMcL LSou WFar WViv
Inticancha Navayo = 'Tesnava'PBR	SPoG WFar
Inticancha Passion = 'Tespassion'	LSou WViv
Inticancha Purple = 'Tespurplin'PBR	CWGN WFar WViv
Inticancha Red = 'Tesrobin'PBR	CWGN EBee GMcL SPoG WFar WViv
Inticancha Sunday = 'Tessunday'PBR	WViv
Inticancha Sunlight = 'Tessunlight'PBR	GMcL LSou WFar WViv
Inticancha White Pink Blush = 'Tesblushin'PBR	WFar WViv
Isabella = 'Stalis'	LSRN
§ ***isabellana***	WCru
'Isabelle' (Midi Series)	XTur
'Jacques' (Maxi Series)	XTur
'Jalesne' (Garden Series)	XTur
'Jazze Purple Rose' (Jazze Series) **new**	GMcL
'Joséphine' (Midi Series)	XTur
'Junon' (Planet Series)	LCro
'Laguna'	WViv
Laura = 'Stalauli'PBR	SCob
'Layon' (Garden Series)	XTur
'Léo' (Mini Series)	XTur
ligtu hybrids	CAvo CBcs ECha EPfP GKev LCro LOPS MNrw NPer SDeJ SRms SWvt WBrk WHoo XLum
- var. ***ligtu***	SMHy
'Liré' (Garden Series)	XTur
'Little Eleanor'	LRHS WViv
'Little Miss Catherine'	WViv
'Little Miss Christina'	see *A.* 'Christina'
'Little Miss Davina'	LRHS WViv
'Little Miss Emily'	WViv
'Little Miss Gina'	WViv
'Little Miss Isabel'	WViv
'Little Miss Jessica'	WViv
'Little Miss Lucy'	CBod WViv
'Little Miss Matilda'	WViv
'Little Miss Miranda'	WViv
'Little Miss Natalie'	see *A.* 'Natalie'
'Little Miss Rosanna'	WViv
'Little Miss Roselind'	see *A.* 'Roselind'
'Little Miss Sophie'	see *A.* 'Sophie'
'Little Miss Tara'	see *A.* 'Tara'
'Little Miss Veronica'	MBNS WViv
'Longué' (Garden Series)	WHlf XTur
'Louis' (Maxi Series)	SHil XTur
'Louise' (Midi Series)	LSRN XTur
'Lucca'	WViv
'Lucinda'	SWvt WViv
'Maestro'PBR	WViv
'Marcé' (Garden Series)	XTur
'Marguerite' (Midi Series)	XTur
'Marie' (Midi Series)	SHil XTur
'Marina'	MBNS
'Marissa'	GMaP IBoy

'Mars' (Planet Series)	LRHS
'Mathilde' (Midi Series)	NLar XTur
'Mauve Majesty'	CBod ECtt ELon EUJe IBoy ILea LLWG LRHS MHol NLar NSti SPoG WBrk WCot
'Mazé' (Garden Series)	LSou XTur
'Montsoreau' (Garden Series)	XTur
'Moulin Rouge'	ELan MBNS WViv
§ 'Natalie'PBR	LRHS WViv
'Neptune'	LCro LOPS
'Nicolas' (Maxi Series)	XTur
'Océane' (Mini Series)	XTur
'Orange Gem' ♀H4	MBNS
'Orange Glory' ♀H4	ELon EWoo GMaP IBoy LRHS MBNS SWvt WViv
'Orange Supreme'	LRHS WViv
'Oriana' ♀H4	SWvt WViv
pallida	SPlb
'Pandora'PBR	WViv
patagonica	ECho
'Pauline' (Mini Series)	SHil
pelegrina	ECho
'Perfect Orange'	WViv
'Philippe' (Maxi Series)	XTur
philippii	WCot
'Phoenix' (v) ♀H4	SWvt WViv
'Pink Lady'	WViv
'Pink Perfection'	NLar
'Pink Sensation'	LRHS WViv
'Polka'	MBNS WViv
presliana RB 94103	WCot
Princess Amina = 'Zapriamin'PBR	CBcs CRos LRHS NRHS SPoG WViv
Princess Angela = 'Staprilan'	ELan MBNS
Princess Anouska = 'Zaprinous'PBR	ELan NLar WViv
Princess Ariane = 'Zapriari'PBR	CBcs WViv
Princess Camilla = 'Stapricamil'	CRos LRHS NRHS SPer SPoG
Princess Claire = 'Zapriclair' **new**	CRos LRHS NRHS
Princess Daniela = 'Stapridani'	SCoo
Princess Diana	see *A.* Diana, Princess of Wales = 'Stablaco', *A.* Princess Diana = 'Zapridapal'
§ Princess Diana = 'Zapridapal'PBR	WViv
Princess Eliane = 'Zaprielia'PBR	CRos LRHS NRHS WViv
Princess Fabiana = 'Zaprifabi'PBR	CBcs CRos ELan LRHS NLar NRHS SPoG WViv
Princess Felicia = 'Zapricia'PBR	ELan SPer
Princess Frederika = 'Stabronza'	ECha
Princess Isabella = 'Zapribel'PBR	CBcs LRHS LSRN WViv
Princess Ivana = 'Staprivane'PBR	ELan SPoG
Princess Julieta = 'Zaprijul'PBR	IBoy NLar
Princess Kate = 'Zaprikate'PBR	CBcs CRos LRHS NRHS
Princess Letizia = 'Zaprilet'PBR	CBcs CRos LRHS NRHS SPoG
Princess Leyla = 'Stapriley'PBR	MBNS SPer

	Princess Lilian = 'Zaprilian' PBR	CBcs CRos EBee LRHS NRHS WViv
	Princess Louise = 'Zaprilou' PBR	LRHS LSRN WViv
	Princess Margaret = 'Staprimar'	NLar
	'Princess Margarita'	CRos
	Princess Marilene = 'Staprilene' PBR	MBNS WViv
	Princess Mary = 'Zaprimary' PBR	NLar
	Princess Mathilde = 'Zaprimat' PBR	LRHS NRHS WViv
	Princess Monica = 'Staprimon' PBR	MBNS
	Princess Oxana = 'Staprioxa' PBR	EBee
	Princess Paola = 'Stapripal' PBR	CBcs CRos LRHS MBNS NRHS SCoo SPoG WViv
	Princess Sara = 'Staprisara' PBR	CBcs CRos EPfP LRHS NRHS SPoG WViv
	Princess Sarah = 'Stalicamp'	MBNS
	Princess Susana = 'Staprisusa'	SCoo
	Princess Theresa = 'Zapriteres' PBR	EPfP NLar
	Princess Zavina = 'Staprivina' PBR	ELan MBNS NLar SPoG
§	***psittacina***	CAvo CBro CHll CMea CPne CSam CTsd ECha EHrv ELan EPfP GBin GBuc GCal GCra LHop MCot MHer SHar SRms WSHC WViv XLum
	- 'Mona Lisa'	CBod GBuc LSou XLum
	- 'Royal Star' (v)	CAby CBod CBro CWCL EAEE ELan ELon EPfP EPri EWTr GBuc LHop LRHS MPie SHar SPoG SRms WCot WHoo WSHC XLum
	pulchella Sims	see *A. psittacina*
	'Purple Rain'	ELan MNrw SPer SWvt WViv
	'Querré' (Garden Series)	XTur
	'Red Beauty' (v)	see *A.* 'Spitfire'
	'Red Beauty'	ELan GMaP LRHS MBNS SPer SWvt
	'Red Elf' 𝕐H4	IBoy MBNS SWvt WPnn WViv
	'René' (Maxi Series)	XTur
	'Rhubarb and Custard'	ELan EPfP
	'Rivale'	LCro
	Rock 'n' Roll = 'Alsdun01' (v)	EBee EPfP MHol SPer SPoG WCot WViv
§	'Roselind'	ELan MBNS SWvt WViv
	'Rosie' (Mini Series)	SHil XTur
	'Saturne' (Planet Series)	EPfP LCro
	'Segré' (Garden Series)	XTur
	'Selina'	EWoo LRHS MBNS MNrw NBre WViv
	'Serenade'	ELan WViv
	'Serrant' (Garden Series)	XTur
	'Sirius' (Planet Series) 𝕐H4	LCro LOPS
	'Sonata' 𝕐H4	WViv
§	'Sophie' PBR	ELan MBNS SWvt WViv
§	'Spitfire' (v) 𝕐H4	EPfP IBoy LCro LOPS LRHS SWvt WCot WViv
	'Strawberry Lace'	EBee ELan EPfP
	'Summer Breeze'	CRos GMcL LRHS LSou NRHS SPoG WViv
	'Summertime' **new**	WViv
	'Sunstar'	GMaP
	'Sweet Laura' PBR	CBod ECtt ELon EWoo LEdu LRHS LSRN MHol MNrw MPie NEgg NGdn NLar NSti SMad SPoG WCot WViv
	'Tangerine Tango'	WViv
	'Tanya'	LRHS MNrw WViv
§	'Tara' PBR	MBNS NLar SWvt WViv
	'Tessa' 𝕐H4	LRHS MBNS NBre WViv
	'Thorigné' (Garden Series)	XTur
	'Tiercé' (Garden Series)	XTur
	'Turkish Delight'	EPfP
	'Ventura'	WViv
	'Venus' (Planet Series)	LCro
	'William' (Maxi Series)	XTur
	'Yellow Friendship' 𝕐H4	MBNS MNrw NLar SWvt WPnn WViv
	'Yellow Queen'	IBoy WBod
	'Zoé' (Mini Series)	XTur

Alternanthera (*Amaranthaceae*)

	reineckii	XBlo
	- 'Lilacina' **new**	XBlo
I	- 'Rosaefolia' **new**	XBlo

Althaea (*Malvaceae*)

	armeniaca	EBee GCal NLar WCot
	cannabina	CAby CArn CFis CSpe ELan EPPr GCal IBoy IPot LHop MAvo MHer MNrw NGBl SHar SPhx WBor WCot WHal WHil WOld WSHC
	officinalis	CArn CBod CHab ELan ENfk GPoy MAvo MHer MNHC NLar SIde SRms WHer WJek XLum
	- ***alba***	LSou NLar
§	- 'Romney Marsh'	MAvo MRav WFar WKif
	rosea	see *Alcea rosea*
	rugosostellulata	see *Alcea rugosa*

Altingia (*Hamamelidaceae*)

	poilanei B&SWJ 11756	WCru

× *Alworthia* (*Asphodelaceae*)

	'Black Gem'	EBee EPfP EShb

Alyogyne (*Malvaceae*)

§	***huegelii***	CCCN EShb EUJe IDee SEle SPlb SRkn SRms WBod
	- 'Santa Cruz'	CCCN CHll CSam LHop
	Magic Moments = 'Hutwow' PBR	CSpe CWGN

Alyssoides (*Brassicaceae*)

	utriculata	GEdr

Alyssum (*Brassicaceae*)

	argenteum	ECho
	bornmuelleri	LLHF
	corningii	LLHF
	montanum	ECha ECho SPlb SRms
§	- 'Berggold'	EPfP MMuc XLum
	- Mountain Gold	see *A. montanum* 'Berggold'
	- 'Tekara' **new**	CMea
	oxycarpum	EPot
	saxatile	see *Aurinia saxatilis*
	- 'Summit'	SRms
	spinosum	ESps
	- 'Roseum' 𝕐H5	CMea CSpe CTri ECha ELan EPot ESps GCrg SIgm WAbe
*	- 'Roseum Variegatum' (v)	EPot
	- 'Rubrum' **new**	EPot
	'Takara Yellow' **new**	GWyn
	tortuosum	SEND
	'Variegatum' (v) **new**	CBod
	wulfenianum	EDAr GAbr GCrg IFoB WIce XLum

Amaranthus (*Amaranthaceae*)

'Autumn Palette'	CSpe
caudatus 'Viridis'	SPhx
hypochondriacus 'Pygmy Torch'	CSpe
'Red Army'	LCro
tricolor	SRms

× *Amarcrinum* (*Amaryllidaceae*)

'Dorothy Hannibal'	WCot
memoria-corsii	CPrp
- 'Howardii'	EPri EShb GKev LEdu NRog SDeJ

× *Amarine* (*Amaryllidaceae*)

'Belladiva' **new**	CBro LAma LRHS
'Fletcheri'	WCot
tubergenii	CAvo
- 'Zwanenburg'	LAma WCot

× *Amarygia* (*Amaryllidaceae*)

§ ***bidwillii*** 'Alba'	CAvo CBro CPrp NRog WCot
- 'Rosea'	NRog

Amaryllis (*Amaryllidaceae*)

§ ***belladonna*** ♀H3	CAby CBcs CBod CBro CPne CPrp CTca CTsd EBee ECho EPfP ERCP EShb GKev LAma MPie NRog SDeJ SEND SPer WCot WWFP
- 'Johannesburg'	WCot
- 'Kimberley'	CPne
- 'Parkeri Alba'	see × *Amarygia bidwillii* 'Alba'
- 'Purpurea'	WCot
- white-flowered	SDeJ

Ambrosina (*Araceae*)

bassii	WCot

Amelanchier ✿ (*Rosaceae*)

alnifolia	CTho EBtc ERea
- 'Forestburg'	MBlu NLar
- 'Obelisk' PBR	CAgr CDul CRos ELan EMOT EPfP GKin GQue LBuc LHop LLHF LRHS LSRN MAsh MCoo MGos MJak NLar NOra NPri SCoo SPer SPoG WCot WHar WMat WPat
- pink-fruited	NLar
§ - var. ***pumila***	LHop MMrt WCot
- 'Regent' (F)	NLar
- 'Smokey'	CDul MBlu NLar
§ ***arborea***	CTho
- Tradition = 'Trazam'	NLar
'Autumn Glory'	EPfP
bartramiana	SSta
- 'Eskimo'	NLar
canadensis K. Koch	see *A. lamarckii*
canadensis Sieb. & Zucc.	see *A. arborea*
canadensis ambig.	CAco CDul CFGn CTsd EMOT ESps GMcL IBoy NEgg NOra NPri SCob SEND SEWo SPoG WFar WHar WHed WMou
canadensis (L.) Medik.	CAgr CJun CLnd CMac CSBt CTho CTri CWib EBee ECrN ELan EPfP LEdu LRHS MGos MRav MSwo NWea SPer WMat WPat
§ - 'Glenn Form'	CEnd EMOT LRHS NOra SGol SLim SPoG WHar WMat
- 'Prince William'	CAgr MCoo
- Rainbow Pillar	see *A. canadensis* 'Glenn Form'
× ***grandiflora***	SCob
- 'Autumn Brilliance'	CEnd CJun EPfP MBlu NHol NLar SGol
- 'Ballerina'	Widely available
- 'Cole's Select'	LRHS SKHP SPoG SWvt
- 'Forest Prince'	NLar
- 'Princess Diana' ♀H6	NLar SCoo
- 'Robin Hill' ♀H6	Widely available
- 'Rubescens'	CEnd CJun EBee NLar SLon SWvt WPat
'La Paloma' ♀H6	EPfP LRHS LSRN MGos NOra NOrn SCoo SLim WHar WMat
laevis	CBcs CDul CTri EPfP NLar
- 'Prince Charles'	NLar
- 'R.J. Hilton' ♀H6	EPfP LRHS NLar NOra SCoo WHar WMat
- 'Snow Cloud'	EPfP
- 'Snowflakes'	CEnd CJun EMOT ESps EWTr LRHS LSRN MAsh NOra NOrn SEWo SLim SPer SPoG SWvt WHar WMat WMou
§ ***lamarckii*** ♀H6	Widely available
ovalis misapplied	see *A. spicata* (Lam.) K. Koch
ovalis Medik.	SPlb
- 'Edelweiss'	CJun IArd MRav NEgg NLar SCoo WPat
pumila	see *A. alnifolia* var. *pumila*
rotundifolia ambig.	CAgr CNWT MCoo NEgg
sanguinea 'Chimney Rock'	NLar
§ ***spicata*** (Lam.) K. Koch	CAgr MCoo
stolonifera	CTri

× *Amelasorbus* (*Rosaceae*)

raciborskiana	MBlu

Amicia (*Papilionaceae*)

zygomeris	CAbb CBcs CCse CDTJ CHGN CHll CSpe EUJe EWes GCal LHop MCot MGil MNHC SDix SEle SMad SPoG WCot WPGP
- 'John's Big Splash' (v)	WCot

Ammi (*Apiaceae*)

majus ♀H6	CBod CSpe CWld LCro LEdu LRHS MNHC SDix SPhx WCot WJek WSFF
visnaga	CBre CHby CLau CSpe CWld LRHS MNHC SPhx SRms WHal

Ammobium (*Asteraceae*)

calyceroides	GBin

Ammocharis (*Amaryllidaceae*)

coranica	WCot
longifolia	WCot

Ammophila (*Poaceae*)

arenaria	CKno IMou SMea XLum XSen
breviligulata	IMou XLum

Amomyrtus (*Myrtaceae*)

§ ***luma***	CBcs CDul CTri CTsd EBee ELan IDee MMuc SEND WJek WPGP

Amorpha (*Papilionaceae*)

canescens	EBee LRHS MNrw NRHS SPhx SPlb
fruticosa	CAco CBcs EBtc MBlu SEND SPlb
herbacea	NLar
nana	XLum
ouachitensis	SMad
paniculata	NLar

Amorphophallus ✿ (*Araceae*)

sp. SDir
albus CDTJ LEdu SPlb WCot
bulbifer CDTJ ESwi EUJe LAma LRHS LTro SBig SDeJ SDir SPlb XLum
dunnii CDTJ LEdu
henryi WCot
kerrii WCot
kiusianus B&SWJ 4845 WCru
§ **konjac** CDTJ CFil CSpe CTal EUJe GCal LEdu LRHS SChF SDeJ SDir SPlb WCot XLum
nepalensis WCot XLum
ongsakulii WCot
rivieri see *A. konjac*
stipitatus LEdu WCot
yuloensis WCot

Ampelaster (*Asteraceae*)

§ **carolinianus** XEll

Ampelocalamus (*Poaceae*)

§ **mocrophyllum** CJng ERod
scandens WPGP

Ampelocissus (*Vitaceae*)

sikkimensis HWJK 2066 WCru

Ampelodesmos (*Poaceae*)

mauritanicus CHid CKno CSam CSpe EBee ECha EHoe EShb EWes GBin MAvo SEND SMad SPlb WCot XSen

Ampelopsis (*Vitaceae*)

aconitifolia NLar WCru
- 'Chinese Lace' EBee EShb EUJe EWTr LRHS MRav NLar WBor
arborea WCru
brevipedunculata ELan LPre MMrt SCoo SKHP SLim SPer WHar
- 'Citrulloides' WCru
- 'Elegans' (v) CBcs CMac CWib EBee ELan EPfP EShb LHop LRHS MGos MRav NBro SNig SPer SPoG SWvt WCot WPat WSHC
delavayana EShb MMuc
glandulosa var. **hancei** B&SWJ 1793 WCru
henryana see *Parthenocissus henryana*
megalophylla CBot ELan EShb GCal NLar SKHP
sempervirens hort. ex Veitch see *Cissus striata*
tricuspidata 'Veitchii' see *Parthenocissus tricuspidata* 'Veitchii'

Amphicome see *Incarvillea*

Amsonia (*Apocynaceae*)

'Blue Ice' CAby CBWd CBod CMos EBee ECGP ECha ECtt EMFm GMaP IBoy IPot LEdu LPla LSun MHol MNrw NAst NDov NPnk SCob SPad WCot WRHF
ciliata ELan IKil LEdu NLar SHar SKHP XLum
§ **elliptica** EBee EPPr SPhx
'Ernst Pagels' LHop MAvo SMHy
fugatei EBee
hubrichtii CAby CBWd CCse CHid CLet CSpe EBee ECha EPPr IPot LEdu LHop LRHS LSun NDov SMHy SMad SPhx SWvt WPGP WPtf WSHC
illustris CAbP CSpe EPPr GCal LEdu LRHS NLar SHar SMHy SPhx WHil WHoo
jonesii EBee SBrt SMHy SPhx
§ **orientalis** CHll CMea CSpe CTri ECha EHrv IPot LEdu LHop LRHS MCot MRav NDov NLar SPhx SVen SWvt WBor WCot WFar WKif XEll XLum
- 'Cally Dark Stem' GCal
peeblesii EBee SPhx
rigida GEdr
sinensis see *A. elliptica*
tabernaemontana Widely available
- 'Montana' SPer SWvt
- var. **salicifolia** EBee IMou IPot LCro LEdu LPla LRHS NDov WCAu
- 'Stella Azul' IPot
tharpii EBee SPhx
tomentosa var. **stenophylla** EBee SPhx

Amygdalus see *Prunus*

Amyris (*Rutaceae*)

madrensis CFil

Anacamptis (*Orchidaceae*)

pyramidalis EFEx WHer

Anacyclus (*Asteraceae*)

pyrethrum GPoy
- var. **depressus** ♀H4 CTri ECho ELan EPfP MMuc NEgg SPlb SRot WCFE
- - 'Garden Gnome' CTri SRms
- - 'Silberkissen' CMea EDAr NSla

Anagallis (*Primulaceae*)

monellii Blue Compact = 'Wesanacomp' LSou
- subsp. **linifolia** 'Blue Light' CSpe
- 'Skylover' CCCN
tenella LLWG MWts
- 'Studland' MHer WAbe

Ananas (*Bromeliaceae*)

comosus (F) CCCN SPre
- 'Champaca' (F) CCCN SPre

Anaphalioides (*Asteraceae*)

§ **bellidioides** CTri SBrt

Anaphalis (*Asteraceae*)

alpicola CHVG EBee
margaritacea CBcs ECha ECtt GMaP GNew NBid NLar SRms WBod WFar WHar WMoo
§ - 'Neuschnee' CTri GJos ILea LPla NBre NLar XLum
- New Snow see *A. margaritacea* 'Neuschnee'
- var. **yedoensis** CTri NBre SDix SPer
§ **nepalensis** var. **monocephala** EBee MCot NBre NSti SRms
nubigena see *A. nepalensis* var. *monocephala*
transnokoensis EBee EWes
§ **trinervis** GCra LSun XLum
triplinervis ♀H7 CBod EHoe ELan ELon EPfP EWTr EWld EWoo GAbr GMaP IBoy IFoB ILea LRHS MMuc MRav NBid NLar

	NSti SBod SPer WBod WCAu WHoo WMoo
- CC 1620	EPPr NBir
§ - 'Sommerschnee' 𝕐H7	CMac EAJP ECha ECtt EHoe EPfP GMcL GWyn IBoy LPot LRHS MCot MHol MRav NEgg NLar NWad SPer WGwG WWtn
- Summer Snow	see *A. triplinervis* 'Sommerschnee'

Anchusa (*Boraginaceae*)

sp.	CHab
§ ***azurea***	NLar
- 'Dropmore'	CTri EBee EPfP GPSL LCro LRHS MRav NEgg NLar SCob SRms WHar WRHF
- 'Feltham Pride'	CDor EBee ELan EPfP SRms SWvt WHoo
- 'Little John'	SRms
- 'Loddon Royalist'	Widely available
- 'Opal'	CWCL ECtt LRHS
capensis 'Blue Angel'	CWCL MNHC SWvt
cespitosa	ECho ELan EWes LLHF WAbe
italica	see *A. azurea*
laxiflora	see *Borago pygmaea*
myosotidiflora	see *Brunnera macrophylla*
officinalis	MNHC SRms
sempervirens	see *Pentaglottis sempervirens*

Ancylostemon (*Gesneriaceae*)

convexus B&SWJ 6624	WCot WCru
- B&SWJ 7182	WCru

Andrachne (*Phyllanthaceae*)

colchica	EWTr WCot

Andromeda (*Ericaceae*)

polifolia	LPar
- 'Alba'	ELan LRHS MAsh SPer SPlb SWvt WFar WThu
- 'Blue Ice'	ELan GBin IDee LPar LRHS LSRN MAsh NHar NLar SPer SPoG WFar
- 'Blue Lagoon'	NLar
- 'Compacta' 𝕐H5	CMac GEdr LRHS LSRN MAsh MGil NLar NWad SWvt WFar WGwG
- 'Grandiflora'	ELan GKev
- 'Kirigamine'	LRHS MAsh NHar
- 'Macrophylla' 𝕐H5	GEdr ITim NHar WThu
- 'Nana'	EPfP
- 'Nikko'	CMac NLar
- 'Shibutsu'	NHar

Andropogon (*Poaceae*)

gerardii	CKno EBee EHoe EPPr LRHS NRHS NWsh XLum
- 'Prairie Sommer' new	NDov
scoparius	see *Schizachyrium scoparium*
ternarius	GCal

Androsace (*Primulaceae*)

alpina	WAbe
amurensis	GKev
* ***bayanharshanensis***	WAbe
bisulca var. ***aurata***	CPBP
brachystegia	EPot
bulleyana	GKev WAbe
carnea	ECho GKev IFoB
- subsp. ***brigantiaca***	GCrg GKev NHpl NSla WAbe WHoo
- var. ***halleri***	see *A. carnea* subsp. *rosea*
- subsp. ***laggeri*** 𝕐H5	ECho GCrg LLHF NSla WAbe
- - 'Andorra'	NHar
§ - subsp. ***rosea*** 𝕐H5	ECho GCrg GKev IFoB ITim NHar NHpl
carnea × ***pyrenaica***	CPBP ECho EPot GKev LLHF
chaixii	IFoB
chamaejasme	ECho
- subsp. ***carinata***	LLHF
ciliata	WAbe
cylindrica	CRos ECho EPot GKev ITim LRHS NRHS
cylindrica × ***hirtella***	CRos ECho EPot LRHS NRHS
delavayi	SPlb WAbe
- ACE 1786	WAbe
elatior	WAbe
flavescens	CPBP
geraniifolia	ECha GKev SRms
globifera	WAbe
halleri	see *A. carnea* subsp. *rosea*
hausmannii × ***hirtella***	LLHF
hedraeantha	GCrg GKev NSla WAbe
himalaica	CPBP EPot GEdr WAbe
hirtella	IFoB ITim LLHF WAbe
idahoensis	WAbe
idahoensis × ***laevigata***	WAbe
incana	GKev
jacquemontii	see *A. villosa* var. *jacquemontii*
lactea	WAbe
laevigata	ITim WAbe
- var. ***laevigata*** new	GKev
lanuginosa 𝕐H5	CBod CMea CPBP CSpe CTal ECho ECtt EDAr EHoe EPfP EPot GBin GEdr MMuc NHol NHpl SBch SRms SRot WAbe WIce WOld WTor
lehmanniana	WAbe
- 'Gotëborg Yellow'	WAbe
limprichtii	see *A. sarmentosa* var. *watkinsii*
mariae	GKev LLHF WAbe
× ***marpensis***	EPot SIgm WAbe
mathildae	LLHF
microphylla	see *A. mucronifolia* G.Watt
'Millstream'	IFoB
minor	WAbe
§ ***mollis***	CPBP
montana	WAbe
mucronifolia misapplied	see *A. sempervivoides*
§ ***mucronifolia*** G.Watt	EPot WAbe
mucronifolia G.Watt × ***sempervivoides***	CPBP CTal SIgm WAbe
muscoidea	WAbe
- 'Breviscapa'	EPot
- 'Dolpo Lilac'	WAbe
- Schacht's form	EPot WAbe
nivalis	SPlb
- Chumstick form	LLHF
ochotensis	WAbe
× ***pedemontana***	LLHF
primuloides	see *A. studiosorum*
pubescens	CRos ECho EPot ITim LLHF LRHS NRHS
pyrenaica	CRos ECho EPot ITim LLHF LRHS NRHS WAbe
rigida	EPot LLHF WAbe
robusta	EPot
- subsp. ***purpurea***	GKev WAbe
- - 'Dolpo Dwarf'	WAbe
rotundifolia	GEdr
sarmentosa misapplied	see *A. studiosorum*
sarmentosa ambig.	NHpl SPlb XLum
sarmentosa Wall.	GKev SRms WHoo
- CC 5557	GKev
- from Namche, Nepal	WAbe

	- Galmont's form	see *A. studiosorum* 'Salmon's Variety'
	- 'Sherriffii'	ECho EPot SIgm SRms WIce
§	- var. ***watkinsii***	CTal EPot GKev
	- var. ***yunnanensis*** misapplied	see *A. studiosorum*
	- var. ***yunnanensis*** Knuth	see *A. mollis*
	selago	WAbe
	- 'Red Eye'	WAbe
§	***sempervivoides*** ♀H5	CRos ECho EDAr EPot GBin GCrg GKev GMaP LHop LRHS NHar NHol NRHS NSla SBch SIgm SPlb SRms WIce WOld
	- 'Susan Joan'	EPot GEdr GKev WAbe WOld
	septentrionalis 'Stardust'	MHol
	spinulifera	GKev LLHF
	stenophylla	MAsh
	strigillosa	GKev NHpl WAbe
	- CC 7533 **new**	GKev
§	***studiosorum*** ♀H5	EPot GAbr GCrg GEdr GKev IFoB WAbe
	- 'Chumbyi'	EPot GEdr LLHF NHpl SIgm SRms WIce WThu
	- 'Doksa'	CPBP CTal EPot GEdr IFoB SIgm WAbe WIce
§	- 'Salmon's Variety'	CMea CTri SBch SIgm WAbe
	tangulashanensis	LLHF
	tapete	WAbe
	- ACE 1725	WAbe
	vandellii	ITim WAbe
	villosa	EPot IFoB WAbe
§	- var. ***jacquemontii***	CTal NHar
	- - lilac-flowered	EPot WAbe
	- - pink-flowered	EPot SIgm WAbe
	vitaliana	see *Vitaliana primuliflora*
	wardii	WAbe
	watkinsii	see *A. sarmentosa* var. *watkinsii*
	yargongensis	LLHF WAbe
	zambalensis	WAbe
	- pink-flowered	GKev

Andryala (*Asteraceae*)

agardhii	GKev
glandulosa **new**	WCot
lanata	see *Hieracium lanatum*

Anemanthele (*Poaceae*)

§	***lessoniana*** ♀H4	Widely available
	- 'Autumn Tints'	EHoe
	- 'Gold Hue'	EHoe
	- 'Sirocco'	CBod WCot WFar

Anemarrhena (*Asparagaceae*)

asphodeloides	WCot

Anemia (*Schizaeaceae*)

mexicana	ISha
tomentosa	ISha LRHS

Anemone ✿ (*Ranunculaceae*)

	Chen Yi T49	WCot
	aconitifolia Michx.	see *A. narcissiflora*
	altaica	NLar SRms
	apennina ♀H4	CAvo ECGP ECho GEdr WShi
	- var. ***albiflora***	ECho EPPr EPot GKev MAvo
	- double-flowered (d)	ECho EPPr LLHF MAvo WCru
	- 'Petrovac'	ECho EPot GKev LEdu LLHF
	baicalensis	WSHC
	baldensis	ECho GBuc GEdr ITim SRms
	barbulata	EAJP EBee EWes GBuc GEdr GKev GPSL
	blanda ♀H4	CAby CRos ECho ESps LAma LRHS MArt NChi NLar NRHS SCob SEND WBor WFar WHar WShi
I	- 'Alba'	CRos LRHS NRHS WBod
	- blue-flowered	CAvo CBro CHVG CMea CRos CTri ECho ELan EPfP EPot ERCP GAbr GKev GMaP LCro LOPS LRHS NPnk NRHS SCob SDeJ SDir SPer SPhx SPoG SRms WCot WHoo
	- 'Charmer'	CGrW EPot GKev NHpl SDeJ SDir
	- 'Ingramii'	EPot GKev WCot
	- var. ***rosea***	CRos ECho ELan GKev LAma LRHS NRHS SDeJ SPoG
	- - 'Pink Star'	CAvo ERCP GKev LAma NBir WRHF
	- - 'Radar' ♀H4	CAvo ECho EPot ERCP GKev LAma MNrw NBir NHpl SDeJ
	- 'Violet Star'	GKev SDeJ
	- 'White Splendour' ♀H4	CAby CAvo CBro CHVG CMea CTri ECho ELan EPfP EPot ERCP GAbr GKev LAma LCro LOPS LRHS LSun NBir SDeJ SDir SPhx SPoG SRms WCot WWFP
	- white-flowered	LRHS
	'Bowles's Mauve'	GEdr MAsh
	caerulea	LEdu
	canadensis	ECGP ELon EPPr GBuc GEdr LEdu NWad WCot
	caroliniana	ECho GKev
	caucasica	LEdu
	chapaensis HWJ 631	WCru
	'Cinderella'PBR (Fantasy Series)	EBee LRHS NRHS SPoG
	coronaria	SCob SVic
	- var. ***coronaria*** **new**	IBoy
	- De Caen Group	CHid CRos EPfP GKev LAma LOPS LRHS NPnk NRHS SCob SDir SPoG WBod WBor
	- - 'Bicolor'	CHid GKev LAma SDeJ WRHF
	- - blue-flowered	LRHS NRHS
	- - 'Bordeaux'	EPfP LCro LOPS SCob
§	- - 'Die Braut'	CMea ERCP GBin GKev LAma LCro NBir SDeJ
	- - 'His Excellency'	see *A. coronaria* (De Caen Group) 'Hollandia'
§	- - 'Hollandia'	GKev IBoy LAma LPot SDeJ
	- - 'Mister Fokker'	CTca ERCP GKev LAma LCro LPot SDeJ WRHF
	- - pink-flowered	LRHS NRHS
	- - red-flowered	LRHS NRHS
	- - The Bride	see *A. coronaria* (De Caen Group) 'Die Braut'
	- - 'The Governor'	CMea GKev SDeJ
	- (Harmony Series) 'Harmony Orchid'	CRos LRHS NRHS
	- - 'Harmony Pearl'	CRos LRHS NRHS
	- - 'Harmony Scarlet'	CRos LRHS NRHS
	- 'Mistral Blue' **new**	NPnk
	- Saint Bridgid Group (d)	CRos EPfP GKev LAma LRHS NRHS SDir
	- - 'Lord Lieutenant' (d)	CMea EPfP ERCP GKev NBir SDeJ
	- - 'Mount Everest' (d)	ERCP GKev NBir SDeJ
	- - 'Saint Bridgid' (d)	CHid
	- - 'The Admiral' (d)	EPfP GKev NBir SDeJ
	- 'Sylphide' (Mona Lisa Series)	ERCP GBin GKev LAma LCro LPot NBir SDeJ
	crinita	NLar
	cylindrica	GEdr MHer NLar XEll
	'Danish White'	MNrw
	decapetala	GBuc LLHF MHer

	deltoidea	GBuc
	demissa	GKev LLHF WCot
	- var. ***major***	EBee
	'Dreaming Swan'	GBin IPot SHar
	drummondii	GBuc GKev
	fasciculata	see *A. narcissiflora*
	filisecta new	EBee MHol SDix WCot
	flaccida	CAby CBro CRos ECho EPPr GEdr LEdu LPla LRHS MAvo MNrw NRHS WCru WHal WSHC
	- 'Ginpai' (d) new	GEdr
	globosa	see *A. multifida* Poir.
	'Guernica'	ECho EWes
	'Hatakeyama Double' (d)	GCal LPla WSHC
	'Hatakeyama Single'	LPla
	hepatica L.	see *Hepatica nobilis*
§	***hortensis***	EBee
§	***hupehensis***	CBod EBee GMaP LSun
	- BWJ 8190	WCru
	- NJM 11.068	WPGP
	- f. ***alba***	CLAP CSpe IFro WPGP
§	- 'Bowles's Pink' 🏆H7	CDor CElw
	- 'Crispa'	see *A.* × *hybrida* 'Lady Gilmour' Wolley-Dod
	- 'Eugenie'	ECtt EPfP GBuc LRHS NBir
	- 'Hadspen Abundance' 🏆H7	Widely available
	- var. ***hupehensis***	WFar
§	- var. ***japonica***	CPou EPed SRms XLum
	- - B&SWJ 4886	WCru
	- - PAB 8884	LEdu
	- - 'Bodnant Burgundy'	LRHS SWvt WBod WBrk
§	- - 'Bressingham Glow'	CMHG CMac ECtt ELan EPfP EPot EShb GKin ILea LRHS LSou NBir NEgg SPer WBrk WCAu WFar WHil
§	- - 'Pamina' 🏆H7	Widely available
	- - 'Pink Saucer'	EBee GMcL
	- - Prince Henry	see *A. hupehensis* var. *japonica* 'Prinz Heinrich'
§	- - 'Prinz Heinrich'	Widely available
§	- - 'Rotkäppchen'	CDor CHVG ECtt GBin GKin GQue IBoy LRHS LSou LSun MHol MSCN NHol NLar NSti SPad SWvt WCot WSHC
	- - 'Splendens'	CMHG CRos EPfP LCro LHop LRHS MCot NAst NGdn NLar NRHS SCob SPer SPoG SRms SWvt WHal XLum
	- 'Little Princess' PBR	ECtt MNrw
	- 'Ouvertüre'	ECtt GBuc GQue
	- 'Praecox'	CMea CNec EPfP LRHS LSou MBNS NBir NSti SHil SWvt WCAu
	- 'September Charm'	see *A.* × *hybrida* 'September Charm'
§	× ***hybrida***	ECho ESps NChi NEgg WHar WMoo
	- 'Alba' misapplied (UK)	see *A.* × *hybrida* 'Honorine Jobert'
	- 'Alba Dura'	see *A. tomentosa* 'Albadura'
	- 'Albert Schweitzer'	see *A.* × *hybrida* 'Elegans'
	- 'Andrea Atkinson'	Widely available
	- 'Bowles's Pink'	see *A. hupehensis* 'Bowles's Pink'
	- 'Bressingham Glow'	see *A. hupehensis* var. *japonica* 'Bressingham Glow'
	- 'Coupe d'Argent'	EBee IKil WCot
§	- 'Elegans' 🏆H7	CSam ECtt GMaP GMcL LCro LHop LOPS LRHS MMuc NBir SEND SWat SWvt WFar
	- 'Frau Marie Maushardt' new	WBrk
§	- 'Géante des Blanches'	LPla
§	- 'Honorine Jobert' 🏆H7	Widely available
	- 'Josephine'	WFar
§	- 'Königin Charlotte' 🏆H7	Widely available
	- 'Lady Gilmour' misapplied	see *A.* × *hybrida* 'Montrose'
	- 'Lady Gilmour' ambig.	GMaP GMcL GWyn MBel WBod XLum
§	- 'Lady Gilmour' Wolley-Dod	CSam CSpe ECtt EPfP GCra LEdu LRHS MRav NBir NChi WCot XLum
	- 'Loreley'	EPfP IKil NLar SCob SHil SWvt WCot
	- 'Luise Uhink'	CPou
	- 'Märchenfee'	MNrw
	- 'Margarete' Kayser & Seibert	CPar ECtt ELan EPfP LRHS NDov NGdn WCot
	- 'Max Vogel'	see *A.* × *hybrida* 'Elegans'
	- 'Monterosa'	see *A.* × *hybrida* 'Montrose'
§	- 'Montrose'	CBod CPou EBee ECha EHrv EWes GCal GMaP LCro LOPS LRHS LSou NBir NLar SHil SRms SWat
	- 'Nightingale' (Fantasy Series)	EBee
	- 'Pamina'	see *A. hupehensis* var. *japonica* 'Pamina'
	- (Pretty Lady Series) 'Pretty Lady Diana' PBR	ECtt LBuc LCro LRHS NPri SCob SLon SPoG SWvt WHil
	- - 'Pretty Lady Emily' PBR	EPfP LBuc LRHS NPri SCob SLon SPoG SWvt WHil
	- - 'Pretty Lady Julia' PBR	LBuc NPri SCob SHar SLon WHil
	- - 'Pretty Lady Maria'	EBee LRHS SPoG
	- - 'Pretty Lady Susan'	CWGN EBee LBuc LRHS NPri SCob SHar SLon SPoG SWvt WHil
	- Prince Henry	see *A. hupehensis* var. *japonica* 'Prinz Heinrich'
	- 'Profusion'	CTri EBee LBuc LRHS WHal
	- Queen Charlotte	see *A.* × *hybrida* 'Königin Charlotte'
	- 'Richard Ahrens'	CBod ECtt EPed EPfP EShb EWoo GBuc GCal GMaP LHop LRHS LSRN MGos MSCN NEgg NGdn NLar SDix SHil SWat SWvt WGwG WHar
§	- 'Robustissima'	CBod EBee EPfP GMaP ILea LLWP LRHS LSRN MCot MNrw NBir NEgg NGdn NLar NSti SEND SPer SWat SWvt WMoo
	- 'Rosenschale'	LRHS MNrw
	- 'Rotkäppchen'	see *A. hupehensis* var. *japonica* 'Rotkäppchen'
§	- 'September Charm' 🏆H7	Widely available
	- 'Serenade'	CSam ECtt EPfP ESps GMcL LHop LRHS LSRN MRav MTis NBir NLar SHil SPoG WCAu WMoo XLum
	- Tourbillon	see *A.* × *hybrida* 'Whirlwind'
§	- 'Whirlwind'	Widely available
	- 'White Queen'	see *A.* × *hybrida* 'Géante des Blanches'
	- Wirbelwind	see *A.* × *hybrida* 'Whirlwind'
	japonica	see *A. hupehensis*, *A. hupehensis* var. *japonica*, *A.* × *hybrida*
	- 'Crustata'	CMac
	keiskeana	GEdr WCru
§	× ***lesseri***	CBro CSpe ECha ECho ELan GKev LHop NDov SPhx SRms
	leveillei	CAby CLAP CSpe CWCL EHrv EPPr EWTr GBin GBuc GEdr GKev IPot LCro LOPS LRHS LSou MSCN NBir NGdn NLar NPnk NQui NSti SPhx SWvt WCru WKif XEll
	- BWJ 7919	WCru
§	× ***lipsiensis***	CAby CBro EBee ECho EPPr EPfP EPot GAbr GMaP IFro LEdu MAvo MBel MNrw NHpl NLar NPnk SBch WCru WFar WHal WPGP WSHC
	- 'Pallida' 🏆H5	CSam CSpe ECho ELon GBuc GEdr GKev LEdu LLWP MAvo NHar NLar SKHP WCot WShi XEll
	- 'Schwefelfeuer'	LEdu MAvo

	- 'Vindobonensis'	GEdr GKev MAvo WCot
	magellanica hort. ex Wehrh.	see *A. multifida* Poir.
	matsudae B&SWJ 1452	WCru
	multifida misapplied, red-flowered	see *A.* × *lesseri*
§	***multifida*** Poir.	ECha ECho EPfP GJos ILea LHop LRHS NBir NRHS NSti SPer SRms WFar WHoo
	- SDR 8101 **new**	GKev
	- Annabella Series	GKev
	- - 'Annabella Deep Rose'	GAbr
	- - 'Annabella White'	GJos
	- var. ***globosa***	GKev
	- 'Major'	CMea CSpe EPfP GPSL SPhx WIce
	- 'Rubra'	EPfP GBin GEdr GKev GPSL GWyn ILea LPot LRHS LSou MPie NBir NEgg NLar NPnk SBod WBor WHar WHil WHoo
	- white-flowered	NPnk
	- yellow-flowered	CBro GEdr
§	***narcissiflora***	CSpe GKev NBir NChi WPtf
	nemorosa 🏆H5	Widely available
	- 'Alba'	LRHS WFar
	- 'Alba Plena' (d)	CSam EAJP ECha ECho EPPr EPfP GBuc GKev MAvo NGdn NLar NPnk WFar WSHC
	- 'Allenii' 🏆H5	CBro CElw ECho ELon EPPr EPot GBuc GEdr GKev GMaP ITim LRHS MAvo MRav NRya WShi
	- 'Amy Doncaster'	ECho
	- 'Apuseni'	LEdu
	- 'Atley'	EBee GEdr GKev MAvo
	- 'Atrocaerulea'	GBuc IBlr NLar NPnk
	- 'Ballyrogan Blue'	MAvo MNrw
	- 'Behemoth Blue'	LEdu MAvo
	- 'Bill Baker's Pink'	CLAP LEdu
	- 'Blue Beauty'	CLAP EBee ELon GBuc GMaP IBlr MAvo SBch
	- 'Blue Bonnet'	CAby ECho GBuc ITim LEdu MAvo
	- 'Blue Eyes' (d)	CElw CLAP EBee GAbr GBuc GEdr GKev GMaP IBlr ITim LEdu MAvo NBir NHpl NPnk WSHC
	- 'Blush'	LEdu
	- 'Bohemia'	MAvo
	- 'Bowles's Purple'	CSam EBee ECho ELon EPot GBuc GEdr GMaP IBlr LRHS MHol NBid NHar NHpl NPnk NRya SKHP WBor WCot WFar
	- 'Bracteata'	CBro CTca ECho EWld GBuc GEdr GKev MMrt
	- 'Bracteata Pleniflora' (d)	CLAP ECho ELon EPot GBuc GKev GMaP IBlr LEdu LHop MAvo MNrw NBir NPnk SBch WCot WHal WShi XEll
	- 'Buckland'	CLAP EBee EPfP EPot IBlr MAvo SKHP
	- 'Caerulea'	EPot GKev ITim
	- 'Cedric's Pink'	CLAP EPPr IBlr LLHF MAvo WFar
	- 'Celestial'	ECho ELan EPPr GBuc MAvo
	- 'Dee Day'	CElw CLAP EBee GBuc LEdu MAvo NHar
	- 'Dell Garden'	EPPr
	- 'Flore Pleno' (d)	ECho GAbr IFro NBir WBor WFar
	- 'Flushing'	EBee GEdr GKev
	- 'Frühlingsfee'	GKev MAvo
	- 'Frühlingsfest'	EBee
	- 'Gerda Ramusen'	CLAP ECho ELan ELon EWes GBuc LEdu LLHF
	- 'Gerry' **new**	MAvo
I	- 'Gigantea Rubra'	MAvo WCot

	- 'Good Blue'	MAvo
	- 'Green Dream'	WSHC
	- 'Green Fingers'	ECho EPPr GBuc GEdr GKev GMaP ITim MMrt WSHC
	- 'Hakumane Senjuizaki'	WCot
	- 'Hannah Gubbay'	CLAP IBlr
	- 'Helsinki' **new**	MAvo
	- 'Hilda'	CBct EBee ECho ECtt GBuc GEdr GKev LEdu MNrw NBir NHar NLar NPnk NRya
	- 'Ice and Fire'	GKev LEdu
	- 'Jack Brownless'	LEdu
	- 'Kentish Pink'	GBin GMaP NPnk
	- 'Knightshayes Vestal' (d)	CLAP MRav WSHC
	- 'Lady Doneraile'	CLAP EPot GBuc LEdu NBir WFar
	- 'Latvian Pink'	EPot GEdr GKev LEdu MAvo
	- 'Leeds' Variety'	CLAP EPot GBuc GKev GMaP ITim LEdu MNrw NPnk
	- 'Lehna' (d) **new**	MAvo
	- 'Lionel Bacon'	LEdu MAvo
	- 'Lismore Blue'	ECho EPPr EPot GKev
	- 'Lismore Pink'	GEdr LEdu
	- 'Lucia'	EPot GEdr GKev LEdu MAvo
	- 'Lychette'	ECho EPPr GAbr GBuc GEdr GKev IBlr ITim MAvo MNrw NPnk
	- 'March Blue'	EPfP
	- 'Marie Rose'	EPot
	- 'Mart's Blue'	EBee EPfP GBuc GKev MAvo WCot WFar
	- 'Monstrosa'	ECho EPot GBuc GKev MAvo NPnk
	- 'New Pink'	IBlr
	- 'Noémie'	XEll
	- 'Parlez Vous'	EPPr GEdr LEdu MAvo MNrw NHpl WPnP XEll
	- 'Pat's Pink'	WShi
	- 'Pentre Pink'	EPot IBlr MAvo
	- 'Picos Pink'	GBuc
	- 'Pink Carpet'	GEdr LEdu
	- 'Pink Delight' **new**	LEdu
	- pink-flowered	ECho MMuc
	- 'Ploeger's Plena' (d)	EBee
	- 'Robinsoniana' 🏆H6	Widely available
	- 'Rosea'	CLAP ECho LEdu NLar NPnk
	- 'Royal Blue'	CAby CBct CBro CLAP CSpe CTca EBee ECho ELon EPPr EPot ERCP GAbr GEdr GKev GMaP LAma LEdu MAvo NDov NHpl NLar NPnk WCot WFar WPnP
	- 'Salt and Pepper'	LEdu MAvo
	- 'Slack Top Pink'	MAvo
§	- 'Stammerberg' (d)	CLAP EPPr MAvo
	- 'Stammheim'	see *A. nemorosa* 'Stammerberg'
	- 'Super Allenii'	GBuc MAvo
	- 'Tilo'	MAvo
	- 'Tinney's Blush'	CLAP
	- 'Tomas'	EBee ECho ELon EPot GBuc GEdr LEdu MAvo NHar NHpl NPnk NRya
	- 'Tups' **new**	LEdu
	- 'Vestal' (d) 🏆H5	Widely available
	- 'Virescens' 🏆H5	CBct CLAP CWCL ECho ELon EPPr EPot GBuc GEdr GKev GMaP LEdu MAvo NBir NHar NLar NPnk SDir WShi
	- 'Viridiflora'	CLAP ECho EPfP GBin GBuc LHop MAvo MNrw NBir WSHC
	- 'Westwell Pink'	CLAP EPPr LLHF MNrw WBor WCot WShi
	- white-flowered	LRHS
	- 'Wilks' Giant'	MAvo
	- 'Wilks' White'	ELon EPPr GEdr MAvo NPnk

	– 'Wisley Pink'	EPot LEdu MAvo
I	– 'Wisley White Form'	MAvo
	– 'Wyatt's Pink'	CLAP ELon EPot GKev LEdu MAvo
	– 'Yerda Ramusem'	ECho EPPr GBuc LEdu MAvo WSHC
	nemorosa* × *ranunculoides	see *A.* × *lipsiensis*
	obtusiloba	GBuc GEdr LLHF SRms WAbe WHal
	– CLD 1549	GEdr
	– 'Alba'	GEdr WAbe
	– 'Large Blue'	GEdr LEdu WAbe
	– 'Pradesh'	GEdr
I	– 'Sulphurea'	GEdr WAbe
	palmata	EWes GEdr GPSL IBoy LEdu NPnk NSum SMad WCot WKif WTor
	parviflora	GKev LLHF XEll
	patens	see *Pulsatilla patens*
	pavonina	CAby CMea CSpe ECha IBoy LPla LRHS MHol NBir SLon SPoG WCot
	– lilac-flowered	NBir
	– pink-flowered	NBir
	'Pocohontas' PBR (Fantasy Series)	EBee ECtt GBin LRHS MNrw NRHS SPoG
	polyanthes	EBee GEdr LRHS
	prattii	EPPr GEdr LEdu
	pseudoaltaica	GEdr LEdu WCru
	– blue-flowered	GEdr
	– pink-flowered **new**	GEdr
	– 'Yuki-no-sei' (d)	GEdr
	pulsatilla	see *Pulsatilla vulgaris*
	raddeana	ECho GKev
*	– f. ***rosea***	GEdr
	ranunculoides ♀H5	Widely available
	– 'Bill Baker'	LEdu MAvo
	– 'Crazy Vienna' **new**	WCot
	– 'Ferguson's Fancy' **new**	GCal
	– 'Frank Waley'	WCot
	– 'Fuchsis Traum'	WCot
*	– ***laciniata***	CLAP GBuc MAvo WCot WFar
	– 'Pleniflora' (d) ♀H5	CLAP ECha ECho EPPr GBuc GKev LRHS MAvo NLar NPnk WFar
	– subsp. ***ranunculoides***	ECho GKev
	– 'Semi-Plena'	ECho GEdr GKev LEdu
	– subsp. ***wockeana***	CSam EBee ECho GBuc LEdu MAvo
	reflexa	EBee GKev LLHF
	rivularis	CAvo CLAP CMea CPar CSpe CTsd EWTr EWoo GBin GBuc GEdr GKev GPoy IPot LHop LRHS MNrw NBir NLar NPnk NWad SBrt SChF SRms WCru WFar WHoo WKif WMoo XEll
	– B&SWJ 13944 **new**	WCru
	– BWJ 7611	WCru
	– PAB 2477	LEdu
	– SDR 4229	GKev
	– 'Glacier'	EBee MAsh NSti WHil
	'Ruffled Swan'	GBin SHar
	rupicola	GKev LLHF NBir
	× ***seemannii***	see *A.* × *lipsiensis*
	stellata Lam.	see *A. hortensis*
	stolonifera double-flowered (d)	GEdr LPla WCot WSHC
	sulphurea misapplied	see *Pulsatilla alpina* subsp. *apiifolia*
	sumatrana B&SWJ 11265	WCru
	sylvestris	Widely available
	– 'Elise Fellmann' (d)	CSpe GBuc WHal
	– 'Macrantha'	EPfP
	tetrasepala	WCot XEll
§	***tomentosa***	LRHS SDix SRms SWat
§	– 'Albadura'	EBee GBin
	– 'Robustissima'	see *A.* × *hybrida* 'Robustissima'
	trifolia L.	EBee EPPr GBuc LEdu NBid NLar SRms WCot
	trullifolia	GBin GBuc GCal GCra LLHF WAbe
	– var. ***linearis***	WAbe
	udensis	GEdr
	vernalis	see *Pulsatilla vernalis*
	vesicatoria **new**	SBrt
	virginiana	EBee LEdu MNrw NBid NWad WCot WHrl
	vitifolia misapplied	see *A. tomentosa*
	vitifolia DC.	GKev
	– WJC 12743 **new**	WCru
	Wild Swan = 'Macane001' PBR	Widely available

Anemonella (*Ranunculaceae*)

thalictroides	CElw CLAP ECho EFEx ELon EPot GAbr GBuc GEdr GKev ITim LAma MAvo NHar NHpl NLar NPnk NRya WAbe WFar WPnP WSHC XLum
– 'Alba Plena' (d)	ECho GBuc NPnk
– 'Amelia'	CLAP EPPr GBuc GEdr NHpl NPnk
– 'Babe'	WCot
– 'Betty Blake' (d)	ECho GBin GEdr LAma LLHF MAvo MMrt NHpl NPnk NRya WCot
– 'Cameo'	ECho EFEx EPPr GEdr LAma MAvo NHar NHpl NPnk NRya SDir WCot
– 'Charlotte'	GEdr NPnk
– 'Dark Pink'	EBee MAvo
– 'Diamante'	CElw WCot
– 'Double Diamante' (d) **new**	WCot
– 'Double Green' (d)	EFEx
– 'Flore Pleno' (d)	GBuc NPnk
– 'Full Double White' (d)	ECho EFEx NHpl
– 'Green Hurricane' (d)	ECho EFEx GEdr LAma NPnk SDir WCot
– 'Hakikomi-fu' (v) **new**	GEdr
– 'Kikuzaki Pink' (d) **new**	LAma
– 'Kikuzaki White' (d) **new**	LAma
– f. ***rosea***	CAby CElw ECho ELan GBuc GKev LLHF NLar WAbe
– – 'Oscar Schoaf' (d)	ECho GBuc GEdr NHpl NPnk WAbe WCot
– – semi-double pink-flowered (d)	CElw MAvo
– 'Rosea Plena' (d)	LAma
– semi-double white-flowered (d)	CElw EPPr WAbe
– 'Snowflakes' (d)	MAvo
– 'Spring Nymph'	SMHy
– 'Tairin'	GEdr LAma

Anemonopsis (*Ranunculaceae*)

macrophylla	CAby CPBP CSpe CTal ECho EPfP EWes GCal GEdr GKev LEdu MNrw MRav NHpl NLar SBch SMad SPhx WCru WFar WOld WPGP WSHC
– 'Alba'	GKev
– double-flowered	GKev WSHC
– 'White Swan'	CTal GEdr WCru WSHC

Anemopsis (*Saururaceae*)

californica	EBee EWay GEdr IFoB LLWG MSKA MWts SBrt WCot WPGP

Anethum (*Apiaceae*)

graveolens	ENfk GPoy MHer MNHC NPri SIde SRms SVic
– 'Dukat'	CLau

angelica see *Angelica archangelica*

Angelica (*Apiaceae*)

acutiloba var. ***iwatensis*** B&SWJ 11197	WCru
anomala B&SWJ 10886	WCru
archangelica	Widely available
atropurpurea	CBod CRos ECtt EPfP GMaP GQue LRHS MHer MNrw MRav NRHS SWat SWvt
cartilaginomarginata B&SWJ 12663	WCru
cyclocarpa WJC 13658 **new**	WCru
dahurica	CBot EWTr NDov WOut
- B&SWJ 8603	WCru
decursiva B&SWJ 5746	WCru
edulis	SPhx WHer WPGP
- B&SWJ 10968	LEdu WCru
gigas	Widely available
- B&SWJ 4170	WCru
- 'Atropurpurea' **new**	CSpe
hendersoni	LEdu
hispanica	see *A. pachycarpa*
japonica B&SWJ 11480	WCru
keiskei	LEdu
montana	see *A. sylvestris*
morii RWJ 9802	WCru
§ ***pachycarpa***	CBod CSpe EBee ELan EPri GBin GMaP LHop LRHS MAvo MHer MRav MSpe NBir NGBl NLar SHil WJek
pubescens	NDov
- B&SWJ 5593	WCru
- B&SWJ 11129	WCru
- var. ***matsumurae*** B&SWJ 6387	WCru
sachalinensis	EBee
sinensis	GPoy LEdu
'Summer Delight'	see *Ligusticum scoticum*
§ ***sylvestris***	CArn CHab LLWG WOut
- PAB 8136	LEdu
- 'Burgundy' **new**	CSpe
- 'Ebony'	CBct CBod CBre CSpe CWld EBee ECtt LEdu LHop LLWG LRHS MHer MHol MNHC MTis NCGa SCob SDix SMDP SMad SPad SPoG WCot WFar WPGP
* - 'Purpurea'	CDor EWes GQue NGBl
- 'Vicar's Mead'	CBot EBee LEdu LRHS NBir NChi NLar NSti SPad SPer SPhx SWvt
taiwaniana	CBre CDTJ CSam EBee ELan ESwi IMou LRHS MBel MMuc NLar
ursina	IMou WCru

Angelonia (*Plantaginaceae*)

Angelface Wedgwood Blue = 'Anwedg'^{PBR} (Angelface Series)	NPri
Archangel Deep Rose	CRos LRHS NRHS SPoG
Archangel Purple = 'Balarcpur'^{PBR} **new**	SPoG

Anigozanthos (*Haemodoraceae*)

'Bush Ranger' (Bush Gems Series)	CCCN
flavidus	SPlb
- 'Ember'	CCCN
- 'Illusion'	CCCN
- 'Opal'	CCCN
- 'Pearl'	CCCN
- red-flowered	SPlb
- 'Splendour'	CCCN
- 'Yellow Gem'	CCCN
manglesii ♀H1c	SPlb SVen
rufus	SEle

Anisacanthus (*Acanthaceae*)

quadrifidus var. ***wrightii***	WCot

anise see *Pimpinella anisum*

Anisodontea (*Malvaceae*)

bryoniifolia	SVen
§ ***capensis***	CCCN CHGN CHll CTre ELan EPri SChF SEle SLim SPlb SRkn SRms SVen SWvt
- 'Elegans Princess' **new**	CCCN
'Crystal Rose'	CRos LRHS MGos NRHS SHil XLum
'Donatella'	SLim
'El Rayo'	CSpe CWGN ECtt LHop LSou MAvo MHol MPie NCou SDys SPad SPoG WBor WCot XLum
'Elegant Lady'	GFai
huegelii	see *Alyogyne huegelii*
× ***hypomadara*** misapplied	see *A. capensis*
§ × ***hypomadara*** (Sprague) D.M. Bates	SEle
julii	Plb SVen
Lady in Pink = 'Nuanilaninp'	NCou
'Large Magenta'	CChe CPne EBee ELon LRHS LSou SWvt
malvastroides	LHop
scabrosa 'Miss Pinky'^{PBR}	LRHS

Anisodus (*Solanaceae*)

carnioliciodes BWJ 7501	WCru
§ ***luridus***	EWld

Anisotome (*Apiaceae*)

imbricata var. ***imbricata***	WAbe

Annona (*Annonaceae*)

cherimola (F)	CCCN XBlo

Anoiganthus see *Cyrtanthus*

Anomalesia see *Gladiolus*

Anomatheca (*Iridaceae*)

cruenta	see *Freesia laxa*

Anopterus (*Escalloniaceae*)

glandulosus	CFil WSHC

Anredera (*Basellaceae*)

§ ***cordifolia***	CRHN ECho EShb GKev LEdu

Antennaria (*Asteraceae*)

aprica	see *A. parvifolia*
dioica	CTri ECtt EDAr EWld GAbr GBin GJos GPoy NSla SPlb SRms XLum
- 'Alba'	EHoe
- 'Alex Duguid'	EPot GPSL NWad
- 'Aprica'	see *A. parvifolia*
- 'Minima'	ECho EPot GCrg ITim NBro NHar NSla WAbe
- 'Nyewoods Variety'	SRms
- red-flowered	ECho

- var. ***rosea***	see *A. rosea*
- 'Rotes Wunder'	CMea ECha EPot GCrg SBch WAbe
* - 'Rubra'	ECha ECho ECtt EDAr MHer MMuc SRms WIce XLum
'Joy'	EPot NWad WHal
§ ***parvifolia***	CTri SRms SRot
plantaginifolia	EBee
§ ***rosea*** ♀H5	CRos ECho GMaP LRHS NRHS NSla SPlb SRms WHal WHoo WIce

Antenoron see *Persicaria*

Anthemis ✿ (*Asteraceae*)

from Turkey	ECtt EWes LLWP
arvensis	CHab
§ 'Beauty of Grallagh'	GBuc
'Cally Cream'	GCal LRHS NCGa SMHy SPhx
'Cally White'	GBin GCal WBrk WHil
carpatica	MMuc NBro SEND
- 'Karpatenschnee'	CRos EPfP LRHS NRHS SAko SRms
cretica subsp. ***tenuiloba***	EWes
frutescens Voss	see *Argyranthemum frutescens*
'Grallagh Gold' misapplied, orange-yellow	see *A.* 'Beauty of Grallagh'
'Grallagh Gold'	ECtt EWes NPer SPhx
§ ***marschalliana***	CRos ECha ECho ECtt EDAr LRHS NHpl NRHS SPlb WCot
- subsp. ***pectinata***	GCrg
nobilis	see *Chamaemelum nobile*
punctata	Widely available
subsp. ***cupaniana*** ♀H4	
- - 'Nana'	NBir NPer SHar
rudolphiana	see *A. marschalliana*
sancti-johannis	CMHG CRos CWib EAEE EPfP ESps LRHS NPer NRHS NWad SAko SRms WMoo
Susanna Mitchell = 'Blomit'	CBod EBee ECtt ELon GMaP LRHS LSRN MAvo MBel MHol MNrw NBir NDov NLar NWad SWvt WHea WSHC XLum
'Tetworth'	ECha ELan EPfP GBin LRHS SAko SMad WCot
tinctoria	CArn CBod CHby CMac EBee ENfk GPoy MHer MNHC NPer SRms SWvt WJek WSFF XLum
- 'Alba'	EBee LRHS MArt NWad WFar
- 'Charme' PBR	EBee EPfP LRHS NLar SPoG SRms SWvt
- 'Compacta'	EWes GCal MNrw WBrk XLum
- dwarf	SAko
- 'E.C. Buxton' ♀H4	Widely available
- 'Eva'	NDov SAko WBrk
- 'Hall Farm Frilly'	ECtt ELon
- 'Kelwayi'	CRos CSBt CTri EPfP ESps GLog GMcL GWyn LRHS NBro NLar NPer NRHS SPer SRms SWat WMoo XLum
- 'Lemon Ice'	EBee GBin GWyn
- 'Lemon Maid'	CRos ECtt ELon LRHS NRHS
- 'Sauce Hollandaise'	Widely available
- 'Wargrave Variety'	CBod CElw CMac CRos CSam CWCL ECha ECtt ELan EPfP GBin GWyn LRHS NBir NChi NGdn NWad SDix SPhx SWvt WCAu WFar
'Tinpenny Sparkle'	CBod CSam EBee ECtt GMaP GMcL GWyn MHol MPie NLar NSti WAul WBrk WCot WFar WHoo WRHF
triumfettii	NDov NPer WCot
tuberculata	NChi SBch

Anthericum (*Asparagaceae*)

algeriense	see *A. liliago*
* ***bovei***	CBro
§ ***liliago***	CSpe ECho ELan EWld GCal GKev GMaP IFoB LHop LRHS LSun MCot MPie MRav NLar SPer WAul WPtf XEll
- 'Major' ♀H5	CAvo CBro EBee ECGP ECha ECho IBlr LEdu SPhx WCot WPGP
plumosum	see *Trichopetalum plumosum*
ramosum	CFis CSpe ECha ECho EPPr EPot EPri EWes GCal GKev IBoy LRHS LSun MBrN NBid NBir NLar SPhx WCot WPGP

Antholyza (*Iridaceae*)

coccinea	see *Crocosmia paniculata*
× ***crocosmioides***	see *Crocosmia* × *crocosmioides*
paniculata	see *Crocosmia paniculata*

Anthoxanthum (*Poaceae*)

odoratum	CHab CLau GPoy XLum

Anthriscus (*Apiaceae*)

cerefolium	CHby CLau ENfk GPoy MHer MNHC SRms WJek WSFF
sylvestris	CBre CHab LRHS NMir SPhx WFar WOut WSFF
- 'Broadleas Blush'	CNat
- 'Going for Gold'	CNat EPPr MAvo WCot WOut
- 'Kabir'	LEdu
- 'Ravenswing'	Widely available

Anthurium (*Araceae*)

andraeanum 'Glowing Pink'	XBlo
- 'Red Heart'	XBlo
- 'Tivolo'	XBlo
'Aztec'	XBlo
Baleno = 'Anthauf4' PBR	XBlo
'Caribo'	XBlo
crenatum	XBlo
'Crimson'	XBlo
'Magenta'	XBlo
'Mikra'	XBlo
'Octavia'	XBlo
Pico Bello = 'Anthcupcup' PBR	XBlo
Pink Champion = 'Antinkeles' PBR	XBlo
'Porcelaine White'	XBlo
Red Champion = 'Anthbnena' PBR	XBlo
'Vitara'	XBlo
White Champion = 'Anthefaqyr' PBR	XBlo

Anthyllis (*Papilionaceae*)

hermanniae 'Compacta'	see *A. hermanniae* 'Minor'
§ - 'Minor'	EPot
montana	XSen
- subsp. ***atropurpurea***	CRos ECho LRHS NRHS
- 'Rubra' ♀H5	ECho EDAr EPot LHop LLHF NSla
vulneraria	CHab NMir NRya SPhx WSFF
- var. ***coccinea***	ELan EWld GAbr GKev IBoy MBel NSla SPhx WCFE WHal WIce
- dark red-flowered	CSpe
- 'Fireberry' **new**	ECtt

Antirrhinum (*Plantaginaceae*)

asarina	see *Asarina procumbens*
australe	GCal
barrelieri	SEND
braun-blanquetii	GCra GLog SEND SPhx WCot
glutinosum	see *A. hispanicum* subsp. *hispanicum*
hispanicum 'Avalanche'	ECtt
§ - subsp. ***hispanicum***	CSpe
- - 'Roseum'	CMea LPot
majus 'Black Prince'	CSpe ECtt LHop SPhx
- 'Cheerio' (mixed)	CWCL
- Liberty Classic Series	NPri
- - 'Liberty Classic Yellow'	NPri
- 'Night and Day'	CSpe WMoo
molle	CSpe GKev MCot NPer SChF WAbe
- pink-flowered	MCot WAbe
- white-flowered	EBee GKev WAbe
Pretty in Pink = 'Pmoore07' **new**	LRHS SLon
sempervirens	EWTr MHer WAbe

añu see *Tropaeolum tuberosum*

Aphelandra (*Acanthaceae*)

squarrosa 'Citrina'	XBlo

Aphyllanthes (*Asparagaceae*)

monspeliensis	SBrt XLum XSen

Apios (*Papilionaceae*)

§ ***americana***	CAgr EWes LEdu NBir WCot WCru WSHC
- 'Nutty'	CAgr
tuberosa	see *A. americana*

Apium (*Apiaceae*)

graveolens	CHab CLau ENfk GPoy MHer MNHC SIde SRms SVic WJek
- var. ***rapaceum*** 'Prinz' 🏆H4	SVic
- (Secalinum Group) 'Par-cel'	MHer SRms

Apium × *Petroselinum* (*Apiaceae*)

hybrid, misapplied	see *A. graveolens* Secalinum Group

Apocynum (*Apocynaceae*)

cannabinum	CArn GPoy

Aponogeton (*Aponogetonaceae*)

desertorum	EWay LLWG
distachyos	CBen CWat EWay LCro MSKA MWts NPer SVic SWat WMAq WPnP XLum

apple see *Malus domestica*

apricot see *Prunus armeniaca*

Aptenia (*Aizoaceae*)

cordifolia	CCCN NPer SChr SPlb SVen
- 'Variegata' (v)	CCCN

Aquilegia ✿ (*Ranunculaceae*)

akitensis misapplied	see *A. flabellata* var. *pumila*
'Alaska' (State Series) 🏆H5	LRHS SHil
alpina	CBot CMea EBee ECho EPfP ESps GMcL LCro MNHC NGdn SCob SPer SRms WMoo XEll XLum
amaliae	see *A. ottonis* subsp. *amaliae*
'Apple Blossom'	NBir
aragonensis	see *A. pyrenaica*
§ ***atrata***	CBot CLAP CPou ECho
aurea misapplied	see *A. vulgaris* golden-leaved
aurea Janka	LLHF
barnebyi	CWCL GKev
bertolonii 🏆H5	CMea CRos ECho EWld GKev LHop LRHS NRHS NSla SIgm SRms WHoo
- 'Blue Berry'	WThu
Biedermeier Group	CRos EAJP EPfP ESps LRHS NGdn NRHS SRot WFar WTou
'Blackcurrant'	CWCL
'Blue Pleats' **new**	CWCL
'Blue Star' (Star Series)	CRos CWCL ELan EPfP GBin GMaP GWyn LRHS NEgg NPnk NRHS SPtp
'Bluebird' (Songbird Series) 🏆H4	LBuc LRHS NBir NPer WFar
buergeriana	GKev SPhx
- 'Calimero'	CFis CTsd LHop MBNS NLar SBee SPtp
- var. ***oxysepala***	see *A. oxysepala*
aff. ***buergeriana***	NPnk
'Bunting' (Songbird Series) 🏆H4	MHer SGbt
canadensis 🏆H3	CBot CLAP CSpe ECho ELan GCrg GKev GLog LCro NBir NBro SPad SPhx SRms WFar XEll XLum
- 'Little Lanterns'	EAJP ECho EPPr GKev LHop NHpl NLar WIce
- 'Nana'	GKev WThu
- 'Pink Lanterns'	LBMP
'Cardinal' (Songbird Series)	LBuc LRHS MHer
chaplinei	GKev NBir SBch
chrysantha	CBot ECho GJos GWyn MCot SIgm SRms SWvt WBod WKif WTou
- 'Denver Gold'	CHVG CSam EShb
I - 'Flore Pleno' (d)	CBot
- 'Yellow Queen' 🏆	CWCL ELon ENor EPPr EPfP EWoo GBin GMaP IKil LBMP LHop LRHS MWat NGdn NPri SCob SDix SGbt SPad SWvt WCFE WTor XEll XLum
clematiflora	see *A. vulgaris* var. *stellata*
Clementine Series	EPfP NPri
coerulea 🏆H5	GJos GKev SRms
- var. ***coerulea***	CBod
- var. ***ochroleuca***	CWCL
'Colorado' (State Series)	LRHS SHil
'Crimson Star'	CRos CWCL ELan EPfP GMcL LRHS NRHS SPoG WHar WMoo WTou
'Danish Dwarf'	LBMP
discolor	GKev LLHF WThu XEll
double black-flowered (d)	WHar
'Double Rubies' (d)	ELan LSRN WMoo WTou
'Dove' (Songbird Series) 🏆H5	LBuc LRHS MHer SGbt SHar SPer
I 'Dragonfly'	CBcs CRos CWib EAJP ELan EPfP LRHS MJak NEgg NGdn NRHS SPoG
'Dragon's Breath' (mixed)	WTou
ecalcarata	see *Semiaquilegia ecalcarata*
einseleana	ECho LLHF
'Elegance'	WTou
elegantula	GKev
flabellata 🏆H5	GCra
- f. ***alba***	CTri ECho ELan
- 'Blackcurrant Ice'	CWCL EPfP LRHS
- Cameo Series	GMaP WFar
- - 'Cameo Blue and White'	CWib GMcL SRms SRot WFar WTor
- - 'Cameo Pink and White'	GMcL MHer
- - 'Cameo Red and White' **new**	GMcL

– – 'Cameo Rose'	WFar
– – 'Cameo Rose and White'	SRms
– – 'Cameo White'	GMcL SRot WFar
– 'Georgia' (State Series) ♀H5	LRHS SHil
– Jewel Series	ECho
– 'Ministar'	ECho EDAr GCrg GWyn MHol SHil WFar WHil XLum
– 'Nana Alba'	see *A. flabellata* var. *pumila* f. *alba*
§ – var. ***pumila*** ♀H5	CRos CWCL ECha ECho EDAr EPPr GEdr GKev LHop LRHS LSun NGdn NRHS
§ – – f. ***alba*** ♀H5	CRos EAJP ECha ECho EDAr GKev LHop LRHS LSun NRHS SRms
– – 'Atlantis'	GMcL LBMP
I – – f. ***kurilensis*** 'Rosea'	WAbe
'Florida' (State Series) ♀H5	LRHS SHil
formosa	CBot ECho EPPr NChi
– var. ***truncata***	SIgm
§ ***fragrans***	CLAP GBin GEdr GJos IBoy MArt SGbt SIgm
'Fruit and Nut Chocolate'	EBee IKil MBNS MHol MPie WCot
glandulosa	GWyn LLHF
glauca	see *A. fragrans*
'Golden Guiness'	ELon GPSL
'Goldfinch' (Songbird Series)	LBuc LRHS MHer NBir SGbt SPer WFar
grahamii	WAbe
'Heavenly Blue'	CBod CDor EBee GWyn LRHS WTou
'Hensol Harebell'	EBee SHar SRms
'Honeydew'	GWyn
hybrida 'Double Pleat Blackberry' (d) new	EPed
japonica	see *A. flabellata* var. *pumila*
jonesii	GKev SIgm SPlb
jonesii × ***saximontana***	GKev SIgm
'Koralle'	CBod CDor GWyn
'Kristall'	EShb LCro SGbt
* ***kuhistanica***	GKev GWyn
laramiensis	CPBP
'Leprechaun Gold' (v)	EPfP MHol NGdn SDix
'Lime Sorbet'	LRHS SRms
longissima	CWld MBel MHer SHar WFar WHoo
long-spurred hybrids	WTou
long-spurred hybrids, white	WTou
'Louisiana' (State Series) ♀H5	EBee LRHS SCob SHil
'Magpie'	see *A. vulgaris* 'William Guiness'
'Maxi'	CBod WHil
McKana Group	Widely available
Mrs Scott-Elliot hybrids	CSBt ECtt EPfP MHol
Music Series	SRms
'Nightingale' (Songbird Series)	SGbt
nigricans	see *A. atrata*
nivalis	LLHF
'Oranges and Lemons'	WFar
(Origami Series) 'Origami Blue and White' new	IBoy
– 'Origami Red and White' ♀H5	IBoy
– 'Origami White' new	IBoy
§ ***ottonis*** subsp. ***amaliae***	CPBP LLHF SIgm
§ ***oxysepala***	GLog MMrt WFar
– B&SWJ 4775	WCru
– var. ***kansuensis*** new	GKev
Perfumed Garden Group	CPla WFar
pleated burgundy-flowered	CBot
'Purple Emperor' PBR	EPfP
§ ***pyrenaica***	GKev
– dwarf	GKev WAbe
'Red Hobbit'	CRos CSpe EAEE EBee ELan EPfP GMcL IBoy LHop LRHS MBel MHol NEgg NGdn NHpl NLar SHil SPtp WBor WFar
'Red Star' (Star Series)	CWCL EAEE EAJP EPfP GBin NEgg SPer WHil
'Robin' (Songbird Series)	SGbt SPer
rockii	CLAP EWld GKev
– B&SWJ 7965	WCru
'Roman Bronze'	see *Aquilegia* × *Semiaquilegia* 'Roman Bronze'
'Rose Queen'	CBod CDor CWCL EPfP GWyn SPtp WFar WHoo
'Roundway Chocolate'	CBot
saximontana	EPot GEdr GKev NSla
§ 'Schneekönigin'	CWCL EBee LRHS WCFE
scopulorum	GKev LLHF SIgm
Shooting Stars (mixed)	WTou
sibirica	GKev LLHF
'Silver Queen'	EBee ELan EWoo GBin LHop
'Simone's White'	EBee
skinneri	CBot CSpe ELan GEdr GLog
– 'Tequila Sunrise'	CSpe CWCL CWib ELan MHer MMrt SPad SPtp
Snow Queen	see *A.* 'Schneekönigin'
'Spitfire'	LRHS NCGa
Spring Magic Series	NPri
– Spring Magic Blue and White	LRHS SCob WTou
– Spring Magic Pink and White	WTou
– Spring Magic Rose and Ivory	WTou
– Spring Magic Rose and White new	GMcL
– Spring Magic White	GMcL SCob WTou
– Spring Magic Yellow	GMcL WTou
stellata	see *A. vulgaris* var. *stellata*
'Sunburst Ruby'	CPla WMoo
(Swan Series) 'Swan Lavender'	NPri
– 'Swan Pink and Yellow'	NPri
– 'Swan Red and White'	CBod NPri
'Sweet Rainbows' (d)	CPla
'Touchwood Black & Bruises' mixed (d)	WTou
'Touchwood Crinoline Ladies' mixed (d)	WTou
'Touchwood Harmony' mixed	WTou
'Touchwood Night Lights' mixed (d)	WTou
'Touchwood Sunrise Surprises' mixed (d)	WTou
triternata	GWyn
'Virginia' (State Series)	EBee LRHS SHil
viridiflora	CBot CLAP EBee ELan EPfP GCal MMrt SBee SIgm WAbe WCot
– var. ***atropurpurea*** new	LEdu
– 'Chocolate Soldier'	CSpe CWCL ENor
'Volcano!' (mixed)	WTou
vulgaris	CArn CHab CMHG CWCL CWld EPfP ESps EWoo GKev GPoy GWyn LLWP LRHS MHer MNHC NBro NGdn NMir SPlb WCAu WMoo WShi
– 'Adelaide Addison'	ECha WHoo
– var. ***alba***	CMea EPfP EWoo LRHS MMuc NDov SCob WTou
– 'Altrosa'	GWyn
– 'Aureovariegata'	see *A. vulgaris* Vervaeneana Group

	- 'Blackbird' (Songbird Series) (d)	CWCL
	- 'Burnished Rose'	CPla
	- ***clematiflora***	see *A. vulgaris* var. *stellata*
	- (Clementine Series) 'Clementine Blue' (d)	CCVN EPfP LRHS NRHS SPoG WCot
	- - 'Clementine Dark Purple' (d)	CRos CWCL EPfP LRHS NRHS SPoG
	- - 'Clementine Purple' (d)	CCVN
	- - 'Clementine Red' (d)	EPfP
	- - 'Clementine Rose' (d)	CCVN LRHS NRHS SPoG
	- - 'Clementine Salmon Rose' (d)	CCVN CRos CWCL EPfP LRHS NRHS SPoG
	- - 'Clementine White' (d)	CCVN CRos EPfP LRHS NRHS SPoG
	- 'Crystal Star'	CRos LRHS NRHS
	- 'Eyecatcher' **new**	WCot
	- var. ***flore-pleno*** (d)	LLWP WFar WTou
	- - bicoloured (d)	WTou
	- - black-flowered (d)	MMuc SEND WCot WTou
	- - blue-flowered (d)	WTou
	- - 'Dorothy Rose' (Dorothy Series) (d)	LHop SPad SPtp
	- - 'Double Pleat' (d)	EPfP
	- - 'Double Pleat' blue/white-flowered (d)	CBot
	- - 'Double Pleat' pink/white-flowered (d)	CWCL
	- - 'Jane Hollow' (d)	CPou
	- - pale blue-flowered (d)	WTou
	- - pink-flowered (d)	WTou
	- - purple-flowered (d)	WTou
	- - red-flowered (d)	WTou
	- - 'Strawberry Ice Cream' (d)	NBro
*	- - 'White Bonnet' (d)	CWCL
	- - white-flowered (d)	WTou
§	- golden-leaved	ECho WTou
	- Grandmother's Garden Group	CBod
	- 'Heidi'	GWyn MMuc SEND
	- 'Mellow Yellow'	CPla CTsd EHoe ELon LRHS SDix WMoo
	- Munstead White	see *A. vulgaris* 'Nivea'
§	- 'Nivea' 🏆H7	CBWd CBod CBot CPou CSpe EBee ECha ELan EPfP EWoo LOPS MArt SEND WCot WTor
	- 'Pink Spurless'	see *A. vulgaris* var. *stellata* pink-flowered
	- 'Pom Pom Crimson' (Pom Pom Series)	NBro WCot
	- scented	WTou
§	- var. ***stellata***	CDor CTsd ELan ESps GAbr GKev GWyn MArt MCot NBir NBro SPad WFar WHea WMoo WTou
	- - Barlow Series (d)	MJak WFar WTou
	- - - 'Black Barlow' (d)	Widely available
	- - black-flowered	WTou
	- - 'Blue Barlow' (Barlow Series) (d)	CBod CBot CRos CSpe EBee ECtt EPfP GMaP GQue ILea IPot LCro LRHS LSRN MJak NRHS SCob SHil SPer SWvt WBor WCot WTou XLum
	- - blue-flowered	MMuc NBir SEND
	- - 'Bordeaux Barlow' (Barlow Series) (d)	LRHS STPC
	- - 'Christa Barlow' (Barlow Series) (d)	CRos EBee EPfP LRHS MBel NLar NRHS WRHF
	- - 'Firewheel'	WMoo
	- - 'Greenapples' (d)	CBod CBre CCVN CNor CWCL EBee ELan EPfP EWoo GKev GQue LRHS MCot SCob WCot WHoo

	- - 'Nora Barlow' (Barlow Series) (d)	Widely available
	- - 'Pink Barlow' (Barlow Series)	GBin SBod
§	- - pink-flowered	WTou
	- - red-flowered	WTou
	- - 'Rose Barlow' (Barlow Series) (d)	EPfP LRHS LSRN
	- - 'Royal Purple' (d)	NBro WMoo
	- - 'Ruby Port' (d)	Widely available
	- - 'White Barlow' (Barlow Series) (d)	CAby EPfP GMaP IBoy LCro LOPS LRHS SHil SPer SWvt WTou
	- - white-flowered	CSpe GCra NBir NBro WTou
	- variegated foliage	see *A. vulgaris* Vervaeneana Group
§	- Vervaeneana Group (v)	CMHG CWCL ELan EPfP LRHS NBir NPer SPlb SRms SWat WBor WHoo WMoo WTou
	- - 'Woodside Blue' (v)	NWad WTou
	- - 'Woodside White' (v)	NBir WBrk WTou
§	- 'William Guiness'	Widely available
	- 'William Guiness Doubles' (d)	GWyn WMoo
	- 'Winky Wooh' (Winky Series)	CWld NEgg WBor
	'White Star' (Star Series)	CDor CWCL EBee ELan EPfP GMaP LRHS NPnk WTou
	white-flowered	WTou
	Winky Series	ELan GJos NCGa SWvt WFar WTou
	- 'Winky Blue-White'	CRos GBin LRHS NLar NPri NRHS WCFE WTou
	- 'Winky Double Red-White' (d)	CRos LRHS
	- 'Winky Double White-White' (d)	NPri
	- 'Winky Purple-White'	CRos GPSL LRHS NPri NRHS
	- 'Winky Red-White'	LRHS NPri NRHS SWvt WTou
	- 'Winky Rose-Rose'	CRos LRHS NPri NRHS
	yabeana	GKev GPSL SPad WMoo
	'Yellow Star' (Star Series) 🏆H4	CDor CWCL ECtt EPfP GBin NPnk

Aquilegia × *Semiaquilegia* (*Ranunculaceae*)

	hybrid, blue-flowered	NGdn
§	'Roman Bronze'	CPla WMoo

Arabis (*Brassicaceae*)

	albida	see *A. alpina* subsp. *caucasica*
	alpina	MAsh SPlb
§	- subsp. ***caucasica***	ECho GKev
	- - 'Arctic Joy' (v) **new**	WCot
	- - 'Corfe Castle'	ECtt
	- - 'Douler Angevine' (v)	CBod ECtt LBMP LHop NEoE NHpl SPoG SRms WIce
	- - 'Flore Pleno' (d) 🏆H5	CElw CFis CHid CSpe CTri CWCL ECho ECtt ELan ESps EWld GAbr GJos SBch SIgm SRms WBrk WHoo WWFP XLum
	- - 'Hedi'	MJak
	- - 'Little Treasure White' **new**	GWyn
	- - 'Lotti Deep Rose' **new**	MHol
	- - 'Pinkie'	ECho
	- - 'Pixie Cream'	ECtt MHol MMuc NGdn
	- - 'Rosea'	GJos LRHS MArt NBir SRms
§	- - 'Schneehaube' 🏆H6	CTri CWib EAJP ECho ECtt EPfP GMaP GWyn LRHS MArt MJak NBir NGdn SPoG SRms WBor
	- - Snowcap	see *A. alpina* subsp. *caucasica* 'Schneehaube'
	- - 'Variegata' (v)	ECho ELan GMaP MJak SPoG SRms

	androsacea	EPot SRms
	× ***arendsii*** 'Compinkie'	SPlb SRms
	blepharophylla	EPfP MHol NPri WSHC
§	- 'Frühlingszauber' 🏆^{H5}	CTri EAJP ELan EPfP GJos MMuc NBir NGdn NPri SPoG SRms WCot WRHF
	- 'Rose Delight'	LRHS
	- 'Rote Sensation'	ELan NGdn WRHF
	- Spring Charm	see *A. blepharophylla* 'Frühlingszauber'
	carduchorum	XLum
	caucasica	see *A. alpina* subsp. *caucasica*
	ferdinandi-coburgi	ECho NHol
	- 'Aureovariegata' (v)	CMea CTri ECho ECtt ELan SWvt
	- 'Old Gold'	CTal ECho EHoe EPfP ESps GWyn LPot MAsh MHer NHol NRya SPoG SRms SRot SWvt WCFE
	- 'Variegata'	see *A. procurrens* 'Variegata'
	procurrens	WCot XLum XSen
	- 'Glacier'	GJos
§	- 'Variegata' (v) 🏆^{H5}	CTal CTri ECho ECtt EHoe ELan EPfP ESps EWes GAbr GKev GPSL MBrN MHer MJak SPlb SRms SRot
	pumila	GKev
	Snow Cap	see *A. alpina* subsp. *caucasica* 'Schneehaube'

Arachniodes (*Dryopteridaceae*)

aristata	NLos
davalliaeformis	EBee ISha LRHS NLos
miqueliana	ISha NLos
simplicior	CCCN EBee EShb EUJe ISha LLWG LRHS NLos SCob SPlb WCot
standishii	EBee EShb ISha LCro LEdu LRHS NLos WCot

Araiostegia (*Davalliaceae*)

	hymenophylloides	SKHP WCot
	parvipinnata	see *A. perdurans*
§	***perdurans***	CFil EBee NLos WCot WPGP
	- B&SWJ 1608	WCru
	pulchra HWJ 1007	WCru

Aralia ✿ (*Araliaceae*)

	CW&T 6257 **new**	CMCN
	apioides	IMou LEdu
	- EDHCH 9720	SBrt WCru
	armata B&SWJ 6916	WCru
	- RWJ 10060	WCru
	bipinnata	WPGP
	- CWJ 12407	WCru
	- RWJ 10101	WCru
	cachemirica	CDTJ CLAP GCal MBrN NBid SDix SMad SPlb WCru WHal WMoo
	californica	EBee GCal GPoy LEdu LTro NLar SBrt SKHP WCru
	castanopsidicola CWJ 12411	WCru
	chapaensis B&SWJ 11812	WCru
	- HWJ 1013	WCru
	chinensis misapplied	see *A. elata*
	chinensis L. BWJ 8102	WCru
	continentalis	CLAP LEdu MPie NLar WHoo
	- B&SWJ 8437	WCru
	- B&SWJ 8524	WCru
	cordata Thunb.	GCal LEdu WFar
	- B&SWJ 5596	WCru
	- var. ***sachalinensis***	NLar
	- - B&SWJ 4773	WCru
	- 'Sun King'	CAby CBct CBod CCht EBee ECtt EPfP ESwi EUJe GBin IBoy LCro LHop LRHS MHol MNrw MPie NBid NLar NSti SCob SDix SPoG SWvt WFar WMoo
	decaisneana B&SWJ 6794	WCru
	- RWJ 9910	WCru
	echinocaulis PAB 9052	LEdu
§	***elata***	CBcs CDul CHll CMac CRos CTsd EBee ELan EPfP LRHS LSRN MBlu MGos MHtn MMuc SArc SCob SGol SPer SPoG SWvt WFar
	- B&SWJ 5480	WCru
	- 'Albomarginata'	see *A. elata* 'Variegata'
	- 'Aureo-marginata' (v)	CMac
	- 'Aureovariegata' (v) 🏆^{H5}	CBcs ELan EWes NLar SCob
	- 'Golden Umbrella' (v)	EUJe LSRN NLar
	- 'Silver Umbrella' (v)	EUJe NLar
§	- 'Variegata' (v) 🏆^{H5}	CBcs CDul ELan NLar SCob SWvt
	foliolosa B&SWJ 8360	WCru
	kansuensis BWJ 7650	WCru
	- CD&R 2289	WCru
	leschenaultii B&SWJ 9515	WCru
	- B&SWJ 11789	WCru
	nudicaulis L.	GPoy
	papyrifera	see *Tetrapanax papyrifer*
	racemosa	CBod GPoy LEdu NLar SRms WJek WMoo
	- B&SWJ 9570	WCru
	searelliana B&SWJ 11736	WCru
	sieboldii de Vriese	see *Fatsia japonica*
	spinosa L.	EBtc GQue LEdu MBlu NChi SPlb
	subcordata HWJK 2385	WCru
	verticillata B&SWJ 11797	WCru
	vietnamensis B&SWJ 12349E	WCru

Araucaria (*Araucariaceae*)

	sp.	LPar MAsh
	angustifolia	WPGP
	angustifolia × ***araucana***	GMcL
§	***araucana***	Widely available
	bidwillii	LPar MMuc SEND
	excelsa misapplied	see *A. heterophylla*
§	***heterophylla*** 🏆^{H2}	CCCN SEND
	imbricata	see *A. araucana*

Araujia (*Apocynaceae*)

sericifera	CBcs CHll CMac CRHN ECre LRHS SVen WCot WSHC

Arbutus ✿ (*Ericaceae*)

andrachne NJM 12.018	WPGP
× ***andrachnoides*** 🏆^{H4}	CAbP CHGN CJun CRos CTho ELan EPfP LEdu LRHS LSRN MAsh MRav SArc SPer SPoG WPGP WPat
menziesii	CBcs CMCN EPfP MBlu MMuc
× ***reyorum*** 'Marina'	CAbP CJun EBee ELan EPfP LEdu LHop LRHS MAsh MBlu NOrn SAko SEND SMad SPer SPoG WPGP WPat
unedo	Widely available
- 'Atlantic' 🏆^{H5}	CCCN CJun CRos EPfP LRHS LSRN MAsh MGos SBig SGbt SGol SHil SWvt WPGP WPat
- 'Compacta'	CBcs CCCN CRos EUJe LRHS MAsh NLar SLon SPoG SWvt WFar
- 'Elfin King'	CRos EPfP LRHS MAsh SLon SWvt
- 'Quercifolia'	CDul CHll CJun ELan LEdu LLHF MAsh NLar WHor WPat
- Roselily = 'Minlily'[PBR]	SBig
- f. ***rubra*** 🏆^{H5}	Widely available
xalapensis	CFil SPlb

Archidendron (*Mimosaceae*)

glandulosum	EBee

Archontophoenix (*Arecaceae*)

cunninghamiana	XBlo

Arctanthemum (*Asteraceae*)

§ ***arcticum***	ECha MMuc NLar XLum
- 'Roseum'	EBee

Arcterica see *Pieris*

Arctium (*Asteraceae*)

lappa	CArn GPoy SIde SRms SVic WHer WSFF
minus	NMir

Arctostaphylos (*Ericaceae*)

uva-ursi	GMcL GPoy NLar SPlb
- 'Snowcap'	MAsh
- 'Vancouver Jade'	CMac CRos ELan GKin LRHS LSRN MAsh NRHS SCoo SLon SPer SPoG SWvt

Arctotheca (*Asteraceae*)

calendula	EBee WPGP WSHC

Arctotis (*Asteraceae*)

Hannah = 'Archnah'PBR	CAby ECtt MBNS
Hayley = 'Archley'PBR	CCCN ECtt MBNS
'Heidi'	CCht MBNS
'Holly'	MBNS
'Hope'	CCht MBNS
× ***hybrida*** hort. 'Apricot'	CCCN CCht ECtt SVen
- 'Flame' ♀H2	CAby CCCN ECtt MBNS SCoo SVen
- 'Red Devil'	CCCN CCht EWoo LSou MBNS SCoo SVen WBod
- 'Wine'	CCCN LSou MBNS SCoo SRkn

Ardisia (*Primulaceae*)

PAB 7988 from Mizoram, India	LEdu
japonica	WCot
- B&SWJ 1032	SMad WCru
- var. ***angusta***	WCot
- 'Houkan' (v)	WPGP
- 'Ito Fukurin' **new**	EBee WPGP
- var. ***minor*** B&SWJ 1841	WCru
- - B&SWJ 3809	WCru

Areca (*Arecaceae*)

triandra	XBlo

Arecastrum see *Syagrus*

Arenaria (*Caryophyllaceae*)

§ ***alfacarensis***	EPot NLar SPlb WAbe WOld
balearica	CWCL ECho EWes GCrg LLWG MAsh NHpl NSla SPlb SRms
capillaris	CTri
festucoides	WAbe
globiflora	GKev
grandiflora	XLum
kansuensis	NLar
ledebouriana	EDAr NLar SBrt
montana ♀H5	CAby CMea ECha ECho ECtt EDAr EPfP EWoo GMaP LHop LRHS MGos NRHS SDix SPhx SPlb SRms SRot WAbe WIce WKif WWFP
- 'Avalanche'	ECtt LSun MHol
- 'Blizzard'	EPfP
pulvinata	see *A. alfacarensis*
purpurascens	ECho EWes GCrg LLHF NLar SRms WAbe
tetraquetra	SIgm
- subsp. ***amabilis***	EPot
'The Pearl'	CBod
verna	see *Minuartia verna*

Arenga (*Arecaceae*)

micrantha	WCot

Argania (*Sapotaceae*)

spinosa	WPGP

Argemone (*Papaveraceae*)

grandiflora	CSpe EPPr SBch
mexicana	ELan IMou

Argyranthemum ✿ (*Asteraceae*)

'Bridesmaid'	MHom
broussonetii	MHom
canariense hort.	see *A. frutescens* subsp. *canariae*
Cherry Harmony = 'Supa532' (Daisy Crazy Series) (d)	MCot
Cherry Love = 'Supacher' (Daisy Crazy Series) (d) ♀H2	CCCN
'Cornish Gold' ♀H2	CBcs CCCN ECtt EShb
'Donington Hero' ♀H2	MHom
double pink-flowered (d)	SVen
'Everest'	CRos LRHS NRHS SPoG
'Flamingo'	see *Rhodanthemum gayanum*
foeniculaceum misapplied pink-flowered	see *A.* 'Petite Pink'
§ ***foeniculaceum*** misapplied	CTri ELan
§ ***foeniculaceum*** (Willd.) Webb & Sch.Bip.	MCot
- 'Royal Haze' ♀H2	CCCN CHll NPer
§ ***frutescens***	SEND WKif
§ - subsp. ***canariae*** ♀H2	CCCN MHom
'Gill's Pink'	MHom WPnn
gracile	CHll
- 'Chelsea Girl' ♀H2	CCCN CSpe MCot MHom WKif
'Guernsey Pink'	MHom
Gypsy Rose = 'M9/18d'	CCCN
'Jamaica Primrose' ♀H2	CSpe CTri ECtt SDix
'Jamaica Snowstorm'	see *A.* 'Snow Storm'
LaRita Banana Split = 'Kleaf10067' (LaRita Series) ♀H2	CRos LRHS NRHS
'Levada Cream' ♀H2	MHom
(Madeira Series) Madeira Crested Ivory = 'Bonmadcivy' (d)	SPoG
- Madeira Crested Pink = 'Bonmadcink'PBR **new**	SPoG
- Madeira Crested Yellow = 'Bonmadcrel'PBR **new**	SPoG
- Madeira Red = 'Bonmadre'PBR **new**	SPoG
- Madeira White Improved = 'Bonmadwitim'PBR **new**	SPoG
§ ***maderense*** ♀H2	CHll MHom
'Mary Wootton' (d)	ECtt MHom
mawii	see *Rhodanthemum gayanum*
Meteor Red = 'Supa742' (Daisy Crazy Series)	CBcs CWGN MBNS

§	'Mrs F. Sander' (d)	MHom
	ochroleucum	see *A. maderense*
	Pacific Gold = 'Pacargone'PBR (d)	CBcs CWGN
§	'Petite Pink' ♀H2	CCCN
	Ping-Pong = 'Innping'PBR (d)	CCCN
	'Pink Australian' (d)	MHom
	'Pink Delight'	see *A.* 'Petite Pink'
	Pomponette Pink = 'Supa392'PBR (d)	CBcs
	'Powder Puff' (d)	ECtt
	'Shirley's Yellow'	MHom
	'Silver Queen'	see *A. foeniculaceum* misapplied
§	'Snow Storm' ♀H2	MHom
	'Snowflake' misapplied	see *A.* 'Mrs F. Sander'
	Sole Mio = 'Supa3047' (d)	CWCL
	'Starlight' ♀H2	MCot MHom
	'Sugar and Ice' (d)	CCCN
	'Sugar Baby' (d)	CCCN
	'Summer Cloud'	MCot
	'Summer Melody' (d)	CBcs CCCN
	'Summer Pink'	CCCN
	'Summer Stars' (Daisy Crazy Series) (d) ♀H2	MHom
	'Vancouver' (d) ♀H2	CCCN CWCL ECtt EShb WBod
	'Vera'	CCCN
	'Weymouth Pink'	MHom
	'White Spider'	CCCN ELan

Argyrocytisus (*Papilionaceae*)

battandieri	Widely available
- 'Yellow Tail' ♀H4	CBot CEnd CRos ELan EPfP EUJe LRHS MGos NLar NOra NOrn NRHS SHil SKHP SPoG SSta WHar WMat

Arisaema ✿ (*Araceae*)

	album	XLum
	amurense	CElw CFil CLAP ECho GBuc GKev LAma LLHF WThu
§	- subsp. ***robustum***	WBor
	asperatum	LAma
	auriculatum	GKev LAma
	- var. ***hungyaense***	LRHS
	brachyspathum	see *A. heterophyllum*
	candidissimum ♀H4	CBro CElw CFil CLAP CPne CSpe CTal ECha ELon EPPr EPfP EPot GBuc GCra GEdr GKev LAma MAvo MRav NHar NLar NSla SDeJ SDir SKHP WBor WCot WHal
	- white-flowered	CFil GEdr GKev LAma SDir
	ciliatum	GBuc GEdr GKev LAma NLar SRot
	- var. ***liubaense***	CAby CFwr CWCL EPfP EPot GBuc GKev WCot
	- - CT 369	CLAP EPfP SDys SKHP WPGP
	- - GG 97091	WCot
	concinnum	EWld GEdr GKev LAma SDir WPnP XLum
	consanguineum	CAby CBcs CBro CFwr CLAP CTal EBee EPfP EWld GBin GCal GEdr GKev LAma NLar WCot WPGP WPnP XLum
	- B&SWJ 071	WCru
	- CLD 1519	ECho GBuc
	- subsp. ***kelung-insulare*** B&SWJ 256	WCru
	- 'The Perfect Wave'	WCot
	- variegated (v)	WCot
	cf. ***consanguineum***	WBod
	costatum	CCCN CFil EBee ECho EPfP EPot GBin GKev LAma SChF SDir WCot WPGP XLum
	dracontium	XLum
	ehimense	LAma
	elephas	LAma
	engleri	GKev LAma LRHS
	exappendiculatum	CAby CFil EBee GKev LAma LRHS
	fargesii	CFil EPot GKev LAma SChF SKHP XLum
	flavum	CFil CWCL ECho EPfP EPot EWld GBin GBuc GCal GKev LAma NHar NPnk SDir SPlb
	- CC 6303	EBee ITim
	- subsp. ***abbreviatum***	GBin GBuc GKev
	- - CC 6300	ITim
	formosanum B&SWJ 280	WCru
§	***franchetianum***	GKev LAma
	galeatum	EPot GKev LAma LRHS WCot XLum
	grapsospadix B&SWJ 7000	WCru
§	***griffithii***	CBro ECho GBuc GEdr GKev LAma LRHS NBid NLar SDeJ SDir XLum
	- 'Numbuq'	GCra
	- var. ***pradhanii***	GEdr GKev LAma XLum
	aff. ***griffithii***	SDir
	helleborifolium	see *A. tortuosum*
§	***heterophyllum***	GKev ITim LAma
	inkiangense	LAma
	intermedium	GKev LAma MNrw XLum
	iyoanum subsp. ***nakaianum***	LAma
	jacquemontii	CAby CFil ECho GCra GEdr GKev GLog LAma NLar SDir XLum
	- CC 5184	ITim
	aff. ***jacquemontii***	SDir
	japonicum Blume	see *A. serratum* var. *mayebarae*
	japonicum Komarov	see *A. serratum*
	kishidae	GEdr GKev LAma
	kiushianum	EFEx GKev LAma LRHS SDir
	- 'Kikkou-fu' **new**	GEdr
	lichiangense	GKev LAma LRHS
	lingyunense	LAma
§	***lobatum***	LAma
	maximowiczii	GEdr LAma
§	***nepenthoides***	CFil ECho EPot EUJe GEdr GKev LAma LRHS SDir WPnP XLum
	ochraceum	see *A. nepenthoides*
	onoticum	see *A. lobatum*
	petelotii B&SWJ 9706	WCru
	propinquum	ECho GKev LAma NLar XLum
	purpureogaleatum	see *A. franchetianum*
	rhizomatum	LAma
	rhombiforme	LAma
	ringens misapplied	see *A. amurense* subsp. *robustum*
	ringens ambig.	EPfP GEdr GKev LRHS SChF SKHP
	ringens (Thunberg) Schott	EFEx LAma LEdu
	- f. ***praecox*** B&SWJ 1515	WCru
	- f. ***sieboldii*** B&SWJ 551	WCru
	aff. ***ringens***	SDir
	robustum	see *A. amurense* subsp. *robustum*
	saxatile	GKev
	sazensoo	GEdr GKev LAma
§	***serratum***	GKev LAma MNrw
§	- var. ***mayebarae***	GEdr GKev LAma
	- var. ***serratum***	LAma
	sikokianum	CBro ECho EFEx EPot GEdr GKev LAma LLHF LRHS NHpl NLar SDir SKHP WPnP
	- variegated (v)	GEdr

speciosum	CFil ECho EWld GEdr GKev LAma LRHS SDeJ SDir SPlb WCot WPnP XLum
* - var. ***magnificum***	CBcs GEdr GKev LAma NLar XLum
- var. ***mirabile***	GKev LAma LRHS XLum
taiwanense	CAby GEdr SKHP
- B&SWJ 269	WCru
- var. ***brevipedunculatum*** B&SWJ 1859	WCru
- f. ***cinereum*** B&SWJ 19121	WCru
tashiroi	GKev LAma
ternatipartitum	GKev LAma LRHS
thunbergii	EFEx GEdr LAma WBor
- subsp. ***autumnale*** B&SWJ 1425	WCru
- subsp. ***urashima***	EFEx GKev LAma
§ ***tortuosum***	CFil CPne ECha ECho EPfP GBin GBuc GKev LAma LEdu LTro NLar SChF SDir WPnP XLum
- 'Black Rod'	CFil
- var. ***helleborifolium***	NBid XLum
tosaense	GKev LAma LRHS
triphyllum	CElw CLAP EPot GKev GPoy LAma NLar SPlb WPnP
- subsp. ***triphyllum*** var. ***atrorubens***	CLAP
§ ***utile***	ECho EPot GBin GEdr GKev LAma XLum
verrucosum	see *A. griffithii*
- var. ***utile***	see *A. utile*
yamatense	GKev
- subsp. ***sugimotoi***	LAma
yunnanense	LAma

Arisarum (*Araceae*)

proboscideum	Widely available
vulgare	ECho
- subsp. ***simorrhinum***	ECho
- - from Spain	ECho

Aristea (*Iridaceae*)

§ ***capitata***	CHll WHil
ecklonii	CBcs CPou CPrp CTsd EBee EPri EShb MHer
- GWJ 9469	WCru
ensifolia	ELan
thyrsiflora	see *A. capitata*

Aristolochia (*Aristolochiaceae*)

bianorii new	SBrt
californica	LEdu SBrt SKHP
chilensis	CCCN SPlb
clematitis	CArn ECho GPoy LEdu
contorta	WCru
- B&SWJ 12613	WCru
cucurbitifolia B&SWJ 7043	WCru
delavayi	SVen
durior	see *A. macrophylla*
fimbriata B&SWJ 13612 new	WCru
gigantea ♀H1b	CCCN CHll
grandiflora	CCCN
griffithii B&SWJ 2118	WCru
heterophylla	see *A. kaempferi* f. *heterophylla*
kaempferi	CCCN
- B&SWJ 293	WCru
§ - f. ***heterophylla*** B&SWJ 3109	WCru
× ***kewensis***	CCCN
liukiuensis B&SWJ 4960	WCru
§ ***macrophylla***	CArn CBcs CCCN CMac EPfP MRav
manshuriensis	EBee
- B&SWJ 12557	WCru
moupinensis BWJ 8181	WCru
onoei B&SWJ 4960	WCru
paucinervis	SBrt
rotunda	CArn SKHP
sempervirens	CMac LEdu SKHP WCru WSHC
serpentaria new	SBrt
sipho	see *A. macrophylla*
tomentosa	SKHP

Aristotelia (*Elaeocarpaceae*)

§ ***chilensis***	IVic LEdu
- 'Variegata' (v)	CCCN CMCN CMac CWib EBee GQui SPlb
macqui	see *A. chilensis*
serrata	GBin SVen

Armeria (*Plumbaginaceae*)

§ ***alliacea*** (Cav.) Hoffmanns. & Link	ECha XSen
- f. ***leucantha***	SRms WMoo
alpina	GJos
'Avalanche' new	MHol
'Bloodgood'	ECho
'Brutus'	MAvo MHCG
caespitosa	see *A. juniperifolia*
- 'Bevan's Variety'	see *A. juniperifolia* 'Bevan's Variety'
curvifolia new	GAbr
gaditana	XSen
Joystick Series	MMuc SEND WHil
- 'Joystick Lilac Shades'	CRos EBee ELan EPfP LRHS NRHS SPoG
- 'Joystick Red'	CRos ELan EPfP EShb LRHS NRHS SPoG WWFP
- 'Joystick White'	CRos ELan EPfP LRHS NRHS SPoG
§ ***juniperifolia*** ♀H5	CMea CRos ECho ELan EPfP GCrg LRHS MHer NRHS NSla SPlb SPoG SRms WIce XLum
- 'Alba'	CMea ECho ELan EPfP EPot GBin GCrg GMaP ITim MHer MMuc NHpl SPoG SRms SRot WAbe WHoo WThu
- 'Beechwood'	GCrg
§ - 'Bevan's Variety' ♀H5	ECha ECho ELan EPfP EPot GEdr GMaP MMuc NCou NLar NRya SPoG SRms SRot WAbe WHoo
- dark-flowered	WAbe
- rose-flowered	ITim
juniperifolia × ***maritima***	ECho
§ ***maritima***	CHab CNec CRos CWld ECho ECtt ELan EPfP GJos LPot LRHS MBel MSCN NEgg NRHS SWvt WCFE WMoo
- 'A Little in the Red'	GCrg
- 'Alba'	CBcs CElw CNec CTri ECha ECho ELan EPfP ESps GJos GMaP LEdu LSun MBel MCot MHol MMuc NHpl NRya SEND SPlb SPoG SRms WCFE WMoo
- 'Armada Rose'	CRos LRHS NRHS
- 'Bloodstone'	CTri ECho ELan
- 'Corsica'	CTri ECha MMuc NBir
- Düsseldorf Pride	see *A. maritima* 'Düsseldorfer Stolz'
§ - 'Düsseldorfer Stolz'	CBod CElw CNec CWld ECha ECho ECtt EDAr ELan EPfP GCrg GMaP LHop LRHS MCot NRHS SPoG SWvt WIce XLum
- 'Glory of Holland'	EPot

- 'In the Red'	CAby CMea ECha EHoe EPPr EShb GBin GCal GCrg GMaP MAvo MHer MMuc NHol NHpl NRya NSla SEND SPoG SRms SRot SWvt WFar WHoo WIce
- 'Laucheana'	WHoo WMoo
- 'Ministicks Rose'	LRHS
- 'Ministicks White'	LRHS
- 'Morning Star White'	CBod
- 'Nifty Thrifty' (v)	CTri ECho ECtt EHoe MHer NLar SPoG SRms
- 'Pink Lusitanica'	NLar
- 'Ruby Glow'	CTri
- 'Schöne von Fellbach'	XLum
- 'Splendens'	CBcs CRos CTri ECho EDAr EPfP ESps GMaP LRHS MHer MHol MJak MMuc NHpl NMir NRHS NRya SEND SPhx SPoG WMoo XLum
- 'Splendens Alba'	XLum
- 'Vindictive' ♀H5	CMea CTri EPfP
- white foliage	LRHS
plantaginea misapplied	see *A. alliacea* (Cav.) Hoffmanns. & Link
pseudarmeria	ELan EPfP LPot XLum
- (Ballerina Series) 'Ballerina'	NBir
- - 'Ballerina Red'	CWld GEdr LRHS SHil SRms WTor
- - 'Ballerina White'	LRHS SHil
- hybrids	CTri ELan
pungens	XSen
splendens 'Perfecta'	LRHS SHil
'Vesuvius'	XLum
vulgaris	see *A. maritima*
welwitschii	IFoB

Armoracia (*Brassicaceae*)

§	***rusticana***	CArn CBod CHby CLau CTri ENfk GPoy LCro LOPS MHer MMuc MNHC NPer NPri SIde SPoG SRms SVic WHer WHrl WJek
	- 'Variegata' (v)	EBee ELan GCal IFoB LEdu LHop NSti SMad SRms WHer WJek WMoo

Arnebia (*Boraginaceae*)

	densiflora	LLHF
	echioides	see *A. pulchra*
	longiflora	see *A. pulchra*
§	***pulchra***	LLHF

Arnica (*Asteraceae*)

angustifolia subsp. ***iljinii***	NBir
chamissonis Less.	CBod CHby EBee ENfk MNHC NLar SRms
montana	EBee GPoy MHer MNHC SRms SWat
- yellow-flowered SDR 6939 **new**	GKev

Arnoglossum (*Asteraceae*)

§	***plantagineum***	SBrt SPhx
	reniforme	SBrt

Aronia ✿ (*Rosaceae*)

arbutifolia	CAco CBcs CDul CTri EPfP LSRN MBlu MMuc SGol SLon SPlb
- 'Erecta'	CDul CTho EBee ELan EWTr GBin LHop LRHS MBlu MGil MMuc NLar SPoG SRms SWvt WCFE
melanocarpa	CCVT CDul CMCN CRos CSpe CTsd CWib ELan EPfP EWTr GKin LEdu LRHS MAsh MMuc WGrn
- var. ***grandifolia***	CJun
- 'Hugin'	CAgr CJun LEdu MCoo NLar
× ***prunifolia***	CFGn GAbr LEdu WGrn
- 'Aron' (F)	CAgr CJun
- 'Autumn Magic'	CBcs CJun CRos CTho EBee ELan GBin LHop LRHS LSou MAsh NEgg
- 'Brilliant'	CBcs CDul CTri EPfP GBin LRHS MMuc NEgg SGol SPer WHar WMat
- 'Karhumäki' (F)	NLar
- 'Nero' (F)	CAgr CBcs GBin LEdu LRHS MCoo NLar WMat
- 'Serina' (F)	CJun
- 'Viking' (F)	CAgr CDul CJun CTho ECrN EPfP EPom EWTr GBin IDee LBuc LCro LEdu LOPS LRHS MBlu MMuc NLar SGol WFar

Arrhenatherum (*Poaceae*)

elatius	CHab
- var. ***bulbosum***	GMcL
- - 'Variegatum' (v)	EBee EHoe ELan EPPr GBin GKev GMaP MMuc NBid NWad SEND WMoo

Artemisia ✿ (*Asteraceae*)

	from Taiwan	WHer
§	***abrotanum***	Widely available
	- 'Courson'	EBee XSen
	absinthium	CArn CBod CEls CHab ELan ENfk ESps GPoy MHer MNHC NLar NSti SIde SRms SVic WHer WJek WTre XSen
	- 'Lambrook Giant'	CEls
	- 'Lambrook Mist'	CEls CFis CMac CRos ECtt ELan EPfP GCal GQue LRHS MRav NRHS SWat XLum
	- 'Lambrook Silver'	CEls CRos CSam EBee ECha ELan EPfP ESps EWoo GCal GMaP LHop LPot LRHS LSRN MHer MMuc MRav NBro NRHS SCob SEND SLim SPer SRms SWat SWvt
	- 'Silver Ghost'	CEls
	afra	CEls XSen
§	***alba***	CBod CEls GPoy MHer SRms WJek XSen
§	- 'Canescens' ♀H4	CBot CEls CSam CTri EBee ECha ELan EPfP GMaP MAsh MHer MRav NLar SBrt SPhx WCFE XSen
	annua	CEls
	anomala	CArn CEls
§	***arborescens*** ♀H3	CBot CEls GAbr GMcL SPer
	- 'Brass Band'	see *A.* 'Powis Castle'
	- 'Faith Raven' ♀H3	CEls GBin MBNS NLar
	- 'Porquerolles'	CEls
	arbuscula **new**	CEls
	arctica var. ***saxatilis***	EBee
	argentea misapplied	see *A. arborescens*
	argentea L'Hér.	CEls
	argyi	CEls
§	***armeniaca***	CEls CRos ECho LRHS WHer XSen
	assoana	see *A. caucasica*
	atrata	CEls
	barrelieri	CEls
	caerulescens	CEls WCot
	subsp. ***cretacea***	
	- subsp. ***gallica***	CEls
	californica	CEls
	- 'Canyon Gray'	CEls
	campestris	XLum XSen
	- subsp. ***borealis***	CEls
	- subsp. ***campestris***	CEls

- subsp. ***maritima***	CEls
- - from Wales	CEls
camphorata	see *A. alba*
cana	CEls
canariensis	see *A. thuscula*
canescens misapplied	see *A. alba* 'Canescens'
canescens Willd.	see *A. armeniaca*
capillaris	CEls XLum
carruthii new	CEls
§ ***caucasica*** ♀H4	CEls ECho EWes MHer SPhx SRms SRot
chamaemelifolia	CBod CEls MHer SRms XSen
cretacea	see *A. nutans*
discolor Dougl. ex Besser	see *A. michauxiana*
douglasiana	CEls
- 'Valerie Finnis'	see *A. ludoviciana* 'Valerie Finnis'
dracunculus	ECha EWTr MJak MNHC MRav SPlb SRms WBrk
- French	CArn CBod CEls CHby CLau CTsd ENfk GPoy LEdu MHer NPri SEND SIde WGwG WJek XLum
- Russian	CEls ENfk SVic
- 'Thüringen'	IMou
ferganensis	CEls
filifolia	CEls
fragrans	CEls
frigida ♀H5	CEls
genipi	CEls
glacialis	CEls
gmelinii	CEls
gnaphalodes	see *A. ludoviciana*
gorgonum	CEls SEND
gracilis hort.	see *A. scoparia*
'Hausserman'	XLum
herba-alba	CEls XSen
indica var. ***momiyamae***	CEls
japonica	CEls
kawakamii B&SWJ 088	WCru
kitadakensis	CEls
- 'Guizhou'	see *A. lactiflora* Guizhou Group
laciniata	CEls
lactiflora ♀H7	CEls EBee ECha ELan GMaP MRav NDov NGdn SDix SPer SRms WMoo XLum
- NJM 11.010	WPGP
- 'Elfenbein'	EBee EPPr GCal IMou LHop MNrw MRav SMHy
§ - Guizhou Group	Widely available
- - 'Dark Delight'	CEls CMos ECtt EWes
- 'Jim Russell'	CDor CEls CElw EBee ECtt EWes MPie SPhx WWFP
- 'Laigong'	LEdu
- ***purpurea***	see *A. lactiflora* Guizhou Group
- 'Weisses Wunder'	EBee
lanata Willd.	see *A. caucasica*
lanata Lam.	XSen
laxa	see *A. umbelliformis*
'Little Mice'	CEls NLar
longifolia	XSen
§ ***ludoviciana***	CEls ELan IFoB NLar NPer SRms WCFE WFar XLum
- var. ***latifolia***	see *A. ludoviciana* subsp. *ludoviciana* var. *latiloba*
- subsp. ***ludoviciana*** var. ***incompta***	CEls
- - var. ***latiloba***	CEls EHoe LHop NBro SWvt WCot
- subsp. ***mexicana*** var. ***albula***	CEls
- 'Silver Queen'	Widely available
- 'Valerie Finnis' ♀H7	Widely available
maritima	CArn
- 'Coca-Cola'	EBee XSen
- var. ***maritima***	CEls
mauiensis	CEls
§ ***michauxiana***	CEls EBee
molinieri	CEls XSen
mutellina	see *A. umbelliformis*
niitakayamensis	CEls
nitida	CEls
nova	CEls
§ ***nutans***	CEls MRav
palmeri hort.	see *A. ludoviciana*
aff. ***parviflora*** CLD 1531	CEls
pedemontana	see *A. caucasica*
pontica	CBod CEls EBee ECha EHoe ELan GMaP GPoy LEdu MAvo MBNS MHer MNHC MRav NBro NLar NSti SEND SPer SPhx SRms WFar WHil WHoo WPGP XSen
§ 'Powis Castle' ♀H3	Widely available
princeps	CArn CEls GPoy LEdu SIde
procera Willd.	see *A. abrotanum*
purshiana	see *A. ludoviciana*
pycnocephala	CEls
- 'David's Choice'	CEls
ramosa	CEls
'Rosenschleier'	CEls EPPr EWes GCal SHar WPGP WWtn
schmidtiana ♀H5	CEls ECha SDix SRms WKif
- 'Nana' ♀H5	Widely available
- 'Nana Attraction'	CBod CRos EUJe LBMP LRHS NLar NRHS SRot
§ ***scoparia***	SMad
selengensis	CEls
splendens misapplied	see *A. alba* 'Canescens'
splendens Willd. var. ***brachyphylla*** Boiss.	MAsh
stelleriana	CEls CTri ECha EDAr GKev IFoB LHop MAvo MHer NBro NLar SRms
- RBS 0207	CEls
- from Alaska new	WCot
- 'Boughton Silver'	CBod CDor CEls CRos CWCL EBee ECtt EHoe ELan EPfP EShb ESps GMaP IKil LRHS LSun MAsh MRav NEgg NLar NRHS NSti SPer SPoG SRms SWvt
- 'Mori'	see *A. stelleriana* 'Boughton Silver'
- 'Nana'	CEls SWvt
- 'Prostrata'	see *A. stelleriana* 'Boughton Silver'
- 'Silver Brocade'	see *A. stelleriana* 'Boughton Silver'
taurica	CEls
§ ***thuscula***	CEls
tridentata	WHer
- subsp. ***tridentata***	CEls
- subsp. ***wyomingensis***	CEls
§ ***umbelliformis***	CEls
vallesiaca	CEls
verlotiorum	CEls
vulgaris	CArn CBod CEls CLau GPoy MNHC WHer
- 'Cragg-Barber Eye' (v)	EBee
- Oriental Limelight = 'Janlim' (v)	CBod CEls CLet CWld EBee EHoe EPPr EPfP GAbr GMcL NBir NEgg NLar SWvt WBod WHrl
- 'Variegata' (v)	CEls EBee ELan EPfP NBir SRms WMoo XLum
× ***wurzellii***	CEls

Arthropodium (*Asparagaceae*)

candidum	CBot ECho MPie

- 'Capri'	LPot
- 'Maculatum'	ECho LEdu NHpl SBrt SPlb
- ***purpureum***	ECho IKil
cirratum	CSpe CTre ECho IDee IKil MHer MPie
- 'Matapouri Bay'	CBcs ECre
milleflorum	SBrt

artichoke, globe see *Cynara cardunculus* Scolymus Group

artichoke, Jerusalem see *Helianthus tuberosus*

Arum (*Araceae*)

alpinum	see *A. cylindraceum*
byzantinum	GKev
'Chameleon'	CDor EPri NBir SEND SKHP SMad SPer WCot WRHF
§ ***concinnatum***	CTal ECho SChr SKHP
- 'Mount Ida'	ECho SKHP
concinnatum* × *cyrenaicum	GKev
cornutum	see *Sauromatum venosum*
creticum	CBro CFil CPne EBee ECho GCal GKev MNrw SDir SKHP WBor
- 'Karpathos'	GKev SKHP WCot
- 'Marmaris White'	EBee
- white-spotted	EWes
creticum* × *italicum	EBee
§ ***cylindraceum***	GKev
cyrenaicum	CFil ECho GKev
dioscoridis	ECho EPot GKev SDir
- JCA 195.197	WCot
- var. ***cyprium***	EBee GKev
§ - var. ***dioscoridis***	GKev LTro
- var. ***liepoldtii***	see *A. dioscoridis* var. *dioscoridis*
- var. ***smithii***	see *A. dioscoridis* var. *dioscoridis*
- var. ***syriacum***	GKev LTro
dracunculus	see *Dracunculus vulgaris*
euxinum	GKev
hygrophilum	WCot
italicum	CBod CLAP CTri ECho GBin GWyn IBoy LAma LCro LOPS MHol SDeJ SWat WCot WShi
- subsp. ***albispathum***	NChi
- 'Angelique'	WCot
- 'Edward Dougal'	MAvo WCot WFar
- 'Green Marble'	MAvo WFar
- subsp. ***italicum***	GKev WBrk
§ - - 'Marmoratum' ♀^{H6}	Widely available
- - 'Tiny'	GCal NChi SMHy SWvt WRHF
§ - - 'White Winter'	WBrk WCot
- subsp. ***neglectum***	SChr
- - 'Miss Janay Hall' (v)	EHoe WCot
- 'Pictum'	see *A. italicum* subsp. *italicum* 'Marmoratum'
- 'Tresahor Beauty'	MAvo
aff. ***italicum***	SDir
italicum* × *maculatum	WHer
korolkowii	WCot
maculatum	EPot GKev GPoy LAma MHer MRav NLar WHer WShi
- 'Pleddel'	MRav
- Tar Spot Group	SEND
nickelii	see *A. concinnatum*
§ ***nigrum***	GKev LLHF SBrt
orientale	EPot
palaestinum	GKev
petteri misapplied	see *A. nigrum*
pictum	CLAP CMac CTal ECho EWes GKev LEdu
- 'Taff's Form'	see *A. italicum* subsp. *italicum* 'White Winter'
purpureospathum	CFil EBee ECho GKev
rupicola var. ***rupicola***	GKev
- var. ***virescens***	GKev

Aruncus ✿ (*Rosaceae*)

aethusifolius ♀^{H7}	Widely available
- 'Little Gem'	ECho WCru
- 'Waddow Scarlet' **new**	NWad
asiaticus B&SWJ 8624	WCru
'Bastei'	IMou
dioicus	Widely available
§ - (m) ♀^{H7}	CBen CMac EHoe ELan IBoy MBNS MRav MWts NBro NSti SMad SPer SRms SWat WMoo
- Child of Two Worlds	see *A. dioicus* 'Zweiweltenkind'
- 'Glasnevin'	ECtt ESps MRav NHol WFar
- var. ***kamtschaticus***	EWes LSun NLar NWad WHrl
- - RBS 0208	NGdn
- 'Kneiffii'	Widely available
§ - 'Zweiweltenkind'	GAbr LRHS NLar SMad XLum
'Guinea Fowl'	ECtt ELon GQue LEdu MHol NGdn NLar SCob
'Horatio'	CBod CDor CSam EBee ECtt ELan GBin GLog IMou IPot LEdu LHop LRHS LSun MAvo MBel MHol MMuc MPie NLar SAko SCob SEND SMHy SMad SPhx SPoG WCot WMoo WWtn
'Johannifest'	EBee ECtt IMou IPot MAvo WCot
'Misty Lace'	ECtt GBin NGdn NLar SAko
'Netzwerk'	IMou
'Noble Spirit'	GMcL LSun MBel NGdn NLar SWat
'Perlehuhn'	EBee IMou
plumosus	see *A. dioicus*
sinensis	NBre
sylvestris	see *A. dioicus*
- 'Sommeranfang'	IMou
'Woldemar Meier'	EBee IMou MAvo SAko WCot

Arundinaria (*Poaceae*)

anceps	see *Yushania anceps*
auricoma	see *Pleioblastus viridistriatus*
disticha	see *Pleioblastus pygmaeus* 'Distichus'
falconeri	see *Himalayacalamus falconeri*
fargesii	see *Bashania fargesii*
fastuosa	see *Semiarundinaria fastuosa*
fortunei	see *Pleioblastus variegatus*
§ ***gigantea***	CDTJ
- subsp. ***tecta***	CBcs
hindsii	see *Pleioblastus hindsii*
hookeriana misapplied	see *Himalayacalamus falconeri* 'Damarapa'
hookeriana Munro	see *Himalayacalamus hookerianus*
humilis	see *Pleioblastus humilis*
japonica	see *Pseudosasa japonica*
jaunsarensis	see *Yushania anceps*
maling	see *Yushania maling*
marmorea	see *Chimonobambusa marmorea*
murielae	see *Fargesia murielae*
nitida	see *Fargesia nitida*
oedogonata	see *Clavinodum oedogonatum*
palmata	see *Sasa palmata*
pumila	see *Pleioblastus argenteostriatus* f. *pumilus*

pygmaea	see *Pleioblastus pygmaeus*
quadrangularis	see *Chimonobambusa quadrangularis*
simonii	see *Pleioblastus simonii*
spathiflora	see *Thamnocalamus spathiflorus*
tessellata	see *Bergbambos tessellata*
vagans	see *Sasaella ramosa*
variegata	see *Pleioblastus variegatus*
veitchii	see *Sasa veitchii*
viridistriata	see *Pleioblastus viridistriatus*
'Wang Tsai'	see *Bambusa multiplex* 'Floribunda'

Arundo (*Poaceae*)

donax	CAbb CKno CLet CPla ELan ELon EPPr ETod EUJe EWes GCra GMaP IDee LRHS LTro MAvo MBlu MBrN MNrw MRav NRHS SArc SCob SDix SEND SMad SPlb SSut WHal
- 'Golden Chain' (v)	CKno EPPr EWes LRHS LTro SMad
- 'Macrophylla'	CFil CHGN CKno ETod LEdu WPGP
- 'Variegata'	see *A. donax* var. *versicolor*
§ - var. ***versicolor*** (v)	CAbb CBcs CBod CKno ELan ELon EPPr ETod EWes LEdu LHop LLWG LRHS MRav NLos NRHS SCob SDix SEND SMad SPlb SPoG XLum XSen
I - - 'Aureovariegata' (v)	CBod CDTJ SEND
formosana	CKno EPPr
- 'Golden Showers'	ESwi EUJe NLos

Asarina (*Plantaginaceae*)

antirrhiniflora	see *Maurandella antirrhiniflora*
barclayana	see *Maurandya barclayana*
erubescens	see *Lophospermum erubescens*
lophantha	see *Lophospermum scandens*
lophospermum	see *Lophospermum scandens*
§ ***procumbens***	CTri CWld EBee ECho IBoy NBir NRya SChF SPhx SRms WAbe WBrk WKif

Asarum (*Aristolochiaceae*)

albomaculatum B&SWJ 1726	WCru
arifolium	EBee EPPr
- 'The Giant'	EBee
- white-flowered **new**	EBee
campaniflorum	ECho WCru
canadense	CArn CDor EBee ECho EWld GEdr GKev GPoy LEdu NLar WCru
cardiophyllum B&SWJ 11742	WCru
caudatum	CLAP EBee ECha ECho EPfP GEdr LEdu LPla NBro NLar SMad SRms WCot WCru
- deciduous	WCru
- white-flowered	SKHP WCru
caudigerum B&SWJ 1517	WCru
- HWJ 641 from Vietnam	WCru
caulescens	ECho LAma WCru
- B&SWJ 5886	WCru
delavayi	ECho LAma LEdu NLar WCot WCru
- giant	EBee XEll
epigynum	CBot GEdr LEdu MNrw NLar NPnk WCot
- 'Silver Web'	GEdr WCru
europaeum ♀H6	Widely available
- PAB 4377	LEdu WPGP
fauriei	WCru
forbesii	ECho
hartwegii	IMou
hypogynum B&SWJ 3628	WCru
infrapurpureum B&SWJ 1994	LEdu WCru
- 'Taroko Web'	WCru
lemmonii	LEdu
leptophyllum B&SWJ 1983	WCru
longirhizomatosum	GEdr WCru
macranthum B&SWJ 1691	WCru
maculatum B&SWJ 1114	WCru
magnificum	LAma WCru
maximum	ECho GKev LAma WCru
- 'Green Panda'	NLos
- 'Silver Panda'	CAby CBct CBod EPot ESwi EUJe GEdr NPnk SKHP WCot WMoo
naniflorum 'Eco Decor'	GMcL
nipponicum B&SWJ 2839	WCru
petelotii HWJ 1043	WCru
pulchellum	WCot WCru
sieboldii	LEdu WCru
splendens	CAby CBct CBod CBro CHid ECho ELan EPfP EPot EUJe GKev ILea LAma LEdu MHol MRav NLar NLos NPnk NSti SKHP SMad SPlb WCot WCru WFar XLum
taipingshanianum B&SWJ 1688	WCru
- 'Elfin Yellow'	WCru
wulingense	CTal WCru

Asclepias ✿ (*Apocynaceae*)

'Cinderella'	GKev SGol
curassavica	CCCN EShb LLWG LTro SRkn XLum
exaltata	SBrt
fruticosa	see *Gomphocarpus fruticosus*
hallii	EBee
incarnata	ELan IFoB LRHS MRav SBrt SPhx SPlb WOld XLum
- 'Ice Ballet'	CAbP CBod ELan GKev IFoB LHop LLWG LTro NLar SPer
* - 'Iceberg'	SGol
- 'Soulmate'	CBod EBee ELan ELon EPfP GKev LPot SPer WHar
latifolia	EBee
purpurascens	CArn EBee
rubra	SBrt
speciosa	EBee NBre SBrt WPGP
syriaca	EBee MBel MMuc XLum
tuberosa	CBcs CBod CSpe CWib EBee ELon GKev GPoy LRHS MHer MNHC MPie NDov SCob SPad SPer SPoG WGwG WWtn XLum XSen
- orange-flowered **new**	MHtn

Asimina (*Annonaceae*)

triloba (F)	CBcs CDTJ EBee IBal MBlu NLar SGol SPlb
- 'Sunflowers'	CCCN

Asparagus (*Asparagaceae*)

hardy, from Malawi	SKHP
PAB 13.0321 from Nagaland **new**	LEdu
acutifolius	XSen
asparagoides ♀H1c	EShb
densiflorus 'Mazeppa'	EShb
- 'Myersii' ♀H1c	EShb SEND
- Sprengeri Group ♀H1c	NGBl SEND
falcatus	SEND
filicinus	XBlo
- var. ***giraldii***	WCot

aff. ***meioclados*** B&SWJ 8309	WCot WCru
officinalis 'Ariane'	LCro LOPS WHar
- 'Backlim' ♀H4	ECrN EMil EPom
- 'Connover's Colossal' ♀H4	CHid CSBt ELan LCro LHop LOPS LSRN MNHC SEND SVic WHar
- 'Crimson Pacific'	SVic
- 'Dariana' ♀H4	SDea
- 'Gijnlim' ♀H4	ECrN EMil EPom LCro LEdu LOPS SDea
- 'Guelph Millennium' ♀H5	EPom LCro LEdu LOPS
- 'Jersey Knight'	SVic
- 'Mondeo'	EPom LCro LOPS
- 'Pacific 2000'	EPfP EPom LCro LOPS LSRN WMat
- 'Pacific Purple'	EPfP EPom LCro LEdu LOPS
- 'Stewart's Purple'	EPom WHar
pseudoscaber 'Spitzenschleier'	EBee EShb SDix WCot
retrofractus	WCot
scandens	EShb WCot
schoberioides	LEdu
- B&SWJ 8814	WCru
setaceus 'Pyramidalis' ♀H1c	XBlo
virgatus	EShb SPlb WPGP

Asperula (*Rubiaceae*)

§ ***arcadiensis*** ♀H3	ECho EPot SIgm WAbe
aristata subsp. ***scabra***	CSpe ECha WCot
- subsp. ***thessala***	see *A. sintenisii*
boissieri	ECho SIgm WAbe
cynanchica	MMuc
daphneola	ECho ELan EWes GKev LLHF WAbe
gussonei	ECho EPot LLHF SIgm WAbe WHoo WOld
lilaciflora var. ***caespitosa***	see *A. lilaciflora* subsp. *lilaciflora*
§ - subsp. ***lilaciflora***	ECho
nitida	ECho EPot
- subsp. ***puberula***	see *A. sintenisii*
odorata	see *Galium odoratum*
§ ***sintenisii***	CMea CPBP ECho LLHF WAbe WHoo WThu
suberosa misapplied	see *A. arcadiensis*
taurina	WPtf
- subsp. ***caucasica***	NLar WBor
tinctoria	CArn GPoy MHer SRms

Asphodeline (*Asphodelaceae*)

§ ***brevicaulis***	XSen
liburnica	CBro CSam ECha ELan EPri IMou MMuc SEND SPhx XSen
§ ***lutea***	Widely available
§ - 'Gelbkerze'	CRos EBee EPfP LRHS NRHS
- Yellow Candle	see *A. lutea* 'Gelbkerze'
taurica	EPot MBNS SMHy

Asphodelus (*Asphodelaceae*)

acaulis	CTal ECho LLHF WCot WWFP
§ ***aestivus***	EBee EWes MBel WCot XSen
albus	CArn CAvo CBot CBro CSam CSpe ECha EPPr EPfP EWTr GJos IFoB NBid NCGa SPlb SRms XLum XSen
brevicaulis	see *Asphodeline brevicaulis*
cerasiferus	see *A. ramosus*
fistulosus	LEdu SVen XSen
lusitanicus	see *A. ramosus*
luteus	see *Asphodeline lutea*
microcarpus	see *A. aestivus*
§ ***ramosus***	CPar CTal ECho GCal MCot WCot XSen

Aspidistra (*Asparagaceae*)

Chen Yi 135	WCot
B&SWJ 6645 from Thailand	WCru
attenuata	IMou
- B&SWJ 377	WCru
aff. ***attenuata*** B&SWJ 2001	WCru
caespitosa 'Jade Ribbons'	see *A. hainanensis* 'Jade Ribbons'
'China Star'	ESwi WCot
daibuensis B&SWJ 312b	ESwi WCru
- B&SWJ 6863	WCru
- 'Totally Dotty' (v)	WCru
aff. ***daibuensis*** 'Tidy Trim'	ESwi WCru
elatior ♀H2	CBct CTsd EBak EBee EShb ESwi LEdu MMuc MRav NLos NPla SAko SEND SMad WCot
- 'Akebono' (v)	WCot
- 'Asahi' (v)	WCot
- 'Hoshi-zora' (v)	WCot
- 'Lennon's Song' (v)	WCot
- 'Milky Way' (v)	EBee EShb ESwi MPie SAko SEND XLum
- 'Okame' (v)	WCot
- 'Variegata' (v) ♀H2	IFoB NBir SEND
- 'Variegata Exotica' (v)	XBlo
§ ***hainanensis*** 'Jade Ribbons'	WCot
linearifolia 'Leopard'	ESwi WCot
lurida	EShb
- 'Ginga'	see *A. sichuanensis* 'Ginga'
- 'Ginga Giant' (v)	WCot
minutiflora	WCot
mushaensis B&SWJ 1953	WCru
- B&SWJ 3727	WCru
aff. ***mushaensis*** 'Spotty Dotty' (v)	ESwi WCru
omeiensis	WCot
saxicola 'Uan Fat Lady'	see *A. zongbayi* 'Uan Fat Lady'
§ ***sichuanensis*** 'Ginga' (v)	WCot
sutepensis B&SWJ 5216	WCru
tonkinensis	WCot WCru
typica 'China Sun'	WCot
zongbayi	WCot
§ - 'Uan Fat Lady'	ESwi WCot WCru

Asplenium ✿ (*Aspleniaceae*)

antiquum 'Osaka'	LRHS
bulbiferum misapplied	see *A.* × *lucrosum*
bulbiferum ambig. × ***oblongifolium***	GBin
bulbiferum Forst.f.	ESwi GBin
§ ***ceterach***	EBee WAbe WHer XLum
integrifolium marbled fronds Chen Yi T-5981 **new**	WCot
§ × ***lucrosum*** ♀H1c	ESwi
'Maori Princess'	EBee GBin WFib
nidus ♀H1b	XBlo
§ ***scolopendrium*** ♀H6	Widely available
- 'Angustatum' ♀H6	Widely available
- Crispum Group ♀H6	CLAP EFer ELan NBid NNys SRms SRot WAbe WFar WFib WPGP
- - 'Crispum Bolton's Nobile'	WFib
- - 'Golden Queen'	CLAP
- Crispum Cristatum Group	CLAP CTal MMuc SCob
- - 'Crispum Cristatum Bolton'	WCot
- Crispum Fimbriatum Group	CLAP

- Cristatum Group	CDor CLAP CWCL EBee ECtt ELan ELon EPfP GMcL LRHS MGos MRav NBro NLar SPer SPoG SRms SRot SWat WBor WFib WHoo WMoo
- Fimbriatum Group	CLAP LRHS
- 'Furcatum'	CDTJ CLAP EBee ELan ELon MMuc NLar SEND SPad
- 'Kaye's Lacerated' ♀H5	CLAP EFer WFib
- Laceratum Group	CLAP
- Marginatum Group	EFer EPed
- 'Muricatum'	CLAP ELan MRav NBid WFib WHoo
- 'Ramocristatum'	CLAP
- Ramomarginatum Group	CLAP
- 'Sagittatoprojectum Sclater'	WFib
- Undulatum Group	CDTJ CLAP EAEE EBee ECha EPed EPfP GEdr LRHS MMuc NBir NEgg NLar SEND SRms WCot WGwG WMoo WPnP XLum
- Undulatum Cristatum Group	CLAP
trichomanes ♀H6	Widely available
- Incisum Group ♀H6	EFer WAbe
- 'Ramocristatum'	WAbe

Astelia (Asteliaceae)

banksii	CBcs CRos CSpe EBee IBal LRHS LSRN MGos SCoo SHil WCot
§ ***chathamica*** ♀H3	Widely available
- 'Silver Spear'	see *A. chathamica*
cunninghamii	see *A. solandri*
fragrans	CBcs IBlr LEdu
graminea	GCal LPar
grandis	IBlr LEdu WPGP
nervosa	IBlr LSRN SArc
- 'Alpine Ruby'	IBlr
- 'Bronze Giant'	IBlr
- 'Silver Sabre'	IBlr
- 'Westland'	CBcs CPne CRos CSpe CTsd GBin GCal IBlr ILea LEdu LHop LPar LRHS LSRN MGos NLos NRHS SCob SEND SHil SWvt
nivicola 'Golden Gem'	IBlr
- 'Red Gem'	LEdu
petriei	IBlr
'Red Devil'	CBcs CRos CSpe EPfP GBin IBoy LRHS MGos MHol SHil SPoG WHer
'Silver Mound'	EPfP SCob
'Silver Shadow' PBR	CBod CRos EBee EPfP LCro LRHS MMrt NLos NRHS SHil SPad SWvt WCot WFar
§ ***solandri***	IBlr

Aster ✿ (Asteraceae)

acris	see *Galatella sedifolia*
ageratoides	see *A. trifoliatus subsp. ageratoides*
§ ***albescens*** WJC 13657 **new**	WCru
alpigenus	see *Oreostemma alpigenum*
alpinus ♀H5	EBee ECho EPfP GKev LPot MHol NRya SIgm SRms XSen
- var. ***albus***	ECho EDAr EPfP ESps MArt WCot
- 'Antje'	MAvo MNrw
- Dark Beauty	see *A. alpinus* 'Dunkle Schöne'
- var. ***dolomiticus***	NSla
§ - 'Dunkle Schöne'	EAJP EDAr MArt SRms XSen
- 'Goliath'	ELan EPfP SPlb
- 'Happy End'	CNec CRos EPfP GMcL LRHS SHil SRms XLum XSen
- 'Pinkie'	EAJP EBee EDAr EPfP MArt
- 'Trimix'	ECho NBir SRms
- violet-flowered	GMcL
amelloides	see *Felicia amelloides*
amellus	ELon
- 'Blue King'	ECtt EWTr EWes GBuc NWsh SWvt
- 'Breslau'	EBee
- 'Brilliant'	CBod ECha ECtt EPPr GBuc LRHS LSou MAvo MBNS MRav MWat NEgg NWsh SAko SEND SPer WFar WGwG WHoo WOld
- 'Butzemann'	WCot
- 'Danzig' **new**	XLum
- 'Doktor Otto Petschek'	EBee ELon WCot
- Empress	see *A. amellus* 'Glücksfund'
- 'Forncett Flourish'	ECtt MHCG WCot WOld
- 'Framfieldii' ♀H7	ECtt SMHy WCot WFar WOld
§ - 'Glücksfund'	SAko
- 'Gründer'	IMou IPot MAvo MHCG WCot WOld
- 'Jacqueline Genebrier' ♀H7	GBuc MHCG NDov WOld
- 'King George' ♀H7	Widely available
- 'Kobold'	ESps WOld
- 'Lac de Genève'	WCot XLum
- 'Lady Hindlip'	CSam ECtt IMou WCot
- 'Louise'	MBrN MHCG SBch
- 'Mira'	EBee GBin MNrw SAko SPtp
- 'Moerheim Gem'	ECtt IMou WCot WOld
- 'Mrs Ralph Woods'	WOld
- 'Nocturne'	IKil WCot WOld
- 'Peach Blossom'	WOld
- Pink Zenith	see *A. amellus* 'Rosa Erfüllung'
§ - 'Rosa Erfüllung'	CBod CDor CMac CRos EBee ECtt ELan ELon EPPr EPfP GBuc GMaP IVic LHop LRHS LSou MAvo MNrw MRav NDov NRHS SBod SCob SPhx SPoG SRGP SWvt WCAu WOld
- 'Rotfeuer'	ELon GQue SAko
- 'Rudolph Goethe'	CNec CRos EBee ECtt ELan EMil EPPr EPfP ESps IKil LPot LRHS NLar NRHS SCob WHar WOld
- 'September Glow'	WOld
- 'Silbersee'	CSam IMou SAko
- 'Sonia'	CRos EBee ECtt GBuc LRHS NRHS SWvt WOld
- 'Sonora'	LHop MAvo MNrw SPhx WKif WOld
- 'Sternkugel'	EBee WOld
- 'Ultramarine'	WOld
- 'Vanity'	WOld
§ - 'Veilchenkönigin' ♀H7	Widely available
- Violet Queen	see *A. amellus* 'Veilchenkönigin'
- 'Weltfriede'	ECtt WOld
× ***amethystinus***	see *Symphyotrichum* × *amethystinum*
'Anita Pfeiffer'	LRHS
'Ann Leys' PBR	SCob WCot XEll
annuus	see *Erigeron annuus*
'Aqua Compact' (Autumn Jewels Series)	CBod EUJe LSou
asperulus misapplied	see *A. peduncularis*
'Beauté du Nord'	WCot
'Betel Nut'	SDix
capensis 'Variegatus'	see *Felicia amelloides* variegated
'Carmen'	WCAu
carolinianus	see *Ampelaster carolinianus*
'Cassandra'	NCGa
'Cheavers'	CRos LRHS NRHS
'Chilly Fingers'	MAvo MNrw MTis
coelestis	see *Felicia amelloides*
coloradoensis	see *Xanthisma coloradoense*
conspicuus	see *Eurybia conspicua*
cordifolius	see *Symphyotrichum cordifolium*
corymbosus	see *Eurybia divaricata*

'Cotswold Gem'	ECtt MHCG WCot WFar WOld
diffusus	see *Symphyotrichum lateriflorum*
diplostephioides	EPPr EPfP GBuc GKev GLog IKil MBNS MMrt SPlb WOld
divaricatus	see *Eurybia divaricata*
'Duchess' (mixed)	CWCL
dumosus	see *Symphyotrichum dumosum*
'Dwarf Barbados'	CRos EPfP LRHS NRHS
'Eleven Purple'PBR new	MNrw
ericoides	see *Symphyotrichum ericoides*
falcatus	see *Symphyotrichum falcatum*
'Fanny's Fall'	see *Symphyotrichum oblongifolium* 'Fanny's'
foliaceus	see *Symphyotrichum foliaceum*
× ***frikartii***	CMac ELan EPfP MRav SWvt WSHC
- 'Eiger'	WOld
- 'Flora's Delight'	CMea EBee ECtt GCal LPla LRHS MMrt MNrw MRav NDov NLar SPoG SRms WCAu WHoo WOld
- 'Jungfrau'	CRos CWGN EBee EPPr GBuc GMaP IKil ILea LRHS MRav NLar NRHS SPhx WOld
- 'Mönch' ♀H7	Widely available
- Wonder of Stafa	see *A.* × *frikartii* 'Wunder von Stäfa'
§ - 'Wunder von Stäfa' ♀H7	CEnd CKno EAEE EBee ECtt ELan ELon EPPr EPed EPfP EWTr GBuc GMaP LHop LRHS LSRN LSou MBNS MCot MHol MWat NBir NLar SRGP SWvt WCot WOld XLum
furcatus	see *Eurybia furcata*
glehnii	SDix
- 'Aglenii'	IMou MNrw NDov
greatae	see *Symphyotrichum greatae*
× ***herveyi***	see *Eurybia* × *herveyi*
himalaicus	NSla
hybridus luteus	see *Solidago* × *luteus*
'Ice Cool Pink' new	SMHy
'Ivy House'	ECtt
* ***kotarimus***	XLum
laevis	see *Symphyotrichum laeve*
lanceolatus Willd.	see *Symphyotrichum lanceolatum*
lateriflorus	see *Symphyotrichum lateriflorum*
linosyris	see *Galatella linosyris*
maackii	WCot
macrophyllus	see *Eurybia macrophylla*
mongolicus	see *Kalimeris mongolica*
'Mrs Dean'	ECtt
natalensis	see *Felicia rosulata*
'Natasha'	LSRN
(Newstars Series) 'Newstars Fantasy'	CBot MArt WCot WOld
- 'Newstars Glory'	CBot ECtt MArt WCot
novae-angliae	see *Symphyotrichum novae-angliae*
'Novemberlaan'	MSpe
novi-belgii	see *Symphyotrichum novi-belgii*
oblongifolius	see *Symphyotrichum oblongifolium*
oolentangiensis	see *Symphyotrichum oolentangiense*
pappei	see *Felicia amoena*
§ ***peduncularis***	CAby CKno CPou EBee EPPr IMou LEdu LRHS MAvo MHol MPie MTis NCou NSti SPoG WCot WFar WOld
petiolatus	see *Felicia petiolata*
pilosus	see *Symphyotrichum pilosum*
'Pinwheel'	WCot
ptarmicoides	see *Solidago ptarmicoides*
puniceum	see *Symphyotrichum puniceum*
'Purple Diamond' (Autumn Jewels Series)	LBMP
pyrenaeus 'Lutetia'	CBod CKno CMea CSam ECha EPPr GBuc GCal GMaP LRHS MAvo MNrw MPie MWat NAst NLar SPoG SPtp SRGP WCAu WKif WOld XLum
radula	see *Eurybia radula*
'Rose Queen'	MNrw MPie NWsh
rotundifolius 'Variegatus'	see *Felicia amelloides* variegated
rugulosus 'Asrugo'	CKno
× ***salignus***	see *Symphyotrichum* × *salignum*
§ ***scaber***	GCal NPnk WCot
scandens	see *Ampelaster carolinianus*
schreberi	see *Eurybia schreberi*
'Sea Spray'	WCot
sedifolius	see *Galatella sedifolia*
sericeus	see *Symphyotrichum sericeum*
sibiricus	see *Eurybia sibirica*
'Small-Ness'	NWad
'Snow Flurry'	see *Symphyotrichum ericoides* f. *prostratum* 'Snow Flurry'
souliei	CPBP
spathulifolius	WCot XLum
spectabilis	see *Eurybia spectabilis*
stracheyi	GKev LLHF
subcaeruleus	see *A. tongolensis*
'Sunhelene'	EBee ECtt WCot
'Sunspring'	SRGP
tataricus 'Jindai'	EBee MAvo
thomsonii	GBin WCot WOld
- 'Nanus'	CAby GBin GMaP ILea LRHS MCot MRav SPer SPhx SPoG WCot WOld
§ ***tongolensis***	GKev NHpl
- 'Berggarten'	CWCL LRHS MHol MNrw MPie NPnk WOld
- 'Napsbury'	LRHS WOld
- 'Wartburgstern'	EPfP LRHS MMuc SEND SGbt SPoG XLum
tradescantii misapplied	see *Symphyotrichum pilosum* var. *pringlei*
tradescantii L.	see *Symphyotrichum tradescantii*
§ ***trifoliatus*** subsp. ***ageratoides***	CPou WOld
- - 'Ashvi'	CBod CBre CKno CMil CSpe ECGP ECtt LSun MAvo MBel MHol MMuc MTis NCou SPoG WCot WFar WOld
- - 'Asran'	EBee ECtt EHoe EPPr EWes GCal LSou MMuc MPie NLar SEND WBrk WCot WFar WOld WTor XLum
- - 'Ezo Murasaki'	CSpe MAvo NDov SAko WCot XLum
- - var. ***firmus***	WPGP
- - - PAB 9347	LEdu
- - 'Harry Smith'	NDov WCot
- - 'Little Theo'	EBee
- - 'Stardust'	NAst WOld
- - 'Starshine'PBR	CKno ECtt EPPr EPfP IBoy LRHS MBel SHil WCot
trinervius var. ***harae***	WOld
tripolium	see *Tripolium pannonicum*
'Triumph'	WCot
turbinellus	see *Symphyotrichum turbinellum*
umbellatus	see *Doellingeria umbellata*
vahlii	GAbr
vimineus Lam.	see *Symphyotrichum lateriflorum*
- 'Ptarmicoides'	see *Solidago ptarmicoides*
'Wood's Blue'	LRHS
'Wood's Pink'	LRHS MTis WHil
'Wood's Purple'	EBee LRHS WHil
'Yvonne'	CBre

Asteranthera (*Gesneriaceae*)

ovata	CRHN CRos EPfP GGGa LRHS LSou SLon SPoG WPGP WSHC

Asteriscus (Asteraceae)

	'Gold Coin'	see *Pallenis maritima*
	maritimus	see *Pallenis maritima*

Asteromoea (Asteraceae)

	mongolica	see *Kalimeris mongolica*
	pinnatifida	see *Kalimeris pinnatifida*

Asteropyrum (Ranunculaceae)

	cavaleriei	GEdr
	peltatum	GEdr

Asterotrichion (Malvaceae)

	discolor	SPlb SVen

Astilbe ✿ (Saxifragaceae)

	'Alive and Kicking'	MAsh SCob
	'Amerika' (× *arendsii*)	CMHG CSBt SRms
	'Amethyst' (× *arendsii*)	CMHG CMac ELon EPfP LRHS MArt MRav NBir NHol SPer WFar WMoo
	'Angel Wings' (× *arendsii*)	NEoE
	'Anita Pfeifer' (× *arendsii*)	CMHG ELon IBoy NLar XLum
	'Aphrodite' (*simplicifolia* hybrid)	CBcs GCal GMcL MAsh XLum
	× ***arendsii***	EPfP IFoB NBre WHar WMoo XLum
	(Astary Series) 'Astary Pink' (× *arendsii*)	CBod LRHS NRHS
	- 'Astary Red' (× *arendsii*)	LRHS NRHS
	- 'Astary White' (× *arendsii*)	CBod CRos LRHS NRHS
	astilboides	CMHG SWvt
	'Avalanche'	CAby CTsd EWTr NHol SPad
§	'Beauty of Ernst' (× *arendsii*)	CBod EBee ELon EPfP LRHS LSou MSCN SRms WMoo
§	'Beauty of Lisse' (× *arendsii*)	ELon LSou MSCN WHil WOut
	'Bergkristall' (× *arendsii*)	CMHG
	'Betsy Cuperus' (*thunbergii* hybrid)	CMHG EBee NBre WCAu
	'Bonn' (*japonica* hybrid)	CWCL CWat NLar NQui SCob SCoo SRms
	'Boogie Woogie'[PBR] (× *arendsii*)	MAsh
§	'Brautschleier' (× *arendsii*) 🏆[H7]	CMHG CMac CTri ECtt EPfP GBin GCra LRHS LSRN MHol NEgg NGdn NLar NQui WPnP XLum
	'Bremen' (*japonica* hybrid)	CMHG
	'Bressingham Beauty' (× *arendsii*)	CLet CMHG CRos CSam CWCL EBee ECtt ELan EPfP EWTr EWoo GBin GMaP ILea LCro LHop LOPS LRHS MHol MJak MRav NEgg NEoE NHol NRHS SPer SWvt WBor WMoo
	Bridal Veil (× *arendsii*)	see *A.* 'Brautschleier'
§	'Bronce Elegans' (*simplicifolia* hybrid) 🏆[H7]	CMHG ECha ELon EPfP GBuc GLog GMaP GMcL GWyn NHol NLar SCob SPer WMoo WOut
	'Bronze Sprite' (*simplicifolia* hybrid)	WFar
	'Bronzelaub' (× *arendsii*)	CMHG
	'Bumalda' (× *arendsii*)	CSBt CWCL ELon GBin GLog GMaP IBoy LRHS MAsh NChi NEoE NGdn SPlb WMoo WWtn
*	***bumalda*** 'Bronze Pygmy'	NHol
	'Bunter Zauber' (× *arendsii*) **new**	XLum
	'Burgunderrot' (× *arendsii*)	MNrw NLar
	'Cappuccino' (× *arendsii*) **new**	MAsh SPad WHlf WTor
*	'Carmine King'	MMuc
	'Carminea'	CMHG
	'Carnea' (*simplicifolia* hybrid)	CMHG
	'Catherine Deneuve'	see *A.* 'Federsee'
	'Cattleya' (× *arendsii*)	CMHG CSam GBin GBuc GMcL GWyn LRHS NLar SAko WMoo XLum
	'Cattleya Dunkel' (× *arendsii*)	CMHG
	'Ceres' (× *arendsii*)	CMHG
	'Cherry Ripe'	see *A.* 'Feuer'
	chinensis	CBWd CMHG ECho GBin LRHS WSHC
	- B&SWJ 8178	WCru
	- from Russia	GCal
	- 'Brokat'	GBin
	- var. ***davidii***	CMHG XLum
	- - B&SWJ 8583	WCru
	- - B&SWJ 8645	WCru
	- 'Diamonds and Pearls'[PBR]	CWGN ECtt LLWG LSou SCob WFar
	- 'Finale'	ELon NHol SPer WOut
	- 'Frankentroll'	CMHG
	- 'Intermezzo'	GBin GCal GMaP NEoE NLar
	- 'Little Vision in Pink'[PBR]	WFar WHil
	- 'Love and Pride'	LSou
	- 'Milk and Honey'[PBR]	CWGN ECtt ELon LSou MBNS WFar
§	- var. ***pumila*** 🏆[H5]	Widely available
	- - 'Serenade'	CMac LRHS NGdn
	- 'Purple Glory'	CMHG ECtt IKil
	- 'Spätsommer'	CMHG
	- var. ***taquetii***	CMac ELan EPfP LRHS NSti SRms XLum
	- - Purple Lance	see *A. chinensis* var. *taquetii* 'Purpurlanze'
§	- - 'Purpurlanze'	Widely available
§	- - 'Superba' 🏆[H7]	CMHG CMac CTri ECha GMcL IBoy LRHS NBro NWad SDix SPer SRms WMoo
	- 'Troll'	GBin
	- 'Veronika Klose'	CMHG GBin NLar
	- 'Vision in Pink'[PBR]	CWCL ELan EPfP LSou LSun MBNS MHol MNrw WFar WHil WMoo
	- 'Vision in Red'[PBR]	CWat ECtt ELan EPfP IBoy LSou MBNS MHol MNrw NEgg NLar SAko SGbt SPoG WCAu WFar WMoo
	- 'Vision in White'	NEoE SAko SPoG WFar WHil WMoo
	- 'Visions'	CMHG CMac EPfP IBoy LRHS LSou MBNS NBro NEoE NGdn WMoo
	'Chocolate Shogun'	EBee ECtt MAsh SCob
	Cologne	see *A.* 'Köln'
	Color Flash	see *A.* 'Beauty of Ernst'
	Color Flash Lime	see *A.* 'Beauty of Lisse'
	'Country and Western'[PBR] (× *arendsii*)	LSou SCob
	'Crimson Feather'	see *A.* 'Gloria Purpurea'
	× ***crispa*** 'Lilliput'	ECtt NBir NEoE NHar NLar NRya NWad SCob SMad
§	- 'Perkeo' 🏆[H5]	CBcs CRos EBee ECtt ELan EPfP GMaP LRHS NBir NEoE NHar NHpl NLar NRHS SPoG SRms WCot WFar WHil WMoo
	- 'Peter Pan'	see *A.* × *crispa* 'Perkeo'
	- 'Red Rog'	NEoE
	- 'Snow Queen'	NBir NEoE
	'Darwin's Dream'	IBoy MNrw NEoE NLar WFar
	'Darwin's Favourite' (× *arendsii*)	CWCL
	'Delft Lace'	CRos EBee LBuc LRHS MAsh NRHS WMoo
	'Deutschland' (*japonica* hybrid)	Widely available

§	'Diamant' (× *arendsii*)	CMHG LSRN MMuc MNrw NBir NGdn NHol SEND WFar
	Diamond	see *A.* 'Diamant'
	'Drayton Glory' (× *arendsii*)	see *A.* × *rosea* 'Peach Blossom'
	'Drum and Bass'[PBR]	IBoy LSou NLar
	'Dunkelachs' (*simplicifolia* hybrid)	EBee
	'Dusseldorf' (*japonica* hybrid)	CMHG CWCL LRHS
	'Eden's Odysseus'	IBoy NHol
	'Eden's Twinkle'	EBee
	'Elegans' (*simplicifolia* hybrid)	CMHG CMac
	'Elisabeth' (× *arendsii*)	NBir
	'Elizabeth' (*japonica* hybrid)	CMHG
	Elizabeth Bloom = 'Eliblo'[PBR] (× *arendsii*)	ELon GAbr LLWG LRHS MHol MRav NDov NEgg NGdn NHol
	'Ellie' (× *arendsii*)	CMHG CMac EPfP EShb GQue LRHS LSRN LSou MAsh MBNS NGdn NHol NLar WFar
	'Else Schluck' (× *arendsii*)	ECha
	'Erica' (× *arendsii*)	CAby CMHG CTri CTsd EWTr GBin GLog LRHS NEoE NLar SHil SPad WMoo
	'Etna' (*japonica* hybrid)	CBcs CMHG CSam ECtt IBoy LRHS NEgg NGdn NLar SRms WFar WHar
	'Europa' (*japonica* hybrid)	CMHG CMac ECtt GMcL GWyn LRHS MGos NEgg NGdn NLar SPoG WHar WMoo
	'Fanal' (× *arendsii*) 🏆[H7]	Widely available
	'Fata Morgana' (× *arendsii* hybrid)	CMHG
§	'Federsee' (× *arendsii*)	CBcs CMHG CWCL EBee ECha ECtt ELan ESps LRHS MBNS NBro NEoE NGdn SPer WFar WWtn XLum
§	'Feuer' (× *arendsii*)	CMHG CMac ECtt ELan GBuc LBMP NEgg NEoE NGdn NHol NLar WBor WMoo
	Fire	see *A.* 'Feuer'
	'Fireberry'[PBR] (Short 'n' Sweet Series)	EBee LSou NLar
	'Flamingo'[PBR] (× *arendsii*)	ECtt MBNS MBel
§	***formosa*** B&SWJ 10946	WCru
	'Gertrud Brix' (× *arendsii*)	CWat MMuc NBir NGdn SEND XLum
§	***glaberrima***	NBid
§	- var. ***saxatilis*** 🏆[H5]	EPfP GBin GCrg GEdr IFro NHar WAbe WHal WThu
	- - 'Candy Floss'	NEoE
	- ***saxosa***	see *A. glaberrima* var. *saxatilis*
	'Gloria' (× *arendsii*)	CMHG CMac CTri ECtt LRHS MRav
§	'Gloria Purpurea' (× *arendsii*)	CMHG ELon NQui WMoo
	Glow	see *A.* 'Glut'
§	'Glut' (× *arendsii*)	CMHG CWCL ECtt LRHS MMuc NGdn NHol SAko SEND SRms WFar WWtn
	'Granat' (× *arendsii*)	CMHG CMac GBuc NBir NDov NEgg NGdn NHol NLar WMoo
*	Grande Group (× *arendsii*)	NBre
	grandis	CMHG WHer
	- BWJ 8076A	NLar
	'Grete Püngel' (× *arendsii*)	ECha WFar
	'Harmony' (× *arendsii*)	CMHG
	'Heart and Soul'[PBR]	CWGN EPfP LSou SAko
	'Hennie Graafland' (*simplicifolia* hybrid)	CBcs CMHG CWCL LSou NLar WFar
	'Holden Clough' (*japonica* hybrid)	NHol
	Hyacinth	see *A.* 'Hyazinth'
§	'Hyazinth' (× *arendsii*)	CMHG EBee GMaP LBMP LLWG LRHS LSou NBir NHol
	'Inshriach Pink' (*simplicifolia* hybrid)	CBcs CCVN CMHG CRos ECtt EHoe ELan GBin LRHS NBir NHar NHol NLar NRHS SBch WHal WOut
	'Irrlicht' (× *arendsii*)	CMHG CMac CMea EBee ELan EPfP EShb GBuc IBoy LHop LRHS NWad SPer SRms WPnP WWtn
	'Isa Hall'	CMHG NEoE NWad
	japonica	GKev
*	- 'Pumila'	NBir NGdn
	- var. ***terrestris***	see *A. glaberrima*
	'Jo Ophorst' (*davidii* hybrid)	CMHG EBee GBuc LRHS NGdn NLar
	'Jump and Jive'[PBR]	LSou MAsh WFar
	'Juno'	XLum
	'Key West' (*simplicifolia* hybrid) **new**	CGar MAsh
	'Koblenz' (*japonica* hybrid)	CMHG CWCL
§	'Köln' (*japonica* hybrid)	CMHG CRos CWat ELon LRHS NRHS
	'König Albert' (*davidii* hybrid)	GCal
	koreana	WCot
	- B&SWJ 8611	WCru
	- B&SWJ 8680	WCru
	'Kriemhilde'	CMHG
	'Kvële' (× *arendsii*)	CMHG LRHS WMoo
§	'Lachskönigin' (× *arendsii*)	CMHG
	'Lilli Goos' (× *arendsii*)	CMHG GBin GCal
	'Lollipop'	ECtt GBin MBNS NEoE SRms
	longicarpa B&SWJ 6711	WCru
	'Look at Me' (× *arendsii*)	LCro LLWG MAsh MBel MHol MSCN SPoG
	'Magenta'	CMHG
	'Maggie Daley'	IBoy NBro NEoE WMoo
	'Mainz' (*japonica* hybrid)	CMHG ECtt
	'Mars' (× *arendsii*)	CMHG
	microphylla	CMHG
	- B&SWJ 11085	WCru
	- pink-flowered	CMHG
	'Midnight Arrow' (*davidii* hybrid)	CMHG
	'Moerheim Glory' (× *arendsii*)	GBin IBoy NBre NGdn NLar
	'Moerheimii' (*thunbergii* hybrid)	CMHG
	'Mont Blanc' (× *arendsii*)	CMHG
	'Montgomery' (*japonica* hybrid)	CMHG EBee ELon EShb GAbr GMcL IKil ILea LBMP LRHS LSRN MAsh MBNS MNrw NBro NEgg NGdn NHol
	'Nikki'	NEoE NLar
§	***okuyamae*** B&SWJ 10975	WCru
	'Opal'	CMHG
	Ostrich Plume	see *A.* 'Straussenfeder'
	'Paul Gårder' (× *arendsii*)	CMHG
	'Peaches and Cream'	NBro NLar
	'Peter Barrow' (*glaberrima* hybrid)	GBin SRms
	'Pink Lightning'[PBR] (*simplicifolia* hybrid)	CWCL ECtt EShb GAbr MBNS NLar SPad WFar
	Pink Pearl (× *arendsii*)	see *A.* 'Rosa Perle'
	'Poschka'	NEoE
	'Professor van der Wielen' (*thunbergii* hybrid)	CMHG EBee ECha GQue LRHS NHol NLar SAko SPer SRms
	pumila	see *A. chinensis* var. *pumila*
	'Radius'	ELon NGdn NLar SPad WPnP
	'Red Baron'	CAby CTsd SPad
	Red Light	see *A.* 'Rotlicht'
	'Red Sentinel' (*japonica* hybrid)	CBcs CWCL CWat EBee ELon EPfP EWoo GBin GMaP GWyn IBoy

		LRHS LSou LSun MHol NBro NCGa NEgg NEoE NGdn NHol NLar WHil WOut WWtn
	'Rheinland' (*japonica* hybrid) 🏆H7	CBcs CLet CMHG CWCL ELon GBin GMcL GWyn LRHS MBel MMuc NGdn NLar SCob SEND SHil SRot WHoo WPnP
	'Rhythm and Blues'PBR	ECtt NEgg NLar
	rivularis	CMHG EBee SDix WCot
	- CC 5201	GKev
	- GWJ 9366	WCru
	- PAB 7353	LEdu
	- PAB 9763	LEdu
I	- 'Grandiflora'	GBin
§	- var. ***myriantha***	EBee NBre WMoo WPGP
	- - BWJ 8076a	WCru
	'Robinson's Pink'	NGdn
	'Rock and Roll'PBR	LSRN MAsh MSCN
§	'Rosa Perle' (× *arendsii*)	CMHG CSam NHol
§	× ***rosea*** 'Peach Blossom'	CBcs CMHG ELon GCra IBoy ILea LRHS NBir NEoE NGdn SGbt SPoG SWvt WHoo WMoo
	- 'Queen Alexandra'	XLum
	'Rosea' (*simplicifolia* hybrid)	NHol
§	'Rotlicht' (× *arendsii*)	CMHG CMac GBin LRHS MWts NEgg NEoE NGdn NHol NLar
	'Salland'	EBee LRHS
	Salmon Queen	see *A.* 'Lachskönigin'
	'Salmonea' (*simplicifolia* hybrid)	CMHG
	'Saxosa'	see *A. glaberrima* var. *saxatilis*
	'Sheila Haxton' (*chinensis*)	LRHS
	Showstar Group (× *arendsii*)	SRms WHil WRHF WWtn
	simplicifolia 🏆H5	CAby CFis SKHP WFar
	- 'Alba'	CMHG
	- Bronze Elegance	see *A.* 'Bronce Elegans'
	- 'Darwin's Snow Sprite'	CMac GBin NHol NLar WFar
	- 'Jacqueline'	LSou NHol
*	- 'Nana Alba'	NEoE
	- 'Rose of Cimarron'	NEoE NWad
	- 'White Sensation'PBR	CRos EBee GQue LRHS NLar NRHS SAko
	'Snowdrift' (× *arendsii*)	CHid CMHG CWat ESps GMaP IKil LBMP LLWG LRHS MBNS MBel MMuc NBir NEgg NEoE SEND SPer
	'Solferino' (× *arendsii*)	CMHG
	'Spartan' (× *arendsii*)	see *A.* 'Rotlicht'
	'Spinell' (× *arendsii*)	CWCL GBuc GMcL NBre WMoo WPnP
	'Spotlight'PBR **new**	GBin
	'Sprite' (*simplicifolia* hybrid) 🏆H7	Widely available
	'Stand and Deliver'PBR	ECtt
§	'Straussenfeder' (*thunbergii* hybrid) 🏆H7	CBod CMHG CMac CMos CTri EBee ECtt EPfP GBin GMaP LBMP LHop LRHS NBid NBir NBro NEgg NGdn NHol NLar SPer WCAu WMoo
	'Sugar Plum' (*simplicifolia* hybrid)	NGdn
	'Sugarberry'PBR (Short 'n' Sweet Series)	NLar
	'Superba'	see *A. chinensis* var. *taquetii* 'Superba'
	thunbergii var. ***congesta*** B&SWJ 10961	WCru
	- var. ***formosa***	see *A. formosa*
	- var. ***hachijoensis***	EBee
	- - B&SWJ 5622	WCru
	- var. ***okuyamae***	see *A. okuyamae*
	- var. ***sikokumontanum*** B&SWJ 11164 **new**	WCru
	- - B&SWJ 11534	WCru
	- var. ***terrestris*** B&SWJ 6125	WCru
	'To Have and To Hold'	LSou MNrw
	'Venus' (× *arendsii*)	ECtt GMaP MBNS MCot MMuc NGdn NHol SEND SPer WFar WMoo
	'Vesuvius' (*japonica* hybrid)	CBcs ECtt NBro NLar
	virescens	see *A. rivularis* var. *myriantha*
	'Walküre' (× *arendsii*)	CMHG
	'Walter Bitner'	GBin LLWG LRHS MBNS NBre NHol
	'Washington' (*japonica* hybrid)	LRHS NBre NGdn WPnP
§	'Weisse Gloria' (× *arendsii*)	CAby CMHG CMac ECha GBuc GMcL LLWG LRHS NBro NEgg NEoE NHol SCoo SHil WBor WCAu WMoo WWtn
	'White Diamond' (× *arendsii*)	WFar
	White Gloria	see *A.* 'Weisse Gloria'
	'William Reeves' (× *arendsii*)	CMHG NHol
	'Willie Buchanan' (*simplicifolia* hybrid)	CBcs CHid CMHG EHoe GAbr GBin GCrg GMaP LRHS NCGa NEgg NHar NHol NHpl NWad SPer SRms WAbe WCFE WFar WMoo
	Younique Carmine = 'Verscarmine'PBR	LSou
	Younique Pink = 'Verspink'PBR	MAsh
	Younique Red = 'Versred'	MAsh
	Younique Silvery Pink = 'Versilverypink'PBR	WFar WHil
	Younique White = 'Verswhite'PBR	MAsh
	'Zuster Theresa' (× *arendsii*)	CMHG CMos EBee ELon IBoy LRHS MBNS MNrw NBro

Astilboides (*Saxifragaceae*)

§	***tabularis***	Widely available

Astragalus (*Papilionaceae*)

canadensis	GJos LRHS
centralpinus	GJos
glycyphyllos	CArn CWld GJos GKev SPhx
looseri	SPlb
neglectus	EBee
odoratus	EBee

Astrantia ✿ (*Apiaceae*)

'Atomic Sunburst'	GQue
bavarica	GCal GKev MFie
'Berendien Stam'	GLet MAvo MFie
'Bloody Mary'	CWCL EBee ELan GBuc GLet MAvo MFie NGdn
'Buckland'	Widely available
'Bury Court'	MAvo NDov
carniolica	NEgg
- ***major***	see *A. major*
- 'Rubra'	CBcs EWoo GKev GMaP MFie WMoo
- 'Variegata'	see *A. major* 'Sunningdale Variegated'
'Clear Pink'	NDov
'Dark Shiny Eyes'	CWCL ECtt GBin GLet IBoy ILea LHop LLHF MTis NGdn NLar NSti SWvt
'Good Pink'	GLet LRHS
'Hadspen Blood'	Widely available

	'Harvington Adrian's Choice Pink' **new**	LRHS NRHS
	'Harvington Selected Red' **new**	LRHS NRHS
	helleborifolia	see *A. maxima*
	'Larch Cottage Clear Pink'	NLar
	'Larch Cottage Magic'	MAvo
	'Madeleine'	see *A. major* 'Madeleine van Bennekom'
§	***major***	Widely available
	- 'Abbey Road'[PBR]	CKno CLAP CWCL ECtt EWTr EWoo GLet IBoy IKil LHop LRHS LSou MFie NLar NPnk SCob SMad SRkn SRms
I	- 'Alba'	CBcs CMHG CWCL EBee GKev GLet IKil LRHS MCot MFie MRav NBir NGdn NPer SPer WMoo WPnP
	- 'Berdien'	EBee
	- 'Best Pink'	MAvo
	- subsp. ***biebersteinii***	EBee LRHS MFie NBir
	- 'Bo-Ann'	CWCL GLet IBoy MFie WFar
	- 'Can Candy'	MAvo
	- 'Celtic Star'	CSpe MFie SWvt
	- 'Claret'	Widely available
	- Cliff's form	MFie
	- 'Cottage Herbery'	MAvo
	- 'Dark Desire'	GLet NDov
	- 'Elaine's Pink'	WHoo
	- 'Elmblut'	IMou MAvo MFie
	- 'Florence'[PBR]	CBct CNor CRos CWCL CWGN ECtt EPfP GLet GPSL LPre LRHS MTis NCGa NDov NLar NRHS SPoG SWvt WHar
	- Gill Richardson Group	Widely available
	- 'Gracilis'	EBee
	- 'Green Tapestry' (v) **new**	WCot
	- 'Greenfingers'	EWes
	- 'Gwaun Valley'	WFar
	- subsp. ***involucrata***	LRHS MFie SWat
	- - 'Barrister'	CSam GBuc GLet MAvo MFie NLar
	- - 'Canneman'	EBee EWes MFie NLar WCot
	- - 'Jumble Hole'	MAvo NDov
	- - 'Margery Fish'	see *A. major* subsp. *involucrata* 'Shaggy'
	- - 'Moira Reid'	CLAP CSam CWCL ECtt ELan GCal GLet GMaP LSRN MFie MRav
	- - 'Orlando'	CLAP MAvo MFie
§	- - 'Shaggy' ♀H7	Widely available
	- - 'Snape Cottage'	EBee MAvo
	- 'Jade Lady'	WFar
	- 'Jitse'	MAvo
	- 'Large White'	LCro
	- 'Lars'	CWCL CWib ECtt ELan ELon EWoo GBin GCra GLet GMcL IFoB LRHS LSRN MFie MHol MNrw NBid NGdn NLar SPer SPoG SRms SRot SWvt WCAu
	- 'Lola'	CBcs CDor EBee EWTr GBuc GLet IBoy MTis NLar WHar
§	- 'Madeleine van Bennekom'	CLAP CNor EBee ECha ECtt GBin GLet
	- 'Midnight Owl'	EBee ECtt MHol MTis WHlf
	- 'Penny's Pink'	CWCL EBee ELan EWoo GLet LCro MAvo MFie NCGa NPnk
	- 'Pink Crush'	CRos EBee EPfP LRHS
	- 'Pink Pride'	CWCL GLet GMcL GWyn IPot LSou MHol MNrw MTis WCAu WFar WHil
	- 'Pink Sensation'	EBee GBin GLet GMcL
	- 'Pink Surprise'	GLet GMcL MAvo NLar
	- 'Primadonna'	CBod EPri GLet GMaP LBMP LRHS MFie MHol MTis NLar SPlb WMoo
	- 'Princesse Sturdza'	CWCL EBee LSou
	- 'Reverse Sunningdale Variegated' (v)	LSou MFie
	- 'Rosa Lee'	CWCL MFie
	- var. ***rosea***	CRos CWCL EPfP EWTr GLet GWyn LHop LRHS LSRN MFie MRav MSpe NGdn SPer WFar WMoo
	- - George's form	CLAP LSRN MFie
	- 'Rosensinfonie'	CWCL EBee GLet GMaP MFie NBro
§	- 'Rubra'	CBod CNec CRos CSBt CSpe CWCL ELan EPfP GKin GMcL IBoy LCro LOPS LRHS MFie MGos MHol MSpe NBir NChi NPer SCob SRms SWat WBod WBor WCAu WHal WHar
	- 'Ruby Cloud'	CBod CHid CWCL ECtt ELon EPri EWTr GBuc GLet LBMP MFie NBro NGdn SRot WHar
	- 'Ruby Giant'	GKin
	- 'Ruby Glow'	MFie
	- 'Ruby Wedding'	Widely available
	- 'Silver Glow'	EBee ECtt
	- 'Star of Beauty'[PBR]	CLAP CRos CWCL ECtt ELan EPed GBin GLet IBoy LRHS LSou MFie NCGa NLar NPri NRHS NSti SCob SPoG SRms SRot SWvt
	- 'Star of Billion'[PBR]	CBod CLAP CRos EBee ECtt ELan GLet IBoy IKil LHop LLWG LRHS LSun MHol NLar NPri NRHS SCob SPoG SWvt WCot WPtf WRHF
	- 'Star of Fire'[PBR]	EBee GLet LSou MBel NCGa SCob SRot WFar WHil
	- 'Star of Magic' (v) **new**	LRHS
	- 'Star of Royals'[PBR]	CLAP ECtt GLet IPot LSou WFar
	- 'Star of Summer'	CBod EBee LSou
	- 'Starburst'	EBee MFie
	- 'Stardust'	EBee
	- 'Sue Barnes' (v)	GCal MFie
§	- 'Sunningdale Variegated' (v) ♀H7	Widely available
	- 'Titoki Point'	MFie WCot
	- 'Venice'[PBR]	CBct CLAP CRos CWCL CWGN ECtt GBuc IBoy LRHS LSou MAvo MHol MNrw NEgg NLar NRHS SPoG SRms STPC SWvt WCAu WFar
§	***maxima*** ♀H6	Widely available
	- 'Mark Fenwick'	MFie NBir
*	- ***rosea***	CDor ECtt EWTr GQue MNrw NBir NGdn
	minor	EBee LRHS WCru
	'Moulin Rouge'[PBR]	Widely available
§	'Mrs MacGregor'	MAvo
	'Old Warwickshire Pink'	see *A.* 'Mrs MacGregor'
	'Queen's Children'	CDor GBuc GLet
	'Rainbow'	MFie NLar
	'Roma'[PBR] ♀H7	Widely available
	rubra	see *A. major* 'Rubra'
	'Ruby Bere'	LEdu
	'Ruby Star'[PBR]	CBod CKno CLAP CMil EBee ECtt ELon EPfP GAbr GMaP IBoy IPot LRHS LSun MFie MHol MSCN NDov NEgg NLar NSti SPer SWvt WCot WHoo WPnP
	'Sheila's Red'	EAEE GLet LRHS LSRN MBNS NDov
	'Snow Star'[PBR]	CRos CWCL CWib EBee EPfP EWoo GLet IKil LRHS MBNS MFie MJak NLar SHil
	'Star of Heaven'	NLar
	'Star of Passion'[PBR]	EBee GLet NCGa NLar SCob
	'Star of Treasure'	GLet IBoy IPot NCGa NLar
	'Superstar'[PBR]	Widely available

'Warren Hills' CCVN CLAP EBee GMaP MFie NLar NPnk
'Washfield' CWCL GLet MAvo NDov

Astrodaucus (*Apiaceae*)

orientalis LEdu

Astrolepis (*Pteridaceae*)

sinuata ISha WCot

Astrophytum (*Cactaceae*)

myriostigma 🏆H2 SRms

Astydamia (*Apiaceae*)

latifolia **new** WCot

Asyneuma (*Campanulaceae*)

campanuloides SIgm
canescens ELan LRHS LSou
limonifolium WAbe
lycium **new** CPBP
pulvinatum CPBP EPot WAbe

Asystasia (*Acanthaceae*)

bella see *Mackaya bella*

Athamanta (*Apiaceae*)

turbith CSpe LEdu MNrw SIgm WPtf
vestina SIgm SPhx

Athanasia (*Asteraceae*)

§ ***parviflora*** SPlb

Atherosperma (*Atherospermataceae*)

moschatum CFil CHll SKHP

Athrotaxis (*Cupressaceae*)

cupressoides CBcs CDul CKen WThu
laxifolia CKen WThu

Athyrium ✿ (*Woodsiaceae*)

'Branford Beauty' CCCN CLAP ISha LRHS NLar WPGP
'Branford Rambler' CLAP ISha
filix-femina 🏆H7 Widely available
§ - subsp. ***angustum*** 🏆H7 CLAP ELan LRHS MRav NGdn WMoo
- - f. ***rubellum*** 'Lady in Red' 🏆H7 CAby CBod CCCN CKel CLAP CWCL EBee ESwi GBin GMcL ISha LBrs LCro LEdu LRHS LSRN MGos MSCN NEgg NLar SCob SHil SPoG WMoo
- 'Crispum Grandiceps Kaye' NGdn
- Cristatum Group CLAP EFer ELan ESps LSRN NGdn SWat WFib
- 'Dre's Dagger' EBee SCob SPoG WFar
- 'Fieldii' CLAP EFer
- 'Frizelliae' 🏆H7 Widely available
- 'Frizelliae Capitatum' CLAP WFib WPGP
- 'Grandiceps' CLAP
- 'Lady Victoria' CLAP
- 'Lady-in-Lace' 🏆H7 CLAP EBee ITim LLHF LLWG SMad WCot
- 'Minutissimum' CLAP ELan ISha LRHS WCot
- Plumosum Group CLAP EShb MRav WFib XLum
- 'Plumosum Axminster' CLAP EFer NLar WFar
- 'Plumosum Druery' EFer
- Red Stem see *A. filix-femina* 'Rotstiel'
§ - 'Rotstiel' CDTJ CLAP EBee NBro NLos WMoo WPnP
- 'Setigerum Cristatum' WFar
- 'Vernoniae' 🏆H7 CLAP ELan MRav NLar
- 'Vernoniae Cristatum' WFib
- 'Victoriae' CCCN CDTJ CWCL EBee EFer ELan GBin GMaP ISha LLWG LRHS NBid NGdn NLar SBod SHil WMoo XLum
- aff. 'Victoriae' CKel CTal EAJP EWTr
- Victoriae Group see *A. filix-femina* subsp. *angustum*
'Ghost' 🏆H6 CCCN CLAP EBee ESwi ISha LRHS MGos MPie NLar NSti SPoG WCot WFar
goeringianum 'Pictum' see *A. niponicum* var. *pictum*
minimum **new** WCot
niponicum LPar WHal
- 'Godzilla' **new** ISha
- f. ***metallicum*** see *A. niponicum* var. *pictum*
§ - var. ***pictum*** 🏆H5 Widely available
- - 'Apple Court' CCCN EBee ESps ESwi ISha LRHS NLar SPoG
- - 'Burgundy Lace' CLAP EBee ECtt ESwi LPre MAvo MPnt NAst NLar SPoG WCot WPat
* - - 'Cristatoflabellatum' CLAP EBee LRHS
- - 'Pewter Lace' EBee ECtt LPre NAst NLar
- - 'Red Beauty' CBcs CBod CDTJ CLAP ECha ECtt ELan EMOT EPfP GBin GMcL IBoy LEdu LRHS LSRN NLar NPri SBod SEND SHil SRkn WCot WMoo
- - 'Regal Red' EBee ISha LRHS NLos
- - 'Silver Falls' 🏆H5 CBcs CLAP EShb ESwi LRHS SPoG WPGP
- - 'Ursula's Red' CCVN CLAP EBee EShb LBMP LCro LHop LOPS LRHS LSRN MNrw MSCN NBid NBir NHpl NLar SPoG WCot WFar WPGP
- - 'Wildwood Twist' CLAP WCot
'Ocean's Fury' CAby CLAP EBee ECtt EShb ESwi GBin LPla SPoG
otophorum 🏆H4 ISha MRav NBid NLos WPGP
- var. ***okanum*** 🏆H5 Widely available
vidalii CLAP EBee ISha LRHS LSou NBro NLar NLos SHil WCot WFar WFib XLum

Atractylodes (*Asteraceae*)

japonica EFEx GEdr LEdu
macrocephala EFEx

Atragene see *Clematis*

Atriplex (*Amaranthaceae*)

canescens CAgr NLar
halimus CAgr CBcs CFGn CLau ECha EHoe EPPr MRav NLar SDix SLon SPer SPlb WCot
- 'Cascais' **new** WCot
- 'Limelight' (v) **new** EPPr
hortensis ENfk
- var. ***rubra*** CSpe ELan LSou MHer MNHC SHDw SIde SRms WJek

Atropa (*Solanaceae*)

belladonna CArn GPoy MMuc SEND
mandragora see *Mandragora officinarum*

Aubrieta (*Brassicaceae*)

'Alba' see *A.* 'Fiona'
albomarginata see *A.* 'Argenteovariegata'
'Alix Brett' CMea ECtt
'Ann Kendall' ECtt
'April Joy' (d) ELon

§ 'Argenteovariegata' (v) ♀H5	CRos ELan LRHS MJak NRHS
'Audrey Blue' (Audrey Series)	GWyn
§ 'Aureovariegata' (v) ♀H5	CMea ELan NPer XLum
(Axcent Series) Axcent Antique Rose = 'Audelanro'PBR	LRHS
- Axcent Blue with Eye = 'Audelbley'PBR	LBuc LRHS
- Axcent Burgundy	CRos LRHS NRHS
- Axcent Deep Purple = 'Audelpur'PBR	LBuc LRHS
- Axcent Light Blue	CRos LRHS NRHS
- Axcent Magenta = 'Audelmag'PBR	LRHS
bicoloured	CMea
Blaue Schönheit	see *A.* 'Blue Beauty'
'Blaumeise'	LRHS MHol
§ 'Blue Beauty'	CBod CMea ECtt EPfP EUJe GBin GMaP NHpl NLar WHoo
'Blue Emperor'	ECtt
'Blue Whale'	CBod ECtt GAbr NLar SRms SRot SWvt
§ 'Bob Saunders' (d)	CMea ECtt ELon
'Bressingham Pink' (d) ♀H5	ECtt ELan EPfP SRms
'Bressingham Red'	ECtt ELan EPfP ESps GCrg GMaP LHop SRms
'Bubble Purple'	EPfP
canescens	CPBP GKev
Cascade Series	CWCL SPoG
- 'Blue Cascade'	GMaP MBNS SPlb SPoG SRms
- 'Lilac Cascade'	SPoG SRms
- 'Purple Cascade'	CTri CWib LBMP LCro LSRN MAsh MBNS MJak SPlb SPoG SRms WRHF
- 'Red Cascade' ♀H5	CTri CWib ECtt LBMP LSRN MBNS MJak SPlb SPoG
× ***cultorum*** new	SVic
deltoidea	WCFE
- Variegata Group (v)	ECtt MHol
- - 'Nana Variegata' (v)	CMea EPot SIgm
'Doctor Mules' ♀H5	ECtt ESps SRms
'Doctor Mules Variegata' (v)	ECtt EHoe ELan ELon EPfP ESps GMaP GWyn MAsh MHer NLar NWad SPoG SRot SWvt WHoo WIce
double pink-flowered (d)	CBod EPfP GMaP MHol WRHF
'Downers Variegata' (v)	ECtt EPot NWad
'Elsa Lancaster'	EPot NHpl NSla
§ 'Fiona'	ECtt EWoo MMuc
glabrescens	CMea CPBP NHpl SIgm WAbe
'Gloria'	CBod ECtt EPot EUJe GAbr NHpl NLar SRot WHoo WIce
'Golden Emperor'	MHer
'Golden King'	see *A.* 'Aureovariegata'
gracilis 'Kitte Rose'	CRos ECtt LBuc LRHS MHol NRHS
'Greencourt Purple' ♀H5	ECtt ELan MHer
'Hamburger Stadtpark'	CWCL ECtt ELan ELon EPfP EWoo GCrg LHop SRms SRot
'Hemswell Purity'	see *A.* 'Snow Maiden'
'Ida'	CSma
'Kati'	LRHS
'Kitte'	CSma ECtt ELan EPfP GCrg LRHS MHer NEoE NLar SPoG SRms
'Kitte Blue'	CRos EPfP LBuc LRHS MHol NPri NRHS SPoG SRms WIce
'Kitte Purple'	CSma ELan EPfP SPoG
'Kitte White' new	LRHS NRHS
'Leichtlinii'	XLum
'Lime Variegated' (v)	NHpl WIce
macedonica	EPot
'Pink Beauty'	ECtt WIce
'Purple Charm'	SRms
'Red Carpet'	ELan EPot MAsh MHer SRms
'Rose Queen'	CMea ECtt
(Royal Series) 'Royal Blue'	EPfP MJak NEgg NLar SRms SRot WMoo
- 'Royal Red'	EPfP GBin GWyn SRms WMoo
- 'Royal Violet'	EPfP WMoo
'Schofield's Double'	see *A.* 'Bob Saunders'
'Shobden' (v)	WIce
'Silberrand' (v)	ECha
§ 'Snow Maiden'PBR	NHpl
'Somerfield Silver'	ELan EPfP
'Somerford Lime' (v)	ECtt ELan EPfP LSou SRms WIce
'Swan Blue' new	EWld
'Swan Red' (v)	CBod ECtt EHoe ELon EPot LBMP MHer NEgg NEoE NHpl NLar NSla SRot
'Valerie' (v)	ECtt EPot
'Westacre Gold' (v)	ECtt MAsh MHol
'Whitewell Gem'	WMoo XLum
'Winterberg'	ECtt

Aucuba ✿ (*Garryaceae*)

chlorascens B&SWJ 11815	WCru
himalaica	CFil
var. ***dolichophylla***	
- - Og 95038	WCru
japonica	CAco CCVT CDul CLet ESps GMcL LPar SCob SEWo WCru WFar
- 'Angelon'	CRos LRHS NRHS
- var. ***borealis*** (f) CWJ 12898	WCru
- 'Crassifolia' (m)	EBtc ELon SArc
- 'Crotonifolia' (f/v) ♀H5	Widely available
- 'Crotonifolia' (m/v)	CMac MAsh SGol SRms
- 'Dentata'	WCru
- 'February Star' (f/v)	SDix
- 'Gold Splash' (v)	WFar
- 'Golden Girl' (v) new	CRos LRHS NRHS
- 'Golden King' (m/v) ♀H5	CLet CMac CWib ELan ELon EMOT EPfP LRHS MAsh MGos NLar NRHS SCob SGol SLim SPoG WFar
- 'Golden Spangles' (f/v)	CBcs EBee IVic LRHS NLar SWvt
- 'Goldstrike' (v)	LRHS MAsh
- 'Hillieri' (f)	EBtc
- f. ***longifolia***	CBot CMac EPfP NLar SArc SDix WCru
- - 'Salicifolia' (f) ♀H5	ESwi MRav NLar SCob WCru WFar WPGP
- 'Maculata' misapplied	see *A. japonica* 'Variegata'
- 'Marmorata' (v)	CRos LRHS SHil
- 'Mr Goldstrike' (m/v)	EPfP ESps LRHS
- Pepper Pot = 'Shilpot' (m/v) ♀H5	EPfP LRHS MAsh MJak SLon WFar
- 'Pepperspot'PBR (m/v)	MJak WMoo
- 'Picturata' (m/v)	CDul CLet CMac CSBt ELan ELon ESps LRHS MAsh MJak MMuc NLar NRHS SEND WFar
- 'Rozannie' (f/m) ♀H5	Widely available
- 'Sulphurea Marginata' (f/v)	CBcs CMac CTri EBee EShb ESwi LRHS NLar NRHS WFar
§ - 'Variegata' (f/v)	Widely available
- 'Variegata' white-flowered male (m/v)	SGbt
omeiensis	CBcs CFil
- B&SWJ 2864	WCru
- BWJ 8048	WCru
- L 614	CFil WPGP

Aulax (*Proteaceae*)

cancellata	CCCN SPlb

Aurinia (*Brassicaceae*)

§	***saxatilis*** ♀H5	ECho ELan EPfP MMuc SEND SPlb WRHF XSen
	- 'Argentea'	ECho
	- 'Citrina' ♀H5	ECha ECtt SRms
	- 'Compacta'	CTri ECtt GJos WIce
	- 'Dudley Nevill'	ELon
	- 'Dudley Nevill Variegated' (v)	ECha ECtt EWes MHer
	- Gold Ball	see *A. saxatilis* 'Goldkugel'
	- 'Gold Dust'	ECho SRms
	- 'Golden Queen'	CNor MHer
§	- 'Goldkugel'	CMea EPfP GWyn MHol SPoG SRms
	- 'Variegata' (v)	SPoG SRms

Austrocedrus (*Cupressaceae*)

§	***chilensis***	CKen SBig SLim

Avena (*Poaceae*)

	candida	see *Helictotrichon sempervirens*

Avenula see *Helictotrichon*

Averrhoa (*Oxalidaceae*)

	carambola (F)	CCCN

avocado see *Persea americana*

Azalea see *Rhododendron*

Azara ✿ (*Salicaceae*)

	sp.	NEgg
	dentata	CBcs CHll CMac WFar
	- 'Variegata'	see *A. integrifolia* 'Variegata'
	integrifolia	CCCN MGil
	- 'Uarie'	CCCN
§	- 'Variegata' (v)	CCCN CWib LRHS
	lanceolata	CBcs CDul CTri CTsd LEdu
	microphylla ♀H4	CBcs CCCN CCht CDul CLet CMac CTri EBee ELan ELon EPfP EUJe LRHS LSRN MAsh MGil MGos MMuc MNHC SArc SDix SEND SLim SPer SPlb SWeb WBod WFar WPGP
*	- 'Albovariegata' (v)	CTri
	- 'Gold Edge' (v)	CBcs EPfP LRHS NRHS WFar
	- 'Variegata' (v)	CBcs CBct CMac CWib EBee EHoe ELan EPfP GMcL GQui LRHS MAsh MGil MMuc NLar NRHS SEND SPoG WFar WPat WSHC
*	***patagonica***	MBlu
	petiolaris	CTri LEdu MGil
	serrata ♀H4	CBcs CBot CCCN CDul CEnd CTsd CWib EPfP EShb EUJe GBin LHop LRHS MGil NLar SDix SEND SGol SPer SPoG SRms SVen WBor WFar WHar WKif WSHC
	uruguayensis	CBcs CCCN CTsd EBtc

Azorella (*Apiaceae*)

	glebaria misapplied	see *A. trifurcata*
	glebaria A. Gray	see *Bolax gummifer*
	gummifer	see *Bolax gummifer*
	lycopodioides	WAbe
	patagonica	SPlb WAbe
§	***trifurcata***	CPar CSpe CTri GAbr GCrg GKev MMuc NBir SIgm SPlb
	- 'Nana'	ECho GEdr GMaP WThu XLum

Azorina (*Campanulaceae*)

§	***vidalii***	SPlb

B

Babiana (*Iridaceae*)

	sp.	SDir
	ambigua	CTal
	angustifolia	ECho
	'Blue Gem'	ECho
	nana	CTal GKev
	patersoniae	SPlb
	purpurea	CTal
	pygmaea	CTal
	sambucina	CTal NRog
	stricta ♀H2	CCCN CTal ECho GKev NNys SDeJ
	- Kew hybrids	GKev
	- 'Purple Star'	ECho GKev NRog
	- 'Tubergen's Blue'	ECho
	thunbergii	CTre
	tubulosa	CTal NRog
	vanzyliae	CTal
	villosa	ECho
*	***volubilis***	NRog
	'Zwanenburg's Glory'	CPrp ECho

Baccharis (*Asteraceae*)

	halimifolia	CBcs SEND
	- 'Baccador'PBR	EBee LRHS
	patagonica	LRHS MMuc SArc SEND SPhx SVen

Backhousia (*Myrtaceae*)

	citriodora	CArn GPoy MHer

Bacopa (*Plantaginaceae*)

	sp.	SEND SWvt
	'Snowflake'	see *Sutera cordata* 'Snowflake'

Baeckea (*Myrtaceae*)

	linifolia	SPlb
	virgata	SPlb

Balbisia (*Ledocarpaceae*)

	peduncularis	CCCN

Baldellia (*Alismataceae*)

	ranunculoides	WMAq
	- f. ***repens***	LLWG

Ballota (*Lamiaceae*)

	acetabulosa	ECha EWes WCot XSen
	'All Hallow's Green'	see *Marrubium bourgaei* var. *bourgaei* 'All Hallows Green'
	hirsuta	XSen
	nigra	CArn GPoy MHer NMir SRms
§	- 'Archer's Variegated' (v)	MAvo
	- 'Variegata'	see *B. nigra* 'Archer's Variegated'
	pseudodictamnus ♀H4	CBcs CBod CMac EBee ECha EHoe ELan EPfP EWoo GMaP LHop LRHS LSRN MBel MRav NPer NSti SCob SDix SEND SLon SPer XLum XSen
	- B&M 8119	WCot WPGP
	- from Crete	ECha
	rupestris 'Frogswell Carolyn' (v)	IFro XSen

Baloskion (*Restionaceae*)

	tetraphyllum	see *Restio tetraphyllus*

Balsamita see *Tanacetum*

Bambusa (*Poaceae*)

glaucescens — see *B. multiplex*
§ **multiplex** — XBlo
- 'Alphonso-Karrii' — SBig
- 'Elegans' — see *B. multiplex* 'Floribunda'
- 'Fernleaf' — see *B. multiplex* 'Floribunda'
§ - 'Floribunda' — EShb XBlo
- 'Golden Goddess' — XBlo
- 'Silverstripe' — see *B. multiplex* 'Variegata'
§ - 'Variegata' (v) — XBlo
- 'Wang Tsai' — see *B. multiplex* 'Floribunda'
pubescens — see *Dendrocalamus strictus*
ventricosa — SBig XBlo
vulgaris — XBlo
- 'Vittata' — ERod XBlo

banana see *Ensete, Musa*

Banksia (*Proteaceae*)

canei — SPlb
ericifolia — CDTJ CTre
- var. **ericifolia** — CCCN
- var. **macrantha** — SPlb
grandis — CCCN CTre LRHS
integrifolia — CBcs CCCN CDTJ CKel CTre LRHS SPlb
marginata — LRHS SPlb
media — SPlb
oblongifolia — SPlb
paludosa — SPlb
robur — CBcs CCCN SPlb
serrata — CCCN SIgm SPlb
speciosa — SPlb
spinulosa — CTre
- 'Birthday Candles' new — CTre
- var. **collina** — SPlb
- var. **spinulosa** — CBcs CCCN
violacea — SPlb

Baptisia (*Papilionaceae*)

§ **alba** — EBee GBin LPla MNrw
- var. **alba** — IPot
- - 'Wayne's World' — EBee
§ - var. **macrophylla** — EWes LRHS SPhx
australis ♀H7 — Widely available
- 'Caspian Blue' — LEdu LHop WHil WSHC
- 'Exaltata' ♀H7 — CGar EBee ECtt GBin LHop LSun MHol NCou WCot
- var. **minor** — GBin MHer MMrt SPhx
- 'Nelson's Navy' — SMHy
× **bicolor** 'Starlite' (Prairieblues Series) — GBin IPot MNrw NDov SKHP SPoG
bracteata var. **leucophaea** — LRHS LSou SPhx
'Carolina Moonlight' — EBee ECtt EWTr EWes GBin IPot LHop MAvo MMrt MNrw NDov NPnk SKHP
'Chocolate Chip' — LHop WHil
'Dutch Chocolate' (Decadence Series) new — LRHS WHlf
lactea — see *B. alba* var. *macrophylla*
leucantha — see *B. alba* var. *macrophylla*
megacarpa — SKHP
pendula — see *B. alba*
'Purple Smoke' — CAbP CAby CSpe EBee ECtt GBuc ILea LCro LEdu LHop LRHS MAvo MHol MNrw NPnk SMHy SPhx WAul WCAu
sphaerocarpa — SPhx SPlb WCot
tinctoria — CArn SPhx
× **variicolor** 'Twilite' (Prairieblues Series) — EBee EPfP EWes GBin MNrw NDov SKHP SPoG

Barbarea (*Brassicaceae*)

praecox — see *B. verna*
§ **verna** — GPoy MHer SRms SVic
vulgaris 'Variegata' (v) — NBro WMoo

Barleria (*Acanthaceae*)

oenotheroides — CCCN
suberecta — see *Dicliptera sericea*

Barosma see *Agathosma*

Bartlettina (*Asteraceae*)

§ **sordida** — CCCN EUJe

Basella (*Basellaceae*)

rubra — SHDw SPre SVic

Bashania (*Poaceae*)

§ **fargesii** — CJng ENBC ERod MMuc MRav MWht SEND
I **qingchengshanensis** — CJng ERod MWht

basil see *Ocimum basilicum*

Bauhinia (*Caesalpiniaceae*)

alba hort. — see *B. variegata*
* **lutea** — CCCN
natalensis — SPlb
purpurea L. — CCCN SPlb
tomentosa — CAco CCCN
§ **variegata** — CAco
'White Lady' — CCCN
yunnanensis — SPlb

Baumea see *Machaerina*

bay see *Laurus nobilis*

Beaucarnea (*Asparagaceae*)

recurvata ♀H1c — SPlb

Beaufortia (*Myrtaceae*)

elegans — SVen
schaueri — SVen
sparsa — CTsd SVen
squarrosa — SPlb

Beauverdia see *Leucocoryne*

Beckmannia (*Poaceae*)

eruciformis — XLum

Bedfordia (*Asteraceae*)

linearis — SPlb SVen

Beesia (*Ranunculaceae*)

§ **calthifolia** — CBct CDTJ CHid CMHG CSpe CTal EBee EPfP GEdr IMou LEdu LHop LLHF SChF SMad WCot WCru WPGP WSHC
deltophylla misapplied — see *B. calthifolia*

Begonia ✿ (*Begoniaceae*)

from Taiwan — GCal
'Abel Carrière' (R) — WDib
aconitifolia (C) — EShb

	'Adam' (T) **new**	WFib
	albopicta (C)	EBak
	- 'Rosea' (C)	WDib
	'Albuquerque Midnight Sky' (R)	SBrm
	'Amoretto' (Be*Adore Series) **new**	NPri
	'Amazon Delta' (R)	SBrm
	Amour = 'Yamour' (Million Kisses Series)	NPri
	'Angela Jane' (T)	WFib
§	***annulata*** ♀H1b HWJK 2424	ESwi WCru
	'Apricot Delight' (T)	WFib
	'Arctic Breeze'PBR (R)	SBrm
	'Argentea' (R)	EBak
	'Argenteo-guttata'	EShb
	'Axel Lange' (R)	SBrm
	'Aya' (C)	WDib
	'Baronessa'	SBrm
	'Benitochiba' (R) ♀H1b	CHll CSpe EBee ECtt ESwi GBin LSou MHol NLar WCot WDib WGrn
	'Beryl Rhodes' (T)	WFib
	'Bethlehem Star'	WDib
§	'Bettina Rothschild' (R)	SBrm WDib
	'Billy Langdon' (T)	WFib
	'Black Fang'	WDib
	'Blackberry Swirl' (R)	WDib
	'Blazing Star' (T)	LOPS
	Blissful (Million Kisses Series)	LSou NPri
	'Blushing Star' (T)	LOPS
	'Bokit'	WDib
	'Bokit' × ***imperialis***	WDib
	boliviensis (T)	ESwi SEND
	- 'Firecracker'	WDib
	Bonfire = 'Nzcone'PBR ♀H1b	EPfP SPoG
	'Bouton de Rose' (T)	SDeJ
	'Buffey'PBR (T) **new**	NPri
	'Buttermilk' (T)	WFib
	'Can-can' (T)	WFib
	'Candy Floss'	WCru
	'Captain Nemo' (R)	SBrm
	carolineifolia ♀H1b	WDib
	'Casey Corwin' (R)	SBrm WDib
	cathayana	EBee GCal
	'Champagne'	LCro LOPS
I	***chapaensis*** HWJ 642	WCru
	Cherry Bon Bon	NPri
	'China Curl' (R) ♀H1b	WDib
	chitoensis B&SWJ 1954	GCal WCru
	'Cleopatra' ♀H1b	WDib
	coccinea (C)	WDib
	'Comte de Lesseps' (C)	WDib
	'Connee Boswell' ♀H1b	CHll WDib
§	***corallina*** (C)	EBak
	cucullata (S)	SKHP
	- var. ***arenosicola*** (S)	CFil ECtt ESwi SEND SKHP WCot
	'Curly Fireflush' (R) ♀H1b	SBrm WDib
	'David Blais' (R) ♀H1b	WDib
	'Dawnal Meyer' (C)	WDib
I	'De Elegans'	WDib
	Devil Series (S)	NPri
	Devotion = 'Yadev'PBR (Million Kisses Series) ♀H1b	NPri
	'Dewdrop' (R) ♀H1b	WDib
	'Dibleys Pink Showers'PBR ♀H1b	WDib
	discolor	see *B. grandis* subsp. *evansiana*
	'Don Miller' (C)	WDib
	Dragon Wing Red = 'Bepared'PBR	EShb
	'Dragoste' (Be*Adore Series) **new**	NPri
§	***dregei*** (T) ♀H1b	CSpe
	'Elda Haring' (R)	SBrm
	Elegance = 'Yagance'PBR (Million Kisses Series) ♀H1b	LSou NPri
	'Embrace' (Million Kisses Series) **new**	NPri
	emeiensis	CFil CSpe EBee SKHP
	'Emerald Beauty' (R) ♀H1b	SBrm
	'Emerald Giant' (R)	WDib
	'Escargot' (R) ♀H1b	SMad WDib
	'Etna' (R)	SBrm
	'Fairy Lights' (T)	WFib
	Fimbriata Group (T)	SDeJ
	'Fire Flush'	see *B.* 'Bettina Rothschild'
	'Fireworks' (R) ♀H1b	WDib
	'Flamboyant' (T)	NNys
	'Flo'Belle Moseley' (C)	WDib
§	***foliosa*** var. ***miniata*** ♀H1b	CHll CSpe CTsd EBak MArl SDix WCot
	- - pink-flowered	CCCN
	Fragrant Falls Improved Series **new**	SPoG
	fuchsioides	see *B. foliosa* var. *miniata*
	'Gay Gordon' (T)	WFib
	'Glowing Embers'	LBuc NWad SPoG
	gracilis (T) F&M 266	CFil
	- F&M 337	CFil
	grandis (T)	IDee WBod XLum
§	- subsp. ***evansiana*** ♀H3	CAby CBot CHll CPne CSpe CTal CTsd ELon EShb EUJe GCal LEdu SBch SDix SEND SKHP SPlb WCot WCru WFar WMoo
	- - B&SWJ 11188	WCru
	- - var. ***alba*** hort. ♀H5	CAby CFil CSpe CTal EBee EPPr EShb ESwi EWld GBin GCal LEdu NLos SBch SDix SKHP WCot WMoo WPGP XLum
	- - 'Claret Jug'	CFil EBee ECtt ESwi WGrn
	- - 'Pink Parasol'	ESwi WCru
	- - pink-flowered	NLos WFar
	- - 'Sublime'	LEdu
	- 'Sapporo'	CFil EBee EPPr ESwi GCal SChr WCru
§	- subsp. ***sinensis*** (T)	EBee
I	- - 'Red Undies'	ESwi WCru
	- - 'Snowpop' **new**	WPGP
	aff. ***grandis*** subsp. ***sinensis*** (T)	SKHP
	- - BWJ 8133	WCru
	'Green Gold' (R) ♀H1b	SBrm WDib
	griffithii	see *B. annulata*
	haageana hort. ex W. Watson	see *B. scharffii*
	hatacoa silver-leaved	WDib
	Heaven Series (S)	NPri
	'Helen Teupel' (R)	WDib
	'Helena Hall' (T)	WFib
	'Hilo Holiday' (R) ♀H1b	WDib
	homonyma	see *B. dregei*
	Honeymoon = 'Yamoon'PBR (Million Kisses Series)	NPri
	'Houston Fiesta' (R)	SBrm
	(Illumination Series) 'Illumination Apricot' (T/d)	ESps NNys SCoo
	- 'Illumination Orange' (T/d)	ESps
	- 'Illumination Peaches 'n' Cream' (T/d) **new**	ESps

- 'Illumination Peachy Pink' (T/d) **new**	ESps
- 'Illumination Rose' (T/d)	ESps SCoo
- 'Illumination Salmon Pink' (T/d)	ESps SCoo
- 'Illumination White' (T/d)	ESps SCoo
'Inca Fire'PBR (R)	SBrm
'Indian Summer'PBR (R)	SBrm
× ***intermedia*** 'Bertinii' (T)	LOPS SDeJ
'Ironstone' (R) ♀H1b	SBrm
'Jennifer Wilson' (T)	WFib
'Jessie Cruickshank' (T)	WFib
'Joburg' (T) **new**	WFib
'John Smith' (T) **new**	WFib
'La Paloma' (C)	WDib
Large-flowered Double Group (T/d)	SDeJ
'Lianne' (T)	WFib
'Lime Swirl'	WDib
'Limeade' ♀H1b	WDib
'Linda Jackson' (T)	WFib
listada ♀H1b	WDib
'Little Brother Montgomery' ♀H1b	EShb SDix WDib
'Little Girl'	LOPS
'Lois Burks' (C)	WDib
'Looking Glass' (C)	WDib
'Lovebirds'PBR **new**	NPri
'Lucerna' (C)	EBak ELan EShb NLos WDib
'Lucky Colours' (R)	SBrm
luxurians ♀H1b	CBod CBot CHll CSpe EBee ECtt ESwi MNrw MPie SMad SPlb WCot WGrn WPGP
macduffieana	see *B. corallina*
maculata 'Wightii' (C)	CSpe WDib
'Magma' (R)	SBrm
'Majesty' (T)	WFib
'Maori Haze'PBR (R)	SBrm
Marginata Group (T)	SDeJ
'Marmaduke' ♀H1b	WDib
'Marmorata' (T)	SDeJ
'Martin Johnson' (R) ♀H1b	WDib
masoniana ♀H1b	GCal WDib WSFF
I 'Matador' (T)	WFib
'Melissa' (T)	WFib
'Merry Christmas' (R)	WDib
'Metallic Mist'PBR	CSpe ESwi LSou
'Midnight Magic' (R) ♀H1b	WDib
'Mikado' (R) ♀H1b	SBrm
Million Kisses Series	LBuc NPri
'Mishmi Silver'	GCal WPGP
'Mother's Day' (T)	LCro LOPS
'Mr Kartuz' (R)	SBrm
'Mrs E. McLaughlan' (T)	WFib
'Mrs Peters' (T)	WFib
'Munchkin' ♀H1b	WDib
'My Best Friend'	WDib
'Namur' (R) ♀H1b	WDib
natalensis	see *B. dregei*
'Nick Woodfield' **new**	WFib
Nonstop Series (T/d)	ESps SDeJ
- 'Nonstop Deep Red' (T/d) **new**	ESps
- 'Nonstop Mocca Mix' (T/d) **new**	ESps
- 'Nonstop Mocca White' (T/d) **new**	ESps
- 'Nonstop Mocca Yellow' (T/d)	ESps
- 'Nonstop Pink' (T/d) **new**	ESps
- 'Nonstop Red' (T/d) **new**	ESps
- 'Nonstop Rose Petticoat' (T/d) **new**	ESps
- 'Nonstop Rosepink' (T/d) **new**	ESps
'Ollykey' (T)	WFib
'Orange Rubra' (C)	WDib
'Pachea' (R)	SBrm
palmata	CDTJ GCal SKHP
panchtharensis	CFil
- B&SWJ 2692	WCru
- PAB 9007 **new**	LEdu
partita	see *B. dregei*
Passion = 'Yabos' (Million Kisses Series)	LSou
'Peardrop'PBR	NPri
pedatifida	SKHP
- DJHC 98473	EWld WCru
Pendula Group (T)	SDeJ
- 'Pink Giant' (T)	LCro LOPS
- 'Red Giant' (T)	LCro LOPS
- 'White Giant' (T)	LCro LOPS
'Picotee' (T)	SDeJ
'Pink Champagne' (R) ♀H1b	WDib
'Pink Flamingo' (T)	LCro LOPS
'Pink Pop' (R)	SBrm
'Pollux' ♀H1b	WDib
'Powder Puff' (T)	WFib
'Princess Alice' (T)	WFib
'Princess of Hanover' (R) ♀H1b	WDib
putii B&SWJ 7245	WCru
'Queen Olympus'	WDib
'Raspberry Swirl' (R)	WDib
ravenii (T)	EBee SKHP
'Ray's Fancy' **new**	WFib
'Razzmatazz' (R)	WDib
'Red Admiral' (T) **new**	WFib
'Red Glory' (T)	LCro LOPS
'Red Kiss' (R)	SBrm
'Red Robin' (R) ♀H1b	SBrm WDib
'Red Undies' (*grandis*)	see *B. grandis* subsp. *sinensis* 'Red Undies'
'Regal Minuet' (R) ♀H1b	SBrm WDib
rex (R)	SBrm
'Rocheart' (R) ♀H1b	SBrm WDib
'Roy Hartley' (T/d)	WFib
'Sal's Comet' (R) ♀H1b	WDib
'Sal's Moondust'	WDib
'Sammy' (T) **new**	WFib
'Sandra Haynes' (T)	WFib
'Savannah Pink Parfait' (R)	SBrm
'Sceptre' (T)	WFib
'Sceptre Cross' (T)	WFib
§ ***scharffii***	EBak SDix
'Scherzo'	WDib
'Sea Urchin'	WDib
Semperflorens Cultorum Group bronze-leaved, red-flowered (S) **new**	ESps
- - white-flowered (S) **new**	ESps
- green-leaved, rose-flowered (S) **new**	ESps
- - scarlet-flowered (S) **new**	ESps
- - white-flowered (S) **new**	ESps
serratipetala ♀H1b	EBak WDib
'Shamus'	WDib
* ***shepherdii***	WDib
Sherbet Bon Bon = 'Yabon' ♀H1b	NPri

sikkimensis	GCal
silletensis	WCot
- subsp. ***mengyangensis***	GCal
'Silver Cloud' (R) 🏆H1b	WDib
'Silver Jewell' 🏆H1b	WDib
'Silver Lace'	WDib
'Silver Splendor'	CSpe EBee ECtt ESwi IBoy SPoG WCot XEll
'Silver Spray' (R)	SBrm
sinensis	see *B. grandis* subsp. *sinensis*
sizemoreae	GCal WDib
'Snow Storm'	WDib
I 'Snowcap' (C) 🏆H1b	WDib
solananthera A. DC. 🏆H1b	WDib
'Solid Silver' (R)	WDib
soli-mutata	WDib
sonderiana (T)	GCal
'Stained Glass'	WDib
'Sugar Candy' (T/d)	WFib
'Sugar Plum'	MAsh
(Summerwings Series) Summerwings Dark Elegance = 'Insumdaele' **new**	CSpe SPoG
- Summerwings Orange = 'Innbolora'[PBR]	ESwi
- Summerwings White = 'Innbolwhi'[PBR]	ESwi
'Susan' (T) **new**	WFib
sutherlandii (T) 🏆H2	CAvo CCCN CFil EBak EBee EShb ESwi EWld NPer SAdn SBch SDix WCot WDib WGrn WPGP
- 'Papaya' (T)	CSpe
'Sweet Dreams' (T/d)	WFib
'Switzerland' (T)	SDeJ
'Tahiti' (T)	WFib
taliensis	SKHP
- EDHCH 042	WCot WCru
- 'White-boned Demon'	SKHP
'Tessa Robinson' (T)	WFib
'Thrush' (R)	SBrm
'Thurstonii' 🏆H1b	EShb
'Tim Anderson' (R)	SBrm
'Tiny Gem'	WDib
* ***tripartita*** (T)	WDib
'Truffle Cream' **new**	NPri
'Truffle Peach' **new**	NPri
'Tuscan Bonfire' (R)	SBrm
'Two Face'	WDib
'Tye Dye'	GCal WPGP
venosa	EShb
'Vera Coates' (T)	WFib
'Vesuvius' (R)	WDib
'Vibrant Star' (T)	LOPS
'Vista' (R)	SBrm
'Wavy Green'	EBee GCal WPGP
'Whispers' (T)	WFib
'Wild Swan'	WCru
* ***wynn-jonesiae*** 'Pink Lady'	WCru
'Ziggy' (T)	WFib

Belamcanda see *Iris*

chinensis	see *Iris domestica*

Bellevalia (*Asparagaceae*)

atroviolacea	GKev
'Cream Pearl'	ECho WCot
desertorum JCA 0.227.690	WCot
dubia	ECho GKev WCot
forniculata	WCot
hyacinthoides	ECho WCot
mauretanica	ECho
§ ***paradoxa***	CAby CHid CMea ECho EHrv ERCP GBin GKev MNrw SDeJ WCot
- white-flowered	ECho GKev
pycnantha misapplied	see *B. paradoxa*
pycnantha ambig.	EPfP EWTr SIgm
pycnantha (K. Koch) Losinsk. 'Green Pearl'	ECho GKev SDeJ
romana	ECho ERCP GKev SDeJ WCot
tabriziana	WCot

Bellis (*Asteraceae*)

§ ***caerulescens***	GAbr
perennis 'Alice'	GAbr WCot
- (Bellissima Series) 'Bellissima Red' **new**	ESps
- - 'Bellissima White' **new**	ESps
- 'Big Bob' (d)	WCot
- 'Dresden China'	EWes WCot
- 'Galaxy White' (Galaxy Series)	EPfP
- Hen and Chickens	see *B. perennis* 'Prolifera' single-flowered
- 'Miss Mason'	WCot
- old strain	WCot
- 'Prolifera' double-flowered (d) **new**	WHer
§ - 'Prolifera' single-flowered	CFis ECtt
- 'Rusher Rose'	EPfP
- 'Single Blue'	see *B. caerulescens*
- 'The Pearl'	GAbr WCot
- 'Upper Seagry'	CNat
rotundifolia 'Caerulescens'	see *B. caerulescens*
sylvestris	WCot

Belloa (*Asteraceae*)

chilensis	SPlb

Beloperone see *Justicia*

guttata	see *Justicia brandegeeana*

Benthamiella (*Solanaceae*)

nordenskjoldii	WAbe
patagonica	CPBP SPlb WAbe
- F&W 9345	ITim WAbe
- white-flowered	WAbe
- yellow-flowered	WAbe

Berberidopsis (*Berberidopsidaceae*)

corallina	CBcs CKel CMac CRHN CRos CTri ELan EPfP IArd IDee IVic LBMP LHop LRHS MGil MGos MRav NLar SLim SNig SPer SPoG SWvt WBod WHar WSHC

Berberis (*Berberidaceae*)

aggregata	NBir SPer SRms
amurensis	WPat
- var. ***latifolia*** B&SWJ 8539	WCru
aquifolium	see *Mahonia aquifolium*
- 'Fascicularis'	see *Mahonia × wagneri* 'Pinnacle'
aristata ambig.	CArn
asiatica	GPoy WPGP
- PAB 5438	LEdu
bealei	see *Mahonia bealei*
'Boughton Red'	WHor
buxifolia 'Nana' misapplied	see *B. microphylla* 'Pygmaea'
calliantha	WFar
candidula C.K. Schneid.	CDul EBee EPfP ESps LRHS MMuc MSwo NLar SCob SEND SPer

	- 'Jytte'	see *B.* 'Jytte'
	× ***carminea*** 'Pirate King'	CSBt EBee EPfP LHop LRHS MAsh SPer SPoG SWvt
	darwinii 🏆H5	Widely available
I	- 'Compacta'	CChe CMac CRos CSBt ELan EPfP ESps GMcL LBuc LHop LRHS MAsh MGos NEgg NLar SBod SCob SHil SLim SPoG SWvt WCot WFar
	deinacantha AC 1010	MHid
	dictyophylla	CBot EBee ELan EPfP LHop LRHS MMuc NLar SCob SKHP SPer SPoG WSHC
	dulcis 'Nana'	see *B. microphylla* 'Pygmaea'
	dumicola	MHid
	empetrifolia	LEdu
	× ***frikartii*** 'Amstelveen' 🏆H5	CCVT CLet ECrN ELan EPfP MBNS MMuc MRav SCob SEND WMoo
	- 'Telstar'	EBtc EMOT ESps EWTr NEoE SCob WMoo
	gagnepainii misapplied	see *B. gagnepainii* var. *lanceifolia*
	gagnepainii C.K. Schneid.	CDul CMac SCob
§	- var. ***lanceifolia***	CBcs CTri EBee MMuc NWea SEND SGol WHar
	- - 'Fernspray'	EBee EPfP MRav SRms
	- 'Purpurea'	see *B.* × *interposita* 'Wallich's Purple'
	'Georgei' 🏆H5	CWib EPfP GQui LRHS WPat
	'Goldilocks'	CDul EBee EPfP MBlu SCob SPoG
	goudotii B&SWJ 10769	WCru
	haematocarpa	SIgm
	hamiltoniana H&M 1919 new	GKev
	heterophylla	GKev
	× ***hybridogagnepainii*** 'Chenault'	ELan
	- 'Robin Hood'	NEgg
	hypokerina	CMac
	insignis	IDee
	- subsp. ***insignis*** var. ***insignis***	ELon LLHF WPat
	- - - B&SWJ 2432	WCru
§	× ***interposita*** 'Wallich's Purple'	CCVT EPfP MRav MSwo SPer WMoo
	jamesiana	CMCN LLHF MHid WCFE WPat
	julianae	CAco CArg CBcs CDul CMac ELan EPfP GMcL MGos MJak MMuc MSwo NBes NEgg NWea SCob SEND SGol SPer SRms SWvt WFar WHar WHed WSHC
§	'Jytte'	EBee
	koreana	EPfP NLar WFar
	'Little Favourite'	see *B. thunbergii* f. *atropurpurea* 'Atropurpurea Nana'
	× ***lologensis*** 'Apricot Queen' 🏆H5	CBcs CLet CMac CRos EBee EPfP LRHS MAsh MGos NLar SCob SPer SPoG SWvt WPat
	- 'Mystery Fire'	GMcL IArd MAsh MGos MJak NEgg NLar SGol SWvt WHar WMoo WRHF
	- 'Stapehill'	CMac ELan EPfP LRHS MAsh SPoG
	× ***media*** 'Dual Jewel' PBR	NLar
	- Park Jewel	see *B.* × *media* 'Parkjuweel'
§	- 'Parkjuweel'	CBcs CMac GMcL IArd MRav SCob SRms WFar WMoo
	- 'Red Jewel' 🏆H5	CMac ECrN EMil EPfP ESps GMcL LRHS MAsh MGos MMuc MRav NEgg SCob SEND SPer SPoG WCFE WFar WMoo
	microphylla	EPfP GKev WCFE WFar
	- SDR 7027 new	GKev
§	- 'Pygmaea'	CBcs CSBt EBee ELan EMil EPfP GMcL LRHS MAsh MGos MMuc MRav SCob SLim SPer
	mitifolia	NLar
	montana	WPGP WPat
	× ***ottawensis*** 'Auricoma'	NBes SGol SWvt
	- f. ***purpurea***	CCVT CMac CWib WHar
§	- - 'Silver Miles' (v)	EHoe MRav NLar WFar WPat
§	- - 'Superba'	Widely available
	panlanensis 'Cally Rose'	GCal WPGP
	polyantha var. ***polyantha***	CTri
	pruinosa	GKev
	'Red Tears'	MRav SPer WFar WMoo WPat
	× ***rubrostilla*** 'Cherry Ripe'	CMac
	- 'Wisley'	LRHS
	sieboldii	ELon LEdu LLHF MAsh MRav WCFE WPat
§	***soulieana***	EPfP NWea
	stenophylla Hance	see *B. soulieana*
	× ***stenophylla*** Lindl. 🏆H5	CCVT CDul CMac CSBt CTri EBee EPfP ESps GMcL LBMP LBuc MMuc MRav NBes NWea SEND SGol SPer WFar WMoo
	- 'Autumnalis'	NEgg
	- 'Claret Cascade'	EMil MRav NLar SPer
	- 'Compacta'	NEgg WFar
	- 'Corallina Compacta' 🏆H5	CMac CMea CRos ECho ELan EPfP EPot GCrg LHop LRHS MAsh MHer SCob SIgm SPer SPoG SRms
	- 'Crawley Gem'	NLar
	- 'Etna'	ELan LRHS MAsh SCoo SPoG
	- 'Irwinii'	CMac LRHS
	- 'Nana'	LRHS
	- 'Pink Pearl' (v)	CMHG
	subacuminata FMWJ 13290	WCru
	- NJM 09.165	WPGP
	sublevis PAB 8943	LEdu
	temolaica 🏆H5	EBtc EHoe EPfP EWes MAsh MGos MHid NLar NWea SCob WCFE WPGP WPat
	thunbergii	CArg CBcs CDul CMac CNec EMOT EPfP ESps GMcL LBuc NBes NWea SCob SPer SWvt WFar WHed WMou
	- f. ***atropurpurea***	Widely available
	- - 'Admiration' PBR 🏆H7	Widely available
§	- - 'Atropurpurea Nana' 🏆H7	Widely available
	- - 'Bagatelle'	CLet CRos ELan EPfP EPot ESps GMcL IArd IVic LBMP LHop LRHS LSRN MAsh MGos MRav NLar SCob SLim SPer SPoG SWvt WCFE WHar WMoo WPat
	- - 'Concorde' 🏆H7	CRos ELan EPfP LRHS MAsh NRHS SCob SHil
	- - 'Dart's Red Lady' 🏆H7	CRos CSBt CWib EHoe ELan EPfP ESps GMcL LRHS MAsh NLar NRHS SCob SPer SWvt WFar
	- - 'Golden Ring' (v) 🏆H7	CAco CBcs CChe CDul CLet CMac CRos EHoe ELan EPfP ESps GMcL LBMP LHop LRHS MAsh MGos MRav NEgg NRHS SCob SGbt SPer SPoG SWvt WFar WMoo WPat
	- - 'Harlequin' (v) 🏆H7	CBcs CChe CRos ELan EPfP ESps GMcL LBMP LCro LOPS LPar LRHS LSRN MAsh MGos NEgg NLar NRHS SCob SEle SGol SHil SPer SPoG SRms SWvt WFar WHar WPat
	- - 'Helmond Pillar'	Widely available

- - 'Pink Queen' (v)	CDul ELan EPfP ESps EWTr LHop LRHS MAsh SCob WFar WPat
- - 'Red Chief'	CBcs CMac CRos EHoe ELan EPfP ESps GMcL LPar LRHS MAsh MGos MJak MSwo NEgg NRHS SCob SGol SHil SLim SLon SPer SPoG SRms SWvt WFar WHar WMoo WPat
- - 'Red Pillar'	CChe CMac CRos EHoe ELan ESps IVic LRHS MAsh MGos NEgg SHil SWvt WPat WRHF
- - 'Red Rocket'	EBee ELan EPfP EUJe GMcL LRHS MPkF NEgg NRHS SCob SCoo SPer WMoo
- - 'Rose Glow' (v) 🏆H7	Widely available
- - 'Rosy Rocket' PBR (v)	CWGN EBee ELan EPfP LRHS MAsh MRav NHol NRHS SHil SPer SPoG WFar
- 'Atropurpurea Superba'	see *B.* × *ottawensis* f. *purpurea* 'Superba'
- 'Aurea'	CBcs CDul CMac CRos EHoe ELan EMOT EPfP EPot ESps GMcL LRHS LSRN MBlu MGos MMuc MRav NLar NRHS SBod SCob SLim SPlb SRms SWvt WMoo
- Bonanza Gold = 'Bogozam' PBR	CBcs CMac CRos EBee ELan EPfP LRHS MAsh MRav NLar SCob SLim SPer WPat
- 'Carpetbagger'	WHar
- 'Crimson Pygmy'	see *B. thunbergii* f. *atropurpurea* 'Atropurpurea Nana'
- 'Diabolic'	CRos ESps LRHS MAsh NHol NPri NRHS SPer SPoG WGrn
- 'Erecta'	CMac EPfP MRav SPer WCFE
- 'Fireball' PBR 🏆H7	EPfP LRHS
- 'Golden Rocket' PBR	CRos EBee ELan EPfP LHop LLHF LRHS MAsh MGos MJak MPkF MRav NEgg NRHS SCoo SPer SPoG WFar
- Golden Ruby = 'Goruzam' (v) **new**	LCro
- 'Golden Torch'	CNec CRos CSBt EBee ELan EPfP ESps LRHS MAsh MRav NEgg NHol NRHS SHil SLim SWvt WPat
- 'Green Carpet'	CDul CMac ESps LHop LRHS MBlu NLar SGol SPoG SWvt WFar
- 'Green Mantle'	see *B. thunbergii* 'Kelleriis'
- 'Green Marble'	see *B. thunbergii* 'Kelleriis'
- 'Green Ornament'	NHol
§ - 'Kelleriis' (v)	GMcL LHop LRHS MRav
- 'Kobold'	CMac CRos EPfP LHop LRHS MAsh MGos NEgg SCob SPer SPoG WMoo
- 'Lutin Rouge' **new**	LCro
- 'Maria' PBR 🏆H7	CRos CWGN EBee EHoe ELon EMOT EPfP ESps GMcL LBMP LLHF LRHS LSou MGos MJak MPkF NBes NLar NPri NRHS SCob SHil SPoG WGrn WHar WMoo
- 'Orange Dream' PBR **new**	EBee
- 'Orange Rocket' PBR	CRos EBee ELan EMil EPfP ESps GMcL LPar LRHS MAsh MGos MPkF MRav NEgg NHol NRHS SCoo SEle SHil SPer SPoG WFar WPat
- 'Pow-wow'	CRos EBee ELan ESps LRHS MAsh MGos NLar NRHS SCob SCoo SLim SPoG SWvt WPat
- 'Silver Beauty' (v)	EHoe
- 'Silver Mile'	see *B.* × *ottawensis* f. *purpurea* 'Silver Miles'
- 'Somerset'	CMac GMcL WPat
- 'Starburst' PBR (v)	CBcs CDul CRos CSBt EBee EPfP ESps LRHS LSRN MAsh MGos MJak MPkF NEgg NHol NRHS SCoo SHil SLim SLon SRms SWvt
- 'Tiny Gold' PBR	CRos ELan LCro LRHS LSou MAsh MGos NEgg SCob SLim SLon SWvt WFar
* - 'Tricolor' (v)	CMac MRav WFar WPat
trigona 'Jewel'	ESps
- 'Orange King'	CBcs CMac CRos CTri ELan EPfP LRHS MAsh MGos NEgg NLar SCob SPer SPoG WPat
valdiviana 🏆H4	CBcs CJun CMHG EBee EPfP IArd IDee SChF SKHP SMad WPGP WPat
verruculosa 🏆H5	CBcs CDul EPfP ESps GMcL LHop LRHS MBlu MGos NLar NWea SCob SPer SRms SWvt WFar
aff. ***verticillata*** B&SWJ 10672	WCru
virescens B&SWJ 2646D	WCru
vulgaris	CAgr CArn CNat GPoy MCoo NWea
- 'Wiltshire Wonder' (v)	CNat
wilsoniae	CBcs CDul CFil CMac CTri ECre ELan EPfP GLog GMcL LHop MMuc NWea SCob SPer SRms WFar
- blue-leaved	MAsh WFar
- var. ***guhtzunica***	EWes
xanthoclada NJM 11.007	WPGP

Berchemia (*Rhamnaceae*)

racemosa	NLar WSHC

bergamot see *Citrus* × *limon* Bergamot Group

Bergbambos (*Poaceae*)

§ ***tessellata***	CJng ERod MMuc MWht SEND

Bergenia ✿ (*Saxifragaceae*)

'Abendglocken'	CMac ECGP ECha ECtt EPfP NSti WCot WFar
§ 'Abendglut'	Widely available
'Admiral'	CBct CMac ECha WCot
afghanica	XLum
* ***agavifolia***	CBct XLum
'Andrea'	WCot
'Angel Kiss' (Dragonfly Series)	EBee ECtt GBin LBrs LRHS MNrw WCot
'Apple Blossom'	CRos EPfP LRHS
'Apple Court White'	CBct
'Autumn Magic'	CBct CBod ELon EPfP LHop LRHS LSou NCou WFar
'Baby Doll'	Widely available
'Bach'	CBct CRos EBee ECGP ECtt EPfP GEdr GQue LPla LRHS LSou LSun MBel MCot MMuc NLar NRHS NSti NWad SCob SWvt WCot WFar WHar WMoo
§ 'Ballawley' clonal	ECha GBin GCal IMou LRHS MRav NEgg WCot XLum
'Ballawley Guardsman'	CBct
§ Ballawley hybrids	CMac
'Ballawley' seed-raised	see *B.* Ballawley hybrids
'Bartók'	CBct CBot CLAP CMil EBee ECtt ESwi GQue IKil LLWG LRHS WCAu WCot WFar WMoo
beesiana	see *B. purpurascens*
'Beethoven'	CBct ECha GBin GCra MRav NBir WCot
Bell Tower	see *B.* 'Glockenturm'
'Biedermeier' 🏆H7	ECha
'Bizet'	CBct XLum
'Borodin'	CBct

	Name	Suppliers
	'Brahms'	CBct WCot
	'Bressingham Bountiful'	CBct
	'Bressingham Ruby'PBR	CBct CBod CHVG CLAP EBee ECha ECtt ELon EPed GBin LBrs LRHS LSRN MBel MGos MHol MRav NBir NEgg SCob SGol SPer SWvt WCot WHoo
	'Bressingham Salmon'	CBct EBee ECha ECtt ELan ELon GMaP MRav NLar SRms WCot
	'Bressingham White' ♀H6	Widely available
	'Britten' ♀H7	CBct CMac GBin IMou WCot
	ciliata	CBct CDor CLAP CMac CTal ECha EPri EShb EUJe GCra GEdr GMaP LEdu LRHS MRav NHol NLar NPnk SDix SPer WKif WPGP WSHC XLum
	- 'Dumbo'	CBct GBin LLHF
	- f. ***ligulata***	see *B. pacumbis*
	- 'Patricia Furness'	CLAP
	- 'Wilton'	CBct CLAP CTal EWld SHar WCot WSHC
	ciliata* × *crassifolia	see *B.* × *schmidtii*
	'Claire Maxine' ♀H7	CBct CLAP ECtt GBin GCal MPie NFav NLar NWad WCAu WCot
	cordifolia	Widely available
	- 'Flore Pleno' (d)	CBct
	- 'Jelle'	CBct EBee GBin WCAu
	- 'Lunar Glow'	CBct EBee ECha ECtt ELan ELon EPfP ESwi EUJe LHop LRHS LSou NEgg NLar SRms
	- 'Purpurea'	CBcs CLet CMac CNec CWCL EBee ECha ELan EPed EPfP GBin GMcL LBuc LCro LOPS LRHS MRav NBir SCob SPer SRms SWvt WCAu WFar XLum
	- 'Rosa Schwester'	CBct ECha
	- 'Rosa Zeiten' ♀H7	CBct GBin IMou
	- 'Rose'	LRHS
	- 'Tubby Andrews' (v)	CBct CMac CTal EShb LEdu LRHS MAvo MBel MBrN NEgg NEoE NLar NPnk SRms WHrl
	- 'Vinterglöd'	CBod CBot EBee ELan ELon EPfP ESps EUJe GMaP GQue IFoB LRHS LSun MGos NGdn NLar SPad SWvt WFar WHar WPnP XLum
	crassifolia	GKev SRms XLum
	- DF 90028	CBct GBin
	- 'Autumn Red'	CBct ECha
	- 'Orbicularis'	see *B.* × *schmidtii*
I	- var. ***pacifica***	XLum
	- - 'Cally Gem'	GCal
	'Croesus'	GBin
*	***cyanea***	CLAP WCot
	'David'	CBct ECha EWes GBin
	'Delbees'	see *B.* 'Ballawley' clonal
	'Doppelgänger'	EBee
	'Eden's Dark Margin'	CBct CBod ECtt ELan ELon GBin GQue IKil LSou MHol MNrw NEoE NLar WCot WHoo
	'Eden's Magic Giant' ♀H7	CAbP CBct ECGP ECtt ELan ELon GBin GMcL IKil LRHS LTro MPie NEgg NLar SDix SRms WCot
	emeiensis	CBct CLAP CTal GCal IMou LEdu SDix WCot WPGP WSHC
	- hybrid	MWat
	'Eric Smith' ♀H7	CBct ECha GCal GCra SWvt WCAu
	'Eroica' ♀H7	Widely available
	'Evening Glow'	see *B.* 'Abendglut'
	'Flower Joy' new	GBin
§	'Glockenturm'	CBct GBin NEgg
	'Godfrey Owen'	EBee
	'Harzkristall'	CBct CBod CDor CMac CMea EPfP GBin GWyn LHop LRHS SHil SPoG STPC SWvt
	'Hellen Dillon'	see *B. purpurascens* 'Irish Crimson'
	'Herbstblute'	GBin WCAu
	'Ice Queen'	CBct CMil EBee ELan EWTr GBin LLHF LPla MBel SWvt WCAu WCot
	'Jo Watanabe'	CBct MRav
	'Kashmir'	XLum
	'Lambrook'	see *B.* 'Margery Fish'
	'Little Pine'	WCot
§	'Margery Fish'	CBct CFis ECha SPer
	milesii	see *B. stracheyi*
§	'Morgenröte' ♀H6	CBcs CBct CBod CMac ECha ELon EPfP GMaP LHop LRHS LSRN MRav NHol NLar NSti SAko SCob SPer SRms SWvt WCFE WCot
	'Morning Light'	ECtt
	Morning Red	see *B.* 'Morgenröte'
	'Mrs Crawford'	ECha
	'Oeschberg'	CBct GBin GCal
	'Opal'	CBct EBee GBin
	'Overture'	Widely available
§	***pacumbis***	CLAP CTal EBee GBin GCal NBid NSti
	- B&SWJ 2693	WCru
	- CC 1793	SBch WCot
	- CC 3616	CBct WPGP
	'Pink Dragonfly'	CBct CMac CTal ECtt ELon EPfP GEdr LRHS NLar SCob SPoG SWvt WCAu WCot
	'Pink Frostwork'	ECtt GBin WCot WWFP
	'Pink Ice'	CBct EBee
	'Pinneberg'	CBct GBin
	'Pugsley's Pink' ♀H7	CBct
§	***purpurascens*** ♀H5	CMac EBee EPfP GMaP LBMP SDix SPer
	- SDR 4548	GKev
	- var. ***delavayi*** ♀H5	CWCL LRHS NLar SRms
§	- 'Irish Crimson' ♀H7	CBct ECha WCot
	aff. ***purpurascens***	NGdn
	- ACE 2175	WCot
	'Purpurglocken'	ECtt GCal WCAu
	'Red Beauty'	EHoe EPfP IBoy LRHS MHid
	'Red Rush'	EBee
	'Rietheim'	CBct EBee GBin
	'Rosenkristall' new	LRHS NRHS
	'Rosi Klose'	CBct CDor CLAP EBee ECha ECtt EHoe ELon EWes GBin GCra GMcL LHop LRHS MHol MRav NGdn WCot WFar
	'Rosi Ruffles'	EBee
	'Rotblum'	CBct CNec ECtt EHoe ELon EPfP GMaP NBir NGdn SCob SHar SRkn WHar
	'Sakura' (Dragonfly Series)	CRos GBin GEdr LRHS MNrw NRHS WHar
§	× ***schmidtii***	CBct CMac GBin MRav NBir NLar
	'Schneekissen'	CBct CMac ECGP ECtt EPri LRHS MCot WCAu WGwG
§	'Schneekoenigin'	CBct ECha GBin GCal SWvt WCot
§	'Silberlicht' ♀H6	Widely available
	Silverlight	see *B.* 'Silberlicht'
	'Simply Sweet'	WCot
	Snow Queen	see *B.* 'Schneekoenigin'
	'Spring Fling' new	GBin
§	***stracheyi***	CBct ECha GBin GCal NBid NLar SDix WCot WFar
	- CC 4609	EBee

	- Alba Group	CTal ECha GCal
	'Sunningdale' ♀H7	CBcs CBct CBod CMac ECha ELan EPfP GCra GMaP LHop LRHS MRav NBir NGdn SWvt WCAu
	'Tim'	EBee
	'Walter Kienli'	GBin
	Winter Fairy Tales	see *B.* 'Wintermärchen'
§	'Wintermärchen' ♀H7	CBct CBot CChe ECha ECtt ELan ELon EPfP EShb GCra LRHS MMuc MRav NEoE NHol SCob SEND SPoG SRms SWvt WCot
	'XXL'	WCot

Bergeranthus (*Aizoaceae*)

multiceps	SChr
vespertinus	XLum

Berkheya (*Asteraceae*)

cirsiifolia	EBee GCal WSHC
macrocephala	SPlb
multijuga	LRHS
- 'Golden Spike'	ECtt WHil
purpurea	CAby CBcs CDor EAJP ELon EPfP ESps EWTr GBin IBoy LRHS MHol MMuc MNrw SHil SPad SPlb WCot WHer WKif WSHC WTor
- 'Silver Spike'	EPfP NGdn
- 'Zulu Warrior'	CMac NGBl SRkn
radula	GCal

Berlandiera (*Asteraceae*)

lyrata	CArn

Berula (*Apiaceae*)

erecta	NPer

Berzelia (*Bruniaceae*)

galpinii	SPlb

Beschorneria (*Asparagaceae*)

albiflora	CFil CSpe EBee WCot
calcicola	WCot
'Red Bells'	WCot
rigida	WCot
septentrionalis	CAbP CAby CDTJ CFil CSpe ESwi IBoy IKil LRHS LSou LSun MBNS MHol MSCN NLos SDix SEND SPad WCot WGrn
- variegated	WCot
septentrionalis* × *yuccoides	CFil CHll EBee
tubiflora	CDTJ CFil
wrightii	CFil WCot
yuccoides ♀H3	CAbb CBcs CFil CPne ESwi SArc SEND SPlb
- subsp. ***dekosteriana***	CFil
- 'Quicksilver'	CBcs CCCN CEnd CSBt ELan EPfP EUJe IVic LRHS MHtn NLos SDix SLim SPoG WGrn

Bessera (*Asparagaceae*)

elegans	CAby CAvo CGrW EBee ECho EPot GKev LAma SDeJ SDir WCot

Beta (*Amaranthaceae*)

vulgaris	SHDw SVic WHer
- 'Bull's Blood'	CSpe
- subsp. ***maritima***	CAgr CFGn

Betonica see *Stachys*

Betula ✿ (*Betulaceae*)

	alba	see *B. pendula*, *B. pubescens*
	albosinensis misapplied	see *B. utilis*
	albosinensis Burkill	CBrP CLnd CMCN EBee EMOT EPfP MMuc SEND
	- W 4106	CSto
	- from Gansu, China	CSto
	- 'Bowling Green'	CJun EBee MBlu WPGP
§	- 'China Rose' ♀H6	CJun CSto WMat WPGP
	- 'China Ruby' K. Ashburner	see *B. albosinensis* 'China Rose'
	- 'China Ruby' ambig.	CJun CLnd EBee EPfP LRHS
	- 'China Ruby' B. Humphrey ♀H6	CBcs CDul ERea
	- 'Chinese Garden'	CJun EBee MBlu WPGP
	- 'Chris Lane' **new**	WPGP
	- clone F	see *B. albosinensis* 'Ness'
	- hybrid	CDul
	- 'Joseph Rock' **new**	CJun
	- 'K. Ashburner'	CJun CTho
§	- 'Ness'	CJun CTho
	- 'Pink Champagne'	CJun CSto EBee EPfP MBlu WPGP
	- 'Red Panda' ♀H6	CJun EBee ERea LPre LRHS SLim WMat WPGP
	- 'Rhinegold'	MBlu
	- 'Sable'	SLim
	- var. ***septentrionalis***	CBcs CCVT CDul CEnd CMac CTho CWib EBee ECrN ELan ELon EPfP ESps EWTr GBin MBlu MGos MMuc MRav MSwo NOrn NWea SCob SGol SLim SPer WMou WPGP
	- - PDM 752	WPGP
	- - 'Kansu'	CEnd CJun CLnd CTsd EBee LRHS NOra NWea SBig WHCr WHar WMat
	- - 'Purdom'	CJun CLnd SBig
§	***alleghaniensis***	CCVT CDul CMCN CSto EPfP MMuc NLar NWea SEND SGol WCru
	apoiensis 'Mount Apoi'	CJun CLnd SBig
	ashburneri	GKev
	- S&L 5297 **new**	GKev
	chichibuensis	CJun CMCN MHid MMrt WHer
	chinensis	CMCN
	'Conyngham'	CJun CTho MBlu SLau
	cordifolia	CSto
	costata misapplied	see *B. ermanii* 'Grayswood Hill'
	costata ambig.	CMCN ESps SGol
	costata Trautv.	CTho EBee MSwo
	- 'Daleside'	EBee ERea NDal NOra WMat
*	- 'Fincham Cream'	CJun SBig
	'Crimson Frost'	EBee GBin
	dahurica Pall.	CBrP CSto
	- 'Maurice Foster'	CJun CSto CTho MBlu WPGP
	- 'Stone Farm'	CJun
	delavayi	EBee
	ermanii	CBcs CCVT CDul CLnd CMCN CMac CTri ECrN ELan EMOT ESps GBin LRHS MBlu MGos MMuc MRav NOrn NWea SCob SGol WMou
	- B&SWJ 8801 from South Korea	WCru WPat
	- B&SWJ 10852 from Aomori, Japan	WCru
	- B&SWJ 12600 from South Korea	WCru
	- from Hokkaido, Japan	CSto
	- 'Blush'	CJun EPfP MBlu SBig SCoo
	- var. ***ermanii*** MSF 825	EBee
§	- 'Grayswood Hill' ♀H6	CDul CEnd CJun CLnd CMCN CMHG CSBt CTho CTri EBee EPfP

GBin LCro LOPS MBlu SAko SCoo SWvt WPGP
- 'Hakkoda Orange' CJun CTho EBee EMOT SCoo WHar WPGP
- 'Holland' IArd
- 'Kwanak Weeping' CJun LLHF MBlu NWea SBig SBir SCoo
- 'Mount Zao' CJun CSto CTho EBee IVic WPGP
- 'Polar Bear' CJun CLnd EBee EPfP LPre MAsh MBlu NLar NOrn SAko SCoo WHCr WMat
- 'Zao Purple' CDul
'Fascination' ♀H6 CCVT CDul CJun CLnd CMCN EBar EBee EPfP ERea IArd IDee LRHS MBlu MGos NOra NOrn NWea SCob SCoo SKHP SLim SSta WHCr WHar WMat WMou
'Fetisowii' CDul CJun EBtc MBlu NOra SBig WHar WMat
fruticosa see *B. humilis*
globispica CJun
'Haywood' WMat
'Hergest' ♀H6 CJun EBee ECrN EPfP ERea MAsh MGos NOra SCoo SLau WHCr WHar WMat WPat
§ ***humilis*** EBee
insignis CSto EBee WPGP
- subsp. ***fansipanensis*** IArd SAko
- - B&SWJ 11751 WCru
'Inverleith' see *B. utilis* var. *jacquemontii* 'Inverleith'
jacquemontii see *B. utilis* var. *jacquemontii*
kamtschatica H. Buek see *B. humilis*
§ ***kenaica*** CTho
lenta CDul CMCN CSto EPfP IArd MBlu MMuc
luminifera CJun EBee EBtc IArd NLar
lutea see *B. alleghaniensis*
maximowicziana CMCN CSto CWib EMOT ESps MBlu NLar SGol
medwediewii CDul CJun CMCN CSto EBee EPfP NLar NWea WPGP
- 'Gold Bark' ♀H7 CJun CMCN EPfP MBlu
megrelica GKev
michauxii GKev NLar WCru
nana GQue MRav NWea
- 'Glengarry' EPot GCrg GEdr NLar
nigra CBcs CCVT CDul CEnd CLnd CMCN CNWT CTho CTri EBee ESps EWTr MAsh NLar SCob SEWo SGol WMou WTSh
- 'Black Star' EBee LRHS NOra WMat
§ - 'Cully' CCVT CDul CLnd CTho ECrN MRav NOra NOrn NWea SBig SGol WHCr WMat
- Heritage see *B. nigra* 'Cully'
- 'Little King' CJun CMCN
- 'Peter Collinson' CJun
- 'Shiloh Splash' SReu SSta
- 'Summer Cascade' [PBR] EBee LRHS LSRN MAsh NOra NOrn SLon WHCr WMat
- Tecumseh Compact = 'Studetec' SGol
- Wakehurst form EPfP SPer SPoG WPGP
papyrifera CAco CCVT CDul CLnd CMCN CMac CSto CTri ECrN ELan EPfP ESps LBuc MBlu MGos MMuc MSwo NOra NWea SCob SEND SGol SPer WHar WMat WTSh
- 'Belle Vue' CSto EBee
- var. ***cordifolia*** 'Clarenville' CJun CSto EBee
- var. ***kenaica*** see *B. kenaica*
- var. ***papyrifera*** CSto
- 'Saint George' CJun CSto CTho EBee WHCr WMat
- 'Vancouver' CTho MBlu
§ ***pendula*** Widely available
- 'Bangor' CJun
- 'Black Prince' WHCr
- f. ***crispa*** see *B. pendula* 'Laciniata'
- 'Dalecarlica' misapplied see *B. pendula* 'Laciniata'
- 'Dalecarlica' ambig. CAco CBcs CSBt ECrN EMOT LRHS MRav NOra SWvt WFar WHCr WMat WTSh
- 'Dark Prince' CJun NOrn
- 'Fastigiata' CCVT CDul CJun CLnd CSBt CTho EBee ECrN ELan EMOT MGos SCoo SGol SPer SPoG
- 'Golden Beauty' CDul CJun CMac EBee EMOT EMil ERea MAsh MGos MJak NOra NOrn NWea SGol SLim SPer WHar WMat
- 'Golden Cloud' MJak
§ - 'Laciniata' ♀H7 CDul CMCN CMac CTho CWib EBee ELan ESps MAsh MBlu MGos MSwo NWea SCob SCoo SGol SPer WCFE WHar WMou WTSh
- 'Long Trunk' CDul EBee LLHF MBlu NOrn SGol SLim WHar
- 'Purpurea' CCVT CDul CMCN CMac CSBt CWib EBee ECrN ELan ELon EMOT ESps GKin LSRN MGos MSwo NOrn NWea SCoo SGol SPer WFar WTSh
- 'Silver Grace' CJun ECrN LSRN SKHP
§ - 'Spider Alley' [PBR] EBee ERea EUJe GBin LRHS NEgg NLar WMat
- 'Tristis' ♀H7 Widely available
- 'Youngii' Widely available
- 'Zwitsers Glorie' CDul CJun NLar SKHP
platyphylla misapplied see *B. platyphylla* subsp. *mandshurica*
platyphylla Sukaczev CDul EBee NLar NOra SCoo WHar
Dakota Pinnacle = 'Fargo' WMat
§ - subsp. ***mandshurica*** CSto MHid MMuc
- subsp. ***platyphylla*** MHid
populifolia CSto EBtc
- 'Whitespire' CDul
potaninii MHid
§ ***pubescens*** CAco CCVT CDul CHab CSto CTho CTri GQue MMuc NWea SCob SEND WHed WMou WTSh
- 'Armenian Gold' **new** CLnd
- var. ***pubescens*** CSto
raddeana EBtc
'Royal Frost' CBcs CDul CJun EBee EUJe GQue LSRN MAsh MBlu NEgg NLar NWea SPoG WHar WMat
'Silver Trestles' see *B. pendula* 'Spider Alley'
szechuanica 'Liuba White' CJun MBlu
§ ***utilis*** CDul CMCN CSto ECrN ESps SSta
- BL&M 100 from central Nepal CSto
- GWJ 9259 WCru
- H&M 1480 from Sichuan, China CSto
- HWJK 2250 WCru
- HWJK 2345 WCru
- Sch 2168 EBee
- SICH 667 from Sichuan, China CSto

- S&L from Nepal	CDul
- Yu 10163 from Yunnan, China	CSto
- from eastern Nepal	CSto
- 'Bhutan Sienna'	CJun CSto
- 'Buckland'	EBee
- 'Buddha'	CJun SAko WPGP
- 'China Bronze'	CSto EBee WPGP
- 'Cobhay Sentinel'	CJun
- 'Dark-Ness'	EBee NOra SLon WHCr WMat WPGP
* - 'Fastigiata'	CJun SBig SSta
- 'Forest Blush' ♀H6	CDul CJun CSto EBee SBig WHar WPGP
- 'Himalayan Pink'	CJun
§ - var. ***jacquemontii***	Widely available
- - Polunin	WPGP
§ - - 'Doorenbos' ♀H6	Widely available
- - 'Grayswood Ghost' ♀H6	Widely available
§ - - 'Inverleith'	CDul CJun EBee GQue SBig SCoo WPGP
- - 'Jermyns' ♀H6	CBcs CDul CEnd CJun CLnd CMHG CTri EBee EPfP IVic LSRN MBlu NOra SCoo SLau SLim SPer SSta SWvt WHCr WHar WMat WPGP
- - 'McBeath'	SLau
- - 'Moonbeam'	CDul CJun CSBt EBee ERea GQue LRHS MAsh NWea SBig SCoo SEWo SLim SPoG WHCr WHar WMat
- - 'Silver Shadow' ♀H6	CDul CEnd CJun CLnd CMCN CTho EBee EPfP LRHS LSRN MAsh MBlu NLar NOra NOrn NWea SBig SCoo SKHP SLau SLim SPer SPoG SSta WHCr WMat WPat
- - 'Snow Leopard' **new**	CSto
- - 'Snow Queen'	see *B. utilis* var. *jacquemontii* 'Doorenbos'
- - 'Trinity College'	CDul CJun CLnd CTri EBee SBig WHCr WHar WMat WPGP WPat
- 'Knightshayes'	CTho EBee WPGP
- 'Mount Luoji'	CJun CSto EBee WPGP
- 'Nepalese Orange'	CJun CSto EBee WPGP
- var. ***occidentalis*** 'Kyelang'	CJun IVic
- 'Park Wood' ♀H6	CJun CSto WPGP WPat
- var. ***prattii***	CJun CTho MBlu
- 'Ramdana River'	CJun CMHG WPGP
- 'Schilling'	CJun
- 'Sichuan Red'	CSto
- subsp. ***utilis*** 'Edinburgh'	CJun CLnd EWTr WMat
- 'Wakehurst Place Chocolate' ♀H6	CJun CSBt EBee ERea GBin MBlu NWea SBig SCoo SLim WHar
* - var. ***yunnanensis***	EBee
cf. ***utilis***	CTri SGol
verrucosa	see *B. pendula*

Biarum ✿ (*Araceae*)

S&L 604	WCot
SB&L 597	WCot
bovei	ECho
carratracense from Spain	WCot
davisii	ECho GKev LAma WCot
dispar SB&L 294	WCot
- SB&L 564	WCot
ditschianum from Turkey	WCot
marmarisense	ECho EPot NRog WCot
tenuifolium	ECho WCot
- LB 295	WCot
- PB 357	WCot
- S&L 174	WCot
- subsp. ***abbreviatum***	GKev
- - MS 974	WCot
- - from Greece	ECho
- subsp. ***arundanum***	GKev WCot
- subsp. ***galianii*** PB 435	WCot
- subsp. ***idomenaeum*** MS 738	WCot
- subsp. ***zelebori***	ECho WCot
- - CRL 502	WCot
- - LB 300	WCot
- - PB 224	WCot
- - PB 334	WCot

Bidens (*Asteraceae*)

atrosanguinea	see *Cosmos atrosanguineus*
§ ***aurea***	EAJP ECtt EPPr ESps EWes LEdu MSpe NPer SBee WBor XLum
- 'Cream Streaked Yellow'	GQue
- cream-flowered	MNrw
- 'Golden Drop'	LSou
- 'Hannay's Lemon Drop'	CAby CCVN CKno EAJP EBee ECtt ELan ELon EPPr EPfP ILea LEdu LHop LPot MNrw MSpe SDix SGbt SPoG SRms WBor WMoo WPGP
* - 'Lemon Queen'	LEdu SMad
- 'Mellow Yellow'	WCot
- 'Rising Sun'	EWes
- 'Super Nova'	EPPr
- white-flowered	EBee EPPr GCal NSti
ferulifolia	NPer
- 'Golden Eye'	LSou SPoG
- Peter's Gold Rush = 'Topteppich'	LSou
- Yellow Charm = 'Danyel9'	LSou
heterophylla Ortega	see *B. aurea*
heterophylla misapplied	CAby ECtt MCot MMuc MRav MWat WFar WHal WMoo XLum
humilis	see *B. triplinervia* var. *macrantha*
integrifolia	SMad SSal
'Pirate's Treasure'	ECtt
'Rockstar'	LSou NPri
§ ***triplinervia*** var. ***macrantha***	LHop

Bignonia (*Bignoniaceae*)

capreolata	CCCN CRHN EBee ECre WSHC
- 'Dragon Lady'	SKHP
lindleyana	see *Clytostoma calystegioides*
tweedieana	see *Macfadyena unguis-cati*
unguis-cati	see *Macfadyena unguis-cati*

Bilderdykia see *Fallopia*

Billardiera (*Pittosporaceae*)

cymosa	CTsd
longiflora ♀H3	CBcs CHid CMac CRos CSBt CTri CWib EBee ELan EPfP GKev IArd IDee ITim LBMP LRHS MAsh MGil MGos MMuc MRav SLim SNig SPer SPoG SWvt WKif WPat WSHC
- 'Cherry Berry'	CBcs CFlo ELan EPfP EUJe LRHS MMuc SLim SPer SPoG SRms SWvt
- 'Fructu-albo'	CBcs CFlo ELan EPfP EWes LRHS NLar SLon SPer SPoG SWvt

Billbergia ✿ (*Bromeliaceae*)

'Borracho'	NLos
distachya var. ***maculata***	NLos
'Fosters Striate'	NLos
nutans	CCCN CHll EBak ESwi EUJe IMou LEdu LTro NLos SChr SEND SPlb WSFF
- var. ***schimperiana***	EShb

* - 'Variegata' (v)	CCCN CHll EShb EUJe LTro NLos SChr WCot
pyramidalis 🏆H1a	NLos XBlo
'Santa Barbara' (v)	SChr
× ***windii*** 🏆H1a	EBak NLos

Bismarckia (*Arecaceae*)

nobilis	CCCN

Bistorta see *Persicaria*

Bituminaria (*Papilionaceae*)

bituminosa	WCot

blackberry see *Rubus fruticosus*

blackcurrant see *Ribes nigrum*

Blechnum ✿ (*Blechnaceae*)

alpinum	see *B. penna-marina* subsp. *alpinum*
attenuatum	NLos
australe	NLos
brasiliense 🏆H1a	EBee EShb ESwi ISha NLos SPlb WCot
- 'Volcano' **new**	CAbb CBct EMFm LLWG NLos SCob WBor WCot
§ ***chilense*** 🏆H4	CBcs CDTJ CKel CLAP EBee EPfP EWes GAbr GBin GCal GCra IBlr LEdu LPar LRHS NBro NLos SArc SBig SKHP SPlb SRms WCru WMoo WPat
cycadifolium	NLos
discolor	GCal NLos
divergens	NLos
fluviatile	CDTJ NLos
gibbum	CKel ISha NLos
- 'Silver Lady'	ISha NLos
gracile	NLos
magellanicum misapplied	see *B. chilense*
magellanicum (Desv.) Mett.	SBig SKHP
novae-zelandiae	NLos
nudum	CDTJ CKel EBee ESwi NLos
penna-marina 🏆H4	CBod CCCN CKel CLAP CTal CWCL EFer ELon GAbr GBin GCal GMaP LEdu LHop LLWG LRHS MMuc MRav NBir NBro NLos SCob WCot WFib WMoo XLum
§ - subsp. ***alpinum***	CLAP ECha EPfP GEdr GKev NWad WMoo
- - BR 68	GEdr
- 'Cristatum'	CLAP GAbr GEdr NWad
procerum	NLos
punctulatum	ISha
spicant 🏆H6	Widely available
tabulare misapplied	see *B. chilense*
tabulare (Thunb.) Kuhn	CBcs CDTJ CKel EPfP NLos
wattsii	EBee NLos

Blepharocalyx (*Myrtaceae*)

§ ***cruckshanksii***	CCCN CTsd EBee ELon LRHS MGil SVen WPGP WPat
- 'Heaven Scent'	see *B. cruckshanksii*

Blephilia (*Lamiaceae*)

ciliata	SPhx

Bletilla (*Orchidaceae*)

sp.	NDav SDir
hyacinthina	see *B. striata*
ochracea	CTal LAma
Penway Paris gx	CTal
Penway Sunset gx	GKev
§ ***striata*** 🏆H4	CAby CBct CTal CTri ECho EPot GKev LAma LCro LEdu LRHS LTro MHer MNrw SDeJ SPer WCot WFar WHlf WPGP XLum
- ***alba***	see *B. striata* f. *gebina*
- 'Albostriata'	CBct ECho ELan LAma WCot XLum
- blue-flowered **new**	GKev
§ - f. ***gebina***	CTal CTri ECho LCro LEdu LOPS LRHS SDeJ SPer WCot WPGP
- - variegated (v)	LEdu WHlf
- 'Kuchi-beni'	LAma WHlf
- purple-flowered **new**	GKev
- 'Soryu'	CTal ECho LAma
- variegated (v)	GKev
- yellow-flowered	GKev
Yokohama gx	CTal

Bloomeria (*Asparagaceae*)

crocea	ECho GKev
- var. ***aurea***	ECho
- var. ***montana***	ECho

blueberry see *Vaccinium corymbosum*

Blumea (*Asteraceae*)

balsamifera	CHab

Bocconia (*Papaveraceae*)

cordata	see *Macleaya cordata* (Willd.) R. Br.
frutescens B&SWJ 10654	WCru
microcarpa	see *Macleaya microcarpa*

Boehmeria (*Urticaceae*)

nivea	GCal WCot
platanifolia	IMou
sieboldiana	EBee EPPr SBrt
tricuspis	IMou SBrt

Boenninghausenia (*Rutaceae*)

albiflora	CPne
- B&SWJ 1479	WCru
- B&SWJ 3112 pink-flowered	WCru
- BWJ 8141 from China	WCru
- CC 7147	ITim

Bolax (*Apiaceae*)

glebaria	see *B. gummifer*
§ ***gummifer***	ECho EPot GEdr WAbe

Bolboschoenus (*Cyperaceae*)

§ ***maritimus***	SMea WDra

Boltonia (*Asteraceae*)

asteroides	GCra MMuc SEND SPer SWat WRHF XLum
- var. ***latisquama***	GMaP GQue LSou MAvo MRav MWat NCGa NLar SHar WBor WHal WHil WTor
- - Jim Crockett = 'Masbolimket'PBR	SPoG
- - 'Nana'	LPla
- - 'Snowbank'	ELan LHop
decurrens	CBod EBee EPPr IMou WBor
- 'Warrior's Blush'	IPot MNrw
incisa	see *Kalimeris incisa*

Bomarea (*Alstroemeriaceae*)

	from Veracruz, Mexico	WCot
	acutifolia	CFil WCot
	- B&SWJ 9094	WCru
	- B&SWJ 9130	WCru
	- B&SWJ 10388	WCru
	- F&M 104	WPGP
	aff. ***andreana*** B&SWJ 10617	WCru
	boliviensis misapplied	see *Alstroemeria isabellana*
	boliviensis Baker	WCot
	caldasii	see *B. multiflora*
	costaricensis	EBee GCal
	- B&SWJ 10467	WCru
	distichifolia	WCot WCru
§	***edulis*** ♀H1c	CHll CPne CRHN WBod WCot
	- B&SWJ 9017	WCru
	'Fiesta'	WCot
	'Flare'	WCot
	frondea	see *B. multiflora*
	aff. ***frondea*** B&SWJ 10681	WCru
	hirtella	see *B. edulis*
§	***multiflora*** ♀H2	CBcs CCCN CPne CTre EBee GCal NLos SKHP WCru WSHC
	'Orange Sunset'	WCot
	patacocensis JCA 13987	WCot
	salsilla ♀H1c	CAvo CCCN CFil CPne EBee NLos SKHP WSHC

Bombax (*Malvaceae*)

ceiba	SPlb

Bongardia (*Berberidaceae*)

chrysogonum	CAvo CRos ECho EPot GKev LLHF LRHS NRHS

Bonia (*Poaceae*)

§	***solida***	CJng ERod MMuc MWht SEND

Boophone (*Amaryllidaceae*)

disticha	LRHS

Boquila (*Lardizabalaceae*)

trifoliolata new	WCru

borage see *Borago officinalis*

Borago (*Boraginaceae*)

	laxiflora	see *B. pygmaea*
	officinalis	CHby CLau ENfk EPfP GPoy LCro MHer MNHC NBir NPri SRms SVic WJek
	- 'Alba'	CBre CLau ENfk MNHC SIde SRms WJek
	- 'Bill Archer' (v)	CNat
§	***pygmaea***	CArn CHid CSpe ELan GCal LEdu MHer MNrw NBir NSti SRms WJek WMoo

Borinda (*Poaceae*)

KR 4558	ERod
KR 5287	MWht
KR 5600	MWht
KR 5950	ERod
KR 6438	MWht
KR 6439	MWht
KR 7346	MWht
KR 7613	MWht
KR 7662	MWht
from Muli County, Sichuan	CJng
albocerea ♀H4	CJng EPfP ERod MWht
- Yunnan 1	CJng ERod
- Yunnan 2	CDTJ CEnt CJng ERod MAvo
- Yunnan 3a	CDTJ CEnt CJng ERod
- Yunnan 3b	CJng ERod
- Yunnan 4	see *B. lushuiensis* Yunnan 4
angustissima	CDTJ CEnt CFil CJng EPfP ERod MMuc MWht SBig
boliana	CJng SBig SSut
edulis	CJng
frigida	CDTJ CEnt CJng
- KR 4059	ERod MWht
fungosa	CBlu CJng ESwi IBoy LTro
grossa	CJng
- KR 5931	MWht
lushuiensis	CJng
§ - Yunnan 4	CDTJ CEnt MWht
macclureana KR 5050	CJng
- KR 5051	MWht
- KR 5177 from Gyala, Nepal	CJng ERod ESwi MWht
- KR 5602	ERod
- KR 5950	ERod
- KR 6236	ESwi
- KR 6243	CJng ERod
- KR 6400 from Show La	ESwi
- KR 6438 from Pasm Tso	ESwi
aff. ***macclureana*** KR 6900	MWht
nujiangensis	CJng
papyrifera	CEnt CJng ERod WPGP
- CS 1046	CJng MAvo MWht
- KR 3968	CJng
- KR 7613	CJng
perlonga	CJng
scabrida ♀H4	CDTJ CEnt CJng ENBC ERod MAvo MWht SSut WPGP
- 'Asian Wonder'	CBod LRHS MBlu NLar SBig
Yunnan 4	see *B. lushuiensis* Yunnan 4

Boronia (*Rutaceae*)

crenulata new	CBcs CCCN
heterophylla	CBcs CCCN CTsd EBee EPfP IDee LRHS MPkF SEle
- 'Ice Charlotte'	CBcs CCCN SEle
- 'Rubra' new	CCht

Bossiaea (*Papilionaceae*)

riparia	SPlb
scolopendria	SPlb

Bothriochloa (*Poaceae*)

§	***bladhii***	CKno EPPr
	caucasica	see *B. bladhii*

Bougainvillea (*Nyctaginaceae*)

	'African Sunset'	SPlb
	'Alexandra'	CCCN SPre SWeb
	'Brilliant' misapplied	see *B.* × *buttiana* 'Raspberry Ice'
§	× ***buttiana*** 'Raspberry Ice' (v)	EShb
	glabra ♀H1c	EShb IDee SPre
	'Sentimento' new	CCCN
	'Tropical Rainbow'	see *B.* × *buttiana* 'Raspberry Ice'
	Vera Series new	CCCN

Boussingaultia (*Basellaceae*)

baselloides Hook.	see *Anredera cordifolia*

Bouteloua (*Poaceae*)

	curtipendula	CBod
§	***gracilis***	CAby EAJP EBee EHoe LRHS NRHS SMea SPoG

Bouvardia (*Rubiaceae*)

ternifolia	CBcs CWGN EBee ESwi EWld LSou MNrw MPie SMad SPad WCot

Bowiea (*Asparagaceae*)

volubilis	EBee GKev LToo

Bowkeria (*Stilbaceae*)

sp.	CCCN
cymosa	SPlb SVen
verticillata	CHll

Boykinia (*Saxifragaceae*)

aconitifolia	CElw CMac GLog IMou MRav NRya SMad WCru WMoo WSHC
elata	see *B. occidentalis*
heucheriformis	see *B. jamesii*
§ ***jamesii***	EBee GKev
lycoctonifolia	LEdu NLar
major	EBee
§ ***occidentalis***	WCru WMoo WPtf XLum
rotundifolia	GJos NBir WCru WMoo
tellimoides	see *Peltoboykinia tellimoides*

boysenberry see *Rubus* 'Boysenberry'

Brachychilum see *Hedychium*

Brachychiton (*Malvaceae*)

acerifolius	SPlb
populneus	SPlb
§ ***rupestris***	EShb

Brachyelytrum (*Poaceae*)

japonicum	NLar

Brachyglottis (*Asteraceae*)

§ ***bidwillii***	CBcs IVic
- 'Basil Fox'	WAbe
§ ***compacta***	ELan EPfP ESps LRHS MAsh SPer
(Dunedin Group) 'Drysdale'	CRos EBee ELan EPfP ESps LRHS NRHS SBod SHil SKHP SLon SRGP SWvt
§ - 'Moira Reid' (v)	CTsd
§ - 'Sunshine' ♀H4	Widely available
'Frosty'	CBod
greyi misapplied	see *B.* (Dunedin Group) 'Sunshine'
§ ***greyi*** (Hook. f.) B. Nord.	CAco CMac EPfP ESps SGol
huntii	SVen
huntii* × *stewartii	SEND
laxifolia misapplied	see *B.* (Dunedin Group) 'Sunshine'
§ ***monroi***	CBcs CMac CSBt CTsd EHoe ELan EPfP IVic LRHS MAsh MRav SGol SKHP SLon SVen WFar
repanda	CBcs EWld
- 'Purpurea'	CBcs
- var. ***rangiora***	CTsd
§ ***rotundifolia***	CCCN
'Silver Waves'	CRos LRHS NRHS
I 'Sunshine Improved'	CBcs EHoe MAsh
'Sunshine Variegated'	see *B.* (Dunedin Group) 'Moira Reid'
Walberton's Silver Dormouse = 'Walbrach'PBR ♀H4	CBct CBot CRos CSBt EBee EPfP ESps GBin LRHS MGos MJak MRav NRHS SPoG SWvt WFar WHil

Brachyotum (*Melastomataceae*)

ledifolium	CPne

Brachypodium (*Poaceae*)

phoenicoides	XSen
pinnatum	EPPr
sylvaticum	CHab MMuc SEND

Brachyscome (*Asteraceae*)

rigidula	CPBP

Brachystachyum (*Poaceae*)

densiflorum	ERod

Bracteantha see *Xerochrysum*

Brahea (*Arecaceae*)

sp.	ETod
armata	CBrP CDTJ CPHo EPfP EShb ETod SPlb WCot
dulcis	NLos
edulis	CCCN CPHo ETod NLos
'Super Silver'	NLos WCot

Brassaia see *Schefflera*

Brassica (*Brassicaceae*)

japonica	see *B. juncea* var. *crispifolia*
juncea	SVic
§ - var. ***crispifolia***	MNHC
oleracea	CAgr SVic WHer
- var. ***acephala*** 'Crème Chantilly' (v) new	WCot
- var. ***ramosa*** 'D'Aubenton Panaché' (v) new	WCot
* ***rapa*** var. ***japonica***	SHDw

Brighamia (*Campanulaceae*)

insignis	CCCN

Brillantaisia (*Acanthaceae*)

kirungae	CCCN
owariensis new	CSpe

Brimeura (*Asparagaceae*)

§ ***amethystina*** ♀H5	ECho GBin GKev LEdu SBrt SDeJ SPhx WCot WPGP WThu
- 'Alba'	ECho GKev SDeJ SPhx

Briza (*Poaceae*)

maxima	CTri EHoe LHop NGdn NSti NWad SPhx WHer WTou
media	Widely available
- 'Golden Bee'	CBWd CKno CRos CWCL EHoe ELon EPPr EPfP EWes LEdu LRHS MMrt NDov NLar NRHS SMad SPhx WPGP
- 'Limouzi'	CElw CKno CWCL EBee EHoe EHrv ELon EPPr GCal LEdu LRHS MAvo NRHS NSti NWsh SMad SMea SPer SPoG WPGP XLum
- 'Russells'PBR	CBod CHid CKno EBee EHoe ELan EPfP LHop LPot LRHS MGos NRHS NWad NWsh SCob SHil SMea SPer SPoG SRms SWvt
subaristata	EPPr
triloba	LRHS NRHS NWsh SMea

Brocchinia (*Bromeliaceae*)

hechtioides	NLos

Brodiaea (*Asparagaceae*)

§ ***californica***	EBee ECho ERCP GKev WCot

	- NNS 00-109	WCot
	- NNS 06-102	WCot
	- 'Babylon'	CAvo EBee ERCP GKev
	capitata	see *Dichelostemma capitatum*
	'Corrina'	see *Triteleia* 'Corrina'
	elegans	ECho
	ida-maia	see *Dichelostemma ida-maia*
	laxa	see *Triteleia laxa*
	peduncularis	see *Triteleia peduncularis*

Bromus (*Poaceae*)

	erectus	CHab
	inermis W&B BG B-5 **new**	WCot
	- 'Skinner's Gold' (v)	EBee EHoe EPPr NLar SMea WCot

Broussonetia (*Moraceae*)

	kazinoki	LHop
	papyrifera	CBcs CDul CMCN CTsd EBtc ELan ESwi IVic MGil SPer WBor
	- 'Billardii'	NLar
	- 'Laciniata'	EBee IDee SChF SMad WCot

Browallia (*Solanaceae*)

	from Sikkim	CSpe
	americana	SPhx

Bruckenthalia see *Erica*

Brugmansia (*Solanaceae*)

	'Angel's Baby' (d)	WOth
§	***arborea***	CBcs CDTJ
§	- 'Knightii' (d) 🏆H1c	CDTJ
	- 'Rosea' variegated (v)	ELan
	- variegated (v)	ELan
	aurea	CCCN SAdn
	'Bergische Symphonie' (d)	WOth
	× ***candida***	CCCN SAdn
	- 'Bergkönigin' (d)	WOth
§	- 'Grand Marnier' 🏆H1c	CDTJ CHll CSam WOth
	- 'Plena'	see *B. arborea* 'Knightii'
	- 'Rosalla'	WOth
§	- 'Variegata' (v)	CCCN CDTJ CHll CSam
	'Dalen's Pink Amour' (d)	WOth
	'Fleming Island Spider' (d)	WOth
	'Flowerdream' (d)	EUJe
§	× ***insignis***	CHll
§	- pink-flowered	SEND
	'L'Amour'	WOth
	'Madame Bovary'	WOth
	'Miss Emily Mackenzie'	WOth
	'Morgensonne'	WOth
	'Nicoline'	WOth
	'Painted Lady'	WOth
§	***sanguinea***	CCCN GCal SEND SPlb WOth
	- 'Rosea'	see *B.* × *insignis* pink-flowered
§	***suaveolens*** 🏆H1c	CBcs CHll EUJe
	- ***rosea***	see *B.* × *insignis* pink-flowered
	- 'Variegata' (v)	EShb
	- yellow-flowered	EShb
	suaveolens* × *versicolor	see *B.* × *insignis*
	'Variegata Sunset'	see *B.* × *candida* 'Variegata'
	versicolor misapplied	see *B. arborea*
§	***versicolor*** Lagerh.	CCCN
*	'Yellow Trumpet'	ELan

Brunfelsia (*Solanaceae*)

	americana	CCCN
	australis **new**	WFib
	calycina	see *B. pauciflora*
	eximia	see *B. pauciflora* 'Eximia'
	lactea	CCCN
§	***pauciflora*** 🏆H1c	CCCN ELan EShb IDee
§	- 'Eximia'	SPer

Brunia (*Bruniaceae*)

	albiflora	SPlb

Brunnera ✿ (*Boraginaceae*)

§	***macrophylla***	Widely available
	- 'Agnes Amez'	IMou
	- 'Aimee Angus'	EPPr
	- 'Alba'	see *B. macrophylla* 'Betty Bowring'
	- 'Alexander's Great'	SCob
§	- 'Betty Bowring'	Widely available
	- 'Blanc d'Adoué'	CBot
	- 'Blaukuppel'	CLAP CTal EWes GCal LRHS NBir WCAu
	- 'Dawson's White' (v)	CBcs CLAP CWCL ECha ECtt ELan ELon EPfP GBuc GEdr GKev GMaP GMcL IKil LHop LRHS NBid NBir NHpl NLar SCob SPer SRGP SRms SWvt WFar
	- 'Diane's Gold'PBR	CBct CTal EBee ECtt LRHS MGos MHol MPnt NBir NLar NPnk SCob SHil SMDP
	- 'Emerald Mist'PBR (v)	CBod EBee ECtt GBin GEdr MGos NLar SWvt
	- 'Gordano Gold' (v)	EHoe NBir WCot
	- 'Green Gold' (v)	EBee SPoG
	- 'Hadspen Cream' (v) 🏆H6	Widely available
	- 'Henry's Eyes'	EBee
	- 'Hopley's Gold'	LHop
	- 'Jack Frost'PBR 🏆H6	Widely available
	- 'Jennifer'	EBee WCAu
	- 'King's Ransom'PBR (v)	CBct CNor CWGN ECtt GPSL NLar NSti WFar
	- 'Langford Hewitt' (v)	MNrw
	- 'Langtrees'	CBct CMac EBee ECha EHoe GAbr GBuc GCal GCra LHop LRHS MCot MHol MMuc NBir NGdn SEND SPer SWat WCFE WHea
	- 'Little Jack' (v) **new**	SPoG
	- 'Looking Glass'PBR 🏆H6	Widely available
	- 'Marley's White'	CLAP ELan LLHF SCob SGbt WPnP
§	- 'Mister Morse'PBR (v)	Widely available
	- 'Sea Heart'	CMea ECtt GBin NLar SCob
	- 'Silver Heart'	CWGN ECtt MTis SCob SMad SPad WBor
	- 'Silver Wings'	CBod CElw CWCL EAEE EBee ECtt EPfP GEdr GKev LRHS LSou MBel MGos NBir NGdn NLar NSti NWad SWat WCAu WFar
	- 'Spring Yellow'	ECtt
	- 'Starry Eyes'	SCob WHlf
	'Mrs Morse'	see *B. macrophylla* 'Mister Morse'
	sibirica	CElw CLAP EBee EPPr EWes NBid

Brunsvigia (*Amaryllidaceae*)

	bosmaniae	WCot
	- white-flowered **new**	WCot
	elandsmontana	WCot
	gregaria	WCot
	josephinae	WCot
	- LAV 30394	WCot
	litoralis	WCot
	marginata	WCot
	multiflora	see *B. orientalis*
§	***orientalis***	WCot
	pulchra	WCot
	radulosa	WCot

rosea 'Minor'	see *Amaryllis belladonna*
striata	CTal WCot

Bryonia (*Cucurbitaceae*)

dioica	CArn GPoy NMir

Bryophyllum see *Kalanchoe*

Buddleja ✿ (*Scrophulariaceae*)

HCM 98.017 from Chile	WPGP
agathosma	CBot CFil SLon WKif WLav WSHC
albiflora	SLon WLav
alternifolia ♀H5	Widely available
- KR 4881 new	GKev
- 'Argentea'	CBcs CBot CNec EBee ELan EMil EPfP EWTr LRHS MBNS MNHC MRav NLar SKHP SPer SWvt WCot WLav WSHC XSen
asiatica ♀H2	CHid IDee SLon WLav
- B&SWJ 11278	WCru
auriculata	CBcs CBot CHll CMCN CNec CWib EBee ELan EPfP LRHS SBod SDix SKHP SLon SPlb SVen WGwG WLav
'Bel Argent'	WPGP
'Blue Chip'PBR (Lo and Behold Series)	CBot EMil EPfP LBuc LRHS MAsh MGos MJak MPkF NLar NRHS SCob SKHP SLim SLon SRms SWvt WCot WFar WLav
caryopteridifolia	EBtc GQui SEND SLon
colvilei	CBcs CDul CWCL CWld ELan EPfP GBin GCal GKin IArd IDee SBrt SLon SWvt WBor WHer
- B&SWJ 2121	WCru
- GWJ 9399	WCru
- WJC 13760 new	WCru
- 'Kewensis'	CBot CHGN CHid CNec CRHN CWCL CWld EWTr EWes GCal NLar SBrt SLon SVen WCFE WCru WLav WPat WSHC
- pink-flowered new	NLar
cordata	CFil LRHS SLon
- B&SWJ 10433	WCru
coriacea	SLon
§ ***crispa***	CBcs CBct CBot CHid CSpe EBee ECha ELan EPfP LRHS SEND SLon SPer SRkn SVen SWvt WFar WKif WPGP WSHC XSen
- var. ***farreri***	CBot CHGN CHid EUJe SLon
crotonoides subsp. ***amplexicaulis***	SLon
'David Griffin'	LRHS
davidii	CCVT ESps NPol NWea SCob WTSh
- B&SWJ 8083	WCru
- Adonis Blue = 'Adokeep'PBR	CBcs CNec CSBt CWCL ESps LBuc LRHS SLon WLav
- 'African Queen'	LRHS SLon SRGP WLav
- var. ***alba***	CWib ESps
§ - 'Autumn Beauty'	CAni CNec SLon WLav
- 'Autumn Delight'	SLon
- 'Bath Beauty'	CAni
- 'Beijing'	see *B. davidii* 'Autumn Beauty'
- 'Bishop's Velvet'	CAni
- 'Black Knight' ♀H5	Widely available
- 'Blue Eyes'	WLav
- 'Blue Horizon' ♀H5	CAni CRos LRHS NLar NRHS SLon SRGP WCot WLav WMoo WRHF
- 'Border Beauty'	CAni CNec LRHS NRHS SCob SLon WLav
- 'Brown's Beauty'	CAni
- 'Butterfly Heaven'PBR	WLav
- Buzz Series	LBuc NHol SLon
- - Buzz Ivory = 'Tobuivo'	CEnd CMac CNec CRos EBee ELan ELon EMOT ESps ESwi GMcL LRHS LSRN LSou MGos MJak NHol NLar NRHS SHil SLim SLon SMDP SPer SPoG WHil WLav
- - Buzz Lilac	ELan MGos NHol SCob SLon
- - Buzz Magenta = 'Tobudpipur'PBR	Widely available
- - Buzz Sky Blue = 'Tobuskyblu'	CMac CRos GMcL LBMP LHop LRHS LSou MGos NEgg NHol NLar NPri NRHS SHil SMDP SPad SPoG SRms WFar WLav
- - Buzz Velvet = 'Tobudvelve'PBR	CRos LRHS NRHS SHil SPad SPer WHil
- - Buzz Violet = 'Tobudviole'	CHid CMac CRos ELan ELon GMcL LRHS LSou MGos MJak NHol NLar NPri NRHS SEle SLim SLon SPer SPoG SWvt WLav
- Camberwell Beauty = 'Camkeep' (English Butterfly Series) ♀H5	CHll CNec ESps LRHS LSRN SLon WLav
- 'Car Wash'	CAni
- 'Castle Blue'	LRHS NRHS SLon
- 'Castle School'	CAni CSam WLav
§ - 'Charming'	CDul WMoo WSHC
- 'Clive Farrell'	see *B. davidii* 'Autumn Beauty'
- 'Corinne Tremaine'	WHer
- 'Cotswold Blue'	WLav
- 'Darent Valley' ♀H5	SLon
- 'Dartmoor' ♀H5	Widely available
- 'Dart's Ornamental White'	CNec MRav SLon WLav
- 'Dart's Papillon Blue'	CAni LRHS SLon WLav
- 'Dart's Purple Rain'	CAni CNec LRHS NRHS SLon WLav
- 'Dubonnet'	CAni SLon WLav
- 'Dudley's Compact Lavender'	CAni
- 'Ecolonia'	CAni SLon WLav
- 'Empire Blue'	CAni CBcs CDul CNec CRos CSBt ECtt EPfP ESps GKin LRHS LSRN MGos NBir NPer NRHS NWea SCob SEND SHil SPer SPlb SPoG SRGP SRms SWat SWvt XSen
- 'Fair Lady'	WLav
- 'Fascinating'	CAni CNec GCal MRav NBir SLon WLav
- 'Flaming Violet'	CAni SLon WLav
- 'Florence'	CNec LLHF LSRN NEgg NLar SLon WFar WMoo
- 'Fortune'	CAni
- 'Foxtail'	WLav
- 'Glasnevin Hybrid'	CAni CNec CRos LRHS NLar SDix SLon WLav
- 'Gonglepod'	CAni CNec LRHS NRHS SLon WLav
- 'Greenway's River Dart'	CAni LRHS SLon
- 'Grey Dawn'	WLav
- 'Griffin Blue'	MAsh WLav
- 'Gulliver'PBR	LRHS NLar NRHS SGol SLon WFar WLav
- 'Harlequin' (v)	Widely available
- 'Île de France'	CAni CBcs CNec CWib NLar NWea SLon SRms WLav
- 'Leela Kapila'	LRHS SLon
- 'Les Kneale'	CAni CNec SLon WLav
- 'Lilac Moon'	WLav
- 'Lyme Bay'	CAni
- Marbled White = 'Markeep'PBR (English Butterfly Series)	CNec EBee LRHS NEoE NRHS SLon WLav WMoo

- Masquerade = 'Notbud' (v)	CLet MRav SLon
- Moonshine = 'Buddma'[PBR]	LSou NEoE WFar
§ - Nanho Blue = 'Mongo'	Widely available
- 'Nanho Petite Indigo'	see *B. davidii* Nanho Blue
- 'Nanho Petite Plum'	see *B. davidii* Nanho Purple
- 'Nanho Petite Purple'	see *B. davidii* Nanho Purple
§ - Nanho Purple = 'Monum' ♀H5	CBcs CMHG CMac CNec CRos CTri CWib EBee ELan EPfP ESps LRHS LSRN MGos MRav NLar SCob SGol SLim SLon SPer SPlb SRms XSen
- Nanho White = 'Monite' ♀H5	CMac CRos ELan EPfP ESps LRHS SCob SGol SLon SPer SRms
- var. ***nanhoensis***	CAni CDul SEND SGol WFar WLav
- - blue-flowered	EPfP NWad SLon SPer
- 'Orchid Beauty'	CAni LRHS SLon WLav
- 'Orpheus'	CAni CNec SLon WLav
- 'Panache'	CNec CRos EPfP LRHS MAsh NRHS SLon WLav
- 'Peace'	CMac CTri CWCL LSRN MRav NLar SLon SPoG WLav
- Peacock = 'Peakeep'[PBR] (English Butterfly Series)	CBcs CNec CSBt GMcL MAsh NEgg SEle SPoG WLav
- 'Persephone'	SLon WLav
- 'Petite Indigo'	see *B. davidii* Nanho Blue
- 'Pink Beauty'	LSRN MBlu SRGP WFar
- 'Pink Charming'	see *B. davidii* 'Charming'
- 'Pink Pearl'	CAni LRHS NRHS SEND SLon WLav
- 'Pink Spreader'	CAni LRHS SLon WLav
- 'Pixie Blue'	CAni GMcL LBMP LRHS MAsh NLar SLon WLav
- 'Pixie Red'	CAni GMcL LBMP LBuc LRHS MAsh NLar SEND WLav
- 'Pixie White'	LBuc MAsh NLar SEND SGol WLav
- Purple Emperor = 'Pyrkeep' (English Butterfly Series)	CNec NBir NEgg SAko SLon SPoG WLav
- 'Purple Friend'	CAni LRHS SLon WLav
- 'Purple Prince'	CAni
- 'Red Admiral'	CAni LLHF LRHS MAsh SLon SRGP
- Rêve de Papillon = 'Minpap'	CNec CRos LRHS MAsh NRHS WLav
- Rêve de Papillon Blue = 'Minpap3'	WLav
- 'Royal Purple'	CAni SLim SWvt
- 'Royal Red' ♀H5	Widely available
- 'Saith Ffynnon Early'	WSFF
- 'Santana' (v)	CAni CBcs CBod CDul CMac CNec EBee EHoe ELon EMil EPfP EWes GMcL LRHS LSou MRav NEgg NHol NLar NRHS SGol SPoG SRms SWvt WCFE WMoo WPat XSen
- 'Shapcott Blue'	CAni
- 'Shire Blue'	WLav
- 'Southcombe Splendour'	CAni LRHS NRHS
- 'Summer Beauty'	CAni CDul CWib MBlu SLon WLav XSen
- 'Summer House Blue'	LRHS SLon WLav
- 'Twotones'	WLav
- 'Variegata' (v)	CAni MAsh SLon SWvt WLav
- 'White Ball'	ELan NLar SLon WLav
- 'White Bouquet'	CAni CCVT CSBt EAEE EPfP GKin MHer MSwo NLar NWea SCob SEND SPer SRGP SWvt WLav XSen
- 'White Cloud'	CAni ECrN GQui LRHS NRHS SRms WGwG
- 'White Harlequin' (v)	SLon WCFE
- 'White Profusion' ♀H5	Widely available
- 'White Wings'	CNec LRHS NRHS SLon WLav
- 'Widecombe'	CAni
- 'Windtor'	CNec LRHS NRHS

§ ***delavayi***	CBot ECre GBin SEND WCru
'Ellen's Blue'	CFil CNec LRHS NLar WLav
fallowiana misapplied	see *B.* 'West Hill'
fallowiana Balf. f. & W.W. Sm.	CRos ELan GQui LRHS WLav
- ACE 2481	LRHS
- BWJ 7803	WCru
- var. ***alba*** ♀H5	CBot CHGN CMac CRos ECrN ELan EPfP LRHS MAsh MRav NLar NRHS SDix SLon SPer WSHC
- 'Bishop's Violet'	CTsd
'Flower Power'	see *B.* × *weyeriana* 'Bicolor'
Flutterby Flow Lavender = 'Podaras No 12' **new**	LCro
Flutterby Petite Blue Heaven = 'Podaras No 8'	CMea LCro NLar
Flutterby Petite Dark Pink = 'Podaras No 10'	LCro NLar
Flutterby Petite Snow White = 'Podaras No 15' **new**	LCro
Flutterby Petite Tutti Fruitti Pink = 'Podaras No 13' **new**	CMea LCro SRms
forrestii	CPne WCru
- BWJ 8020 **new**	WCru
globosa ♀H5	Widely available
- RCB/Arg C-11	WCot
- 'Cally Orange'	GCal WGwG
- 'Lemon Ball'	CNec MBlu NPer SLon WLav
glomerata	CNec CWCL EShb SLon
- 'Silver Service'	CBod CBot EBee ELan LRHS SKHP
heliophila	see *B. delavayi*
'Hocus Pocus' **new**	WHlf
'Ice Chip' (Lo and Behold Series)	EPfP
indica	SLon WLav
InSpired Pink	see *B.* × *weyeriana* 'Pink Pagoda'
japonica	SLon
- B&SWJ 8912	WCru
* ***knappii***	CBot
× ***lewisiana*** 'Margaret Pike'	SLon
'Lilac Chip' (Lo and Behold Series)	LRHS MPkF NLar NRHS
limitanea	SLon
- from Cangshan, Yunnan, China **new**	SBrt
lindleyana	Widely available
- 'Miss Vicie' **new**	LRHS NRHS
aff. ***lindleyana***	CBot EWTr SEle
- B&SWJ 11478	WCru
'Lochinch' ♀H5	Widely available
longifolia	SLon XSen
'Longstock Gem'	SLon
'Longstock Silver'	LRHS SLon
loricata	CBot CHGN CNec CTsd CWib EBee EPfP GBin GCal GQui IDee LRHS SKHP SLon SPlb WLav
macrostachya HWJ 602	WCru
- PAB 4198	LEdu WPGP
- WWJ 12016	WCru
§ ***madagascariensis*** ♀H2	CRHN NLar SLon SPlb SVen
'Malvern Blue'	CAni
megalocephala B&SWJ 9106	WCru WPGP
'Miss Ruby'[PBR] ♀H5	CRos EBee EPfP LBuc LRHS MAsh MPkF NRHS SGol WLav
§ 'Morning Mist'[PBR]	CBcs CBot CMac CNec CRos CSBt CWGN EBee EHoe ELan EPfP GMcL LRHS LSRN NEgg NHol NLar NPri NRHS SCob SEle SGol SLon SPoG SRms SWvt WPGP

myriantha	SLon WPGP XSen
nappii	CBot SLon
nicodemia	see *B. madagascariensis*
nivea	CBot CHid CMHG CWCL EBee SLon WLav XSen
- B&SWJ 2679	WCru
- pink-flowered	SLon
aff. ***nivea***	CBot
officinalis ΨH2	CBot SLon WLav
paniculata	SLon
- GWJ 9286	WCru
- from Sikkim	SBrt
parvifolia	SLon
- MPF 148	WLav
× ***pikei*** 'Hever'	SRms XSen
'Pink Delight' ΨH5	Widely available
'Pink Perfection'	CAni WFar
'Pride of Hever'	SDys
'Pride of Longstock'	SLon SPoG
'Purple Chip' (Lo and Behold Series)	LRHS
saligna	SLon
'Salmon Spheres'	SLon WLav
salviifolia	CBcs CBot CHid CMac CTsd CWCL EBee ELan LRHS MBlu NLar SEND SPlb SVen WGwG WHer WLav WPGP
- white-flowered	EBee SLon WPGP
Silver Anniversary	see *B.* 'Morning Mist'
stachyoides	WLav
stenostachya	SLon
sterniana	see *B. crispa*
'Sugar Plum'	CNec CSBt EPfP LBuc LCro LRHS NRHS SLon
tibetica	see *B. crispa*
tubiflora	SLon WLav
venenifera	SLon
- B&SWJ 895	WCru
- B&SWJ 6036	WCru
wardii KR 4881	WPGP
§ 'West Hill' ΨH5	LRHS NRHS SLon WLav
× ***weyeriana***	CBot CDul ECtt GQui MGil MMuc MNrw MSwo NBir SBod SPad SPlb SWvt WOut
§ - 'Bicolor'	CNec EPPr EPfP IDee LCro LLHF LOPS MNrw NLar SCob SEle SLon SRms WLav
- 'Boy Blue'	SLon WLav
- 'Golden Glow'	CNec CTri ECrN GBin LSRN NLar SLon SWvt WLav WSFF
- 'Honeycomb'	MGos NLar
- 'Lady de Ramsey'	SEND
- 'Moonlight'	CBcs CNec ELan GBin SLon SPer WCot WLav
§ - 'Pink Pagoda' PBR	CNec CRos EPfP LCro LRHS NRHS SLon SPoG
- 'Sungold' ΨH4	Widely available
'White Chip' (Lo and Behold Series)	LRHS
'Winter Sun'	SLon
yunnanensis	CBcs GCal NLar SLon
- B&SWJ 8146	WCru

Buglossoides (*Boraginaceae*)

§ ***purpurocaerulea***	CHll CSpe ECha ELan EPfP EWld LPla MNrw NBid NChi WCot WHea WSHC XLum

Bukiniczia (*Plumbaginaceae*)

cabulica	GKev

Bulbine (*Asphodelaceae*)

SH 74	CCse
alooides	ECho
annua misapplied	see *B. semibarbata*
bulbosa misapplied	see *B. semibarbata*
caulescens	see *B. frutescens*
§ ***frutescens***	CBod CHll IDee MHer SVen WJek
- 'Hallmark'	CCCN EAJP
latifolia	CCCN EBee
§ ***semibarbata***	CCCN

Bulbinella (*Asphodelaceae*)

angustifolia	GKev MHer
hookeri	EBee ECho GBin GEdr GKev LRHS MHer SRms WHal WThu
latifolia	GKev
- subsp. ***latifolia***	IBlr
nutans	EBee ECho
- white-flowered	CPne

Bulbinopsis see *Bulbine*

Bulbocodium (*Colchicaceae*)

vernum	ECho EPot GKev LAma LLHF SDeJ

bullace see *Prunus insititia*

Bunias (*Brassicaceae*)

orientalis	CAgr LEdu

Bunium (*Apiaceae*)

bulbocastanum	CAgr CSpe EBee IMou LEdu SDix SHDw WPGP

Buphthalmum (*Asteraceae*)

salicifolium	EBee ELan EPfP ESps MMuc NBro NGdn SEND SPer SRms SWat WCot WFar WWtn XLum
- 'Alpengold'	CSam ECha GMaP NBre NLar
- 'Dora'	ECtt WCot
- 'Sunwheel'	CBod CRos LRHS MHol NRHS SRms
speciosum	see *Telekia speciosa*

Bupleurum (*Apiaceae*)

angulosum	NBir WTcb
- copper-leaved	see *B. longifolium*
falcatum	CSpe ECGP ECha LPla LRHS NDov SDix WCot
fruticosum	CBcs CFil CSpe EAJP EBee ELan EPfP EUJe GBin LRHS MAsh SCob SDix SEND SKHP SLon SPer SPoG WCot WPGP WPat XSen
- bronze-leaved **new**	LRHS
§ ***longifolium***	CElw CFis CSpe EBee EWes GBin LEdu LRHS MNrw NBir NCGa NChi NSti SBrt SKHP SMad WPGP
- subsp. ***aureum***	SPhx
- 'Bronze Beauty'	GEdr
ranunculoides	LPla SPhx XLum
rotundifolium	CSpe IMou LEdu SPhx WCot

Bursaria (*Pittosporaceae*)

spinosa	CCCN CHll

Butia (*Arecaceae*)

sp.	ETod
capitata	CBcs CCCN CDTJ CPHo ETod LRHS SArc

§	- var. ***odorata***	SPlb
	eriospatha	LRHS
	odorata	see *B. capitata* var. *odorata*
	yatay	LRHS NLos SBig

Butomus (*Butomaceae*)

	umbellatus	CBen CWat ECha EPfP EWay GQue MNrw MRav MSKA MWLS MWts NBir NPer SWat WMAq WWtn XLum
	- f. ***albiflorus***	MSKA
	- 'Rosenrot'	EWay LLWG
	- 'Schneeweisschen'	EWay LLWG MWts

butternut see *Juglans cinerea*

Buxus ✿ (*Buxaceae*)

	aurea 'Marginata'	see *B. sempervirens* 'Marginata'
	'Green Gem'	NWad
	'Green Mound'	LBMP
	harlandii misapplied	CMen SRiv
	japonica 'Nana'	see *B. microphylla*
§	***microphylla***	MHer NWad NWea SGol
	- 'Asiatic Winter'	see *B. microphylla* var. *japonica* 'Winter Gem'
§	- 'Compacta'	CMen LLHF MHer NWad SRiv WCot WPat
	- 'Curly Locks'	NWad
	- 'Faulkner' ♀H5	CCVT ELan EPfP ESps LBuc LHop LTop MAsh MGos SCob SGol SPer SRiv SRms WMoo
	- 'Golden Triumph' PBR	CBot EBee LBMP
	- 'Green Pillow'	MHer SRiv
	- var. ***japonica*** 'Morris Midget'	NWad
	- - 'National'	NLar
§	- - 'Winter Gem'	MHer MRav
	- 'John Baldwin'	SRiv
	- var. ***sinica***	LTop
	sempervirens	Widely available
§	- 'Angustifolia'	MHer MRav NWad SMad
	- 'Arborescens'	CNWT
	- 'Argenteo-variegata' (v)	ESps IFoB MJak SGol WFar
	- 'Aurea'	see *B. sempervirens* 'Aureovariegata'
	- 'Aurea Maculata'	see *B. sempervirens* 'Aureovariegata'
	- 'Aurea Marginata'	see *B. sempervirens* 'Marginata'
§	- 'Aureovariegata' (v)	EBee EPfP EShb ESps LRHS LTop MGos MHer MRav NLar SPer SRiv SRms WMoo
	- 'Bentley Blue'	LTop NWea
	- 'Blauer Heinz'	ELan MHer MRav NWea SRiv WMoo
	- 'Bowles's Blue'	EWes
I	- 'Brilliantissima'	WMoo
	- clipped ball	CLet EPfP LSRN MGos NLar SGol SRiv SRms
	- clipped bird	SRiv
	- clipped cone	CLet LSRN SGol SRiv SRms
	- clipped pyramid	EPfP LSRN MGos NLar SGol SRiv SRms
	- clipped spiral	LSRN SGol SRiv SRms
	- 'Elegans'	IFoB LRHS
§	- 'Elegantissima' (v) ♀H5	Widely available
	- 'Fiesta'	SRms
	- 'Gold Tip'	see *B. sempervirens* 'Notata'
	- 'Golden Frimley' (v)	LHop
§	- 'Graham Blandy' ♀H5	IVic MHer SAko SGol SRiv
	- 'Green Balloon'	EPfP LBuc
	- 'Greenpeace'	see *B. sempervirens* 'Graham Blandy'
	- 'Handsworthensis'	CLnd CTri NWea SEND SRms WMoo
	- 'Japonica Aurea'	see *B. sempervirens* 'Latifolia Maculata'
	- 'King Midas'	IVic SAko
	- 'Kingsville'	see *B. microphylla* 'Compacta'
	- 'Kingsville Dwarf'	see *B. microphylla* 'Compacta'
§	- 'Latifolia Maculata' (v) ♀H5	CAbP CWib EPfP LRHS MHer MMuc NPer SEND SPoG SRiv WRHF
	- 'Longifolia'	see *B. sempervirens* 'Angustifolia'
§	- 'Marginata' (v)	CArn CPne IFoB LHop LRHS LTop SGol
	- 'Memorial'	LTop MHer NWad SMHy SRiv
	- 'Myosotidifolia'	NEoE SRiv WCot
	- 'Myrtifolia'	MHer
§	- 'Notata' (v)	IFoB MAsh WMoo
	- 'Parasol'	MHer
	- 'Prostrata'	NWad
	- 'Raket'	NWea
	- 'Rosmarinifolia'	MRav
	- 'Rotundifolia'	ELan MMuc SEND WMoo
	- 'Silver Variegated'	see *B. sempervirens* 'Elegantissima'
	- 'Suffruticosa'	Widely available
	- 'Suffruticosa Variegata' (v)	SRms SWvt
	- 'Twisty'	WFar
	- 'Vardar Valley'	NEoE SRiv
*	- 'Variegata' (v)	MSwo SArc
	- 'Waterfall'	MHer
	sinica var. ***insularis*** 'Filigree'	NWad
	- - 'Justin Brouwers'	MHer SRiv
	- - 'Tide Hill'	LTop MHer SRiv WFar

C

Cacalia (*Asteraceae*)

	plantaginea	see *Arnoglossum plantagineum*
	suaveolens	see *Hasteola suaveolens*

Cachrys (*Apiaceae*)

	alpina	SPhx

Caesalpinia (*Caesalpiniaceae*)

	gilliesii ♀H1c	CBcs CSpe LRHS NLos SPlb WCot WSHC
	pulcherrima ♀H1b	CCCN
	spinosa	SPlb

Caiophora (*Loasaceae*)

	coronata	SPlb

Caladium (*Araceae*)

	'Candidum' (v)	SDeJ
	'Carolyn Whorton'	SDeJ
	'Florida Cardinal' (v)	SDeJ
	'Frieda Hemple'	SDeJ
§	***praetermissum*** 'Hilo Beauty'	XBlo
	'White Christmas' (v)	SDeJ

Calamagrostis (*Poaceae*)

	× ***acutiflora***	XLum
	- 'Avalanche'	CKno CRos ECha EHoe EPPr EPed EShb EWes GCal GMcL GQue

	GWyn LHop LRHS MAsh MAvo NDov NRHS NWsh WPtf
- 'Eldorado' (v)	CKno MAvo MMuc WCot
- 'England' (v) new	GBin
- 'Karl Foerster'	Widely available
- 'Overdam' (v)	Widely available
- 'Stricta'	EBee EPPr NWsh
- 'Waldenbuch'	CKno EBee
argentea	see *Stipa calamagrostis*
arundinacea	CElw CMac SPlb WMoo XSen
§ ***brachytricha*** ♀H7	Widely available
- 'Mona'	NDov
emodensis	CAby CCVN CMea CSam CSpe EBee ECha EHoe EPPr GCal MAvo NBid NWsh SEND WGrn WHea WMoo WPGP
epigejos	CKno LEdu WHrl WPGP
foliosa	EPPr
splendens misapplied	see *Stipa calamagrostis*
splendens Trin.	NDov
varia	CKno EHoe GBin WHrl

Calamintha (*Lamiaceae*)

alpina	see *Acinos alpinus*
§ ***ascendens***	EBee ECGP WMoo
clinopodium	see *Clinopodium vulgare*
§ ***grandiflora***	CBod ECha ELan GJos GPoy ITim MHer MNHC MNrw MRav NBir NLar NPer SPer SPlb SRms WBod WCAu WHea WJek WMoo XSen
- 'Elfin Purple'	EBee EPfP
- 'Variegata' (v)	ECtt ELan ENfk EPfP LSou MPie SRms
'Harrogate'	NDov
§ ***nepeta***	CArn CBWd CBod CHab CMea ECha ENfk GBin GMaP LRHS MHer MNHC NBro SCob SEND SPhx SPlb SPoG SRms SWat WCAu WHer WJek WMoo WOut WPtf XSen
- subsp. ***glandulosa***	ECGP WMoo
- - ACL 1050/90	EBee WHoo
- - 'White Cloud'	CBWd EBee ECGP ECtt ELan GQue IBoy LLWP MRav NBir SPoG SRms WCAu WHea WMoo
- 'Gottfried Kuehn'	MRav
§ - subsp. ***nepeta***	ELan ELon EPfP IMou MCot MHer MMuc MRav NDov NSti SPer WFar WHal XLum
- - 'Blue Cloud'	CFis CSam CSpe EBee ECha ECtt EPfP EPri MArt MRav MSpe NBir NDov SPhx SPtp SRms WCAu WFar WMoo WTor
- 'Weisse Riese'	CMea EBee SPhx
nepetoides	see *C. nepeta* subsp. *nepeta*
officinalis misapplied	see *C. ascendens*
sylvatica	see *Clinopodium menthifolium*
vulgaris	see *Clinopodium vulgare*

calamondin see *Citrus* × *microcarpa*

Calandrinia (*Portulacaceae*)

sibirica	see *Claytonia sibirica*
umbellata	EDAr MAsh WIce
- 'Ruby Tuesday'	WTor XLum

Calanthe (*Orchidaceae*)

alismifolia	EFEx LAma
arcuata	EFEx
argenteostriata new	WCot
arisanenesis	EFEx
aristulifera	EFEx LAma LRHS
bicolor	see *C. striata*
brevicornu	GKev
discolor	EBee EFEx GKev LAma LRHS SDir WCot
- subsp. ***amamiana***	EFEx
- var. ***flava***	see *C. striata*
- subsp. ***tokunoshimensis***	EFEx
graciliflora	EFEx
Kozu gx	GKev LEdu WPGP
- 'Brown'	GKev
- 'Orange'	GKev
- 'Purple'	GKev
mannii	EFEx
- Chen Yi N-78 new	WCot
nipponica	CBct EFEx LAma LRHS
reflexa	EFEx LAma LRHS SDir
sieboldii	see *C. striata*
§ ***striata***	CBct EBee EFEx GKev LAma LRHS SDir WCot
sylvatica	LAma
tricarinata	CBct EFEx LAma SDir WCot
triplicata	LAma

Calathea (*Marantaceae*)

argyrophylla 'Exotica'	XBlo
louisae 'Maui Queen'	XBlo
majestica ♀H1b	XBlo
makoyana ♀H1b	XBlo
picturata 'Argentea' ♀H1b	XBlo
roseopicta ♀H1b	XBlo
- 'Rosastar'	XBlo
rufibarba ♀H1b	NGBl XBlo
* ***stromata***	XBlo
veitchiana 'Medaillon'	XBlo
zebrina ♀H1b	XBlo
'Zoizia'	XBlo

Calceolaria (*Calceolariaceae*)

arachnoidea	EBee EWes GEdr SKHP SPlb
§ ***biflora***	ECho EWes EWld GAbr GKev
- 'Goldcap'	ECho
- 'Goldcrest Amber'	SPlb
corymbosa	GLog
falklandica	ECho NSla
filicaulis	GKev
fothergillii	GAbr GLog WAbe
'Goldcrest'	ECho LRHS
integrifolia ♀H1c	CAbb CBcs CDTJ CFis CTri ECtt ELan EShb MGil MSCN SAdn SDix SEND SPer SRms WAbe WBor WHer
- bronze	MSCN SPer
- 'Gaines' Yellow'	EBee GCal
'John Innes'	ECho
'Kentish Hero'	CSpe EBee GCal MGil SDys WAbe
mollissima	GKev
pavonii	MGil
aff. ***nivea***	CRHN
perfoliata B&SWJ 10638	WCru
plantaginea	see *C. biflora*
rugosa	see *C. integrifolia*
'Sultan' new	EBee
tenella	NSla WAbe
uniflora var. ***darwinii***	ECho GKev NHpl
'Walter Shrimpton'	ECho WAbe

Calendula ✿ (*Asteraceae*)

arvensis	CCCN
'Bronze Beauty'	CSpe
officinalis	CLau ENfk GPoy LCro MHer MNHC SIde SPav SRms SVic SWvt WJek WSFF

- 'Art Shades' CWCL
- 'Calypso Orange' (Calypso Series) CWCL
- Fiesta Gitana Group WJek
- 'Indian Prince' (Prince Series) LCro SPhx
- 'Touch of Red Buff' (Touch of Red Series) CSpe

'Tarifa' SEND

Calibanus (*Asparagaceae*)

hookeri EShb

Calibrachoa (*Solanaceae*)

(Cabaret Series) Cabaret Bright Red = 'Balcabrite'PBR NPri
- Cabaret Deep Yellow = 'Balcabdepy'PBR NPri

Callie Sunrise = 'Cal Sunre'PBR (Callie Series) LSou
(Can-can Series) Can-can Black Cherry LSou
- Can-can Double Dark Yellow NPri
- Can-can Double Magenta NPri

(Carillon Series) Carillon Burgundy = 'Sk9-354' ESps
- Carillon Lemon **new** ESps
- Carillon Red = 'Sk7-1155' **new** ESps
- Carillon White **new** ESps

Kabloom Deep Blue = 'Pas10203441' **new** NPri
Kabloom Deep Pink = 'Pas1020309' **new** NPri
Kabloom White = 'Pas1020307' **new** NPri
(Million Bells Series) Million Bells Cherry = 'Sunbelchipi'PBR ESps
- Million Bells Pink Morn = 'Sunbelkupapi'PBR ESps
- Million Bells Red = 'Sunbelre'PBR ESps
- Million Bells Trailing Blue = 'Sunbelkubu'PBR ESps
- Million Bells Trailing Fuchsia = 'Sunbelrkup' ESps
- Million Bells Trailing Lavender Vein = 'Sunbelbura'PBR ESps LSou
- Million Bells Trailing Lemon LSou
- Million Bells Trailing Soft Pink = 'Sunbelkuopi'PBR ESps
- Million Bells Trailing White = 'Sunbelkuho' ESps

Noa Tangerine = 'Danoa52' LSou
(Superbells Series) Superbells Banana Chocolate **new** NPri
- Superbells Grape Punch = 'Uscal84704' **new** NPri
- Superbells Imperial Purple = 'Uscali100'PBR LSou
- Superbells Lemon Slice = 'Uscal5302m' NPri
- Superbells Orange = 'Uscali41109' LSou
- Superbells Pink = 'Uscali11'PBR LSou
- Superbells Pomegranate Punch = 'Uscal08501' **new** NPri

Calla (*Araceae*)

aethiopica see *Zantedeschia aethiopica*
palustris CBod CWat ESps EWay MSKA MWts NPer SRms SWat WMAq

Calliandra (*Mimosaceae*)

'Dixie Pink' CCCN
portoricensis CCCN
surinamensis CCCN
tweediei ♀H1c CCCN

Callianthemum (*Ranunculaceae*)

anemonoides GEdr LLHF WAbe WCot
coriandrifolium GEdr
kernerianum GEdr WAbe

Callicarpa (*Lamiaceae*)

CW&T 6228 **new** CMCN
acuminata CFil
americana var. ***lactea*** CMCN
bodinieri CHll WBod WHar
- var. ***giraldii*** ESps MRav NLar SGol
- - 'Profusion' ♀H5 Widely available
- 'Imperial Pearl' **new** LRHS

'Cardinal' CJun
cathayana NLar
dichotoma CBcs NLar SCob
- 'Issai' EPfP ESwi EUJe LRHS MBlu

japonica CMen NLar
- B&SWJ 12621 WCru
- f. ***albibacca*** ESwi LRHS
- 'Heavy Berry' NLar
- 'Koshima-no-homate' NLar
- 'Leucocarpa' CBcs CMac EBee ELan EPfP ESwi EWTr MRav NLar SMad SPer SPoG WGob
- var. ***luxurians*** B&SWJ 8521 WCru

kwangtungensis CBcs EPfP ESwi MMrt NLar
mollis CBcs
psilocalyx NJM 13.057 **new** WPGP
shikokiana NLar
× ***shirasawana*** NLar
aff. ***tikusikensis*** B&SWJ 7127 WCru
Van den Broek selection NLar
yunnanensis NLar

Callirhoe (*Malvaceae*)

bushii EBee
involucrata SBrt WHrl WSHC XLum
- var. ***tenuissima*** GCal

Callisia (*Commelinaceae*)

fragrans EOHP EShb

Callistemon (*Myrtaceae*)

acuminatus CCCN
brachyandrus SVen
citrinus CBcs CHll CTri EPfP EPri ESps SEND SEle SPlb WGrn
- 'Albus' see *C. citrinus* 'White Anzac'
- 'Firebrand' LRHS MAsh SPoG
- 'Splendens' ♀H3 Widely available

§ - 'White Anzac' CHll CMac ELan EMil EPfP LRHS SAko SPoG

comboynensis	CCCN
'Dawson River Weeper'	CMCN
glaucus	see *C. speciosus*
'Inferno'	NEgg
'Kings Park Special'	CMCN
laevis hort.	see *C. rugulosus*
linearifolius	LSRN
linearis ♀H2	CBcs CMac CTri ECrN ELan EPfP ESps IDee LRHS LSRN MAsh MGos MHer SEND SLim SLon SPlb SPoG SWvt WSHC
macropunctatus	SPlb SVen
'Masotti'PBR	MPkF SHil SPoG
'Mauve Mist'	CCCN ELan EMil EPfP LRHS MAsh SAko SEle SPoG SVen WGrn
pallidus	CBcs CCCN CMCN CMac CTsd CWib ELan EPfP EWTr IDee LRHS MAsh MMuc MRav NRHS SAko SEND SEle SPer SPlb SPoG SVen WBod
paludosus	see *C. sieberi* DC.
'Perth Pink'	CBcs CCCN CSBt ELan EPfP LHop LRHS SPad SVen WGrn
pinifolius	SPlb SVen
§ ***pityoides***	CTsd NLar SEle SVen
'Red Clusters'	CBcs CMac ELan EMOT EMil EPfP IArd LRHS MAsh MJak NPri SAko SWvt WFar
rigidus	CBcs CChe CHll CTri CTsd CWib ELan EMOT EPfP ESps EUJe GAbr GMcL IArd LRHS LSRN MGos MHtn MRav NLar NRHS SEle SPer SVen SWvt WBod
§ ***rugulosus***	CBcs CCCN GMcL NPri SVen SWvt
salignus ♀H2	CBcs CCCN CDul CLet CMac CTri CTsd EMOT EPfP MHer MRav NEgg NLar SEle SLim SPer SVen
sieberi misapplied	see *C. pityoides*
§ ***sieberi*** DC.	CBcs CMCN ELan EPfP LRHS MGil MMuc NBir NLar SEND SLim SPlb
§ ***speciosus***	CDul NLar SPlb
subulatus	SArc SPlb
- 'Crimson Tail'	ECrN MGil MMuc NLar SEND SPtp
viminalis	CBcs CCCN CMCN SPlb
- 'Captain Cook'	CMac EMOT LRHS LSRN NEgg SVen SWvt WFar WGrn
- 'Endeavour'	CCCN
- 'Hannah Ray'	EMOT WFar
- Hot Pink = 'Kkho1'PBR	LRHS MPkF SHil SLim
- 'Little John'	LSRN MAsh SPad SWvt
'Violaceus'	NLar SPlb SVen
viridiflorus	CMCN MMuc SEND SPlb WGwG
'White Anzac'	see *C. citrinus* 'White Anzac'

Callistephus (*Asteraceae*)

chinensis	SVic

Callitriche (*Plantaginaceae*)

sp.	WSFF
brutia subsp. ***hamulata***	LLWG
§ ***palustris***	CBen MSKA MWts
stagnalis	WMAq
verna	see *C. palustris*

Callitris (*Cupressaceae*)

endlicheri new	CBrP

Callitropsis see *Chamaecyparis*

× ***leylandii***	see × *Cuprocyparis leylandii*
nootkatensis	see *Xanthocyparis nootkatensis*

Calluna ✿ (*Ericaceae*)

vulgaris	ESps SWhi WOut
- 'Adrie'	SWhi
- 'Alba Elongata'	see *C. vulgaris* 'Mair's Variety'
§ - 'Alba Rigida'	CFst
- 'Alexandra'PBR (Garden Girls Series)	SCoo SPoG
- 'Alicia'PBR (Garden Girls Series) ♀H7	LRHS SCoo SPoG SWhi
- 'Allegro'	EPfP MMuc SCoo
- 'Amethyst'PBR (Garden Girls Series)	MJak MMuc SPoG SWhi
- 'Amilto'	CFst
- 'Anette'PBR (Garden Girls Series)	MJak SCoo SWhi
- 'Angie' new	SWhi
- 'Annabel' (d)	SWhi
- 'Annemarie' (d) ♀H7	CFst CSBt EPfP SCoo SPlb SWhi
- 'Anne's Goldzwerg'	CFst
- 'Anne's Zwerg'	CFst
- 'Aphrodite'PBR (Garden Girls Series)	CFst LRHS NRHS SWhi
- 'Arabella'PBR	SWhi
- 'Arina'	MAsh SCoo
- 'Athene'PBR (Garden Girls Series)	CFst SWhi
- 'Aurea'	MJak
- 'Beoley Crimson'	SCoo
- 'Beoley Gold' ♀H7	CSBt CTri EPfP MAsh NHol SCoo
- 'Beoley Silver'	SCoo SWhi
- 'Blazeaway'	CTri EPfP MAsh MJak SCoo
- 'Bonfire Brilliance'	CSBt NHol
- 'Bonita'PBR (Garden Girls Series)	CFst
- 'Boskoop'	MAsh NHol SWhi
- 'C.W. Nix'	CSBt
- 'Con Brio'	CFst CSBt SCoo SWhi
- 'Cottswood Gold'	SCoo
- 'County Wicklow' (d) ♀H7	CTri EPfP MMuc NHol SCoo SWhi
- 'Cuprea'	EPfP MJak SCoo SWhi
- 'Dark Beauty'PBR (d) ♀H7	CBcs CFst CSBt EPfP LCro MAsh NHol SCoo SPer SWhi
- 'Dark Star' (d) ♀H7	CFst CSBt EPfP LCro MAsh NHol SCoo SWhi
- 'Darkness' ♀H7	CBcs CFst CTri EPfP MAsh MJak SCoo SWhi
- 'David Hagenaars'	SWhi
- 'Disco Queen'	SWhi
- 'Dunnet Lime'	SPlb
- 'Easter-bonfire'	SCoo
- 'Eckart Miessner'	SWhi
- 'Elsie Purnell' (d) ♀H7	CFst EPfP MAsh NHol SCoo SPlb
- 'Feuerwerk'	SCoo
- 'Firefly' ♀H7	CFst CSBt EPfP MJak MMuc NHol NWea SCoo SPer SWhi
- 'Flamingo'	MMuc SCoo
- 'Forest Fire'	CFst
- 'Foxii Nana'	CFst NHol SWhi
- 'Fred J. Chapple'	MJak SWhi
- 'Galaxy'PBR	CFst SPer
- Garden Girls Series	MMuc
- 'Gina'PBR new	SWhi
- 'Glenfiddich'	CSBt MAsh
- 'Gold Haze'	CTri MAsh NHol SCoo
- 'Gold Knight'	EPfP MAsh SCoo
- 'Gold Spronk'	SWhi
- 'Golden Angie' new	SWhi
- 'Golden Carpet'	CFst MAsh NHol
- 'Golden Fleece'	CFst

– 'Golden Turret'	MAsh
– 'Grey Carpet'	CFst
– 'Guinea Gold'	MAsh SWhi
§ – 'H.E. Beale' (d)	CTri EPfP MJak NHol SCoo
– 'Hammondii Aureifolia'	SPlb
– 'Hammondii Rubrifolia'	SWhi
– 'Helena' **new**	LRHS NRHS
– 'Hera'PBR **new**	SWhi
– 'Highland Rose'	SPlb
– 'Hilda'PBR **new**	CRos LRHS NRHS
– 'J.H. Hamilton' (d)	CTri MAsh NHol SCoo SWhi
– 'Jan Dekker'	MAsh SPer
– 'Jana' (d)	CFst
– 'Johnson's Variety'	SCoo
– 'Josefine'	SWhi
– 'Joy Vanstone'	EPfP
– 'Julia'	SWhi
– 'Juliane'PBR **new**	SPer
– 'Kerstin' 🏆H7	CFst NHol SCoo SPlb SWhi
– 'Kinlochruel' (d) 🏆H7	CBcs CFst CSBt CTri EPfP MAsh NHol SPlb SWhi
– 'Kirby White'	MAsh SPlb SWhi
– 'Klaudine'PBR (Garden Girls Series)	CFst
– 'Lemon Queen'	CFst
– 'Leslie Slinger'	SCoo
– 'Lilli'PBR **new**	SWhi
– 'Little John'	LSRN
– 'Loch Turret'	SPer
– 'Loki'PBR **new**	SWhi
– 'Long White'	CFst SWhi
§ – 'Mair's Variety'	SCoo SWhi
– 'Marleen'	CSBt MJak
– 'Melanie' (Garden Girls Series)	CSBt NHol SCoo SWhi
– 'Mrs Pat'	MAsh
– 'Multicolor'	MAsh NHol
§ – 'My Dream' (d)	CSBt EPfP SCoo
– 'Nana Compacta'	CFst
– 'Nora' **new**	SWhi
– 'October White'	CFst
– 'Orange Queen'	CSBt
– 'Peter Sparkes' (d) 🏆H7	CBcs CSBt EPfP MAsh MMuc NHol SCoo
– 'Pink Beale'	see *C. vulgaris* 'H.E. Beale'
– 'Purple Passion'	EPfP SCoo
– 'Radnor' (d)	CSBt
– 'Ralph Purnell'	SCoo
– 'Rebecca's Red'	LRHS NRHS
– 'Red Beauty'	CBcs CFst SWhi
– 'Red Favorit' (d)	CFst SWhi
– 'Red Fred'	SCoo
– 'Red Haze'	EPfP NHol SCoo
– 'Red Pimpernel'	EPfP SCoo SWhi
– 'Red Star' (d)	NHol
– 'Redbud'	SWhi
– 'Rigida Prostrata'	see *C. vulgaris* 'Alba Rigida'
– 'Robert Chapman' 🏆H7	CFst CSBt CTri MAsh NHol SPer SWhi
– 'Rosalind' ambig.	EPfP
– 'Rosalind, Underwood's'	EPfP NHol
– 'Rosita'PBR	CFst CRos LRHS NRHS
– 'Ruby Slinger'	NHol
– 'Ruth Sparkes' (d)	NHol
– 'Sandy'PBR (Garden Girls Series)	CRos LRHS NRHS SPoG SWhi
– 'Serlei Aurea'	CSBt EPfP
– 'Silvana'PBR	CFst SWhi
– 'Silver Fox'	CBcs CFst
– 'Silver Knight'	CSBt EPfP MAsh MJak NHol SCoo SPlb SWhi
– 'Silver Queen' 🏆H7	CFst MAsh MJak NHol SWhi
– 'Sir John Charrington'	CFst EPfP MAsh NHol SWhi
– 'Sister Anne' 🏆H7	CFst CSBt EPfP MJak MMuc SCoo
– 'Snow White'	SWhi
– 'Snowball'	see *C. vulgaris* 'My Dream'
– 'Sonja' (d)	IVic
– 'Spitfire'	MAsh
– 'Spring Cream' 🏆H7	CBcs CFst MAsh MMuc NHol SCoo SPoG SWhi
– 'Spring Torch'	CBcs CFst CSBt MAsh MJak NHol SCoo SPoG SWhi
– 'Stefanie'	SWhi
– 'Strawberry Delight' (d)	EPfP SCoo
– 'Sun Sprinkles'	CFst
– 'Sunrise'	EPfP
– 'Sunset'	CFst
– 'Theresa' (Garden Girls Series)	CFst SWhi
– 'Tib' (d) 🏆H7	CSBt MAsh SWhi
– 'Tricolorifolia'	EPfP MAsh SCoo
– 'Velvet Fascination' 🏆H7	EPfP SCoo SWhi
– 'White Angie' **new**	SWhi
– 'White Coral' (d) 🏆H7	EPfP IVic SCoo
– 'White Lawn'	CFst MMuc NHol
– 'Wickwar Flame' 🏆H7	CBcs CFst CSBt EPfP MAsh MJak NHol SCoo SPlb SWhi
– 'Winter Chocolate'	CSBt EPfP MAsh NHol SCoo
– 'Yellow Beauty'PBR	CFst
– 'Yvette's Gold'	CFst
– 'Yvette's Silver'	CFst

Calocedrus (*Cupressaceae*)

§ ***decurrens*** 🏆H6	CAco CBcs CDul CLnd CMac CTho EPfP EUJe MBlu NWea SLim WTSh
– 'Aureovariegata' (v) 🏆H6	CBcs CWib SCoo
– 'Berrima Gold' 🏆H6	NLar SLim
§ – 'Depressa'	CKen
– 'Maupin Glow' (v)	SLim
– 'Nana'	see *C. decurrens* 'Depressa'
– 'Pillar'	CKen NLar

Calocephalus (*Asteraceae*)

brownii	see *Leucophyta brownii*

Calochortus (*Liliaceae*)

'Cupido'PBR	GKev LAma
luteus 'Golden Orb'PBR	CAby ECho GKev LAma SDeJ SDir
splendens 'Violet Queen'	ECho GKev LAma
superbus	ECho GKev SDeJ SDir
'Symphony'PBR	ECho GKev LAma SDeJ
venustus	CAby ECho GKev LAma SDeJ SDir
– 'Burgundy'	CAby ECho GKev SDeJ

Calomeria (*Asteraceae*)

§ ***amaranthoides***	WJek

Calonyction see *Ipomoea*

Caloscordum see *Allium*

neriniflorum	see *Allium neriniflorum*

Calostemma (*Amaryllidaceae*)

luteum **new**	GKev
purpureum **new**	GKev
– dark **new**	GKev

Calothamnus (*Myrtaceae*)

quadrifidus	CKel
validus	SPlb
villosus	SPlb

Calpurnia (*Papilionaceae*)

aurea	SPlb

Caltha ✿ (*Ranunculaceae*)

howellii	see *C. leptosepala* subsp. *howellii*
introloba	SWat
laeta	see *C. palustris* var. *palustris*
leptosepala	EBee EWay GEdr GKev LLHF LLWG NLar
- SDR 8134 **new**	GKev
§ - subsp. ***howellii*** NNS 07-87	GKev
natans	LLWG
palustris	Widely available
- var. ***alba***	Widely available
- 'Auengold'	EBee LLWG
- 'Auenwald'	LLWG
- var. ***barthei***	GEdr
- 'Flore Pleno' (d) ♀H7	Widely available
- 'Himalayan Snow'	EBee ECtt LLWG
- 'Honeydew'	CAby EWay LLWG WCot WSHC
§ - var. ***major***	CAby
- 'Marilyn'	LLWG
- 'Multiplex' (d)	CDor ECtt GBuc SRot
- Newlake hybrid	LLWG
- 'Pallida Plena' (d)	SCob
§ - var. ***palustris***	CBen CBre ECha ELan EUJe EWay GCal SWat WWtn
- - 'Plena' (d)	CWat EWay GBin LRHS MCot MSKA SBod SGol WGwG
- var. ***radicans***	EWay GEdr
- - 'Flore Pleno' (d)	WWtn
- 'Stagnalis'	MSKA MWts
- 'Yellow Giant'	MSKA
polypetala misapplied	see *C. palustris* var. *major*
polypetala Hochst. ex Lorent	CWat GCal GJos MSCN MSKA NPer SMad SWat WMAq
sagittata	WSHC
scaposa	GKev

Calycanthus (*Calycanthaceae*)

chinensis	CBcs CHll CJun CMCN CRos EBee ELan EPfP EUJe GKin IDee LRHS MBlu MGil MMrt MPkF NLar
fertilis	see *C. floridus* var. *glaucus*
floridus	Widely available
- 'Athens'	CBcs CJun NLar WCot
§ - var. ***glaucus***	EPfP LRHS MAsh SHil
- - 'Purpureus'	CBcs CJun MBlu NLar
- var. ***laevigatus***	see *C. floridus* var. *glaucus*
- 'Michael Lindsay'	CJun NLar
mohrii	NLar
occidentalis	CBcs CDul CMCN CSpe CWib EPPr MBlu MGil SBrt WCFE
× ***raulstonii***	CAbP
- 'Hartlage Wine' ♀H5	CBcs CJun CRos EBee EPfP EUJe GKin IArd IDee LCro LLHF LRHS MAsh MBlu MGos NLar SHil SPoG WKif WPat
'Venus'	CBcs CMCN CRos EPfP IArd LCro LLHF LRHS MBlu NLar SPoG

Calylophus (*Onagraceae*)

§ ***serrulatus***	SIgm

Calystegia (*Convolvulaceae*)

'Angel's Trumpets'	SKHP
§ ***hederacea*** 'Flore Pleno' (d)	SMad
japonica 'Flore Pleno'	see *C. hederacea* 'Flore Pleno'
soldanella NNS 99-85	WCot

Calytrix (*Myrtaceae*)

tetragona	SPlb

Camassia (*Asparagaceae*)

'Blue Candle'	EBee EPot GKev LAma SDir SPhx
'Blue Heaven'	CMea EBee ECGP ERCP GKev LAma NHsp SDeJ SDir SPhx
cusickii	CBWd CBod CBro CRos CTca CTri CWCL EBee ECho ECtt ELan EPfP EPot ERCP EWTr GBin GKev IFro LAma LPot LRHS MCot NBir NLar SDeJ SDir SDix
- white-flowered	IFoB
- 'Zwanenburg'	CTca EBee ERCP GKev IPot LRHS NHpl NHsp NRHS WCot
esculenta Lindl.	see *C. quamash*
'John Treasure' (d)	GCal MAvo
'Lavender Mist' **new**	MAvo
leichtlinii misapplied	see *C. leichtlinii* subsp. *suksdorfii*
leichtlinii (Baker) S.Watson	see *C. leichtlinii* subsp. *leichtlinii*
'Alba' misapplied	
* - 'Alba Plena' (d)	LSun MNrw NBir NHpl
- Blue Danube	see *C. leichtlinii* subsp. *suksdorfii* 'Blauwe Donau'
- 'Blue Wave'	NWad SDir
§ - subsp. ***leichtlinii***	Widely available
- 'Plena' (d)	ECha
- 'Sacajawea'	CAvo CMea CTca EBee ERCP GKev LAma LRHS MAvo NHsp SDeJ SDir WTor
- 'Semiplena' (d)	CAvo CBro CMea CRos CTca EBee ECtt EPfP EPot ERCP GKev LAma LHop LRHS MBel MNrw NSti SDir SPhx WBor WCot WShi
§ - subsp. ***suksdorfii***	LCro WCot
- - 'Alba'	CRos EPot GBin GMaP IBoy LCro LOPS LRHS NRHS NSti SCob
- - 'Albocaerulea' **new**	NPnk
§ - - 'Blauwe Donau'	ILea SMHy
- - Caerulea Group	Widely available
- - 'Electra'	CAvo CMea ECha WCot
§ ***quamash***	Widely available
- 'Blue Melody' (v)	CAvo CBro CSam CTca EBee EPot GKev GMaP LEdu NHsp SDeJ SDir WRHF WTor
- 'Orion'	CBro EBee GKev LRHS NHsp WCot

Camellia ✿ (*Theaceae*)

'Adorable' (*pitardii* hybrid)	LRHS LSRN
'Alpen Glo'	LRHS
'April Blush'	SCog WFar
'Auburn White'	see *C. japonica* 'Mrs Bertha A. Harms'
azalea	LPar
'Baby Bear'	LRHS MPkF
'Barbara Clark' (*reticulata* × *saluenensis*)	LRHS LSRN SCog SCoo
'Bertha Harms Blush'	see *C. japonica* 'Mrs Bertha A. Harms'
'Black Lace' ♀H5	CSgt CTrh CTri EPfP LRHS LSRN MAsh MMuc NPri SArc SCog SCoo SEND SWeb SWvt
'Blissful Dawn'	CBcs CTrh
'Bonnie Marie'	LPar SCam SCog
'Califonia Sunset'	LRHS
'Canterbury'	LRHS MPkF SCam
chekiangoleosa	CPne
'China Lady' (*granthamiana* × *reticulata*)	SCam
'Christmas Daffodil' (*japonica* hybrid)	CBcs MPkF

'Cinnamon Cindy'	LRHS MPkF
'Cinnamon Sensation'	SCog
'Congratulations'	CSBt LSRN
'Contessa Lavinia Maggi'	see *C. japonica* 'Lavinia Maggi'
'Cornish Snow' (*cuspidata* × *saluenensis*) ♀H4	CBcs CSBt CTri ELan EPfP SCam SCog SWvt
'Cornish Spring' (*cuspidata* × *japonica*) ♀H4	CCCN CSBt CTrh CTsd LRHS SCam SCog SPer
crassipes new	CPne
'Crimson Candles' ♀H5	LRHS
'Curly Red' new	ETho
cuspidata	SCam
'Czar'	see *C. japonica* 'The Czar'
'Dainty Dale'	SCam
'Delia Williams'	see *C.* × *williamsii* 'Citation'
'Diamond Head' (*japonica* × *reticulata*)	CBcs LSRN
'Doctor Clifford Parks' (*japonica* × *reticulata*) ♀H4	CBcs CTrh
'Donckelaeri'	see *C. japonica* 'Masayoshi'
edithae	LRHS
'Extravaganza' (*japonica* hybrid) ♀H5	CBcs CTrh IArd
'Fairy Blush'	LRHS MPkF
'Fairy Wand'	LRHS MPkF
'Fascination'	SWvt
'Faustina Lechi'	see *C. japonica* 'Faustina'
'Felice Harris' (*reticulata* × *sasanqua*)	SCog
'Fiesta Grande'	MPkF
'Forty-niner' (*japonica* × *reticulata*)	CBcs CSgt LRHS MAsh
'Fragrant Pink'	CTrh
'Francie L' ♀H4	CBcs CMac EPfP SCam
'Frau Minna Seidel'	see *C. japonica* subsp. *rusticana* 'Otome'
'Free Spirit'	CTrh
'Freedom Bell' ♀H5	CMHG CTrh EPfP GKin LRHS NPri SCam SCog SCoo
'Frosted Star'	LRHS
'Gay Baby'	MPkF
'Golden Anniversary'	see *C. japonica* 'Dahlohnega'
grijsii	CTrh LRHS
'Happy Anniversary'	CSBt LSRN SWvt
§ ***hiemalis*** 'Bonanza'	CSgt CTrh LRHS MPkF SCam
- 'Chansonette'	CSgt ELon SCog
§ - 'Dazzler'	LRHS SCam SCog
- 'Elfin Rose'	LRHS
- 'Interlude'	MPkF
- 'Kanjirō'	SCam
- 'Shishigashira'	CTrh
- 'Shōwa-no-sakae'	LRHS MPkF SCog
'High Fragrance'	LRHS
'Hooker'	CSgt LRHS MAsh SCoo
'Imbricata Rubra'	see *C. japonica* 'Imbricata'
'Inspiration' (*reticulata* × *saluenensis*) ♀H4	CBcs CMac CTrh EPfP LRHS LSRN MGos NLar SCam SCog SPer
japonica	CAco ESps SEWo SPre
- 'Aaron's Ruby'	ELon LRHS SCam SCog
- 'Ace of Hearts'	SHil
- 'ACS Jubilee' new	LRHS
- 'Ada Pieper'	CTrh
- 'Adelina Patti' ♀H5	CBcs CMHG CSgt CTrh ELan
- 'Adeyaka'	CSgt LRHS
- 'Adolphe Audusson' ♀H5	Widely available
§ - 'Akashigata' ♀H5	CBcs ELon EPfP LRHS LSRN MAsh SCam SCog SSta
- 'Alba Plena' ♀H5	CSBt CTrh ELan LRHS SCog SPer SWvt

- 'Alba Simplex'	CMac CSgt CTrh ELan EPfP GMcL IVic NPri SCam SCob SCog SSta SWeb
- 'Alexander Hunter' ♀H5	CSgt LRHS MAsh SCam SCog
§ - 'Althaeiflora'	CBcs ELon LRHS SCam SCog
- 'Amazing Graces'	SCam
- 'Anemoniflora'	CBcs CTsd EPfP LRHS SCog
- 'Angel'	CBcs LSRN SCam WBor
- 'Angela Cocchi'	LPar SWeb
- 'Angello'	CSgt LRHS
- 'Ann Sothern'	CBcs
- 'Annie Wylam' ♀H5	CTrh ELan
- 'Apollo' ambig.	CBcs GMcL LRHS
§ - 'Apollo' Paul, 1911	MSwo SCam SCog
§ - 'Apple Blossom'	CBcs CTrh CTsd ESps LRHS
- 'April Remembered' new	ETho
- 'April Rose' new	ETho
- 'Arajishi' misapplied	see *C. japonica* subsp. *rusticana* 'Beni-arajishi'
- 'Augustine Supreme'	CMac
- 'Ave Maria' ♀H5	CSgt CTrh LRHS
- 'Baby Pearl'	LSRN
- 'Baby Sis'	LRHS
- 'Ballet Dancer' ♀H5	ELon LSRN SCam SCog
- 'Baron Gomer'	see *C. japonica* 'Comte de Gomer'
- 'Baronne Leguay'	SCam
- 'Beau Harp'	LRHS SCam
- 'Bella Lambertii'	SCog
- 'Bella Romana'	SCam
- 'Berenice Boddy' ♀H5	ELan LRHS
- 'Berenice Perfection'	SCam SCog
- 'Betty Foy Sanders'	CTrh
- 'Betty Robinson'	LRHS
- 'Betty Sheffield'	LRHS SCog
- 'Betty Sheffield Pink'	LRHS SCam
- 'Betty Sheffield Supreme'	CBcs SCam
- 'Betty's Beauty'	LRHS
- 'Black Magic'	CSgt CTrh LRHS MAsh SCam
- 'Black Tie'	CBcs CTrh ELan ELon LRHS MGos NEgg SCam SCog WFar
- 'Blackburnia'	see *C. japonica* 'Althaeiflora'
- 'Blaze of Glory'	SCog
§ - 'Blood of China'	CBcs CSBt CSgt ELan LRHS LSRN MGos MMuc NLar SCam SCog SCoo SHil SWvt
- 'Blush Tinsie'	LRHS
- 'Bob Hope' ♀H5	CBcs CTrh CTri LRHS SCam SWeb
- 'Bob's Tinsie' ♀H5	CBcs CMHG CSBt CTsd ECre EPfP LRHS LSRN MGos
§ - 'Bokuhan' ♀H5	MPkF SCam
- 'Bonomiana'	LPar NLar SWeb
- 'Bright Buoy'	LRHS
- 'Brushfield's Yellow'	CBcs CMHG CSBt CSgt CTrh CTsd EBee ELan ELon EPfP IArd LRHS LSRN MGos NLar SCam SCog SCoo SPer SSta
- 'Bush Hill Beauty'	see *C. japonica* 'Lady de Saumarez'
§ - 'C.M. Hovey' ♀H5	CMHG CMac CSgt LRHS
- 'C.M. Wilson'	CMac SCog
- 'Campsii Alba'	CSgt CTsd SCam
- 'Can Can'	ELon SCog
- 'Candy Apple'	CTrh
- 'Cara Mia'	CTsd LRHS SCam
- 'Carolyn Tuttle'	CSgt LRHS
- 'Carter's Sunburst' ♀H5	CBcs ELan EPfP SCog
- 'Cassandra'	EPfP SHil
- 'Centifolia Alba' new	SWeb
- 'Chandleri Elegans'	see *C. japonica* 'Elegans'
- 'Charlotte de Rothschild'	CTrh CTri
- 'Cinderella'	LRHS SCam SCog

	- Classique = 'Kerguelen'PBR	LRHS MPkF SCog
	- 'Colonel Firey'	see *C. japonica* 'C.M. Hovey'
	- 'Commander Mulroy' ♀H5	CTrh
§	- 'Comte de Gomer'	ELan ELon EPfP LRHS NPri SCam SCog
	- 'Conspicua'	CBcs
§	- 'Coquettii' ♀H5	CBcs CSgt LRHS
	- 'Curly Lady'PBR	MJak NPri
§	- 'Dahlohnega'	CSBt CSgt CTrh ELon EPfP LBrs LRHS LSRN MAsh MGos MHtn MPkF
	- 'Daikagura'	SHil
	- 'Dainty'	CBcs
	- 'Daitairin'	see *C. japonica* 'Dewatairin'
	- 'Daphne du Maurier'	LRHS
	- 'Dark of the Moon'	LRHS
	- 'Dear Jenny'	CBcs CSgt
	- 'Debutante'	CBcs CMac ELon SCam SCog
	- 'Desire' ♀H5	CBcs CMHG CSBt CSgt CTrh CTsd ELan EPfP GMcL LCro LMil LRHS LSRN MGos MJak MPkF NEgg SCam SCog SCoo SPoG WFar
	- 'Devonia'	CBcs SCog
§	- 'Dewatairin' (Higo)	CBcs SCam SCog
	- 'Diddy's Pink Organdie'	LRHS
	- 'Dixie Knight'	CBcs LRHS SCam SCog
	- 'Dobreei'	CMac
	- 'Doctor Burnside'	CBcs CTrh EBee LPar LRHS SCam SCog SHil SWeb
	- 'Doctor King'	CSgt EBee EPfP GMcL LRHS NPri SHil SPoG
	- 'Doctor Tinsley' ♀H5	CSgt EPfP LRHS MAsh NPri SCam SCoo
	- 'Dona Herzilia de Freitas Magalhães'	CBcs ELon SCog
	- 'Dona Jane Andresson'	SCam
	- 'Donckelaeri'	see *C. japonica* 'Masayoshi'
	- 'Donnan's Dream'	CTrh
	- 'Drama Girl' ♀H5	CBcs CTsd ELan LRHS SCam SCog
	- 'Dream Time'	CBcs
	- 'Duc de Bretagne'	SCog
	- 'Duchesse Decazes'	CBcs
	- 'Edelweiss'	ELon SCam
	- 'Effendee'	see *C. sasanqua* 'Rosea Plena'
§	- 'Elegans'	ELon EPfP ESps GMcL LCro LMil LPar LRHS MGos SCam SCog SCoo SLim SPoG SWvt
	- 'Elegans Champagne'	CSgt EPfP
	- 'Elisabeth'	LRHS
	- 'Elizabeth Arden'	CTsd
	- 'Elizabeth Cooper'	CTrh LSRN
	- 'Elizabeth Dowd'	CBcs SCog
	- 'Elizabeth Hawkins'	CSgt CTrh LRHS MAsh
	- 'Emmett Pfingstl'	SCam
	- 'Emperor of Russia'	CBcs LRHS WBod
	- 'Eric Baker'	SCam
	- 'Eugène Lizé'	SCam
	- 'Eximia'	EPfP LRHS
	- 'Fanny'	CSgt SCog
§	- 'Faustina'	LRHS
	- 'Finlandia Variegated'	ELon SCam SCog
	- 'Fire Falls' ♀H5	CMHG
	- 'Firebird'	CBcs CTsd
	- 'Flashlight'	EPfP LRHS
§	- 'Fleur Dipater'	CBcs CSgt LRHS SCam
	- 'Flowerwood'	SCam SCog
	- 'Frans van Damme'	CBcs
	- 'Fred Sander'	CBcs ELon LRHS SCam SCog
	- 'Furō-an'	CBcs
§	- 'Gigantea'	LRHS SCam
	- 'Giuditta Rosani'	LRHS
	- 'Gladys Wannamaker'	SCog
	- 'Glen 40'	see *C. japonica* 'Coquettii'
	- 'Gloire de Nantes' ♀H5	CTrh SCam SCog
	- 'Gold Tone'	ELon SCam
	- 'Golden Wedding' (v)	SCog
	- 'Grace Albritton' (d)	LRHS
	- 'Grace Bunton'	CBcs ELon SCog
	- 'Granada'	SCog
	- 'Grand Prix' ♀H5	ELan ELon LSRN NLar SCam SCog SPer SWeb
	- 'Grand Slam' ♀H5	CBcs SCam
	- 'Guest of Honor'	CSgt LRHS
	- 'Guilio Nuccio' ♀H5	CBcs CTri ELan ELon EPfP IArd LRHS LSRN NEgg NPri SCam SCog SCoo SLim SPer SWeb
	- 'Gus Menard'	SCam
	- 'Gwenneth Morey'	CBcs
	- 'H.A. Downing'	SCam
§	- 'Hagoromo' ♀H5	CBcs CSBt CTrh CTsd ELan LPar LRHS SWeb
	- 'Hakugan'	EPfP
§	- 'Hakurakuten' ♀H5	CTrh CTri SCam SCog
	- 'Hanafūki'	LRHS SCam SCog
	- 'Happy Birthday'	LSRN
	- 'Haru-no-utena'	CTrh
	- 'Hatsuzakura'	see *C. japonica* 'Dewatairin'
	- 'Hawaii'	CMac CTrh ELon LRHS SCam
	- Herme	see *C. japonica* 'Hikarugenji'
	- 'High Hat'	CBcs SCog
§	- 'Hikarugenji'	LRHS SCog
	- 'Hinomaru'	CMac
	- 'Holly Bright'	CTrh MPkF
	- 'Ichisetsu'	SCog
§	- 'Imbricata'	CSgt CTrh LRHS MAsh MMuc SCog
	- 'Imperator' **new**	SCam
	- 'Italiana Vera'	CSgt LRHS MAsh
	- 'J.J. Whitfield'	CMac
	- 'Jack Jones Scented'	CMHG
	- 'Janet Waterhouse'	CBcs
§	- 'Japonica Variegata' (v)	LRHS
	- 'Jean Clere'	SCog
	- 'Jingle Bells'	CBcs
	- 'Joseph Pfingstl' ♀H5	CSgt CTri EPfP LRHS MAsh MMuc NLar SCam
	- 'Jovey Carlyon'	CBcs CSgt LRHS
	- 'Joy Sander'	see *C. japonica* 'Apple Blossom'
	- 'Juan XXIII'	SHil
	- 'Jubilee Gem'	CTsd
	- 'Julia France'	SCog
	- 'Juno'	CBcs LRHS SCoo
	- 'Jupiter' Paul, 1904 ♀H5	CMac CSgt CTri EPfP LSRN MAsh SCam SCog WHar
	- 'Kellingtoniana'	see *C. japonica* 'Gigantea'
	- 'Kenny'	CBcs
	- 'Kentucky'	LRHS
	- 'Kick-off'	CBcs CTrh SCam SCog
	- 'Kimberley'	LSRN SCam SCog
	- 'King's Ransom'	CMac CSgt LRHS
	- 'Kingyoba-shiro-wabisuke'	SCam
	- 'Kingyo-tsubaki'	SCam SSta
	- 'Kitty Berry'	CTrh
	- 'Kokinran'	SCam
§	- 'Konronkoku' ♀H5	CBcs CSgt LRHS
	- 'Kouron-jura'	see *C. japonica* 'Konronkoku'
	- 'Kramer's Supreme' ♀H5	CBcs CCCN CSgt ELon GMcL LPar LRHS LSRN MGos SCam SCog SCoo SGol SHil
§	- 'Kumasaka'	CTri LRHS

	- 'Lady Campbell'	CTri EPfP GMcL LRHS NPri SCam SHil WFar
	- 'Lady Clare'	see *C. japonica* 'Akashigata'
§	- 'Lady de Saumarez'	CBcs CMac CTsd
	- 'Lady Loch'	CTrh SCam
	- 'Lady Marion'	see *C. japonica* 'Kumasaka'
	- 'Lady McCulloch'	LRHS
	- 'Lady Vansittart'	CSgt CTrh ELan EPfP LMil LRHS LSRN MAsh MGos NEgg SCam SCog SCoo SHil SLim SPer SPoG SSta
§	- 'Lady Vansittart Pink'	CMac
	- 'Lady Vansittart Red'	see *C. japonica* 'Lady Vansittart Pink'
	- 'Lady Vansittart Shell'	see *C. japonica* 'Yours Truly'
	- 'Latifolia'	SCam
	- 'Laura's Red'	CTsd
	- 'Laurie Bray'	SCog SWeb
§	- 'Lavinia Maggi' ♀H5	CBcs CSgt CTri ELan ELon EPfP GMcL LMil LPar LRHS LSRN MAsh MGos MMuc NPri SCam SCog SCoo SHil SPoG SReu SRms SSta
	- 'L'Avvenire'	SCog
	- 'Lemon Drop'	CTrh LRHS
	- 'Leonora Novick'	SCog
	- 'Lily Pons'	CTrh
	- 'Little Bit'	CBcs CMHG ELon SCam SSta
	- 'Little Man'	LRHS
	- 'Look-away'	LRHS
	- 'Lovelight' ♀H5	CSgt CTrh LRHS
	- 'Ludgvan Red'	LRHS
	- 'Lulu Belle'	CBcs SCog
	- 'Mabel Blackwell'	ELon SCam
	- 'Madame de Strekaloff'	CMac CSBt SCam
	- 'Madame Lebois'	SCam
	- 'Madge Miller'	CSgt LRHS
	- 'Magnoliiflora'	see *C. japonica* 'Hagoromo'
	- 'Magnoliiflora Alba'	see *C. japonica* 'Miyakodori'
	- 'Maiden's Blush'	CMac
	- 'Manuroa Road'	LRHS
	- 'Margaret Davis' ♀H5	CCCN CSBt CSgt EBee ELan ELon EPfP LCro LOPS LRHS LSRN MGos NEgg SCam SCoo SHil SLim SWeb WFar
	- 'Margaret Davis Picotee'	CBcs CMHG CTrh SCog SPer
	- 'Margaret Rose'	SCam
	- 'Margaret Short'	CTsd
	- 'Margherita Coleoni'	CBcs
	- 'Marguérite Gouillon' Drouard-Gouillon	CBcs SSta
	- 'Marian Mitchell'	SCam
	- 'Mariana'	ELon SCog
	- 'Marie Bracey'	CBcs
	- 'Marinka'	CBcs
	- 'Mariottii Rubra'	CMac
	- 'Marjorie Magnificent'	CSgt LRHS SCoo
	- 'Mark Alan'	LRHS LSRN SCam
	- 'Maroon and Gold'	CSgt LRHS SCog
	- 'Mars' ♀H5	CBcs SCam SCog
	- 'Marshmallow'	LRHS
	- 'Mary Costa'	CBcs CTrh SCam
	- 'Mary J. Wheeler'	LSRN
§	- 'Masayoshi' ♀H5	CBcs CSBt LRHS SCog
	- 'Mathotiana Alba'	CMac CTri CTsd ELan EPfP GMcL LSRN MGos SCam SCog SPer
§	- 'Mathotiana Rosea'	CMac NLar
	- 'Mathotiana Supreme'	SCam SCog
	- 'Matilija Poppy'	CTrh SCam
	- 'Matterhorn'	CTrh LCro
	- 'Mattie Cole'	SCam
	- 'Mercury' ♀H5	CMac EPfP GGGa NEgg SCog
	- 'Mercury Variegated' (v)	CMHG

	- 'Mermaid'	LRHS SCam
	- 'Midnight'	CBcs CMHG CTsd LRHS MAsh SCoo
	- 'Midnight Magic'	CSgt CTrh CTri LRHS
	- 'Midnight Serenade'	LRHS
	- 'Midnight Variegated'	LRHS MPkF
	- 'Midsummer's Day'	CBcs
§	- 'Mikenjaku'	CBcs CSgt LRHS SCog SHil
	- 'Miriam Stevenson'	SCam
	- 'Miss Charleston'	CBcs SCog
§	- 'Miyakodori'	SWeb
	- 'Monstruosa Rubra'	see *C. japonica* 'Gigantea'
	- 'Monte Carlo'	SCam SCog
	- 'Moshe Dayan'	CSgt LRHS MAsh SCam SCog SCoo
	- 'Moshio'	SHil
§	- 'Mrs Bertha A. Harms'	LRHS SCam SCog
	- 'Mrs Charles Cobb'	LRHS SHil
	- 'Mrs D.W. Davis'	EPfP
	- 'Mrs William Thompson'	LRHS SCam
	- 'Myorenji' **new**	SCam
	- 'Nagasaki'	see *C. japonica* 'Mikenjaku'
	- 'Nancy Bird' **new**	SCam
	- 'Nigra'	see *C. japonica* 'Konronkoku'
	- 'Nina Avery'	SCam
	- 'Nobilissima' ♀H5	CBcs CMac CSgt CTrh CTri EPfP LCro LMil MBlu MJak MMuc NEgg SCam SCog SCoo SPer SPoG WFar WHar
	- 'Nokogiriba-tsubaki'	MPkF
	- 'Nuccio's Cameo' ♀H5	CBcs CSgt CTrh GMcL LRHS MAsh NPri SCoo
	- 'Nuccio's Gem' ♀H5	CBcs CMHG CSgt EPfP LRHS MAsh MMuc SCoo SGol SHil SWeb
	- 'Nuccio's Jewel' ♀H5	CBcs CSBt CSgt CTrh ELan EPfP LRHS LSRN MAsh SCam SCog SHil
	- 'Nuccio's Pearl' ♀H5	CBcs CSgt EPfP LPar LRHS LSRN MAsh NPri SCog SCoo SHil
	- 'Nuccio's Pink Lace'	CBcs CSgt CTri LRHS
	- 'Oki-no-nami' **new**	SHil
	- 'Onetia Holland'	CBcs EPfP LSRN SCam SCog SLim
	- 'Oo-La-La'	CTrh LRHS
	- 'Optima'	CBcs ELon LRHS SCam SCog SCoo
	- 'Orandakō'	LRHS SCob SHil
	- 'Patricia Ann'	LSRN
	- 'Paulette Goddard'	SCam
	- 'Paul's Apollo'	see *C. japonica* 'Apollo' Paul, 1911
	- 'Peachblossom'	see *C. japonica* 'Fleur Dipater'
	- 'Pearl Harbor'	SCam
	- 'Pearl Maxwell' **new**	SWeb
	- 'Pink Chiffon'	CSgt LRHS
	- 'Pink Clouds'	CBcs
	- 'Pink Perfection'	see *C. japonica* subsp. *rusticana* 'Otome'
	- 'Pope John Paul XXIII' **new**	SCam
	- 'Preston Rose'	CBcs
	- 'Pride of Descanso'	see *C. japonica* 'Yukibotan'
	- 'Primavera'	CTrh SCog
	- 'Prince Murat'	LRHS
	- 'Princess Baciocchi'	SCam
	- 'Princess du Mahe'	CMac
	- 'R.L. Wheeler' ♀H5	CBcs CSBt CSgt CTri EPfP GMcL LRHS LSRN MAsh NPri SCam SCog SCoo SPoG
	- 'Raspberry Ripple'	MPkF
	- 'Red Dandy'	CSgt SCam SCog
	- 'Red Red Rose'	LRHS SCam
	- 'Reg Ragland'	SCog
	- 'Robert Lasson'	LRHS
	- 'Roger Hall'	CBcs CSgt CTrh LRHS LSRN SCoo SPoG

	- 'Rosa Baroveira Nella'	NLar
	- 'Rosularis'	ELon SCog
	- 'Royal Velvet'	CTrh
	- 'Rubescens Major'	CBcs
	- 'Ruddigore'	CTrh
§	- subsp. ***rusticana***	CBcs SCog
	- - 'Arajishi' misapplied	see *C. japonica* subsp. *rusticana* 'Beni-arajishi'
	- - 'Arajishi' Ko'emon	SCam
§	- - 'Beni-arajishi'	CBcs GMcL LRHS
§	- - 'Otome'	SCam
	- - 'Otome' sport **new**	SWeb
	- - 'Reigyoku' (v)	CBcs
	- 'Sabiniana'	LRHS
	- 'Sacco Vera' **new**	SWeb
	- 'Saint André'	CMac CSgt LRHS MAsh SCoo
	- 'San Dimas' ♀H5	CTrh ELon LRHS MPkF SCam SCog SWeb
	- 'Sanpei-tsubaki'	LRHS
	- 'Saturnia'	CSgt ELon LRHS MJak
	- 'Sawada's Dream'	SCam SCog
	- 'Scentsation' ♀H5	CMHG CTri LRHS SCog SHil
	- 'Sea Foam'	LRHS
	- 'Sea Gull'	CTrh
	- 'Shikibu'	CTrh SCam
	- 'Shiragiku'	CBcs EPfP SCog SWeb
	- 'Shiro Chan'	ELon SCam
	- 'Shirobotan'	CSgt ELon LRHS SCam SCog SCoo
	- 'Shūgetsu'	LRHS
	- 'Silver Anniversary' ♀H5	Widely available
	- 'Silver Chalice'	MAsh
	- 'Silver Ruffles'	CTrh ELon LRHS SCam
	- 'Silver Waves'	MPkF
	- 'Something Beautiful'	SCam
	- 'Souvenir de Bahuaud-Litou' ♀H5	CBcs SCam SCog
	- 'Spencer's Pink'	CBcs
	- 'Splendens Carlyon'	CSgt LRHS MAsh SCoo
	- 'Spring Fling'	CTrh
	- 'Spring Formal'	CTrh
	- 'Spring Frill'	SCam
	- 'Stacy Susan'	MPkF
	- 'Strawberry Blonde'	SCog
	- 'Strawberry Swirl'	CBcs SCog
	- 'Sugar Babe'	CTrh LRHS SCam SCoo
	- 'Sweetheart'	SCog
	- 'Sylva' ♀H5	EUJe GGGa
	- 'Sylvia'	CMac
	- 'Takanini'	CBcs CTrh MPkF SCam
	- 'Tama-no-ura'	SCam
	- 'Tammia'	CSgt LRHS
	- 'Teresa Ragland'	SCam
§	- 'The Czar'	CBcs
	- 'The Mikado'	LRHS SCog
	- 'Tiffany'	CBcs ELon LRHS SCam SCog SCoo
	- 'Tinker Bell'	ELon SCam SCog
	- 'Tinker Toy'	CTrh
	- 'Tom Pouce'	LRHS
	- 'Tom Thumb' ♀H5	CTrh LRHS SRms
	- 'Tomorrow'	NEgg SCam SCog
	- 'Tomorrow Park Hill'	SCog
	- 'Tomorrow's Dawn'	SCam
	- 'Touchdown'	SCam
	- 'Trewithen White'	LRHS
§	- 'Tricolor' ♀H5	CBcs CMac CSBt CTrh ELon LRHS MGos MMuc SCam SCog SCoo SHil
	- 'Tricolor Red'	see *C. japonica* 'Lady de Saumarez'
	- 'Trinket' **new**	SCam
	- 'Triphosa' **new**	SHil
	- variegated (v)	SCog
	- 'Vergine di Collebeato' **new**	SHil SWeb
	- 'Victor Emmanuel'	see *C. japonica* 'Blood of China'
	- 'Ville de Nantes'	LRHS
	- 'Virginia Carlyon'	CBcs
	- 'Visconti Nova'	LRHS
	- 'Vittorio Emanuele II'	CSgt CTrh LRHS SCoo
	- 'Volunteer'	EPfP LCro LRHS
	- 'Warrior'	SCam SCog
	- 'Wheel of Fortune'	LRHS
	- 'White Giant'	CBcs
	- 'White Nun'	CBcs SCog
	- 'White Swan'	CMac CSBt CSgt LRHS SCoo
	- 'Wilamina' ♀H5	CMHG
	- 'Wildfire'	LRHS
	- 'William Bartlett'	CTrh
	- 'William Honey'	CTrh
	- 'Wisley White'	see *C. japonica* 'Hakurakuten'
	- 'Witman Yellow'	CTrh
§	- 'Yours Truly'	CMac CSgt CTrh CTsd LRHS LSRN MAsh SCog
§	- 'Yukibotan'	CBcs
	- 'Yukimi-guruma'	SWeb
	'Jury's Yellow'	see *C.* × *williamsii* 'Jury's Yellow'
	'Koto-no-kaori' (*lutchuensis* hybrid) **new**	LRHS
	'Lasca Beauty' (*japonica* × *reticulata*)	CBcs CTrh
	'Leonard Messel' (*reticulata* × (× *williamsii*)) ♀H5	CBcs CMHG CMac CTrh CTri CTsd EPfP LRHS MGos MPkF NLar SCam SCog SCoo SPer SReu SWeb WHor
	'Liz Henslowe'	CTsd
	lutchuensis	LRHS MPkF
	'Magic Mum'	LSRN
	'Maud Messel' (*reticulata* × (× *williamsii*))	SCam
	'Mimosa Jury'	LRHS
	'Nicky Crisp' (*japonica* × *pitardii*)	CSgt CTrh LRHS
	oleifera	CTrh
	'Paolina Guichardini'	LRHS
	'Pink Goddess' (*hiemalis* hybrid)	LRHS MPkF
	'Pink Icicle' (*oleifera* hybrid)	CBcs ELon SCam
	'Pink Spangles'	see *C. japonica* 'Mathotiana Rosea'
	'Polar Ice'	SCog
	'Polyanna'	SCog
	'Portuense'	see *C. japonica* 'Japonica Variegata'
	'Quintessence' (*japonica* × *lutchuensis*)	CTrh SCog
	'Red Crystal'	CTrh
	reticulata Lindl.	CPne
	- 'Arch of Triumph'	LRHS
	- 'Captain Rawes'	LRHS
	- 'Jean Morel'	LRHS
	- 'Mary Williams'	CBcs SCoo
	- 'Mouchang'	CBcs
	- 'Satsuma-kurenai'	LRHS
	- 'Simpatica'	LRHS
	rosthorniana Cupido	see *C. rosthorniana* 'Elina'
§	- 'Elina'	ELan EPfP LCro LRHS NLar
	rusticana	see *C. japonica* subsp. *rusticana*
	saluenensis	WBod
	saluenensis* × *japonica	see *C.* × *williamsii*
I	***sasanqua*** 'Alba'	CMac CTri
	- 'Baronesa de Soutelinho'	ELan ELon SCam SCog
	- 'Bettie Patricia'	SCog
	- 'Bonanza'	see *C. hiemalis* 'Bonanza'
	- 'Cleopatra'	EPfP LPar SCob SWeb
	- 'Cotton Candy'	SCam
	- 'Crimson King' ♀H4	CTrh LRHS

	– 'Dazzler'	see *C. hiemalis* 'Dazzler'
	– 'Dwarf Shishi'	CTrh
	– 'Early Pearly'	LRHS
	– 'Flamingo'	see *C. sasanqua* 'Fukuzutsumi'
	– 'Fragrans'	ELon SCam SCog
	– 'Fuji-no-mine'	ELon SCam SCog
§	– 'Fukuzutsumi'	CSBt
	– 'Gay Border'	LRHS
	– 'Gay Sue'	CTrh SCam
	– 'Hinode-gumo'	SEWo SWeb
	– 'Hiryū'	LPar LRHS SCam
	– 'Hugh Evans' ♀H4	CBcs CTrh ELan EPfP LRHS SCam SCog SCoo SSta
	– 'Jean May' ♀H4	ELan ELon EPfP LRHS SCam SCog SCoo SPer WCot
	– 'Kenkyō'	ELon SCam SCog SPer SSta
	– 'Maiden's Blush'	LRHS SCog WCot
	– 'Mignonne'	CTrh
	– 'Narumigata' ♀	CAbP CBcs CDul CMac CTrh CTsd EPfP LCro LRHS MBlu MGos SCam SCog SPoG SSta WSHC
	– 'New Dawn'	SCam SCog
	– 'Nyewoods'	CMac
	– 'Papaver'	SCam SCog WBod
	– 'Paradise Audrey'	LMil LRHS SPoG
	– 'Paradise Belinda'	CAbP EPfP LMil LRHS SPoG
	– 'Paradise Blush'	CBcs LRHS SCog
	– 'Paradise Glow'	CBcs LMil LRHS
	– 'Paradise Helen'	LRHS
	– 'Paradise Hilda'	CAbP CBcs LRHS
	– 'Paradise Little Liane'	CBcs
	– 'Paradise Pearl'	EPfP LMil LRHS
	– 'Paradise Venessa'	CTsd EPfP LRHS
	– 'Peach Blossom'	CBcs
	– 'Plantation Pink'	CSgt CTrh ELan EPfP LCro LOPS LRHS SCog SRkn WCot
	– 'Rainbow'	CAbP CBcs CTrh ELan ELon EPfP LRHS MPkF SCoo SSta
	– 'Rosea'	CMac ELon LRHS SCam SCog
§	– 'Rosea Plena'	CBcs
	– 'Sasanqua Rubra'	CMac SCam SCog
	– 'Sasanqua Variegata' (v)	CTrh ELon MPkF SCam SCog
	– 'Sekiyō'	LRHS
	– 'Setsugekka'	LRHS SCog
	– 'Shishigashira' Nihon Engei Kai Zasshi, 1894	SCog
	– 'Snowflake'	SSta
	– 'Sparkling Burgundy'	see *C.* 'Sparkling Burgundy'
	– 'Tanya'	CTrh SCam
	– 'Versicolor'	EPfP LRHS
	– 'Winter's Joy'	CBcs SCam
	– 'Winter's Snowman'	LCro LOPS LRHS SCam SCog
	– 'Yae-arare' **new**	IDee
	'Satan's Robe' (*reticulata* hybrid)	SCog
	'Scented Gem'	LRHS
	'Scented Sun'	CTrh
	'Scentuous' (*japonica* × *lutchuensis*)	CBcs
	'Show Girl' (*reticulata* × *sasanqua*) ♀H4	LRHS SCam SCog
§	***sinensis***	CBcs CCCN CPne CSgt CTrh CTsd GPoy LRHS NLar SCam SPlb SPre SWvt
	– var. ***assamica***	CCCN SPre
	– var. ***sinensis***	CCCN
	– 'Tea Breeze'	WCot
	'Snow Flurry'	CBcs CSgt CTrh LRHS NEgg SCog
§	'Sparkling Burgundy' ♀H5	CBcs ELon EPfP LCro LRHS MGos SCam SCog
	'Spring Festival' (*cuspidata* hybrid) ♀H4	CBcs CMHG CSBt CTrh LCro LPar LRHS MAsh MGos NPri SCam SCog SHil SWeb
	'Spring Mist' (*japonica* × *lutchuensis*)	CMHG CTrh
	'Sugar Dream'	CTrh LRHS SCam
	'Superscent'	CTrh
	'Survivor'	LRHS
	'Swan Lake'	EPfP LRHS NPri SCog
	'Sweet Emily Kate' (*japonica* × *lutchuensis*)	LRHS MPkF
	'Sweet Jane'	LRHS MPkF SCam
	'Sweet Olive' (d)	LRHS MPkF
	'Tarōkaja' (wabisuke)	SCam
	thea	see *C. sinensis*
	'Tinsie'	see *C. japonica* 'Bokuhan'
	'Tiny Princess' (*fraterna* × *japonica*)	CMac
	'Tom Knudsen' (*japonica* × *reticulata*) ♀H4	CTrh LRHS
	transnokoensis ♀H4	CMac CTrh LRHS MPkF
	'Tricolor Sieboldii'	see *C. japonica* 'Tricolor'
	'Tristrem Carlyon' (*reticulata* hybrid)	CSgt CTri EPfP LRHS NPri
	'Usu-ōtome'	see *C. japonica* subsp. *rusticana* 'Otome'
	'Valley Knudsen' (*reticulata* × *saluenensis*)	SCog
	× ***vernalis*** 'Star Above Star'	CMHG
	– 'Yuletide'	CTrh LCro LOPS LPar LRHS LSRN MPkF SCam SCob SCog SHil SWeb
	'White Retic' (*japonica* × *reticulata*)	LRHS
§	× ***williamsii***	LPar
	– 'Angel Wings'	LRHS
	– 'Anticipation' ♀H5	CBcs CDul CMHG CMac CSBt CSgt CTrh ELan EPfP GGGa GKin GMcL LCro LMil LRHS MAsh MGos MSwo NEgg SCob SCog SLim SPer SPoG SWvt WFar WHar WHor
	– 'Anticipation Variegated'	LRHS
	– 'Ballet Queen'	CBcs CSBt SCam
	– 'Ballet Queen Variegated' (v)	ELon SCog
	– 'Bartley Number Five'	CMac
	– 'Beatrice Michael'	CBcs CMac
	– 'Bow Bells'	CDul CTri ELan
	– 'Bowen Bryant' ♀H5	CSgt CTrh GGGa GMcL LRHS MAsh SCog
	– 'Brigadoon' ♀H5	CBcs CTri EPfP GGGa LRHS MAsh SCam SCog
	– 'Burncoose'	CBcs
	– 'Buttons 'n' Bows'	LRHS MPkF SCog
	– 'C.F. Coates'	SCam SCog
	– 'Caerhays'	CBcs
	– 'Celebration'	CBcs CSBt LSRN
	– 'Charles Colbert'	LRHS SCam
	– 'Charles Michael'	CBcs
	– 'China Clay' ♀H5	EPfP LRHS
§	– 'Citation'	CBcs CMac SCog
	– 'Contribution'	CTrh
	– 'Coral Delight'	LRHS MPkF
	– 'Daintiness' ♀H5	SCog
	– 'Dark Nite'	CMHG
	– 'Debbie' ♀H5	Widely available
	– 'Debbie's Carnation'	LRHS SCam
	– 'Deloraine'	CTsd
	– 'Donation' ♀H5	Widely available
	– 'Dream Boat'	LRHS MPkF

- 'E.G. Waterhouse'	CBcs CSBt CSgt CTrh CTri ELan ELon EPfP GKin GMcL LRHS MGos MJak NEgg SCam SCog SHil SPoG SSta
- 'E.T.R. Carlyon' 🏆^{H5}	CSgt CTrh CTri ELan EPfP LMil LRHS MAsh MGos NLar SCog SCoo SLim SPoG
- 'Elegant Beauty' 🏆^{H5}	CBcs CTrh ELon LRHS MAsh NLar SCam SCog SPer
- 'Elizabeth Anderson'	CTrh CTsd
- 'Elizabeth de Rothschild'	GGGa
- 'Ellamine'	CBcs
- 'Elsie Jury' 🏆^{H5}	CBcs CMac CTri ELan GKin LRHS MGos NLar SCam SCog SGol SPer
- 'Exaltation'	SCog
- 'Fiona Colville'	SCam
- 'Francis Hanger'	CBcs CTrh LRHS SCam SCog SPer
- 'Galaxie'	CBcs SCam
- 'Gay Time'	LRHS MAsh SCog
- 'George Blandford' 🏆^{H5}	CBcs CMac
- 'Glenn's Orbit' 🏆^{H5}	NLar SCam SCog
- 'Golden Spangles' (v)	CBcs CMac ELan EPfP GKin LRHS MGos MMuc NEgg SCam SCog SEND SPer SPoG WHor
- 'Grand Jury'	LRHS
- 'Gwavas'	CBcs CCCN CSgt CTrh LRHS MAsh SCam SCog SCoo
- 'Hilo'	SCam
- 'Hiraethlyn'	CBcs WBod
- 'J.C. Williams' 🏆^{H5}	CBcs CMac CTri LRHS SCog WBod
- 'Jenefer Carlyon'	CBcs
- 'Jill Totty'	CTrh
- 'John Pickthorn'	CBcs
- 'Julia Hamiter' 🏆^{H5}	CSgt LRHS
§ - 'Jury's Yellow' 🏆^{H5}	CBcs CCCN CSBt CSgt CTrh CTri ELan EPfP GGGa LCro LMil LOPS LRHS LSRN MAsh MGos NEgg NPri SCam SCog SCoo SHil SLim SPer SPoG SSta SWvt
- 'Lady's Maid'	CBcs SCam
- 'Laura Boscawen'	CBcs CTrh SCam
- 'Les Jury' 🏆^{H5}	CBcs CMHG CSBt CTrh LMil LRHS LSRN MGos SCog SLim
- 'Lucky Star' (d)	MPkF
- 'Margaret Waterhouse'	CBcs SCam SCog
- 'Marjorie Waldegrave'	CSgt LRHS MAsh
- 'Mary Phoebe Taylor' 🏆^{H5}	CBcs CSgt NLar SCog SCoo SLim
- 'Mirage'	CTrh
- 'Monica Dance'	CBcs
- 'Muskoka' 🏆^{H5}	CBcs
- 'Night Rider'	MPkF SCam WPGP
- 'November Pink'	CBcs SCam
- 'Philippa Forward'	CBcs CMac
- 'Pink Wave'	CSgt LRHS
- 'Red Dahlia'	CBcs
- 'Rendezvous'	CTrh SCam SCog
- 'Rose Parade'	CSgt
- 'Rose Quartz'	CSgt
- 'Rosemary Williams'	CBcs CMac
- 'Ruby Bells'	CMHG
- 'Ruby Wedding' (d) 🏆^{H5}	CBcs CSBt CSgt CTrh CTsd EPfP GMcL LMil LRHS LSRN MAsh MGos MHtn MJak NEgg NPri SCam SCog SCoo SHil SLim SPer SPoG SWvt WFar
- 'Saint Ewe' 🏆^{H5}	CBcs CSBt CSgt CTrh CTri ELan EPfP LRHS MAsh MGos SCam SCog SCoo SPer WBod
- 'Saint Michael'	CBcs
- 'Sayonara'	SCog
- 'Senorita' 🏆^{H5}	CSgt CTrh ELon GMcL LRHS MAsh NLar SCam SCog
- 'Shocking Pink'	CSgt LRHS MAsh
- 'Sun Song'	SCog
- 'The Duchess of Cornwall'	LRHS SCam
- 'Tiptoe'	CTrh
- 'Toni Finlay's Fragrant'	CTrh
- 'Tulip Time'	LRHS
- 'Twinkle Star'	CSgt LRHS
- 'Water Lily' 🏆^{H5}	CBcs CTri ELan ELon EPfP LRHS NLar SCam
- 'Wilber Foss'	ELon LRHS SCam SCog
- 'William Carlyon'	CSgt LRHS
- 'Winter Gem'	MPkF
'Winter's Charm'	CBcs CSgt LRHS
'Winter's Dream'	SCog
'Winter's Interlude'	CBcs LRHS
'Winter's Joy'	SCog
'Winter's Toughie'	CSgt LRHS SCam SCog
'Winton' (*cuspidata* × *saluenensis*)	CBcs
'Yoimachi' (*fraterna* × *sasanqua*)	CTrh LRHS
'Yume'	LRHS

Camissonia (*Onagraceae*)

bistorta 'Sunflakes'	CSpe

Campanula ✿ (*Campanulaceae*)

RCB AM 13	WCot
from Sicily	WCot
abietina	see *C. patula* subsp. *abietina*
alata	EWTr NBir WMoo XLum
'Albert Kirkham'	EBee
§ ***alliariifolia***	Widely available
- DHTU 0126	WCru
- 'Ivory Bells'	see *C. alliariifolia*
I ***alpestris*** 'Silver Bells'	MSCN
alpina	GAbr GJos
alsinoides	GEdr
americana	XLum
ardonensis	NSla
arvatica	CRos EACa ECho EPot GMaP LRHS NHar NRHS NSla SRms
aucheri	see *C. bellidifolia* subsp. *aucheri*
'Audrey Widdison'	ECtt LRHS WCot
'Barbara Valentine'	SCob
barbata	EACa EBee ECho EPfP EWld GKev SIgm WAbe WMoo
'Belinda'	CPBP EPot SIgm
bellidifolia	LLHF NSla
§ - subsp. ***aucheri***	GEdr GKev
- subsp. ***saxifraga***	GEdr
bellidifolia × ***tridentata***	GKev
§ ***betulifolia*** 🏆^{H5}	EACa GCrg GEdr NSla
biebersteiniana	LLHF NSla
'Birch Hybrid'	CRos EACa ECho ECtt ELan GCrg LRHS MMuc NRHS SAko SEND SIgm SRms WBod XLum
'Blithe Spirit'	WAbe
'Blue Octopus'	CRos IBoy LRHS NPnk NRHS SCob WNPC
bononiensis	LLHF SRms
bornmuelleri	CPBP
'Burghaltii'	CAby NLar SHar WOut
'Campanello White' **new**	WHil
'Cantata'	WAbe
carpatha white-flowered	WHar
carpatica 🏆^{H5}	ECho EPfP NBro NGdn SPlb SRms SWat WFar WHar XLum
- f. ***alba***	CRos ECho LRHS NGdn NRHS SPlb SWat WHar XLum

§ - - 'Weisse Clips'	CBar CRos ECho ECtt ELan EPfP GKin GMaP LCro LHop LRHS MAsh MJak NEgg NGdn NHol NRHS SCob SPer SPoG SRms SWvt WFar WHar
- 'Albescens'	EWoo
§ - 'Blaue Clips'	CBar CBcs ECho ECtt ELan EPfP ESps GKin GMaP IFoB IPot LCro LHop LRHS MAsh MGos MJak NEgg NGdn NRHS SCob SPer SPoG SRms SWvt WFar WHar
- Blue Clips	see *C. carpatica* 'Blaue Clips'
- 'Blue Moonlight'	CRos EACa ECho LHop LRHS NRHS
- 'Chewton Joy'	CRos CTri EACa ECho LLHF LRHS NRHS
- 'Kathy'	EPot GBuc GCrg
- 'Pearl White'	MHol
- var. ***turbinata***	ECho SRms
- - f. ***alba*** 'Snowsprite'	ESps
- - 'Foerster'	CRos EACa ECho GCrg LHop LRHS NRHS XLum
- - 'Isabel'	CRos EACa ECho LLHF LRHS NRHS XLum
- - 'Jewel'	CRos EACa ECho LHop LRHS NRHS
- White Clips	see *C. carpatica* f. *alba* 'Weisse Clips'
§ ***cashmeriana***	WAbe
cenisia	WAbe
cephallenica	see *C. garganica* subsp. *cephallenica*
cervicaria	GJos
§ ***chamissonis***	ECho EPot GEdr GKev LLHF NWad
- 'Major'	EWes
- 'Oyobeni'	EACa NHar
§ - 'Superba' 🏆H5	EACa ECho NHpl SIgm WAbe
choruhensis	LLHF SPlb
§ ***cochlearifolia*** 🏆H5	CRos CSpe CTri EBee ECho EDAr EPfP GJos GMaP LRHS MAsh MMuc NFav NHpl NRHS NWad SBch SEND SPoG WHoo XLum
- var. ***alba***	CSpe CTri EDAr ITim MHer MMuc NHpl NRya SBch SEND SIgm SRms WHoo XLum
- - 'White Baby' (Baby Series)	CRos EACa ECho ECtt EPfP EPot ESps ITim LRHS NRHS NWad SPoG SRms XLum
- 'Bavaria Blue'	ECho ELon GJos IPot NHol XLum
- 'Blue Baby' (Baby Series)	ECho ECtt EPfP ESps GJos LRHS MHer NHpl SPoG SRms SRot
- 'Blue Wonder'	ECtt GCrg ITim
- 'Elizabeth Oliver' (d) 🏆H5	CRos CTri EACa ECho ECtt EDAr EPot GCrg GEdr GMaP LHop LRHS MHer MHol NBir NHpl NRHS SPlb SRms WFar WHoo WIce
- 'Flore Pleno' (d)	WFar
- var. ***pallida*** 'Silver Chimes'	ITim
- 'R.B. Loder' (d)	LRHS MHer NRHS WAbe
- 'Tubby'	CRos EACa ECho EPot ITim LLHF LRHS MHer NRHS SRms
- 'Warleyensis'	see *C.* × *haylodgensis* W. Brockbank 'Warley White'
collina	CTri EACa LLHF WCFE XLum
'Constellation'	EACa
'Covadonga'	CMea CPBP CRos EACa ECho LHop LLHF LRHS NRHS SBch WAbe WThu
cretica	MHol WRHF
'Crystal'	CFis ECtt MAvo MNrw WCot
cymbalaria **new**	GKev
dasyantha	see *C. chamissonis*
dolomitica	EACa GKev LLHF
'E.K. Toogood'	CElw CPBP EACa ECho ECtt MWat SRms XLum
'Faichem Lilac'	LLHF WCot
fenestrellata	EACa XLum
finitima	see *C. betulifolia*
foliosa	EACa
fragilis	ECho IFoB
- 'Hirsuta'	ECho
garganica 🏆H5	EACa ECho EPfP ESps EWoo GMaP GWyn LRHS MAsh MMuc MRav NFav SRms SVic SWvt WFar WMoo XLum
- 'Aurea'	see *C. garganica* 'Dickson's Gold'
- 'Blue Diamond'	EACa ECho IVic LHop NLar
§ - subsp. ***cephallenica***	EACa NBro
§ - 'Dickson's Gold'	Widely available
- 'Erinus Major'	EACa IVic XLum
- 'Major'	SPoG
- 'Mrs Resholt'	ECtt EPau ESwi EWoo LRHS NBir NLar SRms SWvt WIce
- 'Senior' **new**	EWTr
- 'W.H. Paine' 🏆H5	EACa ECho ECtt IFoB NLar NSla WAbe WHoo
'Glandore'	EACa SAko XLum
glomerata	CWld ESps GAbr GJos GNew IBoy LSRN MHer NBir NBro NEgg NGBl NMir WBrk WFar WOut XSen
- var. ***acaulis*** hort.	EACa EPfP GKev GMcL ITim LEdu NEgg NLar SRms WFar XLum
- var. ***alba***	CBcs CRos CSpe EACa EAEE ECtt ELan EPfP GBin GJos GMaP IBoy LRHS MBel NEgg NRHS SBod SCob SPer SPlb SPoG SWat WCAu WGwG
§ - - 'Schneekrone'	ECha LCro LOPS WFar
- (Bellefleur Series) Bellefleur Blue	GMcL
- - Bellefleur White **new**	GMcL
- 'Caroline' 🏆H7	Widely available
- Crown of Snow	see *C. glomerata* var. *alba* 'Schneekrone'
- var. ***dahurica***	EAJP EBee ELon LRHS NEgg NLar XLum
- 'Emerald'	CRos EACa EBee ECtt LRHS MHer NLar NRHS SPad SRms WFar
- 'Freya' PBR 🏆H7	EACa EBee LPla LSun MHol MNrw SCob SPad WCot WFar WHil
- 'Genti Blue' **new**	NPri
- 'Genti Twisterbell'	LSun NPri SPoG WHil
- 'Genti White'	CWGN NLar NPri SPoG
- 'Joan Elliott'	CSam EBee ECha ECtt GBuc LEdu LSRN MWat
- 'Purple Pixie'	LRHS SRms
- 'Superba' 🏆H7	Widely available
grossekii	EBee LLHF LRHS
hakkiarica	WCot
'Hannah'	CRos EACa ECho EPot LHop LRHS NRHS
× ***haylodgensis*** misapplied	see *C.* × *haylodgensis* 'Plena'
§ × ***haylodgensis*** W. Brockbank 'Marion Fisher' (d)	CPBP ECtt EPot WAbe WHoo
§ - 'Plena' (d)	CRos EACa ECho ECtt ELan EPfP EPot LHop LRHS NRHS SRms WAbe WKif
§ - 'Warley White' (d)	ECho EPot XLum
- 'Yvonne'	CBod ECtt EPot GCrg LHop NHpl
'Hemswell Starlight'	WAbe
hercegovina	SIgm
- 'Nana'	CPBP ITim SIgm WAbe
'Hilltop Snow'	NHar
hofmannii	CTsd GJos GKev NWad
hypopolia	CPBP WAbe

§	***incurva***	EACa EWld GKev LHop WAbe WMoo
	Iridescent Bells = 'Iribella'PBR **new**	CWGN EACa EBee EWTr EWes IPot LCro NSti WBor WHil WPnP
	isophylla ♀H2	ECho EPot
	- 'Alba' ♀H2	ECho
	jaubertiana	WAbe
	Jenny = 'Harjen'PBR	CWGN EBee SHar
	'Joe Elliott'	CPBP WAbe
	kemulariae	EDAr LLHF WCot XLum
	- 'Alba'	ITim
	'Kent Belle' ♀H7	Widely available
	khasiana	EBee
	komarovii	WCot
	lactiflora	CAby CElw CMac EACa EBee ECha EPfP ESps GAbr GCra IFoB ITim LRHS MCot MNrw NEgg SDix SPer WBod WCAu WFar WHar WMoo WWtn XLum
	- ***alba***	see *C. lactiflora* white-flowered
	- 'Alba' ♀H7	CAby CBod EBee ECha EPfP EWTr GBin GMaP IBoy IVic MAvo MBel MHol SCob WBod WBrk WCot WRHF
	- 'Assendon Pearl' **new**	EACa
	- 'Avalanche'	EACa EBee ECtt LCro MBNS MTis NCGa WCot
	- 'Blue Cross'	EBee
	- 'Border Blues'	EBee ECtt EPfP EWTr MHol MNrw WFar
	- 'Dixter Presence'	SMHy
	- dwarf pink-flowered	EACa EBee EPfP
	- 'Favourite' ♀H7	CSpe ECtt EWoo NGdn
	- hybrids	CBod GJos
	- 'Lidie's Choice'	CSam
	- 'Loddon Anna' ♀H7	Widely available
	- 'Macrantha'	WRHF
	- 'Moorland Rose'	WMoo
	- 'Platinum' **new**	EACa
	- 'Pouffe'	CHid EACa EAEE EAJP EBee ECtt ELan EPfP GMaP GMcL IVic LRHS MHol MNrw MRav NBro NGdn NLar SGbt SPer SPoG SWat SWvt
	- 'Prichard's Variety' ♀H7	Widely available
	- 'Superba' ♀H7	ECtt IVic
	- 'White Pouffe'	EACa ECtt ELan EPfP EWTr GMaP GMcL IVic LRHS LSRN NChi NLar SGbt SPer SPoG SWat WFar
§	- white-flowered	ECha ESps NBir NEgg SPer SWat
	latifolia	EACa ESps GJos LPot MCot NBid NMir SPer SRms WMoo WShi
	- var. ***alba***	CRos EBee ELan EPfP ESps GCra GJos LRHS MMuc MSCN NGdn NRHS SEND SPav SPer SRms WHal
	- blue-flowered	SEND
	- 'Brantwood'	CFis EBee EPfP GAbr LRHS MRav NLar SPad SWat
	- 'Gloaming'	ECtt LRHS
	- var. ***macrantha***	EBee ELan ELon EPfP GMaP LHop LRHS NEgg NSti SWat SWvt WMoo
	- - 'Alba'	CMea ECtt GLog GMaP LHop MHol MRav NLar WMoo WRHF
	- 'Roger Wood'	WCot
	latiloba	CMHG WCot WKif
§	- 'Alba'	ELan GAbr GCal GCra MCot NEgg NLar NWad WBrk
	- 'Hidcote Amethyst'	CAby CDor CWGN ECtt ELan ELon GBuc GCal IKil LRHS MCot MHol MRav MSpe NBid NBir NChi NGdn NLar SEND SPer WBod WCot
	- 'Highcliffe Variety' ♀H7	CGar EACa ECtt ELan EPfP GBuc GCra LRHS MRav NLar SPer SPoG WCot WRHF

*	- 'Highdown'	GBuc
	- 'Percy Piper' ♀H7	EACa EBee ECtt ELan GBuc LRHS MRav NBro NLar
	- 'Splash'	MAvo
	'Linda'	LSRN
	'Lynchmere'	CMea EPot WAbe
	makaschvilii	CHid CPla CSpe EACa EBee EPfP EWld GKev GWyn ILea LHop MHer SRkn WCot WOut WSHC
	- pink-flowered	EBee
	makaschvilii* × *trachelium	WCot
	'Margaret Brine'	CMea CPBP WAbe
	'Marion Fisher'	see *C.* × *haylodgensis* W. Brockbank 'Marion Fisher'
	medium	CBod EPfP
	'Mevr. V. Vollenhove'	CSpe EBee MAvo MHol NSti
	'Misty Dawn'	MAvo WCot
	modesta	GJos
	moesiaca	GKev
	'Monic'	EPfP
*	***morettiana*** 'Alba'	CPBP
	× ***raineri*** 'Alba' **new**	
	muralis	see *C. portenschlagiana*
	nitida	see *C. persicifolia* var. *planiflora*
	'Norman Grove'	EPot
	ochroleuca	CMea EBee GBin IMou LHop SWat WCFE WCot WNPC
I	- 'Nana' **new**	GEdr
	odontosepala from Iran	EPPr NLar
	'Oliver's Choice'	WHrl
	olympica misapplied	see *C. rotundifolia* 'Olympica'
	orphanidea	IMou
	ossetica	ECtt WBor
	pallida subsp. ***tibetica***	see *C. cashmeriana*
	parviflora Lam.	see *C. sibirica*
	patula	EACa NLar WCot WKif XLum
§	- subsp. ***abietina***	NLar
	'Paul Furse'	ECtt NCGa NSti WCot WHrl
	pendula	EBee GJos MBNS SRot
	persicifolia	Widely available
	- var. ***alba***	Widely available
§	- 'Alba Coronata' (d)	EWoo GAbr SRms WHar
	- 'Alba Plena'	see *C. persicifolia* 'Alba Coronata'
	- 'Azure Beauty'	EBee ECtt ELan NCGa NLar WCot
	- 'Beau Belle'	LSou NLar
§	- 'Bennett's Blue' (d)	EPfP MRav SRms SWat
	- 'Blue Bell'	GWyn
	- 'Blue Bloomers' (d)	CDor CLAP EACa ECtt EPri EWes IKil LRHS MBel MRav MSCN NQui NWad SRms WCAu WCFE WCot WHal WRHF XLum
	- blue cup-in-cup (d)	WPtf
	- 'Blue-eyed Blonde'PBR (v)	LSou NLar WHil
	- blue-flowered	GMcL IFoB SBod SPlb
	- 'Caerulea Coronata'	see *C. persicifolia* 'Coronata'
*	- 'Caerulea Plena' (d)	EWoo
§	- 'Chettle Charm'PBR	CDor CGar CMos CTri CWCL ECtt ELan EPfP EShb GAbr LRHS LSou MAvo MBel MCot MRav NBir NChi NLar SCob SPer SRms SWat SWvt WCot WFar
	- 'Cornish Mist'	EACa EBee ECtt ELan EPfP GBin MBel MHol MPie WCAu WCot WRHF
§	- 'Coronata' (d)	GCra
	- cup and saucer blue (d)	GCra
	- double white-flowered (d)	ELan
	- 'Fleur de Neige' (d)	MRav
	- 'Frances' (d)	WCot

- 'Gawen'	CMac EACa ECtt GMaP LRHS MTis NBre SGbt WCot
- 'George Chiswell'	see *C. persicifolia* 'Chettle Charm'
- 'Grandiflora'	CDor EAJP GBin IBoy
- 'Grandiflora Alba'	EAJP GBin MArt NLar NWad
- 'Hampstead White' (d)	GCal NLar
- 'Kelly's Gold'	CRos LRHS MHol MJak NBir NRHS SRms
- 'La Belle' (d)	EBee MNrw NLar
- 'La Bello' PBR	EBee MNrw
- 'La Bonne Amie' (d)	EBee IBoy IKil MNrw NLar SPoG XEll
- 'Moerheimii' (d)	EPfP
- 'Perry's Boy Blue'	NPer
§ - var. ***planiflora***	CPBP
- - f. ***alba***	CPBP NHpl WCot
- 'Powder Puff' (d)	ECtt EPfP GMcL GWyn LCro LRHS MArt MHol NEgg XEll
- 'Pride of Exmouth' (d) 🏆H7	CDor ELan IBoy LPot MHer MRav
- subsp. ***sessiliflora*** 'Alba'	see *C. latiloba* 'Alba'
- 'Snowdrift'	SRms
- (Takion Series) 'Takion Blue'	EBee ELan GBin GWyn LRHS NPri SPoG
- - 'Takion White'	ELan EPfP GBin GMcL GWyn NPri SPoG
- 'Telham Beauty' ambig.	CBod CLet MCot NEgg NGBl SCob SPad SWvt XLum
- 'Telham Beauty' misapplied	CRos CSBt EBee ELan EPfP LRHS MArt MRav NRHS SPer SRms SWvt
- 'Telham Beauty' D.Thurston	NLar
- 'Tinpenny Blue'	WCot
- 'Wortham Belle' misapplied	see *C. persicifolia* 'Bennett's Blue'
- 'Wortham Belle' ambig.	LPot MRav
- 'Wortham Belle' Blooms	ECtt GBin LRHS MBNS NEgg WGwG
'Peter Nix'	EACa
petrophila	WAbe
pilosa	see *C. chamissonis*
- 'Superba'	see *C. chamissonis* 'Superba'
'Pink Octopus' PBR	CAby CCVN CRos CWGN EAJP ECtt ELon EUJe GCra IBoy LBMP LPot LRHS MBNS MHol MSCN MTis NCGa NGdn NLar NPnk NRHS SCob SEle SPad SPoG SRkn SRms WBod XLum
planiflora	see *C. persicifolia* var. *planiflora*
§ ***portenschlagiana*** 🏆H5	Widely available
- 'Biokovo'	XLum
- 'Catharina'	EACa ECtt EPPr EShb LRHS MHol SHil SPoG SRms
- 'Lieselotte'	CElw CPBP EACa ECtt SAko
- 'Major'	CBod EACa LBMP NCou WGwG WMoo
- 'Resholdt's Variety'	CBar CMea CRos CSam EACa ECho ECtt EDAr ELan EPfP GMaP LHop LRHS MCot MHol MRav NRHS SAko SRms WMoo XLum
poscharskyana	Widely available
- 'Blauranke'	EACa EWes SAko XLum
- 'Blue Gown'	EACa ECtt GCrg SAko XLum
- 'Blue Rivulet' PBR	ECtt
- 'Blue Waterfall'	CCVN CWGN EACa ECtt LSun MBNS NCGa NDov SPoG WBrk WCot XLum
- 'E.H. Frost'	CElw EACa ECho ECtt EDAr ELan EPPr EPfP EWTr GKev GMaP IBoy LHop MCot MMuc NLar NRya SAko SEND SPer SRGP SRms SWvt WAbe WBrk WMoo XLum
- 'Erich G. Arends'	SAko
I - 'Freya'	EACa SAko XLum
- 'Frühlingszauber'	WCot
- 'Hirsch Blue'	EPfP SRms
- 'Lilacina'	EACa EPPr
- 'Lisduggan Variety'	CElw EACa EBee ECtt EDAr EPPr EWes GMaP IBoy LHop LPot MHer NBro NLar SAko SRms WBrk WIce WMoo XLum
- 'Nana Alba'	EACa EPPr SAko WBrk
- 'Pinkins' PBR	CSma EACa ECtt NPri
- 'Silberregen'	SAko
- 'Stella' 🏆H5	ECha ECho ECtt ELan EPPr EPfP EWTr EWoo IBoy IPot LRHS LSRN MAvo MRav NBro NDov SAko SPer SWvt WBrk WHoo WMoo XLum
- 'Trollkind'	EACa EPPr SAko XLum
- variegated (v)	EHoe EPPr
- white-flowered	CTri ECho ELan
× ***pseudoraineri*** hort.	CRos EACa ECho EWes LRHS NRHS
ptarmicifolia	CPBP
pulla	CRos EACa ECho EDAr ELan EPot GCrg GEdr LRHS NHpl NRHS NSla SCob SPoG SRms SRot WIce
- 'Alba'	CRos EACa ECho EPot LRHS NRHS NSla WAbe
× ***pulloides*** hort. 'G.F. Wilson' 🏆H5	EACa ECho ECtt EPot GMaP NLar SBee SIgm SRkn
- 'Jelly Bells' PBR	ECtt IPot NLar
punctata	ESps LEdu MCot NBro NSti SWat WCAu WFar WGwG WMoo WTcb
- f. ***albiflora***	WFar
- - 'Alba'	CCVN
- - 'Nana Alba'	GEdr
- 'Alina's Double' (d)	MSCN MSpe NLar
- 'Cherry Pie'	EPfP
- dwarf	CPBP WAbe
- 'Einhorn JP'	IVic
- 'Golddrache JP'	IVic
- 'Hexe JP'	IVic
- var. ***hondoensis***	GKev
- hose-in-hose (d)	MMrt WGwG
- 'Hot Lips'	CMac EPfP MHol
* - var. ***howozana***	EBee GKev
- 'Kurokawa'	SBrt
- var. ***microdonta*** B&SWJ 5553	WCru
- 'Milly'	IVic
- 'Moorgeist JP'	IVic
* - 'Nana'	CCVN GEdr
- 'Nasachtal'	IVic
- 'Pantaloons' (d)	CMac CWGN EACa NLar NPnk SRms WCot WHlf
- 'Pink Chimes'	CDor IVic LSou MBNS MHol NLar SEle
- 'Plum Wine'	MSpe NWad
- 'Pumpernickel JP'	IVic
- purple-flowered new	LRHS
- 'Reifrock'	IVic
- f. ***rubriflora***	CBod CCVN CDor CRos CSpe ECtt ELan EPfP GCra LHop LRHS MCot MHol MNrw NEgg NRHS SCob SPer SRms WCAu WGwG WHar WTcb
- - 'Beetroot'	GBin GKev IKil IVic MHer NLar
- - 'Bowl of Cherries'	ECtt EPfP IVic LRHS MMrt NPnk SRkn SRms SRot
- - 'Cherry Bells'	CDor ECtt IVic LSRN
- - 'Vienna Festival'	CSBt
- - 'Wine 'n' Rubies'	EACa EBee ECtt MAvo MHol
- 'Seejungfrau JP'	IVic
I - 'Silver Bells'	EACa EBee ECtt EPfP IPot MSpe NSti SRms WFar WHil
- 'Troll JP'	IVic

	- 'Wedding Bells'	CWCL EACa EAJP EBee ELan EPri LRHS LSRN MHer MHol MSpe MTis NEgg NLar NPnk SCob SRkn SRms WHil
	- 'Weisser Schwan JP'	IVic
	- 'Weisser Turm JP'	IVic
I	- 'White Bells'	MJak
	- white hose-in-hose (d)	MNrw XLum
	'Purple Sensation' PBR	CAbP CSpe CWGN EBee EPfP LSou MBel MHol MNrw MSCN NCGa NLar NPnk WCot
	pusilla	see *C. cochlearifolia*
	pyramidalis	CSpe EACa EBee ELan EPfP ESps GJos GMcL MMuc NGBl SEND SPav SPlb WHar XLum
	- 'Alba'	CSpe CWib EACa ELan EPfP GJos NGBl SPav SPlb XLum
	- lavender blue-flowered	CWib GMcL
	raddeana	EACa SBrt WBrk
	raineri ♀H5	CPBP ECho EPot WAbe
*	- 'Alba'	ECho
	- 'Nettleton Gold'	CRos ECho LRHS NRHS
§	***rapunculoides***	GKev LHop SWat WCFE XLum
§	- 'Afterglow'	MAvo
	- 'Alba'	MAvo XLum
	rapunculus	MNHC WCot WOut XLum
	recurva	see *C. incurva*
	rhomboidalis Gorter	see *C. rapunculoides*
	rhomboidalis L.	WCot XLum
	rigidipila	WHer
	'Ringsabell Indigo Blue' (Ringsabell Series) new	WTor
	rotundifolia	CMac CWld EACa ECho ELan EPfP GBin GEdr GJos GLog MCot MHer MNHC NGBl SIde SPhx SPlb SRms SWat WBrk
	- var. ***albiflora***	CElw EWes WAbe
	- 'Jotunheimen'	EACa WAbe
§	- 'Olympica'	EACa EBee ECtt EWoo WHoo
	- 'Superba'	ECho
	- 'Thumbell Blue'	EACa WHar
	- 'White Gem'	CMea EACa EBee EPfP GJos LRHS NBre WHoo
	'Royal Wave'	CAbP EBee ECtt GEdr IPot MBel MHol NCGa NLar SCob WCot WHoo
	rupestris	LLHF
	rupicola	EPot WAbe
	'Samantha'	EACa ECtt ELon GBin IBoy LHop LRHS LSRN NHpl SHar WTor XEll
	'Sarastro'	Widely available
	sarmatica	CFis EACa EBee EPfP NBid SBch SRms
	- 'Hemelstraling'	MAvo NLar
	sartorii	SIgm WAbe
	scheuchzeri	WTcb
	'Senior'	ECtt EPPr EWoo IVic MHol SAko SHar WBrk WCot WRHF
	'Serafinental'	IVic
§	***sibirica***	GAbr GJos
	- 'Royal Wedding'	IPot
	speciosa	EBee
	'Stansfieldii'	CPBP CRos EACa ECho EPot LLHF LRHS NRHS
	suanetica	GMaP
	subramulosa	see *C. cochlearifolia*
	'Summer Pearl'	CBod CPBP ECtt
	'Summertime Blues' PBR	ECtt IBoy LSou NCGa
§	'Swannables'	CPou EACa LRHS MAvo MRav NCGa WOut
	takesimana	CBod CBro CSpe ECtt ELan EPfP ESps GKin LEdu LHop LRHS NEgg NSti SPad SPer SRms SWvt WMoo WTcb XLum
	- B&SWJ 8499	WCru
I	- 'Alba'	GNew IBoy WFar WHea WMoo
	- 'Beautiful Trust'	CCVN CLAP EBee NPnk WCot
	- 'Elizabeth'	Widely available
	- 'Elizabeth II' (d)	EPPr WCot WPtf
	- 'Feenrock JP'	XLum
	- purple-flowered	WWtn
	thyrsoides	CSpe EACa EBee GAbr GKev SPav
	'Timsbury Perfection'	EPot GCrg NHar WAbe
	tommasiniana ♀H5	LLHF WAbe
	topaliana subsp. ***delphica*** SDR 8254 new	GKev
	trachelium	EACa EBee ELon GJos GKev LRHS MHer MNHC MRav NMir SWat WCot WFar WHer WMoo WOut XLum
	- f. ***alba***	CBod CLAP EBee GJos IFro IMou LRHS NLar SGbt SWat WCot WFar WMoo
	- - 'Alba Flore Pleno' (d)	CLAP LEdu SMHy
	- 'Bernice' (d)	CDor CSpe EACa ECtt ELan EPPr EPfP GBuc GMaP IKil LRHS LSou MAvo MBel MHol MNrw MSCN NCGa NLar NSti SCob SKHP SPer WBor WCAu WCot WFar WGwG WHil
	- lilac-blue-flowered	SWat
	- 'Purple Break'	EBee MHol MPie WCot
	- 'Snowball'	CMac LSRN
	tridentata	GEdr
	troegerae	EACa
	'Tymonsii'	ECho
	'Van-Houttei'	CDor EBee EWes NLar SMHy WCot
	versicolor	CPBP SRms
	vidalii	see *Azorina vidalii*
	waldsteiniana	LLHF WAbe
	wanneri	GJos
	'Warley White'	see *C.* × *haylodgensis* W. Brockbank 'Warley White'
	'Warleyensis'	see *C.* × *haylodgensis* W. Brockbank 'Warley White'
	'White Octopus'	ECtt GPSL IBoy SCob SEle WNPC
	× ***wockei*** 'Puck'	CHid CRos EACa ECho ECtt EPot GCrg LHop LLHF LRHS NRHS SIgm WAbe WOld
	zangezura	EACa EDAr GJos GKev IKil SGbt XLum
	zoysii	WAbe

Campanula × *Symphyandra* see *Campanula*

Campanumoea see *Codonopsis*

Campsis (*Bignoniaceae*)

	grandiflora	CArn CBcs CFlo CKel CSBt CWGN ELan EPfP ESps LRHS LSRN MJak SPer SWvt WCFE
	radicans	CArn CBcs CMac CRHN CRos CWCL CWib ECrN ELan EPfP ESps LRHS MGil MJak MSwo NEgg NRHS SLon SNig SPer SPlb
	- 'Atrosanguinea'	SVen
	- 'Flamenco'	CBcs CMac CWCL EBee ELan EUJe LPar LRHS LSRN SAdn SCoo SLim SNig SVen SWvt
§	- f. ***flava*** ♀H4	CBcs CFlo CLet CMac CRos CTri CWCL EBee ELan EPfP ESps LHop

		LRHS MBlu MGos MJak NPla NRHS SLim SNig SPer SPoG SVen SWvt
	- 'Stromboli'	CAco EPfP
	- 'Yellow Trumpet'	see *C. radicans* f. *flava*
	× ***tagliabuana***	ESps
	- Dancing Flame = 'Huidan'PBR	CWCL CWGN EBee LRHS
	- Indian Summer = 'Kudian'PBR	CBcs CFlo CKel CSBt CWCL CWGN ELon EMOT EPfP LRHS LSRN LSou MGos SCoo
	- 'Madame Galen' ♀H4	Widely available
	- (Summer Jazz Series) 'Takarazuka Yellow' **new**	LRHS NRHS
	- - 'Takarazuka Zujin' **new**	LRHS NRHS

Camptosorus see *Asplenium*

Camptotheca (*Nyssaceae*)

acuminata	WPGP

Campylandra see *Tupistra*

Campylotropis (*Papilionaceae*)

macrocarpa	SBrt WSHC

Canarina (*Campanulaceae*)

canariensis ♀H2	CCCN CFil CPne CTsd SVen
- from Anaga Mountains, Tenerife	CLak WCot
- from Los Silos, Tenerife	CLak WCot

Candollea see *Hibbertia*

Canna ✿ (*Cannaceae*)

	'Adam's Orange'	CDTJ XBlo
	'Alaska' ♀H3	SAdu
	'Alberich'	SHaC
	altensteinii	CDTJ SAdu SHaC SPlb XBlo
	'Ambassador'	LAma SAdu SDeJ
	'Ambassadour'	LLWG SAdu SHaC
	'Angel Pink'	SAdu
	'Annaeei' ♀H3	SAdu
	'Annei-Rubra'	SAdu
	'Anthony and Cleopatra' (v)	WCot
	'Argentina'	SAdu SHaC
	'Assaut'	SAdu SHaC
	'Atlantis'	XBlo
	'Australia'	CDTJ EUJe SAdu SHaC XBlo
	'Austria'	SAdu
	'Baron Seguier'	XLum
	'Bethany' ♀H3	SAdu
	'Black Knight'	ECGP EUJe LAma SAdu SDeJ SHaC XBlo XTur
	'Bonfire'	CDTJ SDir
	'Bonnezeaux'	XTur
	brasiliensis	SAdu SHaC XBlo
	'Brillant'	EUJe LAma SAdu SDeJ SHaC XTur
	'Britannia'	SAdu
	'Burbank'	CDTJ
	'Caballero'	SHaC XLum
	'Caliméro'	SHaC
	'Canary'	XBlo
	'Carnaval'	SHaC XTur
	'Centenaire de Rozain-Boucharlat'	SAdu SDeJ SHaC XLum XTur
	'Champion'	SAdu XTur
	'Chocolate Sunrise'	LCro LOPS SAdu
	'Chouchou'	LLWG SHaC
I	'Citrina'	XBlo
§	'City of Portland'	LAma XTur
§	'Cleopatra'	CCCN LAma SAdu SHaC XBlo
*	'Cléopâtre'	SAdu
	coccinea	SArc
	compacta	SHaC
	'Corail'	XTur
	'Corrida'	XLum
	'Corsica' (Island Series)	SAdu
	'Creamy White'	SHaC XBlo
	'Député Hénon'	SAdu
	'Di Bartolo'	XBlo
	'Durban' Hiley, orange-flowered	see *C.* 'Phasion'
	'Durban' ambig.	CWGN EPfP LAma XTur
	'E. Neubert'	ELan LCro SAdu SHaC
	edulis	CDTJ SAdu
	- purple-leaved	SAdu
§	× ***ehemanii*** ♀H3	CAvo CDTJ SAdu SDix SHaC
	'En Avant'	SHaC SPlb XTur
	'Endeavour'	EUJe MSKA SAdu SHaC
	'Erebus' ♀H3	EUJe MSKA SAdu SDix SHaC
	'Ermine'	EUJe
	'Étoile du Feu'	XBlo
	'Fatamorgana'	SHaC
	'Feuerzauber'	SHaC XTur
	'Fiesta'	SHaC
	Firebird	see *C.* 'Oiseau de Feu'
	flaccida	SAdu SHaC
	'Flame'	XBlo
§	'Florence Vaughan'	SAdu
	'General Eisenhower' ♀H3	SAdu SHaC
	generalis × ***indica***	SHaC
	glauca	SAdu SHaC
	'Gnom'	SAdu SDeJ SHaC
	'Golden Girl'	SAdu
	'Golden Lucifer'	LAma
	'Golden Orb'	SHaC
	'Gran Canaria'	SAdu
	'Grande'	SAdu SHaC SPlb XLum
	'Grandiose'	SHaC
	'Heinrich Seidel'	SAdu
	Henlade hybrids	CDTJ
	'Henlade Pink'	SAdu
	'Henlade Red'	SAdu
	'Hercule'	SAdu
	'Horn'	XTur
	'Hossegor'	XLum
	'Hungaria'	SAdu
	hybrids	SHaC
	'Ibis'	XTur
	'Ibiza' (Island Series)	SAdu
	'Indiana'	SHaC
	indica	CAbb CDTJ SAdu SArc SHaC SMHy SPlb
	- 'Kreta' (Island Series)	SAdu
	- 'Purpurea'	CDTJ EUJe SAdu SDix SHaC SPlb
	- 'Red King Rupert'	CCCN
	- 'Russian Red' ♀H3	SAdu SHaC
	- Tropicanna Gold = 'Mactro'PBR	CCCN EPfP LCro LOPS SAdu
	'Ingeborg'	XTur
	'Intrigue'	EUJe SAdu
	iridiflora misapplied	see *C.* × *ehemanii*
	iridiflora Ruiz & Pav.	CDTJ CSpe SArc
	'Italia'	CDTJ SAdu
	jacobiniflora	SAdu SHaC
	jaegeriana	SHaC
	'Jivago'	SHaC
	'Kalimpong'	CDTJ
	King Humbert (orange-red)	see *C.* 'Roi Humbert'
I	'King Humbert' (blood-red)	CBcs CBod CDTJ EPfP XBlo
	'King Midas'	see *C.* 'Richard Wallace'

	'Königin Charlotte'	SAdu SDeJ SHaC
	'La France'	SAdu
	'La Gloire'	XTur
	latifolia	SHaC
	'Lesotho Lil'	CHll SAdu SHaC
	'Libération'	XLum
	'Liberté'	see *C.*'Wyoming'
	'Lion Rouge'	XLum
	'Lippo's Kiwi'	SAdu
	'Llanthony'	SAdu
	'Lolita'	SHaC
	'Louis Cayeux' ♀H3	LAma SHaC XTur
	'Louis Cottin'	CBcs CCCN CDTJ EPfP LAma SAdu XTur
	'Love Child'	SAdu
	'Lucifer'	CCCN LAma NPer XLum
	lutea	SHaC XBlo
	'Madame Angèle Martin'	XBlo XTur
	'Madame Crozy'	SAdu
	'Madeira' (Island Series)	EUJe SAdu
	'Malawiensis Variegata'	see *C.* 'Striata'
	'Marabout'	SAdu XTur
	'Montaigne'	SHaC
	'Moonshine'	CCCN LCro LOPS
	'Mrs Kate Gray'	SAdu
	'Musifolia' ♀H3	CDTJ EUJe EWes SAdu SDix SHaC XBlo
I	'Musifolia Rubra'	SAdu
	'Mystique' ♀H3	EWes SAdu SDix SHaC
	'Ointment Pink'	XBlo
§	'Oiseau de Feu'	SAdu XLum
	'Oiseau d'Or'	XLum XTur
	'Orange Beauty'	SAdu
	'Orange Chocolate'	SHaC
	'Orange Punch'	SAdu XTur
	'Orchid'	see *C.*'City of Portland'
	'Panache'	CDTJ EUJe SAdu SHaC WCot
	'Panama'	SHaC
	paniculata	SHaC
	'Peach Pink'	XBlo
	'Pearlescent Pink'	XBlo
	'Perkeo'	LLWG SAdu SHaC
§	'Phasion' (v) ♀H3	CCCN CHll CSpe ELan EPfP EUJe EWes LAma LCro LOPS NPer NPla SAdu SDix SHaC WCot XBlo
	'Picadore'	XTur
	'Picasso' ♀H3	CBcs CCCN CDTJ LAma SAdu XBlo
	'Pink Champagne'	XBlo
	'Pink Futurity' (Futurity Series)	CCCN
	'Pink Perfection'	SHaC
	'Pink Sunburst' (v)	SAdu
	'Plantagenet'	XTur
	'Plaster Pink'	XBlo
	'Pony'	XTur
	'President'	LAma SAdu SHaC XBlo XLum
	'Pretoria'	see *C.* 'Striata'
	'Pretoria Variegata'	see *C.*'Striata'
	'Prince Charmant'	SHaC XTur
	'Pringle Bay' (v)	SAdu
	'Professor Lorentz'	see *C.*'Wyoming'
	'Puck'	SHaC
	'Ra' ♀H3	MSKA SHaC
	'Red Cherry'	XTur
	'Red Stripe'	SAdu
§	'Richard Wallace'	SAdu SHaC SPlb XBlo
	'Robert Kemp'	SHaC
§	'Roi Humbert'	SAdu SHaC
	'Roi Soleil'	SHaC XLum XTur
	'Roma'	SAdu SHaC

	'Rosemond Coles'	SAdu SHaC XBlo
	'Saladin'	SHaC XLum
	'Saumur'	SHaC
	Savennières = 'Turcasav'	XTur
	'Sémaphore'	EUJe SAdu WCot XBlo
	'Shenandoah' ♀H3	LLWG SAdu SHaC
	'Singapore Girl'	SAdu SHaC
	'Snow-white'	XBlo
	'Society Belle'	SHaC
	'Soudan'	CDTJ SAdu
	speciosa	CDTJ SPlb XBlo
	'Statue of Liberty'	SAdu
	'Strasbourg'	NPer SAdu XLum
	'Strawberry Pink'	XBlo
	'Striata' misapplied	see *C.*'Stuttgart'
§	'Striata' (v) ♀H3	CCCN CDTJ CSpe CWGN EPfP EUJe NLos SAdu SEND SHaC SMad WCot XBlo XTur
	'Striped Beauty' (v)	CCCN CDTJ EUJe LAma SAdu
§	'Stuttgart' (v)	CDTJ CSpe ESwi EWes SAdu SHaC XTur
	'Südfunk'	SAdu
	'Summer Gold'	XBlo
	'Sunset'	WCot
	'Tafraout'	XTur
	'Tali'	SAdu SHaC
	'Talisman'	XBlo
	'Taney'	EUJe MSKA SHaC
	'Taroudant'	SHaC XLum
	'Tenerife' (Island Series)	SAdu
	'Triomphe'	SHaC
	(Tropical Series) 'Tropical Bronze Scarlet'	SAdu SHaC
	- 'Tropical Orange'	XTur
	- 'Tropical Red'	SAdu SHaC XTur
	- 'Tropical Rose'	SAdu SHaC XTur
	- 'Tropical Salmon'	SAdu SHaC
	- 'Tropical White'	SAdu SHaC XTur
	- 'Tropical Yellow'	SAdu SHaC XTur
	Tropicanna	see *C.*'Phasion'
	Tropicanna Black = 'Lon01'PBR	EPfP LCro LOPS SAdu
	tuerckheimii	SAdu SHaC
	'Valentine'	WCot
	'Vanilla Pink'	XBlo
	'Verdi' ♀H3	LAma SAdu SHaC
	warscewiczii	CDTJ SAdu SHaC
	'Weymouth'	CDTJ SAdu
	'Whithelm Pride' ♀H3	SAdu SDeJ SHaC
	'Wintzer's Colossal'	SAdu
	'Woodbridge Pink'	XBlo
§	'Wyoming' ♀H3	CBcs CCCN CDTJ ECGP EUJe LAma LCro LOPS SAdu SDeJ SDir SEND SHaC XBlo XTur
	'Yara'	SAdu SDeJ SHaC
	'Yellow Humbert' misapplied	see *C.*'Cleopatra', *C.* 'Florence Vaughan', *C.*'Richard Wallace'
	'Yellow Humbert'	SAdu
	'Zoodikers!'	SAdu

Cannomois (*Restionaceae*)

grandis	CTre SPlb

Cantua (*Polemoniaceae*)

buxifolia ♀H2	CAbb CBcs CCCN CHid CHll CPne ECre LRHS
- 'Alba'	CBcs CCCN CHid ESwi
- 'Dancing Oaks'	SVen

Cape gooseberry see *Physalis peruviana*

Capnoides see *Corydalis*

Capparis (*Capparaceae*)

spinosa	CCCN
- subsp. ***rupestris***	SPlb WJek

Capsicum (*Solanaceae*)

annuum	CCCN SVic
- 'Ancho'	SVic
- var. ***annuum*** (Cerasiforme Group) 'Piccante Calabresé' new	SVic
- - (Conioides Group) 'Super Chili' ♀^{H1c} new	SPre SVic
- - (Grossum Group) 'Bell Boy'	LCro
- - (Longum Group) 'Bolivian Rainbow' ♀^{H1c}	SVic
- - - cayenne	CCCN
- - - 'Fish' new	SVic
- - - 'Golden Cayenne' new	SVic
- - - jalapeño	SVic
- - - 'Joe's Long Cayenne'	SVic
- - - 'Ring of Fire'	SVic
- - - 'Serrano'	SVic
- - - 'Tokyo Hot' new	SVic
- - 'Marconi Rosso'	SVic
- - 'Prairie Fire' ♀^{H1c}	CCCN
- 'Apache' ♀^{H1c}	CCCN NPri SPre
- 'Basket of Fire' ♀^{H1c}	SPre SVic
- 'Bulgarian Carrot'	SVic
- 'Cayenne Red'	SPre SVic
- 'Demon Red' ♀^{H1c}	SPre SVic
- var. ***glabriusculum***	SVic
- 'Hungarian Hot Wax' ♀^{H1c}	SVic
- 'Las Cruces Cayenne'	SVic
- 'Nosferatu' new	SVic
- 'Numex Big Jim'	SVic
- 'Numex Garnet'	SVic
- 'Numex Piñata'	SVic
- 'Numex Primavera'	SVic
- 'Numex Twilight'	SPre SVic
- 'Peter Pepper'	SVic
- 'Pinocchio's Nose'	SVic
- 'Pot Black' ♀^{H1c} new	SVic
- 'Vampire' new	SVic
baccatum 'Aji Limon'	SVic
- 'Aji Omnicolor'	SVic
- 'Christmas Bell'	SVic
- 'Lemon Drop'	SPre
chinense 'Dorset Naga'^{PBR} new	SPre
- (Habanero Group) 'Habanero Caribbean Red'	SVic
- - 'Naga Morrich'	SVic
- - 'Caribbean Antillais' ♀^{H1c} new	SVic
- 'Numex Suave Orange'	SVic
- 'Numex Suave Red'	SVic
- 'Scotch Bonnet' new	SPre
frutescens Tabasco Group	SVic
'Rodeo'	SVic

Caragana (*Papilionaceae*)

arborescens	CAgr CDul CMCN EBee ELan EPfP NLar NWea SBrt SCob SPer SPlb
- 'Lorbergii'	CEnd GBin MBlu NLar SPer
- 'Pendula'	CAco CMac CWib ELan ESps GBin LHop MAsh MBlu NEgg NLar NOrn SCoo SPer
- 'Walker'	CEnd CMac CWib ELan MAsh MBlu MGos NHol NLar NWea SCoo SPer
aurantiaca	NLar
pygmaea	NLar

Caralluma (*Apocynaceae*)

hesperidum	LToo

carambola see *Averrhoa carambola*

caraway see *Carum carvi*

Cardamine ✿ (*Brassicaceae*)

asarifolia misapplied	see *Pachyphragma macrophyllum*
bipinnata new	WCot
bulbifera	CLAP EBee ELon EPPr GBin GEdr LEdu MAvo NRya WCru
bulbosa	GBuc
californica	EPPr LEdu MAvo NRya WCru WMoo
concatenata	WCru
digitata	CWCL EBee
diphylla	CAby CLAP EBee LEdu SKHP WCot WCru
- 'Eco Cut Leaf'	CAby EBee MAvo WCru
- 'Eco Moonlight'	WCru
aff. ***diphylla***	CTal
enneaphylla	CLAP EWld NBid
glanduligera	CElw EBee ECha ELon EPPr EPri GBuc GEdr LEdu MAvo MNrw WCot WCru
§ ***heptaphylla***	CAby CLAP ECha ECho ELon EWTr GBin GKev ILea LLHF WCru WSHC
- from the Pyrenees	GCal
- 'Big White'	EBee GBuc GCal NCGa WPnP
- Guincho form	CLAP EPPr MAvo WCot
- white-flowered	CLAP
§ ***kitaibelii***	CAby CLAP CTal EPPr GBin GCal LEdu NLar WCot WCru
latifolia Vahl	see *C. raphanifolia*
macrophylla	CLAP EBee GBin LEdu SWat WCot WSHC
- CD&R 561	NCGa
- 'Bright and Bronzy'	IMou WCru
- purple-leaved Chen Yi T-535 new	WCot
maxima	LEdu MAvo WCru
microphylla	GKev
pachystigma	GBuc
pentaphylla ♀^{H5}	CBro CSpe ECho ELan ELon EPPr EPot EWTr GAbr GBin GBuc GKev GMaP IFro LEdu MCot NBir NHar NHpl SPhx WCot WCru WSHC
- bright pink-flowered	CLAP WCot
pratensis	CWat CWld GJos LCro MCot MHer MNHC MSKA NMir SPhx SWat WHer WMoo WSFF WShi
- 'Diane's Petticoat'	MAvo MHer WHoo
- 'Edith' (d)	CLAP EBee
- 'Flore Pleno' (d)	CBre CSpe ECha EPfP GAbr GBuc GCal GMaP IFro LEdu MHer MNrw NBid NBir NBro NCGa NLar SWat WBor WPGP WSFF
- 'Flore Pleno' white-flowered (d)	LEdu
- 'William' (d)	LEdu
quinquefolia	CAby CElw CLAP CMea ECha ELon GBuc ILea LEdu LRHS MAvo MBel

MCot MNrw MPie NCGa NLar SDys WBrk WCot WCru WOut WPnP
- PAB 9992 **new** LEdu
§ ***raphanifolia*** CBre EBee GAbr GBin GCal IFro IMou LLWG MAvo NBid NBro NRya NSti SKHP SWat WBor WMoo WPGP
- PAB 204 LEdu
trifolia CAby CElw CMac CTal EBee ECha EPPr EWld GBin GCal GEdr GMaP IFro ILea IMou LEdu MRav NBir NBro NLar NRya SWat WCot WCru WFar WMoo
waldsteinii CElw CLAP CTal EBee ECho EPPr GBuc GCal GEdr ILea LEdu MAvo NCGa WCru WPGP WSHC
yezoensis GBin
- B&SWJ 4659 EBee WCru

cardamon see *Elettaria cardamomum*

Cardiandra (*Hydrangeaceae*)

alternifolia B&SWJ 5719 WCru
- B&SWJ 5845 WCru
- B&SWJ 6177 WCru
- B&SWJ 6354 WCru
- subsp. ***moellendorffii*** CFil WPGP
- 'Pink Geisha' WCru
amamiohshimensis WCru
formosana WPGP
- B&SWJ 2005 WCru
- 'Crûg's Abundant' WCru
- 'Hsitou' WCru
- 'Hsitou Splendour' WCru

Cardiocrinum ✿ (*Liliaceae*)

cathayanum GEdr GKev
cordatum GAbr
- B&SWJ 2812 WCru
- B&SWJ 4841 WCru
- B&SWJ 5427 WCru
- B&SWJ 6336 WCru
- B&SWJ 11069 **new** WCru
- var. ***glehnii*** CCCN GBuc GKev LRHS
- - B&SWJ 10827 WCru
- - B&SWJ 10843 **new** WCru
- red-veined MNrw
giganteum CAby CBcs CBro CCCN CHid EBee GAbr GBin GBuc GCra GEdr GKev LAma LOPS LRHS MNrw NBid NCGa NHpl NLar SMad WAbe WBod WCot WCru WPnP XLum
- B&SWJ 2419 WCru
- HWJK 2158 from Nepal WCru
- GWJ 9219 from Sikkim WCru
- pure white-flowered **new** GKev
- var. ***yunnanense*** CSpe EPfP GBuc GEdr ITim NBid WCru WPGP
- - PAB 8347 **new** LEdu

cardoon see *Cynara cardunculus*

Carduus (*Asteraceae*)

defloratus SBrt
subsp. ***argemone*** **new**
- subsp. ***defloratus*** **new** SBrt

Carex (*Cyperaceae*)

acuta CHab MSKA
- 'Variegata' (v) CBen CMac CWat EHoe EShb GMaP IFro LLWG NBro WMoo WWtn
acutiformis NMir WDra
alba CKno WCot
'Amazon Mist' NWsh WFar
appalachica EPPr
arenaria CKno
atrata EHoe WHrl
§ - subsp. ***pullata*** GCal
- - KEKE 494 EBee
aurea IFoB WDra
baccans CAby GCal SBrt
berggrenii ELan GBin LPot SPlb
brizoides IMou
brunnea CMac ESps SHDw
- 'Jenneke' (v) ESps LRHS NRHS SHDw SLim SWvt
- 'Variegata' (v) EHoe SHDw WHoo
buchananii Widely available
- 'Firefox' CLet
- 'Green Twist' EBee EShb NWsh
- 'Red Rooster' EWoo NWsh WHar
- 'Viridis' ELan XLum
chathamica LRHS SVen
ciliatomarginata 'Treasure Island' (v) EBee
colchica XLum
comans EPfP NBro
- 'Bronze Perfection' SMea
- bronze-leaved Widely available
- 'Copper Green' SMea
- 'Dancing Flame' CWCL ELon
- 'Frosted Curls' Widely available
- red-leaved CBcs EUJe NLar SRms WHar
- 'Small Red' see *C. comans* 'Taranaki'
§ - 'Taranaki' ELan MBNS SCoo
conica 'Hime-kan-suge' see *C. conica* 'Snowline'
- 'Kiku-sakura' (v) EPPr
§ - 'Snowline' (v) CMac EHoe ELan EShb GKev GMaP LEdu LLWP NBro NLar NWsh SGol SWvt XLum
crinita EPPr
cristatella EPPr
dallii WHrl
davalliana EBee
davisii EPPr
depauperata EHoe
dioica LLWG WDra
dipsacea CKno CMac CWCL EHoe EShb GMaP LRHS NLar NRHS NWad NWsh WHal
- 'Dark Horse' EHoe MMuc SMea WPtf
dissita GAbr
divulsa CKno
- subsp. ***leersii*** EPPr
§ ***dolichostachya*** 'Kaga-nishiki' (v) CSBt ESps LEdu LHop LRHS NRHS SLim
duthiei see *C. atrata* subsp. *pullata*
§ ***elata*** 'Aurea' ♀H6 Widely available
- 'Bowles's Golden' see *C. elata* 'Aurea'
- 'Knightshayes' CKno
elongata CHab
'Evergold' see *C. oshimensis* 'Evergold'
firma 'Variegata' (v) EPot GEdr LLHF NWad WThu
flacca CHab CKno EPPr GBin WBor XLum XSen
- 'Blue Zinger' CKno
§ - subsp. ***flacca*** EBee NSti SMea
flagellifera CBcs CBod CMac CRos CSpe CTri CWCL EBee EHoe ELan ELon EPfP EShb GCal GMaP LRHS LSun MMuc NBir NRHS NWsh SCob SEND SPlb SPoG WWtn
- 'Auburn Cascade' CBod ELan LHop SPtp

- 'Coca-Cola'	WRHF
- 'Kiwi'	EAEE EShb NWsh
- red-leaved **new**	SCob
flava	CKno EHoe EPPr WDra
fortunei	see *C. morrowii* Boott
fraseri	see *Cymophyllus fraserianus*
fraserianus	see *Cymophyllus fraserianus*
glauca Scop.	see *C. flacca* subsp. *flacca*
'Gold Fountains'	see *C. dolichostachya* 'Kaga-nishiki'
granularis	EPPr
grayi	CAby CWCL EAJP EHoe GBin LEdu LLWG LRHS MBlu MSKA NLar NRHS SPlb SPtp WBor WPGP
'Ice Dance' (v)	CKno CRos CWCL EAEE EBee EPPr ESps EWoo GBin GKev GMaP GMcL GQue LPot LRHS LSun MJak MMuc MSCN NHol NRHS NWad NWsh SCob SGol SHil SPad SPtp SWvt WCot
kaloides	EHoe XLum
'Kan-suge'	see *C. morrowii* Boott
laxiculmis 'Bunny Blue'PBR	LRHS NLar
* ***leformeri***	XLum
limosa	LLWG
lupulina	GBin
lurida	EPfP MBNS XLum
- 'Silver'	EPPr
melanocephala	EBee
mertensii NNS 07-98	EPPr
Milk Chocolate = 'Milchoc'PBR (v)	CBod EPfP ESps SCob
morrowii misapplied	see *C. oshimensis*
§ ***morrowii*** Boott	ESps
I - 'Fisher's Form' (v)	CBot CKno CTri ELan EPPr ESps LHop MRav NLar NWsh SCob SWvt WGrn
- 'Gilt' (v)	EHoe EPPr MBNS NWad
- 'Gold Band'	GMcL
- 'Nana Variegata' (v)	CTri
- 'Pinkie'	WPtf
- var. ***temnolepis***	IMou
- 'Variegata' (v)	CBod EHoe ELan EPPr EWoo GCal GMaP MJak MMuc NBir NSti SRms XLum
muricata	XSen
muskingumensis	CKno CWCL CWib EHoe ELan EPPr EPfP EShb ESps GBin GCal LCro LEdu NBro NLar SDix SLim SMad WMoo WPnP
- 'Little Midge'	CKno CMac EPPr EShb GBin GCal LEdu NLar
- 'Little Titch'	SMHy
- 'Oehme' (v)	CBod CKno CWCL EBee EPPr EShb LEdu LLWG LRHS NBid NHol NRHS NWad WPtf
- 'Silberstreif' (v)	CKno EBee EPPr EShb GBin LEdu MMuc XLum
nigra (L.) Reichard	EPPr XLum
§ - 'On-line' (v)	CKno EHrv EPPr
- 'Variegata'	see *C. nigra* 'On-line'
No 4, Nanking (Greg's thin leaf)	EPPr
normalis	EPPr
obnupta	CKno EPPr
ornithopoda 'Aurea'	see *C. ornithopoda* 'Variegata'
§ - 'Variegata' (v)	EBee GBin NHol NWsh WMoo
§ ***oshimensis***	EPPr WCot
- 'Everdi'	LRHS
- Everest = 'Fiwhite'PBR (v)	CBod CKno CSBt EBee EShb ESps GBin GMcL LHop LRHS LSun MAsh NEoE NWad SArc SCob SEND SPoG WCot WFar WRHF WSHC WTor
§ - 'Evergold' (v) ♀H7	Widely available
- 'Evergreen'	LRHS
- 'Everillo'PBR	CBod CKno ESwi GBin LRHS MAsh NLar NWad SPoG WCot WRHF
- 'Everlime' **new**	LRHS
- 'Everoro' (v)	LRHS WCot
- 'Eversheen' **new**	LRHS
- 'J.S. Greenwell'	EBee
- 'Variegata' (v)	NBir
otrubae	CHab WDra XLum
panicea	CKno CWCL EBee EHoe EPPr EShb LLWG MSKA WMoo
paniculata	WDra XLum
parviflora	SMea
pendula	Widely available
- 'Cool Jazz' (v)	EPPr MSKA
- 'Moonraker' (v)	EHoe EPPr ESwi MSKA NWad WCot
petriei	EBee ECha ELon LLWP XLum
phyllocephala	EShb
- 'Sparkler' (v)	EHoe EPfP GMcL LRHS SPad SWvt XLum
plantaginea	EBee EHoe EPPr EShb GBin LEdu WMoo WPGP
praegracilis	CKno EPPr
Pritchard's selection (v)	IFro
projecta	EPPr
pseudocyperus	CBen EHoe GBin MSKA NPer NWsh SWat WMoo WPnP
punctata	XLum
remota	CKno EHoe EPPr EShb SMea WDra
riparia	CHab MMuc MSKA NPer SMea SWat WShi
- 'Bowles's Golden'	see *C. elata* 'Aurea'
sabynensis	see *C. umbrosa* subsp. *sabynensis*
* ***saxatilis*** 'Variegata' (v)	EWoo
scaposa KWJ 12304	WCru
secta	CKno CRos EPPr EPfP GMaP IMou LRHS NRHS SHDw WMoo
- from Dunedin, New Zealand	EPPr
siderosticta	WSHC
- 'Banana Boat'	see *C. siderosticta* 'Golden Falls'
§ - 'Golden Falls' (v)	LEdu SMad SPtp
- 'Golden Fountains'	WCot
- 'Kisokaido' (v)	EShb
- 'Old Barn'	EBee
- 'Shima-nishiki' (v)	EBee EPfP LRHS
- 'Variegata' (v)	CTsd EBee EHoe ELan ELon EShb GCal GMcL LEdu NBir NLar NSti NWsh SLim WBor WWtn
'Silver Sceptre' (v)	CBod EPPr EShb ESps GMaP LPar LRHS MBNS MGos NRHS NSti NWad NWsh SLim SPlb SWvt WBrk WHar WMoo
solandri	CKno NWsh SHDw XLum
spicata	CHab
spissa	MNrw
stricta Gooden. 'Bowles's Golden'	see *C. elata* 'Aurea'
stricta Lam.	MMuc
sylvatica	CHab EHoe WDra
tenuiculmis	CBod CWCL EAJP EBee EPPr LHop LRHS LSRN NRHS NSti NWad SPtp WCot XLum
testacea	Widely available
- dark-leaved	EPfP
- 'Limeshine'	EWes GBin WFar
- 'Old Gold'	ELan EWes SMad SPlb WMoo
- 'Prairie Fire'	CRos CSpe GMaP LHop LRHS NLar NRHS SCob WGrn
texensis	EPPr
'The Beatles'	EHoe ESps EWoo NBir

trifida	CKno EHoe GAbr
- 'Chatham Blue'	CBod GBin MMuc SEND
* - 'Glauca'	CWCL
- 'Rekohu Sunrise'PBR (v)	CKno EBee ELon EPfP ESwi GMcL LHop LRHS NEoE SEND SLon SPoG WCot
umbrosa subsp. ***sabynensis*** 'Thinny Thin' (v)	EBee EShb
vesicaria	WDra

Carica (*Caricaceae*)

papaya (F)	XBlo
- 'Babaco'	CCCN
pubescens	SPlb

Carissa (*Apocynaceae*)

grandiflora	see *C. macrocarpa*
§ ***macrocarpa*** (F)	CCCN

Carlina (*Asteraceae*)

acanthifolia	SPhx
acaulis	ECho ELan SPlb
- subsp. ***acaulis***	GPoy
* - 'Bronze Form'	EBee SMad
- bronze-leaved	ELan
- var. ***caulescens***	see *C. acaulis* subsp. *simplex*
§ - subsp. ***simplex***	ECha ELon NPri
- - bronze-leaved	SPhx
vulgaris 'Silver Star'	SPhx

Carmichaelia (*Papilionaceae*)

australis	WSHC
petriei	SMad
stevensonii	MBlu SBrt WPGP WThu

× *Carmispartium* see *Carmichaelia*

Carpenteria (*Hydrangeaceae*)

californica	CCCN CJun CRos CTri CWCL EBee ELan EPfP ESwi EWTr GBin LCro LOPS LRHS MGil MGos NRHS SCob SPer SWvt WBod WFar WSHC
- 'Bodnant' ♀H4	CBcs CDul CRos ELan LRHS LSRN MAsh MGos NLar NRHS SEle SHil SWvt WFar WPGP
- 'Elizabeth' ♀H4	CAbP CBcs CJun CSBt CWGN ELan EPfP LRHS LSRN MAsh NLar SPoG SSta
- 'Eskimo'	SWvt
- 'Ladhams' Variety'	CBcs CDul CJun CMac EPfP LRHS MRav NLar NPri SEle SPer SRkn SWvt

Carpinus ✿ (*Betulaceae*)

betulus ♀H6	Widely available
* - 'A. Beeckman'	SGol
- 'Columnaris'	CDul CLnd CTho ESps
* - 'Columnaris Nana'	LLHF MPkF WCot WPat
§ - 'Fastigiata' ♀H6	Widely available
- 'Frans Fontaine'	CCVT CDul CEnd CLnd CMCN CMac CTho EBee EMOT EPfP ESps EWTr IArd LHop MBlu MGos NLar NOra NWea SCoo SEWo SGol SLim SPer SPoG WHar WMat
- 'Globus'	MBlu
- 'Incisa'	WMou
- 'Lucas'	EBee EMOT LRHS MBlu NOra SBir SGol WMat
- 'Monument'	MPkF
- 'Pendula'	CDul CEnd CTho EBee IArd LLHF MBlu SWvt WMou WPat
- 'Purpurea'	CDul CEnd MBlu WPat
- 'Pyramidalis'	see *C. betulus* 'Fastigiata'
- 'Quercifolia'	CDul EBee
- 'Rockhampton Red' **new**	EBee
- 'Stegemanns Primus'PBR	EBee WMat
caroliniana	CDul CLnd CMCN EPfP SBir
- 'Red Fall'	EPfP MBlu
- 'Sentinel Dries'	LRHS MBlu
cordata	CDul MBlu SSta
coreana	CMCN SBir
fangiana	CBcs CEnd CMCN CTho EBee EPfP IVic MBlu SKHP WPGP WPat
fargesiana	WPGP
fargesii	see *C. viminea*
henryana	CMen EBtc SBir
- var. ***simplicidentata***	CMCN MBlu
japonica ♀H6	CDul CEnd CLnd CMCN CMen CTho EBee EPfP MBlu NLar NOra SAko SBir SCoo SEWo SMad SSta WMat
- B&SWJ 10803	WCru
- B&SWJ 11072	WCru
- 'Chinese Lantern'	SGol
kawakamii	CMCN
- CWJ 12412	WCru
- CWJ 12449	WCru
laxiflora	CMen
- B&SWJ 10809	WCru
- B&SWJ 11035	WCru
- var. ***longispica*** B&SWJ 8772	WCru
- var. ***macrostachya***	see *C. viminea*
omeiensis	EBee
- KR 280	WPGP
orientalis	CMCN SBir
polyneura	SBir SSta WPGP
pubescens	EBee WPGP
- 'Abbotsbury'	SSta
rankanensis	SSta
- RWJ 9839	WCru
× ***schuschaensis***	EBtc LRHS WPat
shensiensis	CDul EBee WPGP
tschonoskii	EBee
- B&SWJ 10800	WCru
- BBJMT 297	WPGP
turczaninowii	CMCN CMen MBlu NLar SBir SSta
§ ***viminea***	CEnd CMCN SSta WPat

Carpobrotus (*Aizoaceae*)

acinaciformis	SVen
chilensis **new**	LTro
§ ***edulis***	CCCN CCac CDTJ SArc SEND SVen WHer XLum
- 'Gugh Dawn' (v)	CCac SVen
- var. ***rubescens***	CCCN CCac
muirii	CCCN SVen
sauerae	CCCN

Carpodetus (*Rousseaceae*)

serratus	CBcs IVic WPGP

Carrierea (*Salicaceae*)

calycina	IArd IDee IVic SAko WPGP

carrot see *Daucus carota*

Carthamus (*Asteraceae*)

dianius **new**	SBrt
mitissimus	GEdr
tinctorius	MNHC SMad SPav SRms SVen

Carum (*Apiaceae*)

carvi	CBod CLau ENfk GPoy MHer MJak MNHC SIde SRms SVic WJek
petroselinum	see *Petroselinum crispum*

Carya ✿ (*Juglandaceae*)

cordiformis	MBlu
glabra	CMCN
illinoinensis (F)	CAgr CBcs CDul CMCN LRHS MRai
- 'Carlson No 3' seedling (F)	CAgr
- 'Colby' seedling (F)	CAgr
- 'Cornfield' (F)	CAgr
- 'Lucas' (F)	CAgr
laciniosa (F)	EPfP
- 'Henry' (F)	CAgr
- 'Keystone' seedling (F)	CAgr
ovata (F)	CAgr CBcs CDul CLnd EPfP MBlu WPGP
- 'Grainger' seedling (F)	CAgr
- 'Neilson' seedling (F)	CAgr
- 'Weschcke' seedling (F)	CAgr
- 'Yoder No 1' seedling (F)	CAgr
tomentosa	EPfP NLar WPGP

Caryophyllus see *Syzygium*

Caryopteris (*Lamiaceae*)

× ***clandonensis***	CAco CMac ECtt ESps MGil NBir
- 'Arthur Simmonds' ♀H4	CTri ECha ELan LHop SCob SPer
- 'Dark Knight'	CBot CRos CSpe CTsd EBee ECtt ELan EPfP ESps EWTr LBuc LCro LRHS MAsh MCot NCGa NRHS SBod SCob SEle SHil SMDP SPer SPoG SWvt WFar WHil WHoo
- 'Ferndown'	CWib EWTr NLar SEND SRms
- 'First Choice' ♀H5	CLet CMac ECrN ECtt ELan EPfP LHop LRHS LSRN MAsh MGos NRHS SLim SPer SPoG SRkn SWvt
- 'Gold Giant'	CRos EPfP LRHS MAsh NRHS
- Grand Bleu = 'Inoveris' PBR	CDul CMac CSBt ELan EPfP LRHS LSRN MGos NLar NRHS SCob SGbt SGol SWvt WPat
- 'Heavenly Baby' ♀H4	CRos EPfP LRHS MAsh SKHP SLon
- 'Heavenly Blue'	Widely available
- Hint of Gold = 'Lisaura' PBR ♀H4	CRos CSBt ELan EPfP ESps LRHS MAsh NRHS STPC
- 'Kew Blue'	CBcs CDul CMac CRos CSBt EHoe ELan EPfP EShb ESps IVic LRHS LSRN MAsh MGos MHer MSwo NLar NRHS SCob SCoo SGol SLim SLon SPer SRms SSta SWvt XSen
- 'Longwood Blue'	CRos EPfP LRHS
- 'Pershore'	WAvo
- Petit Bleu = 'Minbleu' PBR	EBee LRHS MPkF
- Sterling Silver = 'Lissilv' PBR ♀H4	CMac CRos EBee EPfP GMcL LRHS LSRN MAsh NEoE NRHS SCob SPer SPoG SRms
- 'Summer Gold'	CMac MAsh
- 'Summer Sorbet' PBR (v) ♀H4	CBot CLet CMac CRos CWGN CWld EBee ECrN EHoe ELan EPfP EWes GMcL LRHS MAsh MGos MJak MTPN NLar SCob SCoo SEND SGbt SGol SLim SPer SRms SWvt WHar WHil
- weeping **new**	EPPr
- 'White Surprise' PBR	CBcs CMac CWGN ELan EMil EPfP LPre LRHS MGos NEgg NLar SCob SGol SPer SPoG WCot WFar WHil
- 'Worcester Gold' ♀H4	Widely available
divaricata	CMCN SBrt
- 'Electrum'	EBee LSou WCot WSHC
- 'Jade Shades'	LSou WSHC
§ ***incana***	SPer
- 'Autumn Pink' PBR	ELan
- 'Blue Cascade'	EBtc ELan LRHS MRav NLar SRms WGrn WPat
- 'Delft Blue'	CChe LRHS
§ - 'Jason' PBR	CBcs ECrN ELon NEgg NLar SCob SPoG SWvt WRHF
- Sunshine Blue	see *C. incana* 'Jason'
mastacanthus	see *C. incana*

Caryota (*Arecaceae*)

mitis	CCCN
- 'Himalaya'	NLos

Cassandra see *Chamaedaphne*

Cassia (*Caesalpiniaceae*)

corymbosa Lam.	see *Senna corymbosa*
marilandica	see *Senna marilandica*
nemophila	SPlb

Cassinia (*Asteraceae*)

fulvida	CBcs SVen
leptophylla	CBcs
vauvilliersii	EBee ELan SEle SVen
'Ward Silver'	EHoe EWes LRHS

Cassinia × *Helichrysum* (*Asteraceae*)

hybrid	WKif

Cassiope ✿ (*Ericaceae*)

'Askival Snowbird'	ITim NWad
'Askival Snow-wreath'	see *C.* Snow-wreath Group
'Askival Stormbird'	ITim NWad
'Badenoch'	GKev
'Edinburgh' ♀H5	EPot GBin NHar NWad WThu
lycopodioides ♀H5	ITim
- 'Beatrice Lilley'	EBee EPot GKev NHar NLar WThu
- 'Jim Lever'	ITim NHar WAbe
- 'Rokujō'	ITim
mertensiana 'California Pink'	GKev NWad
- var. ***californica***	ITim NLar NWad WThu
- var. ***gracilis***	NHar NLar NWad WThu
'Muirhead' ♀H5	NHar NLar WThu
'Randle Cooke' ♀H5	EPot GBin NHar WThu
selaginoides LS&E 13284	WAbe WThu
§ Snow-wreath Group	ITim
tetragona	ITim
wardii	EPot

Castanea ✿ (*Fagaceae*)

'Bouche de Bétizac' (F)	CAgr
crenata	CAgr CDul
dentata	CBcs
'Maraval' (F)	CAgr CTho ERea MCoo WHar WMat
'Maridonne' (F)	CAgr
'Marigoule' (F)	CAgr CFGn EPom ERea MCoo NWea SPer WHar WMat
'Marsol' (F)	CAgr ECrN ERea MCoo WMat
mollissima	CBcs
'Précoce Migoule' (F)	CAgr
sativa	Widely available
§ - 'Albomarginata' (v) ♀H6	CEnd EPfP LHop NOra WMat
- 'Anny's Red'	SPer
- 'Anny's Summer Red'	CDul EUJe
- 'Argenteovariegata'	see *C. sativa* 'Albomarginata'

- 'Aspleniifolia'	CDul
- 'Aureomarginata'	see *C. sativa* 'Variegata'
- 'Belle Epine' (F)	CAgr
- 'Bournette' (F)	CAgr
* - 'Doré de Lyon'	CAgr
- 'Marlhac' (F)	CAgr CFGn NOra WMat
- 'Marron Comballe' (F)	CAgr
- 'Marron de Goujounac' (F)	CAgr
- 'Marron de Lyon' (F)	CAgr CDul CEnd CFGn CHab CTho EPfP EPom IVic NWea SVic
- 'Regal' (F)	EPom
§ - 'Variegata' (v)	CMCN ELan SPer
seguinii	EGFP

Castilleja (*Orobanchaceae*)

angustifolia	GKev
integra	SPlb
miniata	GKev SPlb WAbe
sessiliflora	SPlb

Casuarina (*Casuarinaceae*)

cunninghamiana	SPlb

Catalpa ✿ (*Bignoniaceae*)

bignonioides ♀H6	Widely available
- 'Aurea' ♀H6	Widely available
- 'Nana'	EBee WHar WPat
- 'Purpurea'	see *C.* × *erubescens* 'Purpurea'
- 'Variegata' (v)	ELon EPfP LHop LRHS MAsh WPat
bungei	CCVT CMCN CTho MBlu SArc SGol
- 'Purpurea'	EMOT
§ × ***erubescens*** 'Purpurea' ♀H6	Widely available
fargesii f. ***duclouxii*** ♀H5	CBcs CDul CEnd EBee EPfP MBlu SAko SChF WHor WPGP
ovata	CMCN CTho SPad
- 'Slender Silhouette'	NLar
speciosa ♀H6	CDul CMCN CTho GBin SVen
- 'Frederik'	NLar
- 'Pulverulenta' (v)	CDul LLHF MBlu SBig WCot WPat

Catananche (*Asteraceae*)

caerulea	CBod CMea CRos CSBt CSpe CTri EAJP ECha ELan EPfP EShb ESps LRHS MArt MBel MNHC MSpe NEgg SCob SPad SPer SPoG SWvt WCAu WHar WHoo WMoo
- 'Alba'	CMea CRos EAJP ECha ELan EPfP GNew IFoB LRHS MArt MBel MNrw NBir NRHS SCob SPad SPer SPoG SWvt WHar WMoo
- 'Amor Blue'	CRos EPfP LRHS NRHS
- 'Bicolor'	MSpe WMoo
- 'Major' ♀H5	EWTr LRHS SHil SRms

Catha (*Celastraceae*)

edulis	GPoy WJek

Caulokaempferia (*Zingiberaceae*)

petelotii B&SWJ 11818	LEdu WCru
- HWJ 541 **new**	WCru

Caulophyllum (*Berberidaceae*)

thalictroides	EPPr GKev IMou LEdu SRot WCru WPGP WPnP WSHC
- subsp. ***robustum***	WCru

Cautleya ✿ (*Zingiberaceae*)

cathcartii	LEdu
- 'Tenzing's Gold'	EBee WCru WSHC
§ ***gracilis***	CAby CDTJ EBee EPfP EUJe GCal IBlr IBoy SBig
- BWJ 7843	WCru
- NJM 09.105	WPGP
- 'Crûg Gold'	LEdu WCru WPGP
- var. ***gracilis***	NLos
- var. ***robusta***	NLos
lutea	see *C. gracilis*
spicata	CAby CBct CCCN CDTJ CSpe CTsd ECho EUJe GKev IBlr LTro NLos SBig
- 'Arun Flame'	CBct GCal LEdu WCru WPGP
- 'Bleddyn's Beacon'	WCru
- 'Crûg Canary'	LEdu WCru
- 'Crûg Compact' **new**	WCru
* - var. ***lutea***	CBct LEdu WBor WPGP
- 'Robusta'	CAvo EBee GCal GCra IBlr LEdu MNrw SMad WBor WCot WCru WPGP

Cayratia (*Vitaceae*)

japonica B&SWJ 6636	WCru
§ ***thomsonii***	SDea
- BWJ 8123	EPPr WCru

Ceanothus ✿ (*Rhamnaceae*)

'A.T. Johnson'	SGol SRms
arboreus	SArc
- 'Trewithen Blue' ♀H4	Widely available
'Autumnal Blue' ♀H4	Widely available
'Blue Cushion'	CBcs CLet CTri LRHS MAsh MGos MJak NRHS SLon SWvt
'Blue Diamond'PBR	LSRN
'Blue Jeans'	CBcs LRHS MMuc NLar SWeb
'Blue Mound' ♀H4	Widely available
'Blue Sapphire'PBR	CWGN EAEE ELan EPfP GMcL LRHS LSRN MAsh MGos NEgg NEoE NPri SPoG SRms SWvt
'Burkwoodii' ♀H4	CBcs CDul CRos CSBt EMOT EPfP ESps LCro LRHS MAsh MGos MRav NEgg SCob SEle SLim SPer SPoG SWvt
'Cascade' ♀H4	CBcs ESps LSRN SLon SPlb WHar
'Concha' ♀H4	Widely available
§ ***cuneatus*** var. ***rigidus***	WSHC
'Cynthia Postan'	EPfP ESps LRHS LSou MHer NEgg NLar SCob
'Dark Star' ♀H4	CBcs CRos CSBt CTri CWGN ELan ELon EPfP ESps EUJe GMcL LBMP LRHS LSRN MAsh MGos NHol NRHS SBod SCob SNig SPoG SSta SWvt
'Delight'	CBcs EPfP ESps LPar SPer
× ***delileanus*** 'Gloire de Versailles' ♀H4	CBcs CDul CTri CWib ELan EMOT EPfP ESps EWTr GMcL LBMP LHop LRHS MGos MRav MSwo NLar NRHS SCob SCoo SGol SPer SPoG SWvt WSHC
- 'Henri Desfossé'	ELan EPfP LRHS LSRN MRav MSwo NLar NRHS SCob SPer SPoG WKif
- 'Topaze' ♀H4	ELan EPfP GMcL LRHS MRav NLar NRHS SGol SLon WKif
dentatus misapplied	see *C.* × *lobbianus*
dentatus Torr. & A. Gray	SPer SPlb
'Diamond Heights'	see *C. griseus* var. *horizontalis* 'Diamond Heights'
'Edinburgh'	NEgg
El Dorado = 'Perado' (v)	ELan MJak
gloriosus 'Anchor Bay'	EPfP LRHS
- 'Emily Brown'	CBcs ELan MRav NLar
§ ***griseus*** var. ***horizontalis*** 'Diamond Heights' (v)	CBcs CMac EPfP LSRN SPer

- - 'Silver Surprise' PBR (v)	ELan EPfP LBuc LSRN NEgg NLar NPri SRms
- - 'Yankee Point'	CBar CBcs CMac CRos CSBt CWib ECrN EPfP ESps LBrs LPar LRHS LSRN MGos MRav MSwo NRHS SCoo SEND SLim SPlb SPoG SVen SWvt WHar
- 'Kurt Zadnik'	LRHS
impressus	CTri EPfP ESps MAsh SHil SVen SWvt
'Italian Skies'	CBcs CRos CSBt CWib ECrN ELan EPfP ESps GMcL LBMP LHop LPar LRHS LSRN MAsh MGos MSwo NEgg NLar NRHS SCob SCoo SGol SLim SLon SPer SPlb SPoG SWvt WBod
'Lemon and Lime' PBR	LBuc LRHS NRHS
§ × ***lobbianus***	CTri
'Madagascar'	SCoo SPoG WFar
× ***pallidus***	WHar
- 'Marie Simon'	CBcs CWib ELan EPfP GMcL LRHS LSRN MAsh MGos NRHS SCob SGol SPer SPoG SRms SWvt WCFE WKif
- 'Perle Rose' ♀H4	CBcs EMOT EPfP LRHS MGos NRHS SPer WKif WSHC
papillosus	IArd SBrt
§ 'Pershore Zanzibar' PBR (v)	CBcs CBod CChe CLet CMac CRos CSBt CTri EHoe ELan EPfP EShb ESps GMcL LRHS MGos MHtn MJak MRav MSwo NEgg NPri NRHS SGol SLim SPer SPoG SRms SWvt
'Pin Cushion'	CRos CWib EPfP LRHS MAsh
'Point Millerton'	see *C. thyrsiflorus* 'Millerton Point'
'Puget Blue' ♀H4	Widely available
'Puget Blue' × ***thyrsiflorus*** var. ***repens*** **new**	ESps
'Ray Hartman'	NLar
repens	see *C. thyrsiflorus* var. *repens*
rigidus	see *C. cuneatus* var. *rigidus*
'Skylark' ♀H4	Widely available
'Snow Flurries'	see *C. thyrsiflorus* 'Snow Flurry'
'Snow Showers'	CBcs
'Southmead' ♀H4	CTri ECrN ELan EPfP GMcL LBMP LPar LRHS MGos MSwo NEgg NRHS SHil
thyrsiflorus	CTri CWib SRms SWvt
§ - 'Millerton Point'	EPfP LRHS NLar SCoo
- 'Mystery Blue' ♀H4	CRos EPfP LRHS NRHS SHil SWvt
§ - var. ***repens*** ♀H4	Widely available
§ - 'Snow Flurry'	CWib ELan MSwo NEgg
'Tilden Park'	LRHS
'Tuxedo' PBR	GMcL MAsh MRav NLar
× ***veitchianus***	CSBt EPfP LRHS NRHS SEND SPer
'Victoria'	CEnd EAEE EBee ESps LRHS LSRN MSwo NLar NRHS SHil SRGP SRms WHar
'Zanzibar'	see *C.* 'Pershore Zanzibar'

Cedrela (*Meliaceae*)

sinensis	see *Toona sinensis*

Cedronella (*Lamiaceae*)

§ ***canariensis***	CArn CBod EBee ENfk GPoy MHer MNHC SRms SWat WJek
mexicana	see *Agastache mexicana*
triphylla	see *C. canariensis*

Cedrus (*Pinaceae*)

atlantica	CAco CDul CMac ESps LPar NWea SEND SGol WHar WMat WMou WTSh
- 'Aurea' ♀H6	ESwi LPar MJak NLar NWea SLim SSta WHar
- 'Fastigiata'	CDul NEgg NLar SLim
- Glauca Group	Widely available
- - 'Glauca' ♀H6 **new**	CAco WTSh
- - 'Glauca Pendula' ♀H6	CAco CCVT CDul LPar LRHS MBlu MGos NEgg NLar NWea SGol SLim SSta WHar WMat
- - 'Silberspitz'	CKen NLar
- 'Pendula'	CAco MAsh SMad
- 'Sahara Frost'	NLar
- 'Sapphire Nymph'	CKen MAsh NLar SLim
brevifolia	LRHS NLar
- 'Epstein'	NLar
- 'Hillier Compact'	CKen
- 'Jade Medusa'	LRHS
- 'Kenwith'	CKen
deodara ♀H6	Widely available
- 'Albospica' (v)	SWvt
- 'Aurea' ♀H6	CCVT CKen EPfP ESps MAsh MGos NEgg NHol NOra NOrn NWea SGol WFar WHar WMat
I - 'Aurea Pendula'	CAco
- 'Blue Dwarf'	CKen
* - 'Blue Mountain Broom'	CKen
- 'Blue Snake'	CKen
- 'Blue Surprise'	SLim
- 'Bush's Electra'	MBlu NLar
- 'Devinely Blue'	CKen
- 'Eisregen'	LRHS
- 'Feelin' Blue' ♀H6	CKen ELan ESps LRHS MAsh MJak NEgg NLar SLim SMad SWvt WFar
- 'Gold Cascade'	SLim
- 'Golden Horizon'	CKen CMen ELan MAsh NEgg SLim WFar
- 'Golden Jubilee'	SGol
- 'Karl Fuchs'	LRHS NLar
- 'Klondyke'	MAsh
- 'Lime Glow'	CKen NEgg SLim
- 'Nana'	CKen
- 'Pendula' ♀H6	CKen NWea SLim
- 'Pygmy'	CKen
- 'Robusta'	WPGP
- 'Roman Candle'	NEgg WFar
- 'Silver Mist'	CKen
- 'Silver Spring'	NLar WFar
libani ♀H6	CAco CCVT CDul CLnd CMCN CTho ECrN ELan EPfP ESps EUJe EWTr GMcL LPar LRHS MAsh MBlu MMuc NLar NOra NWea SEND SGol SLim SPlb SWvt WFar WHar WMou WTSh
- 'Blue Angel'	NLar SLim
- 'Comte de Dijon'	LRHS NLar
- 'Fontaine'	NLar
- 'Glauca'	CAco
- 'Hedgehog'	CKen
- 'Home Park'	CKen
- 'May'	LRHS NLar
- Nana Group	CAco CKen ELan NEgg
- 'Pendula'	LPar WFar
- 'Sargentii'	LRHS MBlu NEgg NLar
- 'Taurus'	NLar

Ceiba (*Malvaceae*)

pentandra	SPlb

Celastrus (*Celastraceae*)

dependens CWJ 12478	WCru
flagellaris B&SWJ 8572	WCru
hookeri B&SWJ 11667	WCru

kusanoi CWJ 12445	WCru
orbiculatus	CBcs ELan LHop LRHS MRav SLon SPer WBod WHar WHer
- 'Diana' (f)	CMac
- 'Hercules' (m)	CMac
- Hermaphrodite Group Y^{H6}	EWTr MMuc SDix SEND SKHP WSHC
- var. ***papillosus*** B&SWJ 591	WCru
- var. ***punctatus*** CWJ 12439	WCru
scandens	CMac SPhx SPlb
stephanotiifolius B&SWJ 4727	WCru
stylosus WJC 13746 **new**	WCru

Celmisia (*Asteraceae*)

allanii	GKev WAbe
angustifolia Y^{H5}	EPot GKev
argentea	WAbe
armstrongii	WAbe
bellidioides	NSla
bonplandii	GKev
brevifolia	EPot
coriacea misapplied	see *C. semicordata*
discolor	WAbe
'Eggleston Silver'	NBir
glandulosa	GCra
gracilenta	ITim NSla WAbe
haastii × ***viscosa***	NSla
hectorii	ITim WAbe
hookeri	NHpl
longifolia	IBlr
monroi	IBlr
ramulosa	EPot ITim WAbe
- var. ***tuberculata***	NSla
§ ***semicordata***	GCra IBlr ITim NHpl
- subsp. ***stricta***	IBlr
sessiliflora	EPot WAbe
viscosa	GKev

Celsia see *Verbascum*

× *Celsioverbascum* see *Verbascum*

Celtica see *Stipa*

Celtis (*Cannabaceae*)

australis	CBcs CDul CLnd CMCN EBee EBtc LEdu LPar MBlu
biondii	NLar
caucasica	CFil
choseniana B&SWJ 12774	WCru
glabrata	see *C. planchoniana*
occidentalis	CDul ELan EWTr
§ ***planchoniana***	EGFP
sinensis	CMen

Cenolophium (*Apiaceae*)

denudatum	CSam CSpe EPPr EWes GBin LCro LEdu LHop LPla LRHS MMuc MPie MSpe NChi NDov SDix SPtp WCot WPGP

Centaurea ✿ (*Asteraceae*)

HH&K 271	NBid
RCB AM 6	WCot
W&B BGB-1	WCot
alba	IBoy
alpestris	GJos MSpe NLar SPhx
'Amethyst'	CRos LRHS NRHS
'Amethyst on Ice'	LBuc LRHS
§ ***atropurpurea***	CAby CBWd CBod CFis CSpe EAJP EBee EPfP EWes GQue IBoy LPot LRHS MSpe NBid NLar NSti SHar SPhx SPlb WHea WPGP
bella	CRos EAEE EBee ECtt ELon GCal LRHS LSou MBel MRav MSpe NBro NSti SBod SMHy SPhx SWat WKif XLum XSen
- 'Katherine' (v)	MSpe
benoistii misapplied	see *C. atropurpurea*
benoistii ambig.	CSpe EBee MAvo MRav
benoistii ambig. × ***orientalis***	SPhx
'Blewit'	CAby CElw EBee ECtt ELon EPPr MSpe WOut
cana	see *C. triumfettii* subsp. *cana*
candidissima misapplied	see *C. cineraria*
'Caramia'	CMea CRos EBee ECtt EPfP LBMP LEdu LRHS MHol MNrw MSpe NBid NHpl NRHS SPad SPoG WHil
carniolica SDR 5443	EBee
cheiranthifolia	EPPr MNrw MSpe NBid NBir NLar SHar WBrk WPGP
§ ***cineraria***	ECre XSen
- subsp. ***cineraria*** Y^{H3}	SEND WCot
cyanus	CHab CSpe LCro MHer MNHC SVic WJek
- 'Black Ball'	CSpe LRHS MNHC SPhx
- 'Blue Ball'	CSpe
- 'Blue Boy' **new**	LRHS
- 'Pinkie' (d)	MNHC
- 'Snowman'	SPhx
cynaroides	see *Stemmacantha centaureoides*
dealbata	CMac CRos CWib EAJP EBee ELon EPfP ESps GJos GMcL IFoB LRHS MBel MHol MMuc MSpe NBro NLar NMir NRHS SCob SEND SPhx SRms WHar WMoo XLum
- 'Steenbergii'	CMac CRos ELan EPPr GCal LLWP MSpe NBid NBir NEgg NGdn NPer NSti SPer SPoG WCot
declinata RCB UA 18	WCot
drabifolia subsp. ***cappadocica***	SIgm
glastifolia	EBee LEdu
grinensis **new**	WOut
gymnocarpa	see *C. cineraria*
hypoleuca	NBid
jacea	GAbr GQue GWyn LEdu MMuc MSpe NBid NLar SEND SPhx WCot WOut WPGP
- PAB 8821 **new**	LEdu
'John Coutts'	Widely available
'Jordy'	Widely available
karabaghensis	GCal GKev MSpe WPGP
kotschyana	EBee WPGP
macrocephala	Widely available
microptilon	EBee LEdu
mollis	NBid
montana	Widely available
- 'Alba'	Widely available
- 'Amethyst Dream'^{PBR}	CBod CRos EBee LRHS MNrw NLar NRHS SPoG
- 'Amethyst in Snow'	CElw CRos EBee ECtt LRHS LSun MAvo MHol MSpe NAst NHol NLar NRHS NWad SCob SHil SPoG WBor WTor
- 'Black Sprite'	CNor CPar CSpe CWGN EBee ECtt EPfP ILea LPot LRHS MNrw NLar NPnk NSti SPoG STPC WBrk WFar WNPC

§ - 'Carnea' CCVN CElw CSam GCra GMaP LCro LOPS MSpe NBir NChi NLar SPhx WBrk WCAu WFar WMoo WOut
- 'Crinita' **new** EBee
- 'Elworthy Glacier' CElw
- 'Gold Bullion' CSpe EBee ECtt ELan ELon EPfP EWes GMaP LRHS MAvo MHol MRav NBid NLar SMad SPoG WSHC
- 'Grandiflora' EBee ELon MJak MPie MSpe
- 'Joyce' CElw MMuc MSpe MTis NBid NLar SHar WCAu WSHC
- 'Lady Flora Hastings' CBre CCse CElw CSam CSpe EBee ELon EPPr LRHS MMuc MSpe NBid WBrk
- lilac-flowered NBid
- 'Ochroleuca' CElw MSpe NBid
- 'Parham' CBod ECtt ELan ELon GAbr GCal LBMP LLWP LRHS LSou MBel MMuc MNrw MRav NDov NEgg NLar NSti SPer SPlb SPoG WMoo WSHC
- 'Purple Heart' CAby CWGN EBee ECtt ELon EWTr LHop MBNS MBel MHer MMuc MNrw MSpe NLar SPer WCAu WCot WHil
- 'Purple Prose' CElw EPPr LPla
- 'Purpurea' CElw MSpe
- 'Rosea' see *C. montana* 'Carnea'
* - ***violacea*** NBid
- 'Violetta' MAvo MSpe NBid NBir WBrk WMoo
montana* × *triumfettii SHar
nervosa NBid NBro XLum
nigra CArn CHab CWld EPfP GJos MSpe NLar NMir SPhx SRms WMoo WOut WSFF
- var. ***alba*** CBre NBid
- 'Elstead' MSpe
- 'Mardi Gras' (v) ECtt
- subsp. ***rivularis*** MMuc NBid XLum
nogmovii MAvo MSpe
orientalis CSpe ELon EWes IBoy LRHS LSou MHol MPie MSpe NGBl SPhx WHoo WWtn
pannonica EPPr
- subsp. ***pannonica*** HH&K 259 NBid
parilica EBee
pestalozzae GKev
'Phoenix Bronze' LEdu
phrygia MMuc MSpe NFav NLar SEND
pterocaula RCB/TQ 18 WCot
pulcherrima MNrw MSpe NDov SCob SMad XSen
'Pulchra Major' see *Stemmacantha centaureoides*
rupestris EBee EPfP SPhx
ruthenica CFis MSpe NSti SCob SKHP SPer SPhx SPlb
salicifolia NBir
salonitana RCB AM 1 WCot
scabiosa CArn CHab CWib CWld IBoy MHer MNHC MSpe NBid NBir NMir SPhx SRms
'Silver Feather' CAby LRHS
simplicicaulis CSam ELon MAsh MSpe NBir NHpl SBch SHar SRms WHoo WSHC XSen
thracica CSpe EBee WCot
triumfettii CPBP
I - subsp. ***cana*** 'Rosea' WBrk
- 'Hoar Frost' EBee ELon NDov
- subsp. ***stricta*** MSpe
uniflora EBee
woronowii MAvo MSpe

Centaurium (*Gentianaceae*)

erythraea GPoy
scilloides GCrg NSla WAbe

Centella (*Apiaceae*)

§ ***asiatica*** GPoy LEdu WJek

Centradenia (*Melastomataceae*)

inaequilateralis CCCN

Centranthus (*Caprifoliaceae*)

§ ***lecoqii*** ECha ECtt EPPr EWes LRHS SPhx WCot
macrosiphon CMac
§ ***ruber*** Widely available
* - 'Alba Pura' GAbr
§ - 'Albus' Widely available
- 'Atrococcineus' ECha MMuc SPer
- var. ***coccineus*** CBWd CBcs CBod CWld EBee ELan EPed EPfP GAbr GBin GKin GMaP GMcL LBMP LRHS LSun MJak MRav MWat SCob SEND SHil SPhx SRot SWat WCot WFar WGwG XSen
- mauve-flowered misapplied see *C. lecoqii*
- mauve-flowered NBir
- 'Roseus' EBee EPfP LRHS WMoo
- 'Snowcloud' CWld EBee ECtt ENfk EPfP MNHC SRms WHil
'White Cloud' SPad

Centropogon (*Campanulaceae*)

§ ***ayavacensis*** subsp. ***ayavacensis*** B&SWJ 10663 WCru
costaricae B&SWJ 10455 WCru
ferrugineus B&SWJ 10665 WCru
hirsutus B&SWJ 10657 WCru
willdenowianus see *C. ayavacensis* subsp. *ayavacensis*

Cephalanthera (*Orchidaceae*)

falcata EFEx
longibracteata EFEx

Cephalanthus (*Rubiaceae*)

occidentalis CDul CLet CWib EBee EWTr IVic LRHS LSou MAsh MBNS MBlu NLar NQui SLim SMad SPer SPoG WBor WCFE WPat

Cephalaria (*Caprifoliaceae*)

§ ***alpina*** EPPr EPfP LRHS MAsh MHer MNrw SDix SHar SPhx SRms SWat WBrk WCot XLum
caucasica see *C. gigantea*
dipsacoides MSpe SKHP SPhx SRms WMoo WTcb
§ ***flava*** LRHS
galpiniana SPlb
§ ***gigantea*** Widely available
graeca see *C. flava*
leucantha CFis GBin MMuc NLar SEND SPhx WMoo
litvinovii SPhx
natalensis LEdu
radiata NDov
tatarica hort. see *C. gigantea*
tchihatchewii ILea NLar WCot
transsylvanica CSpe
- W&B BGJ-1 WCot

Cephalotaxus (*Taxaceae*)

fortunei	CDul
harringtonia	CMCN LEdu
- 'Fastigiata'	CDul IArd LRHS MAsh MGos NWea SLim SPoG
- 'Gimborn's Pillow'	MAsh NLar
- 'Korean Gold'	SLim

Cephalotus (*Cephalotaceae*)

follicularis 🏆H2	NLos SHmp

Cerastium (*Caryophyllaceae*)

alpinum	ECho IFoB SRms
- var. ***lanatum***	ECho EWes XLum
biebersteinii	XLum
candidissimum	EWes
fontanum	CHab
tomentosum	CBar CNec ECho ELan EPfP ESps GAbr GWyn LPot MMuc NCou SEND SPer SPlb SPoG WFar
- var. ***columnae***	ECha ECho EWes GMaP XLum XSen
- 'Silberteppich'	MArt

Ceratonia (*Caesalpiniaceae*)

siliqua	CBcs SEND SPlb

Ceratophyllum (*Ceratophyllaceae*)

demersum	CBen CWat EWay MSKA MWts SWat WMAq WSFF XBlo
submersum	LLWG

Ceratostigma (*Plumbaginaceae*)

abyssinicum	CBcs ELan ESwi LEdu LHop
asperrimum B&SWJ 7260	WCru
'Autumn Blue'	EPfP LRHS
capensis	CMac
griffithii	Widely available
§ ***plumbaginoides*** 🏆H4	Widely available
willmottianum 🏆H4	Widely available
- BWJ 8140	WCru
- Desert Skies = 'Palmgold'PBR	CBcs CMac ELan EPfP ESps NLar SCob SLim SPer SWvt
- Forest Blue = 'Lice'PBR 🏆H4	CMac CRos CSBt ELan EPfP ESps LCro LOPS LRHS LSRN MAsh MGos MRav NEgg NLar NPri NRHS SAko SBod SCob SCoo SEle SHil SLim SPer SPoG SWvt WPat
- Sapphire Ring = 'Lissbrill'	CRos ELan EPfP LRHS NRHS SCoo SPoG

Cercidiphyllum ✿ (*Cercidiphyllaceae*)

japonicum 🏆H5	Widely available
- 'Boyd's Dwarf'	CJun CRos ELan EPfP LLHF LRHS MAsh MBlu NLar SPoG SSta WCot
- 'Chameleon' (v)	MBlu NLar
- Glowball = 'Jww4' **new**	SPoG
- 'Herkenrode Dwarf'	MBlu NLar
- 'Heronswood Globe' 🏆H5	CJun EPfP MBlu NLar SSta
- 'Kreukenberg Dwarf'	CJun NLar SSta
- f. ***miquelianum***	GBin NLar
- 'Morioka Weeping'	CJun CTho EBee MPkF NLar SChF SMad SSta
- 'Peach'	CJun NLar
§ - f. ***pendulum*** 🏆H5	Widely available
- - 'Amazing Grace'	CTho MBlu NLar SSta
- 'Raspberry'	CJun MBlu NLar
- Red Fox	see *C. japonicum* 'Rotfuchs'
§ - 'Rotfuchs'	CBcs CEnd CJun CLet CMCN CMac CRos CTho EBee ELan EMOT EPfP EWTr GMcL IVic LRHS MAsh MBlu MGos MPkF NLar SCob SPoG SSta WFar WHar WMat WPat
- 'Ruby'	CJun EBee MBlu NLar SChF WPGP
- 'Strawberry'	CBcs CJun MBlu NLar SSta
- 'Tidal Wave'	CJun MBlu NLar SSta
- 'Titania'	NLar SSta
magnificum	CBcs CDul CEnd CMCN IMou MBlu NLar
- f. ***pendulum***	see *C. japonicum* f. *pendulum*

Cercis ✿ (*Caesalpiniaceae*)

canadensis	CAco CBcs CDul CMCN CWGN ESps LPar MGos MMuc NEgg NLar NWea SCob SPer WPat
- 'Ace of Hearts'PBR	MPkF
- f. ***alba***	CBcs ESwi LSRN
- - 'Royal White'	CDul CJun EPfP MBlu
- 'Appalachian Red'	CJun CTho ESwi MBlu MGos NTre SKHP
- 'Cascading Hearts'	CRos ESwi LRHS NRHS NTre
- 'Flame'	CJun NLar SKHP SSta WPat
- 'Forest Pansy' 🏆H5	Widely available
- 'Hearts of Gold'PBR	CRos CTho CWGN EBee EBtc EMOT EPfP IBoy LRHS MAsh MGos MPkF MRav NOra NOrn NRHS NTre SKHP SLon SMad SPoG WHar WMat
- Lavender Twist = 'Covey'	CDul CEnd CRos EBee ELan EPfP ERea ESwi LRHS LSRN MBlu MGos NLar NOra NOrn NTre SCob SGol SKHP SLon SPoG WHar WMat WMou
- Little Woody = 'Litwo'PBR	MGos MPkF SGol
- 'Melon Beauty'	LRHS NLar SKHP SMad WPat
- 'Merlot'	EBee EMOT ESwi NTre NWea WMat
- 'Pauline Lily'	EBee ESwi NLar
- 'Pink Heartbreaker'	SGol
- 'Pink Pom Poms' **new**	NTre
- Red Force = 'Minrouge3'PBR	EBee
- 'Ruby Falls'PBR 🏆H5	CBcs CRos CTho EBee ELan EMOT ERea LRHS MGos NOra NRHS NTre NWea SCob SPoG WMat
- 'Rubye Atkinson'	CJun NLar WPat
- 'Silver Lining' (v)	EBee NTre
- 'Tennessee Pink'	CJun SCob
- var. ***texensis*** 'Oklahoma'	CJun ESwi MGos MPkF NTre SKHP WHar WMat WPGP WPat
- - 'Texas White'	CEnd CJun CMac EPfP ERea MPkF NLar SCob SKHP SPoG WHar WMat WPat
- - 'Traveller'	ESwi NTre SGol
- 'The Rising Sun'	NTre
- 'Vanilla Twist' **new**	NTre
- 'Whitewater' (v)	NTre
chinensis	EGFP NLar SPer WMou
- B&SWJ 12665	WCru
- NJM 11.047	WPGP
- f. ***alba***	CTho MGos
- 'Avondale' 🏆H5	Widely available
- 'Don Egolf' 🏆H5	CJun MBlu MGos MPkF NLar SGol SKHP
- 'Shirobana'	NTre WMat
chingii	WPGP
gigantea	NLar WPGP WPat
griffithii	NLar SSta
occidentalis	LEdu SSta
racemosa	WPGP
siliquastrum	Widely available

	- f. ***albida***	CRos CTho ECrN ELan EPfP EWes LRHS SKHP
	- 'Bodnant' ♀H4	CDul CMac CRos CTho EPfP ESps EWes IArd LLHF LRHS LSRN MBlu MGos NLar NOra NTre SCob WHar WMat WPat
	- 'Rubra'	ESps
	- 'White Swan'	CJun CTho NTre

Cerinthe (*Boraginaceae*)

	glabra	SPlb
	major	SWvt WBod
	- 'Kiwi Blue'	CHll
	- 'Purpurascens'	CSpe CWCL ELan EPfP ESps LBMP LCro LOPS LSun MNHC SPer SPhx SPoG WKif

Ceropegia (*Apocynaceae*)

§	***linearis*** subsp. ***woodii*** ♀H1c	EShb LToo
	sandersonii ♀H1c	CCCN
	woodii	see *C. linearis* subsp. *woodii*

Cestrum (*Solanaceae*)

	aurantiacum	EShb SEND
	× ***cultum***	CHll
	- 'Cretan Pink'	CCCN
	- 'Cretan Purple'	CBcs CCCN CHGN CHll ELan ELon EPfP EShb IDee LHop LRHS SEND SWvt WBod WKif WSHC
	diurnum × ***nocturnum***	EShb
§	***elegans***	CHll CLet CTsd EBee ELon EPfP IDee LHop LRHS NQui SEND SLon SWvt WCFE
	fasciculatum	EShb SDix
	'Newellii' ♀H1c	CBcs CCCN CMHG CRHN CWib EBak EBee ELan ELon EPfP EShb EUJe LRHS SEND SPlb SVen SWvt WKif WSHC
	nocturnum	CBcs CCCN CHll CPne EBak EShb GCal WCFE
	parqui ♀H3	CAbb CBcs CCCN CHll CMCN CTsd CWib ELan EPfP IDee LHop MGil SDix SEND SLon SMad SWvt WJek WKif WSHC
	purpureum (Lindl.) Standl.	see *C. elegans*
	roseum	WBod
	- B&SWJ 10255 from Oaxaca State, Mexico	WCru

Ceterach see *Asplenium*

	officinarum	see *Asplenium ceterach*

Chaenomeles (*Rosaceae*)

	cathayensis	CAgr CDul CTho EBee LEdu NLar SBrt WCru WHer WPGP
§	***japonica***	CAco CCCN ESps MMuc SEND
	- 'Chojubai'	CMen
	- 'Cido'	CAgr LEdu MCoo
	- 'Orange Beauty'	LRHS NHol SPer
	- 'Rising Sun'	NLar
	- 'Sargentii'	CMac ELan MBlu NLar SGol
	lagenaria	see *C. speciosa*
	Madame Butterfly = 'Whitice'	CLet CRos EBee ELan EPfP ESps LRHS LSRN MAsh MMuc MRav NRHS SCob SEND SGol SLim SPer SPoG SRms
	maulei	see *C. japonica*
	'Orange Star'	CEnd
	'Red Kimono' **new**	LCro
	sinensis	see *Pseudocydonia sinensis*
§	***speciosa***	NWea
	- 'Apple Blossom'	see *C. speciosa* 'Moerloosei'
	- 'Brilliant'	EPfP
	- 'Cardinalis'	CMac
	- 'Contorta'	LRHS MAsh WFar
I	- 'Contorta Rosea'	LBMP
	- 'Eximia'	LRHS
	- 'Falconnet Charlet' (d)	CRos LRHS MRav NRHS SRms
	- 'Flocon Rose'	EPfP LRHS
	- 'Friesdorfer'	LRHS
	- 'Geisha Girl' (d) ♀H6	CBcs CEnd CMac CRos CSBt EBee ELan EPfP LCro LHop LRHS LSRN MAsh MGos MRav MSwo NPri NRHS SCob SGbt SGol SHil SLim SPer SPoG SRms SWvt WFar WPat
	- Hot Fire = 'Minvesu'	EBee EPfP LRHS
	- 'Kinshiden'	CLet EBee EPfP LRHS NLar
§	- 'Moerloosei' ♀H6	Widely available
	- 'Nivalis'	Widely available
	- 'Rubra Grandiflora'	LRHS
	- 'Simonii' (d)	CBcs MRav NWea
	- 'Snow'	MAsh MSwo SRms
	- 'Umbilicata'	MBlu SPer SRms
	- 'Winter Snow' (d)	SPer
	- 'Yukigotan' (d)	CRos LCro LLHF LRHS NLar NRHS SCob SGol SHil SWvt WPat
	× ***superba***	ESps IBoy
	- 'Boule de Feu'	CTri CWib MCoo
	- 'Cameo' (d)	CChe CEnd CLet ELon EPfP LHop LRHS MAsh MBNS MRav NLar SGol SRms WBor WFar
	- 'Clementine'	NLar
	- 'Coquelicot'	NLar
	- 'Crimson and Gold' ♀H6	Widely available
	- 'Elly Mossel'	CMac NLar SRms WFar
	- 'Ernst Finken'	NLar
	- 'Etna'	GMcL WFar
	- 'Fascination'	NLar
	- 'Fire Dance'	CDul CHll CWib MSwo NLar SGol SPer WRHF
	- 'Fusion'	CAgr
	- 'Hollandia'	SRms
	- 'Issai White'	MRav NLar
	- 'Jet Trail'	CBcs CMac CRos CSBt ECrN ELan EPfP ESps GMcL LHop LRHS LSRN MAsh MGos MJak MRav MSwo NLar NRHS SCob SGol SHil SLim SPoG SRms SWvt WFar
	- 'Knap Hill Scarlet'	CDul CRos CWCL EBee ELan EPfP LRHS MAsh MGos NRHS SCob SEND SLim SNig SPer SPoG SRms SWvt
	- 'Lemon and Lime'	ELan EWTr LRHS MAsh MGos MRav NLar SLon SRms
	- 'Nicoline' ♀H6	CBcs CDul EAEE EPfP ESps IBoy LRHS MGos NEgg SCob WMoo
	- 'Pink Lady' ♀H6	Widely available
	- 'Pink Trail'	NLar SRms
	- 'Red Joy'	EBee EPfP LHop LRHS MRav NLar WGrn
	- 'Red Trail'	MRav
	- 'Rowallane' ♀H6	CHll ELan EPfP MRav
	- 'Salmon Horizon'	EWTr IArd NLar
	- 'Texas Scarlet'	ELan
	- 'Tortuosa'	EBee LHop LRHS NLar WGrn
	'Toyo-nishiki'	MBlu

Chaenorhinum (*Plantaginaceae*)

	glareosum	NHpl
§	***origanifolium***	CBod SPlb
	- 'Blue Dream'	CSpe EPfP GKev LRHS MAsh SCob SPoG SWvt WIce WMoo

	- 'Dreamcatcher'	EPfP

Chaerophyllum (*Apiaceae*)

	azoricum	LPla SIgm
	hirsutum	IMou
	- 'Roseum'	Widely available
	temulum	LEdu

Chamaebatiaria (*Rosaceae*)

	millefolium	SBrt

Chamaecyparis ✿ (*Cupressaceae*)

	formosensis	CKen
	funebris	see *Cupressus funebris*
	lawsoniana	CAco CDul ESps LPar NWea SLim WHed WMou WTSh
	- 'Allumii Aurea'	see *C. lawsoniana* 'Alumigold'
I	- 'Allumii Green' **new**	CAco
	- 'Allumii Magnificent'	CDul MAsh
	- 'Allumii White Spot'	see *C. lawsoniana* 'White Spot'
§	- 'Alumigold'	MAsh MJak NOrn
	- 'Alumii'	CMac MAsh MJak NOrn NWea
	- 'Aurea'	CDul
	- 'Aurea Densa' 🏆H6	CKen CSBt CTri MAsh MGos
	- 'Bleu Nantais' 🏆H6	CKen EMOT EPfP ESps LBee LRHS MAsh MGos SCoo SLim SPoG WCFE
	- 'Blom'	CKen
§	- 'Blue Gown'	LBee
	- 'Blue Surprise'	CKen
	- 'Brégéon'	CKen
	- 'Broomhill Gold' 🏆H6	CSBt EMOT GMcL LBee MAsh MGos NOrn SCoo SLim SPoG
	- 'Caudata'	CKen
§	- 'Chilworth Silver' 🏆H6	CSBt ESps LBee LRHS MAsh
	- 'Columnaris'	CAco CBcs EMOT EPfP ESps LBee MJak NEgg NWea SCoo SPoG
	- 'Columnaris Glauca'	CLet CMac CWib ESps GMcL MAsh MGos NEgg NLar NPri NWea SCoo SPer
	- 'Cream Crackers'	EMOT
	- 'Cream Glow'	CKen CSBt MAsh
	- 'Dik's Weeping' 🏆H6	NLar NWea SLim
	- 'Duncanii'	EMOT
	- 'Dutch Gold'	MAsh
	- 'Eclipse'	CKen
	- 'Elegantissima' ambig.	CMac SLim
	- 'Ellwoodii' 🏆H6	CDul CMac CSBt CTri CWib ELan EMOT EPfP ESps GMcL LRHS MGos NEgg NPri NWea SCoo SLim SPer
I	- 'Ellwoodii Glauca'	SPlb
	- 'Ellwood's Gold' 🏆H6	CBcs CDul CLet CMac CSBt CWib ELan EMOT EPfP ESps GMcL LBMP LBee LBrs LRHS MAsh MGos MJak NOrn NPri NWea SPer SPlb SPoG
	- 'Ellwood's Gold Pillar' 🏆H6	GMcL LBee MAsh NHol SLim
§	- 'Ellwood's Nymph'	CKen MAsh
	- Ellwood's Pillar = 'Flolar' 🏆H6	CMac EMOT ESps GMcL LBee LRHS MGos NLar SCoo SLim WCFE
	- 'Ellwood's Pygmy'	CMac
	- 'Ellwood's Silver'	MAsh
	- 'Ellwood's Silver Threads'	CMac LBee
	- 'Ellwood's Variegata'	see *C. lawsoniana* 'Ellwood's White'
§	- 'Ellwood's White' (v)	CMac CSBt EMOT GMcL SPoG
	- 'Emerald Spire'	MAsh
	- 'Erecta' **new**	ESps
	- 'Erecta Viridis'	CBcs GMcL MJak NEgg NWea
	- 'Filip's Golden Tears'	ELan MAsh SLim
	- 'Fleckellwood'	CWib MAsh
	- 'Fletcheri' 🏆H6	CMac NWea
	- 'Fletcheri Aurea'	see *C. lawsoniana* 'Yellow Transparent'
	- 'Forsteckensis'	NLar NWea
I	- 'Forsteckensis Aurea'	NLar
	- 'Fraseri'	NWea
	- 'Gimbornii' 🏆H6	CDul
	- 'Glauca'	CDul ESps
	- 'Globosa'	GMcL
	- 'Gnome'	CKen CMac EMOT NHol SCoo SLim SPoG
§	- 'Golden Pot'	CSBt CWib GMcL LBee
	- 'Golden Wonder' 🏆H6	EMOT MAsh NEgg NLar NWea SCoo
	- 'Goldfinger'	NLar
	- 'Grayswood Feather' 🏆H6	ESps GMcL LBee MAsh SPlb
	- 'Grayswood Gold'	GMcL
	- 'Grayswood Pillar'	ESps
	- 'Green Globe' 🏆H6	CKen CMen CSBt ESps LBee LRHS MAsh
§	- 'Green Hedger'	CSBt NWea
§	- 'Green Pillar'	CDul CWib EMOT ESps GMcL LBee NEgg SCoo
	- 'Green Spire'	see *C. lawsoniana* 'Green Pillar'
	- 'Hogger's Blue Gown'	see *C. lawsoniana* 'Blue Gown'
	- 'Imbricata Pendula' 🏆H6	CKen IDee MBlu NLar SMad
	- 'Ivonne' 🏆H6	CDul EMOT EPfP GMcL LRHS MAsh MGos NLar SLim SPoG
	- 'Jackman's Green Hedger'	see *C. lawsoniana* 'Green Hedger'
	- 'Jackman's Variety'	see *C. lawsoniana* 'Green Pillar'
	- 'Jeanette'	CKen
	- 'Killarny Salmon'	CMac
	- 'Kilmacurragh' 🏆H6	CDul CMac MAsh NWea WCFE
	- 'Kilworth Column'	LRHS NLar NWea
	- 'Knowefieldensis'	CMac EMOT
	- 'Lane' misapplied	see *C. lawsoniana* 'Lanei Aurea'
	- 'Lane' den Ouden	CWib EMOT MJak MRav NEgg
§	- 'Lanei Aurea' 🏆H6	ESps MJak NWea
	- 'Lemon Pillar'	WHar
	- 'Lemon Queen'	LBee NOrn
	- 'Little Spire' 🏆H6	ESps LRHS NLar SLim
	- 'Lutea'	CMac
§	- 'Lutea Nana'	CMac ESps MAsh NLar
	- 'Luteocompacta'	LBee
*	- 'MacPenny's Gold'	CMac
	- 'Minima Argentea'	see *C. lawsoniana* 'Nana Argentea'
	- 'Minima Aurea' 🏆H6	CKen CMac CSBt CWib EMOT EPfP ESps GMcL LBee LRHS MAsh MGos MJak NEgg NWea SLim SPoG WCFE
	- 'Minima Glauca' 🏆H6	CLet CMac EMOT ESps GMcL MJak NEgg NWea SCoo SLim
	- 'Moonsprite' 🏆H6	CKen EMOT NLar SCoo SLim SPoG
	- 'Nana'	CMac ESps
	- 'Nana Albospica' (v)	EMOT LBee
§	- 'Nana Argentea'	CKen CMac EMOT EPfP SPoG
	- 'Nana Lutea'	see *C. lawsoniana* 'Lutea Nana'
	- 'Nicole'	EMOT LBrs MAsh NWea SCoo SLim
	- 'Nidiformis'	NWea
	- 'Nyewoods'	see *C. lawsoniana* 'Chilworth Silver'
	- 'Nymph'	see *C. lawsoniana* 'Ellwood's Nymph'
	- 'Pearly Swirls' (v)	LRHS NLar SPoG
§	- 'Pelt's Blue'	CAco CBcs CDul CSBt ESps NLar
	- 'Pembury Blue' 🏆H6	CCVT CDul CLet CWib EMOT EPfP ESps GMcL LBee LRHS MAsh MGos MJak MRav NEgg NLar NOrn NWea SCoo SLim SPer SPoG
	- 'Pina Colada' PBR **new**	LRHS
	- Pot of Gold	see *C. lawsoniana* 'Golden Pot'
	- 'Pottenii'	CMac ESps GMcL LBee MAsh NLar NOrn NWea

	- 'Pygmaea Argentea' (v) ♀H6	CKen CLet CMac CSBt CWib ELan EMOT ESps MAsh MGos NEgg NWea SLim SPoG WCFE
	- 'Pygmy'	ESps NLar NWea SLim
	- 'Rijnhof'	LBee
	- 'Rimpelaar'	NWad
	- 'Silver Queen' (v)	CKen
	- 'Silver Threads' (v)	ELan EMOT EPfP ESps LBee LRHS SPoG
	- 'Silver Tip' (v)	EMOT SLim
	- 'Snow Flurry' (v)	CKen
	- 'Snow White' PBR (v) ♀H6	EMOT ESps GMcL LBee LRHS MAsh MGos NHol NOrn SCoo SLim SPoG
	- 'Springtime' PBR	CSBt LBee LRHS
	- 'Stardust' ♀H6	CBcs CDul CLet CSBt CWib ELan ESps GMcL LRHS MAsh MGos MJak MRav NEgg NOrn NPri
	- 'Stewartii'	CDul ESps NEgg NWea
	- 'Summer Snow' (v) ♀H6	EMOT EPfP GMcL NHol SCoo
	- 'Sunkist'	SLim
	- 'Tamariscifolia'	WCFE
	- 'Treasure' (v)	MAsh SLim
	- 'Van Pelt'	see *C. lawsoniana* 'Pelt's Blue'
	- 'Westermannii' (v)	CMac NOrn
§	- 'White Spot' (v)	EMOT GMcL
	- 'Winston Churchill'	NOrn
	- 'Wisselii' ♀H6	CKen CMac EMOT ESps MGos NLar NWea SCoo SLim WCFE
	- 'Wisselii Nana'	CKen
	- 'Wissel's Saguaro' ♀H6	CKen IVic NLar SLim
	- 'Witzeliana'	CDul NLar
§	- 'Yellow Transparent'	CMac
	× *leylandii*	see × *Cuprocyparis leylandii*
	nootkatensis	see *Xanthocyparis nootkatensis*
	obtusa	ESps LPar
	- 'Albovariegata' (v)	CKen
	- 'Arneson's Compact'	CKen
	- 'Aurea'	SCoo
	- 'Aurora' ♀H7	CKen ELan EMOT MAsh SLim SPoG
	- 'Bambi'	CKen WAbe WThu
	- 'Barkenny'	CKen
	- 'Bartley'	CKen
	- 'Bassett'	CKen
	- 'Bess'	CKen
	- 'Brigitt'	CKen
	- 'Bronze Pygmy'	LRHS NLar
	- 'Butterball'	CKen
	- 'Caespitosa'	WAbe
	- 'Chabo-yadori'	NLar
	- 'Chilworth'	CKen NWad
	- 'Chima-anihiba'	CKen
	- 'Chirimen'	CKen NLar SLim
	- 'Clarke's Seedling'	CKen
	- 'Corley Gold'	NLar
§	- 'Crippsii' ♀H7	CBcs CMac
	- 'Crippsii Aurea'	see *C. obtusa* 'Crippsii'
	- 'Dainty Doll'	CKen NHol NLar NWad
	- 'Densa'	see *C. obtusa* 'Nana Densa'
	- 'Draht'	NLar
	- 'Draht Hexe'	CKen
	- 'Elf'	CKen
	- 'Ellie B'	CKen
	- 'Ericoides'	CKen
	- 'Erika'	NLar
	- 'Fernspray Gold' ♀H7	CCVT CDul CKen CMac CTri EMOT EPfP ESps GMcL LRHS MAsh MGos NEgg NLar SCoo SLim SPoG
	- 'Flabelliformis'	CKen NWad
	- 'Gitte'	SLim
	- 'Gnome'	CKen CMen

	- 'Gold Fern'	CKen
	- 'Golden Fairy'	CKen NLar
	- 'Golden Filament' (v)	CKen
	- 'Golden Nymph'	CKen
	- 'Golden Sprite'	CKen WAbe
	- 'Gracilis'	LPar NEgg
	- 'Gracilis Aurea'	CKen CMac
	- 'Graciosa'	see *C. obtusa* 'Loenik'
	- 'Green Cushion'	CKen
	- 'Green Diamond'	CKen
	- 'Hage'	CKen
	- 'Hannah'	NLar
	- 'Hypnoides Nana'	CKen
	- 'Intermedia'	CKen WAbe
	- 'Ivan's Column'	CKen
	- 'Junior'	CKen
	- 'Juniperoides'	CKen
	- 'Juniperoides Compacta'	WAbe
	- 'Kamarachiba' ♀H7	CKen CSBt EMOT GMcL LBee MAsh NEgg NLar SCoo SLim SPoG
	- 'Kerdalo'	NLar
	- 'Konijn'	GMcL NWea
	- 'Kosteri' ♀H7	CKen CMac ELan EMOT ESps LBee LPot MAsh NHol SCoo SLim
	- 'Kyoto Creeper'	CKen
	- 'Leprechaun'	WAbe
	- 'Limerick'	CKen
	- 'Little Markey'	CKen
§	- 'Loenik'	EMOT
	- 'Lucas' PBR	LRHS NLar
	- 'Marian'	CKen NLar
§	- 'Mariesii' (v)	CKen LRHS
	- 'Melody'	CKen
	- 'Meroke'	NLar
	- 'Minima'	CKen
	- 'Nana' ♀H7	CKen CMac CMen ESps LBee LPar NHol NWad
	- 'Nana Aurea' ♀H7	CMac CSBt EMOT EPfP ESps LRHS MAsh MJak NEgg NHol
§	- 'Nana Densa'	CKen CMac
	- 'Nana Gracilis' ♀H7	CDul CKen CMen CSBt ELan EMOT EPfP GMcL IVic LRHS MAsh MGos MJak NEgg NWad NWea SBod SCoo SLim SPoG
I	- 'Nana Gracilis Aurea'	CMen NEgg
I	- 'Nana Lutea' ♀H7	CKen ELan EMOT GMcL LBee MAsh MGos NHol NWad SLim
	- 'Nana Rigida'	see *C. obtusa* 'Rigid Dwarf'
	- 'Nana Variegata'	see *C. obtusa* 'Mariesii'
	- 'Pygmaea'	CSBt EMOT ESps NEgg SCoo SLim
§	- 'Rigid Dwarf'	CKen LBee SLim
	- 'Saffron Spray'	NLar SLim
	- 'Snowflake' (v)	CKen ELan NEgg NWad
	- 'Snowkist' (v)	CKen
	- 'Sparkles'	NLar
	- 'Spiralis'	CKen
	- 'Split Rock'	NLar
	- 'Stoneham'	CKen NEgg
	- 'Tempelhof'	CKen MAsh NEgg NLar SCoo SLim
	- 'Tetragona Aurea'	CBcs CMac NWad
	- 'Timothy'	CMac
	- 'Tonia' (v)	CKen MAsh NWad
	- 'Tsatsumi'	NLar
	- 'Tsatsumi Gold' ♀H7	CKen ELan EPfP MPkF NLar SCoo SLim SPoG
	- 'Verdon'	CKen
	- 'Villa Marie'	NLar
	- 'Wissel'	CKen
	- 'Wyckoff'	CKen
	- 'Yellowtip' (v)	CKen EPfP MAsh NEgg

	pisifera	LPar
	- 'Aurea'	LPar
	- 'Baby Blue'	ELan EPfP LRHS SCoo SLim SPoG
	- 'Blue Globe'	CKen
	- 'Boulevard' ♀H7	CBcs CDul CJun CLet CMac CSBt CWib ELan EMOT EPfP ESps GMcL LBee LRHS MAsh MGos MJak NEgg NWea SLim SPer WBor
	- 'Compacta Variegata' (v)	MAsh NEgg
	- 'Curly Top' ♀H7	CSBt EMOT EPfP ESps NHol SCoo SLim SPoG
	- 'Devon Cream'	NEgg
	- 'Filifera'	CMac CSBt SCoo
	- 'Filifera Aurea' ♀H7	CKen CLet CMac CWib ELan EMOT EPfP ESps LBee LBrs LPar MAsh MGos MJak NEgg NHol NWea SCoo WCFE
	- 'Filifera Aureovariegata' (v)	ESps
	- 'Filifera Nana'	ELan LRHS SLim
	- 'Filifera Nana Aurea'	see *C. pisifera* 'Golden Mop'
	- 'Filifera Sungold'	see *C. pisifera* 'Sungold'
	- 'Fuiri-tsukomo'	CKen
	- 'Gold Cushion'	CKen
	- 'Gold Dust'	see *C. pisifera* 'Plumosa Aurea'
	- 'Gold Spangle'	CKen
§	- 'Golden Mop'	CKen NLar
	- 'Green Pincushion'	CKen CMen
	- 'Hime-himuro'	CKen
	- 'Hime-sawara'	CKen CMen
	- 'Iceberg'	NLar
	- 'Lime Tart'	CKen
	- 'Nana'	CKen CMen EMOT ESps GMcL MAsh NHol
I	- 'Nana Albovariegata' (v)	MAsh
	- 'Nana Aureovariegata' (v)	CSBt LBee
I	- 'Nana Compacta'	CMac
	- 'Nana Variegata' (v)	CMac LBee NWad
I	- 'Parslorii'	CKen
	- 'Pici'	CKen
§	- 'Plumosa Aurea'	CKen MAsh NWea
	- 'Plumosa Aurea Compacta'	CKen NWad
	- 'Plumosa Aurea Nana'	MAsh
I	- 'Plumosa Aurea Nana Compacta'	CMac
	- 'Plumosa Aurescens'	CMac
§	- 'Plumosa Compressa' ♀H7	CKen NWad
	- 'Plumosa Densa'	see *C. pisifera* 'Plumosa Compressa'
I	- 'Plumosa Juniperoides'	CKen ESps
I	- 'Plumosa Pygmaea'	ESps
§	- 'Plumosa Rogersii'	GMcL
I	- 'Pygmaea Tsukumo'	NLar
	- 'Rogersii'	see *C. pisifera* 'Plumosa Rogersii'
	- 'Silver Lode' (v)	CKen
	- 'Snow' (v)	CKen
	- 'Snowflake'	CKen
	- 'Spaan's Cannon Ball'	CKen
	- 'Squarrosa Dumosa'	CKen
I	- 'Squarrosa Lombarts'	CLet CMac CSBt
	- 'Squarrosa Lutea'	CKen
	- 'Squarrosa Sulphurea'	CSBt ELan ESps
§	- 'Sungold' ♀H7	CKen CSBt ELan ESps LRHS MAsh MGos NWea SCoo SLim SPoG
	- 'Tama-himuro'	CKen
	- 'Teddy Bear'	NEgg NLar
	- 'True Blue'	ELan NWea
	- 'White Beauty' (v)	EMOT
	thyoides 'Andelyensis'	CMac CSBt EMOT
	- 'Conica'	MAsh
	- 'Ericoides'	CKen CTri EMOT ESps LBee SPlb
	- 'Little Jamie'	CKen
	- 'Red Star'	see *C. thyoides* 'Rubicon'
§	- 'Rubicon'	CLet CMac CSBt EMOT EPfP ESps LBee LRHS MAsh NEgg SLim SPoG
	- 'Top Point'	LBee LRHS MAsh SCoo SPoG

Chamaecytisus see *Cytisus*

Chamaedaphne (*Ericaceae*)

	calyculata	CBcs
	- 'Nana'	NHar

Chamaedorea (*Arecaceae*)

	elegans ♀H1a	NLos
	metallica misapplied	see *C. microspadix*
§	***microspadix***	CPHo SChr
	radicalis	CBrP CPHo NLos SChr

Chamaemelum (*Asteraceae*)

§	***nobile***	CArn CBod CHby CLau CPrp CTri CWld ENfk EPfP GPoy LCro MHer MMuc MNHC NGdn NPri SEND SPlb SRms SVic WJek WTre
	- dwarf	SMor SVic
	- dwarf, double-flowered (d)	LEdu
	- 'Flore Pleno' (d)	CBod CBre CElw CLau CMea CPrp CTri ECha ENfk EPfP GPoy MHer MHol MMuc MNHC MRav NBro NGdn SEND SIde SPer SRms WHal WJek WTre
	- 'Treneague'	CBod CBre CPrp CTri ECha ECho ELan ENfk EPfP GAbr GKin GPoy MCot MHer MNHC MRav NPri SIde SMor SPer SPlb SRms WHal WHer WJek WTre

Chamaenerion (*Onagraceae*)

§	***angustifolium***	SWat WSFF
§	- 'Album'	Widely available
	- 'Isobel'	MRav WCot
	- 'Stahl Rose'	CAby CHid CMea EPfP EWes LEdu NSti SGbt SMad SPhx SWat WCot WSHC
§	***dodonaei***	CFis ELan EWes IMou SMHy SPhx WCot
§	***fleischeri***	MMuc SEND

Chamaepericlymenum see *Cornus*

Chamaerops (*Arecaceae*)

	sp.	ETod LPar
	excelsa misapplied	see *Trachycarpus fortunei*
	excelsa Thunb.	see *Rhapis excelsa*
	humilis ♀H4	CAbb CAco CBcs CBrP CTsd ELan EPfP ESps ESwi ETod EUJe LPar LRHS MGos NPla SArc SChr SEND SPlb SPoG STrG WCot XSen
§	- var. ***argentea***	CBlu CBrP CDTJ CPHo ETod LPar LRHS LTro MGos SChr SPlb WCot
	- var. ***cerifera***	see *C. humilis* var. *argentea*
	- var. ***humilis*** 'Nana' **new**	LPar
	- 'Stella'	ETod
	- 'Vulcano'	CDTJ SChr

Chamaespartium see *Genista*

Chamaesphacos (*Lamiaceae*)

	ilicifolius misapplied	see *Siphocranion macranthum*

Chamelaucium (*Myrtaceae*)

	uncinatum	CCCN

Chamerion see *Chamaenerion*

Chasmanthe (*Iridaceae*)

	aethiopica	CTre EPri
	bicolor	CPrp CTal CTca EPri EWld
	floribunda	CPrp EBee EPri GKev LTro
	- var. ***duckittii***	CPrp ECho EPfP GKev
	- - 'Golden Wave'	CPrp GKev
	- 'Saturnus'	GKev MHer

Chasmanthium (*Poaceae*)

§	***latifolium***	CBWd CBod CKno CLet CSpe EAJP ECha EHoe ELan ELon EPPr EShb EUJe GMcL LEdu LHop LRHS MAvo MBrN NRHS SCob SDix SGol SMad SPad SPoG SRms WBor WCot XLum
	- 'Golden Spangles'	CKno
	- 'Little Tickler' **new**	CBod
	- 'River Mist' (v)	CBod EBee ECha LRHS SCob
	laxum	CBod SMea

Cheilanthes ✿ (*Pteridaceae*)

	argentea	EBee ISha
	distans	WAbe
	eatonii	WAbe
	lanosa	CBod CCCN CHid CLAP EBee EFer EPot EWes ISha LRHS NLos SPlb SPoG WCot
	lindheimeri	WAbe
	myriophylla	WAbe
	tomentosa	CCCN CLAP EBee ISha LRHS
	wootonii	WAbe

Cheiranthus see *Erysimum*

Cheirolophus (*Asteraceae*)

	benoistii misapplied	see *Centaurea atropurpurea*
	benoistii (Humb.) Holub	CSpe EBee MRav SKHP WSHC

Chelidonium (*Papaveraceae*)

	japonicum	see *Hylomecon japonica*
	majus	CArn GEdr GPSL GPoy GQui NMir WHer WHil WSFF
	- 'Flore Pleno' (d)	CBre GJos NBid NBro WHer WTou
	- var. ***laciniatum***	WCot

Chelone (*Plantaginaceae*)

	barbata	see *Penstemon barbatus*
§	***glabra***	CBod CMac EBee ECha ELan EPfP GMaP GMcL GPoy GQui ILea LRHS MBel MMuc NBid NBro NEgg NGdn NHol NLar SEND SPer SPlb SRms WFar WHar WMoo WPnP WSHC WWtn
	lyonii	EBee ELan ILea NLar SPad SPhx WShi
	- 'Hot Lips'	LHop WCAu WPnP
	- 'Pink Temptation'	EBee GEdr
	obliqua	Widely available
	- var. ***alba***	see *C. glabra*
	- 'Forncett Foremost'	GQui
	- 'Ieniemienie'	EBee LEdu
	- 'Pink Sensation'	WFar
I	'Pink Turtle'	EBee GBin

Chelonopsis (*Lamiaceae*)

	moschata	EBee GEdr LEdu MHer SBrt SMad SPlb WHil WMoo
	yagiharana	CAby CMea NBid WMoo

Chengiopanax (*Araliaceae*)

	sciadophylloides	WCru

Chenopodium (*Amaranthaceae*)

	bonus-henricus	CAgr CHab CHby ENfk GPoy LPot MCoo MHer MNHC SIde SRms WHer WJek WTre
	giganteum	MNHC SHDw SRms WJek

cherimoya see *Annona cherimola*

cherry, Duke see *Prunus* × *gondouinii*

cherry, sour or morello see *Prunus cerasus*

cherry, sweet see *Prunus avium*

chervil see *Anthriscus cerefolium*

chestnut, sweet see *Castanea sativa*

Chiastophyllum (*Crassulaceae*)

§	***oppositifolium*** 🏆^{H5}	CAby CElw CRos CSam CTri EBee ECha ECho EDAr ELan EPfP GAbr GJos GKev GLog ITim LRHS MMuc MRav NBid NRHS NSla SIgm SPlb SRms WKif WMoo WSHC XLum
	- 'Frosted Jade'	see *C. oppositifolium* 'Jim's Pride'
	- 'Jane's Reverse' (v)	EBee WCot
§	- 'Jim's Pride' (v)	ECha ECho ECtt EHoe EWes GBuc GKev GMaP MHer MPie MRav NHar NHpl NPer NWad SPlb SRGP SRms SRot WFar WIce WKif WMoo WSHC WTor
	simplicifolium	see *C. oppositifolium*

Chiliotrichum (*Asteraceae*)

	diffusum	CWib MMuc

Chimonanthus ✿ (*Calycanthaceae*)

	fragrans	see *C. praecox*
	nitens	CMCN NLar
§	***praecox***	Widely available
	- 'Grandiflorus' 🏆^{H5}	CEnd CJun EPfP LRHS MAsh SPoG WCot WPat
	- 'Luteus' 🏆^{H4}	CBcs CEnd CJun ELan EPfP LEdu LRHS MAsh MGos NLar SPoG WCot WPat
	- 'Sunburst'	CJun
	- 'Trenython' 🏆^{H4}	CEnd CJun
	yunnanensis misapplied	IDee

Chimonobambusa (*Poaceae*)

	KR 7592	MWht
	hookeriana misapplied	see *Himalayacalamus falconeri* 'Damarapa'
§	***marmorea***	CDTJ CEnt ERod MMuc MWht SBig
	- 'Variegata' (v)	CDTJ ERod ESwi
§	***quadrangularis***	CBcs CDTJ CEnt EPfP ERod ESwi IMou MWht SBig
	- 'Nagaminei' (v)	ERod
	- 'Suow' (v)	CDTJ
	- 'Tatejima'	ERod
	tumidissinoda	CDTJ CEnt CJng ERod ESwi IMou MWht SBig

Chinese chives see *Allium tuberosum*

Chiogenes see *Gaultheria*

Chionanthus (*Oleaceae*)

retusus CBcs CCCN CMCN EBee EPfP LRHS MPkF NLar SAko SKHP SPer
- 'Arnold's Pride' NLar WPGP
virginicus CBcs CCCN CDul CJun CMCN ECrN ELan EPfP EWTr GBin IArd LHop LRHS MBlu MMuc MRav NEgg NLar SAko SKHP SPer SPlb WCot

Chionochloa (*Poaceae*)

conspicua CAby CBod EBee GAbr GCal GKev MAvo NBid NBir SMea WPGP
- 'Rubra' see *C. rubra*
flavescens EBee EHoe MAvo WPGP
flavicans GBin IMou SMad SMea
rigida MAvo
§ ***rubra*** 🏆H7 CBcs CCht CElw CKno CSpe EBee EHoe ELan EWes GBin GCal IMou MAsh MRav SMad WCot WMoo WPGP
- PAB 67 LEdu
- subsp. ***cuprea*** CAby CBod

Chionodoxa ✿ (*Asparagaceae*)

§ ***forbesii*** CBro CRos ECGP ECho EPfP EPot GKev LAma LRHS NBir NHpl NRHS SCob SDeJ SDir SPer SRms WShi
- 'Alba' ECho SDir
- 'Blue Giant' ECho ELan EPot ERCP GKev SCob SDir
- 'Rosea' GKev LAma NHpl
- Siehei Group see *C. siehei*
- 'Violet Beauty' GKev SDeJ SDir
gigantea see *C. luciliae* Gigantea Group
luciliae misapplied see *C. forbesii*
luciliae ambig. CAvo ECho LCro LOPS LRHS NRHS SEND
luciliae Boiss. 🏆H5 CAby CBro EPfP LAma SPer
- 'Alba' CRos ECho LAma LRHS NHpl NRHS SDeJ SDir SPer
§ - Gigantea Group GKev
- - 'Alba' EPot GKev SCob
- 'Rosy Queen' GKev LAma
'Pink Giant' CAvo CBro CRos ECho ELan EPfP EPot ERCP GKev LAma LRHS NRHS SCob SDeJ SDir WBor XLum
sardensis 🏆H5 CBro CRos ECho EPot ERCP GKev LAma LRHS NNys NRHS SDeJ SPhx WShi
§ ***siehei*** 🏆H5 GKev
'Valentine Day' EPot

Chionographis (*Melanthiaceae*)

japonica EFEx GEdr WCru

Chionohebe (*Plantaginaceae*)

pulvinaris NSla WAbe
'Vera Cox' WAbe

× *Chionoscilla* (*Asparagaceae*)

§ ***allenii*** ECho SPhx WCot

Chiranthodendron (*Malvaceae*)

pentadactylon SPlb

Chirita (*Gesneriaceae*)

'Aiko' WDib
'Candy' WDib
'Chastity' WDib
'Diane Marie' WDib
'Erika' WDib
flavimaculata WDib
heterotricha WDib
'Keiko' WDib
linearifolia WDib
linearifolia* × *sinensis WDib
longgangensis WDib
'New York' WDib
sinensis 🏆H1c WDib
- 'Hisako' WDib
speciosa 'Crûg Cornetto' WCot WCru
'Stardust' WDib
'Sweet Dreams' WDib
tamiana WDib

Chironia (*Gentianaceae*)

baccifera SPlb

× *Chitalpa* (*Bignoniaceae*)

tashkentensis CBcs CEnd EPfP ESwi IDee MMrt MTPN SBrt
- 'Morning Cloud' MBlu
- 'Pink Dawn' ESwi MBlu SPad
- Summer Bells = 'Minsum' ELon LHop WCot

chives see *Allium schoenoprasum*

Chlidanthus (*Amaryllidaceae*)

fragrans CCCN ECho GKev SDeJ SEND

Chloranthus (*Chloranthaceae*)

fortunei SCob
- 'Domino' WCot
glaber B&SWJ 11102 WCru
- var. ***flavus*** see *Sarcandra glabra* f. *flava*
henryi WCot
japonicus GBuc GEdr WCru
oldhamii CTal WPGP
- B&SWJ 2019 GEdr LEdu WCru
serratus GEdr WCru

Chloris (*Poaceae*)

distichophylla see *Eustachys distichophylla*

Chlorogalum (*Asparagaceae*)

pomeridianum CLak
- 'Berkeley Hills' **new** SBrt
- tall, from Siskiyou Mountains, Oregon, USA **new** SBrt

Chlorophytum (*Asparagaceae*)

comosum EShb SEND SVic
- 'Aureomarginata' (v) SEND
- 'Variegatum' (v) 🏆H2 CTsd EShb NGBl SEND SPre SRms
- 'Vittatum' (v) 🏆H2 EShb NGBl SRms
graminifolium **new** EBee
krookianum WCot
macrophyllum EShb
nepalense IMou
- B&SWJ 2528 WCru

Choisya (*Rutaceae*)

× ***dewitteana*** 'Aztec Gold' PBR CBcs CRos EPfP LRHS MAsh MGos NRHS SCob SHil WFar
- 'Aztec Pearl' 🏆H4 Widely available
- Golden Gift = 'Lismarty' PBR LRHS NRHS
- Goldfingers = 'Limo' PBR CBcs CDul CMac CRos CWGN EBee ELan EMOT EPfP EShb ESps GMcL

	LHop LRHS LSRN MGos MJak MRav NEgg NHol NLar NPri NRHS SCob SGbt SLon SPer SPoG SWvt
- Snow Flurries = 'Lisflurry'PBR	CRos ELan EPfP LLHF LRHS MAsh MRav NRHS SPoG
- White Dazzler = 'Londaz'PBR 🏆H4	Widely available
dumosa	LHop
'Royal Lace'	SLon SPoG
ternata 🏆H4	Widely available
- Moonshine = 'Walcho'PBR	CBcs EBee NLar
- Moonsleeper	see *C. ternata* Sundance
§ - Sundance = 'Lich'PBR 🏆H4	Widely available

Chondrosum (*Poaceae*)

gracile	see *Bouteloua gracilis*

Chordospartium see *Carmichaelia*

Chorisia (*Malvaceae*)

speciosa	CCCN SPlb

Chorizema (*Papilionaceae*)

cordatum 🏆H2	SVen
dicksonii	SPlb

Chronanthus see *Cytisus*

Chrysalidocarpus see *Dypsis*

Chrysanthemopsis see *Rhodanthemum*

Chrysanthemum ✿ (*Asteraceae*)

E.H. Wilson s.n.	MNrw WCot
'Action Bronze' (22)	EPfP NWsh
'Agnes Ann' (21d)	EWoo MNrw
'Alan Brown' (25a)	MCms
'Alan Foxall Yellow' (3b)	MCms
'Alec Bedser' (25a)	NHal
'Alehmer Rote' (21)	MNrw
'Alex Young' (25b)	MCms
'Aline' (21)	EWoo MNrw
'Alison' (29c)	ELon EWoo MNrw
'Alison's Dad'	MNrw
'Allouise' (25b) 🏆H3	NHal
'Allouise Orange' (25b)	MCms NHal
'Allouise Pink' (25b)	MCms
'Allyson Peace' (14a)	MCms NHal
alpinum	see *Leucanthemopsis alpina*
'Amber Matlock' (24b)	MCms
'American Beauty Lemon' (5b)	MCms
'American Beauty Snowball' (5b) **new**	MCms
'American Beauty White' (5b)	MCms
'Anastasia' ambig.	SAko
'Anastasia' (21c)	CHid EBee ELon GCal LRHS MNrw MRav NSti SRms WBor
'Anderton' (6b)	MCms
'Angela Blundell' (19b)	WCot
'Angela Cosimini' (25b)	MCms
'Angelic' (21b) 🏆H4	EBee EWoo
'Anne Ratsey' (21)	CHVG CSam MNrw WBrk
'Anne, Lady Brocket' (21d)	ECtt NWsh
'Anthony Peace' (25b)	MCms
'Antigua'PBR	MCms
'Apollo' H. Shoesmith	LLHF MNrw WCot
'Apollo' (21)	SPhx WHoo
'Apricot'	see *C.* 'Cottage Apricot'
'Apricot Chessington' (25a)	MCms NHal
'Apricot Courtier' (24a)	MCms NHal
'Apricot Enbee Wedding'	see *C.* 'Bronze Enbee Wedding'
'Apricot Mundial' (6b)	MCms
'Arctic Queen'PBR (23a)	MCms
'Arctic Queen Yellow'	MCms
arcticum L.	see *Arctanthemum arcticum*
argenteum	see *Tanacetum argenteum*
'Artist Orange' **new**	MCms
'Astro' (25b)	MCms NHal
'Aunt Millicent' (21d) 🏆H4	EWoo LLHF NHal WCot
'Balcombe Perfection' (5a)	MCms NHal
balsamita	see *Tanacetum balsamita*
Barbara = 'Yobarbara' (22)	NHal
'Barca'	MCms
'Beacon' (5a) 🏆H2	MCms NHal
'Beechcroft' (29Rub)	MNrw
'Belle' (21d)	EWoo MNrw NWad
'Beppie Bronze' (29e)	MCms
'Beppie Purple' (29e)	MCms
'Beppie Red' (29e)	MCms
'Beppie Rose' (29e)	MCms
'Beppie Yellow' (29e)	MCms
'Best Man' (29d)	MCms
'Betty' (21)	EWoo
'Bill Holden' (14a)	MCms NHal
'Bill Wade' (25a)	MCms NHal
'Billy Bell' (15a)	MCms NHal
'Blanche Poitevene' (5b)	EMal MCms NHal
'Bob Green' (13b)	MCms
'Bobby Swinburn' (13b)	MCms NHal
'Branroyal'PBR	NLar
Bravo = 'Yobra' (22c) 🏆H3	NHal
* 'Breitner's Supreme'	ECtt MHCG MNrw
'Brennpunkt'	MNrw
'Bretforton Road'	ECtt MNrw WCot WFar WOld
'Brierton Violet' (17b)	NHal
'Brightness' (21)	EWoo MNrw
'Bronze Cassandra' (5b) 🏆H2	MCms NHal
'Bronze Darren Pugh' (3b)	NHal
'Bronze Dee Gem' (29c)	MCms NHal
§ 'Bronze Elegance' (21b) 🏆H4	CTri ECtt LRHS MNrw NBir NGdn NSti NWsh SRms WBor
§ 'Bronze Enbee Wedding' (29d) 🏆H3	MCms NHal
'Bronze Gigantic' (1)	NHal
'Bronze Matlock' (24b)	NHal
'Bronze Max Riley' (23b) 🏆H3	MCms NHal
'Bronze Mayford Perfection' (5a) 🏆H2	MCms
'Bronze Mei-kyo'	see *C.* 'Bronze Elegance'
'Bronze Talbot Parade' (29c) 🏆H3	MCms
'Bronze William Florentine' (15a)	MCms
'Brooke Farm Red' **new**	NWsh
'Brown Eyes' (21b) 🏆H4	EWoo
'Bryony Wade' (13b)	MCms NHal
'Buff William Florentine' (15a)	MCms
'Bunty' (28)	SMad
burnt orange-flowered	CAby CFis MNrw
'Burntwood Belle' (3b)	MCms
'Buxton Ruby'	EWTr EWoo
'Candy John Wingfield' (14b)	MCms
'Capel Manor'	EBee MHCG MNrw WCot
'Capella' (10a)	MCms
'Cardinal Red'	LRHS
'Carlene Welby' (25b)	MCms

'Carmine Blush' (21d) ♀H4	EWoo GAbr LHop MNrw WBrk WCot
'Caroline Barclay' (14b)	MCms
'Casablanca' (25a)	NHal
'Cassandra' (5b) ♀H2	MCms NHal
'Cawthorne' (29d)	MCms
'Charles Tandy' (5a)	MCms
'Charles Tandy Primrose' (15a) **new**	MCms
'Charles Tandy Yellow' (15b)	MCms
'Charlie' (24b)	MCms
'Chatsworth' (29c)	NHal
'Chelsea Physic Garden'	CAby EBee EWoo GAbr LEdu MHCG MNrw WCot
'Chempak Rose' (14b)	MCms
'Cherilyn Arlett' (5a) **new**	MCms
'Cherry Chessington' (25a)	MCms NHal
'Cherry Riley's Dynasty' (14a)	MCms
'Chesapeake Primrose' (10a)	MCms
Chesapeake = 'Yochesapeake'PBR (10a)	GBin MCms NHal
'Chessington' (25a)	MCms
'Chessington Oyster' (25a)	MCms
'Chesswood Beauty' (7b)	MCms
'Chestnut Talbot Maid' (29c)	MCms
'Chestnut Talbot Parade' (29c) ♀H3	MCms
'Chloe Ball' (13b)	MCms
'Christmas'	MNrw
'Christopher Lawson' (24b)	MCms NHal
cinerariifolium	see *Tanacetum cinerariifolium*
'Clapham Delight' (23a)	MCms NHal
'Clara Curtis' (21d)	Widely available
'Clare Louise' (24b)	MCms
'Clarksdale' (15b)	MCms NHal
coccineum	see *Tanacetum coccineum*
'Colsterworth'	MNrw
'Contralto' (22)	EWoo
'Coral Reef' (10b)	MCms NHal
'Corinna' (21d)	GBin MNrw
'Cornetto' (25b)	MCms NHal
corymbosum	see *Tanacetum corymbosum*
§ 'Cottage Apricot' (21)	ECGP EPfP EWoo LRHS MBNS MRav SRms
'Cottage Bronze'	MNrw
'Cottage Lemon'	MNrw
'Cottage Pink'	see *C.* 'Emperor of China'
'Courtier' (24a)	NHal
'Cousin Joan' (21d) ♀H4	EBee EWoo LHop MNrw NCGa WCot WOld
'Cream Dorridge Crystal' (24a)	MCms
'Cream Elegance' (9c)	NHal
'Cream John Hughes' (3b)	MCms
'Cream Patricia Millar' (14b)	NHal
'Cream Talbot Maid' (29c)	MCms
'Cream Talbot Parade' (29c) ♀H3	MCms
'Cream West Bromwich' (14a)	MCms
'Crimson Purple Glow' (5a) **new**	MCms
Dana = 'Yodana' (25b) ♀H3	MCms NHal
Dance = 'Fidance'PBR (9f)	MCms
'Dance Red' (9f)	MCms
Dance Salmon = 'Fidancesal' (9f)	GBin MCms
'Dance Sunny' (9f)	MCms
'Dance White' (9f)	MCms
'Daniel Cooper' (21d) ♀H4	EBee EWoo MNrw SBch
'Danny Peace' (25b)	MCms
'Daphne' (21d)	EWoo
'Daphne Davis' (29d)	NHal
'Darren Pugh' (3b)	MCms NHal
'Darren Pugh Primrose' (3b) **new**	MCms
'David Shoesmith' (25a)	MCms
'Dawn Charlton' (14a)	MCms
'Dee Gem' (29c) ♀H3	MCms NHal
'Delianne'PBR	MCms
'Delianne Yellow'PBR	MCms
'Delistar'PBR (9f)	MCms
'Delistar Bronze' (9f)	MCms
'Delistar Cream'PBR (9f)	MCms
'Delistar Lemon' (9f)	MCms
'Delistar Lilac' (9f)	MCms
'Delistar Mint' (9f)	MCms
'Delistar Pink' (9f)	MCms
'Delistar Pink Star' (9f)	MCms
'Delistar Saffira' (9f)	MCms
'Delistar Sunny' (9f)	MCms
'Delta' (5b)	NHal
'Delta Copper Bronze' (9d)	NHal
'Delta Crimson' (29d)	NHal
'Delta Yellow' (29)	NHal
'Denise Oatridge' (5a)	MCms
'Dennis Gill' (25b)	MCms
'Dennis Turner' (25b)	MCms
'Dennis Turner Primrose' (15b)	MCms
'Dernier Soleil'	EBee MNrw XLum
'Deva Glow' (25a)	MCms
'Disco Club' **new**	MCms
'Dixter Orange'	EBee GCal MHCG SBee SDix SMad WBor
§ 'Doctor Tom Parr' (21c)	ELan EWoo LHop MNrw
'Domingo' (14b)	MCms
'Don't Start' (7a)	MCms
'Doreen Hall' (15a)	MCms NHal
'Doreen Statham' (4b)	MCms NHal
'Doris Ozols' (25a)	MCms NHal
'Dorothy Stone' (25b)	MCms NHal
'Dorridge Crystal' (24a)	MCms NHal
'Downpour' (10a)	MCms
'Dublin'	MCms
'Duchess of Edinburgh' (21d)	EBee ECtt ELan EPfP EWoo LRHS LSun MNrw SPhx XLum
'Dulwich Pink' (21d) ♀H4	WCot WOld
'Dutchy'PBR (9d)	MCms
'Early Yellow'	EBee ELon EWoo MNrw WCot
'Edelweiss' (21)	CAby NWad
'Edina' (29d) **new**	NHal
'Edmund Brown'	WCot
'Edward Shaw' (5a)	MCms
'Egret' (23b)	MCms NHal
'Elegance' (9c)	NHal
'Elizabeth Lawson' (5b)	MCms NHal
§ 'Emperor of China' (21)	CAby CElw ECha ECtt EWoo LSun MNrw MRav NHal SBee SPhx SRms WBor XLum
'Enbee Wedding' (29d) ♀H3	MCms NHal
'Energy'PBR (9)	MCms
'Esther' (21d)	EBee ELon MNrw SMad
'Eva Allen' (25b)	MCms
'Exopolis' **new**	MCms
'Fairweather' (3b)	MCms NHal
'Fairweather Cream' (3b)	MCms

'Fairweather Peach' (3b)	MCms
'Fanfare Cherry'	LRHS
'Fanfare Claret'	LRHS
'Fanfare Flame'	LRHS
'Fanfare Glowing Embers'	LRHS
'Fanfare Orange'	LRHS
'Fanfare Pink Blush'	LRHS
'Fanfare Pink Pastel'	LRHS
'Fanfare Rosetta'	LRHS
'Fanfare Ruby'	LRHS
'Fanfare Sunset'	LRHS
'Feeling Green Dark'^{PBR}	MCms
'Fleur de Lis' (10a)	MCms
'Flo Cooper' (25a) **new**	MCms
foeniculaceum misapplied	see *Argyranthemum foeniculaceum* misapplied
foeniculaceum (Willd.) Desf.	see *Argyranthemum foeniculaceum* (Willd.) Webb & Sch. Bip.
'Folk Song' (4b)	MNrw
'Fondant'	NHal
'Formcast' (24a)	MCms
'French Rose'	MNrw
'Froggy'^{PBR} (9)	MCms
frutescens	see *Argyranthemum frutescens*
'Gala Burgundy'	EPfP
'Gambit' (24a)	MCms NHal
'Geoff Aird' (15b)	MCms
'Geoff Amos' (3b)	MCms
'Geoff Brady' (5a)	MCms NHal
'George Griffiths' (24b) ♀^{H3}	MCms NHal
'Gillette' (23b)	MCms
'Ginger Nut' (25b)	MCms
'Ginger Nut Yellow' (25b)	MCms
I 'Gladys' (12a)	NHal
'Gladys Emerson' (3b)	MCms NHal
'Gold Enbee Wedding' (29d) ♀^{H3}	MCms
'Gold Mundial' (6b) ♀^{H2}	MCms
'Golddukaten' (21)	NWad
'Golden Cassandra' (5b) ♀^{H2}	MCms NHal
'Golden Chalice' (12a)	NHal
'Golden Courtier' (24a)	MCms NHal
'Golden Masons' (7b)	MCms
'Golden Mayford Perfection' (5a) ♀^{H2}	MCms
'Golden Plover' (22)	NHal
'Golden Rain' (10a) ♀^{H2}	MCms NHal
'Golden Roy Coopland' (5b)	MCms
'Golden Shoesmith Salmon' (4a) **new**	MCms
'Golden Splendour' (10a)	MCms
'Golden Wedding' (21)	MNrw
'Golden William Florentine' (15a)	MCms
'Golden Woolman's Glory' (7a)	NHal
'Goldengreenheart' (21d) ♀^{H4}	EBee ECtt ELon EShb LLHF MHCG MNrw WBrk WHoo
'Goldmarianne' (21)	GBin XLum
'Goodlife Sombrero' (29a) ♀^{H3}	MCms
'Goshu Penta' (10a)	MCms
'Grace Wade' (25b)	MCms
'Grand Cherry' **new**	MCms
'Grand Pink' **new**	MCms
'Grandchild' (21c) ♀^{H4}	MNrw NHal SBch
'Hanenburg' (25b)	MCms NHal
haradjanii	see *Tanacetum haradjanii*
'Harold Lawson' (5a)	MCms NHal
'Harry Tolley' (14b)	MCms
'Heather James' (3b)	MCms NHal
'Hebe' (21d)	EBee
'Heide' (29c) ♀^{H3}	NHal
'Helen Louise' (25b)	MCms NHal
'Herbie McCauley' (24b)	MCms
'Herbstbrokat'	GBin XLum
'Herbstfeuer' (21)	NWad
'Hesketh Knight' (5b) ♀^{H2}	MCms
'Hillfield Apricot'	EShb
'Hoagy' (29d)	MCms NHal
'Holly Elizabeth' (14a)	MCms
Holly = 'Yoholly' (22b) ♀^{H3}	NHal
'Honey Enbee Wedding' (29d)	MCms NHal
'Horningsea Pink' (19d)	ECGP WBor
hosmariense	see *Rhodanthemum hosmariense*
'Imp' (21e) ♀^{H4}	EWoo
indicum	SVic
'Innocence' (21d) ♀^{H4}	CFis ECtt ELan EWoo LEdu MNrw MRav NGdn SHar WBrk WHoo
'Jack Wood' (25a) **new**	MCms
'Janet South'	EWoo MNrw
'Jante Wells' (21b) ♀^{H4}	MNrw WBor
'Jennifer Shephard' (25b)	MCms
'Jenny Wren' (12a)	NHal
'Jessie Cooper' misapplied	see *C.* 'Mrs Jessie Cooper' (21)
'Jessie Cooper' Perry	CElw
'Jimmy Simpson' (25b)	MCms
'Jimmy Tranter' (14b)	NHal
'Joan Waugh' (14b)	MCms
'John Harrison' (25b)	MCms NHal
'John Hughes' (3b)	MCms NHal
'John Lowry' (24a)	MCms NHal
'John Riley' (14a)	MCms NHal
'John Wingfield' (14b)	MCms NHal
'John Wingfield Honey' (14b)	MCms
'John Wingfield Pearl' (14b)	MCms
'Jolie Rose'	WCot
'Joyce Fountain' (24a)	MCms NHal
'Joyce Frieda' (13b)	MCms NHal
'Julia' (28)	EPfP MNrw
'Julia Arnold'	WHoo
'Julia Peterson'	LLHF MHCG MHer MNrw WCot WFar WHoo
'Julie Lagravère' (28)	EWoo LHop MNrw XLum
'Karen Taylor' (29c) ♀^{H3}	NHal
'Kath Stephenson' (7b)	MCms NHal
'Kath Stephenson Honey' (7b)	MCms
'Kath Stephenson Peach' (7b)	MCms
'Kath Stephenson Primrose' (7b)	MCms NHal
'Kath Stephenson Rose' (7b)	MCms NHal
'Kath Stephenson Salmon' (7b)	MCms
'Kay Woolman' (13b)	MCms NHal
'Kay Woolman Primrose' (13b) **new**	MCms
'Kay Woolman Yellow' (13b)	MCms
'Killerton Tangerine'	MNrw
'Kimberley Marie' (15b)	MCms NHal
'Kiyomi-no-meisui'	MCms NHal
'Kleiner Bernstein'	MNrw
'La Damoiselle'	WCot
§ 'Lady in Pink' (21)	MPie
'Lakelanders' (3b)	MCms NHal

'Laura Jayne' (25a)	MCms
'Laura Norris' (15a) **new**	MCms
'Lava' (10a)	MCms
'Leo' (21b) ♀H4	EBee EWoo
leucanthemum	see *Leucanthemum vulgare*
'Lexy'PBR (9)	GBin MCms
'Lexy Red'PBR (9)	GBin MCms
'Lighthouse'	NHal
'Lilac Chessington' (25a)	MCms NHal
'Lilian Shoesmith' (5b)	MCms
Linda = 'Lindayo' (22c) ♀H3	NHal
'L'Innocence' (21)	CAby
'Little Dorrit' (21f) ♀H4	EWoo
'Little Ricky' (25b) **new**	MCms
'Liverpool Festival' (23b)	MCms
'Lollipop'PBR (9)	GBin MCms
Lollipop Purple = 'Filollipop Purple'PBR	MCms
'Lorna Wood' (13b)	MCms NHal
'Louise Park' (24a)	MCms
'Luba' (9c)	MCms
'Luba Bronze' (9c)	MCms
'Luba Orange' (9c)	MCms
'Lucy' (29a)	MCms NHal
'Lucy Simpson' (21d)	EWoo
'Lydia Mannion' (7b)	MCms
'Lynn Johnson' (15a)	MCms
Lynn = 'Yolynn' (22c) ♀H3	NHal
macrophyllum	see *Tanacetum macrophyllum* (Waldst. & Kit.) Sch.Bip.
'Malcolm Perkins' (25a)	MCms NHal
'Mancetta Comet' (29a)	MCms NHal
'Mancetta Symbol' (5a)	MCms
'Mandarin' (5b)	SAko
maresii	see *Rhodanthemum hosmariense*
'Margaret Dear' (25a)	MCms
'Margaret Lawson' (14b)	MCms NHal
'Margery Fish'	MNrw
'Marion' (25a)	MNrw WCot
'Martin Bell' (29d)	MCms
'Mary' (21f)	NHal
'Mary Stoker' (21d)	CAby EBee ECtt ELan EPfP EPri EWoo LRHS MNrw MPie MRav NCGa NHal NLar NWsh SPer WAul WCAu XLum
'Mary's Miracle' (24a)	MCms
'Mason's Bronze' (7b)	MCms
'Matlock' (24b)	NHal
'Mauve Gem' (21f) ♀H3	MNrw NHal
'Mavis' (21) ♀H3	MHCG MNrw
mawii	see *Rhodanthemum gayanum*
'Max Riley' (23b) ♀H3	MCms NHal
maximum misapplied	see *Leucanthemum* × *superbum*
maximum Ramond	see *Leucanthemum maximum* (Ramond) DC.
'Maxine Charlton' (24b)	MCms NHal
'Maxine Johnson' (25b)	MCms NHal
'May Shoesmith' (5a) ♀H2	MCms NHal
'Maybach' (9)	MCms
'Mayford Perfection' (5a) ♀H2	MCms
'Mei-Kyō' (28b) ♀H4	CFis CMea CTri ECtt EPPr EWoo LRHS MNrw MPie SRms WBor WBrk WCAu
'Membury' (24b)	MCms NHal
'Michelle Preston' (13b)	NHal
'Millennium' (25b) ♀H3	MCms NHal
'Millie Mathews' (14b)	MCms
'Misty Cream' (25b)	MCms
'Misty Golden' (25b)	MCms
'Misty Lemon' (25b)	MCms
'Moonlight' (29d/K)	CRos MRav
'Moonlight' (24a)	LRHS NRHS
'Morning Star' (12a)	NHal
'Mount Fuji' (10b)	MCms
§ 'Mrs Jessie Cooper' (21d) ♀H4	CAby CHGN EBee ELon EWoo GQue LHop MNrw MPie NLar SDys SRms WCot WHoo WPtf
'Mrs Jessie Cooper No 1'	NCGa NWsh SBch
'Mrs Jessie Cooper No 2'	MNrw
'Mundial' (6)	MCms
'Mundial Peach' (6b/9a)	MCms
'Mundial Rose' (6b)	MCms
'Mundial Ruby' (6b)	MCms
'Muriel Odell' (7b)	MCms
'Music' (23b)	MCms NHal
'Muxton Sable' (10a)	GBin MCms
'Myss Debbie' (29e)	NHal
'Myss Dorothy' (29c)	MCms NHal
'Myss Eliza' (29c)	MCms
'Myss Goldie' (29c)	MCms
'Myss Rihanna' (29c)	MCms NHal
'Myss Saffron' (29c) ♀H3	MCms NHal
'Nancy Perry' (21d)	CSam MNrw MRav XLum
'Nantyderry Sunshine' (28b) ♀H4	ELon LLHF LRHS MHCG MNrw MPie NWsh SPhx WBor WCot WFar WOld
'Naru' (9c)	NHal
'Naru Crimson' (9c)	NHal
'Natalie Rachelle' (25b)	MCms
'Natalie Sarah' (29d) ♀H3	MCms NHal
'Nell Gwynn' (21d)	EWoo MNrw NHal
'New Stylist' (24b)	MCms
Nicole = 'Yonicole' (22c) ♀H3	NHal
nipponicum	see *Nipponanthemum nipponicum*
'Nora Brook' (25b)	MCms
'Olwyn' (4b)	MCms
'Olwyn Yellow' (4b)	MCms
'Optimist' **new**	MCms
'Orange Enbee Wedding' (29d)	NHal
'Paloma Mist' (29d)	NHal
'Paloma Redeye' (29d)	NHal
'Paloma Regent' (29d)	NHal
'Paloma Sands' (29d)	NHal
parthenium	see *Tanacetum parthenium*
'Pat Bahn' (29c) **new**	NHal
'Patricia Millar' (14b)	MCms NHal
'Patricia Millar Cerise' (14b)	MCms
'Patricia Millar Coral' (14b)	MCms
'Patricia Millar Orange' (14b)	MCms
'Patricia Millar Yellow' (14b)	MCms NHal
'Paul Boissier' (30Rub)	CAby CFis ECtt EWoo MNrw NSti SPhx WBor
'Paul Cornelius' (24b)	MCms NHal
'Pauline White' (15a)	MCms
'Peach Courtier' (24a)	NHal
'Peach Enbee Wedding' (29d) ♀H3	MCms NHal
'Peach John Wingfield' (14b)	MCms NHal
'Peach Patricia Millar' (14b)	MCms
'Peach Southway Sheeba' (29d) **new**	NHal
'Pearl Celebration' (24a)	MCms
'Pearl Enbee Wedding' (29d)	MCms
'Pearl Smith' (25b) **new**	MCms
'Pennine Bullion'	NHal
'Pennine Gambol' (29a)	MCms

'Pennine Jude' (29a)	MCms
'Pennine Marie' (29a) ♀H3	MCms
'Pennine Oriel' (29a) ♀H3	MCms NHal
'Pennine Point' (19c)	NHal
'Pennine Polo' (29d) ♀H3	MCms NHal
'Pennine Poppet' (29a)	MCms
'Pennine Swan' (29c)	MCms NHal
'Penny's Yellow'	LHop LLHF WBrk
'Percy Salter' (24b)	NHal
'Perry's Peach' (21d) ♀H4	EWoo LLHF MHCG MNrw NCGa NHal NPer SPhx
'Peter Jolley' (25b)	MCms
'Peter Rowe' (23b)	MCms NHal
'Peterkin'	CMac EBee ECtt ELon LRHS XLum
'Picasso'	MNrw
'Ping Pong' (8a)	MCms
'Pink John Wingfield' (14b)	NHal
'Pink Progression'	see *C.* 'Lady in Pink'
'Pocahontas' (10a)	MCms
'Poesie'	SAko WCot
'Polar Gem' (3a)	MCms NHal
'Pomander' (25b)	MCms
'Pot Black' (14b)	MCms
'President Osaka'	MNrw
'Primrose Allouise' (24b) ♀H3	MCms NHal
'Primrose Chessington' (25a)	MCms
'Primrose Courtier'	see *C.* 'Yellow Courtier'
'Primrose Dorothy Stone' (25b)	MCms NHal
'Primrose Dorridge Crystal' (24a)	MCms
'Primrose Egret' (23b)	MCms
'Primrose Enbee Wedding' (29d) ♀H3	MCms NHal
'Primrose Fairweather' (3b)	MCms
'Primrose John Hughes' (3b)	MCms
'Primrose Mayford Perfection' (5a) ♀H2	MCms
'Primrose Olwyn' (4b)	MCms
'Primrose Pauline White' (15a)	MCms
'Primrose Pennine Oriel' (29a)	MCms
'Primrose West Bromwich' (14a)	MCms
'Princess' (21d)	LLHF
'Promise' (25a)	MCms NHal
'Purleigh White' (28b)	ECtt ELon EPPr MNrw NSti WCot
'Purple Chempak Rose' (14b)	MCms
'Purple Dee Gem' (29c)	NHal
'Purple Doreen Hall' (15a)	MCms
'Purple Glow' (5a)	MCms
'Quinty' (19) **new**	GBin
'Raquel' (21)	MNrw
'Red Balcombe Perfection' (5a)	MCms NHal
'Red Chempak Rose' (14b)	MCms
'Red Goodlife Sombrero' (29a)	MCms
'Red Louise Park' (14a)	MCms
'Red Mayford Perfection' (5a)	MCms
'Red Pennine Gift' (29c)	NHal
'Red Regal Mist' (25b)	MCms NHal
'Red Shirley Model' (3a)	MCms NHal
'Redbreast' (12a)	NHal
'Regal Mist' (25b)	NHal
'Regal Mist Purple' (25b)	MCms
'Rejoyce' **new**	GBin
I 'Rhumba'	WCot
'Rihanna' **new**	MCms
'Riley's Dynasty' (14a)	MCms
'Ringdove' (12a)	NHal
'Rita Fox' (25b)	MCms
'Rita McMahon' (29d) ♀H3	NHal
Robin = 'Yorobi' (22c)	NHal
'Roen Sarah' (29c)	NHal
'Romantica'	MNrw WOld
'Rose Enbee Wedding' (29d)	MCms NHal
'Rose Madder'	EWoo GAbr LPot MNrw WCot
'Rose Mayford Perfection' (5a) ♀H2	MCms
'Rose Patricia Millar' (14b)	MCms NHal
'Rose Talbot Parade' (29c)	MCms
'Rosensilber'	SAko
'Rosetta'	MNrw
roseum	see *Tanacetum coccineum*
'Roter Spray'	NWad
'Roy Bevan' (29d)	MCms
'Roy Coopland' (5b) ♀H2	MCms
'Royal Command' (21a)	MNrw WCot
rubellum	see *C. zawadskii*
'Ruby Enbee Wedding' (29d) ♀H3	MCms NHal
'Ruby Glow' (7b)	MCms
'Ruby Mound' (21c) ♀H3	CSpe EWoo MHCG MNrw NHal SDys SHar SPhx WCot WFar
'Ruby Raynor' (21c) ♀H4	MNrw NHal WCot WFar
'Rumpelstilzchen' (21d)	CFis CMea ECtt EWoo MNrw NWsh
'Salhouse Dream' (10a)	MCms NHal
'Salhouse Joy' (10a)	MCms NHal
'Salmon Allouise' (25b)	MCms NHal
'Salmon Enbee Wedding' (29d) ♀H3	NHal
'Salmon Fair Lady' **new**	LRHS
'Salmon Fairweather' (3b)	MCms
'Salmon John Wingfield' (24b)	MCms
'Salmon Patricia Millar' (14b)	MCms
'Salmon Pauline White' (15a)	MCms
'Salmon Talbot Maid' (29c)	MCms
'Salmon Talbot Parade' (29c) ♀H3	MCms
'Salmon Venice' (24b)	MCms
'Sam Vinter' (5a)	MCms NHal
'Samba'	WCot WFar
'Sarah Louise' (25b)	NHal
'Savanna Charlton' (25a)	MCms NHal
'Sea Urchin' (21f) ♀H3	NHal SDys
'Seaton's Ashleigh' (10b)	MCms
'Seaton's Galaxy' (10a)	MCms NHal
'Senkyo Karyu' (10a)	MCms
'Senkyo Kenshin' (10a)	GBin MCms NHal
'Shamrock' (10b)	MCms
'Sheffield'	XLum
'Sheila Coles' (7b)	MCms NHal
'Sheila Harris' (3b)	MCms
'Shining Light' (21f)	EWoo
'Shoesmith Salmon' (4a) **new**	MCms
'Shoesmith Salmon Bright Bronze' (4a) **new**	MCms
'Shoesmith Salmon Crimson' (4b) **new**	MCms

'Shoesmith Salmon Purple' (4a) **new**	MCms
'Showmaker Action Bronze' **new**	ESps
'Sonnenschein'	LHop
'Sound' (9d)	MCms
'Southway Semtex' (29d)	MCms
'Southway Sheba' (29d) ♀^{H3}	MCms NHal
'Southway Sheba Bronze' (29d)	MCms NHal
'Southway Shimmer' (29d)	MCms NHal
'Southway Shiraz' (29d)	MCms
'Southway Sloe' (29d)	MCms NHal
'Southway Spectacular' (29d)	MCms
'Southway Spritzer' (29d)	MCms NHal
'Southway Strontium' (29d)	MCms NHal
'Southway Sunbeam' (29d)	MCms
'Spartan Canary' (21d) ♀^{H4}	EWoo
'Spartan Display'	EWoo
'Spartan Seagull' (21d)	MNrw
'Stallion'^{PBR} (9)	GBin MCms
'Stallion Yellow'	MCms
'Stan Addison' (5b)	MCms
'Starlet' (21f) ♀^{H4}	EWoo NHal
'Steve Packham' (23b)	MCms NHal
'Stockton' (3b) ♀^{H2}	MCms NHal
'Suffolk Pink'	ECtt EShb EWoo MNrw
'Sunny John Wingfield' (14b)	MCms
'Super-Bronze Shoesmith Salmon' (4a) **new**	MCms
'Susan Kate' (25b) **new**	MCms
'Swan Cream' **new**	MCms
Swan = 'Fiswan'^{PBR} (9)	MCms
'Sweetheart Pink' **new**	MNrw
'Syllabub' (21f) ♀^{H3}	ECtt MNrw
'Symphony' (10a)	MCms NHal
'Talbot Maid' (29c)	MCms
'Talbot Parade' (29c) ♀^{H3}	MCms
'Talbot Parade Pink' (29c)	MCms
'Tapestry Rose' (21d)	CMea EWoo MNrw NCGa NWsh SPhx WBor WHoo
'Tara Olivio' (24b)	MCms
'Terry Brook' (29e)	MCms NHal
'Terry Morris' (7b)	MCms
'Thoroughbred' (24a)	MCms NHal
'Tickle Pink' (29f/K)	MNrw NWad
'Tim Sandall' (25a)	MCms
'Tom Parr'	see *C.* 'Doctor Tom Parr'
'Tom Snowball' (3b)	MCms
'Topsy' (21d) ♀^{H4}	EWoo
'Tracey Waller' (24b)	MCms
Triumph = 'Yotri' (22)	NHal
uliginosum	see *Leucanthemella serotina*
'Uri'	CAby CFis EBee LHop SPhx
'Vagabond Prince'	ELon EWoo LHop MHCG MNrw NCGa WBor WBrk WFar WHoo WOld
'Venice' (24b)	MCms NHal
'Venice Peach' (24b)	MCms
'Venice Rose' (24b)	MCms
'Venus' (21)	WCot
'Venus One'	ECtt EWoo MNrw NHal SPhx
'Vibrant' (9c) ♀^{H2}	NHal
'Viking' (9)	MCms
'Viscount' (4b) **new**	MCms
'Vision On' (24b)	MCms
'Vulcano Dark' (9)	MCms
'Wedding Day' (29k)	EWoo MNrw
'Wedding Sunshine' (21)	MNrw NWad
welwitschii	see *Glebionis segetum*
'Wembley' (24b)	MCms
'Wendy Tench' (21d)	EBee ECtt EWoo NWsh
'West Bromwich' (14a)	MCms
weyrichii	EBee ECho GCrg GPSL IKil LEdu NHpl NLar SBch SRms
'White Allouise' (25b) ♀^{H3}	MCms NHal
'White Beppie' (29e)	MCms
'White Cassandra' (5b)	MCms NHal
'White Denise Oatridge' (5a)	MCms
'White Enbee Wedding' (29d)	MCms NHal
'White Fairweather' (3b)	MCms NHal
'White Gem' (21f)	NHal
'White Gloss' (21e)	MNrw SPhx
'White Pearl Celebration' (24a)	MCms
'White Tower' (27)	MNrw MPie NWad
'William Florentine' (15a)	MCms NHal
'Win' (9c)	NHal
'Wind Dancer' (10a)	MCms
'Winning's Red' (21)	EWoo NCGa SMad WCot
'Winter Queen' (5b)	MCms
'Winter Queen Yellow' (5b)	MCms
'Woolley Globe' (15b)	MCms
'Woolman's Glory' (7a)	MCms NHal
'Woolman's Glory Red' (7a)	MCms
'Woolman's Star' (3a)	MCms NHal
'Woolman's Venture' (14b)	MCms NHal
'Woolman's Venture Red' (14b) **new**	MCms
'Xiang'	NWad
'Yellow Allouise' (25b)	MCms
'Yellow American Beauty' (5b) ♀^{H2}	MCms
'Yellow Billy Bell' (15a)	NHal
'Yellow Clapham Delight' (23a)	MCms NHal
§ 'Yellow Courtier' (24a)	MCms NHal
'Yellow Duke of Kent' (1)	NHal
'Yellow Egret' (23b)	MCms
'Yellow Enbee Wedding' (29d)	MCms NHal
'Yellow Goodlife Sombrero' (29a)	MCms
'Yellow Heide' (29c) ♀^{H3}	NHal
'Yellow John Harrison' (25b)	MCms
'Yellow John Hughes' (3b) ♀^{H2}	MCms NHal
'Yellow John Wingfield' (14b)	MCms NHal
'Yellow May Shoesmith' (5a)	NHal
'Yellow Mayford Perfection' (5a) ♀^{H2}	MCms
'Yellow Pennine Oriel' (29a) ♀^{H3}	MCms NHal
'Yellow Spider' (10a)	MCms
'Yellow Starlet' (21f) ♀^{H4}	EWoo LLHF MNrw
'Yellow Talbot Parade' (29c)	MCms
'Yellow Woolman's Glory' (7a)	MCms
yezoense	CDor MNrw SRms
– B&SWJ 10872	WCru
– 'Roseum'	ECtt
'Yvonne Gray' (25b)	MCms
'Yvonne's Rot-Goldene'	SAko

§ ***zawadskii***	CMac SRms
'Zembla'^{PBR}	MCms
'Zembla Yellow'^{PBR}	MCms

Chrysocephalum (*Asteraceae*)

'Desert Flame'	LRHS NRHS

Chrysogonum (*Asteraceae*)

australe	LRHS
virginianum	CMea EBee EWes SPer WFar
- 'Golden Acres'	ECtt

Chrysopogon (*Poaceae*)

gryllus	WPGP

Chrysopsis (*Asteraceae*)

§ ***mariana***	WOld

Chrysosplenium (*Saxifragaceae*)

alternifolium	GEdr
davidianum	CBre CSam CSpe EBee EPot EWld GCal GEdr GJos GKev IMou NHpl NLar WBor WCru WMoo WSHC
flagelliferum B&SWJ 8902	WCru
lanuginosum	GEdr
var. ***formosanum***	
- - B&SWJ 6979	ESwi WCru
macrophyllum	CSpe CTal EBee EPPr EWld GBin GCal GKev GMaP IMou LEdu MAvo MPie MTPN NLar SHar WBor WCot WCru WSHC
oppositifolium	ECha NMir WSFF WShi

Chusquea (*Poaceae*)

breviglumis misapplied	see *C. culeou* 'Tenuis'
culeou 🏆H4	CAbb CBcs CEnt CHid CJng EPfP LEdu MAvo MGos MWht SBig SPlb SSta
- 'Breviglumis'	see *C. culeou* 'Tenuis'
- 'Purple Splendour'	CJng
§ - 'Tenuis'	ERod
- weeping	CDTJ
delicatula from Machu Picchu, Peru	CFil
gigantea 🏆H3	CDTJ CEnt CFil CHid CJng EPfP ERod ESwi MWht SBig WPGP
montana	CDTJ
nigricans	CFil MAvo

Cibotium (*Cibotiaceae*)

barometz	NLos

Cicerbita (*Asteraceae*)

§ ***alpina***	GAbr NBid SPlb
bourgaei	MMuc
macrorhiza CC 6912	EBee
plumieri	GAbr SBrt WCot WFar WMoo WSHC
- 'Blott' (v)	WCot

Cichorium (*Asteraceae*)

intybus	Widely available
- f. ***album***	CBod ECha ECtt LHop LRHS MBel MCot NPnk SPer SPoG SWat
- 'Palla Rossa' 🏆H4	SRms
- 'Red Rib'	SRms
- 'Roseum'	CBod CMos CWld ECha ECtt ELan GKin LHop LRHS MBel MPie NCGa NPnk SBod SHar SPer SPoG SWat WCAu

Cicuta (*Apiaceae*)

virosa	LLWG

Cimicifuga see *Actaea*

acerina	see *Actaea japonica*
americana	see *Actaea podocarpa*
cordifolia (DC.) Torrey & A.Gray	see *Actaea cordifolia*
cordifolia Pursh	see *Actaea podocarpa*
foetida	see *Actaea cimicifuga*
racemosa var. ***cordifolia***	see *Actaea cordifolia*
- 'Purpurea'	see *Actaea simplex* Atropurpurea Group
ramosa	see *Actaea simplex* 'Prichard's Giant'
rubifolia	see *Actaea cordifolia*
simplex var. ***matsumurae***	see *Actaea matsumurae*

Cineraria (*Asteraceae*)

× ***hybrida***	see *Pericallis* × *hybrida*
maritima	see *Senecio cineraria*

Cinnamomum (*Lauraceae*)

camphora	CBcs LRHS SPlb

Circaea (*Onagraceae*)

alpina	EBee
lutetiana	WHer
- 'Caveat Emptor' (v)	NBid WCot

Cirsium (*Asteraceae*)

arvense	WSFF
* ***atroroseum***	SWat
canum	CSpe GQue
ciliatum	EBee
diacantha	see *Ptilostemon diacantha*
helenioides	see *C. heterophyllum*
§ ***heterophyllum***	CBod CHid EBee EWld GQue LEdu LRHS MAvo MMuc NChi NLar SHar WHil
- PAB 067	LEdu WPGP
- 'Pink Blush' **new**	GBin NSti
japonicum 'Pink Beauty'	CBod
- 'Rose Beauty'	EBee SCob
'Mount Etna'	CBod CFis CMHG EBee ELan GCal GKin GQue LHop LRHS MBNS MMuc MSpe NDov NGdn SEND WCAu
oleraceum	LEdu NBid NLar SBrt
purpuratum	MNrw
rivulare 'Atropurpureum'	Widely available
- 'Trevor's Blue Wonder'	CBod CDor CSam EBee ECtt ELon EPfP IBoy LEdu LPla MAvo MBel MCot MHol MNrw NDov NEgg NLar SCob SPer WCAu WCot WTor
tuberosum	CAby LEdu LPla LRHS SKHP SPhx
vulgare	WSFF

Cissus (*Vitaceae*)

antarctica 🏆H1c	CCCN EShb SEND
pedata B&SWJ 2371	WCru
rhombifolia 🏆H1c	EOHP EShb
- 'Ellen Danica' 🏆H1c	EShb
§ ***striata***	CBcs CMac CRos CWCL EBee ELon EShb IBoy LRHS MGil MRav NChi SBrt SEND SLim SWvt WSHC

Cistus ✿ (*Cistaceae*)

acutifolius misapplied	see *C. inflatus*, *C.* × *pulverulentus*

× ***aguilarii***	CBcs CSBt CTri MRav SPhx WSHC XSen
- 'Maculatus' ♀H4	CBcs CDul CSBt CSam ELan EPfP GMcL LRHS LSRN MMuc NLar NRHS SEle SPer SPoG SWvt WBod WKif WPGP
albidus	CArn SVen XSen
algarvensis	see *Halimium ocymoides*
'Anne Palmer'	see *C.* × *fernandesiae* 'Anne Palmer'
× ***argenteus*** 'Blushing Peggy Sammons'	ELan NLar SVen SWvt XSen
- Golden Treasure = 'Nepond' (v)	SWvt
- 'Paper Moon'	EWTr LSRN NLar SVen
§ - 'Peggy Sammons'	CBot CDul ECha ELan EPfP EWTr LPot LRHS LSRN MAsh MGos MNHC NLar SAko SCob SEND SLim SPer SPhx SWvt XSen
- 'Silver Ghost'	EPfP LRHS SVen SWvt
- 'Silver Pink' ambig.	Widely available
atriplicifolius	see *Halimium atriplicifolium*
'Blanche'	see *C. ladanifer* 'Blanche'
× ***bornetianus*** 'Jester' ♀H4	CSBt EPfP EWTr LRHS MAsh NLar NRHS SVen SWvt
× ***canescens***	SVen
- f. ***albus***	CWib WKif XSen
§ ***clusii***	SBod
- subsp. ***multiflorus***	XSen
× ***corbariensis***	see *C.* × *hybridus*
creticus	CBcs CRos CSam ESps LRHS MAsh MGos NEgg NRHS SHil SLon SPoG SRms SVen SWvt WBod WKif
- subsp. ***corsicus***	XSen
§ - subsp. ***creticus***	EBee ELan EPfP MRav SCoo SPer
§ - subsp. ***incanus***	WCot
× ***crispatus***	XSen
§ - 'Warley Rose'	GMaP SIgm WKif XLum
crispus misapplied	see *C.* × *pulverulentus*, *C.* × *purpureus*
§ ***crispus*** L.	ELan SEND SGol
- 'Prostratus'	see *C. crispus* L.
- 'Sunset'	see *C.* × *pulverulentus* 'Sunset'
§ × ***cyprius*** ♀H4	CArn CDul EBee ELan EPfP ESps LRHS SDix SEND SPer SRms SWvt WKif
§ - var. ***ellipticus*** 'Elma' ♀H4	ELan EPfP EWTr LRHS MAsh NLar NRHS SPer XSen
§ × ***dansereaui***	CBot CMac CSBt CWib EAEE LRHS NLar SVen SWvt
- 'Decumbens' ♀H4	CChe CDul CLet CRos CTri CTsd EBee ELan EPau EPfP ESps LRHS MAsh MBNS MJak MRav MSwo NEgg NLar NRHS SAko SArc SCoo SGbt SHil SPer SPhx SPoG SWvt WPGP
- 'Jenkyn Place' ♀H4	CBod EBee GMaP IVic LSRN MBNS MMuc NLar SPer SPoG WKif
× ***dubius***	SVen
'Elma'	see *C.* × *cyprius* var. *ellipticus* 'Elma'
§ × ***fernandesiae*** 'Anne Palmer'	CRos EPfP LLHF LRHS MAsh MNHC NLar
× ***florentinus*** misapplied	see × *Halimiocistus* 'Ingwersenii'
× ***florentinus*** ambig.	SVen XLum
§ × ***florentinus*** Lam.	GMaP XSen
- 'Fontfroide'	SVen
* - 'Tramontane'	XSen
'Gordon Cooper' ♀H4	LSRN MMuc NLar SCob SPoG
× ***heterocalyx*** 'Chelsea Bonnet'	CBod GMaP MBNS NLar SCoo SPoG XSen
heterophyllus	SVen
'Highlights'	EPfP LRHS MAsh
hirsutus Lam. 1786	see *C. inflatus*

- var. ***psilosepalus*** misapplied	see *C. inflatus*
§ × ***hybridus***	Widely available
- 'Gold Prize' (v)	CWGN ELan NLar SWvt WGrn
- Little Miss Sunshine = 'Dunnecis'PBR (v)	LRHS MAsh MGos NHol NLar NRHS SRms SWvt
- Rospico = 'Rencis'PBR (v)	LRHS NLar
incanus	see *C. creticus* subsp. *incanus*
§ ***inflatus***	XSen
ingwerseniana	see × *Halimiocistus* 'Ingwersenii'
'Jessamy Beauty'	SVen WHar
'Jessamy Bride'	SVen
'Jessamy Charm'	SPhx
ladanifer misapplied	see *C.* × *cyprius*
ladanifer ambig.	CMac ECha SArc WKif
ladanifer L.	CBcs CBot CLet CSBt CTri ELan EPfP GPoy LRHS MRav MSwo SWvt XSen
§ - 'Blanche'	CBot EPfP LLHF LSRN NLar SEND SPer SWvt WKif
§ - 'Paladin'	CRos EPfP LRHS MNHC NRHS
- Palhinhae Group	see *C. ladanifer* var. *sulcatus*
- 'Pat'	CRos ELan EPfP LRHS LSRN MAsh NBir NLar NRHS SAko SPer SPoG SWvt
§ - var. ***sulcatus***	ELan LHop LRHS
lasianthus	see *Halimium lasianthum*
laurifolius	CLet EPfP LRHS MGos NBir SCob SEND SKHP SPer SVen SWvt XSen
- subsp. ***atlanticus***	XSen
× ***laxus*** 'Snow White' ♀H4	CWGN EBee EPfP GMcL MGos NLar NPer SLon
× ***ledon***	EBee
§ × ***lenis*** 'Grayswood Pink' ♀H4	Widely available
libanotis	SVen
- 'Major'	XSen
× ***longifolius***	see *C.* × *nigricans*
× ***loretii*** misapplied	see *C.* × *dansereaui*
× ***loretii*** Rouy & Foucaud	see *C.* × *stenophyllus*
× ***lusitanicus*** Maund	see *C.* × *dansereaui*
'Merrist Wood Cream'	see × *Halimiocistus wintonensis* 'Merrist Wood Cream'
monspeliensis	CAbP CMac EPfP GMcL LRHS MAsh MBNS MMuc SLon SPer SPoG XSen
- 'Vicar's Mead'	CCCN MBNS
monspeliensis × ***salviifolius***	see *C.* × *florentinus* Lam.
§ × ***nigricans***	XSen
× ***oblongifolius***	SWvt XSen
× ***obtusifolius*** misapplied	see *C.* × *nigricans*
× ***obtusifolius*** ambig.	ELan LRHS MRav SAko SKHP
× ***obtusifolius*** Sweet	EPfP WPGP XSen
§ - 'Thrive' ♀H4	CRos EPfP LRHS MGos NRHS SCoo SHil WBod
ocymoides	see *Halimium ocymoides*
'Paladin'	see *C. ladanifer* 'Paladin'
palhinhae	see *C. ladanifer* var. *sulcatus*
parviflorus misapplied	see *C.* × *lenis* 'Grayswood Pink'
parviflorus Lam.	WSHC
× ***pauranthus***	GMcL
* - 'Natacha'	XSen
'Peggy Sammons'	see *C.* × *argenteus* 'Peggy Sammons'
× ***platysepalus***	SPhx
populifolius	CBot CMac ECha EPfP LLHF LRHS NLar SGol SPer SWvt
- var. ***lasiocalyx***	see *C. populifolius* subsp. *major*
§ - subsp. ***major***	EPfP LRHS LSRN SKHP WPGP
psilosepalus misapplied	see *C. inflatus*
§ × ***pulverulentus***	CTri ECha SVen WSHC XSen
* - Delilei Group	XSen
- - 'Fiona'	XSen

§	- 'Sunset' ♀H4	Widely available
	- 'Warley Rose'	see *C.* × *crispatus* 'Warley Rose'
§	× ***purpureus*** ♀H4	Widely available
	- 'Alan Fradd'	Widely available
	- 'Betty Taudevin'	see *C.* × *purpureus*
	- f. ***strictus***	EPfP LRHS SVen XSen
	× ***rodiaei*** 'Jessabel'	CBot CRos EPfP EWTr LRHS MAsh MRav NLar NRHS SPer SWvt WPGP
	- 'Jessica'	NLar
	rosmarinifolius	see *C. clusii*
	'Ruby Cluster'	CCCN LRHS MMuc NLar
	sahucii	see × *Halimiocistus sahucii*
	salviifolius	CAbP CArn CCCN SVen XSen
	- 'Avalanche'	MRav WAbe
	- 'Gold Star'	ELan NLar
	- 'May Snow'	EHoe LRHS MAsh
	- 'Prostratus'	ELan EPfP LRHS SAko SWvt
	'Silver Pink' misapplied	see *C.* × *lenis* 'Grayswood Pink'
	× ***skanbergii***	CLet CMac CTri CWib ELan EPfP LHop MGos MMuc MRav NBir NLar SCob SDix SEND SPer WCFE XLum XSen
	'Snow Fire' ♀H4	CCCN CRos EBee ELan EPfP LRHS LSRN MAsh MGos MMuc NEgg NLar SAko SBod SCoo SEle SWeb SWvt WGrn WHar
§	× ***stenophyllus***	CWib
	'Stripey'	SVen
	× ***tephreus***	XSen
	'Thrive'	see *C.* × *obtusifolius* 'Thrive'
	× ***verguinii***	LHop XSen
	villosus	see *C. creticus* subsp. *creticus*
	wintonensis	see × *Halimiocistus wintonensis*

Citharexylum (*Verbenaceae*)

	quadrangulare Jacq.	see *C. spinosum*
	spicatum	CFil WBor
§	***spinosum***	CHll

citrange see *Citrus* × *insitorum*

× *Citrofortunella* (*Rutaceae*)

	mitis	see *Citrus* × *microcarpa*

citron see *Citrus medica*

Citronella (*Icacinaceae*)

§	***gongonha***	SVen
	mucronata	see *C. gongonha*

Citrullus (*Cucurbitaceae*)

	lanatus 'Charleston Gray'	SVic

Citrus (*Rutaceae*)

§	× ***aurantiifolia*** (F)	CCCN EPfP ETod SCit SPre
	- key lime	see *C.* × *aurantiifolia*
	× ***aurantium*** 'Aber's Narrowleaf' (F)	SCit
	- subsp. ***bergamia***	see *C.* × *limon*
	- 'Bouquet de Fleurs'	see *C.* × *aurantium* (Sour Orange Group) 'Bouquet'
	- 'Gou-tou Cheng' (F)	SCit
§	- Grapefruit Group (F)	CCCN SPre SVic
	- - 'Foster' (F)	SCit
	- - 'Golden Special' (F)	SCit SVic
	- - 'Marsh' (F)	SCit
	- - 'Oroblanco' (F)	SCit
	- - 'Red Blush' (F/S)	SCit
	- - 'Star Ruby' (F/S)	CCCN SCit SPre
	- - 'Wheeny'	see *C. maxima* 'Wheeny'
	- 'Robinson' (F)	SCit
§	- (Sour Orange Group) 'Bouquet' (F)	SCit
	- - 'Bouquetier de Nice' (F)	SCit
	- - 'Chinotto' (F)	SCit SPre
	- - 'Seville' (F)	LSRN SCit SPre
	- - 'Smooth Flat Seville' (F)	SCit
§	- Sweet Orange Group (F)	CCCN ETod SCit SPre SVic
§	- - 'Baia' (F/S)	SCit
	- - 'Embiguo' (F)	SCit
	- - 'Fukumoto' (F)	CCCN
	- - 'Jaffa'	see *C.* × *aurantium* (Sweet Orange Group) 'Shamouti'
	- - 'Lane Late' (F)	CCCN NLar SCit
§	- - 'Malta Blood' (F)	SCit
	- - 'Maltaise Sanguine'	see *C.* × *aurantium* (Sweet Orange Group) 'Malta Blood'
	- - 'Navelate' (F)	SCit
	- - 'Navelina' (F/S)	CCCN SCit SPre SVic
	- - 'Newhall' (F/S)	NLar SCit
	- - 'Ruby' (F)	ELan
	- - 'Salustiana' (F/S)	SCit
§	- - 'Sanguinelli' (F)	CCCN SCit SPre SVic
§	- - 'Shamouti' (F)	SCit
	- - 'Spanish Sanguinelli'	see *C.* × *aurantium* (Sweet Orange Group) 'Sanguinelli'
	- - 'Succari' (F)	SCit
	- - 'Tarocco' (F)	SCit
	- - 'Valencia' (F)	CCCN SCit
	- - 'Washington'	see *C.* × *aurantium* (Sweet Orange Group) 'Baia'
	- - 'Washington Navel'	see *C.* × *aurantium* (Sweet Orange Group) 'Baia'
§	- (Tangelo Group) 'Minneola' (F)	SCit
§	- - 'Nova' (F/S)	CCCN SCit SVic
	- - 'Orlando' (F)	SCit
	- - 'Ugli' misapplied	see *C.* × *aurantium* (Tangelo Group) 'Minneola'
	- - 'Ugli' (F)	SCit
	- (Tangor Group) 'Ellendale' (F)	SCit
	- - 'Murcott' (F)	SCit
	bergamia	see *C.* × *limon*
	- bergamot	see *C.* × *limon* Bergamot Group
	'Buddha's Hand'	see *C. medica* 'Fingered'
	calamondin	see *C.* × *microcarpa*
§	***cavaleriei*** (F)	WPGP
	deliciosa	see *C. reticulata* 'Willowleaf'
	× ***floridana*** 'Eustis' (F)	SCit SPre
§	***hystrix***	CCCN ELan IDee LSRN MHtn NLar NPla SCit SPre
	Ichang lemon	see *C. cavaleriei*
	ichangensis	see *C. cavaleriei*
	× ***insitorum*** 'C-35' (F)	SCit
	- 'Carrizo' (F)	SCit
	- 'Swingle' (F)	SCit
	jambhiri	see *C.* × *taitensis*
§	***japonica*** (F) ♀H1c	CBcs ELan EPfP SCit SPre SVic
	- Hong Kong kumquat (F)	SCit
	- 'Nagami' (F)	SPre
	- 'Reale' PBR (F) **new**	SPre
	kinokuni	see *C. japonica*
	'Kucle' (F)	SCit SPre
	'Kulci' (F)	CCCN
	kumquat	see *C. japonica*
	'La Valette' (F)	CCCN LSRN SPre
	× ***latifolia*** (F/S)	CCCN EPfP NLar SCit SPre
	- 'Bearss' (F)	SCit SVic
	- variegated (v)	SPre

latipes Hook. f. & Thomson ex Hook. f. — see *C. hystrix*
limetta (F) — CCCN SPre SVic
limettioides (F) — SCit SPre
§ × ***limon*** (F) — ETod LSRN SCit SVic
§ - Bergamot Group (F) — SPre
- 'Eureka' — see *C.* × *limon* 'Garey's Eureka'
- 'Eureka Variegated' (F/v) — SCit
- 'Fino' (F) — CCCN SCit
- 'Four Seasons' — see *C.* × *limon* 'Garey's Eureka'
§ - 'Garey's Eureka' (F) — CCCN ELan EPfP LSRN NLar SCit SPre SVic
- 'Imperial' (F) — SCit
- 'Improved Meyer' — see *C.* × *limon* 'Meyer'
- 'Lemonade' (F) — SCit
- 'Lisbon' (F) — SCit
- 'Lunario' (F) — SCit
§ - 'Meyer' (F) ♀H2 — CBcs CCCN CHll CTri ELan EPfP LSRN NLar SCit SPre
- 'Ponderosa' (F) — SCit
- 'Quatre Saisons' — see *C.* × *limon* 'Garey's Eureka'
- 'Rangpur' (F) — SCit
- 'Sfusato d'Amalfi' (F) — SCit
- 'Siracusano' (F) — SCit
- 'Variegata' (F/v) ♀H2 — CCCN SCit SPre
- 'Verna' (F) — CCCN SCit
- 'Villa Franca' (F) — SCit
- 'Yen Ben' (F) — SCit
- 'Zagara Bianco' (F) — SCit
× ***limonia*** — see *C.* × *limon*
'Lipo' (F) — CCCN NLar SPre
macrophylla (F) — SCit
madurensis — see *C. japonica*
§ ***maxima*** 'Wheeny' (F) — SCit
medica 'Cedra' (F) **new** — SPre
- 'Cidro Digitado' — see *C. medica* 'Fingered'
- var. ***digitata*** — see *C. medica* 'Fingered'
- 'Ethrog' (F) — SCit SPre
§ - 'Fingered' (F) — SCit SPre
* - 'Rubra' **new** — SPre
- var. ***sarcodactylis*** — see *C. medica* 'Fingered'
× ***meyeri*** — see *C.* × *limon*
§ × ***microcarpa*** (F) ♀H1c — CCCN NLar SCit SPre
- Philippine lime — see *C.* × *microcarpa*
§ - 'Tiger' (F/v) — SCit SPre
- 'Variegata' — see *C.* × *microcarpa* 'Tiger'
× ***mitis*** — see *C.* × *microcarpa*
× ***nobilis*** Lour. — see *C. reticulata* 'Willowleaf'
- var. ***inermis*** — see *C. japonica*
- Ortanique Group — see *C.* × *aurantium* Sweet Orange Group
× ***obovata*** (F) — SPre
§ - 'Fukushu' (F) — CCCN SCit
× ***paradisi*** — see *C.* × *aurantium* Grapefruit Group
- 'Wheeny' — see *C. maxima* 'Wheeny'
'Pursta' (F) — CCCN
§ ***reticulata*** (F) — CCCN SPre
- 'Clausellina' (F/S) — SCit
- 'Clemenlate'PBR (F) — ELan
- var. ***deliciosa*** — see *C. reticulata* 'Willowleaf'
- 'Fina' (F/S) — SCit
- 'Hashimoto' (F/S) — SCit
- 'Hernandina' (F) — CCCN
- Mandarin Group (F) — EPfP
- - 'Clemenpons'PBR (F) — ELan
- - 'Clementine' (F) — EPfP SPre
- - 'Encore' (F) — SCit
- - 'Esbal' (F) — CCCN
- - 'Fortune' (F) — SCit
- - 'Fremont' (F) — SCit
- - 'Nules' (F/S) — CCCN SCit
- 'Marisol' (F/S) — SCit
- 'Miyagawa' (F) — CCCN SCit
- 'Nour' (F) — SCit
- 'Nova' — see *C.* × *aurantium* (Tangelo Group) 'Nova'
- 'Okitsu' (F/S) — CCCN SCit
- 'Owari' (F/S) — SCit
- Satsuma Group — see *C. reticulata*
§ - 'Willowleaf' (F) — SCit
sinensis — see *C.* × *aurantium* Sweet Orange Group
- 'Jaffa' — see *C.* × *aurantium* (Sweet Orange Group) 'Shamouti'
- 'Washington' — see *C.* × *aurantium* (Sweet Orange Group) 'Baia'
§ × ***taitensis*** (F) **new** — SPre
- 'Otaheite' (F) — CCCN
§ - rough lemon (F) — SCit
- Schaub rough lemon — see *C.* × *taitensis* rough lemon
§ ***trifoliata*** — CAgr CBcs CCCN CDul EBee ELan EPfP IDee LRHS MBlu MGil MMuc MRav SCit SMad SPer SPlb SVic
- 'Flying Dragon' — IVic LEdu SCit
unshiu — see *C. reticulata*
volkameriana — see *C.* × *limon*

Cladium (*Cyperaceae*)

mariscus — XLum

Cladrastis (*Papilionaceae*)

§ ***kentukea*** — CBcs CDul CLnd CMCN CTho EBee ELan EPfP EUJe EWTr MBlu MRav NLar NOra WHar WMat
§ - 'Perkins Pink' — MBlu
- 'Rosea' — see *C. kentukea* 'Perkins Pink'
lutea — see *C. kentukea*
sinensis — CBcs CFil EPfP IArd MBlu SChF SKHP WPGP
wilsonii **new** — WPGP

Clavinodum (*Poaceae*)

§ ***oedogonatum*** — MWht

Claytonia (*Portulacaceae*)

alsinoides — see *C. sibirica*
caroliniana — GKev WCot
§ ***perfoliata*** — GPoy MNHC WHer
§ ***sibirica*** — CAgr IMou LPot LSou MSCN XLum
- f. ***albiflora*** — EWld MPie WCot WMoo
virginica — EBee ECho GKev LAma MPie WFar WMoo WPnP

Clematis ✿ (*Ranunculaceae*)

BWJ 7630 from China — WCru
SDR 6151 — GKev
SDR 7835 **new** — GKev
'Abigail' (Vt) — NHaw
Abilene = 'Evipo027' (EL) — CFlo CKel CLng CRos ELan EPfP ETho LRHS NRHS NTay SNig SPoG SWCr
'Abundance' (Vt) ♀H6 — CBcs CFlo CKel CRHN CWCL EPfP ESps ETho GMcL LCro LRHS LSRN MAsh NHol NTay SDix SNig SPer WBod WFar
Acropolis = 'Evipo078' (Boulevard Series) **new** — CWGN
acuminata — WCru
var. ***sikkimensis*** B&SWJ 7202

	addisonii	ESps NHaw
	'Advent Bells' (C) **new**	CWGN
	afoliata	WThu
	'Ai-Nor' (EL)	ETho
	'Akaishi' (EL)	ETho
	akebioides	NHaw
	akoensis **new**	NHaw
	Alabast = 'Poulala'PBR (EL) ♀H6	ETho LRHS SCoo
	Alaina = 'Evipo056' (EL)	CRos LRHS NRHS NTay SLon SPoG SWCr
	'Alba Luxurians' (Vt)	CBcs CFlo CKel CRHN CRos CSam CTri CWCL ELan ELon EPfP ETho LCro LRHS LSRN MAsh MGos NHol NRHS NTay SCob SDix SLim SNig SPer SPoG SWCr
	'Albatross' (EL)	LSRN
	albicoma	LLHF
	'Albiflora' (A)	NTay
	'Albina Plena' (A/d)	ETho
	'Aleksandrit' (EL)	NHaw
	'Alice Fisk' (EL)	CKel ETho LSRN MSwo NHaw SNig
	'Aliide' (LL)	NHaw
	'Alionushka' (I) ♀H6	CKel CRHN CWCL ELan EPfP ETho LPre LRHS LSRN NLar SDix SLim SPoG SWCr
	Alita = 'Evipo070' (Vt)	CLng NTay SNig
	'Allanah' (LL)	CWCL ELon ETho LRHS LSRN NHaw SCoo SLim SNig WHar
	alpina	ESps GKev GKin GLog IBoy LCro LPar LRHS LSRN MAsh MRav NHaw NPer SCob SEWo SPlb SPre SWvt WFar
	- 'Albiflora'	see *C. sibirica*
	- 'Columbine White'	see *C.* 'White Columbine'
I	- 'Odorata' (A)	NHaw
§	- 'Pamela Jackman' (A) ♀H6	CKel CLng CMac CRos CWCL ELan LRHS LSRN MAsh MJak MMuc NEgg NRHS NTay SCoo SDix SLim SNig SPer SPoG SRkn SWCr SWvt WFar
	- 'Stolwijk Gold' (A)	CWGN ETho IBoy MBlu NHaw NTay SRms
	alternata	CWGN EBee ETho NHaw
	'Amelia' (I)	SMDP
	'Ameshisuto'	see *C.* 'Amethyst' (EL)
§	'Amethyst' (EL)	ETho
	'Amethyst Beauty' (A)	EPfP LRHS
	Amethyst Beauty = 'Evipo043'PBR (LL)	CRos ETho NTay SLon SPoG
	'Andante' (I)	CWGN
	'Andromeda' (EL)	CRos ETho LRHS NHaw NRHS NTay SDix SNig SWCr
	Aneta = 'Evipo055'PBR	CFlo CRos CWGN EBee LCro LRHS NRHS NTay
	Angela = 'Zoang'PBR (EL)	ELan NTay
	Angelique = 'Evipo017' (EL)	CFlo CKel CLng CRos CWGN ELan EPfP ETho LRHS MGos NRHS NTay SCoo SLon SNig SPer SWCr
§	***angustifolia***	EBee
	'Anita' (Ta)	CFlo EBee EPfP ETho IPot LSRN NHaw SMDP
	Anna Louise = 'Evithree'PBR (EL) ♀H6	CLng CRos CWCL EPfP ETho LRHS LSRN MGos NTay SCoo SLim SLon SNig SWCr
	'Annabel' (EL)	LSRN MAsh
	Anniversary = 'Pynot' (EL)	LSRN SCoo
	'Aotearoa' (LL) ♀H6	ETho IPot NHaw
	'Aphrodite' (I)	CRos
	'Aphrodite Elegafumina' (I)	CRHN CRos CWGN LRHS NHaw SBrt
	apiifolia	SBrt
	'Apollonia'	CWGN IPot
	'Apple Blossom' (Ar) ♀H4	Widely available
	'Arabella' (I) ♀H6	Widely available
§	Arctic Queen = 'Evitwo'PBR (EL) ♀H6	CFlo CKel CRos EPfP ETho LBuc LCro LRHS LSRN MAsh NPri NRHS NTay SCoo SLon SPoG SWCr WHar
	armandii	Widely available
	- 'Enham Star'	CRos LRHS MGos NRHS SHil
§	- 'Little White Charm'	CRos EBee ELan LRHS NRHS SHil SKHP SWCr
	- 'Meyeniana'	see *C. armandii* 'Little White Charm'
§	- 'Snowdrift'	CBcs CFlo CKel CLet CRos CSBt ELan EPfP ESps ETho GMcL LCro LRHS LSRN MAsh MGos MSwo NLar NRHS NTay SCob SEle SKHP SPer SPoG SRms SWCr
	× ***aromatica***	CFlo CKel CWGN EAEE ELan EPfP ETho LRHS NTay SCoo SDix SMDP WHlf
	'Asao' (EL)	CLng CRos ELan EPfP ETho IBoy LRHS NTay SCoo SNig SPoG SWCr WFar
	'Ascotiensis' (LL)	CLng CRHN CRos EPfP LRHS NHaw NTay SCoo SDix SLim SLon SNig
	'Ashva' (LL)	CWGN
	Astra Nova = 'Zo09085' (Vt) **new**	CWGN EBee ETho IPot
	Avant-garde = 'Evipo033'PBR (Vt)	CFlo CKel CLng CRos CWCL CWGN ELan EPfP ETho EUJe LRHS NTay SLon
§	Aztek = 'Daihelios' (Ta)	CKel LRHS SCoo
	Baby Doll = 'Zobadol'PBR (EL)	CWGN ETho NTay
	Baby Star = 'Zobast'PBR (EL)	CWGN ETho NTay
§	'Bagatelle' (LL)	CLng GMcL LRHS NHaw SNig
	'Bal Maiden' (Vt)	CRHN NHaw
	'Barbara' (LL)	LSRN NTay SDix
	'Barbara Dibley' (EL)	CFlo CKel CRos CTri CWCL LRHS MAsh NHaw SCoo SLim SNig
	'Barbara Harrington'PBR (LL)	CLng CRos LRHS LSRN SLon
	'Barbara Jackman' (EL)	CKel CRos CWCL ESps ETho LRHS LSRN MAsh MGos MSwo NEgg NTay SCoo SLon SNig SWCr
	'Beata' (LL)	CWCL NHaw SNig
	'Beautiful Bride'PBR (EL)	LCro LPre NTay
	'Beauty of Worcester' (EL)	CKel CRos CWCL ELan ELon EPfP ESps ETho LRHS LSRN MAsh MSwo NEgg NHaw NTay SCoo SDix SLim SNig SPer
	'Bees' Jubilee' (EL)	CBcs CKel CMac CRos CWCL ELan ELon ESps ETho LCro LRHS LSRN MAsh MGos MSwo NBir NEgg NLar NTay SLim SNig SPer SPoG SWvt
	'Bella' (EL)	LSRN
	'Belle Nantaise' (EL)	LRHS NRHS NTay SCoo SRms
	'Belle of Woking' (EL)	CLng CRos ELan ELon ESps LRHS LSRN MAsh NEgg NTay SCoo SPoG SWCr SWvt
	'Ben's Beauty' (A)	CFlo
	Bernadine = 'Evipo 061'	CLng LRHS NRHS NTay
	'Berry Red' (A)	CWGN
	'Best Wishes'	CKel CRos ETho LRHS NRHS NTay SNig SPoG SWCr
§	'Beth Currie' (EL)	CLng CRos EPfP LRHS SNig SWCr
	'Betty Corning' (Vt)	CFlo CKel CLng CRHN CRos CWGN EBee ELan EPfP ETho IPot LRHS LSRN MGos NRHS NTay SCoo SLon SNig SPoG SRms SWCr SWvt
	'Betty Risdon' (EL)	ETho
	Bijou	see *C.* Thumbelina
	'Bill MacKenzie' (Ta) ♀H6	Widely available

	'Black Prince' (Vt)	CFlo CKel CRHN CRos CWGN ELan EPfP ETho IPot LCro LPre LRHS LSRN NHaw NLar NRHS NTay SLim SLon SMDP SNig SPer SPoG SRms SWCr
	'Black Tea' (LL)	CKel CRos EPfP IPot LRHS LSRN NEgg NHaw NRHS NTay SLim SLon SWCr
§	'Błękitny Anioł' (LL) 𝕐^{H6}	CFlo CKel CLng CMac CRHN CWCL CWGN EBee ELon ETho LRHS MAsh NLar NRHS NTay SCob SCoo SNig SPer SPoG SWCr WBor
	Blue Angel	see *C.* 'Błękitny Anioł'
	'Blue Belle' (Vt)	CRHN ELan LRHS NEgg SLon WFar
	'Blue Bird' (A/d)	CBcs CWCL ELan GMcL LRHS MAsh NTay SRms
	Blue Blood	see *C.* 'Königskind'
	'Blue Boy' (EL)	see *C.* 'Elsa Späth'
	'Blue Boy' (I)	see *C.* × *diversifolia* 'Blue Boy' (I)
	'Blue Dancer' (A)	CBcs CKel CLng CRos EPfP ETho LRHS MGos NLar NTay SNig
	'Blue Eclipse' (A)	CFlo CKel CWGN ETho MMrt NHaw NHol NTay SNig
	'Blue Eyes' (EL)	ELon ETho LSRN NHaw NTay SNig
§	'Blue Light'^{PBR} (EL/d)	CFlo CWGN ELan LRHS NLar NTay
	Blue Moon = 'Evirin'^{PBR} (EL)	ETho LRHS LSRN NLar NTay SCoo SLon SNig SWCr
	Blue Ocean = 'Zo09045' (I) **new**	IPot
	Blue Pirouette = 'Zobluepi'^{PBR} (I)	CWCL IPot LRHS MJak NEgg
	Blue Rain	see *C.* 'Sinii Dozhd'
	'Blue Ravine' (EL)	EPfP LRHS NLar NTay SCoo
	Blue River = 'Zoblueriver'^{PBR}	CWGN ELan ETho
	'Bolam Belle' (Vt)	NHaw
	Bonanza = 'Evipo031'^{PBR} (Vt)	CLng CRos EPfP LRHS NLar NTay SCoo SLon SNig SPoG SWCr
	× ***bonstedtii*** 'Crépuscule' (H)	ECtt SMDP
	Bourbon = 'Evipo018'^{PBR} (EL)	CLng CRos ELan EPfP ETho LRHS NTay SCoo SLon SNig
	'Brianna' (Vt) **new**	NHaw
	'Brocade' (Vt)	CRHN NHaw
	'Broughton Bride' (A)	CBot CFlo CKel CLng CWGN ETho LRHS NHol NTay SMDP SRms WHar
	'Broughton Star' (M/d) 𝕐^{H4}	Widely available
	'Brunette' (A)	CFlo CKel CRos ELan EPfP ETho LRHS MAsh NHaw NLar NTay SLon SNig
	buchananiana Finet & Gagnep.	see *C. rehderiana*
	buchananiana DC. B&SWJ 8333a	WCru
	'Buckland Beauty' (V)	CFlo CWGN ETho LCro MJak NHaw SMDP
	'Buckland Cascade'	ETho SMDP
	'Buckland Pixie' (Vt)	NHaw
	'Burford Bell' (V)	NHaw
	'Burford Princess' (Vt)	CRHN NHaw
	'Burford White' (A)	NLar
	'Burma Star' (EL)	CFlo CKel CWCL CWGN EPfP ETho NTay SDix SNig
	'By the Way' (M)	SMDP
	Caddick's Cascade	see *C.* 'Semu'
	calycina	see *C. cirrhosa* var. *balearica*
§	***campaniflora***	CMea EShb ETho GCal NHaw
	- dark-flowered **new**	CMea
	'Candleglow' (A)	NHaw
	'Candy Stripe'	CLng CRos LRHS NTay SCoo SNig SPoG
	'Capitaine Thuilleaux'	see *C.* 'Souvenir du Capitaine Thuilleaux'
	'Cardinal Wyszyński'	see *C.* 'Kardynał Wyszyński'
	'Carlotta' (Vt) **new**	NHaw
	'Carmencita' (Vt)	CRHN EBee LRHS LSRN NHaw SCoo SLon
	'Carnaby' (EL)	CBcs CKel CRos CWCL ELan ELon EPfP ETho LRHS LSRN MAsh NEgg NTay SCoo SLim SNig SWCr SWvt WHar
	'Carol Klein' (I)	NHaw
	'Carol Leeds' (Vt)	NHaw
	'Caroline' (LL)	CWGN ETho LSRN NTay SDix
	× ***cartmanii*** hort. 'Avalanche'^{PBR} (Fo/m)	CFlo CKel CRos ELan EPfP ETho LPre LRHS MGos NLar NPri NRHS NTay SCoo SLon SNig SPoG SWCr SWvt
	- 'Joe' (Fo/m) 𝕐^{H4}	CBcs CFlo CKel CRos CWCL ELan EPfP ETho EWes ITim LPre LRHS LSRN NRHS NTay SCob SCoo SPoG SWCr SWvt WIce
	- 'Joe' × *marmoraria* (Fo)	ECho MAsh SWCr
	- 'Joe' × 'Sharon'	LSRN
	- Michiko = 'Evipo044'^{PBR} (Fo)	CLng CRos LRHS NRHS NTay
	- Tai Yang = 'Evipo045'^{PBR} (Fo)	CLng
	- 'White Abundance'^{PBR} (Fo/f)	LRHS NLar SPoG
	× ***cartmanii*** hort. × ***petriei*** (Fo)	ECho
	Cassis = 'Evipo020'^{PBR}	CKel CLng CRos ELan ETho LRHS LSRN NTay SCoo SLon SNig SPer SWCr
	'Catherine Clanwilliam' (T)	CWGN SMDP
	'Celebration' Caddick	see *C.* 'Pink Celebration'
	'Celebration' Godfrey ^{PBR} (EL)	CFlo ETho NTay
	Cezanne = 'Evipo023'^{PBR} (EL)	CFlo CKel CLng CRos ELan EPfP ETho LRHS MGos NRHS NTay SCoo SLon SNig SWCr
	'Chacewater' (Vt)	CRHN
	'Chalcedony' (EL)	CWCL CWGN ETho SNig
	Chantilly = 'Evipo021'^{PBR} (EL)	CFlo CKel CLng CRos ELan EPfP ETho LBuc LRHS LSRN NRHS NTay SCoo SLon SNig SWCr
	'Charissima' (EL)	CWGN LRHS NLar SCoo
	'Charlie Brown' (LL)	CRHN NHaw
	Charmaine = 'Evipo022'^{PBR} (EL) **new**	CWGN
	'Chatsworth' (Vt)	CRHN CRos CWGN LRHS NHaw SLon SNig
	Chelsea = 'Evipo100'	CRos ETho LRHS NRHS NTay SLon SWCr
	Cherokee	see *C.* Ooh La La
	Chevalier = 'Evipo040'^{PBR} (EL)	CLng CRos ELan EPfP LRHS NRHS NTay SLon SNig SPoG SWCr
	chiisanensis	WSHC
	- B&SWJ 4560	WCru
	- B&SWJ 8800	WCru
	- B&SWJ 12725	WCru
	- 'Korean Beauty' (A)	CRos
	- 'Lemon Bells' (A)	CRos ELan EPfP LRHS MAsh SCoo SLon SPoG SWCr
	- 'Love Child' (A)	ELan IPot NTay
	chinensis misapplied	see *C. terniflora*
	chinensis Osbeck PAB 3751	LEdu
	- RWJ 10042	WCru
	Chinook = 'Evipo013'^{PBR}	CLng LRHS SRms
	'Chris' (H)	SMDP

chrysantha	see *C. tangutica*
chrysocoma misapplied	see *C. spooneri*
chrysocoma Franch.	SMDP
'Cicciolina' (Vt)	CRHN ETho NHaw
cirrhosa	CRos CTri LRHS MAsh SArc SCob SNig
§ - var. ***balearica***	CBcs CFlo CKel CMac CRos CTri CWCL ELan EPfP ETho LCro LHop LRHS LSRN MAsh MGos MRav MSwo NTay SBrt SCob SDix SEND SLim SNig SPer SPoG SWCr SWvt
- 'Jingle Bells' (C)	CFlo CKel CLng CMac CRos CWCL EPfP ETho LCro LOPS LRHS LSRN MAsh MGos NLar NRHS NTay SCob SCoo SLim SLon SNig SPoG SRms SWCr
- 'Ourika Valley' (C)	CWGN ELon ETho LRHS MAsh NLar NTay
- var. ***purpurascens*** 'Freckles' (C) ♀H4	Widely available
- - 'Lansdowne Gem' (C)	CFlo CKel CMac CRos CWCL CWGN CWib LCro LRHS NLar NTay SKHP SMDP SNig SPoG SWCr SWvt
- 'Wisley Cream' (C) ♀H4	Widely available
clarkeana misapplied	see *C. urophylla* 'Winter Beauty'
'Cloudburst' (LL) **new**	ETho
coactilis	NHaw SBrt
§ ***columbiana*** var. ***tenuiloba***	LLHF
- - 'Ylva' (A)	WAbe
'Columbine' (A)	CDul EBee LRHS MSwo NTay SDix SNig SPer
'Columella' (A)	EBee ETho NLar
'Comtesse de Bouchaud' (LL) ♀H6	CFlo CKel CMac CRos CTri CWCL EBee ELan ELon EPfP EShb ESps ETho LRHS LSRN MAsh MGos MRav NPri NRHS NTay SDix SLim SNig SPer SPoG SWCr WBor
Confetti = 'Evipo036'PBR (Vt)	CFlo CLng EBee EPfP ETho LRHS LSRN NTay SLim SLon
'Congratulations' (EL)	CRos ELon LRHS LSRN NRHS SNig
connata	GQui
aff. ***connata*** GWJ 9431 from West Bengal	WCru
- HWJK 2176 from Nepal	WCru
'Constance' (A) ♀H6	CFlo CKel CLng CMac CRos CWCL EBee EPfP ESps ETho GMcL LRHS LSRN NEgg NLar NRHS NTay SCoo SNig SPre SRms SWCr WFar
'Continuity' (M)	CWGN
'Cora' (I)	CWGN
Corinne = 'Evipo063' (EL) **new**	CLng LRHS NRHS NTay SNig SPoG
'Cornish Spirit' (Vt)	CRHN
'Corona' (EL)	ELon EPfP LRHS SCoo
'Côte d'Azur' (H)	CBcs CCse GCal LRHS MNrw NTay
'Countess of Lovelace' (EL)	CBcs ELan EPfP ETho LRHS LSRN NTay SCoo SNig
Country Rose = 'Zocoro'PBR (A)	EPfP
§ 'Crimson King' (LL)	NHaw NLar
'Crinkle'PBR (M)	CCCN
§ ***crispa***	CWGN NHaw
§ Crystal Fountain = 'Evipo038'PBR (EL)	CFlo CKel CLng CRos CWCL CWGN ELan EPfP ETho LBuc LCro LRHS LSRN MGos NTay SCoo SLim SLon SNig SPoG SRms SWCr
'Danae' (Vt)	NHaw
Dancing Dorien = 'Zodado'PBR (EL)	IPot
Dancing Queen = 'Zodaque'PBR (EL)	ETho NTay
Dancing Smile = 'Zodasmi'PBR (EL)	NTay
'Daniel Deronda' (EL) ♀H6	CFlo CKel CLng CRos CWCL CWGN ELan ETho IBoy IPot LRHS LSRN MAsh NBir NRHS NTay SCoo SDix SLim SNig SPoG SWCr
'Darius' (EL)	SNig
'Dark Eyes' (Vt)	CKel CWGN ETho IPot LPar
'Dark Secret' (A)	NHaw NHol NTay
dasyandra NJM 11.075	WPGP
'Dawn' (EL)	CCCN CFlo CRos ETho LRHS LSRN NTay SCoo
'De Vijfhoeven' (Vt)	NHaw
'Débutante' (EL)	NHaw
delavayi	ESps
'Denny's Double' (EL/d)	CWGN ETho LRHS NTay SNig
'Destiny' (EL)	CWGN SNig
Diamantina = 'Evipo039'PBR (EL)	CFlo CKel CLng CRos EPfP ETho LBuc LCro LRHS NRHS NTay SLon SNig SPoG SWCr
'Diamond Anniversary' (A)	CWCL LPre NTay
'Diamond Ball'PBR (EL) **new**	ETho
'Diana' (LL)	ETho LSRN NHaw
Diana's Delight = 'Evipo026'PBR	CKel CLng CRos EPfP ETho LRHS LSRN NRHS NTay SLon SPoG SWCr
dioscoreifolia	see *C. terniflora*
§ × ***diversifolia***	CRHN LRHS NHaw SWvt WCot
- 'Benedikt' (I) **new**	CWGN
§ - 'Blue Boy' (I)	CRHN NHaw
- 'Heather Herschell' (I)	CFlo CRHN CTsd NHaw SMDP
§ - 'Hendersonii' (I)	CFlo CWCL ELan ETho GBuc LHop LRHS LSRN MCot MRav NBir SMHy SPer SWat SWvt WCot WHoo
§ - 'Olgae' (I)	NHaw
'Doctor Mary' (V)	NHaw
'Doctor Ruppel' (EL)	CFlo CKel CMac CRos CWCL EBee ELon ESps ETho GMcL IBoy LRHS LSRN MAsh MSwo NBir NRHS NTay SCob SDix SLim SNig SPer SWCr WFar
'Dominika' (LL)	NHaw
'Dorath'	CKel CRos CWGN EPfP LRHS NHaw NTay SWCr
'Dorothy Barbara' (M)	SMDP
'Dorothy Tolver' (EL)	ETho
'Dorothy Walton'	see *C.* 'Bagatelle'
'Double Delight' (M)	CFlo CWGN
'Duchess of Albany' (1897) (T)	CFlo CKel CLng CRos CTri CWCL CWib ELan EPfP ETho LRHS LSRN MAsh MGos NEgg NHol SDix SNig SPer SWCr
'Duchess of Edinburgh' (EL)	CBcs CKel CMac CWCL EBee ELan ELon EPfP ESps ETho IBoy LRHS LSRN MAsh MGos MSwo NEgg NHol NRHS NTay SDix SLim SNig SPoG SWCr SWvt WHar
'Duchess of Sutherland' (EL)	NHaw
× ***durandii*** ♀H6	CBcs CFlo CKel CRHN CRos CSpe CWCL ELan EPfP ETho LRHS LSRN MAsh MGos MRav NRHS NTay SCoo SDix SNig SPer SPoG SWCr SWvt WCot
'Dutch Sky' (LL)	CWGN ETho LPar
'Early Sensation' (Fo/f)	Widely available
East River = 'Zoeastri'PBR (I)	ELan
'Eclipse' (H)	EBee

Edda = 'Evipo074' (Boulevard Series) (EL)	CRos LRHS NRHS NTay SWCr
'Edith' (EL) ♀H6	CWCL ETho LSRN NHaw NLar NTay SNig
'Édouard Desfossé' (EL)	LRHS
'Edward Prichard'	CFlo CKel EPfP ETho MAsh NTay SDix SMDP SNig
'Eetika' (LL)	CRHN ETho NHaw
'Ekstra' (LL)	NHaw
'Eleanor' (Fo/f)	GEdr
'Elf' (Vt)	CWGN
'Elisabeth Foster' (EL) **new**	CRos
'Elizabeth' (M) ♀H4	Widely available
§ 'Elsa Späth' (EL)	CKel CLng CMac CRos CTri ELan EMOT EPfP ESps ETho LRHS LSRN MAsh NEgg NRHS NTay SLim SNig SPer SPoG SWCr SWvt
'Elten' (M)	CKel
'Elvan' (Vt)	CRHN NHaw NLar SNig
'Ember' (I)	CWGN
'Emerald Dream'	EBee NPnk
'Emilia Plater' (Vt)	CRHN EPfP ETho NHaw NTay SLon
'Empress Amy Lai' **new**	CWCL LPre NHaw
Empress = 'Evipo011'PBR (EL)	CFlo CLng CRos EBee ELan EPfP LRHS NRHS NTay SLon SNig
Endellion = 'Evipo076' (EL)	CRos LRHS NRHS NTay SPoG SWCr
'Entel' (Vt)	CRHN NHaw SNig
× ***eriostemon***	see *C.* × *diversifolia*
'Ernest Markham' (LL) ♀H6	CBcs CKel CMac CRos CWCL ELan EPfP ESps ETho IBoy LRHS LSRN MAsh MGos MJak MSwo NEgg NPri NRHS NTay SDix SLim SNig SPer SPoG SWCr SWvt
Esme = 'Evipo048'	CLng NTay SNig
'Esperanto' (LL)	EBee NHaw
'Étoile Rose' (Vt)	CMac CRHN CRos CTri CWCL EBee ELan EPfP ESps ETho IPot LRHS LSRN MAsh NEgg NHaw NHol NTay SCoo SDix SLim SLon SNig SPer SWCr WBod
'Étoile Violette' (Vt) ♀H6	Widely available
Evening Star = 'Evista' (EL)	EPfP
'Everett' (V)	SMDP
Exciting = '20exci' (EL)	NTay
'Fair Rosamond' (EL)	NHaw NLar NTay
Fairy Blue	see *C.* Crystal Fountain
'Fairydust' (Vt)	NHaw
fargesii var. ***souliei***	see *C. potaninii* var. *potaninii*
× ***fargesioides***	see *C.* 'Paul Farges'
fasciculiflora	CMHG
- KWJ 12160	WCru
- L 657	CBot EBee EPfP WCru WPGP
'Fascination'PBR (I)	CFlo CWGN EBee NTay
Filigree = 'Evipo029'PBR (EL)	CFlo CLng CRos ETho LBuc LRHS MGos NRHS NTay SWCr
'Filomae' (Vt) **new**	NHaw
'Fireworks' (EL)	CFlo CKel CRos CWCL CWGN ELon EPfP ESps ETho IBoy LRHS LSRN MAsh MRav NEgg NLar NTay SLim SNig SPer SPoG SWCr
flammula	CFlo CKel CRos CWib ELan EPfP ETho LCro LRHS LSRN MAsh MBlu MRav NRHS NTay SDix SNig SPer SPoG SRms SWCr SWvt XSen
- 'Rubra Marginata'	see *C.* × *triternata* 'Rubromarginata'
Fleuri = 'Evipo042'PBR (Boulevard Series) (EL)	CFlo CKel CLng CRos CWCL EPfP ETho LBuc LRHS LSRN LSou NRHS NTay SCoo SLon SNig SPoG SWCr
florida	CWGN SWvt
- 'Bicolor'	see *C. florida* var. *florida* 'Sieboldiana'

- var. ***flore-pleno*** 'Plena' (d)	CCCN CFlo CLng CWCL ELan EPfP ETho IPot LRHS LSRN MAsh NEgg NRHS NTay SNig SPoG SWCr
§ - var. ***florida*** 'Sieboldiana' (d)	CBcs CFlo CKel CRos CWCL CWGN ELan ELon EPfP ETho LCro LOPS LRHS LSRN MAsh NEgg NRHS NTay SNig SPoG SRkn SWCr SWvt WFar
- var. ***normalis*** Pistachio = 'Evirida'PBR (LL)	CCCN CFlo CKel CLng CRos CWGN ELan EPfP ETho LRHS MAsh MGos NLar NTay SLon SNig SPoG SWCr
- - 'Thorncroft' (LL)	ETho
'Floris V' (I)	MCot NHaw NLar
'Fluffy Duck' (Vt/d)	NHaw
foetida × 'Lunar Lass' (Fo)	ECho
foetida × ***petriei***	ECho
'Fond Memories' (EL)	CFlo CKel CRos CWCL CWGN EPfP ETho IPot LCro LOPS LRHS LSRN NLar NRHS NTay SLon SNig SWCr
Forever Friends = 'Zofofri'PBR (LL)	CRos CWGN ETho IPot LRHS NRHS NTay SLon SWCr
'Forget-me-not NLP1'	LSRN NLar WHar
forrestii	see *C. napaulensis*
§ ***forsteri***	IDee WSHC
'Foxtrot' (Vt)	CRHN
'Foxy' (A) ♀H6	CFlo CLng LRHS NLar NTay SLon SNig
Fragrant Oberon = 'Hutbron'PBR (Fo)	CFlo LCro LOPS NTay SMDP SWvt
'Fragrant Spring' (M)	CKel CRos CSBt CWGN ELon ETho GMcL IBoy LCro LOPS LRHS NLar NRHS NTay SLim SMDP SNig SWCr
'Frances Rivis' (A) ♀H6	CBot CFlo CKel CMac CWCL ELan EPfP ETho LCro LOPS LPar LRHS LSRN MAsh MBlu MRav MSwo NFav NLar NTay NWea SDix SNig SPer SPoG SRms SWCr
'Francesca' (A)	LSRN
'Frankie' (A) ♀H6	CFlo CKel CLng CRos EBee ELan EPfP ETho LCro LRHS LSRN MAsh MGos MHer NTay SCoo SNig SWCr
Franziska Maria = 'Evipo008' (EL)	CFlo CLng CRos EPfP LCro LRHS MAsh MGos NTay SCoo SLon
'Frau Susanne' (EL)	ETho
'Freda' (M) ♀H4	CKel CRHN CTri CWGN ELan EPfP ESps ETho LCro LRHS LSRN MAsh MBlu MRav NEgg NHol NRHS NTay SDix SLim SNig SPer SRms SWCr
fremontii	NHaw SBrt
'Fryderyk Chopin' (EL)	EBee NHaw NLar SNig
'Fudō' (V)	NHaw
'Fujimusume' (EL) ♀H6	CFlo CKel CRos CWGN ETho IPot LRHS MAsh NHaw NRHS NTay SPoG SWCr
fujisanensis B&SWJ 11370	WCru
'Fukuzono'	CRos LPar LRHS LSRN NHaw NRHS NTay SDix SNig SWCr
fusca misapplied	see *C. japonica*
fusca Turcz. dwarf	CWGN
§ - var. ***fusca***	ETho WSHC
- var. ***kamtschatica***	see *C. fusca* Turcz. var. *fusca*
- large-flowered B&SWJ 8431 **new**	WCru
'Fusca Peveril' (V)	NHaw
'Fuyu-no-tabi' (EL)	ETho
'Gabrielle' ambig.	LSRN
Galore	see *C.* Vesuvius
'Garnet' (V)	NHaw
Gazelle = 'Evipo014'PBR (I)	CLng LRHS SKHP SRms
'Generał Sikorski' (EL)	CBcs CFlo CKel CMac CRos CWCL ELan EPfP ESps ETho LRHS LSRN

		MAsh MGos NRHS NTay SCoo SLim SNig SPer SWCr SWvt
	gentianoides	WAbe
	'Geoffrey Tolver' (LL)	CWGN ETho NHaw SNig
	'Georg' (A/d)	EBee
	'Georg Ots' (LL)	NHaw
	Giant Star = 'Gistar'^{PBR} (M)	CKel CLng EBee ELon GMcL IBoy LRHS NEgg NLar NPer SLim SRkn
	'Gillian Blades' (EL) 🏆^{H6}	CFlo CKel CLng CRos ELan EPfP ETho LBuc LRHS LSRN MAsh MGos NHaw NRHS NTay SCoo SNig SPoG SWCr SWvt
§	'Gipsy Queen' (LL) 🏆^{H6}	CBcs CMac CRos CWCL ELan ELon EPfP ESps ETho IBoy LRHS LSRN MAsh MGos NEgg NTay SDix SLim SNig SPer SPoG SWCr SWvt
	Giselle = 'Evipo051'	CRos EPfP ETho LRHS NRHS NTay SLon SPoG SWCr
	'Gladys Picard' (EL)	NHaw
	glaucophylla	WCru
	'Golden Harvest' (Ta)	NLar
	Golden Tiara = 'Kugotia'^{PBR} (Ta) 🏆^{H6}	CKel CWGN ESps ETho LSRN NLar NTay SRms WCot
	'Grace' (Ta)	EPfP NHaw NLar
	gracilifolia BWJ 8002	WCru
I	'Grandiflora' (F)	WFar
	grandiflora	ETho LBuc SRms
	'Grandiflora Sanguinea' (Vt)	NHaw
	grata misapplied	see *C.* × *jouiniana*
	'Gravetye Beauty' (T)	CFlo CKel CMac CRHN CRos CWCL ELan EPfP ETho LRHS LSRN MAsh MGos MJak NHol NTay SDix SLon SNig SPoG SRms SWCr SWvt
§	'Grażyna' (LL)	ETho
	grewiiflora B&SWJ 2956	WCru
	'Guernsey Cream' (EL)	CFlo CRos CWCL EPfP ETho LCro LOPS LRHS LSRN MAsh MGos NLar NTay SCoo SDix SLim SNig SRkn SWCr
	Guiding Promise = 'Evipo053'^{PBR}	CLng LRHS NRHS NTay SLon SNig
	'Gunta' (LL)	NHaw
	'H.F. Young' (EL)	CFlo CKel CRos ELan EPfP ETho LRHS LSRN MAsh MGos NLar NTay SCoo SDix SNig SPer SWCr SWvt
	'Hågelby Pink' (Vt) 🏆^{H6}	CRHN CWGN NHaw
	'Hagley Hybrid' (LL)	CMac CRos CWCL EBee ELan EPfP ESps ETho GMcL LRHS LSRN MAsh MGos MJak MRav NEgg NLar NRHS NTay SCob SDix SLim SNig SPer SPoG SRms SWCr SWvt
	'Hakuōkan' (EL)	EPfP ETho LRHS LSRN NLar SCoo
	'Hakuree' ambig.	CKel
	'Hakuree' K. Ozawa (I)	EBee ETho SMDP
	'Hanaguruma' (EL)	CKel ETho LSRN NTay SNig
	'Hanajima' (I)	ETho SChF SMDP
	'Hania' (EL)	EBee ETho
	'Happy Anniversary' (EL)	LBuc LSRN NLar NTay
§	Happy Birthday = 'Zohapbi'^{PBR} (LL)	LCro LSRN NTay
	Harlow Carr = 'Evipo004'^{PBR}	CLng CMac CRos EPfP LRHS NRHS NTay SCoo SLim SRms
	'Haru Ichiban' (EL)	ETho
	'Hayate'	CWGN EBee
	'Helen Cropper' (EL)	ETho
	'Helios'	see *C.* Aztek
	'Helsingborg' (A) 🏆^{H6}	CFlo CKel CLng CRos EBee ELan EPfP ETho LRHS MAsh NPri NTay SCoo SNig SPoG SRms SWCr
I	'Hendersonii' (I)	CFlo CKel GBuc LSRN
	hendersonii Koch	see *C.* × *diversifolia* 'Hendersonii'
	hendersonii Stand.	see *C.* × *diversifolia*
I	'Hendersonii Rubra' (Ar)	LRHS
	'Hendryetta'^{PBR} (I)	EMOT LRHS NEgg SWvt
	henryi	EShb ESps LSRN MAsh NTay SNig
	- B&SWJ 3402	WCru
	- var. ***morii*** B&SWJ 1668	WCru
	'Henryi' (EL)	CFlo CKel CMac CRos CTri CWCL EBee ELan EPfP ETho LCro LRHS LSRN MRav MSwo NEgg NRHS SDix SPer SPoG SWCr
	heracleifolia	CBod CFis CMac CPou ECtt GLog LRHS MArt NLar WBor WOld
	- Alan Bloom	see *C. tubulosa* Alan Bloom
	- 'Blue Dwarf' (H)	CWGN ETho SMDP WAbe
	- 'Cassandra' (H)	CBot CFlo CSpe CWGN CWld EAEE ECtt ELon EPfP ETho GLog LCro LRHS LSRN MCot NCGa NRHS SChF SMDP
	- 'China Purple' (H)	CPou GBin LRHS MHol MSCN NDov NLar SNig WHar
	- var. ***davidiana***	see *C. tubulosa*
	- 'Pink Dwarf' (H)	CWGN ETho NLar NTay SMDP WAbe
	- 'Roundway Blue Bird' (H)	CBot LHop NHaw SMDP
	'Herbert Johnson' (EL)	NHaw
	hexapetala Pall.	see *C. angustifolia*
	hexapetala Forster	see *C. forsteri*
	hexasepala	see *C. forsteri*
	hirsutissima	SBrt
	'Honora' (LL)	CFlo CWGN LRHS MAsh NTay SCoo SNig
	'Horn of Plenty' (EL)	CRos LRHS NHaw
	'Hoshi-no-flamenco' (T) <u>new</u>	CWGN ETho
	huchouensis <u>new</u>	NHaw
	'Huldine' (LL) 🏆^{H6}	CBcs CKel CLng CRHN CRos CWCL ELan EPfP ETho LRHS LSRN MAsh MRav NTay SDix SLon SNig SPer SWCr SWvt
	'Huvi' (LL)	CWGN ETho NHaw
	'Hybrida Sieboldii' (EL)	SCoo
	Hyde Hall = 'Evipo009'^{PBR} (EL)	CFlo CKel CMac CRos CWGN ELan EPfP LRHS MAsh MGos NRHS NTay SCoo SLim SLon SNig SPer SRms SWCr
	'Hythe Egret' (Fo)	ECho LLHF
	I Am a Little Beauty = 'Zolibe' (Vt)	CRHN NHaw NTay
	I am Happy = 'Zoiamha' (Vt)	SCob
	I am Lady J = 'Zoiamlj' (Vt)	IPot NHaw SCob
	I Am Lady Q = 'Zoiamladyq'^{PBR} (Vt)	CWGN LRHS NHaw NTay SCob
	I Am Red Robin = 'Zorero'^{PBR} (A)	CWGN
	ianthina 'Josie's Midnight Blue' (V)	NHaw
	- var. ***kuripoensis***	NHaw
	- - B&SWJ 700	WCru
	'Ibi' (EL)	CWGN
	Ice Blue = 'Evipo003'^{PBR} (Prairie Series) (EL)	CLng CRos ELan EPfP ETho LRHS NTay SCoo SLim SLon SNig SWCr
	'Ice Queen' (EL)	MAsh
	'Ilka' (EL)	NHaw
	'Ingrid Biedenkopf' (Vt)	NHaw
	'Innocent Blush'^{PBR} (EL) <u>new</u>	ETho
	'Innocent Glance'^{PBR} (EL) <u>new</u>	ETho
	Inspiration = 'Zoin'^{PBR} (I)	ELan NLar SCoo

	integrifolia	CFis CPou ELan EPfP GKev IFoB LHop LRHS MArt MHer NLar NPer NTay SRms WHoo
	- RCB UA 10	WCot
I	- 'Alba' (I)	CFlo ECtt LRHS LSRN NBir NHaw NTay SCoo SRms
	- 'Blue Ribbons' (I)	CSpe SPhx
	- dark blue-flowered **new**	GKev
	- 'Hendersonii' Koch	see *C.* × *diversifolia* 'Hendersonii'
	- 'Olgae'	see *C.* × *diversifolia* 'Olgae'
	- 'Ozawa's Blue' (I)	CWGN ETho MBNS
	- white-flowered	see *C. integrifolia* 'Alba'
	'Intermedia Rosea' (I)	NChi
	ispahanica	NHaw
	'Iubileinyi-70' (LL)	NHaw
	'Ivan Olsson' (EL)	CWCL ETho IPot
	'Izumi' M.Takeuchi (LL)	ETho
	'Jackmanii' (LL) ♀H6	CBcs CKel CMac CRos CTri EBee EPfP ESps ETho GMcL IBoy LCro LRHS LSRN MAsh MGos MJak NTay NWea SCoo SLim SNig SPoG SWCr SWvt WHar
	'Jackmanii Alba' (EL)	CRos CWCL ELan ELon EPfP ETho LRHS LSRN MAsh SCoo SLim SNig SPoG
	Jackmanii Purpurea = 'Zojapur'PBR (LL)	ETho NTay
	'Jackmanii Rubra' (EL)	ETho
	'Jackmanii Superba' misapplied	see *C.* 'Gipsy Queen'
	'Jackmanii Superba' ambig. (LL)	CDul CFlo CKel CMac CRos CWCL ELan EPfP ESps ETho LCro LRHS MAsh MGos MRav MSwo NEgg NPer NPri NTay SCob SDix SLim SPer SPoG SWCr
	'Jacqueline du Pré' (A) ♀H6	CBcs CFlo CKel CMac EBee ELan EPfP ETho LPre LRHS NTay SMDP SNig
	'Jacqui' (M/d)	CKel CWCL
	'James Mason' (EL)	ETho LSRN SNig
	'Jan Fopma'PBR (I)	CWGN NTay
	'Jan Lindmark' (A/d)	CLng CRos ETho LRHS MAsh NLar NTay SCoo SNig SPoG SPre SWCr
§	'Jan Paweł II' (EL)	ELan ETho LRHS SCoo SPer
§	***japonica***	NHaw
	- B&SWJ 11204	WCru
	'Jasper' (V)	ETho IPot
	'Jean Caldwell' (Vt)	NHaw
	'Jean Cumpston' (C) **new**	NHaw
	'Jeanne's Pink'	CWCL ETho LCro LPre
	'Jenny' (M/d)	CFlo CKel CRos CWCL ETho LRHS LSRN SNig SPoG SWCr
	'Jenny Caddick' (Vt)	NHaw
	'Jerzy Popiełuszko' (EL)	ETho
	Jessica = 'Evipo012'PBR (I)	CLng LRHS
	Jewel of Merk	see *C.* Happy Birthday
	John Howells = 'Zojohnhowells'PBR (Vt)	CFlo CWCL ETho LSRN NTay SLon
	'John Huxtable' (LL) ♀H6	CFlo CKel CLng CRos ETho LRHS NHaw NTay SNig
	John Paul II	see *C.* 'Jan Paweł II'
	'John Treasure' (Vt)	CRHN NHaw NLar NTay
	'John Warren' (EL)	CRos LRHS MAsh NHaw NRHS NTay SCoo SWCr
	'Jolly Jake' (Vt)	CFlo
	Josephine = 'Evijohill'PBR (EL)	CFlo CKel CLng CRos CWCL CWGN EPfP ETho EUJe LCro LRHS LSRN MAsh MGos NLar NRHS NTay SCoo SLim SNig SPer SPoG SRkn SWCr SWvt WHar
§	× ***jouiniana***	MRav SEND SWvt WSHC

	- 'Chance' (H)	NHaw
	'Julka' (EL)	CFlo CWCL ETho NHaw NTay
	'Justa' (Vt)	NHaw SNig
	'Juuli' (I)	LSRN
	'Kaaru' (LL)	CRHN
	'Kacper' (EL)	NHaw
	'Kaen' (EL)	EBee ETho NTay
	'Kaiser'PBR **new**	ETho
	'Kaiu' (V)	CFlo CKel CRos CWCL CWGN ETho LRHS NHaw NTay SMDP
§	'Kakio' (EL)	CLng CRos CWCL ETho LRHS LSRN MAsh MGos NEgg NTay SDix SLim SNig SPer SPoG SWCr
	'Kamila' (EL) **new**	SNig
I	'Kamilla' (EL)	CWGN
§	'Kardynał Wyszyński' (EL)	ETho
§	'Kasmu' (Vt)	NHaw
	Kassia = 'Evipo067' (Flora Series) **new**	LRHS NRHS
	'Kathleen Dunford' (EL)	LSRN NHaw NTay SCoo
	'Kathryn Chapman' (Vt)	CRHN NHaw
	'Kaunitar' (LL)	NHaw
	'Ken Donson' (EL) ♀H6	LRHS SCoo
	'Ken Pyne' (LL)	CFlo
	'Kermesina' (Vt) ♀H6	CKel CRHN CRos EBee ELan EPfP ETho IBoy LCro LRHS MAsh MJak SCoo SDix SLim SNig SPer SPoG SRms SWCr
	'Ketu Õde' (LL)	NHaw
	'Kiev' (Vt)	NHaw
	'Killifreth' (Vt)	CRHN NHaw
	'King Edward VII' (EL)	LRHS NHaw
	Kingfisher = 'Evipo037'PBR (EL)	CFlo CKel CLng CRos ELan EPfP LBuc LRHS NTay SCoo SLon SNig
	'Kinju Atarashi' (LL)	ETho NTay
	'Kiri Te Kanawa' (EL)	CKel CWCL ELon ETho LRHS LSRN NLar NTay SNig
	'Kirsi' (LL) **new**	NHaw
	'Kommerei' (LL)	NHaw
§	'Königskind' (EL)	ETho NLar
	koreana	MAsh WCru
	'Krakowiak'PBR (Vt)	NHaw
	'Külli' (LL)	NHaw
	ladakhiana	GQui NHaw
	'Lady Betty Balfour' (LL)	CMac CRos ETho LRHS NTay SCoo SNig SWvt
	'Lady Bird Johnson' (T)	CFlo CRos CWCL LRHS LSRN NTay SCoo SNig
	'Lady Caroline Nevill' (EL)	LRHS NRHS
	'Lady Londesborough' (EL)	NHaw NTay SCoo SDix
	'Lady Northcliffe' (EL)	CKel CLng CRos CTri CWCL EPfP ETho LRHS MAsh NTay SDix SNig
	'Lambton Park' (Ta) ♀H6	CKel CRHN CWCL ETho NHaw NLar NTay SMDP
	lasiandra	NHaw
	'Last Dance' (Ta)	CRHN
	Lasting Love	see *C.* 'Grażyna'
	'Lasurstern' (EL) ♀H6	CBcs CFlo CKel CMac CTri ELan EPfP ETho LCro LRHS LSRN MAsh NEgg NTay SDix SNig SPer SPoG SWCr SWvt WFar
	'Laura Denny' (EL)	ETho
	'Lavender Twirl' (Vt)	CRHN
	'Lawsoniana' (EL)	CMac LRHS SNig
	'Lech Wałęsa' (EL)	ETho
	'Lemon Beauty' (A) **new**	ETho
	'Lemon Chiffon' (EL)	CLng CRos LRHS
	'Lemon Dream'PBR (A) **new**	ETho
	Lianne = 'Evipo064' (EL) **new**	CLng

	Liberation = 'Evifive'^{PBR} (EL)	CLng CRos LRHS NLar NTay SCoo SLim SLon SNig
	Liberty = 'Zo08095' (EL) **new**	ETho IPot
§	***ligusticifolia***	NHaw
	'Lily the Pink' (V/Vt)	NHaw
	'Lincoln Star' (EL)	CLng CMac CRos ELon ESps LRHS MAsh NEgg SDix SLim SNig SPer SWvt
	'Lisboa' (Vt)	NHaw
	'Little Bas' (Vt)	CRHN CWGN IPot NHaw NLar NTay SLon SNig
	'Little Butterfly' (Vt)	CRHN NHaw
	'Little Mermaid' (EL)	CFlo EBee ETho NTay
	'Little Nell' (Vt)	CCCN CRHN ELan EPfP ETho LRHS LSRN MAsh NTay SCoo SDix SLon SNig WFar
I	'Longiflora'	CFlo
	'Lord Herschell'	CFlo CKel CWCL CWGN ETho NHaw SMDP
	'Lord Nevill' (EL)	EPfP LRHS SNig
	'Louise Rowe' (EL)	CFlo CLng CRos CWCL ELan ETho LRHS LSRN NHaw NTay SNig SWCr
	loureiroana HWJ 663	WCru
	'Love Jewelry' (EL)	ETho SNig
	Lula = 'Evipo057' (Boulevard Series) **new**	CWGN
	'Lunar Lass' (Fo/f)	CFlo EBee ECho ETho LRHS NTay WAbe
	'Lunar Lass Variegata' (Fo/v)	ECho LLHF
	'Luther Burbank' (LL)	SNig
	'Luxuriant Blue' (Vt)	CRHN NHaw
	'M. Koster' (Vt)	CRHN ETho LPar LRHS NHaw SLon SRms
	macropetala (d)	CBcs CLng CRos CSBt ELan EPfP ESps ETho GKev GMcL LRHS MAsh MGos MMuc MRav NRHS NTay SDix SNig SPer
	- 'Blue Lagoon'	see *C. macropetala* 'Lagoon' Jackman 1959
	- 'Lagoon' Jackman 1956	see *C. macropetala* 'Maidwell Hall' Jackman
	- 'Lagoon' ambig.	LSRN SNig
§	- 'Lagoon' Jackman 1959 (A/d) Υ^{H6}	CRos ETho LCro LRHS LSRN MAsh MSwo NHol NRHS NTay SCoo
	- 'Maidwell Hall' ambig. (A)	SCob
§	- 'Maidwell Hall' Jackman (A/d)	CTri EPfP LSRN MAsh NTay
	- 'Wesselton' (A/d) Υ^{H6}	CFlo CKel CRos CTri CWCL EBee EPfP ETho LCro LRHS MAsh NHaw NTay SPoG SPre SRms SWCr
	- 'White Moth'	see *C.* 'White Moth'
	'Madame Baron-Veillard' (LL)	CLng CRos LRHS SCoo SNig
	'Madame Edouard André' (LL)	CLng CRos CWCL EPfP LRHS MAsh NRHS NTay SCoo SNig
	'Madame Grangé' (LL) Υ^{H6}	CRos LRHS NHaw SCoo
	'Madame Julia Correvon' (Vt) Υ^{H6}	Widely available
	'Madame le Coultre'	see *C.* 'Mevrouw Le Coultre'
	'Majojo' (Fo)	GEdr LLHF
	mandschurica	ETho GBin GCal NHaw NLar XEll
	marata	GKev WThu
	'Margaret Hunt' (LL)	ELan ETho IBoy LSRN NHaw NTay
	'Mari' (LL)	NHaw
	'Maria' Kivistik (LL)	NHaw
	'Maria Błăsescu'	NTay
	'Maria Cornelia'^{PBR} (Vt)	CWGN EBee ETho LCro LOPS NTay
	'Maria Skłodowska-Curie'^{PBR} (EL) **new**	ETho
	'Marie Boisselot' (EL) Υ^{H6}	CBcs CFlo CKel CMac CRos CTri CWCL ELan EPfP ETho IBoy LRHS LSRN MAsh MGos MRav MSwo NPri NTay SDix SNig SPer SPoG SWCr SWvt
	'Marie-Louise' (EL)	EBee
	'Marinka'	CWGN EBee
	'Marjorie' (M/d)	CBcs CKel CRos CTri CWCL ELan EPfP ESps GKin GMcL IBoy LRHS LSRN MAsh MGos MRav NEgg NRHS NTay SLim SNig SPer SPoG SRms SWCr WFar
	'Markham's Pink' (A/d) Υ^{H6}	Widely available
	marmoraria	CRos EAEE ECho EPot LHop LRHS NRHS SPlb SRms WAbe
	- 'Timpany Treasure'	ITim
	marmoraria* × *petriei	ECho
	'Marmori' (LL)	CWGN ETho NHaw
	Marta = 'Evipo071' **new**	CLng NTay SNig
	'Mary Habberley' (Vt)	NHaw
	'Mary Rose'	see *C. viticella* 'Flore Pleno'
	'Mary-Claire' (EL/d)	SNig
	maximowicziana	see *C. terniflora*
	'Mayleen' (M) Υ^{H4}	CPou CRos CSam CTri EPfP ETho IBoy LRHS MAsh MRav NEgg NRHS NTay SCoo SLim SNig SPer SPoG SRms SWCr SWvt WFar
	'Mazury' (LL)	ETho
	'Meeli' (LL)	NHaw
I	'Melodie' (Vt)	NHaw
§	'Mevrouw Le Coultre' (EL)	GMcL MJak
	meyeniana* var. *insularis B&SWJ 6700	WCru
	Mienie Belle = 'Zomibel'^{PBR} (T)	CWGN ETho IPot NHaw
	'Mikelite' (Vt)	NHaw
	'Miniseelik' (LL)	NHaw
	'Minister' (EL)	SNig
	'Minuet' (Vt) Υ^{H6}	CRHN CRos ELon EPfP ETho LCro LOPS LPre LRHS MAsh MGos NTay SCob SCoo SDix SLon SPer SWvt
	Miranda = 'Floclemi'^{PBR} (I)	CWGN SMDP
	'Miss Bateman' (EL)	CFlo CKel CMac CRos CTri CWCL ELan EPfP ESps ETho GMcL LCro LRHS LSRN MAsh MGos NEgg NRHS NTay SDix SLim SNig SPer SPoG SWCr WBor
	'Miss Christine' (M)	CFlo CSam ELan LCro LPre LSRN NTay SMDP
	Mississippi River = 'Zomisri' (I)	IPot
	'Mister Hans Horn' (Vt)	NHaw
	Mon Amour = 'Zomoa' (EL)	CWGN EBee NTay
	Mon Cherry = 'Zomonch' (EL) **new**	CWGN IPot
	'Moniuszko' (EL)	CWGN
	montana	CSBt ESps LPar MAsh SCob SDix SEWo
	- B&SWJ 6724 from Taiwan	WCru
	- B&SWJ 6930	WCru
	- var. ***alba***	see *C. montana* var. *montana*
	- 'Alexander' (M)	CPou CRos EPfP LRHS NRHS SWCr
	- 'Da Yun' (M)	CWGN
	- var. ***grandiflora*** (M) Υ^{H4}	Widely available
§	- var. ***montana***	CBar CBcs GMcL LCro LRHS MAsh MJak SCob SPer SPoG WFar
	- var. ***rubens*** misapplied	see *C. montana* var. *montana*
	- var. ***rubens*** E.H.Wilson	CSBt CTri ELan EPfP ESps GMcL LRHS NHol NRHS NWea SDix SNig SPlb
I	- - 'Odorata' (M)	EPfP ETho GKin LRHS MRav SCoo SLim WHar

	- - 'Pink Perfection' (M)	CKel CMac CRHN CRos EBee ECrN ELan EPfP ESps GKin LCro LRHS LSRN MAsh NRHS NTay SCob SCoo SLim SNig SPer SPoG SWCr SWvt WFar WHar
	- - 'Tetrarose' (M) 🏆H4	Widely available
	- - 'Veitch' (M)	LPar
I	- 'Rubens Superba' (M)	CTri GKin NEgg NTay SRms SWCr WFar
	- var. ***sericea***	see *C. spooneri*
	- var. ***wilsonii***	CFlo CKel CRos CSam ELan EPfP ETho GKin GLog LRHS LSRN MRav MSwo NTay SDix SMDP SNig SPer SPoG SRms SWCr SWvt
	'Monte Cassino' (EL)	CWGN EBee NTay SNig
	'Moonbeam' (Fo)	EPot GEdr ITim MRav
	Moonfleet = 'Evipo046'PBR (LL)	CRos LRHS NTay
§	'Moonlight' (EL)	LRHS MAsh
	'Moonman' (Fo)	LLHF
	Morning Cloud	see *C.* 'Yukikomachi'
	'Morning Heaven' (Vt)	NHaw
	Morning Star = 'Zoklako'PBR (EL)	CWGN ETho IPot LRHS
	Morning Yellow = 'Cadmy'PBR (M)	CCCN GMcL IBoy LRHS
	'Mrs Cholmondeley' (EL) 🏆H6	CKel CRos CWCL ELan EPfP ESps ETho LRHS LSRN MAsh MGos MSwo NPri NTay SCob SLim SNig SPer SPoG SWCr
	'Mrs George Jackman' (EL) 🏆H6	CFlo CLng CRos CWCL ESps ETho LRHS NLar NTay SCoo
	'Mrs James Mason' (EL)	EBee
	'Mrs N. Thompson' (EL)	CKel CMac CRos CTri CWCL ELan ELon ETho IBoy LRHS LSRN MAsh MGos NBir NEgg NHol NPer NTay SDix SLim SNig SPer
	'Mrs P.B. Truax' (EL)	CRos LRHS NTay
	'Mrs Robert Brydon' (H)	ECtt NLar NTay SNig SRms
	'Mrs T. Lundell' (Vt)	CRHN NHaw
	'Multi Blue' (EL)	CBcs CFlo CKel CRos CWCL ELan ELon EPfP ESps EUJe GMcL IBoy LRHS LSRN MAsh MGos NTay SLim SNig SPer SPoG SRkn SRms SWCr WHar
	'My Angel'PBR (Ta)	ELan NHaw NLar NTay SCob
	'Myōjō' (EL)	LRHS
	'Nadezhda' (LL)	NHaw
§	***napaulensis***	CFlo CTri CWCL EPfP ETho LCro NHaw SMDP WCru WSHC
I	'Natacha' (EL)	CRos NHaw NTay SCoo
	'Natascha' (EL)	CLng CWCL LRHS LSRN SNig SWvt
	'Negritianka' (LL)	LRHS LSRN NHaw
	'Negus' (LL)	NHaw
	'Nelly Moser' (EL) 🏆H6	Widely available
	'Nelly Moser Neu' (EL)	GMcL NTay
	Neva = 'Evipo050' (Boulevard Series) (EL)	CLng CRos LRHS NRHS NTay
	'New Dawn' (M)	NHaw
	'New Love'PBR (H)	EBee ETho LSRN NHaw NLar NTay
	'Night Veil' (Vt)	NHaw
	Ninon = 'Evipo052' (Boulevard Series) **new**	CWGN
	'Niobe' (EL) 🏆H6	Widely available
	'North Star' (EL)	CKel EPfP SNig
	North Star (LL)	see *C.* 'Põhjanael'
	'Nunn's Gift' (Fo)	ETho LPre NTay
	nutans var. ***thyrsoidea***	see *C. rehderiana, C. veitchiana*
	'Oberek' (Vt)	NHaw
	'Ocean Pearl' (A)	CFlo ETho LSRN NLar NTay
	ochotensis	LLHF
	Octopus = 'Zooct'PBR (A)	CFlo NTay
	'Odoriba' (V)	CRHN CWGN ETho NHaw SMDP
	'Olimpiada-80' (EL)	NHaw
	'Omoshiro' (EL)	CWGN ETho IPot LRHS NHaw NTay
§	Ooh La La = 'Evipo041'PBR (Boulevard Series) (EL)	CFlo CKel CLng CRos CWCL ELon EPfP ETho LBuc LRHS LSou NRHS NTay SCoo SNig SPer SPoG SWCr
	orientalis misapplied	see *C. tibetana* subsp. *vernayi*
	orientalis ambig.	SRms
	orientalis L.	EBee EPfP GCra SCoo SWvt
*	- 'Rubromarginata' (Ta)	MMrt
	- 'Orange Peel'	see *C. tibetana* subsp. *vernayi* var. *vernayi* 'Orange Peel'
	- 'Sherriffii'	see *C.* 'Sherriffii'
	- var. ***tenuiloba***	see *C. columbiana* var. *tenuiloba*
	orientalis × tangutica	SWvt
	otophora	NHaw SBrt
	'Ovation'PBR (Fo)	EBee NPnk
	'Paala' (EL)	NHaw
	'Pagoda' (Vt)	CRHN EBee EPfP LRHS SCoo SLon SNig SRms
	Palette = 'Evipo034'PBR (Vt)	CLng LRHS SLon
	'Pamela' (F)	ETho NHaw NTay
	'Pamela Jackman' (A)	see *C. alpina* 'Pamela Jackman'
	'Pamela Jackman' (Vt)	NEgg
	'Pamiat Serdtsa' (I)	ELon ETho NHaw
	'Pamina' (EL)	ETho
	'Pangbourne Pink' (I) 🏆H6	CFlo CKel CRos CWCL EPfP ETho LRHS NHaw NRHS NTay SCoo SWCr
	paniculata Thunb.	see *C. terniflora*
	paniculata J.G. Gmel. (f)	ETho
	'Paradise Queen' (EL)	LBuc NLar
	'Parasol' (EL)	EBee
	Parisienne = 'Evipo019'PBR (Boulevard Series) (EL)	CFlo CLng CRos CWCL EPfP ETho LRHS LSou NRHS NTay SCoo SLon SNig SPoG SWCr
	parviflora DC.	see *C. campaniflora*
	parviloba var. ***bartlettii*** B&SWJ 6788	WCru
	'Pastel Blue' (I)	ETho
	'Pastel Princess' (EL)	NHaw
	'Pat Coleman' (EL)	CWCL ETho
	patens 'Korean Moon' (EL)	WCru
§	- 'Manshuu Ki' (EL)	CFlo CWCL ELon ETho LRHS NEgg SNig
	- 'Yukiokoshi' (EL)	ETho IPot
§	'Paul Farges' (Vb) 🏆H6	CKel CWGN EShb ETho GLog LPre MNrw NEgg NHaw NTay SMDP
	'Pauline' (A/d) 🏆H6	CBcs CRos LRHS LSRN NTay SCoo
	'Pendragon' (Vt)	CRHN NHaw
	'Pennell's Purity' (LL)	CFlo NTay
	Peppermint = 'Evipo005'PBR (d)	CFlo CLng CRos ELan EPfP LRHS NTay SCoo SLon SNig
	'Perida' (LL)	CWGN EBee
	'Perle d'Azur' (LL)	CBcs CKel CMac CRHN CRos CTri CWCL ELan ELon EPfP ETho LCro LOPS LRHS LSRN MAsh MGos MSwo NEgg NTay SCob SDix SLim SNig SPer SPoG SRms SWCr WFar
	'Perrin's Pride' (Vt)	CLng CRos LRHS MGos NHaw NLar NTay SCoo SNig SWCr
	Petit Faucon = 'Evisix'PBR (I) 🏆H6	CFlo CLng CRos EPfP ETho LRHS LSRN MGos NLar NTay SCob SCoo SLim SNig SPer SRms SWCr SWvt
	petriei	WThu
	'Peveril Pristine' (Vt)	CWGN NHaw
	Picardy = 'Evipo024'PBR (EL)	CFlo CLng CRos EPfP ETho LRHS NRHS NTay SCoo SLim SNig SPoG SWCr

I 'Picton's Variety' (M) CTri
'Piilu' (EL) CKel CRos CWCL CWGN ELan ETho GMcL LRHS LSRN LSou MAsh MBNS NHaw NLar NTay SCob SCoo SLim SNig SRkn SWCr
'Pille' (LL) NHaw
§ 'Pink Celebration' (EL) ETho
Pink Champagne see *C.* 'Kakio'
'Pink Dream' (A) **new** ETho
'Pink Fantasy' (LL) CFlo CRHN CRos CTri ETho LRHS MAsh NLar NTay SCob SCoo SLim SNig SRkn
'Pink Flamingo' (A) 🏆H6 CLng CWCL ELan EPfP LRHS MGos NRHS NTay SCoo SLim SNig SPoG SWCr WBor
'Pink Ice' (I) CKel CWCL NHaw NTay
'Pink Swing' (A) **new** ETho
'Pirko' (Vt) NHaw
§ ***pitcheri*** CWGN NHaw WSHC
'Pixie' (Fo/m) CFlo CKel CLng EBee ELan ELon EPfP ETho GMcL LRHS MGos NLar NPnk NTay SCoo SPoG
pogonandra NHaw
§ 'Põhjanael' (LL) NLar
Polar Bear see *C.* Arctic Queen
'Poldice' (Vt) 🏆H6 CRHN
'Polish Spirit' (LL) 🏆H6 CBar CBcs CFlo CKel CMac CRHN CRos CTri CWCL ELan EPfP ESps ETho LCro LRHS LSRN MGos NEgg NHol NRHS NTay SCob SLon SNig SPer SRkn SWCr SWvt WBor WFar
'Polonez' (Vt) NHaw
potaninii ETho GCra NSti
§ - var. ***potaninii*** WSHC
- var. ***souliei*** see *C. potaninii* var. *potaninii*
- 'Summer Snow' see *C.* 'Paul Farges'
'Praecox' (H) 🏆H6 CBod CRHN CWCL CWld EAEE EBee ELan EPfP ETho LHop LRHS MCot NBir NSti NTay SDix SPer WAul WCot
Pretty in Blue = 'Zopre'[PBR] (F) SCob SWvt
'Primrose Star' see *C.* 'Star'
'Prince Charles' (LL) 🏆H6 CFlo CKel CPou CRHN CTri CWCL ELan EPfP EShb ETho LRHS LSRN MAsh MJak NHaw NLar NTay SCoo SDix SLim SNig SPer SWCr SWvt WBod
'Prince George' (LL) CWCL ETho LCro LOPS LPre LSRN NPri NTay
§ 'Princess Diana' (T) 🏆H5 CBcs CFlo CKel CRHN CTri CWGN EBee ELan ESps ETho IPot LBuc LCro LRHS LSRN MAsh MBlu MJak MSwo NHol NTay SCob SCoo SLim SNig SPer SPoG SRms SWCr SWvt
Princess Kate = 'Zoprika'[PBR] (T) CWGN EBee EPfP ETho IPot LCro LOPS LRHS MBlu NRHS NTay SPoG SWCr WBor
§ 'Princess of Wales' (1875) (EL) CWCL LSRN NLar SLon SWvt
'Prinsesse Alexandra'[PBR] (EL) ETho NTay
'Propertius' (A) CFlo CKel CWCL CWGN EBee ETho GEdr LRHS MGos NHaw NTay SMDP
'Prosperity' (M) CRHN ETho
'Proteus' (EL) CLng CRos EBee ELan ELon EPfP LRHS MAsh MGos NTay SCoo SNig WHar
psilandra CWJ 12377 WCru
'Purple Dream'[PBR] (A) **new** ETho
'Purple Haze' (Vt) CRHN NHaw
'Purple Spider' (A/d) CFlo CMac EPfP ETho LPre LRHS MAsh MBlu NHaw NLar NTay SCoo
'Purpurea Plena Elegans' (Vt/d) 🏆H6 Widely available
quadribracteolata NHaw
'Queen Alexandra' (EL) EBee
Queen Mother = 'Zoqum' (Vt) CWGN EPfP ETho LRHS NTay
'Radiance' CWGN
'Ragamuffin' (EL/d) SNig
'Rahvarinne' (LL) ETho
'Ramona' (LL) CLng LRHS LSRN NHaw SNig
ranunculoides NHaw
'Rasputin' (LL) CWCL ETho
Rebecca = 'Evipo016'[PBR] (EL) CFlo CKel CLng CRos CWCL CWGN EBee ELan EPfP ETho EUJe LBuc LCro LOPS LRHS LSRN NRHS NTay SCob SCoo SLon SNig SPer SPoG SWCr
recta CWCL ECtt MNrw NLar
- PAB 9005 **new** LEdu
- 'Lime Close' seedlings CAby
- 'Purpurea' (F) CDor CFlo CMea CRos CWld EHoe ELan EPfP ETho GKev IPot LHop LRHS MArt MNrw NBir NChi NSti NTay SEND SPer SWCr XLum
- 'Velvet Night' (F) CSpe ECtt ETho EUJe GBuc LRHS MAvo MBel NEgg NLar SMDP WCot
'Red Ballon' (Ta) IPot
'Red Cooler' see *C.* 'Crimson King'
'Red Pearl' (EL) CFlo CRos LRHS LSRN NTay SNig SWCr
I 'Red Star' (d) NTay
Reflections = 'Evipo035' (LL) CRos EPfP LRHS NTay SLon SNig SWCr
§ ***rehderiana*** 🏆H5 CDul CKel CRHN CSam EBee ELan EPfP ETho MBlu NBir NSti NTay SChF SDix SPer SWvt WCot WPGP WSHC
'Reiman' (LL) NHaw
'Remembrance' (LL) CFlo EPfP ETho LSRN
repens 'Bells of Emei Shan' ETho NTay
'Rhapsody' ambig. CLng EPfP ETho LBuc MAsh MGos NTay SCoo SNig SWCr
'Rhapsody' B. Fretwell (EL) LRHS LSRN NHaw
'Ribble Red' (V) NHaw
'Richard Pennell' (EL) 🏆H6 CRos LRHS MAsh SNig SWCr
'Richard's Picotee' (Vt) NHaw
'Rising Star' NHaw SNig
'Ristimägi' (LL) NHaw
'Rituaal' (LL) **new** NHaw
'Robud'[PBR] (M/d) NPer
'Roelie' (Vt) NHaw
'Roko-Kolla' (LL) ETho NHaw
'Romantika' (LL) CFlo ELan ELon ETho IBoy LCro LRHS LSRN MAsh NHaw NTay SCoo SNig XEll
'Rooguchi' (I) CFlo CWCL CWGN EBee ETho LRHS NHaw SDix
'Rooran' (EL) EBee ETho
'Rosa Königskind' (EL) ETho
Rosalyn = 'Zo09087' (Vt) **new** CWGN
'Rosamunde' (LL) ETho
I 'Rosea' Westphal. (Vt) NHaw
I 'Rosea' (I) EPfP ETho LHop LRHS LSRN NTay WHoo
Rosemoor = 'Evipo002'[PBR] (EL) CFlo CKel CLng CRos CWCL CWGN EPfP ETho LRHS MAsh NRHS NTay SCoo SLim SLon SNig SWvt
'Rosy O'Grady' (A) 🏆H6 MAsh NLar NTay SRms

	'Rosy Pagoda' (A)	CRos ELan LRHS NHaw NLar NTay WBod
	'Rouge Cardinal' (LL)	CBcs CFlo CMac CRos ELan ELon EPfP ESps ETho GMcL IBoy LRHS LSRN MAsh MGos MJak NEgg NRHS NTay SCob SDix SLim SNig SPer SRms SWCr
	'Royal Velours' (Vt)	CFlo CKel CRHN CRos CTri CWCL ELan EPfP ETho LCro LRHS LSRN MAsh MGos NHol NRHS NTay SCob SCoo SDix SLim SNig SPer SPoG SWCr
	Royal Velvet = 'Evifour'PBR (EL)	CRos LRHS LSRN SCoo
	'Royalty' (EL)	CRos CWCL ELan EPfP LRHS LSRN MAsh MJak NBir NTay SCoo SNig SWCr
	'Rubens Superba'	see *C. montana* 'Rubens Superba'
	'Ruby' (A)	CLng CWCL ELan EPfP ETho LRHS LSRN MAsh NEgg NTay SCoo SNig SPer SRms WFar
	'Ruby Glow' (EL)	CLng CRos EBee EPfP LRHS LSRN NTay SCoo SNig
	'Ruby Wedding' Fretwell (T)	CFlo CWCL CWGN EPfP LBuc LCro LPre LSRN NTay SWvt
	'Rüütel' (EL)	CFlo CKel ELon ETho LRHS MAsh NHaw NTay SCoo SNig
	'Saalomon' (LL)	NHaw
	'Saladus' (EL) new	NHaw
	'Sally Cadge' (EL)	NHaw
	Sally = 'Evipo077' (EL)	CRos LRHS NRHS NTay SPoG
	Samaritan Jo = 'Evipo075'	CRos ETho LRHS NRHS NTay SPoG SWCr
	'Sander' (H)	SMDP
	Savannah = 'Evipo015'PBR (Vt)	CLng LRHS
	'Scartho Gem' (EL)	CLng CRos LRHS SCoo SNig
	'Sealand Gem' (EL)	NHaw SNig
§	'Semu' (LL)	CWGN ETho NHaw
	serratifolia	CRHN ECtt ETho GAbr GLog SDix SPlb
	- B&SWJ 8458 from Korea	WCru
	'Sheila Thacker' (EL)	ETho
I	'Sherriffii' (Ta)	SWvt
	'Shikoo' (EL)	CWCL ETho LSRN NTay
	Shimmer = 'Evipo028'PBR (LL)	CKel CLng CRos EPfP LRHS NRHS NTay SLon SPoG SWCr
	'Shirayukihime' (EL)	NLar SNig
	'Sialia' (A/d)	CFlo CKel
§	***sibirica***	EPfP ESps LRHS NRHS
	- var. ***tianschanica*** new	NHaw
	'Signe' (Vt)	see *C.* 'Kasmu'
	'Siirus' (EL)	NHaw
	'Silmakivi' (EL)	NHaw
	'Silver Moon' (EL)	CFlo CLng CWCL EPfP ETho LRHS MAsh NLar NTay SCoo
	simensis	LEdu
	simsii Small	see *C. pitcheri*
	simsii Sweet	see *C. crispa*
	'Sinee Plamia' (LL)	NHaw
§	'Sinii Dozhd' (I)	CWCL NHaw
	'Sir Eric Savill' (M)	EBee ETho
	'Sir Garnet Wolseley' (EL)	SDix
	'Sir Trevor Lawrence' (T)	CRos LRHS NHaw
	'Sireen' (LL)	NHaw
	'Skyfall' (LL) new	ETho
	smilacifolia NJM 10.094	WPGP
	aff. ***smilacifolia*** HWJ 1049	WCru
	'Snow Queen' (EL)	CFlo CKel CRos ELon EPfP ETho LRHS NTay SLim SNig SRms WBod
	'Snowbird' (A/d)	CFlo CKel CRos LRHS NHaw NTay SNig SPer SPoG SWCr
	'Snowdrift'	see *C. armandii* 'Snowdrift'
	'Södertälje' (Vt)	CRHN EPfP ETho SCoo
	'Solidarność' (EL)	ETho
	'Solina' (Vt)	NHaw
	songarica	NHaw
	'Sonnette' (V)	CFlo CWGN EBee ETho IPot NHaw
§	'Souvenir du Capitaine Thuilleaux' (EL)	CKel ELon NTay SNig
	'Special Occasion' (EL)	CLng CRos CWGN LRHS LSRN NHaw NLar NTay SCoo SPoG SWCr
	Spiky = 'Zospi'PBR (A/d)	CFlo
§	***spooneri***	CTri EPfP LPar LRHS NTay SCoo SWvt
	'Sputnik' (I)	CWGN NHaw
	stans	CPou CRos EBee ETho EWTr IFro LLHF LRHS NLar SWCr
	- B&SWJ 5073	WCru
	- B&SWJ 6345	WCru
§	'Star'PBR (M/d)	ELan EPfP LPre LRHS MSwo NLar NTay SPer
	'Star of India' (LL)	CKel CLng CRos CWCL EPfP ETho LRHS MGos NTay SCoo SLim SNig SPer
	Star of Pakistan = 'Zostapa' new	CWGN
	Star River = 'Zostarri'PBR (I)	ELan IPot
I	'Starfish' (EL)	NHaw
	'Starlight' (M)	CKel CWCL ELon NTay SNig
	'Stasik' (LL)	NHaw
	'Stefan Franczak' (EL) new	ETho
	'Stephanie' (A)	CFlo CKel
	Still Waters = 'Zostiwa'PBR (EL)	CWGN ETho NTay
	'Strawberry Kiss' (V)	NHaw
	Sugar Candy = 'Evione'PBR (EL)	LRHS MAsh NTay SCoo SLim SNig
	Summer Snow	see *C.* 'Paul Farges'
	Summerdream = 'Zosumdre' (EL)	ETho IPot NTay
	'Sundance' (Ta)	SMDP
	Sunny Sky = 'Zosusk'PBR (Vt)	CFlo CKel NHaw NTay
	'Sunrise' (M/d)	IPot MSwo NHaw NLar NTay
	'Sunset' (EL) ♀H6	CLng CRos CWCL ELon LRHS LSRN MGos NEgg NLar NTay SCoo SLim SNig
	'Swedish Bells' (I)	CWGN
	'Sweet Scentsation' (F)	CFlo EPfP LCro LOPS NHaw NLar NTay
	'Sweet Summer Love'PBR (F)	CWGN ETho NHaw
	Sweetheart = 'Witswe'PBR (I)	ELan EPfP ETho LPar NTay
	'Sylvia Denny' (EL)	ELan EPfP ETho MAsh
	'Syrena' (LL)	NHaw
	szuyuanensis B&SWJ 6791	WCru
	- CWJ 12455	WCru
	'Tae'	see *C.* 'Toltae'
	'Tage Lundell' (A)	CFlo EBee EPfP LRHS NLar
	'Tango' (Vt)	CRHN NHaw
§	***tangutica***	Widely available
	'Tapestry' (I)	NHaw
	'Tartu' (EL)	NHaw
	tashiroi	NHaw
	- purple-flowered B&SWJ 7005	WCru
	- 'Yellow Peril'	WCru
	Tekla = 'Evipo069' (LL)	CLng NTay

'Teksa' (LL)	NHaw
Temptation = 'Zotemp'^{PBR} (EL)	MJak NTay
tenuiloba	see *C. columbiana* var. *tenuiloba*
§ ***terniflora***	EPfP ETho NHaw SKHP WHar
- B&SWJ 5751	WCru
'Teshio' (EL)	IPot
texensis	ETho NHaw WSHC
- 'The Princess of Wales'	see *C.* 'Princess Diana'
'The Bride' (EL)	CWCL CWGN EBee ETho LRHS LSRN
The Countess of Wessex = 'Evipo073' (EL)	CRos EPfP ETho LRHS NRHS NTay SPoG SWCr
'The First Lady' (EL)	CWCL ETho SNig
'The President' (EL) 🏆H6	Widely available
'The Princess of Wales' (EL)	see *C.* 'Princess of Wales' (1875) (EL)
'The Princess of Wales' (T)	see *C.* 'Princess Diana' (T)
'The Vagabond' (EL)	CRos CWCL ELan EPfP ETho LRHS LSRN MAsh NHaw NLar NTay SCoo SLim SNig
'The Velvet' (EL)	SNig
§ Thumbelina = 'Evipo030'^{PBR} (EL)	CKel CLng CRos CWCL ETho GMcL LRHS NRHS NTay SNig SPoG SWCr
thunbergii misapplied	see *C. terniflora*
'Thyrislund' (EL)	CKel SNig
'Tibetan Mix' (Ta)	NHaw
tibetana	NHaw
- CC 7447 **new**	GKev
- 'Black Tibet' (Ta)	CWGN
§ - subsp. ***vernayi***	LLHF
- - 'Glasnevin Dusk' (Ta)	SMDP WSHC
§ - - var. ***vernayi*** 'Orange Peel' LS&E 13342 (Ta)	CBcs ETho LRHS SEND
'Tie Dye' (LL)	CWGN ELan EPfP ETho LPre NHaw NTay
'Tiiu' (LL)	NHaw
'Titipu' (V)	NHaw
'Together' (I) **new**	NHaw
'Toki' (EL)	CWGN
§ 'Toltae'^{PBR} (EL)	ETho
tongluensis GWJ 9358	WCru
- HWJK 2368	WCru
tosaensis f. ***cremea*** **new**	NHaw
'Tranquility'	CWGN
'Treasure Trove' (Ta)	SMDP
'Triinu' (Vt)	NHaw
'Trikatrei' (LL)	EBee
§ × ***triternata*** 'Rubromarginata'	CFlo CKel CMac CRHN CRos CWCL CWGN ELan ELon EPfP ETho LCro LOPS LRHS LSRN MAsh MGos MJak MRav NRHS NTay SCob SDix SLim SLon SNig SPer SPoG SRms SWCr
'Tsunami Child' (M)	IMou
§ ***tubulosa***	ETho SMDP
§ - Alan Bloom = 'Alblo'^{PBR} (H)	LRHS
- 'Wyevale' (H)	CFlo CMac CWld EAEE ELan ELon EPfP LHop LRHS MCot MRav NCGa NSti NTay SBod SCoo SDix SMDP SPad SPer SPoG WAul WCAu WGwG
'Tuchka' (EL)	NHaw
'Twilight' (EL)	CFlo CKel CLng CRos EPfP LRHS MAsh NTay SNig SWCr
Twinkle = 'Zotwi' (I)	CWGN
uncinata CWJ 12373	WCru
'Uno Kivistik'^{PBR} (LL)	NHaw
§ ***urophylla*** 'Winter Beauty'	CFlo CWCL EBee ETho LCro LOPS LPre LRHS LSRN NTay SBrt SMDP SPoG WPGP
urticifolia B&SWJ 8651	WCru
- B&SWJ 8852	WCru
'Utopia' (EL)	CWGN
'Valge Daam' (LL)	CWGN ETho NHaw SNig
'Valle' (LL)	NHaw
'Van Gogh' (M)	CWGN ETho SMDP
'Vanessa' (LL)	CRHN
'Vanso'	see *C.* 'Blue Light'
§ ***veitchiana***	NHaw
'Venosa Violacea' (Vt) 🏆H6	CFlo CKel CRHN CRos ELan EPfP ETho LCro LRHS LSRN MAsh NHaw NHol NTay SCoo SDix SNig SPer SPoG SRms SWCr
'Vera' (M)	LRHS LSRN NTay SCoo SLim
vernayi	see *C. tibetana* subsp. *vernayi*
'Veronica's Choice' (EL)	CFlo CWCL ELan LPre NHaw NTay SNig
Versailles = 'Evipo025'^{PBR} (EL)	CLng CRos EPfP LRHS NTay SLim SNig
§ Vesuvius = 'Evipo032'^{PBR} (Vt)	CLng LRHS SCoo SLim SLon
'Vetka'^{PBR} (LL)	NHaw
Victor Hugo = 'Evipo007'^{PBR} (LL)	CFlo CLng EBee LRHS NLar NTay SCoo SNig
'Victoria' (LL) 🏆H6	CRHN CRos ETho LRHS LSRN NHaw NTay SCoo
Viennetta = 'Evipo006'^{PBR} (d)	CFlo CKel CLng CRos CWCL CWGN EPfP ETho LRHS MGos NTay SCoo SLon SNig SRms SWCr
'Vihma' (LL)	NHaw
'Ville de Lyon' (LL)	CBcs CFlo CKel CRHN CWCL ELan EPfP ESps GMcL IBoy LRHS LSRN MAsh MGos NEgg NRHS NTay SDix SLim SNig SPer SPoG SWCr WBod WHar
vinacea **new**	NHaw
'Vince Denny' (Ta)	EBee ETho NHaw SMDP SNig
Vino = 'Poulvo'^{PBR} (EL)	CLng LRHS NHaw NTay SCoo SLim
'Viola' (LL)	CFlo CWGN ELon ETho LSRN NHaw NTay SDix SMDP
'Violet Charm' (EL)	NEgg SNig
'Violet Elizabeth' (EL)	EBee
viorna	CWGN NHaw WCru WSHC
virginiana misapplied	see *C. vitalba*
virginiana Hook.	see *C. ligusticifolia*
§ ***vitalba***	CArn CWld ECrN ETho NHaw NTay NWea WHer WSFF
- SDR 6610	GKev
viticella	CDul CRHN CWib ESps ETho GKev NHaw SNig WSHC
- subsp. ***campaniflora***	see *C. campaniflora*
§ - 'Flore Pleno' (Vt/d)	CFlo CKel CRHN CRos EBee ELan ELon EPfP ETho IPot LCro LRHS LSRN NHaw NRHS NTay SLon SNig SPoG SWCr WHlf
- 'Hågelby Blue' (Vt)	NHaw
- 'Hågelby White' (Vt)	CRHN CWGN NHaw
- 'Hanna' (Vt)	CRHN LSRN NHaw
- 'Mary Rose'	see *C. viticella* 'Flore Pleno'
'Viva Polonia'^{PBR} (EL) **new**	ETho
'Vivienne'	see *C.* 'Beth Currie'
'Voluceau' (Vt)	CLng CPou CRHN CRos CWCL ELan LRHS LSRN SNig SRms SWCr
'Vostok' (LL)	NHaw NTay
'Vyvyan Pennell' (EL)	CBcs CFlo CKel CMac CRos CTri CWCL ELan EPfP ESps ETho EUJe GBin IBoy LRHS LSRN MAsh MSwo NEgg NLar NTay SLim SNig SPer SPoG SWCr SWvt WFar
'W.E. Gladstone' (EL)	ETho LRHS
Wada's Primrose	see *C. patens* 'Manshuu Ki'

'Walenburg' (Vt) ♀H6	CKel CRHN CWGN ETho NHaw SLon
'Walter Pennell' (EL)	CBcs CRos LRHS SCoo
'Warsaw' (Ta)	NLar
'Warszawska Nike' (EL) ♀H6	CLng CMac CRHN CWCL ELan EPfP ETho GMcL LCro LRHS MAsh MGos NTay SCob SCoo SNig SPer SPoG SWCr
'Warszawska Olga' (EL)	ETho
'Warwickshire Rose' (M)	CFlo CKel CLng CMac CRHN CRos CTri CWGN ELan ESps ETho LRHS LSRN MAsh NEgg NHaw NTay SLim SNig SPoG SWCr WHar
'Wedding Day' (EL)	CFlo ETho LCro LPre LSRN NLar NTay
'Wee Willie Winkie' (M)	GMcL SCoo SRms
'Westerplatte' (EL)	CFlo CKel CLng CRos CWCL CWGN EPfP ETho LRHS MGos NHaw NTay SLim SNig SPoG SWCr WHar
§ 'White Columbine' (A) ♀H6	CWCL ELan ETho LRHS NTay SDix SNig SPer
'White Lady' (A/d)	NHaw
'White Magic' PBR (Vt)	ETho
§ 'White Moth' (A/d)	ETho LSRN MAsh NHaw NHol SLim
'White Prince Charles' (LL)	NHaw
'White Satin' (A)	CRos EPfP LRHS SRms
'White Swan' (A/d)	MAsh NHol NLar SCoo
'White Wings' (A/d)	CFlo LSRN
'Will Goodwin' (EL) ♀H6	CBcs CLng CRos CWCL ELan EPfP LRHS SLim SNig SRms
'William Kennett' (EL)	CWCL ELan ETho IBoy LRHS MJak
williamsii	SMDP
'Willy' (A)	CBcs CLng CRos CWCL EBee ELan EPfP ETho LRHS MAsh MGos NLar NRHS NTay SDix SPer SRms WBod WFar
Wisley = 'Evipo001' PBR (Vt) ♀H6	CKel CLng CRos EPfP LRHS MGos NLar NTay SLim SLon SWCr
'Xerxes' misapplied	see *C.* 'Elsa Späth'
'Yatsuhashi' ambig.	SNig
'Yellow Queen' Holland	see *C. patens* 'Manshuu Ki'
'Yellow Queen' Lundell/ Treasures	see *C.* 'Moonlight'
§ 'Yukikomachi' (EL)	ETho NHaw NTay
yunnanensis	EBee WPGP
'Yvonne Hay' (I)	SMDP
Zara = 'Evipo062' (EL)	CRos ELan ETho LRHS NRHS NTay SLon
'Zephyr' (Vt)	NHaw

Clematopsis see *Clematis*

Clementsia see *Rhodiola*

Cleome (*Cleomaceae*)

hassleriana 'Helen Campbell' ♀H2	CSpe
§ Senorita Rosalita = 'Inncleosr' PBR	CSpe NPri

Cleretum (*Aizoaceae*)

§ ***bellidiforme***	ESps

Clerodendrum (*Lamiaceae*)

CW&T 6506 **new**	CMCN
bungei	Widely available
- PAB 8953	LEdu
- 'Pink Diamond' (v)	CCCN CWGN ELan EWes LRHS LSRN LSou MGos NLar SKHP SMDP SPer SPoG SWvt
§ ***chinense*** var. ***chinense*** (d) ♀H1b	CCCN CHll
- 'Pleniflorum'	see *C. chinense* var. *chinense*
colebrookianum B&SWJ 6651	WCru
- PAB 7794	LEdu
fragrans var. ***pleniflorum***	see *C. chinense* var. *chinense*
myricoides 'Ugandense' ♀H1b	CCCN CCse CHll CRHN EShb WSFF
philippinum	see *C. chinense* var. *chinense*
aff. ***subscaposum*** WWJ 11735	WCru
thomsoniae ♀H1b	EShb WSFF
trichotomum	CBcs CDul CEnd CMCN CSam CSpe CTho CTri CWib EPfP EUJe IArd LCro LOPS LRHS NLar SLim SLon SPer WBor WHor WMat
- var. ***fargesii*** ♀H4	Widely available
- - 'Carnival' (v) ♀H4	CAbP CBcs CCCN CMac CWCL EBee ELan ELon EPfP EWes LRHS MAsh NLar SEND SEle SKHP SLim SMDP SMad SPer SPoG SWvt WCot WPat
- 'Purple Blaze'	EBee
- 'Purple Haze'	CJun MMrt NLar
- 'Shiro'	WCru
wallichii	EShb IDee

Clethra ✿ (*Clethraceae*)

CW&T 6497 **new**	CMCN
acuminata	NLar
alnifolia	CBcs CDul CMHG CTsd MPkF SPer SRms WCFE WCot WFar
- 'Anne Bidwell'	MBlu NLar
- 'Creel's Calico' (v)	NLar
- 'Fern Valley Pink'	CCCN CMac EBee ELon LLHF LRHS NLar SRms WFar
- 'Hokie Pink'	NLar
- 'Hummingbird' ♀H5	CCCN CEnd CMac CRos CWib ECrN ELan EPfP LRHS MAsh MBlu NEgg NLar SChF SEle SPad SPoG SWvt WFar
- 'Paniculata'	ELon EPfP LRHS MGil MMuc WBor
- 'Pink Spires'	CAco CWld ECrN GKin LEdu LSou MMuc MRav NEgg NLar SCob SCoo SEle
- 'Rosea'	CTri GKin GQui MPkF SPer
- 'Ruby Spice' ♀H5	CBcs CCCN CEnd CJun CLet CMac CWib CWld EBee ELan ELon GBin GGGa GKin IDee LRHS LSRN MAsh MBlu NLar SEle SPad SPer SPoG SWvt
- 'September Beauty'	CJun NLar
- 'Sixteen Candles'	GGGa MPkF NLar
- Vanilla Spice = 'Caleb'	NLar
arborea	CBcs EBee NLar
barbinervis ♀H5	CBcs CTho EPfP GGGa IDee IVic LRHS MBlu MGil NLar WFar WPGP WSHC
- B&SWJ 11562	WCru
- Great Star = 'Minbarb'	EPfP LRHS
- 'White Star'	EBee LRHS SPer
delavayi Franch.	CBcs CCCN CFil CPne EBee EPfP GGGa GQui IDee LLHF MGil MNHC NLar SKHP
- KR 10414 **new**	GKev
- Stone's hardy strain	SKHP
fabri B&SWJ 11702	WCru
fargesii	CFil EPfP NLar
kaipoensis NJM 11.020	WPGP
- NJM 11.058	WPGP

- PAB 8571 new	LEdu
luzmariae	CFil
mexicana	CFil
monostachya	EBee GGGa NLar WPGP
pringlei	CFil EBee NLar WPGP WSHC
tomentosa 'Cottondale'	CJun NLar

Cleyera (*Pentaphylacaceae*)

fortunei	see *C. japonica* 'Fortunei'
- 'Variegata'	see *C. japonica* 'Fortunei'
§ ***japonica*** 'Fortunei' (v)	CCCN CMHG CMac CWib LRHS SHil
- var. ***japonica***	EBee WPGP
- 'Tricolor' (v)	CBcs IDee SAko

Clianthus ✿ (*Papilionaceae*)

maximus	GDun
- 'Kaka King'	CBcs EWes GDun SPoG
§ ***puniceus*** ♀H3	CAbb CBcs CHll CKel CSpe CTsd CWib EBee EPfP GDun IBoy LHop LRHS MGil NRHS SEle SGbt SIgm SPer SPlb SPoG SWvt WBor WSHC
§ - 'Albus' ♀H3	CBcs CHGN CKel CSpe CWib EBee EPfP EWld GDun IBoy LRHS MGil NRHS SPer SPoG SWvt
- 'Flamingo'	see *C. puniceus* 'Roseus'
- 'Red Admiral'	see *C. puniceus*
- 'Red Cardinal'	see *C. puniceus*
§ - 'Roseus' ♀H3	CBcs CKel EPfP GDun IVic LRHS NRHS SPer SPoG
- 'White Heron'	see *C. puniceus* 'Albus'

Clinopodium (*Lamiaceae*)

ascendens	see *Calamintha ascendens*
calamintha	see *Calamintha nepeta*
grandiflorum	see *Calamintha grandiflora*
§ ***menthifolium***	NBre NLar SRms WJek
§ ***vulgare***	CHab CSpe EBee GPSL MHer MNHC NMir SRms WJek WMoo WOut
- PAB 7562	LEdu

Clintonia (*Liliaceae*)

andrewsiana	ECho
udensis	WCru
umbellulata	GCal WCru
uniflora	ECho

Clivia ✿ (*Amaryllidaceae*)

'Bertress Bicolor' new	WCot
caulescens	WCot
- pink-flowered	WCot
gardenii	WCot
gardenii × ***miniata***	WCot
miniata ♀H1c	CAbb CBcs CCCN CTca CTsd ECho EWoo SAdn SEND SPlb WCot
- 'Anshan Variegated' (v)	WCot
- 'Arturo's Yellow'	WCot
- 'Ato-Shan'	WCot
- 'Aurea'	CSpe EWoo
- Belgian hybrids	WCot
- 'Beverley's Delight'	WCot
- broad-leaved	EWoo
- - dark orange-flowered	EWoo
- - variegated (v)	WCot
- var. ***citrina*** ♀H1c	CTca ECho LAma WCot
- - variegated (v)	WCot
- 'Dancing Sisters'	WCot
× 'Terracotta Green Throat' new	
- Daruma Group	WCot
- green-centred	EWoo WCot
- 'Light of Buddha' (v)	WCot
- 'Mitsuhashi Multipetal'	WCot
- 'Orange Spider'	CFwr
- pastel shades	CFwr EWoo WCot
- 'Pink Perfection'	WCot
- 'Red Dawn'	WCot
- 'Striata' (v)	CBlu WCot
- 'Terracotta Treasure' (v)	WCot
- 'Vico Shima'	WCot
- 'Vico Yellow'	EWoo
- 'Wide Leaf Monk'	WCot
nobilis ♀H1c	SPlb WCot
robusta	WCot
'San Marcus Yellow'	WCot
× 'Solomone Yellow'	
'Sweet Undress'	WCot

Clusia (*Clusiaceae*)

rosea	CCCN

Clytostoma (*Bignoniaceae*)

§ ***calystegioides***	CBcs CCCN CHll CRHN

Cneorum (*Rutaceae*)

tricoccon	SKHP

Cnidium (*Apiaceae*)

officinale	GPoy LEdu

Cobaea (*Polemoniaceae*)

paneroi new	CFil
pringlei	CRHN WPGP WSHC
- CD&R 1323	SBrt WCot
scandens ♀H2	CBot CCCN CDTJ CSpe EShb SPer
- f. ***alba***	CSpe EShb LCro SPer

cobnut see *Corylus avellana*

Cocculus (*Menispermaceae*)

laurifolius	EBee EUJe IArd
§ ***orbiculatus*** B&SWJ 535	WCru
trilobus	see *C. orbiculatus*

Cochlearia (*Brassicaceae*)

armoracia	see *Armoracia rusticana*
officinalis	WHer

Cocos (*Arecaceae*)

plumosa	see *Syagrus romanzoffiana*

Codonanthe (*Gesneriaceae*)

gracilis	WDib
'Paula'	WDib

× *Codonatanthus* (*Gesneriaceae*)

'Golden Tambourine'	WDib
'Sunset'	WDib
'Tambourine'	WDib

Codonopsis ✿ (*Campanulaceae*)

ACE 1625	EWld
HWJK 2105 from Nepal	WCru
RJN 245 new	GKev
affinis	EBee
- HWJCM 70	WCru
- HWJK 2151	WCru
benthamii GWJ 9352	WCru
bhutanica	GKev
cardiophylla	EBee EWld GCal

clematidea	CDor CSpe EBee ECha EPfP EWld GCal GKev MNHC MNrw NEgg NLar SPhx SPlb SWvt WRHF WSHC
- 'Lilac Eyes'	NEgg
convolvulacea misapplied	see *C. grey-wilsonii*
convolvulacea ambig.	GBin
- 'Alba'	see *C. grey-wilsonii* 'Himal Snow'
- Forrest's form	see *C. forrestii* Diels
- var. ***hirsuta*** B&SWJ 7812	WCru
'Dangshen'	see *C. pilosula*
aff. ***deltoidea*** SSSE 86	EBee EWld
dicentrifolia	NLar
forrestii misapplied	see *C. grey-wilsonii*
§ ***forrestii*** Diels	CPne EBee EWld GKev NHar WCot WTcb
- BWJ 7776	WCru
- BWJ 7847	WCru
§ ***grey-wilsonii*** 🏆H5	CAby CBro CPne EPot EWld GEdr MNrw
- B&SWJ 7532	WCru
§ - 'Himal Snow'	CAby CPne EPot EWld GEdr WCru
inflata GWJ 9442	WCru
kawakamii	EBee
- B&SWJ 1592	WCru
- RWJ 10007	WCru
§ ***lanceolata***	CAby EWld GCal GKev SBrt
- B&SWJ 562	EBee WCru
nepalensis Grey-Wilson	see *C. grey-wilsonii*
obtusa	EBee EWld
ovata	CPne EBee EWld NBro NLar
§ ***pilosula***	CDor EBee EWld GKev GPoy SBrt WSHC WTcb
- BWJ 7910	WCru
- var. ***modesta***	EBee EWld
§ ***rotundifolia*** var. ***angustifolia***	EBee EWld SBrt WCru
- var. ***grandiflora***	EBee EWld GKev
silvestris	see *C. pilosula*
tangshen misapplied	see *C. rotundifolia* var. *angustifolia*
ussuriensis	see *C. lanceolata*
vinciflora	CPne EWld GEdr
viridiflora	WCru
viridis HWJK 2435	WCru

Coffea (*Rubiaceae*)

arabica	CCCN SPlb SPre

coffee see *Coffea*

Coincya (*Brassicaceae*)

wrightii PJL 20098	CHid

Colchicum (*Colchicaceae*)

agrippinum 🏆H4	CAvo CBro CTal ECha ECho EPot GBin GKev LAma MRav NBir NRog WAbe WHoo WThu
alpinum	GKev
'Antares'	ECha NRog
atropurpureum	LAma
'Autumn Herald'	LAma NRog
'Autumn Queen' 🏆	CTca NRog
§ ***autumnale***	CAvo CBro CHab EPot GBin GKev GPoy IFro LAma NRog NRya SDeJ SEND WShi
- CH 871	GKev
- 'Alboplenum'	ERCP GKev LAma NBir NRog
- 'Album'	CAvo CBro CTca ELan EPot ERCP GKev LAma LCro LOPS NBir WShi
- 'Atropurpureum'	NRog
- 'Karin Persson'	GKev
- var. ***major*** hort.	see *C. byzantinum* Ker Gawl.
- var. ***minor*** hort.	see *C. autumnale*
§ - 'Nancy Lindsay' 🏆H5	CBro CTal EPot GKev NRog WShi XEll
- 'Pannonicum'	see *C. autumnale* 'Nancy Lindsay'
§ - 'Pleniflorum' (d)	GKev LAma NRog
- 'Roseum Plenum'	see *C. autumnale* 'Pleniflorum'
baytopiorum	GKev NRog
'Beaconsfield'	NRog
§ ***bivonae***	EPot
- 'Apollo'	GKev NRog
- 'Mount Giona'	GKev
- 'Petrovac'	GKev
§ ***boissieri***	GKev
bornmuelleri misapplied	see *C. speciosum* var. *bornmuelleri* hort.
bornmuelleri Freyn	CBro GKev LAma NRog
bowlesianum	see *C. bivonae*
byzantinum ambig.	NRog
§ ***byzantinum*** Ker Gawl. 🏆H5	CBro ELan GKev LAma SDeJ WShi
- ***album***	see *C. byzantinum* 'Innocence'
§ - 'Innocence'	NRog WCot
cilicicum	LAma NRog
- 'Purpureum'	CTca EPot GKev LAma NRog
'Conquest'	see *C.* 'Glory of Heemstede'
corsicum	ECho GKev WThu
cupanii AH 9707 **new**	GKev
- var. ***pulverulentum***	GKev NRog
davisii	CTal GKev NRog
'Dick Trotter'	EPot GKev NRog SDeJ SDir WOld
'Disraeli'	EPot GKev NRog
falcifolium	NRog
§ ***giganteum***	GKev LAma NRog
§ 'Glory of Heemstede'	GKev NRog WCot
'Gracia'	NRog
graecum	GKev
'Hannibal' **new**	GKev
'Harlekijn'	GKev NRog
hungaricum	ECho EPot GKev NRog
- f. ***albiflorum***	EPot GKev NRog
- 'Roseum' **new**	GKev
- 'Valentine'	GKev
- 'Velebit Star'	GKev NRog
illyricum	see *C. giganteum*
'Jaroslavna'	NRog
'Jochem Hof'	NRog
kesselringii	NRog
laetum misapplied	see *C. parnassicum*
laetum Stev.	NRog
'Lilac Bedder'	GKev NRog
'Lilac Wonder'	ELan EPfP GKev LAma MRav NRog SDeJ WCot
longifolium	see *C. neapolitanum*
lusitanum	LAma
luteum	NRog
'Lysimachus' **new**	GKev
macrophyllum	GKev LAma NRog
minutum	NRog
munzurense	NRog
§ ***neapolitanum***	GKev NRog
'Neptun'	NRog
'Oktoberfest'	EPot
parlatoris	NRog
§ ***parnassicum***	ECha GKev NRog WThu
'Pink Goblet' 🏆H5	CBro LAma
'Poseidon'	GKev NRog
procurrens	see *C. boissieri*
psaridis	GKev
pusillum	GKev NRog
'Rosy Dawn' 🏆H5	CBro ECha GKev NRog WOld

	'Rosy Wonder'	GKev
	sibthorpii	see *C. bivonae*
	'Spartacus' **new**	GKev
	speciosum ♀H5	CAvo CBro ELan EPot GBin GKev LAma NBir NRog WCot WShi
	- 'Album' ♀H5	CAvo CBro ECha EPfP EPot ERCP GAbr GKev LAma NBir NRog SDeJ
	- 'Atrorubens' ♀H5	ECha EPot LAma
I	- var. ***bornmuelleri*** hort.	WHoo WOld
	- 'Dombai'	NRog
	- var. ***illyricum*** hort.	see *C. giganteum*
	szovitsii subsp. ***brachyphyllum*** **new**	GKev
	- pink-flowered	GKev
	- 'Snow White'	GKev
	- 'Tivi'	ECho NRog
	- white-flowered	ECho GKev
	tenorei ♀H4	CTal EPot GKev LAma NBir NRog
	'The Giant'	CAvo CBro EPfP EPot GAbr GKev LAma NRog SCob SDeJ
	triphyllum	GKev NRog
	'Violet Queen'	EPot GKev LAma NRog
	'Waterlily' (d) ♀H5	CAvo CBro CTca ECho ELan EPfP EPot ERCP GBin GKev GMcL LAma LCro LOPS NBir NRog SCob SDeJ WHoo
	'William Dykes'	NRog
	'Zephyr'	LAma

Coleonema (*Rutaceae*)

	album	EBee
§	***pulchellum***	CCCN CSpe SVen
§	- 'Pink Fountain'	CAbb CRos EBee ELan EPfP LRHS MPkF NRHS SEle SPoG
	pulchrum misapplied	see *C. pulchellum*
§	'Sunset Gold'	CAbb CBod CCCN CRos CSpe CWGN ELan EPfP LBuc LRHS MPkF NRHS SAko SCoo SEle SPlb SPoG

Coleus see *Plectranthus, Solenostemon*

Colignonia (*Nyctaginaceae*)

	ovalifolia B&SWJ 10644	WCru

Colletia (*Rhamnaceae*)

	armata	see *C. hystrix*
	cruciata	see *C. paradoxa*
§	***hystrix***	CBcs CMac CTri CTsd ELon IVic LTro NLar SMad
	- 'Rosea'	CMac GCal MBlu SArc SKHP
§	***paradoxa***	CBcs CCCN CWib EBee ELan EPfP SArc SKHP SMad
	paradoxa* × *spinosissima	SMad
	ulicina	SVen

Collinsonia (*Lamiaceae*)

	canadensis	CArn LEdu

Collomia (*Polemoniaceae*)

	grandiflora	WCot

Colobanthus (*Caryophyllaceae*)

	canaliculatus	EPot

Colocasia (*Araceae*)

	affinis var. ***jeningsii***	CDTJ
	antiquorum	see *C. esculenta*
§	***esculenta*** ♀H1a	CDTJ EUJe LCro LLWG LOPS MSKA NLos SDir SPlb XBlo
	- 'Black Coral'	CAbb LRHS SPad
	- 'Black Magic'	CBct CDTJ EUJe LAma LRHS NLos SBig SDir SDix XBlo
	- burgundy-stemmed	CDTJ EUJe LAma SBig
	- 'Diamond Head'	CWGN EUJe LRHS
	- 'Fontanesii'	CDTJ EUJe MPkF SDix
	- 'Hawaiian Eye'	LRHS
	- 'Hilo Beauty'	see *Caladium praetermissum* 'Hilo Beauty'
	- 'Hilo High Colour'	EUJe
	- 'Illustris'	CDTJ EUJe LLWG
	- 'Mammoth'	EUJe
	- 'Pink China'	MPkF
	- 'Ruffles'	EUJe
	- 'Sangria'	EUJe
	fallax	SPlb
	formosana B&SWJ 6909	WCru
	gigantea	CDTJ
	- 'Thailand Giant'	EUJe
	'Himalayan Dragon'	SKHP
	'Kachhu'	LAma

Colquhounia (*Lamiaceae*)

	coccinea	CCCN CHll CMHG ESwi EUJe LRHS MBlu MGil MRav NLar SBrt SChF SLon WBod WSHC
	- Sch 2458	WPGP
§	- var. ***mollis*** B&SWJ 7222	WCru
	- var. ***vestita*** misapplied	see *C. coccinea* var. *mollis*
	- var. ***vestita*** (Wall.) Prain	CBcs CTsd EBee EPfP LRHS SEND

Columnea (*Gesneriaceae*)

	'Aladdin's Lamp'	WDib
	× ***banksii*** ♀H1c	WDib
§	'Broget Stavanger' (v) ♀H1c	WDib
	'Chanticleer' ♀H1c	WDib
I	'Firedragon'	WDib
	'Gavin Brown'	WDib
	gloriosa	EBak
	'Inferno'	WDib
	'Katsura'	WDib
	'Merkur'	WDib
I	'Midnight Lantern'	WDib
	'Rising Sun'	WDib
	schiedeana	WDib
	'Sherbert'	WDib
	'Stavanger' ♀H1c	WDib
	'Stavanger Variegated'	see *C.* 'Broget Stavanger'

Coluria (*Rosaceae*)

	geoides	WCot

Colutea (*Papilionaceae*)

	arborescens	CAgr CBcs CWib ELan EWTr LRHS MBlu MGil MGos MMuc NWea SCob SEND SPer SPlb XSen
	× ***media***	CTsd MArt
	- 'Copper Beauty'	CBcs ELan LRHS NLar SCob SPer
	orientalis	CCCN

Colvillea (*Caesalpiniaceae*)

	racemosa	SPlb

Comarum see *Potentilla*

Combretum (*Combretaceae*)

	fruticosum	CCCN

Commelina (*Commelinaceae*)

	benghalensis **new**	XBlo

coelestis see *C. tuberosa* Coelestis Group
dianthifolia GCal GEdr LEdu NHpl SBrt SMad
- 'Electric Blue' ELan LRHS SVic WCot
robusta SBrt WCot
tuberosa GKev MAvo NWad
- B&SWJ 10353 WCru
- blue-flowered SDeJ
§ - Coelestis Group CAby CSpe ECha LHop SDys WKif WSHC
- - 'Sleeping Beauty' MSpe WHea

Comptonia (*Myricaceae*)

peregrina WPGP

Conandron (*Gesneriaceae*)

ramondoides B&SWJ 8929 WCru

Conicosia (*Aizoaceae*)

pugioniformis SVen

Coniogramme (*Pteridaceae*)

japonica WFib
- 'Flavomaculata' ♀H4 CBod CSpe EBee MPie WCot

Conium (*Apiaceae*)

maculatum CArn

Conoclinium (*Asteraceae*)

§ ***coelestinum*** EBee LHop MArt SBrt XLum

Conopodium (*Apiaceae*)

majus CEls WOut WShi

Consolida (*Ranunculaceae*)

§ ***ajacis*** CSpe LRHS
- Giant Imperial Series SVic
ambigua see *C. ajacis*

Convallaria ✿ (*Asparagaceae*)

japonica see *Ophiopogon jaburan*
keiskei EPPr MAvo
I - 'Marginata' (v) WCot
- 'Shiro-shima-fu' (v) **new** GEdr
majalis ♀H7 Widely available
- 'Albostriata' (v) CBct CBot CFwr CLAP CTal CWCL ECho EHoe ELan EPPr EUJe GKev GMaP LEdu LRHS MAvo MHol MNrw MRav NBir NEgg NPnk NSti WCot WFar WHer WHoo WPnP
- 'Berlin Giant' NRya SDeJ
- 'Bordeaux' CBro CWld EBee EPPr GKev GPSL MAvo NEgg NLar WCot
- 'Bridal Choice' EBee ELan GKev NLar
- 'Dorien' CBct CBre EPPr IMou MAvo
- 'Fernwood's Golden Slippers' CAvo GEdr LLHF
- 'Flore Pleno' (d) GEdr WFar
- 'Géant de Fortin' CAvo CBct CBro CLAP CLet ECho EPot GCal GEdr MRav NBir NLar SBch WFar
- 'Gerard Debureaux' see *C. majalis* 'Green Tapestry'
- 'Golden Jubilee' CBct
§ - 'Green Tapestry' (v) CBct MAvo
- 'Haldon Grange' (v) CLAP EPPr MAvo
- 'Hardwick Hall' (v) CBct CCse CLAP CTal EBee ECho EHoe GEdr GKev LEdu MAvo WAul WCot WFar WHil XEll
- 'Hitschberger Riesenperle' XLum
- 'Hofheim' (v) CBct CLAP GEdr GKev LEdu MAvo WCot WHal
- 'Landgraaf' (v) **new** MAvo
- 'Marcel' (v) MAvo
- 'Prolificans' CBct CBod CCse CLAP CTal EBee ECho ECtt EPPr EPfP GKev LAma LCro LOPS LSou MAvo MRav NBir NLar NPnk NSti WCot WFar WPnP
- var. ***rosea*** Widely available
- 'Rosea Plena' (d) EWoo
- 'Silbercconfolis' (v) WCot
- 'Variegata' (v) CAvo EAJP EPot GCal LHop SBch SMad WThu
- 'Vic Pawlowski's Gold' (v) CAby CBct CBro CLAP CMac ELon EPPr GEdr LEdu MAvo WPGP WSHC
transcaucasica EBee GKev

Convolvulus (*Convolvulaceae*)

althaeoides CFis CMea ECho ELan EPri SEND WSHC
§ - subsp. ***tenuissimus*** EWes
§ ***boissieri*** WAbe XEll
cantabrica LRHS SPhx XLum XSen
chilensis CCCN
cneorum ♀H4 Widely available
- 'Snow Angel' LRHS LSou SWvt
compactus LLHF
elegantissimus see *C. althaeoides* subsp. *tenuissimus*
lineatus ECho EWes
mauritanicus see *C. sabatius*
nitidus see *C. boissieri*
§ ***sabatius*** ♀H3 CCCN CSam CTri ECho ECtt ELan EPfP EPot EShb EWoo LHop MCot SEND SLim SPer SPlb SPoG SVen SWvt WCFE WSHC XLum XSen
- dark-flowered CCCN CSpe ECho
- 'Moroccan Beauty'PBR CSpe ECtt
- white-flowered **new** CCCN

× *Cooperanthes* see *Zephyranthes*

Cooperia see *Zephyranthes*

Coprosma (*Rubiaceae*)

baueri misapplied see *C. repens*
'Beatson's Gold' (f/v) CBcs CDTJ CHGN CHll ELan EShb IVic LRHS SEND SEle SLim SWvt WGrn WSHC
'Black Cloud' CBcs ELon LRHS SEND
'Blue Skies' NHar WThu
'Brunette' (f) MAsh
brunnea (f) WThu
- (m) WThu
'Cappuccino' CBcs EShb SEle
depressa WThu
'Evening Glow'PBR (f/v) CCCN CDTJ CRos CSBt ELan ESps EUJe IVic LRHS MGos SEle SHil SLim SRms WHar
'Fire Burst'PBR (f/v) CAbb CBcs CCCN CRos EBee ELan ESps LHop LRHS MGos SEle SHil SLim SLon SRms WHar
'Green Globe' CHll
'Inferno' CAbb CCht CRos LRHS SEle SHil
'Karo Red'PBR (v) CBcs SLim SRms
I × ***kirkii*** 'Kirkii' (f) CHll
- 'Variegata' (f/v) CBcs CTsd ELan EPfP EShb GBin LRHS SLim
'Lemon and Lime'PBR (v) CRos EBee ELan ESps EUJe LHop LRHS MGos NRHS SEle SHil SPoG SRms WHar

petriei	GAbr WThu
- 'White Pearls'	WThu
'Rainbow Surprise'PBR (v)	CCCN CRos CSBt ELan ESps LRHS MGos SHil SLim SRms WHar
§ ***repens***	CBcs EShb SPlb SVen
- 'County Park Plum' (v)	CBcs
- 'Marble Queen' (m/v) ♀H2	EShb
- 'Midnight Martini' (v)	CRos LRHS NRHS SHil SPoG
- Pacific Night = 'Hutpac'PBR (m)	CCht CRos CSBt ELan ESps EUJe IVic LHop LRHS MGos SHil SLon
- Pacific Sunset = 'Jwncopps' (v)	EBee ELan ESps LCro SEle SHil
- 'Painter's Palette' (m)	SEle SVen
- 'Picturata' (m/v) ♀H2	EShb
- 'Pina Colada'PBR (v)	CAbb CRos CSBt LRHS NRHS SEle SHil SPoG
- 'Pink Splendour' (m/v)	CBcs
- 'Tequila Sunrise'	CAbb CRos EBee ESps LRHS NRHS SBod SEle SHil
'Roy's Red' (m)	CCht EShb LRHS LSRN
'Scarlet O'Hara'	CCht SEle SPoG
'Walter Brockie'	CHGN CHll EShb

Coptis (*Ranunculaceae*)

chinensis B&SWJ 12865 **new**	WCru
japonica	GPoy WCru
- var. ***dissecta***	WCru
- var. ***major***	EBee WCru WSHC
omeiensis	CTal WCru
quinquefolia	CTal
- B&SWJ 1677	WCru
ramosa B&SWJ 6000	WCru
- B&SWJ 6030	WCru
trifolia	WCru

Corallospartium see *Carmichaelia*

Cordyline ✿ (*Asparagaceae*)

australis ♀H3	Widely available
- 'Albertii' (v) ♀H3	CCCN SArc
- 'Atlantic Green'	LRHS NRHS SHil
- 'Atropurpurea'	CCCN
- 'Black Night'	CCCN
- Burgundy Spire = 'Jel01'PBR	EPfP
- Charlie Boy = 'Ric01'PBR (v)	EBee SPad
- 'Claret'	CBcs
- 'Karo Kiri'	CCCN
- multi-stemmed	CLet
- 'Olive Fountain'	CCCN
- 'Peko'PBR	CCCN
- 'Purple Heart'	CCCN MSwo
- Purpurea Group	CBcs CDTJ ELan ESps LPar MGos MMuc SEND SPer SPlb WFar
- 'Red Sensation'	CCCN LRHS NRHS SWvt
- 'Sparkler'	CCCN LRHS NRHS SCob
- 'Torbay Dazzler' (v) ♀H3	CAbb CBcs CLet CSBt ELan EMOT EPfP ESps EUJe IVic LPar LRHS LSRN MAsh MGos MJak NEgg NPla NPri SCob SEND SHil SLim SPer SPoG SWvt WFar
- 'Torbay Sunset'	CCCN LRHS NRHS SCob
- 'Variegata' (v)	LPar
'Autumn'	CCCN
banksii	CTsd
'Cardinal'PBR	CBcs
'Cha Cha'PBR **new**	CCCN
'Cherry Sensation' (v)	EPfP LBuc LRHS NRHS SHil WFar
'Coffee Cream'	CCCN
'Dark Star'	CCCN CDTJ SLim
Electric Pink = 'Sprilecpink'	EBee
'Eurostar'	CCCN
'Eurostripe'PBR	LRHS NRHS
'Firecracker'	CCCN LRHS
fruticosa 'Kiwi'	LRHS NRHS
- 'Red Edge' ♀H1b	XBlo
§ ***indivisa***	CBcs CBrP CCCN CDTJ CTre CTsd EUJe NLos SArc SPlb WPGP
kaspar	CCCN CTsd
obtecta	CCCN
'Pink Champagne'	CCCN ELan EMOT LRHS MSwo SCob
Pink Passion = 'Seipin'PBR	CCCN EPfP EUJe LBuc LRHS NRHS
'Pink Stripe' (v)	CCCN ELan EPfP LSRN SLim SWvt
pumilio	LRHS
'Purple Sensation'	CBcs CCCN LRHS NRHS
'Purple Tower' ♀H3	ESps MJak
'Red Bush'	XBlo
'Red Heart'	CCCN MJak
'Red Star'	CAbb CBcs CCCN CChe CEnd CLet CSBt CWGN CWib EMOT EPfP EUJe GMcL LCro LPar LRHS MJak MSwo NPer NRHS SCob SHil SPoG SWvt WFar
'Southern Splendour'	CCCN ELan ESps LRHS NPri NRHS SHil SPoG
'Sundance' ♀H3	CBcs CBod CWib EMOT EPfP LRHS MAsh MGos MMuc MSwo NPer SCob SEND SLim SPoG SRms SWvt WFar
'Sunrise' (v)	CEnd CWGN LRHS NRHS SHil
terminalis	see *C. fruticosa*
'Torbay Red' ♀H3	CCCN CLet CMac CTsd EPfP ESps LRHS LSRN MAsh NPri SWvt

Coreopsis (*Asteraceae*)

'Astolat'	CBod EPed LSou MRav NEgg SPer
auriculata Cutting Gold	see *C.* 'Schnittgold'
- 'Elfin Gold'	EDAr
- 'Nana'	ELon MNrw NBre
- 'Superba'	MRav
- 'Zamphir'	CDor EBee EPfP MNrw WCot
'Baby Gold'	see *C. lanceolata* 'Sonnenkind' (unblotched)
Baby Sun	see *C.* 'Sonnenkind' (red-blotched)
'Calypso' (v)	EWes XLum
'Cha Cha Cha'	SEle
'Cherry Pie'PBR (Pie Series)	SCob
'Citrine'PBR (Hardy Jewel Series)	CWGN SPoG
'Cosmic Evolution' (Big Bang Series) **new**	EBee LRHS
'Cosmic Eye' (Big Bang Series)	EBee
'Cranberry Ice'	CWGN EBee LRHS
'Desert Coral'PBR (Hardy Jewel Series)	CWGN LBMP LSou SPoG
'Dream'	SRkn
'Fool's Gold'	EBee
'Fruit Punch'PBR (Punch Series)	CRos LRHS NRHS
'Full Moon'PBR (Big Bang Series)	CBod EBee STPC WFar XLum
'Galaxy' (Big Bang Series)	EBee
'Garnet'PBR (Hardy Jewel Series)	EBee
gigantea	SPlb
'Golden Pompom' (d)	EBee
grandiflora	ESps NEgg NPnk

	- 'Bernwode' (v)	CMac EBee LSou SWvt
	- 'Domino'	EAJP EBee LSun
	- 'Early Sunrise' ♀H5	CBod CRos CSBt EAJP EBee ECtt EPed EPfP IBoy LPot LRHS MAsh MNHC NBir NGBl NPer NRHS SCob SGbt SPoG SWvt WHar XLum
	- Flying Saucers = 'Walcoreop'PBR	EPfP LRHS SCoo SPoG
	- 'Illico'	EBee
	- 'Mayfield Giant'	CSBt EBee ELan EPfP LHop MNrw NPri SPer SRms SWvt WHrl
	- 'Presto' (d)	CNor NGBl SPad
	- 'Rising Sun'	ELan
	- 'Sunburst'	EPfP NBre XLum
	- 'Sunfire'	IBoy LRHS MHer NPri SHil WFar
	- 'Sunray'	CBcs CRos CSBt CWib EAJP ECtt ELon EPed EPfP GMcL LRHS MAsh NGdn NRHS SHil SPlb SPoG SRms SWvt WCAu WHar WMoo XLum
	- 'Tetra Riesen'	NBre
	'Jethro Tull'PBR	CBod EBee LSou
	'Jive'PBR (Coloropsis Series)	CWGN NPnk SCob SEle
	lanceolata	NBre
	- 'Goldfink'	MRav SRms
	- 'Goldteppich'	CRos EBee EPfP LRHS NRHS
	- 'Little Sundial'	IKil LSou
§	- 'Sonnenkind' (unblotched)	GMaP MAsh XLum
	- 'Walter'	CBod LSou MNrw MPie NDov NEgg SPoG WCot WFar WGwG XLum
	'Limbo' (Coloropsis Series)	SCob
	'Limerock Passion'PBR	CRos EPfP ILea LRHS MBNS NRHS SRkn
	'Limerock Ruby'PBR	CRos EWoo GMaP ILea LRHS LSou NRHS SCob SPer SRkn SWvt WFar WHar XLum
	major	EBee
	'Mambo' (Coloropsis Series) **new**	SEle
	'Mango Punch' (Punch Series)	EBee GMcL
	maximiliani	see *Helianthus maximiliani*
	'Mercury Rising' (Big Bang Series) **new**	SHar
	'Pineapple Pie'PBR (Pie Series)	SCob
	'Pink Lady'PBR	WBod
	pubescens	LSou
	- 'Sunshine Superman'	EBee ELan
	'Pumpkin Pie'PBR (Pie Series)	SCob
	'Red Satin' (Permathread Series) **new**	WTor
	'Redshift'	ILea
	rosea	NGBl
	- 'American Dream'	CBod CSBt CSam ELan EPed EPfP GMaP LRHS MArt NBir NEgg NGdn SPer SPlb SRms SWvt WGwG XLum
	- 'Heaven's Gate'PBR	LRHS MHol NGBl SCob WFar
	- 'Nana'	XLum
	- 'Sweet Dreams'PBR	SRkn
	'Route 66'PBR	EBee WFar
	'Ruby Frost' (Hardy Jewel Series)	CCVN EBee NAst SPoG
	'Rum Punch'PBR (Punch Series)	LHop
	'Salsa' (Coloropsis Series)	SEle
§	'Schnittgold'	NBre SHar
	'Snowberry'	LRHS
I	'Sonnenkind' (red-blotched)	EBee LRHS NBre NRHS
	'Star Cluster' (Big Bang Series)	CWGN EBee MHol WFar
	'Sterntaler'	EBee ECtt ELon EPfP GWyn LHop LRHS LSun NCou NPri SEle SPad SWvt WHrl XLum
	Sun Child	see *C.* 'Sonnenkind' (red-blotched)
	'Sweet Marmalade'PBR **new**	NCGa
	'Tequila Sunrise' (v)	MNrw
	tinctoria	MNHC SRms
	tripteris	CAby CBWd ELan EPfP SMad WMoo XLum
	- 'Mostenveld'	EBee GBin
	- 'Pierre Bennerup'	SAko
	- 'Red November' **new**	MNrw
	verticillata	CMac EBee ECha GCal MBel MBrN MHer MWat NLar NPer SRms WCAu WHal WOld
	- 'Bengal Tiger' **new**	CMea
	- Crème Brûlée = 'Crembru'PBR	ECtt EWes LRHS MJak SCoo SRkn
I	- 'Golden Gain'	CBod ECtt GBuc LHop MArl NGdn WFar
	- 'Golden Shower'	see *C. verticillata* 'Grandiflora'
§	- 'Grandiflora' ♀H5	CBcs CBod EAEE ELan EPfP GMaP LRHS MAvo MRav NGdn NHol NWad SHar SPer WFar XLum
	- 'Limerock Dream'PBR	EBee ILea MBNS SCob
	- 'Moonbeam'	Widely available
	- 'Old Timer' ♀H5	SDix
	- 'Ruby Red'	CAbP EAJP LRHS
	- 'Sunbeam'	ELon SCob
	- 'Tweety'PBR	WFar
	- 'Zagreb' ♀H6	Widely available

coriander see *Coriandrum sativum*

Coriandrum (*Apiaceae*)

*	***citratus***	CLau
	sativum	ENfk GPoy MHer MNHC NPri SIde SPoG SRms
	- 'Leisure'	SVic
	- 'Santo'	CLau
	- 'Slobolt'	CLau

Coriaria ✿ (*Coriariaceae*)

	arborea	WCru
	intermedia B&SWJ 019	WCru
	japonica	NLar SVen WCru
	- B&SWJ 2833	WCru
	- subsp. ***intermedia*** B&SWJ 3877	WCru
	kingiana	WCru
§	***microphylla***	WCru
	- B&SWJ 8999	WCru
	myrtifolia	NLar WCru
	- B&SWJ 14003 **new**	WCru
	nepalensis	NLar WCru
	- BWJ 7755	WCru
	pteridoides	WCru
	ruscifolia	WCru
	- HCM 98178	WCru
	sarmentosa	WCru
	terminalis	GCal SBrt WCru
	var. ***xanthocarpa***	
	- - GWJ 9204	WCru
	- - HWJK 2112c	WCru
	thymifolia	see *C. microphylla*

Cornus ✿ (*Cornaceae*)

	alba L.	CArg CBar CCVT CDul CLnd ECrN EMOT ESps MRav NWea SCob SEWo SRms WHed WMou WTSh

	- 'Alleman's Compact'	LRHS SPoG
	- 'Argenteovariegata'	see *C. alba* 'Variegata'
	- 'Atrosanguinea'	WWtn
	- 'Aurea' $\mathbb{Y}^{H7}$	Widely available
	- Baton Rouge = 'Minbat' PBR	CRos ELon EPfP LHop LRHS MAsh NRHS SPoG SWvt WFar
	- 'Bloodgood' **new**	SPoG
	- 'Cream Cracker' PBR (v)	EBee MRav
	- 'Elegantissima' (v) $\mathbb{Y}^{H7}$	Widely available
	- 'Gouchaultii' (v)	CBcs CMac CRos EPfP ESps GKin LRHS MGos MRav NEgg NLar NRHS SGol SHil SPer SRms WFar WMoo
	- 'Hessei' misapplied	see *C. sanguinea* 'Compressa'
	- 'Hessei' Hesse	WPat
	- Ivory Halo = 'Bailhalo' PBR	EAEE EBee EMil EPfP ESps LRHS LSRN MAsh MRav NWea SPer
	- 'Kesselringii'	Widely available
	- Red Gnome = 'Regnzam'	ELon EPfP LLHF MAsh SPoG
	- 'Ruby'	SPoG
	- 'Siberian Pearls'	ELan GKin MBlu NLar
§	- 'Sibirica' $\mathbb{Y}^{H7}$	Widely available
	- 'Sibirica Variegata' (v) $\mathbb{Y}^{H7}$	CMac CRos EBee ECrN ELon EPfP ESps GCra GKin GMcL LRHS LSRN MAsh MBlu MGos NEgg NRHS SCob SHil SLim SPer SWvt WCFE WHar WMoo
	- 'Spaethii' (v) $\mathbb{Y}^{H7}$	Widely available
§	- 'Variegata' (v)	WFar
	- 'Westonbirt'	see *C. alba* 'Sibirica'
	alternifolia	CBcs CCVT CMCN CTho EAEE ELan ESps EWTr WMou
§	- 'Argentea' (v) $\mathbb{Y}^{H6}$	Widely available
	- 'Brunette'	CJun MBlu NLar
	- Golden Shadows = 'Wstackman' PBR (v)	CRos EBee IArd LRHS NLar SAko WHor
	- 'Golden Surprise'	CJun
	- 'Goldfinch' (v)	CJun MBlu
	- 'Moonlight' (v)	CJun
	- Pinky Spot = 'Minpinky'	LSRN NLar
	- 'Silver Giant' (v)	CJun IArd NEgg NLar SAko
	- 'Variegata'	see *C. alternifolia* 'Argentea'
	- 'Yellow Spring'	CJun NLar
	amomum	CAbP EBtc NLar
	- 'Blue Cloud'	EPfP LRHS MBlu SPoG
	- 'Lady Jane'	NLar
	'Ascona'	CBcs CEnd CJun EWTr NLar SPer SSta WGob
	Aurora = 'Rutban' (Stellar Series)	CJun MBlu NLar SGol
	canadensis	Widely available
	capitata	CAby CBcs CDul CHid CJun CMac CPne CRos CTsd EBee EPfP ESwi EWTr GKev IArd IDee IMou LRHS MGos MMuc NRHS SAko SEND SKHP SMad WCru WFar WPGP
	- subsp. ***emeiensis***	CJun
	- 'Foreness Fog' (v)	SEND
§	Celestial = 'Rutdan' (Stellar Series)	CBcs CDul CJun CRos LRHS NEgg NLar NRHS SGol SKHP WGob
	'Celestial Shadow'	MGos MPkF SGol
	'Centennial'	LRHS
	chinensis	SSta SWvt
	Constellation = 'Rutcan' (Stellar Series)	CJun MAsh SGol
	controversa	CBcs CCVT CDul CLnd CMCN CTri ECrN ELan EPfP ESps GBin LCro LOPS LPar MBlu MJak NLar NWea SEND SEWo SGol SSta SWvt WHar
I	- 'Aurea'	LRHS MAsh
	- 'Candlelight'	MBlu NLar
§	- 'Frans Type' (v)	CJun LSRN
	- 'Green Carpet'	NLar
	- 'Laska'	CJun NLar
	- 'Lucia'	CJun NLar
I	- 'Marginata Nord'	NLar
	- 'Pagoda'	CJun MBlu NLar
	- 'Troya Dwarf'	CJun NLar
	- 'Variegata' (v) $\mathbb{Y}^{H5}$	Widely available
	- 'Variegata' Frans type	see *C. controversa* 'Frans Type'
	'Dorothy'	CJun NLar
	'Eddie's White Wonder' $\mathbb{Y}^{H5}$	Widely available
	elliptica	EBee IArd SKHP
	- 'Full Moon'	CJun
	florida	CAco CDul CLnd CMCN CTho ESps ESwi EWTr LCro LPar MMrt MMuc NOra NOrn NWea SPer WHar WMat WTSh
	- 'Alba Plena' (d)	LPar
	- 'Apple Blossom'	CJun CMac CMen WGob
	- 'Autumn Gold'	SSta
	- Cherokee Brave = 'Comco No 1'	CBcs CJun CMen ESwi LMil LRHS MAsh NEgg NRHS SGol SPoG SSta WGob
	- 'Cherokee Chief'	CBcs CEnd CJun CLet CMac CMen CTho CTri EWTr IVic LSRN NEgg SAko WGob WHar
	- 'Cherokee Daybreak'	see *C. florida* 'Daybreak'
	- 'Cherokee Princess'	CJun CRos EWTr LRHS MAsh NOra SGol SPoG SSta WMat
	- 'Cherokee Sunset'	see *C. florida* 'Sunset'
	- 'Clear Moon'	LPar
	- 'Cloud Nine'	CBcs CJun CLet CMen CTho EWTr GKin NEgg SAko WGob WHar
§	- 'Daybreak' (v) $\mathbb{Y}^{H5}$	CBcs CJun CLet CRos ESwi LRHS LSRN MAsh NOra NOrn NRHS SHil SPer WHar WMat
	- 'Eternal Dogwood' (d)	ESwi LSRN SGol
	- 'First Lady' (v)	CJun CMac CMen NEgg WGob
	- 'Fragrant Cloud'	SWvt
	- 'Golden Nugget' (v)	CJun
	- 'Granary Gold'	SSta
	- 'Junior Miss'	CEnd
	- 'Moonglow'	CJun
	- 'Pendula'	CJun
	- 'Pink Flame' (v)	SSta
	- 'Purple Glory'	CBcs CJun SPer
	- 'Rainbow' (v) $\mathbb{Y}^{H5}$	CAbP CBcs CDul CJun CLet CRos CWib GKin LPar LRHS MAsh NOra NRHS NWea SHil SPoG WHar WMat
	- f. ***rubra***	CLnd CTri CWib ELan ESps ESwi GKin LCro LPar LRHS MRav NEgg SPer WGob WMat
	- - 'Red Giant'	CAbP CBcs CJun EWTr
	- - 'Spring Song'	CJun CMac CMen NEgg WGob
	- 'Spring Day'	CMac CMen NEgg WGob
	- 'Springtime'	CJun
	- 'Stoke's Pink'	CEnd CJun CMac CMen NEgg WGob
§	- 'Sunset' (v)	CBcs CEnd CLet CMen CWib ELan ESps LCro LPar LRHS MAsh NEgg NOrn NRHS SSta SWvt WGob WHar WMat
	- 'Sweetwater'	CJun WGob
	- subsp. ***urbiniana***	WPGP
	- 'Variegata'	GKin
	- 'White Cloud'	CJun NOra WMat
	'Gloria Birkett'	CAbP CJun CRos ELan LMil LRHS MAsh NEgg WGob
	'Gold Splash' (v)	NEgg
	hessei misapplied	see *C. sanguinea* 'Compressa'
	hongkongensis	CRos LRHS NLar NRHS WPGP

- B&SWJ 11700	WCru
- HWJ 1033	EBee EPfP WPGP
- PAB 8237	LEdu
- subsp. ***gigantea*** KWJ 12225	WCru
- subsp. ***melanotricha***	EBee SChF
- subsp. ***tonkinensis*** B&SWJ 11791	WCru
'Jerry Mundy'	CMac IVic NEgg
'Kelsey Dwarf'	see *C. sericea* 'Kelseyi'
'Kenwyn Clapp'	CJun
kousa	CBcs CCVT CMCN CMHG CMac CTho ELan EPfP ESps GKin GMcL LCro LPar MJak NEgg NLar SCob SPer SPlb WFar WHar WMou
- B&SWJ 12610 from Korea	WCru
- 'Akabana'	CJun
- 'Akatsuki' (v)	CJun MPkF NLar SSta
- 'All Summer'	CJun
- 'Autumn Rose'	CJun NLar SAko
- 'Beni-fuji'	CJun EBee EWTr LRHS MPkF NLar SMad
- 'Big Apple'	CJun CRos LLHF LMil LRHS MAsh NLar SBir WGob
- 'Blue Shadow'	CJun LRHS MBlu NLar SSta
- 'Bultinck's Beauty'	LRHS NLar
- 'Bultinck's Giant'	LRHS NLar SMad WGob
- 'Cherokee'	CJun LPar NLar
- 'China Dawn' (v)	CJun SSta
- var. ***chinensis***	Widely available
- - 'Bodnant Form'	CAby CEnd CJun CMac CTho EPfP ESwi EUJe NEgg NLar SSta WBor WGob
- - 'China Girl' 𝕐H5	Widely available
- - 'Claudia'	EPfP IArd IVic LRHS NLar SAko SSta
- - 'Great Star'	LRHS MAsh
- - 'Greta's Gold' (v)	CJun SSta
- - 'Ikone'	IVic
- - 'PVG'	CJun
- - 'Snowflake'	CJun
- - 'Spinners'	CJun NEgg
- - 'Summer Stars'	CJun
- - 'Tri-Splendor'	NLar
- - 'White Dusted' (v)	CJun EPfP MBlu NLar
- - 'White Fountain'	EPfP LSRN MPkF MPnt NLar NOra NOrn SLim WHar WMat
- - 'Wieting's Select'	CJun EWTr MBlu MPkF NEgg NLar SAko
- - 'Wisley Queen' 𝕐H5	CAbP CJun CRos EBee EPfP LMil LRHS MAsh SSta WPGP
- 'Claudine'	CJun
- 'Copacabana'	MBlu
- 'Daybreak'	SGol
- 'Doctor Bump'	CJun
- 'Doubloon'	CJun WPat
- 'Dwarf Pink'	CJun LRHS
- 'Ed Mezitt'	CJun NLar
- 'Eline'PBR	MPkF
- 'Elizabeth Lustgarten'	CJun MBlu MPkF SSta
- 'Eurostar'	ELan IVic LRHS MBlu
- 'Fanfare'	CJun
- 'Fernie's Favourite'	CJun
- Galilean = 'Galzam'	CJun MPkF WGob
- 'Gay Head'	CJun
I - 'Girard's Nana'	CJun
- 'Gold Cup' (v)	CJun MPkF SSta
- 'Gold Star' (v)	CBcs CEnd CJun CMac CRos ELan ESps LMil LRHS MAsh MBlu MPkF NEgg NLar SPoG SSta WGob
- 'Greensleeves'	CJun CRos EPfP GKev LLHF LMil LRHS MAsh SPoG SSta WGob

- 'Heart Throb'	CJun NLar SGol WGob
- 'Highland'	CJun
- 'John Slocock' 𝕐H5	CJun NLar WGob
- 'Kim'	NEgg
- 'Koree'	NLar
- 'Kreutzdame'	CJun LRHS MBlu
- 'Laura'	IArd MBlu SSta
- 'Little Beauty'	CJun
- 'Lizzie P'	NLar
- 'Lustgarten Weeping'	CJun
- 'Madame Butterfly'	CJun CRos LRHS MBlu NEgg NLar SPoG
- 'Marwood Dawn'	CMHG SSta
- 'Marwood Twilight'	CMHG
- 'Melanie'PBR	GQue WMat
- 'Milky Way'	CBod CJun CLnd CMCN CTho EPfP ESwi GMcL LRHS LSRN MAsh MBlu MGos MPkF MRav NEgg NLar SGol WGob WPat
- 'Milky Way Select'	CBcs CJun CRos LRHS NRHS
- 'Miss Petty'	CJun MPkF NLar
- 'Miss Satomi' 𝕐H5	Widely available
- 'Moonbeam'	CJun LPar MPkF NLar WPat
- 'Mount Fuji'	CJun MBlu NLar SSta
- 'National'	CJun LMil MAsh NLar SSta WGob WPat
- 'Nicole'	LRHS NLar WGob WPat
- 'Ohkan'	CJun
- 'Pevé Foggy'	LRHS NLar
- 'Pevé Limbo' (v)	CJun NLar
- 'Pevé Satomi Compact'	CJun NLar
- 'Piff Frocky'	EBee
- 'Polywood'	CJun NLar
- 'Radiant Rose'	CJun MPkF NLar SBir SSta WGob
- 'Rasen'	CJun NLar
- 'Rel Whirlwind'	CJun NLar
* - 'Robert'	NLar
- 'Rosea'	CJun LPar
- Samaratin = 'Samzam' (v)	CBcs CEnd CJun LRHS LSRN MPkF SGol SKHP SSta
- 'Schmetterling'	CJun EWTr MBlu NLar SAko WPat
- 'Snowbird'	CJun
- 'Snowboy' (v)	CBcs CDul CEnd CMac MBlu SMad
- 'Snowflurries'	CJun
- 'Southern Cross'	CJun WGob
- 'Square Dance'	CJun
- 'Steeple'	CJun NEgg
- 'Summer Fun' 𝕐H5	CJun CRos LRHS SPoG SSta
- 'Summer Majesty'	CJun
- 'Sunsplash' (v)	CJun LRHS SPoG SSta
- 'Temple Jewel' (v)	CJun
- 'Teresa'	LRHS
- 'Teutonia' 𝕐H5	CJun IArd IVic MGos NLar SAko SHil SSta WGob WPat
- 'Trinity Star'	CJun
- 'Triple Crown'	CJun WPat
- 'Tsukubanomine'	CJun CLnd NLar
- 'Weaver's Weeping'	CJun MPkF NLar
- 'Weisse Fontäne'	CJun NLar
- 'White Dream'	CJun LRHS NLar
- 'White Giant'	CJun SLim SPer
- 'Willy Boy'	WHor
- 'Wolf Eyes' (v) 𝕐H5	CBcs CJun LMil MAsh MBlu MPkF NLar SGol SPoG SSta
macrophylla Wall.	WCru
mas	Widely available
- 'Aurea' (v) 𝕐H6	CAbP CBcs CJun CRos ELan EPfP LRHS MAsh MBlu MGos MRav NEgg NLar SGol SSta WPat

§ - 'Aureoelegantissima' (v)	CJun CMac CRos LRHS MAsh NLar SPer WCot WPat
- 'Devin' (F)	NLar
- 'Elegant' (F)	CAgr
- 'Elegantissima'	see *C. mas* 'Aureoelegantissima'
- 'Golden Glory' ♀H6	CJun EPfP NLar SKHP WHor
- 'Gourmet' (F)	CAgr
- 'Happy Face'	NLar
- 'Hillier's Upright'	CJun
- 'Jolico' (F) ♀H6	CAgr CFGn CJun LEdu MBlu NLar SKHP WMat
- 'Kasanlaker' (F)	CAgr NLar
- 'Pancharevo' (F)	CAgr
- 'Pioneer' (F)	CJun NLar
- 'Redstone' (F)	CJun
- 'Shan' (F)	CAgr
- 'Shumen' (F)	CAgr
- 'Spring Glow'	CJun NLar
- 'Titus' (F)	NLar
- 'Variegata' (v) ♀H6	CAbP CBcs CJun CMCN CMac CRos CTho EBee EPfP ESps LRHS MAsh MBlu MGos NLar SKHP SPer WPat
- 'Xanthocarpa'	CJun NLar
- 'Yellow'	CAgr
mas* × *officinalis new	CJun
'Norman Hadden' ♀H5	Widely available
nuttallii	CDul CLnd CTri CWib ELan EPfP ESwi SPer SWvt
- 'Colrigo Giant'	CJun
- 'Gold Spot' (v)	CJun CMac
- 'Monarch'	CJun NEgg SKHP WPat
- 'North Star'	CDul CJun NLar SPer
- 'Portlemouth'	CEnd CJun LRHS NLar
- 'Zurico'	CJun
oblonga	LEdu WPGP
officinalis	CAgr CBcs CDul CJun CMCN EPfP IMou LRHS MBlu NLar SKHP SWvt
- 'Kintoki' ♀H6	ESwi NLar SKHP
'Ormonde' ♀H5	CJun EPfP NEgg NLar SMad SSta WGob WPGP WPat
'Pink Blush'	CJun
'Porlock' ♀H5	CDul CJun CMCN CRos EPfP ITim LRHS MAsh NLar SHil SWvt WGob WHor WPat
pumila	NLar
racemosa	EBtc NLar
rugosa	EBtc NLar
I × ***rutgersiensis***	LRHS
- Galaxy	see *C.* Celestial
Ruth Ellen = 'Rutlan' (Stellar Series)	CJun NLar
sanguinea	CBcs CCVT CDul CHab CLnd CMac CTho CTri ECrN EPfP ESps LBuc MJak MMuc MRav MSwo NBes NWea SCob SEWo SGol SPer SVic WHar WHed WMat WMou WTSh
§ - 'Anny'	CJun MBlu MRav WCot WPat
- 'Anny's Winter Orange' ♀H6	CJun CRos LRHS MAsh NRHS
- 'Beteramsii' new	LRHS
§ - 'Compressa'	MBlu MGil MRav NLar
- 'Magic Flame' ♀H6	CJun CRos ELon EMil EPfP LRHS MAsh NLar NRHS SPoG SWvt WPat
- 'Midwinter Fire'	Widely available
- 'Winter Beauty'	CJun CSBt CWib EBee EPfP ESps EUJe LBMP MAsh MBlu NEgg NLar NWea SLon SWvt WCFE WHar WPat WWtn
- 'Winter Flame'	see *C. sanguinea* 'Anny'
sericea 'Bud's Yellow'	CRos ELon EPfP LRHS MBlu NLar SHil SPoG
- 'Cardinal'	CHGN CRos ELon EPfP ESwi LRHS MAsh MGos NLar NRHS SHil SPoG
- 'Flaviramea' ♀H7	Widely available
- 'Hedgerows Gold' (v) ♀H7	CRos EBee ELan ELon EMil EPfP LHop LRHS MAsh MGos NEoE NRHS SCob SHil SPoG WCot WPat
§ - 'Kelseyi'	CMac EBee ELan EPfP ESps GMcL MRav NLar SCob WMoo
- Kelsey's Gold = 'Rosco'	LRHS MAsh SPoG WPat
- subsp. ***occidentalis*** 'Sunshine'	EPfP NEoE NLar SPoG
§ - 'White Gold' (v)	EAEE EHoe ELon EPfP EWTr MRav NLar SBod SMad SPer SPoG SRms WFar WMoo
- 'White Spot'	see *C. sericea* 'White Gold'
Stardust = 'Rutfan' (Stellar Series)	CJun
Stellar Pink = 'Rutgan' (Stellar Series)	CBcs CJun LRHS MGos MPkF NLar NRHS SGol SKHP WGob WPGP
suecica	NHar
× ***unalaschkensis***	LLHF
- NNS 08-101	GKev
Venus = 'Kn30 8' PBR	CBcs CJun CWGN ELan EPfP LBuc LCro MAsh MBlu MPkF NLar SLon SSta WPGP
walteri	CBcs EBtc
- B&SWJ 8776	WCru
'Winter Orange'	CJun NLar WHor

Corokia (*Argyrophyllaceae*)

buddlejoides	CBcs CHGN CMHG CTsd GBin NLar SEND WFar
'Coppershine'	CMHG
cotoneaster	CAbP CBcs CDul CMac CTri ECre ELan EPfP EPot EUJe LRHS MAsh MGil MGos NLar SBod SCob SEle SIgm SPer SPoG SWvt WCot WFar WGrn WPat
× ***virgata***	CAbP CChe CTri CTsd ELan EPfP LRHS NLar SArc SWvt WKif WSHC
- 'Bronze King'	LRHS SPer SVen
- 'Frosted Chocolate'	CCht CMHG CTsd EBee ELan EPfP IVic LHop LLHF LPre LRHS SEND SKHP SLim SPoG SVen SWvt WGrn
- 'Geenty's Green'	LRHS WGrn
- 'Pink Delight'	EPfP ESwi MAsh MRav
- 'Red Wonder'	CMHG CMac EBee ELan EPfP IVic LPre LRHS SEND SPoG SVen WGrn
- 'Sunsplash' (v)	CBcs CMac CTsd EBee ELan EPfP ESwi LHop LLHF LRHS MAsh NLar SEND SEle SPoG SWvt WGrn
- 'Yellow Wonder'	CBcs CMHG EBee ELan ESwi LRHS NLar SBod SEND SWvt

Coronilla (*Papilionaceae*)

comosa	see *Hippocrepis comosa*
coronata	LRHS
emerus	see *Hippocrepis emerus*
glauca	see *C. valentina* subsp. *glauca*
juncea	XSen
minima	WAbe XSen
'Nan Hicks'	EWld
valentina	CRHN GMcL LHop MGil SDix WSHC
- 'Clotted Cream'	CHid
- 'Cotswold Cream' (v) new	WCot
§ - subsp. ***glauca*** ♀H4	CDul CMac CRos CSBt CTri CWib EBee ELan EPfP LRHS LSRN MGil

	MMuc SEND SLim SNig SPer SRms SVen SWvt WAbe WBod WOut WPat XSen
- - 'Brockhill Blue'	EBee EPfP IVic LRHS SAko WCot
- - 'Citrina' 𝕐H4	Widely available
* - - 'Pygmaea'	LRHS SEle SRms WAbe WCot
- - 'Variegata' (v)	CBcs CKel CMac CTri CWCL CWib CWld EBee EHoe ELan EPfP LBMP LRHS MAsh MCot MGil MRav NQui SEle SLim SLon SNig SPer SPoG SRms SVen WCot
- 'Variegata'	SEle SMad
varia	see *Securigera varia*

Correa (*Rutaceae*)

alba	CCCN EPfP
- 'Pinkie' 𝕐H2	CCCN CTsd
alba* × *backhouseana	SEle
backhouseana 𝕐H2	CAbb CBcs CCCN CHll CMac CTri CTsd ELan EPfP GCal IDee IVic LHop LPot LRHS NLar SEle SVen WSHC
- 'Peaches and Cream'	CCCN IVic SEle SRkn
'Dusky Bells' 𝕐H2	CAbb CBcs CCCN CHll CTri CTsd ELan EPfP IVic LBMP LHop LRHS MAsh MHtn SEND SEle SPlb SRkn SVen
'Dusky Maid'	CCCN
'Federation Belle'	CCCN SPlb SVen
glabra	SEle
'Harrisii'	see *C.* 'Mannii'
'Ivory Bells'	LRHS
lawrenceana	CFil CTsd LRHS SEND SVen WPGP
- var. ***grampiana***	SVen
§ 'Mannii' 𝕐H2	CBcs CCCN CTsd ECre ELan ELon EPfP IVic LRHS WSHC
'Marian's Marvel' 𝕐H2	CBcs CCCN ELan EPfP LBMP MAsh SEND SEle SPoG SRkn SVen
'Peachy Cream'	CAbb CCCN LRHS
'Poorinda Mary'	CCCN SEle
pulchella 𝕐H2	CTri SEle
- 'Pink Mist'	WAbe
reflexa	MAsh MGil WAbe WCot
var. ***nummulariifolia***	
schlechtendalii	CCCN LHop SEle SVen

Cortaderia ✿ (*Poaceae*)

argentea	see *C. selloana*
fulvida misapplied	see *C. richardii* (Endl.) Zotov
§ ***fulvida*** (Buchanan) Zotov 𝕐H6	EWes IArd IDee SMad SWvt WCot
richardii misapplied	see *C. fulvida* (Buchanan) Zotov
richardii ambig.	CBod EHoe IMou MMuc NBir SDix SMad SWvt WHrl
§ ***richardii*** (Endl.) Zotov 𝕐H5	CAby CBcs CBot CCht CKno EBee ECha ESwi EWes IMou LRHS NRHS SArc SRms WPGP
- Brown's strain	LSun WCot
§ ***selloana***	CBcs CBod CDul CLet CTri CWib EMOT ESps IBoy LPar MGos MHtn MJak NBir SCob SGol SPlb
§ - 'Albolineata' (v)	CBcs CBot ELon EWes MWht SEND SPoG SWvt
§ - 'Aureolineata' (v) 𝕐H5	CBcs CBot CLet CMac ELan EPfP GMaP IVic LRHS NBid NRHS SCob SEND SLim SPer SPoG SWvt
- 'Evita'PBR 𝕐H5	CKno ECtt NLar SMad SPer SWvt WFar
- 'Gold Band'	see *C. selloana* 'Aureolineata'
- 'Golden Goblin'PBR	EHoe NLar NPri SCob
- 'Icalma'	EPPr
- 'Monstrosa' 𝕐H5	SEND SMad
- 'Patagonia' 𝕐H5	EHoe EPPr
- 'Pink Feather'	EPfP GMcL SEND SHil SPer WFar
- 'Pointe du Raz'	CBot SWvt
- 'Pumila' 𝕐H5	Widely available
- 'Rendatleri'	CBcs ELan LSRN SCoo SLim SWvt
- 'Rosea'	CBod CLet EMOT EPfP ESps MJak NGdn NLar SCob SGol WHar
- 'Senior'	NLar
- Silver Feather = 'Notcort' (v) 𝕐H5	SCob
- 'Silver Fountain' (v)	ELan EPfP LRHS MAsh NRHS
- 'Silver Stripe'	see *C. selloana* 'Albolineata'
- 'Splendid Star'PBR (v)	CBcs EHoe LHop LRHS MAsh MGos MJak NLar NRHS SLim SPoG SWvt
- 'Sunningdale Silver' 𝕐H5	CDul CMac ECha ELan EPfP ESps GMcL LRHS LSRN MGos NRHS SCob SEND SLim SMad SPer SPoG SWvt
* - 'White Feather'	CBod GMcL NGdn SCob SHil SPer WFar WHar
- 'White Plume' **new**	EPed
Toe Toe	see *C. richardii* (Endl.) Zotov

Cortia (*Apiaceae*)

depressa CC 7379	EWld

Cortusa (*Primulaceae*)

altaica	CPne
- 'Amelia Chekiangolios'	CPne
brotheri	EBee ECho
* ***caucasica***	EBee GKev
* - 'Alba'	EBee GKev
matthioli	ECho GEdr GKev GPSL NHpl WFar
- 'Alba'	ECho GBuc GKev NLar
- var. ***congesta***	GEdr GKev
- subsp. ***pekinensis***	ECho EDAr MPnt NBid NLar
- - var. ***sachalinensis***	EBee GKev
turkestanica	ECho GEdr LLHF

Corydalis ✿ (*Papaveraceae*)

angustifolia	WCot
anthriscifolia	CLAP CSpe EWes MMrt
'Blackberry Wine'	CSpe CWCL EBee ECtt EPfP EWTr MPnt SPad
Blue Line = 'Couriblue'	CWGN GBin LSou SPoG
'Blue Panda'	see *C. flexuosa* 'Blue Panda'
bracteata	EPot
'Bronze Beauty'	WMoo
brunneovaginata	WCot
bulbosa misapplied	see *C. cava*
bulbosa (L.) DC.	see *C. solida*
buschii	CAby EBee ECho ELon GBuc GEdr GKev NHar NRya WCot
calycosa **new**	GKev WCot
'Canary Feathers'PBR	ECtt LRHS MBNS NHpl NPri SHil
cashmeriana	LRHS NBid NRHS WAbe WHal
- 'Kailash'	EBee LRHS
cashmeriana* × *flexuosa	CBro CLAP ECho LHop WAbe
caucasica	ECho GBuc
- var. ***alba*** misapplied	see *C. malkensis*
§ ***cava***	CLAP EBee ECho GKev LAma NHpl WShi
- 'Albiflora'	CLAP ECho
cheilanthifolia	CSpe EPfP EWld IMou LEdu SRms WHea
- 'Manchu'	NPri
'Craigton Blue'	CLAP EBee EPPr EWTr EWld GBuc GEdr GKev IMou IPot MNrw NHar WAbe

curviflora	WAbe
- subsp. ***rosthornii*** 'Blue Heron'	CWGN ECtt GEdr LBMP MPnt NCGa WSHC
decipiens Schott, Nyman & Kotschy	see *C. solida* subsp. *incisa*
decipiens misapplied	EPot GKev
densiflora	GKev
'Early Bird'	GKev
elata	CLAP CSpe EWes GAbr GBin GBuc GEdr GWyn IFro LHop LRHS MArl MBel MCot MMuc MNrw NBid NBir NChi NSla SPhx SPoG SPtp WCot WCru WHal WHoo WOut WSHC
- 'Blue Summit'	CLAP ECtt EPPr IMou LRHS
elata* × *flexuosa	IMou
elata* × *flexuosa clone 1	CCse CLAP GEdr
flexuosa ♀H5	CHVG CSpe EPfP GMcL GWyn MArl MNrw WAbe WSHC XLum
- CD&R 528	CBot IFro NRya
- 'Balang Mist'	CLAP
- 'Blue Dragon'	see *C. flexuosa* 'Purple Leaf'
§ - 'Blue Panda'	CWCL EPPr EWes GBuc GKev GMaP MPnt NLar WCru
- 'Blue Skies'	MHol
- 'China Blue'	Widely available
- 'Golden Panda' (v)	NHpl NLar
- 'Hale Cat'	ECtt EPPr
- 'Hidden Purple'	CHid
- 'Nightshade'	LLHF NBid WCot
I - 'Norman's Seedling'	EPPr IVic WPGP
- 'Père David'	CBod CDor CLet CMac CRos CSBt CSpe CWCL EBee ECha ECho ELan EPPr EPfP GBin GWyn LRHS MHer NBir NCGa NEgg SPlb SPoG SRms SWvt WCru WPnP WSHC XLum
§ - 'Purple Leaf'	Widely available
'Golden Spinners'	IVic
heterocarpa	EBee IMou
incisa	ECho LAma SDir
- B&SWJ 4417	WCru
'Kingfisher'	CAby CBot CLAP CSma GBuc LEdu NHar NLar NSla WAbe WSHC
leucanthema DJHC 752	CLAP
linstowiana CD&R 605	CLAP
§ ***lutea***	CBcs EPfP IFoB IFro MMuc NBir NPer NPri NWad SEND SRms WCot WMoo
§ ***malkensis*** ♀H5	CMea CWCL EBee ECho EPot GBuc GKev LLHF NBir NRya WThu
'Maya' (v)	XLum
nobilis	ECho IFoB LLHF SPhx
ochotensis	IMou LRHS
§ ***ochroleuca***	CElw CSpe EPot EWTr GCal NLar WMoo
omeiana	WCot
ophiocarpa	EHoe ELan GCal WMoo
ornata	EPot
pachycentra	WAbe
paczoskii	CRos ECho GBuc GKev LRHS NRHS
pseudobarbisepala **new**	GKev
pseudofumaria alba	see *C. ochroleuca*
'Rainier Blue'	IVic
'Red Majesty' **new**	GKev
'Rukšāns Red'	CWCL
'Sapphire'	CBro
scandens	see *Dactylicapnos scandens*
scouleri	IMou NBir
sempervirens 'Alba'	MArt

shimienensis 'Berry Exciting'PBR	CAby CBod CDor CWGN EBee ECtt EPfP LHop LSou MBNS MHol MPnt NPer SPoG
siamensis	IFoB IMou
- B&SWJ 7200	WCru
§ ***solida***	CAvo CBro CElw CRos EBee ECho ECtt ELan EPfP EPot GKev LAma LEdu LHop LRHS MPie MRav NLar NRHS NRya SDeJ SPhx WCot WShi
- 'Advocet'	GEdr
- 'Endres Traum'	EBee
- 'Evening Shade'	GEdr SDir
- 'Fire Bird'	ECho GEdr GKev WHlf
- 'Firecracker'	CBro CRos ECho GKev LHop LLHF LRHS NRHS SPhx
- 'Frodo'	LAma
- 'Gandalf'	NHar
- 'Gaviota'	GEdr
§ - subsp. ***incisa*** ♀H5	ECho EPot GKev SDeJ SPhx
- lilac-flowered	IFoB
- 'Lucky Bird' **new**	GKev
- pink and red shades	GBuc
- 'Purple Beauty'	EBee GEdr GKev SPhx
- 'Purple Bird'	CAvo EBee GKev LLHF WHlf
- 'Quiet Elegance'	SDir
- Rainbow Mixed **new**	GKev
- 'Rosefinch'	GKev
§ - subsp. ***solida***	CLAP EPot GKev MArt NBir NRya SPhx WCot
- - from Penza, Russia	GBuc GKev LLHF SDir
- - 'Beth Evans'	Widely available
- - 'Blushing Girl'	ECho GEdr LAma
- - 'Dieter Schacht' ♀H5	EPPr EPot LAma NLar
- - 'Evening Shade'	ECho GEdr LAma
- - 'George Baker' ♀H5	Widely available
- - 'Nettleton Pink'	GKev
- - Prasil Group	GEdr GKev NHpl SPhx WBor
- - 'White Knight'	ECho GKev LAma NHpl SDir WCot
- f. ***transsylvanica***	see *C. solida* subsp. *solida*
- 'Turaco' **new**	GKev
- 'White King'	WCot
- 'White Swallow'	ECho EPot GEdr GKev SDeJ WHlf
- 'Zwanenberg'	GKev
'Spinners'	CAby CDor CElw CFis CLAP CSpe EBee ECha ECtt ELon EPPr GKev GLog GPSL IMou IVic NEgg NQui WPnP WSHC XLum
stipulata B&SWJ 2951	WCru
'Sylvia's Castle Haven' **new**	MPie
taliensis	GCal GKev GLog
tauricola	GEdr
temulifolia 'Chocolate Stars'	CBod CHVG CSpe CWGN EBee ECtt EWld LEdu LHop LLHF MBNS MHol MPie NCGa SCob SPoG WCot WSHC WWFP
'Tory MP'	CDor CHid CLAP CSam CSpe EBee EPPr GEdr IFro LRHS MNrw MPie NBid NCGa NChi NHar WHoo WPGP
transsylvanica hort.	see *C. solida* subsp. *solida*
turtschaninovii	EPot SKHP
vittae	GKev IFoB
vivipara	EPPr
wendelboi	IFoB
'Wildside Blue'	CLAP EWld WSHC
wilsonii	IFoB

Corylopsis (*Hamamelidaceae*)

glabrescens	CHGN CJun CRos LRHS
- var. ***gotoana***	CJun EPfP LRHS MAsh NLar WPat
- - 'Chollipo'	CAbP CBcs LRHS NLar SSta

- 'Lemon Drop' — CJun IArd NLar
glandulifera — CJun
pauciflora ♀H5 — Widely available
platypetala — see *C. sinensis* var. *calvescens*
- var. ***laevis*** — see *C. sinensis* var. *calvescens*
sinensis — CBcs EPfP
§ - var. ***calvescens*** — CBcs CJun CTho EPfP WPat
§ - - f. ***veitchiana*** ♀H5 — CJun CRos EPfP IArd IDee IMou LRHS MAsh NLar
§ - var. ***sinensis*** ♀H5 — CDul CJun CMCN CTho ELon EPfP IVic LRHS MAsh NLar SLon
- - 'Spring Purple' — CAbP CBcs CEnd CJun CMac EPfP GMcL IDee IVic LRHS MGos NLar SChF SHil SKHP SPoG WPGP WPat
- 'Veitch's Purple' — CJun NLar
spicata — CBcs CDul CJun CMCN IArd IDee LRHS MBlu MRav NEgg NLar SCob SGol SLim SPoG WHor WPat
- 'Golden Spring' — CBcs NLar
- 'Red Eye' — CJun NLar
veitchiana — see *C. sinensis* var. *calvescens* f. *veitchiana*
willmottiae — see *C. sinensis* var. *sinensis*

Corylus ✿ (*Betulaceae*)

avellana (F) — Widely available
- 'Anny's Purple Dream'PBR — MBlu NLar
- 'Anny's Red Dwarf' — NLar
- 'Aurea' — CBcs CDul CEnd CLet CRos CTho CTri EBee ELan EPfP ESps EUJe LRHS MAsh MBlu MGos MRav NLar NWea SCob SLim SPer SPoG SSta SWvt WFar
- 'Bollwylle' — see *C. maxima* 'Halle'sche Riesennuss'
§ - 'Butler' (F) — CAgr CDul CMac CTho CTri EMOT ERea IArd MJak SDea SRms WHar
- 'Casina' (F) — CAgr CTho
- 'Contorta' ♀H6 — Widely available
- 'Corabel' (F) — CAgr NOra SKee SRms WMat
- 'Cosford' (F) — CAgr CCVT CDul CFGn CMac CSBt CTho CTri EBee ECrN EPom ERea GTwe IArd LBuc LEdu MBlu MGos NLar NOra SDea SEWo SGol SKee SPer SRms SWvt WHar WMat
- Emoa Series — WMat
§ - 'Ennis' (F) — CAgr EMOT NOra SDea WHar
§ - 'Fuscorubra' (F) — EPom EShb MRav NLar SPoG SWvt WFar
- 'Gustav's Zeller' (F) — NOra SKee WMat
§ - 'Heterophylla' — CDul EBee NLar SSta WHar WPat
- 'Laciniata' — see *C. avellana* 'Heterophylla'
§ - 'Lang Tidlig Zeller' (F) — CAgr ERea NOra NWea WMat
- 'Merveille de Bollwyller' — see *C. maxima* 'Halle'sche Riesennuss'
- 'Nottingham Prolific' — see *C. avellana* 'Pearson's Prolific'
- 'Pauetet' (F) — CAgr
§ - 'Pearson's Prolific' (F) — CAgr CFGn CSBt CTho GTwe LBuc SDea SGol SKee
- 'Pendula' — EBee MAsh MBlu SCoo SRms WCot WHar WPat
- 'Princess' (F) — SVic
- 'Purpurea' — see *C. avellana* 'Fuscorubra'
- 'Red Majestic'PBR ♀H6 — Widely available
- 'Tonda di Giffoni' (F) — NOra SKee WMat
- 'Webb's Prize Cob' (F) — CAgr CDul CTho ELan ERea GTwe IArd LEdu MBlu MJak NLar SDea SEND SGol SKee SVic
colurna ♀H5 — CAgr CCVT CDul CMCN CMac EBee ECrN ELan EPfP ESps IArd LEdu MBlu MGos NLar NOra NOrn NPri NWea SCoo SGol SPer SRms WHar WMat WMou
× ***colurnoides*** 'Chinoka' (F) — CAgr MCoo WHar WMat
- 'Freeoka' (F) — CAgr MCoo WHar WMat
Early Long Zeller — see *C. avellana* 'Lang Tidlig Zeller'
fargesii — WPGP
ferox — CJun
maxima (F) — CDul CLnd CMac CTri EPom ESps GTwe MSwo NWea SDea
- 'Butler' — see *C. avellana* 'Butler'
- 'Ennis' — see *C. avellana* 'Ennis'
- 'Fertile de Coutard' — see *C. maxima* 'White Filbert'
- 'Frühe van Frauendorf' — see *C. maxima* 'Red Filbert'
- 'Grote Lambertsnoot' — see *C. maxima* 'Kentish Cob'
- 'Gunslebert' (F) — CCVT CDul CMac CTho CTri ECrN EMOT ERea GTwe NOra SDea SKee SPoG SRms WHar WMat
- Halle Giant — see *C. maxima* 'Halle'sche Riesennuss'
§ - 'Halle'sche Riesennuss' (F) — CAgr CTho ECrN EMOT ERea GTwe MMuc NLar NOra SDea SEND SKee WHar WMat
§ - 'Kentish Cob' (F) — CAgr CBcs CDul CMac CSBt CTho ECrN ELan EMOT EPfP EPom ERea GTwe IArd LBuc LRHS MGos NLar SDea SEWo SKee SLim SPer SPoG SRms SVic SWvt WHar WMat WMou
- 'Lambert's Filbert' — see *C. maxima* 'Kentish Cob'
- 'Longue d'Espagne' — see *C. maxima* 'Kentish Cob'
- 'Monsieur de Bouweller' — see *C. maxima* 'Halle'sche Riesennuss'
- 'Nottingham Cobnut' (F) — ERea SVic
- 'Purple Filbert' — see *C. maxima* 'Purpurea'
§ - 'Purpurea' (F) — Widely available
§ - 'Red Filbert' (F) ♀H6 — CDul CEnd CHab CTho EMOT EPom ERea GTwe IArd LEdu MAsh MBlu NLar NOra SCoo SGol SKee SLim SRms SSta WHar WPat
- 'Red Zellernut' — see *C. maxima* 'Red Filbert'
- 'Spanish White' — see *C. maxima* 'White Filbert'
§ - 'White Filbert' (F) — CHab ERea SKee WHar
- 'White Spanish Filbert' — see *C. maxima* 'White Filbert'
- 'Witpit Lambertsnoot' — see *C. maxima* 'White Filbert'
'Nottingham Early' (F) — NLar
sieboldiana B&SWJ 11056 — WCru
- var. ***mandshurica*** — MBlu
'Te Terra Red' — CDul CMCN EBee EPfP MAsh MBlu NOrn SLon SRms WHar WMat
tibetica — CMCN LEdu

Corymbia see *Eucalyptus*

Corynabutilon see *Abutilon*

Corynephorus (*Poaceae*)

canescens — NBir

Corynopuntia (*Cactaceae*)

grahamii SB 1885 from Candelaria, Texas — CCac

Cosmos (*Asteraceae*)

§ ***atrosanguineus*** — CBcs CMea CSBt CSpe CWGN CWib ECtt ELan ENor EPfP EWTr IVic LCro LHop LOPS LSRN MRav NLar SCob SDeJ SPer SPoG SWvt WHoo
- Chocamocha = 'Thomocha'PBR — CAvo CBcs CCCN CChe CHid CSpe CWGN ECtt EPfP ESps GMaP IBoy

	LBMP LCro LHop LOPS LRHS MGos NCGa NLar SCob SEle SHil SPer SPoG SRot WBor
- 'New Choco'PBR	LSou
- 'Spellbound'	ECtt
bipinnatus 'Antiquity'	NPri SPhx
- 'Dazzler'	LCro SPhx
- 'Purity'	CSpe LCro LRHS SPhx
- 'Rubenza'	LCro SPhx
- 'Sea Shells' (mixed)	CWCL
- Sonata Series **new**	SEle
- - 'Sonata Carmine'	LSou NPri SPoG
- - 'Sonata Pink'	LSou NPri SPoG
- - 'Sonata White'	CSpe LSou NPri SPoG
- 'Sweet Sixteen'	SPhx
caudatus	WJek
peucedanifolius	CSpe GPSL NGBl WSHC
- 'Flamingo'	CGrW EBee EPfP ERCP SDeJ
'Razzmatazz Pink'	NPri
sulphureus 'Bunte Lichter'	CSpe

Cosmos × *Dahlia* (*Asteraceae*)

'Mexican Black'	ECtt ERCP NJRG SMHy WPGP

costmary see *Tanacetum balsamita*

Costus (*Costaceae*)

pulverulentus **new**	LRHS

Cotinus ✿ (*Anacardiaceae*)

americanus	see *C. obovatus*
'Candy Floss' **new**	SHil
§ ***coggygria***	CAco CArn CBcs CDul CMCN CMac EBee ECrN ELan EPfP ESps LHop LPar MRav MSwo NLar NWea SCob SEND SGol SPer SRms SWvt WFar XSen
- Golden Spirit = 'Ancot'PBR 🏆H5	Widely available
- Green Fountain = 'Kolcot'PBR	EBee EMil LHop
- 'Kanari'	NLar WPat
- 'Nordine'	WPat
- 'Notcutt's Variety'	MRav
- 'Old Fashioned'PBR	GMcL MPkF
- 'Pink Champagne'	CBcs EPfP MAsh NLar SSta WPat
- Purpureus Group	EPfP IBoy LPar SGol SRms
- 'Red Beauty'	NLar
- 'Royal Purple' 🏆H5	Widely available
- Rubrifolius Group	CBcs CDul EPfP SEND SGol SPer SWvt
- Selection	EPfP
- Smokey Joe = 'Lisjo'PBR	CRos EPfP LRHS MAsh SLon SPoG SSta SWvt
- 'Smokey Joe Purple'	LSou
- 'Velvet Cloak'	CAbP EBee ELan EPfP ESps LRHS MGos MPkF NLar SLon SWvt
- 'Young Lady'PBR 🏆H5	Widely available
Dusky Maiden = 'Londus'PBR	CRos CSBt ELon EPfP LLHF LRHS MAsh MGos NLar NRHS SCob SLon WPat
'Flame' 🏆H5	CBcs CDul CRos ECrN ELan ELon EPfP ESps LRHS MAsh MGos MRav NLar NRHS SCob SGbt SKHP SLim SPer SPoG SWvt WFar WPat
'Grace'	Widely available
'Grace' × ***obovatus*** **new**	GMcL
§ ***obovatus***	CMCN EBtc ELon EPfP IArd LLHF LRHS MBlu MPkF MRav NLar SSta WPGP WPat
'Ruby Glow'	CRos LRHS NRHS SHil

Cotoneaster ✿ (*Rosaceae*)

acuminatus	SRms
acutifolius var. ***laetevirens***	see *C. laetevirens*
adpressus	CAco SCob
§ - 'Little Gem'	ECho NHar NLar
- var. ***praecox***	see *C. nanshan*
- 'Tangstedt'	SGol
- 'Tom Thumb'	see *C. adpressus* 'Little Gem'
affinis	SRms
albokermesinus	SRms
ambiguus Rehder & E.H. Wilson	NLar
amoenus	NLar SRms
- AC 829	MHid
§ ***apiculatus***	NLar SRms
§ ***ascendens***	SRms
assamensis	SRms
§ ***astrophoros***	CMac MBlu NHar NLar
atropurpureus	NLar SRms
§ - 'Variegatus' (v) 🏆H6	Widely available
aurantiacus	NLar
boisianus	NLar SRms
bradyi	SRms
brickellii	NLar
§ ***bullatus***	CDul CTri EPfP ESps MMuc NLar SPer SRms WHil
- 'Firebird'	see *C. ignescens*
- f. ***floribundus***	see *C. bullatus*
- var. ***macrophyllus***	see *C. rehderi*
bumthangensis	NLar SRms
buxifolius blue-leaved	see *C. lidjiangensis*
- 'Brno'	see *C. marginatus* 'Brno'
- f. ***vellaeus***	see *C. astrophoros*
cambricus	NLar
camilli-schneideri	NLar SRms
canescens	NLar SRms
chadwelli	NLar
chuanus	NLar
chungtiensis	NLar
cinnabarinus	SRms
§ ***cochleatus***	SRms
§ ***congestus***	CDul CSBt CWib ESps MSwo NLar SPer SPlb SRms XLum
- 'Nanus'	CMea ELan GCrg GEdr
conspicuus	CBcs EWTr SRms
- AC 3176	MHid
- 'Decorus' 🏆H6	CDul CLet CRos CSBt EAEE EPfP ESps GMcL LHop LRHS MGos MJak MMuc MSwo NEgg NLar NWea SCob SEND SGol SHil SLim SPer SPlb SPoG SWvt WMoo
- 'Leicester Gem'	SRms
- 'Red Glory'	CMac
cooperi	SRms
cordifolius	MBlu NLar SRms
cornifolius	SRms
§ 'Cornubia' 🏆H6	Widely available
crispii	NLar
cuspidatus	MBlu NLar
dammeri	Widely available
§ - 'Major'	CBar CDul ESps LBuc NLar WFar
§ - 'Mooncreeper'	SCob
- var. ***radicans*** misapplied	see *C. dammeri* 'Major'
dammeri × ***microphyllus***	MJak
dielsianus	NLar NWea SPer SRms
divaricatus	EPfP NLar NWea SPer SRms
duthieanus	NLar
- 'Boer'	see *C. apiculatus*

	elatus	SRms
	elegans	SRms
	emeiensis	NLar SRms
	encavei	NLar
	'Erlinda'	see *C.* × *suecicus* 'Erlinda'
	'Exburiensis'	CBcs CBod CCVT CDul ECrN EMOT EPfP ESps MGos MMuc MRav NLar NOra SCob SEND SGol WFar WHar WMat
	falconeri	SRms
	fastigiatus	SRms
	flinckii	NLar SRms
	floccosus	GMcL IArd NWea SEND
	floridus	SRms
	forrestii	NLar SRms
	franchetii	Widely available
	frigidus	EWTr NOrn SRms
§	- 'Pershore Coral'	WAvo
	fulvidus	NLar
	gamblei	SRms
	ganghobaensis	CMCN SRms
	- B&L 12234	WCru
	glabratus	SRms
	glacialis	SRms
	glaucophyllus	IArd NLar SRms
§	***glomerulatus***	NLar SRms
	gonggashanensis new	NLar
	gracilis	SRms
	granatensis	NLar SRms
	harrovianus	NLar SRms
	harrysmithii	NLar
	hebephyllus	NLar
I	***hedegaardii*** 'Fructu Luteo'	SRms
	henryanus	SRms
	- 'Corina'	SRms
	'Herbstfeuer'	see *C. salicifolius* 'Herbstfeuer'
	'Highlight'	see *C. pluriflorus*
	hillieri	NLar
§	***hjelmqvistii***	LBuc NLar SRms
	- 'Robustus'	see *C. hjelmqvistii*
	- 'Rotundifolius'	see *C. hjelmqvistii*
	hodjingensis	SRms
	horizontalis	Widely available
	- 'Variegatus'	see *C. atropurpureus* 'Variegatus'
	- var. ***wilsonii***	see *C. ascendens*
	hualiensis	NLar SRms
	- B&SWJ 3143	WCru
	humifusus	see *C. dammeri*
	hummelii	SRms
	hupehensis	NLar
§	'Hybridus Pendulus'	Widely available
§	***hylmoei***	NLar SRms
	hypocarpus	SRms
	ignavus	SRms
§	***ignescens***	NLar NWea SRms
	ignotus	SRms
	incanus	NLar
	induratus	SRms
	insculptus	SRms
	insolitus	NLar
	integerrimus	SRms
§	***integrifolius***	MAsh NLar SRms WMoo
	kangdingensis	SRms
	kingdonii	NLar
	kitaibelii	NLar
	konishii	NLar
	kweitschoviensis	NLar
	lacteus ♀H6	Widely available
	- 'Milkmaid' (v)	NLar
§	***laetevirens***	NLar
	lancasteri	NLar SRms
	langei	SRms
	laxiflorus	SRms
§	***lidjiangensis***	SRms
§	***linearifolius***	GCra
	lucidus	NLar SRms
	ludlowii	SRms
	magnificus	SRms
§	***mairei***	NLar NWea SRms
	marginatus Lindl. ex Loudon	SRms
§	- 'Blazovice'	NLar SRms
§	- 'Brno'	SRms
	marquandii	NLar SRms
§	***meiophyllus***	MBlu NLar
	melanocarpus	NLar
	meuselii	NLar SRms
	meyeri	NLar
	microphyllus misapplied	see *C. purpurascens*
	microphyllus ambig.	CBcs ESps GMcL SCob
	microphyllus Wall. ex Lindl.	CDul CTri LRHS MGos NWea SBod SDix SPer SPoG WHed WMoo
	- NICE 004	WCFE
	- var. ***cochleatus*** (Franch.) Rehder & E.H.Wilson	see *C. cochleatus*
	- var. ***cochleatus*** ambig.	NSla
	- 'Donard Gem'	see *C. astrophoros*
	- 'Tanja' new	LRHS NRHS
	- 'Teulon Porter'	see *C. astrophoros*
	- var. ***thymifolius*** misapplied	see *C. linearifolius*
	- var. ***thymifolius*** (Lindl.) Koehne	see *C. integrifolius*
	- var. ***thymifolius*** ambig.	CRos LRHS
	milkedandaensis	SRms
	miniatus	SRms
	mirabilis	NLar SRms
	monopyrenus	SRms
	- F 11422	GKev
	'Mooncreeper'	see *C. dammeri* 'Mooncreeper'
	morrisonensis	SRms
	moupinensis	GLog SRms
	- BWJ 8167	WCru
	mucronatus	NLar SRms
§	***nanshan***	CAbP NLar NWea SRms
	- 'Boer'	see *C. apiculatus*
	naoujanensis	EPfP NLar
	- 'Berried Treasure'	CRos EPfP LRHS NRHS SHil
	nepalensis	NLar
	newryensis	SRms
	nitens	NLar SRms
	nitidifolius	see *C. glomerulatus*
	nohelii	NLar SRms
	notabilis	SRms
	nummularioides	SRms
	nummularius Fisch. & C.A.Mey.	SRms
	obscurus	SRms
	obtusus Wall. ex Lindl.	NLar SRms
	ogisui	NLar
	- Og 95105 new	GKev
	omissus	NLar
	pangiensis	SRms
	pannosus	SRms
	paradoxus	SRms
	parkeri	NLar SRms
	pekinensis	SRms
	permutatus	see *C. pluriflorus*
	perpusillus	SRms
	'Pershore Coral'	see *C. frigidus* 'Pershore Coral'
§	***pluriflorus***	NLar SRms

	poluninii	NLar SRms
	polycarpus	SRms
	praecox 'Boer'	see *C. apiculatus*
	procumbens	SRms
	- 'Queen of Carpets' ♀H6	CBod CLet CRos ELan EPfP ESps IBoy LHop LRHS LSRN MAsh MGos MRav NEgg NLar NRHS SBod SCoo SHil SLim SPoG SRms SWvt WMoo
	- 'Streib's Findling'	see *C.* 'Streib's Findling'
	prostratus	SRms
	przewalskii	SRms
	pseudo-obscurus	SRms
§	***purpurascens***	CSBt LRHS NLar NRHS
	pyrenaicus misapplied	see *C. congestus*
	qungbixiensis	NLar SRms
	raboutensis	NLar
	racemiflorus	SRms
§	***rehderi***	NLar SRms
	reticulatus	NLar
	rokujodaisanensis	NLar
	roseus	NLar SRms
	'Rothschildianus' ♀H6	Widely available
	rubens W.W. Sm.	NLar
	rugosus E. Pritz. ex Diels	NLar SRms
	'Saint Monica'	MBlu
	salicifolius	CTri MSwo NLar NWea SRms WFar
	- Autumn Fire	see *C. salicifolius* 'Herbstfeuer'
§	- 'Avonbank'	CEnd NLar WAvo
	- 'Brno Orangeade'	SRms
	- 'Emerald Carpet'	SEND
	- 'Gnom' ♀H6	CDul CMac CRos ELan EPfP ESps GMcL LRHS MAsh MGos MMuc MRav NBir NEgg SCob SLim SPer SPoG SRms WHar WMoo
§	- 'Herbstfeuer'	GMcL MRav MSwo SRms WMoo
	- Park Carpet	see *C. salicifolius* 'Parkteppich'
§	- 'Parkteppich'	NWea
	- 'Pendulus'	see *C.* 'Hybridus Pendulus'
	- 'Pink Champagne' ♀H6	CMac MRav
	- 'Repens'	CWib EPfP ESps NOra NPla NWea SCob SGol SLim SPer SPoG SRms WMat
	- var. ***rugosus***	see *C. hylmoei*
	salwinensis	SRms
	sandakphuensis	SRms
	Saphyr Green = 'Belka'PBR	EAEE
	scandinavicus	SRms
	schantungensis	NLar SRms
	schlechtendalii 'Blazovice'	see *C. marginatus* 'Blazovice'
	- 'Brno'	see *C. marginatus* 'Brno'
	schubertii	SRms
	serotinus misapplied	see *C. meiophyllus*
	serotinus Hutch.	SRms
	shannanensis	SRms
	shansiensis	NLar SRms
	sherriffii	NLar SRms
	sikangensis	GBin GLog SRms
	simonsii	CBcs CCVT CDul CLnd CMac EBee ECrN ELan EPfP ESps GMcL LBuc LRHS MGos MMuc NBes NHol NLar NWad NWea SCob SGol SPoG SRms WHed
	soczavianus	NLar
§	***splendens***	SRms
	- 'Sabrina'	see *C. splendens*
	spongbergii	NLar SRms
	staintonii	SRms
	sternianus ♀H6	EPfP NLar SRms
	- ACE 2200	MSwo
§	'Streib's Findling'	IBoy LRHS MAsh NRHS SCob SGol
	suavis	SRms
	subacutus	SRms
	subadpressus	SRms
	submultiflorus	NLar
	× ***suecicus*** 'Coral Beauty' ♀H6	Widely available
§	- 'Erlinda' (v)	SRms
	- 'Ifor'	SRms
	- 'Juliette' (v) ♀H6	CRos EHoe EMOT EShb GMcL LRHS LSRN MAsh MJak MMuc MRav NLar NOrn NRHS SCob SCoo SHil SLim SPer SPoG WMat
	- 'Skogholm'	CBcs CRos CWib ELan EPfP ESps LRHS MAsh MGos NWea SCob SPer SRms WHar
	svenhedinii	NLar
	taoensis	SRms
	tardiflorus	NLar SRms
	tauricus	SRms
	teijiashanensis	NLar SRms
	tengyuehensis	SRms
	thimphuensis	NLar SRms
	tomentellus	WCFE
	tomentosus	SRms
	transcaucasicus	NLar
	turbinatus	NLar SRms
	'Valkenburg'	SRms
	vandelaarii	NLar SRms
	veitchii	MAsh NLar SRms
	verruculosus	SRms
	vestitus	NLar
	villosulus	SRms
	vilmorinianus	SRms
	wardii misapplied	see *C. mairei*
	wardii W.W. Sm.	SRms
	washanensis	NLar
	× ***watereri***	CBod CCVT CWib EAEE ECrN ELon EMOT ESps MJak MMuc MSwo NWea SHil WJas
	- 'Avonbank'	see *C. salicifolius* 'Avonbank'
	- 'Cornubia'	see *C.* 'Cornubia'
	- 'John Waterer'	EPfP SHil SPer SPoG
	- 'Pendulus'	see *C.* 'Hybridus Pendulus'
	wilsonii	NLar SRms
	yalungensis	SRms
	yinchangensis	SRms
	zabelii	SRms

Cotula (*Asteraceae*)

	coronopifolia	CBen CWat NPer SWat
	hispida ambig.	ECtt SIgm
§	***hispida*** (DC.) Harv.	CTri CWCL ECho EDAr EHoe GMaP MAsh MHer NPer NRya SPoG SRms WIce WJek XLum
	lineariloba (DC.) Hilliard	ECha ECho EWes
	minor	see *Leptinella minor*
	pectinata	see *Leptinella pectinata*
	'Platt's Black'	see *Leptinella squalida* 'Platt's Black'
	potentilloides	see *Leptinella potentillina*
	pyrethrifolia	see *Leptinella pyrethrifolia*
	reptans	see *Leptinella scariosa*
	scariosa	see *Leptinella scariosa*
	squalida	see *Leptinella squalida*

Cotyledon (*Crassulaceae*)

	chrysantha	see *Rosularia chrysantha*
	oppositifolia	see *Chiastophyllum oppositifolium*
	orbiculata	CTal CTre ETod SPlb
	- var. ***oblonga***	EShb LToo WCot
	- 'Silver Waves'	MCot

simplicifolia	see *Chiastophyllum oppositifolium*
tomentosa subsp. ***ladismithensis*** ♀H1c	LAll

Craibiodendron (*Ericaceae*)

yunnanense	CBcs

Crambe (*Brassicaceae*)

cordifolia ♀H5	Widely available
maritima	CEls CSpe ECha EMil EPfP GJos GMaP GPoy IPot LRHS MCoo MHol MRav NLar NPnk NPri NSti SEND SMad SPer SWat WCot WFar WJek WPGP WTre
- 'Lilywhite'	CAgr LEdu SVic
tatarica	GJos

cranberry see *Vaccinium macrocarpon*, *V. oxycoccos*

Crassula ✿ (*Crassulaceae*)

	anomala	see *C. atropurpurea* var. *anomala*
	arborescens	EShb EUJe SChr
	argentea	see *C. ovata*
§	***atropurpurea*** var. ***anomala***	SChr
	- subsp. ***arborescens*** 'Blue Mist'	LAll SEND
	coccinea	CTre EShb SPlb
	muscosa	SChr SPlb SRot
	obtusa	SRot
	orbicularis	WCot
§	***ovata*** ♀H2	EBak LAll NPer NPla SChr SEND SPlb SPre SVen WThu
	- 'Blue Bird'	LToo
	- 'Gollum' ♀H2	LAll
	- 'Hummel's Sunset' (v) ♀H2	EShb LAll
	- 'Minima'	LAll
	- 'Undulata'	WCot
	- 'Variegata' (v)	EBak EShb LAll WCot
	pellucida subsp. ***marginalis*** f. ***rubra***	EShb
	perfoliata var. ***falcata*** ♀H2	SRot WCot
	perforata 'Variegata' (v)	NWad SRot
	portulacea	see *C. ovata*
§	***sarcocaulis*** ♀H3	CBcs CTri ECho ELon GCrg GMaP LTro MAsh NHpl SBrt SIgm SPlb SPoG SRms SRot SVen WAbe WHoo WIce WSHC XSen
I	- 'Alba'	LTro NHpl
	sedifolia	see *C. setulosa* 'Milfordiae'
	sediformis	see *C. setulosa* 'Milfordiae'
	setulosa	SPlb
§	- 'Milfordiae'	CTri ECho NBir NRya WAbe
	socialis	LLHF WAbe
	tetragona	LAll SEND
*	***tomentosa*** 'Variegata' (v)	EShb

+ *Crataegomespilus* (*Rosaceae*)

'Jules d'Asnières'	NLar

× *Crataegosorbus* (*Rosaceae*)

miczurinii 'Ivan's Belle'	CAgr

Crataegus (*Rosaceae*)

	F&M 196	WPGP
	arnoldiana	CAgr CDul CLnd CTri ECrN EPfP MAsh MCoo MMuc NLar NWea SEND WMat
	'Autumn Glory'	CEnd CLnd EBee ECrN
	azarolus	CTho
	- var. ***aronia***	WCot
	chrysocarpa	EPfP
	coccinea ambig.	NWea
§	***coccinea*** L.	CAgr CDul CLnd CNWT CTho EBee WMat
	coccinioides	EPfP
	cordata	see *C. phaenopyrum*
	crus-galli misapplied	see *C. persimilis* 'Prunifolia'
	crus-galli L.	CCVT CDul CLnd ECrN EPfP LCro MAsh NWea SPer WJas
	dahurica	EPfP
	dsungarica	EPfP
	× ***durobrivensis***	CAgr CDul CLnd EPfP LRHS MBlu
	ellwangeriana	CAgr ECrN EPfP SDix WCot
	- 'Fire Ball'	MBlu
	gemmosa	CAgr MAsh
	greggiana	EPfP
	× ***grignonensis*** ♀H6	CDul CLnd CTho ECrN MAsh SPer WJas
	harbisonii **new**	IArd
	jonesiae	EPfP
	laciniata misapplied	see *C. orientalis*
§	***laevigata***	CCVT ESps NWea SCob
	- 'Coccinea Plena'	see *C. laevigata* 'Paul's Scarlet'
	- 'Crimson Cloud'	see *C. laevigata* 'Punicea'
	- 'Gireoudii'	CBod CDul CWib EMOT NLar NSti WJas
	- 'Mutabilis'	CTri EWTr SGol
§	- 'Paul's Scarlet' (d) ♀H6	Widely available
	- 'Pink Corkscrew'	EPfP LLHF MAsh MBlu WCot WPat
	- 'Plena' (d)	CBcs CDul CLnd CMac CSBt CTri CWib EBee ECrN ELan EMOT EPfP ESps MGos MRav MSwo NOra NOrn NWea SEWo SGol SLim SPer SWvt WHar WMat
§	- 'Punicea' ♀H6	Widely available
	- 'Rosea'	GKin
	- 'Rosea Flore Pleno' (d) ♀H6	Widely available
	× ***lavalleei***	CCVT CDul CLnd CMCN CTri ECrN ELan EMOT ESps MMuc MRav MSwo NOrn NWea SCoo SEND SLon SPer WTSh
	- 'Aurora'	NLar
	- 'Carrierei' ♀H6	CDul CMac CTho EPfP EWTr IVic LHop LSRN NWea SCoo SEWo SPoG WMat WMou
	mexicana	see *C. pubescens* f. *stipulacea*
	mollis	CAgr CTho ECrN EPfP
	monogyna	Widely available
§	- 'Biflora'	CDul CEnd CTho CTri EBee MAsh MCoo MGos NLar NWea SLim WMat
	- 'Compacta'	LLHF MAsh MBlu WCot WPat
	- 'Flexuosa'	WCot
	- 'Praecox'	see *C. monogyna* 'Biflora'
	- 'Stricta'	CCVT CDul CLnd CSBt ECrN EPfP IDee MMuc SGol SPer
	- 'Variegata' (v)	ECrN
	× ***mordenensis*** 'Toba' (d)	CDul CLnd LRHS SGol
	nigra	CDul
§	***orientalis*** ♀H6	CCVT CDul CEnd CLnd CMCN CTho CTri ECrN EMOT EPfP ESps IArd MAsh MCoo MGos NLar NOrn NWea SCoo SLim WHar WJas WMat WMou
	oxyacantha misapplied	see *C. laevigata*
	pedicellata	see *C. coccinea* L.
	persimilis	NOrn
§	- 'Prunifolia' ♀H6	Widely available

- 'Prunifolia Splendens' CAgr CCVT EBar EBee ESps EWTr LBuc NOra NOrn WMat WPat

§ ***phaenopyrum*** CDul CLnd CTho EBee EPfP
pinnatifida EPfP
- var. ***major*** CDul CEnd EPfP LEdu MCoo NOrn
- - 'Big Golden Star' CAgr CLnd CTho ECrN EMOT EPfP MBlu MCoo NOra WMat
'Praecox' see *C. monogyna* 'Biflora'
prunifolia see *C. persimilis* 'Prunifolia'
§ ***pubescens*** f. ***stipulacea*** CDul CTho ECrN EPfP
punctata EPfP
- f. ***aurea*** EPfP MBlu
sanguinea EPfP
schraderiana CAgr CDul CLnd CTho EBtc EPfP IVic NLar WHar WMat
submollis CLnd
succulenta 'Jubilee'PBR EBee LRHS MCoo NOra WMat
- var. ***macracantha*** CMCN
tanacetifolia CAgr CDul CTho EPfP MBlu WPGP
viridis 'Winter King' CAgr EPfP
wattiana CDul CLnd EBee ELan EPfP

× *Crataemespilus* (*Rosaceae*)

grandiflora CDul CLnd IArd WPat

Craterocapsa (*Campanulaceae*)

congesta CPBP

Cremanthodium (*Asteraceae*)

SDR 7968 new GKev
arnicoides EBee GKev
oblongatum new GKev
reniforme WJC 13872 new WCru

Crenularia see *Aethionema*

Crepis (*Asteraceae*)

incana ♀H4 CMea CPla ECho ECtt GBin GCrg NChi NSla SRms WAbe
rubra CSpe

Crinitaria see *Aster*

Crinodendron (*Elaeocarpaceae*)

hookerianum ♀H4 Widely available
- 'Ada Hoffmann' CBcs CBot CEnd CMac CTsd EBee ELan ELon EPfP GCal GKin GMcL IBoy IVic LRHS MBlu MGil MGos MPkF NLar SAko SCob SEle SKHP SLim SWvt WBor WFar WSHC
patagua CBcs CBot CCCN CDul CHid CMac CTsd CWib EBee ELan ELon EPfP ESwi GBin LRHS MGil MMuc NLar SAko SEND SEle SPlb SVen WSHC

Crinum (*Amaryllidaceae*)

amoenum CCCN EBee GKev
asiaticum WCot
§ ***bulbispermum*** CPrp
campanulatum EBee
capense see *C. bulbispermum*
'Carolina Beauty' WCot
'Cintho Alpha' EPfP GKev SDeJ SPer
'Elizabeth Traub' WCot
'Ellen Bosanquet' CCCN EBee ELan EPri GKev LRHS SDir WCot
'Emma Jones' WCot
'Hanibal's Dwarf' CFil WCot WPGP
moorei CBro CTca IVic LEdu SChr WPGP
- f. ***album*** CCCN CFil CTca EBee EPri GKev
'Ollene' WCot
§ × ***powellii*** CBcs CBod CBro CPrp CTca EBak ECha ECho ELan ELon EPfP GCal LAma LEdu LRHS MAvo MNrw MRav MWat NWad SDeJ SDix SEND SMad SPer SRms WCot
- 'Album' CBro CPrp CTca CTri EBee ECha ECho ELan ELon EPfP EWTr EWes GCra GKev LAma LEdu LRHS MRav SDeJ SDir SEND SMad SPer SRms WCot WFar WPGP WSHC
- 'Harlemense' EBee
- 'Krelagei' EBee
- 'Longifolium' see *C. bulbispermum*
- 'Roseum' see *C.* × *powellii*
'Sangria' WCot
'Summer Nocturne' WCot
'White Queen' WCot
yemense misapplied GKev IMou

Criogenes see *Cypripedium*

Crithmum (*Apiaceae*)

maritimum CArn CEls GPoy MNHC SPlb SRms WHoo WJek WTre

Crocosmia (*Iridaceae*)

'African Beauty' ECtt IBal
'Anna Marie' CTca EBee ECtt GKev LRHS MAvo NRHS
'Anniversary' IBlr
'Apricot' CTca ECrc IBal
'Apricot Surprise' ECtt IBal
aurea misapplied see *C.* × *crocosmiiflora* 'George Davison' Davison
aurea ambig. EShb GCal LRHS
aurea (Pappe ex Hook.f.) Planch. CPou IBal IBlr LEdu
- from Swaziland GCal IBal
- subsp. ***aurea*** CTca GKev IBlr
- - 'Maculata' IBlr
- subsp. ***pauciflora*** IBlr
- 'Zomba' new GCal
'Auricorn' CTca IBal IBlr LEdu
'Auriol' IBlr
'Aurora' NGdn
'Ballyrogan Sundown' IBlr
'Baywalker' MAvo
'Beth Chatto' CTca ECrc IBal
'Blaze' IBal
'Bowland Blaze' IBal MAvo
Bressingham Beacon = 'Blos' IBlr LRHS MSpe
'Bressingham Blaze' CBre CMHG CTca ECrc IBal IBlr LRHS NGdn NHol
Bridgemere hybrid ECrc
Bright Eyes = 'Walbreyes'PBR CRos EPfP LRHS NRHS
'Buttercups' EWoo MTis
'Cadenza' IBal IBlr NWad
'Caistor Sunset' IBal
'Carnival' IBlr
'Cascade' IBal IBlr
'Chinatown' IBal IBlr
'Chrome' CSam
'Chrome Spray' CTca IBlr
'Citronella' misapplied see *C.* × *crocosmiiflora* 'Honey Angels'
'Comet' Knutty CTca ECrc IBal IBlr LRHS MAvo SDix WMoo

	'Cornish Copper'	CTca SMad
	× ***crocosmiiflora***	CTca CTri IBlr SPlb SRms WBrk WMoo WShi
	- 'A.E.Amos'	ECrc
	- 'A.J. Hogan'	CPrp CTca IBal IBlr NHol
	- 'African Glow'	CTca EBee ECrc IBal
	- 'Amberglow'	CElw GWyn IBal IBlr NHol NPer
	- 'Apricot Queen'	CTca IBlr NHol
	- 'Autumn Gold'	ECrc IBlr
	- 'B.A.Walker'	ECrc
	- 'Baby Barnaby'	CBre CSam EBee
	- 'Babylon'	Widely available
	- 'Best of British'	ECtt
	- 'Bicolor'	CElw CTca IBlr
	- 'Burford Bronze'	CTca IBal IBlr NHol
	- 'Burnt Umber'	IBal
	- 'Butterball'	LRHS
	- 'Buttercup'	CDor CRos CSam CTca ECrc ECtt EPfP GKev IBal IBlr IKil LRHS MAvo MCot NHol SHar SHil SMad SRkn WMoo
	- 'Canary Bird'	CBro CSam ECtt IBal NGdn NHol WBrk
	- 'Cardinale'	IBlr
§	- 'Carmin Brillant' ℽ[H4]	Widely available
	- 'Challa'	ECtt IBal
	- 'Citrina'	MNrw
	- 'Citronella' J.E. Fitt	CBro CSam CTri EBee ECrc EPfP GMaP GQue LRHS MBel NGdn NHol
§	- 'Coleton Fishacre'	Widely available
§	- 'Columbus'	CAvo CMos CPrp CSam CTca ECrc EPfP EPri GKev IBal IBlr ILea LHop LRHS LSou MAvo MSCN MTis NHol SMad SPer SRms WFar WMoo
	- 'Colwall'	IBal IBlr NWad
	- 'Comet'	EBee IBal
	- 'Constance'	CBro CDor CSam CTca ECrc ECtt GKev IBal IBlr LRHS MAvo NBid NGdn NHol WBrk
	- 'Corona'	CPrp IBal IBlr MAvo NHol
	- 'Corten'	IBlr
§	- 'Croesus'	IBal IBlr
	- 'Custard Cream'	CPrp ECrc IBlr LRHS NHol
	- 'D.H. Houghton'	IBlr
	- 'Daisy Hill'	IBlr
	- 'David Fitt'	MAvo
	- 'Debutante'	CPrp CTca EBee ECrc EPri IBal IBlr NHol WSHC
§	- 'Diadème'	CSam CWCL IBal
	- 'Dusky Maiden'	CMac CTca ECrc ECtt EHoe EPri ESps GKin GMaP IBal IBlr LSou MSwo NHol SRms SWvt
	- 'Dwarf Gold'	IBal
§	- 'E.A. Bowles'	CPou ECrc
	- 'Eastern Promise'	CBre IBal IBlr MAvo
	- 'Elegans'	ECrc ECtt IBal
§	- 'Emily McKenzie'	Widely available
	- 'Fantasie'	ECrc IBal
	- 'Festival Orange'	ECrc
	- 'Fire Jumper'	CTca EBee IBal MAvo
	- 'Fireglow'[PBR]	ECtt GKev IBal
	- 'George Davison' misapplied	see *C.* × *crocosmiiflora* 'Golden Glory' ambig., *C.* 'Sulphurea'
§	- 'George Davison' Davison	Widely available
	- 'Gillian'	ECrc IBal
	- 'Gloria'	CTca ECrc IBal MAvo
	- 'Golden Glory' misapplied	see *C.* × *crocosmiiflora* 'Diadème'
§	- 'Golden Glory' ambig.	CBod CDor CRos CWCL ELan EWoo GBuc GMcL IBal IBoy LCro MSwo NBir SCob SEND SRms WHar
	- 'Goldfinch'	ECrc
	- 'Goldie'	CTca ECrc MAvo
	- 'Hades'	IBal IBlr
	- 'Harvest Sun'	IBlr
	- 'His Majesty'	CBro CSam CTca ECrc IBal IBlr NHol
	- 'Hoey Joey'	ECrc
§	- 'Honey Angels'	Widely available
	- 'Honey Bells'	ECrc WBrk WOld
	- 'Irish Dawn'	ECrc IBal IBlr MAvo NHol NWad
§	- 'Jackanapes'	ECtt ELan GCal IBal IBlr LRHS MNrw SRms STPC
	- 'Jackanapes VI'	IBal
	- 'James Coey' misapplied	see *C.* × *crocosmiiflora* 'Carmin Brillant'
	- 'James Coey' J.E. Fitt	CBod ECha EHoe EPfP GKin IBal IFoB NGdn NLar SPoG WMoo
	- 'Judith'	IBlr
	- 'Kapoor'	IBlr
	- 'Kiautschou'	CWCL IBal IBlr NGdn NHol
	- 'Lady Hamilton'	CSam CTca ECtt GCal GCra IBal IBlr LRHS MAvo NHol WMoo WOut
	- 'Lady McKenzie'	see *C.* × *crocosmiiflora* 'Emily McKenzie'
	- 'Lady Oxford'	ECrc IBal IBlr NHol
	- 'Lambrook Gold'	CAvo ECrc IBal IBlr MAvo
	- 'Lemon Fleece'	CCVN
	- 'Lord Nelson'	IBal NHol
	- 'Loweswater'	ECrc IBal MAvo
	- 'Lutea'	ECtt IBal
	- 'Marjorie'	ECrc IBal
	- 'Mars'	ECrc EWes IBal IFoB MAvo NGdn SRkn
	- 'Mephistopheles'	CPrp CTca IBlr MAvo NHol
	- 'Merryman'	ECrc IBal MAvo
	- 'Météore'	ECtt EPfP GKev GQue LRHS MBNS NEgg WFar
	- 'Morgenlicht'	MAvo NHol
	- 'Mount Usher'	CCse CPrp CTca EBee ECrc ECtt GCal IBal MNrw NHol
§	- 'Mrs Geoffrey Howard'	CSam IBal IBlr LRHS NCGa NHol SRms WCru
	- 'Mrs Morrison'	see *C.* × *crocosmiiflora* 'Mrs Geoffrey Howard'
	- 'Newry Seedling'	see *C.* × *crocosmiiflora* 'Prometheus'
	- 'Nimbus'	CTca IBal IBlr
§	- 'Norwich Canary'	CMHG CTca ECha ECtt EPri GBuc GCra GKev IBal IBlr LCro LEdu LRHS MRav NBir NGdn NHol SPer WMoo WOut
	- 'Olympic Fire'	ECrc IBlr NHol
	- 'Pepper'	IBlr
	- 'Ping Pong'	CTca
	- 'Plaisir'	IBal IBlr NBid NHol
	- 'Polo'	CSam CTca CWCL ECtt IBal LRHS
	- 'Princess'	see *C. pottsii* 'Princess'
§	- 'Princess Alexandra'	IBlr
	- 'Prolificans'	ECrc IBal
§	- 'Prometheus'	CTca IBal IBlr LRHS NHol
	- 'Queen Alexandra' misapplied	see *C.* × *crocosmiiflora* 'Princess Alexandra'
§	- 'Queen Alexandra' J.E. Fitt	CTca EBee ECha EWes IBlr WHal WMoo
	- 'Queen Charlotte'	ECrc IBal IBlr
	- 'Queen Mary II'	see *C.* × *crocosmiiflora* 'Columbus'
	- 'Queen of Spain'	CTca IBal
	- 'Rayon d'Or'	ECrc IBal
	- 'Red King'	CBro CDor CWld EBee EPfP GKev IBal IBoy LHop LRHS NLar NNys WBrk WMoo WRHF
	- 'Red Knight'	IBal

	- 'Rheingold' misapplied	see *C.* × *crocosmiiflora* 'Diadème'
	- 'Saint Clements'	CTca IBal IBlr NHol
	- 'Saracen'	CBcs CMac CTca CWCL EBee ECtt GBin GBuc GCal GKin IBal IBoy LEdu LRHS LSou MAvo MBNS MHer MHol MNrw SKHP WAul WCot WMoo
	- 'Severn Seas'	ECrc ECtt
	- 'Sir Mathew Wilson'	IBal
	- 'Solfatare' ♀[H4]	Widely available
	- 'Solfatare Coleton Fishacre'	see *C.* × *crocosmiiflora* 'Coleton Fishacre'
	- 'Star of the East' ♀[H4]	Widely available
	- 'Starfire'	ECrc
	- 'Sultan'	WFar WMoo
	- 'Twilight Fairy Gold'	CBod CPou EBee ECtt IBal LLWG LSou MHol NHpl SMad SPer WCot WRHF
	- 'Venus'	CBre CDor CTca ECtt GPSL IBal MAvo MHer NHol WMoo
	- 'Vesuvius'	ECrc GCal WSHC
	- 'Vic's Yellow'	ECrc IBal
	- 'Voyager'	ECtt ERCP GKev IBal LRHS NHol NLar SDeJ WHar WOut
	- Wasdale strain	ECrc IBal
	- 'Zeal Tan'	CElw CMHG CSam CTca EBee ECtt ELan ELon EPri GBin IBal LEdu LLWG LRHS MBNS NEgg NLar NSti SDix SPoG WCot WFar WHoo WMoo
§	× ***crocosmioides***	IBlr
	- 'Castle Ward Late'	CBod CPrp ECrc ECtt EPfP GCal GCra GQue IBal IBlr LEdu LRHS MAvo NEgg NHol NLar SRms WCot WFar WMoo
	- 'Mount Stewart Late'	IBlr
§	- 'Vulcan' Leichtlin	CTca IBlr
	'Darkleaf Apricot'	see *C.* × *crocosmiiflora* 'Coleton Fishacre'
	'Doctor Marion Wood'	IBal
	'Eggs and Bacon'	ECrc
	'Eldorado'	see *C.* × *crocosmiiflora* 'E.A. Bowles'
	'Elegance'	IBlr
	'Ellenbank Canary'	MAvo
	'Ellenbank Firecrest'	CTca EBee MAvo MHCG NCGa
	'Ellenbank Goldcrest'	NLar WSHC
	'Ellenbank Skylark'	MAvo
	'Emberglow'	Widely available
	'Fandango'	IBal IBlr NHol
	'Fernhill'	ECrc IBal IBlr
	'Fire King' misapplied	see *C.* × *crocosmiiflora* 'Jackanapes'
	'Fire King' ambig.	ECrc EPot ERCP GKev IBal LRHS NLar NSti SWvt
	'Fire Sprite'	IBlr
	'Firebird'	CAby CTca ECtt ELon GCra IBal IBlr LRHS MHol NHol SRms WCot
	'Firecracker'	IBlr
	'Firefly'	ECtt GKev IBlr IBoy MAsh
	'Flaire'	IBlr
	'Fleuve Jaune'	ECrc IBal
	'Forest Fire'	IBal LLHF LSou
	fucata	IBlr
	- 'Jupiter'	see *C.* 'Jupiter'
	fucata* × *paniculata	IBal
	'Fugue'	CTca IBlr
	'Fusilade'	IBlr
	'Gold Sprite'	IBlr
	'Golden Ballerina'[PBR]	CAbb EBee ECtt EWes IBal LBMP LSou MWat NCGa SCob SHar SPoG
	'Golden Dew'	ECrc ECtt GQue IBal MBNS SKHP WCot WFar WMoo

	Golden Fleece *sensu* Lemoine	see *C.* × *crocosmiiflora* 'Coleton Fishacre'
	'Harlequin'	CElw CPrp CTca GKev IBal ILea MAsh MAvo MHer MTis WTor
	'Harmonia'	EBee
	'Hellfire'	Widely available
	'Highlight'	ECrc IBal IBlr MAvo NHol NWad
	'Jennine'	IBal
	Jenny Bloom = 'Blacro'[PBR]	EBee IBal LRHS
	'John Boots'	CRos ECtt ELon GBuc GKev IBal IBoy LRHS MCot NBid NLar SMad SRms
§	'Jupiter'	CBot CBre CDor CSam CTca CWCL EBee GCal IBal MAvo MNrw NCGa NChi NHol NLar
	'Karin' **new**	CMos GKev
	'Kathleen'	ECrc WBod
	'Krakatoa'	CAbb CHll CPrp ECrc IBal LBMP LLHF MAvo MBel MHer SKHP SWvt WFar WMoo
	'Lady Ann' **new**	GKev
	'Lady Jane' **new**	GKev
	'Lady Wilson' misapplied	see *C.* × *crocosmiiflora* 'Norwich Canary'
	'Lana de Savary'	CTca EBee ECtt EWes GCal IBal IBlr MNrw NBid NHol NWad WCot
	'Late Cornish'	see *C.* × *crocosmiiflora* 'Queen Alexandra' J.E. Fitt
	'Late Lucifer'	CTri GCal IBal IBlr MNrw SDix SMHy
	'Late Yellow'	IBal
	× ***latifolia***	see *C.* × *crocosmioides*
	'Lemon Spray'	CTca IBlr
	'Limpopo'	Widely available
	'Lowen Daa'	CTca
	'Lucifer' ♀[H5]	Widely available
	Lucifer's Children	EPfP
	'Malahide Castle Red'	GBin SBod SMad WMoo
	'Mandarin'	ECrc IBlr
	'Marcotijn'	GNew IBal
	masoniorum ♀[H4]	Widely available
	- from Satan's Nek, South Africa	IBal
	- 'African Dawn'	CTca EBee ECrc ECtt
	- 'Amber'	IBlr
	- 'Dixter Flame'	IBlr IFoB SDix WOut
	- 'Flamenco'	IBlr
	- 'Golden Swan'	SRms
	- Holehird strain	ECrc ECtt
	- 'Kiaora'	IBlr
	- 'Moira Reid'	ECtt IBal IBlr
	- red-flowered	IBlr
	- 'Rowallane Apricot'	IBlr
	- 'Rowallane Orange'	CHVG CTca GBin IBal IBlr
	- 'Rowallane Yellow' ♀[H4]	CTca EBee GAbr GCal IBal IBlr IMou LRHS NCGa NHol SMHy WSHC
	- 'Sherbert Orange'	IBal MAvo
	- Slieve Donard selection	ECrc IBal
	- 'Sunflare'	IBlr
	- 'Tropicana'	IBlr
	mathewsiana	IBlr
	'Mex'	MAvo
	'Ministar' **new**	GKev
	'Minotaur'	IBlr
	'Miss Scarlet'	CRos EPfP LRHS NRHS SAko
	'Mistral'	CCCN CRos CTca ECtt EPfP EPot GAbr GBuc GKev IBal IBlr LEdu LRHS NHol NLar SCob SPer WFar WMoo
	'Moorland Blaze'	WMoo
	'Moorland Sunset'	IBal
	'Mr Bedford'	see *C.* × *crocosmiiflora* 'Croesus'
	'Mullard Pink'	ECrc

	'Okavango' PBR	CBre CBro CMac CTca ECtt ELon EPfP EPot EPri GAbr GBin GQue IBal LPla LSun MAvo MBNS MHol MNrw NEgg NLar NSti SDix SKHP WCot WFar
	Old Hat	see *C.* 'Walberton Red'
	'Orange Devil'	CBod CBre ECtt GKin IBal IBlr LLHF LRHS MBNS NCGa
	'Orange River'	MAvo WCot
	'Orangeade'	CTca ECtt GKev IBal IBlr NHol SRms
	'Pageant'	ECrc IBal
§	***paniculata***	CMac CPou CTca ECtt GAbr GBin NBid SCob WBrk WMoo WOut WShi
	- from Kologha	CTca
	- brown/orange-flowered	IBlr
	- 'Cally Greyleaf'	EBee GCal IBal MAvo MNrw WCot
	- 'Cally Sword'	GCal IBal MAvo
	- 'Major'	CTri IBlr
	- 'Natal'	CPrp CTca ECtt IBal NHol
	- red-flowered	IBlr SWvt
	- triploid	IBlr
	aff. ***paniculata***	IBlr
	'Paul's Best Yellow'	Widely available
	pearsei	IBlr
	'Phillipa Browne'	CTca ECtt IBal SCob WCot WMoo
	pottsii	CTca EBee GMcL GWyn IBlr LEdu WPtf
	- CD&R 109	CPou
	- 'Culzean Pink'	CElw CHVG CPrp CTca EBee GBin GCal GNew IBal IBlr MNrw NBid NBir NHol NLar WFar WOut
	- deep pink-flowered	IBlr WMoo
	- 'Grandiflora'	IBlr
§	- 'Princess'	ECrc ECtt GKev IBal
	- tall	IBal MSpe
	'Pride of Plantation' **new**	CTca GKev ILea
	'Prince of Orange'	ERCP GKev
	'Quantreau'	IBlr
	'Queen Alexandria'	LRHS
	'R.W.Wallace'	IBal
	'Raspberry Spray'	IBlr
	'Red Star'	IBal
	rosea	see *Tritonia disticha* subsp. *rubrolucens*
	'Rowden Bronze'	see *C.* × *crocosmiiflora* 'Coleton Fishacre'
	'Rowden Chrome'	see *C.* × *crocosmiiflora* 'George Davison' Davison
	'Ruby Velvet'	IBlr
	'Rubygold'	CPrp IBlr
	'Saffron Queen'	IBlr
	'Sampford Yellow'	IBal
	'Saturn'	see *C.* 'Jupiter'
	'Scarlatti'	CTca ECtt GAbr GKev IBal IBlr NHol
	'Scarlet Wonder'	CTca
	'Severn Sunrise' ♀H5	CElw CMac CPrp CTca CWCL ECha ECtt EPfP GKin GMaP IBal IBlr LRHS LSou MAvo MHer MMuc NBir NEgg NGdn NHol NLar SRms SWvt WBrk WFar WMoo WSHC
	'Shocking'	IBlr MAvo
	'Sorento'	IBlr
	'Spitfire'	CPrp CSam CTca ECha ECtt ELan GAbr GQue IBal IBlr LHop MArl MAvo MRav NHol SWvt WOld
§	'Sulphurea'	CPou CSam ECtt EPfP IBal IBlr LRHS MSpe NHol
	'Sunglow'	EBee EPfP ERCP GKev IBal MAsh MNrw SHar WHil
	'Sunzest'	ECrc ECtt MAvo WHoo
	'Suzanna'	EBee ECtt GKev
	'Tamar Double Red'	CTca SMad
	'Tamar Glow'	CTca WOld
	'Tamar Golden Ring' **new**	CTca
	'Tamar New Dawn'	CTca
	'Tamar Peace'	CTca
	'Tangerine'	ECrc
	'Tangerine Dream'	IBlr
	'Tangerine Queen'	CTca ECrc GAbr IBal IBlr NHol NWad WMoo
	'Tangerine Spray'	IBlr
	'Tiger'	CElw CTca ECrc MAvo
	'Toccata'	IBlr
	'Twilight Fairy Crimson'	CAbb CWGN EBee ECrc ECtt GBin LEdu LSou MAvo NHpl
I	'Vulcan' A. Bloom	CTca IBal IBlr MAvo
	'Vulcan' Leichtlin	see *C.* × *crocosmioides* 'Vulcan' Leichtlin
§	'Walberton Red'	CSam CTca ECrc EWes IBal MAvo NCGa NWad SKHP SMad
	Walberton Yellow = 'Walcroy' PBR	CRos EPfP LRHS NRHS SMHy SMad
	'Zambesi' PBR	CMac ECtt ELon GBin GQue IBal LHop MAvo MBNS MCot MNrw NEgg SKHP WCot
	'Zeal Giant'	CTca ECrc ECtt IBal IBlr MAvo NHol
	'Zeal Unnamed'	CTca ECrc ECtt IBal IBlr NHol

Crocus ✿ (*Iridaceae*)

	adanensis	EPot GKev
	'Advance'	ECho EPot ERCP GKev LAma SDeJ SDir
§	***albiflorus***	GKev
	ancyrensis	EPot GKev SDeJ
	- 'Golden Bunch'	ECho SDeJ WShi
§	***angustifolius*** ♀H5	ECho EPot GKev MGib SDeJ WShi
	- 'Berlin Gold'	GKev
	- bronze-flowered **new**	GKev
	- 'Minor'	EPot
	'Ard Schenk'	ECho GKev LAma LRHS NRHS SDir
	asturicus	see *C. serotinus* subsp. *salzmannii*
	asumaniae	EPot GKev NRog
	- white-flowered	NRog
	'Aubade'	EPot GKev LAma
	aureus	see *C. flavus* subsp. *flavus*
	autranii **new**	NRog
	banaticus ♀H5	ECho EPot GKev LLHF NHar NHpl NRog WThu
	- 'Early Bird'	NRog
	- 'Snowdrift'	GKev NHar
	baytopiorum	ECho
	biflorus 'Blue Pearl' ♀H5	CAvo CBro ECho EPfP EPot ERCP GKev LCro NBir SCob SDeJ SDir SPer SPhx WCot WShi
	- subsp. ***melantherus***	GKev NRog
	- 'Miss Vain'	ECho EPot ERCP GKev LAma MGib
	- 'Serevan'	EPot
	- subsp. ***tauri***	EPot
	- subsp. ***weldenii*** 'Albus'	ECho EPot GKev LAma
	- - 'Fairy'	ECho GKev LAma
	'Blue Bird'	ECho EPot GKev LAma
	boryi	CRos ECho LRHS NRHS NRog
	cambessedesii	NRog
	cancellatus	SDeJ
§	- subsp. ***cancellatus***	EPot GKev LAma NRog
	- var. ***cilicicus***	see *C. cancellatus* subsp. *cancellatus*

- subsp. ***damascenus***	NRog
- subsp. ***lycius***	ECho EPot NRog
- subsp. ***mazziaricus***	EPot NRog
- subsp. ***pamphylicus***	NRog
candidus var. ***subflavus***	see *C. olivieri* subsp. *olivieri*
cartwrightianus $\mathbb{Y}^{H4}$	CRos GKev LRHS NRHS NRog WShi
- 'Albus' misapplied	see *C. hadriaticus*
- 'Albus' Tubergen $\mathbb{Y}^{H4}$	EPot GKev NRog SDeJ
- 'Marcel'	NRog
- 'Michel'	NRog
chrysanthus $\mathbb{Y}^{H5}$	CHab
- VV GB 235 **new**	GKev
- 'Blue Peter'	EPot
- 'Constellation'	EPot
- 'Cream Beauty' $\mathbb{Y}^{H5}$	CAvo CBro ECho EPfP EPot GKev LAma LCro LOPS NBir SCob SDeJ WShi
- 'E.A. Bowles' misapplied	see *C. chrysanthus* 'E.P. Bowles'
§ - 'E.P. Bowles'	LAma
- var. ***fuscotinctus***	ECho EPfP EPot LAma LCro LOPS SDeJ
- 'Goldene Sonne'	EPot
- 'Uschak Orange'	ECho
- 'Warley'	ECho
- 'Zwanenburg Bronze' $\mathbb{Y}^{H5}$	ECho EPfP GKev LCro LOPS SDeJ WShi
'Cloth of Gold'	see *C. angustifolius*
clusii	see *C. serotinus* subsp. *clusii*
corsicus $\mathbb{Y}^{H4}$	ECho EPot GKev
dalmaticus	EPot
- 'Petrovac'	GKev
danfordiae	ECho
'Dorothy'	EPot GKev
'Dutch Yellow'	see *C.* × *luteus* 'Golden Yellow'
'Ego'	GKev
etruscus $\mathbb{Y}^{H5}$	GKev
- 'Rosalind'	ECho GKev
- 'Zwanenburg' $\mathbb{Y}^{H5}$	ECho EPot GKev LAma SDeJ SDir
'Fantasy'	ECho GKev WShi
§ ***flavus*** subsp. ***flavus*** $\mathbb{Y}^{H5}$	ECho EPot GKev LAma WShi
fleischeri	ECho EPot GKev LAma
'Flower Record'	GKev LAma LRHS NBir SDeJ SDir
gargaricus	GKev
gilanicus	GKev
'Gipsy Girl'	CAvo EPfP EPot ERCP GKev LAma LCro LOPS SCob SDir SPer
'Golden Mammoth'	see *C.* × *luteus* 'Golden Yellow'
'Goldilocks' $\mathbb{Y}^{H5}$	GKev LAma SDeJ
goulimyi $\mathbb{Y}^{H4}$	CAvo CBro CRos CTal ECho EPot GKev LAma LRHS NRHS NRog SDeJ WCot
- 'Albus'	see *C. goulimyi* subsp. *goulimyi* 'Mani White'
§ - subsp. ***goulimyi*** 'Mani White' $\mathbb{Y}^{H4}$	CAvo CTal ECho EPot
- subsp. ***leucanthus***	NRog
'Grand Maître'	CAvo GKev LAma MGib SDeJ
'Haarlem Gem'	GKev
§ ***hadriaticus*** $\mathbb{Y}^{H4}$	CRos ECho LAma LRHS NRHS NRog
- 'Alepohori'	GKev
- 'Annabelle' **new**	GKev
- var. ***chrysobelonicus***	see *C. hadriaticus*
- 'Jumbo'	NRog
'Herald'	CAvo GKev LAma SDeJ SPhx
heuffelianus subsp. ***heuffelianus***	WShi
§ - subsp. ***scepusiensis***	GKev WShi
imperati subsp. ***suaveolens***	EPot
- - 'De Jager'	ERCP GKev LAma
'Jeanne d'Arc'	CAby CAvo CBro ECho EPfP EPot GKev LAma LCro LOPS LRHS NBir SDeJ WShi
'Jeannine'	GKev SDeJ
karduchorum	EPot GKev LAma NRog
'Karin'	EPot
'King of the Striped'	ECho GKev LAma SDeJ SPer
korolkowii	ECho GKev LAma MGib
- 'Golden Nugget'	EPot GKev
- 'January Gold' **new**	GKev
- 'Kiss of Spring'	ECho EPot GKev
kosaninii	GKev
- 'April View'	GKev
kotschyanus $\mathbb{Y}^{H5}$	SDeJ
- 'Albus'	GKev NRog SDeJ
- subsp. ***cappadocicus***	NRog
§ - subsp. ***kotschyanus***	EPot GKev NRog SDeJ
- 'Reliance'	GKev NRog
'Ladykiller' $\mathbb{Y}^{H5}$	CAvo CBro ECho EPot ERCP GKev LAma LCro LOPS NNys SPhx WShi
laevigatus $\mathbb{Y}^{H3}$	NRog
- CE&H 612	EPot
- 'Fontenayi'	EPot ERCP GKev NRog
'Large Yellow'	see *C.* × *luteus* 'Golden Yellow'
§ ***ligusticus*** $\mathbb{Y}^{H5}$	EPot GKev LAma
- 'Millesimo'	NRog
longiflorus $\mathbb{Y}^{H4}$	CRos EPot LRHS NRHS NRog
§ × ***luteus*** 'Golden Yellow' $\mathbb{Y}^{H5}$	CAvo EPot GKev LAma LCro LRHS WShi
§ - 'Stellaris' $\mathbb{Y}^{H5}$	EPot
malyi $\mathbb{Y}^{H4}$	ECho GKev
- 'Sveti Roc'	GKev
mathewii	EPot NHpl
- 'Dream Dancer'	EPot GKev
medius	see *C. ligusticus*
minimus	ECho EPot ERCP GKev LAma LLHF
- 'Spring Beauty'	EPfP ERCP GKev NNys SDeJ
'Negro Boy'	ECho EPot GKev LAma
niveus	CRos ECho EPot GKev LAma LLHF LRHS NRHS NRog
nudiflorus	ECho EPot GKev LAma LLHF NRog
ochroleucus	ECho EPot GKev NRog SDeJ
olivieri AH 0156 **new**	GKev
- subsp. ***balansae*** 'Zwanenburg'	EPot GKev
§ - subsp. ***olivieri***	GKev
'Orange Monarch'	EPfP ERCP LAma LLHF SCob SDir
oreocreticus	NRog
pallasii VV KR 75 **new**	GKev
- subsp. ***dispathaceus***	NRog
- subsp. ***turcicus***	GKev
paschei	EPot
pestalozzae	GKev
- var. ***caeruleus***	GKev
'Pickwick'	CAby CAvo EPfP EPot GKev LAma LCro LRHS NBir NNys SDeJ WShi
'Prins Claus'	ECho EPfP EPot ERCP GKev LAma NBir SDeJ SDir SPer
pulchellus $\mathbb{Y}^{H4}$	CAvo ERCP GKev LAma NNys NRog SDeJ WCot
- 'Albus'	ECho EPot GKev NRog
- 'Inspiration'	GKev NRog
- 'Michael Hoog'	ECho NRog
'Purple Heart'	GKev NRog
'Purpureus'	see *C.* 'Purpureus Grandiflorus'
§ 'Purpureus Grandiflorus'	CBro EPot SDeJ
'Queen of the Blues'	CBro EPot SDeJ
'Remembrance'	CAby CAvo CBro ECho EPfP EPot GKev LAma LCro LRHS NBir SDeJ WShi
reticulatus	EPot

robertianus	NRog
'Romance'	CAvo CBro EPot GKev LAma NBir SDeJ
'Ruby Giant'	CAvo CBro CRos ECho EPfP EPot ERCP GKev LAma LCro LOPS LRHS NBir NRHS SCob SDeJ SPer SPhx WShi
rujanensis	EPot
salzmannii	see *C. serotinus* subsp. *salzmannii*
sativus	CAvo CBod CBro CTca CTsd ECho ELan EPot ERCP GKev GPoy ILea LAma LCro LOPS NBir NCGa NNys NRog SCob SDeJ SVic
'Saturnus'	EPot LAma
scepusiensis	see *C. heuffelianus* subsp. *scepusiensis*
§ ***serotinus*** subsp. ***clusii***	GKev LAma NRog
§ - subsp. ***salzmannii***	GKev LAma NRog
- - f. ***albus***	NRog
- - 'Erectophyllus'	GKev NRog
sibiricus	see *C. sieberi*
§ ***sieberi*** ♀H5	EPot
- 'Albus'	see *C. sieberi* 'Bowles's White'
- subsp. ***atticus***	ECho
- - 'Amfiklia' **new**	GKev
- - 'Firefly'	ECho EPfP EPot GKev LAma SDeJ
- - 'Stunner'	GKev
§ - 'Bowles's White' ♀H5	CBro ECho EPot GKev SDeJ
- 'Hubert Edelsten' ♀H5	ECho EPot GKev LAma
- 'Ronald Ginns'	EPot
- subsp. ***sublimis*** **new**	GKev
- - 'Tricolor' ♀H4	CAvo CBro CRos CTca ECho EPfP EPot GKev LAma LCro LRHS NBir NRHS SDeJ SPer WOld
- 'Violet Queen'	LAma
'Snow Bunting' ♀H5	CAvo CBro CTca ECho ELan EPfP EPot GKev LAma LCro LOPS NBir NNys SCob SDeJ SDir SPer WShi
speciosus ♀H4	CAvo CBro CTca EPfP LAma LCro LOPS NBir SDeJ WCot WShi
- 'Aino'	ECho NRog
- 'Aitchisonii'	CRos ECho GKev LAma LRHS NRHS NRog
- 'Albus' ♀H4	CAvo CBro ECho EPot ERCP GKev LCro LOPS NRog SDeJ WShi
- 'Artabir'	CRos ECho GKev LRHS NRHS NRog SDeJ
- 'Cassiope'	CRos ECho GKev LAma LRHS NRHS NRog SDeJ
- 'Conqueror'	CRos ECho ELan EPfP ERCP GKev LAma LCro LOPS LRHS NRHS NRog SDeJ
- 'Oxonian'	CRos ECho ELan EPot GKev LAma LRHS NRHS NRog WOld
- subsp. ***speciosus***	ECho EPot GKev NBir NRog SDeJ
- subsp. ***xantholaimos***	NRog
× ***stellaris***	see *C.* × *luteus* 'Stellaris'
'Striped Beauty'	GKev
susianus	see *C. angustifolius*
suterianus	see *C. olivieri* subsp. *olivieri*
thomasii	EPot GKev NRog
tommasinianus ♀H5	CAvo CBro CGrW CHab CTca ECho EPot GKev LAma LCro LLWP MRav NBir NNys SDeJ SDir SPhx SRms WShi
- 'Albus'	ECho EPot GKev LAma WShi
- 'Barr's Purple'	ECho EPot GKev LAma LCro NBir SDeJ SDir
- 'Claret'	ECho
- 'Eric Smith'	EPot GKev
- 'Lilac Beauty'	ECho EPfP EPot GKev LAma
- 'Pictus'	ECho EPot GKev LAma LLHF WShi
- 'Roseus'	CAvo ECho EPot ERCP GKev LAma SDeJ SDir SPhx WCot WShi
- 'Rubinetta' **new**	GKev
- 'Whitewell Purple'	CAvo CBro CRos ECho EPot ERCP GKev LAma LCro LOPS LRHS NBir NRHS SDeJ WShi
tournefortii ♀H3	CAvo CRos ECho EPot GKev LRHS NRHS NRog
'Twinborn'	EPot
vallicola	GKev
'Vanguard' ♀H5	EPfP EPot GKev LAma LCro LOPS SDeJ WCot
veluchensis	LLHF
veneris	NRog
vernus	GKev
- subsp. ***albiflorus***	see *C. albiflorus*
- 'Drina Marvel' **new**	GKev
- 'Graecus'	EPot GKev
- 'Krasno Polje'	GKev
- Uklin strain	ECho GKev
- subsp. ***vernus*** 'Grandiflorus'	see *C.* 'Purpureus Grandiflorus'
versicolor JMH 8215 **new**	GKev
- 'Picturatus'	EPot GKev LAma LLHF SDeJ WShi
vitellinus	EPot
'White Triumphator'	LAma
'Yalta'	ECho ERCP GKev MGib NNys SDir SPhx WCot
'Yellow Giant'	SDeJ
'Yellow Mammoth'	see *C.* × *luteus* 'Golden Yellow'
'Zenith'	EPot
'Zephyr' ♀H4	CBro GKev NRog SDeJ WOld
zonatus	see *C. kotschyanus* subsp. *kotschyanus*

Croomia (*Stemonaceae*)

heterosepala	WCru

Crossandra (*Acanthaceae*)

infundibuliformis ♀H1a	EShb

Crossyne (*Amaryllidaceae*)

flava	NRog WCot
guttata	WCot

Crotalaria (*Papilionaceae*)

laburnifolia ♀H2	CCCN

Crucianella (*Rubiaceae*)

stylosa	see *Phuopsis stylosa*

Cruciata (*Rubiaceae*)

§ ***laevipes***	NMir

Crusea (*Rubiaceae*)

coccinea	CSpe SBrt WCot
- 'Crûg Crimson'	CAby WCot WCru

Cryptocarya (*Lauraceae*)

alba	GBin SVen

Cryptocoryne (*Araceae*)

× ***willisii***	XBlo

Cryptogramma (*Pteridaceae*)

crispa	WHer

Cryptomeria ✿ (*Cupressaceae*)

fortunei	see *C. japonica*

§	***japonica***	CAco CDul CLau CLet CMen CTho EPfP ESps LPar MBlu MMuc NWea SEND SWvt WMou WTSh
	- 'Antique Gold'	LRHS
	- Araucarioides Group	NEgg SLim
	- 'Atawai'	NLar
	- 'Aurea'	EUJe
	- 'Bandai-sugi' 🏆H6	CKen CMac CMen EPfP IArd MGos NHol NLar SRms
	- 'Barabits Gold'	LRHS
	- 'Birodo'	CKen
	- 'Black Dragon'	SLim
	- 'Blue Diamond' **new**	CAco
	- 'Compressa'	CKen EMOT EPfP LBee LRHS MAsh NWad SRms
§	- 'Cristata'	CBcs CMac ELan ESwi LRHS MGos MPkF NEgg NOrn SRms
	- 'Dacrydioides'	NLar
	- 'Dinger'	CKen LRHS NLar
	- Elegans Group	CAco CBcs CDul CLet CMac CSBt ELan EMOT EPfP ESps EUJe LRHS MGos NEgg NLar NOra NOrn NWea SCoo SEND SLim SPoG SRms WMat
	- 'Elegans Aurea'	CCVT CLet ELan MAsh NEgg SPoG SWvt
	- 'Elegans Compacta' 🏆H6	CLet CMac CSBt CWib ELan GBin GMcL LBee LRHS MAsh MMuc NLar NWea SRms SWvt
	- 'Elegans Nana'	SRms
	- 'Elegans Viridis' 🏆H6	NOra SLim WHar WMat
I	- 'Elegantissima'	CCVT
	- 'Globosa Nana' 🏆H6	CAco EMOT EPfP ESps GMcL LBee MGos NEgg NHol SArc SCoo SPoG
	- 'Golden Promise' 🏆H6	CBcs MAsh NHol NWad SLim SPer SWvt
	- Gracilis Group	LPar
	- 'Jindai-sugi'	NLar
	- 'Kamasan'	NLar
	- 'Kilmacurragh'	CKen NWea
	- 'Kohui-yatsubusa'	CKen
	- 'Koshiji-yatsubusa'	NLar
	- 'Koshyi'	CKen
	- 'Little Champion'	CKen LRHS SLim
	- 'Little Diamond'	CKen NEgg
	- 'Little Sonja'	CKen SLim
	- 'Little Yoko'	CKen NLar
	- 'Littleworth Dwarf'	see *C. japonica* 'Littleworth Gnom'
§	- 'Littleworth Gnom'	LRHS NLar
	- 'Lobbii'	CAco GMcL
	- 'Lobbii Nana' hort.	see *C. japonica* 'Nana'
	- 'Monstrosa'	NLar
§	- 'Nana'	CMac SRms
	- 'Osaka-tama'	CKen
	- 'Pipo'	CKen
	- 'Pygmaea'	NHol NLar NWad SRms
	- 'Rasen-sugi'	IDee IVic NLar SMad
	- 'Rein's Dense Jade'	SLim
	- 'Sekkan-sugi' 🏆H6	CBcs CCVT CDul CLet CMac EPfP ESwi GBin GKin IArd LBee LRHS MAsh MGos NEgg NLar SCoo SLim SPoG SWvt
	- 'Sekka-sugi'	see *C. japonica* 'Cristata'
§	- 'Spiralis' 🏆H6	CKen CMac ELan EPfP ESps LBee LRHS MAsh MGos MHer NEgg NHol NLar NWea SCoo SLim SPoG SRms SWvt
§	- 'Spiraliter Falcata'	NLar
§	- 'Tansu'	CKen LRHS
	- 'Tenzan-sugi' 🏆H6	CKen NHol WThu
	- 'Tilford Gold'	EMOT GMcL NHol
	- 'Toda'	CKen
	- 'Vilmorin Gold'	NHol
	- 'Vilmoriniana' 🏆H6	CKen CLet CMen CTri ELan EPfP ESps GKin GMcL LRHS MAsh MGos MMuc NEgg NHol NLar SCoo SEND SLim SPer SPoG SWvt WMoo
	- 'Winter Bronze'	CKen
	- 'Yatsubusa'	see *C. japonica* 'Tansu'
	- 'Yore-sugi'	see *C. japonica* 'Spiralis', 'Spiraliter Falcata'
	- 'Yoshino'	CKen NEgg SLim
	sinensis	see *C. japonica*

Cryptostegia (*Apocynaceae*)

	grandiflora	CCCN

Cryptotaenia (*Apiaceae*)

	japonica	CAgr CHby CPou GPoy LEdu MHer MNHC SRms WHer WJek
	- f. ***atropurpurea***	CDor CSpe EBee EHoe LEdu LPla MNrw SDix WBor WPGP

Ctenanthe (*Marantaceae*)

	lubbersiana 🏆H1b	XBlo
	oppenheimiana	XBlo

Cucubalus (*Caryophyllaceae*)

	baccifer	CArn NLar

Cudrania see *Maclura*

cumin see *Cuminum cyminum*

Cuminum (*Apiaceae*)

	cyminum	CLau SRms SVic

Cumulopuntia (*Cactaceae*)

§	***boliviana*** subsp. ***dactylifera***	CCac

Cunninghamia (*Cupressaceae*)

§	***lanceolata***	CAco CBcs CDTJ CDul CKen CMCN CMac CTho EPfP SSta WPGP
	- 'Glauca'	CAco CJun IVic
	sinensis	see *C. lanceolata*
	unicaniculata	see *C. lanceolata*

Cuphea (*Lythraceae*)

	caeciliae	CSam
	cyanea	CMHG SDix
	hyssopifolia 🏆H1c	CTsd EShb SWvt
	- 'Alba'	CCCN CTre EShb SWvt
	- pink-flowered	CCCN CTre
	- red-flowered	CCCN
	- 'Rosea'	SWvt
§	***ignea*** 🏆H1c	CTsd WHea
	- 'Matchless' **new**	SVic
	'Lilac Belle'	CSpe
§	***llavea*** 'Georgia Scarlet'	CCCN
	- 'Tiny Mice'	see *C. llavea* 'Georgia Scarlet'
I	***macrophylla*** hort.	CHII
	maculata	CCCN
	platycentra	see *C. ignea*
	'Regal Purple'	CPla
	'Torpedo'	NPri
	viscosissima	CFis CSpe ELan MCot

× *Cupressocyparis* see × *Cuprocyparis*

Cupressus (*Cupressaceae*)

	arizonica	ESps LPar
	- 'Conica Glauca'	CAco
I	- 'Fastigiata Aurea' new	ESps
§	- var. ***glabra***	CPne
	- - 'Angaston'	SLim
	- - 'Aurea'	CLet CMac MAsh SGol SLim
	- - 'Blue Ice'	CAco CDul CMac CTho ESps MAsh MGos NEgg SLim SWvt WHar
	- - 'Compacta'	CKen
I	- - 'Fastigiata'	CCVT ECrN EPfP ETod NPri
*	- - 'Lutea'	NEgg
	- 'Pyramidalis' ♀H5	SEND SGol
	cashmeriana ♀H3	CAco CBcs CDTJ IVic SLim
§	***funebris***	CDul
	glabra	see *C. arizonica* var. *glabra*
	× ***leylandii***	see × *Cuprocyparis leylandii*
	lusitanica 'Brice's Weeping'	CKen NEgg SLim
	- 'Brookhall'	IArd
	- 'Pygmy'	CKen
	macnabiana new	GLog
	macrocarpa	CBcs CCVT CDul CTho LPar SEND
	- 'Compacta'	CKen
	- 'Gold Spread'	SLim
	- 'Goldcrest' ♀H4	CBcs CCVT CDul CLet CMac ECrN ELan EMOT ESps GMcL LBMP LPar LRHS MGos NBir NPri SEWo SGol SLim SWvt
	- 'Golden Cone'	ESps
	- 'Golden Pillar'	SWvt
	- 'Lohbrunner'	CKen
	- 'Pygmaea'	CKen
	- 'Sulphur Cushion'	CKen
	- 'Wilma' ♀H4	CSBt ELan EMOT LBee LRHS MAsh MGos SCoo SEND SGol SLim SPer SPoG SWvt
	- 'Woking'	CKen
	nootkatensis	see *Xanthocyparis nootkatensis*
	sempervirens	CLet ELan EUJe LPar SPlb SWeb
	- 'Agrimed'	CCVT
	- 'Bolgheri'	SBig
	- 'Green Pencil'	CKen
	- 'Pyramidalis'	see *C. sempervirens* Stricta Group
	- var. ***sempervirens***	see *C. sempervirens* Stricta Group
§	- Stricta Group	CAco CBcs CCVT CDul CTho EPfP ESps LPar NLar SArc SEND SEWo SGol WCFE
	- 'Swane's Gold'	CBcs CKen MAsh NEgg
	- 'Totem Pole'	CAco CCVT CKen CSBt CTho CTri ELan EMOT EPfP EUJe LBee LPar LRHS MAsh MGos SCoo SEND SPoG SWvt

× *Cuprocyparis* ✿ (*Cupressaceae*)

§	***leylandii***	Widely available
I	- '2001'	CCVT SGol WHed
	- 'Blue Jeans'PBR	SEND
§	- 'Castlewellan'	CBcs CCVT CDul CMac CSBt CTri EMOT EPfP ESps LBuc LSRN MAsh MGos MJak MMuc NBes NPri NWea SCob SEND SGol SLim SPer SPoG SWvt WFar WHar WHed WTSh
	- Excalibur Gold = 'Drabb'PBR	NWea
	- 'Ferngold'	MAsh
	- 'Galway Gold'	see × *C. leylandii* 'Castlewellan'
	- 'Gold Rider' ♀H6	CLet CMac ELan ESps LPar MAsh MGos MMuc NEgg NWea SCob SCoo SEND SGol SMad SPer SPoG SWvt WHar
§	- 'Harlequin' (v)	CMac SEND SWvt
	- 'Leighton Green'	WTSh
	- 'Naylor's Blue'	CMac
	- 'Olive's Green'	SWvt
	- 'Robinson's Gold'	CLet CMac GQui NWea SGol WHar
	- 'Variegata'	see × *C. leylandii* 'Harlequin'
	- 'Winter Sun'	WCFE

Curculigo (*Hypoxidaceae*)

capitulata	XBlo
crassifolia B&SWJ 2318	WCru
- HWJ 683 from Vietnam	WCru

Curcuma ✿ (*Zingiberaceae*)

alismatifolia	SDeJ
longa	CArn SPlb SPre
roscoeana	LAma SDeJ
zedoaria 'Bicolor Wonder'	CCCN
- 'Pink Wonder'	CCCN
- 'White Wonder'	CCCN SDeJ

Curtonus see *Crocosmia*

Cussonia ✿ (*Araliaceae*)

gamtoosensis	WCot
natalensis new	WCot
paniculata	CDTJ CWGN
sphaerocephala	WCot
spicata	CDTJ SPlb
zuluensis	WCot

custard apple see *Annona cherimola*

Cyananthus (*Campanulaceae*)

	incanus	GEdr
	integer misapplied	see *C. microphyllus*
	lobatus ♀H5	GKev LLHF
	- SDR 7476	GKev
	- 'Albus'	EPot WAbe
	- giant	EPot GEdr NHar WAbe
	lobatus × ***microphyllus***	GCrg GEdr WAbe
	macrocalyx	EPot
§	***microphyllus*** ♀H5	EPot GCrg GEdr NHar NSla WAbe
	microphyllus × 'Sherriff's Variety'	NHar
	sherriffii	EPot GJos IFoB WAbe
	spathulifolius	WAbe

Cyanastrum (*Tecophilaeaceae*)

cordifolium new	GKev

Cyanella (*Tecophilaeaceae*)

orchidiformis	NRog

Cyanotis (*Commelinaceae*)

somaliensis ♀H1c	EShb

Cyathea ✿ (*Cyatheaceae*)

	atrox	CKel
	australis	CBct CDTJ CKel ESwi IDee NLos SPlb
	baileyana	NLos
	brownii	CKel NLos
	cooperi	CDTJ CKel ESwi ISha NLos WFib
*	- 'Brentwood'	EBee ESwi ISha NLos
	- 'Cinnamon'	NLos
	- single-crested	NLos
	cunninghamii	CKel
	dealbata	CDTJ CKel GBin

	dregei	SPlb
	exilis	NLos
	glauca	NLos
	leichardtiana	NLos
	medullaris	CKel NLos
	rebeccae	NLos
	robusta	CKel
	smithii	CDTJ CKel
	tomentosissima	CDTJ CKel
	woollsiana	NLos

Cyathodes (*Ericaceae*)

	colensoi	see *Leucopogon colensoi*
	fraseri	see *Leucopogon fraseri*

Cycas (*Cycadaceae*)

	panzhihuaensis	CBrP SPlb
	revoluta ♀H2	CAbb CBrP CCCN EPfP ESps ETod EUJe LPar NLos SArc SChr SEND SMad SPlb XBlo
	revoluta* × *taitungensis	CBrP
§	***rumphii***	CBrP
	taitungensis	CBrP
	thouarsii	see *C. rumphii*

Cyclamen ✿ (*Primulaceae*)

	abchasicum	see *C. coum* subsp. *caucasicum*
	africanum	CBro CRos ECho GKev LRHS MAsh NRHS
§	***alpinum***	CBro CRos ECho EPot GKev LAma LRHS MAsh NRHS SDeJ XEll
	- 'Nettleton White'	MAsh
	balearicum	CBro CRos ECho EPot GKev LAma LRHS MAsh NRHS
	cilicium ♀H3	CBro CRos ECho EPfP EPot ERCP GBuc GJos GKev GMcL LAma LCro LOPS LRHS MAsh NHpl NRHS NSla WHoo WShi XEll
	- f. ***album***	CBro CRos ECho EPot GBuc GKev LAma LLHF LRHS MAsh NRHS XEll
	colchicum	MAsh
§	***coum*** ♀H5	Widely available
	- var. ***abchasicum***	see *C. coum* subsp. *caucasicum*
§	- subsp. ***caucasicum***	GKev
	- subsp. ***coum***	CBro ECho
	- - f. ***albissimum***	GBuc GKev
	- - - 'George Bisson'	MAsh
	- - - 'Golan Heights'	MAsh
	- - f. ***coum*** Pewter Group ♀H5	ECho GBuc GEdr GKev WCot
	- - - - 'Blush'	GBuc
	- - - - 'Maurice Dryden' ♀H5	CBro CLAP CRos ECho EPot GKev LAma LHop LRHS MAsh NPnk NRHS WHoo
	- - - - red-flowered	WPat
	- - - - 'Tilebarn Elizabeth'	MAsh NBir WHoo
	- - - 'Roseum'	CAvo GBuc
	- - - Silver Group	CAvo CBro CRos ECho EWoo GKev LHop LRHS NRHS NRya WHoo
	- - - - bicoloured	EWTr
	- - - - red-flowered	WHoo
	- - magenta-flowered	WHoo
	- - f. ***pallidum*** 'Album'	CAvo EPot EWoo GEdr GKev GMaP LAma SDeJ SDir SPer WHoo WPat WShi
	- dark pink-flowered	CAvo CLAP ECho WHoo
	- hybrid	ERCP
	- marble-leaved	LHop WHoo
	- 'Meaden's Crimson'	GKev
	- plain-leaved	CLAP
	- red-flowered	CLAP ECho
I	- 'Rubrum'	GKev
	- 'Something Magic'	IPot
	creticum	ECho MAsh
	cyprium	CBro CRos ECho GKev LRHS MAsh NRHS XEll
	- 'E.S.'	WThu
	× ***drydeniae***	MAsh
	elegans	GKev
	europaeum	see *C. purpurascens*
	graecum	CBro CPne CRos ECho EPot GKev LLHF LRHS MAsh NRHS WThu XEll
	- subsp. ***candicum***	MAsh
	- subsp. ***graecum*** f. ***album***	CBro CRos LRHS MAsh NRHS
	- - f. ***graecum*** 'Glyfada'	EPot GKev MAsh XEll
§	***hederifolium*** ♀H5	Widely available
	- S&L 175/1	WCot XLum
	- 'Amaze Me'	ECtt LEdu MHol MPie WCot
	- arrow-head	CLAP ECho
	- var. ***confusum***	GKev
	- 'Crassifolium' **new**	GKev
	- var. ***hederifolium*** f. ***albiflorum*** ♀H5	CAby CAvo CBro CTri ECho EWoo GKev LCro LEdu LOPS NWad SCob SDeJ WHoo WPat WPnP XLum
	- - - 'Album'	CWCL EWTr WShi
	- - - Bowles's Apollo Group	GBuc
	- - - 'Discovery' **new**	WCot
	- - - 'Nettleton Silver'	see *C. hederifolium* var. *hederifolium* f. *albiflorum* 'White Cloud'
	- - - 'Perlenteppich'	GMaP
	- - - silver-leaved	SDys
§	- - - 'White Cloud' ♀H5	CLAP MAsh NHpl WHoo
	- - f. ***hederifolium*** Bowles's Apollo Group	CHid CLAP GBuc
	- - - 'Fairy Rings'	MAsh
	- - - 'Rosenteppich'	CAby
	- - - 'Ruby Glow'	CRos CWCL GBuc LRHS MAsh NBir NRHS WPat WThu
	- - - Silver Cloud Group ♀H5	CAby CBro CHid CLAP GBuc MAsh NBir WHoo WPat
	- island scented strain	WCot
	- 'Lysander'	ECho EPot GKev MAsh
	- 'Pewter Mist'	LAma SDir
	- 'Red Sky'	CBro LAma NWad
	- 'Rose Pearls'	SRot
	- 'Silver Mist'	SDir
	- Silver-leaved Group	CRos ECho EPot GKev LHop LRHS NPnk NRHS SRot
	- - 'Silver Leaf Pink'	GMaP NWad
	- - 'Silver Leaf Red'	NWad
	- - 'Silver Leaf White'	GMaP NWad
	× ***hildebrandii***	LLHF
	ibericum	see *C. coum* subsp. *caucasicum*
	intaminatum	CBro CPne CRos ECho EPot GKev LAma LLHF LRHS MAsh NRHS XEll
	- plain-leaved	WThu
	latifolium	see *C. persicum*
	libanoticum	CBro CRos ECho GKev LAma LRHS MAsh NRHS XEll
	mirabile ♀H4	CBro CPne CRos ECho EPot GBuc GKev LAma LLHF LRHS MAsh NHpl NRHS SDeJ WThu
	- 'Alba'	GKev SDeJ XEll
	- f. ***mirabile*** 'Tilebarn Nicholas'	MAsh WCot
	neapolitanum	see *C. hederifolium*
	orbiculatum	see *C. coum*
	parviflorum	MAsh
§	***persicum***	CBro CRos CWCL ECho GBuc GKev LRHS MAsh NRHS WCot

- white-flowered MAsh
pseudibericum ♀H4 CBro CPne CRos ECho EPot GKev LAma LHop LLHF LRHS MAsh NRHS SDeJ WCot
- AC&W 664 NWad
- f. ***roseum*** MAsh
§ ***purpurascens*** CAby CBro ECho GBuc GKev LLHF MAsh NHpl NSla WBor WHoo WPat WThu
repandum CAvo CBro CRos ECho EPot GKev LAma LLHF LRHS NRHS WHer
- 'Pelops' misapplied see *C. rhodium* subsp. *peloponnesiacum*
rhodium GKev
§ - subsp. ***peloponnesiacum*** ECGP
rohlfsianum CRos GKev LRHS MAsh NRHS WThu XEll
× ***schwarzii*** MAsh
'Trena' SDeJ
trochopteranthum see *C. alpinum*

Cyclea (*Menispermaceae*)

polypetala KWJ 12157 WCru

Cydonia ✿ (*Rosaceae*)

japonica see *Chaenomeles japonica*
oblonga (F) ECrN ESps
- 'Agvambari' (F) SKee
- 'Aromatnaya' (F) ERea MCoo NOra SKee WHar WMat
- 'Champion' (F) CAgr CHab ECrN EMOT EPom ERea GTwe LBuc MCoo NEgg NOra SBdl SKee SVic WHar WMat
- 'Early Prolific' (F) SEND
- 'Ekmek' (F) SKee
- 'Gamboa' (F) **new** MRai SKee
- 'Iranian' (F) CAgr
- 'Isfahan' (F) ERea SKee WMat
- 'Krymsk' (F) CAgr WWct
- 'Leskovac' (F) CAgr CLnd EPom ERea NLar NOra WWct
§ - 'Lusitanica' (F) CAgr CHab CLnd ELan EMOT EPom ERea GTwe LPre LRHS NLar SBdl SKee WHar WMat
- 'Meech's Prolific' (F) ♀H5 CAgr CDul CHab CLnd CTri ECrN EMil EPom ERea GTwe LRHS MAsh MGos MRav NLar NOra NWea SDea SKee SLim SPer SPoG WHar WMat WWct
- pear-shaped (F) CHab ECrN NEgg SPer
- Portugal see *C. oblonga* 'Lusitanica'
- 'Rea's Mammoth' (F) CHab ECrN ERea NLar
- 'Serbian Gold' (F) CDul CFGn CMac CTho ECrN EMOT EPom ERea GQue GTwe LPre LRHS MAsh NLar NOra SBdl SKee WHar WMat
- 'Shams' (F) SKee
- 'Smyrna' (F) NLar NOra SKee WHar WMat
- 'Sobu' (F) SKee
- 'Vranja' ambig. (F) CBcs CFGn EMOT MAsh NBes NWea SBdl
- 'Vranja' Nenadovic (F) ♀H5 Widely available

Cylindropuntia (*Cactaceae*)

acanthocarpa from Meadview, Arizona CCac
§ ***echinocarpa*** MUG 167 CCac
imbricata CCac SPlb XLum XSen
- DJF 928.19 from Union County, New Mexico CCac
- DJF 1575 from Delhi, Colorado CCac
- KMR 429 CCac
- SB 99 from Manzano Mountains, New Mexico CCac
- from Caon City, Colorado CCac
- from Fremont County, Colorado CCac
- 'Pinky' CCac
kleiniae CCac
leptocaulis XSen
- from Valencia County, New Mexico CCac
rosea PG CCac
§ ***spinosior*** XLum
versicolor CCac XSen
× ***viridiflora*** CCac
- SB 957 from Santa Fe, New Mexico CCac
whipplei from Coconino County, Arizona CCac
- DJF 131.24 from Show Low, Arizona CCac
- DJF 167 from Snowflake, Arizona CCac
- MUG 125 from San Juan, New Mexico CCac
- 'Monstrosus' CCac
* - var. ***multidigitata*** from Meadview, Arizona CCac
- 'Waiblingen' CCac
- 'Würzburg' CCac

Cymbalaria (*Plantaginaceae*)

aequitriloba 'Alba' GAbr GEdr NRya
§ ***hepaticifolia*** CSma SBrt SPlb
§ ***muralis*** ECtt GAbr GJos MArt MHer MSCN WHer WIce WTor
- 'Kenilworth White' GJos WCot WMoo
- 'Nana Alba' MSCN WIce
- 'Rosea' WAbe
§ ***pallida*** CPBP CSma MAsh MMuc SBch SEND SPlb WAbe WMoo
- 'Alba' EWTr WMoo
§ ***pilosa*** ECtt NLar
'Snow Wave' ECtt LSou

Cymbopogon (*Poaceae*)

citratus CArn CBod CCCN CTsd ENfk ERea GPoy MNHC SHDw SIde SRms SVic WJek WTre
flexuosus CCCN CLau MHer SRms WJek
martini GPoy
nardus GPoy

Cymophyllus (*Cyperaceae*)

§ ***fraserianus*** CFil EBee

Cynanchum (*Apocynaceae*)

ascyrifolium EBee GEdr IPot LEdu WHil

Cynara (*Asteraceae*)

§ ***baetica*** subsp. ***maroccana*** SBrt WHil
cardunculus ♀H6 Widely available
- ACL 380/78 SWat
- 'Bianco Avorio' SVic
I - 'Cardy' LCro NCGa
- dwarf SDix SMHy
- subsp. ***flavescens*** **new** SBrt
I - 'Florist Cardy' NLar

	- from Chelsea Physic Garden **new**	MAvo
	- 'Gobbo di Nizza'	LEdu SRms WHer
	- 'Porto Spineless'	CAgr WFar
§	- Scolymus Group	CBcs EPfP EWes GPoy IBoy LRHS LSRN MNHC MRav SEND SPav SPhx SPoG SVic WHer
	- - 'Bere'	LEdu
	- - 'Carciofo Violetto Precoce'	WHer
	- - 'Gros Camus de Bretagne'	MAvo WCot
	- - 'Gros Vert de Lâon' 🏆^{H5}	CBcs ELan LRHS WCot
	- - 'Monica Lynden-Bell'	WCot
	- - 'Purple Globe'	LEdu SRms
	- - 'Romanesco'	SRms SVic
	- - 'Rouge d'Alger'	CAgr
	- - 'Tavor'	SVic
	- - 'Vert Globe'	CSBt ENfk LEdu NLar NPer SPad SRms SVic SWvt WHil
	- - 'Violet de Provence'	CSBt LEdu MHer SRms
*	***gomerensis***	WCot
	humilis	SBrt
	hystrix misapplied	see *C. baetica* subsp. *maroccana*
	scolymus	see *C. cardunculus* Scolymus Group

Cynodon (*Poaceae*)

	aethiopicus	EBee EHoe EPPr SEND

Cynoglossum (*Boraginaceae*)

	amabile 🏆^{H3}	SPhx
	- f. ***roseum*** 'Mystery Rose'	LLWG
	grande	SBrt
	nervosum	EBee ELan EPPr GPSL MMuc MRav SEND SPer WCAu WCot WGwG
	officinale	CArn MHer

Cynosurus (*Poaceae*)

	cristatus	CHab NMir

Cypella (*Iridaceae*)

	aquatilis	EWay LLWG
§	***coelestis***	CSpe SChr WHil
	peruviana	WHil
	plumbea	see *C. coelestis*

Cyperus (*Cyperaceae*)

§	***albostriatus***	CCCN EShb
	alternifolius misapplied	see *C. involucratus*
	alternifolius L.	CBen CCCN EPfP MHtn MSKA SArc WMAq WMoo XBlo
	- 'Compactus'	see *C. involucratus* 'Nanus'
	'Chira'	NWsh
§	***cyperoides***	NLos
	diffusus misapplied	see *C. albostriatus*
	diffusus ambig.	NLos
§	***eragrostis***	EHoe GCal LPot MWts NSti SDix SPlb SWat WGrn WMAq WMoo
	esculentus	CAgr CArn EShb LEdu
	fuscus	WMoo
	glaber	IBoy
	haspan misapplied	see *C. papyrus* 'Nanus'
	haspan L.	MSKA NLos
§	***involucratus*** 🏆^{H1c}	EShb EWay MSKA MWts SEND SWat WMoo
§	- 'Nanus'	EShb NLos
	longus	CBen CWat EHoe EWay MMuc MWts NPer SEND SWat WMAq WWtn XLum
	papyrus 🏆^{H1a}	CAby CCCN CDTJ LRHS LTro MHer MSKA NLos SBig SPlb XBlo
§	- 'Nanus' 🏆^{H1a}	SKHP XBlo
	- 'Perkamentus'^{PBR}	CCCN LLWG
	prolifer	LLWG
	sumula hort.	see *C. cyperoides*
	vegetus	see *C. eragrostis*
	'Zumila'	EShb

Cyphomandra see *Solanum*

Cypripedium (*Orchidaceae*)

	acaule	GEdr
	Achim gx	GEdr XFro
	Aki gx	GEdr LAma XFro
	- 'Pastel'	GEdr XFro
	× ***andrewsii***	GEdr
	Anna gx	GEdr XFro
	Annette gx	GEdr
	Bärbel Schmidt gx	GEdr
	× ***barbeyi***	see *C.* × *ventricosum*
	Barry Phillips gx	GEdr
	Bernd gx	GEdr
	Bill gx	GEdr
	Birgit gx pastel-flowered	GEdr XFro
	Boots gx	GEdr
	calceolus	GKev LAma
	calceolus × ***henryii***	LAma
	californicum	LAma
	Carol Ilene gx	GEdr
	Chauncey gx	GEdr XFro
	Cleo Pinkepank gx	GEdr XFro
	corrugatum	see *C. tibeticum*
	Dawn Edwards gx	GEdr
	debile	LAma
	Dietrich gx 🏆^{H5}	GEdr XFro
	Emil gx	GEdr XFro
	Eurasia gx **new**	XFro
	fasciolatum	GEdr LAma LRHS
	flavum	GEdr GKev LAma
	- white-flowered	GKev
	- white-flowered × ***reginae***	LAma
	formosanum 🏆^{H3}	GEdr GKev LAma SKHP
	Gabriela gx 'Kentucky Maxi'	GKev LAma NHpl
	Gisela gx	CAvo GEdr LAma XFro
	- 'Pastel'	GEdr
	guttatum	GKev
	Hank Small gx 🏆^{H5}	GEdr XFro
	Hans Erni gx	GEdr XFro
	henryi	LAma
	Inge gx	GEdr XFro
	Ingrid gx	GEdr XFro
	Irene gx	GEdr XEll
	Ivory gx	GEdr LAma
	James Armitage gx	GEdr
	Jens gx	GEdr
	Judith Merrick gx	GEdr
	Julia Barclay gx	GEdr
	Kathleen Anne Green gx	GEdr
	kentuckiense 🏆^{H5}	CCCN GEdr GKev LAma LRHS NHpl XEll
	- Lady Dorine gx	LAma
	'Kentucky Pink'	see *C.* Philipp gx 'Kentucky Pink'
	Kristi Lyn gx	GEdr XFro
	Lothar Pinkepank gx	GEdr LAma
	Lucy Pinkepank gx	GEdr XFro
	- 'Kentucky Pink Blush'	GKev LAma LRHS NHpl
	macranthos	GEdr GKev
	- 'Hotei'	GEdr

- var. ***hotei-atsumorianum*** Sadovsky	GEdr
- John Hagger Group	XFro
- var. ***speciosum***	GEdr
Maria gx	GEdr XFro
Memoria Gerd Kohls gx	GEdr
Memoriam Shawna Austin gx	GEdr LAma
Michael gx 🏆H5	GEdr XFro
- 'Pastel'	GEdr
Monto gx **new**	XFro
Neil Lancaster gx	GEdr
Otto gx	GEdr
parviflorum	GEdr GKev
- var. ***parviflorum***	LAma
§ - var. ***pubescens***	GEdr GKev LAma
'Parville'	LRHS NHpl
Paul gx	GEdr XFro
Peter gx	GEdr XFro
Philipp gx 🏆H5	GEdr LAma XFro
§ - 'Kentucky Pink'	GKev LAma NHpl
Piccolo gx **new**	GKev
Pixi gx	GEdr
Pluto gx	GEdr XFro
pubescens	see *C. parviflorum* var. *pubescens*
'Pueblo'	GKev LRHS NHpl
Rascal gx	GEdr
reginae 🏆H5	CCCN GEdr GKev LAma LRHS NHpl SKHP WHlf XEll
- f. ***albolabium***	NHpl
- f. ***album***	GEdr GKev LAma LRHS XEll
Renate gx	GEdr
- pastel-flowered	XFro
Rhodopoxis gx	GEdr
Sabine gx 🏆H5	GEdr XFro
- pastel-flowered	GEdr XFro
Sebastian gx	GEdr XFro
- 'Frosch's Mountain King'	XFro
- 'Multiflower White'	LAma NHpl
segawae	LAma
Selston High School gx	GEdr
Siggi gx	GEdr
Sunny gx	GEdr XFro
§ ***tibeticum***	GEdr LAma
Tilman gx	GEdr LAma XFro
Tower Hill gx	GEdr
Ulla Silkens gx 🏆H5	GEdr GKev LAma XEll XFro
Ursel gx	GEdr XFro
§ × ***ventricosum***	GEdr LAma XFro
- 'Pastel'	XFro
Victoria gx	GEdr XFro
Werner Frosch gx	GEdr

Cyrilla (*Cyrillaceae*)

racemiflora	CMac

Cyrtanthus (*Amaryllidaceae*)

§ ***brachyscyphus***	ECho EShb
breviflorus	CTre ECho WPGP
'Edwina'	CCCN ECho
§ ***elatus*** 🏆H1c	CPne CTal ECho GKev LEdu NSti
- 'Pink Diamond'	ECho
- salmon-flowered **new**	GKev
- white- and orange-flowered **new**	GKev
- white-flowered **new**	GKev
- yellow-flowered **new**	GKev
elatus × ***fergusoniae*** **new**	CPne
'Elizabeth'	CCCN ECho
eucallus	WCot
falcatus 🏆H2	CPne
mackenii	ECho EShb WPGP
- var. ***cooperi***	CAby CPne
- cream-white-flowered	CCCN ECho GKev
- 'Himalayan Pink'	CCCN ECho GKev
- orange-flowered	ECho
- pink-flowered	GKev
- red-flowered	CCCN ECho GKev
- white-flowered	ECho
- yellow-flowered	ECho
montanus	ECho WCot
parviflorus	see *C. brachyscyphus*
purpureus	see *C. elatus*
sanguineus	ECho WCot
speciosus	see *C. elatus*

Cyrtomium ✿ (*Dryopteridaceae*)

§ ***caryotideum***	CLAP ISha
devexiscapulae **new**	LLWG
§ ***falcatum*** 🏆H2	CAby CBod CKel CLAP CPne EFer ELan ELon EPfP GBin GMaP IVic LEdu LHop LPar LRHS NLar NLos SBod SDix SEND SHil SPlb SPoG SPtp SRot WCot WMoo XBlo XLum
- 'Rochfordianum'	CCCN GBin ISha LRHS MRav WFib
§ ***fortunei*** 🏆H3	Widely available
- var. ***clivicola***	CKel EBee EPfP EShb ISha LPot LRHS MGos MRav NBro NLar SPad SPtp WCot XLum
macrophyllum	CLAP LRHS
tukusicola	EBee NLos

Cystopteris ✿ (*Woodsiaceae*)

bulbifera	CLAP WCot
dickieana	CLAP WFib
fragilis	EFer WFib
moupinensis B&SWJ 6767	WCru

Cytisus (*Papilionaceae*)

'Andreanus'	see *C. scoparius* f. *andreanus*
× ***beanii*** 🏆H5	CLet ELan EPfP LRHS MAsh NLar SLon
'Boskoop Glory'	NLar
× ***boskoopii*** 'Apricot Gem'	NLar
- 'Boskoop Ruby' 🏆H5	CLet CMac CSBt EPfP ESps EUJe GKin GMcL LBMP LCro LRHS LSRN MAsh MJak NEgg NHol NPri SCob SHil SPer SWvt WBor WHar
- 'Dukaat'	NLar
- 'Hollandia' 🏆H5	CBcs CSBt EPfP ESps GKin LBMP MRav SGol
- 'La Coquette'	CRos ELon EPfP LRHS NEgg NRHS SPlb
- 'Windlesham Ruby'	CRos ELan EPfP LRHS LSRN MMuc NEgg NLar NRHS SLim SPer WFar
- 'Zeelandia' 🏆H5	CMac EPfP ESps LRHS NHol SCob SPer WFar
'Burkwoodii' 🏆H5	CBcs CDul CRos ELan ELon EPfP ESps GMcL LRHS LSRN MMuc MSwo NEgg NRHS SPoG WFar
canariensis	see *Genista canariensis*
'Cottage'	EPot
§ ***decumbens***	MAsh
'Dorothy Walpole'	WFar
'Golden Cascade'	CBcs CRos ELan LBMP LRHS MAsh NEgg NRHS SLim
'Goldfinch'	CSBt ELan GMcL MJak MSwo NEgg NHol NLar SCob WFar
× ***kewensis*** 🏆H5	CLet CRos ELan EPfP LRHS MAsh MGos MRav NLar NRHS NWea SPer SRms

	- 'Niki'	EPfP GMcL LRHS MAsh MMuc NLar SPer WRHF
	'Killiney Red'	ELan
	'Killiney Salmon'	GKin LSRN MRav
	'Lena' ♀H5	CLet CMac CRos CSBt EPfP GKin GMcL LRHS LSRN MGos NBir NEgg NHol NLar NPri NRHS SCob SGol SHil SLim SPoG WFar WHar
	'Luna'	EPfP GMcL NEgg SHil
	maderensis	see *Genista maderensis*
	'Maria Burkwood'	NLar
	'Minstead'	ELan SPer
	'Moyclare Pink'	LCro
	'Mrs Norman Henry'	NLar
	'Newry Seedling'	CMac
	nigricans 'Cyni' ♀H5	ELan ESwi IArd LRHS MAsh MMuc SPer SPoG
	'Porlock'	see *Genista* 'Porlock'
	× ***praecox***	CMac CRos ELon ESps LRHS MAsh NEgg NRHS SGol SPlb SPoG WFar WHar
	- 'Albus'	CBcs CDul CMac CRos ELan EPfP ESps GMcL LPar LRHS LSRN MAsh MGos MJak MRav NHol NRHS SCob SEND SHil SPer WFar WHar
	- 'Allgold' ♀H5	Widely available
	- 'Frisia'	WFar
	- 'Lilac Lady'	LRHS
	- 'Warminster' ♀H5	EPfP GKin MMuc MRav NWea SEND SPer SRms
	purpureus	ELan EPfP GMcL LHop LRHS MRav SPer WCot WPat WSHC
	- 'Atropurpureus'	EPfP NWea SPer
	racemosus	see *Genista* × *spachiana*
	'Red Wings'	MMuc SPer
	scoparius	CDul CPer NWea WTSh
§	- f. ***andreanus***	CTri EPfP NWea
	- - 'Splendens'	SPer
	- 'Cornish Cream'	CDul CSBt ELan EPfP NEgg SPer
	- 'Firefly'	CBcs CMac
	- 'Fulgens'	EPfP
	- 'Golden Sunlight'	CSBt GMcL MSwo
§	- subsp. ***maritimus***	CMac
	- Monarch strain	GJos
	- var. ***prostratus***	see *C. scoparius* subsp. *maritimus*
	× ***spachianus***	see *Genista* × *spachiana*
	supranubius	SBrt
	'White Lion'	CMac

D

Daboecia ✿ (*Ericaceae*)

	cantabrica	MMuc
§	- f. ***alba***	CSBt NWad SWhi
	- - 'Creeping White'	CFst
	- - 'David Moss'	MMuc
I	- - 'Early Bride'	CFst
	- 'Alberta White'	CFst IVic SWhi
	- 'Amelie'PBR	CFst IVic LCro SWhi
	- 'Andrea'	CFst SWhi
	- 'Arielle'	CFst SWhi
	- 'Atropurpurea'	CFst CSBt NWad SWhi
	- 'Bicolor'	CFst
	- f. ***blumii*** 'Purple Blum'	CFst
	- - 'White Blum'	CFst SPer SWhi
	- 'Bubbles'	CFst
	- 'Celtic Star'	CFst
	- 'Chaldon'	CFst
	- 'Cinderella'	IVic
	- 'Covadonga'	CFst
	- 'Cupido'	IVic SWhi
	- 'Glamour'	CFst SPer
I	- 'Globosa Pink'	NWad SWhi
	- 'Heather Yates'	CFst
	- 'Hookstone Purple'	NWad
	- 'Praegerae'	CTri
	- 'Rainbow' (v)	CFst
	- 'Romantic Muxoll'	CFst
	- subsp. ***scotica*** 'Ben'	CFst
	- - 'Cora'	CFst
	- - 'Ellen Norris'	CFst
	- - 'Golden Imp'	CFst SWhi
	- - 'Goscote'	MGos SWhi
	- - 'Jack Drake'	CFst
	- - 'Katherine's Choice'	CBcs CFst CTri
	- - 'Red Imp'	CFst
	- - 'Robin'	CFst
	- - 'Silverwells' ♀H5	CBcs MAsh SWhi
	- - 'William Buchanan' ♀H5	CFst GAbr GJos MAsh NWad SCoo SWhi
	- 'Stardust Muxoll'	CFst
	- 'Tinkerbell'	CFst GJos SWhi
	- 'Vanessa'PBR	CFst IVic SWhi
	- 'Waley's Red' ♀H5	NWad SWhi

Dacrycarpus ✿ (*Podocarpaceae*)

§	***dacrydioides***	CBrP LEdu

Dacrydium ✿ (*Podocarpaceae*)

	cupressinum	SPlb WThu
	franklinii	see *Lagarostrobos franklinii*
	laxifolium	see *Lepidothamnus laxifolius*

Dactylicapnos (*Papaveraceae*)

	macrocapnos	CBcs CSpe IDee IFro SNig WBor WCru
	platycarpa	WPGP
§	***scandens***	CRHN EBee GEdr IRos MSCN SBrt SMad
	- GWJ 9438	WCru
	- WJC 13793 **new**	WCru
	torulosa	WTou
§	***ventii*** GWJ 9376	WCru

Dactylis (*Poaceae*)

	glomerata	CHab SVic WSFF
	- 'Variegata' (v)	MMuc NBid SEND SHDw

Dactylorhiza (*Orchidaceae*)

	sp.	SDir
	aristata	EFEx
	baltica	LAma
	× ***braunii***	ECha
§	***elata*** ♀H5	GKev IBlr LAma WCot
§	***foliosa*** ♀H4	CCCN ECha GCra IBlr
§	***fuchsii***	CCCN CMil ECho EPot GKev LEdu MNrw NRya SKHP WHer WHlf WSFF
	× ***grandis***	IBlr
	- Blackthorn hybrid	IBlr
	hybrid	LEdu NRya
	incarnata	LAma NBid
§	***maculata***	CHid EPfP GKev LAma LRHS WBor WHlf
	maderensis	see *D. foliosa*
§	***majalis***	LAma MNrw WHlf WSFF XEll
	- subsp. ***sphagnicola***	GKev
	mascula	see *Orchis mascula*

	praetermissa	CCCN GKev LRHS SKHP
	- subsp. ***praetermissa*** hybrid	SKHP
	purpurella	EPot GAbr GJos GKev NRya

Dahlia ✿ (*Asteraceae*)

	'A la Mode' (D)	CWGr
	'Abba' (D)	CWGr ECtt
	'Abbie' (D)	NHal
	'Abingdon Ace' (D)	SGbt
	'Abridge Ben' (D)	CWGr
	'Abridge Florist' (WL)	CWGr
	'Abridge Taffy' (D)	CWGr
I	'Acapulco' (S-c)	ERCP
	'Addison June' (Ba) **new**	ERCP
	'Adelaide Fontane' (D)	CWGr
	'Admiral Rawlings' (D)	CWGr
	'African Garden' (D)	CSut
	'Aitara Caress' (C)	NHal SGbt
	'Akita' (Misc)	CWGr ELan NBri SGbt
	'Aladdin's Lamp' (WL)	NJRG
	'Alauna Clair-Obscur' (Fim)	CWGr ERCP
	'Albert Schweitzer' (S-c)	CWGr SGbt
	'Alden Regal' (C)	CWGr
	'Alfred C' (S-c)	CWGr
	'Alfred Grille' (S-c)	LCro LOPS SDeJ SGbt SPer
	'Alf's Mascot' (D)	NJRG
	'Aljo' (S-c)	CWGr
	'Allan Snowfire' (S-c)	NHal
	'Allan Sparkes' (WL) 🏆H3	CWGr
	'Alloway Candy' (Misc)	ERCP
	'Alloway Cottage' (D)	CWGr NHal SGbt
	'Alltami Apollo' (S-c)	CWGr
	'Alltami Cherry' (Ba)	CWGr
	'Alltami Classic' (D)	CWGr
	'Alltami Corsair' (S-c)	CWGr
	'Alltami Ruby' (S-c)	CWGr
	'Almand's Climax' (D) 🏆H3	CWGr SGbt
	'Alpen Beauty' (Col)	CWGr
	'Alpen Fern' (Fim)	CWGr
	'Alpen Flame' (C)	CWGr
	'Alpen Mildred' (S-c)	CWGr
	'Alpen Sun' (S-c)	CWGr
	'Alva's Doris' (S-c) 🏆H3	CWGr LAyl
	'Alva's Lilac' (D)	CWGr
	'Alva's Supreme' (D) 🏆H3	CWGr LAyl NHal
	'Amaran Guard' (D)	CWGr
	'Amaran Relish' (D)	CWGr SGbt
	'Amaran Return' (D)	CWGr
	'Amaran Royale' (D)	CWGr
	'Amaran Troy' (WL)	CWGr
I	'Amazone' (Sin/DwB)	SPoG
	'Amber Banker' (C)	CWGr SGbt
	'Amber Festival' (D)	NHal
	'Amberglow' (Ba)	CWGr
	'Amberley Joan' (D)	CWGr
	'Ambition' (S-c)	CAvo CWGr ERCP LCro LOPS
	'Amelia's Surprise' (D)	CWGr
	'American Copper' (D)	CWGr
	'American Dawn' (D)	LCro LOPS
	'American Moon' (D)	LCro LOPS
	American Pie = 'Vdtg26'PBR (Dark Angel Series) (Sin)	CRos LRHS NRHS SDeJ
	'Amethyst' (D)	CWGr
	'Amgard Coronet' (D)	CWGr
	'Amgard Delicate' (D)	CWGr SGbt
	'Amgard Rosie' (D)	CWGr
	'Amira' (Ba)	CWGr
	'Amorangi Joy' (C)	CWGr
	'Amy Cave' (Ba)	NHal
	'Anchorite' (D)	CWGr
	'Andrea Clark' (D)	NHal
	'Andrea Lawson' (Ba)	NHal
	'Andrew Lockwood' (Pom)	CWGr
	'Andrew Mitchell' (S-c)	CWGr NHal
	'Andries' Amber' (S-c)	CWGr
	'Andries' Orange' (C)	ECtt
	'Andries' Orange As' (S-c) **new**	CWGr
	'Andy Murray' (Sin) **new**	CWGr
	'Angora' (Fim)	SGbt
	'Anita Summerhayes' (Misc)	CWGr
	'Ann Breckenfelder' (Col) 🏆H3	CWGr ECtt ERCP EUJe NHal NJRG SDix
	'Annika' (Sin)	LCro LOPS SDeJ
	'Anniversary Ball' (Ba)	CWGr
	'Another Pet'	see *D.* 'Mystic Enchantment'
	'Antique' (Sin) **new**	LRHS
	'Apache' (Fim)	CAby CWGr ERCP SDeJ SGbt SPer
	'Apache Blauw' (Fim)	ERCP
	'Apple Blossom' (C)	SGbt
I	'Appleblossom' (Col)	CWGr
	'Apricot Honeymoon Dress' (D)	CWGr
I	'Apricot Parfait' (Fim)	CWGr
	'Apricot Star' (Fim)	NBri
	'April Dawn' (D)	CWGr
	'April Heather' (Col) 🏆H3	NHal
	'Arabian Night' (D)	CAby CAvo CBcs CSut CWGr ECtt ELan EPfP ERCP LAyl LCro LOPS LRHS LSRN LSun MHol NBri NLar SDeJ SEND SGbt WCot
	'Arc de Triomphe' (D)	CWGr
	'Arlequin' (D)	SGbt
	'Arnhem' (D)	CWGr
	'Arthur Godfrey' (D)	CWGr
	'Arthur Hankin' (D)	CWGr
	'Arthur's Delight' (D)	CWGr
	'Asahi Chohje' (Anem) 🏆H3	CWGr
	'Askwith Joan' (D)	NHal
	'Askwith Minnie' (D)	NHal
	'Atilla' (D)	CWGr
I	'Atlanta' (D)	CWGr SGbt
	atropurpurea **new**	CWGr
	'Audacity' (D)	CWGr LAyl SGbt
	'Aurora's Kiss' (Ba)	CWGr ERCP NHal SGbt
	'Aurwen's Violet' (Pom)	CWGr NHal
	australis	CSpe CWGr EBee IFro SEND SSal
	- B&SWJ 10208	WCru
	- B&SWJ 10389	WCru
I	'Autumn Fairy' (S-c)	ERCP SDeJ
	'Autumn Lustre' (WL)	CWGr
	'Avignon' (D)	SDeJ
	'Avoca Amanda' (D)	NHal
	'Avoca Comanche' (S-c)	NHal
	'Avoca Salmon' (D)	NHal
	'Awaikoe' (Col)	CWGr
	'B.J. Beauty' (D)	NHal NJRG
	'Babette' (S-c)	WBor
	'Baby Fonteneau' (S-c)	CWGr
	'Babylon' (D)	LRHS SGbt
§	'Babylon Brons' (D)	ERCP LRHS SGbt
	'Babylon Bronze'	see *D.* 'Babylon Brons'
	'Babylon Lila' (D)	SGbt
§	'Babylon Paars' (D)	LRHS SDeJ SGbt
	'Babylon Purple'	see *D.* 'Babylon Paars'
	'Babylon Rose' (D)	LRHS SGbt
	'Bacardi' (D)	ERCP
	'Badger Twinkle' (S-c) **new**	CWGr
	'Bahama Lemon'	see *D.* 'Lemon Cane'

'Balham' (Sin) **new**	WCot
'Ballego's Glory' (D)	CWGr SGbt
'Bambino' (Lil)	CWGr
'Banker' (C)	CWGr
'Bantling' (Ba)	CWGr ERCP SDir SGbt
'Barbara Schell' (D)	CWGr
'Barbara's Pastelle' (S-c)	CWGr NJRG SGbt
'Barbarossa' (D)	CWGr
'Barbarry Ball' (Ba)	CWGr
'Barbarry Banker' (D)	CWGr LAyl
'Barbarry Bluebird' (D)	NHal SGbt
'Barbarry Cadet' (D)	CWGr
'Barbarry Carousel' (Ba)	CWGr
'Barbarry Cosmos' (D)	CWGr
'Barbarry Dominion' (D)	CWGr
'Barbarry Drifter' (D)	CWGr
'Barbarry Flag' (D)	CWGr
'Barbarry Gem' (Ba)	CWGr
'Barbarry Melody' (D)	NHal
'Barbarry Monitor' (Ba)	CWGr SGbt
'Barbarry Olympic' (Ba)	CWGr
'Barbarry Oracle' (D)	CWGr
'Barbarry Pinky' (D)	CWGr
'Barbarry Pip' (D)	NHal
'Barbarry Sultan' (D)	NHal
'Barbarry Sunbeam' (D)	NHal
'Barbarry Triumph' (D)	CWGr
'Barbette' (D)	CWGr
'Bareham's Beauty' (D)	CWGr
'Baret Joy' (S-c)	CWGr NHal
'Bargaly Blush' (D)	NHal
'Baron Ray' (D)	CWGr
'Barry Williams' (D)	CWGr SGbt
'Bart' (D)	CWGr
'Bassingbourne Beauty' (D)	CWGr
'Bayou'^{PBR} (Misc)	CWGr ERCP LCro LOPS NHal NJRG SGbt SPer
'Bedford Sally' (D)	CWGr
'Bednall Beauty' (Misc/DwB) ♀^{H3}	CHll CSpe CWCL CWGr ECtt ELan EUJe EWes LHop LRHS NJRG NLar WHoo
'Bell Boy' (Ba)	SGbt
'Belle Epoque' (C)	CWGr
'Berger's Rekord' (S-c)	CWGr
'Berliner Orange' (D)	ERCP
'Bernice Sunset' (S-c)	CWGr
'Berolina' (D)	CWGr
'Berwick Banker' (Ba)	CWGr
'Berwick Wood' (D)	CWGr NHal SGbt
'Bess Painter' (D)	CWGr
'Best Bett'	see *D.* Mystic Spirit
'Beth's Chaplet' (Sin)	WCot
'Betty Ann' (Pom)	CWGr
'Biddenham Fairy' (D)	CWGr
'Biddenham Strawberry' (D)	CWGr SGbt
'Biddenham Sunset' (S-c)	CWGr
'Big Orange' (D)	CWGr
'Bilbao'^{PBR} (Jumbo Collection) (D)	NBri
'Bill Holmberg' (D)	CWGr SGbt
'Bingo' (D)	SGbt
'Bishop of Auckland'^{PBR} (Misc)	CAby CAvo CHVG CSut CWGN CWGr ECtt EPfP EPot ERCP EWoo LAma LCro LOPS LRHS MGos SDeJ SGbt SHil WCot
'Bishop of Cambridge' (Sin)	CWGr
'Bishop of Canterbury'^{PBR} (P)	CWGr ECtt ELan EPfP LAma LCro LOPS LRHS MGos NHal NNys SDeJ SGbt SHil SPoG WBod
'Bishop of Dover' (Sin)	CSut CWGr EPfP EPot LAma LCro LOPS LRHS NBri NNys SDeJ SGbt WBrk
'Bishop of Lancaster' (Misc)	CWGr LAma LCro LOPS NLar NNys SDir
'Bishop of Leicester' (Misc)	CWGr ECtt ELan EPfP EPot LAma LCro LOPS LRHS NBri NNys SDeJ SGbt SHar
'Bishop of Llandaff' (P) ♀^{H3}	Widely available
'Bishop of Oxford' (Misc)	CAby CWGr ELan EPfP EPot ERCP LAma LCro LOPS LRHS MGos NNys SDeJ SDir SGbt SHil SPoG
'Bishop of York' (Misc)	CAby CAvo CBod CWGr ECGP ECtt ELan EPfP EPot LAma LAyl LCro LOPS LRHS MGos NGdn NNys SDeJ SGbt SHil SPoG
'Bishop Peter Price' (Sin)	CWGr
'Black Fire' (D)	CWGr ECtt
'Black Jack' (D)	ERCP NHal
'Black Monarch' (D)	CWGr NHal SGbt SSal
'Black Narcissus' (C)	CWGr SGbt
I 'Black R Jack'	NJRG
'Black Spider' (S-c)	CWGr
'Black Star' (Sin)	EPfP
'Black Touch' (Fim)	CWGr ERCP
'Black Tucker' (Pom)	CWGr
'Black Wizard' (S-c)	EWoo
'Blackberry Ripple' (S-c)	CWGr
'Blaisdon Red' (D)	CWGr
'Blaze' (D)	CWGr
'Bliss' (WL)	CWGr
'Blithe Spirit' (D)	CWGr
'Bloemfontein' (D)	CWGr
'Bloodstone' (D)	CWGr SGbt
'Bloom's Graham' (S-c)	CWGr
'Bloom's Kenn' (D)	CWGr SGbt
'Blue Beard' (S-c)	CWGr
'Blue Bell' (D)	ERCP SPer
'Blue Boy' (D)	CWGr ERCP LCro LOPS SSal
'Blue Record' (S-c/DwB)	ERCP
'Blue Wish' (WL)	CSut ERCP LCro LOPS NJRG
'Blyton Golden Girl' (D)	NHal
'Blyton Lady in Red' (D)	LAyl NHal NJRG
'Blyton Romance' (D)	NHal
'Blyton Softer Gleam' (D) ♀^{H3}	CWGr NHal NJRG SGbt
'Bob's Bonaventure' (D)	CWGr NHal
'Bokay' (WL)	CWGr
'Bonesta' (D)	CWGr NBri
'Bonny Blue' (Ba)	CWGr
'Boogie Woogie' (Anem)	CWGr SDeJ
'Boom Boom White' (Ba)	ERCP
'Boom Boom Yellow' (Ba)	ERCP
'Bora Bora' (S-c)	NBri
'Border Princess' (C/DwB)	CWGr SGbt
'Boy Scout' (Ba)	CWGr
'Bracken Lorelei' (WL)	NJRG
'Brackenridge Ballerina' (WL)	CWGr NHal NJRG SGbt
'Brandaris' (S-c)	CWGr SGbt
'Brandon James' (D)	SDeJ
'Brandysnap' (D)	CWGr SGbt
'Brantwood' (Sin)	CWGr
Braveheart = 'Vdtg67'^{PBR} (Dark Angel Series) (Sin)	LCro LOPS SDeJ
'Brian's Dream' (D)	LAyl NHal
'Bride's Bouquet' (Col)	ERCP LRHS
'Bridge View Aloha' (S-c) ♀^{H3}	CWGr SGbt
'Bright Eyes' (Sin)	ERCP

	'Brigitta Alida' (S-c)	EBee
	'Bristol Petite' (D)	CWGr
	'Bristol Stripe' (D) **new**	CWGr
	'Brookfield Delight' (Sin/Lil) ♀^{H3}	CWGr
	'Brookfield Rachel' (Ba)	CWGr
	'Brookfield Rene' (D)	CWGr
	'Brookfield Snowball' (Ba)	CWGr
	'Brookfield Sweetie' (Misc/DwB)	CWGr
	'Brookside Cheri' (C)	CWGr
	'Brookside Snowball' (Ba)	CWGr
	'Bryce B. Morrison' (D)	CWGr
	'Bryn Terfel' (D)	CWGr GWyn NHal SGbt
	'Bull's Pride' (D)	CWGr
	'Butch' (D)	CWGr
	'Butterball' (D/DwB)	SDeJ
*	'Buttercup' (Pom)	CWGr
	'By George' (D)	CWGr
	'Caballero' (WL)	CWGr
	'Café au Lait' (D)	CAby CWGr ELan EPfP ERCP LCro LOPS LRHS NBri NNys SDeJ SGbt SPer
	'Calgary' (D)	CWGr
	'Camano Ariel' (C)	CWGr
	'Camano Choice' (D)	CWGr
	'Camano Passion' (S-c)	CWGr
	'Camano Poppet' (Ba)	CWGr
	'Camano Regal' (S-c)	CWGr
	'Cambridge' (D)	NBri
I	'Cameo' (WL)	LAyl NHal NJRG SGbt
	campanulata	CWGr
	'Campos Hush' (S-c)	CWGr
	'Campos Philip M' (D)	CWGr
	'Canary Fubuki' (Fim)	CWGr ERCP SDeJ SGbt
	'Candy Cane' (Ba)	CWGr
	'Candy Cupid' (Ba)	CWGr
	Candy Eyes	see *D.* 'Zone Ten'
	'Candy Hamilton Lilian' (D)	CWGr
	'Candy Keene' (S-c)	CWGr NHal
	'Caproz Jerry Garcia' (D)	CWGr
	'Capulet' (Ba)	CWGr
	'Careless' (D)	CWGr
	'Caribbean Fantasy' (D)	CWGr
	'Carolina Moon' (D)	CWGr GWyn NHal SGbt
	'Carol's Spanish Dancer' (C)	LAyl NHal NJRG
	'Carstone Firebox' (Col)	LAyl NHal NJRG
	'Carstone Ruby' (D)	NHal
	'Carstone Sunbeam' (D)	CWGr
	'Carstone Suntan' (C)	CWGr
	'Carstone Valiant' (Ba)	NHal
	'Castle Drive' (D)	CWGr
	'Catherine Deneuve' (Misc)	CWGN CWGr SGbt SSal
	'Catherine Ireland' (D)	CWGr
	'Cerise Prefect' (S-c)	CWGr
	'Cha Cha' (S-c)	CWGr SGbt
	'Challenger' (D) **new**	GWyn
	'Chanson d'Amour' (D)	CWGr
	'Charles de Coster' (D)	CWGr
	'Charles Dickens' (Ba)	CWGr
	'Charlie Briggs' (Ba)	NHal
	'Charlie Dimmock' (WL) ♀^{H3}	NHal NJRG SGbt
	'Charlie Two' (D)	CWGr NHal
	'Charlotte Bateson' (Ba)	CWGr
	'Chat Noir' (S-c) ♀^{H3}	CWGr ERCP LAyl LCro LOPS LRHS SGbt
	'Chee' (WL)	CWGr
	'Cheerio' (S-c)	CWGr
	'Cherokee Beauty' (D)	CWGr
	'Cherry Wine' (D)	CWGr
	'Cherrywood Millfield' (S-c)	CWGr
	'Cherrywood Turnpike' (D)	CWGr
	'Cherrywood Wilderness' (D)	CWGr
	'Cherubino' (Col)	CWGr
	'Cherwell Goldcrest' (S-c)	CWGr NHal SGbt
	'Cherwell Skylark' (S-c)	NHal
	'Chessy' (Sin/Lil) ♀^{H3}	CWGr
	'Chic en Rouge' (Misc)	LSou
	'Chilson's Pride' (D)	CWGr SGbt
	'Chiltern Amber' (D)	CWGr
	'Chiltern Sylvia' (S-c)	CWGr
	'Chimacum Topaz' (S-c)	CWGr
	'Chimborazo' (Col)	CWGr EUJe LAyl SDix SGbt
	'Chinese Lantern' (D)	CWGr
	'Chloe's Keene' (S-c)	CWGr
	'Chorus Girl' (D)	CWGr
	'Christine' (D)	CWGr SPer
I	'Christine' (WL)	SGbt
	'Christmas Carol' (Col)	CWGr ECtt GWyn NHal NJRG
	'Christmas Star' (Col)	CWGr
	'Christopher Nickerson' (S-c)	CWGr SGbt
	'Christopher Taylor' (WL)	NHal SGbt
	'City of Alkmaar' (C)	SSal
	'City of Leiden' (S-c)	LCro LOPS NHal
	'Clair de Lune' (Col) ♀^{H3}	CWCL CWGr ECtt ERCP LRHS MCot NHal NJRG NLar SGbt WCot
	'Claire Diane' (D)	CWGr
	'Claire Louise Kitchener' (WL)	CWGr
	'Clara May' (Fim)	CWGr
	'Clarion' (S-c)	LRHS
I	'Clarion' (Sin)	CHVG CWGr
	'Classic A.1' (C)	CWGr
	'Classic Poème'^{PBR} (Misc)	ERCP
	'Classic Rosamunde'^{PBR} (Misc)	CWGr ERCP NHal NJRG NNys
	'Classic Summertime' (Misc)	CWGr
§	'Classic Swanlake'^{PBR} (Misc)	CWGr EPfP ERCP EWoo LCro LOPS LRHS NJRG
	'Claudette' (D)	ECtt
	'Clayt's Candy' (S-c) **new**	NHal
	'Clearview Irene' (S-c)	NHal
	'Clearview Louise' (S-c) **new**	NHal
	'Clearview Sundance' (C) **new**	NHal
	'Cloverdale' (D)	CWGr
	coccinea	CFil CSpe CWGr EBee MCot SDix SGbt SMHy WPGP
	- NJM 05.072	WPGP
	- hybrids	NSti
	- orange-flowered **new**	CWGr
	- var. ***palmeri***	CAvo CFil EBee WPGP XEll
	- yellow-flowered **new**	CWGr
	'Cocktail' (S-c)	CWGr
	'Colac' (D)	CWGr
	'Color Spectacle' (S-c)	CWGr LRHS
	'Colour Magic' (S-c)	CWGr
	'Coltness Gem' (Sin/DwB)	CWGr
	'Comet' (Anem)	CWGr
	'Como Polly' (D)	CWGr
	'Connie Bartlam' (D)	CWGr
	'Contessa' (WL)	CWGr SDeJ
	'Coral Jupiter' (S-c)	CWGr
	'Coral Strand' (D)	CWGr
	'Cornel' (Ba)	CWGr ERCP NHal NJRG SGbt
	'Cornel Brons' (Ba)	ERCP

	'Cornish Minx' (Pom)	CWGr
	'Cornish Ruby' (Sin)	EPfP
I	'Corona' (S-c/DwB)	SDeJ
	'Coronella' (D)	CWGr SGbt
	'Cortez Silver' (D)	CWGr
	'Cortez Sovereign' (S-c)	CWGr
	'Corton Bess' (D)	CWGr
	'Corton Olympic' (D)	CWGr
	'Corydon' (D)	CWGr
	'Cottontail' (Col)	CWGr
	'Country Boy' (S-c)	CWGr
	'Coupe de Soleil' (D)	CSut CWGr
	'Craigowan' (S-c)	NHal
	'Crazy Legs' (D)	CWGr SGbt
	'Cream Alva's' (D) ♀H3	CWGr
I	'Cream Beauty' (WL)	CWGr
	'Cream Klankstad' (C)	CWGr
	'Cream Linda' (D)	CWGr
	'Cream Moonlight' (S-c)	CWGr SGbt
	'Cream Reliance' (D)	CWGr
	'Creme de Cassis' (D) **new**	CWGr ERCP
	'Crève Coeur' (D)	CWGr
	'Crichton Cherry' (D)	CWGr
	'Crichton Honey' (Ba)	CWGr
	'Croesus' (S-c)	CWGr
	'Crossfield Allegro' (S-c)	CWGr
	'Crossfield Anne' (D)	CWGr
	'Crossfield Ebony' (Pom)	CWGr
	'Crossfield Festival' (D)	CWGr
	'Croydon Ace' (D)	CWGr
	'Croydon Jumbo' (D)	CWGr
	'Croydon Snotop' (D)	CWGr
	'Croydon Superior' (D)	SGbt
	'Cryfield Harmony' (Ba)	CWGr
	'Cryfield Jane' (Ba)	CWGr
	'Cryfield Keene' (S-c)	CWGr
	'Cryfield Max' (C)	CWGr
	'Cryfield Rosie' (Ba)	CWGr
	'Culdrose' (D)	SGbt
	'Curate' (Misc)	CWGr
	'Curiosity' (Col)	NJRG
	'Currant Cream' (Ba)	CWGr SGbt
	cuspidata	CFil EBee
	'Cyclone' (D)	CWGr
	'Cycloop' (S-c)	CWGr
	'Cynthia Chalwin' (Ba)	CWGr
	'Cynthia Louise' (D)	CWGr
	'Czar Willo' (Pom)	CWGr
	'Czardas' (C)	GCal
	Dahlietta Jenny	see *D.* 'Jenny'
	'Daily Mail' (D)	CWGr
	'Daisy Duke' (D) **new**	ERCP
	Dalaya Devi = 'Kledh13037' **new**	NPri
	Dalaya Shiva = 'Kledh13033' **new**	NPri
	Dalaya Yogi = 'Kledh11031' PBR **new**	NPri
	'Daleko Gold' (D)	CWGr
	'Daleko Jupiter' (S-c)	CWGr NHal
	'Daleko National' (D)	CWGr
	'Daleko Tangerine' (D)	CWGr
	'Dame Deidre' (S-c) **new**	CWGr
	'Dana Audrey' (C)	CWGr
	'Dana Dream' (S-c)	CWGr
	'Dana Iris' (S-c)	CWGr
	'Dana Sunset' (C)	CWGr
	'Dancing Queen' (S-c)	CWGr
I	'Dandy' (Col)	CWCL SVic
	'Danjo Doc' (D)	CWGr SGbt
	'Dannevirke' (Sin)	CWGr
	'Danum Belle' (D)	CWGr
	'Danum Chippy' (D)	CWGr
	'Danum Fancy' (D)	CWGr
	'Danum Gail' (D)	CWGr
	'Danum Hero' (D)	CWGr
	'Danum Meteor' (S-c)	CWGr
	'Danum Rebel' (S-c)	CWGr
	'Danum Rhoda' (D)	CWGr
	'Danum Salmon' (S-c)	CWGr
	'Danum Torch' (Col)	CWGr ECtt SGbt
	'Dark Desire' (Sin/DwB)	CAvo CWGN CWGr ECtt EWoo LHop WCot
	'Dark Fubuki' (Fim)	ERCP
§	'Dark Side Of The Sun' PBR (Sin)	LRHS SPoG
	'Dark Spirit' (D)	CSpe ECtt SGbt
	'Dark Stranger' (C)	CWGr
	'Darlington Diamond' (S-c)	CWGr
	'Darlington Jubilation' (S-c)	CWGr
	'Davenport Anita' (D)	CWGr
	'Davenport Honey' (D)	CWGr
	'Davenport Lesley' (D)	CWGr
	'Davenport Sunlight' (S-c)	CWGr
	'Dave's Snip' (D)	CWGr
	'David Digweed' (D)	CWGr NHal SGbt
	'David Howard' (D) ♀H3	CHVG CWGr ECtt ELan EPfP ERCP EUJe EWoo LAyl LCro LHop LOPS LRHS NBri NHal NJRG SDix SGbt SPer SWvt WBrk WCot WFar
	'David's Choice' (D)	CWGr
	'Dawn Chorus' (D)	CWGr
	'Dawn Sky' (D)	LAyl
	'Dazzler' (D/DwB) **new**	CWGr
	'Deborah's Kiwi' (C)	CWGr NHal SGbt
	'Debra Anne Craven' (S-c)	CWGr NHal
	'Decorette' (D/DwB)	CWGr SGbt
	'Deepest Yellow' (Ba)	CWGr SDeJ SGbt
	'Demi Schneider' (Col)	CWGr
	'Dentelle de Venise' (C)	CWGr
	'Deuil du Roi Albert' (D)	CWGr
	'Deutschland' (D)	CWGr
	'Devon Elegance' (S-c)	CWGr
	'Devon Joy' (D)	CWGr
	'Devon Temptation' (C)	CWGr
	'Diamond Rose' (Anem/DwB)	CWGr
	'Diamond Wedding' (D)	SGbt
	'Diamond Years' (D)	SGbt
	'Diana Gregory' (Pom)	CWGr SGbt
	'Dick Westfall' (S-c)	CWGr
	'Dikara Jodie' (D)	NHal
	'Dikara Moon' (D)	NHal
	'Dikara Superb' (D)	CWGr NHal
	'Dilys Ayling' (Col)	NHal
	'Dinah Shore' (S-c)	CWGr
I	'Disneyland' (Col)	SGbt
	dissecta	CFil CWGr EBee
	'Diva US' (D) **new**	ERCP
	'Doc van Horn' (S-c)	CWGr
	'Doctor John Grainger' (D)	LRHS SSal
	'Doktor Hans Ricken' (D)	CWGr
	'Don Hill' (Col) ♀H3	CWGr NJRG
	'Doris Bacon' (Ba)	CWGr
	'Doris Day' (C)	CWGr NHal SGbt
	'Doris Rollins' (C)	CWGr
	'Dorothy Rose' (D) **new**	NHal
	'Dottie D.' (Ba)	CWGr
	'Double Dream Fantasy' (Dreamy Series) (Misc)	CRos EPfP LRHS NRHS

'Dovegrove' (Sin) Y^{H3}	CWGr
'Downham Royal' (Ba)	CWGr ERCP LCro LOPS
'Dr Caroline Rabbit' (D)	CWGr SGbt
Dracula = 'Vdtg17'^{PBR} (Dark Angel Series) (Sin)	CRos ERCP LRHS NRHS
Dragon Ball = 'Vdtg31'^{PBR} (Dark Angel Series) (Sin)	SDeJ WHil
'Dream Fantasy' (Dream Series) (Misc)	ELan LRHS
'Dream Seeker' (Col)	CWGr
(Dreamy Series) 'Dreamy Eyes' (Misc)	CWGr
- 'Dreamy Fantasy' (Misc)	CWGr
- 'Dreamy Fusion' (Sin)	CWGr LRHS
- Dreamy Inspire (Misc)	NLar
- 'Dreamy Kiss' (P) **new**	LRHS NRHS
- 'Dreamy Lips' (P) **new**	CWGr LRHS NRHS SHil
- 'Dreamy Nights' (Misc)	CRos CWGr LRHS NPri NRHS
- 'Dreamy Passion' (Sin)	LRHS SHil
'Drummer Boy' (D)	CWGr
'Duddon Grace' (WL)	NHal
'Duet' (D)	CSut CWGr ECtt ELan NBri SGbt
'Dusky Harmony' (WL)	CWGr SGbt
'Dutch Boy' (D)	CWGr
'Dutch Explosion' (S-c)	ELan
'Dutch Triumph' (D)	CWGr
'Earl Haig' (D)	CWGr
'Earl Marc' (C)	CWGr
'Early Bird' (D)	CWGr
'Early Harvest' (D)	SGbt
'Easter Sunday' (Col)	CWGr
'Eastwood Moonlight' (S-c)	CWGr NHal SGbt
'Eastwood Star' (S-c)	CWGr
'Ebbw Vale Festival' (D)	CWGr
'Edge of Gold' (D)	CWGr
'Edge of Joy' (D)	EPfP LCro LOPS
'Edgeway Joyce' (Ba)	CWGr
'Edinburgh' (D)	CWGr ERCP GWyn NBri NHal SDeJ SGbt
'Edith Jones' (Col)	CWGr NJRG
'Edith Mueller' (Pom)	CWGr
'Edmund' (Sin) **new**	WCot
'Edna C' (D)	CWGr
'Edwin's Sunset' (WL) Y^{H3}	NHal
'Eileen Denny' (S-c)	CWGr
'El Cid' (D)	CWGr
'El Paso' (D)	CWGr
'Elaine Huston' (S-c)	NJRG
'Eldon Wilson' (Misc)	CWGr
'Elga-Bergerhoff' (C)	ERCP LRHS
'Elgico Leanne' (C)	CWGr SGbt
'Elizabeth Snowden' (Col)	NJRG
'Ella Britton' (D)	LRHS
'Ellen Huston' (Misc/DwB) Y^{H3}	CWGr ECtt ERCP NHal SGbt
'Elma E' (D)	CWGr ERCP NHal
'Elmbrook Chieftain' (D)	CWGr
'Elmbrook Rebel' (S-c)	CWGr
I 'Embrace' (C)	NHal NJRG
'Emma's Coronet' (D)	CWGr
'Emmie Lou' (D)	CWGr
'Emory Paul' (D)	CWGr ERCP
'Emperor' (D)	CWGr
I 'Encore' (Fim) **new**	CWGr ERCP
'Engadin' (D)	CWGr
'Engelhardt's Matador' (D)	ECtt ERCP EUJe LRHS MCot MHol NJRG SGbt WCot
'England's Glory' (D)	SPer
'Enid Adams' (D)	CWGr
'Epping Forest' (D)	CWGr
'Eric's Choice' (D)	CWGr
'Ernie Pitt' (D)	CWGr
'Esau' (D)	CWGr
'Essex Chronicle' (D) **new**	CWGr
'Etheral' (Sin)	CAvo CWGr
'Eunice Arrigo' (S-c)	CWGr
'Eveline' (D)	CAby CWGr ERCP LCro LOPS SGbt
'Evelyn Foster' (D)	CWGr
'Evelyn Rumbold' (D)	CWGr SGbt
'Evelyn Taylor' (S-c)	NJRG
'Evening Lady' (D)	CWGr
I 'Evita' (Anem)	NJRG
excelsa (B)	CHII
- B&SWJ 10238	WCru
- 'Penelope Sky' (Sin)	SSal WCru
'Excentrique' (Misc)	CWGr ECtt ERCP NJRG
'Exotic Dwarf' (Sin/Lil) Y^{H3}	ECtt NHal NJRG
'Explosion' (S-c)	CWGr
'Extase' (S-c)	CWGr
'Eye Candy' (Sin)	LRHS NJRG
'Eyed Beauty' (Anem) **new**	EPfP
'Fabula' (Col)	CWGr
'Fairfield Frost' (Col)	NHal
'Fairway Pilot' (D)	CWGr
'Fairway Spur' (D)	CWGr NHal
'Fairy Queen' (C)	CWGr SGbt
§ 'Famoso' (Col)	CAby ERCP
'Fantastico' (Col)	CWGr ERCP WBor
'Fascination' (P) Y^{H3}	CAby CBcs CBod CRos CWGr ECGP ECtt ERCP LAyl LRHS MCot NJRG NLar NRHS SDeJ SGbt WHoo
'Fascination Aus' (Col)	CWGr
'Fashion Monger' (Col)	CWGr ECtt ERCP NHal NJRG SGbt
'Fata Morgana' (Anem)	CWGr NJRG SGbt
'Fay Dyer' (Col) **new**	NJRG
'Fern Irene' (WL)	CWGr
'Ferncliff Illusion' (D)	CWGr ERCP SGbt
'Ferncliff Inspiration' (S-c) **new**	ERCP
'Fernhill Champion' (D)	CWGr
'Fernhill Surprise' (D)	CWGr
'Festivo' (Col)	CWGr
'Feu Céleste' (Col)	CWGr
'Fidalgo Blacky' (D)	CWGr
'Fidalgo Bounce' (D)	CWGr
'Fidalgo Climax' (Fim)	CWGr
'Fidalgo Magic' (D)	CWGr
'Fidalgo Snowman' (S-c)	CWGr
'Fidalgo Splash' (D)	CWGr
'Fidalgo Supreme' (D)	CWGr LAyl
I 'Fiesta' (Pom)	SDeJ
Figaro Series (Misc/DwB)	NPri
'Figurine' (WL) Y^{H3}	NJRG
'Fille du Diable' (S-c)	CWGr SGbt
'Finchcocks' (WL) Y^{H3}	CWGr LAyl
'Fiona Stewart' (Ba)	CWGr
'Fire and Ice' (Misc)	CWGr WBor
'Fire Magic' (S-c)	CWGr
'Fire Mountain' (D)	CWGr LAyl NHal NJRG SSal
'Firebird' (Sin)	CWGr
'Firebird' (S-c)	see *D.* 'Vuurvogel'
'Firebrand' ambig. (S-c)	CWGr SGbt
'Firepot' ambig. (WL)	ERCP SGbt
'First Lady' (D)	CWGr
'Flavien' (D) **new**	ERCP
'Fleur'	see *D.* 'Fleurel'
'Fleur Mountjoy' (Col)	CWGr
§ 'Fleurel'^{PBR} (Fim)	ERCP SDeJ SPer
'Floorinoor' (Anem)	ERCP GWyn SGbt
'Florence Vernon' (Ba)	CWGr

	'Flutterby' (WL)	CWGr
	foeniculifolia	CFil
	'Fontmell Kaz' (Col)	NJRG SGbt
	'Formby Art' (D)	NHal
	'Formby Supreme' (D)	CWGr SGbt
	'Forrestal' (S-c)	CWGr
	'Fortuna' (Col/DwB)	CWGr ERCP
	'Frank Holmes' (Pom)	CWGr NHal
	'Frank Hornsey' (D)	CWGr
	'Frank Lovell' (S-c)	CWGr
	'Franz Kafka' (Pom)	CAvo CWGr ERCP NHal NJRG SDeJ SSal
	'Fred Wallace' (C)	CWGr
	'Freelancer' (C)	CWGr SGbt
	'Freestyle' (C)	CWGr NJRG
§	'Freya's Paso Doble' (Anem) ♀H3	CWGr LAyl NJRG SGbt WCot
	'Freya's Thalia' (Sin/Lil)	CWGr
	'Friendship' (C)	CWGr
	'Frigoulet' (C)	CWGr ERCP SGbt
	'Fringed Star' (S-c)	NBri
	'Funfair' (D)	CWGr
	'Funny Face' (Misc)	CWGr
	'Furswood Park' (Pom)	NJRG
	'Fusion' (D) ♀H3	CWGr SGbt SHar WCot
	'G.F. Hemerik' (Sin)	CWGr
	'G.I. Joe' (D)	SGbt
	'Gala Parade' (D)	CWGr
	'Gale Lane' (Pom)	CWGr
	(Gallery Series) 'Gallery Art Deco'PBR (D) ♀H3	CWGr ERCP LRHS NHal NNys SGbt SHil
	- 'Gallery Art Fair'PBR (D) ♀H3	CWGr ERCP LRHS NHal NNys SDeJ SHil
	- 'Gallery Art Nouveau'PBR (D) ♀H3	CWGr ERCP LRHS NHal NNys SHil
	- 'Gallery Bellini'PBR (D)	LRHS SDeJ SHil
	- 'Gallery Cézanne'PBR (D)	CWGr LRHS NRHS SGbt
	- 'Gallery Cobra'PBR (D)	ERCP
	- 'Gallery La Tour'PBR (D) ♀H3	SDeJ
	- 'Gallery Leonardo'PBR (D) ♀H3	CWGr SDeJ
	- 'Gallery Matisse'PBR (D)	LRHS
	- 'Gallery Monet'PBR (D)	CWGr
	- 'Gallery Pablo'PBR (D) ♀H3	CWGr LRHS SGbt SHil
	- 'Gallery Pinto'PBR (D)	CWGr LRHS SHil
	- 'Gallery Rembrandt'PBR (D) ♀H3	CWGr
	- 'Gallery Renoir'PBR (D) ♀H3	CWGr LRHS SHil
	- 'Gallery Rivera'PBR (D)	LRHS NRHS SDeJ SHil
	- 'Gallery Salvador'PBR (D)	ERCP SGbt
	- 'Gallery Serenade'PBR (D)	ERCP
	- 'Gallery Singer'PBR (D)	CWGr
	- 'Gallery Valentin'PBR (D)	LRHS
	- 'Gallery Vermeer'PBR (D)	CWGr SGbt
	- 'Gallery Vincent'PBR (D) ♀H3	CWGr
	'Garden Festival' (WL)	CWGr ERCP
	'Garden Party' (C) ♀H3	LAyl
	'Garden Princess' (C/DwB)	CWGr SGbt
	'Garden Wonder' (D)	CWGr NBri SDeJ SPer
	'Gargantuan' (S-c)	CWGr
	Gateshead Festival	see *D.* 'Peach Melba'
	'Gaudy' (D)	CWGr
	'Gay Mini' (D)	CWGr
	'Gay Princess' (WL)	CWGr
	'Gay Triumph' (S-c)	CWGr
	'Geerlings Babette' (Ba)	ERCP
	'Geerlings Beatrice' (Ba)	CWGr
	'Geerlings Cupido' (WL)	CWGr SGbt
	'Geerlings Indian Summer' (S-c)	CWGr NHal
	'Geerlings Moonlight' (D)	CWGr
§	'Geerlings Sorbet' (S-c)	CAby NHal SGbt
	'Geerlings Yellow' (S-c)	CWGr
	'Gelber Vulkan' (S-c)	SGbt
	'Gemma Darling' (D)	CWGr
	'Gemma's Place' (Pom)	CWGr
	'Genova' (Ba)	CAvo EPfP ERCP SGbt SPer
	'Gentle Giant' (D)	CWGr
	'Gerald Grace' (S-c)	CWGr
	'Gerlos' (D)	CWGr
	'Gerrie Hoek' (WL)	CWGr ECtt ERCP EWoo NBri SDeJ SGbt
	'Gilt Edge' (D)	CWGr
	'Gilwood Terry G' (C)	NHal
	'Gina Lombaert' (S-c)	CWGr SEND
	'Ginger Willo' (Pom)	CWGr
	'Gipsy Boy' (D)	CWGr LAyl
	'Gipsy Night' (Ba)	ERCP SDeJ
	'Giraffe' (DblO)	CAby CWGr ERCP SGbt
	'Gitty' (Ba)	CWGr
	'Glad Huston' (S-c/DwB)	CWGr
	'Glen Afton' (Pom)	CWGr
	'Glen Gharry' (Col)	CWGr
	'Glenbank Paleface' (Pom)	CWGr
	'Glenbank Twinkle' (C)	CWGr
	'Globular' (Ba)	CWGr
	'Glorie van Heemstede' (WL) ♀H3	CWGr ERCP LAyl NHal NJRG SDeJ SEND SGbt
	'Glorie van Naardwijk' (D)	CWGr
	'Glorie van Noordwijk' (S-c)	ERCP SDeJ SGbt SSal
	'Glow Orange' (Ba)	CWGr
	'Go American' (D)	CWGr NHal
	'Gold Crown' (S-c)	SDeJ
	'Goldean' (D)	CWGr
I	'Golden Emblem' (D)	CWGr ECtt NBri SDeJ
	'Golden Fizz' (Ba)	CWGr
	'Golden Glitter' (S-c)	CWGr
	'Golden Heart' (S-c)	CWGr
	'Golden Horn' (S-c)	CWGr
	'Golden Impact' (S-c)	CWGr
	'Golden Scepter' (D)	CWGr ERCP SDeJ SGbt
	'Golden Symbol' (S-c)	CWGr
	'Golden Torch' (D)	NBri
	'Golden Turban' (D)	CWGr
	'Goldfield' (D)	CWGr
	'Goldie Gull' (Anem)	NJRG
	'Goldorange' (S-c)	CWGr
	'Good Earth' (C)	CWGr SDeJ SSal
I	'Good Hope' (D)	CWGr
	'Good Intent' (Ba)	CWGr
	'Goshen Beauty' (WL)	CWGr
	'Goya's Venus' (S-c)	CWGr
	'Grace Rushton' (WL)	CWGr
	'Gracie S' (C)	CWGr NHal NJRG
	'Gramma's Lemon Pie' (D) **new**	CWGr
	'Grand Duc' (Col)	CWGr
	'Grand Prix' (D)	CWGr ERCP SDeJ SGbt
	'Grand Willo' (Pom)	CWGr
	'Grenadier' (D) ♀H3	CWGr ECtt ERCP EWoo LRHS NJRG NLar SDix SGbt WCot
	'Grenidor Pastelle' (S-c)	CWGr NHal NJRG
	'Gretchen Heine' (D)	CWGr
	'Grock' (Pom)	CWGr
	'Gunyuu' (D)	CWGr

'Gurtla Twilight' (Pom)	CWGr NHal NJRG
'Gute Laune' (C)	CWGr
'Gwyneth' (WL)	NHal NJRG
'Gypsy Girl' (D)	CWGr SGbt
'Hadrian's Sunlight' (Sin)	NHal SSal
'Hallmark' (Pom)	CWGr GWyn NJRG
'Hallwood Coppernob' (D)	CWGr
'Hallwood Satin' (D)	CWGr
'Hallwood Tiptop' (D)	CWGr
'Hamari Accord' (S-c) ♀H3	CWGr LAyl
'Hamari Bride' (S-c) ♀H3	CWGr
'Hamari Girl' (D)	CWGr NHal SGbt SSal
'Hamari Gold' (D) ♀H3	CWGr NHal SGbt
'Hamari Katrina' (S-c)	CWGr
'Hamari Rosé' (Ba) ♀H3	CWGr NHal SGbt
'Hamari Sunshine' (D)	NHal SGbt
'Hamilton Amanda' (D)	CWGr
'Hamilton Lillian' (D) ♀H3	CWGr
'Hans Ricken' (D)	CWGr
* 'Happy Birthday' (S-c)	CWGr
'Happy Caroline' (D)	CWGr
Happy Days Cream = 'Hdw79'PBR (Sin)	LRHS
Happy Days Purple = 'Hdpu165'PBR (Sin) **new**	ERCP
'Happy Halloween' (D)	CWGr
(Happy Single Series)	CWGr ERCP LRHS SDeJ
Happy Single Date = 'HS Date'PBR (Sin)	
- Happy Single First Love = 'HS First Love'PBR (Sin)	CWGr ERCP LRHS SDeJ
- Happy Single Flame = 'HS Flame'PBR (Sin) ♀H3	CAvo CWGr ERCP LRHS NRHS
- Happy Single Juliet = 'HS Juliet'PBR (Sin)	CWGr ERCP LRHS SDeJ
- Happy Single Kiss = 'HS Kiss'PBR (Sin)	CAvo CWGr LRHS
- Happy Single Party = 'HS Party'PBR (Sin)	CAvo CWGr NBri SDeJ
- Happy Single Princess = 'HS Princess'PBR (Sin) ♀H3	CWGr ERCP LRHS
- Happy Single Romeo = 'HS Romeo'PBR (Sin)	CWGr LRHS SDeJ
- Happy Single Wink = 'HS Wink'PBR (Sin) ♀H3	CWGr ERCP IBoy LCro LOPS LRHS LSou NPri SDeJ
'Haresbrook' (Sin)	NGdn SHar
'Harriet G' (WL)	NHal NJRG
'Harvest' (Fim)	CWGr
§ 'Harvest Samantha' (Sin/Lil) ♀H3	CWGr NHal
'Haseley Bridal Wish' (Fim)	CWGr
'Haseley Goldicote' (D)	CWGr
'Haseley Triumph' (D)	CWGr
'Hawai'PBR	CWGr
'Hawaiian Dreams' (Sin) **new**	CWGr IBoy LRHS
'Hayley Jayne' (C)	CWGr ERCP NBri NJRG SGbt
'Heather Huston' (D)	CWGr
'Heather Jean' (Col)	NJRG
'Heather Linford' (Fim) **new**	NHal
'Helma Rost' (S-c)	CWGr
'Henri Lewi' (S-c)	CWGr
'Henriette' (C)	CWGr
'Herbert Smith' (S-c)	CWGr
'Hexton Copper' (Ba)	CWGr SGbt
'Hi Ace' (C)	CWGr
'Highgate Bobby' (Ba)	CWGr

'Highgate Torch' (S-c)	CWGr
'Highness' (S-c)	CWGr
'Hilda Clare' (Col)	CWGr
'Hildepuppe' (Pom)	CWGr
'Hillcrest Albino' (S-c)	CWGr
'Hillcrest Amour' (D)	CWGr SGbt
'Hillcrest Bobbin' (Ba)	CWGr
'Hillcrest Camelot' (S-c)	CWGr
'Hillcrest Candy' (S-c) ♀H3	CWGr NHal NJRG SGbt
'Hillcrest Carmen' (D)	CWGr
'Hillcrest Cheryl' (SinO)	NHal
'Hillcrest Contessa' (Ba)	CWGr
'Hillcrest Delight' (D)	NHal SGbt
'Hillcrest Duncan Edwards' (S-c) **new**	NHal
'Hillcrest Fiesta' (S-c)	CWGr
'Hillcrest Heights' (S-c)	CWGr
'Hillcrest Jake' (S-c)	NHal
'Hillcrest Kismet' (D)	LAyl NHal NJRG
'Hillcrest Pearl' (D)	CWGr
'Hillcrest Regal' (Col) ♀H3	CWGr SGbt
'Hillcrest Royal' (C) ♀H3	CWGr LAyl NHal SDix SGbt
'Hillcrest Suffusion' (D)	CWGr NJRG
'Hillcrest Ultra' (D)	CWGr
'Hill's Delight' (S-c)	CWGr
'Hindu Star' (Ba)	CWGr
hjertingii	CWGr
'Hockley Maroon' (D)	CWGr
'Hockley Nymph' (WL)	CWGr
'Holbrook Amber' **new**	CSam
'Holbrook Lilac' **new**	CSam
'Holbrook Magenta' **new**	CSam
'Holland Festival' (D)	CWGr SGbt
'Hollyhill Big Pink' (S-c)	SGbt
'Home Run' (Sin)	CWGr
'Homer T' (S-c)	CWGr
'Honest John' (C)	CWGr
'Honey' (Anem/DwB)	CWGr
'Honeymoon Dress' (D)	CWGr
'Honeypot' (Ba)	SGbt
'Honka' (SinO) ♀H3	CBod CWGr ECtt ERCP LAyl LCro LOPS LRHS NHal NJRG NSti SDeJ WCot
'Honka Fragile' (SinO)	CAby ERCP
'Honka Orange' (SinO)	ERCP NJRG
'Honka Pink Edge' (SinO)	NJRG
'Honka Red' (SinO)	CAby CWGr ERCP LCro LOPS SSal
'Honka Rose' (SinO)	ERCP NJRG
'Honka Surprise' (SinO)	CAby CWGr EBee ECtt ERCP EUJe NJRG SDeJ WBrk WCot
'Honka White' (SinO)	CAby CWGr ERCP
'Honor Francis' (Misc)	WCot
I 'Hootenanny' (Col)	NHal NJRG
'Hot Chocolate' (D)	CWGr NJRG SGbt
'Hugh Mather' (WL)	CWGr
'Hulin's Carnival' (D)	CWGr
'Hy Clown' (D)	CWGr
'Hy Fire' (Ba)	CWGr
'Ian Hislop' (Sin)	CWGr
'Ice Crystal' (Fim)	ERCP
'Ice Cube' (D)	ERCP SDeJ
'Ice Queen' (WL)	CWGr
'Ike' (Fim) **new**	CWGr
imperialis (B)	CDTJ CHll CWGr EBee EWes LEdu LRHS SBig SChr SDix SGbt
- B&SWJ 8997	WCru
- 'Alba' (B)	CWGr SSal
- pink double-flowered (B)	CFil
aff. ***imperialis***	CWGr SDir XLum
'Impression Famosa'	see *D.* 'Famoso'

'Inca' (Anem)	IBoy
'Inca Dambuster' (S-c)	CWGr NHal SGbt
'Inca Glamour' (D)	CWGr
'Inca Matchless' (D)	CWGr
'Inca Metropolitan' (D)	CWGr
'Inca Panorama' (D)	CWGr
'Inca Spectrum' (S-c)	CWGr
'Inca Vanguard' (D)	CWGr
'Inca Vulcan' (S-c)	CWGr
'Independence' (D)	SGbt
'Inglebrook Jill' (Col)	CWGr
'Inland Dynasty' (S-c)	CWGr
'Inn's Gerrie Hoek' (D)	CWGr
'Iola' (D)	CWGr
'Irene van der Zwet' (Sin)	CWGr
'Iris' (Pom)	CWGr GWyn
'Islander' (D)	CWGr ERCP
'Ivanetti' (Ba)	CWGr NHal SGbt
'Ivy Della' (D)	CWGr
'J.R.G.' (Misc) 🏆H3	NJRG
'Jack Hood' (D)	CWGr SGbt
'Jack O'Lantern' (Col)	CWGr
'Jackie Magson' (S-c)	CWGr
'Jacqueline Tivey' (D)	CWGr
'Jaldec Jerry' (S-c)	CWGr
'Jaldec Joker' (C)	CWGr
'Jamaica' (WL)	CWGr SGbt
'Jamie' (S-c)	CWGr
'Jan Lennon' (S-c)	CWGr
'Jan van Schaffelaar' (Pom)	ERCP SDeJ
'Janal Amy' (S-c)	CWGr NHal SGbt
'Jane Cowl' (D)	CWGr
'Jane Horton' (Col)	CWGr SGbt
'Janet Beckett' (C)	CWGr
'Japanese Waterlily' (WL)	CWGr
'Jayne Warton' (S-c) **new**	NHal
'Jazzy' (Col)	CWGr
'Je Maintiendrai' (D)	CWGr
'Jean Fairs' (WL) 🏆H3	CWGr SGbt
'Jean Marie'PBR (D)	CWGr ERCP
'Jean Melville' (D)	CWGr
'Jean Shaw' (D)	NHal
'Jeanne d'Arc' (C)	CWGr EPfP
'Jeannie Leroux' (Fim)	CWGr
'Jean's Carol' (Pom)	CWGr
I 'Jennie' (Fim)	CWGr
§ 'Jenny' (Dahlietta Select Series) (Misc)	SGbt
'Jersey Beauty' (D)	CWGr
'Jescot Buttercup' (D)	CWGr
'Jescot India' (D)	CWGr
'Jescot Jess' (D)	CWGr
'Jescot Jim' (D)	CWGr
'Jescot Julie' (DblO)	CWGr ERCP LAyl LCro LOPS NNys
'Jescot Lingold' (D)	CWGr SGbt
'Jescot Redun' (D)	CWGr
'Jessica' (S-c)	CWGr
'Jessie G' (Ba)	CWGr NJRG
'Jessie Ross' (D/DwB)	CWGr
'Jill Day' (C)	CWGr
'Jill Doc' (D)	CWGr
'Jill's Delight' (D)	CWGr
'Jim Branigan' (S-c)	CWGr NHal
'Jive' (Anem)	ELan ERCP SDeJ
'Jo Anne' (S-c)	CWGr
'Joanne Taylor' (WL)	NJRG
'Jocondo' (D)	CWGr NHal SGbt
'Jodie Wilkinson' (Ba)	NHal
'Joe Swift' (Sin)	CWGr
'Johann' (Pom)	CWGr NHal SSal

'John Butterworth' (D)	CWGr
'John Hill' (D)	NHal SSal
'John Prior' (D)	CWGr
'John Street' (WL)	CWGr
'John's Champion' (D)	CWGr
'Jomanda' (Ba) 🏆H3	CWGr NHal NJRG SGbt
'Jo's Choice' (D)	CWGr
'Josie Gott' (Ba) 🏆H3	NJRG SGbt
'Jowey Winnie' (Ba) **new**	ERCP
'Joy Donaldson' (C)	CWGr
'Joyce Green' (S-c)	CWGr SGbt
'Joyce Margaret Cunliffe' (D)	CWGr
'Juanita' (S-c)	CWGr
'Jules Dyson' (Misc)	SDys
'Julie One' (DblO)	CWGr SGbt
'Julie's Delight' (S-c)	CWGr
'Julio' (Ba)	CWGr
'Jura' (S-c)	CWGr EPfP
'Juul's Allstar' (SinO) 🏆H3	CWGr
'Kaftan' (D)	CWGr
'Kaga-komachi' (D) **new**	LRHS
'Kaiser Wilhelm' (Ba)	CWGr
'Kaiserwalzer' (Col)	CWGr
'Kaisha Lea' **new**	ERCP
'Karenglen' (D) 🏆H3	NHal NJRG SGbt
'Kari Quill' (C)	CWGr
'Karma Amanda'PBR (D)	CWGr WHlf
'Karma Bon Bini'PBR (C)	CAby SGbt
'Karma Choc'PBR (D) 🏆H3	CAby CAvo CSpe CWGr EBee EPfP ERCP EWes IBoy LCro LOPS LRHS MHol MSCN NNys SBod SEND SGbt SPer WBor WCot WFar WHoo
'Karma Corona'PBR (C)	CWGr SGbt
'Karma Fiesta'PBR (D)	ERCP
'Karma Fuchsiana' (D)	CWGr ERCP IBoy LCro LOPS SGbt
'Karma Irene'PBR (D)	CWGr ERCP
'Karma Lagoon'PBR (D)	CWGr ERCP LRHS SGbt WHlf
'Karma Maarten Zwaan'PBR (WL)	CWGr ERCP
'Karma Naomi'PBR (D)	ERCP SGbt
'Karma Pink Corona'PBR (C)	LCro LOPS
'Karma Prospero'PBR (D)	ERCP LCro LOPS WHlf
'Karma Red Corona'PBR (C)	SDeJ SGbt
'Karma Sangria'PBR (C)	CWGr SDeJ SGbt
'Karma Serena'PBR (D)	NNys SDeJ
'Karma Yin Yang' (D)	SGbt
'Karras 150' (S-c)	CWGr
'Kasasagi' (Pom)	CWGr
'Kate Mountjoy' (Col)	CWGr SGbt
'Kathryn's Cupid' (Ba)	CWGr
'Katie Dahl' (D)	NHal
'Katisha' (D)	CWGr
'Kayleigh Spiller' (Col)	SGbt
'Keith's Choice' (D)	CWGr NHal SGbt
'Keith's Pet' (Sin) 🏆H3	CWGr
'Kelsea Carla' (S-c) 🏆H3	CWGr
'Kelvin Floodlight' (D)	CWGr NBri SDeJ SGbt
'Kennemerland' (S-c)	EPfP SDeJ SGbt
'Kenora Canada' (S-c)	CWGr
'Kenora Challenger' (S-c)	CWGr NHal NJRG SGbt
'Kenora Christmas' (Ba)	CWGr
'Kenora Clyde' (S-c)	CWGr
'Kenora Frills' (Fim)	NHal
'Kenora Jubilee' (S-c)	GWyn SGbt
'Kenora Lisa' (D)	CWGr
'Kenora Macop-B' (Fim)	CWGr ERCP NHal
'Kenora Moonbeam' (D)	CWGr
'Kenora Ontario' (S-c)	CWGr
'Kenora Sunset' (S-c) 🏆H3	CWGr NHal SGbt
'Kenora Superb' (S-c)	CWGr SGbt

	'Kenora Valentine' (D) ♀H3	CWGr NHal SGbt
	'Kenora Wildfire' (D)	CWGr
	'Kenora Wow' (S-c)	NHal
	'Ken's Coral' (WL)	CWGr
	'Ken's Flame' (WL)	CWGr SGbt
	'Ken's Rarity' (WL)	NHal NJRG SGbt
	'Key West' (D)	CWGr
	'Kidd's Climax' (D) ♀H3	CWGr
	'Kiev' (Jumbo Collection) (D)	NBri
	'Kikoski' (C)	SGbt
	'Kilburn Fiesta' (S-c)	NHal
	'Kilburn Glow' (WL)	NHal
	'Kilburn Rose' (WL)	NJRG
	'Kilmorie' (S-c)	NHal
	'Kingston' (D)	CWGr SGbt
	'Kismet' (Ba)	CWGr
	'Kiss' (D)	CWGr
	'Kiss Me' (D)	EPfP
	'Kit Kat' (C)	CWGr
	'Kiwi Brother' (S-c)	CWGr
	'Kiwi Cousin' (C)	CWGr
	'Kiwi Gloria' (C)	CWGr NHal NJRG
	'Kiwi Sister' (S-c)	CWGr
	'Klondike' (S-c)	CWGr ERCP NJRG
	'Knock Out' (S-c)	CAby
I	'Knockout'PBR (Sin) ♀H3	CBcs CBod CChe CWGr EPfP ERCP LRHS LSRN LSou NBri SPoG
	'Kochelsee' (Ba)	CWGr
	'Kogane Fubuki' (Fim)	CWGr
	'Kotare Jackpot' (S-c)	CWGr
	'Kung Fu' (D)	CWGr
	'Kym Willo' (Pom)	CWGr
I	'Kyoto' (WL)	CWGr SGbt
	'L.A.T.E.' (Ba)	CWGr NHal NJRG SGbt
	'La Cierva' (Col)	CWGr
	'La Gioconda' (Col)	CWGr
	'La Recoleta' (D)	CWGr ERCP
	'Labyrinth' (D) **new**	ERCP
	'Lady Darlene' (D) **new**	CWGr ERCP
	'Lady Kerkrade' (C)	CWGr
	'Lady Liberty' (D)	ERCP
	'Lady Linda' (D)	CWGr NHal SGbt
	'Lady Orpah' (D)	CWGr
	'Lady Sunshine' (S-c)	CWGr
	'Lakeland Polly' (Pom)	CWGr NHal NJRG
	'Lambada' (Anem)	ELan ERCP
	'L'Ancresse' (Ba)	LAyl NHal NJRG
	'Larkford' (D)	CWGr
	'Last Dance' (D)	CWGr
	'Laura's Choice' (D)	CWGr
	'Lauren Kitchener' (Misc)	NJRG
	'Lavendale' (D)	CWGr
	'Lavender Chiffon' (S-c)	CWGr
	'Lavender Freestyle' (C)	CWGr
	'Lavender Leycett' (D)	CWGr
	'Lavender Line' (S-c)	NHal
	'Lavender Nunton Harvest' (D)	CWGr
	'Lavender Perfection' (D)	CWGr
	'Lavengro' (D)	CWGr
	'Le Baron' (D)	CSut ERCP
	'Le Castel' (WL) ♀H3	CWGr SDeJ
	'Le Feu du Soleil' (Fim) **new**	NHal
	'Le Patineur' (D)	CWGr
	'Le Vonné Splinter' (S-c)	CWGr
	'Leander' (S-c)	CWGr
§	'Lemon Cane' (D)	CWGr
	'Lemon Elegans' (S-c) ♀H3	CWGr NHal
	'Lemon Meringue' (D)	CWGr ECtt SGbt
	'Lemon Puff' (Anem)	CWGr
	'Lemon Symbol' (S-c)	CWGr
	'Lemon Zing' (Ba)	LAyl NHal SGbt
	'Leopold Chloe' (D)	NHal
	'Leopold Sophie' (D) **new**	CWGr
	'Lexington' (Pom)	CWGr
	'Leycett' (D)	CWGr
	'Libretto' (Col)	CWGr
	'Life Force' (D)	CWGr SGbt
	'Life Style' (Anem)	GWyn
	'Light Music' (S-c)	CWGr
	'Lilac Athalie' (C)	CWGr
	'Lilac Bull' (D)	LRHS
	'Lilac Marston' (D) ♀H3	NHal
	'Lilac Shadow' (S-c)	CWGr
	'Lilac Taratahi' (C) ♀H3	CSam CWGr
I	'Lilac Time' (D)	CWGr ERCP NBri SDeJ SGbt
	'Lilac Willo' (Pom)	CWGr
	'Lilianna W' (Sin/Dw.B.)	NJRG
	'Linda's Baby' (Ba)	SPer
	'Linda's Chester' (C)	CWGr
	'Linda's Diane' (D)	CWGr
	'Linda's Polly' (Pom) **new**	NJRG
	'Lismore Carol' (Pom)	CWGr GWyn NHal
	'Lismore Moonlight' (Pom)	CWGr NHal
	'Lismore Robin' (D)	NHal
	'Lismore Sunset' (Pom)	CWGr SGbt
	'Lismore Willie' (WL) ♀H3	CWGr NJRG
	'Little Dorrit' (Sin/Lil)	CWGr NJRG
	'Little Fawn' (S-c)	CWGr
	'Little Lamb' (S-c)	CWGr
	'Little Laura' (Ba)	CWGr
	'Little Matthew' (Pom)	CWGr SGbt
	'Little Reggie' (S-c)	CWGr
	'Little Robert' (D)	CAvo CWGr ERCP NBri SGbt
	'Little Sally' (Pom)	CWGr SGbt
	'Little Scottie' (Pom)	CWGr
	'Little Shona' (D)	CWGr
	'Little Snowdrop' (Pom)	CWGr SGbt
	'Little Tiger' (D)	CWGr
	'Little Willem' (Pom)	SGbt
	'Lloyd Huston' (S-c)	CWGr
	'Lois Walcher' (D)	CWGr
	'Lololove' (Sin)	SPer
	'Lorona Dawn' (SinO)	ERCP LAyl NJRG
	'Loud Applause' (C)	CWGr
	'Louie Meggos' (D) **new**	NHal
	'Louis V' (Fim)	SGbt
*	'Louis Walchen' (D)	CWGr
	'Louise Bailey' (D)	CWGr
	'Louise'PBR (Dahlietta Surprise Series) (D/DwB) **new**	CWGr
	lovatii **new**	CWGr
	'Lovelife'PBR **new**	ERCP
	'Lucky Devil' (WL)	CWGr
	'Lucky Number' (D)	CWGr ERCP
	'Ludwig Helfert' (S-c)	CWGr SEND
	'Luka Johanna' (WL)	ERCP
	'Lupin Dixie' (C)	CWGr
	'Lyn Mayo' (D)	CWGr
	'Mabel Ann' (D)	CWGr LAyl
	'Madaline Ann' (D)	CWGr
	'Madame Simone Stappers' (WL)	CWGr ECtt EUJe LAyl LRHS
	'Madame Vera' (D)	CWGr
	'Maddie Grace' (D) **new**	CWGr
	'Mafolie' (S-c)	CWGr
	'Magenta Magenta' (D)	LAyl SGbt
	'Magenta Magic' (Sin/DwB)	NHal
	'Magenta Star' (Sin) ♀H3	CAvo CWGr SGbt
I	'Magic Moment' (S-c)	CWGr

'Magnificat' (D)	CWGr
'Maiko Girl' (DblO) ♀H3 **new**	LAyl
'Maisie' (D)	CWGr
'Maisie Mooney' (D)	CWGr
'Majestic Kerkrade' (C)	CWGr
'Majjas Symbol' (S-c)	CWGr
'Maldiva' (D)	ERCP
'Malham Portia' (WL)	CWGr
'Maltby Fanfare' (Col)	CWGr
I 'Mambo' (Anem)	SDeJ
'Manhattan Island' (D)	CWGr ERCP NBri
'Marble Ball' (D)	CWGr EPfP ERCP SDeJ SGbt
'March Magic' (D)	CWGr
'Margaret Anne' (D)	CWGr
'Margaret Brookes' (D)	CWGr
'Marie' (D)	CWGr
'Marie Schnugg' (SinO) ♀H3	CWGr NJRG SGbt
'Mariposa' (Col)	CWGr
'Mark Damp' (S-c)	CWGr
'Mark Hardwick' (D)	CWGr
'Mark Lockwood' (Pom)	CWGr
'Market Joy' (S-c)	CWGr
'Marla Lu' (C)	CWGr
'Marlene Joy' (Fim)	CWGr SGbt
I 'Mars' (Col)	CWGr NJRG SGbt
'Marshmallow Sky' (Col)	CWGr
'Marston George' (Ba)	CWGr NHal
'Marston Suzanne' (D) **new**	NHal
'Martin's Yellow' (Pom)	NHal
I 'Mary Eveline' (Col)	ECtt NHal
'Mary Evelyn' (C)	ERCP SGbt
'Mary Layton' (Col)	CWGr
'Mary Lunns' (Pom)	CWGr
'Mary Partridge' (WL)	CWGr
'Mary Pitt' (D)	CWGr SGbt
'Mary Richards' (D)	CWGr
'Mary's Jomanda' (Ba) ♀H3	CWGr GWyn NHal NJRG SGbt
'Mascot Maya' (D)	NJRG
'Master Michael' (Pom)	CWGr
'Match' (S-c)	CWGr
'Matchless' (C)	CWGr
'Matilda Huston' (S-c)	CWGr LAyl NHal
'Matt Armour' (Sin)	CWGr
'Maureen Hardwick' (D)	CWGr SGbt
'Maureen Jones' (Col)	NJRG
'Maxime' (D)	ERCP
'Maxine Bailey' (D)	CWGr
'Mayan Pearl' (DblO) ♀H3	CWGr LAyl NHal SGbt
'Mayan Swan' (S-c)	SGbt
'Mediterranee' (D)	ERCP
'Megan Dean' (Ba)	NHal
'Meiro' (D)	CWGr
'Melanie Jane' (S-c)	CWGr
'Melody Allegro'PBR (D) **new**	ERCP
'Melody Bolero'PBR (D)	CWGr
'Melody Dixie'PBR (D)	CWGr ERCP
'Melody Dora'PBR (D)	CWGr
'Melody Fanfare'PBR (D)	LCro LOPS
'Melody Gipsy'PBR (S-c)	CWGr ERCP
'Melody Harmony'PBR (D) ♀H3	EPfP ERCP
'Melody Pink Allegro' (D) **new**	ERCP
'Melody Swing'PBR (D)	CWGr ERCP
'Mel's Orange Marmalade' (Fim)	LCro LOPS
'Melton' (D)	CWGr
merckii	CBot CFil CSpe CWGr EUJe EWes EWoo LRHS MCot MMrt MNrw MRav NSti SEND SHar SPtp SSal WBod
– 'Alba' (B)	CFil CSpe
– compact	CFil
– dark-leaved	WPGP
'Mero Star' (D)	SPer
'Mevrouw Clement Andries' (Fim)	ERCP
'Mexico Mogul' (D)	SGbt
'Miami' (D)	CWGr
'Michael J' (D)	CWGr
'Michigan' (D)	CWGr
'Mick' (C)	CWGr
'Mick's Peppermint' (S-c)	CAby CWGr SGbt
'Midas' (S-c)	CWGr
'Midnight' (Pom)	CWGr SGbt
'Midnight Star' (SinO)	NJRG
'Mies' (Sin)	CWGr LCro LOPS
'Mingus Alex' (S-c)	CWGr
'Mingus Gregory' (S-c)	CWGr ERCP
'Mingus Kyle D' (D)	CWGr
* 'Mingus Max'	ERCP
'Mingus Nichole' (D)	CWGr
'Mingus Randy' (S-c)	SPer SSal
'Mingus Toni' (D)	ERCP
'Mingus Tracy Lynn' (S-c)	CWGr
'Mini Red' (S-c)	CWGr
'Minley Carol' (Pom)	CWGr NHal
'Minley Iris' (Pom)	CWGr
'Miramar' (D)	CWGr
'Miss Blanc' (WL)	CWGr
'Miss Campbell' (Ba)	NJRG
'Miss Ellen' (Misc) ♀H3	CWGr
'Miss Rose Fletcher' (S-c)	CWGr
'Miss Swiss' (D)	CWGr
'Misterton' (D)	CWGr SGbt
'Mistill Beauty' (C)	CWGr
'Mistill Delight' (D)	CWGr
mollis	CFil
'Mom's Special' (D)	CWGr ERCP
'Monet Mystique' (WL)	SGbt
'Monet Sunlight' (WL)	SGbt
'Monk Marc' (C)	CWGr
'Monkstown Diane' (C)	CWGr
'Monrovia' (Ba)	CWGr
'Moonfire' (Misc/DwB) ♀H3	CAby CWCL CWGN CWGr ECtt ELan EPfP ERCP EUJe LAyl LRHS NHal NJRG SDix SGbt SPer WCot WHoo
'Moonglow' (S-c)	CWGr ERCP LRHS
'Moor Place' (Pom)	CWGr NHal NJRG SGbt
moorei	WPGP
'Moray Susan' (WL)	CWGr
'Moret' (S-c)	CWGr
'Morley Lady' (D)	CWGr
'Morning Dew' (WL)	CWGr
'Motto' (D)	CWGr
'Mount Noddy' (Sin)	CWGr
'Mrs A. Woods' (D)	CWGr
'Mrs Black' (Pom)	CWGr
'Mrs Eileen' (D)	ERCP SGbt
'Mrs H. Brown' (Col)	SGbt
'Mrs McDonald Quill' (D)	CWGr SGbt
'Mrs Silverston' (D)	CWGr
'Ms Kennedy' (Ba) **new**	NHal
'München' (D)	SDeJ SGbt
'Murdoch' ambig. (D)	ECtt EWoo LRHS MHol WCot
'Murillo' ambig. (Sin)	LAyl
'Murray May' (WL)	CWGr
'Murray Petite' (S-c)	CWGr
'Musette' (D)	CWGr SGbt
'My Irene' **new**	NJRG
'My Joy' (Pom)	CWGr

	'My Love' (S-c)	CWGr ERCP LCro LOPS NBri SEND SGbt
	'My Neddy' (D)	SGbt
	'Myama Fubuki' (Fim)	ELan ERCP
	'My-nute Blend' (Misc)	CWGr
	'Myrtle's Folly' (Fim)	ERCP
	'Mystery Day' (D)	CWGr
	Mystic Desire	see *D.* 'Scarlet Fern'
§	'Mystic Enchantment'PBR (Sin)	CAvo EBee IBoy LRHS LSou SPoG
	'Mystic Haze'	see *D.* 'Dark Side Of The Sun'
	Mystic Illusion	see *D.* 'Knockout' (Sin)
	Mystic Mars	see *D.* 'Scarlet Fern'
§	Mystic Spirit ='Hamspirit'PBR (Sin) **new**	LRHS
	'Nadia Ruth' (Fim) **new**	ERCP
	'Nagano' (D)	CWGr SDeJ
	'Nancy H' (Ba)	CWGr
	'Naples' (D)	EWoo
	'Nargold' (Fim)	CWGr LAyl
	'Natal' (Ba)	CAvo ECtt NBri SDeJ
	'Natalie G' (D)	EPfP NJRG
	'Nathalie's Wedding' (WL)	ERCP
	'Nationwide' (D)	CWGr
	'Neal Gillson' (D)	CWGr
	neglecta	CWGr
	'Nelly Geerlings' (Sin)	CWGr
	'Nenekazi' (Fim)	CWGr LAyl
	'Nepos' (WL)	CWGr GWyn NJRG SGbt
	'Nescio' (Pom)	CWGr ERCP SDeJ
	'Nettie' (Ba)	CWGr
I	'New Baby' (Ba)	CWGr ERCP LCro LOPS SGbt
	'New Look' (S-c)	CWGr
	'Newby' (D)	CWGr
	'Newquay' (Sin) **new**	CWGr
	'Newsham Wonder' (D)	CWGr
	'Nicholas' (D) **new**	ERCP
	'Nicola' (S-c)	CWGr
	'Nicolette' (D)	CWGr
	'Night Butterfly' (Col) **new**	NNys
	'Night Editor' (D)	CWGr
I	'Night Queen' (Ba)	EPfP ERCP
	'Nijinsky' (Ba)	CWGr
	'Nina Chester' (D)	CWGr
	'Nippon' (Sin)	EBee EPfP LRHS
	'Nonette' (WL)	CWGN CWGr EBee ECtt SGbt WBrk WCot
	'Norbeck Dusky' (S-c)	CWGr
	'Noreen' (Pom)	CWGr NHal
	'Norman Lockwood' (Pom)	CWGr
	'Northland Primrose' (C)	CWGr
	'Northwest Cosmos' (Sin) 🏆H3	CWGr
	'Ntac Eileen' (Col) **new**	NJRG
§	'Nuit d'Eté' (S-c)	CAby CAvo CWGr ELan ERCP EWoo LCro LRHS NBri SGbt
	'Nuland's Josephine' (Ba)	NHal NJRG
	'Nunton Form' (D)	CWGr
	'Nunton Harvest' (D)	CWGr
	'Nymphenburg' (WL)	CWGr
	'Oakwood Diamond' (Ba)	CWGr
	'Oakwood Goldcrest' (S-c)	NHal
	'Offshore Dream' (D)	ERCP
	'Old Boy' (Ba)	CWGr
I	'Old Gold' (D)	CWGr SGbt
I	'Olivia' (Col)	CWGr NJRG
	'Olivia Mari' (WL)	NHal
	'Omo' (Sin/Lil) 🏆H3	CWGr NJRG
	'Onesta' (D)	CWGr ERCP SDeJ
	'Only Love' (S-c)	CWGr
	'Onslow Michele' (D)	CWGr
	'Onslow Renown' (S-c)	CWGr
	'Opal' (Ba)	CWGr
	'Optic Illusion' (D)	CWGr
	'Opus' (D)	CWGr SGbt
	'Orange Cushion' (D)	CWGr
	'Orange Explosion' (Misc)	SGbt
	'Orange Fire' (S-c)	CWGr
	'Orange Fubuki' (D)	ERCP
	'Orange Keith's Choice' (D)	CWGr
	'Orange Mullett' (D/DwB)	CWGr
	'Orange Nugget' (Ba)	CWGr SDeJ
	'Orange Pathfinder' (Misc)	CWGr
I	'Orange Queen' (C)	CWGr SGbt
	'Orange Sun' (D)	CWGr
	'Orange Turmoil' (D) **new**	CWGr
	'Orchid Lace' (C)	CWGr
	'Orchid Princess' (S-c)	ERCP
	'Orel' (Col)	CWGr SGbt
	'Oreti Bliss' (C)	LAyl NHal
	'Oreti Classic' (D)	NHal
	'Oreti Duke' (Pom)	CWGr
	'Orfeo' (C)	CWGr ECtt ERCP MNrw SDeJ SGbt
I	'Orion' (D)	CWGr
	'Ornamental Rays' (C)	CWGr
	'Osaka' (D)	CWGr
	'Osirium' (D)	ERCP
	'Ossie Latham' (Sin)	CWGr SGbt
	'Othello' (S-c)	CWGr
	'Otto's Thrill' (D)	ERCP
	'Our Dad' (S-c) **new**	NHal
	'Pacific Argyle' (D)	NHal
	'Pacific Ocean' (WL) **new**	ERCP
	'Paint Box' (S-c)	CWGr
	'Painted Girl' (D)	ERCP
	'Paisley Gem' (Sin) **new**	CWGr
	'Pale Excentrique' (Sin/DwB)	NJRG
	'Pale Roxy'	NJRG
	'Palomino' (D)	CWGr
	'Pam Howden' (WL)	NHal NJRG SGbt
	'Pamela' (D)	CWGr
	'Paradise City' (D)	CAby SSal
	'Pari Taha Sunrise' (S-c)	CWGr
	'Park Princess' (C/DwB)	CSut CWGr LAyl NBri NHal SDeJ SGbt
	'Park Record' (S-c)	NBri
	'Parkland Rave' (S-c)	CWGr
	'Paroa Gillian' (C)	CWGr
	'Paso Doble' misapplied	see *D.* 'Freya's Paso Doble'
	'Pat Knight' (Col)	CWGr NHal NJRG
	'Pat Mark' (S-c)	CWGr
	'Pat 'n' Dee' (D)	CWGr
	'Pat 'n' Perc' (Col)	NJRG SGbt
	'Pat Seed' (D)	CWGr
	'Paul Chester' (C)	CWGr
	'Paul Critchley' (C)	CWGr
	'Paul Smith' (Ba)	CWGr
	'Peace Pact' (WL)	CWGr
	'Peach Athalie' (C)	CWGr
	'Peach Cupid' (Ba)	CWGr
	'Peach Delight' (S-c)	NHal SGbt
§	'Peach Melba' (D)	CWGr NHal
I	'Peaches' (Ba)	ERCP
	'Peaches and Cream'PBR (D)	CWGr
	'Peachette' (Misc/Lil)	CWGr
	'Pearl Hornsey' (D)	CWGr
	'Pearl of Heemstede' (D) 🏆H3	CWGr LAyl NHal NJRG
	'Pearl Sharowean' (S-c)	CWGr

	'Pearson's Ben' (S-c)	CWGr NJRG
	'Pearson's Melanie' (C)	CWGr
	'Pearson's Patrick' (S-c)	CWGr
	'Pembroke Levenna' (Ba)	LAyl NHal
	'Penhill Autumn Shade' (S-c)	NJRG SGbt
	'Pennsclout' (D)	CWGr
	'Pennsgift' (D)	CWGr
	'Penny Lane' (D)	ERCP
	'Pensford Marion' (Pom)	CWGr
	'Perfect Partner' (Sin)	CWGr
	'Perfectos' (C)	CWGr
	'Peter' (D)	CWGr ECtt SGbt
	'Petit Byoux' (Col/DwB)	CWGr
	'Petite Harvest' (Misc/DwB)	NJRG
	'Petite Sunrise' (Sin)	NJRG
	'Petite Sunset' (Misc/Lil)	NJRG
	'Petra's Wedding' (Ba)	NBri
	'Pfitzer's Joker' (C)	CAby
	'Pianella' (S-c)	CWGr SGbt
	'Pineapple Lollipop' (Ba)	CWGr
	'Pineholt Princess' (D)	CWGr
	'Pinelands Pam' (Fim)	CWGr
	'Pinelands Princess' (Fim)	ERCP EUJe SGbt
	'Pink Attraction' (D)	CWGr
	'Pink Breckland Joy' (D)	CWGr
	'Pink Carol' (Pom)	CWGr NJRG
	'Pink Giraffe' (DblO) ♀H3	CAby CWGr ERCP SGbt
	'Pink Honeymoon Dress' (D)	CWGr
	'Pink Isa'PBR (D)	CWGr ERCP
	'Pink Jean Fairs' (WL)	CWGr
	'Pink Jupiter' (S-c)	CWGr NHal SGbt SSal
	'Pink Katisha' (D)	CWGr
	'Pink Kerkrade' (C)	CWGr
	'Pink Leycett' (D)	CWGr
	'Pink Loveliness' (WL)	CWGr
	'Pink Pastelle' (S-c) ♀H3	NHal SGbt
	'Pink Pat and Perc' (Col) **new**	NHal NJRG
	'Pink Preference' (S-c)	CWGr
	'Pink Risca Miner' (Ba)	CWGr
	'Pink Robin Hood' (Ba)	CWGr
	'Pink Sensation' (C) ♀H3	CWGr
	'Pink Shirley Alliance' (C)	CWGr
	'Pink Skin' (D)	ECtt EWoo LRHS SDeJ
	'Pink Sylvia' (D)	CWGr
	'Pink Symbol' (S-c)	CWGr
	'Pink Worton Ann' (D)	CWGr
	pinnata	CFil
	- B&SWJ 10240	SSal WCru
	'Piperoo' (C)	CWGr SGbt
	'Piper's Pink' (S-c/DwB)	CWGr ECtt LRHS NLar SGbt
I	'Pippa' (WL)	CWGr
I	'Pippi' (D) **new**	CWGr
	'Playa Blanca' (C/DwB)	SGbt
	'Playboy' (D)	CWGr
	'Plum Surprise' (Pom)	CWGr
	'Polar Sight' (C)	CWGr
I	'Polka' (Anem)	NJRG SDeJ SGbt
	'Polly Peachum' (D)	CWGr
	'Polventon Supreme' (Ba)	CWGr
	'Polyand' (D)	CWGr
	'Pontiac' (C)	CWGr SGbt
	'Pooh' (Col)	see *D.* 'Pooh - Swan Island'
§	'Pooh - Swan Island' (Col) ♀H3	CHVG CWGr EBee ERCP EUJe LAyl NHal NJRG WCot
	'Pop Harris' (D)	CWGr
I	'Poppet' (Pom)	CWGr
	'Poppyscotland' (Sin) **new**	CWGr
	'Popular Guest' (Fim)	CWGr
	'Pot Black' (Ba)	CWGr
	'Potgeiter' (Ba)	CWGr
	'Pow Wow' (Anem)	EWoo
	'Prefect' (S-c)	CWGr
	'Prefere' (Sin)	CWGr
	'Preference' (C)	CWGr ERCP SDeJ SGbt SSal
	'Preston Park' (Sin/DwB) ♀H3	CWGr LAyl NHal
	Pretty Woman = 'Vdtg43'PBR (Dark Angel Series) (Sin)	CRos ERCP LCro LOPS LRHS NRHS
	Pride of Berlin	see *D.* 'Stolz von Berlin'
	'Prime Minister' (D)	CWGr
	'Primrose Diane' (D)	CWGr
	'Primrose Pastelle' (S-c)	NHal
	'Primrose Rustig' (D)	CWGr
	'Prince Valiant' (D)	CWGr
I	'Princess' (Col)	SDeJ
	'Princess Beatrix' (D)	CWGr
	'Princess Marie José' (Sin)	CWGr
	'Princesse Elisabeth' (D)	ERCP
	'Princesse Gracia' (D)	ERCP
	'Princesse Laetitia' (D)	ERCP
	'Procyon' (D)	CWGr NBri SGbt
	'Prom' (Pom)	CWGr
	'Promise' (Fim)	CWGr ECtt ERCP
	pteropoda **new**	CWGr
	aff. ***pteropoda***	CWGr
	- F&M 312	WPGP
	Pulp Fiction = 'Vdtg61'PBR (Dark Angel Series) (Sin)	ERCP
	'Punky' (Pom)	CWGr
	'Purbeck Lydia' (S-c)	CWGr
	'Purity' (S-c)	CWGr
	'Purpinca' (Anem)	CWGr
	'Purple Cottesmore' (WL)	CWGr
	'Purple Flame'PBR (D)	ERCP
	'Purple Gem' (S-c)	CWGr ERCP EUJe LCro LOPS SGbt
	'Purple Haze' (Misc)	ERCP NBri NQui
	'Purple Pearl' (D)	ERCP NHal
	'Purple Petite' (Sin)	NJRG
	'Purple Puff' (Anem)	NHal NJRG
	'Purple Sensation' (S-c)	CWGr
	'Purple Splash' (WL)	CWGr
	'Purple Taihey?' (D)	CWGr
	'Purpurröschen' (D)	CWGr
	purpusii	CWGr
	aff. ***purpusii*** B&SWJ 10321	SSal WCru
	'Pussycat' (D)	CWGr
	'Que Sera' (Misc)	CWGr
	'Quel Diable' (S-c)	CWGr
	'Quick Step' (Anem)	NJRG
	'Rachel de Thame' (Sin)	CWGr
	'Rachel's Place' (Pom)	CWGr
	'Radiance' (C)	CWGr
	'Raffles' (D)	CWGr
	'Ragged Robin' (Misc)	CSpe CWGN CWGr ECtt ERCP LCro LRHS
	'Raiser's Pride' (C)	NHal
	'Raspberry Ripple' (S-c)	CWGr
	'Raspberry Valiant' (B)	NHal
*	'Raymond Guernsey'	ECtt
	'Razzle Dazzle' (D)	ERCP
	'Rebecca Lynn' (D)	CWGr
	'Rebecca's World' (D)	EPfP SPer SSal
	'Red Alert' (Ba)	CWGr
	'Red and White' (D)	CWGr SGbt
	'Red Arrows' (D)	CWGr
	'Red Balloon' (Ba)	CWGr
	'Red Cap' (D)	CWGr
	'Red Carol' (Pom)	CWGr

	'Red Diamond' (D)	CWGr NHal
	'Red Fox'PBR (Ba)	LCro LOPS
	'Red Fubuki' (D)	SDeJ
	'Red Highlight' (S-c)	CWGr
	'Red Kaiser Wilhelm' (Ba)	CWGr
	'Red Majorette' (S-c)	CWGr SDeJ
	'Red Pathfinder' (Sin)	NJRG
	'Red Pimpernel' (D)	CWGr
	'Red Pygmy' (S-c)	CWGr SDeJ
	'Red Riding Hood' (Ba)	CWGr
	'Red Rock' (D) **new**	ERCP
	'Red Sun' (D) **new**	CWGr
	'Red Velvet' (WL)	CWGr
	'Red Warrior' (Pom)	CWGr
	'Reddy' (Sin/Lil)	CWGr
	'Reedly' (D)	CWGr
	'Rees' Dream' (D)	CWGr
	'Regal Boy' (Ba)	CWGr
	'Reginald Keene' (S-c)	CWGr NHal
	'Reliance' (Ba)	CWGr
	'Renato Tosio' (D)	CWGr
	'Reputation' (C)	CWGr SGbt
	'Requiem' (D)	CWGr ECtt ERCP NJRG
	'Reverend P. Holian' (S-c)	CWGr SGbt
	'Revive' (Misc)	CWGr
	'Rhonda' (Pom)	NHal
	'Richard Marc' (C)	CWGr
	'Richard S' (S-c)	NHal
	'Richstone' (D)	CWGr
	'Ridlings Salmon Wheels' (Col)	NJRG
	'Riisa' (Ba)	CWGr
	'Rip City' (S-c)	CAvo CWGr ERCP LCro LOPS LRHS MCot
	'Risca Miner' (Ba)	CWGr
	'Rita Easterbrook' (D)	CWGr
	'Rita Shrimpton' (Misc)	CWGr NJRG
	'Roan' (D)	CWGr
	'Robann Regal' (D) **new**	CWGr
	'Robann Royal' (Ba)	CWGr
	'Robert Too' (D)	CWGr
I	'Robin Hood' (Ba)	CWGr
	'Rocco' (Ba)	ERCP LCro LOPS SGbt WBor
	'Rockcliffe Billy' (S-c)	NJRG
	'Rockcliffe Gold' (S-c)	CWGr
	'Rokewood Opal' (C)	CWGr
	'Rosalinde' (S-c)	CWGr
	'Rose Jupiter' (S-c)	CWGr NHal
	'Rose Tendre' (S-c)	CWGr
	'Rosella' (D)	CWGr SDeJ SGbt
	'Rosemary Webb' (D)	CWGr SGbt
I	'Rosita' (Col) **new**	CWGr
	'Rossendale Flamenco' (D) **new**	NHal
	'Rossendale Heide' (D)	NHal
	'Rossendale Luke' (D)	CWGr
	'Rossendale Mollie' (D) **new**	NHal
	'Rossendale Natasha' (Ba)	NHal SGbt
	'Rossendale Stephanie' (D)	NHal
	'Rosy Cloud' (D)	CWGr
	'Rothesay Castle' (D/DwB)	CWGr
	'Rothesay Herald' (D/DwB)	CWGr
	'Rothesay Reveller' (D)	CWGr
	'Rothesay Rose' (WL)	CWGr
	'Rothesay Superb' (Ba)	CWGr
	'Rotonde' (C)	CWGr
I	'Roxy' (Sin/DwB)	CAby CBcs CBod CWGr EBee ECtt ELan EPfP ERCP GMaP LAyl LRHS LSRN NHal NJRG SGbt WBrk WCot
	'Royal Amethyst' (D)	CWGr
	'Royal Mail' (D)	SGbt
	'Royal Visit' (D)	CWGr SGbt
	'Royal Wedding' (S-c)	CWGr
	'Ruby Puff' (Anem)	CWGr
	'Ruby Red' (Ba)	CWGr
	'Ruby Wedding' (D)	CWGr SGbt
	rudis	CFil CWGr WPGP
	'Ruskin Andrea' (S-c)	LAyl NHal
	'Ruskin Avenger' (S-c)	NJRG
	'Ruskin Belle' (S-c)	CWGr
	'Ruskin Bride' (S-c)	NHal
	'Ruskin Buttercup' (D)	CWGr SGbt
	'Ruskin Charlotte' (S-c)	CWGr
	'Ruskin Diana' (D)	CWGr NHal
	'Ruskin Dynasty' (D)	CWGr
	'Ruskin Emile' (S-c)	CWGr
	'Ruskin Gypsy' (Ba)	CWGr
I	'Ruskin Harmony' (S-c)	CWGr NHal
	'Ruskin Limelight' (C)	NHal
	'Ruskin Marigold' (S-c)	CWGr NHal
	'Ruskin Mars' (D) **new**	GWyn
	'Ruskin Michelle' (S-c)	NHal
	'Ruskin Myra' (S-c)	CWGr NHal NJRG
	'Ruskin Petite' (Ba)	CWGr
	'Ruskin Respectable' (S-c)	NJRG
	'Ruskin Sensation' (S-c)	NHal
	'Ruskin Tangerine' (Ba)	NHal SGbt
	'Russell Turner' (S-c)	CWGr
	'Rustig' (D)	CWGr
I	'Rusty' (Sin) **new**	CWGr
	'Rusty Hope' (D)	CWGr
	'Ryecroft Brenda T' (D)	NHal NJRG
	'Ryecroft Claire' (D)	NHal
	'Ryecroft Delight' (Ba)	NHal
	'Ryecroft Ice' (D)	SGbt
	'Ryecroft Jan' (Ba) 🏆H3	NHal NJRG
	'Ryecroft Jim' (Anem)	NHal
	'Ryecroft Laura' (Ba)	NHal
	'Ryecroft Magnum' (D)	CWGr
	'Ryecroft Pixie' (C)	NHal
	'Ryecroft Punch' (Ba) **new**	NHal
	'Ryecroft Rebel' (D)	NHal
	'Ryecroft Sparkler' (C)	NHal SGbt
	'Ryecroft Yellow Orb' (Ba)	NHal
	'Ryecroft Zoe' (S-c)	NHal
	'Ryedale Pinky' (D)	CWGr
	'Ryedale Prince' (D)	CWGr
	'Ryedale Rebecca' (S-c)	CWGr
	'Safe Shot' (D)	CWGr
	'Sailor' (Fim)	CWGr
	'Saint Fagans' (S-c) **new**	CWGr
	'Saint-Saëns' (S-c)	ERCP SDeJ
	'Sakura Fubuki' (Fim)	ERCP
I	'Saladin' (Misc)	CWGr
	'Salmon Athalie' (C)	CWGr
	'Salmon Carpet' (D)	CWGr
	'Salmon Hornsey' (D)	CWGr
	'Sam Hopkins' (D)	ERCP LAyl NHal SSal
	'Sam Huston' (D)	CWGr SGbt
	'Samantha'	see *D.* 'Harvest Samantha'
	'Sandia Rose' (WL)	NHal
	'Sandia Shomei' (WL)	EWoo
	'Sandra' (D)	ERCP
	'Sans Souci' (C)	CWGr
	'Santa Claus US' (D)	CWGr SGbt
	'Sarabande' (S-c)	CWGr
	'Sarah' (S-c)	CWGr ECtt EUJe LRHS
	'Sarah G' (S-c)	CWGr
	'Sarah Louise' (WL)	CWGr
	'Sarah Thomas' (Col)	CWGr

	'Sarum Aurora' (D)	CWGr
	'Sassy' (D)	SGbt
	'Satellite' (S-c)	CWGr
	scapigeroides **new**	CFil
	'Scarborough Ace' (D)	CWGr
	'Scarlet Comet' (Anem)	CWGr
§	'Scarlet Fern' (Sin)	CWGr LRHS
	'Scarlet Kokarde' (D)	CWGr
	'Scarlet O'Hara' (D)	NJRG
	'Scarlet Rotterdam' (S-c)	CWGr
	'Scarlet Star' (S-c)	CWGr
	'Scarlett Claire' (Col)	CWGr
	'Scaur Sunrise' (D)	NJRG
	'Scaur Swinton' (D)	CWGr NHal SGbt
	'Schweitzer's Kokarde' (D)	CWGr
	'Scottish Rhapsody' (S-c)	CWGr
	'Scura' (Sin)	CWGr
	'Seattle' (D)	CWGr NBri
	'Seduction' (D)	EPfP ERCP
	'Seirō' (S-c)	SGbt
	'Senior Ball' (Ba)	CWGr
	'Senzoe Ursula' (D)	CWGr
	'Severin's Triumph' (D)	CWGr
	'Shandy' (S-c)	CWGr LAyl
	'Shannon' (D)	CWGr
	'Sheila Mooney' (D)	CWGr
	'Shep's Memory' (WL) ♀^{H3}	NJRG
	sherffii	CWGr
	- dwarf	WPGP
	'Sherwood Monarch' (S-c)	CWGr
	'Sherwood Titan' (D)	CWGr
	'Sherwood's Peach' (D)	CWGr
	'Shining Star' (C)	CWGr
	'Shirley' (D)	CWGr
	'Shirley Pillman' (Misc)	CWGr
	'Shirwell Greta' (D)	NHal
	'Shooting Star' (S-c)	CWGr NBri
	'Show 'n' Tell' (Fim)	CWGr SGbt
	'Shy Princess' (C)	CWGr
	'Siedlerstolz' (D)	CWGr
	'Silver City' (D)	CWGr NHal SGbt
	'Silver Years' (D)	CWGr
	'Sir Alf Ramsey' (D)	CWGr LAyl NHal SGbt
	'Sisa' (D)	CWGr
	'Skipley Spot' (D)	CWGr
	'Skipper Rock' (D)	CWGr
	'Small World' (Pom) ♀^{H3}	CWGr LAyl NHal
	'Smokey' (D)	CWGr
	'Smoots' (Fim)	CWGr
	'Sneezy' (Sin/Dw.B.)	CWGr
	'Snip' (S-c)	CWGr
	'Snoho Tammie' (Ba)	CWGr
	'Snow Cap' (S-c)	CWGr SDeJ
	'Snow Fairy' (C)	CWGr
	'Snowbound' (D)	SGbt
I	'Snowflake' (WL)	CWGr ERCP SDeJ
I	'Snowstorm' (D)	CWGr LRHS SGbt
	'Snowy' (Ba)	CWGr
	'So Dainty' (S-c) ♀^{H3}	CWGr
	'Song of Olympia' (WL)	CWGr
	'Sonia Henie' (Ba)	CWGr
	'Sophie Taylor' (SinO)	NJRG
I	'Sorbet' (D)	NHal
	'Sorbet' (S-c)	see *D.* 'Geerlings' Sorbet' (MS-c)
	sorensenii	CWGr
	'Sorrento Flush' (D)	NJRG
	'Soulman' (Anem)	CWGr EWoo NJRG SGbt
	'Souvenir d'Eté' (Pom)	CWGr SDeJ
	'Spanish Conquest' (D)	CWGr NHal SGbt
I	'Sparkler' (S-c)	ERCP

	'Spartacus' (D)	CWGr NHal
	'Spassmacher' (S-c)	CWGr NBri
	spectabilis	CWGr
	'Spectacular' (D)	CWGr SGbt
	'Spencer' (D)	CWGr
	'Spennythorn King' (D)	CWGr
I	'Spike' (S-c)	SGbt
	'Spikey Symbol' (S-c)	CWGr
	'Sprinter' (C)	CWGr
	'Staleen Condesa' (S-c) ♀^{H3}	NHal SGbt
	'Star Child' (SinO)	CWGr
	'Star Elite' (C)	CSut CWGr NBri
	'Star Spectacle' (S-c)	CWGr
	'Star Surprise' (C)	CWGr SDeJ
	Star Wars = 'Vdtg14'^{PBR} (Dark Angel Series) (Sin)	CRos ERCP LCro LOPS LRHS NRHS SDeJ WHil
	'Starlight Keene' (S-c)	CWGr
	'Starry Eyes - Red' (Sin) **new**	CRos
	'Starry Night' (S-c)	CWGr
	'Star's Favourite' (C)	ERCP NBri
	'Star's Lady' (C)	CWGr
	'Stellyvonne' (Fim)	CWGr
	'Stephanie' (S-c)	CWGr
	'Stevie D' (D) ♀^{H3}	CWGr SGbt
§	'Stolz von Berlin' (Ba)	CWGr ERCP SDeJ SGbt
	'Stoneleigh Joyce' (Pom)	CWGr
	'Storm Warning' (D)	CWGr
	'Storrs Julie' (Pom)	NJRG
	'Strike a Light' (C) **new**	CWGr
	'Striped Vulcan' (S-c)	CAby
	'Sue Mountjoy' (Col)	CWGr
	'Sue Willo' (Pom)	CWGr
	'Sue's Kilmorie' (S-c) **new**	NHal
	'Suffolk Fantasy' (D)	CWGr
	'Suffolk Punch' (D)	CWGr LAyl
	'Sugar Diamond' (C)	EPfP ERCP
	'Suitzus Julie' (Misc)	CWGr
	'Summer Festival' (D)	CWGr SGbt
	'Summer Night' (S-c)	see *D.* 'Nuit d'Eté'
	'Summer Night' ambig.	ECGP NHal
	'Summer Nights' (Misc)	LOPS NJRG
	'Sunlight' (Ba)	CWGr
	'Sunlight Pastelle' (S-c)	CWGr
	'Sunny Boy' (D)	NBri
	'Sunray Silk' (S-c)	CWGr
I	'Sunshine' (Sin)	LCro LOPS LRHS
	'Sunshine Girl' (Col)	NJRG
	'Super Trouper' (D)	CWGr
	'Superfine' (C)	CWGr
	'Sure Thing' (C)	CWGr
	'Susan Gilbert' (Col)	NHal NJRG SSal
	'Susan Gilliott' (S-c)	NHal
	'Susan Willo' (Pom)	CWGr
I	'Suzanne' (Col)	NJRG
	'Suzette' (D/DwB)	SGbt
	'Swallow Falls' (D)	CWGr
	'Swan Lake'	see *D.* 'Classic Swanlake'
	'Swanvale' (D)	CWGr SGbt
	'Sweet Content' (D)	CWGr SGbt
	'Sweetheart' (D)	CWGr NJRG
	'Swiss Miss' (Ba)	CWGr
I	'Sylvia' (Ba)	CWGr ERCP NBri NJRG
	'Sylvia's Desire' (C)	CWGr
	'Symbol' (S-c)	CWGr
	'Sympathy' (WL)	CWGr
	'Syston Harlequin' (D)	CWGr
	'Syston Sophia' (Ba)	CWGr
	'Tahiti Sunrise' (S-c)	CWGr EPfP
	'Tahoma Hope' (Misc)	CWGr
	'Tahoma Moonshot' (SinO)	CWGr

'Tahoma Star' (SinO) LCro LOPS
'Take Off' (Anem) WBor
'Tally Ho' (Misc) ♀H3 CWGr ECGP ECtt EPfP LRHS NJRG SDys WCot
'Tam Tam' (Ba) CWGr EPfP SPer
'Tamburo' (S-c) EPfP ERCP SPer
I 'Tapestry' (Sin) CWGr SGbt
'Taratahi Ruby' (WL) ♀H3 CWGr ERCP NHal NJRG
'Tartan' (D) CWGr
Taxi Driver = 'Vdtg57'PBR (Dark Angel Series) (Sin) CRos ERCP LRHS NRHS
'Teesbrooke Audrey' (Col) CWGr ECtt NHal
'Teesbrooke Red Eye' (Col) CWGr ERCP NHal NJRG SGbt
'Temptress' (S-c) CWGr
'Tender Moon' (D) CWGr
tenuicaulis CDTJ CWGr SBig
- F&M 257 CFil
- F&M 355 CFil
aff. ***tenuicaulis*** CWGr
'Terracotta' (Misc/DwB) NHal
'Terrie Bandey' (Fim) LAyl NHal
'Thais' (Col) NJRG
'Thames Valley' (D) CWGr
'That's It!' (D) CWGr
'The Baron' (D) CWGr
'The Phantom' (Anem) ERCP NJRG WBor
I 'The Queen' (S-c) CWGr
'Thelma Clements' (D) CWGr
'Theo Sprengers' (D) CWGr
'Thika' (D) CWGr
'Thomas A. Edison' (D) CAvo CWGr ERCP NNys SDeJ SGbt
'Thoresby Jewel' (D) CWGr
I 'Tiara' (D) CWGr
'Tiffany Lynn' (SinO) CWGr
I 'Tiger' (Sin/DwB) **new** CWGr
'Tiger Eye' (D) CWGr SGbt
'Tiger Tiv' (D) CWGr
'Timeless' (D) SPer
'Tina Burden' (Ba) CWGr
'Tinker's White' (D) CWGr
'Tioga Spice' (Fim) CWGr SSal
'Toga' (WL) CWGr
'Tohsuikyoh' (Misc) CWGr SGbt
'Tom McLelland' (S-c) **new** NHal
'Tommy Doc' (S-c) CWGr
'Tommy Keith' (Ba) CWGr
'Tomo' (D) LAyl NHal
'Top Affair' (S-c) CWGr
'Top Choice' (S-c) CWGr
'Top Totty' (D) NHal
I 'Topaz Puff' (Anem) CWGr
'Topmix' (Sin/DwB) SDeJ
'Topmix Mama' (Sin) NJRG
'Topmix Orange' (Sin) NJRG
'Topmix Pink' (Sin/DwB) SDeJ
'Topmix Purple' (Sin) NJRG
'Topmix Red' (Sin/DwB) NJRG SDeJ
'Topmix Reddy' (Sin) NJRG
I 'Topmix Rose' (Sin) NJRG
'Topmix White' (Sin/DwB) SDeJ
'Topmix Yellow' (Sin/DwB) NJRG SDeJ
'Toto' (Anem) CWGr ERCP
'Towneley Class' (D) CWGr
'Tramar' (C) CWGr
'Trampolene' (S-c) CWGr
'Trelissick Purple' **new** CWGr
'Trelyn Crimson' (Col) NHal
'Trelyn Daisy' (Col) ♀H3 CWGr
'Trelyn Kiwi' (S-c) ♀H3 CWGr NHal NJRG SGbt
'Trelyn Red Dragon' (SinO) NHal
'Trelyn Seren' (SinO) LAyl NHal
'Trendy' (D) CWGr
'Trengrove Autumn' (D) CWGr SGbt
'Trengrove Jill' (D) CWGr
'Trengrove Millennium' (D) CWGr NHal NJRG SGbt
'Trengrove Tauranga' (D) CWGr
I 'Trevor' (Col) CWGr ECtt SGbt
'Tricolor' ambig. MSCN
'Trooper Dan' (S-c) NHal
'Trotter's Jo-Anne' (S-c) CWGr
'Troy Dyson' (Misc) SDys
'Truly Scrumptious' (S-c) SGbt
'Tsuki-yori-no-shisha' (Fim) CWGr LCro LOPS
tubulata CFil EBee
'Tudor 1' (Misc/DwB) NHal
'Tui Avis' (C) CWGr NJRG
'Tui Orange' (S-c) CWGr
'Tula Rosa' (Pom) CWGr
'Tutankhamun' (Pom) CWGr
'Tu-tu' (S-c) CWGr SGbt
'Twiggy' (WL) CWGr SGbt
'Twilight Time' (D) CWGr SDeJ
* 'Twinkle Stars' SDeJ
'Twyning's After Eight' (Sin) ♀H3 CAby CAvo CBod CBot CHVG CSpe CWGN CWGr EAJP ECtt ELan EPfP ERCP EWoo LAyl LCro LOPS LRHS LSun NHal NJRG NSti SDix SDys SGbt SPer WBor WCot WHoo
'Twyning's Aniseed' (Sin) CWGr
'Twyning's Black Cherry' (D) CWGr
'Twyning's Candy' (Sin) CWGr
'Twyning's Chocolate' (Sin) CWGr
'Twyning's Peppermint' (Sin) CWGr
'Twyning's Purple Cherry' (D) **new** CWGr
'Twyning's Revel' (Sin) ♀H3 CAvo CWGr
'Twyning's Smartie' (Sin) CWGr EBee ECtt LCro
'Twyning's White Chocolate' (Sin) CWGr
'Tyrell' (D) EPfP
'Uchuu' (D) CWGr
'Uncle Hankey' (D) ERCP
'Union Jack' (Sin) CWGr
'United' (D) CWGr
'Usugesho' (D) CWGr
'Vader Abraham' (D) CWGr
'Vaguely Noble' (Ba) CWGr
I 'Valentino' (Dw) **new** CWGr
'Val's Candy' (S-c) NHal
'Vancouver' (Misc) CWGr ERCP SDeJ
'Variace' (Ba) CWGr
'Vassio Meggos' (D) **new** ERCP NHal
'Vera's Elma' (D) CWGr
'Veritable' (S-c) CSut NBri
'Verrone's Obsidian' (SinO) **new** ERCP
'Vicky Jackson' (WL) CWGr
'Victory Day' (C) CWGr
'Vigor' (WL) CWGr
'Viking' (Pom) CWGr NBri
'Vino' (Pom) CWGr
'Violet Davies' (S-c) CWGr
'Vivex' (Pom) CWGr
'Vivian Russell' (WL) NJRG
'Volkskanzler' (Sin) CWGr
'Vulcan' (S-c) CWGr ERCP SGbt
§ 'Vuurvogel' (S-c) CWGr ERCP NBri SDeJ
'Walter Hardisty' (D) CWGr

	'Walter James' (D)	CWGr
	'Waltzing Mathilda' (Misc)	ERCP LCro LOPS
	'Wanborough Gem' (Ba)	CWGr
	'Wanda's Capella' (D)	CWGr
	'Wanda's Moonlight' (D)	CWGr
	'Wandy' (Pom)	CWGr
	'War of the Roses' (D)	CWGr EWes WHer
	'Warkton Willo' (Pom)	CWGr
I	'Waterlily' (Sin) **new**	LRHS NRHS
I	'Welcome Guest' (S-c)	CWGr
I	'Wendy' (Ba)	CWGr
	'Wendy Spencer' (D)	CWGr
	'Westerton Folly' (Ba) 🏆H3	NHal
	'Westerton Harry' (D) **new**	NHal
	'Westerton Lilian' (D)	NHal
	'Westerton Southside' (D)	NHal
	'Weston Aramac' (S-c)	CWGr
	'Weston Buccaneer' (C)	NHal
	'Weston Corsair' (C)	NJRG
	'Weston Forge' (C)	CWGr
	'Weston Kelpie' (C)	NJRG
	'Weston Miss' (S-c)	CWGr GWyn NHal NJRG
	'Weston Nugget' (C)	CWGr
	'Weston Pirate' (C) 🏆H3	LAyl NHal NJRG
	'Weston Princekin' (S-c)	CWGr
	'Weston Spanish Dancer' (C) 🏆H3	CWGr NHal NJRG SGbt
	'Weston Stardust' (C) 🏆H3	NJRG
	'Weston Tea-time' (C)	CWGr
	'Wheels' (Col)	NJRG
	'White Alva's' (D) 🏆H3	CWGr LAyl NHal SGbt
	'White Aster' (Pom)	CWGr ERCP
	'White Ballerina' (WL)	NHal SGbt
	'White Ballet' (D) 🏆H3	CWGr LAyl SGbt
	'White Charlie Two' (D)	NHal
	'White Hallelujah' (Sin) **new**	CWGr
	'White Hunter' (D)	CWGr
	'White Klankstad' (C)	CWGr
	'White Knight' (D)	NHal
	'White Linda' (D)	CWGr NHal
	'White Magenta Star' (Sin)	CWGr
	'White Moonlight' (S-c)	CWGr NHal
	'White Nettie' (Ba)	CWGr SGbt
	'White Onesta' (D)	ERCP SDeJ
	'White Perfection' (D)	CWGr ECtt EPfP ERCP NBri SDeJ
	'White Rebel'	NBri
	'White Rustig' (D)	CWGr
	'White Seedling' (Sin) **new**	CWGr
	'White Star' (S-c)	CWGr ERCP LCro LOPS SDeJ
	'White Swallow' (S-c)	NHal
	'Who Dun It' (D)	ERCP
	'Wicky Woo' (D)	CWGr
	'Wildwood Marie' (WL)	CWGr NJRG
	'William B' (D)	CWGr
	'William John' (Pom)	CWGr
	'Williamsburg' (S-c)	CWGr
	'Willo's Borealis' (Pom)	CWGr NHal
	'Willo's Flecks' (Pom)	CWGr
	'Willo's Night' (Pom)	CWGr
	'Willo's Surprise' (Pom)	CWGr NHal SGbt
	'Willo's Violet' (Pom)	CWGr NHal NJRG SGbt
	'Willowfield Mick' (D)	CWGr
	'Wilma McCulloch' **new**	GWyn
	'Wine & Roses' (WL)	CWGr SGbt
	'Winholme Diane' (D)	CWGr NHal
	'Winkie Colonel' (D)	CWGr
	'Winnie' (Pom)	CWGr
	'Winsome' (WL)	CWGr
	'Winston Churchill' (WL)	CWGr
	'Winter Springs' (S-c)	ERCP
	'Wise Guy' (D)	CWGr
	'Wishes n Dreams' (Sin)	NJRG
	'Wisk' (Pom)	CWGr
	'Wittem' (D)	CWGr
	'Witteman's Best' (S-c)	CWGr ERCP MCot NBri SGbt
	'Witteman's Superba' (S-c) 🏆H3	CWGr NHal SDix
	'Wizard of Oz' (Ba)	CWGr ERCP LCro LOPS
	'Woodbridge' (Sin)	CWGr SGbt
	'Woodside Finale' (D)	NHal
	'Wootton Carnival' (C)	CWGr
	'Wootton Cupid' (Ba) 🏆H3	CWGr
	'Wootton Impact' (S-c) 🏆H3	NHal
	'Wootton Phebe' (D)	CWGr
	'Wootton Tempest' (S-c)	CWGr
	'Wootton Windmill' (Col)	CWGr
	'Worton Blue Streak' (S-c)	CWGr ERCP SGbt
	'Worton Revival' (D)	CWGr
	'Worton Superb' (D)	CWGr
	'Wyndal Horizon' (S-c)	CWGr
	'XXL Grand Central' (D) **new**	CWGr
	'XXL Grand Sonata' (D) **new**	CWGr
	'Yamabiraki' (D)	CWGr
	'Yellow Baby' (Pom)	CWGr
I	'Yellow Bird' (Col)	CWGr
	'Yellow Bulldog' (Sin) **new**	CWGr
	'Yellow Galator' (C)	CWGr SGbt
	'Yellow Hammer' (Sin/DwB) 🏆H3	CWGr NHal SGbt
	'Yellow Happiness' (C)	NBri
	'Yellow Heaven' (D)	NBri
	'Yellow Linda's Chester' (C)	CWGr
	'Yellow Lorona Dawn' (Col)	NJRG
	'Yellow Pages' (D)	CWGr
	'Yellow Passions' (D)	ERCP
	'Yellow Pet' (D)	CWGr
	'Yellow Spiky' (S-c)	CWGr
	'Yellow Star' (S-c)	CWGr ERCP EUJe SDeJ
	'Yellow Vulcan' (S-c)	CWGr
	'Yelno Enchantment' (WL)	CWGr LAyl
	'Yelno Petite Glory' (D)	CWGr
	'York and Lancaster' (D)	CWGr EBee SGbt WBrk
	'Yukino' (Col)	CWGr
	'Zagato' (D)	CWGr
	'Zakuro-hime' (D)	CWGr
I	'Zelda' (D)	CWGr
	'Zest' (D)	CWGr
*	'Zingaro'	LCro
	'Zingaro' (D)	LOPS
	'Zirconia' (D) **new**	ERCP
§	'Zone Ten'PBR (Sin/DwB)	CAvo CWGr EPfP IBoy LRHS LSou SHar SPoG WBor
	'Zorro' (D) 🏆H3	CWGr ERCP NHal SGbt
	'Zundert Mystery Fox'PBR (Ba) **new**	ERCP
	'Zurich' (S-c)	CWGr

Daiswa see *Paris*

Dalea (*Papilionaceae*)

	purpurea	EBee SPhx WHil
	- 'Stephanie'	LRHS

damson see *Prunus insititia*

Danae (*Asparagaceae*)

§	***racemosa*** 🏆H5	CBcs CFil CLet CMac CTri EBee EPfP EWes MGil MGos MMuc MRav SEND SPer SRms SWvt WCot WCru WPGP

Danthonia (*Poaceae*)

§	***cincta***	WCot

Daphne ✿ (*Thymelaeaceae*)

	DJHC 98164 from China	WCru
	acutiloba	GKev SMDP
	- 'Fragrant Cloud'	CJun EWes WPGP
	albowiana	CJun GKev
	alpina	WThu
	altaica	CJun
	arbuscula ♀H5	EPot SIgm
	arisanensis B&SWJ 6983	WCru
	aurantiaca	WAbe
	- 'Gang-ho-ba'	CJun WThu
	bholua	CAbP CJun EPfP LRHS
	- B&SWJ 8275 from Fansipan, Vietnam **new**	WCru
	- NJM 13.115 **new**	WPGP
I	- 'Alba'	EPfP SSta WPGP
	- 'Cobhay Snow'	CJun
	- 'Darjeeling'	CJun EPfP GKev SKHP WPGP
	- 'Garden House Enchantress'	WPGP
	- 'Garden House Ghost'	WPGP
	- 'Garden House Red Stem' **new**	WPGP
	- 'Garden House Sentinel'	WPGP
	- var. ***glacialis*** 'Gurkha' ♀H4	CJun EPfP SKHP WPGP
	- 'Glendoick'	CJun
	- 'Hazel Edwards'	LRHS
	- 'Heale House' **new**	WPGP
	- 'Jacqueline Postill' ♀H4	CJun CTri CWib EPfP GKev LCro LSRN MAsh MBlu MGil MGos SCob SKHP SReu SSta SWvt WPGP WPat
	- 'Limpsfield'	CJun LRHS SSta WPGP
	- 'Penwood'	CJun
	- 'Peter Smithers'	CJun EPfP SSta WPGP
	- 'Wisley Purple'	CJun
	blagayana	NBir SRms
	- 'Brenda Anderson'	CJun EPot WAbe
	'Bramdean'	see *D.* × *napolitana* 'Bramdean'
	× ***burkwoodii***	ECrN LSRN SCob
	- 'Albert Burkwood'	CJun
	- 'Astrid' (v)	CBcs GMcL NLar SCob
§	- 'Carol Mackie' (v)	CJun
	- 'G.K.Argles' (v)	CJun MAsh
I	- 'Gold Sport'	CJun
	- 'Golden Treasure'	CJun MAsh SChF
	- 'Lavenirii'	CJun
	- 'Somerset' ♀H4	CBcs CJun ELan ESwi LCro MGos MRav MSwo NWea SCob
§	- 'Somerset Gold Edge' (v)	CJun
§	- 'Somerset Variegated' (v)	EPot WThu
	- 'Variegata' broad cream edge	see *D.* × *burkwoodii* 'Somerset Variegated'
	- 'Variegata' broad gold edge	see *D.* × *burkwoodii* 'Somerset Gold Edge'
	- 'Variegata' narrow gold edge	see *D.* × *burkwoodii* 'Carol Mackie'
	caucasica	CJun
	circassica	SChF
	cneorum	CBcs ELan EWTr GKev
	- 'Eximia' ♀H5	WAbe
	- var. ***pygmaea***	EPot
	- 'Variegata' (v)	GEdr GKev
	- var. ***verlotii***	EPot
	collina	see *D. sericea* Collina Group
	domini	EPot GKev
	euboica	GKev
	gemmata	CBcs LCro NLar
	genkwa	SKHP
	giraldii	GKev
	gnidium	CMCN
	- PAB 8371	LEdu
	'Guardsman'	CJun MAsh
	× ***hendersonii*** 'Aymon Correvon'	WThu
	- 'Blackthorn Rose'	WAbe
	- 'Ernst Hauser'	GKev SChF WAbe WIce WThu
	- 'Fritz Kummert'	WAbe WThu
	- 'Jeanette Brickell'	WAbe WThu
	- 'Kath Dryden'	EPot GEdr
	- 'Marion White'	SIgm WAbe
	- 'Rosebud'	WAbe WThu
	- 'Solferino'	WAbe
	'Hinton'	CJun
	× ***houtteana***	CJun
	japonica 'Striata'	see *D. odora* 'Aureomarginata'
	jasminea upright **new**	EPot
	'Kilmeston Beauty'	CJun
	kurdica	GKev
	× ***latymeri*** 'Spring Sonnet'	SChF WAbe
	laureola	CJun EPfP GKev GPoy MMrt NBid NBir NLar NPer SChr SMDP
	- 'Margaret Mathew'	NLar SChF
	- subsp. ***philippi***	CBcs CCCN CJun CMac ELan EPfP EWes MAsh MBlu MGil MGos NLar SKHP WCot WPGP
	'Leila Haines'	GKev
	limprichtii **new**	GKev
	longilobata	GKev SMDP
	× ***mantensiana*** 'Audrey Vockins'	CJun
	- 'Manten'	CJun
	× ***mauerbachii*** 'Perfume of Spring'	CJun
	'Meon'	see *D.* × *napolitana* 'Meon'
	mezereum	CTri EWld GKev GMaP GPoy IFoB MAsh MGil MGos NChi NWea SChF SCob SGol SWvt WCot WHar WHil WPGP
	- PAB 7643	LEdu
	- f. ***alba***	CJun CMac EWld GKev GLog MAsh MGos NChi SRms SWvt WAbe
	- - 'Bowles's Variety'	CJun EPot
	- var. ***alpina*** hort **new**	GKev
	- 'Rosea'	MAsh SRms
	- var. ***rubra***	CBcs CJun CMac CWib ELan GKin LRHS MGos MJak MNHC MRav MSwo SPer WAbe
	× ***napolitana*** ♀H4	CJun
§	- 'Bramdean'	CJun SChF
§	- 'Meon'	CJun ELan GEdr MAsh SChF WAbe WThu
	odora	CBcs CJun CRos EPfP EWTr LCro LOPS LRHS LSRN MSwo NRHS SCob SEle
§	- f. ***alba***	CBcs CCCN CMac
	- - 'Sakiwaka'	CCCN SKHP WPat
§	- 'Aureomarginata' (v)	Widely available
I	- 'Aureomarginata Alba' (v)	SEle
	- 'Double Cream' (v) **new**	CJun
	- 'Geisha Girl' (v)	MAsh
	- var. ***leucantha***	see *D. odora* f. *alba*
	- 'Mae-jima' (v)	CAbP ELan EPfP GMcL MAsh MGos SLon SPer
	- 'Marginata'	see *D. odora* 'Aureomarginata'
	- Marianni = 'Rogbret' (v)	CCCN LCro LHop LOPS MJak NLar SGol SWvt

- Rebecca = 'Hewreb' (v)	CBct CMea CRos CWib EPfP LBuc LRHS MAsh MGos NRHS SHil SLon SPer SPoG
- var. ***rubra***	CCCN CMac GKev
- 'Walberton' (v)	CRos EPfP LRHS NRHS
oleoides	GKev NLar
- var. ***buxifolia***	GKev
papyracea	CFil
petraea	WAbe
- 'Garnet'	WAbe
- 'Grandiflora'	WAbe
pontica	CBcs CJun CMac CRos EBee EPfP LRHS MAsh NLar NRHS SChF SDix SKHP SPoG WPGP
retusa	see *D. tangutica* Retusa Group
× ***rollsdorfii*** 'Arnold Cihlarz'	CJun SChF WAbe
- 'Wilhelm Schacht' ♀H5	CAbP CJun EPot MAsh SChF WThu
'Rosy Wave'	SChF
× ***schlyteri*** 'July Glow'	EPot GEdr SChF
- 'Lovisa Maria'	GEdr
§ ***sericea*** Collina Group	CAbP SChF WIce
'Spring Beauty'	CJun WPGP
'Spring Herald'	CJun WPGP
× ***suendermannii*** 'Franz Suendermann'	WOld
× ***susannae*** 'Anton Fahndrich'	SChF WThu
- 'Cheriton' ♀H5	ELan EPot NLar SChF WThu
- 'Tichborne'	CAbP EPot SChF WIce WThu
tangutica ♀H5	CBcs CJun CMac CRos CSpe CTri ECho ELan EPfP GKev LSRN MAsh MGil MGos NBir NHol SCoo SEND SKHP SPoG SRkn SRms WAbe WBod WKif WOld WPGP
- 'Golden Thread' (v)	EPfP
§ - Retusa Group ♀H5	CJun ECho ELan ELon EPot GAbr GBin GEdr GKev GMaP LCro LHop MGil MHer NBir SIgm SRms WSHC
× ***transatlantica***	CBot
- 'Beulah Cross' (v)	CAbP CJun MAsh SChF
- Eternal Fragrance = 'Blafra'PBR ♀H5	CAbP CBcs CCCN CRos CWGN ELan EPfP EUJe GBin GKev LCro LOPS LRHS LSRN MAsh MGos MJak MPkF NLar NRHS SCoo SKHP SLon SPer SPoG XEll
- 'Jim's Pride'	SChF
§ - Pink Fragrance = 'Blapink'PBR	CBcs CRos ELan EPfP GKev LCro LOPS LRHS MAsh NRHS SKHP SPoG XEll
- Spring Pink Eternal Fragrance	see *D. × transatlantica* Pink Fragrance
- 'Summer Ice' (v)	WAbe
'Valerie Hillier'	CJun GKev
velenovskyi 'Weber's Findling' **new**	SChF
× ***whiteorum*** 'Beauworth'	WAbe WOld
- 'Kilmeston'	WAbe
wolongensis 'Kevock Star'	GKev SChF

Daphniphyllum (*Daphniphyllaceae*)

aff. ***angustifolium*** B&SWJ 8225	WCru
- B&SWJ 11804	WCru
- WWJ 12020	WCru
chartaceum KWJ 12244	WCru
- KWJ 12313	WCru
glaucescens subsp. ***oldhamii*** var. ***kengii*** B&SWJ 6872	
- - - B&SWJ 7119	WCru
- - var. ***oldhamii*** B&SWJ 7056	WCru
- - - CWJ 12351	WCru
humile	see *D. macropodum* var. *humile*
aff. ***longeracemosum*** B&SWJ 11788	WCru
- NJM 10.147	WPGP
macropodum	CBcs CBct CCCN CFil CMCN EBee EPfP LRHS NLar SArc SDix SKHP SVen WCru WHor WPGP
- B&SWJ 581	WCru
- B&SWJ 2898	WCru
- B&SWJ 6809 from Taiwan	WCru
- B&SWJ 8507 from Ulleungdo, South Korea	WCru
- B&SWJ 8763 from Cheju-do, Korea	WCru
- B&SWJ 11489 from Yakushima, Japan	WCru
- dwarf	WCru
§ - var. ***humile*** B&SWJ 11232	WCru
majus B&SWJ 11744	WCru
paxianum B&SWJ 9755	WCru
pentandrum B&SWJ 6888	WCru
- B&SWJ 7056	WCru
- CWJ 12393	WCru
- RWJ 9836	WCru
teysmannii B&SWJ 11110 from Japan	WCru
- B&SWJ 11112	WCru
- B&SWJ 11358 from Japan	WCru
aff. ***teysmannii*** CWJ 12350 from Taiwan	WCru

Darlingtonia (*Sarraceniaceae*)

californica ♀H3	EFEx SHmp WSSs

Darmera (*Saxifragaceae*)

peltata ♀H6	Widely available
- 'Nana'	EBee ECha ELan EPfP GBuc GCal NBid NHol NLar SWat WFar WMoo

Dasylirion (*Asparagaceae*)

sp.	LPar
§ ***acrotrichum***	CDTJ EShb SArc
cedrosanum	CDTJ CJun SPlb
glaucophyllum	CJun
gracile Planchon	see *D. acrotrichum*
longissimum	CCCN EShb ETod SChr XSen
miquihuanense	SMad
- F&M 321	EBee
quadrangulatum	EBee SPlb
serratifolium	ETod EUJe LPar
wheeleri ♀H2	CBrP SIgm SPlb XSen

date see *Phoenix dactylifera*

Datisca (*Datiscaceae*)

cannabina	CArn CDTJ CSpe EBee ECha GCal IMou NChi SBrt SDix SMHy SMad WMoo WSHC

Datura (*Solanaceae*)

arborea	see *Brugmansia arborea*
cornigera	see *Brugmansia arborea*
rosea	see *Brugmansia × insignis* pink-flowered
rosei	see *Brugmansia sanguinea*
sanguinea	see *Brugmansia sanguinea*
stramonium	EBtc
suaveolens	see *Brugmansia suaveolens*

versicolor	see *Brugmansia versicolor* Lagerh.
- 'Grand Marnier'	see *Brugmansia* × *candida* 'Grand Marnier'

Daucus (*Apiaceae*)

carota	CHab LRHS NMir SVic WHer WSFF

Davallia ✿ (*Davalliaceae*)

canariensis ♀H1c	CMen
divaricata	NLos
fejeenis	see *D. solida* var. *fejeensis*
mariesii ♀H2	CMen CPne ISha NLos
- var. ***stenolepis***	CMen
§ ***solida*** var. ***fejeensis***	IDee
tasmanii	CMen
trichomanoides	CMen NLos
- f. ***barbata***	CMen

Davidia (*Nyssaceae*)

involucrata ♀H5	Widely available
- 'Sonoma'	MBlu NLar SWeb
- var. ***vilmoriniana*** ♀H5	CBcs CRos CWCL ELan EPfP LRHS MAsh MBlu MGos NOrn SLim SPer SPtp

Daviesia (*Papilionaceae*)

cordata	SPlb
* ***ovalifolia***	SPlb
pectinata	SPlb

Debregeasia (*Urticaceae*)

CW&T 6451 **new**	CMCN
longifolia	SVen
- WWJ 11686	WCru

Decaisnea (*Lardizabalaceae*)

fargesii	Widely available
- B&SWJ 8070	WCru
insignis WJC 13740 **new**	WCru

Decodon (*Lythraceae*)

verticillatus	LLWG

Decumaria (*Hydrangeaceae*)

barbara	CMac MMuc NLar WCru WSHC
- 'Vicki'	NBro NLar
sinensis	CBot EPfP ESwi EUJe IDee LRHS MMuc NRHS SKHP SLon WCru WSHC

Degenia (*Brassicaceae*)

velebitica	WOld

Deinanthe ✿ (*Hydrangeaceae*)

bifida	CBct CMil EBee EPfP EWes GEdr LRHS MMrt WCru WPGP
- B&SWJ 5436	EWld WCru
- B&SWJ 5551	WCru
- B&SWJ 5655	LEdu
- 'Pink-Kii'	WCru
- 'Pink-Shi'	CMil WCru WSHC
bifida × ***caerulea***	CLAP WCru
'Blue Blush'	WCru
caerulea	CMil CPne ECho GCra GEdr GKev IMou LEdu LHop MMrt NLar NPnk SKHP WCru WSHC
- 'Blue Wonder'	CLAP LLHF MNrw SPoG
- white-flowered	IMou

Delonix (*Caesalpiniaceae*)

decaryi	SPlb
regia	SPlb

Delosperma (*Aizoaceae*)

from Graaf Reinet, South Africa	EPot, NSla XLum
from Ouberg Pass, South Africa	CPBP
from Sani Pass, South Africa	see *Ectotropis seanii-boganii*
§ ***aberdeenense*** ♀H3	SAko XLum
alpinum	see *Ectotropis alpina*
ashtonii	CCCN EWes NSla WThu XLum
basuticum	NHpl NSla
'Beaufort West'	CRos EDAr EPot EWes LRHS NRHS NSla WIce XLum
congestum misapplied	see *Malotigena frantiskae-niederlovae*
cooperi	CCCN CRos CTri EAEE ECho ECtt EDAr EPfP EPot EUJe GBin GKev ITim LRHS LSou MHer MSCN NHpl NRHS SChr SIgm SPlb SRot SVen WIce WPnn XLum
dyeri Red Mountain = 'Psdold'	ECho EDAr LRHS NRHS SAko XLum
ecklonis	GKev
Fire Spinner = 'P001s'	EDAr WHlf WIce XLum
floribundum Sequins = 'Balosquin'	CAbb
- 'Starburst'	MHol
- 'Stardust'	EWes
Golden Wonder = 'Wowd20111' (Wheels of Wonder Series) **new**	CCCN
harazianum	CPBP
jansei	NSla
(Jewel of Desert Series) 'Jewel of Desert Garnet'PBR	CAbb CCCN CRos ECtt LRHS NHpl NRHS SPad
- 'Jewel of Desert Moon Stone'PBR	CCCN CRos ECtt LRHS NHpl NRHS WIce
- 'Jewel of Desert Peridott'PBR	CCCN CRos CWGN ECtt LRHS NHpl NRHS SPad WIce
- 'Jewel of Desert Rosequartz' **new**	CCCN LRHS NRHS
- 'Jewel of Desert Ruby'PBR	CCCN CWGN LRHS NHpl WIce
- 'Jewel of Desert Topaz'PBR	CAbb CCCN CRos CWGN ECtt LRHS NHpl NRHS WIce
§ 'John Proffitt'	CCCN GKev SAko SPlb XLum
lavisiae	ELon NSla SPlb
'Lesotho Pink'	EWes
lineare	XLum
Mesa Verde = 'Kelaidis'	ECtt SAko XLum
nubigenum	CSma CTal CTri ECho ECtt EPot EUJe GAbr GCrg GKev NHpl SPlb
Orange Wonder = 'Wowdoy3' (Wheels of Wonder Series) **new**	CCCN SPad
'Ruby Coral'	CRos ECho ECtt EPot LRHS NRHS
sphalmanthoides	CPBP GEdr NHpl NSla SPlb
sutherlandii ♀H3	CCCN CSma CTal EDAr GBin NHpl SRot XLum
- 'Peach Star'	CCCN EDAr GEdr NHpl WIce
Table Mountain	see *D.* 'John Proffitt'
Violet Wonder = 'Wowdrw5' (Wheels of Wonder Series) **new**	CCCN
White Wonder = 'Wowdw7' (Wheels of Wonder Series) **new**	CCCN

Delphinium ✿ (*Ranunculaceae*)

	'Alice Artindale' (d)	EWes EWld IFoB WCot
	alpestre new	EWld
	ambiguum	see *Consolida ajacis*
	'Ann Woodfield'	CNMi
	'Ariel' ambig.	LRHS
	Astolat Group	CBcs CBod CSBt CTri CWib ELan EPfP ESps GMaP GMcL IBoy LRHS MGos MHol NHol NLar SHil SPer SPoG SWvt WCAu WHar
	'Atholl' 🏆H5	CNMi
	'Augenweide'	IPot
	'Baby Doll'	ESps
	'Bambi'	CNMi
	Belladonna Group	CWCL ELan EPfP WHar
	- 'Atlantis'	ECha IBoy LRHS NLar WCot
	- 'Casa Blanca'	EBee EPfP GMaP LRHS NLar
	- 'Cliveden Beauty'	CWCL EPfP GMaP LHop LRHS NLar WHar
	- 'Gute Nacht'	EBee
§	- 'Janny Arrow'	LRHS
	- 'Piccolo'	ECha NLar
	- 'Pink Sensation'	see *D.* × *ruysii* 'Pink Sensation'
	- 'Snow White' new	IBoy
	- 'Völkerfrieden'	GMaP IBoy LRHS MNrw MRav NLar WCot
	× ***bellamosum***	EPfP GMaP LRHS MNrw
	'Berghimmel'	EBee LRHS
	'Beryl Burton'	CNMi
	Black Knight Group	Widely available
	'Black Pearl'	ECtt IKil
	'Black-eyed Angels' (New Millennium Series)	IPot LSun SCob SGbt
	'Black-eyed Beauty'	MHol
	'Blauwal'	LRHS
	'Blue Arrow'	see *D.* (Belladonna Group) 'Janny Arrow', *D.* 'Blue Max Arrow', *D.* 'Kings Blue Arrow'
	Blue Bird Group	CBcs CRos CSBt CTri CWCL ELan EPfP ESps GMaP GMcL LRHS MGos MJak NMir NRHS SGbt SPer SPoG WCAu
	'Blue Butterfly'	see *D. grandiflorum* 'Blue Butterfly'
	'Blue Dawn' 🏆H5	CNMi
	Blue Fountains Group	CSBt EPfP LSRN SPoG SRms
	'Blue Jay'	CBcs CTri EPfP EWoo LSRN MWat
	'Blue Lace'	IPot LRHS NCGa
§	'Blue Max Arrow'	LRHS
	'Blue Nile' 🏆H5	CNMi LRHS
	'Blue Oasis'	CNMi
	Blue Springs Group	NGdn
	'Blue Tit'	CNMi IKil
	'Bob Geldof'	CNMi
	'Bolero' new	IBoy WCot
	'Boudicca'	CNMi
	'Bruce' 🏆H5	CNMi
	'Butterball'	CNMi
	Cameliard Group	CBcs CSBt ELan EPfP LHop LRHS NLar SHil SPer SPoG
	'Can-can' 🏆H5	CNMi
	carolinianum	SBrt
	cashmerianum	CPne
	(Centurion Series) 'Centurion Gentian Blue'	LOPS
	- 'Centurion Lavender'	LOPS
	- 'Centurion Sky Blue' 🏆H5	LOPS
	'Cha Cha' new	WCot
	'Chelsea Star'	CNMi EBee LRHS
	'Cher'	CNMi
	'Cherry Blossom'	EPfP NLar
	'Cherub' 🏆H5	LRHS
	chinense	see *D. grandiflorum*
	'Christel'	IKil LRHS LSRN NLar
	'Claire'	CNMi
	'Clifford Sky' 🏆H5	LRHS
	'Conspicuous' 🏆H5	CNMi
	'Coral Sunset' (d)	LBuc
	'Cranberry Delight'	CNMi
	'Crown Jewel'	EBee EWes LRHS
	'Dark Blue Black Bee' (Excalibur Series) new	GMcL
	'Dark Blue White Bee' (Excalibur Series)	GMcL NPri
	'Darling Sue'	CNMi
	'Diamant'PBR	IKil LRHS
	'Dreaming Spires'	SRms
	'Dunsden Green'	CNMi
	Dusky Maidens Group	ELan IFoB LRHS LSun MHol NAst NCGa SGbt SPoG
	dwarf, dark-blue-flowered	LRHS
	elatum	GCal
	- 'Blushing Brides' (New Millennium Series)	EBee LRHS SPoG
	- 'Dasante Blue'	GMcL MHol NPri
	- 'Double Innocence' (New Millennium Series) (d)	GBin IPot LRHS MHol NCGa
	- ex GORK	SMHy
	- 'Morning Lights' (New Millennium Series)	EPfP IPot LRHS MHol NCGa SPoG
	- 'Sweethearts' (New Millennium Series) 🏆H5	EBee LSun
	'Elizabeth Cook' 🏆H5	CNMi
	'Elmfreude'	IBoy LRHS
	'Emily Hawkins' 🏆H5	CNMi
	exaltatum	CSpe LPla
	'Fanfare'	CNMi
	'Faust' 🏆H5	CNMi IKil LRHS
	'Fenella' 🏆H5	CNMi LRHS
	'Finsteraarhorn'	IKil LRHS MAvo
	'Flamenco' new	WCot
	'Florestan'	CNMi
	Galahad Group	CBcs CSBt CTri CWCL CWib ECtt ELan EPfP ESps EWoo GMaP GMcL LRHS MJak MWat NGdn NHol SPer SPlb SPoG WCAu WHar
	'Galahad' (Pacific Hybrid Series)	LCro LOPS LSun MGos MHol
	'Galileo' 🏆H5	CNMi
	'Gemini'	CNMi
	'Gemma'	CNMi
	'Gillian Dallas'	IKil LRHS
	glaciale HWJK 2299	WCru
	'Gossamer'	CNMi ECtt IKil
§	***grandiflorum***	GKev
§	- 'Blauer Zwerg'	MNHC SPoG WHar
§	- 'Blue Butterfly'	CSpe EPfP ESps LHop SPlb SPoG WSHC
	- Blue Dwarf	see *D. grandiflorum* 'Blauer Zwerg'
	- Delfix Series	LRHS
	- - 'Delfix Blue' new	WTor
	- - 'Delfix Rose' new	WTor
	- - 'Delfix White' new	WTor
	- 'Summer Blues' (Summer Series)	LRHS SRot
	- 'Summer Nights' (Summer Series)	EPfP LRHS SPoG WHar
	- 'White Butterfly'	LRHS
	'Green Twist' (New Millennium Series)	LRHS SCob SPoG

	(Guardian Series) 'Guardian Blue'	EBee LCro LOPS LRHS NPri SHil SPoG
	- 'Guardian Lavender'	LCro LOPS LRHS MHol SHil SPoG
	- 'Guardian White'	LCro LOPS LRHS NPri SHil SPoG
	Guinevere Group	CBcs CSBt CWCL CWib ECtt EPfP SPer SPoG
	- 'Lady Guinevere'	IBoy
	'Guy Langdon'	CNMi
	'Highlander Blueberry Pie'	ECtt IBoy LRHS SPoG WCot
	'Highlander Crystal Delight'	ECtt LRHS SPoG WCot
	'Highlander Morning Sunrise'	IKil SPoG WCot
	himalayae	GKev
	'Honey Pink'	CNMi
I	'Independence'	IKil LRHS
	'Innocence'	LRHS SCob
	'Jenny Agutter'	CNMi
	'Jill Curley' ♀H5	LRHS
	'Kathleen Cooke'	CNMi
	'Kestrel' ♀H5	CNMi
	King Arthur Group	CBcs CSBt CWCL ELan EPfP EUJe LSRN LSun MGos MHol MWat SHil SPer SPoG WHar
§	'Kings Blue Arrow' PBR	LRHS
	'La Bohème'	CWCL
§	'Langdon's Royal Flush'	LRHS
	'Lanzenträger'	LRHS
	'Leonora'	CNMi
	'Loch Leven'	CNMi
	'Lord Butler' ♀H5	CNMi EBee EWes LRHS
	'Lucia Sahin' ♀H5	CNMi
	maackianum	IMou LLHF WCot
	Magic Fountains Series	IFoB LRHS SPlb SPoG SVic
	- 'Magic Fountains Blue/White Bee'	IBoy LRHS
	- 'Magic Fountains Bright Eye' **new**	ESps
	- 'Magic Fountains Cherry Blossom'	EPfP SHil SPoG
	- 'Magic Fountains Dark Blue'	EAJP EPfP GMaP IBoy LRHS LSRN NEgg NLar SPoG
	- 'Magic Fountains Deep Rose/White Bee'	LRHS
	- 'Magic Fountains Lavender'	EAJP EPfP NLar
	- 'Magic Fountains Lilac Pink'	EPfP SPoG
	- 'Magic Fountains Lilac Rose'	EAJP LRHS
	- 'Magic Fountains Pure White'	EAJP EPfP IBoy LRHS NEgg
	- 'Magic Fountains Sky Blue'	EPfP SPoG
	- 'Magic Fountains The Blues' **new**	ESps
	'Marilyn Clarrissa'	CNMi
	'Merlin' ambig.	LRHS
	'Michael Ayres' ♀H5	CNMi
	'Mighty Atom'	CNMi IKil IPot LRHS
	'Min' ♀H5	CNMi
	'Misty Mauves' (New Millennium Series) (d)	LRHS
	'Molly Buchanan'	CNMi
	'Moon Light' (Highlander Series) (d)	ECtt EPfP EWTr IKil LBuc LRHS MHol NAst NLar SPad SPoG WCot
	'Moonbeam'	LRHS
	'Moonlight Blues' (New Millennium Series)	LSun SGbt
	'Morgentau'	EBee LRHS
	'Morning Sunrise' PBR **new**	IBoy
	'Mrs Newton Lees'	IKil LRHS NLar
	'Ned Rose'	IKil
	'Ned Wit'	IKil
	nudicaule	GKev SPlb
	- 'Laurin'	LRHS
	'Ouvertüre'	LRHS
	oxysepalum	LLHF
	Pacific hybrids	CWCL EPfP ESps IBoy LSRN MHer NLar SRms SWvt WHar
	'Pagan Purples' (New Millennium Series) (d)	EWTr IFoB IPot LRHS NCGa
	'Patricia Johnson'	CNMi
	Percival Group	EPfP
	'Pericles'	CNMi LRHS
	'Pink Punch' (New Millennium Series)	ELan EPfP LHop LRHS SCob
	'Pink Ruffles'	CNMi
	'Plagu Blue' PBR	MAvo NLar
	Princess Caroline = 'Odabar' PBR	CBcs
	'Purple Passion' (New Millennium Series)	EAJP ELan EPfP LRHS LSun SCob SPoG
	'Red Caroline'	CBcs
	requienii	CBgR CSpe MNHC
	'Rona'	CNMi
	'Rose Butterfly' (d)	LRHS NRHS
	Round Table Mixture	CTri
	'Royal Aspirations' (New Millennium Series)	ELan LHop LRHS SCob SGbt SPoG
	'Royal Flush'	see *D.* 'Langdon's Royal Flush'
	'Ruby'	CNMi
	'Ruby Tuesday'	CNMi
	'Ruby Wedding'	CNMi
§	× ***ruysii*** 'Pink Sensation'	CWCL EWTr IBoy NLar
	'Sandpiper'	CNMi
	'Schildknappe'	EBee
	'Schönbuch'	LRHS
	'Secret' PBR	LRHS WCot
	'Shieldbearer'	LRHS
	'Silver Jubilee'	CNMi
	'Sky Sensation'	IBoy LRHS
	'Snow Queen Arrow'	LRHS
	'Sommerabend'	LRHS
	'Sommerwind'	EBee
	'Sooty'	CNMi
	'Spindrift' ♀H5	CNMi LRHS
	'Starlight' PBR	LRHS
	'Strawberry Fair'	IKil LRHS NLar
	Summer Skies Group	CBcs CSBt CTri CWCL ELan EPfP ESps EWTr EWoo LRHS LSun MGos MWat NNys SHil SPer SPoG WCAu
	'Summerfield Diana'	CNMi
	'Summerfield Oberon'	WCot
	'Sungleam' ♀H5	ECtt IKil
	'Sunkissed' ♀H5	CNMi
	'Sunny Skies' (New Millennium Series)	ELan LRHS SPoG
	sutchuenense	EWld
	- BWJ 7867	WCru
	'Sweet Sensation' PBR (Highlander Series) (d)	EBee ECtt EPfP IBoy IKil LCro LRHS NAst NLar WCot WHlf
	'Sweetheart'	LRHS
	tatsienense	IFoB
	'Tiger Eye'	CNMi
	'Trudy'	CNMi
	'Vanessa Mae'	CNMi
	'White Swan'	EPfP
	Woodfield strain	WHrl
	'Yvonne'	LRHS NLar
	'Zauberflöte'	EBee LRHS

Dendranthema see *Chrysanthemum*

Dendriopoterium see *Sanguisorba*

Dendrobenthamia see *Cornus*

Dendrocalamus (*Poaceae*)

asper	XBlo
calostachys	SPlb
giganteus	XBlo
§ ***strictus***	XBlo

Dendromecon (*Papaveraceae*)

rigida	CBcs EPfP LRHS SKHP WPGP WSHC

Dendropanax ✿ (*Araliaceae*)

cf. ***kwangsiensis*** FMWJ 13274	WCru
trifidus B&SWJ 11230	WCru

Dennstaedtia ✿ (*Dennstaedtiaceae*)

punctilobula	CLAP

Dentaria see *Cardamine*

pinnata	see *Cardamine heptaphylla*
polyphylla	see *Cardamine kitaibelii*

Deparia (*Woodsiaceae*)

conilii	NLos
okuboana	ISha

Dermatobotrys (*Scrophulariaceae*)

saundersii	ECre

Derwentia see *Parahebe*

Deschampsia (*Poaceae*)

cespitosa	CBod CKno CLet CWib EPPr EPfP LCro LOPS LPot LRHS MWat SCob SPhx SPlb WCot WMoo XLum XSen
- Bronze Veil	see *D. cespitosa* 'Bronzeschleier'
§ - 'Bronzeschleier'	CBod CDor CMea CWCL EAEE EBee EHoe ELan EPPr EPed EPfP GBin GMaP LRHS MAsh MAvo MBel NGdn NRHS NWsh SCob SPer SPhx SRms SWvt WMoo WPtf XLum
- 'Coral Cloud'	GQue
- 'Fairy's Joke'	see *D. cespitosa* var. *vivipara*
- 'Garnet Schist'	GQue LRHS SPhx
- Gold Dust	see *D. cespitosa* 'Goldstaub'
- Golden Dew	see *D. cespitosa* 'Goldtau'
- Golden Pendant	see *D. cespitosa* 'Goldgehänge'
- Golden Shower	see *D. cespitosa* 'Goldgehänge'
- Golden Veil	see *D. cespitosa* 'Goldschleier'
§ - 'Goldgehänge'	CSam EHoe NBir XLum
§ - 'Goldschleier'	CBod CSam CSpe EBee ECha EPPr EPfP GBin GMaP GQue LHop LRHS NGdn NRHS NWsh SCob SPhx SWvt WMoo XLum
§ - 'Goldstaub'	EPPr
§ - 'Goldtau'	Widely available
- 'Mill End'	CKno
- 'Morning Dew'	WFar
- 'Northern Lights' (v)	CSBt ELan EPfP LRHS MBel NBro SLim SPer SPoG SRms SWvt XLum
- 'Pixie Fountain'	CBWd EBee GQue LHop LRHS LSun MWat SPhx SPtp
- 'Schottland'	CKno EBee ELon EPPr EPed GBin LEdu MAvo
- 'Tardiflora'	CKno EPPr
- 'Tauträger'	CKno EBee ELon EPPr GQue SMHy XLum
§ - var. ***vivipara***	EHoe EPPr GBin NBro
- 'Waldschatt'	CKno EBee EPPr
- 'Willow Green'	GCal SCoo
flexuosa	CBWd CKno EHoe LRHS NBir NRHS NWsh SPhx
- 'Tatra Gold'	CBWd CWCL ECha EHoe ELan ELon EPed EPfP ESps GMaP LBMP LRHS MAsh MHtn MMuc MRav NBir NBro NGdn NRHS NSti SCob SLim SPer SPoG SRot SWvt

Desfontainia (*Loganiaceae*)

§ ***spinosa*** ♀H4	CAbb CBcs CBot CDul CMHG CMac CTri CTsd CWib EBee ELan ELon EPfP GAbr GKin GMcL IArd LRHS MAsh MBlu MGil MMuc SLim SPer SPoG WBod WFar WPat WSHC
- 'Harold Comber'	CMac NLar WHor
- f. ***hookeri***	see *D. spinosa*

Desmodium (*Papilionaceae*)

callianthum	CMac LRHS SBrt WSHC
canadense	EBee MNrw NLar SBrt SPhx
cuspidatum var. ***longifolium***	SPhx
§ ***elegans***	CBcs CRos EBee ELan EPfP LRHS NLar NRHS SBrt SChF SKHP SVen WBod WHer WPGP WSHC
paniculatum	SBrt
praestans	see *D. yunnanense*
tiliifolium	see *D. elegans*
§ ***yunnanense***	WSHC

Deuterocohnia (*Bromeliaceae*)

brevifolia ♀H2	CFil WCot WPGP
lotteae	WCot

Deutzia ✿ (*Hydrangeaceae*)

bhutanensis HWJK 2180	WCru
'Bright Eyes'	WPGP
calycosa	GQui
- B&SWJ 7742	WPat
- BWJ 8007	WCru
- 'Dali'	CFil NLar SDys
chunii	see *D. ningpoensis*
compacta	CMCN SLon WPGP
- GWJ 9202	WCru
- GWJ 9203	WCru
- GWJ 9339	WCru
- 'Lavender Time'	CBot CMac EPfP LRHS NLar SWvt
cordatula B&SWJ 3720	WCru
- B&SWJ 6917	WCru
corymbosa	MRav
crenata	CBot
- B&SWJ 8886	WCru
- B&SWJ 8896	WCru
- B&SWJ 8924	WCru
- 'Flore Pleno'	see *D. scabra* 'Plena'
- var. ***heterotricha*** B&SWJ 5805	WCru
- - B&SWJ 8879	WCru
- var. ***nakaiana***	SBrt WPat
- - B&SWJ 11184	WCru
- - 'Nikko'	see *D. gracilis* 'Nikko'
§ - 'Pride of Rochester' (d) ♀H5	CAco CBcs CMCN CWib ECrN GKin LRHS LSou MBlu MMuc MRav NLar SCob SEle SGol SLim SPoG SWvt WGrn

'Dark Eyes'	CFil EBee SAko SMad
discolor 'Major'	CFil IDee WPGP WPat
× ***elegantissima***	SRms
- 'Fasciculata'	CBod ELan EPfP EWTr LRHS NLar SPer SWvt WBor
- 'Rosealind' 🏆H5	CBar CBcs CBot CCCN CDul CMac CTri EBee ELan EPfP GKin IArd LHop LRHS LSRN LSou MGil MRav SLim SPer SRms SWvt WCFE WKif WPat WSHC
glabrata B&SWJ 617	GQui WCru
- B&SWJ 8427	WCru
glomeruliflora BWJ 7742	WCru
gracilis	CBod CRos CSBt EAEE ELan EPfP EWTr GKin GQui LPot LRHS MAsh MGos MRav MSwo NRHS SPad SPer WFar WHar WPat
- B&SWJ 8927	WCru
- 'Aurea'	CBcs CMac EPfP LRHS
- 'Carminea'	see *D.* × *rosea* 'Carminea'
§ - 'Nikko' 🏆H4	CBcs CBot CMCN CMac CRos EBee ECho ELan EPfP EShb EWes GKin LHop LRHS MAsh MGos MHer MMuc MRav NGdn NLar NRHS SGol SHil SPlb SWvt WKif WSHC
- var. ***ogatae*** B&SWJ 8911	WCru
- 'Rosea'	see *D.* × *rosea*
grandiflora	NChi WPGP
'Hillieri'	CFil
hookeriana	CRos EBee EPfP LBuc LLHF LRHS NRHS SWvt WBod
× ***hybrida*** 'Contraste' 🏆H5	CMac SPer
- 'Iris Alford'	CRos EPfP LRHS MGos NRHS SAko SChF SHil SLon WFar WPGP
- 'Joconde' 🏆H5	WFar
- 'Magicien' misapplied	see *D.* × *hybrida* 'Strawberry Fields'
- 'Magicien' Lemoine	Widely available
- 'Mont Rose' 🏆H5	Widely available
§ - 'Strawberry Fields' 🏆H5	Widely available
× ***kalmiiflora***	CMac CSBt CTri GKin GQui MAsh MJak MRav NLar SPer SRms WFar WPat
× ***lemoinei***	MJak NGdn
longifolia	CMCN WPGP WPat
- 'Veitchii'	CSBt EPfP GQui MGil MRav
- 'Vilmoriniae'	MRav
× ***magnifica***	CBcs CDul GQui NLar SGbt SRms
- 'Rubra'	see *D.* × *hybrida* 'Strawberry Fields'
× ***maliflora***	CFil
maximowicziana B&SWJ 11567	WCru
monbeigii 🏆H5	CBot CFil EPfP LLHF LRHS MRav SWvt WKif
- BWJ 7728	CBot WCru
multiradiata	CFil EBee WPGP
§ ***ningpoensis***	CFil CTsd EBee EPfP GQui MNHC NLar SMad SPer WCFE WPGP
paniculata B&SWJ 8592	WCru
parviflora var. ***barbinervis*** B&SWJ 8478	WCru
'Pink Pompon'	see *D.* 'Rosea Plena'
prunifolia B&SWJ 8588	WCru
pulchra	CAbP CBot CDul CMCN ELan EPfP EWTr IDee LRHS MMuc MRav SBrt SLon SPer SPoG SWeb WPGP WPat
- B&SWJ 1738	WCru
- B&SWJ 3870	WCru
- B&SWJ 6908	WCru
- pink-tinged	WPGP
purpurascens BWJ 7859	WCru
rehderiana	CFil
§ × ***rosea***	CDul CWib EPfP ESps LRHS MAsh NRHS SRms WKif
- 'Campanulata'	MAsh MSwo
§ - 'Carminea'	SDix SPlb SRms WPat
§ 'Rosea Plena' (d)	CBot CLet CMac CRos CSBt CWib ECrN ELan EPfP GKin GMcL LBuc LRHS MAsh MGos MMuc NLar NRHS SEle SLim SPoG SWvt WFar
rubens	LLHF WPat
scabra	CAco CDul CTri
- B&SWJ 11127	WCru
- B&SWJ 11168	WCru
- B&SWJ 11178	WCru
§ - 'Candidissima' (d) 🏆H5	CDul GQui MGil MMuc MRav SCob SPer WPat
- 'Codsall Pink' 🏆H5	CFil MRav
§ - 'Plena' (d)	ECrN EPfP GKin NLar SPer SPoG WCFE
- 'Pride of Rochester'	see *D. crenata* 'Pride of Rochester'
- 'Punctata' (v)	EHoe MMuc SEND SRms
- 'Robert Fortune'	SPlb
- 'Variegata' (v)	CDul CMac
setchuenensis	CMac GQui MRav WPat WSHC
- PAB 7449	LEdu
- var. ***corymbiflora*** 🏆H5	CBcs CBot CDul CTri ECre ELan EPfP EWTr IDee LHop LRHS MSwo NLar SAko SChF SEle SPoG SWvt WFar WKif WPGP
- - NJM 11.096 **new**	WPGP
taiwanensis	EPfP SAko SGol WPGP WPat
- B&SWJ 6858	WCru
- CWJ 12443	WCru
- CWJ 12459	WCru
× ***wellsii***	see *D. scabra* 'Candidissima'
× ***wilsonii***	SRms

Dianella ✿ (*Hemerocallidaceae*)

caerulea	CBcs CMac EBee ELan EPri IBoy IMou NBir NLar
- Cassa Blue = 'Dbb03'PBR	CBod CHll CLet EPfP LRHS SPad SPer SPoG
- Little Jess = 'Dcmp01'PBR	EBee
- 'Variegata'	see *D. tasmanica* 'Variegata'
ensifolia	LEdu
nigra	CBcs IMou LEdu LTro
- 'Margaret Pringle' (v)	CBcs
§ ***revoluta*** 'Allyn Citation'PBR **new**	EBee LRHS
- 'Blue Stream' **new**	EBee
- Coolvista	see *D. revoluta* 'Allyn Citation'
- Little Rev = 'Dr5000'PBR	EBee EPfP ESwi
'Silver Streak' (v)	LRHS SPoG
'Streetscape' **new**	EBee
tasmanica	CAbb CBcs CElw CKno CMac CPne CTal CTri CTsd ECre ELan EPfP EShb EUJe GBin IBoy LEdu LHop LTro SMad SRms WSHC
- from Logan	EBee GCal
- 'Emerald Arch'	ESwi LEdu SPer
- 'Splice'	CDTJ MJak
- Tasred = 'Tr20'PBR	CBod CTsd ELan EPfP ESwi EUJe NPla SPer
§ - 'Variegata' (v)	CCCN CDTJ ELan LHop NLar

Dianthus ✿ (*Caryophyllaceae*)

'Alan Titchmarsh' (p)	CRos CWCL CWhe ECtt EPfP ESps LRHS LSRN MGos MTis NEgg NRHS SBod SPoG SWvt
'Albert Hill' (p)	LAll

	'Albus Plenus' (p)	MJak
	'Aldridge Yellow' (b)	LAll
	'Alfriston' (b) ♀^{H6}	LAll
	'Alice' (p)	LAll LSRN
	'Alice Lever' (p)	WAbe
§	'Allen's Maria' (p)	LAll
	'Allspice' (p)	CFis MRav WHoo
	Allwoodii Alpinus Group (p)	NGdn SRms XLum
	(Allwoodii Group) 'Doris' (p)	CRos CWhe SHil
	'Allwood's Celebration' (p)	LAll
	'Allwood's Crimson' (pf)	LAll
	'Allwood's Delight' (p)	LAll
	alpinus ♀^{H6}	ESps GCrg GJos MMuc
	- 'Albus' (p)	GCrg NWad SIgm
	- 'Joan's Blood' (p) ♀^{H6}	ECho GBuc GCrg LSRN NHpl WAbe
	'Alyson' (p)	LAll
	amurensis	EPPr GCal SPhx XLum
	- 'Siberian Blue'	EPPr GPSL
	anatolicus	CRos CTri ECho EDAr LRHS MHer NGdn NRHS XLum
	'Anders Fay Seagrave' (p)	LAll
	'Anders Irene Ann' (pf)	CNMi
	'Anders Kath Phillips' (pf) ♀^{H2}	CNMi
	'Anders Melody' (p)	LAll
	'Anders Patricia Griffiths' (p)	CNMi LAll
	'Andrew Morton' (b)	LAll
	'Angela Carol' (pf)	CNMi
	'Angelo' (b)	LAll
	'Ann Franklin' (pf) ♀^{H2}	CNMi
	'Annabelle' (p)	LAll
	'Annette' (p)	CPBP CRos EAJP ECho EDAr GCrg IPot LRHS LSRN MAsh NGdn NHol NRHS SRGP SWvt
	'Annie Claybourne' (pf)	CNMi
	'Apricot Sue' (pf)	LAll
	Arctic Star	see *D.* 'Devon Arctic Star'
	arenarius	GKev LAll LEdu NGdn SPhx SPlb WWFP XLum
	- 'Little Maiden' (p)	CSpe GWyn MMuc NCGa NGdn WIce
	- 'Snow Flurries' (p)	ITim
	'Argus'	LAll
	armeria	CBgR CFis WHer WOut
	arpadianus	GKev
	- var. ***pumilus***	EPot
	'Arthur Leslie' (b)	LAll
§	× ***arvernensis*** (p) ♀^{H6}	ECha ECho SBch
	- 'Albus'	ECho
	'Audrey Robinson' (pf)	CNMi
	'Aurora' (b)	LAll
	'Auvergne'	see *D.* × ***arvernensis***
	'Averiensis'	see *D.* 'Berlin Snow'
	'Badenia' (p)	ECha
	'Bailey's Celebration' (p)	CWhe MTis SRGP
	barbatus	SVic
	- SDR 6404	GKev
	- 'Black Adder' (p,a)	CSpe
	- 'Heart Attack' (p,a)	WCot
	- 'Indian Carpet' (p,a)	LCro
	- Midget Group (p,a)	CBod
	- 'Monksilver Black' (p,a)	CSpe EBee ECtt EUJe MAvo MHol MPie NCou NSti SBod SDix SMad WCot WRHF
	- Nigrescens Group (p,a) ♀^{H7}	CBre CSpe SPhx
	- - 'Sooty' (p,a)	CBod CTsd CWCL CWld EDAr GWyn WHer
	- 'Oeschberg' (p,a)	GWyn
*	- 'Roseus' (p,a) **new**	GWyn
	- (Super Parfait Series) 'Super Parfait Raspberry' (p,a) **new**	CRos
	- - 'Super Parfait Strawberry' (p,a)	LRHS NRHS
	- 'Tuxedo Black' (p,a)	WMoo
	'Barley Sugar' (pf)	CNMi
	basuticus	CTre GKev
§	'Bat's Double Red' (p)	LAll
	'Becky Robinson' (p) ♀^{H6}	CNMi LAll
	'Belmont Duchess' (p)	LAll
§	'Berlin Snow' (p)	CPBP CRos ECho EPot GCrg ITim LRHS NRHS
	'Betsy' (pf)	LAll
	'Betty Miller' (b)	LAll
	'Betty Morton' (p) ♀^{H6}	CRos IFoB LRHS NRHS WKif
	'Betty's Choice' (pf)	CNMi
	'Bill Smith' (pf)	CNMi
	'Blue Hills' (p)	ECho GKev
	'Blue Ice' (b)	LAll
	'Blush'	see *D.* 'Souvenir de la Malmaison'
	'Bobby' (p)	LAll
	'Bob's Highlight' (pf)	CNMi
	'Bombardier' (p)	ECtt
	'Bookham Gleam' (b)	LAll
	'Bookham Grand' (b)	LAll
	'Bookham Heroine' (b)	LAll
	'Bookham Lad' (b)	LAll
	'Border Special' (b)	LAll
	'Bouquet Purple' (p)	CSpe
	'Bovey Belle' (p)	LAll
	'Bramdean' (pf)	CNMi
	brevicaulis subsp. ***brevicaulis***	LLHF
	'Brian Tumbler' (b) ♀^{H6}	LAll
	'Bridal Veil' (p)	LAll SBch WHer
	Bright Eyes = 'Wp07 Ame02'^{PBR} (p)	CWhe
	'Brilliance' (p)	WMoo
	'Brilliant'	see *D. deltoides* 'Brilliant'
	'Brilliant Star' (p) ♀^{H6}	CRos ECho ECtt LRHS NRHS SEND SWvt WIce
	'Brockenhurst' (pf)	CNMi
	'Brympton Red' (p)	CFis ECha LAll
	'Bryony Lisa' (b) ♀^{H6}	LAll
	Bubblegum = 'Wp15val12' (p) **new**	CWhe
	caesius	see *D. gratianopolitanus*
	callizonus	LLHF
	'Calypso' (pf)	CTri
	'Calypso Star' (p)	ECho ECtt SPoG
	'Camilla' (b)	CNMi
	'Can-can' (pf)	ECho ECtt MHol
	'Candy Clove' (b)	LAll
	Candy Floss	see *D.* 'Devon Flavia'
	'Candy Spice' (p)	MRav
§	'Carmine Letitia Wyatt'^{PBR} (p) ♀^{H6}	CRos CWhe ECtt LRHS NRHS SPoG
	Carmine Valda	see *D.* 'Devon Louise'
	carthusianorum	Widely available
	- W&B BGL-1	WCot
I	- 'Rupert's Pink' (p)	EBee NGdn SWvt
	caryophyllus	ENfk SVic WOut WSFF
	Cassandra = 'Bardranasca'^{PBR} (pf)	LAll
	'Cecil Wyatt'	see *D.* 'Rose Devon Pearl'
	'Charles' (p)	LAll
	'Charles Edward' (p)	LAll
	'Charles Musgrave'	see *D.* 'Musgrave's Pink'
	'Chastity' (p)	LAll LLHF WHoo

	Cheddar pink	see *D. gratianopolitanus*
	'Cherly'	LSRN
	'Cherry Clove' (b)	LAll
	Cherry Daiquiri = 'Wp15 Pie42' (p) **new**	CWhe
	'Cheryl'	see *D.* 'Houndspool Cheryl'
	'Chesswood Dorothy Cottam' (b)	LAll
	'Chetwyn Ruth Gillies' (pf)	CNMi
	'Chianti Double' (p)	LAll
	Chili	see *D.* Cracker
	chinensis 'Black and White' (p,a)	CSpe
I	- 'Valentine' (p,a)	LAll
	'Chris Crew' (b) 🏆H6	LAll
	'Christopher' (p)	LAll
	'Clare' (p)	LAll
	'Claret Joy' (p) 🏆H6	ECtt EPfP ESps LAll MMuc SEND
	'Cleopatra' (pf) **new**	EMal
	'Clifford Pipperoo' (pf)	LAll WCot
	'Clunie' (b)	LAll
§	'Cockenzie Pink' (p)	LAll SBch WHer
	Coconut Sundae = 'Wp 05 Yves'PBR (Scent First Series) (p)	CRos CWhe ECtt ELan ELon LCro LOPS LRHS LSRN MCot NPri NRHS SRot WTor
	'Constance' (p)	LAll
	'Constance Finnis'	see *D.* 'Fair Folly'
	'Consul' (b)	LAll
	'Conwy Silver' (p)	WAbe
	'Conwy Star' (p)	WAbe
	'Coral Reef'PBR (Scent First Series) (p)	CWhe ECtt ELan LCro LRHS MTis NRHS SHil SPoG
	'Coronation Ruby' (p) 🏆H6	LAll
	Cosmopolitan = 'Wp15 Pie43' (p) **new**	CWhe
	'Coste Budde' (p)	SBch WSHC
§	Cracker = 'Wp10 Sab06'PBR (Early Bird Series) (p)	CWhe GAbr LRHS SHil
	'Cranberry Crush' (pf)	CNMi
	'Cranmere Pool' (p) 🏆H6	CBcs CWhe ECtt ELan EPfP LRHS SEND SPoG SWvt WBrk WTor
	Crimson Valda	see *D.* 'Devon Kitty'
	'Crimson Warrior' (pf)	CNMi
	'Crock of Gold' (b)	LAll
	'Crompton Classic' (pf)	CNMi
	'Crompton Princess' (pf)	CNMi
	cruentus	CAby CFis CSpe ELan EPPr EWTr GCal LCro LRHS MBel NDov SDix SHar SPhx SPtp SWvt WCAu WPtf
	'D.D.R.'	see *D.* 'Berlin Snow'
	'Dad's Favourite' (p)	LAll
	'Dainty Dame' (p) 🏆H4	CRos CSpe CTri ECho ECtt EPfP LAll LRHS MNHC NRHS SBch SIgm WBod
§	'Dancing Queen'PBR (p)	MTis
	'Daphne' (p)	LAll
	'David' (p)	LAll LSRN SCob
	'David Russell' (b) 🏆H6	LAll
	'David Saunders' (b) 🏆H6	LAll
	'Dawn' (b)	LAll
	'Dedham Beauty' (p)	MPie SEND WCot
	deltoides 🏆H6	CTre CWld ECha ECho ENfk EPfP EWld LEdu MAsh MBel MMuc MNHC SDix SIgm SPlb SRms WJek WPtf
	- 'Albus' (p)	ECha EPfP GBin GWyn NGdn WMoo
	- 'Arctic Fire' (p)	CWib ECho EPfP GJos GWyn MBel NGdn NHol WMoo
	- 'Bright Eyes' (p)	ECho
§	- 'Brilliant' (p)	CTri EAJP ECho GJos GWyn LAll NGdn NHol SPhx SRms WHar
	- 'Broughty Blaze' (p)	GCrg
	- 'Dark Eyes' (p)	EWes
	- 'Erectus' (p)	EPfP
	- Flashing Light	see *D. deltoides* 'Leuchtfunk'
§	- 'Leuchtfunk' (p)	ECho GJos GPSL MJak SPoG WMoo WRHF WTor
I	- 'Luneburg Heath Maiden Pink' (p)	NGdn SPhx
	- Microchips Group (p)	WMoo
	- 'Nelli' (p)	NGdn WMoo
	- red-flowered (p)	SVic
	- 'Shrimp' (p)	EAJP NGdn
	'Dennis' (p)	LAll LSRN
	'Desert Song' (b)	LAll
	'Desmond'	EPfP
§	'Devon Arctic Star' (Early Bird Series) (p)	CMea CRos CTri CWhe ELan EWoo GMaP LHop LRHS NRHS SHil SPoG SRot SWvt WHlf
	'Devon Cream'PBR (p)	CWhe ECtt ELan ESps LRHS NEgg
	'Devon Dove'PBR (p) 🏆H6	CRos CSBt CTri CWhe ECtt ELan EPfP LRHS MRav MTis NEgg NRHS
	'Devon Esther'	see *D.* Popstar
	'Devon Fatima'	see *D.* Iced Gem
§	'Devon Flavia'PBR (Scent First Series) (p) 🏆H6	CWhe ELan LCro LOPS LRHS LSou MTis SHil SPoG
	'Devon Flores'	see *D.* Shooting Star
	'Devon General'PBR (p)	CTri CWhe
	'Devon Glow' (p)	EPfP
§	'Devon Isolde'PBR (p)	CWhe
§	'Devon Judith'PBR (p)	CWhe
§	'Devon Kitty'PBR (p)	CWhe
§	'Devon Louise'PBR (p)	CWhe
	'Devon Magic'PBR (p)	CWhe ECtt LRHS
	'Devon Opal'	see *D.* Lady Madonna
	'Devon Pearl'PBR (p)	CWhe
	'Devon Sapphire'	see *D.* Mystic Star
	'Devon Verity'	see *D.* 'Dancing Queen'
§	'Devon Winnie'PBR	CWhe MAsh MTis
	'Devon Wizard'PBR (p) 🏆H6	CRos CSBt CWhe ECtt EPfP LRHS MRav MSpe MTis NDov NEgg NRHS SBod SEND WCAu
§	'Devon Xera' (p) 🏆H6	CWhe MTis
§	'Devon Yolande'PBR (Scent First Series) (p)	CRos CWhe ECtt ELan EPfP LBMP LCro LOPS LRHS LSRN NRHS SEND SHil SPoG
	'Devon Yvette'	CWhe
	'Dewdrop' (p)	CFis CMea CTri EPot EWTr LAll MAsh MHer MMuc NBir NGdn SEND WHal
	'Dian Cape' (b)	LAll
	'Diana'	see *D.* Dona
	'Diane' (p) 🏆H6	CWhe ELan EPfP ESps LAll NEgg SPoG SWvt WHar
	'Dinetta Lilac' (p) **new**	LRHS NRHS
	'Dinetta Pink' (p) **new**	LRHS NRHS
	'Diplomat' (b)	LAll
	'Doctor James Dennison' (pf)	CNMi
§	Dona = 'Brecas' (pf)	LSRN SRGP
	'Dora' (p)	CRos LRHS NRHS
	'Doreen Hodgson' (p)	ECtt LAll
	'Doris' (p) 🏆H6	Widely available
	'Doris Allwood' (pf)	CNMi CSBt EMal LAll
	'Doris Elite' (p)	LAll
	'Doris Galbally' (b)	LAll
	'Doris Majestic' (p)	LAll
	'Doris Ruby'	see *D.* 'Houndspool Ruby'
	'Doris Supreme' (p)	LAll
	'Double Lace'	ECtt
	Dubai = 'Bardibua'PBR (pf)	LAll
	'Dubarry' (p)	CTri ECtt
	'Duchess of Fife' (p)	EPfP

'Duchess of Roxburghe' (pf)	EMal LAll
'Duchess of Westminster' (M)	EMal LAll
'Duke of Norfolk' (pf)	EMal LAll
'Dunkirk Spirit' (pf)	CNMi
'Dusky Janelle' (pf)	CNMi
'Earl Kelso' (pf)	EMal
'Earl of Essex' (p)	LAll
'Edenside Scarlet' (b)	LAll
'Edenside White' (b)	LAll
'Edna' (p)	LAll
'Edward Allwood' (pf)	LAll
'Edwin Cross' (b)	LAll
'Eileen' (p)	LAll
'Eileen Lever' (p)	CPBP IFoB SIgm WAbe
'Eileen Neal' (b) ♀H6	LAll
'Eileen O'Connor' (b) ♀H6	LAll
'Eira Wen' (p)	WAbe
'Eleanor Parker' (p)	WAbe
'Eleanor's Old Irish' (p)	ECtt ELon LRHS MBel MHol MPie NDov SEND WCot WHoo
'Elizabethan' (p)	CFis CSpe EWTr MCot MHCG SBch SDys
* 'Elizabethan Pink' (p)	LAll
'Elsie Ketchen' (pf)	CNMi
'Emile Paré' (p)	CFis
'Emjay' (b)	LAll
'Emmeline Pankhurst' (pf)	CNMi
'Emperor'	see *D.* 'Bat's Double Red'
erinaceus	ECho EPot GCrg GJos SIgm
- var. ***alpinus***	EPot ITim
- Duguid's	WAbe
'Erycina' (b)	LAll
'Ethel Hurford' (p)	WHoo
'Eva Humphries' (b)	LAll
'Evelyn Berry' (p)	CNMi
'Evening Star' (p) ♀H6	CRos CTri CWhe ECho EWoo LRHS NRHS SPoG SWvt WIce
'Eve's Holly' (pf)	CNMi
'Exquisite' (b)	LAll
§ 'Fair Folly' (p)	LAll WHer
'Farnham Rose' (p)	LAll
'Fenbow Nutmeg Clove' (b)	SDix
'Fettes Mount' (p)	WBrk WCot
'Feuerhexe' (p)	ECtt GCrg XLum
'Fimbriatus' (p)	WHoo
'Fiona' (p)	LAll
Fire Star	see *D.* 'Devon Xera'
'Firestar' (p)	CRos CTri ELan GMaP LRHS MAsh NRHS SHil SRot SWvt
'First Lady' (b)	LAll
Fizzy = 'Wp08 Ver03'PBR (Early Bird Series) (p)	CWhe ELan LRHS MHol SHil WHlf
'Flanders' (b) ♀H6	LAll
'Flashdance' (pf)	CNMi
'Fleur' (p)	LAll
'Florence Franklin' (pf)	CNMi
'Forest Princess' (b)	LAll
'Forest Sprite' (b)	LAll
'Forest Treasure' (b)	LAll
'Forest Violet' (b)	LAll
'Forge Pink'	LLHF
'Fortuna' (p)	LAll
'Fragrant Ann' (pf) ♀H6	CNMi EMal LAll
'Fragrant Phyllis' (pf)	CNMi
'Frances Isabel' (p)	LAll
'Frank Bruno' (pf)	CNMi
'Freda' (p)	LAll
'Freda Woodliffe' (p)	ECtt GCrg SBch WAbe WHoo
freynii	ECho EWes GKev WAbe
* - var. ***nana***	GKev
Frilly = 'Wp08 Ulr03'PBR (Early Bird Series) (p)	CWhe LRHS SHil WHlf
fringed pink	see *D. superbus*
furcatus	GKev SIgm
'Fusilier' (p)	CBod CRos CTri CWhe EAJP ECho ECtt EDAr EPfP GAbr GBuc GCrg GMaP LAll LHop LRHS MAsh NRHS SHar SHil SRot SWvt
'Gail Graham' (b)	LAll
'Gail Tilsley' (b)	LAll
'Garland' (p)	CTri
'Gaydena' (b)	LAll
giganteus	WSHC
'Gingham Gown' (p)	ECtt LAll NBir
* ***glacialis elegans***	GKev
'Gold Dust' (p)	ECtt EPot EWTr LAll SBch
'Gold Embrace' (pf)	CNMi
'Golden Cross' (b) ♀H6	LAll
'Grace's Scarlet Clove' (b)	LAll
'Grandma Calvert' (p)	LAll
'Gran's Favourite' (p) ♀H6	CBcs CSBt CTri CWCL CWhe ECtt ELan EPfP ESps EWoo GAbr LAll LHop LPot LRHS LSRN MCot MGos MMuc MTis NEgg NGdn SEND SPlb SPoG SRGP SWvt WGwG WHer
§ ***gratianopolitanus*** ♀H6	CBod CPBP CTri CWld EDAr ENfk EPfP EPot GJos LAll LEdu MHer MNHC MRav NBid
- 'Albus' (p)	MHer
- 'Babi Lom' (p)	GCrg
- dwarf	SIgm WAbe
- 'Grandiflorus' (p)	SPhx
* - 'Karlik' (p)	GKev
- 'Rosenfeder' (p)	SPhx
§ - 'Tiny Rubies' (p)	EDAr GCrg LLHF SDys WAbe
'Greensides' (p)	LAll
'Grey Dove' (b) ♀H6	LAll
'Gypsy Star' (p)	SPoG
haematocalyx	EPot
- 'Alpinus'	see *D. haematocalyx* subsp. *pindicola*
§ - subsp. ***pindicola***	LLHF NSla WAbe
'Hamish Berry' (p)	CNMi
'Hampshire' (pf)	CNMi
'Hannah Gertsen' (p)	LAll
'Hannah Louise' (b) ♀H6	LAll
'Harkell Special' (b)	LAll
'Hayden' (pf)	CNMi
'Hayley's Choice' (b)	LAll
Haytor	see *D.* 'Haytor White'
'Haytor Rock' (p) ♀H6	CWhe ELan EPfP MTis WGwG
§ 'Haytor White' (p) ♀H6	CBcs CTri CWhe CWib EPfP ESps LAll SCob
'Hazel Ruth' (b) ♀H6	LAll
'Heath' (p)	LAll
'Helen' (p)	ELon LAll LSRN
'Helena Allwood' (pf) **new**	EMal
'Helena Hitchcock' (p)	LAll
'Herbert's Pink' (p)	ECtt SPhx
'Hercules' (pf)	CNMi
'Hereford Butter Market' (p)	EBee
'Hidcote' (p)	CRos CTri LLHF LRHS NRHS SIgm
'Hidcote Red' (p)	ECho
Highland Group (p)	SGbt
'Highland Fraser' (p)	WKif
'Hope' Allwood 1946 (p)	LAll
'Hope' Clifford 2007 (p)	SBch
'Hot Spice' (p)	SPoG
§ 'Houndspool Cheryl' (p) ♀H6	CBcs CSBt CTri CWhe EPfP ESps LAll SRGP
§ 'Houndspool Ruby' (p) ♀H6	CBcs CWhe EPfP ESps LAll LSRN

hyssopifolius	WOut
'Ian' (p)	LAll LSRN
§ Iced Gem = 'Wp06 Fatima'PBR (Scent First Series) (p)	CWhe ELan ELon LHop LRHS LSRN LSou MTis NPnk NPri SHil SPoG SRot
'Icomb' (p)	WHoo
'Inchmery' (p)	LAll LRHS WHer WHoo
'India Star'PBR (p) 🏆H6	CRos CTri CWhe ESps LRHS MTis NEgg NRHS SEND SRot WIce
'Inglestone' (p)	CTri
'Inshriach Dazzler' (p) 🏆H6	CPBP ECho ECtt EPot GCrg GMaP LLHF MAsh MHer NEgg NHar NHol NSla SRot WAbe WHal WTor
'Inshriach Startler' (p)	CMea
'Irene Della-Torré' (b) 🏆H6	LAll
'Janelle Welch' (pf)	CNMi
'Janet Walker' (p)	GMaP
'Jess Hewins' (pf)	CNMi LAll
'Joan Schofield' (p)	CPBP
'Joanne' (pf)	CNMi
'Joanne's Highlight' (pf)	CNMi
'Joy' (p) 🏆H6	EPfP ESps LAll SPoG
'Julian' (p)	LAll
'Julie Ann Davis' (b)	LAll
'Julie Martin' (pf)	CNMi
'Just Jodie' (pf)	CNMi
'Kathleen Hitchcock' (b) 🏆H6	LAll
'Kelly's Kiss' (p)	CNMi
'Kent' (pf)	CNMi
'Kessock Charm' (p)	MNrw
'Kesteven Chamonix' (p)	SBch
'Kesteven Kirkstead' (p) 🏆H6	LAll MNrw
'Kim' (p)	NDov
'King of the Blacks' (p,a)	CWld
knappii	SDix SPhx WHer XLum
- 'Yellow Harmony' (p,a)	LAll
'La Bourboule' (p) 🏆H6	CMea CRos CTri ECho ECtt EDAr GAbr GCrg GMaP LRHS NRHS
'La Bourboule Alba' (p) 🏆H5	CTri ECho ECtt GCrg MAsh
'Laced Joy' (p)	LAll
'Laced Monarch' (p)	CBcs CSBt CWhe ECtt ELan EPfP GCra LAll LHop LRHS MCot MMuc NEgg SEND SPlb SPoG WGwG
'Laced Mrs Sinkins' (p)	LAll WHer
'Laced Prudence'	see *D.* 'Prudence'
'Laced Romeo' (p)	LAll
'Laced Treasure' (p)	LAll
'Lady Granville' (p)	LAll MHCG SBch
Lady in Red = 'Wp04 Xanthe'PBR (p)	CRos CWhe ECtt ELan EPfP LRHS MTis NRHS
§ Lady Madonna = 'Wp04 Opal'PBR (p) 🏆H6	CWhe ELan
'Lady Wharncliffe' (p)	SBch
'Lady Windermere' (M)	EMal LAll
'Lancing Monarch' (b)	LAll
'Lancing Supreme' (p)	LAll WHer
'Langford Manor' (pf)	CNMi
'Langport Lady' (pt)	CNMi
'Laura' (p)	LAll
'Layla Jane' (p)	CNMi
'Leatham Pastel' (pf)	CNMi
'Lemsii' (p) 🏆H6	NGdn
'Len Hutton' (p) **new**	SBch
'Leslie Rennison' (b)	LAll
'Letitia Wyatt' (p) 🏆H6	CMea CWhe LRHS NRHS SBch SPoG SRGP
'Leuchtkugel' (p)	CPBP ECho LLHF WAbe
'Lily Lesurf' (b)	LAll
Lily the Pink = 'Wp05 Idare'PBR (p) 🏆H6	CRos CWhe ELan LRHS NRHS
'Lime Crush' (pf)	CNMi
'Linfield Annie's Fancy' (pf)	CNMi
'Linfield Doreen Ashmore' (p)	LAll
'Linfield Dorothy Perry' (p) 🏆H6	LAll
'Linfield Isobel Croft' (p)	LAll
'Linfield Julie' (p)	LAll
'Linfield Kathy Booker' (p) 🏆H6	LAll
'Linfield Pink Margaret' (p)	CNMi LAll
'Little Ben' (p)	LAll
'Little Jock' (p)	ECho ECtt EDAr EPot GCrg LAll LRHS MAsh NRHS SBch SPlb
'Liz Rigby' (b)	LAll
'London Brocade' (p)	LAll
'London Glow' (p)	LAll
'London Lovely' (p)	LAll
'London Poppet' (p)	ECtt LAll
'Lord Nuffield' (b)	LAll
lumnitzeri	XLum
'Lustre' (b)	LAll
'Maggie' (p)	LSRN
'Maisie Neal' (b) 🏆H6	LAll
'Mandy' (p)	LAll
'Manon des Sources' (pf)	CNMi
'Margaret Taylor' (p)	LAll
'Maria'	see *D.* 'Allen's Maria'
'Marian Allwood' (pf) **new**	EMal
'Marielle' (pf)	LAll
'Marilyn's Highlight' (pf)	CNMi
'Marjery Breeze' (p)	LAll
'Marmion' (M)	EMal LAll
'Ma's Choice' (p)	LAll
'Matthew' (p)	WHoo
'Maudie Hinds' (b)	LAll
'Maxine' (pf)	CNMi
'Maybole' (b)	LAll
'Maybush' (pf)	CNMi
Memories = 'WP11 Gwe04'PBR (Scent First Series) (p)	CMea CWhe EBee ELan LBuc LRHS LSun MCot MHol MTis NDov SHil WCot WWFP
'Mendip Hills' (b)	LAll
Mendlesham Minx = 'Russmin'PBR (p)	CRos CWhe ECho EDAr ELan EPfP LAll LRHS MTis NRHS SWvt
'Messines Pink' (p)	LAll
'Michael Saunders' (b) 🏆H6	LAll
microlepis	ECho EDAr MMuc NGdn NSla WAbe
- f. ***albus***	NSla
- ED 791562	NGdn
- var. ***musalae***	ECho EPot LLHF
- 'Rivendell' (p)	ECho WAbe
'Mike Briggs' (b)	LAll
'Miss Farrow' (p)	LRHS SCob SPhx
'Miss Sinkins' (p)	CTri IFoB
Mojácar = 'Barjamocar'PBR (pf)	LAll
Mojito = 'Wp15 Pie41' (p) **new**	CWhe
'Monica Wyatt' (p) 🏆H6	CBcs CWhe ECtt ELan EPfP LRHS NEgg NRHS SPoG
'Montrose Pink'	see *D.* 'Cockenzie Pink'
'Monty Allwood' (p)	ECtt LAll
'Monty's Pink' (pf)	EMal
'Moor Editha' (p)	CNMi
Morning Star	see *D.* 'Devon Winnie'
'Morrissey' (pf)	CNMi
Mother of Pearl = 'Wp10 Ele04'PBR (Perfume Pinks Series) (p)	ELan
'Mottisfont Pink'	NWad

'Moulin Rouge' (p) ♀H6	CMea CRos CTri CWCL CWhe ECtt ELan EPfP GAbr GCra LHop LRHS MTis NRHS SPoG
'Mrs Macbride' (p)	GAbr LAll
'Mrs Sinkins' (p)	Widely available
'Musgrave's Pink' (p)	CFis ECha LAll MRav WHer
'Musgrave's White'	see *D.* 'Musgrave's Pink'
myrtinervius	ECho EDAr GKev GPSL MHtn NGdn SIgm
'Mystic Dawn' (b)	LAll
§ Mystic Star = 'WP 05 Saphire' (p) ♀H6	CMea CWhe ELan EWoo IPot MTis WIce WSHC
'Napoleon III' (p)	LAll
nardiformis	XLum
'Natalie Saunders' (b) ♀H6	LAll
'Nautilus' (b)	LAll
neglectus misapplied	see *D. pavonius*
'Neon Star'PBR (p) ♀H6	CRos CTri CWhe ECho EDAr ELan GBuc GKev LRHS MTis NCou NRHS SMad SPoG SRot
'Night Star' (p) ♀H6	CRos ECho ELan EPfP EUJe EWoo GBin GKev GMaP GWyn LHop LPot LRHS NCou NEgg NRHS SBch SEND SRot WPtf
noeanus	see *D. petraeus* subsp. *noeanus*
'Nomie' (pf)	CNMi
'Northland' (pf)	CNMi EMal LAll
'Nyewoods Cream' (p)	CMea CTri ECho EPot GCrg GMaP MHer NGdn NHar NWad SBch
§ 'Oakington' (p)	CTri
'Oakington Rose'	see *D.* 'Oakington'
'Oakwood Erin Mitchell' (p)	CNMi
'Oakwood Sweetheart' (p)	LAll
'Old Blush'	see *D.* 'Souvenir de la Malmaison'
'Old French Red' (pf)	EMal
'Old Man's Head' (p) **new**	SBch
'Old Mother Hubbard' (p)	SBch
'Old Red Clove' (p)	CAby ECtt GAbr MBel MCot MHol MPie NSti SBch SPer WCot
'Old Rose' (pf) **new**	EMal
§ 'Old Square Eyes' (p)	LAll MNrw SHar WHer
'Old Velvet' (p)	LAll MNrw WHoo
'Oliver' (p)	LAll
'Orange Maid' (b)	LAll
'Oscar' (b)	CRos LRHS NRHS
'Owston Third Avenue' (p)	LAll
'Oxford Magic' (p)	LAll
'Painted Lady' (p)	LAll
'Paisley Gem' (p)	LAll
Passion = 'Wp Passion'PBR (Scent First Series) (p)	CWhe EBee ECtt ELan EPfP LRHS LSou MBel MHer MHol MPie MTis NDov SAko SEND SHil SPoG WCot
§ ***pavonius***	EWes NGdn NSla SIgm WRHF
'Peach' (p)	SEND
'Pendle Doris Delight' (p)	LAll
'Pennine Reflections' (b)	LAll
'Peter Wood' (b) ♀H6	LAll
§ ***petraeus***	EWes NGdn WThu
§ - subsp. ***noeanus***	EPot LHop LLHF WHal
'Petticoat Lace' (p)	LAll
'Phantom' (b)	LAll
'Pheasant's Eye' (p)	LAll WHer
* 'Picton's Propeller' (p)	GBuc GCal WSHC
Pierrot = 'Kobusa' (pf)	CNMi
'Pike's Pink' (p) ♀H6	CRos CSpe CTri ECho EDAr ELan EPfP EPot EWoo GCrg LAll LHop LRHS MAsh MMuc NBir NGdn NRHS SEND
Pinball Wizard = 'Wp15mow08' (p) **new**	CWhe MTis

pindicola	see *D. haematocalyx* subsp. *pindicola*
pinifolius	SBrt
'Pink Doris' (pf)	CNMi
'Pink Fantasy' (b)	LAll
Pink Fizz = 'Wp10 Xav04'PBR (Scent First Series) (p)	LRHS SHil
'Pink Jewel' (p)	CMea CPBP ECha EDAr LAll LCro LOPS MAsh MNHC SBch XLum
'Pink Mrs Sinkins' (p)	LAll MHer MNrw
'Pink Pearl' (b)	LAll
Pink Valda	see *D.* 'Devon Judith'
'Pixie' (b)	EPot
'Pixie Star'PBR (p) ♀H6	CWhe EPfP SPoG SRot WIce
plumarius	LAll SIgm XLum
- 'Albiflorus' (p)	XLum
- subsp. ***praecox***	CPBP
§ Pop Star = 'Wp04 Esther'PBR (p)	CBod CWhe LRHS MTis SGbt SHil
'Pretty' (p)	ECtt LAll
Pretty Flamingo	see *D.* 'Carmine Letitia Wyatt'
'Prince Charming' (p)	ECho MAsh
'Princess of Wales' (M)	EMal LAll
'Priory Pink' (p)	LAll
§ 'Prudence' (p)	LAll
'Pudsey Prize' (p)	EPot
'Purple Frosted' (pf)	EMal
'Purple Jenny' (p)	LAll
'Queen of Hearts' (p)	CTri SEND
§ 'Queen of Henri' (p)	CRos EBee ECho LRHS NRHS
'Queen of Sheba' (p)	LAll SBch WHer WHoo WKif
'Rachel' (p)	LAll
'Rainbow Loveliness' (p,a)	LAll WOut
'Ralph Gould' (p)	ECho
'Raspberry Parfait' (p,a)	CRos LRHS NRHS
Raspberry Sundae	see *D.* 'Devon Yolande'
Rebekah = 'Wp09 Mar05'PBR (Early Bird Series) (p)	CMea CWhe ELan LRHS SHil
'Red Dwarf'	see *D.* 'Red Star'
§ 'Red Star'PBR (p) ♀H6	CWhe ELan GJos LRHS MAsh NRHS SRot WIce WTor
'Reine de Henri'	see *D.* 'Queen of Henri'
'Richard Pollak' (b)	LAll
'Ringwood Belle' (pf)	CNMi
'Rizalene' (p)	CNMi
'Robert Allwood' (pf)	EMal LAll
'Robin Ritchie' (p)	WHoo
Romance = 'Wp09 Wen04'PBR (Scent First Series) (p)	CWhe ELan LRHS LSou MTis SHil
'Romsey' (pf)	CNMi
'Roodkapje' (p)	XLum
'Rose de Mai' (p)	CFis CNMi CSam LAll WHer WHoo
§ 'Rose Devon Pearl'PBR (p)	CWhe
'Rose Joy' (p) ♀H6	CBcs CRos EPfP ESps LRHS NRHS
§ 'Rose Monica Wyatt'PBR (p) ♀H6	CWhe
Rosebud = 'Wp08 Ros03'PBR (Early Bird Series) (p)	CWhe LRHS NRHS SHil
'Rötkappchen' (p)	ELon WCot
'Royal Crimson' **new**	EMal
'Royal Fragrance' (pf)	EMal
'Royal Salmon' (pf)	EMal
'Ruby'	see *D.* 'Houndspool Ruby'
'Ruby Doris'	see *D.* 'Houndspool Ruby'
'Ruby Wedding' (p)	LSRN
rupicola	WCot
'Saint Nicholas' (p)	WThu
'Sam Barlow' (p)	LAll SBch
'Santa Claus' (b)	LAll

	'Seraphina' (pf)	CNMi
	'Seren Wen' (p)	WAbe
	serotinus	WCot
	Sherbet = 'Wp08 Ros03'^{PBR} (Early Bird Series) (p)	CWhe ELan LRHS NRHS SHil
	Shirley Temple = 'Wp15 Pie44' (p) **new**	CWhe
§	Shooting Star = 'Wp04 Flores'^{PBR} (p)	CWhe ELan MTis SHil SRms
	'Shot Silk' (pf)	EMal LAll
	'Show Aristocrat' (p)	LAll
	'Show Beauty' (p)	LAll
	Show Girl = 'Hilshow' (pt)	LRHS
	'Show Glory' (p)	LAll
	'Show Harlequin' (p)	LAll
	'Show Satin' (p)	LAll
	Showgirl = 'Wp08 Uni02'^{PBR} (Scent First Series) (p)	ELan LSou MTis
	'Shrimp' (b)	CWib
	Silver Star = 'Wp10 Hel01'^{PBR} (p)	CWhe LRHS MTis SHil
	'Singapore Girl' (Kiwi Series) (p)	CWGN
*	'Six Hills'	NWad
	Slap 'n' Tickle = 'Wp 05 Pp 22'^{PBR} (Scent First Series) (p)	CWhe EBee ECtt ELon LRHS LSRN LSou SHil SPoG SRot
	'Snowshill Manor' (p)	ECtt
	'Solomon' (p)	LAll
	'Somerset' (pf)	CNMi
	'Sops-in-wine' (p)	CFis CSam ECha ECtt LAll MSCN
§	'Souvenir de la Malmaison' (M)	EMal LAll
	'Spangle' (b)	LAll
	'Spencer Bickham' (p)	MNrw
	spiculifolius	CAby EPot MMuc SPhx
	'Spinfield Joy' (b) ♀H6	LAll
	Spooky Group (p)	MBel
	'Spring Star' (p)	ECtt SRot WJek
	'Square Eyes'	see *D.* 'Old Square Eyes'
	squarrosus	CPBP ECho EPot WAbe
*	- ***alpinus***	ECho
	- 'Nanus'	see *D.* 'Berlin Snow'
	'Starburst'^{PBR} (p)	CBod CMea CWhe LRHS MTis WIce
	Stardust = 'Wp07 Opr04'^{PBR} (Early Bird Series) (p)	CWhe WIce
	Stargazer = 'Wp13 Gil05' (Whetman Stars Series) (p)	CRos CWhe LRHS MTis NRHS
	Starlette = 'Wp11evi08' (p) **new**	CWhe
	Starlight = 'Hilstar' (pf)	CMea SRms
	Starlight = 'Wp 06 Parnia'^{PBR} (p)	CWhe
	'Starry Eyes' (p) ♀H6	CSam CWhe EAJP ECho ELan GCrg GMaP LRHS NRHS SRms SRot SWvt WTor
	'Storm' (pf)	CNMi EMal LAll
	'Strawberries and Cream' (p)	ECtt NEgg SPoG
	strictus	WCot
*	- subsp. ***pulchellus***	GEdr
	subacaulis	EDAr IFoB NSla XLum
	- subsp. ***brachyanthus***	EPot
	- - 'Murray Lyon' (p)	WThu
	suendermannii	see *D. petraeus*
	Sugar Plum = 'Wp08 Ian04'^{PBR} (Scent First Series) (p)	CWhe EBee ECtt ELan LRHS LSou MTis SHil
	'Summerfield Adam' (p)	LAll
	'Summerfield Amy Francesca' (p)	LAll
	'Summerfield Blaze' (p)	LAll
	'Summerfield Blush' (p)	LAll
	'Summerfield Daniel' (b)	LAll
	'Summerfield Debbie' (p)	LAll
	'Summerfield Emma Louise' (p)	LAll
	'Summerfield Jo' (p)	CFis LAll
	'Summerfield Rebecca' (p)	LAll
	Summertime	see *D.* 'Rose Monica Wyatt'
	'Sunray' (b)	LAll
	'Sunstar' (b)	LAll
§	***superbus***	CMHG EPPr LRHS SBch SHar SIgm SPhx WMoo
	- 'Crimsonia' (p)	WOut
I	- 'Primadonna' (p)	GQue
	Supernova = 'Wp11 Tyr04'^{PBR} (pf)	CWhe MTis
	'Susan' (p)	LAll
	'Susannah' (p)	LAll
*	'Susan's Seedling' (p)	LAll
	'Swanlake' (p)	LAll
	'Sway Lass' (p)	SEND
	'Sweet Cecille' (pf)	CNMi
	'Sweet Sue' (b)	LAll
	sylvestris	CMea WOut
	'Tamsin Fifield' (b) ♀H6	LAll
	'Tatra' (pf)	NQui
	'Tatra Blush' (p)	GCal
	'Tatra Fragrance' (p)	CCse GCal LAll
	'Tatra Ghost' (p)	LAll SDys
	'Tayside Red' (M)	EMal LAll
	Tequila Sunrise = 'Wp15 Pie45' (p) **new**	CWhe
	'Terranova' (pf)	CNMi
	The Wessex Pink = 'Wp15val11' (p) **new**	CWhe MTis
	'Thora' (M)	EMal LAll
	'Thunderstorm' (pf)	CNMi
	Tickled Pink = 'Devon Pp 11'^{PBR} (Scent First Series) (p)	CWhe ECtt ELan ELon LBMP LCro LOPS LRHS LSRN LSou SHil SPoG
	'Tiny Rubies'	see *D. gratianopolitanus* 'Tiny Rubies'
	'Tony's Choice' (pf)	CNMi
	'Treasure' (p)	LAll
	'Trevor' (p)	LAll
	tristis	XLum
	'Tropic Butterfly' (p)	LPot
	'Tudor'	ELon MHCG MNrw
	turkestanicus	WPtf
	'Twinkle' (p) **new**	EBee
	Tyrolean trailing carnations	LAll
	'Uncle Teddy' (b) ♀H6	LAll
	'Unique' (p)	LAll
	'Valda Wyatt' (p) ♀H6	CBcs CWhe ELan EPfP LAll MCot NEgg NSti SEND SPoG SWvt WBod WGwG
	'Velvet Pelargonium' (pf) **new**	EMal
	'Vic Masters' (p)	SBch
	'Violet Clove' (b)	LAll
	'Violet Yates' (pf)	CNMi
	'W.A. Musgrave'	see *D.* 'Musgrave's Pink'
	'Waithman Beauty' (p)	CFis CTri ECtt LAll WHoo
	'Waithman's Jubilee' (p)	LAll SBch
	'Warden Hybrid' (p)	CRos CTri CWhe ECho ECtt GCrg LRHS MNHC NGdn NRHS NWad SPoG SWvt WAbe
	'Waterloo Sunset'^{PBR} (p)	CMea CWhe MTis
	'Weetwood Double' (p)	LPot SBch

'Welton Raspberry Ice' (p)	LAll
'Wessex' (pf)	CNMi
weyrichii	ECho EPot
'Whatfield Anona' (p)	LAll
'Whatfield Beauty' (p)	ECho ECtt
'Whatfield Cancan' (p) 🏆H6	CBod CRos CWhe ECho ECtt ELan EPot GMaP LAll LHop LRHS MNHC NEgg NGdn NHol NRHS SBch SPoG SWvt WJek
'Whatfield Cyclops' (p)	ECho LAll
'Whatfield Dorothy Mann' (p)	ECho LAll
'Whatfield Fuchsia Floss' (p)	LAll
'Whatfield Gem' (p)	CFis CWhe ECho ECtt ELan ELon EPfP GCrg LAll MNHC NGdn SIgm SWvt WHoo WTor
'Whatfield Joy' (p)	CRos ECho ECtt ELan EPfP GCrg GPSL LAll LRHS NGdn NRHS
'Whatfield Magenta' (p) 🏆H6	CRos CSam ECho ECtt ELan EPot EWTr GCrg LAll LHop LRHS NRHS SBch SPoG WAbe
'Whatfield Mini' (p)	LAll SBch
'Whatfield Miss' (p)	LAll SBch
'Whatfield Misty Morn' (p)	ECho LAll
'Whatfield Peach' (p)	LAll
'Whatfield Pretty Lady' (p)	ECho LAll
'Whatfield Ruby' (p)	ECho ECtt ELan GJos LAll
'Whatfield Supergem' (p)	ECho
'Whatfield White' (p)	ECho ECtt LAll
'Whatfield Wisp' (p)	CPBP CTri ECho EPfP EPot GEdr MRav NBir
'White and Crimson' (p)	LAll
'White Joy'PBR (p) 🏆H6	MRav
'White Ladies' (p)	LAll MRav
White Valda	see *D.* 'Devon Isolde'
'Whitehill' (p)	ECho
'Whitesmith' (b) 🏆H6	LAll
'Widecombe Fair' (p) 🏆H6	CRos CTri CWhe ELan EPfP LAll LRHS MTis NRHS SPoG
'Yellow Alice' (b)	LAll
'Zebra' (b)	LAll

Diapensia (*Diapensiaceae*)

lapponica var. ***obovata***	NHar

Diarrhena (*Poaceae*)

obovata	EPPr

Diascia (*Scrophulariaceae*)

'Alice Cap'	SBch
'Andrew'	SBch
'Apricot'	see *D. barberae* 'Hopleys Apricot'
Apricot Delight = 'Codicot' (Sun Chimes Series)	EDAr
barberae 'Belmore Beauty' (v)	EWes
- 'Blackthorn Apricot' 🏆H4	CRos EBee ECha ELan EPfP EWoo GBin GMaP GWyn LRHS LSRN NDov NLar NRHS SPer SPlb SPoG SWvt XEll
§ - 'Hopleys Apricot'	NLar
- Juliet Orange = 'Balajulor'	NPri
§ - 'Ruby Field' 🏆H4	CRos EBee ECha ELan EPfP GBin LHop LRHS LSRN NRHS SPer SPoG SRms SWvt
Blue Bonnet = 'Hecbon'	SWvt
'Bluebelle' (Maritana Series)	NDov
'Blush'	see *D. integerrima* 'Blush'
(Breezee Series) Breezee Apple Blossom	NLar
- Breezee Apricot = 'Diaspritwo'PBR	LHop NLar
- Breezee Red	NLar
- Breezee Snow = 'Inndiabzsno'PBR	LHop NLar
'Coldham'	LPla
Coral Belle = 'Hecbel'PBR 🏆H3	EWoo LHop LRHS LSou NRHS
'Denim Blue'	EDAr NLar WHea
elegans misapplied	see *D. fetcaniensis*, *D. vigilis*
'Emma'	LPla NDov SMHy SWvt
felthamii	see *D. fetcaniensis*
§ ***fetcaniensis***	CMea CPne CPrp EBee EPfP GMaP LPla LRHS MCot MHer NEgg SPer WBod WHal WHea WKif
- 'Daydream'	LBuc MNrw MPie SBch WHrl
flanaganii misapplied	see *D. vigilis*
(Flying Colours Series) Flying Colours Appleblossom = 'Diastara'	EPfP
- Flying Colours Apricot = 'Diastina'	EPfP
- Flying Colours Red = 'Diastonia'	EPfP
'Hector Harrison'	see *D.* 'Salmon Supreme'
Ice Cracker = 'Hecrack'	CMea CRos ELan LHop LRHS NRHS
Iceberg = 'Hecice'	NDov SWvt
§ ***integerrima*** 🏆H4	CSam ECha MCot MHer SIgm
- 'Alba'	see *D. integerrima* 'Blush'
§ - 'Blush'	CSpe NDov
- 'Ivory Angel'	see *D. integerrima* 'Blush'
integrifolia	see *D. integerrima*
'Jacqueline's Joy'	NPer
'Joyce's Choice' 🏆H3	CRos LRHS NRHS
'Katherine Sharman' (v)	EWes
'Lady Valerie' 🏆H3	GPSL
'Lilac Belle' 🏆H3	CRos EDAr ELan LHop LRHS NBir NEgg NRHS SPlb SPoG
'Lilac Mist' 🏆H3	NPer
Little Dancer = 'Pendan'PBR	ELan LSou NLar
Little Dreamer = 'Pender'PBR	NLar
Little Drifter = 'Pendrif'PBR	LSou NLar
Little Maiden = 'Penmaid'PBR	NLar
Little Tango = 'Pentang'PBR	LHop LSou NLar WRHF
'Peaches and Cream' (v) **new**	CMea
personata	CAby CBod CHll CMea CPne CPrp CSam CSpe EBee ECtt EHoe EPfP GBin ITim LBMP LLHF LRHS MCot MHer MHol MNrw MPie NDov SDix SPer SPhx WBod WCot WSHC WWFP
- 'Hopleys'	EPPr EWes LHop LRHS MAvo MHCG MPie MSCN NCGa SHil SMHy WHea
'Peter'	NDov
Pink Panther = 'Penther'	SWvt
Red Ace = 'Hecrace'PBR	EPfP LHop NPer SWvt
Redstart = 'Hecstart'	SWvt
rigescens 🏆H3	CBod CCht CPne CPrp CSpe CWCL ECtt ELan EPfP EPot GWyn ILea LHop LRHS MHer NLar NPer SPer SPlb SPoG SWvt WCFE WSHC
§ - 'Anne Rennie'	LRHS SWvt
- pale-flowered	see *D. rigescens* 'Anne Rennie'
'Ruby Field'	see *D. barberae* 'Ruby Field'
'Rupert Lambert' 🏆H3	NDov
§ 'Salmon Supreme'	CRos LRHS NPer NRHS SPoG

(Sundiascia Series) Sundiascia Blush Pink LBMP LCro LOPS SHil
- Sundiascia Orange LSou SHil
- Sundiascia Rose Pink LBMP LSou SHil
'Twinkle' ♀H3 CRos LRHS NBir NPer NRHS
* 'Twins Gully' EWes MAvo
§ ***vigilis*** ♀H3 CMea CRos EPot LHop LRHS NBro NCGa NRHS SIgm WHal WPnn

Dicentra ✿ (*Papaveraceae*)

'Adrian Bloom' ECtt EPfP GBuc GLet MAsh MCot SPer SWvt WFar WMoo
(Amore Series) 'Amore Pink' CWGN NLar WHil WHlf
- 'Amore Rose' CWGN GBin GEdr MAsh NLar
'Aurora' CElw CWCL EBee ECtt ELon EPfP EWTr GBuc IBoy LCro LRHS MBel MRav MTis NGdn NLar NSti SCob SPer SPoG SWvt WHil WMoo
'Boothman's Variety' see *D.* 'Stuart Boothman'
'Bountiful' CMac ECtt EPau GLet LRHS LSou MRav NGdn SWvt
'Brownie' GBuc
'Burning Hearts'PBR CMos CWCL CWGN ECtt EPot EWoo GLet IKil LHop LRHS LSou MPnt NCGa NSti SCob SPer WHil
canadensis CLAP EBee GBuc GKev LEdu MAvo MNrw NLar WAbe WHal
'Candy Hearts'PBR EBee ECtt ELan EWTr LHop NLar SCob SGol
cucullaria CAby CElw CLAP CPBP CRos CTal CWCL EBee ECho ELon EPPr EPot GAbr GBuc GEdr GKev GLet ITim LRHS MNrw MRav NHar NHpl NLar NRHS WAbe WFar XEll
- 'Pink Punk' CTal CWCL EBee EPPr GBin LEdu MNrw NHar NLar
- 'Pittsburg' CAby EBee EPPr GBuc MNrw
eximia misapplied see *D. formosa*
eximia ambig. CRos GKev GPSL MHol
eximia (Ker Gawl.) Torr. 'Alba' see *D. eximia* (Ker Gawl.) Torr. 'Snowdrift'
§ - 'Snowdrift' CLAP ELan MCot MTis NLar SRms WMoo
'Filigree' new CSpe
'Firecracker' ECtt MPnt
§ ***formosa*** CBcs CLet CSpe CTri ECha ELan EPfP GAbr GKev GMcL IFro LRHS MArt NBro NGdn NRHS SPlb SRms WMoo
- f. ***alba*** GAbr GCra GLet GLog GMaP NBir SRms WCru WFar WKif
- 'Bacchanal' ♀H5 Widely available
- 'Cox's Dark Red' CLAP EWes GBin GBuc GKev GLet LLHF NHpl SKHP
- 'Langtrees' ♀H5 CMac CSam ECha EPau GBuc LEdu LHop MRav NBro NLar SRms SSut SWvt WCru WFar WHea WMoo WOut
- 'Moorland Pearl' WOut
- subsp. ***oregana*** EPPr NChi SKHP WHal
- - 'Rosea' EPPr
- Snowflakes = 'Fusd' EWes MRav
- 'Spring Gold' EBee ECha ELon EPPr LRHS NLar SPad WHil WMoo
- 'Spring Magic' CMos EBee ECtt EPPr GBin GWyn LRHS MRav NLar
'Ivory Hearts'PBR CWGN EBee ELan EWoo GKev GLet IKil LHop MAvo MCot NCGa NLar NPnk NSti SPer
§ 'Katie' EPPr
'Katy' see *D.* 'Katie'
'King of Hearts' Widely available
'Luxuriant' ♀H5 CBcs CLet CSBt ECtt ELan EPfP GBuc GKev LHop LRHS LSRN MAsh MCot MGos MHol MRav MTis SCob SPer SPoG SRms SRot SWvt WMoo
macrantha see *Ichthyoselmis macrantha*
'Pearl Drops' ELan GKev GLog GMaP GMcL GWyn LRHS MCot MHCG MMrt NBid NLar SRms WHil WMoo
peregrina WAbe
'Red Fountain'PBR ECtt GLet LHop NCGa NLar NPnk NSti SMad WFar WHil
'Rekka'PBR new GEdr
scandens see *Dactylicapnos scandens*
spectabilis see *Lamprocapnos spectabilis*
'Spring Morning' CElw CMHG CSam CTal EAEE ECtt EPPr EPau GLet NGdn
§ 'Stuart Boothman' ♀H5 CMac CWCL ECtt ELan ELon EPfP GBuc GLet GMaP ILea LHop LRHS MCot MRav MTis NBro NGdn NLar SPoG SRms SWvt WFar WKif WMoo
thalictrifolia see *D. scandens*
ventii see *Dactylicapnos ventii*

Dichelachne (*Poaceae*)

crinita SMea

Dichelostemma (*Asparagaceae*)

§ ***capitatum*** GKev
congestum CAvo ECho GKev LCro SDeJ WCot
§ ***ida-maia*** CAvo CGrW CWCL EPot GKev SDeJ
- 'Pink Diamond' EBee GKev SDeJ
pulchellum see *D. capitatum*
volubile ECho GKev
- 'Pink Giant' SDeJ

Dichocarpum (*Ranunculaceae*)

§ ***dicarpon*** B&SWJ 11555 WCru

Dichondra (*Convolvulaceae*)

argentea 'Silver Falls' EShb LBMP LSou NPri SCoo SPer SPoG
§ ***micrantha*** EShb
repens misapplied see *D. micrantha*

Dichopogon (*Asparagaceae*)

strictus SBrt WSFF

Dichroa ✿ (*Hydrangeaceae*)

cyanea NJM 13.104 new WPGP
febrifuga B&SWJ 9734 new WCru
- B&SWJ 9753 new WCru
- HWJK 2430 WSHC
- NJM 10.042 WPGP
- PAB 8639 new LEdu
hirsuta B&SWJ 8207 from Vietnam WCru
aff. ***hirsuta*** B&SWJ 8371 from Laos WCru
aff. ***yunnanensis*** B&SWJ 9734 WCru

Dichroa × *Hydrangea* see × *Didrangea*

Dichromena see *Rhynchospora*

Dichrostachys (*Mimosaceae*)

cinerea SPlb

Dicksonia ✿ (*Dicksoniaceae*)

	antarctica ♀H3	Widely available
	arborescens	NLos
	fibrosa ♀H3	CDTJ CKel
	sellowiana	CDTJ CKel
	squarrosa ♀H3	CCCN CDTJ CKel NLos
	thyrsopteroides	NLos
	youngiae	CKel

Dicliptera (*Acanthaceae*)

§	***sericea***	CCCN CHll EShb LHop MCot MSCN SBch SRkn WPGP XSen
	suberecta	see *D. sericea*

Dictamnus (*Rutaceae*)

	albus	CBcs CHll CTri CWCL EBee ECha ELan EPfP EWTr EWoo GMaP LEdu LHop LRHS LSun MBel MCot MNrw MRav SKHP SMHy SPer SPoG SWat SWvt WCAu
	- var. ***albus*** ♀H6	IBoy SWvt WAul
§	- var. ***purpureus*** ♀H6	EAEE ECha ELan EPfP GMaP GPoy IBoy LHop LRHS LSun MBel MNrw MRav NEgg SKHP SPer SPoG SRms SWat SWvt WAul WKif
*	- var. ***roseus***	EWTr IMou
*	- ***turkestanicus***	GCal
	caucasicus	SBrt SMHy WSHC
	fraxinella	see *D. albus* var. *purpureus*

× *Didrangea* (*Hydrangeaceae*)

	B&SWJ 6605 from Thailand	WCru
	versicolor	CAbb CBcs CBot CHll CMCN CMil CWib EBee EPfP LRHS MGil SCob SPoG SWvt WPGP
	- B&SWJ 6565	WCru
	ytiensis B&SWJ 11790	WCru

Didymochlaena (*Dryopteridaceae*)

	lunulata	see *D. truncatula*
§	***truncatula***	XBlo

Dierama ✿ (*Iridaceae*)

	CD&R 192	CElw
	adelphicum	LLHF
	ambiguum	CElw EBee GAbr NLos XLum
	argyreum	CCCN CElw CMac CMos CPla CTsd CWCL EBee EPri EWTr GAbr GBin GKev GPSL ITim NLar SPad SPoG SRot WGob WHil XLum
	atrum	EBee
	'Ballyrogan Red'	IBlr
	Barr hybrids	CBro CWCL GAbr WHil
	'Black Knight'	IBlr
	'Blackberry Bells'	CWCL CWGN ELon GBin GPSL LRHS MAvo NLar NLos SPer WHil
	Blue Belle = 'Rowblu'PBR	CBod EBee ECtt GBin GEdr IBal IVic LBuc LRHS SPoG
	'Blush'	IBlr
	'Buckland White'	WPGP
	'Candy Stripe'	CPla EBee GMcL IBal
	'Carmine'	CWCL
	'Cinnamon Fairy'	EBee EPfP IBal
	cooperi	CElw CPou NBir
	'Coral Belle'	EBee IBal LRHS
	'Coral Bells'	CKno GCal IBal
	'Cosmos'	CWCL EBee EPri EUJe EWTr GAbr LRHS MHer MMrt SPad WFar WGob WHil
	'Delicacy'	IBlr
	'Desire'	IBlr
	'Donard Legacy'	IBlr
§	***dracomontanum***	Widely available
	- JCA 3.141.100	WPGP
	dracomontanum × ***pulcherrimum***	SMad
	dubium	IBlr
	ensifolium	see *D. pendulum*
	erectum	CBcs CBod CCCN CHid CMac CTsd CWCL EBee EPri GPSL NLar NLos SRot WGob
	formosum	EBee WPGP
	galpinii	CCCN CPla CWCL EBee EPri LHop LLHF NLos WPGP
	grandiflorum	CPou IBlr
	'Guinevere'	Widely available
	igneum	Widely available
	- CD&R 278	CPou ELon GBuc
	insigne	CCCN CHid CWCL EBee ESwi LRHS MMrt NLos NWad WHil
	'Iris'	IBlr
	jucundum	CWCL EBee EWTr GBuc LRHS
	'Knee-high Lavender'	WPGP
	'Lancelot'	CElw CKno CPne EBee ECtt GMcL IBal IBlr LRHS NBir SWvt WFar WKif WSHC
	latifolium	CHid IBlr WGob
	luteoalbidum	GAbr
	'Mandarin'	IBlr
	medium	ELon SWat WPGP
	'Milkmaid'	IBlr
	'Miranda'	CBod CKno CWCL EBee ECtt EPri GMcL IBal LRHS LSRN NLar SPhx
	mossii	CBcs CCCN CHid CMHG CPne CWCL EBee EPri EWTr LHop LRHS NHpl NLar NLos NWad SPhx SPlb SRot SVen WGob WHil WPGP XLum
	'Painted Lady'	EBee EPfP IBal SKHP SLon
	'Pamina'	CPrp IBlr
	'Papagena'	IBlr
	'Papageno'	IBlr
	pauciflorum	CAbb CBod CCCN CHid CPrp CWCL CWib EBee EPri EWTr GBin IKil LHop MNrw NBir NLar NLos NSla SPhx SRot SWat WGob WPGP WSHC
§	***pendulum***	CBro IBlr LRHS MArt MRav SWvt WFar WGob
	pictum	IBlr
	'Pink Rocket'	CBod CMos CWCL MHer NHol
	Plant World hybrids	ELon
	Plant World Jewels	CWCL NLos NWad
	'Pretty Flamingo'	CPrp IBlr
	'Puck'	EBee GCal IBlr ITim MRav WPGP
	pulcherrimum	Widely available
	- var. ***album***	CCCN CWCL GAbr IBlr MHer MNrw NDov NLos WHil WPGP
	- 'Blackbird'	Widely available
	- dark cerise seedlings	MAvo NDov
	- dark pink-flowered	IBoy
	- 'Falcon'	IBlr
	- 'Flamingo'	IBlr
	- 'Merlin'	CElw CKno CPou CWCL EBee ECtt ELon EWoo GEdr GMaP GMcL IBal IBlr IBoy LRHS MBel NBir SCob SVen SWvt WGwG
	- pale-flowered	ECha
	- 'Peregrine'	IBoy
	- Slieve Donard hybrids	CWCL GBuc NLos SMad WFar WHrl

pumilum misapplied	see *D. dracomontanum*
'Queen of the Night'	IBlr
reynoldsii	CBcs CCCN CHid CPla CTsd CWCL EBee EPri GAbr GBin IBlr IVic MBel NHpl SBrt SPhx SPlb SPoG SRkn SVen WFar WKif
robustum	CAbb CPou CWCL EWes LRHS WHoo WPGP
'Sarastro'	IBlr
sertum	EBee
'Spring Dancer'	CWCL EBee EHoe MHer NHol NLos SPlb
'Tamino'	IBlr
'Tiny Bells'	EDAr GCal IBal SMHy
'Titania'	IBal IBlr
trichorhizum	CBod CCCN CElw CPla CPrp CWCL EPri GKev LHop WHil WPGP
'Tubular Bells'	IBlr
tyrium	LLHF
'Violet Ice'	IBlr
'Westminster Chimes'	IBlr MAvo
white-flowered	MBel
'Zulu Bells'	ELon

Diervilla ✿ (*Caprifoliaceae*)

middendorffiana	see *Weigela middendorffiana*
rivularis 'Troja Black'	EPPr NLar
§ ***sessilifolia***	CBcs CHGN CMac EBee EPPr IDee LCro MBlu MRav SLon WBod WCot WFar WMoo
- 'Butterfly'	CMac EPPr LCro LSou NLar SCob WMoo
- Cool Splash = 'Lpdc Podaras'^{PBR} (v)	CBod CMac CWGN EBee ELan EMil LHop LRHS NEoE SPoG SWvt WCot
× ***splendens***	CMHG CWib EHoe ELan EPPr EPfP GAbr IDee LHop LRHS MBNS MBlu MGil MSwo NLar SPer SPoG SWvt

Dietes (*Iridaceae*)

bicolor	CAbb CAby CBod CPrp CTca CTre EBee EPri IBoy LEdu LRHS LSou SChr SPoG WSHC
grandiflora	CAbb CAby CBod CHIl CPne CTre ECho ESwi SVen WCot WHil
§ ***iridioides***	CPrp CSpe ECho ESwi IBoy LRHS WCot WGob XLum
robinsoniana	WCot

Digitalis ✿ (*Plantaginaceae*)

'Albino'	CRos EPfP LRHS NRHS
ambigua	see *D. grandiflora*
apricot hybrids	see *D. purpurea* 'Sutton's Apricot'
canariensis	CAbb CBot CCCN CCht CDTJ CHIl CRHN CRos CSpe CTsd GCal GCra LRHS MGil SEND SEle SPad SPlb SVen WCFE
cariensis	CBot
§ 'Chelsea Gold' (Illumination Series)	CHid CRos EPfP GBin ILea LRHS NAst
ciliata	EPPr GKev NSti NWad
davisiana	GKev GLog WMoo
dubia	CBot WAbe
'Elsie Kelsey'	ECtt SWvt
eriostachya	see *D. lutea*
ferruginea 🏆^{H7}	Widely available
- 'Gelber Herold'	CDor CLAP GBin GMaP WCot WFar
- 'Gigantea'	CBar CLAP ECtt ELan EPfP EWTr EWoo GQue LEdu MBNS SCob SHar SPlb SWat WPGP WWtn
'Foxtrot'	CRos EPfP LRHS SHil
'Glory of Roundway'	CBod CBot CDor CLAP CMos ECtt IBoy LEdu LSou MBel MHol MNrw MPie NLar SPer STPC WCot WGob
§ ***grandiflora*** 🏆^{H5}	Widely available
- 'Carillon'	CBod ELan EPfP GJos GPSL IFoB NBir SCob SRot WHoo
- 'Cream Bell'	EPfP LRHS MHol WHar
- 'Temple Bells'	CBot
aff. ***grandiflora***	IBoy
heywoodii	see *D. purpurea* subsp. *heywoodii*
Illumination Series	EPfP LRHS SCob
- Illumination Apricot	see *D.* 'Chelsea Gold'
- Illumination Chelsea Gold	see *D.* 'Chelsea Gold'
- Illumination Cherry Brandy **new**	LRHS NRHS SHil
- Illumination Dark Pink **new**	LRHS NRHS SHil
- Illumination Flame = 'Tomdigharpink' **new**	SHil
- Illumination Pink = 'Tmdgfp001'^{PBR}	CAbb CBot CDor CHid CRos CWGN ELan EPfP GBin IPot LBMP LBrs LBuc LHop LSou MAvo MHol MNrw NAst NLar NPnk SCob SHil SPad SPoG STPC WCot
- Illumination Raspberry	CBod CBot CMea EPfP GBin LBMP LBuc LRHS LSou MAvo MHol NAst NDov NLar NPnk SCob SHil
isabelliana	CCCN GCal
'John Innes Tetra'	CBot EPPr MNrw SPtp WHoo
kishinskyi	see *D. parviflora* Jacq.
laevigata	CBot GKev LEdu MArt NBro SBrt SEND SPav WMoo
- subsp. ***laevigata***	SPtp
- white-flowered	ESwi MCot WCot
lamarckii misapplied	see *D. lanata*
§ ***lanata***	CArn CBot CRos EBee ECtt ELan EPfP GKev IBoy LRHS MBNS MNHC NGdn NWad SPav SPlb SPtp SRms
- 'Café Crème'	CBot CDor CLAP WHar WTor
§ ***lutea***	CAby CBod CBot CSam EBee ECha ECtt ELan EPPr EPfP EWTr EWoo GCra GMaP IBoy LRHS MArt MRav NBid NBro NLar SCob SEND SGbt SRms SSut SWvt WMoo
- 'Flashing Spires' (v)	CPla
× ***mertonensis*** 🏆^{H5}	Widely available
- 'Raspberry'	CLAP
- 'Summer King'	CChe CDor ECtt ELan EWld GJos IKil LSRN LSun MHol WFar
minor var. ***palaui***	SBrt
obscura	CBot EAJP IFoB SBrt SEND SPlb SVen WCot WHer
- B&SWJ 14010 **new**	WCru
* - 'Dusky Maid'	LHop WFar
orientalis	see *D. grandiflora*
§ ***parviflora*** Jacq.	CBot CRos CSam ECha ECtt ELan EPPr EPfP EWTr GBin GCra GJos IBoy LCro LEdu LOPS LRHS MArt MBNS MMuc NBro NChi SBrt SEND SPav WMoo WWtn
- 'Milk Chocolate'	CAbb CBcs CBod CBot CDor CLAP CSpe ECtt ELan EPfP GBin GBuc GJos GKev GQue IBoy LHop LOPS LRHS LSRN MCot MHer NBir NEgg NLar NWad SCob SKHP SPtp WHar
'Pink Chapel'	ECtt
(Polkadot Series) 'Polkadot Pippa'	CBot LRHS SHil
- 'Polkadot Polly'	CBot
- 'Polkadot Princess'	CBot

	purpurea	CHab CWld ELan ENfk EPfP ESps EWoo GPoy LSun MHer MMuc MNHC NMir SCob SHil SIde SPlb SPoG WBrk WHar WMoo WOut WSFF
	- 'Alba'	see *D. purpurea* f. *albiflora*
§	- f. ***albiflora***	Widely available
	- - 'Anne Redetzky'[PBR]	CSpe LRHS
	- 'Apricot Delight'	EBee WHar
	- Camelot Series	CNec SHar SVic
	- - 'Camelot Cream'	CBot ELan EPfP LRHS SWvt
	- - 'Camelot Lavender'	CBot ELan EPfP ESps LRHS SWvt
	- - 'Camelot Rose'	CBot ELan EPfP ESps LRHS SWvt
	- - 'Camelot White'	ELan EPfP
*	- 'Campanulata Alba'	CBot
	- 'Candy Mountain'	CBod CBot
	- CEN-type mutant	CNat
	- 'Chedglow' (v)	CNat
	- (Dalmatian Series) 'Dalmatian Cream'	CBot LRHS MAsh NPri
	- - 'Dalmatian Peach'	CBod CBot EBee EPfP IBoy LRHS LSou MAsh NPri
	- - 'Dalmatian Purple'	CBot EPfP ESps LCro LOPS LRHS LSou MAsh MHtn NPri
	- - 'Dalmatian Rose'	CBod CBot EPfP LCro MAsh NPri
	- - 'Dalmatian White'	CBod EBee LCro LRHS LSou
	- Excelsior Group	CBcs CBot CDor CMac CRos CSBt CTri CWCL EAEE ECtt EPfP ESps GJos GMaP IBoy LCro LRHS MJak NHol NMir NRHS SCob SPer SPoG SRms SVic SWvt WHar XLum
	- - (Suttons; Unwins) ♀H7	ECtt MRav
	- Foxy Group	CBot CRos CWib EAJP EPfP GMcL LRHS MJak MNHC NNys NRHS SPoG WHar
	- - 'Foxy Apricot'	SPtp SWvt WCot
	- - 'Foxy Pink'	ELan LHop SPtp
	- Giant Spotted Group	CRos ECtt EPfP LRHS NRHS SPoG
	- Glittering Prizes Group	CBot SWat
	- Gloxinioides Group	CBot LCro LOPS
	- - 'The Shirley' ♀H7	WMoo
§	- subsp. ***heywoodii***	CBot IBoy WMoo
	- - 'Silver Fox'	CBod LSRN
	- 'Pam's Choice'	Widely available
	- 'Pam's Split'	CBot EBee GAbr SCob
	- 'Primrose Carousel'	CBot NEgg NLar SCob STPC
	- 'Serendipity'	EPfP LRHS SHil
	- 'Snow Thimble'	CAby CBod CBot CDor CLAP EAJP ELan GJos IBoy LRHS LSun MHol NLar STPC
	- 'Sugar Plum'	CBot LBrs
§	- 'Sutton's Apricot' ♀H7	Widely available
*	- 'Sutton's Giant Primrose'	CBot
	- (Virtuosa Series) 'Virtuosa Red' **new**	GMcL
	- - 'Virtuosa Rose' **new**	GMcL
	- - 'Virtuosa White' **new**	GMcL
	- white CEN-type mutant	NChi
	'Red Skin'	GJos NLar NWad
	sceptrum	CCCN MGil SPlb SVen
	'Silver Cub' **new**	GAbr
	'Spice Island'	CBod CDor CHVG CLAP CMos EBee ECtt ELon ESwi GJos IBoy LEdu LHop LRHS LSou NLar NSti SCob SPer SPoG STPC WCot
*	***stewartii***	EWes GLog LEdu NWad WMoo
	'Strawberry Fayre'	GJos
	thapsi	ELan EPPr EPfP GJos NChi
	- 'Spanish Peaks'	CBod GJos IBoy MArt
	trojana	CFis EAJP ECtt GKev IFoB SCob SDix WWtn
	- 'Helen of Troy'	CLAP ELan LHop MArt SKHP SPtp WHer
	viridiflora	CSam ECtt NBro

Dilatris (*Haemodoraceae*)

ixioides	CLak
pillansii	CLak

dill see *Anethum graveolens*

Dimorphotheca (*Asteraceae*)

cuneata	WHil

Dionaea ✿ (*Droseraceae*)

	muscipula	CHew EECP NLos SHmp SKHP SPlb WSSs
	- 'Akai Ryu' ♀H3	NLos SHmp WSSs
	- 'All Green'	EECP
	- 'B52'	EECP WSSs
	- 'Big Mouth'	EECP
	- 'Bohemian Garnet'	EECP WSSs
	- 'Darwin' **new**	WSSs
	- (Dentate Traps Group) 'Dentate Traps'	WSSs
*	- f. ***heterodoxa***	NLos
	- large clone	NLos
	- long-toothed	NLos
	- 'Mk1979' **new**	WSSs
	- 'Pink Venus'	NLos
	- 'Royal Red'	CHew NLos WSSs
	- 'Sawtooth'	EECP NLos WSSs
	- shark-toothed	EECP NLos
	- Slack's red clone	NLos
	- 'South West Giant' ♀H3	NLos WSSs
	- 'Spider'	EECP NLos
	- 'Tiger Fangs'	WSSs
	- upright	NLos

Dionysia (*Primulaceae*)

'Annielle'	WAbe
aretioides ♀H5	WAbe
- 'Bevere'	EPot WAbe
- 'Gerben' **new**	WAbe
- 'Phyllis Carter'	ECho
bryoides	WAbe
'Charlson Emma'	WAbe
'Charlson Gem'	EPot WAbe
'Charlson Jake'	WAbe
'Charlson Petite'	WAbe
'Charlson Pip'	WAbe
'Charlson Primrose'	WAbe
'Corona'	WAbe
curviflora	WAbe
'Eric Watson'	WAbe
'Ewesley Iota'	WAbe
'Ewesley Kappa'	WAbe
'Ewesley Theta'	WAbe
'Geist'	WAbe
involucrata	WAbe
- white-flowered	WAbe
janthina	WAbe
'Judith Bramley'	WAbe
'Lycaena'	WAbe
'Mike Bramley' **new**	WAbe
'Monika'	WAbe
'Pascal'	WAbe
sarvestanica	WAbe
tapetodes	EPot WAbe
- 'Brimstone'	WAbe
- 'Peter Edwards'	WAbe

'Tess'	WAbe
'Zdeněk Zvolánek'	WAbe

Dioon (*Zamiaceae*)

argenteum new	CBrP
califanoi	CBrP
caputoi	CBrP
edule ♀H1b	CBrP SPlb
- var. ***angustifolium***	CBrP
merolae	CBrP
rzedowskii	CBrP
spinulosum	CBrP SBig

Dioscorea (*Dioscoreaceae*)

araucana	LSou
batatas	CAgr CArn CRHN LEdu
elephantipes ♀H1c	LToo
japonica	CAgr LEdu
quinqueloba	WCru
villosa	CArn LEdu

Diosma (*Rutaceae*)

ericoides L.	SWvt
'Pink Fountain'	see *Coleonema pulchellum* 'Pink Fountain'
'Sunset Gold'	see *Coleonema* 'Sunset Gold'

Diosphaera (*Campanulaceae*)

asperuloides	see *Trachelium asperuloides*

Diospyros (*Ebenaceae*)

austroafricana	SPlb
glabra	SVen
* ***hyrcanum***	NLar
kaki (F)	CBcs CMCN EPfP NLar NPla WCot
- 'Fuyu' (F)	CAgr
- 'Hana Fuyu' (F) new	MRai
- 'Kostata' (F)	CAgr
- 'Mazelii' (F)	CAgr WPGP
- 'Rojo Brillante' (F)	MRai
lotus	CAgr CBcs CMCN EBee ESwi GBin LEdu NLar SPlb WMat
- PAB 10032 new	LEdu WPGP
- (f)	CAgr
- (m)	CAgr
lycioides	CTre SPlb
'Nikita's Gift' (F)	CAgr
'Nikita's Russian' (F)	CAgr
'Nikshoo' (F)	CAgr
ramulosa	SPlb
rhombifolia	NLar
'Russian Beauty' (F)	CAgr
'Russian Red' (F)	CAgr
virginiana (F)	CBcs CMCN EBee NLar SPlb
- 'Morris Burton' (F)	CAgr
- 'Nc-10' (F)	CAgr

Diostea (*Verbenaceae*)

juncea	MGil

Dipcadi (*Asparagaceae*)

ciliare	CLak
serotinum	ECho EPot GKev
viride	CLak CTal
white-flowered	CLak

Dipelta (*Caprifoliaceae*)

floribunda ♀H5	CBcs CBot CDul CFil CJun CMCN CTho EBee ELan EPfP IDee LRHS MBlu NLar SKHP SWvt WPGP WPat
ventricosa	CAbP CBcs CFil CJun EBee ELan EPfP LRHS MBlu NLar SBrt SKHP SPoG WPGP
yunnanensis	CBcs CBot CDul CJun CTho ELan EPfP IArd IDee LRHS NLar SBrt SKHP SWvt WPGP

Diphylleia (*Berberidaceae*)

cymosa	CAby CTal ECha GCal GEdr LEdu MRav SPhx WCot WCru
grayi	GEdr LEdu WCru
sinensis	WCru

Dipidax see *Onixotis*

Diplacus see *Mimulus*

Dipladenia see *Mandevilla*

Diplarrena (*Iridaceae*)

§ ***latifolia***	CNor EBee GCal IBlr LRHS NCGa
moraea	CAbP CAby CElw CJun CMac CWCL EBee ECho GAbr GCal IBlr IBoy IKil LEdu MBel NCGa WSHC
- ***minor***	IBlr
- 'Slieve Donard'	CBot IBlr
- West Coast form	see *D. latifolia*

Diplazium (*Woodsiaceae*)

maximum	NLos

Diplopanax (*Cornaceae*)

stachyanthus B&SWJ 11803	WCru

Diplotaxis (*Brassicaceae*)

muralis	CLau WJek
tenuifolia	CAgr CLau ENfk MNHC SRms

Dipsacus (*Caprifoliaceae*)

asper PAB 8884	LEdu
§ ***fullonum***	CBod CHab ENfk EPfP LCro MHer MNHC NMir SDix SEND SIde SRms WHer WSFF
inermis	CSam ECha NBid NLar
japonicus	SKHP
- HWJ 695	SPhx WCru
pilosus	CBgR NDov
sativus	NLar NWad
strigosus	SPhx
sylvestris	see *D. fullonum*

Dipteracanthus see *Ruellia*

Dipteronia (*Sapindaceae*)

sinensis	CBcs CMCN

Disa (*Orchidaceae*)

aurata	NDav
Bride's Dream gx	NDav
Child Safety Transvaal gx	NDav
- 'Sonia'	NDav
Colette Cywes gx	NDav
'Blush' new	
Constantia gx	NDav
Diores gx	NDav
- 'Inca City'	NDav
- 'Inca Gold'	NDav
- 'Inca Princess'	NDav
- 'Inca Warrior'	NDav
Diorosa gx	NDav

Foam gx NDav
- 'Zoe' NDav
Glasgow Orchid Conference gx NDav
Ivan Watson gx NDav
Kalahari Sands gx NDav
- 'Tina' **new** NDav
Kewbett gx NDav
- 'Pink Gem' **new** NDav
Kewdior gx NDav
Kewensis gx 'Alice' NDav
- 'Ann' NDav
- 'May' NDav
- 'Milkmaid' NDav
- 'Ruth' NDav
Reheat gx NDav
Riette gx NDav
Robert Parkinson gx NDav
Sealord gx NDav
Tracey Parkinson gx NDav
tripetaloides NDav
Unidiorosa gx 'Tracey' NDav
uniflora NDav SPlb
- carmine-flowered NDav
- pink-flowered NDav
- red-flowered NDav
Unifoam gx NDav
- 'Firebird' NDav
Unilangley gx NDav
Watsonii gx 'Bramley' NDav
- 'Candy' NDav
- 'Don' NDav
- 'Sandra' NDav

Disanthus (*Hamamelidaceae*)

cercidifolius ♀H5 CAbP CBcs CMCN CMac CRos EPfP GBin GKin IArd IDee LRHS MBlu MPkF NLar SPer SPoG WHor WMat WPGP
- 'Ena-nishiki' (v) MBlu NLar WPGP

Discaria (*Rhamnaceae*)

chacaye LEdu

Diselma (*Cupressaceae*)

archeri CKen SCoo SLim
- 'Read Dwarf' CKen

Disepalum (*Annonaceae*)

petelotii B&SWJ 11690 WCru
- FMWJ 13375 WCru

Disphyma (*Aizoaceae*)

crassifolium SChr

Disporopsis (*Asparagaceae*)

B&SWJ 229 from Taiwan WCru
B&SWJ 1864 from Taiwan WCru
aspersa CAvo CBro EBee ECho EPPr EWld GEdr GKev LEdu MAvo MNrw NBir WCru WPGP
- tall CBct WCru
fuscopicta CAby CBct CLAP EBee EPPr LEdu MAvo MPie WCru
longifolia CLAP
- B&SWJ 5284 WCru
luzoniensis IMou
- B&SWJ 3891 CBct ESwi GEdr LEdu WCru
'Min Shan' CTal ELon
* ***nova*** EPPr MAvo
§ ***pernyi*** Widely available
- B&SWJ 1864 CBct EPPr GEdr
- 'Bill Baker' CBct EBee EPPr LEdu MAvo WSHC
taiwanensis EBee IMou LEdu
- B&SWJ 3388 CBct GEdr WCru
undulata CBct CSpe EPPr ILea IMou LEdu MAvo NBid WCru WPGP

Disporum (*Colchicaceae*)

austrosinense B&SWJ 9777 WCru
bodinieri CBct EPfP
- DJHC 765 WCru
cantoniense CBct IMou LEdu LRHS WCru WFar
- B&L 12512 CLAP
- B&SWJ 1424 WCru
- B&SWJ 9715 WCru
- DJHC 98485 LEdu SKHP WPGP
- PAB 8339 LEdu
I - 'Aureovariegata' CBct EPfP LEdu WCot
- var. ***cantoniense*** f. ***brunneum*** B&SWJ 5290 WCru
- 'Leigong' WPGP
- var. ***multiflorum*** B&SWJ 11252 WCru
- - B&SWJ 11291 WCru
- 'Shirui Pink' **new** LEdu
- var. ***sikkimense*** B&SWJ 2337 WCru
- - B&SWJ 2358 LEdu WCru
- - PAB 13.1711 **new** LEdu
- - PAB 4973 LEdu
- var. ***y-tiense*** HWJ 1045 WCru
hookeri see *Prosartes hookeri*
kawakamii B&SWJ 350 WCru
- RWJ 10103 CBct WCru
lanuginosum see *Prosartes lanuginosa*
leschenaultianum B&SWJ 9484 WCru
- B&SWJ 9505 WCru
leucanthum CTal WCru
- B&SWJ 2389 WCru
longistylum CTal EBee LEdu
- B&SWJ 2859 WCru
- BWJ 8128 **new** WCru
- L 1564 CBct ESwi LEdu WCru
- 'Green Giant' CBct CLAP CTal EBee EPfP GEdr IDee IFoB ILea LEdu LPla LRHS LSou MAvo MSCN NLar WCot WFar WHil WPtf
- 'Night Heron' CBct CTal IFoB IMou LEdu LPla LRHS MAvo WCot WFar
- 'Night Heron' seedlings WPGP
lutescens CTal WCru
maculatum see *Prosartes maculata*
megalanthum CBct CLAP IFoB LEdu WCru
- CD&R 2412B CTal
menziesii see *Prosartes smithii*
nantouense CTal
- B&SWJ 359 CBct LEdu WCru
- B&SWJ 6812 WCru
oreganum see *Prosartes hookeri* var. *oregana*
sessile EBee ECho LEdu WCru
- AGSJ 146 GBuc
- B&SWJ 2824 WCru
I - 'Aureovariegatum' (v) ECho EWld WCru
- 'Awa-no-tsuki' (v) GEdr
- 'Ginsekai' GEdr
- 'Kinga' (v) GEdr LEdu

	- f. ***macrophyllum*** B&SWJ 4316	WCru
I	- 'Robustum Variegatum' (v)	EBee
	- 'Snow Stream' (v)	GEdr
	- 'Variegatum' (v)	CAby CNor CTal EBee ECho ELan ELon EPPr EPfP GCal IMou LEdu LRHS NHpl NLar SPhx WCru WFar WPGP
	- var. ***yakushimense***	ECho LEdu
	shimadae	GKev
	- B&SWJ 399	WCru
	smilacinum	CTal NLar WCru
	- B&SWJ 713	CBct WCru
*	- 'Aureovariegatum' (v)	LEdu WCru
	- pink-flowered	CBct WCot WCru
	smithii	see *Prosartes smithii*
	taiwanense B&SWJ 1513	WCru
	- B&SWJ 2018	WCru
	tonkinense B&SWJ 11672	WCru
	- B&SWJ 11814	WCru
	- HWJ 882	WCru
	trabeculatum	CBct WCru
	- 'Nakafu'	IMou LEdu WCru
	uniflorum	CAby CAvo CBct CLAP CTal ECho EPPr EPfP ETho LEdu LRHS MMrt MNrw NBid SMad WSHC
	- B&SWJ 651	CBct LEdu WCru
	- B&SWJ 872	WCru
	- B&SWJ 4100	WCru
	- MSF 800 new	LEdu
	viridescens	CBct EBee EPPr LEdu SKHP WCru WPnP
	- B&SWJ 4598	WCru

Distictis (*Bignoniaceae*)

	buccinatoria	CHII

Distyliopsis (*Hamamelidaceae*)

	tutcheri new	CJun

Distylium (*Hamamelidaceae*)

	myricoides	NLar WPat
	racemosum	CBcs CCCN CMac EBee EPfP MBlu NLar SSta WSHC

Dittrichia (*Asteraceae*)

	viscosa	WCot

Diuranthera see *Chlorophytum*

Dizygotheca see *Schefflera*

Dobinea (*Anacardiaceae*)

	vulgaris B&SWJ 2532	WCru

Dodecatheon (*Primulaceae*)

	alpinum	GKev NHar
	- subsp. ***alpinum***	EBee
	'Aphrodite'PBR	ECtt MHol NLar WFar
	austrofrigidum	EBee GEdr GKev NCGa NHar SBrt
	clevelandii	GEdr WAbe
	- subsp. ***insulare***	EBee LLHF
	- subsp. ***patulum***	CRos ECho LRHS NRHS
	conjugens	GKev LLHF XEll
	cusickii	see *D. pulchellum* subsp. *cusickii*
	dentatum ♀H5	CPBP GEdr GKev LEdu NHar SBrt WAbe WFar
	- subsp. ***utahense***	NHar
	frigidum	GEdr GKev WAbe
§	***jeffreyi***	CRos ECho ECtt EPPr EPfP GBuc GEdr GKev LEdu LRHS MNrw NLar NPnk NRHS NSum WAbe WBor WFar
	- subsp. ***pygmaeum***	GKev
§	***meadia*** ♀H5	Widely available
	- from Cedar County, USA	WAbe
	- f. ***album*** ♀H5	CBro CRos ECho ELan EPfP EPot GKev IBoy LAma LEdu LHop LRHS NHol NHpl NPnk NRHS NSum NWad SKHP SPer SWvt WPnP
	- 'Aphrodite'	EPfP WFar
*	- 'Goliath'	GAbr GWyn NSum
	- membranaceous	WAbe
	- 'Purple Rose'	SPad
	- 'Queen Victoria'	ECho GBuc LEdu NLar SKHP WFar
	- red shades	GBuc NSum
	pauciflorum misapplied	see *D. pulchellum*
	pauciflorum (Dur.) E. Greene	see *D. meadia*
	poeticum	SPlb
	- NNS 00-259	NCGa
§	***pulchellum*** ♀H5	CBro CRos EBee ECho EDAr GEdr IBoy LHop LLWG LRHS MArt MNrw NRHS NRya WIce
	- ***album***	ECho
§	- subsp. ***cusickii***	LEdu
	- subsp. ***pulchellum*** 'Red Wings'	CPne CRos ECho ELan ELon EPot GWyn IBoy LLHF LRHS NBir NHar NHpl NLar NRHS SKHP SPoG WHoo
	- ***radicatum***	see *D. pulchellum*
	- 'Sooke Variety'	WAbe
	radicatum	see *D. pulchellum*
	redolens	GBuc
	tetrandrum	see *D. jeffreyi*

Dodonaea (*Sapindaceae*)

	viscosa	CBcs SPlb
	- 'Purpurea'	CBcs CHGN CTsd EUJe IVic SPoG SVen

Doellingeria (*Asteraceae*)

	scabra	see *Aster scaber*
§	***umbellata***	CBWd CBre CKno EBee ECha EPPr GQue LEdu MMuc NBir NDov NLar WCot WOld

Dolichos (*Papilionaceae*)

	purpureus	see *Lablab purpureus*

Dombeya (*Malvaceae*)

	× ***cayeuxii***	SVen
	wallichii	CCCN

Dondia see *Hacquetia*

Doodia ✿ (*Blechnaceae*)

	media	CBct EBee EShb EUJe ISha LCro LEdu LRHS NLos SPlb WCot

Doronicum (*Asteraceae*)

	austriacum	MMuc NBid
	- PAB 5641	LEdu
	caucasicum	see *D. orientale*
§	***columnae***	CBcs
	cordatum	see *D. columnae*
§	× ***excelsum*** 'Harpur Crewe'	EBee LEdu MRav NPer SHar

	'Finesse'	CRos GCal GJos LRHS LSun NRHS SRms
	'Little Leo'	CBod CRos ELan ELon EPfP GJos GMaP LRHS LSRN NLar NRHS SPoG SRms WHil
§	***orientale***	EPed EPfP GJos MMuc SEND SPoG SWat WHea
	- 'Leonardo'	CRos GMcL LRHS NPri NRHS WHar
	- 'Leonardo Compact'	LPot WTor
	- 'Magnificum'	CRos CSBt EBee EPfP ESps GMaP LRHS MBNS NRHS SPoG SRms WHar
	pardalianches	CArn CFis CMea GCal GJos MMuc WBrk WHal WRHF
	- 'Goldstrauss'	EBee
	plantagineum 'Excelsum'	see *D.* × *excelsum* 'Harpur Crewe'

Dorotheanthus (*Aizoaceae*)

bellidiformis	see *Cleretum bellidiforme*

Doryanthes (*Doryanthaceae*)

palmeri	CBrP

Dorycnium see *Lotus*

Doryopteris (*Pteridaceae*)

pedata var. ***palmata***	NLos

Douglasia see *Androsace*

vitaliana	see *Vitaliana primuliflora*

Dovyalis (*Salicaceae*)

caffra (F)	XBlo

Doxantha see *Macfadyena*

Draba (*Brassicaceae*)

	acaulis	WAbe
	aizoides	CRos ECho GJos LRHS NRHS SPlb SRms
	aizoon	see *D. lasiocarpa*
	bertolonii Boiss.	see *D. loeseleurii*
	bruniifolia	NHar
	bryoides	see *D. rigida* var. *bryoides*
	'Buttermilk'	WAbe
	compacta	see *D. lasiocarpa* Compacta Group
*	***condensata*** new	GJos
	cusickii	GKev
	cuspidata	GJos
	dedeana	GJos WAbe
	densifolia	IFoB
	gilliesii new	GJos
	imbricata	see *D. rigida* var. *bryoides*
	'John Saxton'	EPot WAbe
	kotschyi	SPlb
§	***lasiocarpa***	XLum
§	- Compacta Group	SIgm
§	***loeseleurii***	GJos
	longisiliqua ♀H4	LLHF WAbe
	mollissima	EPot WAbe
	- 'Göteborg'	EPot
	nivalis	SPlb
	norvegica new	GJos
	oligosperma	EDAr GJos IFoB
	ossetica	WAbe
	parnassica	GJos
	paysonii	SIgm
	- var. ***treleasei***	LLHF
	polytricha	NSla
	ramosissima	GJos
§	***rigida*** var. ***bryoides***	WThu
	- - compact	EPot WAbe
*	- var. ***imbricata***	GCrg NSla
	rosularis	EDAr GJos WAbe
	scardica	see *D. lasiocarpa*
	sphaeroides	SPlb
	stellata new	GJos
	ventosa	WAbe
	yunnanensis	WAbe

Dracaena ✿ (*Asparagaceae*)

cochinchinensis	SPlb
draco ♀H1c	CArn CCCN EShb SPlb WCot XBlo
fragrans (Compacta Group) 'Compacta' new	XBlo
- Deremensis Group	XBlo
- - 'J.A. Truffaut' new	XBlo
- - 'Souvenir d'August de Schrijver' (v) new	XBlo
indivisa	see *Cordyline indivisa*
'Lemon Lime Tips'	XBlo
marginata (v) ♀H1b	XBlo
- 'Tricolor' (v) ♀H1b	XBlo

Dracocephalum (*Lamiaceae*)

	altaiense	see *D. imberbe*
	argunense	CAby SPhx SRms
	- 'Blue Carpet'	LEdu NLar
	- 'Fuji Blue'	CSma EDAr EWes SPoG WIce
	- 'Fuji White'	SPhx SPoG
	austriacum	LRHS
	botryoides	CPBP MMuc SPhx
	calophyllum var. ***smithianum***	IMou
	forrestii	GKev SBrt
	grandiflorum	GBin GEdr MMrt SPhx WCot XLum
	hemsleyanum	LLHF
§	***imberbe***	GBin
	mairei	see *D. renatii*
	moldavica	GBin
	paulsenii	CPBP
	peregrinum	GBin
	- 'Blue Dragon'	SPhx
	prattii	see *Nepeta prattii*
§	***renatii***	LLHF SPhx
	rupestre	EBee SBrt SPhx
	ruyschiana	ELan MMrt SPhx XLum
	sibiricum	see *Nepeta sibirica*
*	***tataricum***	LRHS
	virginicum	see *Physostegia virginiana*

Dracophyllum (*Ericaceae*)

prostratum	EPot

Dracunculus (*Araceae*)

	canariensis	CBod GKev WCot
	muscivorus	see *Helicodiceros muscivorus*
§	***vulgaris***	CAby CHid EBee ECho EPfP EPot ESwi GKev LTro SDix SEND SMad SPlb SPoG WCot
	- white-flowered	WCot

Dregea (*Apocynaceae*)

sinensis	CBcs CBot CCCN CHll CRHN EBee ECre ELan EPfP EShb EWes LRHS MRav SEND SKHP SNig SPer SPoG SWvt WPGP WSHC
- 'Brockhill Silver'	CBot EPfP LRHS SKHP SWvt
- 'Variegata' (v)	EWes

Drepanostachyum (*Poaceae*)

	falconeri J.J.N. Campbell. ex D. McClintock	see *Himalayacalamus falconeri*, *H. falconeri* 'Damarapa'
	hookerianum	see *Himalayacalamus hookerianus*

Drimia (*Asparagaceae*)

	anomala	CLak
	basutica	CLak
	elata	CLak
	involuta	CLak
	mzimvubuensis	CLak
	sphaerocephala	CLak
	uniflora	CLak

Drimiopsis (*Asparagaceae*)

	maculata	EShb GKev LToo MPie WCot

Drimys (*Winteraceae*)

	andina	CBct EPfP MMuc
	aromatica	see *Tasmannia lanceolata*
	colorata	see *Pseudowintera colorata*
	granadensis	WCru
	var. ***grandiflora*** B&SWJ 10777	
	latifolia	see *D. winteri* var. *chilensis*
	winteri 🏆H4	Widely available
§	- var. ***chilensis***	CBcs EPfP LRHS WCru WPGP
	- Latifolia Group	see *D. winteri* var. *chilensis*
	- var. ***winteri***	SRms

Drosanthemum (*Aizoaceae*)

	hispidum	CRos ECho ELan EPot LRHS MAsh NRHS SPlb SPoG
*	***sutherlandii***	ECho

Drosera ✿ (*Droseraceae*)

	admirabilis	CHew
	aliciae 🏆H3	CHew EECP NLos SHmp
	andersoniana	EFEx
	ascendens	CHew
	binata	CHew EECP SHmp
§	- subsp. ***dichotoma*** 🏆H3	CHew NLos SHmp
	- 'Extrema'	NLos
	- 'Giant'	NLos
	browniana	EFEx
	bulbigena	EFEx
	bulbosa subsp. ***bulbosa***	EFEx
	- subsp. ***major***	EFEx
	capensis	CHew NLos SHmp SPlb
	- 'Albino' 🏆H3	CHew EECP NLos SHmp
	dichotoma	see *D. binata* subsp. *dichotoma*
	dichrosepala	EECP
	erythrorhiza	EFEx
	- subsp. ***collina***	EFEx
	- subsp. ***erythrorhiza***	EFEx
	- subsp. ***magna***	EFEx
	- subsp. ***squamosa***	EFEx
	filiformis	NLos
	- var. ***filiformis***	CHew EECP SHmp
	- var. ***tracyi***	NLos
	gigantea	EFEx
	graniticola	EFEx
	heterophylla	EFEx
	loureiroi	EFEx
	macrantha	EFEx
	- subsp. ***macrantha***	EFEx
	macrophylla subsp. ***macrophylla***	EFEx
	madagascariensis	NLos SHmp
	marchantii subsp. ***prophylla***	EFEx
	menziesii subsp. ***basifolia***	EFEx
	- subsp. ***menziesii***	EFEx
	- subsp. ***thysanosepala***	EFEx
	modesta	EFEx
	nidiformis	CHew NLos
	orbiculata	EFEx
	paradoxa new	NLos
	peltata	EFEx
	platypoda	EFEx
	ramellosa	EFEx
	rosulata	EFEx
	rotundifolia	SHmp WHer
	salina	EFEx
	scorpioides	EECP SHmp
	slackii 🏆H3	CHew SPlb
	spatulata	SHmp
	stolonifera subsp. ***compacta***	EFEx
	- subsp. ***humilis***	EFEx
	- subsp. ***porrecta***	EFEx
	- subsp. ***rupicola***	EFEx
	- subsp. ***stolonifera***	EFEx
	tubaestylus	EFEx
	zonaria	EFEx

Dryandra (*Proteaceae*)

	formosa	CTre SPlb
	quercifolia	SPlb

Dryas (*Rosaceae*)

	drummondii	EPot LLHF
§	***integrifolia***	CMea EPot LLHF WAbe
	- 'Greenland Green'	WAbe
	octopetala 🏆H5	CArn CMea CRos ECho GKev LHop LRHS NChi NRHS SPoG SRms SWvt WAbe
	- subsp. ***hookeriana***	LLHF
§	- 'Minor' 🏆H5	EPot NHar SIgm WAbe
	× ***suendermannii*** 🏆H5	EPot GCrg GMaP LLHF NHar NSla SBch WAbe WTor
	tenella misapplied	see *D. octopetala* 'Minor'
	tenella Pursh	see *D. integrifolia*

Drynaria (*Polypodiaceae*)

	baronii new	WCot

Dryopteris ✿ (*Dryopteridaceae*)

	from Kunming, China	NLos
	from Mount Zijin, China	NLos
	from Nanjing Botanical Garden, China	NLos
	aemula	EFer
§	***affinis*** 🏆H5	CDor CLAP CMac CWCL EAEE ECha EPfP ERod ESps EWoo GMaP LBuc LRHS MCot MGos NPnk NPri SCob SPer SPoG WCot WFib WShi XLum
	- 'Angustata Crispa'	EBee
	- subsp. ***cambrensis***	ISha
	- - 'Insubrica'	EFer
	- 'Congesta'	CKel CLAP
	- 'Congesta Cristata'	CLAP CTal CWCL ECtt EFer GMaP SRot
	- Crispa Group	CBod CLAP EPfP LRHS SCob
§	- 'Crispa Gracilis' 🏆H5	CBod CKel CLAP ELan ERod ISha NBir NEgg NHol NLar
*	- 'Crispa Gracilis Congesta'	GEdr MRav NGdn NWad SBod WCot WFib WPat

§	– 'Cristata' ♀H5	Widely available
	– 'Cristata Angustata' ♀H5	CLAP CTal EFer ELan EPed EPfP NBid NBro NGdn NHol WBor WFib WMoo
	– 'Cristata The King'	see *D. affinis* 'Cristata'
	– 'Grandiceps Askew'	EFer WFib
	– 'Pinderi'	CLAP EBee EPfP EUJe GBin ISha LPla LSun MAvo MPie NCou NLar SCob WCot WRHF
	– Polydactyla Group	CLAP CLet
	– – 'Polydactyla Dadds'	CLAP EBee LLHF NLar
	– – 'Polydactyla Mapplebeck' ♀H5	CLAP CLet NBid WFib
	– 'Revolvens'	CLAP EFer
	atrata misapplied	see *D. cycadina*
	atrata (Wall. ex Kunze) Ching	CDTJ CWCL LLWG LRHS NEgg NLar SPoG WPat XLum
	× ***australis***	CLAP EBee ISha NLos
	austriaca	see *D. dilatata*
	bissetiana	ISha
	blanfordii from Kashmir	ISha
	buschiana	CLAP EBee EWTr MRav NLar WCot
	carthusiana	CLAP EBee EFer NLar XLum
	– 'Cristata'	EFer
	celsa	ISha NLos
	championii	CCCN CLAP EBee ISha LRHS NBro
	clintoniana	CLAP EBee ECtt EFer GBin GEdr LLWG LPla LRHS WCot
	× ***complexa***	ISha NLos
	– 'Stablerae' ♀H7	CLAP CLet EFer WFib
	– 'Stablerae' crisped ♀H7	WFib
	coreanomontana	NLar
	crassirhizoma ♀H6	CAby CBod CCCN CKel CLAP EBee ECGP ECtt EPfP EUJe GBin ISha LLWG LPla LRHS LSun MAvo WCot WPtf WRHF
	cristata	CLAP CWCL EBee EPfP WMoo XLum
§	***cycadina*** ♀H4	CBcs CLAP CTal EBee EFer ELan EPfP ERod EShb EUJe GBin ISha LRHS MGos NBid NBir NLos SCob SPtp WFib WMoo WPnP
	cystolepidota	EFer
§	***dilatata*** ♀H6	ECha EFer ELan EPfP ERod ESps LEdu LRHS MMuc MRav WCot WFib WHal WShi
	– 'Crispa Whiteside' ♀H6	CDor CLAP CLet CWCL EAEE EBee EFer ELan EPfP ERod EShb GBin LRHS MRav NBro NEgg NLar SHil SPlb WCot WFib WMoo WPat
	– 'Grandiceps'	CLAP CMac EFer WFib
	– 'Jimmy Dyce'	CLAP GBin ISha LRHS
	– 'Lepidota Crispa Cristata'	CLAP EBee WPat
	– 'Lepidota Cristata' ♀H6	CLAP CWCL ELan EMOT ERod GKev NBro NGdn NLos WFib WMoo
	– 'Lepidota Grandiceps'	CLAP
*	– 'Recurvata'	CLAP ISha LLHF NLar
	erythrosora ♀H4	Widely available
	– 'Brilliance' ♀H5	CCCN CLAP CSpe EBee ECtt ELon EMFm EUJe GQue ISha LLWG LPla LRHS LSou MAvo MPie NCou WCot WRHF
	– var. ***koidzumiana***	ISha LRHS WCot
	– var. ***prolifica***	CBod CKel CLAP EBee ELan EPfP GBin GMaP ISha LRHS MGos NBir NEgg NLar NPri SBod SHil SPoG WFib WPat
	– 'Radiance' **new**	ISha
	× ***euxinensis***	CLAP
	filix-mas ♀H7	CKel CSBt CTri CWCL ECha ELan EPfP ERod ESps EWoo GBin GMaP GMcL IBoy LCro LEdu LOPS LRHS LSun MCot MMuc MWat NHol SCob SEND SPer WFib WSFF WShi XLum
	– 'Barnesii'	CLAP CLet CWCL ECGP EFer ELan EMOT ERod ISha LRHS NEgg NLar SEND SHil SPlb
	– 'Crispa'	CLAP LRHS SHil WFib
	– 'Crispa Congesta'	see *D. affinis* 'Crispa Gracilis'
	– 'Crispa Cristata' ♀H7	CLAP CWCL EBee ECtt EFer ELan EPfP ERod ESps EUJe GBin GMaP IKil LHop LLWG LRHS NBid NBir NBro SCob SPoG WFib XLum
	– 'Crispatissima'	EBee
	– 'Cristata' ♀H7	CLAP CTal EBee ECtt EFer ELan LLWG LOPS LPot MJak NBro SEND WMoo
	– Cristata Group	EFer
*	– – 'Cristata Grandiceps'	EFer
	– – 'Cristata Jackson'	CLAP SPlb
	– – 'Cristata Martindale'	CLAP NBid WFib
	– – 'Fred Jackson'	CLAP WFib
	– 'Depauperata'	CLAP
	– 'Furcans'	CLAP EBee ECtt WMoo
	– 'Grandiceps Wills' ♀H7	NBid WFib
	– 'Linearis'	EFer ELan EWoo ISha LRHS MCot MGos WFib
	– 'Linearis Polydactyla' ♀H7	CBod CDor CLAP CMac CWCL EAJP EFer ELan EMOT EPfP EShb EWTr GBin LRHS MMuc MRav NEgg NGdn NHol NLar NLos SCob SEND SPoG SPtp WMoo WPnP XLum
	– 'Parsley'	CLAP ISha
*	– Polydactyla Group	ECha MRav NEgg SCob
I	– 'Revolvens'	WFib
	fragrans	SKHP
	goldieana	CBod CDTJ CLAP CLet CTal EBee ECha ECtt EFer EMOT EWTr GMaP ISha LLWG LRHS NBid NBir NEgg NLar WFar WFib WMoo WPnP XLum
	hirtipes misapplied	see *D. cycadina*
	intermedia	ISha
	labordei	EBee GBin ISha LRHS
	lacera	ISha
	lepidopoda	CAby CBcs CBod CDor ECtt EUJe GBin LLWG LPla LRHS MAvo MPie WCot WPtf WRHF
	ludoviciana	ISha LRHS
	marginalis	CDTJ CKel CLAP EMOT LRHS NLar SCob WMoo
	neorosthornii	NLos
	oreades	WCot
	pacifica	CLAP
	paleacea	CLAP
	pseudofilix-mas	ISha
	pseudomas	see *D. affinis*
	pulcherrima	LRHS
	× ***remota***	EFer ISha NLos
	× ***separabilis***	ISha
	sichotensis	EBee
	sieboldii ♀H6	Widely available
	stewartii	CLAP GEdr LLHF NBro NLar
	tokyoensis ♀H6	CDTJ CLAP ISha LRHS NLar
	uniformis	CLAP EFer NLos
	wallichiana ♀H5	Widely available
	– from Yunnan, China	GCal
	yigongensis	NLos

Duchesnea (*Rosaceae*)

	chrysantha	see *D. indica*
§	***indica***	GJos MRav SEND WHea WMoo WOut XLum

Dudleya (*Crassulaceae*)

brittonii ΥH3	SMad
calcicola	SPlb
cymosa	SPlb
- subsp. ***cymosa***	SIgm
lanceolata	SIgm SPlb

Dugaldia (*Asteraceae*)

hoopesii	see *Hymenoxys hoopesii*

Dulichium (*Cyperaceae*)

arundinaceum	LLWG
- 'Tigress'	LLWG

Dunalia (*Solanaceae*)

australis	see *Iochroma australe*
- blue-flowered	see *Iochroma australe* 'Bill Evans'
- white-flowered	see *Iochroma australe* 'Andean Snow'

Duranta (*Verbenaceae*)

§	***erecta***	CCCN CHII
§	- 'Geisha Girl'	CCCN
	- 'Sapphire Swirl'	see *D. erecta* 'Geisha Girl'
	- 'Variegata' (v)	CCCN
	- white-flowered	SVen
	plumieri	see *D. erecta*
	repens	see *D. erecta*
	serratifolia	CCCN

Duvernoia see *Justicia*

Dyckia (*Bromeliaceae*)

brevifolia	WCot
'Cherry Coke'	WCot
frigida	WCot WGrn
goehringii	WCot
jonesiana	WCot
leptostachya	WCot WGrn
marnier-lapostollei	CBlu WCot
'Morris Hobbs'	WCot
remotiflora	SChr
velascana	WCot

Dypsis (*Arecaceae*)

§	***decaryi***	CCCN XBlo
	lutescens ΥH1a	NLos XBlo

Dysosma see *Podophyllum*

E

Ecballium (*Cucurbitaceae*)

elaterium	CArn CDTJ CFil LEdu WCot WPGP
- 'Lahij'	WPGP

Eccremocarpus (*Bignoniaceae*)

	ruber	see *E. scaber* 'Ruber'
	scaber	CBcs CKel CRos CWCL ELan EPfP GKev LHop LRHS MArt NPer SEND WHea
	- 'Carmineus'	EPfP
	- cream-flowered	ESwi NLar
	- orange-flowered	ESwi
	- red-flowered	NLar
§	- 'Ruber'	GKev
	- 'Tangerine'	CSpe
	- Tresco Series	GKev

Echeandia (*Asparagaceae*)

formosa B&SWJ 9147	WCru

Echeveria ✿ (*Crassulaceae*)

	affinis	CBod CDTJ MHer SRot
	agavoides ΥH1c	CDTJ MRav
	- 'Ebony'	WCot
	- 'Lipstick'	WCot
	albicans	SPlb
	alpina	see *E. secunda*
	ballsii	WCot
*	'Black Prince'	CDTJ ELan NPer SPlb SRot WCot
	'Blue Waves'	WCot
*	***cana***	CDTJ SRot
	cante ΥH2	SPlb
	coccinea	ELan
	'Corymbosa'	WCot
	'Curly Locks'	EBee ECtt EMFm WCot
	derenbergii ΥH2	MHCG
	× ***derosa***	CDTJ
	'Duchess of Nuremberg'	CBod EUJe SPlb SRot
	elegans ΥH2	CBod CDTJ EPfP EUJe LSou LSun NWad SEND SPlb
	'Ghost Buster'	WPGP
*	× ***gilva*** 'Red'	LSun MHol WCot
	glauca Baker	see *E. secunda* var. *glauca*
	lilacina ΥH2	SPlb SRot
	'Mahogany'	WCot WGrn
	'Mauna Loa'	CDTJ WGrn
	maxonii B&SWJ 10396	WCru
	minima ΥH2	SPlb
	montana B&SWJ 10277	WCru
	nodulosa	WCot
	peacockii	MHer MSCN SPlb
	'Perle von Nürnberg' ΥH2	CAbb SMad
	'Pollux'	LToo
	prolifica	SPlb
	pulidonis ΥH1c	LToo MHer
	pulvinata ΥH1c	MHCG
I	- 'Rubra'	SPlb
	purpusorum	SPlb
	rosea ΥH1c	MHer WCot
	runyonii 'Topsy Turvy' ΥH2	CDTJ SRot
§	***secunda***	CAbb CCac SPlb
§	- var. ***glauca***	CDTJ ELan EShb NBir SEND WPGP
	- - 'Compton Carousel'	WCot
*	- - 'Gigantea'	NPer
	'Set-Oliver' × ***setosa*** <u>**new**</u>	WCot
	setosa ΥH1c	CDTJ LToo
	- var. ***ciliata***	EShb
	shaviana ΥH2	CDTJ SPlb SRot WCot
	subsessilis	WCot

Echinacea ✿ (*Asteraceae*)

	'12th of July' <u>**new**</u>	EBee
§	'Adam Saul'	LRHS
§	'After Midnight'PBR (Big Sky Series)	EBee ECtt IBoy
	'Aloha'PBR	LRHS NLar
	'Amazing Dream'PBR	CWGN EBee ECtt IBoy LCro LRHS
	angustifolia	ENfk EPfP GPoy LRHS SPhx
§	'Art's Pride'PBR	MJak SCob SPer

'Big Kahuna' **new**	ECtt SCob
'Buttercream'	EBee
'Butterfly Kisses'PBR (d)	EBee LCro
'Caribbean Green'	EBee
'Cheyenne Spirit' (mixed)	CBod CDor GMcL LCro LOPS LPla SPhx WTor
'Chiquita' (Prairie Pixie Series) **new**	EBee
'Cleopatra'PBR	EBee
'Colorburst Orange' (Colorburst Series) (d) **new**	CWGN
'Coral Reef'PBR	ECtt
'Coupe Soleil' (d)	EBee
'Cranberry Cupcake'PBR (d)	EBee ECtt
Crazy Pink	see *E.* 'Adam Saul'
Crazy White	see *E.* 'Noam Saul'
'Daydream'PBR	CWCL CWGN ECtt LSou
Double Scoop Bubblegum = 'Balscblum'PBR	EBee
Double Scoop Raspberry = 'Balsceras'PBR (d)	EBee
'Eccentric'PBR (d)	CWCL CWGN EBee IBoy IPot LRHS SMad WNPC WTor
'Emily Saul'	see *E.* 'After Midnight'
'Evan Saul'	see *E.* 'Sundown'
'Evening Glow'	CWGN EBee WWtn
'Ferris Wheel' (Carnival Series)	EBee SCob
'Flame Thrower'PBR	CWGN ECtt LBMP LCro LSou NLar SCob SPoG WCAu
'Gemini Pink'	EBee LRHS
'Glowing Dream' **new**	CMos
'Golden Skipper' **new**	ECtt
'Green Envy'PBR	CBcs CWGN EBee ECtt ELan EPfP EWoo GMaP IBoy LOPS LRHS MBNS MBel MNrw NLar NPnk SCob SKHP SMad WTor
'Greenline'PBR	EBee ECtt
'Guava Ice'PBR	EBee LLHF
§ 'Harvest Moon'PBR (Big Sky Series)	CBcs EBee ECtt EPfP LHop LOPS LRHS NSti SCob SKHP SPer SWvt WFar
'Heavenly Dream'PBR	CWCL ECtt ELon
'Hot Lava'PBR	CWGN EBee ECtt LCro LRHS MAvo SPoG
'Hot Papaya'PBR (d)	CWCL CWGN ECtt EWoo IBoy IPot LCro LLHF LOPS MBNS NPla SCob SMad SWvt
'Hot Summer'PBR	CBcs CPar CWCL CWGN EBee EWoo LHop LRHS NLar SCob SGbt SPoG
'Indian Summer' **new**	EBee
'Intermezzo' (d) **new**	WTor
'Irresistible'PBR (d)	CWGN EBee IPot LCro LOPS
'Julia' **new**	ECtt
'Jupiter' (Big Sky Series)	ECtt SCob
'Katie Saul'	see *E.* 'Summer Sky'
'Leilani'PBR	WCAu
'Mac 'n' Cheese'PBR	EBee LCro LOPS LRHS SCob
'Mama Mia'PBR	CWCL CWGN EBee ECtt LCro LRHS NLar SGbt SPoG
Mango Meadowbrite = 'CBG Cone3'	EPfP LRHS
'Marmalade'PBR	CBcs CWCL CWGN EBee LLHF NCGa SCob WCAu
'Matthew Saul'	see *E.* 'Harvest Moon'
'Maui Sunshine'PBR	CAbb EBee ECtt NHpl
'Maya Raya'	IBoy WNPC
'Meditation'PBR	EBee WCot
'Meteor Red' (Meteor Series) **new**	ECtt
'Moodz Shiny Yellow' **new**	LRHS
'Mozzarella' (d)	EBee GBin
§ 'Noam Saul'	EBee LRHS
'Now Cheesier' **new**	LCro
Orange Meadowbrite	see *E.* 'Art's Pride'
'Orange Passion'	CBod CWGN EBee ECtt SHil
'Pacific Summer'	CWGN EBee
pallida	Widely available
- 'Hula Dancer'	CDor GWyn NGdn SHar SPhx
paradoxa	CBod CHid CRos ELan EPfP EPri GPoy LHop LPla LRHS MBel MCot NGdn NRHS SPav SPer SPhx SPlb SPtp SWvt WHil WTcb XLum
- var. ***paradoxa***	EAJP SPtp
paradoxa* × *purpurea	IBoy
'Piccolino'	CWGN EBee ECtt LLHF LRHS WCot
'Pink Mist'PBR (Mistical Series)	EBee
Pixie Meadowbrite = 'CBG Cone 2'	CAbP CWGN EBee ECtt IKil MNrw
'Purple Emperor' **new**	ECtt
§ ***purpurea***	Widely available
- 'Alaska'PBR	IBoy NGdn NLar
- 'Alba'	CBod CRos EPfP EWTr GMcL LBMP LRHS SHil WCot XLum
- 'Amber Mist'PBR (Mistical Series)	EBee
- 'Augustkönigin'	CKno EBee LRHS MNrw NDov WCot
- 'Avalanche'PBR	EBee ELon
- 'Baby Swan Pink'	EAEE GPSL LRHS SHil SPhx
- 'Baby Swan White'	CRos EBee ELon GPSL LRHS NLar NRHS SHil WCot WFar
- Bressingham hybrids	CMea CNec EShb LRHS MRav MSpe NCGa SPer WGwG WWtn
- 'Catharina'PBR	CWGN EBee ECtt
- 'Coconut Lime'PBR	CWGN EPfP LSou
- 'Cotton Candy' **new**	CWCL
- Doppelganger	see *E. purpurea* 'Doubledecker'
§ - 'Doubledecker'	CNor CWCL EBee ELan EPfP ESps GWyn IBoy LLHF NGdn SGbt SWat WCAu WFar WHar XLum
- Elton Knight = 'Elbrook'PBR ♀H7	ECtt LOPS LRHS STPC SWvt
- 'Fancy Frills'	ECtt LSou
- 'Fatal Attraction'PBR	Widely available
- 'Firebird'PBR	CWCL ECtt LRHS SCob SGbt SPoG
- 'Fragrant Angel'PBR	CBcs CWCL ECtt ELon EPfP IBoy LHop LRHS MBel NLar SKHP SPoG SWat SWvt WCot WNPC
- 'Green Eyes'	EBee ECtt NLar
- 'Green Jewel'PBR	CDor CWGN EBee ECtt EUJe EWoo LPla LRHS LSou MBel MCot MNrw NDov NLar NSti SBod SCob SGbt SPad WCAu WCot
- 'Gum Drop'PBR	EBee LRHS SPoG
- 'Happy Star'	CDor EAEE EBee EPed LRHS LSou SHil
- 'Hope'PBR	EBee ECtt LRHS LSou NLar WCAu
- 'Jade'	CAbP EBee LSRN MBNS NLar SWat
- 'JS Purple Prairie'	IPot
- 'Kim's Knee High'PBR	CKno ECtt ELan EPfP EWoo GMaP LCro LRHS LSou MBel MCot NGdn NLar SCob SPer SWat SWvt WCot
- 'Kim's Mop Head'	CKno CRos ECtt ELan EPfP EWes LRHS MCot MRav NGdn NLar WCot
§ - 'Leuchtstern'	CKno CRos ELan EPfP LRHS NBir NGdn NRHS SWat XLum

- 'Lilliput'PBR	ECtt NLar
- 'Little Angel'	ECtt
- 'Little Magnus'PBR	CKno ECtt LRHS SHil SPoG
- 'Lucky Star'	ELan EPfP LRHS SPhx WCFE
- 'Magnus'	Widely available
- 'Magnus Superior'	CBod CDor CRos EAEE GBin LRHS LSou LSun MAvo NRHS SHil SPhx SWvt WHoo
- 'Mars'	SCob
- 'Maxima'	CAbP CRos ECtt LRHS NRHS
- 'Meringue'PBR	IBoy SCob
- 'Merlot'PBR	ECtt LRHS LSou
- 'Milkshake'PBR	CWCL CWGN EBee LLHF LRHS MBel
- 'Mistral'	EBee LRHS
- 'Pica Bella'	CRos CWGN ECtt EPfP LRHS NRHS
- 'Pink Double Delight'PBR	CRos LHop LRHS MRav NGdn NRHS SWat
- 'Pink Glow'	NDov
- 'Pink Poodle'PBR	EBee IBoy
- 'Pink Sorbet'PBR	NLar
- (PowWow Series) PowWow White = 'Pas709018'	CBod CRos GMcL LRHS NRHS SPoG WCAu WTor
- - PowWow Wild Berry = 'Pas702917'PBR	CRos IPot LRHS NRHS SCob SPoG WFar WTor
- 'Prairie Splendor'	EHoe EPed EPfP GMcL LRHS NDov SPhx WHar
- 'Primadonna Deep Rose'	CNec GPSL IFro LEdu NGBl SRot SVic
- 'Primadonna White'	LRHS MArt SRot WWtn
- 'Purity'PBR	ECtt LRHS SPoG WCAu
- 'Razzmatazz'PBR (d)	CAbP CMac EBee ECtt ELan IBoy MNrw MRav NGdn NSti SPer SWat SWvt WCot
- 'Red Baron'	EBee WHlf
- 'Red Knee High'PBR	ECtt
- 'Robert Bloom'	ECtt GQue LHop NBir SWvt
- 'Rubinglow'	ECtt IBoy LCro LOPS NBir NDov NLar SWvt
- 'Rubinstern'	Widely available
- 'Ruby Giant' ♀H7	CKno CRos ECtt ELan EWoo GMaP IBoy LHop LRHS LSRN LSou LSun MBel MTis NEgg NLar NRHS SGbt SPer WCot
- 'Sensation Pink' new	CWGN
- 'Southern Belle'PBR	CWCL EBee IPot NPla SMad
- 'Summer Salsa'PBR	CWGN EBee EUJe LLHF WCot
- 'The King'	CRos LRHS NGdn NLar NRHS
- 'Tom Thumb'	EBee
- 'Verbesserter Leuchtstern'	NLar
- 'Vintage Wine'PBR	CKno CRos ECtt ELan EPfP EWoo LCro LRHS MBel NEgg NLar NRHS SCob SPer SWvt WCAu WCot
- 'Virgin'PBR	EBee EWoo IPot LCro MAvo NDov NLar SCob WCAu
- 'White Lustre'	ECha EPfP SRms
- White Natalie = 'Norwhinat'PBR	EBee
- 'White Swan'	Widely available
- 'Yellow Prairie' new	IPot MAvo
'Quills and Thrills'PBR (Prairie Pillars Series)	CWGN ECtt SCob
'Raspberry Tart'	ECtt
'Raspberry Truffle'PBR	EBee ECtt
(Secret Series) 'Secret Desire' (d) new	EBee NHpl
- 'Secret Joy' (d)	NHpl
- 'Secret Love' (d)	CWGN SCob
- 'Secret Lust'PBR (d)	EBee ECtt
- 'Secret Passion'PBR (d)	CWGN EBee ECtt IPot LRHS NHpl SGbt
- 'Secret Pride' (d)	SCob
- 'Secret Romance'PBR	LRHS NHpl
'Solar Flare'PBR (Big Sky Series)	CPar EBee ECtt LRHS
(Sombrero Series) 'Sombrero Flamenco Orange' new	LRHS NPnk
- 'Sombrero Hot Coral'	EBee MAsh WFar
- 'Sombrero Salsa Red'	LRHS MAsh NPnk WFar
- 'Sombrero Sandy Yellow'	EBee MAsh WFar
'Spider' new	EBee
'Starlight'	see *E. purpurea* 'Leuchtstern'
'Strawberry Shortcake'	EBee
'Summer Breeze'	EBee SCob
'Summer Cloud'	EBee LRHS SCob WTor
'Summer Cocktail'PBR	CMos ELan LCro LRHS SCob SPoG WTor
'Summer Passion'	CBod ELan
'Summer Samba' (d)	EBee IPot
§ 'Summer Sky'PBR (Big Sky Series)	ECtt EPfP LRHS MBNS NLar NPnk
'Summer Sun'PBR	LRHS NLar
§ 'Sundown'PBR (Big Sky Series)	CBod CPar EBee ECtt EPfP GMaP IBoy LOPS LRHS MBNS NLar NSti SCob SGbt SPoG SWvt
'Sunrise'PBR (Big Sky Series)	CKno EBee ECtt ELan EPed EPfP EWes GMcL LHop LLHF LRHS MCot NEgg NSti SCob SGbt SKHP SPer SPoG SWat SWvt WCot
'Sunset'PBR (Big Sky Series)	CAbP ECtt ELan EWes GMaP LLHF LSRN MBNS NEgg SWat SWvt
'Supreme Cantaloupe' (d) new	ECtt
'Supreme Elegance' (d)	EBee
'Tangerine Dream'PBR	EBee ECtt EPfP GMcL LRHS SCob SPoG WNPC
tennesseensis	CArn SPhx
- 'Rocky Top'	CBcs CBod CDor EPfP IBoy LRHS MGos SKHP SPhx
'Tiki Torch'PBR	CBcs CDor CMea ECtt LCro LHop LOPS LRHS SCob SPer SPoG SSal SWvt WCot WTor
'Tomato Soup'PBR	Widely available
'Twilight'PBR (Big Sky Series)	ECtt LRHS
'White Meditation'	LRHS SHil
'White Mist'PBR (Mistical Series)	EBee
'White Spider'	SCob
'Yellow Spider'	EBee SCob

Echinocereus (*Cactaceae*)

§ ***coccineus***	CCac
- SB 236	CCac
- from Belen, New Mexico	CCac
- from Jarilla Mountains, New Mexico	CCac
engelmannii var. ***variegatus*** LZ 867	CCac
reichenbachii ♀H2 HK 1228	CCac
- from Montemorelos, Mexico	CCac
- subsp. ***baileyi***	CCac
- subsp. ***caespitosus***	CCac
- - from Mason County, Texas	CCac
triglochidiatus	CCac
- SB 223	CCac
- from Sandoval County, New Mexico	CCac
- var. ***melanacanthus***	see *E. coccineus*
- var. ***mojavensis***	CCac
- - SB 686	CCac

	viridiflorus DJF 713.1 from Larimer County, Colorado	CCac
	- SB 876 from Chaffee County, Colorado	CCac
	- SB 137/18 from Sandia Mountains, New Mexico	CCac
*	- var. ***robustior*** HK 1007	CCac

Echinops (*Asteraceae*)

	albus	see *E.* 'Nivalis'
§	***bannaticus***	CBcs CMac CSBt NBid SCob WWtn
*	- 'Albus'	EBee
	- 'Blue Globe'	CBod CMHG EBee EHoe ELan EPed EPfP GBin GCal GMcL IBoy LRHS LSRN LSun MBel MGos MHol NGdn NHol SBod SCob SPoG WCAu WFar
	- 'Star Frost'	CBod EBee ELan EPfP GQue LRHS NLar SPhx
	- 'Taplow Blue'	Widely available
	maracandicus	WCot
§	'Nivalis'	CBre LRHS
*	***perringii***	GCal
	ritro misapplied	see *E. bannaticus*
§	***ritro*** L. 🏆H7	Widely available
	- 'Baby Globes'	EBee
	- subsp. ***ruthenicus*** 🏆H7	ELan MRav WCot WWtn
	- - 'Platinum Blue'	CMea ECtt ELon LRHS NDov NEgg SPhx SRms WHar
	- 'Veitch's Blue' misapplied	see *E. ritro* L.
	- 'Veitch's Blue'	Widely available
	sphaerocephalus	MSCN NBir NDov SPlb
	- 'Arctic Glow'	CBWd CBod CMHG CMac CPou EBee ECha ECtt EHoe ELan EPfP ESps GMaP IBoy LRHS MMuc MTis NDov NGdn NLar SCob SPer SPlb SPoG SWvt WFar WHar WWtn
	spinosissimus new	GKev
	tjanschanicus	GPSL LRHS MMuc NLar SEND

Echium (*Boraginaceae*)

	amoenum	MArt SPhx
	bethencourtianum	SVen
	'Blue Steeple'	MEch NLos
	boissieri	CCCN
§	***candicans*** 🏆H1c	CAbb CBcs CCCN CHll CPne CTre CTsd ECre ELan IBoy MEch NLos SArc SCob SEND SVen
	- 'Dwarf Blue' new	CCCN
	decaisnei subsp. ***decaisnei***	SVen
	fastuosum	see *E. candicans*
	gentianoides	EBee MEch SPlb SVen
	italicum	CCCN MEch
	lusitanicum	CCCN
	onosmifolium	SVen
	pininana 🏆H2	CAbb CBcs CBod CPla CTre CTsd ECre ELan EUJe GBin IBoy IKil NLos SArc SChr SCob SDix SEND SIde SPav SPhx SVen
	- 'Snow Tower'	CCCN CDTJ CPla ELan EUJe IBoy LRHS MEch NLos SVen
	'Pink Fountain'	CCCN CDTJ CPla ELan EUJe LRHS MEch NLos
	rosulatum	CCCN
	russicum	CCCN CFis CSpe EAJP EBee ELan ESps GPSL IBoy LHop MArt SPad SPav SPhx SPlb XEll
	strictum	CCCN
	sventenii	SPlb
	tuberculatum	EWld SPhx WMoo
	virescens	SVen
	vulgare	CCCN CHab CSpe CWld ELan ENfk IBoy MHer MNHC NLar NMir SBch SIde SPhx WHer WJek WOut WSFF WTre
	- 'Blue Bedder' 🏆H7	CSpe SPhx WSFF
	- Drake's form	SPhx
	webbii	MMrt SVen
	wildpretii 🏆H1c	CCCN CDTJ CPla CPne CTsd ECre ELan NLos SIgm SPlb SVen
	- subsp. ***wildpretii***	SPav

Ectotropis (*Aizoaceae*)

§	***alpina***	CRos ECho EWes GEdr LRHS NRHS
§	***seanii-hoganii***	CPBP CTal ECtt GCrg GEdr LLHF NSla WAbe

Edgeworthia (*Thymelaeaceae*)

§	***chrysantha***	CCCN CHGN EBee ELan EPfP LCro LRHS MGos MTPN NCGa NLar SBig SPer SPoG
I	- 'Grandiflora'	CBcs EBee ELon ESwi GBin LOPS LRHS MGos MPkF NLar SMad WPGP
§	- 'Red Dragon'	NLar SPer
	- f. ***rubra*** hort.	see *E. chrysantha* 'Red Dragon'
	papyrifera	see *E. chrysantha*

Edraianthus (*Campanulaceae*)

	croaticus	see *E. graminifolius*
	dalmaticus	GKev
§	***graminifolius***	GKev
	- subsp. ***graminifolius***	LLHF
	niveus new	GKev
	owerinianus	LLHF WAbe
	pilosulus	WAbe
§	***pumilio*** 🏆H5	CPBP EPot GEdr GKev NSla SIgm SRms WAbe
	- silver-leaved new	GKev
	serbicus	GKev
§	***serpyllifolius***	EPot GKev
	- 'Major'	WAbe
	zogovicii	see *E. graminifolius*

Egeria (*Hydrocharitaceae*)

§	***densa***	CBen

Ehretia (*Boraginaceae*)

	anacua	CBcs
	dicksonii	IVic
	rigida	SPlb

Eichhornia (*Pontederiaceae*)

	crassipes	CBen MSKA
	- 'Major'	NPer

Elaeagnus (*Elaeagnaceae*)

	angustifolia	CAgr CArg CBcs CDul CTho EPfP ESps MCoo MGos NLar SCob SPer SRms
	- Caspica Group	see *E.* 'Quicksilver'
	argentea Pursh	see *E. commutata*
§	***commutata***	CBcs CDul CMac ECrN EHoe EPfP LHop MBlu NLar SPer
	- 'Zempin'	EPfP LRHS
§	× ***ebbingei*** 🏆H5	Widely available
	- 'Coastal Gold' (v)	CBcs CDul CLet EBee EPfP LBMP LRHS LSRN MAsh MGos SGol SLim SRms WFar WRHF
I	- 'Compacta'	LRHS LSou MGos NRHS SHil
	- 'Gilt Edge' (v) 🏆H5	Widely available

- Gold Splash = 'Lannou' (v)	CMac EPfP LRHS SGol SWvt
- 'Limelight' (v)	Widely available
- 'Moonlight'	EPfP LRHS MAsh
- 'Salcombe Seedling'	CCCN
- 'Viveleg'^{PBR} (v)	ELan EPfP LRHS SCob SEWo SHil
macrophylla	CMac EPfP LRHS
multiflora	MBlu SPer WPGP
- 'Sweet Scarlet'	CAgr
parvifolia	CCCN ELan
pungens	CLet
- 'Argenteovariegata'	see *E. pungens* 'Variegata'
- 'Aureovariegata'	see *E. pungens* 'Maculata'
- 'Dicksonii' (v)	CWib LRHS NLar SLon SPer SRms
- 'Forest Gold' (v)	ELan EPfP LRHS MAsh
- 'Frederici' (v)	CBcs CMac EBee EHoe ELan LBMP LHop LRHS MAsh MRav NLar SCob SPer SWvt
- 'Goldrim' (v)	ESps
- 'Hosoba-fukurin' (v)	EBee ELan LRHS MAsh NLar SLon
§ - 'Maculata' (v)	Widely available
§ - 'Variegata' (v)	CBcs CMac GMcL NBir SPer
§ 'Quicksilver'	Widely available
× ***submacrophylla***	see *E.* × *ebbingei*
umbellata	CAco CBcs CDul CTho EBee EPfP EWTr LEdu MBlu NLar SPer WSHC
- 'Amber' (F)	CAgr CFGn
- 'Big Red' (F)	CAgr CFGn
- var. ***borealis*** 'Polar Lights'	NLar
- 'Brilliant Rose' (F)	CAgr
- 'Garnet' (F)	CAgr
- 'Hidden Springs' (F)	CAgr
- 'Jewel' (F)	CAgr
- 'Late Scarlet' (F)	CAgr CFGn
- 'Newgate' (F)	CAgr CFGn
- 'Red Cascade' (F)	CAgr LEdu
- var. ***rotundifolia*** CWJ 12835	WCru
- 'Ruby' (F)	CAgr CFGn LEdu
- 'Sweet 'n' Tart' (F)	CAgr LEdu

Elaeocarpus (*Elaeocarpaceae*)

sylvestris var. ***ellipticus***	LEdu WPGP

elderberry see *Sambucus nigra*

Elegia (*Restionaceae*)

capensis	CBod CCCN CDTJ CLet CTre LRHS MPkF NLos SPlb WPGP
cuspidata	NLos
elephantina	CTre NLos
equisetacea	CTre NLos
filacea	NLos
grandis	SPlb
macrocarpa	CCCN CTre NLos SPlb
stipularis	LRHS
tectorum ♀^{H2}	CTre EAEE LRHS MPie NLos SHDw SPlb SPoG
- dwarf	CTre
- 'Fish Hoek'	CTre

Eleocharis (*Cyperaceae*)

acicularis	MSKA
parvula	MSKA
vivipara new	XBlo

Elettaria (*Zingiberaceae*)

cardamomum	CArn GPoy LEdu SPre WJek

Eleutherococcus ✿ (*Araliaceae*)

from Manipur	WPGP
divaricatus B&SWJ 5027	WCru
giraldii BWJ 8091	WCru
hypoleucus B&SWJ 5532	WCru
nodiflorus PAB 8119	LEdu
pictus	see *Kalopanax septemlobus*
senticosus	GPoy LEdu
- B&SWJ 4568	WCru
septemlobus	see *Kalopanax septemlobus*
sessiliflorus B&SWJ 4528	WCru
- B&SWJ 8457	WCru
- B&SWJ 8618	WCru
sieboldianus	MMuc MRav SEND
- 'Variegatus' (v)	CBcs CCCN CLet EBee EHoe ELan ELon EPfP ESwi EUJe LRHS MGil MRav NLar SEND SPoG WCFE WHer WSHC WWFP
trifoliatus PAB 7113	LEdu
- RWJ 10108	WCru

Elisena (*Amaryllidaceae*)

longipetala	see *Hymenocallis longipetala*

Ellisiophyllum (*Plantaginaceae*)

pinnatum	SBrt
- B&SWJ 197	EBee LEdu WCru

Elmera (*Saxifragaceae*)

racemosa	EWes WMoo

Elodea (*Hydrocharitaceae*)

canadensis	MSKA NBir WMAq
densa	see *Egeria densa*

Elsholtzia (*Lamiaceae*)

stauntonii	CBcs EBee ECha ELan GPoy IDee IVic LRHS MHer MNrw NLar SBch SBrt SPer SRms SWvt WBor WJek XLum

Elymus (*Poaceae*)

arenarius	see *Leymus arenarius*
canadensis	EHoe
glaucus misapplied	see *E. hispidus*
§ ***hispidus*** ♀^{H6}	CBod EPPr MBlu NDov SPer WCFE WCot
§ ***magellanicus***	Widely available
- 'Blue Sword'	CRos ELan LRHS MGos NRHS SHil SRkn SRms
riparius	EPPr
sibiricus	EPPr
villosus	EPPr
- var. ***arkansanus***	EPPr
virginicus	EPPr

Embothrium ✿ (*Proteaceae*)

coccineum	CBcs CFil CPne CTri EPfP GBin GMcL LRHS LSou MGil NRHS SPlb WBod WPGP WPat
* - var. ***andina***	MGil
- Lanceolatum Group	CBcs CEnd CHll CTsd ELon EPfP EUJe LRHS MBlu MMuc MPkF SArc SLim SPer SSta SWvt WAbe WBor WPat
- - 'Inca Flame'	CCCN CJun EPfP LRHS MAsh SPoG SWvt
- Longifolium Group	CCCN EPfP IBlr WPGP

Emmenopterys (*Rubiaceae*)

henryi	CBcs EPfP IArd MBlu NLar SAko WCot

Empetrum (*Ericaceae*)

nigrum	GPoy WThu
rubrum	MGil

Empodium (*Hypoxidaceae*)

namaquensis	NRog
plicatum	GKev NRog

Encephalartos ✿ (*Zamiaceae*)

altensteinii	CBrP
ferox	CBrP
horridus	CBrP
lebomboensis	CBrP
lehmannii	CBrP
natalensis	CBrP
villosus	CBrP

Endymion see *Hyacinthoides*

Engelmannia (*Asteraceae*)

peristenia new	GLog

Enkianthus ✿ (*Ericaceae*)

campanulatus ♀H5	Widely available
- var. ***campanulatus*** f. ***albiflorus***	CBcs GKin IVic NLar NPnk
I - 'Pagoda'	CBcs IArd IDee NLar NPnk SAko
- var. ***palibinii***	CAbP CBcs CLet CRos EPfP GGGa GKin LRHS MAsh NLar
- 'Red Bells'	CBcs CDul EPfP GKin LRHS MAsh NLar SWvt WFar
- 'Red Velvet'	CBcs GKin NLar
- 'Ruby Glow'	CBcs IVic SAko
- var. ***sikokianus***	EPfP GGGa GKin NLar
- 'Sinsetu'	NLar
- 'Tokyo Masquerade' (v)	MAsh SPoG
- 'Venus'	CBcs GKin NLar
- 'Victoria'	CBcs IArd NLar
- 'Wallaby'	CBcs IArd LRHS NLar
cernuus f. ***rubens*** ♀H5	CBcs EPfP GGGa GKin ITim NLar
chinensis	CAbP CBcs CRos EPfP GGGa LRHS MAsh
deflexus	CRos GGGa LRHS MAsh WPGP
I 'Pagoda Red' new	LRHS
perulatus ♀H5	CBcs CDul LRHS MGos MMrt NLar SPer WFar
serrulatus	GGGa

Ennealophus (*Iridaceae*)

fimbriatus	GKev

Ensete (*Musaceae*)

gilletii	XBlo
- from Malawi	XBlo
- from Mozambique	XBlo
glaucum	CDTJ
§ ***ventricosum*** ♀H1c	CCCN CDTJ CHll EUJe NLos SEND XBlo
§ - 'Maurelii' ♀H1c	CCCN CDTJ CHll CSpe CTsd EBee ESwi EUJe LCro NLos NPla SChr SDix SEND WCot
- 'Rubrum'	see *E. ventricosum* 'Maurelii'
- 'Tandarra Red'	CAbb

Entelea (*Malvaceae*)

arborescens	EShb SPlb

Eomecon (*Papaveraceae*)

chionantha	CSam CSpe EBee GAbr GBuc GCal GCra GEdr LEdu MRav NHpl SBrt WCru WMoo WPGP XLum

Epacris (*Ericaceae*)

microphylla	ITim
serpyllifolia	WThu

Ephedra (*Ephedraceae*)

sp.	MPie SArc
andina	IMou
chilensis	MGil
distachya	GPoy
equisetina	CArn
- RCB/TQ K-1	WCot
fragilis	XSen
gerardiana	LRHS
- var. ***sikkimensis***	GEdr WOld
§ ***major***	EBee XSen
monosperma	GEdr WThu
nebrodensis	see *E. major*
nevadensis	CArn GPoy
sinica	CArn GPoy
viridis	CArn MGil

Epigaea (*Ericaceae*)

gaultherioides	GGGa

Epilobium (*Onagraceae*)

angustifolium	see *Chamaenerion angustifolium*
- f. ***leucanthum***	see *Chamaenerion angustifolium* 'Album'
californicum misapplied	see *Zauschneria californica*
canum	see *Zauschneria cana*
dodonaei	see *Chamaenerion dodonaei*
fleischeri	see *Chamaenerion fleischeri*
garrettii	see *Zauschneria californica* subsp. *garrettii*
glabellum misapplied	NSla WCFE
glabellum G. Forst.	CSpe MMuc SPhx WKif
hirsutum 'Album'	EWTr GMaP
microphyllum	see *Zauschneria cana*
rosmarinifolium	see *Chamaenerion dodonaei*
septentrionale	see *Zauschneria septentrionalis*
villosum	see *Zauschneria californica* subsp. *mexicana*
'White Wonder Bells'[PBR]	GMcL

Epimedium ✿ (*Berberidaceae*)

from Jian Xi, China	GEdr
from Yunnan, China	CLAP IFoB WPGP
acuminatum	CAby CCse CFil CLAP CSam EFEx ESMi GEdr LEdu MNrw NLar SCob WMoo WPGP WSHC
- L 575	CElw CFil
- 'Galaxy'	CFil CJun CLAP CMil LEdu
- 'Night Mistress'	GPSL
- 'Quinquin'	IMou
'Akakage'	CLAP GBuc
'Akebono'	Widely available
Alabaster = 'Conalba'	NEgg
alpinum	CBod CFil CFis CMac EBee EPot EWTr GBin GKev GLog IFro LEdu LRHS SHar SKHP SPer WMoo XLum
'Amanogawa'	CAby CJun CMil GEdr IFoB LEdu
'Amber Queen'[PBR]	Widely available
'Anju'	GEdr

'Arctic Wings'[PBR]	CLAP CSpe EBee EPfP GEdr LHop NGdn SMHy SWvt
'Asiatic Hybrid'	CJun CLAP WHal
'Autumn Raspberry'	CJun
'Beni-goromo'	GEdr
'Beni-kujaku'	CAby CJun CLAP EBee GEdr GPSL IFoB MHol
'Beni-yushima'	GEdr
'Bieke'	SMHy
'Black Sea'	CElw CFil CJun CLAP CMil CSpe EBee EPPr EPot ESMi EWTr GBin GBuc GPSL IFoB IMou LHop MAvo MNrw NPnk SCob
brachyrrhizum	CAby CJun GPSL NLar
- 'Elfin Magic'	IFoB
brevicornu	CFil GEdr SKHP WPGP
- Og 82.010	CAby CFil CJun
- Og 88.010	CJun
'Buckland Spider'	CFis CLAP EBee ELon EPPr GEdr IFoB MNrw SMHy WCot WPGP
campanulatum	CAby LLHF
- Og 93.087	CFil CJun
× ***cantabrigiense***	CBro CDor CMac CTal ECtt ESwi GBuc GEdr GKev GMaP GPSL ILea MRav NEgg NHpl NLar SRms XLum
chlorandrum	CAby EBee IFoB LEdu WPGP
- Og 94.003	EBee
creeping yellow	EBee LSou MNrw WHil
cremeum	see *E. grandiflorum* subsp. ***koreanum***
davidii	CFil EPPr ESMi GEdr LEdu MNrw NLar SCob SKHP WHal WHil WPGP WSHC
- CPC 960079	EBee
- EMR 4125	CElw CJun CLAP
- dwarf	CAby
diphyllum	CFil CTsd EBee EPfP GEdr IFoB IVic WHal WPGP
- dwarf white	CSam
dolichostemon	CElw IFoB LHop
- Og 81.010	CJun
'Domino'	GPSL
ecalcaratum	CMil EBee LEdu WPGP
- Og 93.082	CJun
'Egret'	CMil EBee SMHy
elongatum	CLAP
'Emperor'	see *E.* 'Phoenix'
'Enchantress'	CElw CJun CLAP CTal ESMi EWTr EWld IFoB MNrw NLar WHal WHoo
epsteinii	CAby CFil CLAP CMil CTal EBee EPPr ESMi GEdr IFoB LEdu LLHF MNrw SKHP WPGP WSHC
- CPC 940347	CElw CJun IVic
fangii	IFoB SKHP
fargesii	CAby CFil EBee GEdr IFoB LEdu MAvo MNrw WPGP
- Og 93.057	CTal
- 'Pink Constellation'	CAby CFil CJun EBee GEdr ITim LEdu LHop SBch WPGP
'Fire Dragon'[PBR]	CLAP CWCL EBee EPfP GEdr IFoB LLHF MBNS MNrw SPoG
flavum	CFil EBee SKHP WPGP
- Og 92.036	CJun
'Flowers of Sulphur'[PBR]	CLAP EBee EPfP GEdr WHil
franchetii	CAby CElw ELon GEdr IFoB SKHP
- 'Brimstone Butterfly'	CAby CFis CJun EPPr ESMi GEdr GPSL LHop NLar SKHP WCot WPGP
'Fukujuji'	GEdr
'Genpei'	GEdr
'Golden Eagle'	CJun EBee EWes MNrw SMHy
§ ***grandiflorum*** ♀H5	CBcs CBod CElw CPla CTri ELan ELon EPfP EWTr GBuc GLog IBoy LRHS MArt NBir NHpl NLar NPnk SCob SPer WPnP
- 'Album'	CLAP
- 'Bandit'	GEdr IFoB
- 'Beni-chidori'	CJun CLAP GEdr
- 'Crimson Beauty'	CAby CJun CLAP ECha NLar WHal WHoo WSHC
- 'Elfenkönigin'	GPSL LRHS NLar
- 'Freya'	EBee IFoB SMHy WSHC
- 'Freya Mk II' **new**	SMHy
§ - var. ***higoense***	CJun GEdr WHal WPGP
- 'Jennie Maillard'	ELon WCot
- 'Koji'	CLAP EBee ESMi IFoB WSHC
§ - subsp. ***koreanum***	CLAP CPla ECha EFEx GEdr IFoB
- 'Kourin' **new**	GEdr
- 'La Rocaille'	CAby CElw EBee
- lilac-flowered	CAby CLAP WHal
- lilac-pink-flowered	SMHy
- 'Lilafee'	Widely available
- 'Mount Kitadake'	CLAP WAbe
- 'Nanum' ♀H5	CAby CJun CPBP EBee ECho EPot ESMi EWTr GBuc GKev MNrw NEgg NHar SKHP SMHy WAbe WPGP
- pink-flowered	MCot
- 'Purple Pixie'[PBR]	ECtt EWTr MHol NEgg WHil WTor
- 'Purple Prince'	CLAP CTal EBee WPGP
- 'Queen Esta'	CAby CJun CLAP CMil EBee IFoB LEdu MNrw MRav WPGP WSHC
- 'Red Beauty'	CLAP CWCL CWld ECtt ELan ELon EPfP EWTr GEdr IFoB LEdu LRHS LSou MAvo MCot MNrw NCGa SEle WGrn WGwG WPnP
- 'Red Queen'	CMac
- 'Rose Queen' ♀H5	CAby CSam EBee ELan ELon EPfP ESMi EWTr GBin IFoB LEdu LRHS MNrw MRav NBir NEgg NSti SCob SHil SWvt WFar WMoo WPGP
- 'Roseum'	CLAP CMac CMil ESwi GMaP GPSL IFoB SWvt
- 'Rubinkrone'	CWCL GBuc GEdr GMaP IMou MNrw
- 'Sirius'	CAby CJun CLAP
- f. ***violaceum***	CJun CLAP EBee WCFE WSHC
- 'White Beauty'	WSHC
- 'White Queen' ♀H5	CElw CJun EBee EPPr EWTr IFoB LLHF LRHS MBel SMHy WCot WHal WHil
- 'Wildside Red'	CJun
- 'Yellow Princess'	CAby CElw CJun EBee
- 'Yubae'	GEdr IFoB
'Hagoromo'	GEdr
'Hakubai'	GEdr
'Harugasumi'	GEdr
'Heavenly Purple'	CJun
higoense	see *E. grandiflorum* var. *higoense*
'Hina Matsuri'	GEdr
ilicifolium	CAby CFil CJun EBee LEdu WPGP
'Jean O'Neill'	CAby CLAP CMil EBee EPPr LEdu SMHy WCot WPGP WSHC
'Jenny Pym'	EBee
'Kaguyahime'	CElw CJun CMil EPPr GPSL IFoB MArt WSHC
'King Prawn'	LEdu SMHy WPGP
'Koki'	GEdr
'Kotobuki'	GEdr
latisepalum	CPne CTal EBee GEdr LEdu MNrw WCot WPGP
- Og 91.002	CJun

'Lemon Meringue Pie'	CJun
leptorrhizum	CAby CDor CElw CFil CJun CLAP CWCL EBee ELon EPPr ESMi EWld GBuc GEdr IFoB IVic LEdu MArt MNrw NCGa NHar NLar SKHP WCot WHal
- Og Y44	WSHC
- 'Mariko'	CAby CJun CMil LEdu MNrw WPGP
lishihchenii	CAby CFil CJun CTal GEdr WPGP
'Little Shrimp'	CJun CTal CTri EBee ELon EPot GMaP GPSL LLHF LRHS MNrw NLar WSHC
macranthum	see *E. grandiflorum*
macrosepalum	GEdr
'Madame Butterfly'PBR	WCot
'Mandarin Star'	CWCL GEdr GPSL
'Marchant's Sulphur Queen' **new**	SMHy
membranaceum	CAby CFil CMil EBee ESMi GEdr LEdu LLHF NCGa SKHP WHal WPGP XEll
- Og 93.047	CJun EPPr GEdr
mikinorii	GEdr
'Milky Way'	CAby
'Mine-no-fubuki'	GEdr
'Myojo'	GEdr
myrianthum	CAby CJun EBee GEdr LEdu WPGP
ogisui	CAby CElw CLAP CMil IFoB LEdu MArt MRav SMHy WPGP
- Og 91.001	CFil CJun EBee MNrw SKHP
§ × ***omeiense*** 'Akame'	CJun CMil EPPr GEdr WPGP
- 'Emei Shan'	see *E.* × *omeiense* 'Akame'
- 'Pale Fire Sibling'	CJun GEdr
- 'Stormcloud'	CAby CElw CFil CJun CMil EBee EPPr MAvo WPGP
pauciflorum	CFil EBee EPPr GEdr LEdu NHar WPGP
- Og 92.123	CJun CLAP
× ***perralchicum***	CAby CBro CJun CTri ECha GKev IFro NLar WSHC
- 'Fröhnleiten'	Widely available
- 'Lichtenberg'	EBee EWes
- 'Wisley'	CDor CElw CJun CSam EWes
perralderianum	CBod CMac CSam CTal EPot GMaP MBel MCot MNrw SRms WHal WPnP
- 'Weihenstephan'	CWCL LRHS NLar WPnP
'Perrine's Pink' (Magique Elfes Series) **new**	WCot
§ 'Phoenix'	CAby EBee WCot WPGP
'Pink Champagne'	EPfP GEdr LEdu WCot WFar
'Pink Elf'PBR	CLAP CMil CMos CWCL ECGP EPfP EWoo GBin GEdr GMcL IFoB LLHF MNrw MPie NCGa NGdn NLar NSti SCob SRms WCot WFar
pinnatum	EBee ECho GMaP WHal XLum
§ - subsp. ***colchicum*** ♀H7	CJun CLAP CWCL ELan EPfP EWTr GBuc GLog LEdu LRHS MCot MRav NGdn NLar SCob SDix SPer WCot WFar WPnP XEll
- - L 321	GEdr WPGP
- ***elegans***	see *E. pinnatum* subsp. *colchicum*
platypetalum	CAby CFil CLAP SBrt WCot WPGP
- Og 93.085	CJun
pubescens	CAby IFoB
- Og 91.003	CFil CJun WPGP
pubigerum	CDor CJun CSam CWCL EAEE EBee ESMi EWTr GAbr GBuc GLog IFro ILea LEdu LRHS MMuc NEgg NHpl NLar SCob SEND SWvt WCAu WHal WPGP XEll
reticulatum	GEdr
rhizomatosum	CAby EPPr ESMi GEdr GMaP WPGP WSHC
- Og 92.114	CJun WCot
× ***rubrum*** ♀H7	Widely available
- 'Galadriel'	GBin
- 'Sweetheart'	GEdr
sagittatum	EFEx
'Sakura-maru'	GEdr
'Sasaki'	CLAP EPot GBuc GPSL IFoB MNrw NLar XEll
sempervirens	CAby CJun WHal
- 'Creamsickle' (v)	GEdr
- 'Okuda's White'	EBee WPGP
× ***setosum***	CJun ESMi WHal
'Shiho'	EBee GEdr GPSL MNrw
'Sphinx Twinkler'	see *E.* 'Spine Tingler'
§ 'Spine Tingler'	CAby CBod CMil CSpe EBee ECtt ESwi EUJe GBin GEdr GPSL LEdu MBel MNrw MPie MSCN SCob SMad SPoG WCot WPGP
'Spinners'	EBee WCot
'Starcloud'	LRHS WGrn
stellulatum	GEdr
- 'Wudang Star'	CFil CJun CLAP CMil EWes IFoB IMou ITim IVic SCob WPGP WSHC
sulphureum 'Plena'	see *E.* × *versicolor* double-flowered
'Sunshowers' **new**	CFil
'Suzuka'	GEdr LEdu WPGP
'Tama-no-genpei'	CJun GEdr IFoB LEdu WPGP
'Tanima-no-yuki'	GEdr
'The Giant'	WCot
'Togen'	WCot
'Tokiwa-gozen'	GEdr
'Totnes Turbo'	EBee
× ***versicolor***	EShb SCob SSut
- 'Cherry Tart'	CLAP
- 'Cupreum'	CFis CJun CLAP CWCL EBee GBuc LEdu LRHS SHil WCAu
§ - 'Discolor'	CAby CElw CFis CTal ECha EPPr EWld NBir SMHy WCot
§ - double-flowered (d) **new**	LSun
- 'Neosulphureum'	CAby CBro CLAP CTal EPPr WPGP WSHC WThu
- 'Sulphureum' ♀H7	Widely available
- 'Versicolor'	see *E.* × *versicolor* 'Discolor'
× ***warleyense***	Widely available
- 'Orangekönigin'	Widely available
'Wildside Ruby' **new**	CMil
'William Stearn'	CJun CLAP GEdr WCot
wushanense	CAby CFil CLAP EPPr ESMi GEdr LEdu
- Og 93.019	CJun
- 'Caramel'	CAby CJun CLAP EBee GEdr GPSL IFoB LEdu MAvo SKHP WCot WPGP WSHC
- spiny-leaved	WCot WHil
'Yachimata-hime'	GEdr
'Yokihi'	GEdr
× ***youngianum***	IFoB NEgg
- 'Beni-kujaku'	NEgg
- 'Fairy Dust' **new**	CFil
- 'Merlin'	CDor CElw CJun CLAP CMil EBee EPfP ESMi EWTr GBuc GEdr GPSL IFoB NSti WHal WSHC
- 'Niveum' ♀H5	Widely available
- 'Roseum'	Widely available
- 'Shikinomai'	CJun EPPr
- 'Tamabotan'	CAby CLAP CMil EBee GEdr MNrw MRav

§ - 'Typicum'	CElw GBuc WSHC
- 'Yenomoto'	CJun CLAP
- 'Youngianum'	see *E.* × *youngianum* 'Typicum'
zhushanense	CTal EBee LEdu WCot

Epipactis (*Orchidaceae*)

Catalina gx	GEdr MNrw
gigantea	CAvo CBro EBee ECha ECho ELan GBin GEdr GKev LRHS MHer MNrw MRav NDav WPGP
gigantea* × *veratrifolia	see *E.* Lowland Legacy gx
helleborine	WHer
§ **Lowland Legacy gx**	GEdr
- 'Edelstein'	MNrw
- 'Frankfurt'	GEdr
palustris	GEdr LRHS MNrw MWts NDav WHer WPnP
Passionata gx Light Royals Group	GEdr
royleana	GEdr
Sabine gx	CAby GEdr WHlf
- 'Frankfurt'	MNrw
thunbergii	EFEx GEdr

Epipremnum (*Araceae*)

pinnatum 'Marble Queen' (v)	XBlo

Episcia (*Gesneriaceae*)

dianthiflora	WCot WDib
'San Miguel'	WDib

Equisetum ✿ (*Equisetaceae*)

'Bandit' (v)	CNat EBee MAvo SMad WMoo
× ***bowmanii***	CNat
* ***camtschatcense***	EWay SArc SBig SMad SPlb XLum
fluviatile	CNat MSKA
giganteum	LLWG
hyemale	CBen CKno EHoe EWay GQue LRHS MAvo MSCN MSKA NPer NSti SCob SPlb WCot WMoo WWtn XLum
§ - var. ***affine***	CNat EBee ELan EUJe LEdu MSKA SCob WMAq WPGP
- var. ***robustum***	see *E. hyemale* var. *affine*
ramosissimum	LEdu MMuc NLos NPla SCob SWat
var. ***japonicum***	WPGP
robustum	SCob
scirpoides	EBee EFer EHoe EWay MSKA MWts NPer NWad SPlb SWat WMAq WMoo XLum
sylvaticum	CNat
telmateia	LEdu SMad
variegatum	EBee EFer

Eragrostis (*Poaceae*)

RCB/Arg S-7	EBee
airoides misapplied	see *Agrostis montevidensis*
airoides ambig.	CBod WMoo
chloromelas	EPPr
curvula	CBod CElw CKno CMea CWCL ECha EHoe EPPr LRHS MAvo MBel MRav NBir NChi NGdn NWsh SEND SPhx WMoo XLum
- S&SH 10	CElw EPPr SMHy WPGP
- 'Totnes Burgundy'	CAby CKno CMos CRos EBee ECha EPPr EPfP EShb LRHS MAvo NRHS NWsh SMea SPhx SPoG SRms WMoo WPGP
elliottii	CBod CKno ECha EPPr EShb LBMP LRHS MAvo SEND SHDw SMea
- 'Wind Dancer'	EBee WHar XSen
prolifera	IMou
spectabilis	CBod CKno CSBt CTsd EBee ELan EPfP LBMP NGdn NLar NWsh SDix SMea WMoo XLum XSen
trichodes	CBod CKno EBee EHoe LEdu NWsh SMea WCot

Eranthemum (*Acanthaceae*)

pulchellum 🏆H1b	ECre

Eranthis (*Ranunculaceae*)

cilicica	see *E. hyemalis* Cilicica Group
§ ***hyemalis*** 🏆H5	CBro CMea CRos CSpe CTca ECho ELan ELon EPfP GKev LAma LCro LOPS LRHS NHpl NPri SCob SDeJ SDir SPhx SWvt WCot WHoo WShi
§ - Cilicica Group	CRos ECho ELan ELon EPot GEdr GKev GMaP LRHS NLar NPnk NRHS SCob SDeJ SDir SPer SPhx WBor WCot WShi
- 'Flore Pleno' (d)	ECho EPot GEdr GKev WCot
- 'Grünling'	CAvo ECho GKev WCot
- 'Grünspecht' **new**	GKev
- 'Orange Glow'	ECho GEdr GKev
- 'Schwefelglanz'	CAvo CBro ECho EPot GEdr GKev WCot
§ - Tubergenii Group	CBro ECho EPot
- - 'Guinea Gold' 🏆H5	ECho
pinnatifida	EFEx GEdr
× ***tubergenii***	see *E. hyemalis* Tubergenii Group

Ercilla (*Phytolaccaceae*)

volubilis	CBcs CBod CFil CRHN CWGN EPfP EWld IArd IDee LRHS MGil SAko SEND SMad WCot WCru WSHC

Eremophila (*Scrophulariaceae*)

glabra	SVen
longifolia	SPlb

Eremurus (*Asphodelaceae*)

'Brutus'	EBee GKev
bungei	see *E. stenophyllus* subsp. *stenophyllus*
'Charleston'	EBee GKev
'Disco'	EBee
'Emmy Ro'	EBee GKev LAma LRHS NLar WCot
'Foxtrot'	EBee GKev
fuscus	EBee GKev SPhx
'Grace'	LAma NLar
'Helena'	LAma LRHS SDir
himalaicus	EBee ELan EPot ERCP GBin GKev GMaP ILea LAma LRHS MHer NLar SCob SDeJ SDir SPer SPhx
'Image'	EBee
× ***isabellinus*** 'Cleopatra'	CBod CWCL EBee EPfP EPot ERCP GKev GMaP LAma LCro LOPS LRHS MBNS MHer SCob SDeJ SPhx WHar
- 'Obelisk'	EBee LAma LRHS
- 'Pinokkio'	CWCL EBee EPot GKev LAma LCro LOPS SDeJ SPad SPer
- Ruiter hybrids	ELan EPfP GKev GMaP LAma LRHS MGos MNrw NLar
- Shelford hybrids	CBcs ELan GKev LAma SDeJ SPer SPhx
- 'Tropical Dream'	GKev
'Jeanne-Claire'	LAma LRHS NLar
'Joanna'	LAma LRHS NLar SDir
'Line Dance'	EBee GKev LAma
'Luca Ro'	EBee NLar

'Moneymaker'	CWCL EBee EPot GKev LAma
'Oase'	EBee GKev LAma LRHS SDeJ
'Paradiso'	EBee GKev
'Pink Persuasion'	EBee
'Pink Sky'	EBee
'Rexona'	GKev LAma MBNS SDeJ
robustus 🏆H7	CBcs ELan EPot ERCP GBin GKev LAma LRHS MHer NLar SDeJ SPer SPhx SPlb
'Romance'	CBod EBee EPot ERCP GKev LAma MBNS MNrw NLar SCob SDeJ SPhx
'Rumba'	EBee GKev LAma
'Samba'	LAma
'Sarah Cato' new	EBee GKev
stenophyllus 🏆H6	CBod CGar CTri CWib EPot ERCP GKev LCro LHop LOPS LRHS NLar SDeJ SDir SPhx SPoG
§ - subsp. ***stenophyllus***	CBcs CWCL EBee EPfP GMaP IBoy MHer MNrw NPer SPer
'Tap Dance'	EBee LAma
'Twist'	EBee
'White Beauty Favourite'PBR	ERCP GKev LCro LOPS NNys
'White Plume'	EBee
'White Sensation'	LRHS SDir
'Yellow Giant'	GKev
zenaidae JCA 0.444.409	WCot

Erepsia (*Aizoaceae*)

lacera	SPlb

Erianthus see *Saccharum*

Erica ✿ (*Ericaceae*)

aestiva	SPlb
alopecurus	SPlb
andevalensis f. ***albiflora***	CFst
arborea	CBcs SPlb XSen
- var. ***alpina*** 🏆H5	CTri EPfP GAbr LPar LRHS NRHS SCob SPer SWhi
§ - - f. ***aureifolia*** 'Albert's Gold' 🏆H5	CFst CRos CSBt CTri ELan EPfP GAbr LRHS MGos NHol NRHS SCob SCoo SPer SPoG SWhi
- 'Arbora Gold'	see *E. arborea* var. *alpina* f. *aureifolia* 'Albert's Gold'
- 'Arnold's Gold'	see *E. arborea* var. *alpina* f. *aureifolia* 'Albert's Gold'
- 'Estrella Gold' 🏆H5	CBcs CFst CRos CSBt CTri ELan EPfP GAbr LRHS NHol NRHS SCob SCoo SPer SPoG SWhi
- 'Golden Joy'	CFst
australis f. ***albiflora*** 'Mr Robert' 🏆H2	CFst GCal
- 'Holehird'	CFst
- 'Riverslea' 🏆H4	CFst CRos CTri GCal LRHS NRHS SCob SPer SPoG SWhi
- 'Trisha'	CFst
bauera	CTre
caffra	CTre SPlb
canaliculata 🏆H2	CBcs
carnea	ESps
- 'Adrienne Duncan' 🏆H7	SCoo SRms
- f. ***alba*** 'Golden Starlet' 🏆H7	CFst CSBt CTri EPfP MAsh MJak NHol NWea SCoo SPer SRms SWhi
- - 'Ice Princess' 🏆H7	ELan EPfP MAsh SCoo SRms SWhi
- - 'Isabell' 🏆H7	CBcs CFst CSBt EPfP IVic MAsh SCoo SRms SWhi
- - 'Rosalinde Schorn'	SRms
- - 'Schneekuppe'	SWhi
- - 'Schneesturm'	SRms
- - 'Snow Queen'	SRms SWhi
- - 'Springwood White' 🏆H7	CFst CSBt CTri ELan EPfP ESps MAsh MMuc NHol SEND SLon SRms SWhi
- - 'Whitehall'	CFst LCro SCoo SRms SWhi
- - 'Winter Snow' 🏆H7	CFst CSBt ELan SCoo SPer SRms SWhi
- 'Amy Doncaster'	see *E. carnea* 'Treasure Trove'
- 'Ann Sparkes' 🏆H7	CBcs CFst CSBt CTri ELan EPfP MAsh NHol SCoo SRms SWhi
- 'Atrorubra'	SWhi
- f. ***aureifolia*** 'Aurea'	SCoo SRms
- - 'Barry Sellers'	SRms
§ - - 'Bell's Extra Special'	EPfP SRms SWhi
- - 'Foxhollow' 🏆H7	CBcs CFst CTri EPfP IArd MAsh MJak NHol SCoo SRms SWhi
- - 'Gelber Findling'	SRms
- - 'Hilletje'	CFst SRms
- - 'January Sun'	SRms
- - 'Westwood Yellow' 🏆H7	CSBt MAsh NHol SRms SWhi
- 'Aztec Gold'	CFst SPer SWhi
- 'Beoley Pink'	SRms
- 'C.J. Backhouse'	SRms
- 'Challenger' 🏆H7	ELan EPfP MAsh SCoo SLon SRms SWhi
- 'Clare Wilkinson'	SRms
- 'Claribelle'	CFst SWhi
- 'Columbia' new	SWhi
- 'Corinna'PBR	SWhi
- 'December Red'	CFst ELan EPfP MAsh MMuc SCoo SEND SPer SRms SWhi
- 'Diana Young'	SCoo SWhi
- 'Dømmesmoen'	CFst SRms
- 'Dorset Sunshine'	CFst
- 'Early Red'	SRms
- 'Eileen Porter'	SEND
- 'Eva' 🏆H7	CBcs CFst IVic SRms SWhi
- 'Foxhollow Fairy'	SPer SRms
- 'Gracilis'	SRms
- 'Heathwood'	MAsh SRms
- 'James Backhouse'	CTri
- 'Jason Attwater'	SRms
- 'Jennifer Anne'	SRms
- 'John Kampa'	SRms
- 'John Pook'	SCoo SRms
- 'Kathy' new	SWhi
- 'King George'	CFst CTri SRms
§ - 'Kramer's Rubin'	CFst SRms SWhi
- 'Lena'	see *E.* × *darleyensis* 'Lena'
- 'Lesley Sparkes'	CFst
- 'Lohse's Rubin'	NWea SRms SWhi
- 'Loughrigg' 🏆H7	CTri MAsh MJak NHol SCoo SRms
- 'March Seedling' 🏆H7	CFst EPfP MAsh NHol SCoo SLon SPer SRms SWhi
- 'Margery Frearson'	SRms
I - 'Martin'	SRms
- 'Memory'	SWhi
- 'Myretoun Ruby' 🏆H7	CBcs CFst CSBt CTri EPfP LCro MAsh NHol SCoo SPer SRms SWhi
- 'Nathalie' 🏆H7	CFst CSBt IVic MAsh SCoo SRms SWhi
- 'Pink Cloud'	CFst
- 'Pink Mist'	SRms
- 'Pink Spangles' 🏆H7	CBcs CFst CSBt CTri MAsh MJak SCoo SPer SRms SWhi
- 'Pirbright Rose'	SRms
- 'Polden Pride'	SRms
- 'Praecox Rubra'	NHol SCoo SRms SWhi
- 'Queen Mary'	SRms
- 'Queen of Spain'	SRms
- 'R.B. Cooke'	EPfP MAsh MJak SCoo SRms SWhi
- 'Robert Jan'	SRms
- 'Rosalie' 🏆H7	CFst EPfP IArd LCro MAsh SCoo SRms SWhi

	- 'Rosantha'	CFst SRms
	- 'Rosea'	SPlb
	- 'Rosy Morn'	SRms
	- 'Rotes Juwel'	SRms
	- 'Rubens' Palette' **new**	SWhi
	- 'Rubinette' **new**	SWhi
	- 'Rubinteppich'	SRms
	- 'Ruby Glow'	MJak NHol
	- 'Saskia' **new**	SWhi
	- 'Scatterley'	SRms
	- 'Schatzalp'	SRms
	- 'Sherwood Creeping'	SRms
	- 'Smart's Heath'	SRms
	- 'Springwood Pink'	CSBt CTri NHol SRms SWhi
	- 'Tanja'	CFst SWhi
§	- 'Treasure Trove'	CFst
	- 'Viking'	MAsh
	- 'Vivellii' ♀H7	CFst CTri MAsh MJak NHol SCoo SRms SWhi
	- 'Walter Reisert'	SRms
	- 'Wentwood Red'	SRms
	- Whisky	see *E. carnea* f. *aureifolia* 'Bell's Extra Special'
	- 'Winter Beauty'	MJak NHol
	- Winter Rubin	see *E. carnea* 'Kramer's Rubin'
	- 'Winterfreude'	SWhi
	- 'Wintersonne' ♀H7	CFst MMuc SRms SWhi
	cerinthoides	CTre
	ciliaris 'Bretagne'	SWhi
	- 'Corfe Castle'	CFst
	- 'David McClintock'	CFst SWhi
	- 'Globosa'	SWhi
	cinerea	SWhi
	- f. ***alba*** 'Alba Major'	SWhi
	- - 'Alba Minor'	CFst MAsh SWhi
	- - 'Celebration'	SWhi
	- - 'Domino'	MAsh
	- 'Atropurpurea'	MAsh
	- 'Atrorubens'	CFst MJak
	- f. ***aureifolia*** 'Apricot Charm'	CSBt
	- - 'Fiddler's Gold'	MAsh SWhi
	- - 'Golden Drop'	CFst CSBt MAsh
	- - 'Golden Hue'	MAsh
	- - 'Golden Sport'	SWhi
	- - 'Goldilocks'	CFst
	- - 'Summer Gold'	SWhi
	- 'Bucklebury Red'	CFst
	- 'C.D. Eason' ♀H7	CFst CSBt CTri IVic MAsh SCoo SWhi
	- 'Champs Hill'	CFst
	- 'Coccinea'	SWhi
	- 'Discovery'	CFst
	- 'Eden Valley'	CFst SCoo
	- 'Glasnevin Red'	IVic
	- 'Glencairn'	MMuc
	- 'Harry Fulcher'	SWhi
	- 'John Ardron'	CFst
	- 'Joseph Murphy'	CFst
	- 'Joyce Burfitt'	CFst
	- 'Katinka'	CFst IVic SWhi
	- 'Lilac Time'	CFst
	- 'Mrs E.A. Mitchell'	SPlb SWhi
	- 'My Love'	CFst SWhi
	- 'Ockham'	CFst
	- 'Pentreath'	SWhi
	- 'Pink Ice' ♀H7	CFst CTri EPfP MAsh NHol SWhi
	- 'Providence'	CFst
	- 'Purple Beauty'	SWhi
	- 'Rosita'	CFst
	- 'Roter Kobold'	SWhi

	- 'Sandford Heritage'	CFst
	- 'Sandpit Hill'	CFst SWhi
	- 'Sherry'	NHol SWhi
	- 'Stephen Davis' ♀H7	NHol SCoo SWhi
	- 'Ted Oliver'	CFst
	- 'Velvet Night' ♀H7	CSBt MAsh NHol SWhi
	- 'Vivienne Patricia'	CFst
	coccinea **new**	CTre
	cooperi	SPlb
	curviflora	SPlb
	× ***darleyensis***	ESps
	- 'Alba'	see *E.* × *darleyensis* f. *albiflora* 'Silberschmelze'
	- f. ***albiflora*** 'Ada S. Collings'	MAsh SRms
	- - 'Bing'	CFst SCoo
	- - 'N.R. Webster'	SRms
§	- - 'Silberschmelze'	CSBt CTri EPfP MAsh MJak MMuc SCoo SEND SRms SWhi
	- - 'White Glow'	CTri MAsh SRms
	- - 'White Perfection' ♀H6	CBcs CFst EPfP IArd IVic MAsh MJak NHol SCoo SPoG SRms SWhi
	- 'Archie Graham'	SRms
	- 'Arthur Johnson' ♀H6	CFst CTri MAsh SRms
§	- f. ***aureifolia*** 'Eva Gold'[PBR]	CFst SWhi
	- - 'Jack H. Brummage'	CSBt CTri MAsh SRms
	- - 'Mary Helen'	CSBt EPfP MAsh NHol SCoo SRms SWhi
	- - 'Moonshine'	CFst SRms SWhi
	- - 'Tweety'	CBcs CFst CSBt SRms SWhi
	- 'Aurélie Brégeon'	CFst SRms
	- 'Bert'	CFst SCoo
	- 'Cherry Stevens'	see *E.* × *darleyensis* 'Furzey'
§	- 'Darley Dale'	CFst CSBt ELan EPfP ESps MAsh MJak MMuc SCoo SEND SLon SPer SPoG SRms SWhi
	- 'Epe'	CFst SRms
	- 'Eva'	see *E.* × *darleyensis* f. *aureifolia* 'Eva Gold'
§	- 'Furzey' ♀H6	CSBt EPfP ESps LCro MAsh NHol NWea SCoo SRms SWhi
	- 'George Rendall'	CTri EPfP MAsh SCoo SRms
	- 'Ghost Hills' ♀H6	CSBt EPfP ESps LCro MAsh MJak SCoo SPoG SRms
	- 'Golden Perfect'	CFst SWhi
	- 'Irish Treasure'	CFst
	- 'J.W. Porter' ♀H6	EPfP ESps MJak MMuc SCoo SEND SLon SRms SWhi
	- 'James Smith'	SRms
	- 'Jenny Porter' ♀H6	ELan EPfP ESps SCoo SLon SWhi
	- 'Katia'[PBR] (Winter Belles Series)	CFst SWhi
	- 'Kramer's Rote' ♀H6	CFst CSBt CTri ELan EPfP MJak NHol SCoo SPer SPoG SRms SWhi XLum
§	- 'Lena'	CFst
	- 'Lucie'[PBR] (Winter Belles Series)	CFst SWhi
	- 'Margaret Porter'	CFst EPfP SCoo
	- Molten Silver	see *E.* × *darleyensis* f. *albiflora* 'Silberschmelze'
	- 'Phoebe'[PBR] (Winter Belles Series)	CFst SPer SWhi
	- 'Pink Perfection'	see *E.* × *darleyensis* 'Darley Dale'
	- 'Rubina'[PBR]	CFst SWhi
	- 'Snow Surprise'	SWhi
	- 'Spring Surprise'[PBR] ♀H6	CFst EPfP SCoo SWhi
	- 'W.G. Pine'	SRms
	- 'White Spring Surprise'	SWhi
	- 'Winter Spring Surprise'	SWhi
	- 'Winter Surprise'	CFst SWhi

	- 'Winter Treasure'	CFst SWhi
	discolor	CTre
	erigena f. ***alba*** 'Brian Proudley'	CFst
	- - 'W.T. Rackliff' ♀^{H5}	CBcs CSBt EPfP MAsh NHol SCoo SRms SWhi
	- f. ***aureifolia*** 'Golden Lady'	CFst CSBt MAsh NHol SCoo SRms
	- - 'Thing Nee'	CFst SRms SWhi
	- 'Brightness'	CSBt EPfP NHol SCoo
	- 'Golden Jubilee' **new**	SWhi
	- 'Irish Dusk' ♀^{H5}	CBcs CSBt CTri EPfP MAsh NWea SCoo SEND SRms SWhi
	- 'Rosslare'	CFst
	- 'Superba'	MAsh SRms
	formosa	CTre
	glandulosa	CTre
	glauca var. ***glauca***	SPlb
	× ***griffithsii*** 'Jacqueline'	SWhi
	- 'Valerie Griffiths'	NHol
	× ***krameri*** 'Rudi'	IVic
	lusitanica ♀^{H2}	CFst
	- f. ***aureifolia*** 'George Hunt'	CFst ELan EPfP LRHS SLon SPer
	- Great Star	see *E. lusitanica* 'La Vasterival'
§	- 'La Vasterival'	CFst
	- 'Sheffield Park'	CFst EPfP LRHS NRHS SPer SPoG
	mackayana f. ***eburnea*** 'Doctor Ronald Gray'	CFst
	- - 'Shining Light'	CFst SWhi
	- 'Errigal Dusk'	CFst
	- f. ***multiplicata*** 'Ann D. Frearson' (d)	CFst
	- - 'Plena' (d)	CFst WHer
	mammosa ♀^{H2}	CTre SPlb
	- cream-flowered	CTre
	- pink-flowered	CTre
	- red-flowered	CTre
	- white-flowered	CTre
	mediterranea misapplied	see *E. erigena*
	multiflora	XSen
	× ***oldenburgensis*** 'Ammerland' ♀^{H6}	SCoo SRms
	patersonii	SPlb
	perspicua	CTre SPlb
	platycodon subsp. ***maderincola*** f. ***aureifolia*** 'Levada Gold'	CFst
	plukenetii	CTre
	scabriuscula	CTre
	sessiliflora	CTre
	spiculifolia	WThu
	- 'Balkan Rose'	GCal
	straussiana	SPlb
	× ***stuartii*** 'Irish Lemon' ♀^{H5}	CFst CSBt NHol SWhi
	- 'Irish Orange'	CSBt NHol SWhi
	terminalis	WBod
	tetralix	SWhi
	- f. ***alba*** 'Alba Mollis' ♀^{H7}	CFst CSBt MAsh SWhi
	- f. ***aureifolia*** 'Ruth's Gold'	NHol
	- 'Con Underwood'	CFst CSBt SWhi
	- 'Riko'	CFst
	- 'Samtpfötchen'	CFst
	- 'Silver Bells'	CSBt
	- f. ***stellata*** 'Pink Star' ♀^{H7}	CFst NHol SWhi
	vagans f. ***alba*** 'Cornish Cream' ♀^{H6}	EPfP NHol SWhi
	- - 'Diana's Gold'	SRms
	- - 'Golden Triumph'	CFst
	- - 'Lyonesse' ♀^{H6}	MAsh MMuc NHol SWhi
	- f. ***aureifolia*** 'Valerie Proudley' ♀^{H6}	CSBt MAsh NHol
	- - 'Yellow John'	CFst SRms
	- 'Birch Glow' ♀^{H6}	EPfP
	- 'Keira'	CFst SRms
	- 'Mrs D.F. Maxwell' ♀^{H6}	CBcs CFst CSBt MAsh MMuc NHol SWhi
	- 'Mrs Donaldson'	CFst
	- 'Saint Keverne'	CFst CSBt IArd IVic MMuc NHol SWhi
	- 'Summertime'	CFst
	× ***veitchii*** 'Exeter' ♀^{H5}	CFst CRos CSBt ELan EPfP LRHS MAsh NRHS SPer SWhi
	- 'Gold Tips' ♀^{H5}	CFst CSBt EPfP LRHS NRHS
	versicolor	CTre SPlb
	verticillata	CTre
	× ***watsonii*** 'Claire Elise'	CFst
	- 'Mary'	SWhi
	- 'Pink Pacific'	CFst SWhi
	× ***williamsii*** 'Ken Wilson'	CFst
	'Winter Fire'	CTre
	woodii	SPlb

Erigeron ✿ (*Asteraceae*)

	acris subsp. ***angulosus***	GKev
	'Adria'	EBee ECtt EUJe LLHF LRHS MMuc
§	***annuus***	CSpe MAvo MNrw NCGa NDov SDix WSHC
	aurantiacus	CBcs IBoy NBro WHal
	aureus 'Canary Bird' ♀^{H4}	CPBP ECtt EPot GCrg NSla WAbe
	- 'The Giant'	WAbe
	'Azure Beauty'	WHar
	Azure Fairy	see *E.* 'Azurfee'
§	'Azurfee'	CSBt ELan EPfP GMaP MArt MBNS MHol NBir NLar SPer SPoG SWvt WFar WMoo
	Black Sea	see *E.* 'Schwarzes Meer'
	'Blue Beauty'	CMac CRos EPfP LRHS NRHS
	borealis	GKev
	caespitosus	CPBP
	'Charity'	MRav NPnk WBrk
	chrysopsidis	MHer
	- 'Grand Ridge'	ECho LHop LRHS NRHS WAbe
	compositus	CTri SRms
§	- var. ***discoideus***	CMea NSla SIgm SPlb WHal WHoo WOld
	- 'Rocky'	CBod ECho MMuc
	Darkest of All	see *E.* 'Dunkelste Aller'
	'Dignity'	ECGP ELan GBuc LHop LLHF MBrN MMuc MPie MRav NHol SBod SPoG SWvt WBrk WFar
	'Dimity'	ECha NBir NBre WFar WHal
	'Dominator'	MNrw WCot
I	'Dunkelste Aller'	CAby CBcs CBod CSam ELan EPfP GBin GLog GMaP LHop LRHS LSou MBel MRav MSpe MTis NLar NPnk SCob SGbt SPer SPoG SRms SWvt WCAu WCot
*	***ereganus***	NBre
	flettii	ECho GKev
	'Foersters Liebling' ♀^{H5}	EBee LHop MBel MNrw MTis
	formosissimus	GBin
	'Four Winds'	CAbP ECho ECtt ELan EWes GKev LRHS NGdn NHpl WBrk
	'Gaiety'	NBre
	glaucus	CBod CCCN CRos CSBt ECho GJos LRHS MArt MMuc MRav NGdn SEND SMad WBrk WFar
	- 'Albus'	ELon LHop LRHS MArt NLar WBor WFar
	- 'Elstead Pink'	CTri ECtt ELan WFar

- large-flowered	ELon LRHS
- 'Roger Raiche'	CFis CMea MRav
- 'Rose Purple'	CFis
- 'Roseus'	CBcs SEND
- 'Sea Breeze'	CBod CCCN CNec EBee ECtt ELon ENor GBin GJos GMaP GMcL LHop LOPS LRHS MHol NDov NLar NPri NRHS SCob SGbt SHil SPoG SRms SWvt WBor WBrk WFar WHoo
- 'Sennen'	MHCG WBrk
- 'Viewpoint Blue'	ELon LRHS
§ ***karvinskianus*** 🏆H4	Widely available
- 'Kew Profusion'	LRHS MHol SHil
- 'Sea of Blossom'	CBod MArt NCou
- 'Stallone'	LSun MHol NLar
leiomerus	GEdr GKev LLHF
linearis	LLHF
'Mrs F.H. Beale'	LSou MSpe WCot
mucronatus	see *E. karvinskianus*
multiradiatus	GCal
'Nachthimmel'	NBre NGdn NPnk
philadelphicus	CElw MArt MNrw MPie NBir NBro WHal
'Pink Beauty'	SKHP
Pink Jewel	see *E.* 'Rosa Juwel'
Pink Triumph	see *E.* 'Rosa Triumph'
'Professor Korodi' (d) **new**	EBee
'Profusion'	see *E. karvinskianus*
pumilus	MAvo
pygmaeus	CPBP LLHF
pyrenaicus Rouy	see *Aster pyrenaeus*
'Quakeress'	CAby CBod CMea ECtt EPri GBuc GMaP IKil LHop LRHS MBel MMuc MNrw MRav MSpe NGdn NPnk SCob SDix SPoG SWvt WBrk WFar WGwG
§ 'Rosa Juwel'	CBod CSBt CTri ECtt ELan EPfP GBin GMaP LRHS MBNS MHol MRav NBir NPnk NRHS SPad SPer SPoG SRms SWvt WFar WHar WMoo
§ 'Rosa Triumph'	EBee
'Rotes Meer'	CMac EBee ELan MRav
rotundifolius 'Caerulescens'	see *Bellis caerulescens*
salsuginosus misapplied	see *Eurybia sibirica*
§ 'Schneewittchen'	CBod CRos CSam EBee ELan EPPr EPfP LHop LRHS MBNS MBel MPie MRav NCGa NGdn NPnk SRms SWvt WGwG
§ 'Schwarzes Meer'	EBee WCot
scopulinus	SBch WAbe WHal WOld
simplex	CRos ECho LRHS NRHS
'Sincerity'	XLum
'Snow Queen'	SWvt
Snow White	see *E.* 'Schneewittchen'
'Sommerneuschnee'	MTis NDov NPnk SCob SPhx
speciosus 'Grandiflora'	CBod MArt
'Strahlenmeer'	MSpe NBre
'Synehurst'	WCot
trifidus	see *E. compositus* var. *discoideus*
uniflorus	LLHF SRms
'Wayne Roderick'	CBod ELan EPfP LRHS NRHS WCot WTor
'White Quakeress'	CFis CMea MHCG MRav WCot

Erinacea (*Papilionaceae*)

§ ***anthyllis*** 🏆H5	SBrt WAbe WThu
pungens	see *E. anthyllis*

Erinus (*Plantaginaceae*)

alpinus 🏆H4	CTri ECho ECtt EDAr GAbr GJos GKev NBir NSla SBch SRms XLum
- var. ***albus***	ECho GJos NSla SRms WHoo XLum
- 'Doktor Hähnle'	ECho EDAr GJos GMaP NRya SRms WHoo XLum

Eriobotrya (*Rosaceae*)

sp.	ETod LPar
'Coppertone'	see × *Rhaphiobotrya* 'Coppertone'
deflexa	CBcs EBee
japonica (F) 🏆H3	CAbb CBcs CCCN CDul CLet CTsd ELan EPfP ETod EUJe LPar LRHS MGos MMuc NLar NLos NPla SArc SCoo SEND SPer SPlb SPtp SSta SVic WHer WPGP
- 'Gold Nugget' (F)	XBlo
- 'Mrs Cookson' (F)	CFGn EBee WMat
- 'Oliver' (F)	CFGn EBee LRHS WMat
- 'Rose-Anne'	LRHS SGol

Eriocapitella see *Anemone*

Eriocephalus (*Asteraceae*)

africanus	CBod SPlb WJek

Eriogonum (*Polygonaceae*)

alatum	WCot
alleni	WCot
- 'Little Rascal'	EBee ELan
cespitosum	LLHF WAbe
fasciculatum	EBee SEND
grande var. ***rubescens***	EBee
ovalifolium var. ***nivale***	WAbe
umbellatum	ECho GKev
- var. ***porteri***	GKev SIgm
- var. ***torreyanum***	CMea

Eriophorum (*Cyperaceae*)

angustifolium	CBen CWat EHoe MSKA MWts SPlb SWat WMAq WPnP WWtn XLum
chamissonis	MWts
latifolium	LLWG MSKA MWts XLum
rousseauianum	MSKA
vaginatum	EHoe EWay LLWG MSKA XLum

Eriophyllum (*Asteraceae*)

lanatum	EBee ECha ELan EPfP MMuc NBid NGBl SHar

Eriostemon (*Rutaceae*)

myoporoides	see *Philotheca myoporoides*

Eritrichium (*Boraginaceae*)

aretioides	SPlb

Erodium (*Geraniaceae*)

absinthoides	CRos LRHS NRHS XSen
- from Genoa	CElw
- var. ***amanum***	see *E. amanum*
§ ***acaule***	EPPr
'Almodovar'	WCot
§ ***amanum***	CSpe ECtt EWes
balearicum	see *E.* × *variabile* 'Album'
'Bidderi'	XSen
'Carmel'	XSen
'Caroline'	CMea WHoo
§ ***castellanum***	EBee GKev LLHF NLar
- 'La Féline'	GCrg

	celtibericum	EPot XSen
	- 'Javalambre'	XSen
	- 'Peñagolosa'	XSen
	'Cézembre'	WCot XSen
	chamaedryoides	see *E. reichardii*
	- 'Roseum'	see *E.* × *variabile* 'Roseum'
§	***cheilanthifolium***	XSen
	- 'David Crocker'	EPot WAbe
	chrysanthum	CElw CSam CSpe CTri EAJP ECha ECho ECtt EDAr ELan EPfP EPot EWoo GBuc GJos GMaP ITim LHop MMuc MPnt NChi NLar SEND SRot SWvt XLum XSen
	- (f)	WFar
	- (m)	NRya
	- 'Arcadia'	CMea SPhx
	- pink-flowered	CSpe ECtt EPot LHop MMuc SEND SRot
	- 'Special Rose' **new**	CSpe
	corsicum	ECho
	- 'Album'	ECho
	'County Park'	ECha EPPr NLar SHar SRms XSen
	daucoides misapplied	see *E. castellanum*
	'Fran's Delight'	CMea CSpe ECtt EPot GJos WAbe WHoo
	'Freedom'	EBee MHol SCob WCot XEll
	'Fripetta'	WIce XSen
	'Géant de Saint Cyr'	ECtt
	'Gini's Choice'	WCot
	glandulosum ♀H5	ELan EPfP MAsh MMuc NLar SBch SEND SPtp SRms SRot WSHC XLum XSen
	- 'Marie Poligné'	XSen
	'Grey Blush'	SMHy
	gruinum	CHid SPhx
	guicciardii	XSen
	guttatum misapplied	see *E.* 'Katherine Joy'
	guttatum (Desf.) Willd.	EPot EWTr LHop SRms
	hymenodes L'Hér.	see *E. trifolium*
	'Julie Ritchie'	CPBP CSpe WHoo
§	'Katherine Joy'	ECtt EWes GCrg MHer NRya SBch SRot XSen
	× ***kolbianum***	SMHy WAbe WCot WHoo WPnn XSen
	- 'Natasha'	ECtt EPPr EPot EWes GBuc MHer MMuc SEND SPoG WIce WKif XSen
	'Las Meninas'	ECtt WCot
	× ***lindavicum***	GCrg NChi WPnn XSen
	macradenum	see *E. glandulosum*
	manescavii	Widely available
	'Marchants Mikado'	WKif
	'Maryla'	CMea WIce
	'Merstham Pink'	ELon SRms XLum XSen
	'Mesquita'	CMea
	'Milly' **new**	CMea
	'Pallidum'	CSam
	pelargoniiflorum	CFis CHid CSpe ELan EPfP EWTr LRHS MCot MNHC NLar SAko SBee SEND SRms SWvt WFar WKif WPnn
	'Peter Vernon'	MHer XSen
	petraeum subsp. ***crispum*** misapplied	see *E. cheilanthifolium*
	- subsp. ***petraeum***	EPot
	'Pickering Pink'	EBee
	'Princesse Marion'	XSen
*	'Purple Haze'	EBee ELan SRms SRot WFar
§	***reichardii***	CRos CTri ECho ECtt LRHS MBrN NRHS SPoG SRms WCFE
	- 'Album'	CRos ECho GCrg LRHS MAsh MMuc MSCN NHpl NRHS SPoG WHoo WPnn
	- 'Bianca'	ELan EPfP
	- 'Jenny' **new**	NHpl
*	- 'Rubrum'	CElw ECho MAsh
	'Robertino'	WAbe
	rodiei	EWes
	romanum	see *E. acaule*
§	***rupestre***	ECho ECtt SRms SRot WIce
	'Sarck'	XSen
	sibthorpianum	XSen
	'Souvenir d'Hélène'	XSen
	'Spanish Eyes'	CBod CSpe CWGN EBee ECtt EWTr GCrg LRHS LSou LSun MHol SPoG SRot SWvt WCot WKif WRHF
	'Stephanie'	ECho ECtt ELan EPPr EWes MHer MMuc SEND WIce XSen
	supracanum	see *E. rupestre*
	'Tiny Kyni'	XSen
	trichomanifolium misapplied	see *E. cheilanthifolium*
	trichomanifolium L'Hér.	EWes
§	***trifolium***	ECho ELan MHer SBch SPhx
	× ***variabile***	WFar
§	- 'Album'	CMea CRos ECho EPfP EPot GMaP LRHS MHer NEgg NRHS SRms SRot SWvt WAbe WBrk WFar WTor
I	- 'Bishop's Form'	CBod CMea CNec CRos ECho ECtt EPfP EPot GCrg GJos GMaP LRHS MAsh MHol NEgg NQui NRHS NRya SPoG SRms SRot SWvt WAbe WBrk WCFE WFar WHoo WIce
	- 'Candy'	ECtt MHer NHpl WBrk
	- 'Derek'	ECho SRGP
	- 'Flore Pleno' (d)	CRos ECho ELan EPfP EWes GMaP ITim LRHS MHer NHpl NRHS SPoG SRms SRot WBrk WRHF WTor
	- 'Red Rock'	CTri
§	- 'Roseum' ♀H4	CBod ECho ECtt ELan MMuc NCou SEND SIgm SPlb SRms WBrk
	- 'Timpany Seedling'	ITim
	'Whitwell Superb'	XSen

Erpetion see *Viola*

Eruca (*Brassicaceae*)

	vesicaria	ENfk
	- subsp. ***sativa***	CLau CSpe GPoy MHer MNHC SIde SRms SVic

Eryngium (*Apiaceae*)

§	***agavifolium***	Widely available
	- giant	WPGP
	alpinum	CSpe ECha ELan ESps EWTr GKev GMaP GMcL IBoy LHop MGos MHer MMuc MPie NBir SCob SKHP SPer SRms SRot WFar WHar
	- 'Amethyst'	LRHS LSRN
	- 'Blue Star'	CBcs CBot CSpe EBee ECtt ELan ELon EWTr EWoo GBuc GPSL MHer NDov NLar SAko SMad WBor WCFE
	- 'Slieve Donard'	see *E.* × *zabelii* 'Donard Variety'
	- 'Superbum'	ECtt GCal GLog LRHS MNrw SRms SWat
	amethystinum	ELon EPri LRHS
	'Blue Jackpot'	EBee EPfP EWes MBel MHol MNrw
	'Blue Spikes'	EBee
	'Blue Steel'	EBee LLHF
	bourgatii	Widely available
	- Graham Stuart Thomas's selection	CAbP CAby CEnd CLet CRos CSpe ECtt ELan EPPr EWes GAbr GMaP LHop LRHS MBel MCot MHol NBid

	NBir NEgg NLar SDix SPad SPer SRms WCAu WCot WHoo WHrl WPGP
- 'Oxford Blue' ♀H5	ENor MHer NLar NSla SKHP SWvt
- 'Picos Amethyst'	CBcs CMac CWCL EBee EPfP LCro LHop LRHS LSRN NLar NSti SCob SCoo SKHP SRms WSHC
- 'Picos Blue'PBR	CBcs CBct CBot CSpe EAEE ECtt ELan EPfP EShb EWoo LRHS LSRN MBel MRav MSpe NCGa NDov NEgg NHol NLar NSti SKHP SWat SWvt
bromeliifolium misapplied	see *E. agavifolium*, *E. eburneum*
bromeliifolium ambig.	LRHS
'Broughton Blue' **new**	GKev
'Cobalt Star'	MAvo MRav NLar WHoo
creticum	MNrw NBro NChi
cymosum B&SWJ 10267	WCru
decaisneanum misapplied	see *E. pandanifolium*
deppeanum	CFil CSpe
- F&M 54	WPGP
- NJM 05.031	LEdu
Dove Cottage hybrid	MAvo
ebracteatum	CSpe LEdu
- var. ***poterioides***	LRHS SMad SPhx
§ ***eburneum***	ECha EPfP EWes GMaP ILea LRHS NChi SIgm SKHP SMad
aff. ***eburneum***	CMac
'Electric Haze'	CSam ECtt GBuc LSou
§ ***giganteum*** ♀H7	Widely available
- 'Silver Ghost' ♀H7	CAby CSam CSpe ECtt EWoo GMaP LCro LHop LOPS LRHS MBel NChi NDov NGdn NLar NSti SKHP SMad SPhx SWat SWvt WCot
gracile B&SWJ 10351	WCru
- B&SWJ 10441	WCru
'Green Jade'	LRHS
guatemalense B&SWJ 10322	WCru
- B&SWJ 10397 **new**	WCru
horridum misapplied	see *E. eburneum*
horridum ambig.	EWes MNrw NLar NLos SArc
humile B&SWJ 10464	WCru
'Indigo Star'	MAvo
leavenworthii	LRHS
maritimum	CArn CEls CPou GPoy MNHC SPhx SPlb SRms
Miss Willmott's ghost	see *E. giganteum*
monocephalum	EBee
× ***oliverianum*** ♀H6	CMea ECtt ELan EPfP GBuc GKev LHop LRHS MAvo MCot MRav MTis NBir NChi NLar SDix SMad SPoG SWat SWvt WCot
§ ***pandanifolium*** ♀H3	CBot CKno ELan EUJe EWes GCal LTro MNrw SArc SEND SMad SPlb SWvt
- 'Physic Purple'	CAby CFis CSpe EBee GPSL MAvo SDix SPhx
paniculatum	LTro
'Pen Blue'	CAby CSpe CWld EBee ECha ECtt IPot LSun MAvo MGos MHol MNrw NCGa SAko SCob WCot WTor
planum	Widely available
- 'Bethlehem'	NLar SWat
§ - 'Blauer Zwerg'	GMaP NLar
- 'Blaukappe'	CMea EAEE EBee ELan ELon EPfP EWoo LHop LRHS LSun MMuc NLar SEND SKHP SPhx SRms WTcb
- Blue Dwarf	see *E. planum* 'Blauer Zwerg'
- 'Blue Glitter'	CBod EBee ELon GPSL LRHS LSun NLar SPhx SWvt
- 'Blue Hobbit'	CBod CMea CNec EAJP EHoe ELan ELon EPfP ESps EUJe EWoo GEdr GMcL LBuc LHop LRHS LSun MGos MHer NGdn NLar NQui NWad SCob SMad SPad SRms SWvt WFar WHar
- 'Blue Ribbon'	CSam
- 'Flüela'	CBod EPed EWes GBuc GCal LRHS LSRN NEgg SWat
- 'Jade Frost'PBR (v)	Widely available
- 'Little Blue Wonder'PBR	NHol
- 'Naughty Jackpot' (v)	EBee NLar
- 'Paradise Jackpot'PBR	SRms
- 'Seven Seas'	LRHS MBNS NEgg
- 'Silver Salentino'	CBod ELon GPSL WOut
- 'Silver Stone'	SRms
- 'Tetra Petra'	LRHS SRms
- 'Tiny Jackpot'	CWGN GMaP IBoy NLar NPnk
- 'White Glitter'	CBod EBee ELan
proteiflorum	EPfP LRHS NChi SBrt SKHP SMad SPlb
serbicum	GCal SDix WCot
serra	EWes LRHS NLos
tricuspidatum	EBee ECtt LRHS
× ***tripartitum*** ♀H5	CBcs CBod CTri ECha ECtt ELan EPPr EPfP GMaP LHop LRHS LSRN MNrw MRav NBro NEgg NLar SDix SRkn SWat SWvt
* ***umbelliferum***	GCal IMou MBNS SKHP
variifolium	Widely available
- 'Miss Marbel'	CNec EPfP LSun SRms WHar WSHC WWtn
venustum	EBee LRHS SDix SMad
yuccifolium	CBWd CSpe EBee EPfP EWes GCal LEdu MAvo MSpe NLar SDix SMad SPhx SPlb SWvt XLum XSen
× ***zabelii***	CDor ECha NChi
- 'Big Blue'	Widely available
- 'Blaue Ritter'	SKHP SWat
§ - 'Donard Variety'	ECtt EUJe GBuc GCal ILea LRHS MAvo NLar SWat
- 'Forncett Ultra'	GCal MNrw NChi SDix
- 'Jos Eijking'PBR	Widely available
- 'Neptune's Gold'	CBct CWGN EBee ECtt EMFm EUJe GBin ILea LCro NLar NPri NSti SCob SHar SPoG WBor
- 'Violetta'	MCot NLar

Erysimum ✿ (*Brassicaceae*)

* ***altaicum*** var. ***humillinum***	LLHF
'Andy's Oranges and Lemons' (v)	WCot
'Apricot Delight'	see *E.* 'Apricot Twist'
§ 'Apricot Twist'	Widely available
arkansanum	see *E. helveticum*
'Audrey's Pink'	WHoo
bicolor from La Gomera **new**	MArt
'Bowles's Mauve' ♀H4	Widely available
'Bowles's Purple'	SRms SWvt
'Bowles's Yellow'	MHCG WCot
'Bredon'	NPer WKif
'Butterscotch'	MMrt WHoo
'Canaries Yellow'	GMcL WHar
capitatum var. ***purshii***	WAbe
'Caribbean Island'	WHlf
cheiri	MHer
- 'Baden-Powell' (d)	GCal
- 'Bloody Warrior' (d)	CElw ECtt WCot
- 'Fire King'	LCro
- 'Harpur Crewe' (d)	CBot NPer SRms WHer
concinnum	see *E. suffrutescens*

	'Constant Cheer'	CElw CMea CSBt CWCL EAJP ECtt ELan EPfP IFoB MAvo MCot MMuc NPer SCob SEND SPoG SRGP SRkn SRms SWvt WHoo WKif
	'Cotswold Gem' (v)	ELon GPSL LSou MHer MMuc NPer SEND SIgm SWvt
	'Dawn Breaker'	ECtt MRav
	'Desert Island'	ECtt MAsh
	'Dorothy Elmhirst'	see *E.* 'Mrs L.K. Elmhirst'
	'Emm's Variety'	ECtt EPot
	'Gogh's Gold'	WHlf
	'Gold Shot'	EAJP
	'Golden Gem'	EPfP
	'Golden Jubilee'	ECtt EPPr GBuc LRHS SRms WIce
	'Hector's Gatepost'	SRGP
§	***helveticum***	MMuc SRms
	'Jacob's Jacket'	ECha ECtt MBNS MHer NPer
	'John Codrington'	GBin LHop NPer WKif
	'Joseph's Coat'	EWld MHCG
	kotschyanum	ECho EPot GCrg GEdr NSla SIgm SRms WHal WIce
	'Lemon Light'	WHoo
	linifolium	SRms
	- 'Super Bowl Mauve' **new**	WHil
§	- 'Variegatum' (v)	CCCN CSBt EAJP EBee ECtt ELan EPfP IBoy LPot LRHS MHol NPer NPri SCob SPer SPoG SRot WHar WHer XLum
	- 'Variegatum' peach-flowered (v)	NQui
	'Moonlight'	GBuc GMaP MHer MRav NBir SRms WHoo
§	'Mrs L.K. Elmhirst'	MMrt NPer
	mutabile	CTri EPfP MRav WHal
	'Orange Flame'	CMea ECha ECho ELon GCrg MHer MMuc NPer SEND WHoo
	'Orange King'	WIce
	'Orange Zwerg'	MMuc WIce
	'Paintbox'	WHlf
	'Parish's'	CElw CFis CSpe CWld WHea
	'Parkwood Gold'	ECho NHpl
	'Pastel Patchwork'	CBod CSpe ECtt WCot
	Perry's hybrid	NPer
	'Perry's Peculiar'	NPer
	'Perry's Surprise'	NPer
	'Perry's Variegated' (v)	NPer
	'Picasso Purple' (Artist Series) **new**	WHlf
	'Plant World Lemon'	CAby CHGN ELon NLar
§	***pulchellum***	ECha
	pumilum DC.	see *E. helveticum*
	'Purple Jep' **new**	LRHS NRHS SHil
	'Ray's Early Giants' (mixed)	CPla
	'Red Jep' **new**	EBee EPfP LRHS NRHS SHil SPoG
	'Rembrandt' (Artist Series) **new**	WHlf
	rupestre	see *E. pulchellum*
	'Ruston Royal'	ECha
	Rysi Bronze = 'Innrysibro'	LRHS
	Rysi Gold = 'Innrysigol'^{PBR}	LRHS
	Rysi Moon	IKil LRHS
	Rysi Star = 'Inneryrysistar'	LRHS
	scoparium	ECha ELon
	'Sissinghurst Variegated'	see *E. linifolium* 'Variegatum'
	'Spice Island'	ECtt MAsh
	'Sprite'	CMea CTri EPot MMuc NPer SEND
	'Stars and Stripes' (v)	CBod ECtt LRHS LSou SRkn
§	***suffrutescens***	SBrt
	Sunburst = 'Listrace'	CAby CMea CWGN ECtt LSou SPoG WCot
	'Sweet Sorbet'	CElw ELon NLar SPoG SRkn SWvt
	Walberton's Fragrant Star = 'Walfrastar'^{PBR} (v)	CRos EPfP LRHS NRHS SPoG SRms WHlf
	Walberton's Fragrant Sunshine = 'Walfrasun'	CBod CRos EPfP LRHS NRHS SCoo SPoG
	'Wenlock Beauty'	CFis SRms
	'Winter Joy'	EPfP LLHF LRHS MBNS
	Winter Orchid	CWGN GBin NLar
	'Winter Party' **new**	MAvo NPnk WHlf
	Winter Rouge	CBod CMea CWCL MAvo WTor
	Winter Sorbet = 'Inneryws'^{PBR}	ECtt EPfP IKil LRHS SPoG

Erythraea see *Centaurium*

Erythrina (*Papilionaceae*)

	abyssinica	SPlb
	amazonica	SPlb
	arborescens	SPlb
	× ***bidwillii***	CCCN LRHS
	crista-galli $\mathbb{Y}^{H3}$	CBcs CCCN CDTJ CHll CSpe EBee ELan EPfP ESwi LRHS MPie MPkF SPlb WCot WPGP
	flabelliformis	SPlb
	guatemalensis	SPlb
	herbacea	SPlb
§	***humeana***	SPlb
	latissima	SPlb
	lysistemon	SPlb
	princeps	see *E. humeana*
	rubrinervia	SPlb
	speciosa	SPlb
	vespertilio	SPlb

Erythronium ✿ (*Liliaceae*)

albidum	ECho EPot GBuc GEdr GKev IBlr LAma SDir
americanum	ECho EPot GKev IBlr LAma MNrw NRog SDir SKHP WAbe
'Apple Blossom'	ECho IBlr
'Ballyrogan's Blaze'	IBlr
'Beechpark'	IBlr
'Blush'	ECho IBlr
'Bronze Beauty'	IBlr
'Bryn Meifod' **new**	WAbe
'Californian Star'	IBlr
'Californian Sunshine'	IBlr
californicum $\mathbb{Y}^{H5}$	CLAP EBee ECho ENun GBuc GKev IBlr LRHS MNrw NHar NRog
- J&JA 13216	CLAP
- 'Ballyrogan Bronze Bounty'	IBlr
- 'Brimstone'	IBlr
- 'Brocklamont Inheritance'	IBlr
- 'Bronze Edge'	IBlr
- 'Dark Delight'	IBlr
- 'Harvington Snowgoose'	see *E.* 'Harvington Snowgoose'
- Plas Merdyn form	IBlr
- 'Stellar'	IBlr
- 'White Beauty' $\mathbb{Y}^{H5}$	Widely available
californicum × ***hendersonii***	IBlr NRog
'Carol Scott'	IBlr
caucasicum	EPot NRog
citrinum	GBuc LLHF NRog
- J&JA 13462	CLAP
- subsp. ***citrinum***	GBuc
- var. ***roderickii***	NRog
citrinum × ***hendersonii***	IBlr NRog
'Citronella'	CBro CLAP GBuc GKev IBlr NRog WAbe

	cliftonii hort.	see *E. multiscapideum* Cliftonii Group
	'Craigton Beauty'	IBlr
	'Craigton Cover Girl'	IBlr
	'Craigton Cream'	IBlr
	'Delicacy'	IBlr
	dens-canis ♀H5	Widely available
	- JCA 470.001	CLAP
	- 'Charmer'	ECho GEdr MNrw NRog
	- 'Frans Hals'	ECho EPot GBuc GCra GEdr GKev IPot MNrw NRog SKHP WAbe WHal
	- large-flowered	IBlr
	- 'Lilac Wonder'	EBee ECho EPot GBuc GEdr GKev GMaP IPot LAma LEdu MNrw NRog NWad SDeJ SKHP
*	- 'Moerheimii' (d)	ECho GEdr GKev IBlr NRog
	- var. ***niveum***	EPot GEdr IBlr NRog
	- 'Old Aberdeen'	CAvo CLAP CWCL ENun IBlr LRHS MNrw NHar NRog WAbe
	- 'Pink Perfection'	EBee ECho GEdr GKev LEdu MNrw NRog SDeJ WAbe
	- 'Purple King'	EBee ECGP ECho EPot GBuc GEdr GKev GMaP IPot LAma LEdu MAvo MNrw NHol NHpl NPnk NRog NWad SDeJ WAbe
	- 'Rose Queen'	ECho EPot GBuc GEdr GKev GMaP LAma LEdu MAvo MNrw NRog NWad SDeJ WHal
*	- 'Semi-plenum' (d)	IBlr
	- 'Sheer Delight' **new**	IRob
	- 'Snowflake'	CAvo CLAP ECho ENun EPot GBuc GEdr GKev LAma LEdu LRHS MNrw NBir NHol NHpl NRog NWad SDeJ SKHP WAbe
	- 'White Splendour'	ECho EPot GEdr IBlr MNrw NRog
	- white-flowered, from Serbia	ECho
	'Eirene'	IBlr
	elegans	EBee ECho GBuc GKev NRog
	'Flaire'	IBlr
	'Flash'	IBlr
§	***grandiflorum***	CLAP ECho NRog
	- M&PS 007	CLAP
	- var. ***candidum***	EPot
	- subsp. ***chrysandrum***	see *E. grandiflorum*
§	'Harvington Snowgoose'	CAvo CBro CLAP EBee ENun IBlr LLHF LRHS NHar SKHP
	helenae	CLAP ECho GKev IBlr MNrw NRog
	hendersonii	CAvo CLAP EBee ECho ENun GBuc LAma LRHS NHar NRog SKHP SPlb WAbe
	- J&JA 12945	CLAP
	'Hidcote Beauty'	ENun LLHF LRHS
	howellii	CLAP EBee ENun SKHP
	- J&JA 13441	CLAP
	'Janice'	IBlr
	japonicum	ECho EFEx EPot GKev LAma MNrw NRog
	'Jeanette Brickell'	CLAP GBuc IBlr
	'Jeannine'	GBuc IBlr
	'Joanna'	CTal GBuc GEdr IBlr MAvo MNrw NRog
	'John Brookes'	IBlr
	'Kinfauns Pink'	CWCL EPot GBin GBuc GEdr IBlr LAma LLHF NHar NRog WCot
	'Kondo'	CTri ECho EPfP GKev GMaP IBlr LAma LRHS NBir NHol NLar NRog NWad SCob SPer WPnP
	'Lavender Eye'	IBlr
	'Margaret Mathew'	CLAP IBlr WAbe
	'Minnehaha'	GBuc IBlr
	montanum	ECho
§	***multiscapideum***	CLAP ECho GBuc GKev LLHF MNrw WCot WSHC
	- NNS 02-166	WCot
§	- Cliftonii Group ♀H4	CLAP GBuc SKHP WAbe WCot
	'Oregon Encore'	IBlr
	oregonum	CBro CLAP EBee ECha ECho ENun GBuc GEdr GKev IBlr LAma LLHF LRHS MNrw NHar NRog
	- 'Ballyrogan Yellow'	IBlr
	- subsp. ***leucandrum***	GBuc
	- - 'The Giant'	IBlr
	- subsp. ***oregonum***	SKHP
	oregonum × revolutum	IBlr
	'Pagoda' ♀H5	Widely available
	purdyi	see *E. multiscapideum*
	'Purple Heart'	IBlr
	revolutum ♀H5	CBro CLAP ECho ENun GBin GBuc GEdr GKev GMaP IBlr LAma LCro LRHS MNrw NHar NLar NRog SChF SKHP SRot WCru
	- from God's Valley, Oregon	CPne IBlr MNrw
	- 'Ballyrogan White Blusher'	IBlr
	- 'Dark Dapple'	IBlr
	- 'Guincho Splendour'	IBlr
I	- 'Inshriach Form'	IBlr
	- Johnsonii Group	EBee EPot GKev WAbe WCru
	- 'Knightshayes'	CAvo EBee GBuc IBlr LRHS NHar SKHP
	- 'Knightshayes Pink'	CLAP CWCL ENun IBlr LAma LLHF NBir WShi
	- 'Pink Beauty'	NRog
	- Plas Merdyn form	IBlr
	- 'Rose Beauty'	ECho
	- 'Wild Salmon'	CLAP EBee ENun LLHF LRHS NHar SKHP
	'Rippling Waters'	IBlr
	'Rosalind'	IBlr NRog WAbe
	sibiricum	ECho LAma NHpl NRog
	'Spring Fresh'	IBlr
	'Sundisc'	CTal ECha ECho GBuc IBlr NRog WAbe
	'Sunshine'	IBlr
	'Susannah'	EBee ENun IBlr LRHS NHar
	tuolumnense ♀H5	CBro CLAP CTal CWCL ECho GBuc GEdr GKev GMaP IBlr LAma MCot MNrw NHpl NRog NWad SDeJ WAbe
	- EBA clone 2	IBlr
	- EBA clone 3	IBlr
	- 'Edgar Klein'	CTal
	- Plas Merdyn form	IBlr
	- 'Spindlestone'	CTal CWCL EBee ENun GBuc GEdr IBlr LAma LLHF LRHS NHar SKHP WAbe
	umbilicatum	EBee ECho EPot GEdr GKev IBlr NHpl
	'White Star'	IBlr
	'Winifred Loraine'	IBlr

Escallonia (*Escalloniaceae*)

	'Alice'	SCob SPer
§	***alpina***	MGil
	'Apple Blossom' ♀H5	Widely available
§	***bifida*** ♀H4	CBot CDul CHGN CRos ECre ELan LRHS NRHS SDix WPGP
	'C.F. Ball'	CBcs CTri ELan EPfP ESps GKin GMcL IArd LBMP LBuc LRHS MAsh MSwo NEgg NPla NWea SEND SGol SRms WMoo
	'Cardinalis'	LRHS NRHS

'Compacta Coccinea'	LRHS
'Dart's Rosy Red'	WMoo
'Donard Beauty'	SRms
'Donard Brilliance'	SRms
'Donard Radiance' 🏆^{H5}	CBcs CDul CMac CSBt CWib EMOT EPfP EShb ESps LBMP LHop LRHS NLar NWad NWea SCob SGol SLim SPer SPoG SRms SWvt WMoo
'Donard Seedling'	CBcs CCVT CDul ECrN ELan EMOT EPfP ESps GKin GMcL LBuc LRHS MAsh MGos MMuc MSwo NBes NEgg NPer NRHS NWea SCob SGol SHil SLim SPer SRms SWvt WMoo
'Donard Star'	CWib EPfP NLar NWad NWea WCFE WHar
'Donard White'	CBod EPfP NLar SPoG
'Edinensis'	EAEE EPfP NLar SLim SRms WMoo
'Everest'	EPfP LRHS MMuc SLon
× ***exoniensis***	SRms
fonkii	see *E. alpina*
Golden Carpet = 'Alcaura'	GBin LRHS MAsh NEoE NRHS SCob SPoG
'Hopleys Gold'	see *E. laevis* 'Gold Brian'
illinita	CDul NLar
'Iveyi' 🏆^{H4}	Widely available
'Jamie'^{PBR}	EAEE EShb LLHF LSRN
§ ***laevis***	LRHS
§ - 'Gold Brian'^{PBR}	CDul CLet CMac EHoe EPfP ESps GMcL LRHS LSRN MAsh MGos MJak NLar NRHS SCob SGol SPer
- 'Gold Ellen' (v)	Widely available
- Pink Elle = 'Lades'^{PBR}	CRos EPfP LCro LRHS MAsh MGos NRHS SCob
'Langleyensis' 🏆^{H5}	CMac CTri CWib NWea SCob SGol SRms WHar
mexicana	CBot
montevidensis	see *E. bifida*
organensis	see *E. laevis*
'Peach Blossom' 🏆^{H5}	CBar CDul CRos CWib ELan EPfP ESps GKin GMcL LHop LRHS MAsh MMuc MSwo NEgg NHol NRHS SCob SCoo SEND SGol SLim SPer SRms
'Pride of Donard' 🏆^{H5}	CAco CSBt EPfP ESps GKin MGos SCob SRms WBod
Red Carpet = 'Loncar'^{PBR}	CBcs EAEE GBin LRHS SLon WMoo WNPC
'Red Dream'	CLet CSBt EPfP ESps GMcL LBMP LRHS MAsh MGos MSwo NLar NWad SCob SCoo SHil SPoG SRms SWvt
'Red Dwarf'	LPar
'Red Elf'	CMac ELan EMOT EPfP ESps GKin GMcL LRHS MGos NEgg SBod SCob SHil SPer SPlb SPoG SRms SWvt
'Red Hedger'	CBod CSBt CTsd CWib EAEE ECrN ELan EShb MRav SCob SRms WMoo
'Red Knight'	LRHS MAsh NEgg NHol NRHS WNPC
resinosa	CBod CTsd SArc SPlb SRms SVen WJek
revoluta	CTri MGil
rubra 'Crimson Spire' 🏆^{H5}	Widely available
- 'Ingramii'	CWib NWea SEND
- var. ***macrantha***	Widely available
* - - ***aurea***	NPla
- 'Pygmaea'	see *E. rubra* 'Woodside'
§ - 'Woodside'	ECho LLHF NWad SGol SRms
'Silver Anniversary'	MSwo
'Slieve Donard'	CMac MRav NWad NWea SLim SRms
tucumanensis	SPlb SVen
'Ventnor'	SPlb SVen
virgata	MGil

Eschscholzia (*Papaveraceae*)

californica	MBel WBod
- 'Alba'	CSpe
- subsp. ***mexicana*** 'Sun Shades'	SPhx
- 'Red Chief'	LRHS SPhx

Escobaria (*Cactaceae*)

missouriensis	CCac
vivipara SB 128 from Manzano, New Mexico	CCac

Espeletia (*Asteraceae*)

aff. ***killipii*** new	WCru
aff. ***summapacis***	WCru

Esterhuysenia (*Aizoaceae*)

alpina	CPBP SPlb

Eucalyptus ✿ (*Myrtaceae*)

aggregata	CBlu SArc SKin
alpina	SPlb
amygdalina	SPlb
approximans	SKin
archeri	CDTJ CDul EPfP LRHS MGos MMuc NLar SHil SKin WCot
baeuerlenii	SKin
caesia 🏆^{H2}	SPlb
camaldulensis	SPlb
camphora	CCCN CTsd EMOT ESwi MMuc SKin
cinerea	SBig SKin SPlb
citriodora	CWCL MHer SKin SPlb SVic
coccifera	CBcs CSBt CTsd EPfP EUJe MMuc NPer SBig SKin SPlb
cordata	EBee SKin WPGP
crenulata	SKin
crucis subsp. ***crucis***	SPlb
cypellocarpa	SPlb
dalrympleana 🏆^{H4}	EPfP EUJe LRHS LSRN MGos NLar NPer SBig SEND SHil SKin SLim SPer SPlb WCot WPGP
debeuzevillei	see *E. pauciflora* subsp. *debeuzevillei*
delegatensis	NPer SKin
divaricata	see *E. gunnii* subsp. *divaricata*
erythrocorys	SPlb
eximia	SPlb
* - 'Nana'	SPlb
ficifolia	CDTJ IDee
fraxinoides	SPlb
gamophylla	SPlb
glaucescens	CAbb CAco ELan EPfP IDee LPar LRHS SArc SEWo SKin SPer
globulus	CWCL SPlb
§ ***gregsoniana***	CDul EPfP EUJe SKin SPlb
gunnii 🏆^{H5}	Widely available
- Azura = 'Cagire'^{PBR}	LCro LPre LRHS LSRN SCob SLon WMat
§ - subsp. ***divaricata***	EPfP SKin
* - 'Silver Drop'	CBlu
johnstonii	CAco CDul IDee SKin SPer
kitsoniana	SKin
kruseana	SPlb
kybeanensis	SKin WCot
§ ***lacrimans***	CRos

	leucoxylon subsp. ***megalocarpa***	SPlb
	'Little Boy Blue'	CWib
	macarthurii	SKin
	macrocarpa	SPlb
	mitchelliana	SKin
	moorei var. ***nana***	CDTJ
	neglecta	SKin
	nicholii	CAbb CBcs CSpe ECre EPfP EWes LRHS MGos MMuc SCoo SKin WCot
	niphophila	see *E. pauciflora* subsp. *niphophila*
	nitens	CAco CDTJ CTsd SBig SKin SPlb
§	***nitida***	SKin
	parviflora	SKin
	parvula	CAco CCCN CMac EPfP MRav SCoo SEND
	pauciflora	CCCN CSBt CTsd EMOT ESps EUJe MMuc SPer
§	- subsp. ***debeuzevillei*** ♀H5	CBlu EPfP NOrn SArc SBig SKin
	- subsp. ***hedraia***	SKin
	- var. ***nana***	see *E. gregsoniana*
§	- subsp. ***niphophila*** ♀H5	Widely available
	- - 'Pendula'	see *E. lacrimans*
	perriniana	CAco CBcs CDul CMHG ECrN EPfP EUJe LRHS MGos NLar NOrn SBig SCoo SHil SKin SPlb SPoG SWvt WFar WMat
	pulverulenta	CAco SKin SPlb
	- 'Baby Blue'	ELan LHop LRHS NRHS SHil SKin SPer SWvt
	regnans	SKin
	rodwayi	SKin
	rossii	SPlb
	rubida	CCCN GAbr IDee SKin
	sideroxylon	SPlb
	- 'Rosea'	SPlb
	simmondsii	see *E. nitida*
	stellulata	SKin
	stricta	SKin
	subcrenulata	ELan EPfP SKin
	tetraptera	SPlb
	torquata	SPlb
	urnigera	CMCN SKin
	vernicosa	SKin
	viminalis	CAco SKin

Eucharis (*Amaryllidaceae*)

§	***amazonica*** ♀H1b	CCCN LAma SDeJ SPav
	grandiflora misapplied	see *E. amazonica*

Eucomis ✿ (*Asparagaceae*)

	Aloha	see *E.* 'Leia'
	autumnalis misapplied	see *E. zambesiaca*
§	***autumnalis*** (Mill.) Chitt. ♀H3	CBlu CBro CGar ECho EPot ERCP GKev LAma LRHS SDeJ SPav SPer SPlb WCot
	- subsp. ***autumnalis***	IBoy LTro
	bicolor ♀H3	Widely available
	- 'Alba'	CTca ECho EPot GKev LAma
	- 'Stars and Stripes'	WCru WHil
§	***comosa***	CAvo CBro CHll CPrp CSam CTal CTca EBee ERCP EShb GKev LAma LEdu LRHS SDeJ SPav
	- 'Cornwood'	CAvo CTca
	- 'Johannesburg'	GKev
	- 'Kilimanjaro'	CTca EBee WHil
	- 'Lotte'	CTca EBee GKev
	- 'Oakhurst'	CAby CBct CBod CKno CMos ECtt ESwi GMcL LRHS LTro SPad SPtp
	- purple-leaved	CAvo EShb
	- 'Sparkling Burgundy' ♀H6	Widely available
	- 'Sparkling Rosy'	ECho ERCP GKev LAma SArc SCob WFar
	- var. ***striata***	CAby EBee
	'Dark Star' **new**	ECtt WCot
	'Freckles'	CMos LSou SMad SPad
	'Glow Sticks'	CWGN ECtt WHil
	humilis	XEll
	- 'Twinkle Stars'	EPot ERCP GKev LAma SCob
	'John Treasure'	SMHy
	'Joy's Purple'	CBro CPar CPne CTca EPri
§	'Leia'PBR	CBro CTca ERCP GKev LAma LRHS
	montana	CBlu CBro CPar CPrp CTca EBee ECho EPot ERCP GKev LAma WCot
	pallidiflora ♀H3	CAvo CTal LEdu SMHy WPGP
	'Pink Gin'	CAvo
	'Playa Blanca'	CTca GKev LAma
	pole-evansii	CBro CPar CPne CTal CTca EAEE ELan EPri EUJe GKev IVic LAma LTro MRav SDeJ SDir WCru WPtf
	- dark **new**	GKev
	- pink-flowered **new**	CPar
I	- 'Purpurea'	GCal
	punctata	see *E. comosa*
	regia JCA 3.230.709	WCot
	undulata	see *E. autumnalis* (Mill.) Chitt.
	vandermerwei ♀H3	CAvo CBlu CBro CPne CTal CTca EBee ECho EPot GKev LAma LEdu SDeJ SKHP SPlb
	- 'Octopus'	CCCN CPrp CTca ECho ELan EPfP ESwi EUJe GBin GKev LSou LTro MHer SDir WCot WFar
§	***zambesiaca***	CAvo CTal CTca EBee GCal GKev LAma SMHy
	- JCA 3.230.709	WCot
	- JCA 3.231.010	WCot
	- 'White Dwarf'	ECho SPer
	'Zeal Bronze'	CMHG CTal CTca GCal GCra

Eucommia (*Eucommiaceae*)

	ulmoides	CMCN EBtc EPfP IDee NLar

Eucryphia ✿ (*Cunoniaceae*)

	cordifolia	CAbP CMac CWib IDee MBlu
§	***cordifolia*** × ***lucida***	CCCN
	glutinosa ♀H4	CCCN EPfP GGGa GKev IDee LRHS MAsh WBod
	- 'Miniature'	CBct EBee EPfP SChF WPGP
	× ***hillieri*** 'Winton'	CMHG EBee GQui WPGP
	× ***intermedia***	CMac NLar SRms SSta
	- 'Rostrevor' ♀H4	CBcs CDul CJun CMHG CMac CTho ELan EPfP GBin GGGa GQui LRHS LSRN MAsh MBlu MMuc NLar SAko SReu SSta WPGP
	lucida	CCCN LLHF LRHS MMuc NLar NRHS
	- 'Ballerina' ♀H4	CBcs CBct CJun CMHG CMac CRos CTho EBee ELan ELon EPfP GKin IDee LRHS MAsh MPkF SAko SChF SCoo WPGP
I	- 'Chaplin's Variety'	CBct EBee WPGP
	- 'Dumpling'	WPGP
	- 'Gilt Edge' (v)	CBcs CRos GKin LLHF LRHS
	- 'Leatherwood Cream' (v)	WHor
	- 'Pink Cloud'	CBcs CDul CEnd CJun CMac CRos CTho ELan EPfP GKin GQui IDee IVic LHop LRHS LSRN MBlu MGil NLar SAko SLim SWvt WPGP
	- 'Spring Glow' (v)	CRos ELan LLHF LRHS MAsh SPoG

milliganii	CDul CFil CTho EPfP GQui LHop LRHS MBlu MRav SAko SRms WPGP
moorei	CBcs CCCN CMac IDee SAko WPGP
× ***nymansensis***	CHab CWib SArc SRms
- 'George Graham'	CMHG GGGa
- 'Nymans Silver' (v)	CBot CDul CJun CMac CRos ELan EMil GGGa LLHF LRHS MAsh SPer SPoG WPat
- 'Nymansay' 🏆H4	Widely available
'Penwith' misapplied	see *E. cordifolia* × *lucida*
'Penwith' ambig.	GQui IDee

Eugenia (*Myrtaceae*)

uniflora	CCCN

Eumorphia (*Asteraceae*)

sericea	CFis GBin

Eunomia see *Aethionema*

Euodia (*Rutaceae*)

daniellii	see *Tetradium daniellii*
hupehensis	see *Tetradium daniellii* Hupehense Group

Euonymus ✿ (*Celastraceae*)

	B&L 12543	EWes
	NJM 09.109	CRHN WPGP
	NJM 10.106	WPGP
	alatus	Widely available
	- B&SWJ 8794	WCru
	- var. ***apterus***	EBee EPfP WGrn
	- 'Blade Runner'	CRos EPfP LRHS MGos NRHS SHil
	- Chicago Fire	see *E. alatus* 'Timber Creek'
	- 'Ciliodentatus'	see *E. alatus* f. *striatus*
	- 'Compactus' 🏆H5	Widely available
	- 'Fastigiata' **new**	CJun
§	- 'Fire Ball'	CJun
*	- 'Macrophyllus'	CJun EPfP
	- 'Rudy Haag'	CJun
	- 'Select'	see *E. alatus* 'Fire Ball'
	- 'Silver Cloud'	EPfP NLar
§	- f. ***striatus***	CJun WPat
	- - B&SWJ 11051	WCru
§	- 'Timber Creek'	CJun EPfP IDee LEdu LLHF MBlu NLar WPat
	americanus	EPfP MBlu NLar
	- var. ***angustifolius*** B&SWJ 12905	WCru
	- 'Evergreen'	EPfP
	- narrow-leaved	EPfP
	bungeanus	EPfP
	- B&SWJ 8782 from South Korea	WCru
	- 'Dart's Pride'	CJun EPfP NLar
	- 'Fireflame'	CJun WPat
*	- var. ***mongolicus***	EPfP
	- 'Pendulus'	MBlu
	- var. ***semipersistens***	CJun WCru
§	***carnosus***	CJun CMCN
	- CWJ 12425	WCru
	- 'Red Wine'	CJun CTho EBee ELon EPfP ESwi LEdu LHop MBlu NLar SKHP WCot WPat
	chibae B&SWJ 11159	WCru
§	***clivicola***	CJun EPfP WCru
	'Copper Wire'	EHoe
	cornutus	WPGP
	- var. ***quinquecornutus*** 🏆H5	CBot CJun CMCN ELan EPfP MBlu WPGP WPat
	'Den Haag'	CJun EPfP NLar
	echinatus	IDee
	europaeus	Widely available
	- from Slovakia	WCru
	- f. ***albus***	CTho EPfP LRHS NLar
	- 'Atropurpureus'	CMCN CTho EPfP NLar
	- 'Atrorubens'	CJun
	- 'Aucubifolius' (v)	CMac
*	- 'Aureus'	CNat
	- 'Brilliant'	CJun EPfP LRHS NLar
*	- f. ***bulgaricus***	EPfP
	- 'Chrysophyllus'	EPfP MBlu
	- 'Howard'	EPfP NLar
	- var. ***intermedius***	CJun EPfP MBlu NLar
	- 'Miss Pinkie'	CEnd
	- 'Red Cascade' 🏆H5	Widely available
	- 'Scarlet Wonder'	CJun EPfP IArd
	- 'Thornhayes'	CTho EPfP NLar
	farreri	see *E. nanus*
	fimbriatus	CJun
	fortunei	ESps LEdu LPar SBod
	- Blondy = 'Interbolwi'^{PBR} (v)	CDul CLet CTri CWib ELan EPfP ESps GMcL LRHS MAsh MGos MJak MMuc MSwo NEgg NLar NPri NRHS SCob SCoo SEND SGol SHil SLim SPoG SRms WHar
	- 'Canadale Gold' (v)	EPfP ESps LRHS MAsh NHol NRHS SLon
	- 'Coloratus'	CBod CMac ECrN EPfP MBlu MSwo SEND
	- 'Country Gold'	WFar
	- Dan's Delight = 'Dandel' (v) **new**	EBee SPoG
	- 'Dart's Blanket'	CDul ELan EPfP GMcL MRav SCob SSal
	- 'Emerald Gaiety' (v) 🏆H5	Widely available
	- 'Emerald 'n' Gold' (v) 🏆H5	Widely available
	- 'Emerald Surprise' (v) 🏆H5	SRGP
	- 'Gaiety Silver'	IBoy
	- 'Gold Spot'	see *E. fortunei* 'Sunspot'
	- 'Gold Tip'	see *E. fortunei* 'Golden Prince'
	- Golden Harlequin = 'Hoogi'^{PBR} (v)	CLet GMcL LHop LRHS MAsh MPkF NRHS NWad SHil SPoG SWvt
§	- 'Golden Pillar' (v)	GMcL
§	- 'Golden Prince' (v)	CMac EHoe GMcL MRav MSwo SRms
	- Goldy = 'Waldbolwi'^{PBR}	LRHS NLar NRHS SGol SHil SPoG
	- 'Harlequin' (v)	CBcs CMac CSBt CWGN EBee EHoe ELan ELon ESps LBuc LPar LRHS LSRN MAsh MBlu MGos MJak MRav NBir NRHS SGol SHil SLim SPer SPoG SRms SWvt WBod WFar
	- 'Heins Silver'^{PBR}	LRHS
	- 'Hort's Blaze'	EBee
	- 'Kewensis' 🏆H5	CHid CMac CWib ELan EUJe GCal GEdr LRHS MSCN SArc SCob SPoG WCru
	- 'Kewensis Variegatus' (v)	MRav
	- 'Longwood'	LRHS
	- 'Minimus'	CDul CTri EPPr MSwo SCob SMad WBor WPGP XLum
*	- 'Minimus Variegatus' (v)	EPPr SPlb
	- 'Prince John' **new**	CSBt
	- 'Sheridan Gold'	CTri MRav
	- 'Silver Gem'	see *E. fortunei* 'Variegatus'
	- 'Silver Queen' (v)	Widely available
	- 'Silverstone'^{PBR} (v)	EMil EPfP LRHS NRHS SPoG
	- 'Sunshine' (v)	EBee ELan EPfP LRHS MAsh SLon

§	- 'Sunspot' (v)	CBcs CBod CMac ELan ELon ESps MJak MMuc MSwo SEND SRms WRHF
§	- 'Variegatus' (v)	ESps SRms
	- 'Wolong Ghost' ♀H5	CBot CRos EPPr GKin LRHS MBlu MGos MMuc NLar NRHS SGol SKHP SWvt WCot WPat
	frigidus	EPfP
	- var. ***elongatus*** GWJ 9378	WCru
	grandiflorus misapplied	see *E. carnosus*
§	***grandiflorus*** Wall.	CJun EBee EPfP NLar SCoo WFar
	- f. ***salicifolius*** misapplied	see *E. grandiflorus* Wall.
	- f. ***salicifolius*** Stapf. & F. Ballard	CJun EPfP
	hamiltonianus	CMCN EBtc ECrN EPfP EWTr LRHS MMuc SEND
	- NJM 11.006	WPGP
	- 'Fiesta'	CJun LRHS
	- subsp. ***hians***	see *E. hamiltonianus* subsp. *sieboldianus*
	- 'Indian Summer'	CJun ELon EMil EPfP LPre LRHS MAsh NLar NOra SAko SCoo SKHP SPoG WMat WPat
	- 'Koi Boy'	CJun EPfP LPre MAsh SPoG WMat WPat
	- 'Miss Pinkie'	CJun EPfP MAsh NLar SCoo WPat
	- 'Pink Delight'	CJun
	- 'Poort Bulten'	CJun LRHS
	- 'Popcorn'	CJun EPfP WPat
	- 'Rainbow'	CJun EPfP
	- 'Red Chief'	CJun EPfP
	- 'Red Elf'	CJun LRHS NLar
	- 'Rising Sun'	CJun EPfP NLar
§	- subsp. ***sieboldianus***	CJun CTho EPfP MRav WPat
	- - B&SWJ 10941	WCru
	- - PAB 5337	LEdu
	- - 'Calocarpus'	CJun EPfP SCoo
	- - 'Coral Charm'	CJun EPfP NLar WPat
*	- - var. ***yedoensis*** f. ***koehneanus***	EPfP
	- 'Snow'	CJun EBee WCot WPat
	- 'Winter Glory'	CJun LRHS MMrt
	- var. ***yedoensis***	see *E. hamiltonianus* subsp. *sieboldianus*
§	***huangii***	CJun WPat
	- B&SWJ 3700	WCru
	japonicus	CBcs CBod CDul CMac CTri ECrN EPfP ESps GMcL LPar SArc SBod SCob SEND SEWo SPer
	- 'Albomarginatus' (v)	CBcs CTri EHoe EPfP NPri SEND SRms
	- 'Argenteovariegatus' (v) **new**	ESps
§	- 'Aureomarginatus'	CCVT GBin GMcL LPar NPri
	- 'Aureopictus'	see *E. japonicus* 'Aureus'
	- 'Aureovariegatus'	see *E. japonicus* 'Ovatus Aureus'
§	- 'Aureus' (v)	CBcs CDul CSBt CTsd CWib EPfP ESps GMcL LRHS NPri SCoo SEND SLon SPer
	- 'Benkomasaki'	ECrN EPfP LRHS
	- 'Bravo' (v)	CBar CCVT CDul ECrN EHoe EPfP ESps GMcL LPar LRHS MAsh MGos NLar NPri NRHS SArc SCob SCoo SEWo SHil SLim SPer SPoG SWvt WCot WFar
	- 'Chollipo' (v) ♀H5	ELan EPfP LRHS MAsh NRHS SEND SHil SPoG
	- 'Compactus'	SCoo
	- 'Duc d'Anjou' Carrière (v)	EBee EHoe ELan EPfP EWes MRav SPoG
	- 'Elegantissimus Aureus'	see *E. japonicus* 'Aureomarginatus'
	- Exstase = 'Goldbolwi'PBR (v)	SPoG WCot
	- 'Francien' (v)	LRHS NLar NRHS SHil
	- 'Gold Queen'PBR	LRHS NLar
	- 'Golden Maiden' (v)	ELan EPfP LRHS MAsh SLim SLon SPoG SRms SWvt
	- 'Golden Pillar'	see *E. fortunei* 'Golden Pillar'
	- Green Millenium = 'Minmil'PBR	LRHS
	- 'Green Rocket'	CCVT CRos EBee EPfP GBin LRHS MGos MRav NPnk NRHS SGol SHil SLim SPoG WCot WFar WPat
	- 'Green Spider'	SPoG
	- 'Green Spire'	LHop LRHS
	- 'Grey Beauty'	NLar
	- 'Happiness'PBR	MPkF NEoE
	- 'Hibarimisaki' (v)	EPfP
	- 'Kathy'PBR	CRos ELan ELon EPfP ESps LRHS MAsh NBes NRHS SCob SHil SPoG SRGP
§	- 'Latifolius Albomarginatus' (v)	CTsd ELan EPfP ESps MRav MSwo SPer SWvt
	- 'Luna'	see *E. japonicus* 'Aureus'
	- 'Macrophyllus'	LPar
	- 'Macrophyllus Albus'	see *E. japonicus* 'Latifolius Albomarginatus'
	- 'Maiden's Gold'	CSBt
	- 'Marieke'	see *E. japonicus* 'Ovatus Aureus'
	- 'Microphyllus'	CMac MRav NEgg SBod SRms
§	- 'Microphyllus Albovariegatus' (v)	CBcs CDul CMac CRos CSBt CTri ELan EPfP ESps LRHS MGos SCob SEND SHil SIgm SLim SRms SWvt WFar
§	- 'Microphyllus Aureovariegatus' (v)	CMac CRos CSBt ELan ELon EPfP ESps LRHS MAsh MMuc NLar NRHS SHil WHar
	- 'Microphyllus Aureus'	see *E. japonicus* 'Microphyllus Pulchellus'
§	- 'Microphyllus Pulchellus' (v)	CBcs CMac CSBt EBee ECrN EPfP ESps LRHS MAsh MGos SEND SHil SPoG SWvt
	- 'Microphyllus Variegatus'	see *E. japonicus* 'Microphyllus Albovariegatus'
§	- 'Ovatus Aureus' (v) ♀H5	CBar CDul CLet CMac CSBt CTri EBee ELon EPfP ESps GMcL LPar LRHS MGos MRav NLar NRHS SCob SEND SGol SHil SLim SPer SPlb SPoG SRms SWvt WFar
	- Paloma Blanca = 'Lankveld03' **new**	LCro LRHS NRHS SPoG
	- 'Président Gauthier' (v)	CAco EBee ESps GMcL LRHS SCob SCoo SLim SPer SWvt WCFE
	- 'Pulchellus Aureovariegatus'	see *E. japonicus* 'Microphyllus Aureovariegatus'
I	- 'Pyramidatus'	EPfP
	- 'Rokujo'	GEdr
	- 'Silver King'	CMac
	- 'Silver Krista' (v)	NLar
	- 'Susan' (v) ♀H5	CMac EShb MAsh SAko SRGP
	kachinensis B&SWJ 11668	WCru
	kiautschovicus 'Berry Hill'	NLar
	- 'Manhattan'	NLar
	latifolius	CJun CMCN CTho EPfP IDee IMou LEdu WCru WPat
§	***laxiflorus*** GWJ 9351	WCru
	- HWJ 890	WCru
	lucidus	CBcs CHll EBee
	macropterus	CJun EPfP
	mexicanus	CFil
	morrisonensis	see *E. huangii*
	myrianthus	CJun ELan EPfP EUJe EWes MBlu MPkF NLar

§ ***nanus***	CWib NLar WSHC
- var. ***turkestanicus***	GKin LHop LRHS SBrt SLon SRms
obovatus	NLar
occidentalis	SBrt
oxyphyllus ♀H5	CDul CJun CMCN CTho EPfP LRHS MMuc NLar WCot WCru WHar WPat
- 'Waasland'	CJun EPfP
phellomanus ♀H5	CBot CDul CTho EBee EPfP GKin IDee LHop LRHS MBlu MGil MGos MPkF MRav MSCN NLar NOra NOrn SCoo SKHP SPer SPoG SWvt WFar WMat WPGP
- 'Silver Surprise' (v)	CJun ELon EPfP WPat
Pierrolino = 'Heespierrolino'PBR	LRHS MRav NLar SCoo
§ ***planipes***	Widely available
- B&SWJ 8660	WCru
- 'Dart's August Flame'	CJun EPfP
- 'Sancho' ♀H5	CJun EPfP LRHS WPat
porphyreus GWJ 9377	WCru
quelpaertensis	CJun
'Rokojō Variegated' (v)	WCot
rongchuensis 'Cliuicolus'	see *E. clivicola*
rosmarinifolius	see *E. nanus*
rubescens	see *E. laxiflorus*
sachalinensis misapplied	see *E. planipes*
sachalinensis (F. Schmidt) Maxim.	EPfP NLar WPat
- B&SWJ 10835	WCru
sacrosanctus	CJun MBlu
sanguineus	CJun
sieboldianus	WCru
var. ***sanguineus*** B&SWJ 11140	
- - B&SWJ 11386	WCru
spraguei	NLar
- CWJ 12446	WCru
tingens	CJun
trapococcus	EPfP
vagans Wall.	EPfP WCot
verrucosus	CJun NLar
vidalii	EPfP
wilsonii	LRHS NLar
yedoensis	see *E. hamiltonianus* subsp. *sieboldianus*

Eupatoriadelphus see *Eupatorium*

Eupatorium ✿ (*Asteraceae*)

B&SWJ 9052 from Guatemala	WCru
FMWJ 13428 from Northern Vietnam	WCru
album misapplied	see *Ageratina altissima*
album L.	NBid
altissimum	SRms
aromaticum	see *Ageratina aromatica*
atrorubens	see *Bartlettina sordida*
cannabinum	CArn CBod CHab ELan EShb GLog GPoy IFoB MBNS MHer MMuc MNHC MWts NBir NMir NPer SEND SPav SWat WHer WSFF
- f. ***cannabinum*** 'Flore Pleno' (d)	CMac ECtt ELan ELon GBin IBoy LHop MBel MHer MRav MSpe NBir NGdn NLar SDix SWat WCot WFar WSFF WWtn XLum
- - 'Spraypaint' (v)	WSFF
capillifolium ♀H3	CAby EBee ECtt ESwi EWes LHop MNrw MPie SDix SHar SPad SPhx WCot
- 'Elegant Plume' **new**	IPot
coelestinum	see *Conoclinium coelestinum*
dubium 'Baby Joe'PBR	CMea CWGN ECtt IPot LRHS MNrw NEgg NLar SHar SPad WNPC WSFF WWtn
- 'Little Joe'	EBee EPPr LEdu NDov WSFF
fistulosum	EBee
- f. ***albidum***	MMuc
- - 'Bartered Bride'	CKno EBee ECtt EWes GCal WCot WSFF
- - 'Ivory Towers'	EShb LRHS LSun SPtp WCot WPtf WSFF
- - 'Massive White' ♀H6	EBee GCal MNrw NBir NSti
- 'Berggarten'	GCal WSFF
- 'Carin'	WSFF
fortunei 'Capri' (v) **new**	WHil
- 'Fine Line' (v)	LSou WSFF
- 'Pink Elegance' (v)	CAby CBod EBee ECtt EShb LHop LLWG LRHS MPie SDix SPoG SRms WWtn
- 'Pink Frost' (v)	LBMP MWts
japonicum	GPoy
ligustrinum	see *Ageratina ligustrina*
lindleyanum	CKno EBee WSFF
- var. ***trisectifolium*** B&SWJ 12742	WCru
maculatum	NGdn NLar WHrl
- Atropurpureum Group	Widely available
- - 'Ankum's August'	EBee IMou LPla
- - 'Gateway'	CBod CKno EBee ECtt ELon GCal LEdu LHop LRHS NBid NBre NLar SMad SWvt WMoo WSFF WWtn
- - 'Glutball'	CKno ELon GCal IMou LBMP LRHS MNrw NChi SMad
- - 'Little Red'	GBin WSFF
- - 'Orchard Dene' ♀H6	MAvo SMHy
- - 'Phantom'PBR	CBot EBee ECtt ELon EWTr EWoo GBin GQue IKil LHop LRHS MHol MWts NCGa NLar SAko SMad WMoo WPtf
- - 'Purple Bush' ♀H6	CDor CKno EBee ECtt ELon EPPr GBin GCal GQue ILea LCro LOPS LRHS MHer MTis NCGa NDov NEgg SDix SPhx SWvt WSFF
- - 'Red Dwarf'	CBod ECtt ELon EShb GBin GQue IKil ILea IPot LEdu LRHS MBel MHol SCob SHar SPoG SWvt
- - 'Riesenschirm' ♀H6	Widely available
- 'J.S. Humble' **new**	IPot MNrw
- 'Snowball'PBR **new**	CBot
makinoi var. ***oppositifolium*** B&SWJ 8449	WCru
'Mask' **new**	IPot MNrw
micranthum	see *Ageratina ligustrina*
perfoliatum	CArn GPoy MNrw NBre NLar SPhx WSFF
purpureum	Widely available
- 'Album'	CTri MBel SWvt
rugosum	see *Ageratina altissima*
* 'Snowball'	NDov SCob
weinmannianum	see *Ageratina ligustrina*

Euphorbia ✿ (*Euphorbiaceae*)

'Abbey Dore'	SPhx WCot
alfredii **new**	LToo
altissima	NWit
ambovombensis	LToo
amygdaloides	ECtt SWat SWvt WOut XSen
- 'Craigieburn'	EWes GBuc GCra LRHS MRav

§ - 'Purpurea'	Widely available
§ - var. ***robbiae***	Widely available
- - dwarf	EWes
- - 'Pom Pom'	LSou
- - 'Redbud'	EWes LSou
- 'Rubra'	see *E. amygdaloides* 'Purpurea'
- Ruby Glow = 'Waleuphglo' **new**	SWeb
ankarensis	LToo
atropurpurea **new**	IBoy
baselicis	CPla EWes
biglandulosa Desf.	see *E. rigida*
Blackbird = 'Nothowlee'PBR	CBcs CMac CWGN EBee ECtt ELan EPfP EWes GBuc IBoy LCro LLHF LRHS MBel MGos MRav NLar NPnk NSti SCob SKHP SLim SWvt WCot XEll XSen
'Blue Dome'	CSpe
'Blue Haze'	ECrN MAvo WCot WRHF WSHC
bupleurifolia* × *susannae	LToo
caerulescens	LToo
capitulata	SBrt
cashmeriana CC&McK 607	EWes
ceratocarpa	CBod CFil ECtt EWes EWoo GMaP LSou NWit SEND SIgm SMad WCot WSHC
characias	CBcs CLet CMac CWCL ECtt EPfP EWoo IBoy LRHS LSun MCot MRav NPer SPer SRms SWvt WBrk WCot XSen
- 'Black Pearl'	CAbb CBcs CBod CLet CRos ECtt ELan ELon EPfP GBin GMcL LHop LRHS MAvo MBel MPnt NPnk NQui NRHS SGbt SGol SHil SLim SMad SPoG SRkn SWvt WFar
- 'Blue Wonder'	CBod ECtt ELan EMFm EPfP GAbr GMaP LRHS MAvo NEgg NLar NWit WCot WRHF
- 'BQ'	WCot
- subsp. ***characias***	GMaP NLar SEND
- - 'Blue Hills'	ECtt
- - 'Burrow Silver' (v)	MRav NEgg SWvt
- - 'Humpty Dumpty'	CBod CRos EBee ECtt ELan ELon EPfP ESps EWTr GMaP IBoy LRHS LSRN NGdn NLar NPer NWit SBod SCob SPer SRms SWvt
- - 'Joshua' **new**	WCot
- 'Dwarf Black Pearl'	ECtt
- 'Forescate'	EBee EPfP
- 'Glacier Blue'PBR	CAby CBct CBot CHVG CMea CSpe CWGN EBee ECha EHoe ELan EMFm EShb LRHS MHol MMrt MNrw NHpl NLar NPri SCob SHeu SHil SPoG WCot WNPC WTor
- 'Goldbrook'	CBod CWCL ECtt EPfP GBin LRHS MRav NGdn
- 'Kestrel' (v)	WCot
- 'Portuguese Velvet' ♀H5	CBod ECtt ELan ELon EPed EPfP EUJe LHop LRHS MBel MCot MRav NLar NWit SArc SBod SKHP SLim SPhx SPtp WCot XSen
- Silver Swan = 'Wilcott'PBR (v) ♀H2	Widely available
- 'Tasmanian Tiger'PBR (v)	CBct CBod CWGN ECtt EWTr EWes GMaP LHop LRHS LSou MAvo MGos MHol MHtn MJak NHpl NLar SCob SEle SHeu SKHP SMDP SMad SPad SPoG SRms SWvt WCot WHil WNPC
- subsp. ***wulfenii***	Widely available
- - 'Emmer Green' (v)	ECtt ELon EWes GMaP IKil MHol NSti NWit WCot
- - 'Jayne's Golden Giant'	SMad
- - 'Jimmy Platt'	SRms WCot
§ - - 'John Tomlinson' ♀H5	EWes LSRN MRav
- - 'Joyce's Giant' **new**	WKif
- - Kew form	see *E. characias* subsp. *wulfenii* 'John Tomlinson'
- - 'Lambrook Gold' ♀H4	CSam CWCL MNrw MRav NPer SCob SMad WCot
- - 'Lambrook Gold' seed-raised	see *E. characias* subsp. *wulfenii* Margery Fish Group
§ - - Margery Fish Group	CBot LRHS MCot NBir SPer
- - 'Perry's Tangerine'	EWes NPer
§ - - 'Purple and Gold'	ECtt EWes MAvo MNrw NWit SWvt
- - 'Purpurea'	see *E. characias* subsp. *wulfenii* 'Purple and Gold'
- - 'Shorty'	EBee ECtt GBin LRHS LSou XSen
- - var. ***sibthorpii***	IBoy
- - 'Silver Shadow'	EBee MHol WCot
- - 'Westacre Giant'	EWes
clavarioides var. ***truncata***	WCot
'Copton Ash'	CBcs CSpe EBee ECtt EWes LRHS SKHP SPhx WCot WNPC XSen
corallioides	ECha GWyn LPla LSun NLar NPer NSti WHer
§ ***cornigera*** ♀H6	EBee ECha EPfP GBuc LRHS MMuc NBid NGdn NLar NSti NWit SEND SPhx SWat WCru WFar
- 'Goldener Turm'	CSpe ECtt EPfP ESwi GBin GBuc GMcL LCro LOPS LRHS LSou NWit SCob SDix SPer WCot
corollata	MNrw SBrt
cylindrifolia var. ***tubifera***	LToo
cyparissias	CBcs ECha ELan EWoo MRav NBir NGdn NLar SBod SPav SRms WBrk WFar XLum XSen
- 'Betten'	see *E.* × *gayeri* 'Betten'
- 'Clarice Howard'	see *E. cyparissias* 'Fens Ruby'
- clone 2	WCot
§ - 'Fens Ruby'	Widely available
- 'Orange Man'	CBod CNec ECtt EPfP EWes LRHS LSou NBro NEgg NGdn NLar SPoG SVen SWat SWvt WAul WBrk WFar
- 'Purpurea'	see *E. cyparissias* 'Fens Ruby'
- 'Red Devil'	NWit
- 'Tall Boy'	EWes
decaryi	LToo
- var. ***cap-saintemariensis***	LToo
deflexa	EBee EWes MAvo
dendroides	CKel LRHS
'Despina'PBR	LRHS
§ ***donii***	ECha EWes MAvo NWit SDix XEll
- HWJK 2405	WCru
- 'Amjillasa'	ECha LPla NWit SDix SMHy WWtn
dulcis	CBre IFro NBro NWit
- 'Chameleon'	CLet CWCL ECtt EHoe ELan ELon EPfP GCal IBoy IFro MArt MGos MRav NBid NBir NLar NPer NWit SCob SPhx SPlb SRot SWat SWvt WBrk WCot WFar WMoo
'Efanthia'PBR	CEnd CRos ELon EWes GBin GMcL LHop LPla LRHS LSou MAvo SHil SPoG
enormis	LToo
§ ***epithymoides***	Widely available
- 'Bonfire'PBR	ECtt IPot SAko SMDP SPoG WHil
§ - 'Candy'	EBee ECha ELan EPfP LPla MBel MNrw WFar

	- compact	NWit
	- 'First Blush' (v)	EBee ECtt EMFm NWit WCot
	- 'Geisha'	EWes
	- 'Golden Fusion'	EPfP WFar
§	- 'Lacy' (v)	EWes NBir NGdn NWit SKHP
§	- 'Major' ♀H6	EBee SDix WKif
	- 'Midas'	MNrw NWit SCob
	- 'Senior'	LRHS MAvo MNrw NLar NRHS
	esula Baker's form	NWit
	Excalibur = 'Froeup'PBR	CBod CMac CWCL ELan ELon GBin IVic LHop LSRN MBNS MMuc MNrw MRav NBir NLar NSti SEND SPtp SWvt
	fischeriana B&SWJ 8575	WCru
	fragifera	NWit
	francoisii	LToo
	var. ***crassicaulis*** **new**	
§	× ***gayeri*** 'Betten'	EBee EWes GBin
	glauca	SKHP
	'Golden Foam'	see *E. stricta*
	'Grey Hedgehog'	CBod LSou WNPC
	griffithii	CHll ESps IFoB NBro SWat WFar WMoo WWtn
	- 'Dixter' ♀H7	Widely available
	- 'Dixter Flame'	IFoB NWit
	- 'Fern Cottage'	CElw EWes GBin
	- 'Fireglow'	Widely available
	- 'King's Caple'	ELon EWes LRHS NLar SPoG WCru
	- 'Wickstead'	CWCL EBee ESwi GBin LRHS NLar SPoG
	griseola **new**	LToo
	'Helena'PBR (v)	LSRN NLar SWvt
	horrida ♀H2	LToo SPlb
	hyberna	SWat WFar
	hypericifolia Diamond Frost = 'Inneuphe'PBR	CAbP CSpe ESwi LBMP LHop LSou SRkn WCot
	- 'Diamond Star' **new**	WCot
	inermis	LToo
	ingens	CAbb
	jacquemontii	IFoB MRav NLar WCot
	'Jade Dragon'	LRHS SWvt
	'Jessie'	NWit
	Kalipso = 'Innkalff'	CRos LRHS NLar SHil SPoG SRot
	knobelii	LToo
	'Lambrook Silver'	SRkn
	lathyris	CBre NLar NPer NWit SRms SVic
	leuconeura **new**	LToo
	longifolia misapplied	see *E. cornigera*
	longifolia D. Don	see *E. donii*
	longifolia Lam.	see *E. mellifera*
	margalidiana	EWes NWit
	× ***martini***	Widely available
	- 'Ascot Rainbow'PBR (v)	Widely available
	- 'Baby Charm'	CNec CRos EBee ECtt ELon EPed EPfP EUJe GBin GKin IPot LHop LRHS LSRN MGos NLar SHil SPoG WFar WNPC
	- 'Cherokee'	WCot
	- 'Helen Robinson'	WCot
	- Helena's Blush = 'Inneuphhel' (v)	EPfP
	- 'Kolibri'	EBee MBel MPnt SWvt
	- 'Little John'	LRHS
	- 'Rudolph'PBR	CRos ECtt EPfP LRHS
	- Tiny Tim = 'Waleutiny'	CBod CRos EBee ECtt EPfP ESps GBin LRHS LSRN LSou NRHS SWvt
	- 'Walberton's Red Flush'	EPfP LRHS NRHS
§	***mellifera*** ♀H2	Widely available
	meloformis ♀H2	LToo
	milii ♀H1b	EBak
*	- 'Variegata' (v)	CBlu
	moratii	LToo
	myrsinites ♀H4	Widely available
	nereidum	EWes NWit
	nicaeensis	CSpe EBee GCal LRHS SEND SPhx WCot XSen
	- subsp. ***glareosa***	NWit
	- subsp. ***nicaeensis***	CBot
	obesa ♀H2	LToo
	oblongata	NLar NPnk SEND WCot
	palustris ♀H7	Widely available
	- 'Walenburg's Glorie'	CBot CWCL EBee ECha ELan EWTr EWoo GBin IBoy LCro MAvo MNrw MRav NLar NSti NWit SWat WCot WKif
	- 'Woodchippings'	WCot
	- 'Zauberflöte'	ELon SRms
	paralias	WHer
	× ***pasteurii***	CBct CBod CDTJ CKel EPfP EWes GBin GCal GWyn LSou MNrw NBir NLos NSti NWit SDix SMad SPhx WCot WPGP
	- Brown's strain	EBee EMFm WCot WRHF
	- 'Devil's Honey'	CHid
	- 'John Phillips'	CBct CFil EBee EPfP IVic LRHS MAvo SChF SMad SSal WPGP
	- 'Phrampton Phatty'	LRHS WCot WPGP
	pekinensis	SKHP
	pentagona	SVen
	pilosa 'Major'	see *E. epithymoides* 'Major'
	pithyusa	CBot ECha ELan SEND SPlb WCot WSHC XSen
	polychroma	see *E. epithymoides*
	- 'Purpurea'	see *E. epithymoides* 'Candy'
	- 'Variegata'	see *E. epithymoides* 'Lacy'
	portlandica	SVen WHer
	pseudocactus 'Lyttoniana'	LToo
	pulcherrima	SPre
	Redwing = 'Charam'PBR ♀H5	CBcs CBod CMac ECtt EHoe ELan EPfP EWoo GMcL IKil LBuc LRHS LSou MAvo MBel MHol MNrw MRav NLar NSti NWit SGol SLim SPer SPoG SWvt WCot
	reflexa	see *E. seguieriana* subsp. *niciciana*
§	***rigida*** ♀H6	CAby CBod CBro CSpe EBee EHoe ELan EPfP EUJe EWes GCal GJos SDix SEND SIgm SPhx WCot XSen
	robbiae	see *E. amygdaloides* var. *robbiae*
	'Roundway Titan'	CBot CFil EBee EMil EPfP LRHS SAko SWvt WSHC
	sarawschanica	ECha GBin GKev GQue LRHS NWit SMad SPhx WCot
	schillingii ♀H5	Widely available
	schoenlandii	LToo SPlb
	seguieriana	ECha EWes SPhx
§	- subsp. ***niciciana***	CSpe GBin IMou LRHS MAvo SCob WHoo
	serrulata Thuill.	see *E. stricta*
	sikkimensis ♀H5	ECha ELan EWes GBin GCal GLog GMcL IMou LRHS MAvo NEgg NLar NPer SCob SRms WBod WCru
	- 'Crûg Contrast'	WCru
	soongarica	NWit
	spinosa	NWit SPlb XSen
	stellata	LToo
	stellispina	LToo
§	***stricta***	CBgR CFil GWyn NWad
	stygiana	CAbb CDTJ CPne CSam CSpe ELon EMFm EUJe EWes GBin IBoy LPla LRHS SPlb SPtp WCot WCru WPGP WSHC

- subsp. ***santamariae*** CFil WPGP WSHC
- subsp. ***stygiana*** CFil WPGP
susannae LToo
tirucalli EShb
tortirama LToo
valdevillosocarpa GWyn NLar SPhx WFar
'Velvet Ruby' GBin LSRN LSou SWvt WNPC
viguieri LToo
villosa Waldst. & Kit. ex Willd. GBin LEdu NWit
§ ***virgata*** EWes NWit
× ***waldsteinii*** see *E. virgata*
wallichii misapplied see *E. donii*
wallichii Kohli see *E. cornigera*
wallichii ambig. GBin MRav SCob
wallichii Hook. f. EPfP MNrw SKHP SPhx WCot
- 'Lemon and Lime' CWib NWit
'Whistleberry Garnet' CMac EBee ELan EPfP EWoo LBMP LLHF LRHS LSou NSti SCob SKHP SWvt WBod WNPC
'Whistleberry Ruby'PBR EWTr

Euphrasia (*Orobanchaceae*)

officinalis SIde

Euptelea (*Eupteleaceae*)

franchetii see *E. pleiosperma*
§ ***pleiosperma*** NLar
polyandra EPfP NLar SBrt WPGP

Eurya (*Pentaphylacaceae*)

japonica 'Moutiers' (v) EBee
- 'Variegata' misapplied see *Cleyera japonica* 'Fortunei'

Eurybia (*Asteraceae*)

§ ***conspicua*** MAvo
§ ***divaricata*** Widely available
§ - 'Eastern Star' IBoy NCGa WCot WFar WOld
- Raiche form see *E. divaricata* 'Eastern Star'
- 'Snow Heron' **new** MAvo
- 'Tradescant' IMou MNrw SMad
§ ***furcata*** XLum
§ × ***herveyi*** CBod CSam ECha ECtt ELan EPPr GLog GQue IKil IMou LCro LEdu LOPS LRHS MSpe MTis NDov NLar NSti SDix SPer SPhx WCot WFar WOld WSHC XLum
§ ***macrophylla*** CFis EBee ELan LRHS MArt MMuc MSpe NLar SPhx WFar WOld WWtn
- 'Albus' EPPr WFar WOld
- 'Twilight' see *E.* × *herveyi*
§ ***radula*** CSam EPPr EWes IMou MAvo MNrw NLar WOld WSHC
- 'August Sky' CBre CKno EBee EPPr MBel MTis NDov WCot WFar WHoo WRHF
§ ***schreberi*** CDor EPPr EWes LEdu MAvo MPie MSpe NCGa NWsh WCot WFar WHoo WOld WPGP WWtn
§ ***sibirica*** NLar WOld
§ ***spectabilis*** EBee IMou LRHS SPhx WOld
- 'JS Macho Blue' MNrw

Euryops (*Asteraceae*)

abrotanifolius CCCN SVen
§ ***acraeus*** ♀H4 CSBt ECho ELan EPot EWes GCrg GEdr GKev WAbe
brachypodus SVen
§ ***chrysanthemoides*** CBcs CCCN EShb SEND SVen
- 'Sonnenschein' SPtp
evansii Schltr. see *E. acraeus*
lateriflorus SPlb
pectinatus ♀H3 CBcs CBod CCCN CDTJ CLet CRos CTri CTsd ELan EPfP EShb IKil IVic LRHS MGil MSCN SEND SPtp SVen SWvt
tenuissimus SVen
tysonii EWes SPlb SVen
virgineus CCCN SBod SPlb SVen

Euscaphis (*Staphyleaceae*)

japonica B&SWJ 11359 WCru
- B&SWJ 12739 WCru

Eustachys (*Poaceae*)

§ ***distichophylla*** NWsh

Eutrochium see *Eupatorium*

Ewartia (*Asteraceae*)

planchonii SPlb WAbe

Exochorda (*Rosaceae*)

alberti see *E. korolkowii*
giraldii var. ***wilsonii*** CDul EBee ELan EPfP LHop LRHS MBlu MMuc MNHC MRav NLar SWvt
§ ***korolkowii*** LRHS MAsh NLar
× ***macrantha*** LRHS
§ - 'Niagara' CBcs CMac CRos EBee EPfP LRHS LSRN MGos MPkF NLar NPnk NRHS SCob SEle SGol SHil SPoG
- Snow Day Surprise see *E.* × *macrantha* 'Niagara'
- 'The Bride' ♀H6 Widely available
racemosa EPfP MMuc NLar SPer
serratifolia CBcs ELan EPfP LRHS MMuc SPoG
- 'Snow White' CJun EPfP EWes GKin IArd IMou LRHS MAsh MBlu NLar NOrn SLon SPoG SWvt

F

Fabiana (*Solanaceae*)

foliosa 'Cliftonville Limelight' WAbe
imbricata CAbP CTre ELon LLHF LRHS MGil SLon SPlb
- 'Prostrata' CBcs ELan LRHS SVen WThu
- f. ***violacea*** ♀H4 CSBt CTri EBee ELan EPfP LLHF LRHS MMuc SPad SPer SPoG SWvt WKif
- - dark-flowered CBcs
nana WAbe

Fagopyrum (*Polygonaceae*)

from India GCal
cymosum see *F. dibotrys*
§ ***dibotrys*** CSpe EBee ECha EWld LEdu MMuc XLum
I - 'Cally Form' **new** EMFm

Fagus ✿ (*Fagaceae*)

§ ***crenata*** CMCN CMen MBlu
- 'Mount Fuji' CMen LLHF NEgg SBir
engleriana SBir
grandifolia subsp. ***mexicana*** SBir
japonica SBir
- var. ***multinervis*** SBir

	longipetiolata	CMCN EBee WPGP
	orientalis	CMCN SBir
	- 'Iskander'	IArd MBlu SGol
	sieboldii	see *F. crenata*
	sylvatica ♀H6	Widely available
	- 'Albovariegata' (v)	CMCN
	- 'Aniek'	SGol
	- 'Arcuata'	SBir
	- 'Asterix'	LRHS MBlu
	- Atropurpurea Group	Widely available
	- - 'Purpurea Pendula'	CAco CBcs CCVT CEnd CMCN CMac CSBt CTri CWib ELan EPfP ESps GKin IBoy IVic LPar MAsh MGos MJak NEgg NWea SCoo SGol SLau SLim SPer SPoG WHar WMat WTSh
	- - 'Riversii' ♀H6	CBcs CDul CEnd CLnd CMCN CTho CTri CWib ECrN ELan EMOT EPfP ESps GKin MAsh MGos NOrn NWea SPer WHar WMat
	- 'Aurea Pendula'	CEnd CMCN LPar MBlu SBir WPat
	- 'Bicolor Sartini'	MBlu
	- 'Birr Zebra'	CEnd
	- 'Black Swan'	CDul CLnd CMCN EBee ELan LSRN MAsh MBlu MGos NEgg NHol NOra NOrn SBir SLon SMad SPoG WMat
	- 'Bornyensis'	MBlu
	- 'Brathay Purple'	MBlu
	- 'Cochleata'	CMCN
	- 'Cockleshell'	MBlu SBir
	- 'Cristata'	MBlu
§	- 'Dawyck' ♀H6	CBcs CDul CLnd CMac CSBt CTho ECrN ELan EPfP ESps LPar MGos NEgg NLar NWea SBir SCob SGol SLau SPer WMou
	- 'Dawyck Gold' ♀H6	CBcs CDul CEnd CMCN CMac CSBt CTri EBee ELan EMOT ESps GKin IBoy IVic MAsh MBlu MGos NEgg NLar NOra NOrn NWea SBir SCob SGol SLau SPer WHar WMat WMou
	- 'Dawyck Purple' ♀H6	Widely available
	- 'Eugen'	SBir
	- 'Fastigiata' misapplied	see *F. sylvatica* 'Dawyck'
	- 'Felderbach'	SBir
	- 'Franken' (v)	CAco LLHF MBlu SBir
	- 'Green Obelisk'	MBlu
	- 'Greenwood'	LLHF MBlu NEgg
	- var. ***heterophylla***	CLnd CSBt CTho NWea
	- - 'Aspleniifolia' ♀H6	CBcs CDul CEnd CMCN CMac EBee ECrN ELan EPfP ESps ESwi GKin MBlu MGos NEgg SBir SCoo SGol SLau SPer SPoG WMat WMou
	- - (Atropurpurea Group) 'Ansorgei'	CEnd MBlu
	- - 'Incisa'	MBlu
	- - f. ***laciniata***	ESps MBlu
	- - 'Mercedes'	CDul CMCN LLHF MBlu NEgg SMad WCot WPat
	- 'Horizontalis'	MBlu
	- 'Pendula' ♀H6	CAco CBcs CCVT CDul CEnd CMCN CMac CSBt CTho EBee ECrN ELan ESps MGos MSwo NEgg NOra NWea SGol SLau SPer WHar WMat WMou WTSh
	- 'Prince George of Crete'	CDul CMCN
	- 'Purple Fountain' ♀H6	CAco CDul CEnd CMCN EBee ELan ESps LHop MAsh MBlu MGos NLar NOra NWea SBir SLau WMat
	- Purple-leaved Group	see *F. sylvatica* Atropurpurea Group
§	- 'Purpurea Tricolor' (v)	CAco CDul CEnd CMCN CMac MAsh MBlu MGos NEgg NOra NWea SBir SCoo SPer WMat WMou
	- 'Red Obelisk'	see *F. sylvatica* 'Rohan Obelisk'
	- 'Rohan Gold'	CEnd CMCN SGol
	- 'Rohan Minaret'	SGol
§	- 'Rohan Obelisk'	CAco CDul CEnd CMCN CTho ELan IBoy MBlu NEgg NLar SBir SGol SPoG
I	- 'Rohan Pyramidalis'	CEnd
	- 'Rohan Trompenburg'	CMCN MBlu
	- 'Rohan Weeping'	MBlu SBir
	- 'Rohanii'	CBcs CDul CEnd CMCN CTri EBee ELan EMOT EPfP ESps GKin LHop MGos NEgg NWea SBir SLau SPer WHar
	- 'Roseomarginata'	see *F. sylvatica* 'Purpurea Tricolor'
	- 'Rotundifolia'	CDul MBlu NEgg SGol
	- 'Spaethiana'	GKin
	- 'Striata'	CAco NEgg
	- f. ***tortuosa***	MPkF NEgg
	- - 'Rot Süntel'	CDul NEgg
	- 'Tricolor' misapplied (v)	see *F. sylvatica* 'Purpurea Tricolor' (v)
	- 'Tricolor' ambig. (v)	SLau
	- 'Tricolor' (v)	CBcs CLnd CSBt CWib ELan LLHF NHol SGol
	- 'Viridivariegata' (v)	CMCN
	- 'Zlatia'	CBcs CDul CLnd CMCN CSBt CWib ELan EPfP MBlu MGos NLar NWea SBir SGol SLau

Fallopia (*Polygonaceae*)

	aubertii	see *F. baldschuanica*
§	***baldschuanica***	Widely available
§	***japonica*** var. ***compacta***	WMoo XLum
	- - 'Fuji Snow'	see *F. japonica* var. *compacta* 'Milk Boy'
§	- - 'Milk Boy' (v)	EShb
	- - 'Variegata' misapplied	see *F. japonica* var. *compacta* 'Milk Boy'
§	***multiflora***	CArn CBod LEdu
	- var. ***hypoleuca***	SCoo
	- - B&SWJ 120	WCru

Farfugium (*Asteraceae*)

§	***japonicum***	CTal
	- B&SWJ 884	WCru
	- 'Argenteum' (v)	SMad WCot
§	- 'Aureomaculatum' (v) ♀H3	ECtt LEdu
	- 'Bumpy Ride'	WCot
	- 'Crispatum'	CAbP CTal LEdu
	- double-flowered (d)	WCru
	- 'Kaimon Dake'	WCot
	- 'Kinkan' (v)	WCot
	- 'Ryuto'	WCot
I	- 'Tsuwa-buki'	WCot
	'Last Dance' ^{PBR}	EBee ECtt NLar
	tussilagineum	see *F. japonicum*

Fargesia (*Poaceae*)

	from Jiuzhaigou, China	CDTJ CEnt CJng EPfP ERod ETod EUJe GMcL MAvo MMuc MWht NLar SBig WPGP
	adpressa	CJng MWht
	confusa	CDTJ
	denudata	CDTJ CEnt CFil CJng ENBC ERod NLar SBig
	- L 1575	MWht
	- 'Huanglong'	CJng
	- Xian 1	CDTJ CJng

dracocephala	CEnt CFil CJng ERod ESwi LRHS MAvo MBrN MMuc MWht NRHS SBig WMoo
- 'White Dragon'	CFil SMad
§ ***murielae*** 🏆H4	CAgr CEnt CFil CJng CLet ELan ENBC EPau EPfP ERod ESps ETod LCro LOPS LRHS MGos MJak MMuc MWht NGdn NLos SArc SCob SPlb SPoG WMoo
- 'Bimbo'	CBod CEnt CJng CSBt EPfP ERod ESps ESwi ETod LRHS MWht NLar NRHS SCob SPoG SWvt WMoo
- 'Dana Jumbo'	LRHS NRHS
- 'Grüne Hecke'	ERod MWht SBig
- 'Harewood'	CFil GMcL MWht SWvt
- 'Joy'	NLar WMoo
- 'Jumbo'	CBod CEnt CJng CSBt ELan ELon EPfP ERod ESps ESwi ETod EUJe GBin GMcL LRHS MAvo MGos MJak MWht NGdn NLar NRHS SBig SPer SPoG SRms SWvt
- 'Mae'	CDTJ MWht
- 'Simba'	Widely available
- 'Vampire'	ERod EUJe LRHS SBig
murieliae 'Superjumbo'[PBR]	ETod
§ ***nitida***	CAbb CBcs CDul CEnd CEnt CJng CLet CSBt ELan EPfP ERod ESps IFro LRHS MGos MJak MWht NRHS SCob SPoG SRms SWvt WHer WMoo WPGP
- 'Great Wall'	CBod CSBt ETod EUJe GBin MWht NLar SCob
- Jiuzhaigou 1	see *F.* Red Panda
- 'Jiuzhaigou 2'	CJng
- 'Jiuzhaigou 4'	CDTJ CFil WPGP
- 'Jiuzhaigou 8'	CDTJ WPGP
- 'Jiuzhaigou Genf'	CDTJ CFil NLar WPGP
- 'Nymphenburg'	SBig
perlonga Yunnan 6	ERod WPGP
§ Red Panda = 'Jiu' 🏆H4	CFil CJng EBee LCro LOPS LRHS NRHS SPoG SWvt
robusta 🏆H4	CAbb CChe CDTJ CEnt CJng CSBt ELan ENBC EPfP ERod ETod LRHS MAvo MBrN MMuc MWht NGdn NLos NRHS SBig SSut
- 'Campbell'	MJak NLar
- 'Ming Yunnan'	CJng LEdu WPGP
- 'P. King'	ERod MWht
- 'Pingwu'	CBod CDTJ CEnt CJng ENBC ERod ETod GMcL MGos MJak MWht SBig
- 'Red Sheath'	CEnt CJng CJun ERod MWht WPGP
- 'Wolong'	CJng ERod ETod MWht WPGP
rufa 🏆H4	CAbb CBod CEnt CFil CJng CSBt ELan ENBC EPfP ERod ETod EUJe GBin LCro LRHS LSRN MAvo MBlu MBrN MGos MJak MMuc MWht NLar NLos NRHS SBig SWeb WPGP
spathacea misapplied	see *F. murielae*
utilis	CEnt CJng ERod ETod MMuc MWht SEND
yulongshanensis	CJng ERod MWht
yunnanensis	LTro

Farsetia (*Brassicaceae*)

clypeata	see *Fibigia clypeata*

Fascicularia (*Bromeliaceae*)

andina	see *F. bicolor*
§ ***bicolor***	Widely available
- subsp. ***bicolor***	CFil CMac CPne IBoy NLos SMad
- subsp. ***canaliculata***	CFil GEdr IBlr LEdu MNrw SChr SKHP SPad WCot WPGP
kirchhoffiana	see *F. bicolor*
litoralis	see *Ochagavia litoralis*
pitcairniifolia misapplied	see *F. bicolor*
pitcairniifolia (Verlot) Mez	see *Ochagavia litoralis*

× *Fatshedera* ✿ (*Araliaceae*)

lizei 🏆H3	CBcs CDul CMac CRos CTri EBee ECrN ELon EMOT EPfP ESps EUJe GBin LRHS MAsh MRav SArc SCob SDix SEND SPer SPlb SWvt
§ - 'Annemieke' (v) 🏆H3	CBcs CBot CLet CRHN ELan ELon EMOT EPfP ESps EUJe LHop LRHS MAsh MMuc MRav SCob SEND SEle SPer SPoG
- compact	EBee EMil EPfP
- 'Lemon and Lime'	see × *F. lizei* 'Annemieke'
- 'Maculata'	see × *F. lizei* 'Annemieke'
- 'Variegata' (v) 🏆H3	CRos EBee ELan ELon EMOT EPfP ESps EUJe LRHS MAsh SCob SDix SEND SPer SWvt
- 'Variegata' compact	EMil

Fatsia ✿ (*Araliaceae*)

§ ***japonica*** 🏆H5	Widely available
- 'Annelise' (v)	SEND SMad
- 'Annemie' (v) **new**	NLos
- 'Moseri'	ELan ESwi LHop NGdn NLar SWvt WCot
- 'Murakumo-nishiki' (v)	CBot
- 'Spider's Web' (v)	CAbb CBcs CHid CWGN EBee ECtt ELon ESwi ETod EUJe LCro LHop LRHS MNrw MRav NHpl NLos NRHS SBig SCob SDix SEle SMad SPad SPer SPoG WCot WGrn WHar
- 'Variegata' (v) 🏆H3	CAbb CBcs CBot CLet CMac CRos EBee ELan EPfP ESps ESwi LPar LRHS MAsh MGos MRav MSCN NLos SCob SEND SHil SLim SLon SPer SPoG WCot WGrn WWFP
papyrifera	see *Tetrapanax papyrifer*
polycarpa	CBot CDTJ CFil
- B&SWJ 1776	WCru
- B&SWJ 3467	WCru
- B&SWJ 7144	WCru
- RWJ 10133	WCru
- from Tregye	CFil
- deeply cut leaf	WCot
- - BWJ 12499	WCru
- giant-leaved **new**	CFil

Feijoa see *Acca*

Felicia (*Asteraceae*)

aethiopica	CTre
§ ***amelloides***	CCCN SPlb
- 'Santa Anita'	CTri SVen
§ - variegated (v)	CCCN ECtt MSCN NPer
§ ***amoena***	CTri
- 'Variegata' (v)	CCCN CTri
capensis	see *F. amelloides*
coelestis	see *F. amelloides*
echinata	CCCN IDee
Felicitara Blue = 'Wigetablue'[PBR]	LRHS NRHS
filifolia blue-flowered	SVen
fruticosa	CHll
natalensis	see *F. rosulata*
pappei	see *F. amoena*

§	***petiolata***	CFis CTri EWes MMuc MNrw NSti SDix
§	***rosulata***	CFis CSma ECho GAbr GCrg GEdr MBrN MHol NBro NLar SBrt SRot WHal WIce
	uliginosa	EWes SBrt SPlb WIce
	wrightii	GEdr

Fenestraria (*Aizoaceae*)

rhopalophylla subsp. ***aurantiaca*** ♀H2	LToo

fennel see *Foeniculum vulgare*

fenugreek see *Trigonella foenum-graecum*

Ferraria (*Iridaceae*)

	LP 18095	WCot
§	***crispa***	ECho NRog WCot
	- var. ***nortieri***	NRog WCot
	divaricata	EBee NRog WCot
	- subsp. ***arenosa***	NRog
	schaeferi	NRog WCot
	undulata	see *F. crispa*

Ferula (*Apiaceae*)

	assa-foetida	WJek
	chiliantha	see *F. communis* subsp. *glauca*
§	***communis***	CAby CSpe ECGP ECha EHoe ELan EWes GBin GCra IBoy LEdu LRHS NDov SDix SEND SPav SPhx SPlb SPoG SPtp WJek
	- 'Gigantea'	see *F. communis*
§	- subsp. ***glauca***	ECha EWes GKev SDix SMHy SSut WCot
	- - B&SWJ 12999	WCru
	'Giant Bronze'	see *Foeniculum vulgare* 'Giant Bronze'
	szowitsiana	NDov
	tingitana	WCru
	B&SWJ 14005 **new**	
	- 'Cedric Morris'	ECha GCra SDix SMHy WCot

Ferulago (*Apiaceae*)

cassia	WCot
stellata **new**	WCot
sylvatica PAB 2875	LEdu WPGP

Festuca (*Poaceae*)

	actae	XLum
	amethystina	CBod CKno CWib EHoe EShb LOPS LRHS MBel NGdn SCob SEND SMea SPhx SRot WMoo XLum
	- 'Aprilgrün'	XLum
	arundinacea	CHab MMuc SEND
	californica	CKno EPPr
	coxii	CHid
	curvula	EShb
	subsp. ***crassifolia***	
	durissima	XLum
	'Eisvogel'	EPPr
	elegans	EPPr XLum
	eskia	EHoe XLum
	filiformis	CHab
	gamisansii	XLum
§	***gautieri***	EBee LRHS SMea XLum
	- 'Hobbit'	CBod
	- 'Pic Carlit'	NLar XLum
	gigantea	CHab SEND XLum
	glacialis	XLum
	- 'Czakor'	XLum
	glauca Vill.	CBar CBcs CBod CWib ELan EShb ESps GMaP GWyn LPot MBNS MGos MRav MSCN NGdn SLim SPlb SRms WHea XSen
I	- 'Auslese'	EShb LBMP NGdn
	- 'Azurit'	EHoe EWes LHop NLar NWad SPoG SRms
§	- 'Blaufuchs'	CLet CRos CSBt EAEE ELan EPfP EWes GMaP LRHS MAsh MAvo MBlu MGos NLar NRHS NWad NWsh SLim SPer SPlb SWvt WFar XLum
§	- 'Blauglut'	EBee LRHS MRav NRHS SRms
	- Blue Fox	see *F. glauca* 'Blaufuchs'
	- Blue Glow	see *F. glauca* 'Blauglut'
	- 'Elijah Blue'	Widely available
	- 'Golden Toupee'	CRos CTsd ECha EHoe ELan EPfP ESps LRHS MAsh MBlu MGos NBir NEgg NLar NRHS NSti SLim SPer SPlb SPoG SWvt WHar XLum
	- 'Harz'	EHoe XLum
	- Intense Blue = 'Casblue'PBR	CAbP CKno CRos EHoe EPfP EWes GBin GMcL LCro LRHS LSRN MGos NRHS SHil SMad SPoG SRms
*	- ***minima***	CCCN NWsh
	- 'Pallens'	see *F. longifolia*
	- Sea Urchin	see *F. glauca* 'Seeigel'
§	- 'Seeigel'	LRHS NWad
	- Select	see *F. glauca* 'Auslese'
	- 'Seven Seas'	see *F. valesiaca* 'Silbersee'
	- 'Silberreiher'	EPPr
	- 'Solling'	XLum
	- 'Uchte'	ELan EPPr WPtf
	'Hogar'	EPPr
	idahoensis	EShb
	- 'Tomales Bay'	CKno
§	***longifolia***	EPPr
	mairei	CKno ECha EHoe EPPr LPla NDov SPhx XLum
	novae-zelandiae	CWCL
	ovina	CHab WSFF
	- var. ***gallica***	NWsh
*	- 'Tetra Gold'	SWvt
	paniculata	CKno EHoe EPPr XLum
	- subsp. ***spadicea***	XLum
	pratensis	CHab
	punctoria	MMuc SMea
	rubra	CHab CKno WSFF XLum
	scoparia	see *F. gautieri*
	'Siskiyou Blue'	CKno
	tatrae	MBel MMuc SEND
	valesiaca	SMea XLum
	- var. ***glaucantha***	CWib NGdn XLum
§	- 'Silbersee'	EAEE EHoe SRms WFar
	- Silver Sea	see *F. valesiaca* 'Silbersee'
	violacea	EPPr
	vivipara	EHoe LEdu NBid XLum
*	'Willow Green'	SPlb

Fibigia (*Brassicaceae*)

§	***clypeata***	GPSL MAvo
I	- 'Select'	CSpe

Ficaria (*Ranunculaceae*)

	verna 'Aglow in the Dark'	CHid
	- Alba Group	CHid CSam LEdu NRya WOut
	- anemone-centred	see *F. verna* 'Collarette'
§	- Aurantiaca Group	ECha ECho GCrg MHer NLar NRya SPhx

	- var. ***aurantiacus***	see *F. verna* Aurantiaca Group
	- 'Bowles's Double'	see *F. verna* 'Double Bronze', 'Picton's Double'
	- 'Brambling'	CHid EBee ECha ECho LEdu NLar
	- 'Brazen Child'	SHar
	- 'Brazen Hussy'	Widely available
	- subsp. ***bulbilifer***	see *F. verna* subsp. *verna*
§	- subsp. ***chrysocephala***	EBee ECha IFro MNrw WCot
§	- 'Collarette' (d)	CHid ECho GBuc LEdu MHer NBir NLar NRya
	- 'Coppernob'	CHid ECho WCot WPnP
	- 'Cupreus'	see *F. verna* Aurantiaca Group
	- 'Dahlem'	EPPr
	- 'Damerham' (d)	CHid
§	- 'Double Bronze' (d)	CHid ECho GBuc LEdu MHer NBir NLar NRya SHar
§	- 'Double Mud' (d)	CHid ECho EPPr EWTr GAbr GBuc IFro LEdu NLar NRya SHar WHal
	- double, cream-flowered	see *F. verna* 'Double Mud'
	- double, green-eyed (d)	CHid LEdu
	- double, yellow-flowered	see *F. verna* Flore Pleno Group
	- 'Dusky Maiden'	ECho NLar NRya
	- 'E.A. Bowles'	see *F. verna* 'Collarette'
	- 'Edna' **new**	WOut
§	- Flore Pleno Group (d)	CBod CHid CMac CTri ECha ECho ELan EPPr GAbr NRya SRms WCot WPnP
	- 'Green Mantle'	ECho
	- 'Green Petal'	CAby CHid EBee ECho EPPr GBuc LEdu MCot MHer NBir NRya WHal WHer
	- 'Holly'	see *F. verna* 'Holly Green'
§	- 'Holly Green'	ECho
	- 'Hyde Hall'	NLar WCot
	- 'Jake Perry'	MNrw
	- 'Jane's Dress'	CHid
	- 'Ken Aslet Double' (d)	EPPr LEdu MHer WHal
	- 'Lambrook Variegated' (v)	CFis
	- 'Lemon Queen'	CHid
	- 'Leo'	MNrw
	- subsp. ***major***	see *F. verna* subsp. *chrysocephala*
	- 'Mobled Jade'	CHid
	- 'Monksilver'	IFro
	- 'Montacute'	CFis
	- 'Newton Abbot'	CBre
	- 'Old Master'	WCot
	- 'Orange Sorbet' (d)	LEdu MNrw NLar
	- 'Petrol Spillage' **new**	CNat
§	- 'Picton's Double' (d)	MNrw
	- 'Primrose'	CHid NRya
	- 'Primrose Elf'	EBee
	- 'Ragamuffin' (d)	EBee
	- 'Randall's White'	CAby SHar
	- 'Richard and Val'	WCot
	- 'Rita Pirouet'	WCot
	- 'Salmon's White'	CBre ECho EPPr NBir NLar NRya SHar WHal
	- 'Sheldon Silver'	CHid
	- 'Silver Collar'	LEdu
	- 'Single Cream'	MNrw
	- 'Tomas'	ECho
	- 'Tortoiseshell'	CHid EPPr
§	- subsp. ***verna***	CTri ESwi MHer WHer WOut WSFF WShi
	- - 'Chedglow'	WCot
	- 'Wisley Double'	see *F. verna* 'Double Bronze'
	- 'Yaffle'	CHid ECho

Ficinia (*Cyperaceae*)

	truncata 'Ice Crystal' (v)	LRHS SPoG

Ficus (*Moraceae*)

	afghanistanica	ERea
	- 'Silver Lyre'	EBee WPGP
I	***binnendijkii*** 'Alii'	WCot
	carica (F)	CCCN ESps ETod EUJe LPar SArc SEWo SLon SPad
	- 'Abicou' (F)	ERea
	- 'Adam' (F)	CCCN ERea LEdu MRai NLar SEND SMad
	- 'Alma' (F)	ERea
	- 'Angélique' (F)	ERea
I	- 'Bauern Feige' (F)	NLar SRms
	- 'Beall' (F)	CCCN
	- 'Bellone' (F)	CCCN
	- 'Black Ischia' (F)	CCCN ERea SDix
	- 'Black Jack' (F)	ERea
	- 'Bornholm' (F)	CCCN LSRN SPre
	- 'Bourjassotte Grise' (F)	CAgr ERea SDea XSen
	- 'Brogiotto' (F)	CCCN
	- 'Brogiotto Bianco' (F) **new**	EMOT
	- 'Brown Turkey' (F) ♀H4	Widely available
	- 'Brunswick' (F)	CAgr CCCN CDul CHll CLet CRHN ELan ELon EPfP EPom ERea EShb EUJe GTwe LEdu LRHS NLar SDix SEND SKee SLim SRms WCot WFar WMat
	- 'Califfo Blue' (F)	SRms
	- 'Castle Kennedy' (F)	CCCN ERea
	- 'Celeste' (F)	CBcs CCCN ERea SRms
	- 'Col de Dame Blanc' (F)	ERea XSen
	- 'Col de Dame Noir' (F)	ERea
	- 'Colummaro Black Apulia' (F)	CCCN
	- 'Colummaro White Apulia' (F)	CCCN
	- 'Dalmatie' (F)	CAgr CCCN CFGn EBee ELan EPfP ERea LRHS MGos MRai NPri SEND SRms WMat WPGP XSen
§	- 'Desert King' (F)	ERea
I	- 'Digitata' (F)	MBlu
	- 'Digredo' (F)	CCCN
	- 'Dorée' (F)	EPom
	- 'Dorée de Porquerolles' (F)	CCCN
	- 'Drap d'Or' (F)	ERea
	- 'Excel' (F)	ERea
	- 'Figue d'Or' (F)	ERea
	- 'Filacciano' (F)	CCCN
	- 'Flanders' (F)	CCCN
	- 'Gentile' (F) **new**	MRai
	- 'Goutte d'Or' (F)	CAgr CCCN EPfP EPom ERea SDea
	- 'Green Ischia' (F)	CCCN ERea
	- 'Grise de Marseille' (F)	CCCN
	- 'Grise de Saint Jean' (F)	CCCN ERea
	- 'Ice Crystal' (F) ♀H5	ECrN ELan EMil EPfP ERea EShb EUJe LPar LRHS MBlu SPoG SRms WCot WMat WPGP
	- 'Jordan' (F)	CFGn EMOT LRHS
	- 'Kadota' (F)	CCCN EMOT ERea MRai
	- 'King'	see *F. carica* 'Desert King'
	- 'Lisa' (F)	ERea
	- 'Little Yellow Wonder' (F)	ERea
	- 'Longue d'Août' (F)	XSen
	- 'LSU Gold' (F)	ERea
	- 'LSU Purple' (F)	ERea
	- 'Madeleine des Deux Saisons' (F)	EBee EPom ERea MRai SEND
	- 'Malvern Prolific' (F) **new**	LRHS
	- 'Marseillaise' (F)	EPfP GTwe SDea
	- 'Melanzana' (F)	CCCN

- 'Morena' (F)	SRms
- 'Moscatel' (F)	CCCN
- 'Napolitana' (F)	ERea
- 'Negrétte de Porquerolles' (F)	CCCN
- 'Nero' (F)	ELon SGol
- 'Newlyn Harbour' (F)	ELon
- 'Noire de Caromb' (F)	CAgr CCCN CFGn EPfP ERea LRHS SKee SRms WMat
- 'Noire de Provence'	see *F. carica* 'Reculver'
- 'Orphan' (F)	ERea
- 'Osborn's Prolific' (F)	EPfP SEND SGol SWvt
- 'Panachée' (F)	CCCN CSut EMOT EPom ERea LRHS SMad SRms
- 'Pastilière' (F)	ERea
- 'Peter's Honey' (F)	ERea
- 'Petite Nigra' (F)	ERea
- 'Pied de Boeuf' (F)	CCCN
- 'Pingo de Mel' (F)	ERea
- 'Précoce de Dalmatie' (F)	CCCN CTho ERea LEdu NLar SRms
- 'Précoce Ronde de Bordeaux' (F)	ERea SEND
- 'Quinta' (F)	CCCN
§ - 'Reculver' (F)	SEND
- 'Ronde de Bordeaux' (F)	CCCN EPfP XSen
- 'Rouge de Bordeaux' (F)	CCCN EPom ERea NPri SDea SPlb SRms
- 'Safi' (F)	CCCN
- 'Saint Johns' (F)	ERea SDea
- 'San Pedro Miro' (F)	ERea
- 'Sugar 12' (F)	ERea
- 'Sultane' (F)	CAgr EPom ERea
- 'Tena' (F)	ERea
- 'Texas Everbearing' (F)	ERea
- 'Verte d'Argenteuil' (F)	CCCN
- 'Violette Dauphine' (F)	EPfP ERea LEdu MRai NLar SEND
- 'Violette de Bordeaux' (F)	ERea
- 'Violette de Sollies' (F)	ERea SVic
- 'Violette Normande' (F)	SEND
- 'Violette Sepor' (F)	ERea
- 'White Adriatic' (F)	CBcs ERea MRai SRms
- 'White Genoa'	see *F. carica* 'White Marseilles'
- 'White Ischia' (F)	ERea
§ - 'White Marseilles' (F)	CAgr CCCN CMac CRHN CWib ECrN ERea LRHS SDea SEND SKee SRms WMat WPGP
- 'Zidi' (F)	CCCN
pumila ΨH1c	CBcs CTsd EShb
- 'Variegata' (v) ΨH1c	EShb
tikoua	CFil

fig see *Ficus carica*

filbert see *Corylus maxima*

Filipendula ✿ (*Rosaceae*)

alnifolia 'Variegata'	see *F. ulmaria* 'Variegata'
camtschatica	ECha ELan IMou MMuc NBid NLar SEND WPGP WWtn
- B&SWJ 10987	WCru
- RBS 0224	NLar
- 'Rosea'	LHop MRav
digitata 'Nana'	see *F. multijuga*
hexapetala	see *F. vulgaris*
- 'Flore Pleno'	see *F. vulgaris* 'Multiplex'
'Kahome'	EAJP ELon EShb GLog GMaP IFoB IKil LLWG LRHS MHol NBid NBir NGdn NLar NSti SCob SPer SPhx SWat WMoo WPnP
kiraishiensis	EBee
- B&SWJ 1571	WCru
§ ***multijuga***	EBee GCal IFoB LLWG MSCN NHol NLar NWad WBor WMoo
- B&SWJ 10950	WCru
- 'Hjördis'	CBod EBee ELon LLWG SPad WHil
- var. ***yezoensis*** B&SWJ 10828	IMou WCru
palmata	ECha IBlr LLWG LRHS NBre SWat WMoo
- 'Digitata Nana'	see *F. multijuga*
- 'Elegantissima'	see *F. purpurea* 'Elegans'
- 'Nana'	see *F. multijuga*
- 'Rosea'	CMac LLWG NBir
- 'Rubra'	CTri EBee GCra LRHS MRav NGdn
purpurea	CKno CSBt ECha ELon IBlr ILea MMuc SBod SEND SRms WCru WMoo
- f. ***albiflora***	LLWG WMoo
§ - 'Elegans'	EBee ELon EWTr ILea LLWG LRHS NBid NDov NHol NWad SCob SPer SRms SWat WFar WMoo WPnP
- 'Pink Dreamland'	SPhx
* - 'Plena' (d)	NLar
'Queen of the Prairies'	see *F. rubra*
§ ***rubra***	GNew IFro WSFF
§ - 'Venusta' ΨH5	Widely available
- 'Venusta Magnifica'	see *F. rubra* 'Venusta'
rufinervis B&SWJ 8469 **new**	WCru
- B&SWJ 8611	WCru
§ ***ulmaria***	CArn CBen CBod CHab CHby CLau CWat CWld EBee ENfk GJos GMaP GPoy MCot MHer MMuc MNHC MWLS MWts NMir SIde SWat WHer WJek WMoo WOut WPnP WSFF WShi XLum
- 'Aurea'	CBod CDor CMac CNor CTri CWCL EBee ECha ECtt EHoe ELan GMaP LEdu LRHS MAvo MRav NBid NLar SPer SRms WCot WFar WMoo WSHC
- 'Flore Pleno' (d)	CBre EBee LHop LLWG LRHS MRav NBid SPer SWat WCot WFar WHil
- 'Rosea'	LRHS MBel MHer
§ - 'Variegata' (v)	CBen CWCL EBee ECtt EHoe ELan GBuc IFoB LRHS NBid NGdn NLar SPer SRms WFar WHil WMoo
§ ***vulgaris***	CArn CDor CHab CWld GLog ILea MBel MMuc MNHC NBro NMir NQui SWat WHer WJek
- 'Flore Pleno'	see *F. vulgaris* 'Multiplex'
- 'Grandiflora'	CBre
§ - 'Multiplex' (d)	CDor CMac CSpe ECha ELan EWTr GMaP LLWG LRHS MHer MMuc MRav NBid NBir NRya NSti SRms WFar WMoo XLum
- 'Plena'	see *F. vulgaris* 'Multiplex'
- 'Rosea'	NBre

Firmiana (*Malvaceae*)

simplex	CBcs EBee EShb ESwi EUJe MBlu SPad WPGP

Fitzroya (*Cupressaceae*)

cupressoides	CAco CBcs CMac CTho IArd IDee SLim WThu
- 'Borde Hill' (f)	WThu
- 'Westonbirt' (m)	WThu

Flueggea (*Phyllanthaceae*)

suffruticosa	SBrt

Fockea (Apocynaceae)

edulis	LToo

Foeniculum (Apiaceae)

sp.	LBMP
vulgare	CAgr CHby CLau ECha ECrN ELan ENfk EPfP ESps EWoo GPoy MGos MHer MJak MNHC NPnk NPri SCob SEND SIde SPer SPhx SPlb SPoG SRms SVic SWvt WJek
- 'Bronze'	see *F. vulgare* 'Purpureum'
- var. ***dulce***	ENfk SIde
§ - 'Giant Bronze'	CBod EBee IBoy LCro LEdu LOPS LRHS SCob SMad SPhx WCot WGrn XSen
§ - 'Purpureum'	Widely available
- 'Smoky'	ECha MRav
- 'Sweet Florence'	SVic

Fontanesia (Oleaceae)

fortunei	EBtc
phillyreoides	CBcs

Fontinalis (Fontinalaceae)

antipyretica	XBlo

Forsythia (Oleaceae)

'Arnold Dwarf'	ECrN NBir SRms
'Beatrix Farrand' ambig.	CTri NWea SEND SRms
'Beatrix Farrand' K. Sax	MMuc NLar
'Fiesta' (v)	CRos ELon EPfP LRHS MAsh MRav MSwo NEgg NLar SPer WCot
giraldiana	MSwo SRms
Gold Tide	see *F.* Marée d'Or
'Golden Nugget'	CMac ELan EPfP LBuc LRHS MAsh NLar SLon SPoG WCFE WFar
'Golden Times' (v)	CMac GMcL LBuc LPot LSRN MAsh MSwo NHol NWea SPoG SWvt
'Goldstream' (v)	NWad
× ***intermedia***	CAco EShb ESps IBoy WHar
- 'Arnold Giant'	MBlu
- 'Goldrausch'	ELan GMcL LCro LRHS MAsh NLar NRHS SHil
- 'Goldzauber'	NWea
- 'Lynwood Variety' ♀H5	Widely available
- 'Lynwood Variety' variegated (v)	CWib
- Minigold = 'Flojor'	CMac CNec CSBt ELan ESps LBMP MSwo NLar SRms
- 'Nimbus'PBR **new**	LRHS NRHS
- Show Off = 'Mindor'PBR	LRHS NRHS
- 'Spectabilis'	CDul EPfP LBuc NWea SCob SCoo SGol SLim WFar
- 'Spectabilis Variegated' (v)	MBNS NEoE
- 'Spring Glory'	MHer
- 'Variegata' (v)	SRms
- Week End = 'Courtalyn'PBR ♀H5	CBod CEnd CLet CNec EPfP ESps LBMP LBuc LRHS MAsh MJak MMuc NHol NLar NRHS SCob SEND SGol SLon SPlb WFar
'Kanarek'	NLar
× ***mandshurica***	IDee IMou SAko
§ Marée d'Or = 'Courtasol'PBR ♀H5	CRos ELon EPfP IVic LRHS MAsh MJak MRav NLar NWea SLon SPer SPoG
Mêlée d'Or = 'Courtaneur'	SGol WBor
Melissa = 'Courtadic'	NWea
'Northern Gold'	MBlu
ovata 'Tetragold'	NWea
'Paulina'	GEdr NLar WAbe
suspensa	CMac CTri CWib EPfP NWea SPlb SRms
- f. ***atrocaulis***	CDul
- 'Nymans'	MRav NLar NSti SBrt SEND SPer
'Tremonia'	ECrN
viridissima	NWea
- 'Bronxensis'	CMac CTal ECho LHop LLHF MAsh NBir NLar SIgm WAbe WPat
- Citrus Swizzle = 'Mckcitrine'PBR	NLar
- var. ***koreana*** 'Kumsom' (v)	EBee IArd IDee NLar SAko SPoG
- 'Weber's Bronx'	NLar

Fortunella (Rutaceae)

× ***crassifolia***	see *Citrus japonica*
'Fukushu'	see *Citrus* × *obovata* 'Fukushu'
hindsii	see *Citrus japonica*
margarita	see *Citrus japonica*

Fothergilla (Hamamelidaceae)

gardenii	CBcs CJun EPfP LRHS MBlu MRav NLar SPer SWvt
- 'Blue Mist'	CAbP CCCN CEnd CJun EBee ELan ELon EPfP IVic LRHS MAsh SKHP SMad SPer SPoG WHor WPat
- 'Glaucophylla'	NLar
- 'Suzanne'	CJun NLar
- 'Zundert'	NLar
'Huntsman'	CCCN CJun CTho EPfP SPer WHor
× ***intermedia*** Beaver Creek = 'Klmtwo'	NLar
- 'Blue Shadow'	CBcs CCCN CJun EPfP IDee LCro LRHS LSRN MGos MPkF MRav NLar NRHS SGol SKHP
- 'Mount Airy' ♀H5	CJun CMCN EBee EPfP LRHS MPkF NLar NRHS SKHP SSta
- 'Red Licorice'	CJun EPfP NLar
- 'Sea Spray'	CJun NLar
- 'Windy City'	CJun NLar
major ♀H5	CBcs CDul CJun CLet CRos CWib EBee ELan EPfP ESps LCro LRHS LSRN MAsh MBlu MGos MJak NEgg NLar NPri SHil SPer SReu SWvt WBod WFar WHor WMat WPat WTSh
- 'Bulkyard'	CJun
- Monticola Group	CEnd CJun CTho EPfP LRHS MAsh MMuc SLim SPer SSta WHar

Fouquieria (Fouquieriaceae)

columnaris	SPlb
splendens	SPlb

Fragaria (Rosaceae)

from Taiwan	WHer
alpina 'Alba'	see *F. vesca* 'Semperflorens Alba'
× ***ananassa*** 'Albion'PBR (F)	CSBt LCro LOPS LRHS LSRN NRHS SBdl SPer
- 'Alice'PBR (F) ♀H6	CAgr CMac EPom LBuc
- 'Anablanca' (F)	EMil LRHS
- 'Aromel' (F)	EPfP LBuc
- 'Buddy' (F)	EPom LCro LOPS LRHS NRHS SPer
- 'Calypso' (F)	CSBt LBuc SDea SFrt SPer
- 'Cambridge Favourite' (F) ♀H6	CAgr CMac CRos CSBt CTri EMil EPfP EPom GAbr GTwe LBuc LCro LOPS LRHS MGos MJak NPri NRHS SBdl SDea SEND SFrt SPlb WHar
- 'Cambridge Vigour' (F)	LRHS NRHS

	- 'Christine' (F)	CAgr CRos EPom LRHS NRHS SDea
	- 'Cupid'^{PBR} (F)	CArg LCro LOPS
	- 'Darselect'^{PBR} (F)	EPom LOPS
	- 'Delia' (F)	CRos LCro LOPS LRHS NRHS
	- 'Elan'^{PBR} (F)	CRos LRHS NRHS
	- 'Elegance'^{PBR} (F)	EPom GTwe SFrt
	- 'Elsanta' (F)	CRos CSBt CTri EMil EPfP EPom GTwe IArd LBuc LEdu LRHS NEgg NPri NRHS SBdl SDea SPer WHar WMat
	- 'Elvira' (F)	EPfP
	- 'Eros'^{PBR} (F)	LBuc
	- 'Everest'^{PBR} (F)	LRHS NRHS
	- 'Fenella'^{PBR} (F)	CMac EMil EPom GTwe LCro LOPS
	- 'Finesse' (F)	GTwe LRHS NRHS
	- 'Flamenco'^{PBR} (F)	CArg CSut EPom LEdu NWad SDea
	- 'Florence'^{PBR} (F)	CAgr CArg CRos CSBt CTri EPfP EPom GTwe LBuc LEdu LRHS NRHS SDea SFrt SPer
	- 'Florian' (F)	LEdu
	- Fraise des Bois	see *F. vesca*
	- 'Framberry' (F)	LEdu LRHS
	- 'Frau Mieze Schindler' (F)	SFrt
	- 'Gariguette' (F)	EPom
	- 'Gasana' (F)	CRos LRHS NRHS
	- 'Hapil' (F) Υ^{H6}	CTri EMil EPfP EPom LBuc LEdu LRHS NRHS SBdl
	- 'Honeoye' (F) Υ^{H6}	CAgr CRos CSBt EMil EPfP EPom GTwe LBuc LCro LEdu LOPS LRHS NRHS NWad SBdl SEND SPer WHar
	- 'Judibell'^{PBR} (F)	GTwe SFrt
	- 'Korona'^{PBR} (F)	CMac EPom
	- 'Leo Alba' (F)	CArg
	- 'Loran' (F)	CRos LRHS NRHS
	- 'Lucy'^{PBR} (F)	LCro LOPS SFrt
	- 'Malling Centenary' (F) **new**	EPom
	- 'Malling Opal'^{PBR} (F)	CSut EPom
	- 'Malwina'^{PBR} (F)	CSut EPom SVic
	- 'Manille' (F)	EPom
	- 'Merlan'^{PBR} (F)	LRHS NRHS
	- 'Pandora' (F)	LEdu
	- 'Pegasus'^{PBR} (F) Υ^{H6}	CAgr CRos CSBt EPfP EPom LRHS NRHS
	- pineberry (F)	LEdu
	- Pink Panda = 'Frel' (F)	CBod CMac CTri EAEE EBee ELan GMcL LHop LRHS MBel MRav NEgg NGdn NLar SPer SPoG WCAu WWFP
	- pink-flowered (F)	GAbr LPot
	- 'Red Glory'^{PBR} (F)	LRHS NRHS
	- 'Red Princess'^{PBR} (F)	LRHS NRHS
	- Red Ruby	see *F.* × *ananassa* 'Samba'
	- 'Redgauntlet' (F)	CRos EPfP LBuc LRHS NRHS
	- 'Rhapsody' (F) Υ^{H6}	CRos GTwe LRHS LSRN NRHS SBdl
	- 'Rosie'^{PBR} (F)	SDea
	- 'Royal Sovereign' (F)	CMac CSut CTri EPom GTwe LEdu NBir SDea SVic
§	- 'Samba'^{PBR} (F)	CBod ELan GLog GMcL LEdu LRHS MBel MNrw NDov NGdn NLar SPer SPoG
	- 'Senga Sengana' (F)	SVic
	- Snow White = 'Hansawhit' (F) **new**	CSut EPom
	- 'Sonata'^{PBR} (F)	ELan EPom NWad
	- 'Sophie'^{PBR} (F)	LEdu NWad
	- 'Sweetheart' (F)	CSut LCro
	- 'Symphony'^{PBR} (F) Υ^{H6}	CAgr CRos CSBt EPfP EPom LBuc LRHS LSRN NRHS SFrt SPer
	- 'Temptation' (F)	CRos LRHS NRHS
	- 'Toscana'^{PBR} (F)	CRos LRHS NRHS
§	- 'Variegata' (v)	CMea CTri EAEE EBee MRav SPer SPoG WHea WMoo WOut
	- 'Vibrant'^{PBR} (F)	CSut EMil EPom GTwe
	- 'White Dream' (F)	LCro LOPS
	'Bowles's Double'	see *F. vesca* 'Multiplex'
	chiloensis (F)	IFro LEdu
	- 'Chaval' (F)	CHid ECha EPPr IMou MRav NChi WMoo
	- 'Variegata' misapplied	see *F.* × *ananassa* 'Variegata'
	daltoniana	GCra
	indica	see *Duchesnea indica*
	'Lipstick'	EBee LHop NFav NLar
	moschata	CAgr
	nubicola	CAgr GPoy
	- 'Mount Omei'	EBee
	'Roman'	LRHS NRHS
	'Variegata'	see *F.* × *ananassa* 'Variegata'
§	***vesca*** (F)	CAgr CArn CBcs CWld ELan EPfP GPoy LCro LOPS MHer MNHC NMir NPri SFrt SIde SPlb SRms SVic WGwG WJek WOut WSFF WShi
	- 'Alexandra' (F)	CLau ENfk ERea NLar SIde WHar
	- 'Alpina Scarletta' (F)	ENfk
	- 'Alpine Yellow' (F)	EWTr
	- 'Baron Solemacher' (F)	ERea SHDw SPhx WHer
	- 'Capron Royale' (F)	CAgr
	- 'Flore Pleno'	see *F. vesca* 'Multiplex'
	- 'Fructu Albo' (F)	CAgr CArn CBre WMoo
	- 'Golden Alexandra' (F)	ECha EWes WHer
	- 'Golden Surprise' (F)	SHDw
	- 'Mara des Bois'^{PBR} (F)	EPom LRHS
	- 'Monophylla' (F)	SIde WHer
§	- 'Multiplex' (d)	EPPr NChi WBor WHer WOut
§	- 'Muricata'	CBre LEdu LOPS
	- 'Pineapple Crush' (F)	WHer
	- 'Plymouth Strawberry'	see *F. vesca* 'Muricata'
	- 'Reine des Vallées' (F)	ERea
	- 'Scarlet Beauty' (F)	EPom LCro LOPS MCoo
§	- 'Semperflorens Alba' (F)	CAgr WJek
	- 'Variegata' misapplied	see *F.* × *ananassa* 'Variegata'
	- 'Variegata' ambig. (v)	EHoe
	- 'White Surprise' (F)	LCro LOPS
	virginiana	CAgr
	- subsp. ***glauca***	EPPr
	viridis	CAgr

Francoa (Francoaceae)

	appendiculata	GAbr ILea NBir WHer WMoo
	- red-flowered	LHop
	Ballyrogan strain	IBlr
	'Confetti'	IKil
*	dwarf purple	CElw
	'Purple Spike'	see *F. sonchifolia* Rogerson's form
	ramosa	CCVN CTri IBlr ILea NBro SDix WKif WMoo
*	- 'Alba'	CSpe
	sonchifolia	Widely available
	- 'Alba'	WMoo
	- 'Cally Dwarf Purple'	MHer
	- 'Culm View Lilac'	CCVN MSCN
	- 'Molly Anderson'	MAvo
	- 'Petite Bouquet'	EWes SHar
	- 'Pink Bouquet'	CAbb CKno CMac CMos CWGN EBee SHar SRkn WOut
	- 'Pink Giant'	CBod GBuc GCal IPot LPot LRHS MBel NWad SPad WMoo
§	- Rogerson's form	CBWd CCVN CElw CTri ELon EShb GBin IBoy IMou IVic LHop LRHS NBir NChi SDix SPad WMoo

Frangula (*Rhamnaceae*)

§	***alnus***	CArg CCVT CDul CHab CPer CTri ECrN EShb LBuc MBlu MGos MMuc NWea SEWo WFar WHed WMou WSFF WTSh
	- 'Aspleniifolia'	CTho ELan EPfP LCro LRHS MBlu MGil MMuc MPkF MRav NLar SMad WCFE WGrn WPat
	- 'Fine Line'	CRos ELan LRHS NLar NRHS SPoG
	- 'Minaret'	MBlu
	- 'Ron Williams'	MBlu WMat

Frankenia (*Frankeniaceae*)

	laevis	SRms
	thymifolia	CTri ECho ECtt EPot MAsh MHer MMuc SIgm SPlb WIce WOld WRHF XLum

Franklinia (*Theaceae*)

	alatamaha	CBcs EBee IArd IVic MBlu MGil SAko WPGP

Fraxinus ✿ (*Oleaceae*)

	americana	CDul CMCN NWea
	- 'Autumn Purple'	CDul CEnd CMCN EBee EPfP MAsh NWea
	angustifolia	CMCN
	- 'Raywood'	CCVT CDul CEnd CMCN CTri CWib ECrN ELan EPfP EWTr GBin LCro MAsh MGos MMuc MSwo NWea SCob SEND SGol
	anomala	CDul
	chiisanensis B&SWJ 12719	WCru
	chinensis	CDul CMCN
	excelsior	CAco CCVT CDul CHab CTri CWib ECrN EPfP MAsh MGos MJak MMuc NWea SCob SEWo SGol
	- 'Althena'	CDul
	- 'Aurea Pendula'	CDul CEnd
	- 'Crispa'	NLar
	- f. ***diversifolia***	CDul
	- 'Jaspidea'	CCVT CDul CEnd CMCN CWib ECrN EMOT EPfP ERod MAsh MGos MMuc MSwo NWea SCob SGol
	- 'Pendula'	CCVT CDul CEnd CTsd EBee ECrN NWea SGol
	- 'R.E. Davey'	CDul
	- 'Westhof's Glorie'	CCVT CDul EMOT
	insularis var. ***henryana***	CDul CMCN
	latifolia	CMCN
	mariesii	see *F. sieboldiana*
	nigra 'Fallgold'	CEnd
	ornus	CCVT CDul CMCN CTri ECrN EPfP MMuc MSwo NWea SEND WTSh
	- 'Arie Peters'	CDul
	- 'Obelisk'	EBee EBtc MAsh
	- 'Rotterdam'	EBee
	pennsylvanica	CDul CMCN
	quadrangulata	CDul
§	***sieboldiana***	CDul CMCN EPfP
	sogdiana Potamophila Group	CFil EBee
	velutina	CDul
	xanthoxyloides	CDul

Freesia (*Iridaceae*)

	alba Foster	see *F. lactea*
	alba Watson	see *F. caryophyllacea*
	alba (G.L. Mey.) Gumbl.	CTre
§	***caryophyllacea***	NRog
	corymbosa	NRog
	'Delta River' **new**	SPoG
	'Fragrant Sunburst'	SPoG
	fucata	ECho
	'Gold River' **new**	SPoG
	grandiflora	CHll ECho
	'Grumpy'	LRHS
§	***lactea***	ECho
§	***laxa*** 🏆H3	CSpe CTal CTre CTri ECho EPri GKev LRHS NHpl NLos WAbe
	- var. ***alba*** 🏆H3	CSpe CTre ECho EPri GKev LLWP WAbe
	- blue-flowered	ECho WAbe
	- 'Joan Evans'	CSpe ECho LLHF SChF
	- red-spotted	ECho
	- ***viridiflora***	ECho
	leichtlinii	NRog
	'Red River' **new**	SPoG
	refracta	CTal NRog
	viridis	CTal ECho NRog
	'White River' **new**	SPoG
	xanthospila	NRog

Fremontodendron (*Malvaceae*)

	'California Glory' 🏆H4	Widely available
	californicum	CTri EBee ELan MPkF NLar SEND SLim SNig SPlb WFar
	'Pacific Sunset'	CBcs EPfP LRHS MGos MRav SGol
	'Tequila Sunrise' 🏆H4	CWGN LHop LLHF LRHS WFar

Freylinia (*Scrophulariaceae*)

	cestroides	see *F. lanceolata*
§	***lanceolata***	CBcs CCCN CWib SPlb SVen
	tropica	CHll GFai
	visseri	SVen

Frithia (*Aizoaceae*)

	pulchra 🏆H2	LToo

Fritillaria ✿ (*Liliaceae*)

	acmopetala 🏆H4	CAvo CBro CTal CWCL ECho EPot ERCP GAbr GBuc GKev ITim LAma MNrw MPie SDeJ SDir WCot WIce
	- 'Brunette'	EPot GKev LAma
	- subsp. ***wendelboi***	ECho GKev LAma NPnk
	- - 'Zwanenburg'	GKev
	affinis	CWCL ECho GBuc GKev NHpl
	- 'Sunray'	GKev
§	- var. ***tristulis***	GKev
	- 'Vancouver Island'	LAma
	- yellow-flowered **new**	CWCL
	amana	CWCL ECho EPot ERCP GKev ITim LLHF WCot
	- 'Cambridge' 🏆H4	WCot
	- 'Goksan Gold'	ECho
	arabica	see *F. persica*
	armena	GKev
	assyriaca	EPot GBuc
	aurea	LAma
	- 'Golden Flag'	ECho EPot LAma LLHF
	ayakoana	GEdr
	'Beethoven' (Rascal Series)	GKev
	biflora	ECho
	- 'Martha Roderick'	ECho LAma SDeJ
§	***bithynica***	ECho GKev ITim LAma
	bucharica	ECho EPot GKev LAma
	- 'Nurek Giant'	ECho
	camschatcensis	CBro CWCL ECho EFEx EPfP EPot ERCP GBin GBuc GEdr GKev GMaP

		LAma LRHS NBir NHar NHpl SDeJ SDir SPhx WAbe WCot WCru
	- 'Alaska'	NHar
	- 'Aurea'	ECho GBuc NHar SPhx
	- black-flowered	CAby ECho NHar
	- double-flowered (d)	ECho GBuc
	- f. ***flavescens***	EFEx GBuc GEdr LAma
	- green-flowered	CAby
	carduchorum	see *F. minuta*
	carica	ECho EPot GKev
	'Chopin' (Rascal Series)	CAvo GKev
	citrina	see *F. bithynica*
§	***crassifolia*** subsp. ***kurdica***	ECho EPot GKev ITim
	- - 'Talish'	GKev
	davisii	ECho EPfP EPot GKev LAma LLHF WCot
	eduardii	ECho EPot GKev
	- 'Castor' new	LAma
	elwesii	CAvo ECho EPot ERCP GKev ITim LAma LLHF SDeJ SDir WTor
*	***glauca*** 'Golden Flag'	GKev LLWG
	- 'Goldilocks'	LAma SDeJ
	graeca	ECho EPot GBuc GKev LAma SDeJ
	- subsp. ***graeca***	GBuc
	hermonis	GKev
	hispanica	see *F. lusitanica*
	imperialis 🏆H6	ECGP SDir
	- 'April Flame'	LAma SDir
	- 'Argenteovariegata' (v)	GKev LAma SDir
	- 'Aureomarginata' (v)	GKev LAma SDir
	- 'Aurora'	EPot ERCP GKev GMcL LAma LRHS NLar NPer SDeJ SDir SPhx WFar
	- 'Early Fantasy' new	LAma
	- 'Early Passion' new	LAma
	- 'Garland Star'	GKev LAma LSun NLar
	- 'Grenadier'	LAma
	- var. ***inodora***	GKev LAma
	- 'Inodora Purpurea'	LAma
	- 'Lutea'	CAvo CRos ELan ERCP GKev LAma LRHS SPoG WFar
	- 'Maxima'	see *F. imperialis* 'Rubra Maxima'
	- 'Maxima Lutea' 🏆H6	CBro ELan EPfP EPot ERCP GKev GMcL LRHS LSun NLar SDeJ SPer SPhx SPoG
	- 'Orange Beauty'	GKev LAma LRHS
	- 'Orange Brilliant'	LAma
	- 'Pollux' new	LAma
	- 'Prolifera'	GKev LAma SDeJ
	- 'Rubra'	CBod EPfP ERCP GKev LAma NLar SPer WFar
§	- 'Rubra Maxima'	CBro ELan EPfP EPot ERCP GKev GMcL LRHS SDeJ
	- 'Slagzwaard'	GKev LAma
	- 'Striped Beauty'	EPot GKev LAma LSun SDeJ
	- 'Sulpherino'	GKev LAma SDir
	- 'Sunset'	LAma SDir
	- 'The Premier'	GKev LAma SDeJ
	- 'William Rex'	CAvo CRos EPot ERCP GKev LAma LBuc LRHS LSun SDeJ SPhx SPoG
	involucrata	ECho WCot
	japonica	EFEx
	var. ***koidzumiana***	
	karadaghensis	see *F. crassifolia* subsp. *kurdica*
	kotschyana	ECho GKev
	lanceolata	see *F. affinis* var. *tristulis*
	latakiensis	ECho EPot GKev
§	***lusitanica***	ITim
	'Mahler' (Rascal Series) new	GKev
	meleagris 🏆H5	Widely available
	- 'Artemis'	GBuc

	- var. ***unicolor*** subvar. ***alba*** 🏆H5	CAby CAvo CBro ECho ERCP GBuc GKev IBoy LCro LLWG LOPS MWat NHol SCob SDeJ SPer SPhx WShi
	- - - 'Aphrodite'	EPot NBir
	messanensis	GKev
	subsp. ***gracilis***	
	michailovskyi	CAby CHid CRos CTri ECho EPfP EPot ERCP GBuc GKev LAma LHop LRHS MNrw NHpl NPnk NRHS SDeJ SDir SRms WFar
	- 'Multiflorum' new	GKev IBoy
	minima	ECho
§	***minuta***	ECho EPot ERCP GKev LAma NPnk SDeJ
	montana	ECho GKev
	muraiana	GEdr
	nigra Mill.	see *F. pyrenaica*
	olivieri	ECho
	pallidiflora 🏆H5	CBro ECho EPot ERCP GBuc GCra GKev LAma NBir NHpl NPnk SDeJ SPhx
§	***persica***	ECha ECho EPfP EPot ERCP GKev LAma LHop LRHS NNys NPnk SCob SPhx
	- 'Adiyaman' 🏆H4	ELan SDeJ
	- 'Alba'	GKev SDeJ
	- 'Chocolate'	CWCL
	- 'Ivory Bells'	ECho ELan EPot ERCP GKev LAma SDeJ SKHP SPhx
	- 'Ivory Queen'	CBro
	- 'Midnight Bells'	ECho GKev
	- 'Pastel' new	GKev
*	- 'Senkoy'	GKev
	pinardii	ECho EPot GKev LAma
	- 'Ole Sonderhause'	ECho
	pontica 🏆H4	CAvo CBro CWCL ECho EPot ERCP GBuc GKev ITim LAma NHpl SDeJ
	pudica	ECho LAma
*	- 'Fragrant'	ECho
	- 'Giant'	ECho EPot SDeJ
	purdyi	ECho
§	***pyrenaica*** 🏆H5	ECho GCra LAma LLHF
	raddeana	ECho EPot ERCP GBin GKev LAma SDeJ SPhx WCot
	reuteri	ECho EPot GKev LAma
	roylei 'Lowndes' Variety' new	GKev
	rubra major	see *F. imperialis* 'Rubra Maxima'
	ruthenica	ECho GKev
	sewerzowii	ECho EPot GKev LAma
	- 'Brown Eyes'	GKev
	- brown-flowered new	GKev
	shikokiana	GEdr
	stenanthera	ECho EPot GKev LAma
	thunbergii	CTal ECho GKev LAma LLHF WCot
	uva-vulpis	CAby CMea CRos CTca ECho ECtt ELon EPfP EPot ERCP GKev GWyn LAma LHop LLWG LRHS MNrw NBir NPri NRHS SDeJ SDir WFar
	verticillata	CBro ECha LAma WCot WCru
	whittallii	ECho EPot GKev LAma

Fuchsia ✿ (*Onagraceae*)

'A.M. Larwick'	EBak SLBF SRiF
'A.W. Taylor'	EBak
'Aalt Groothuis' (d)	SRiF
'Abbé Farges' (d)	CLoc CWVF EBak EPts LHop MSmi SRiF SVic WOth
'Abbigayle Reine' (v)	SRiF
'Abigail' ambig.	CWVF SRiF

'Achievement' ♀H4	CLoc LCla MJac MSmi SRiF SVic
'Adinda' (T) ♀H1c	EPts LCla SRiF
'Adriaan van Bylant' (d)	WOth
'Adrienne' (d)	SRiF
'Ailsa Garnett' (d)	EBak
'Aintree'	CWVF
'Airedale'	CWVF
'Ajax' (d)	SRiF
'Aladna's Sander' (d)	CWVF SRiF
'Alan Ayckbourn'	CWVF SRiF WOth
'Alan Titchmarsh' ♀H2	EPts ESps LCla SLBF SRiF
'Alaska' (d)	CLoc SRiF SVic
'Alberttina'	SRiF SVic WOth
'Albertus Schwab'	LCla
'Alde'	CWVF SRiF WOth
'Alderford'	SLBF
'Alexandra Meles'	WOth
'Alf Thornley' (d)	CWVF SRiF WOth
'Alfie' (d)	SRiF
'Alfonso' (d)	SLBF
'Alfred Rambaud' (d)	SRiF
'Alice Ashton' (d)	EBak
'Alice Blue Gown' (d)	CWVF
'Alice Doran'	LCla SRiF
'Alice Hoffman' (d) ♀H4	Widely available
'Alice Mary' (d)	SRiF
'Alice Sweetapple' (d)	CWVF SRiF
'Alicia Sellars'	SLBF
'Alisha Jade'	SRiF
'Alison Ewart'	CLoc CWVF SPet SRiF SVic
'Alison Patricia' ♀H2	CWVF EBak LCla MJac SLBF SRiF SVic WOth
'Alison Reynolds' (d)	CWVF SRiF WOth
'Alison Ruth Griffin' (d)	MJac
'Alison Ryle' (d)	EBak
'Alison Sweetman' ♀H2	CWVF MJac
'Allan Taylor'	WOth
'Allen Jackson'	LCla SLBF WOth
'Alma Hulscher' (d)	SRiF
'Aloha'	WOth
'Aloys Hetterscheid'	WOth
alpestris	EBak GCal LCla SRiF SVic
'Alsa Garnet' (d)	SRiF
'Alton Water' (d/v)	SRiF WOth
'Alwin' (d)	CWVF SRiF
'Alyce Larson' (d)	CWVF EBak MJac SRiF SVic
'Alyssa May Garcia' (d)	EPts SLBF WOth
'Amanda Bridgland' (d)	SRiF
'Amanda Jones'	SRiF
'Amaranth'	WOth
'Amazing Grace' (d)	MJac
'Amazing Maisie' (d)	MSmi SLBF SRiF WOth
'Ambassador'	SRiF SVic WOth
'Amelia Rose'	SLBF
'Amelie Aubin'	CLoc CWVF EBak SVic
'America'	CWVF
'Amerika' (d)	WOth
'Amethyst Fire' (d)	SRiF
'Amigo' ambig.	SRiF
§ ***ampliata***	LCla
'Amy'	MJac
'Amy Lye'	CLoc SVic
'Amy Ruth'	CWVF
§ 'Andenken an Heinrich Henkel' (T)	CLoc CWVF EBak SRiF SVic WOth
'André Le Nostre' (d)	CWVF EBak SRiF SVic
'Andreas Schwab'	LCla
andrei	LCla SRiF
'Andrew'	SRiF
'Andrew Carnegie' (d)	CLoc
'Andrew Hadfield'	CWVF SRiF SVic WOth
'Andrew Ryle'	SRiF
'Andromeda' De Groot	WOth
'Angela' (d)	WOth
'Angela King'	SLBF WOth
'Angela Leslie' (d)	CLoc EBak SRiF SVic
'Angela Rippon'	CWVF
'Angel's Flight' (d)	EBak SRiF
'Angel's Kiss' (E)	SLBF
'Angie Baby'	WOth
'Anhaltiner'	WOth
'Anita'	CLoc CWVF EPts MJac SLBF SRiF SVic WOth
'Anjo' (v)	CWVF SRiF WOth
'Ann Allen'	SLBF
'Ann Howard Tripp'	CLoc CWVF EPts MJac SRiF SVic
'Ann Lee' (d)	SRiF
'Anna of Longleat' (d)	CWVF MJac SPet SRiF
'Anna Sunshine' (T)	EPts SLBF
'Annabel' (d) ♀H4	CCCN CLoc CTri CWVF EBak EPts ESps LCla MJac SLBF SPet SRiF SVic WOth
'Annabelle Stubbs' (d)	SRiF
'Anne Strudwick' (d)	SRiF
'Anneke de Keijzer'	LCla WOth
'Annie den Otter'	WOth
'Annie Earle'	SRiF WOth
'Annie M.G. Schmidt'	EPts LCla WOth
'Anniek Geerlings' (T)	WOth
'Another Storey'	SRiF
'Ant and Dec' (d/v)	MJac
'Anthea Day' (d)	CLoc
'Anthony Heavens'	SRiF
'Antigone'	SLBF SRiF WOth
'Apart'	SLBF WOth
'Aphaia' **new**	WOth
'Aphrodite' (d)	CLoc CWVF SRiF
'Applause' (d)	CLoc CWVF EBak EPts SPet SRiF SVic
aprica misapplied	see *F.* × *bacillaris*
aprica Lundell	see *F. microphylla* subsp. *aprica*
'Apricot Ice'	CLoc SVic
'Aquarius'	SRiF
'Arabella'	CWVF
'Arabella Improved'	CWVF SRiF SVic
arborea	see *F. arborescens*
§ ***arborescens***	CBcs CBot CHll CLoc CWCL CWVF EBak EWld IDee LCla MCot MHer SDys SRiF SVic WHil WJek
- B&SWJ 10475	WCru
'Arcadia Gold' (d)	CWVF SRiF WOth
'Arcady'	CLoc CWVF
'Archie Owen' (d)	SRiF
'Arels Nina'	WOth
'Arels Tojo'	WOth
'Ariel' (E)	CRos LRHS NRHS SVic WOth
'Arkie'	MJac
'Arlendon' (d)	CWVF
'Army Nurse' (d) ♀H4	CLoc CRos CWCL CWVF ELan ELon EPfP EPts LRHS MGos MSmi NBir NLar NRHS SHil SLBF SPet SRiF SVic WOth
'Art Deco' (d)	SRiF
'Ashley'	LCla
'Ashley and Isobel'	CWVF SRiF
'Ashtede'	SLBF
'Ashville'	SLBF WOth
'Atahualpa'	WOth
'Athela'	SRiF
'Athene'	SRiF
'Atlantic Star'	CWVF MJac SRiF

	'Atlantis' (d)	CWVF
	'Atlas'	SRiF
	'Atomic Glow' (d)	SRiF SVic
	'Aubergine'	see *F.* 'Gerharda's Aubergine'
	'Aubrey Harris' (d)	SRiF
	'Audray'	SRiF
	'Audrey Booth' (d)	SRiF
	'Audrey Dahms'	SRiF
	'Audrey Hepburn'	CWVF
	'Auenland'	MJac
	'Aunt Juliana' (d)	SRiF
	'Auntie Jinks' ♀H2	CWVF EBak MJac SPet SRiF SVic WOth
	'Auntie Kit'	SRiF
	'Aurora Superba'	CLoc CWVF EBak SLBF SRiF
	'Australia Fair' (d)	CWVF SRiF
§	***austromontana***	SRiF
	'Autumnale' ♀H2	CLoc CWVF EBak EPts MSmi SLBF SPet SPoG SVic WOth
	'Avalanche' ambig. (d)	CLoc EBak SLBF
	'Avalanche' Henderson (d)	WOth
	'Avocet'	CLoc SRiF
	'Avon Celebration' (d/v)	CLoc WOth
	'Avon Gem'	CLoc SRiF
	'Avon Glow' (d)	CLoc
	'Avon Gold'	CLoc
	'Awake Sweet Love' (T)	EPts
	ayavacensis	LCla
	'Aylisa Rowan' (E)	SLBF
	'Azure Sky' (d)	MJac WOth
	'Babette' (d)	SRiF
	'Baby Blue Eyes' ♀H4	CLoc CRos CWVF ELan ELon EPfP ESps LRHS LSRN MAsh NRHS SLBF SVic WOth
	'Baby Bright'	CWVF LCla SRiF
	'Baby Brooke'	WOth
	'Baby Chang'	SRiF WOth
	'Baby Face' ambig.	SRiF
	'Baby Love'	SRiF
	'Baby Pink' (d)	CWVF
	'Baby Thumb' (v)	EPts SRiF
	'Babyface' Tolley (d)	SVic
§	× ***bacillaris*** (E)	CAbb CHGN EWes GCal LRHS SEle SLBF SPoG XLum
§	- 'Cottinghamii' (E)	EWld ILea WOth WSHC
§	- 'Reflexa' (E)	CAbP CCCN LSou WOth
	'Baden Powell' (E)	SRiF SVic
	'Bagworthy Water'	CLoc
	'Baker's Tri' (T)	EBak
	'Balkonkönigin'	CLoc CWVF SRiF
	'Ballerina Girl' (E)	SLBF
	'Ballet Girl' (d) ♀H2	CLoc CWVF EBak SLBF SRiF
	'Balmoral' (d)	SRiF
	'Bambini'	CWVF EPts SLBF SRiF
	'Banks Peninsula'	GQui
	'Barbara'	CLoc CWVF EBak EPts LCla MJac SPet SRiF SVic WOth
	'Barbara Evans'	SLBF SRiF
	'Barbara Pountain' (d)	CWVF
	'Barbara Reynolds'	WOth
	'Barbara Windsor'	CWVF MJac MSmi SRiF
	'Baron de Ketteler' (d)	SRiF
	'Barry's Queen'	see *F.* 'Golden Border Queen'
	'Bashful' (d)	EPts LCla SPet SRiF SVic
	'Basketfull' (d)	SRiF
	'Beacon'	CLoc CMac CRos CWVF EBak EPfP EPts ESps LCla LRHS MJac NRHS SLBF SPet SPoG SRiF SVic
	'Beacon Rosa' ♀H4	CLoc CRos CWVF ELon EPfP EPts LCla LRHS MJac NRHS SLBF SPet SPoG SRiF SVic
	'Bealings' (d)	CWVF SRiF SVic
	'Beauty of Bath' (d)	CLoc
	'Beauty of Bexley' (d)	SRiF
	'Beauty of Clyffe Hall' Lye	EBak WOth
	'Beauty of Exeter' (d)	CWVF EBak SRiF WOth
	'Beauty of Prussia' (d)	CLoc CWVF
	'Beauty of Purbeck' (d)	WOth
	'Beauty of Swanley'	SRiF
	'Beauty of Trowbridge'	CWVF LCla WOth
	'Beckey' (d)	SRiF
	'Beckie Lou' PBR	EBee
	'Beebop'	MSmi
	'Belinda Jane'	WOth
	'Bella Forbes' (d) ♀H2	MSmi
	'Bella Harris' (d)	SRiF
	'Bella Rosella' (California	CLoc EPts MJac MSmi SCoo SLBF
	Dreamers Series) (d) ♀H2	SRiF
	'Bellbottoms'	SRiF
	'Belle de Spa'	SRiF
	'Belsay Beauty' (d)	CWVF MJac SRiF
	'Belvoir Beauty' (d)	CLoc
	'Ben de Jong'	LCla SLBF SRiF
	'Ben Jammin'	CLoc CRos CWVF EPfP EPts LRHS MSmi NRHS SRiF SVic WOth
	'Ben Jiggins' (d)	SRiF
	'Ben-Ben'	SLBF
	'Beninkust'	WOth
	'Berba's Happiness' (d)	CWVF
	'Berba's Trio'	SRiF WOth
	'Berliner Kind' (d)	CWVF EBak SRiF
	'Bermuda' (d)	CWVF SRiF
	'Bernadette' (d)	CWVF
	'Bernie's Big-un' (d)	MJac SLBF
	'Bernisser Hardy' ♀H4	EPts LCla SAko SLBF SLim SRiF WOth XLum
	'Beryl's Choice' (d)	SRiF
	'Berys Elizabeth'	SRiF
	'Bessie Kimberley' (T)	LCla
	'Beth Robley' (d)	CWVF SRiF
	'Betsy Huuskes'	SLBF
	'Bette Sibley' (d)	SRiF
	'Beverley'	CWVF EBak EPts SRiF
	'Beverley Hills' (d)	WOth
	'Bianca' (d)	CWVF SRiF SVic
	'Bicentennial' (d)	CLoc CWVF EBak EPts MJac MSmi SPet SRiF SVic
	'Big Slim'	SRiF WOth
	'Bill Gilbert'	SRiF
	'Billy Green' (T) ♀H2	CLoc CWVF EBak EPts LCla MHer MJac MSmi SRiF SVic
	'Bishop's Bells' (d)	CWVF SVic
	'Bittersweet' (d)	SVic
	'Black Beauty' (d)	CWVF
	'Black Prince'	CWVF SRiF SVic WOth
	'Black to the Future'	WOth
	'Blackmore Vale' (d)	CWVF
	'Blacky' (d)	CCCN EBak EUJe GBin SDix SDys SEND SPet SRiF SVic
I	'Blanche Regina' (d)	CWVF MJac
	'Bland's New Striped'	EBak EPts LSou MSmi SLBF SRiF WOth
§	'Blauer Engel' (d)	MJac WOth
	'Blaze Away' (d)	MJac SRiF
	'Blood Donor' (d)	MJac SRiF
	'Blowick'	CWVF MJac SPet SRiF WOth
	Blue Angel	see *F.* 'Blauer Engel'
	'Blue Beauty' (d)	SRiF
	'Blue Bush'	CWVF EPts MJac SRiF SVic WOth XLum
	'Blue Butterfly' (d)	CWVF SRiF
	'Blue Eyes' (d)	SPet SRiF

'Blue Gown' (d)	CLoc CWVF EBak MSmi SRiF SVic
'Blue Lace' (d)	SVic
'Blue Lagoon' ambig. (d)	CWVF
'Blue Lake' (d)	CWVF
'Blue Mink'	SRiF
'Blue Mirage' (d)	CLoc CWVF SRiF SVic
'Blue Pearl' (d)	CWVF EBak SRiF
'Blue Pinwheel'	CWVF EBak
'Blue Sails'	SRiF
'Blue Satin' (d)	WOth
'Blue Sleighbells'	WOth
'Blue Tit'	LCla SRiF
'Blue Veil' (d)	CLoc CWVF MJac SCoo SRiF SVic WOth
'Blue Waves' (d)	CLoc CSBt CWVF EBak MJac SRiF SVic
'Blueberry Fizz' (d)	SRiF
'Blush o' Dawn' (d)	CLoc EBak MSmi SLBF SRiF SVic
'Blythe' (d)	SRiF
'Bob Pacey'	CWVF
'Bob Paisley' (d)	SRiF
'Bobby Dazzler' (d)	CWVF SRiF
'Bobby Shaftoe' (d)	EBak SRiF
'Bobby Wingrove'	EBak
'Bobby's Girl'	EPts
'Bobolink' (d)	EBak SRiF
'Bob's Best' (d)	CWVF EPts SRiF
'Boerhaave'	SRiF
boliviana Britton	see *F. sanctae-rosae*
boliviana ambig.	CBcs MHer
§ ***boliviana*** Carrière	CHll CLoc CWVF LCla SRiF WOth
§ - var. ***alba*** ♀H2	CHll CLoc EBak EPts LCla SRiF SVic WOth
- var. ***boliviana***	CRHN SVic
- var. ***luxurians*** 'Alba'	see *F. boliviana* Carrière var. *alba*
- f. ***puberulenta*** Munz	see *F. boliviana* Carrière
'Bon Accorde'	CLoc CWVF EBak EPts SLBF SRiF
'Bon Bon' (d)	CWVF SRiF SVic
'Bonita' (d)	CWVF SVic
'Bonnie Bambini'	SRiF
'Bonnie Lass' (d)	EBak
'Boogie'	MSmi
'Bora Bora' (d)	CWVF SRiF SVic
'Borde Hill' (d)	EPts
'Border Princess'	EBak SRiF
'Border Queen' ♀H4	CLoc CWVF EBak EPts MJac SLBF SRiF SVic WOth
'Border Reiver'	CWVF SVic
'Börnemann's Beste'	see *F.* 'Georg Börnemann'
'Bosom Pals'	SRiF
'Boson's Norah'	SRiF
'Bouffant'	CLoc SVic
'Bountiful' Lye	SRiF
'Bountiful' Munkner (d)	CLoc CWVF
'Bouquet' (d)	SLBF SRiF
'Bow Bells'	CLoc CWVF MJac SPet SRiF SVic WOth
'Boy Marc' (T) ♀H1c	LCla SRiF
'Brancaster'	SRiF
'Brandt's 500 Club'	CLoc SRiF
'Brann's Blossom'	SRiF
'Breakaway'	SRiF
'Breckland'	EBak SRiF
'Breeders' Delight'	CWVF SRiF
'Breeder's Dream' (d)	EBak
'Breevis Minimus'	SLBF
'Brenda' (d)	CWVF
'Brenda Megan Hill'	SRiF
'Brenda Pritchard' (d)	SRiF
'Brenda White'	CLoc CWVF EBak SRiF SVic WOth
'Brian C. Morrison' (T)	LCla SRiF
'Brian G. Soanes'	EBak SRiF
'Brian Kimberley' (T)	LCla
'Brian McFetridge' (d)	WOth
'Bridal Pink' (d)	SRiF
'Bridal Veil' (d)	SRiF
'Bridesmaid' (d)	CWVF EBak SRiF SVic
'Brighton Belle' (T)	CWVF SRiF
'Brilliant' ambig.	CWVF
'Brilliant' Bull, 1865	CLoc EBak LCla
'British Jubilee' (d)	CWVF SVic WOth
'British Sterling' (d)	SRiF WOth
'Brixham Orpheus'	CWVF
'Broadbent' (d)	SRiF
'Bromley Beauty' **new**	MJac
'Brookwood Belle' (d) ♀H3	CWVF EPts LCla MJac SLBF SRiF
'Brookwood Joy' (d)	CWVF SRiF
'Brutus' ♀H4	CLet CLoc CRos CWVF EBak EPfP EPts LRHS MAsh MSmi NRHS SCoo SLBF SPet SRiF SVic WFar WOth
'Bryan Breary' (E)	LCla SRiF WOth
'Bubble Hanger'	SRiF
'Buddha' (d)	EBak
'Bugle Boy'	LCla SRiF
'Bunny' (d)	CWVF ESps SRiF SVic
'Burgundy Velvet'	WOth
'Buster' (d)	LCla SRiF
'Buttercup'	CLoc CWVF SRiF SVic
'Butterfly Dance'	SLBF WOth
'C.J. Howlett'	EBak SRiF
'Cabaret' (d)	SRiF
'Cable Car' (d)	SRiF
'Caesar' (d)	CWVF EBak SRiF
'Caledonia'	SRiF WOth
'Callaly Pink'	CWVF
'Calverley'	WOth
'Cambridge Louie'	CWVF EBak SPet SRiF WOth
'Camelot'	SRiF
campos-portoi	CFil LCla MGil WOth WPGP
'Candy Bells' (d)	CSBt
'Candy Kisses' (d)	SRiF
canescens misapplied	see *F. ampliata*
'Cannell's Gem'	SRiF
'Cannenburgh Floriant' (d)	SRiF
'Canny Bob'	MJac WOth
'Canopy' (d)	CWVF
'Capri' (d)	CWVF SRiF
'Captivating Kelly'	SRiF
'Cara Mia' (d)	CLoc SPet SRiF
'Caradela' (d)	CLoc MJac
'Cardinal'	CLoc SRiF
'Cardinal Farges' (d)	CLoc CWVF SLBF SRiF SVic
'Careless Whisper'	LCla SLBF WOth
'Carisbrooke Castle' (d)	SRiF
'Carl Drude' (d)	SRiF SVic
'Carl Wallace' (d)	SRiF
'Carla Johnston' ♀H2	CLoc CWVF EPts MJac SVic WOth
'Carl's Brummagem Beauty'	MJac
'Carmel Blue'	CCCN CLoc LCla SRiF SVic
'Carnea'	CWib
'Carnival' (d)	SRiF
'Carnoustie' (d)	EBak
'Carol Grace' (d)	CLoc
'Carol Lynn Whittemore' (d)	SRiF
'Carol Nash' (d)	CLoc
'Caroline'	CLoc CWVF EBak EPts SLBF SRiF SVic WOth
'Caroline's Joy'	MJac SCoo SPet SRiF
'Cascade'	CLoc CWVF EPts ESps MJac SLBF SPet SRiF
'Caspar Hauser' (d)	CWVF SLBF SRiF SVic

'Catharina' (T)	SRiF
'Catherine Bartlett'	CWVF
'Cecil Glass'	SRiF WOth
'Cecile' (d)	CCCN CWVF EPts LCla MJac MSmi SLBF SRiF SVic
'Celadore' (d)	CWVF SRiF
'Celebration' (d)	CLoc CWVF SRiF
'Celia Smedley' ♀H3	CLoc CRos CWVF EBak EPts LCla LRHS MJac NRHS SLBF SPet SRiF SVic WBod WOth
'Centenary' (d)	SRiF
'Centerpiece' (d)	EBak
'Ceri'	CLoc
'Cerrig'	SVic
'Chameleon'	SRiF
'Champagne Celebration'	CLoc WOth
'Champagne Gold'	SRiF
'Champion'	SRiF WOth XLum
'Chandleri'	CWVF SRiF SVic
'Chang' ♀H2	CLoc CWVF EBak LCla SLBF SRiF SVic WOth
'Chantelle Garcia' (d)	EPts MJac SLBF WOth
'Chantry Park' (T)	LCla SRiF
'Chapel Rossan' (E)	SLBF
'Charisma'	SVic
'Charles Edward' (d)	SRiF
'Charles Lester'	SRiF
'Charles Welch'	EPts
Charlie Dimmock = 'Foncha'PBR (d)	CLoc SRiF
'Charlie Gardiner'	CWVF EBak
'Charlie Girl' (d)	SRiF SVic
'Charlie Pridmore' (d)	SRiF
'Charlotte'	SRiF
'Charlotte Clyne'	SRiF
'Charming'	CLoc CRos CWVF EPfP LRHS MAsh MJac NRHS SVic WOth XLum
'Chartwell'	WOth
'Chatt's Delight'	SLBF
'Checkerboard' ♀H3	CLoc CWVF EBak EPts LCla MHer MJac MSmi SLBF SPet SVic WOth
'Cheers' (d)	CWVF
'Chelsea Louise'	EPts
'Chenois Godelieve'	SEND
'Cherry Lee'	SLBF WOth
'Chessboard'	CLoc
'Chillerton Beauty' ♀H4	CLoc CRos CTri CWVF ELan ELon EPts LCla LRHS MJac NLar NRHS SEND SLBF SPer SPet SVic WOth
'Chilli Red'	EPts
'China Doll' (d)	CWVF SRiF
'China Lantern'	CLoc CWVF MSmi SRiF SVic
'Chomal' (d)	SRiF
'Chor Echo'	SLBF WOth
'Chris Bright'	MJac
'Chris Coleman'	SRiF
'Chris Tarrant' (d)	EPts
'Christina Becker'	SRiF SVic
'Christine Bamford'	CWVF SRiF
'Christine Truman' (d)	SRiF
'Christmas Ribbons' (d)	MSmi
'Churchtown'	CWVF SRiF
'Cicely Ann'	SRiF
cinerea	LCla
'Cinnabarina' (E)	CLoc SRiF SVic WOth
'Cinnamon' (d)	SRiF
'Cinque Port Liberty' (d)	SRiF
'Cinvenu'	LCla
'Cinvulca'	LCla
'Circe' (d)	CWVF
'Circus Spangles' (d)	CLoc
'Citation'	CLoc CWVF EBak SVic
'City of Adelaide' (d)	CLoc SRiF
'City of Leicester'	CWVF SPet
'Clair de Lune'	CWVF EBak SLBF SRiF SVic
'Claire Oram'	CLoc
'Claudia' (d)	LCla MJac SLBF
'Cliantha' (d)	SRiF
'Clifford Gadsby' (d)	SRiF
'Cliff's Hardy'	LCla MSmi SRiF SVic
'Cliff's Own'	SVic
'Cliff's Unique' (d)	CWVF EPts
'Clifton Beauty' (d)	CWVF MJac SRiF
'Clifton Belle' (d)	CWVF
'Clifton Charm'	EPts LCla MJac SVic
'Clipper'	CWVF WOth
'Cloth of Gold'	CLoc CWVF EBak MJac SLBF SPet SRiF SVic WOth
'Cloverdale Jewel' (d)	CWVF MSmi SPet SRiF SVic WOth
'Cloverdale Joy'	SRiF
'Cloverdale Pearl'	CWVF EBak MSmi SPet SPoG SVic WOth
'Coachman' ♀H4	CLoc CWVF EBak EPts LCla MSmi SLBF SRiF SVic WOth
coccinea	CTsd WOth
'Codex' (d) **new**	SLBF
× ***colensoi***	LCla
* - var. ***purpurascens***	WOth
'Colibri'	SRiF
'Colin Chambers' (d)	SRiF
'Collingwood' (d)	CLoc CWVF SRiF WOth
'Colne Fantasy' (v)	SRiF
'Come Dancing' (d)	CWVF SPet SRiF SVic
'Comet' ambig.	SRiF
'Comet' Banks	CWVF
I 'Comet' Tiret (d)	CLoc
'Conchetta Garcia'	SLBF
'Conchilla' (d)	SRiF
'Connie' (d)	EBak SRiF SVic XLum
'Connor's Cascade'	SLBF
'Conspicua' ♀H4	CWVF LRHS SLBF SRiF SVic WOth
'Constable Country' (d)	CWVF SRiF
'Constance' (d)	CLoc CWVF LCla MJac MSmi SLBF SPet SRiF SVic
'Constance Comer'	MJac SRiF
'Constellation' ambig.	CWVF
'Constellation' Schnabel, 1957 (d)	CLoc EBak
'Continental' (d)	SRiF
'Coquet Bell'	CWVF EBak SRiF
'Coquet Dale' (d)	CWVF SRiF
'Coquet Gold' (d/v)	SRiF
'Coral Baby' (E)	LCla SLBF
'Coral Rose' (d)	SVic
'Coralle' (T) ♀H1c	CCCN CLoc CWVF EBak EPts LCla MJac MSmi SLBF SRiF SVic WOth
'Corallina' ♀H4	CLoc MMuc SEND SRiF SVic WOth WPnn
* ***cordata*** B&SWJ 9095	WCru
- B&SWJ 10325	WCru
cordifolia misapplied	see *F. splendens*
'Core'ngrato' (d)	CLoc CWVF SRiF
'Cornelia Smith' (T)	LCla
'Cornish Blue' **new**	CLoc
'Cornwall Calls' (d)	EBak
'Coronation' (d)	SRiF WOth
'Corsage' (d)	CWVF SVic
'Corsair' (d)	EBak SRiF SVic
corymbiflora misapplied	see *F. boliviana* Carrière
corymbiflora Ruíz & Pav.	SVic

'Cosmopolitan' (d)	SRiF
'Costa Brava'	CLoc
'Cotta Bright Star'	CWVF LCla
'Cotta Carousel'	LCla
'Cotta Christmas Tree'	LCla SLBF SRiF
'Cotta Fairy'	CWVF
'Cotta Vino'	SRiF SVic
'Cottinghamii'	see *F.* × ***bacillaris*** 'Cottinghamii'
'Cotton Candy' (d)	CLoc CWVF SRiF SVic
'Countdown Carol' (d)	EPts
'Countess of Aberdeen'	CWVF EBak SLBF SRiF WOth
'Countess of Maritza' (d)	CLoc CWVF
'Court Jester' (d)	CLoc SRiF
'Cover Girl' (d)	EPts SRiF
'Coxeen'	EBak WOth
I 'Cracker' (d)	SRiF
'Crackerjack'	CLoc SRiF
'Creampuff' (d)	SRiF
'Crescendo' (d)	CLoc CWVF
'Crinkley Bottom' (d)	EPts MJac SLBF SRiF
'Crinoline' (d)	SRiF
'Crosby Serendipity'	CLoc
'Crosby Soroptimist'	CWVF SRiF WOth
'Cross Check'	CWVF
'Crusader' (d)	CWVF SRiF
'Crystal Aniversary' (d)	SRiF
'Crystal Blue'	EBak SRiF SVic
'Crystal Stars' (d)	SVic
'Cumbrian Lass'	WOth
'Cupid'	EBak
'Curly Q'	EBak SRiF SVic
'Curtain Call' (d)	CWVF EBak SRiF SVic
cylindracea misapplied	see *F.* × ***bacillaris***
cylindracea Lindl. (E)	SRiF
'Cymon' (d)	CWVF SRiF
'Cymru' (d)	SVic
'Cyndy Robyn' (d)	SRiF
'Cyril Holmes'	SRiF
'Dainty'	EBak
'Dainty Lady' (d)	EBak WOth
'Daisy Bell'	CLoc CWVF EBak LCla MJac SPet SRiF SVic WOth
'Dana Samantha'	EPts
'Dancing Bloom'	EPts SRiF
'Dancing Flame' (d) 🏆H3	CLoc CWVF EBak EPts LCla MJac SLBF SRiF SVic
'Daniel Pfaller' (d)	MJac
'Daniel Smith' (d) **new**	SRiF
'Danielle'	SRiF
'Danish Pastry'	CWVF SPet SRiF
'Danny Boy' (d)	CLoc CWVF EBak SRiF SVic
'Danson Belle' (d)	SRiF
'Darenth Pride' (d) **new**	SRiF
'Darenth Treasure' (d) **new**	SRiF
'Dark and Delicious' (Mojo Series)	MSmi WOth
'Dark Eyes' (d) 🏆H4	CCCN CLoc CWVF EBak MJac SLBF SPer SPet SRiF SVic WOth
'Dark Mystery' (d)	SRiF WOth
'Dark Secret' (d)	EBak
'Dark Treasure' (d)	SRiF
'Daryn John Woods'	ECre LCla WOth
'David' 🏆H4	CLoc CWVF ELon EPfP EPts LCla LSRN MJac SEND SLBF SPoG SRiF WHil WOth
'David Alston' (d)	CLoc CWVF
'David Lockyer' (d)	CLoc CWVF SVic
'David Savage' (d)	LCla
'Dawn'	SRiF
'Dawn Carless' (d)	SRiF
'Dawn Fantasia' (v)	CLoc EPts SRiF
'Dawn Redfern' (d)	CWVF
'Dawn Star' (d)	CLoc CWVF SVic WOth
'Dawn Thunder' (d)	SVic
'Daytime Live'	SRiF
'De Berckt'	SRiF
'De Groot's Dream'	WOth
'De Groot's Floriant'	LCla
'De Groot's Moonlight'	SRiF
'De Groot's Tricolore'	SRiF
'Deal Marine' (d)	SRiF
'Debby' (d)	EBak SRiF
'Deben Petite' (E)	LCla
'Deben Rose'	SRiF
'Deborah Jane'	SLBF WOth
'Deborah Louise'	SRiF
'Deborah Street' (d)	CLoc
'DebRon's Beau Dean Richard'	WOth
'DebRon's Black Cherry'	SLBF
'DebRon's Party Girls'	WOth
'DebRon's Snow Fairy'	WOth
'DebRon's Tonii Nicole' (d)	WOth
'DebRon's White Linen' (d)	WOth
'Dee Copley' (d)	EBak
'Deep Purple' (d)	CLoc MJac SCoo SLBF SRiF
'Delia Smith' (d)	EPts
'Delicate Purple'	EPts WOth
'Delilah' (d)	CWVF
'Delphobe'	EPts WOth
'Delta's Bride'	SLBF
'Delta's Dream'	CWVF SRiF WOth
'Delta's Drop'	SRiF SVic
'Delta's Fellow'	WOth
'Delta's Groom'	LCla SLBF SRiF
'Delta's Ko' (d)	SRiF SVic
'Delta's Paljas'	SRiF
'Delta's Parade' (d)	SRiF WOth
'Delta's Pim'	SRiF
'Delta's Prelude'	SRiF
'Delta's Rien'	SRiF
'Delta's Sara'	CRos ELon EPfP EShb IDee LBuc LCro LRHS MJac NRHS SHil SLim SLon SPoG SRiF WBor WFar WHar WOth
'Delta's Song'	SRiF
'Delta's Sprinkler'	SRiF
'Delta's Symphonie' (d)	CWVF
'Delta's Trick'	SRiF
'Delta's Wonder'	SRiF SVic
§ ***denticulata*** 🏆H2	CBot CLoc CRos CWVF EBak EPts LCla LRHS MHer NRHS SLBF SRiF SVic WBod WOth
'Derby Imp'	CWVF SRiF
'Derrick's Folly' **new**	WOth
'Desperate Daniel'	EPts
'Deutsche Perle'	WOth
'Devonshire Dumpling' (d) 🏆H2	CCCN CLoc CWVF EBak EPts MJac MSmi SLBF SPet SRiF SVic
'Dharlah' (T)	SLBF WOth
'Diablo' (d)	EBak SRiF
'Diament'	SRiF
'Diamond Celebration' (d)	SRiF WOth
'Diamond Wedding'	SRiF SVic WOth
'Diana' (d)	SRiF
'Diana Simpson'	SRiF
'Diana Wills' (d)	CWVF
'Diana Wright'	SRiF
Diana, Princess of Wales = 'Fucdpw'^{PBR}	MSmi

'Diane Brown'	CWVF
'Diane Stephens'	SLBF
'Dick Swinbank' (d)	SRiF
§ 'Die Schöne Wilhelmine'	SVic
'Dilly-Dilly' (d)	CWVF SRiF
'Dimples' (d)	SRiF
'Dipton Dainty' (d)	CLoc EBak SRiF SVic
'Display' ♀H4	CLoc CRos CWVF EBak EPfP EPts LCla LRHS MAsh MGos MJac NPer NRHS SHil SLBF SPet SPoG SRiF SVic WHar
'Diva'	WCot
'Do Little' **new**	SRiF
'Doc'	EPts SPet SRiF SVic
'Docteur Topinard'	CLoc
'Doctor'	see *F.* 'The Doctor'
'Doctor Becky Reynolds' (d)	SRiF
'Doctor Foster' ♀H4	CLoc CTri EBak MSmi SPoG SRiF SVic
'Doctor Mason'	CWVF
'Doctor Olson' (d)	CLoc SRiF
'Doctor Robert'	CWVF EPts MJac SRiF
'Dodo'	LCla SLBF
'Doffie'	WOth
§ 'Dollar Prinzessin' (d) ♀H4	CLoc CMac CRos CWVF EBak EPfP EPts EShb LCla LRHS MAsh MGos MJac MSmi NPer NRHS SHil SLBF SLim SPet SPlb SRiF SVic WFar
'Dolly Harris'	SRiF
'Dominyana'	EBak LCla
'Dopy' (d)	EPts SPet SRiF SVic
'Doray'	EPts WOth
'Doreen Redfern'	CLoc CWVF MJac SPet SRiF SVic
'Doreen Stroud' (d)	CWVF
'Dorian Brogdale'	SRiF
'Doris Coleman' (d)	SRiF
'Doris Joan'	SLBF SRiF WOth
'Doris Yvonne' (d)	SRiF
'Dorking Blue' (d)	SRiF
'Dorking Delight'	SRiF
'Dorothea Flower'	CLoc CWVF EBak SRiF WOth
'Dorothy'	EPts LCla SLBF SRiF
'Dorothy Ann'	LCla SLBF
'Dorothy Cheal'	CWVF
'Dorothy Day' (d)	CLoc
'Dorothy Hanley' (d)	CCCN CLoc ELon EPts LSou MAsh MJac SLBF SPet SRiF SVic WOth
'Dorothy Shields' (d)	CWVF MJac SRiF WOth
'Dorrian Brogdale' (T)	LCla
'Dorset Abigail'	CWVF
'Dorset Delight' (d)	CWVF SRiF
'Dot Woodage'	SRiF
'Dovercourt Pride'	SRiF
'Drake 400' (d)	CLoc
'Drama Girl' (d)	CWVF SRiF
'Drame' (d)	CWVF EBak MSmi SRiF SVic WHea
'Duchess of Albany'	CLoc SRiF WOth
'Duchess of Cornwall' (d)	EPts SRiF
'Duet' (d)	SRiF SVic
'Duke of Wellington' Haag, 1956 (d)	CLoc
'Dulcie Elizabeth' (d)	CWVF EBak MJac SPet SRiF
'Dunrobin Bedder'	SLBF
'Dusky Beauty'	CWVF SRiF SVic
'Dusky Blue'	SRiF
'Dusky Rose' (d)	CLoc CWVF EBak MJac SVic
'Dusted Pink' (d)	SRiF
'Dutch Flamingo'	SRiF
'Dutch Mill'	CLoc CWVF EBak SRiF
'Dutch Shoes' (d)	SRiF

'Duyfken'	CWVF SRiF
'Dying Embers'	CLoc MHer MSCN SVen WOth
'Dymph Werker van Groenland' (E)	LCla
'Earre Barré'	SLBF SRiF
'East Anglian'	CLoc SRiF WOth
'Easter Belle'	CRos LRHS NRHS
'Easter Bonnet' (d)	CLoc CWVF
'Ebb 'n' Flow'	EBak SRiF
'Ebbtide' (d)	CLoc
'Echo'	CWVF SRiF WOth
'Ed Largarde' (d)	EBak SRiF
'Edale'	MSmi
'Ede Staal' **new**	WOth
'Eden'	SRiF
'Eden Lady'	CLoc SPet SRiF
'Eden Princess'	CWVF MJac
'Eden Rock' (d)	CLoc MSmi WOth
'Edie Lester'	SRiF
'Edith' ambig.	EPts
'Edith' Banks	SRiF
'Edith' Brown (d)	LCla SLBF
'Edith Emery' (d)	SPet SRiF
'Edna May'	CWVF
'Edna W. Smith'	CWVF
'Eisleban'	SRiF
'El Camino' (d)	CWVF SRiF
'El Cid'	CLoc EBak SRiF SVic
'Elaine Ann'	EPts MJac
'Elaine Taylor' (d)	MJac
'Elburg's Minibel' **new**	WOth
'Eleanor Clark'	WOth
'Eleanor Grace'	WOth
'Eleanor Leytham'	CWVF EBak SRiF SVic WOth
'Eleanor Rawlins'	SRiF
Electric Lights = 'Nufu1'PBR	EPts
'Elfin Glade'	CLoc CWVF EBak SRiF SVic
'Elfrida' (d)	MSmi
'Elfriede Ott' (T) ♀H1c	CLoc EBak LCla SRiF
'Eliza' (d) **new**	SRiF
'Elizabeth' ambig.	SRiF
'Elizabeth' Whiteman, 1941	WOth
'Elizabeth Honnorine'	SVic
'Ellen Morgan' (d)	CWVF SRiF
'Ellen White' (d)	SRiF
'Elma'	LCla MJac
'Elsa' (d)	CWVF SRiF SVic
'Elsie Maude' (d)	SRiF
'Elsie Mitchell' (d)	CWVF SPet SRiF
'Elsie Vert' (d)	SRiF
'Elsstar' (d)	SRiF
'Elysée'	SRiF
§ 'Emile de Wildeman' (d)	CWVF SPet SRiF
'Emile Zola'	SRiF
'Emily'	WOth
'Emily Austen'	CWVF SRiF
'Emily Bright'	SRiF
'Emily Eve' (d) **new**	MJac SLBF WOth
'Emma Alice' (d)	CWVF
'Emma Louise' (d)	SRiF
'Emma Margaret'	SRiF
'Emma Massey'	SRiF
'Empress of Prussia' ♀H4	CLoc CWVF EBak EPts MSmi SLBF SRiF SVic WOth
'Enchanted' (d)	CWVF
encliandra subsp. ***encliandra*** (E)	WOth
§ 'Enfant Prodigue' (d)	CLoc SDix SLBF SPet SRiF SVic XLum
'English Rose' (d)	CWVF

'Enstone'	see *F. magellanica* var. *molinae* 'Enstone'
'Eppsii'	SLBF
'Eric's Majestic' (d)	MJac SRiF
'Erik'	WOth
'Erika Köth' (T)	SRiF
'Ernest Rankin'	SRiF SVic
'Ernie'PBR	EPts SLBF
'Ernie Bromley'	CWVF SRiF WOth
'Ernie Wise' (d)	SCoo SRiF
'Eroica'	SVic
'Eruption'	CLoc MCot
'Estelle Marie'	CLoc CWVF EBak SPet SRiF SVic
'Eternal Flame' (d)	CWVF EBak EPts SRiF SVic
'Ethel May' (d)	MJac
'Ethel May Lester' (d)	SRiF
'Eureka Red' (California Dreamers Series) (d)	SRiF
'Eusebia' (d)	SRiF SVic
'Eva Boerg' 🏆H4	CCCN CLoc CTri CWVF EBak ESps SPet SRiF SVic WKif
'Evelyn Stanley' (d)	CWVF
§ 'Evelyn Steele Little'	SRiF
'Evening Sky' (d)	SRiF
'Evensong'	CLoc CWVF EBak SRiF SVic WOth
excorticata	CBcs CTsd EBee IDee MCot SPlb WBor
'Exmoor Woods'	SRiF
'Expo '86' (d)	SRiF
'Eynsford' (d)	SRiF
'Fabian Franck' (T)	LCla SRiF
'Falklands' (d)	EPts SLBF SRiF
'Falling Stars'	CLoc CWVF SRiF SVic
'Fancy Pants' (d)	CLoc CWVF SRiF SVic
'Fanfare'	LCla SRiF SVic
'Farningham'	SRiF
'Fascination'	see *F.* 'Emile de Wildeman'
'Favourite'	SRiF
'Felicity Kendal' (d)	SCoo
'Feltham's Pride'	CWVF
'Fenman'	CWVF SRiF SVic
'Fergie' (d)	SRiF
'Festival Lights' (E)	SLBF
'Festoon'	WOth
'Fey' (d)	CWVF SRiF
'Ffion'	EPts SRiF WOth
'Fiery Spider'	EBak SRiF SVic
'Finn'	CWVF EPts
'Fiona'	CLoc CWVF EBak SRiF SVic WOth
'Fiona Pitt' (E)	WOth
'Fire Mountain' (d)	CLoc SRiF SVic
'Firecracker'	see *F.* 'John Ridding'
'Firefly'	SRiF SVic
'Firelite' (d)	EBak SRiF
'Firenza' (d)	CWVF SRiF
'First Kiss' (d)	CWVF WOth
'First Lady' (d)	CWVF SRiF
'First Lord'	CWVF SRiF
'First of the Day'	SRiF
'First Success' (E)	CWVF LCla SRiF SVic WOth
'Flair' (d)	CLoc CWVF SRiF WOth
'Flamenco Dancer' (California Dreamers Series) (d)	CLoc
'Flamingo' (d)	SVic
'Flamingo Wings' (d)	EPts
'Flash' 🏆H4	CLoc CTri CWVF ELan EPts LCla MJac MRav MSmi SLBF SPet SPoG SRiF SVic WOth
'Flashlight'	CWVF EWld LCla MJac MSmi SCoo SRiF WOth
'Flat Jack o' Lancashire' (d)	SLBF SRiF
'Fleur de Picardie'	SLBF
'Flirtation Waltz' (d)	CLoc CWVF EBak MJac SRiF SVic
'Flocon de Neige'	SLBF
'Flogman'	EWld LCla
'Floral City' (d)	CLoc
'Florence Taylor' (d)	CWVF
'Florence Turner'	EBak SRiF WOth
'Florentina' (d)	CLoc CWVF EBak SRiF SVic
'Florrie Lester' (d)	SRiF
'Florrie's Gem' (d)	SLBF
'Flowerdream' (d)	CWVF
'Flyaway' (d)	SRiF
'Fly-by-night' (d)	CWVF
'Flying Cloud' (d)	CLoc CWVF EBak SRiF SVic WOth
'Flying Scotsman' (d)	CLoc CWVF EBak EPts SCoo SRiF SVic WOth
'Fokko's Katrientje'	WOth
'Folk'	MSmi
'Foolke'	EBak SRiF
'Forfar's Pride' (d)	SRiF
'Forget-me-not'	CLoc CWVF SVic WOth
'Formosissima'	WOth
'Fort Bragg' (d)	CWVF EBak SRiF
'Forward Look'	SRiF
'Fountains Abbey' (d)	CWVF
'Four Farthings' (d)	EPts
'Foxgrove Wood' 🏆H4	CWCL CWVF EBak ELon EPts SLBF SRiF WOth
'Foxtrot' (d)	CWVF
'Foxy Lady' (d)	CWVF MTis SRiF
'Frank Sanford' (d)	SRiF
'Frank Saunders'	CWVF LCla SLBF
'Frank Unsworth' (d)	CWVF EPts MJac SPet SRiF
'Frankfurt 2006'	MJac
'Frankie's Magnificent Seven' (d)	EPts
'Franz von Zon'	LCla
'Frau Hilde Rademacher' (d)	CWVF EBak EPts SLBF SRiF SVic
'Frauke'	SVic
'Fred Hansford' (v)	CWVF SRiF WOth
'Fred Shepherd'	SRiF
'Fred Swales' (T)	WOth
'Fred's Choice' (d) **new**	SRiF
'Fred's First' (d)	SRiF SVic
'Friendly Fire' (d)	CLoc SRiF
'Friendship' (d)	SRiF
'Frosted Flame'	CLoc CWVF LCla MJac SLBF SPet SRiF
'Frozen Tears'	EPts SRiF WOth
'Frühling' (d)	EBak
'Fuchsiade '88'	CLoc CWVF SRiF
'Fuchsiarama '91' (T) 🏆H2	CWVF
'Fuji-san'	ELon EPts
'Fuksie Foetsie' (E)	SRiF WOth
fulgens (T) 🏆H2	GCal LCla
* - 'Variegata' (T/v)	CLoc EPts LCla SRiF
'Fulpila'	LCla SLBF SRiF
'Funk'	MSmi
'Gala' (d)	EBak SRiF
'Galadriel'	SAko WOth
'Garden News' (d) 🏆H4	CLoc CRos CWCL CWVF ELon EPfP EPts LCla LRHS MAsh MJac MSmi NBir NGBl NPer NRHS SHil SLBF SPer SPet SRiF SVic WFar WHar
'Garden Week' (d)	CWVF SRiF SVic
'Gartenmeister Bonstedt' (T) 🏆H1c	CLoc CWVF EWld LCla SRiF SVic
'Gary Rhodes' (d)	EBak SCoo SRiF
'Gay Anne' (d)	WOth

	'Gay Fandango' (d)	CLoc CWVF SRiF
	'Gay Future'	WOth
	'Gay Parasol' (d)	SRiF
	'Gay Señorita'	EBak
	'Gay Spinner' (d)	CLoc
	'Geeskie Guskie'	SRiF
	'Gemma Fisher' (d)	EPts
	Gene = 'Goetzgene'PBR (Shadowdancer Series)	SCoo
	'Général Monk' (d)	CWVF EBak EPts MSmi SRiF SVic WOth
	'General Wavell' (d)	SRiF SVic
	'Genii' ♀H4	Widely available
	'Geoff Amos' (d)	MSmi
	'Geoff Oke'	WOth
	'Geoffrey Smith' (d)	EPts SRiF
§	'Georg Börnemann' (T) ♀H2	CLoc EBak MJac SRiF WOth
	'Georgana' (d)	SRiF
	'George Allen White' (d)	CWVF
	'George Barr'	CRos LRHS NRHS SRiF
	'George Johnson'	SRiF
	'George Travis' (d)	SRiF
	'Georges Remy'	WOth
§	'Gerharda's Aubergine'	CLoc CWVF SRiF WOth
	'Gesaüseperle' **new**	WOth
	'Gesneriana'	CLoc EBak SRiF
	'Ghislaine' (d)	SRiF
	'Giant Pink Enchanted' (d)	CLoc
	'Gilda' (d)	CWVF MJac SVic
	'Gillian Althea' (d)	CWVF SRiF
	'Gilt Edge' (v)	CLoc
I	'Gina'	WOth
	'Gina Bowman' (E)	EPts LCla SLBF
	Ginger = 'Goetzginger'PBR (Shadowdancer Series)	LSou SCoo
	'Gingham Girl' (d)	SRiF
	'Giovanna and Wesley' (d)	SRiF
	'Gipsy Princess' (d)	CLoc
	'Girls' Brigade'	CWVF SRiF
	'Gladiator' (d)	CMac EBak SRiF SVic WOth
	'Gladys Lorimer'	CRos CWVF EPts LRHS NRHS WOth
	'Gladys Miller'	CLoc
	glazioviana ♀H2	CWVF EPts GCal LCla LHop MHer SLBF SMHy SRiF SVen WOth
	'Glenby' (d)	CWVF SRiF
	'Glendale'	CWVF WOth
	'Glitters'	CWVF EBak
§	'Globosa'	CAgr SRiF WOth
	'Gloria Golding'	SRiF
	'Glow'	SRiF WOth
	'Glowing Embers'	EBak SDix SRiF
	'Glowing Lilac' (d)	EPts
	'Gold Brocade'	ELan SRiF
	'Gold Crest'	SRiF
	'Gold Leaf'	CWVF SRiF
	'Golden Amethyst' (d)	SRiF
	'Golden Anniversary' (d)	CLoc CWVF EBak MSmi SRiF SVic
	'Golden Arrow' (T)	LCla SRiF SVic
§	'Golden Border Queen'	CLoc EBak SPet
	'Golden Dawn'	CLoc CWVF SPet SRiF SVic
	'Golden Girl'	SLBF
	'Golden Herald'	SLBF
	'Golden la Campanella' (d/v)	CLoc
	'Golden Lena' (d/v)	CWVF
	'Golden Marinka' (v) ♀H2	CLoc EBak ESps SPet SRiF SVic
	'Golden Melody' (d)	SRiF
	'Golden Peppermint Stick' (d)	SRiF
	'Golden Swingtime' (d)	MJac SPet SRiF SVic
	'Golden Treasure' (v)	CLoc CWVF MSmi SRiF
	'Golden Vergeer' (v)	SLBF
	'Golden Wedding'	SRiF
	'Goldsworth Beauty'	SRiF
	'Golondrina'	CWVF
	'Good Girl'	WOth
	'Goody Goody'	SRiF SVic
	'Gooseberry Hill'	SRiF
	'Goosebery Belle'	SRiF
	'Gordon's China Rose'	LCla
	'Göttingen' (T)	SRiF WOth
	'Governor Pat Brown' (d)	EBak SRiF
	'Grace Darling'	CWVF EBak SRiF
	gracilis	see *F. magellanica* var. *gracilis*
	'Graf Witte'	CWVF SPet SRiF SVic
	'Granada' (d)	SRiF WOth
	'Grand Duke' (T/d)	CWVF
	'Grand Prix' (d)	SVic
	'Grandad Fred' (d)	SLBF SRiF
	'Grandad Hobbs' (d)	LCla
	'Grandma Sinton' (d)	CLoc CWVF SRiF
	'Grandpa George' (d)	SRiF
	'Grandpa Jack' (d)	SLBF
	'Granny Charlton'	WCFE
	'Grasmere'	SRiF WOth
	'Grayrigg'	ELon EPts LCla LSRN MSmi SLBF SRiF WOth
	'Great Ouse' (d)	EPts SRiF
	'Great Scott' (d)	CLoc SRiF
	'Green 'n' Gold'	EBak
	'Greenpeace'	SLBF SRiF SVic
	'Greg Walker' (d)	SRiF
	'Gregory Wallis'	SRiF
	'Greta' (T)	SRiF
	'Grey Lady' (d)	MSmi SRiF SVic
	'Grietje' (E)	WOth
	'Gris'	SRiF WOth
	'Groene Kan's Glorie'	SVic
	'Grumpy'	CWVF EPts SPet SRiF SVic WOth
	'Gruss aus dem Bodethal'	CLoc CWVF EBak EPts SLBF SRiF
	'Guinevere'	CWVF
	'Gunar Reich' (d)	WOth
	'Gustave Doré' (d)	EBak SRiF
	'Gwen Dodge'	SRiF SVic
	'Gwend-a-ling'	SRiF
	'Gypsy Girl' (d)	CWVF SRiF
	'H.G. Brown'	EBak SRiF
	'Hage Pinokkio'	WOth
	'Halsall Belle' (d)	SRiF
	'Hampshire Blue'	CWVF SRiF WOth
	'Hanna' (d)	CRos LRHS WOth
	'Hanna Improved'	SRiF
	'Hannah Amelia'	MJac
	'Hannah Louise' (d)	EPts
	'Hannah Rogers'	SRiF
	'Hans Callaars'	LCla
	'Happiness' (d)	SVic
	'Happy'	CWVF EPts LCla MSmi SPet SRiF SVic
	'Happy Anniversary'	CLoc SVic WOth
	'Happy Fellow'	CLoc EBak SRiF WOth
	'Happy Wedding Day' (d)	CLoc CWVF EPts EShb MJac MSmi SCoo SPet SRiF SVic
	'Hapsburgh'	EBak SRiF
	'Harbour Lites'	SLBF
	'Harlow Car'	CWVF EPts SRiF WOth
	'Harlow Perfection'	WOth
	'Harmony' Niederholzer, 1946	EBak
I	'Harmony' Tabraham	WOth

'Harnser's Flight'	SRiF
'Harold Smith'	SRiF
'Harriet Lye'	SRiF WOth
'Harriett' (d)	SRiF WOth
'Harry Gray' (d) $\mathbb{Y}^{H2}$	CLoc CWVF EBak EPts MJac SPet SRiF SVic
'Harry Lye'	WOth
'Harry Taylor' (d)	EPts SRiF
'Harry's Sunshine'	SLBF
hartwegii	LCla MHer
'Harvey's Reward'	SLBF WOth
'Hathersage' (d)	EBak
hatschbachii $\mathbb{Y}^{H2}$	CRos EBee EShb EWes GCal LCla LRHS MCot MHer SBrt SCob SDix SLon SMHy SMad SPlb SVen WOth WPGP WPnn
'Haute Cuisine' (d)	CLoc SVic
'Hawaiian Sunset' (d)	CLoc CWVF EPts SLBF SRiF WOth
'Hawkshead' $\mathbb{Y}^{H4}$	Widely available
'Hayley Jay' (d)	SLBF WOth
'Hazel' (d)	CWVF SRiF SVic WOth
'Heather Rose' (d)	SRiF
'Heavenly Hayley' (d)	SRiF
'Hebe'	SRiF
'Heidi Ann' (d) $\mathbb{Y}^{H4}$	CLoc CRos CWVF EBak EPts ESps LRHS MAsh MRav SLBF SPet SRiF SVic
'Heidi Blue' (d)	SLBF
§ 'Heidi Weiss' (d)	CLoc CWVF SPet
'Heinrich Henkel'	see *F.* 'Andenken an Heinrich Henkel'
'Helen Clare' (d)	CLoc CWVF
'Helen Gair' (d)	CWVF SRiF
'Helen Storer'	MJac
'Hellen Devine'	CWVF
'Hello Moideer'	SRiF
'Hemsleyana'	see *F. microphylla* subsp. *hemsleyana*
'Hendrikje Stoffels' (d)	WOth
'Henkelly's Chloris'	WOth
'Henkelly's Gitano'	WOth
'Henkelly's Hermine'	WOth
'Henkelly's Trubia'	WOth
'Henkelly's Vitalia'	WOth
'Henning Becker' $\mathbb{Y}^{H3}$	CWVF ELan
'Henri Poincaré'	EBak SRiF
'Henriette Ernst'	SRiF WOth
'Her Majesty's Crown' (T) **new**	WOth
'Herald' $\mathbb{Y}^{H4}$	CRos CWCL CWVF EPfP LRHS LSou MGos SHil SLBF SRiF SVic WOth
'Herbé de Jacques'	see *F.* 'Mr West'
'HeRi Asagi'	WOth
'HeRi Buffalo' (d) **new**	WOth
'HeRi Qat' (d) **new**	SLBF
'HeRi Trevally'	SLBF WOth
'Heritage' (d)	CLoc EBak SRiF
'Herman de Graaff' (d)	SLBF
'Hermiena'	CLoc CWVF EPts SLBF SRiF SVic WOth
'Heron'	SRiF
'Herps Bazuin'	WOth
'Herps Buggy'	WOth
'Herps Buikorgel'	WOth
'Herps Conga' (d) **new**	WOth
'Herps Kipkar'	WOth
'Herps Martina'	WOth
'Herps Mignon' (d)	WOth
'Herps Piccolo'	WOth
'Herps Pierement'	SLBF
'Herps Schalmei'	WOth
'Herps Steekkar'	WOth
'Herps Tamboerijn'	WOth
'Hessett Festival' (d)	CWVF EBak SRiF
'Heston Blue' (d)	CWVF SRiF
'Heydon'	CWVF SRiF
'Hi Jinks' (d)	SRiF
hidalgensis	see *F. microphylla* subsp. *hidalgensis*
'Hidcote Beauty' $\mathbb{Y}^{H2}$	CLoc CWVF LCla SLBF SPet SRiF SVic WOth
'Highland Pipes'	LCla SVic
'Hilda May Salmon'	CWVF
'Hindu Belle'	EBak SRiF
'Hinnerike' (E)	CWVF LCla SVic
'Hiroshige' (T)	LCla SRiF
'His Excellency' (d)	SRiF
'Hobo' (d)	SRiF
'Hobson's Choice' (d)	CWVF SLBF SRiF
'Holly's Beauty' (d)	CLoc EPts SRiF
'Hollywood' (d)	SRiF
'Horsforth Beauty'	WOth
'Horsforth in Bloom'	WOth
'Hot Coals'	CWVF EPts MJac SRiF SVic
'Howard's Own'	SRiF
'Howlett's Hardy' $\mathbb{Y}^{H4}$	CLoc CWVF EBak MSmi SRiF SVic WOth
'Huet's Baraketh'	WOth
'Hugh Morgan' (d)	SRiF
'Hula Girl' (d)	CWVF EBak MJac SRiF
'Humboldt Holiday' (d)	SRiF
'Huntsman' (d)	CCCN SRiF
'I Love You'	WOth
'Ian Leedham' (d)	SRiF
'Ian Storey'	CRos LRHS
'Ice Cool' (d)	MSmi
'Ice Cream Soda' (d)	SRiF
'Iceberg'	CWVF EBak SRiF SVic
'Icecap'	CWVF SVic
'Iced Champagne'	CLoc CWVF EBak MJac
'Ichiban' (d)	CLoc SRiF
'Ida' (d)	EBak
'Igloo Maid' (d)	CLoc CWVF EBak SRiF SVic
'Imogen Faye' (d)	SLBF WOth
'Impala' (d)	CWVF SRiF
'Imperial Crown'	WOth
'Imperial Fantasy' (d)	CWVF SRiF
'Impudence'	CLoc CWVF EBak SRiF
'Impulse' (d)	CLoc WOth
'Independence' (d)	SRiF SVic
'Indian Maid' (d)	CWVF EBak SRiF
'Inekris' **new**	WOth
'Insetta' (d)	WOth
'Insulinde' (T)	CWVF EPts LCla MHer MJac SLBF SRiF
'Iolanthe' (T)	CWVF
'Irene L. Peartree' (d)	CWVF LCla
'Irene Sinton' (d)	MJac
'Iris Amer' (d)	CLoc CWVF
'Isis' ambig.	WOth
'Isle of Purbeck'	SRiF SVic
'Italiano' (d)	CWVF MJac SVic
'Ivana van Amsterdam'	WOth
'Ixion'	SRiF WOth
'Izabela Cieszyńska' (d)	WOth
'Jack Acland'	CWVF SRiF
'Jack Coast'	SRiF
'Jack King'	SRiF
'Jack Rowlands' (d)	SRiF
'Jack Shahan' $\mathbb{Y}^{H2}$	CCCN CLoc CWVF EBak ESps LCla MJac SRiF WOth

'Jack Siverns'	WOth
'Jack Stanway' (v)	CWVF MSmi SRiF WOth
'Jackie Bull' (d)	CWVF
'Jackpot' (d)	EBak
'Jackqueline' (T)	CWVF SRiF
'Jacky'	SRiF
'Jadi Messingtetra'	WOth
'Jamboree' (d)	SRiF
'James Bamber'	WOth
'James Eve' (d)	SRiF
'James Hammond'	SRiF
'James Lye' (d)	CWVF EBak SRiF WOth
'James Travis' (E)	LCla SRiF
'Jan Baptist David' **new**	WOth
'Jan Bremer'	SVic
'Jan Everett' (d) **new**	WOth
'Jan Murray'	SRiF
'Jan van Erp'	WOth
'Jandel'	CWVF SRiF
'Jane Amanda' (d)	SRiF
'Jane Humber' (d)	CWVF SRiF
'Jane Lye'	SRiF
'Janet Yvonne' **new**	SRiF
'Janice Perry's Gold' (v)	CLoc MJac SRiF
'Janie' (d)	CRos EPfP LBuc LRHS MAsh SRiF SVic
'Jap Vantveer' (T)	LCla
'Jasper Marnix'	WOth
'Jasper's Red Ruby' **new**	SLBF
'Jasper's Zuurstok'	WOth
'Jaunty Jack'	WOth
'Javelin'	WOth
'Jean Frisby'	CLoc WOth
'Jean Smith' (d)	MSmi
'Jean Taylor'	EPts
'Jean Webb' (v)	WCot
'Jeeves' (d)	WOth
'Jennie Rachael' (d)	SRiF
'Jennifer'	MJac SRiF
'Jennifer Ann'	SLBF WOth
'Jenny May'	CLoc EPts LCla WOth
'Jenny Sorensen' $\mathbb{Y}^{H2}$	CWVF SRiF
'Jess'	LCla SLBF SRiF WOth
'Jessica Reynolds'	SRiF
'Jessie Pearson'	CWVF
'Jessimae'	CWVF SPet SRiF
'Jester' Holmes (d)	CLoc
'Jet'	MJac
'Jezebel' (d)	SRiF SVic
'Jiddles' (E)	LCla SRiF
'Jill Holloway' (T)	SLBF
'Jill Whitworth'	WPnn
'Jim Coleman'	CWVF SRiF SVic
'Jim Dodge' (d)	EPts
'Jim Hawkins'	SRiF
'Jim Missin' (d/v)	SRiF
'Jim Muncaster'	CWVF
'Jim Todd'	SRiF
'Jim Watts'	WOth
'Jimmy Cricket' (E)	SLBF WOth
'Jingle Bells'	SRiF
'Joan Barnes' (d)	CWVF SRiF
'Joan Cooper'	CLoc CWVF SLBF SRiF SVic
'Joan Gilbert' (d)	SRiF
'Joan Goy'	CWVF MJac SRiF SVic
'Joan Knight'	CLoc
'Joan Margaret' (d)	MJac
'Joan Morris'	SLBF
'Joan Pacey'	CWVF SRiF
'Joan Pawley'	SRiF
'Joan Smith'	SRiF
'Joan Waters' (d)	CWVF
'Joanna Lumley' (d)	EPts SRiF
'Joanne'	WOth
'Jo-Anne Fisher' (d)	EPts
'Joanne Jackson'	MJac
'Joan's Delight'	SVic WOth
'Joe Kusber' (d)	CWVF EBak SRiF
'Joel'	WOth
'Johannes Nowinski'	SRiF
'John Bartlett'	CLoc
'John Grooms' (d)	CLoc SRiF SVic
'John Hitchcock' (d) **new**	SLBF
'John Lockyer'	CLoc CWVF SRiF
'John Maynard Scales' (T) $\mathbb{Y}^{H2}$	CWVF LCla MJac SRiF WOth
'John Nicholass'	SLBF WOth
§ 'John Ridding'^{PBR} (T/v) $\mathbb{Y}^{H1c}$	CLoc EPts SPoG
'John Wright'	LCla
'Johnny Boy' **new**	SLBF
'Jomam'	CWVF SRiF
'Jon Oram'	CLoc CWVF
'Jose's Joan' (d)	CWVF SRiF SVic
'Jotu'	WOth
'Joy Patmore'	CLoc CWVF SLBF SPet SRiF WOth
'Joyce Adey' (d)	CWVF SRiF
'Joyce Forward'	SRiF
'Joyce Sinton'	CLoc CWVF SRiF
'Jubilee Queen' **new**	SRiF
'Judith Coupland'	CWVF
'Judith Louise'	WOth
'Juella'	SRiF
'Jülchen'	CWVF
'Jules Daloges' (d)	EBak SRiF
'Julie'	SRiF
'Julie Ann'	SRiF
'Julie Marie' (d)	CWVF MJac WOth
'June Gardner'	CWVF SRiF
'June Marie Shaw'	MJac
'Jungle'	LCla SLBF SRiF WOth
juntasensis	SRiF WOth
'Jupiter Seventy'	SRiF
'Just Pilk'	SLBF
'Just Pink' (E)	WOth
'Just William'	SRiF
'Justin's Pride'	SRiF
'Kalang Talinga' (d)	SRiF
'Kaleidoscope' (d)	SRiF
'Kaley Jackson'	MJac
'Kames Bay'	WOth
'Karen Isles' (E)	LCla SLBF
'Karen Louise' (d)	CLoc
'Karl Hartness'	SRiF
'Kate Harriet' (d)	SRiF
'Kate Taylor' (d)	SLBF
'Kath van Hanegem'	CLoc SLBF SRiF
'Kathleen Galea'	SRiF
'Kathryn Maidment'	SVic
'Kathy Louise' (d)	SRiF
'Kathy's Sparkler' (d)	SRiF
'Katie'	WOth
'Katie Coast'	SRiF
'Katie James'	SRiF
'Katie Reynolds' (d)	SRiF
'Katie Rogers'	EPts
'Katinka' (E)	CWVF LCla WOth
'Katjan'	LCla SLBF SRiF WOth
'Katrien Michiels'	SRiF
'Katrina' (d)	SRiF
'Katrina Thompsen'	CLoc CWVF EPts SLBF SRiF WOth
'Katy Flynn'	CWVF WOth

	'Kegworth Carnival' (d)	CWVF SRiF
	'Kelly Jo'	SRiF
	'Ken Goldsmith' (T)	CWVF
	'Ken Jennings'	CWVF
	'Ken Shelton'	SRiF
	'Ken Tudor'	MJac
	'Kenny Dalglish' (d)	SRiF
	'Kenny Holmes'	CWVF
	'Kenny Walkling'	MJac SLBF
	'Ken's Pixie'	MJac
	'Kent Boy' **new**	SRiF
	'Kent Girl' **new**	SRiF
	'Kentish Maid'	SRiF
	'Kernan Robson' (d)	CWVF EBak SRiF
	'Keystone'	EBak SRiF
	'Kim Wright' (d)	SRiF
	'Kimberly' (d)	SRiF
	'King George V'	SRiF
	'King of Hearts' (d)	SRiF
	'King's Ransom' (d)	CLoc CWVF EBak SPet SRiF SVic
	'Kirsten de Keijzer' (E)	WOth
	'Kiss 'n'Tell'	CWVF SRiF
	'Kit Oxtoby' (d)	CWVF MJac SRiF WOth
	'Kiwi' (d)	EBak SRiF
	'Knockout' (d)	CWVF SVic
	'Kobold'	SLBF
	'Kocarde'	WOth
	'Kolding Perle'	CWVF SLBF SRiF
	'Kuniko Atarashi' (d)	EPts
	'Kwintet'	CWVF EBak MJac SPet SRiF
	'La Bianca'	EBak
	'La Campanella' (d) $\mathbb{Y}^{H2}$	CCCN CLoc CWVF EBak EPts ESps MJac SRiF SVic
	'La France' (d)	EBak SRiF
	'La Neige' ambig.	CWVF
	'La Porte' (d)	CLoc CWVF
	'La Rosita' (d)	EBak SRiF
I	'La Traviata' Blackwell (d)	EBak SRiF
	'Lace Petticoats' (d)	EBak SRiF SVic
	'Lady Bartle Frere' (d)	SRiF
	'Lady Beth' (d)	SRiF SVic
	'Lady Boothby' $\mathbb{Y}^{H4}$	Widely available
	'Lady Edwards' (d)	SRiF
	'Lady Framlingham' (d)	EPts
	'Lady Heytesbury'	SRiF WOth
	'Lady in Black' (d)	CBcs CRos MHer SPoG
	'Lady in Grey' (d)	SRiF SVic
	'Lady Isobel Barnett'	CLoc CWVF EBak MJac SLBF SRiF SVic WOth
	'Lady Kathleen Spence'	CWVF SPet SVic WOth
	'Lady Lupus'	SRiF
	'Lady Patricia Mountbatten'	CWVF SRiF SVic WOth
	'Lady Ramsey'	EBak SRiF
	'Lady Rebecca' (d)	CLoc
	'Lady Thumb' (d) $\mathbb{Y}^{H3}$	Widely available
	'Laepines'	WOth
	'Laing's Hybrid'	CWVF EBak SRiF WOth
	'Lakeland Princess'	EBak
	'Lakeside'	SRiF
	'Lambada'	CLoc SLBF SRiF
	'Lancashire Lad' (d)	MJac
	'Lancashire Lass'	CWVF SRiF WOth
	'Lancelot'	EBak SRiF
	'Land van Beveren'	WOth
	'Landgoed Hulshorst'	WOth
	'Langsford'	SRiF
	'Larissa' **new**	WOth
	'Lark' (T)	CWVF SRiF
	'Lassie' (d)	CLoc CWVF EBak SRiF
	'Last Chance' (E)	SLBF

	'Laura' ambig.	CWVF SVic WOth
I	'Laura' (Dutch)	CLoc EPts LCla SLBF SRiF
	'Laura Cross' (E)	SLBF WOth
	'Lavender Beauty' (d)	SRiF
	'Lavender Kate' (d)	CWVF EBak
	'Lazy Lady' (d)	CWVF SRiF
	'Lechlade Apache'	LCla
	'Lechlade Bullet'	LCla
	'Lechlade Chinaman'	SRiF SVic
	'Lechlade Debutante'	WOth
	'Lechlade Fire-eater' (T)	SRiF
	'Lechlade Gorgon'	CWVF LCla SLBF
	'Lechlade Magician'	EPts LCla SEND SLBF SPet SRiF WOth
	'Lechlade Maiden'	CWVF SRiF WOth
	'Lechlade Martianess'	LCla SRiF SVic WOth
	'Lechlade Potentate'	LCla
	'Lechlade Tinkerbell' (E)	LCla SRiF
	'Lechlade Violet' (T)	LCla SRiF SVic
	lehmanii	LCla
	'Len Bielby' (T)	CWVF LCla SRiF
	'Lena' (d) $\mathbb{Y}^{H2}$	CLoc CMac CTri CWVF EBak EPts MJac MSmi SLBF SPer SPlb SRiF SVic
	'Lena Dalton' (d)	CLoc CWVF EBak SRiF SVic
	'Leonora'	CLoc CWVF SLBF SPet SRiF SVic
	'Lesley' (T)	CWVF LCla SRiF
	'Lesley's Wonder'	MJac
	'Leslie Bowman'	LCla SLBF
	'Lett's Delight' (d)	CWVF EPts SRiF
	'Letty Lye'	EBak SRiF WOth
	'Leverhulme'	see *F.* 'Leverkusen'
§	'Leverkusen' (T)	CLoc EBak LCla MJac SRiF WOth
	'Li Kai Lin'	SRiF
	'Lidie Bartelink'	WOth
	'Liebriez' (d) $\mathbb{Y}^{H4}$	EBak SRiF SVic
	'Liemers Lantaern'	CWVF
	'Likalin'	CWVF
	'Lilac Lustre' (d)	CLoc CWVF SPet SRiF SVic
	'Lilac Mist'	SLBF
	'Lilac Princess'	SRiF
	'Lilac Queen' (d)	EBak
	'Lilian'	SRiF WOth
	'Lillian Annetts' (d) $\mathbb{Y}^{H2}$	CWVF MJac SLBF SRiF WOth
	'Lillibet' (d)	CLoc CWVF SRiF
	'Lillydale' (d)	SRiF
	'Lilo Vogt' (T)	SRiF
	'Lime Lite' (d)	MJac
	'Lincoln Castle'	WOth
	'Linda Goulding'	CWVF EBak SVic
	'Linda Grace'	MJac WOth
	'Linda Hinchliffe'	MJac
	'Lindisfarne' (d)	CLoc CWVF EBak MJac WOth
	'Lindsey Victoria' (d)	SVic
	'Lionel'	SRiF WOth
	'Lisa' (d)	EPts SRiF
	'Lisa Ashton'	SRiF
	'Lisi'	WOth
	'Little Baby'	SRiF
	'Little Beauty'	CWVF SVic WOth
	'Little Boy Blue'	EPts SRiF
	'Little Brook Gem'	SLBF
	'Little Catbells' (E)	SLBF
	'Little Cracker'	SPoG
	'Little Fellow'	WOth
	'Little Gene'	EBak
	'Little Jessica' **new**	LCla SLBF WOth
	'Little Jewel'	SPet SRiF
	'Little Nan'	SLBF
	'Little Orphan Annie'	SRiF
	'Little Ouse' (d)	CWVF

	'Little Ronnie' (d)	SRiF
	'Little Scamp'	SLBF
	'Little Tony'	SLBF
	'Little Witch'	SRiF WOth
	'Liz' (d)	SRiF
	'Liza Todman' (d)	SRiF
	'Lochinver' (d)	CWVF
	'Loeky'	CLoc CWVF SRiF SVic WOth
	'Logan Garden'	see *F. magellanica* 'Logan Woods'
	'Lolita' (d)	CWVF EBak SRiF
	'London 2000'	EPts LCla MJac SLBF SRiF WOth
	'London Eye'	WOth
	'London in Bloom'	LCla SLBF
	'Lonely Ballerina' (d)	CLoc CWVF SRiF
	'Long Distance' (T)	LCla
	'Long Wings'	LCla SRiF SVic
I	'Longfellow' Lockerbie	WOth
	'Lord Byron'	CLoc SRiF
	'Lord Jim'	LCla
	'Lord Lonsdale'	CWVF EPts LCla SRiF SVic
	'Lord Roberts'	CLoc CWVF SLBF SRiF WOth
	'Lorna Swinbank'	CWVF SRiF SVic
	'Lorraine's Delight' (d)	SRiF SVic
	'Lottie Hobby' (E) ♀H3	CLoc CMac CWVF EPfP EPts EShb LCla MSmi SRiF SVic WCot WHea
	'Louise Emershaw' (d)	CWVF EBak MJac SRiF SVic
	'Louise Nicholls'	MJac SRiF
	'Loulabel'	SVic
	'Loveliness'	CLoc CWVF SRiF SVic WOth
	'Lovely Les' (d)	SRiF
	'Lovely Linda'	SLBF SRiF
	'Love's Reward' ♀H2	CLoc CWVF MJac SLBF SRiF SVic
	'Lower Raydon'	SRiF
I	'Loxensis'	CWVF SVic
	loxensis misapplied	see *F.* 'Loxensis', *F.* 'Speciosa'
	loxensis Kunth	WOth
	'Loxhore Lullaby' (E)	LCla
	'Loxhore Mazurka' (T)	SRiF
	'Loxhore Minuet' (T)	LCla SRiF
	'Lucinda'	CWVF SRiF
	'Lucky Strike' (d)	SRiF
	Lucy = 'Goetzlucy' (Shadowdancer Series)	SRiF
	'Lucy Locket'	MJac WOth
	'Lunter's Trots' (d)	SRiF
	'Luscious' (d)	SRiF
	'Lustre'	CWVF SVic WOth
	'Lutz Bogemann'	SRiF
I	'Lycioides'	LCla
	lycioides misapplied	see *F.* 'Lycioides'
§	***lycioides*** Andrews	WOth
	'Lydia'	WOth
	'Lye's Elegance'	SRiF WOth
	'Lye's Excelsior'	SRiF
	'Lye's Own'	SLBF SPet SRiF
	'Lye's Unique' ♀H3	CLoc CWVF EBak EPts LCla MJac SLBF SPet SRiF SVic WOth
	'Lyndon' **new**	MJac
	'Lynette' (d)	CLoc
	'Lynne Marshall'	WOth
	'Lynne Patricia' (d)	EPts SLBF WOth
	'Maartje'	SRiF
	'Mabel Greaves' (d)	CWVF
	'Machu Picchu'	CLoc CWVF EPts LCla SRiF SVic WOth
	macrophylla	WMoo
	'Madame Butterfly' (d)	CLoc
	'Madame Cornélissen' (d) ♀H4	CLet CLoc CMac CRos CSBt CTri CWVF EBak EBee ELan EPfP EPts ESps LRHS MAsh MRav NLar SCob SCoo SHil SLBF SLim SPer SPet SPoG SRiF SVic WFar XLum
	'Madame Eva Boye'	SRiF
	'Madeleine Sweeney' (d)	MJac
	'Maetsuycker'	WOth
	magellanica ♀H4	CBcs CTsd CWib ESps MGil MMuc NPer NWea SPer SVic WGwG WMoo WPnn
	- 'Alba'	see *F. magellanica* var. *molinae* 'Alba'
	- 'Alba Variegata' (v)	CLet WFar
	- 'Folius Aureus'	WFar
§	- var. ***gracilis*** ♀H4	CAgr CLoc CRos CTri CWVF EPfP LRHS NBro SVic WMoo WOth WPnn
	- - 'Aurea' ♀H4	CBcs CMac CRos CTsd CWVF ELan ELon EPfP ESps LCla LRHS MHer MRav MSmi SCoo SDix SLBF SPer SPet SRms SVic WMoo WOth XLum
	- - 'Purple Mountain'	CRos EPfP LRHS SPoG
	- - 'Variegata' (v) ♀H4	CRos CTsd EBak EPfP LRHS MGos MRav SDix SPer SPet SRiF SVic WPnn
§	- - 'Versicolor' (v) ♀H4	Widely available
	- 'Lady Bacon'	CBot CRos ELon EPri EPts EWes GBuc GCal LHop LRHS MCot MMuc SBod SDys SEND SLBF SMHy SPoG SRiF WBod WOth WPGP WSHC
§	- 'Logan Woods'	CAby ELon GKin SLBF WPGP
	- var. ***magellanica***	SCob
	- var. ***molinae***	Widely available
§	- - 'Alba' ♀H4	CBar EUJe GMcL NLar SPet WGwG
I	- - 'Alba Aureovariegata' (v)	CBcs CMac EPfP SPer SVic WFar XLum
§	- - 'Enstone' (v)	ELon GBuc SRiF
	- - 'Golden Sharpitor' (v)	CCCN WFar
	- - 'Mr Knight's Blush'	CDul
§	- - 'Sharpitor' (v) ♀H2	CLet CTsd EBak ELan ELon EPfP LRHS MAsh NChi NPer SPer SRiF SVic WFar WKif WMoo WSHC
	- var. ***myrtifolia***	CTsd
	- 'Pumila'	CAby ESps EWes GCal MHer SMHy SRot SVic WAbe WHal WPGP
	- 'Red Mountain'	EWes
§	- 'Thompsonii' ♀H4	ECGP SMHy SRiF
	'Magenta Flush'	CWVF
	'Magic Flute'	CLoc CWVF MJac SVic
	'Maharaja' (d)	SRiF
	'Majebo' (d)	SRiF
	'Majestica'	SRiF
	'Major Heaphy'	CWVF EBak MHer MSmi SRiF WOth
	'Malibu Mist' (d)	CWVF SRiF
	'Mama Bleuss' (d)	EBak SRiF
	'Mancunian' (d)	CWVF SRiF
	'Mandarin Cream'	MSmi WOth
	'Mandi Oxtoby' (T)	LCla SRiF
	'Mantilla' (T)	CLoc CWVF LCla MJac MSmi SRiF SVic
	'Maori Maid'	MSmi SRiF
	'Maori Pipes' (T)	SRiF
	'Marble Crepe' (T) **new**	WOth
	'Marbled Sky'	SVic
	'Marcia' PBR (Shadowdancer Series)	CLoc
	'Marcus Graham' (d)	CLoc CWVF EBak SCoo SRiF SVic
	'Marcus Hanton' (d)	CWVF SRiF
	'Mardi Gras' (d)	SRiF
	'Margaret' (d) ♀H4	CDul CLoc CTri CWVF EBak EPts SEND SLBF SPet SRiF SVic WFar
	'Margaret Bird'	LCla

	Name	Suppliers
	'Margaret Brown' ♀H4	CLoc CRos CTri CWVF LCla LRHS SLBF SPet SRiF SVic WOth
	'Margaret Hazelwood'	SRiF
	'Margaret My Own' **new**	EPts
	'Margaret Pilkington'	CWVF SRiF SVic WOth
	'Margaret Roe'	CWVF EBak MJac SPet SRiF
	'Margaret Rose'	SRiF
	'Margaret Susan'	EBak
	'Margaret Viscountess Thurso'	SLBF
	'Margarite Dawson' (d)	SRiF SVic
	'Margery Blake'	SRiF
	'Margharita' (d)	SRiF
	'Maria Landy'	CWVF MJac SLBF SRiF WOth
	'Maria Mathilde' (d)	SLBF
	'Maria Merrills' (d)	SRiF
	'Maria Shaw'	EPts
	'Mariah' (Diva Series)	SRiF
	'Marietta' (d)	SRiF
	'Marilyn Jane'	WOth
	'Marilyn Olsen'	CWVF SRiF
	'Marin Belle'	SRiF
	'Marin Glow' ♀H3	CLoc CWVF EBak SRiF SVic
	'Marina Kelly'	SRiF WOth
	'Marinka' ♀H2	CLoc CWVF EBak EPts ESps LCla MJac SPet SRiF SVic
	'Marja'	SRiF
	'Mark Kirby' (d)	CWVF SRiF
	'Marlies de Keijzer' (E)	EPts LCla SLBF SVen WOth
	Martha = 'Goetzmart' PBR (Shadowdancer Series)	LHop
	'Martina'	SLBF
	'Martin's Double Delicate' (d)	WOth
	'Martin's Inspiration'	LCla WOth
	'Martin's Yellow Surprise' (T)	LCla SLBF SRiF SVic
	'Marty' (d)	EBak SRiF
	'Martyn Smedley'	WOth
	'Mary' (T) ♀H1c	CLoc CWVF EPts LCla MSmi SLBF SRiF SVic WOth
	'Mary Lockyer' (d)	CLoc EBak SRiF
	'Mary Poppins'	CWVF SRiF SVic
	'Mary Reynolds' (d)	CWVF WOth
	'Mary Sturman' (E)	SRiF
	'Mary Thorne'	EBak
	'Mary's Beauty' (d)	MSmi
	'Mary's Millennium'	CWVF
	'Mauve Beauty' (d)	CWVF MSmi SLBF WOth
	'Mauve Lace' (d)	SRiF
	'Mauve Wisp' (d)	SVic
	'Mavis Enderby'	MJac SLBF
	'Max Jaffa'	CWVF SRiF
I	'Maxima'	EPts LCla SLBF SRiF
	'Maxine's Smile'	SLBF
	'Maybe Baby'	SRiF
	'Mayblossom' (d)	CWVF
	'Mayfield'	CWVF
	'Maytime' (d)	SRiF
	'Mazda'	CWVF SRiF WOth
	'Meadowlark' (d)	CWVF SRiF
	'Meditation' (d)	CLoc
	'Melanie'	SRiF SVic WOth
	'Melissa Heavens'	CWVF
	'Melody'	SPet SRiF SVic
	'Melody Ann' (d)	EBak SRiF
	'Melting Moments' (d)	SCoo SRiF
	'Mendocino Mini' (E)	WOth
	'Mendocino Rose'	SVic
	'Mephisto' ♀H2	CWVF WOth

	Name	Suppliers
	'Mercurius' ♀H4	WOth XLum
	'Merlin'	LCla SRiF
	'Merry Go Round' (d) **new**	SRiF
	'Merry Mary' (d)	CWVF EBak SRiF
	'Mersty' (d)	SLBF WOth
	'Meteor Storm'	SRiF
I	'Mexicali Rose' Machado	CLoc
	'Michael' (d/v)	CWVF EPts SRiF WOth
	'Michael Wallis' (T)	LCla SLBF SRiF WOth
	'Michelle Wallace'	SVic
	michoacanensis misapplied	see *F. microphylla* subsp. *aprica*
	michoacanensis Sessé & Moç. (E) B&SWJ 9027	WCru
	- B&SWJ 9148	WCru
	'Micky Goult' ♀H2	CLoc CWVF EPts MJac SLBF SRiF SVic WOth
	'Microchip' (E)	LCla
	microphylla (E)	CAby CBcs CElw CLoc CRos CTsd CWVF EBak EBee ELon GBin GCal IDee LRHS MGil SDix SIgm SMHy SVic
	- B&SWJ 10331	WCru
§	- subsp. ***aprica*** (E)	LCla
	- - B&SWJ 9101	WCru
	- - 'Dolly's Dress' (E)	WCru
§	- subsp. ***hemsleyana*** (E)	CLet SRiF SVic
	- - B&SWJ 10478	WCru
	- - 'Silver Lining' (E)	GCal SCob WCot WCru WOth
§	- subsp. ***hidalgensis*** (E)	LCla
§	- subsp. ***minimiflora*** (E)	SVic
	- 'Variegata' (E/v)	EWes
	'Midas'	CWVF
	'Midnight Sun' (d)	SRiF
	'Midwinter'	CWVF SRiF SVic
§	'Mieke Meursing' ♀H2	CLoc CWVF EBak MJac SPet SRiF SVic
	'Miep Aalhuizen'	LCla WOth
	'Mike Oxtoby' (T)	CWVF
	'Millennium'	CLoc EBak EPts MJac SCoo SRiF SVic
	'Millfield Alpha' **new**	EPts
	'Millfield Bravo' **new**	EPts
	'Millfield Charlie' **new**	EPts
	'Millfield Delta' **new**	EPts
	'Millfield Echo' **new**	EPts
	'Millie'	SRiF
	'Millie Butler'	CWVF
	'Ming'	CLoc SRiF
	'Mini'	WOth
	'Mini Skirt' (d)	SRiF
	'Miniature Jewels' (E)	SLBF
	minimiflora misapplied	see *F.* × *bacillaris*
	minimiflora Hemsl.	see *F. microphylla* subsp. *minimiflora*
	'Minipani' **new**	SLBF
	'Minirose'	CWVF EPts SLBF SRiF WOth
	'Minnesota' (d)	EBak WOth
	'Miramere'	EPts
	'Mirjana'	SRiF
	'Mischief'	SVic
	'Miss California' (d)	CLoc CWVF EBak ESps SRiF
	'Miss Debbie' (d)	SRiF
	'Miss Grace' (d)	SRiF
	'Miss Great Britain'	CWVF SRiF
	'Miss Lye'	SRiF
	'Miss Marilyn'	SRiF
	'Miss Muffett' (d)	EPts SRiF
	'Miss Vallejo' (d)	EBak SRiF WOth
	'Mission Bells'	CLoc CWVF EBak EPts SPet SRiF SVic
	'Mistoque'	SRiF

'Misty Blue' (d)	SVic
'Misty Haze' (d)	CWVF SRiF SVic
'Molesworth' (d)	CWVF MJac SRiF
'Mollie Beaulah' (d)	SRiF
'Molly Bellamy'	SRiF
'Monarch Mammoth'	SRiF
'Money Spinner'	CLoc SRiF
'Monica' (d)	SRiF
'Monica Dare' (T) ♀H1c	SRiF
'Monsieur Thibaut' ♀H4	SPer SRiF
'Monte Rosa' (d)	CWVF SRiF
'Monterey'	SRiF
'Montevideo' (d)	CWVF SRiF
'Montrose'	SRiF
'Monty Python'	WOth
'Monument' (d)	SRiF
'Mood Indigo' (d)	CWVF MSmi SRiF SVic WOth
'Moody Blues'	SRiF
'Moonbeam' (d)	CLoc SRiF
'Moonglow'	MJac SRiF WOth
'Moonlight Sonata'	CLoc CWVF SPet
'Moonraker' (d)	CWVF SRiF SVic
'More Applause' (d)	CLoc SRiF
'Morning Cloud' (d)	SRiF
'Morning Light' (d)	CLoc SRiF SVic
'Morning Mist'	SRiF
'Morrells' (d)	EBak SRiF
'Moth Blue' (d)	CWVF EBak SRiF
'Mountain Mist' (d)	CWVF SVic
'Moyra' (d)	CWVF WOth
'Mr A. Huggett'	CLoc CWVF EPts SLBF SRiF WOth
'Mr W. Rundle'	EBak SRiF SVic WOth
§ 'Mr West' (v)	LSou MCot SPet WMoo
'Mrs Churchill'	CLoc
'Mrs Hobhouse' (d)	SRiF
'Mrs Lee Belton' (E)	LCla SLBF WOth
'Mrs Lovell Swisher' ♀H4	CWVF EBak LCla SRiF SVic WOth
'Mrs Marshall'	CWVF SLBF SRiF WOth
'Mrs Popple' ♀H4	Widely available
'Mrs W. Castle'	SVic
'Mrs W.P. Wood' ♀H4	CLoc CWVF ELon LRHS MSCN SRiF SVic
'Mrs W. Rundle'	CLoc CWVF SLBF WOth
'Mrs Wilks'	SLBF
'Multa'	SRiF
'Muriel' (d)	CLoc CWVF SRiF WOth
'Murru's Pierre Marie' (d)	SLBF
'Musetta' **new**	WOth
'My Delight'	CWVF
'My Fair Lady' (d)	CLoc CWVF EBak SRiF
'My Grandchildren' **new**	SLBF
'My Honey'	WOth
'My Little Cracker'	MJac
'My Mum'	LCla SLBF SRiF WOth
'My Pat'	SLBF SRiF
'My Reward' (d)	CWVF
'Naaldwijk 800'	WOth
'Nananice'	SRiF
'Nancy Lou' (d)	CLoc CWVF MJac SLBF SPet SRiF SVic
'Nanny Ed' (d)	CWVF
'Napoléon'	WOth
'Natal Bronze'	SRiF
'Natalie Jones'	SRiF
'Natasha Lynn' (d)	WOth
'Natasha Sinton' (d)	CCCN CWVF MJac SPet SRiF
'Nathan Rhys'	EPts WOth
'Native Dancer' (d)	CWVF
'Naughty Nicole' (d)	SRiF
'Navy Blue'	SRiF
'Neapolitan' (d)	SLBF
'Neck'	LCla
'Nell Gwyn'	CLoc CWVF SRiF SVic
'Nellie Nuttall' ♀H2	CLoc CWVF EBak EPts SPet SRiF SVic
'Neopolitan' (E)	CLoc EPts LCla SVic WOth
'Nephele'	EPts WOth
'Nettala'	SRiF SVic WOth
'Neue Welt'	CWVF SRiF
'New Millennium' (d)	EShb LHop
'Nice 'n' Easy' (d)	CRos LRHS MJac SRiF
'Nicki Fenwick-Raven' (E)	LCla
'Nicki's Findling'	CWVF EPts LCla MJac SRiF
'Nicola'	EBak
'Nicola Jane' (d)	CLet CWVF EBak EPts LCla MJac SLBF SPet SRiF SVic
'Nicolette'	CWVF MJac
§ ***nigricans*** B&SWJ 10664	WCru
'Nikki'	SRiF
'Nimue'	SRiF
'Niula'	LCla SRiF
'Noblesse'	WOth
'Noel Freeman'	SRiF
'Nonchalance' (T)	LCla
'Nordseebrandung'	WOth
'Norfolk Belle' (d)	SRiF
'Norfolk Ivor' (d)	SRiF
'Norman Greenhill'	SRiF
'Norman Welton'	MJac SLBF
'Normandy Bell'	EBak SVic
'Northern Jewel'	EPts SLBF
'Northern Pride' (d)	WOth
'Northilda'	SVic
'Northumbrian Belle'	SRiF
'Northumbrian Pipes'	LCla WOth
'Northway'	CLoc CWVF MJac MSmi SPet SRiF SVic
'Norvell Gillespie' (d)	EBak SRiF
'Novato'	SRiF
'Novella' (d)	CWVF SRiF
'Noyo Star' (d)	SRiF
'Nuance'	LCla
'Nunthorpe Gem' (d)	SRiF
'O Sole Mio'	SVic
'Obcylin' (E)	EPts LCla SRiF WOth
'Obergärtner Koch' (T) ♀H1c	SRiF
'Ocean Beach'	EPts SRiF WOth
'Oddfellow' (d)	SRiF WOth
'Oetnang' (d)	CTri SCoo
'Oh Carol' (E)	LCla WOth
'Old Lottie Hobby'	SRiF
'Old Rose'	SRiF
'Old Somerset' (v)	CCCN SRiF SVic WOth
'Oldbury'	SRiF
'Oldbury Gem'	SRiF
'Oldbury Pearl'	SRiF
'Olga Storey'	CRos LRHS
'Olive Moon' (d)	WOth
'Olive Smith'	CWVF EPts LCla MJac SRiF
'Olympia'	WOth
'Olympic Lass' (d)	WOth
'Olympic Sunset'	SVic WOth
'Olympic Twenty Twelve' **new**	SRiF
'Omeomy'	SRiF
'Onward Dingle'	SRiF
'Oosje' (E)	LCla SRiF SVic
'Oostveens Thymen'	WOth
'Opalescent' (d)	CLoc CWVF SVic

'Orange Crush'	CLoc CWVF EBak MJac SPet WOth
'Orange Crystal'	CWVF MJac SLBF SVic WOth
'Orange Drops'	CLoc CWVF EBak EPts SRiF SVic WOth
'Orange Flare'	CLoc CWVF EBak SLBF SRiF SVic
'Orange King' (d)	CLoc CWVF
'Orange Mirage'	CLoc CWVF SLBF SPet SVic
'Orange Queen'	SRiF
'Orange Star' (E)	LCla SLBF WOth
'Orangeblossom'	SLBF SRiF WOth
'Oranje van Os'	CWVF
'Orient Express' (T) ♀^{H1c}	CLoc CWVF MJac SRiF SVic WOth
'Oriental Lace'	SRiF
'Oriental Sunrise'	CWVF
'Ornamental Pearl' (v)	CLoc CWVF SLBF SRiF
'Orwell' (d)	CWVF
'Oso Sweet'	CWVF SRiF
'Other Fellow'	CWVF EBak EPts LCla MJac SLBF SPet SRiF SVic WOth
'Oulton Empress' (E)	LCla SLBF
'Oulton Fairy' (E)	SLBF
'Oulton Hoya' (E)	WOth
'Oulton Red Imp' (E)	LCla SLBF
'Oulton Travellers Rest' (E)	SLBF
'Oulton Tu-Fu' (E)	WOth
'Our Carol'	SLBF
'Our Darling'	CWVF SRiF
'Our Dereck'	SRiF
'Our Fred' **new**	SRiF
'Our Hilary'	SLBF WOth
'Our Joyce'	SRiF
'Our Kid'	SLBF
'Our Lillian' **new**	SRiF
'Our Nan' (d)	MJac
'Our Nell'	SRiF
'Our Pamela'	MJac
'Our Spencer'	SLBF
'Our Ted' (T)	EBak SRiF
'Our Topsy'	SRiF
'Overbecks'	see *F. magellanica* var. *molinae* 'Sharpitor'
'P.E. King' (d)	SLBF
'Pabbe's Belle'	WOth
'Pabbe's Kirrevaalk'	WOth
'Pabbe's Klompnoagel'	WOth
'Pabbe's Kopstubber' (d)	WOth
'Pacific Grove' Greene	see *F.* 'Evelyn Steele Little'
'Pacific Queen' (d)	EBak
'Pacquesa' (d)	CWVF EBak SPet SRiF SVic
'Padre Pio' (d)	CWVF EBak MJac
'Pale Flame' (d)	SRiF
'Palm Springs' (d)	SRiF
'Pam Plack'	LCla SLBF SRiF WOth
'Pamela Hutchinson'	SRiF
'Pamela Knights' (d)	EBak
'Pam's People'	LCla
'Pan'	WOth
'Panache' (d)	LCla
paniculata (T) ♀^{H2}	CBot CCCN CRHN CWVF EBak EPts LCla MCot MHer SLBF SRiF WCot WCru
'Panique'	LCla
'Pantomine Dame' (d)	CWVF SRiF
'Panylla Prince'	LCla SRiF
'Papa Bleuss' (d)	CWVF EBak SRiF
'Papoose' (d)	EBak SLBF SRiF SVic
'Parkstone Centenary' (d)	CWVF
'Party Frock'	CLoc CWVF EBak SPet WOth
parviflora misapplied	see *F. × bacillaris*
parviflora Lindl.	see *F. lycioides* Andrews
'Pastel'	SRiF

'Pat Meara'	CLoc EBak SRiF
'Pathétique' (d)	CLoc
'Patience' (d)	CWVF EBak SLBF SRiF
'Patio Princess' (d)	CLoc CWVF EPts
'Patty Evans' (d)	CWVF SRiF
'Patty Sue' (d)	SRiF
'Paul Cambon' (d)	EBak SRiF
'Paul Meredith'	SRiF
'Paul Pini' (d)	SRiF
'Paul Roe' (d)	MJac
'Paul Storey'	SRiF
'Paul und Carola' (d)	WOth
'Paula Jane' (d) ♀^{H2}	CWVF MJac SLBF SRiF SVic
'Pauline Rawlins' (d)	CLoc
'Pavilion Princess' **new**	WOth
'Peace' (d)	SRiF
'Peachy' (California Dreamers Series) (d)	CLoc SCoo SRiF
'Peachy Keen' (d)	EBak SRiF
'Peacock' (d)	CLoc
'Pearly Gates'	SRiF
'Pearly Queen' (d)	WOth
'Peasholm'	WOth
'Pee Wee Rose'	EBak SRiF SVic
'Peggy Burford' (T)	LCla
Peggy = 'Goetzpeg'[PBR] (Shadowdancer Series)	LSou SCoo SRiF
'Peggy King'	EBak SPet SRiF
'Peloria' (d)	CLoc EBak
'People's Princess'	SRiF
'Peper Harow'	EBak SRiF
'Pepi' (d)	CWVF EBak SRiF
'Peppermint Candy' (d)	CWVF MJac
'Peppermint Stick' (d)	CLoc CWVF EBak MSmi SPet SVic
'Periwinkle'	SRiF
'Perky Pink' (d)	EBak EPts SRiF
'Perry Park'	CWVF MJac SRiF SVic
'Perry's Jumbo'	NPer
perscandens	CBcs LCla WOth
'Personality' (d)	SRiF
'Peter Bielby' (d)	CWVF SRiF
'Peter Crookes' (T)	CWVF SRiF
'Peter James' (d)	SRiF
'Peter Meredith'	MJac WOth
'Peter Pan'	CWVF SRiF
'Peter Sheewood' **new**	SRiF
petiolaris	LCla
- B&SWJ 10675	WCru
'Petit Four'	CWVF SRiF WOth
'Petit Point'	SRiF
'Petronella' (d)	SRiF
'Phaidra' (T)	LCla WOth
'Pharaoh'	CLoc
'Phénoménal' (d)	CWVF EBak MSmi SRiF
'Phryne' (d)	SRiF SVic WOth
'Phyllis' (d) ♀^{H4}	CLoc CRos CWVF EBak EPts LCla LRHS MJac MSmi SEND SLBF SPet SRiF SVic
'Piet van der Sande'	LCla SLBF
'Piggelmee'	WOth
'Pinch Me' (d)	CWVF EBak SPet SRiF SVic
'Pink Aurora'	CLoc SRiF
'Pink Ballet Girl' (d)	CLoc SVic
'Pink Bon Accord'	CLoc CWVF SRiF SVic
'Pink Cloud'	CLoc EBak SRiF
'Pink Cornet'	LCla SRiF
'Pink Darling'	CLoc EBak SRiF
'Pink Dessert'	EBak
'Pink Fairy' (d)	SPet SRiF
'Pink Fandango' (d)	CLoc

'Pink Fantasia' ♀H2	CLoc CWVF EBak EPts LCla MJac SLBF SRiF SVic
'Pink Flamingo' (d)	SRiF
'Pink Frills'	SRiF
'Pink Galore' (d) ♀H2	CLoc CWVF MJac SLBF SPet SRiF
'Pink Goon' (d)	MSmi SLBF SRiF SVic
'Pink Haze'	SRiF SVic
'Pink Jade'	CWVF
'Pink la Campanella'	CWVF EBak SRiF WOth
'Pink Lace' (d)	SPet
'Pink Marshmallow' (d) ♀H4	CLoc CWVF EBak MJac SLBF SPet SRiF SVic
'Pink Panther' (d)	SRiF
'Pink Pearl' ambig.	SRiF
'Pink Princess'	SRiF
'Pink Profusion'	EBak SRiF
'Pink Quartet' (d)	CLoc CWVF EBak SRiF WCot
'Pink Rain'	CWVF MJac SRiF WOth
'Pink Slippers'	CLoc
'Pink Spangles'	see *F.* 'Mieke Meursing'
'Pink Sprite'	WOth
'Pink Temptation'	CLoc CWVF SVic
'Pinnochio' (T) **new**	WOth
'Pinto de Blue' (d)	MSmi SRiF
'Pinwheel' (d)	CLoc EBak SRiF
'Piper' (d)	CWVF SRiF
'Piper's Vale' (T)	MJac SLBF WOth
'Pippa Rolt'	SRiF
'Pirbright'	CWVF
'Pixie'	CLoc CWVF EBak MJac SLBF SPet SRiF SVic
'Playboy' (d)	SVic
'Playford'	CWVF EBak SRiF
'Pledle' (T)	WOth
'Plenty'	EBak SVic
'Plumb Bob' (d)	CWVF
'Pol Jannie' (d)	SRiF
'Polar' **new**	WOth
'Pole Star'	SRiF
'Pop Whitlock' (v)	CWVF SLBF SPet SRiF SVic
'Poppet'	CWVF WOth
'Popsie Girl' (v)	SLBF SRiF WOth
'Port Arthur' (d)	EBak SRiF
'Postiljon'	CWVF EBak SRiF
'Postman'	SRiF
'Powder Puff' ambig.	CWVF
'Powder Puff' Hodges (d)	CLoc SRiF SVic
'Prelude' Blackwell	CLoc
'President'	EBak LRHS SRiF
'President B.W. Rawlins'	SRiF
'President Barrie Nash'	CLoc
'President Carol Gubler' (d)	SLBF
§ 'President Elliot'	SRiF
'President George Bartlett' (d) ♀H2	CLoc EPts MJac SLBF SRiF WOth
'President Jim Muil'	SLBF
'President Joan Morris' (d)	SLBF
'President John Porter'	MJac SLBF
'President Leo Boullemier'	CWVF MJac MSmi SPet SRiF SVic WOth
'President Margaret Slater'	CLoc CWVF SPet SRiF SVic WOth
'President Moir' (d)	SLBF SRiF WOth
'President Norman Hobbs'	CWVF WOth
'President Stanley Wilson' (d)	EBak EPts SRiF WOth
'President Wilf Sharp' (d)	SRiF SVic
'Preston'	CMac
'Preston Guild' ♀H3	CLoc CWVF EBak NPer SDys SPet SRiF SVic WOth
'Prestonfield' (v)	WOth
'Pride of Ipswich'	SRiF
'Pride of the West'	SRiF
'Prince of Orange'	CLoc SRiF SVic WOth
'Prince Syray'	SRiF WOth
'Princess Dollar'	see *F.* 'Dollar Prinzessin'
'Princessita'	CWVF EBak SPet WOth
procumbens	CBcs CCCN CLoc CWVF EBak EPfP EPts EUJe LCla MCot MHer SBrt SLBF SRiF WAbe WHea WOth
- 'Argentea'	see *F. procumbens* 'Wirral'
- 'Variegata'	see *F. procumbens* 'Wirral'
§ - 'Wirral' (v)	CLoc CTsd EShb ITim SRiF WOth
'Prodigy'	see *F.* 'Enfant Prodigue'
'Profusion' ambig.	SVic
'Profusion' Wood	SRiF
'Prosperity' (d) ♀H3	CLoc CRos CWVF EBak EPfP EPts LCla LRHS MJac MSmi SEND SLBF SPet SRiF SVic WOth
'Pumila'	CMac CWib EBee ELan EPfP LRHS SDix SPet SRiF SVic
'Purbeck Mist' (d)	CWVF
'Purperklokje'	CWVF EBak SRiF SVic WOth
'Purple Emperor' (d)	CLoc
'Purple Heart' (d)	CLoc EBak SRiF
'Purple Lace'	SRiF SVic
'Purple Rain'	EPts
'Purple Showers'	SRiF
'Purple Splendour' (d)	SRiF
'Pussy Cat' (T)	CLoc CWVF EBak SRiF SVic WOth
'Putney Pride'	EPts
'Put's Folly' ♀H2	CWVF EBak MJac SPet SRiF WOth
putumayensis	EBak SRiF
'Quasar' (d)	CCCN CLoc CWVF EPts EShb MJac SLBF SRiF SVic
'Queen Elizabeth'	WOth
'Queen Ester'	SRiF WOth
'Queen Mabs'	SRiF
'Queen Mary'	CLoc EBak SRiF
'Queen of Bath' (d)	SVic
'Queen of Derby' (d)	CWVF
'Queen of Hearts' Kennett (d)	SVic
'Queen of Mercia'	MJac
'Queen Victoria' Smith (d)	SRiF
'Queen's Park' (d)	EBak
'Query'	SRiF SVic WOth
'R.A.F.' (d)	CLoc CWVF EBak EPts SPet SRiF SVic
'Rachel Sinton' (d)	SRiF
'Radings Gerda' (E)	LCla SLBF
'Radings Mia' (T)	SLBF
'Radings Michelle'	CWVF WOth
'Ragtime'	MSmi
'Rahnee'	CWVF SRiF
'Rainbow'	CWVF MSmi
'Raintree Legend' (d)	SRiF
'Ralph's Delight' (d)	CWVF SRiF
'Rambling Rose' (d)	CLoc CWVF SRiF
'Rambo' (d)	SRiF
'Rams Royal' (d)	CWVF SRiF
'Raspberry' (d)	CLoc CWVF EBak SRiF SVic
'Raspberry Red'	SRiF
'Raspberry Ripple' (d)	WOth
'Raspberry Sweet' (d)	CWVF SRiF
'Raspberry Twist'	WOth
'Ratae Beauty'	CWVF
'Ratatouille' (d)	SRiF WOth
ravenii	WOth
'Ray Redfern'	CWVF
'Razzle Dazzle' (d)	SRiF
'Reading Show' (d)	CWVF EPts SLBF

'Rebecca Williamson' (d)	CWVF MJac
'Rebeka Sinton' (v)	CLoc EBak SRiF
'Red Ace' (d)	WOth
'Red Jacket' (d)	CWVF EBak SRiF
'Red Petticoat'	CWVF SRiF
'Red Rain'	CWVF SRiF WOth
'Red Rover'	SRiF
'Red Rum' (d)	SPet
'Red Shadows' (d)	CLoc CWVF EBak SRiF
'Red Spider'	CCCN CLoc CWVF EBak SCoo SPet SRiF SVic WOth
'Red Wing'	CLoc
'Reflexa'	see *F.* × *bacillaris* 'Reflexa'
'Reg Gubler'	SLBF
'Regal'	CLoc WOth
'Regal Robe' (d)	SRiF
regia subsp. ***regia***	LCla SRiF XLum
- subsp. ***reitzii***	CDul LCla XLum
- subsp. ***serrae***	CBcs WOth
'Remember Carole Anne' (d)	SLBF WOth
'Remember Eric'	SRiF WOth
'Remembering Claire'	EPts WOth
'Remembrance' (d)	EPts LCla MSmi SLBF SRiF
'Remus' (d)	SRiF SVic
'Remy Kind' (d)	SRiF
'Rene Schwab'	LCla
'Renée-Madeleine'	WOth
'Requiem'	CLoc
'Reverend Elliott'	see *F.* 'President Elliot'
'Reverend Frank Pagden'	WOth
'Revival'	SRiF
'Rhapsody' ambig.	SVic
I 'Rhapsody' Blackwell (d)	CLoc
'Riant' (d)	SRiF
'Riccartonii' ♀^{H6}	Widely available
'Richard John' (v)	SRiF SVic
'Ridestar' (d)	CLoc CWVF SRiF
'Rigoletto'	SVic
'Rijs 2001' (E)	SLBF SRiF WOth
'Ringwood Gold'	SVic
'Ringwood Market' (d)	CWVF EPts MJac SCoo SPet SRiF SVic
'Rivendell'	EPts
'Riverdancer Claire'	WOth
'Riverdancer Liam'	WOth
'Riverside' (d)	SRiF
'Robbie'	SRiF
'Robert Lutters'	SVic
'Robin Hood' (d)	SRiF
'Rocket Fire' (California Dreamers Series) (d)	SRiF SVic
'Roesse Amold' **new**	WOth
'Roesse Duck'	WOth
'Roesse Meton'	WOth
'Roger de Cooker' (T)	CLoc EPts LCla SRiF SVic WOth
'Rohees Izar'	SRiF
'Rohees Lava'	SLBF
'Rohees Leada' (d)	SLBF SRiF
'Rohees Matar' (d)	WOth
'Rohees Merope'	SRiF
'Rohees Naos' (d)	SRiF
'Rohees New Millennium' (d)	SLBF SRiF
'Rohees Reda' (d)	SRiF
'Rolla' (d)	CWVF EBak SRiF
'Rolt's Bride' (d)	SRiF
'Rolt's Ruby' (d)	CWVF SRiF SVic WOth
'Roman City' (d)	CLoc SRiF SVic
'Romance' (d)	CWVF SRiF
'Romany Rose'	CLoc
'Ron Holmes'	SRiF
'Ronald L. Lockerbie' (d)	CLoc CWVF SRiF SVic
'Ron's Ruby'	SRiF
'Roos Breytenbach' (T)	CCCN LCla MJac SRiF WOth
'Rosamunda' (d)	CLoc
'Rose Aylett' (d)	EBak
'Rose Bradwardine' (d)	EBak SRiF
'Rose Churchill' (d)	MJac
'Rose Fantasia' ♀^{H2}	CLoc CWVF EPts MJac SLBF SRiF
'Rose of Castile'	CLoc EBak EPts LCla MJac MSmi SLBF SVic
'Rose of Castile Improved' ♀^{H4}	CWVF LCla MJac SPet SRiF WOth
'Rose of Denmark'	CCCN CLoc CWVF EBak MJac SCoo SLBF SPet SRiF WOth
'Rose van der Bergh'	SRiF
'Rose Winston' (d)	SCoo
rosea misapplied	see *F.* 'Globosa'
rosea Ruíz & Pav.	see *F. lycioides* Andrews
'Rosebud' (d)	SRiF
'Rosecroft Beauty' (d/v)	CWVF EBak SRiF SVic WOth
'Rosemarie Higham' (v)	MJac SCoo WOth
'Rosemary Day'	CLoc
'Rosemoor' (T)	SRiF
'Roswitha'	SRiF
'Rosy Bows'	CWVF SRiF
'Rosy Frills' (d)	CWVF MJac SRiF SVic
'Rosy Morn' (d)	CLoc
'Rothbury Beauty'	SRiF
'Rough Silk'	CLoc CWVF EBak SRiF
'Roy Castle' (d)	CWVF
'Roy Walker' (d)	CWVF SRiF
'Royal Academy' (d)	EPts
'Royal and Ancient'	CWVF
'Royal Mosaic' (California Dreamers Series) (d)	MJac SRiF
'Royal Purple' (d)	EBak SRiF
'Royal Ruby'	SRiF
'Royal Serenade' (d)	CWVF
'Royal Velvet' (d) ♀^{H2}	CCCN CLoc CRos CWVF EBak EPts LRHS MJac SLBF SPet SRiF SVic
'Royal Wedding'	SRiF
'Rozientje'	SRiF
'Rubra Grandiflora'	CWVF LCla SLBF SRiF WOth
'Ruby' (d)	SRiF
'Ruby Wedding' (d)	CWVF SLBF SRiF
'Ruddigore'	CWVF SRiF
'Ruffles' (d)	CWVF SRiF
'Rufus' ♀^{H4}	CDul CLoc CMac CWVF EBak ELan EPts LCla MJac MRav SLBF SPet SRiF SVic
'Ruth'	SRiF SVic WOth
'Ruth King' (d)	CWVF EBak SRiF
'Rutland Water'	SRiF
'Ryan' **new**	SLBF
'S'Wonderful' (d)	CLoc EBak SRiF
'Sailor'	EPts SVic
'Sally Ann' (d)	SRiF
'Salmon Cascade'	CWVF EPts LCla MJac SLBF
'Salmon Glow'	CWVF SVic
'Sam Sheppard'	SLBF
'Samantha Reynolds'	SRiF WOth
'Sammy Girl'	SRiF
'Sam's Song' (d)	SRiF
'Samson' (d/v)	SRiF
'San Diego' (d)	CWVF
'San Mateo' (d)	EBak
§ ***sanctae-rosae***	LCla SRiF
'Sandboy'	CWVF EBak
'Santa Cruz' (d)	CMac CWVF MSmi SLBF SRiF SVic WOth

	'Santa Lucia' (d)	CLoc
	'Santa Monica' (d)	EBak SRiF
	'Sapphire' (d)	EBak SRiF
	'Sappho Phaoon' (T)	EPts
	'Sara Helen' (d)	CLoc EBak
	'Sarah Brightman' (d)	CLoc
	'Sarah Eliza' (d)	EShb MSmi SCoo
	'Sarah Jane' (d)	EBak SVic
	'Sarah Louise'	CWVF
	'Sarina'	SRiF
	'Satellite'	CLoc CWVF EBak SPet SRiF SVic
	'Saturnus' ♀^{H4}	CRos CWVF EBak LRHS SEND SPet SPoG SRiF
	'Saxondale Sue'	SRiF SVic
	scabriuscula	LCla SRiF
	'Scarborough Rosette' (d)	SRiF
	'Scarcity'	CWVF EBak MSmi SRiF SVic WOth
	'Scarlet Jester'	EPts
	'Schneeball' (d)	EBak SRiF SVic
	'Schneekoppen' (d)	SRiF
	'Schneewitcher'	EPts SRiF
	'Schöne Hanaurin'	SLBF
	'Schöne Wilhelmine'	see *F.* 'Die Schöne Wilhelmine'
	'Scion of Longleat'	SRiF
	'Scotch Heather' (d)	CWVF SRiF
	'Sea Shell' (d)	CWVF SRiF
	'Seaforth'	SRiF
	'Sealand Prince'	CWVF LCla SRiF SVic WOth
	'Seattle Blue' (T/d)	SLBF
	'Sebastopol' (d)	CLoc
	'Sensation'	WOth
	serratifolia Hook.	see *F. austromontana*
	serratifolia Ruíz & Pav.	see *F. denticulata*
	'Seventh Heaven' (d)	CLoc CWVF MJac SCoo SRiF
	'Shady Blue'	CWVF
	'Shania' (Diva Series)	SRiF
	'Shanley'	CWVF SVic
	'Sharon Allsop' (d)	SRiF
	'Sharpitor'	see *F. magellanica* var. *molinae* 'Sharpitor'
	'Shatzie B' **new**	SLBF
	'Shawna Ree' (E)	WOth
	'Sheila Crooks' (d)	CWVF EBak SRiF
	'Sheila Kirby'	CWVF
	'Sheila Purdy'	SRiF
	'Sheila Steele' (d)	CWVF SRiF
	'Sheila's Surprise' (d)	SRiF
	'Shelford'	CLoc CWVF EBak EPts MJac SLBF SRiF SVic WOth
	'Shell Pink'	SVic
	'Shelley Lyn' (d)	SRiF
	'She's a Beauty'	MJac
	'Shirley Halladay' (d)	LCla SRiF
	'Shirley'^{PBR} (Shadowdancer Series)	SCoo SRiF
	'Shirley Teece'	EPts
	'Shooting Star' (d)	SRiF
	'Showfire'	EBak
	'Showtime' (d)	CWVF
	'Shrimp Cocktail'	CLoc EShb SRiF
	'Shuna Lindsay'	LCla WOth
	'Shy Lady' (d)	SPet SRiF
	'Siberoet' (E)	LCla SLBF WOth
	'Sierra Blue' (d)	CLoc CWVF EBak SRiF
	'Silver Anniversary' (d)	SRiF SVic
	'Silver Dawn' (d)	SRiF WOth
	'Silver Dollar'	SVic
	'Silver Surfer' **new**	SLBF WOth
	'Silver Wedding' (d)	SRiF
	'Silverbell'	SRiF
	'Silverdale'	EPts SRiF
	'Simon J. Rowell'	LCla SRiF
	'Simple Simon'	SRiF
	simplicicaulis	EBak LCla
	'Sincerity' (d)	CLoc SVic
	'Siobhan'	CWVF
	'Siobhan Evans' (d)	SLBF
	'Sir Alfred Ramsey'	CWVF EBak
	'Sir David Jason'	MJac
	'Sir Ian Botham' (d)	SRiF
	'Sir Matt Busby' (d)	EPts MJac SRiF
	'Sister Ann Haley'	EPts SRiF
	'Sister Sister' (d)	SLBF
	'Skater's Waltz' (d) **new**	CLoc
	'Sleepy'	EPts SPet SRiF SVic
	'Sleigh Bells'	CLoc CWVF EBak SRiF SVic WOth
	'Small Pipes'	CWVF SRiF
	'Smokey Mountain' (d)	SRiF SVic
	'Sneezy'	EPts SRiF SVic
	'Snow Burner' (California Dreamers Series) (d)	CLoc SRiF
	'Snow White' (d)	SRiF SVic
	'Snowbird' (d)	SLBF
§	'Snowcap' (d) ♀^{H4}	CCCN CLoc CRos CWVF EBak ELon EPfP EPts ESps GKin LCla LRHS MAsh MGos MJac MSmi NPer SCoo SHil SLBF SLim SPet SPoG SRiF SVic WFar
	'Snowdon' (d)	CWVF SRiF
	'Snowdrift' ambig.	SRiF
	'Snowdrift' Colville (d)	CLoc
	'Snowdrift' Kennett (d)	EBak
	'Snowfall'	CWVF
	'Snowfire' (d)	CLoc CWVF SCoo SRiF SVic
	'Snowflake' (E)	EPts LCla WBor WOth
	'Snowstorm' (d)	SRiF
	'So Big' (d)	SRiF
	'Softpink Jubelteen'	WOth
	'Software' (d)	SRiF
	'Sombrero' (d)	SRiF
	'Son of Thumb' ♀^{H4}	CLoc CRos CWVF EPts ESps LRHS MAsh MJac MRav SCob SLBF SLim SPer SPet SRiF SVic
	'Sonata' (d)	CLoc CWVF SRiF SVic
	'Sophie Grace'	WOth
	'Sophie Louise'	CWVF EPts SLBF SRiF WOth
	'Sophisticated Lady' (d)	CWVF EBak EPts SRiF SVic
	'Soroptimist International'	SRiF
	'South Gate' (d)	CLoc CWVF EBak EPts MSmi SPet SRiF SVic
	'South Lakeland'	SRiF
	'South Today' (d)	SRiF
	'Southwell Minster'	SRiF
	'Space Shuttle'	CLoc LCla SRiF
	'Sparky' (T)	CLoc CWVF EPts LCla SRiF WOth
	'Speciana'	EPts
§	'Speciosa'	EBak LCla SRiF
	'Spice of Life' (d)	SRiF
	'Spion Kop' (d)	CCCN CWVF EShb SPet SRiF
§	***splendens*** ♀^{H2}	CBot CCCN CLoc EBak LCla MCot NPer SLBF SRiF WOth
	- B&SWJ 10469	WCru
	'Spotlight'	SRiF
	'Spring Bells' (d)	CRos LRHS SRiF
	'Spring Classic' (d)	SRiF
	'Squadron Leader' (d)	CWVF EBak EPts SRiF
	'Square Peg' (d)	SRiF
	'Squirtie'	SLBF
	'Stan'	WOth
	'Stanley Cash' (d)	CLoc CWVF SPet SRiF SVic
	'Star Wars'	CLoc EPts MJac SRiF WOth

'Stardust'	CWVF WOth
'Starlight'	WOth
'Steeley' (d)	SVic
'Steirerblut' (T)	SRiF
'Stella Ann' (T)	CWVF EPts LCla SRiF
'Stolze von Berlin' (d)	SRiF
'Stoney Creek' (d)	SRiF
'Straat Cumberland'	LCla
'Straat Futami' (E)	EPts LCla
'Straat Kobe' (T)	LCla
'Straat La Plata'	LCla
'Straat Magelhaen'	LCla WOth
'Straat Malakka'	SRiF
'Straat of Plenty'	LCla WOth
'Strawberry Daiquiri' (d)	WOth
'Strawberry Delight' (d)	CLoc CWVF MJac SPet SVic
'Strawberry Fizz' (d)	SRiF
'Strawberry Sundae' (d)	CLoc CWVF EBak SRiF
'Strike the Viol' (T)	SLBF WOth
'String of Pearls'	CLoc CWVF MJac SLBF SPet SRiF SVic WOth
'Stuart Joe'	CWVF
'Stuart Lockyer' (d)	CLoc
'Stuart Martin'	SRiF
'Sue'	SLBF SRiF WOth
'Suffolk Punch'	SRiF
'Suffolk Splendour' (d)	EPts
'Sugar Almond' (d)	CWVF
'Sugar Blues' (d)	SRiF
'Summerdaffodil'	SRiF WOth
'Summerwood' (d)	SRiF
'Sunbeam Hillary' (Sunbeam Series)	WOth
'Sundance'	SRiF
'Sunny'	SRiF
'Sunny Jim'	SVic
'Sunny Smiles'	CWVF SRiF
'Sunray' (v)	CLoc CWVF EBak ELon EPfP ESps LBuc LRHS MAsh MGos NEgg SCoo SHil SLBF SLim SPoG SPtp SRiF SVen WCot WOth
'Sunset'	CLoc CWVF SRiF WOth
'Sunset Boulevard' (d)	SRiF
'Sunshine'	WOth
'Supersport' (d)	SVic
'Superstar'	CWVF SRiF SVic
'Susan' (d)	SRiF
'Susan Ford' (d)	CWVF SPet SRiF
'Susan Green'	CWVF EBak MJac SRiF WOth
'Susan McMaster'	CLoc
'Susan Olcese' (d)	CWVF EBak SRiF
'Susan Travis'	CLoc CWVF EBak SRiF SVic
'Swanley Beauty'	WOth
'Swanley Gem' ♀H2	CLoc CWVF EBak SLBF SPet SRiF SVic
'Swanley Pendula'	CLoc WOth
'Swanley Yellow'	CWVF EBak SRiF SVic WOth
'Sweet Hollie'	SLBF
'Sweet Lavender' (d)	SRiF
'Sweet Leilani' (d)	SRiF
'Sweet Sarah' (E)	EPts WOth
'Sweetheart' ambig.	SRiF
I 'Sweetheart' van Wieringen	EBak
'Swingtime' (d) ♀H2	CCCN CLoc CWVF EBak EPts ESps LCla MJac SLBF SPet SRiF SVic
sylvatica misapplied	see *F. nigricans*
'Sylvia Barker' ♀H2	CWVF LCla SLBF SRiF WOth
'Sylvia Gale'	SRiF
'Sylvia Rose' (d)	CWVF SRiF
'Sylvia's Choice'	EBak
'Sylvy'	SRiF
'Symphony'	CLoc CWVF
'Syreme' (d)	SLBF
'Szilvia Ócsai' (d)	WOth
''t Binnenland'	WOth
'T.I.S. Herentals' **new**	SLBF
'T.S.J.' (E)	LCla
'T'Vöske' (d/v)	SRiF
'Taatje'	SRiF
'Taco'	LCla SRiF WOth
'Taddle'	CWVF SLBF
'Taffeta Bow' (d)	CLoc SLBF SRiF SVic
'Tam O'Shanter' (d)	SRiF
'Tammy'	SRiF
'Tamworth'	CLoc CWVF EBak MJac SRiF SVic
'Tangerine'	CLoc CWVF SRiF SVic
'Tania Leanne'	SRiF
'Tanya Bridger' (d)	EBak SRiF WOth
'Tarra Valley'	LCla SRiF SVic WOth
'Task Force'	CWVF SRiF SVic
'Taudens Heil'	WOth
'Tausendschön' (d)	CLoc WOth
'Ted Perry' (d)	CWVF
'Ted Stiff' (d)	SRiF
'Ted's Tribute'	SRiF
'Television' (d)	SRiF
'Temptation' ambig.	CWVF
'Temptation' Peterson	CLoc EBak SRiF WOth
'Tennessee Maiden' (d)	SRiF
'Tennessee Waltz' (d) ♀H2	CLoc CWVF EBak EPts SLBF SPer SPet SRiF SVic
'Tequila Sunrise'	SRiF
'Teresa' (d)	SRiF
'Tess'	EPts SLBF
tetradactyla misapplied	see *F.* × *bacillaris*
'Texas Longhorn' (d)	CLoc CWVF EBak MSmi SRiF SVic
'Thalia' (T) ♀H1c	CBot CCCN CLoc CWVF EBak EPts ESps EUJe LCla LSRN MCot MHer MJac MSmi NEgg SLBF SPer SPlb SPoG SRiF SVic SWeb WBod WOth
'Thamar'	CLoc CWVF EPts SRiF SVic WOth
'That's It' (d)	SVic
'The Aristocrat' (d)	CLoc EBak SRiF
'The Cannons' (d)	SRiF
§ 'The Doctor'	CLoc CWVF EBak SRiF WOth
'The Jester' (d)	EBak
'The Madame' (d)	CWVF SRiF
'The Marvel'	SRiF
'The Speedbird'	SRiF
'The Tarns'	CWVF EBak SRiF SVic WOth
'Théroigne de Méricourt'	SRiF
'Think Pink'	WOth
'This England' (d)	SRiF
'Thistle Hill' (d)	WOth
'Thomas' (d)	EPts
'Thomas Ritchie'	SRiF
'Thompsonii'	see *F. magellanica* 'Thompsonii'
'Thornley's Hardy'	SRiF SVic
'Three Cheers'	CLoc SRiF
'Three Counties'	EBak SRiF
'Thumbelina'	CRos LRHS
'Thunderbird' (d)	CLoc CWVF SRiF
thymifolia (E)	CWVF GCra LRHS MHer SDys SEND SMHy WKif WOth
- subsp. ***minimiflora*** (E)	CBot
- subsp. ***thymifolia*** (E)	SEle WOth
'Tiara' (d)	EBak
'Tiffany' ambig.	SRiF
'Tillingbourne' (d)	SLBF
'Time After Time'	CLoc EShb SLBF SRiF

'Timlin Brened' (T)	CWVF EBak SRiF
'Timothy Titus' (T) ♀H1c	LCla SRiF
'Ting-a-ling'	CLoc CWVF EBak SLBF SPet SRiF SVic WOth
'Tinker Bell' ambig.	SRiF
'Tinker Bell' Hodges	EBak SVic
'Tintern Abbey'	CWVF
'Tjinegara'	LCla
'Toby Bridger' (d)	CLoc EBak SRiF
'Toby Foreman'	SLBF
'Toby S' (d)	SLBF WOth
'Tolling Bell'	CWVF EBak SPet
'Tom Boy'	SRiF
'Tom Goedeman'	LCla
'Tom H. Oliver' (d)	SRiF
'Tom Knights'	EBak SPet SRiF WOth
'Tom Thumb' ♀H4	Widely available
'Tom West' misapplied	see *F.* 'Mr West'
'Tom West' Meillez (v)	CLet CLoc CMHG CRos CSBt CWVF CWib EBak EHoe EPfP EPts ESps LCla LRHS MHer MJac MRav MSCN MSmi SHil SLBF SLim SPtp WFar WOth
'Tom Woods'	CWVF SRiF
'Tomarama' (E)	WOth
'Tommy Tucker'	SRiF
'Ton Ten Hove'	LCla SRiF
'Tony Galea'	SRiF
'Tony Porter' (d)	SRiF
'Tony Talbot'	MJac
'Tony's Treat' (d)	EPts
'Toos'	SVic
'Toosje Vantveer'	WOth
'Topaz' (d)	CLoc
'Topper' (d)	CWVF SRiF
'Torch' (d)	CLoc CWVF EBak SRiF SVic
'Torchlight'	CWVF EPts LCla
'Torvill and Dean' (d)	CLoc CWVF EPts MJac SLBF SPet
'Tosca'	CWVF SRiF
'Touch the Lute' (T) **new**	WOth
'Town Crier'	SLBF
'Tracid' (d)	SVic
'Tracie Ann' (d)	SRiF
'Trail Blazer' (d)	CLoc CWVF MJac SRiF
'Trailing King'	WOth
'Trailing Queen'	MJac SRiF
'Trase' (d)	CWVF CWib EBak SRiF SVic
'Traudchen Bonstedt' (T) ♀H1c	CLoc CWVF LCla SRiF SVic
'Traviata'	see *F.* 'La Traviata' Blackwell
'Treasure' (d)	EBak
'Tresco'	SRiF
'Tricolor'	see *F. magellanica* var. *gracilis* 'Versicolor'
'Trident'	SRiF
'Trientje'	LCla SLBF
'Trimley Bells'	SRiF
triphylla (T)	EBak MHer
'Trish's Triumph'	EPts SRiF
'Tristesse' (d)	CLoc CWVF EBak SRiF
'Troika' (d)	SRiF
'Troon'	CWVF SRiF
'Tropic Sunset' (d)	SRiF
'Tropicana' (d)	CLoc CWVF SRiF SVic
'Troubador' Waltz (d)	CLoc
'Troubadour' Bland (d)	SRiF
'Trudi Davro'	MJac SCoo SRiF
'Trudy'	CWVF EPts SRiF SVic
'Truly Treena' (d)	SLBF SRiF
'Trumpeter' ambig.	CWVF SRiF
'Trumpeter' Fry	SRiF SVic
'Trumpeter' Reiter (T)	CLoc EPts LCla MJac MSmi
'Tsjiep'	SRiF
'Tubular Bells' (T)	LCla SRiF WOth
'Tuonela' (d)	CLoc CWVF
'Turkish Delight'	SRiF WOth
'Tutone' (d)	SRiF
'Tutti-frutti' (d)	CLoc
'Twiggy'	SRiF
'Twinkling Stars'	CWVF MJac SVic WOth
'Twinny'	CWVF EPts SRiF
'Twist and Shout' **new**	WOth
'Twister'	SRiF
'Two Tiers' (d)	CWVF SRiF
'Twydale'	SRiF
'U.B.' (d)	SRiF
'U.F.O.'	CWVF SVic
'Ullswater' (d)	CWVF EBak SRiF WOth
'Ultramar' (d)	SRiF
'Uncle Charley' (d)	EBak MSmi SRiF SVic
'Uncle Jinks'	SPet SRiF
'Uncle Steve' (d)	SRiF SVic
'University of Liverpool'	CLoc MJac SRiF
'Upward Look'	EBak SRiF
'Valda May' (d)	CWVF
'Vale of Belvoir'	SRiF SVic
'Valerie Ann' (d)	EBak SPet SVic
'Valerie Bradley'	EPts
'Valiant'	SRiF
'Vanessa Jackson'	CLoc CWVF MJac SRiF SVic
'Vanessa Wright'	CRos LRHS
'Vanity Fair' (d)	CLoc EBak SRiF
'Variegated Lottie Hobby' (E/v)	SRiF
'Variegated Pixie' (v)	MSmi SRiF
'Variegated Procumbens'	see *F. procumbens* 'Wirral'
'Variegated Swingtime' (v)	SRiF
'Variegated Triphylla' (T/v)	SRiF
'Veenlust'	EBak MJac SRiF
'Velvet Crush'	EPts EShb
'Vendeta'	LCla WOth
'Venus Victrix'	EBak SRiF
venusta	EBak LCla
'Vera Garcia'	EPts MJac SLBF WOth
'Versicolor'	see *F. magellanica* var. *gracilis* 'Versicolor'
'Vespa'	SRiF
'Vicky'	SRiF
'Vicky Bradshaw' **new**	SLBF
'Ville de Paris'	WOth
'Vincent van Gogh'	SRiF WOth
'Vintage Dovercourt'	LCla
'Violet Bassett-Burr' (d)	CLoc EBak SRiF
'Violet Gem' (d)	CLoc
'Violet Rosette' (d)	CWVF SRiF SVic
Violetta = 'Goetzviol' (Shadowdancer Series)	LSou SCoo
'Violette Szabo'	SRiF
'Viva Ireland'	EBak SRiF
'Vivien Colville'	CLoc SVic
'Vobeglo'	CWVF
'Vogue' (d)	SRiF
'Voltaire'	SRiF
'Voodoo' (d)	CCCN CLoc CWVF EBak EPts EShb LCla SCoo SPet SRiF SVic
'Vuurwerk'	SRiF
'Vyvian Miller'	CWVF
'Wagtails White Pixie'	EBak
'Wake the Harp' **new**	WOth
'Waldfee' (E)	CCVN
'Waldis Grafin'	WOth

'Waldis Spezi'	LCla
'Wally Yendell' (v)	SRiF
'Walsingham' (d)	CWVF SRiF
'Walton Jewel'	EBak SRiF
'Waltzing Matilda' (d)	SRiF
'Walz Banjo'	WOth
'Walz Bella'	LCla SRiF
'Walz Blauwkous' (d)	CWVF SRiF WOth
'Walz Bombardon'	SRiF
'Walz Bruintje' **new**	WOth
'Walz Cimbaal'	SRiF
'Walz Doedelzak'	SRiF WOth
'Walz Duimelot'	SRiF
'Walz Estafette' (d)	SRiF SVic
'Walz Fagot'	SRiF
'Walz Fanclub'	SRiF
'Walz Fluit'	MJac
'Walz Fonola'	SRiF
'Walz Freule'	CWVF MJac WOth
'Walz Harp'	CWVF SRiF WOth
'Walz Hoorn'	WOth
'Walz Jubelteen' 🏆H2	CLoc CWVF ELon EPts LCla MJac SAdn SEle SLBF SRiF SVen SVic WOth
'Walz Klarinet'	SRiF
'Walz Lucifer'	CWVF LCla SLBF SRiF WOth
'Walz Luit'	SRiF
'Walz Mandoline' (d)	CWVF SRiF SVic WOth
'Walz Nugget'	SRiF
'Walz Panfluit'	LCla
'Walz Parasol'	WOth
'Walz Polka'	LCla SRiF WOth
'Walz Rail'	SRiF
'Walz Sitar'	WOth
'Walz Toeter'	WOth
'Walz Triangel' (d)	SRiF SVic
'Walz Trompet'	WOth
'Walz Tuba'	SRiF WOth
'Wapenveld 150'	LCla
'Wapenveld's Bloei'	EPts LCla SLBF SRiF
'War Paint' (d)	CLoc SRiF
'Warton Crag'	CWVF SRiF SVic
'Wassernymphe' **new**	WOth
'Water Color'	SLBF
'Water Nymph'	CLoc MHer SLBF SRiF SVic
'Wattenpost'	SLBF WOth
'Wave of Life'	CWVF SRiF
'Waveney Gem'	CLoc CWVF EBak LCla MJac SLBF SRiF WOth
'Waveney Queen'	CWVF SVic WOth
'Waveney Sunrise'	CWVF MJac SRiF SVic WOth
'Waveney Unique'	CWVF
'Waveney Valley'	CWVF SRiF WOth
'Waveney Waltz'	CWVF EBak SRiF WOth
'Wedding Bells' ambig.	SRiF SVic
'Welsh Dragon' (d)	CLoc CWVF EBak SRiF WOth
'Wendy' Catt	see *F.* 'Snowcap'
'Wendy Bendy'	EPts SLBF
'Wendy Jane Webster'	EPts
'Wendy's Beauty' (d)	CLoc EBak EPts MJac SRiF
'Wentworth'	CWVF SRiF SVic WOth
'Wessex Belle' (d/v)	CWVF
'Westham'	LCla SRiF
'Westminster Chimes' (d)	CLoc CWVF SPet SRiF
'Wharfedale' 🏆H4	ELon EPts LRHS MJac SEND SLBF SRiF SVic WOth
'What's-it' (E)	LCla SLBF
'Whickham Blue'	CWVF
'Whirlaway' (d)	CLoc CWVF SRiF SVic
'Whispering Dawn' **new**	WOth
'White Academy'	EPts

'White Ann'	see *F.* 'Heidi Weiss'
'White Bride' (d)	SVic
'White Clove'	SRiF SVic WOth
'White Fairy' (d)	SRiF
'White Galore' (d)	CWVF SRiF SVic
'White Gold' (v)	SRiF
'White Heidi Ann' (d)	SRiF
'White Joy'	EBak SRiF
'White King' (d)	CLoc CWVF EBak SRiF SVic
'White Lace'	SRiF
'White Pixie' 🏆H4	EPts MJac MSmi SLBF SPet SRiF SVic
'White Princess'	SRiF
'White Queen' ambig.	CWVF
'White Queen' Doyle	WOth
'White Sincerity' (d)	SRiF
'White Spider'	CLoc CWVF EBak SRiF SVic WOth
'White Veil' (d)	CWVF
'White Water' (d)	SRiF
'Whiteknights Amethyst'	WOth
'Whiteknights Blush'	CCse EBee EWes GCal GQui LHop LRHS MSmi SRiF
'Whiteknights Cheeky' (T)	CWVF EBak EPts LCla SRiF SVic
'Whiteknights Green Glister'	SRiF
'Whiteknights Pearl' 🏆H3	CBot CLet CTsd CWVF ECha EPfP EPts LCla LCro MMuc SDys SEND SLBF SRiF SVic WHar WOth WPnn
'Whiteknights Ruby' (T)	SRiF WOth
'Whitney' (Diva Series)	SRiF
'Whitton Starburst'	LCla
'Whoopee' **new**	MJac SLBF WOth
'Wicked Queen' (d)	SVic
'Widnes Wonder'	MJac SLBF WOth
'Widow Twanky' (d)	CWVF
'Wiebke Becker'	SRiF
'Wigan Peer' (d)	EPts MJac SRiF WOth
'Wight Magic' (d)	MJac SRiF
'Wild and Beautiful' (d)	CWVF SRiF SVic
'Wilf Langton'	WOth
'Wilhelmina Schwab'	LCla
'Willie Tamerus'	SRiF
'Willow Tinsdale'	LSou
'Willy Nijhuis' (T)	WOth
'Willy Winky'	SRiF
'Wilma van Druten'	LCla WOth
'Wilma Versloot'	SRiF
'Wilson's Colours'	EPts LCla
'Wilson's Joy'	MJac
'Wilson's Pearls' (d)	CWVF SLBF SPet SRiF
'Wilson's Sugar Pink'	EPts LCla MJac SRiF WOth
'Win Oxtoby' (d)	CWVF
'Windhapper'	LCla SLBF WOth
'Windmill'	CWVF
'Wine and Roses' (d)	EBak SRiF
'Wingrove's Mammoth' (d)	SRiF SVic
'Wings of Song' (d)	CWVF SRiF
'Winifred'	SRiF
'Winston Churchill' (d) 🏆H2	CLoc CWVF EBak ESps MJac SCoo SPet SRiF SVic
'Winter Hymn' **new**	WOth
'Winter's Touch'	SRiF
'Witchipoo'	SLBF
'Woodnook' (d)	CWVF SRiF
'Woodside' (d)	SVic
'Wrotham' (d)	SRiF
'Wyre Light' (E)	SLBF
'Y Me'	SRiF
'Yattendon Lady'	SLBF
'York Manor'	EShb MSmi
'Yours'	SRiF
'Yuletide' (d)	SRiF

'Yvonne Priest'	SRiF
'Yvonne Schwab'	LCla SRiF
'Zara'	SRiF
'Zeebrook'	SRiF SVic
'Zeeuwse Parel'	WOth
'Zellertal'	WOth
'Zets Alpha'	SRiF
'Zets Bravo'	SRiF
'Ziegfield Girl' (d)	SRiF SVic
'Zifi'	SLBF
'Zulu King'	SRiF SVic WOth
'Zus Liebregts' (d)	WOth
'Zwarte Snor' (d)	CWVF
'Zyzy'	SRiF

Fumaria (*Papaveraceae*)

capreolata	WSFF
lutea	see *Corydalis lutea*

Furcraea (*Asparagaceae*)

bedinghausii	see *F. parmentieri*
§ ***foetida***	CCCN WCot
gigantea	see *F. foetida*
longaeva misapplied	see *F. parmentieri*
macdougalii	SPlb
§ ***parmentieri***	CBcs CCCN CDTJ CHGN CHll CPne CTsd EBee GBin LEdu LRHS NLos SMad SPlb SVen

G

Gahnia (*Cyperaceae*)

sieberiana	SPlb

Gaillardia (*Asteraceae*)

'African Sunset' **new**	GMcL
aristata misapplied	see *G.* × *grandiflora*
aristata Pursh 'Maxima Aurea'	EBee EPfP MSpe NBre SPhx
'Arizona Sun'	EAJP ESps LRHS MHer MMuc MNHC SCob SHil SVic
'Bijou'	EBee ELon LSun SWvt
'Celebration'	LRHS NRHS SPoG
'Dwarf Goblin'	NGBl
§ 'Fackelschein'	IBoy MSpe
'Fanfare'PBR	CWGN EBee ECtt ENor LHop LRHS NRHS SCoo
Goblin	see *G.* × *grandiflora* 'Kobold'
§ × ***grandiflora***	ESps
- 'Amber Wheels'	CDor EPfP MSpe NCGa SPhx
- 'Arizona Apricot'	CDor LRHS
- 'Arizona Red Shades'	LRHS NRHS
- 'Burgunder'	CSBt CSpe EAJP ELan ELon EPfP EWoo LHop LRHS LSou MSpe NGBl NRHS SBod SCob SPer SPhx SPoG SWvt WHar
- 'Dazzler'	CSBt EAEE EBee ELan EPfP LRHS SPer SPoG WHar WMoo
- 'Fanfare Blaze'	GMcL LRHS NRHS
- (Gallo Series) 'Gallo Dark Bicolor'	CBod LRHS NRHS
- - 'Gallo Fire'	NRHS
- - 'Gallo Peach'	LRHS NRHS
- - 'Gallo Yellow'	LRHS NRHS
- - 'Gallo Yellow Trumpet'	LRHS NRHS
- (Galya Series) 'Galya Coral Spark' (d) **new**	WHlf
- - 'Galya Orange Spark' (d) **new**	WHlf
- - 'Galya Red Spark' (d) **new**	WHlf
§ - 'Kobold'	CBcs CDor CMac CSBt CTsd EBee ELan ELon EPfP ESps GMaP GMcL IBoy LRHS NLar NRHS SPer SPlb SPoG SWvt WGwG WHar
- 'Mesa Peach' (Mesa Series) **new**	SPad
- 'Red Sun'PBR	CWGN NLar
- 'Sun Flare'PBR	SPad
- (Sunburst Series) Sunburst Burgundy Picotee = 'Granretip'	GMcL LRHS
- - Sunburst Burgundy	LRHS SHil
- - Sunburst Orange = 'Granoran'	LRHS SHil
- Sunburst Yellow = 'Granyel'	LRHS NRHS SHil
- 'Sunset Cutie' **new**	SPad
- 'Tokajer'	EAJP EBee ELan EPfP LRHS MSpe NBre NRHS SPhx WCAu
'Naomi Sunshine'	SHar
§ 'Oranges and Lemons'PBR	EBee ECtt LSou SCob SHar
Saint Clements	see *G.* 'Oranges and Lemons'
'Solar Flare'	SCob
Torchlight	see *G.* 'Fackelschein'

Galactites (*Asteraceae*)

tomentosa	EHoe EWTr SPav
- white-flowered	CPla

Galanthus ✿ (*Amaryllidaceae*)

'Acton Pigot No. 3'	CAvo
'Ailwyn'	CAvo GEdr
'Alan's Treat'	CAvo
'Alison Hilary'	EHrv GEdr MAsh
× ***allenii***	CBro EHrv GKev
alpinus var. ***bortkewitschianus***	GKev
'Anglesey Not Galatea'	EHrv
'Anne of Geierstein'	IFoB WCot
'Ann's Millennium Giant'	CBro
'Armine'	CElw CTal IFoB LRHS NRHS WCot
'Art Nouveau'	CAvo CElw EHrv
'Atkinsii' ♀H5	CAvo CBro CElw CLAP CMea CRos ECho EHrv EPot EWoo GEdr GKev IFoB LAma LRHS MAsh MRav MWat NBir NPnk NRHS SDir SDix WCot WFar WHoo WShi XEll
'Autumn Beauty'	CBro LRHS NRHS
'Babraham Scented'	CAvo GEdr
'Backhouse Spectacles'	GEdr ITim
'Ballerina' (d) **new**	CAvo
'Bankside'	CAvo
'Barbara's Double' (d)	CAvo EWes MAsh NHar
'Barbara's Hybrid'	EHrv
'Benhall Beauty'	CElw EHrv EWes GEdr
'Benton Magnet'	ITim
'Bertram Anderson' ♀H5	EHrv GEdr MAsh WCot
'Bess'	CAvo CElw CTal EHrv GEdr IFoB
'Bill Bishop'	CBro CTal EHrv EWoo GEdr IFoB MAsh WCot
'Bitton' ambig.	NPol
'Blewbury'	EHrv IFoB
'Brenda Troyle'	CBro CElw CLAP ECho EPot GEdr LRHS MAsh MHom NPol NRHS WCot WFar
'Brigadier Mathias'	EHrv

	'Byfield Special'	CAvo EHrv IFoB
	byzantinus	see *G. plicatus* subsp. *byzantinus*
	'Caryl Baron' **new**	CAvo
	'Castlegar'	IFoB
	caucasicus misapplied	see *G. elwesii* var. *monostictus*
	caucasicus ambig.	IFoB NPol
	- 'Comet'	see *G. elwesii* 'Comet'
	- var. ***hiemalis***	see *G. elwesii* Hiemalis Group
	'Chthonic' **new**	CAvo
	'Cicely Hall'	IFoB
	'Clare Blakeway-Phillips'	CAvo
	corcyrensis spring-flowering	see *G. reginae-olgae* subsp. *vernalis*
	- winter-flowering	see *G. reginae-olgae* subsp. *reginae-olgae* Winter-flowering Group
	'Cordelia' (d)	CElw CLAP IFoB MAsh
	'Cornwood Gem'	CAvo IFoB
	'Cowhouse Green'	CAvo CSna EHrv GEdr
	'Curly'	CAvo EHrv EWes GEdr IFoB MAsh
	'Daglingworth'	GEdr
	'David Baker'	GEdr
	'Desdemona' (d)	CBro CLAP EHrv EPot GAbr LLHF WCot WFar
	'Devon Marble' **new**	CAvo
	'Ding Dong'	CAvo EHrv GEdr IFoB
	'Dionysus' (d)	CBro CLAP EHrv EPot EWes EWoo GAbr GEdr GKev LLHF MHom NBir NPnk WBrk WFar WShi XEll
	'Drummond's Giant'	IFoB
	'Dymock' **new**	CAvo
	'Ecusson d'Or'	CAvo
§	***elwesii*** 🏆H5	CBro CTri ECho ELan EPfP EPot ERCP IFoB LAma LCro LRHS MMuc MWat NBir NNys NPnk NPol NRHS SCob SDeJ SDir SEND SRms WCot WFar WHoo WShi
	- 'Abington Green'	CSna
	- 'Bo Bette'	GEdr
	- 'Broadleigh Gardens'	EHrv
	- 'Bubble' **new**	CAvo
	- 'Cedric's Prolific'	ECha EHrv EWoo GEdr IFoB ITim WFar
§	- 'Comet' 🏆H5	CElw EHrv GBuc GEdr IFoB MAsh WFar
	- 'Daphne's Scissors'	CElw CSna GEdr
	- 'David Shackleton'	CElw EHrv IFoB MAsh
	- 'December Green Tip'	WCot
	- 'Deer Slot' **new**	CAvo
	- 'Early Twin'	WCot
	- 'Echoes'	WCot
	- Edward Whittall Group	CLAP
	- - 'Two Eyes'	EHrv
	- 'Elmley Lovett'	CAvo CElw
	- var. ***elwesii***	EHrv
	- - 'Fenstead End'	GEdr
	- - 'Fred's Giant'	GMaP
	- - 'Kite'	EHrv GEdr
	- - 'Magnus'	NBir
	- - 'Maidwell L'	CBro CTal EHrv
	- - 'Sibbertoft Magnet'	IFoB
	- 'X Files' **new**	CAvo
*	- 'Flore Pleno' (d)	NPol
	- 'Godfrey Owen'	CAvo GEdr IFoB
	- 'Green Brush'	CBro EWes GKev IFoB LAma LRHS
	- 'Grumpy'	CAvo EHrv GEdr MAsh
§	- Hiemalis Group	CBro EHrv EPot GKev MHom WCot XEll
	- - 'Barnes'	EHrv GKev WCot
	- - 'Donald Sims'	EHrv
	- - 'Rainbow Farm Early'	EHrv
	- 'J. Haydn'	LAma
	- 'Jessica'	IFoB
	- 'Kyre Park'	GEdr MAsh
	- 'Long 'drop'	GEdr IFoB
	- 'Mandarin'	CElw EWes
	- 'Marielle'	EPPr
	- 'Marjorie Brown'	CAvo CFis EHrv GEdr ITim
	- var. ***maximus***	see *G. elwesii* 'Yvonne Hay'
	- 'Milkwood'	see *G. elwesii* 'Mrs Macnamara'
	- 'Miss Mowcher'	WCot
§	- var. ***monostictus*** 🏆H5	CBro ECha ECho EHrv GKev IFoB LLHF LRHS NPnk NRHS WBrk WFar WShi
	- - 'B. Britten'	LAma
	- - 'G. Handel'	IFoB LAma LLHF LRHS NPnk
	- - 'Grayswood'	GEdr
	- - 'H. Purcell'	CTal GEdr LAma LLHF LRHS NPnk
	- - late-flowering	ECho
	- - 'Lord Monostictus'	CAvo
	- - 'Miller's Late'	CAvo EHrv
	- - 'Mozart'	LAma
	- - 'Rogers Rough'	SDys
	- - 'Warwickshire Gemini'	CAvo MHCG
	- aff. var. ***monostictus***	WFar
	- 'Mr Omer'	WCot
	- 'Mr Peggotty'	WCot
§	- 'Mrs Macnamara'	CAvo CTal EHrv EWoo GEdr IFoB MAsh WFar
	- November-flowering	WCot
	- 'Penelope Ann'	EHrv GEdr
	- 'Peter Gatehouse'	EHrv
§	- 'Ransom's Dwarf'	GEdr
*	- 'Robustus Praecox'	GKev
	- 'Selborne Green Tips'	EHrv
	- 'Sickle'	CSna CTal EHrv NHar
	- 'Sir Edward Elgar'	LAma LLHF
	- 'Three Leaves'	CAvo IFoB
	- 'Washfield Colesbourne'	see *G.* 'Washfield Colesbourne'
§	- 'Yvonne Hay'	EHrv
	- 'Zwanenburg'	EHrv
	'Epiphany'	CAvo EHrv
	'Ermine House' (d)	EHrv
	'Erway'	CAvo MHom
I	'Excelsis'	CAvo
	'F63'	IFoB
	'Falkland House'	CElw GEdr
	'Faringdon Double' (d)	EHrv MAsh
	'Fieldgate Forte' **new**	CAvo
	'Fieldgate Prelude'	EHrv GEdr
	'Fieldgate Superb'	EHrv IFoB
	'Fieldgate Tiffany'	CAvo
	'Fly Fishing'	CAvo
	fosteri	CBro ECho EHrv GEdr
	'Framlingham Double' (d)	EHrv
	'G71' (d)	IFoB
	'Gabriel'	CAvo
	'Galadriel'	CAvo GEdr
	'Galatea'	CAvo CBro CSna EHrv EPot EWes EWoo GAbr MAsh MHom SDys WFar
	'George Elwes'	CAvo
	'Ginns'	CLAP EHrv EWoo IFoB
	'Gloria'	MAsh
§	***gracilis***	CBre CBro GKev NPol WCot
	- 'Highdown'	CElw EHrv GKev IFoB MAsh MHom
	- Kew	CElw
	- 'Vic Horton'	CElw EHrv WThu
	graecus misapplied	see *G. gracilis*
	graecus Orph. ex Boiss.	see *G. elwesii*
	'Grande Juge'	IFoB

'Grayling'	see *G. plicatus* 'Percy Picton'
Greatorex double (d)	CLAP
'Green Arrow'	CAvo
'Green Man'	EHrv GEdr IFoB WFar
'Green Necklace'	CAvo EWes LRHS
'Green Ribbon'	CAvo
'Greenfields'	CSna IFoB MAsh
green-tipped double (d) **new**	GEdr
'Heffalump' (d)	EHrv GEdr IFoB MAsh
'Hill Poë' (d)	CAvo CBro CElw CLAP EHrv EPot GEdr IFoB LLHF MAsh MHom MWat
'Hippolyta' (d)	CAvo CBro CElw CLAP ECha EHrv EPot EWoo GEdr GKev IFoB LAma LRHS MAsh MHom NPol SDir SKHP WCot WShi
'Hobson's Choice'	EHrv
'Homersfield'	EHrv
'Honeysuckle Cottage'	CAvo
× ***hybridus*** 'Merlin' ♀H5	CBro CElw EHrv GEdr IFoB WCot WFar WHoo
- 'Robin Hood'	EHrv GAbr GEdr IFoB
'Icicle'	CAvo GEdr
§ ***ikariae*** Bak.	EPfP GEdr GKev LRHS
- subsp. ***ikariae*** Butt's form	NPol
- Latifolius Group	see *G. platyphyllus*
- subsp. ***snogerupii***	see *G. ikariae* Bak.
'Imbolc'	CAvo EHrv GEdr IFoB
'Irish Green'	CAvo IFoB
'Ivy Cottage Corporal'	EHrv
'Ivy Cottage Green Tip'	EHrv
'Jacquenetta' (d)	CBro CElw CLAP CSna EHrv EWes GEdr IFoB ITim LAma MCot MHom
'Jade'	CAvo
'James Backhouse'	EHrv WHoo WShi
'John Gray'	CBro EHrv EWes GEdr IFoB MAsh
'June Boardman'	CAvo
'Kersen' **new**	CAvo
'Ketton'	CBro CElw CSna CTal EHrv EWoo GEdr GKev IFoB LLHF NRya
'Kew Green' **new**	CAvo
'Kildare'	CTal IFoB
'Kingston Double' (d)	CLAP EHrv
'Kinn McIntosh' **new**	WCot
krasnovii	GKev
'Lady Beatrix Stanley' (d) ♀H5	CAvo CBro CElw CLAP ECha EHrv EPot GEdr IFoB ITim LLWP LRHS MAsh MHom WCot WFar
lagodechianus	CBro GKev MPhe
'Lapwing'	CAvo EHrv GEdr IFoB MAsh
latifolius Rupr.	see *G. platyphyllus*
'Lavinia' (d)	CElw EHrv EWes GEdr MAsh MHom WFar
'Lerinda'	EHrv IFoB
'Limetree'	CElw CLAP EHrv EPri EWes EWoo GKev ITim MHom NPol WFar
'Little Ben'	CElw EHrv GEdr GMaP
'Little Dorrit'	GEdr
'Little John'	EHrv GEdr WBrk
'Little Magnet'	CAvo SDir
'Longstowe'	CTal MAsh
'Louise Ann Bromley'	CAvo
lutescens	see *G. nivalis* Sandersii Group
'Lyn'	CBro EHrv GEdr NBir
'Magnet' ♀H5	CAvo CBro CElw CLAP CMea CTal EHrv ELon EPfP EPot EWoo GEdr GKev LAma LEdu LRHS MAsh MHom MWat NBir NPol NRHS SDir SKHP WBrk WCot WFar WHoo WShi XEll
aff. 'Magnet'	GMaP SDir
'Maidwell'	IFoB
'Melanie Broughton'	CAvo IFoB
'Midwinter'	CAvo
'Mighty Atom'	CBro CLAP GAbr WBrk
'Mill House'	EHrv
'Moccas'	CElw CSna MHom
'Modern Art'	CAvo GEdr IFoB MAsh
'Mrs Backhouse No 12'	EHrv IFoB
'Mrs Thompson'	CAvo CElw EHrv GEdr IFoB MAsh
'Mrs Wrightson's Double' (d)	CAvo
'Myddelton Giant' **new**	CAvo
'Natalie Garton'	CAvo EHrv IFoB
'Neill Fraser'	EHrv GEdr MHom
'Nerissa' (d)	GEdr
nivalis ♀H5	Widely available
- 'Anglesey Abbey'	CElw EHrv EWes GEdr IFoB MHom
- 'April Fool'	MHom
- 'Ballynahinch'	ITim
- 'Bitton'	EHrv GEdr
- 'Blonde Inge'	CAvo GEdr IFoB MAsh
- 'Chedworth'	CElw GEdr WBrk
- 'Cornwood'	CAvo
- 'Dreycott Greentip'	IFoB
- dwarf	ITim
- 'Elfin'	CAvo CElw EHrv EWes GKev IFoB MAsh WCot
- 'Fluff'	EHrv
- 'Fuzz'	CAvo
- 'Gloucester Old Spot'	GEdr
- 'Lutescens'	see *G. nivalis* Sandersii Group
- 'Major Pam'	IFoB
- 'Margery Fish' **new**	CAvo
- 'Maximus'	WShi
- 'Melvillei'	CAvo MAsh
- f. ***pleniflorus*** (d)	GKev MAsh NPri SPoG
- - 'Bagpuize Virginia' (d)	CAvo
- - 'Blewbury Tart' (d)	CAvo CBro CElw CLAP CSna EHrv EWes EWoo GEdr IFoB WBrk WFar
- - 'Boyd's Double' (d) **new**	CAvo
- - 'Doncaster's Double Scharlock' (d) **new**	CAvo
- - 'Flore Pleno' (d) ♀H5	CBro CWCL EPfP EPot ERCP ESps IFoB LAma LBMP LCro LHop LLWP LOPS LRHS MMuc NHpl NPnk NRya SCob SDeJ SEND SPer SRms WBrk WCot WHoo WShi
- - 'Lady Elphinstone' (d)	CAvo CBro CLAP CSna EHrv IFoB LLHF LRHS MAsh MHom NPol NRya WCot
- - 'Pusey Green Tips' (d)	CAvo CBro CElw CLAP EPot GAbr IFoB NPol WCot
- - Scharlockii Group double (d)	GKev
- - 'Walrus' (d)	EHrv GEdr MAsh NHar
§ - - 'Wonston Double' (d)	EHrv IFoB
- Poculiformis Group	CElw CLAP EHrv MAsh
- - 'Angelique'	CAvo
- - 'Henry's White Lady'	GEdr
- cf. Poculiformis Group	CElw
- 'Puck' **new**	CAvo
§ - Sandersii Group	GMaP IFoB WFar
- - 'Lowick' **new**	CAvo
- - 'Ray Cobb' **new**	CAvo
§ - Scharlockii Group	CElw MAsh MHom WBrk
- 'Sibbertoft White'	MAsh
- 'Tiny'	IFoB LRHS MHom WFar
- 'Tiny Tim'	ITim MAsh WFar
- 'Virescens'	CLAP IFoB
- 'Viridapice'	CAvo CBro CElw ECha EPot ERCP GKev GMaP IFoB LAma LRHS MAsh

MWat NBir NPnk NPol NRHS SDeJ SKHP WCot WFar WHoo WShi
- 'Warei' EHrv
- 'White Dream' GEdr IFoB WShi
'Nothing Special' GKev MAsh
'One Drop or Two' **new** CAvo
'Ophelia' (d) CAvo CBro EHrv EPot EWoo GEdr LRHS MAsh MHom MWat NPol SKHP WBrk WFar WHoo
'Peardrop' EHrv GEdr NHar
'Peg Sharples' EHrv GEdr IFoB LRHS MHom
peshmenii ECho LEdu
'Philippe André Meyer' **new** CAvo
§ ***platyphyllus*** LLWP LRHS NRHS
plicatus 🏆H5 CAvo CBro CElw EHrv GKev LRHS MCot MHom NPnk NPol NRHS WBrk WCot WHoo WShi
- from Coton Manor EHrv MCot
- 'Augustus' CBro CElw EHrv EPot EWes GEdr IFoB MAsh MHom WCot WHoo
- 'Babraham Dwarf' EHrv
- 'Baxendale's Late' CAvo CLAP GEdr
- 'Beth Chatto' EHrv
- 'Bill Clark' IFoB
- 'Bolu Shades' IFoB
- 'Bowles's Large' EHrv
§ - subsp. ***byzantinus*** CBro EHrv MHom WThu
- - 'Fox Farm' EHrv
- 'Colossus' CBro CTal ECho EHrv EWes GKev IFoB WCot
- 'Diggory' CAvo EHrv GEdr IFoB MAsh
- 'Duckie' GEdr WFar
- 'E.A. Bowles' GEdr
- 'Edinburgh Ketton' EHrv
- 'Florence Baker' CAvo EHrv GEdr
- 'Gerard Parker' EHrv IFoB
- 'Green Hayes' EHrv
- 'Green Teeth' MAsh
- 'Greenpeace' CSna
- 'Henham No. 1' EHrv
- 'John Long' GEdr
- late flowering GKev
- 'Limey' EWoo
- 'Madelaine' CAvo MAsh
§ - 'Percy Picton' CAvo EWes GEdr
- 'Phil Cornish' **new** CAvo
- subsp. ***plicatus*** **new** GKev
- 'Sally Pasmore' CAvo GKev
- 'Sophie North' CElw CTal IFoB LLHF
- 'The Pearl' EHrv GEdr IFoB
- 'Three Ships' 🏆H5 EHrv GEdr IFoB MHom NHar
- 'Trym' CAvo EHrv GEdr IFoB NPol WFar
- 'Wandlebury Ring' EHrv
- 'Warham' CBro CElw EPot IFoB ITim MHom NPnk WCot
- 'Warham Rectory' EHrv
- 'Wendy's Gold' 🏆H5 CAvo CBro CSna EHrv IFoB MAsh WFar
- 'Woodtown' IMou
'Pom-pom' CAvo
'Porlock No 2' EHrv
'Pride o' the Mill' CAvo GEdr
'Primrose Warburg' CAvo EHrv GEdr IFoB LRHS MAsh WFar
'Ransom's Dwarf' see *G. elwesii* 'Ransom's Dwarf'
reginae-olgae ECho EHrv GKev IFoB MHom
- subsp. ***reginae-olgae*** 🏆H3 EPot GKev
- - 'Cambridge' EHrv MHom
- - 'Tilebarn Jamie' MHom
§ - - Winter-flowering Group CBro
§ - subsp. ***vernalis*** EPot GKev IFoB LEdu WCot
- - 'Miss Adventure' EHrv
'Reverend Hailstone' CAvo EHrv GEdr IFoB
'Richard Ayres' (d) CAvo EHrv GEdr IFoB LRHS WCot
rizehensis CAvo CLAP GKev IFoB MHom
- Baytop 34474 EHrv IFoB
'Rodmarton' EHrv GEdr IFoB
'Ruth Birchall' EHrv
'S. Arnott' 🏆H5 CAvo CBro CElw CLAP CMea ECha ECho EHrv EPot ERCP EWoo GBuc GKev IFoB LAma LCro LOPS LRHS MAsh MWat NBir NPnk NPol NRHS NRya SDeJ WBrk WCot WFar WHoo
'Saint Anne's' CElw CSna GEdr IFoB MHom
'Scharlockii' see *G. nivalis* Scharlockii Group
'Seagull' CElw EHrv GEdr
'Sentinel' CElw EHrv
'Silverwells' CSna CTal EHrv GEdr IFoB
'Sir Herbert Maxwell' ITim MAsh
'Spindlestone Surprise' CAvo EHrv EWoo GEdr NHar
'Sprite' CAvo
'St Pancras' CAvo EHrv
'Starling' **new** CAvo
§ 'Straffan' 🏆H5 CAvo CBro CElw ECho EHrv EPot GEdr GKev IFoB MHom NPol WBrk WCot WFar
'Sutton Courtenay' CSna
'The Apothecary' EHrv
'The O'Mahoney' see *G.* 'Straffan'
'The Wizard' CAvo
'Titania' (d) EHrv GEdr IFoB MAsh MHom WShi
'Trotter's Merlin' CAvo CElw
'Trumps' CAvo NHar
'Trymming' CAvo
'Trympostor' CAvo EHrv
'Tubby Merlin' CElw EHrv EWoo IFoB
'Uncle Dick' CAvo
× ***valentinei*** 'Compton Court' CBro IFoB ITim
'Vertigo' **new** CAvo
§ 'Washfield Colesbourne' CElw EHrv EWoo
'Washfield Warham' CElw ECha EHrv EWoo ITim MAsh
'Wasp' CAvo GEdr MAsh NHar WCot
'Welshway' CAvo GEdr
'White Admiral' SKHP
'White Dreams' GEdr IFoB
'White Swan' Ballard (d) CElw EWes ITim
'William Thomson' CSna EWes
'Winifrede Mathias' CElw EHrv MAsh
'Wisley Magnet' EHrv
'Wonston Double' see *G. nivalis* f. *pleniflorus* 'Wonston Double'
woronowii 🏆H5 CBro CElw CLAP CTca CTri ECho EHrv EPfP EPot GAbr GKev IFoB LAma LCro LEdu LRHS MHom MWat NBir NPnk SCob SDeJ SDix SPer WBrk WCot WFar WShi

Galatella (*Asteraceae*)

§ ***linosyris*** EBee EWes MAvo NLar SPer SPhx WHer WOld XLum
§ ***sedifolia*** ECtt ELan ELon GAbr GQue LEdu LRHS MAvo NBid NEgg NSti SDix SEND SPoG WCot WOld
- RCB AM 5 WCot
- 'Nana' EBee ELan GCal MRav NBir NLar NWsh SPer WCot WFar WOld WTor XLum
- 'Rosea' IMou

Galax (*Diapensiaceae*)

aphylla	see *G. urceolata*
§ ***urceolata***	EBee GAbr IBlr MNrw WSHC

Galega (*Papilionaceae*)

bicolor	NBir SRms SWat
'Duchess of Bedford'	GBin
× ***hartlandii*** 'Alba' ♀H7	ELon EWes GBin GNew IBlr LRHS MArl MCot MRav SHar SMHy SWat WCot WHoo WSHC WWtn
- 'Lady Wilson' ♀H7	CWld ECtt ELon EPPr EWes EWld GBin MArl MAvo MMrt SHar SRms WCot WHrl
'Her Majesty'	see *G.* 'His Majesty'
§ 'His Majesty'	EBee ECtt EPPr IFro LEdu MAvo MCot MRav WCot
officinalis	Widely available
- 'Alba'	CBod ECtt ELan EPfP GJos LEdu LPot LSun MAvo MBel MBrN MHer MMuc MNHC SEND SPer SRms WHer WHrl WKif WMoo
- 'Lincoln Gold'	MTPN
orientalis	EBee ECtt EWes LEdu MArl MAvo MCot MRav SBrt WMoo WPGP WSHC

Galeobdolon see *Lamium*

Galeopsis (*Lamiaceae*)

tetrahit	WSFF

Galium (*Rubiaceae*)

cruciata	see *Cruciata laevipes*
mollugo	CHab CWld
§ ***odoratum***	Widely available
verum	CArn CHab CWld ENfk GJos GPoy MHer MMuc MNHC NMir SEND SIde SRms

Galtonia (*Asparagaceae*)

candicans ♀H4	Widely available
- 'Moonbeam' (d)	EBee GKev
princeps	CSam ECha GBin GCra IMou LRHS WHil WPGP
regalis	CTca WPGP
viridiflora	CTca CWld EBee ECha ELan EPot ERCP GBin GCal GKev IBoy LRHS MNrw NChi NNys NWad SDeJ SDir XLum

Galvezia (*Plantaginaceae*)

speciosa	CCCN CHll CSpe LRHS MCot

Gamblea (*Araliaceae*)

pseudoevodiifolia B&SWJ 11707	WCru

Garcinia (*Clusiaceae*)

mangostana	CCCN

Gardenia (*Rubiaceae*)

augusta	see *G. jasminoides*
'Crown Jewel' PBR	EBee EPfP LCro LRHS SEle SPoG
florida L.	see *G. jasminoides*
grandiflora	see *G. jasminoides*
§ ***jasminoides*** ♀H1c	CBcs CCCN EBak
- 'Kleim's Hardy'	CDTJ CHll CRos CSBt CWld EBee ELon EPfP ESps IDee LCro LRHS LSRN MAsh MBlu MMuc NPri SChF SCoo SEND SEle SLim SPad SPer SPlb SPoG SRkn SSta WCot

garlic see *Allium sativum*

garlic, elephant see *Allium ampeloprasum* 'Elephant'

Garrya ✿ (*Garryaceae*)

sp.	ESps LPar
congdonii	IArd
elliptica	CBcs CDul CMac CRos EBee EPfP ESps LPar LRHS LSRN MAsh MGos NPnk NPri NWea SCob WFar WHar
- (f)	MJak MRav MSwo SWvt
- (m)	CTri LPar MBlu NLar SGol SLim
- 'James Roof' (m) ♀H4	Widely available
flavescens new	SIgm
× ***issaquahensis*** 'Glasnevin Wine' (m) ♀H4	CDul CJun CRos ELan EPfP IArd LRHS MAsh MGos SCob SCoo SPoG
- 'Pat Ballard' (m)	EPfP NLar
× ***thuretii***	CBcs EBee GMcL NLar SEND SGol SPer WFar

Gasteria ✿ (*Asphodelaceae*)

batesiana ♀H2	SEND
bicolor var. ***liliputana*** ♀H2	SPlb
carinata var. ***verrucosa***	EShb SEND SPlb
ellaphieae	LToo
nitida var. ***nitida*** variegated (v)	WCot
'Smokey'	EShb

× *Gaulnettya* see *Gaultheria*

Gaultheria ✿ (*Ericaceae*)

NJM 10.032	WPGP
antarctica	WThu
cardiosepala	WThu
crassa 'John Saxton'	WAbe
cuneata	CRos ECho GEdr LRHS MAsh NHar WThu
forrestii BWJ 7809	WCru
hispida	CPne
itoana	GEdr GJos NHar WThu
miqueliana	GEdr NLar WThu
mucronata	CDul EPfP ESps MAsh MJak NWea WFar
- (m)	CMac CSBt CTri ELan EPfP GMcL MGos MMuc NEgg NWad SPer SRms WFar
- 'Alba' (f)	MJak
- 'Bell's Seedling' (f/m) ♀H6	CBcs CDul CLet CTri ELan EPfP ESps GMcL LRHS MAsh MMuc NBir NEgg NLar SCob SGbt SPer SPoG
- 'Cherry Ripe' (f)	CMac MMuc
- 'Crimsonia' (f) ♀H6	CBcs CLet CMac EPfP SRms
- 'Indian Lake'	NWad
- 'Lilacina' (f)	CMac MAsh
- 'Lilian' (f)	CSBt EPfP NWad
- Mother of Pearl	see *G. mucronata* 'Parelmoer'
- 'Mulberry Wine' (f) ♀H6	CBcs CSBt CTri ELan MHtn MMuc NEgg NHol SPer
§ - 'Parelmoer' (f)	CSBt SPer
- 'Pink Pearl' (f) ♀H6	CLet SRms
- pink-berried (f)	GMcL
- red-berried (f)	GMcL MJak
- 'Rosea' (f)	MJak
§ - 'Signaal' (f)	CBcs ELan EPfP LRHS MAsh NEgg NLar NWad SCob SPer

	- Signal	see *G. mucronata* 'Signaal'
§	- 'Sneeuwwitje' (f)	CBcs CDul CSBt ELan EPfP LRHS MAsh MMuc NBir SPer
	- Snow White	see *G. mucronata* 'Sneeuwwitje'
	- 'Thymifolia' (m)	EPfP
	- 'White Pearl' (f)	ESps
	- white-berried (f)	GMcL
	- 'Wintertime' (f) ♀H6	CMac SRms
§	***myrsinoides***	WThu
	'Pearls'	EPot NHar NWad WAbe WThu
	'Pink Champagne'	ITim
	procumbens ♀H4	Widely available
	- 'Very Berry'	EShb NWad WFar
	prostrata	see *G. myrsinoides*
	pumila	LEdu NHar
	schultesii	WThu
	shallon	CAgr CBcs CSBt EPfP GMcL MCoo MJak MMuc NLar SPer SRms SWvt WFar
	sinensis	NHar
	- lilac-berried	GEdr
	thymifolia	NWad
	trichophylla	NHar
	× ***wisleyensis***	CRos LRHS SLon SRms
	- 'Pink Pixie'	CRos LRHS MAsh NLar
	- 'Ruby'	CMac
	- 'Wisley Pearl'	MMuc SCoo WFar

Gaura (*Onagraceae*)

	'Experimental Deep Rose' **new**	LRHS NRHS
§	Gaudi Pink = 'Florgaucompi'[PBR]	LRHS NRHS
	lindheimeri ♀H4	Widely available
	- 'Bargau' (Pink Panache) (v) **new**	EBee WTor
	- Belleza Series	CRos CWCL EPau EPfP LRHS SHil
	- - Belleza Dark Pink = 'Kleau04263' **new**	LRHS NRHS
	- - Belleza White = 'Kleau04264' **new**	LRHS NRHS
	- 'Blaze'[PBR]	LRHS
	- Cherry Brandy = 'Gauchebra'[PBR]	CRos EAEE EBee ECtt ELan EPfP IPot LRHS SHil SWvt WHar
	- 'Chiffon'	SHar
	- 'Corrie's Gold' (v)	CAby EBee ECha ECtt EHoe ELan EPfP LRHS MHer NRHS SPer
	- 'Crimson Butterflies'[PBR]	ELan EPfP
	- 'Freefolk Rosy' (v)	LCro SHar
	- 'Gambit Rose'	EBee
	- 'Gambit White'	EBee
	- Gaudi Red = 'Florgaured'	EPfP LRHS NRHS
	- (Geyser Series) Geyser Pink = 'Gaudros'[PBR]	CBod EBee EPfP LRHS NRHS
	- - Geyser White = 'Gaudwwhi'[PBR]	EBee EPfP
§	- 'Heather's Delight'	MRav
	- 'Ice Cool Rosy' **new**	EBee
	- In the Pink	see *G. lindheimeri* 'Heather's Delight'
	- 'Jo Adela' (v)	ECha EPfP
	- Karalee Petite = 'Gauka'	CWCL EPfP
	- Karalee Petite Improved	see *G. lindheimeri* Lillipop Pink
	- Karalee White = 'Nugauwhite'[PBR]	CBod CKno CRos ELan EPfP LHop LRHS NLar SCoo SHil SPer SPoG
§	- Lillipop Pink = 'Redgapi'[PBR]	CAby EPfP LRHS MBrN NLar SCob SPoG
	- 'My Melody'[PBR] (v)	WTor
	- 'Occitania' (v)	XLum
	- Papillon = 'Nugaupapil'[PBR]	ECtt SHil SPer SPoG
	- 'Passionate Blush'[PBR]	CBcs CChe EAEE ECtt ENor EPfP LRHS LSou MGos SLon SPoG SRms WHil
	- 'Passionate Pink'	LRHS
	- 'Passionate Rainbow'[PBR] (v)	CRos CWCL EPfP LBMP LRHS SHil SPad SPoG SRms
	- 'Pink Dwarf'	EBee EPfP SAdn
	- Pink Fountain = 'Walgaupf'	LRHS NRHS
	- 'Pink Gin'	EBee LSou SPoG
	- 'Rosy Shimmer' **new**	EBee
	- Rosyjane = 'Harrosy'[PBR]	Widely available
	- Ruby Ruby = 'Harruby'[PBR]	MNHC SHar
	- 'Siskiyou Pink'	CBcs CSBt CSpe CWCL EAEE EAJP EBee ECha ECtt EHoe ELan EPfP LCro LOPS LRHS MMuc MWat SAdn SCob SMad SPer SWat SWvt WCFE XLum XSen
	- Snow Fountain = 'Walsnofou'	LRHS NRHS
	- 'Sparkle White' **new**	LSun
	- 'Summer Breeze'	CBod CDor CSpe EAJP LRHS LSun MArt NGBl SPhx
	- 'Summer Emotions'	CBod MNrw
	- 'The Bride'	CTri CWCL EAEE EBee ECtt ELan EPfP GAbr LRHS LSRN MBel MMuc MNHC MRav MWat SAdn SBod SGbt SPav SPer SWvt
	- 'Tutti Frutti'	LSou SCob SPoG
	- 'Vanilla'	CKno CWCL LRHS LSou SPoG
I	- 'Variegata' (v)	CRos CWCL LRHS SHil SRms
	- 'Whirling Butterflies'	CBWd CKno CSpe CWCL ECtt ELan EPfP ESps GMaP IBoy LCro LOPS LRHS MWat SCob SMad SPer SWat SWvt
	- 'White Dove'	LRHS LSou
	- 'White Heron'	MNrw
	sinuata	CAby CFis SHar
	Stratosphere Pink Picotee	see *G.* Gaudi Pink

Gaylussacia (*Ericaceae*)

baccata (F)	CMac

Gazania (*Asteraceae*)

'Aztec'	CCCN
'Bicton Orange'	CCCN CSam ECtt SCoo SVen
'Big Kiss White Flame' (Kiss Series)	LBuc SPoG
'Big Kiss Yellow Flame' (Kiss Series)	LBuc SPoG
'Blackberry Ripple'	CCCN EBee SCoo
'Blackcurrant Ice'	MCot
'Christopher'	SCoo
'Christopher Lloyd'	CCCN ECtt
'Cookei'	CSpe
'Cornish Pixie'	CCCN
'Cream Beauty'	MCot
Gazoo Series	SPoG
krebsiana	CCCN
'Lemon Beauty'	ECtt
'Magic'	CCCN SCoo
Nahui = 'Suga119' (Sunbathers Series)	CCCN
'Orange Beauty'	ELan
rigens 'Variegata' (v)	CCCN ELan
Rumi = 'Suga116' (Sunbathers Series)	CCCN
Sunset Jane = 'Sugaja'[PBR] (Sunbathers Series)	CCCN
Sunset Jane Lemon Spot = 'Sugajale' (Sunbathers Series)	CCCN

	'Talent'	SEND
	Tiger Eye = 'Gazte' (v)	CCCN LSou SPoG
	Toptokai = 'Suga407' (Sunbathers Series)	CCCN
	Totonaca = 'Suga212' (Sunbathers Series)	CCCN

Geissorhiza (*Iridaceae*)

	aspera	CTre
	tulbaghensis	CTre

Gelidocalamus (*Poaceae*)

	fangianus	see *Ampelocalamus mocrophyllum*

Gelsemium (*Gelsemiaceae*)

	rankinii	LRHS
	sempervirens ♀H1c	CCCN CHll CRHN EBee LRHS LSRN SBrt SLim SPoG WCot

Genista (*Papilionaceae*)

	aetnensis ♀H5	CDul ELan EPfP LRHS MGil MMrt SArc SBrt SEND SPer SRms WPat WSHC
§	***canariensis*** ♀H1c	CSBt CWib
	carinalis	GJos
	cinerea	WCFE
	decumbens	see *Cytisus decumbens*
	'Emerald Spreader'	see *G. pilosa* 'Yellow Spreader'
	fragrans	see *G. canariensis*
	hispanica	CBcs CDul CSBt ELan EPfP ESps GMcL LPot NLar SCob SEND SPer SRms SWvt WCFE
	humifusa	see *G. pulchella*
	lydia ♀H5	Widely available
§	***maderensis***	CRos LRHS SHil
	monosperma	see *Retama monosperma*
	pilosa	EPot MAsh
	- 'Goldilocks'	LRHS MMuc
	- 'Lemon Spreader'	see *G. pilosa* 'Yellow Spreader'
	- var. ***minor***	NLar WAbe
	- 'Procumbens' ♀H5	CMea EPot GEdr SRot
	- 'Vancouver Gold'	CMac ELan EPfP MRav SPer SRms
§	- 'Yellow Spreader'	CBcs MAsh MSwo
§	'Porlock' ♀H3	CBcs CDul CLet CMac CRos CSBt CTri CWib EPfP LBMP LRHS MAsh MMuc MRav SEND SHil WHor
§	***pulchella***	CTri GCrg
	sagittalis	CTri GJos LRHS MMuc NBir SPer WWFP
§	× ***spachiana*** ♀H1c	CEnd CTri SHil SPoG
	tinctoria	CArn CHab GJos GPoy MCot MHer WHer
§	- 'Flore Pleno' (d) ♀H6	CLet ECho
	- 'Humifusa'	EPot GEdr
	- 'Plena'	see *G. tinctoria* 'Flore Pleno'
	- 'Royal Gold' ♀H6	CWib ESps MRav NWad SPer SPlb
	villarsii	see *G. pulchella*

Gennaria (*Orchidaceae*)

	diphylla	GKev

Gentiana ✿ (*Gentianaceae*)

§	***acaulis*** ♀H5	CMea CPla CRos ECho EPfP EPot GKev LHop LRHS MAsh NGdn NHar NLar NRHS NSla SBch SIgm SPlb SRms WAbe
	- SDR 1323	GKev
	- f. ***alba***	WThu
	- - 'Snowstorm'	GKev
	- 'Belvedere'	EPot
	- 'Coelestina'	WThu
	- 'Dinarica'	see *G. dinarica*
	- 'Holzmannii'	IVic WAbe
	- 'Krumrey'	EPot GEdr GKev
	- 'Luna' PBR	NLar
	- 'Max Frei'	NHar
I	- 'Maxima Enzian'	EPot GEdr
	- 'Rannoch'	EPot GEdr
	- 'Stumpy'	GEdr
	- 'Trotter's Variety'	WAbe
	- 'Undulatifolia'	EPot
	- 'Velkokvensis'	EPot
	'Alex Duguid'	CRos GCrg GEdr IVic LRHS NHar
	'Amethyst'	CRos EPot GEdr LRHS NHar WAbe
	angulosa misapplied	see *G. verna* 'Angulosa' hort.
	angustifolia	WAbe XEll
	'Ann's Special'	GEdr
	asclepiadea ♀H5	CLAP CSpe CTal CTri ECho ELan GCra GEdr GKev GMaP LEdu LRHS MNrw NBid NBir NCGa NLar NSti SIgm SPer SRms WBor WCFE WCot WHoo WKif WSHC
	- 'Alba'	CLAP EBee GCal GEdr GKev GMaP LEdu LRHS NBid NRHS SPer SRms WCFE WHoo
	- dark blue-flowered	GCal WPGP
	- 'Hoo House'	WHoo
	- 'Knightshayes'	EBee GKev
I	- 'Nana'	GKev
	- 'Phyllis'	WHoo
	- 'Pink Swallow'	GEdr GQue MArt
	- 'Rosea'	GEdr GKev MNrw
	- 'White Swallow' **new**	GEdr
	'Balmoral' PBR	GMaP NHar
	'Barbara Lyle'	WAbe
	bavarica var. ***subacaulis***	SPlb
	× ***bernardii***	see *G.* × *stevenagensis* 'Bernardii'
	'Berrybank Dome'	GEdr GMaP LRHS
	'Berrybank Sky'	CRos GAbr GEdr GMaP LRHS
	'Berrybank Snowflakes'	GMaP
	'Berrybank Star'	GEdr GMaP
	bisetaea	SRms
	'Blauer Diamant'	GEdr
	'Blauer Kobold'	GEdr
	'Blauer Stern'	IVic
	'Blauer Zwerg'	GEdr
	'Blue Flame'	GEdr
	'Blue Heaven'	GEdr
	'Blue Magic' PBR	EBee LRHS
	'Blue Sea'	LRHS
	'Blue Silk' ♀H5	CRos CSma EPfP GCrg GEdr GKev IVic LRHS NHar NRHS SPoG WAbe
	brachyphylla	WAbe
	'Braemar' PBR	GMaP NHar
*	***burrowthii***	GEdr
	cachemirica	SIgm
	'Cairngorm'	GEdr LRHS NHar
	'Carmen'	GEdr
	× ***caroli***	WAbe
*	***clusii alboviolacea***	LLHF
	'Compact Gem'	GEdr NHar WAbe
§	***cruciata***	ELan GEdr MMrt NLar
§	***dahurica***	ECho GEdr GLog MMuc NGdn NLar
	'Dark Hedgehog'	GEdr
	decumbens	GKev
	depressa	EPot GEdr WAbe
	'Devonhall'	GEdr IVic NHar NWad
	'Diana' PBR	LRHS NLar
§	***dinarica***	ECho GKev NHar SIgm
	- 'Colonel Stitt'	GEdr WThu
	- 'Frocheneite'	EPot

'Dumpy'	GEdr
'Elehn'	GEdr NHar
'Elizabeth'	GEdr
'Ettrick'	GEdr IVic
'Eugen's Allerbester' (d)	CRos CSma EWld GEdr GKev GMaP IVic LRHS NHar NHol NLar NWad SPer WAbe
'Eugen's Bester'	NHar
farreri Silken Star Group	WAbe
'Faszination'	GEdr
fetissowii	see *G. macrophylla* var. *fetissowii*
'Gellerhard'	GEdr
georgei	EPot
'Gewahn'	GEdr IVic NHar
I 'Glamis Strain'	CRos GEdr LRHS NHar
'Glen Moy'	GEdr
'Glendevon'	GEdr
§ ***gracilipes***	GEdr GKev LLHF SPlb SRms
- 'Yuatensis'	see *G. macrophylla* var. *fetissowii*
'Henry'	GEdr
hexaphylla	EPot GEdr
Inshriach hybrids	LRHS
'Inverleith'	GEdr LRHS NHol SPlb
'Iona'PBR	GMaP NHar
'Joan Ward'	CRos LRHS SPer
'John Aitken'	GEdr
'Juwel'	GEdr
'Kobold'	GEdr
kochiana	see *G. acaulis*
kurroo var. ***brevidens***	see *G. dahurica*
lagodechiana	see *G. septemfida* var. *lagodechiana*
ligustica	EPot
'Little Diamond'PBR	LRHS NLar
'Lucerna'	EPfP GCrg GEdr GKev LRHS
lutea	EBee GCal GPoy LLHF SMad SRms
× ***macaulayi***	CPla
- 'Blue Bonnets'	GEdr
- 'Elata'	IVic NWad
- 'Kidbrooke Seedling'	GEdr GMaP LRHS WAbe
- 'Kingfisher'	CPla GEdr IVic LRHS NBir WAbe
§ ***macrophylla*** var. ***fetissowii***	LLHF
makinoi 'Marsha'PBR	CHll GEdr LRHS MMrt NHpl NLar SPoG
- 'White Magic'PBR	GEdr
'Margaret'	GEdr
'Maryfield'	GEdr
'Melanie'	GEdr NHar
microdonta	EPot LLHF
'Multiflora'	LRHS
'Mystic'PBR	NLar
occidentalis	EPot
ornata	LRHS
paradoxa 🏆H5	EPot GKev LLHF SBrt SIgm WAbe
- 'Blauer Herold'	GKev
phlogifolia	see *G. cruciata*
pneumonanthe	LRHS NLar SPlb
pumila subsp. ***delphinensis***	WAbe
purdomii	see *G. gracilipes*
robusta CC 7494 new	GKev
'Sapphire Blue'	GEdr
saxosa	GCrg GKev ITim LRHS NBir NHpl NSla WAbe
scabra	LRHS
- 'Zuikorindo'	NLar
'Selektra'	GEdr IVic
septemfida 🏆H5	CRos LHop LRHS MAsh MJak NBir NHpl NRHS NSla SPlb SRms WHoo WKif
- 'Alba'	GKev LLHF
- var. ***kolakovskyi***	LLHF
§ - var. ***lagodechiana*** 🏆H5	LLHF LRHS SRms XLum
'Serenity'	CSma GEdr IVic LRHS NHar NLar NWad WAbe
'Shot Silk' 🏆H5	CRos EWes GAbr GCrg GEdr GMaP LRHS MGos NBir NHar NHol NHpl SPoG WAbe WIce
'Silken Giant'	GEdr WAbe
'Silken Night'	GEdr NHar WAbe
'Silken Seas'	CSma GCrg GEdr NHar NWad WAbe
'Silken Skies' 🏆H5	GEdr NHar WAbe
'Silken Surprise'	WAbe
sino-ornata 🏆H5	CPla CSma CTri ECho GAbr GMaP GMcL LSRN MAsh NCGa NHpl SRms WAbe WIce
- SDR 5127	MGos
- 'Alba'	CPla
- 'Angel's Wings'	GEdr LRHS
- 'Bellatrix'	GEdr IVic NHar
- 'Blautopf'	GEdr IVic
- 'Brin Form'	SRms
- 'Downfield'	GKev LRHS
- 'Edith Sarah'	GEdr IVic
- 'Gorau Glas'	WAbe
- 'Mary Lyle'	GEdr
- 'Oha'	GEdr IVic
- 'Purity'	GEdr LRHS NHar WAbe
- 'Starlight'	GEdr NHar
- 'Weisser Traum'	GEdr IVic LRHS NHar NHol NLar
- 'White Wings'	GEdr
'Sir Rupert'	GEdr IVic NHar
× ***stevenagensis***	CPla LRHS
§ - 'Bernardii'	GEdr NHar
- dark-flowered	WAbe
straminea	EPot
'Strathmore' 🏆H5	CRos CSma EWes EWld GAbr GEdr GKev GMaP LRHS NBir NHar SPer SPlb
'Surprise'	GEdr
syringea	WAbe
szechenyii	LLHF
ternifolia 'Cangshan'	EPot GEdr
- 'Dali'	GEdr NHar
'The Caley'	GEdr GMaP NHar
tibetica	CArn GCal GPoy XLum
- PAB 2357	LEdu WPGP
Tough's form	GEdr
triflora var. ***japonica***	NLar
'True Blue'	SPad
veitchiorum	GKev LLHF
verna	CRos CSma ECho EDAr EPfP EPot EWes GKev LCro LHop LOPS LRHS LSRN NHpl NPri NRHS NSla SIgm SPlb SPoG WAbe WHoo
- 'Alba'	GEdr NSla WAbe
§ - 'Angulosa' 🏆H5	MAsh
- subsp. ***pontica***	WIce
'Violette'	GEdr LRHS NWad
waltonii	EWes
wilsonii	GKev ITim
wutaiensis	see *G. macrophylla* var. *fetissowii*
zekuensis	WCot

Gentianopsis (*Gentianaceae*)

paludosa new	GKev

Geranium ✿ (*Geraniaceae*)

aconitifolium misapplied	see *G. palmatum*

aconitifolium L'Hér.	see *G. rivulare*
'Adam Moreland'	WOut
'Alan Mayes'	CBod CElw CMac CNec ECtt EPPr EWoo GBin GBuc GKin LRHS LSou NGdn SBod SRGP WCra WFar WPnP WPtf
'Alan's Blue'	WCra
albanum	CElw EPPr GLog GPSL GWyn LLWP MMuc SDix SRGP WMoo
anemonifolium	see *G. palmatum*
'Ann Folkard' 🏆H7	Widely available
'Ann Folkard' × ***psilostemon***	LSRN
'Anne Thomson' 🏆H7	Widely available
× ***antipodeum*** 'Pink Spice'PBR	CWGN EWoo GKin GMcL LBuc LRHS SRms
- 'Purple Passion'PBR	LBuc LRHS
- 'Sea Spray'	NBro
- 'Stanhoe'	LEdu MHCG
- (***sessiliflorum*** subsp. ***novae-zelandiae*** 'Nigricans' × ***traversii*** var. ***elegans***)	SRms
argenteum	NSla
aristatum	ECGP EPPr EWes GCal MNrw MRav NBir SGbt SRGP WCru WMoo
armenum	see *G. psilostemon*
asphodeloides	CBod CElw IFro LRHS MBNS MNrw NBid NBir SGbt SPav SRGP WBrk WFar WMoo WPnP
- subsp. ***asphodeloides*** white-flowered	CElw SRGP WMoo
- subsp. ***sintenisii***	EPPr
- 'Starlight'	GCal NBid
atlanticum Hook. f.	see *G. malviflorum*
'Azure Rush'	CDor CMos EBee ECtt EWTr ILea IPot LBMP LRHS NDov SPoG SRms WCAu WCra WFar WPnP
'Azzurro'	EBee LRHS MAsh
'Baby Blue'	see *G. himalayense* 'Baby Blue'
'Bertie Crûg'	CBod CWld ECtt ELon GMcL LLHF NBir NCou NLar SRms SRot SWat SWvt
biuncinatum	IFro
'Blue Boy'	NLar
'Blue Cloud' 🏆H7	Widely available
'Blue Pearl'	EPPr MAvo NBir NSti SRGP WMoo
§ Blue Sunrise = 'Blogold'PBR 🏆H7	CBod CSam EBee ECtt ELan ELon EPfP GMaP ILea LLWG LPla LRHS LSRN MAvo MHol MNrw MRav MTis NCGa NEgg NLar NSti SPer SPoG SRms SRot WCot WCra WFib WPnP
'Blue Thunder' **new**	EPPr
'Blushing Turtle'PBR	CBod CMos EBee EPfP LBuc NLar NSti WCAu WCra
'Bob's Blunder'	ECtt EPfP IBoy LHop LLWG LRHS MBNS MBel MHol MNrw SAko SPoG SRGP SRms SWvt WCot WCra WFar WHoo WRHF
bohemicum	SRGP WHer
- 'Orchid Blue'	SWvt WTor
'Brookside' 🏆H7	Widely available
'Buckland Beauty'	EBee EWes SBch
'Buxton's Blue'	see *G. wallichianum* 'Buxton's Variety'
caeruleatum	EBee EPPr GCal NLar SBrt
caffrum	CPla SPlb SRGP
canariense	see *G. reuteri*
candicans misapplied	see *G. lambertii*

§ × ***cantabrigiense***	CMac CRos CSBt ECtt ESps GMcL LRHS MHer MNrw NBir NBro NLar NPer NSti SRms WBor WCru WHea WMoo
- 'Andrew Clarke' **new**	WBrk
- 'Berggarten'	EBee EPPr NLar SAko SRGP WBrk WCra WPtf
- 'Biokovo'	Widely available
- 'Cambridge'	CBcs CBod CMHG CNec CPrp EBee ECha ECtt ELan EPPr EPfP ESps GAbr GKin LHop LRHS MCot MRav MSwo SCob SPer SPoG SWat SWvt WBrk WCra WFar WFib WMoo WPnP
- Crystal Rose = 'Abpp'	EBee EPPr MAsh NSti
- 'Hanne'	EBee ECtt EPPr EWes WCra
- 'Harz'	CDor EPPr SAko WBrk WCra
- 'Hilary Rendall'	ECtt EPPr
- 'Karmina'	CBod CDor CRos EBee EPPr EPfP GBin GCal LRHS NLar NRHS SBod SHil SRGP SWat WCra WFar WHoo WMoo WPnP XEll XLum
- 'Rosalina'	EPPr WBrk
- 'Show Time'	EPPr
- 'St Ola'	CBod CHVG EBee ECtt EPPr EPfP GBuc GMaP ILea LRHS MNrw MRav MSpe NBro NChi NEgg NGdn NSti SAko SCob SHil SRGP WCot WCra WCru WFib WHoo WMoo WPnP WWtn
- 'Vorjura'	EBee EPPr SAko WBrk WCra
- 'Westray'PBR	CBod CHVG CMac CNec CPrp EBee ECtt EPPr EPfP GBuc GLog GMaP LBMP LSou MBel MHol MMuc NGdn NLar NRya NSti SCob SEND SRkn SRms SWvt WCra WFib WIce WPnP
'Chantilly'	CBod CFis CLAP EBee ECtt EPPr EPfP EWTr LRHS MAvo MNrw NBir WCra WCru WFib WGwG WMoo WPtf
'Chipchase Castle'	NChi
christensenianum B&SWJ 8022	WCru
cinereum	CNec ECho
- 'Album'	IBoy
- 'Apple Blossom'	see *G.* × *lindavicum* 'Apple Blossom'
- 'Elizabeth'	ECtt GBuc LSRN
- 'Sateene'PBR	CMos CSma ECtt EPPr GMaP SRms SRot WCra
(Cinereum Group) 'Alice'PBR	CMos CSma EBee EPPr EWTr GMaP LSRN MAsh MBNS NHar NLar NSti SRms SRot WCra WFar
- 'Ballerina' 🏆H5	Widely available
- 'Carol'	CSma CWGN EAEE ECtt EPPr EWes GKin LRHS LSRN LSou MAsh MBNS MRav NHar NLar NSti SWvt WFar WIce
I - 'Heather'	CSma
- 'Lambrook Helen'	CFis
- 'Laurence Flatman'	CKno CLet CPla CSpe ECtt ELan EPfP EPri EWoo GBuc GCrg GMaP LBMP LRHS LSou NBid NEgg NHar NQui NRHS NRya NSla SRms SRot SWat WCra WHoo
- 'Lizabeth'PBR	ECtt EPPr LSou NHar NLar WCra
- 'Melody'PBR **new**	CMos CSma WCra
- 'Penny Lane'PBR	CMos CSma MAsh WCra
- 'Purple Pillow'	CBcs CMos CWGN ECtt ELan EPPr EPot EWoo LLHF LSRN LSou MCot

		MHer MRav NDov NHar NSti SCob SPer SRms SRot STPC SWvt WCra WFar WIce
	- René Macé = 'Progera'	SRkn
	- Rothbury Gem = 'Gerfos'PBR ♀H5	CGar ECtt ELon MRav SKHP SPer SWvt WCra
	- 'Signal'	ECtt EPPr EPot NHar WCra
	- 'Sophie'PBR **new**	CMos CSma WCra
§	- 'Thumbling Hearts'	CWGN EBee ECtt IPot LCro LLWG LPla MHol MSCN NCou NSti SCob WCot WHoo
	- Thumping Heart	see *G.* 'Thumbling Hearts'
	'Claridge Druce'	see *G.* × *oxonianum* 'Claridge Druce'
	clarkei 'Kashmir Pink'	Widely available
§	- 'Kashmir White'	Widely available
	- 'Mount Stewart'	CHid EBee EPfP WCra WCru WPGP
	- (Purple-flowered Group) 'Kashmir Purple'	Widely available
	- Raina 82.83	MNrw
	clarum B&SWJ 10246	WCru
	collinum	EPPr NBir SRGP WCra WCru
	'Colour Carousel'	EBee GBin
	'Coombland White'	CHid ECtt EWTr GBuc GCal LRHS LSou MAvo MMuc NLar SKHP SPer SRGP WCra WMoo WPnP
	'Coquet Island'	EBee EPPr
	'Criss Canning'	EBee EPPr
	'Cyril's Blue'	EBee
	'Cyril's Fancy'	EPPr
	dalmaticum ♀H5	Widely available
	- 'Album'	EBee ECho ECtt EPPr EPfP GBuc LRHS MRav NHpl NRHS NRya SBch SRGP SRms SWat WAbe WCru
	- 'Bressingham Pink'	EBee ECtt EPPr
	- 'Bridal Bouquet'	ECtt EPot GCrg LLHF NChi NSla
	- 'Croftlea'	GBuc
	- 'Stades Hellrosa'	EPPr
	dalmaticum* × *macrorrhizum	see *G.* × *cantabrigiense*
	'Danny Boy' ♀H7	EBee MAvo
	delavayi misapplied	see *G. sinense*
	'Deux Fleurs'	GBin MAvo MNrw
	'Devon Pride'	CElw EBee EPPr SRGP
	'Dilys' ♀H7	CBod CElw CFis CMos CPrp EBee ELan EPPr GBuc MAvo MNrw MTis NBir NChi NDov NGdn NLar SRGP WCra WCru WHal WMoo WPnP
	'Distant Hills'	EBee EPPr SRGP WCra
	'Diva'	EBee ELan EPPr EPfP LLHF
	'Double Jewel'	see *G. pratense* 'Double Jewel'
	Dragon Heart = 'Bremdra'PBR	CLAP CMos ECtt EPfP EWoo IPot LPla LRHS LSRN MAsh MNrw MPnt NDov NLar NSti SCob SKHP STPC WBor WCAu WCra WHil WPnP
	Dreamland = 'Bremdream'PBR	CBod CDor CPou CWGN EBee ECtt EWoo LCro LPla LSou LSun MAsh MHol STPC WCot WCra WPnP
	'Dusky Crûg'	CSBt CSam ECtt EHoe ELan ELon EPPr EPfP EWTr GKin GMcL MBel MHol MJak MPie NEgg NHpl NLar SPoG SWvt WCot WCra WCru WFar
	'Dusky Rose'	CAby CDor CPrp CSpe ECtt EWoo GKev GMcL GWyn LBuc NLar SHar SRot WCra WFar
	'Edith May'	EBee WCra
	'Elizabeth Ross'	MAvo
	'Elke'	Widely available
	'Ella'	CWGN
	'Elworthy Eyecatcher'	CElw MAvo MNrw SRGP WPGP
	'Elworthy Tiger'	CElw MAvo WCra
	'Emily'	SRGP
	endressii ♀H7	CBod CBre CElw CNec ECha EPfP ESps GLog GMaP GMcL LPot MBNS MCot MHer MMuc NBro NPer NPol SCob SEND SPlb SRGP SRms SWvt WCra WHar WMoo WPtf XLum
	- 'Album'	see *G.* 'Mary Mottram'
	- 'Castle Drogo' ♀H7	EPPr
	- 'Prestbury White'	see *G.* × *oxonianum* 'Prestbury Blush'
	- 'Rose'	MAvo
	- 'Wargrave Pink'	see *G.* × *oxonianum* 'Wargrave Pink'
	erianthum	GLog GMaP IMou NLar SRGP WCru WMoo
	- 'Axeltree'	WCot
	- 'Cally Pearl'	GCal
	- 'Calm Sea'	WCru WMoo
	- 'Neptune'	WCru
	- 'Pale Blue Yonder'	EBee EWes WCra
	eriostemon Fischer	see *G. platyanthum*
	'Eureka Blue'	CPou ECtt LPla LRHS LSun MAvo MHol MTis NLar NSti SPoG WCot WCra WPnP WRHF
	'Eva'	WCra WPnP
	'Expression'	see *G.* 'Tanya Rendall'
	'Extravaganza'	EWes WCra
	'Farncombe Cerise Star'	CElw MAvo WCra
§	***farreri***	CRos ECho EPot LHop LLHF LRHS NBir NRHS
	'Fay Anna'	CBct GBin SCob WCra WFar
	goldmannii	SKHP
	gracile	CFis EBee GMaP LRHS LSou MNrw NBir SRGP WBrk WCru WMoo WPtf
	- 'Blanche'	EPPr LRHS MNrw
	- 'Blush'	CElw EPPr EWes WCra
	grandiflorum	see *G. himalayense*
	'Grasmere'	ECtt
	'Gwen Thompson'	WOut
	gymnocaulon	CMac SRGP WCru
	- from Lagonaki, Caucasus	SBrt
	gymnocaulon* × *platypetalum	EBee
	'Harmony'	EBee EPPr
	harveyi	EWes GKev NChi SPhx SRGP WKif
§	***hayatanum***	LRHS
	- B&SWJ 164	NLar WCru WMoo
	'Hilary'	WWtn
§	***himalayense***	CBcs CMHG CNec ECha ELan EPfP ESps LRHS MBNS MMuc MRav MWat NBir NBro SEND SPlb SRGP SRms SRot SWat WCra WFar WMoo WPnP XLum
	- CC 1957 from Tibetan border	EPPr
	- ***alpinum***	see *G. himalayense* 'Gravetye'
§	- 'Baby Blue'	CElw EBee ECtt ELon EPPr GBin GBuc GCal GCra LRHS MAvo MNrw MTis NGdn NLar NSti SRGP WBrk WCAu WCra WCru WFib WMoo WPnP WPtf
	- 'Birch Double'	see *G. himalayense* 'Plenum'
	- 'Derrick Cook'	CElw CLAP CMos EBee ECtt EPPr EPfP GBuc MAsh MAvo MNrw MSpe MTis NSti SPer STPC WBrk WCAu WCra WHal WHil WHoo
	- 'Devil's Blue'	EPPr SRGP WCra WPtf
§	- 'Gravetye'	Widely available
	- 'Irish Blue'	CBod CDor CElw EBee EPPr EWoo GBuc GCal GCra LRHS MSpe NLar

		NPol NSti SRGP WCra WCru WFib WMoo WPnP WPtf
	- ***meeboldii***	see *G. himalayense*
	- 'Pale Irish Blue'	EBee EPPr GCal
§	- 'Plenum' (d)	Widely available
	- 'Spiti Valley'	WPtf
	himalayense* × *pratense	WFib
	'Hola Guapa' **new**	GBin
	ibericum misapplied	see *G.* × *magnificum*
	ibericum ambig.	SRms
	ibericum Cav.	CSBt CTri LRHS NBre SPav SRGP SRms
	- 'Blue Springs'	ECtt LAll
	- subsp. ***ibericum***	CMac EPPr
	- subsp. ***jubatum***	EPPr MNrw SGbt SRms WCru
	- - 'White Zigana'	CAby CBod CFis EBee ECtt EPPr EPed EWoo LRHS LSRN NLar NSti SRms WCra WFar WGwG WPnP WWtn
	- subsp. ***jubatum* × *renardii***	SWvt
	- var. ***platypetalum*** misapplied	see *G.* × *magnificum*
	- var. ***platypetalum*** Boiss.	see *G. platypetalum* Fisch. & C.A. Mey.
§	- var. ***platypetalum*** Cav. 'Ushguli Grijs'	EBee EPPr IMou NLar WCot
	ibericum* × *libani	EBee
	incanum	CAbP CHVG EBee ELon EWes GCal NBir NHpl SBrt SRGP SVen
	- var. ***incanum***	SBch
	- white-flowered	SRGP
	'Ivan' ♀H7	CBod CElw CLAP CMos CPrp EBee ECtt EPPr GBuc LRHS NChi NLar SRGP WCra WCru WFib WHoo WMoo
	'Jean Armour'	CBod CPrp ECtt GBuc LRHS MAvo NLar SPoG SRGP WCra WFar WGwG
	'Jennifer'	MAvo
	'Johnson's Blue'	Widely available
	'Jolly Bee'	see *G.* Rozanne
	'Joy'	CBod CCht CDor CPrp EBee ECtt EPPr GBuc LRHS LSou LSun MAvo MBel MCot MRav NBir NEgg NLar NSti NWad SBch SRGP SRms WCot WCra WFib WGwG WMoo WPnP
§	'Kanahitobanawa'	EBee WCra WSHC
	'Karen Wouters'	EPPr WPtf
	'Kashmir Blue'	ECtt ELan EPfP EWTr GMaP LRHS MAvo MTis NLar SWat SWvt WCra WFar WKif WPtf
	'Kashmir Green'	CLAP ECtt EPfP EWTr LLHF WCra WMoo
§	'Khan'	CElw CFis EPPr EWes IFro LRHS MAvo NEoE SDys SMHy SRGP WCra WCru
	'Kirsty'	EBee EWes WCra
	kishtvariense	GCal IMou MRav NSti WCra WCru
	koraiense	CFis WCra WMoo
	- B&SWJ 797	WCru
	- B&SWJ 878	EBee WCru
	koreanum misapplied	see *G. hayatanum*
	koreanum ambig.	CPla GCal LRHS NLar WMoo
	- B&SWJ 602	WCru
	krameri	IMou NLar
	- B&SWJ 1142	WCru
	'Lakwijk Star'	CBod ECtt ILea IPot LHop NLar SPoG WCra
§	***lambertii***	EWes GBuc NBir
	- 'Swansdown'	GBuc GCal
	'Larch Cottage Velvet'	MAvo
I	***libani***	CDor ELon EPPr LLWP MCot NBid NSti WBrk WCot WSHC
	- RCB RL B-2	WCot WCra
	'Light Dilys'	CMos EBee EPPr LCro NDov WCra
	'Lilac Ice'	CMil CMos CWGN EBee ECtt EPfP GMaP LPla LRHS MAsh MNrw NDov NLar NSti SCob SPoG WCAu WCra
	× ***lindavicum***	NSla
§	- 'Apple Blossom'	EBee EPot MAsh NSla WCra WFar
	linearilobum subsp. ***transversale***	SRot WPnP
I	- - 'Laciniatum'	GKev WCot
	- - 'Rose Foundling'	SBrt
§	'Little David'	NLar WCra
	'Little Devil'	see *G.* 'Little David'
	'Little Gem'	EBee ECtt EPPr LRHS NChi NDov SBch WFar WHoo WMoo
	lucidum	WOut WPtf WSFF
	'Luscious Linda'	MAvo
	'Lydia'	EBee SRGP
§	***macrorrhizum***	CArn CBod CSBt ECrN EPed EPfP ESps GBin GKev GKin GMcL IFro LEdu LOPS LSun MCot MRav MWat NBro NCGa SBod SRms SWat WCAu WCra WFar WHar XLum
	- AL & JS 90179YU	CHid EPPr
	- 'Album'	CBre CElw CPrp ECha EPPr EWTr GMaP LRHS MBel MSpe MSwo NBid NBro NChi SAko SWat WBrk WCot WCra WCru WFib WMoo
	- 'Bevan's Variety'	Widely available
	- 'Bulgaria'	EPPr WBrk WCra
	- 'Cham-ce'	ECtt EPPr WCra
	- 'Czakor'	CBod CBre CMac CNec EBee ECtt ELan ELon EPPr EPfP LHop LRHS MCot MRav MSpe NEgg NGdn NLar SAko SRGP SWat SWvt WBrk WCot WCra WCru WFar WMoo XLum
I	- 'De Bilt'	EPPr EWes WBrk
	- 'Freundorf'	EBee EPPr EWes GBin GCal SAko WCra
	- 'Glacier'	EPPr EWes
	- 'Ingwersen's Variety' ♀H7	Widely available
	- 'Lohfelden'	CLAP EPPr EWes GBuc GCal SRGP WBrk WCra WCru
	- 'Mount Olympus'	see *G. macrorrhizum* 'White-Ness'
	- 'Mytikas'	EPPr WBrk WPtf
	- 'Olympos'	EBee EPPr
	- 'Pindus'	CBod CLAP CPrp EBee EPPr GAbr GBuc LRHS MHer NLar NSti SPoG SRGP WCra WCru WFar WPnP WPtf
	- 'Prionia'	EPPr GCal SAko WBrk
	- 'Purpurrot'	WBrk
	- 'Ridsko'	EPPr GCal SRGP WBrk WCra WCru
	- ***roseum***	see *G. macrorrhizum*
	- 'Rotblut'	EPPr SRGP WBrk
	- 'Sandwijck'	EBee EPPr MAvo WCra
	- 'Snow Sprite'	CMea CPla EPPr LLHF MHer NEoE NLar WBrk WHrl WPtf XLum
	- 'Spessart'	CBar CBod EBee ELan ELon EPPr EPfP EWoo GBin GMaP LBMP LHop LRHS MMuc NBid NLar SCob SEND SGbt SHil SPer SPhx SPoG SWvt WCra WFib WHar WRHF XLum
	- 'Variegatum' (v)	CFis CNec EBee ELan GMaP GMcL LEdu LPot NBir SRGP SRms WCot WFar
	- 'Velebit'	EPPr SRGP WBrk WCru XLum

§	- 'White-Ness' ♀H7	Widely available
	macrostylum	WCot WCru
I	- 'Caeruleum'	WPtf
	- 'Leonidas'	EPPr WPnP
	- 'Talish'	EPPr
	- 'Uln Oag Triag'	EPPr
	maculatum	CFis LRHS MAvo MCot MMrt MNrw MRav NLar NSti SRGP SWat WCru WHal
	- from Kath Dryden	EPPr
	- f. ***albiflorum***	CElw CLAP EBee ELan ELon EPPr EPfP EWoo GBin LRHS MAsh MBel MNrw MTis NChi NLar NSti SRGP SSut WBrk WCru WMoo WPnP
	- 'Beth Chatto'	Widely available
	- 'Elizabeth Ann' PBR ♀H7	CLAP CSam CWGN EBee ECtt EPPr EWoo GAbr GBin LHop LRHS LSou MBel MHol MNrw MTis NGdn NLar NSti NWad WCot WCra WFar WFib WHil WMoo WPnP
	- 'Espresso'	Widely available
	- purple-flowered	EPPr
	- 'Putnam County'	EPPr WCra
	- 'Shameface'	EPPr WCra WMoo
	- 'Silver Buttons'	EBee
	- 'Smoky Mountain'	EPPr
	- 'Spring Purple'	CElw EBee EPPr MAvo NLar WCra
	- 'Sweetwater'	EPPr
	- 'Vickie Lynn'	EBee EPPr EWTr WCra
	maderense ♀H3	CAbb CBcs CBod CPla CPne CSpe CTre ECre ELan EUJe EWes IBoy LRHS NBir NLos NPer SArc SChr SDix SPav SPhx SRGP SRkn SVen SWvt WFar
	- 'Guernsey White'	CBod NLos WOut
	- white-flowered	CSpe EBee
§	× ***magnificum*** ♀H7	Widely available
	- 'Blue Blood'	CAbP CElw CLAP EBee ECtt EMFm EPPr EPfP GAbr GCal GMcL LRHS LSou MBNS MCot MHol NGdn NSti SWvt WCot WCra WRHF
	- 'Ernst Pagels'	CBod GBin MHol WOut
	- 'Hylander'	EPPr
	- 'Peter Yeo'	EBee EPPr SRGP WCra
	- 'Rosemoor'	CBod CElw CHid CNec ECtt ELan EPPr EPed EPfP GBuc GCal IKil LCro LOPS LRHS MBel NEoE SPer SPtp WCra WFib WHoo WPtf XLum
	- 'Vital'	XLum
	magniflorum	EBee EWes GKev NBid NGdn
	'Maître Hugo'	EBee
§	***malviflorum***	CFis ECha ELan EPPr LLWP NSti SBrt WCot WCru WHea WHoo
	- from Spain	EWes
	- pink-flowered	EPPr WSHC
§	'Mary Mottram'	CElw EPPr WCra
	'Mavis Simpson' ♀H4	Widely available
	maximowiczii	WPtf
	'Maxwelton'	EBee
	'Melinda' PBR	CMos EBee ECtt EPPr EWTr EWoo IKil LCro LHop LOPS MMuc MNrw MTis NLar NMir NSti WCot WCra WFib WPnP WRHF
	'Memories' PBR	CMos CSma ECtt LSRN MBNS SRms
	'Menna Bach'	WCra
	'Meryl Anne'	SRGP WPtf
	microphyllum	see *G. potentilloides*
	'Midnight Clouds'	CMos CWGN EBee ECtt EPPr EPfP EWTr LBuc MAsh MAvo NSti SCob SPoG WCra WFar
	'Midnight Star'	EPPr EWes WFar
	molle	WSFF
	× ***monacense***	CBod EBee ELan IFoB IMou LEdu LRHS MBNS MWat SRGP SWat WCra WCru WGwG WMoo WPnP WWtn
	- var. ***anglicum***	ECtt EPPr EPfP GMaP LRHS NLar WCra WMoo
	- - 'Eric Clement'	EBee
	- 'Anne Stevens'	EBee WPtf
	- 'Claudine Dupont'	CElw EBee EPPr IFro NWad WCot WCra WFib WPtf
	- dark-flowered	WMoo
	- 'Emma White'	EBee EPPr
	- 'Jackie' **new**	EBee EPPr
	- var. ***monacense*** 'Breckland Fever'	EBee EPPr SRGP WCra
§	- - 'Muldoon'	EPPr EPfP NBir SRGP WMoo WPnP
*	'Money Peniche'	XEll
	'Mourning Widow'	see *G. phaeum* 'Lady in Mourning'
	'Mrs Jean Moss'	EBee EPPr EWes MAvo SRGP
	napuligerum misapplied	see *G. farreri*
	'Natalie'	EBee EPPr LRHS LSRN MAsh MAvo NChi WCra
	nepalense	SRGP SRms
	'Nicola'	CElw EPPr EPfP IFro LRHS NLar SRGP WCra
	'Nimbus' ♀H7	Widely available
	nodosum	Widely available
	- 'Blueberry Ice'	CElw CLAP MAvo
	- 'Clos du Coudray'	EBee EPPr EWTr EWoo ILea MAvo NLar NSti WCAu WCra WHil WPnP
	- 'Dark Heart'	MCot WCra
	- dark-flowered	see *G. nodosum* 'Swish Purple'
	- 'Darkleaf'	EBee
	- 'Hexham Big Eyes'	CElw CLAP EBee EWes MAvo
	- 'Hexham Face Paint'	EPPr
	- 'Hexham Feathers'	CElw
	- 'Hexham Freckles'	EBee EPPr
	- 'Hexham Lace'	CElw EPPr
	- 'Julie's Velvet'	CElw LEdu SBch WBor WHoo WPGP
	- pale-flowered	see *G. nodosum* 'Svelte Lilac'
	- 'Pascal'	EPPr
	- 'Saucy Charlie'	SBch
	- 'Silverwood'	CDor CElw CLAP CSpe EBee ECtt EPPr EWoo GCal LPla LSou MBel MTis NSti SAko SBch SPoG SRGP WCot WCra WHoo WRHF WWFP
	- 'Simon'	MAvo SRGP
§	- 'Svelte Lilac'	CBod CElw EAEE EPPr LPla LRHS LSou NBro NDov NHol SPoG SRGP SWat WBrk WCra WCru WFar WFib WMoo WPnP
§	- 'Swish Purple'	CElw ELon EPPr LRHS MAvo NLar SRGP WCru WMoo WPnP
	- 'Tony's Talisman'	EBee MAvo
	- 'Whiteleaf'	CElw CFis CMac CMea EPPr GBin GCal NChi SRGP WCru WFar WHal WMoo WPnP
	- 'Wreighburn House White'	EBee MAvo
	'Northumberland Lavender Queen'	EBee
	'Nunwood Purple'	EBee EPPr EWes MAvo WCra
	ocellatum	IFro
	'Old Rose'	LRHS SRGP WCru
§	***orientalitibeticum***	CSpe ECtt EPPr GAbr GKev IFro MCot MHer MMuc NBid NLar NRya SEND SKHP SMad SRGP WCot WMoo
	'Orion' ♀H7	Widely available

	'Orkney Blue'	CElw EPPr WCru
	Orkney Cherry = 'Bremerry'PBR	CMac EBee ECtt EPfP GBin LLHF MBel SCob SRkn SRms WCra
	'Orkney Dawn'	MAvo WPnP
	'Orkney Flame' **new**	EBee EPPr
	'Orkney Mist'	EBee EPPr
	'Orkney Pink'	ECtt EPPr EPfP LEdu LHop SRGP SWat
	'Out of the Blue'	WOut
	× ***oxonianum***	CNec WMoo
	- 'A.T. Johnson' ♀H7	CAby CBcs EBee ECtt ELan EPPr EPfP ESps GKin GMaP LHop LRHS MRav MWat NBir NEgg NGdn NSti SCob SPer SRGP SRms SWat SWvt WCra WCru WMoo WWtn
	- 'Ankum's White'	CLAP EBee EPPr EWes
	- 'Anmore'	SRGP
	- 'Beholder's Eye' ♀H7	CPrp EPPr MMuc NLar SRGP WPnP
	- 'Breckland Sunset'	EBee EPPr NLar SRGP
	- 'Bregover Pearl'	CBre EPPr SRGP WMoo
	- 'Bressingham's Delight'	LRHS SRGP WCra
	- 'Buttercup'	EPPr SRGP
	- Caborn hybrids	LLWP
I	- 'Cally Seedling'	EBee EWes GCal
	- 'Chocolate Strawberry'	EBee EPPr EWes WCra
§	- 'Claridge Druce'	CBod CMac CNec CTri ECha ELan EPPr EPfP EShb ESps EWoo GKin GMaP LPot LRHS MCot MRav MSwo MWat NBir NGdn NLar SCob SPer SRms WCra WHar WMoo WWtn XLum
	- 'Coronet'	GCal SRGP WCra WMoo
	- 'Cream Chocolate'	EBee EPPr
	- 'David Rowlinson'	EBee EPPr WCra
	- 'Diane's Treasure'	EBee
	- 'Elworthy Misty'	CElw CFis EPPr SRGP WCra
	- 'Frank Lawley'	CPrp LLWP NBid SRGP WMoo
§	- 'Fran's Star' (d)	SRGP WCru
	- 'Frilly Gilly'	WCra
	- 'Hexham Pink'	EBee EPPr EWes NChi SRGP
	- 'Hollywood'	ELan EPPr NLar NPer SAko SRGP SRms WCra WMoo
	- 'Iced Green Tea'	EBee
	- 'Julie Brennan'	EBee LRHS
	- 'Kate Moss'	EPPr EWes NSti SRGP
	- 'Katherine Adele'	CMea CMos CSpe ECha ECtt EPPr EPfP EShb EWes GCal LLWP LSou MAsh MAvo MMuc MSpe NLar SEND SRGP SRms WCra WFar WFib
§	- 'Kingston'	CElw EBee EPPr
	- 'Königshof'	EPPr EWes
	- 'Kurt's Variegated'	see *G.* × *oxonianum* 'Spring Fling'
	- 'Lace Time'	CAby CBod CBre CPrp EBee ECtt EPPr GBuc GKin LBMP LRHS LSRN MAsh MSpe NEgg SHil SPer SPoG SRGP SRms WCAu WCra WGwG WMoo
	- 'Lady Moore'	SRGP WMoo
	- 'Lambrook Gillian'	CFis EPPr SRGP WBrk
	- 'Lasting Impression'	EPPr SRGP
	- 'Laura Skelton'	CElw EBee
	- 'Little John'	EPPr EWes
	- 'Maid Marion'	EWes
	- 'Maurice Moka'	EBee ECtt NLar WCra
	- 'Miriam Rundle'	EPPr SRGP WCru WMoo
	- 'Moorland Jenny'	WMoo
	- 'Moorland Star'	WMoo
	- 'Mrs Molly Kisby'	EBee
	- 'Music from Big Pink'	EBee EPPr EWes WCra
	- 'Pat Smallacombe'	EBee EPPr SRGP WMoo
	- 'Pearl Boland'	EBee EPPr SRGP
	- 'Phantom'	EBee EPPr WCra
	- 'Phoebe Noble'	CBre EBee EPPr LRHS MNrw NLar SRGP WCra WFib WMoo
	- 'Phoebe's Blush'	EPPr SRGP
	- 'Pink Cluster'	CLAP
§	- 'Prestbury Blush'	CElw EPPr SRGP
	- 'Prestbury White'	see *G.* × *oxonianum* 'Prestbury Blush'
	- 'Raspberry Ice'	EBee EWes WCra
	- 'Rebecca Moss'	CPrp ECha ECtt ELan EPPr GAbr GCra LRHS LSRN NSti SAko SRGP WCra WCru WFib WOut WPtf
	- 'Red Sceptre' **new**	EBee
	- 'Robin's Ginger Nut'	EBee EWes WCra
	- 'Robin's Red Eye'	EPPr
	- 'Rose Clair'	CNec ELan EPPr LRHS NBir NLar SRGP WCAu WCra WCru WHar WMoo
	- 'Rosenlicht'	EAEE EBee EPPr EWoo GKin LRHS MAsh MRav SRGP WCra WCru WMoo XLum
	- 'Rothbury Sarah'	EBee EPPr
	- 'Sandy'	EBee EPPr EWes
	- 'Something Special' **new**	EBee EPPr
§	- 'Spring Fling' (v)	ECtt EWes MSpe NWad SRGP WCra WFar
	- 'Stillingfleet Keira'	EBee EPPr NSti SRGP
	- 'Summer Surprise'	EBee EPPr EWes WCra WCru
	- 'Susan'	EPPr EWes
	- 'Susie White'	EPPr SRGP WCru
§	- f. ***thurstonianum***	Widely available
	- - 'Armitageae'	EPPr SRGP
	- - 'Breckland Brownie'	CElw EBee EPPr EWes MAvo SRGP WCra
	- - 'Crûg Star'	WCru
	- - 'David McClintock'	EBee SRGP WMoo
	- - 'Red Sputnik'	EPPr SRGP
	- - 'Sherwood'	EPPr GCal GQue MSpe NBro NSti SRGP WCra WFar WMoo
	- - 'Southcombe Double' (d)	CBod CLAP CMos CNec CPla ECtt ELan EPPr EWTr GCra LRHS LSou MHol SPer SRGP SRms WCra WCru WGwG WMoo
§	- - 'Southcombe Star'	EBee EPPr GAbr NBro NGdn SRGP WCru WMoo
	- - 'Sue Cox' (d)	EPPr NLar
	- - 'White Stripes'	EBee EPPr
	- 'Trevor's White'	CLAP EBee EPPr LLWP LRHS SRGP WCra WCru
	- 'Tyne Salmon' **new**	EBee
	- 'Wageningen' ♀H7	CBod CBre CNec EBee EPPr GCal LRHS LSou NGdn SEND SRGP SRms WCot WCra WCru WGwG WHoo WMoo
	- 'Walter's Gift'	CBod CNec ECtt EPPr EPri EShb EWoo GBin LLWP LRHS LSou MAsh MAvo MRav NBir NBro NChi NLar NPer SAko SDix WCra WCru WFar WHoo WMoo WPnP WWtn
§	- 'Wargrave Pink'	Widely available
	- 'Waystrode'	EBee EPPr SRGP
	- 'Westacre White'	EPPr EWes WCra
	- 'Whitehaven'	SRGP
	- 'Whiter Shade of Pale'	EBee EPPr
	- 'Winscombe'	EPfP GCal SRGP WMoo
	× ***oxonianum*** × ***sessiliflorum*** subsp. ***novae-zelandiae*** 'Nigricans'	WHar

§	***palmatum*** ♀H4	Widely available
	palustre	EBee EPPr GLog MMuc MNrw NLar SRGP WCot WMoo WPtf
	'Pastel Clouds'	GWyn WFar
	Patricia = 'Brempat' ♀H7	Widely available
	peloponnesiacum	CElw EAEE EPPr EWes GQue NLar NWad WMoo
	'Perfect Storm'	CLAP ECtt LLHF
	phaeum	Widely available
	- 'Acorn Bank'	EBee EPPr WCra
	- 'Advendo'	EBee EPPr WCra
	- 'Album'	Widely available
	- 'Alec's Pink'	EBee EPPr LLWP WCra WPnP WPtf
	- 'All Saints'	EBee EPPr LEdu SRGP WCra WPtf
	- 'Angelina'	EBee EPPr GBin WCra
	- 'Ann Logan' **new**	EBee EPPr
	- 'Aureum'	see *G. phaeum* 'Golden Spring'
	- 'Basket of Lavender'	EBee
	- 'Blauwvoet'	EPPr LBMP NChi WCra WPtf
	- 'Blue Shadow'	CElw CLAP EBee EPPr LEdu MAvo SRGP WPtf
	- 'Caborn Lilac'	LLWP
	- 'Calligrapher'	EPPr LLHF NChi SRGP WCra WMoo
	- 'Chocolate Chip'	EPPr
	- 'Conny Broe' (v)	CLAP EShb MAvo WSHC
	- 'Dark Angel'	EBee
	- 'Dark Dream'	EBee
	- 'David Bromley'	WCru
	- 'David Martin'	EBee EPPr SRGP
	- 'Enid'	EPPr
	- 'Garage Door' **new**	EBee
	- 'George Stone'	EPPr
	- 'Golden Samobor'	CElw EPPr
§	- 'Golden Spring'	EBee EPPr MAvo NEoE SRGP WOut
	- 'Green Ghost'	EBee EPPr
	- 'Hector's Lavender'	EBee SRGP WOut
	- var. ***hungaricum***	EBee EPPr SRGP WCra
	- 'James Haunch'	EPPr WCra
	- 'Judith's Blue'	EBee EPPr
	- 'Klepper'	EBee EPPr GBin
§	- 'Lady in Mourning'	EBee EPPr GBin GCal NChi SRGP SRms SWat WCru WMoo WPnP
	- 'Lavender Pinwheel'	CBod CMos EBee EPfP MSpe SPer WCot WCra WHar
	- 'Lilacina'	ECha
	- 'Lily Lovell'	Widely available
	- 'Lisa' (v)	CElw CFis CLAP EPPr MAvo MNrw SMHy WCot WCra
	- 'Little Boy'	EPPr
	- var. ***lividum***	CBre EPfP GMaP LLWP MRav SRGP SRms WFar WPnP XLum
	- - 'Joan Baker'	CFis CSam EBee EPPr NChi NGdn NSti SDys SPer SRGP WCru WFib WMoo WOut WPnP
	- - 'Majus'	EBee ECtt ELan EPPr EPfP LLWP LRHS WFar WMoo
	- 'Lustige Witwe' (v)	WCot
	- 'Marchant's Ghost'	IFro
	- 'Margaret Wilson' (v)	CMos CWGN EBee ECtt EPPr EWes GAbr GCal LBMP LEdu MAvo MSpe NBir NEgg NGdn NLar NSti SRGP WCot WHil WMoo WSHC
	- 'Mierhausen'	EBee EPPr WPtf
	- 'Misty Samobor' **new**	ECha
	- 'Mojito' (v)	WCot
	- 'Moorland Dylan'	WMoo WOut
	- 'Mottisfont Rose'	CElw CLAP SBch
	- 'Mourning Widow'	see *G. phaeum* 'Lady in Mourning'
	- 'Mrs Charles Perrin'	CFis WPtf
	- 'Mrs Withey Price'	WHil
	- 'Night Time'	EBee EPPr LLWP
	- 'Nightshade'	EBee EPPr
	- 'Our Pat' ♀H7	CLAP EBee EPPr MAvo NChi WCot
	- var. ***phaeum***	WPtf
	- - 'Langthorns Blue'	CWCL EBee ELan EPPr EPfP EWes LEdu LRHS MNrw SRGP SWvt WCra WPGP
	- - 'Samobor'	Widely available
	- 'Phantom of the Opera' (v)	EBee EPPr
	- 'Pink Palava' **new**	LEdu
I	- 'Ploeger de Bilt'	EBee EPPr
	- 'Purple Moon' **new**	EBee EPPr
	- 'Rachel's Rhapsody'	EBee EPPr MAvo MSpe SRGP
	- 'Raven'	CBod CLAP CMos EBee ECtt EPPr EWoo LRHS NChi NLar SCob WCAu WCra WFar WHar
	- 'Ray of Light'	EPPr
	- 'Rise Top Lilac'	EBee WPGP WPtf
	- 'Robin's Angel Eyes'	EBee EPPr
	- 'Rose Air'	EPPr MAvo SRGP WMoo WPnP
	- 'Rose Madder'	CElw EPPr GBuc GCal LEdu LLWP MNrw NChi NLar SPhx SRGP WCru WGwG WMoo WPnP
	- 'Rothbury Ruby'	EBee EPPr
	- 'Saturn'	EPPr WPtf
	- 'Séricourt'	MAvo WCot WCra WFib
	- 'Shadowlight'	EBee ECtt EPPr NLar SPoG WCra WFar
	- 'Slatina'	EPPr WPtf
	- 'Springtime'PBR	CMos EBee EPPr LBMP LLHF MBNS MSpe NGdn NLar WCra WFib
	- 'Stillingfleet Ghost'	EBee EPPr LEdu MNrw NChi NSti
	- 'Taff's Jester' (v)	MSpe NHol SRGP WHil
	- 'Trevor's Recall'	EBee
	- 'Tyne Mist'	EBee EPPr
§	- 'Variegatum' (v)	CBre CFis CMac EBee EHoe ELan EPPr GMaP IFro MSpe NBir NBro SRGP WCru WHer WMoo
	- 'Vintage Dave'	WOut
	- 'Walküre'	EPPr EWTr EWes EWoo MTis NLar WCra
	- 'Waterer's Blue' **new**	CLAP
	'Philippe Vapelle'	Widely available
	'Pink Delight'	CElw SBch
	'Pink Penny'	CLAP CMos EBee ECtt EPPr EPfP GBin LRHS MNrw NLar NSti SPoG SRGP WCra WFar WMoo
§	***platyanthum***	EPPr MNrw SRGP WCru
	- var. ***reinii***	GCal WCru
	- 'Russian Giant'	EPPr
	platypetalum misapplied	see *G.* × ***magnificum***
	platypetalum Franch.	see ***G. sinense***
§	***platypetalum*** Fisch. & C.A. Mey.	EBee EPPr LRHS NBir SRGP WCru XLum
	- 'Dark Side of the Moon'	EBee
	- 'Genyell'	EBee EPPr WCra
	- 'Georgia Blue'	WCru
	- 'Turco'	EBee EPPr NLar WCra
§	***pogonanthum***	CHid GLog NBir
	polyanthes	EWes NChi
§	***potentilloides***	GCal NBir SRGP WMoo
	pratense	CArn CBre CHab CMac CNec CWld EBee ECtt ELan EPPr ESps GJos GMaP MHer MNHC NMir SCob SPer SPlb SPoG SRGP SRms SWat WCot WHar WMoo WPnP WSFF XLum
	- 'Akaton'	NLar WCra
I	- 'Alboroseum'	EBee
	- 'Algera Double'	LLHF MHol MSCN WCot WCra
	- 'Bittersweet'	EPPr

	– Black Beauty = 'Nodbeauty'PBR	CAby CBcs CMea CWCL CWGN CWld EBee ECtt EPfP EUJe EWes LBuc LCro LOPS LRHS MBel MGos MHol MPnt NHpl NLar SPer SPoG SRkn SRot SWat WFar WHoo
	– 'Blue Lagoon'	EBee EPPr WCra
*	– 'Blue Skies'	LSou WFar
	– 'Cluden Sapphire'	EBee EPPr EWTr NEoE NHol WCra WCru
§	– 'Double Jewel' (d)	CWGN EBee EPfP LLHF MAvo MBNS MHol NBir NLar SPoG WBor WCra WFar
	– 'Else Lacey' (d)	CElw EBee WCra
	– 'Flore Pleno'	see *G. pratense* 'Plenum Violaceum'
I	– 'Himalayanum'	NLar
	– 'Hocus Pocus'	CBod CMos CRos CWGN CWld ECtt ELan EWTr EWoo LRHS MAvo MBNS MHol MNrw MSCN NBro NLar NRHS NSti SCob WCAu WCra
	– 'Ilja'	EBee EPPr MNrw
	– 'Janet's Special'	WHoo
	– 'Marshmallow' **new**	EBee MHol WCot
	– 'Midnight Blues'	CMos CWGN EBee SCob WCra
	– Midnight Reiter strain	CBct CWGN CWld ECtt ELan EWTr GBuc GCal GWyn IBoy IFoB MAvo MBel MHol NBro NChi NGdn NHpl NLar NQui SCob SDys SMad SWat SWvt WCra WFar WPnP
	– 'Milou' **new**	MAvo
	– 'Mrs Kendall Clark' ♀H7	Widely available
	– 'New Dimension'	CBcs EBee WCra WFib
	– 'Okey Dokey'	EBee
	– 'Pink Splash'	WMoo
	– 'Plenum Caeruleum' (d)	CMHG ECtt EPPr GCra MRav NBid NEgg NLar SWat WSHC
§	– 'Plenum Violaceum' (d) ♀H7	Widely available
	– var. ***pratense*** f. ***albiflorum***	CSam EPPr EPfP EWoo GCra GMaP IFro LRHS MNrw NBid SCob SGbt SPer WCra WMoo WPtf
	– – – 'Galactic'	CBod CLAP CMea ECtt LRHS LSun MHol MMuc NBir NEgg NLar SEND WCot WCra WCru WFib WMoo WPnP
	– – – 'Laura'PBR (d)	CBod EBee EPPr EPfP EWTr EWes LSRN LSou NLar NSti SCob SKHP SPer WCra WPnP
	– – – 'Plenum Album' (d)	CBot CLAP EBee ECtt ELan EPPr EPfP EWes GBin LLHF LRHS MBel MMuc MNrw MRav NEgg NGdn NLar SGbt SWvt WBor WCot WFar WGwG WPnP
	– – – 'Silver Queen'	CAby CNec EBee ECtt EPed GQue LRHS LSou NBir SPoG SRGP WCra WGwG WMoo
	– 'Purple Ghost' **new**	MSCN WHar WHlf
	– 'Purple Heron'	LSRN
*	– 'Purple-haze'	CPla GPSL GWyn SMad WMoo WSHC WTou
	– 'Rectum Album'	see *G. clarkei* 'Kashmir White'
	– 'Robin's Grey Beard'	EBee EPPr
§	– 'Rose Queen'	NBir SGbt SRGP WCru
	– 'Roseum'	see *G. pratense* 'Rose Queen'
	– 'Splish-splash'	see *G. pratense* 'Striatum'
	– 'Stanton Mill'	NBid
	– var. ***stewartianum***	MRav
	– – 'Elizabeth Yeo'	CBod CLAP CNec ECtt EPPr EWoo LRHS NWad WCra WCru
	– – 'Raina'	EPPr
§	– 'Striatum'	Widely available

	– 'Striatum' dwarf	WCru
	– variegated, white-flowered (v)	WCot
§	– Victor Reiter Junior strain	CSpe ELan EPPr LEdu NBir NGdn NHpl SPoG SRot WCot
	– 'Wisley Blue'	EPPr SRGP WCra WHal
	– 'Yorkshire Queen'	EBee NGdn NSti WCru
	'Prelude'	CBre CElw EBee ELon EPPr NBir NEoE NLar SHar SRGP WCra WFib WPtf
	procurrens	CBre CElw CTri EPPr GAbr GCal GCra WBor WBrk WCru WMoo WPtf
§	***psilostemon*** ♀H7	Widely available
	– 'Bressingham Flair'	CKno CLAP ECtt GBuc GCra LRHS MRav NBid NChi NLar SRms WCra WCru WFar WMoo WPnP
	– 'Catherine Deneuve'PBR	CWGN EBee EWTr EWes ILea SCob STPC WCra
	– 'Coton Goliath'	EPPr EWes MAvo
	– 'Jason Bloom'	EBee EPPr LRHS
	– 'Madelon'	CElw MAvo NLar
	– 'Moorland Jack'	WMoo
	pulchrum	CFil CSpe EBee EWes GWyn SRGP
	punctatum hort.	see *G.* × *monacense* var. *monacense* 'Muldoon'
	– 'Variegatum'	see *G. phaeum* 'Variegatum'
	'Purple Rain'	EBee EPPr WCra
	pylzowianum	NBid NRya WMoo
	pyrenaicum	GAbr NSti WTou
	– f. ***albiflorum***	EPPr GAbr IFro MNrw NBir SRGP WBrk WCot WCra WFar WTou
	– 'Barney Brighteye'	SRGP
	– 'Bill Wallis'	CSpe ELan EPPr EPfP EWoo GBuc IFro LBMP LLWP LRHS LSRN LSun MBrN MMuc MRav NBir NDov NHpl NPer SEND SPhx SPtp SRGP SWvt WCFE WCot WFar WHoo WPnP
	– 'Bright Eyes'	LLWP
	– 'Isparta'	EPPr IFro MNrw SHar SPhx SRGP WBrk
	– 'Summer Sky'	CBod SPav SRGP SWvt
	– 'Summer Snow'	GPSL GWyn
	'Rainbow'PBR	EWoo MBNS WCra
	Rambling Robin Group	CSpe ECre EPri EWes LLHF
	'Ray's Pink'	CPla
	rectum	EPPr NBre NLar WCra WCru
	– 'Album'	see *G. clarkei* 'Kashmir White'
	'Red Admiral'	CBod CMea CNec CSam ECtt EHoe EPPr GBuc GCal LRHS MAvo NCGa NDov NLar NQui NSti SBod SRGP WCot WCra WFar WGwG WHoo WPnP
	'Red Propellers'	CElw WSHC
	reflexum	CDor CFis EPPr EPfP LRHS WCru
	– 'Katara Pass'	EPPr
	refractoides	WCot
	regelii	EPPr GWyn WCru WMoo
	renardii ♀H5	Widely available
	– 'Beldo'	MAvo
	– blue-flowered	see *G. renardii* 'Whiteknights'
	– 'Rothbury Hills'	EBee EPPr
	– 'Tcschelda'	CBod ECha ECtt EPPr EShb GBuc LRHS NBir NLar SRms WCra WFar WMoo
§	– 'Whiteknights'	EBee NBir
	– 'Zetterlund'	CBod CMos EBee ELan EPPr EPfP EPri EWTr LHop LRHS NEgg NQui WCra WMoo

§	***reuteri***	CHid CPla CTsd EBee NLos SChr SRGP WCru
	'Richard Nutt'	EBee
	richardsonii	CBod CFis EBee EPPr GCal LRHS MCot NBir NWad SBod SPoG SRGP WCra WCru WGwG
	- pink-flowered	MAvo
	- white-flowered	NChi
	× ***riversleaianum*** 'Russell Prichard' ♀H4	Widely available
§	***rivulare***	GLog NLar
	robertianum	ENfk EPPr LLHF SRms WSFF
§	- 'Album'	CBod EPPr SHar SRGP SRms WHer
	- f. ***bernettii***	see *G. robertianum* 'Album'
	- 'Celtic White'	CBre EPPr GCal IFro MMuc SEND SPav SRGP WTou
	robustum	EPri NBir SKHP SPav SPlb SRGP WKif
	'Rosetta'PBR	MSCN WCra
	'Rosie Crûg'	SWvt
	rosthornii	WCru
	'Rothbury Red'	EBee NChi
§	Rozanne = 'Gerwat'PBR ♀H7	Widely available
	rubescens	see *G. yeoi*
	rubifolium	WCru
	ruprechtii (Grossh.) Woronow	EPPr MNrw SRGP
	Sabani Blue = 'Bremigo'PBR	CAbP CLAP CMac CMos CSpe CWGN EBee ECtt EPPr EWTr EWes EWoo LCro LOPS MHol NLar NSti SMHy SPer SPoG WCot WCra WSHC
	'Salome'	CBcs CBod CLAP EBee ECtt ELan GAbr ILea LHop MBel MCot NBir NLar NSti SCob SPoG SRms SRot SWat SWvt WCot WCra WGwG WHoo WKif WMoo WPnP
	'Sandrine'PBR	CBcs CLAP CSam CWGN EBee EPfP IMou IPot LHop LLHF LRHS LSou MHol MNrw NSti SAko SCob SPoG SRms WCot WCra WHil WPnP
	sanguineum	Widely available
	- Alan Bloom = 'Bloger'PBR	EBee EPPr LHop LRHS WCra WFib
	- 'Album' ♀H5	Widely available
	- 'Alpenglow'	EBee EPPr SRGP WBrk WCra
	- 'Ankum's Pride' ♀H7	CDor CElw CMos CPrp EPPr EPfP EWoo LHop LRHS LSou MAsh MTis NDov NGdn NHar NLar NSti SBch SRGP SWat WBrk WCra WCru WFib WMoo WPnP WPtf
	- 'Apfelblüte'	ELon EPPr GBin GJos NLar WCAu WCra
	- 'Aviemore' ♀H7	CElw CFis EPPr GBin GCal
	- 'Barnsley'	CPrp EPPr NBro NEoE WCra
	- 'Belle of Herterton'	CElw EPPr MAvo NBid NEoE WBrk WCra WCru
	- 'Bloody Graham'	EPPr LRHS MAvo WBrk WCra WMoo
	- 'Canon Miles'	CBod CElw CMos ECtt EPPr EWTr NLar SRGP SRms WCra
	- 'Catforth Carnival'	EBee EPPr MAvo
	- 'Cedric Morris'	CElw ECha ELon EPPr GCra MAvo NBid SRGP WBrk WCra WCru WPnP
	- 'Compactum'	EPPr WCra WMoo XLum
	- 'Connie Hansen'	WCra
	- dark purple **new**	SSut
§	- 'Droplet'	SRGP
	- dwarf **new**	WAbe
	- 'Elsbeth'	CBod CElw CNec CPrp EBee ECha ECtt ELan ELon EPPr EWes GBin GCal LRHS MSpe NGdn NLar NSti SPoG SRGP WBrk WCra WCru WFar WFib WHal WMoo WPnP XLum
	- 'Feu d'Automne'	EBee EPPr WBrk WCra
	- 'Fran's Star'	see *G.* × *oxonianum* 'Fran's Star'
	- 'Glenluce'	CDor CElw CPrp ECtt EPPr EPfP EShb GBuc GCal LHop LRHS MRav MSpe MTis NChi NDov NLar NWad SPoG SRGP SRms SWat WBrk WCra WHal WPnP
	- 'Hampshire Purple'	see *G. sanguineum* 'New Hampshire Purple'
	- 'Holden'	CElw EBee EPPr WBrk
	- 'Inverness'	EBee EPPr XLum
	- 'Joanna'	CFis EPPr MAvo WBrk WCra
	- 'John Elsley'	EAEE EBee ECtt EHoe EPPr LLWP LRHS LSou MSpe NBro NGdn NSti SRGP SWat WCra WPnP
	- 'John Innes'	EPPr
	- 'Jubilee Pink'	GCal WCru
	- 'Kristin Jacob'	EPPr
	- var. ***lancastrense***	see *G. sanguineum* var. *striatum*
	- 'Leeds Variety'	see *G. sanguineum* 'Rod Leeds'
§	- 'Little Bead' ♀H5	ECho EPPr NHpl NWad WBrk WCra XLum
	- 'Max Frei'	Widely available
	- 'Minutum'	see *G. sanguineum* 'Droplet'
	- 'Nanum'	see *G. sanguineum* 'Little Bead'
§	- 'New Hampshire Purple'	CLAP CPrp EBee ECtt ELon EPPr EPfP EWTr GLog IPot LRHS MAvo NBro NDov NGdn NLar WBrk WCra WFib WHar
	- 'Nyewood'	CBod CNec EBee ECGP ECtt EPPr LRHS MAsh SEND SRGP WBrk WCra WCru WFib
	- 'Pink Pouffe'	CWGN EBee ECtt MAsh SCob
I	- 'Plenum' (d)	EPPr
	- 'Prado'	XLum
	- var. ***prostratum*** (Cav.) Pers.	see *G. sanguineum* var. *striatum*
	- 'Purple Flame'	see *G. sanguineum* 'New Hampshire Purple'
§	- 'Rod Leeds'	CFis CLAP EBee SRGP
	- 'Sandra'	SRGP
	- 'Sara'	LLWP MAvo
§	- 'Shepherd's Delight'	ECtt EPPr
	- 'Shepherd's Warning' misapplied	see *G. sanguineum* 'Shepherd's Delight'
	- 'Shepherd's Warning' ♀H7	CMea CTri ECtt GCal MMuc MRav NBir NLar SEND SRGP SWat WCru WFib WHoo WIce WPnP
	- 'Shooting Star'	EPPr
	- 'South Nutfield'	CElw
§	- var. ***striatum*** ♀H5	Widely available
	- - deep pink-flowered	CSBt MSwo SWvt
	- - 'Mottisfont'	SBch
	- - 'Reginald Farrer'	WCru
	- - 'Splendens' ♀H7	CRos EBee EPPr GCal LHop LRHS NBid NRHS SAko WCru
	- 'Vision Light Pink'	CBod CNec EPPr WCra WFar
	- 'Vision Violet'	CBod CNec EBee IFoB MAvo SWvt WBrk WCra WFar WHar WPnP
	- 'Westacre Poppet'	EWes WCra
	'Sanne'	CBod EPPr EWes EWoo LRHS MHol NLar SCob STPC WCot WCra WFib WPGP
	saxatile	EPPr
*	- var. ***candidum*** **new**	EBee
	'Scapa Flow'	EBee EPPr GCal MAvo WCra WSHC
	schlechteri	EWes MMuc SEND

	'Sea Spray' **new**	GMcL
	sessiliflorum	GBin
	- subsp. ***novae-zelandiae*** 'Mandy' **new**	GBin
I	- - 'Nigricans'	CFis ECha ECho ELan GAbr LPot MHer SBch SCob SRGP WFar
§	- - 'Porters Pass'	EHoe EWes NHpl SBch SPlb WCra WFar WHoo
	- - red-leaved	see *G. sessiliflorum* subsp. *novae-zelandiae* 'Porters Pass'
	shikokianum	EBee GLog GWyn NLar SRGP WCra WPnP
	- var. ***kaimontanum***	WCru
	- var. ***quelpaertense***	CFis EBee MAvo
	- - 'Crûg's Cloak'	WCru
	- var. ***yoshiianum*** B&SWJ 6147	WCru
	'Shocking Blue'	NLar NSti WCra WFib
	'Shouting Star'	see *G.* 'Kanahitobanawa'
	'Silva'	CElw EPPr MRav SWat WCru
*	'Silver Shadow'	SPhx
	'Simonside'	EBee
§	***sinense***	CBod CMos EBee ECtt GBuc GCal LRHS MCot WCra WGwG XLum
	'Sirak' ♕H7	Widely available
	soboliferum	CBod EPPr NBir NDov NLar SPer SRGP WCra WCru WMoo
	- Cally strain	EBee EPPr GCal LPla MAvo NSti
	- var. ***kiusianum***	CElw
	- 'Rothbury Star'	EBee
	- 'Starman'	CMos EBee ECtt EPPr EWoo MSCN NLar SCob SKHP STPC WCra WMoo WSHC
	'Solitaire'	CFil EBee WCot
	'Southcombe Star'	see *G.* × *oxonianum* f. *thurstonianum* 'Southcombe Star'
	'Southease Celestial'	SMHy
	'Spinners'	CBod CHid CMac CPrp EBee ECtt EPPr EPfP GCal GMaP LHop LRHS LSRN MAvo MRav NBid NBir NGdn NLar NSti SPer SWat WCra WCru WFar WFib WMoo WPnP
	stapfianum var. ***roseum***	see *G. orientalitibeticum*
	'Stephanie'	CElw CNec EPPr EPfP EWes GBuc LPla LRHS LSRN MAvo MBNS MNrw MRav MSpe NChi NGdn NLar NSti WBor WCra WPnP WSHC
	'Storm Chaser'	CLAP EBee LRHS SCob
	'Strawberry Frost'	LLHF
	subcaulescens ♕H4	Widely available
	- 'Giuseppii' ♕H5	CGar CRos EAEE ECtt ELon EPPr EPot GAbr GBuc GCrg LRHS LSou MAsh MRav NBir NDov NFav NRHS SBod SRGP SRot SWvt WCra
	- 'Splendens' ♕H5	CTri EAEE ECtt EPPr GBuc GCrg GMcL LHop LRHS LSou MAsh MHer NEgg NRHS NSla SRms SWat WFar
	'Sue Crûg'	EBee ECtt ELan EPfP GCra LLWP LPla LRHS LSou NEgg SRGP WCra WCru WMoo WSHC
	'Sue's Sister'	WCru
	'Summer Cloud'	EPPr SRGP WOut
	Summer Skies = 'Gernic'PBR (d)	Widely available
	suzukii B&SWJ 016	WCru
	'Sweet Heidy'PBR	CMos EBee ECtt EPPr EPfP EWTr LBMP LLHF LPla MNrw MSwo NLar NSti SCob SPoG WBor WCra WFar WPnP
	sylvaticum	MArt NBid NGdn NMir WFar WMoo WShi
	- 'Afrodite'	EPPr
	- f. ***albiflorum***	CBre ELan EWoo NSti WCru
	- - 'Cyril's Superb White'	EBee EPPr
	- 'Album' ♕H7	Widely available
	- 'Amanda'	EBee EPPr
	- 'Amy Doncaster'	Widely available
	- 'Angulatum'	CElw EPPr WMoo
	- 'Birch Lilac'	CElw CLAP EBee EPPr EPri GBuc GCal LRHS NLar NPnk WCAu WCra WFib WMoo
	- 'Coquetdale Lilac'	EBee EPPr WCra
	- 'Greek Fire'	EBee EPPr MAvo
	- 'Ice Blue'	EBee EPPr NChi
	- 'Immaculée'	EPPr MRav
	- 'Jonah P' **new**	EBee
	- 'Kanzlersgrund'	CElw EPPr
	- 'Lilac Time'	EPPr
	- 'Mayflower' ♕H7	Widely available
	- 'Meran'	EPPr
	- 'Miss Connie Wilson'	EBee EPPr
	- 'Nikita'	CLAP EPPr
	- f. ***roseum***	CFis NLar
	- - 'Baker's Pink'	CLAP EBee EPPr GCra MNrw MRav NBir SRGP WCra WCru WMoo
	- subsp. ***sylvaticum*** var. ***wanneri***	EPPr WCru
§	'Tanya Rendall'PBR	EBee ECtt ELan ELon EPPr GMcL IPot LHop MHer NLar SPer SRms WCot WCra WFar WFib WPnP
	'Terre Franche'	EPPr MAvo NLar SPhx WCra
§	***thunbergii***	CHid EWes LSou SRGP WMoo XLum
	- 'Jester's Jacket' (v)	CPla EPPr GMcL MNrw SRGP WFar WMoo WOut
	- pink-flowered	EPPr SRGP
	- white-flowered	EPPr SRGP
	thurstonianum	see *G.* × *oxonianum* f. *thurstonianum*
	'Tinpenny Mauve'	MAvo WCra WHoo
	'Tiny Monster'	Widely available
	transbaicalicum	CFis EPPr XLum
	traversii var. ***elegans***	ECho LRHS NRHS
	tuberosum	CDor CElw CHid ECha ELan EPfP GEdr GKev IMou MRav NBir NBro NGdn NQui SKHP SPhx WCra
	- subsp. ***linearifolium***	EPPr
	- 'Richard Hobbs'	EPPr
	- 'Rosie's Mauve'	EPPr MAvo
	'Ushguli Grijs'	see *G. ibericum* Cav. 'Ushguli Grijs'
	'Vectis' **new**	CElw
	'Verguld Saffier'	see *G.* Blue Sunrise
	versicolor	CGar CMea EBee EPPr EPfP GAbr GCal GPSL MHer MMuc SRms WCra WHea WMoo WPnP XEll
	- 'Kingston'	see *G.* × *oxonianum* 'Kingston'
§	- 'Snow White'	EPPr SEND SRGP WCru WFib WMoo WRHF
	- 'White Lady'	see *G. versicolor* 'Snow White'
	'Victor Reiter'	see *G. pratense* Victor Reiter Junior strain
	violareum	see *Pelargonium* 'Splendide'
	viscosissimum	WFib
	wallichianum	CFis CMac CPou EBee IFro NBir NChi NSti WMoo
§	- 'Buxton's Variety'	Widely available
	- 'Chris'	EWes SRGP
	- 'Crystal Lake'PBR	CWGN EBee ECtt EPfP EWoo IPot MBNS MNrw MTis NBir NDov NLar

	NSti SCob WCra WFar WHil WPnP WPtf
- 'Havana Blues'	CMos EBee ECtt EWoo GBin IPot LCro LHop LRHS MAvo MHol NLar NSti SCob STPC WBrk WCot WCra WFar
- magenta-flowered	GBuc
- pale-blue-flowered	CElw
- 'Pink Buxton'	EWes NLar
- pink-flowered	CLAP GBuc GCal WCru
- 'Rise and Shine'PBR	CWGN EBee ECtt EWoo LCro MAsh STPC WCot WCra
- 'Rosetta'	IMou
- 'Rosie'	SRGP
- 'Syabru'	CElw CMea MArt MNrw SMHy WMoo
- 'Sylvia's Surprise'PBR	CLAP CMos IMou LPre NLar SCob WCra
'Wednesday's Child'	WFar
'White Doves'	MAvo NDov
wilfordii misapplied	see *G. thunbergii*
Wisley hybrid	see *G.* 'Khan'
wlassovianum	Widely available
- 'Blue Star'	EBee MRav NEoE SRGP WCra WFar
§ ***yeoi***	CSpe NBir NBro NSti SEND WCru WOut
yesoense	IFro NSti
- var. ***nipponicum***	WCru
yoshinoi misapplied	see *G. thunbergii*
yunnanense misapplied	see *G. pogonanthum*

Gerbera (*Asteraceae*)

(Everlast Series) Everlast Carmine = 'Amgerbcar'	MBNS
- Everlast Honey	MBNS
- Everlast Pink = 'Amgerbpink'	MBNS
'Fleurie'PBR (Garvinea Series)	LRHS MBNS
Garvinea Crista = 'Garcrista' (Garvinea Series)	LRHS
- Garvinea Jilly	LRHS
- Garvinea Lisa = 'Garlisa'PBR	MHol
- Garvinea Nikki = 'Garnikki'	LRHS
- Garvinea Pam = 'Pam'PBR	EUJe LRHS
- Garvinea Rachel = 'Garrachel'PBR	MHol MNrw
- Garvinea Romy = 'Garromy'PBR	LRHS NRHS
- Garvinea Sunny	see *G.* 'Sunny'
- Garvinea Sylvana = 'Garsylvana'PBR	MHol WCot
- Garvinea Valerie = 'Garvalerie'PBR	LRHS
- Garvinea Vivian = 'Garvivian'PBR	LRHS
§ 'Sunny'PBR (Garvinea Series)	LRHS

Gesneria (*Gesneriaceae*)

cardinalis	see *Sinningia cardinalis*

Gethyum (*Alliaceae*)

atropurpureum	GKev

Geum ✿ (*Rosaceae*)

'Abbeydore Burnt Orange' new	CElw
'Abendsonne'	CElw MAvo MRav MSpe NEoE WOut
'Alabama Slammer' (Cocktails Series)	EBee ECtt GBin IKil LRHS MAsh MAvo MSpe MTis NDov NEgg NLar NPri SBri SCob SHil SPad WHlf
alpinum	see *G. montanum*
'Apricot Beauty'	CWCL
'Apricot Delight'	LLHF NEoE NWad
'Baked Beans'	NEoE
'Banana Daiquiri' (Cocktails Series)	CMea EBee IKil LLWG LRHS MAsh MSpe MTis SCob SHil WTor
'Beech House Apricot'	CDor CLAP EAJP ECtt EPri GCra ILea LRHS MAvo MNrw MRav NEoE NHol NWad SBri SPoG WMoo WPnP XEll
'Beech's Double' new	EWes
'Bell Bank'	Widely available
'Birkhead's Creamy Lemon'	EBee NBir
'Blazing Sunset' (d)	Widely available
'Blood Orange'	EPed LRHS MAsh MAvo NEoE
'Borisii'	Widely available
'Bremner's Gold'	NEoE SBri
'Bremner's Nectarine'	CElw MNrw MSpe NChi NEoE SHar
'Broomrigg Beauty'	NEoE
'Brown Sugar'	NEoE
bulgaricum	CElw EBee MRav NBir NEoE NLar NRya XLum
'Butterscotch'	EBee
calthifolium	EPPr
camschaticum new	EBee
'Can-can' (d)	CElw MAvo WHoo
'Cantamos'	NEoE
capense	NBre NEoE SPlb
chiloense 'Red Dragon'	CBre CElw CWld GPSL LLHF MMrt MMuc SEND SWvt WHrl WOut
'Chipchase'	CElw MAvo NChi NPnk WHoo
coccineum ambig.	GKev NCGa
coccineum Sibth. & Sm.	GLog WHoo
- 'Ann'	EPri MSpe
- 'Cooky'	CElw CRos EBee EPfP ESps GMcL GPSL LRHS MMuc NEoE NLar NRHS SHil SPhx SPoG SRms SWvt WFar WRHF WWtn
- 'Eos'	CElw CSpe CWCL EBee ECtt ELon EWes GBin IBoy LEdu LHop LRHS MAvo MHol MNrw MPnt MRav MSpe NEoE NGdn NLar SCob SPoG SRms WGwG WHrl WMoo
- 'Koi'	EAJP EBee GBin GPSL GWyn LEdu NCou NEoE SPad WMoo
- 'Queen of Orange'	CBod CBre CElw GBin GJos NEoE SRms SRot
- 'Werner Arends'	CElw ECtt GAbr GCal LRHS MAvo MNrw MRav WFar WMoo
'Copper Pennies'	CElw NEoE
'Coppertone'	CElw CLAP CPla CWCL ELan EPri LPla MRav NBir NBro NChi NRya SCob XEll
'Cosmopolitan' (Cocktails Series)	CSpe EBee EWTr GBin IBoy IKil LCro LLWG LRHS MAvo MSCN MSpe MTis NDov NLar SCob SHil SPad WHlf
'Cotton Candy'	NEoE WOut
'Country Rock Star'	NEoE WFar
'Cream Crackers'	NEoE
'Cumbrian Candy'	NEoE
'Cumbrian Cheddar'	NEoE
'Cumbrian Cherrypie'	NEoE WFar
'Cumbrian Cream'	NEoE
'Custard Pie'	NEoE

	'Custard Tart'	NEoE
	'Dawn'	NEoE SBri SMHy
	'Deano's Delight'	NEoE
	'Diana'	MAvo MNrw NEoE NLar
	'Dingle Apricot'	ECtt GAbr GCal MNrw MRav NBir
	'Dolly North' (d)	CElw EBee EWoo GWyn MArl MCot MRav MSpe MTis NBro NGdn SHar WCAu WHal XEll
	'Double Sunrise' (d)	EBee
	'East of Eden'	NEoE
	'Eden Valley Angel'	MAvo NEoE WWtn
	'Eden Valley Elf'	NEoE
	'El Wano'	NEoE
	'Elworthy Amber'	CElw
	'Emory Quinn'	ECtt LLHF LRHS NEoE
	'Fancy Frills'	CElw ECtt MAvo WHoo
	'Farmer John Cross'	CAby CBre CElw CLAP EBee ECtt ELon EPri GBin GJos MAvo MSpe MTis NLar WHal WMoo WOut WWtn
	'Feuermeer'	CElw MAvo NEoE NLar
	'Fire Opal' (d) 🏆H7	CElw CWCL EAJP GWyn MAvo MNrw NBir NEoE SBri WMoo
	'Fire Storm' PBR	CBod CBre CMea CMos CWGN EBee ECtt GBin IKil LBMP LBrs LRHS LSun MBel MNrw MPnt NEgg NLar SBri SPoG WCot WFar WGrn WWFP
	'Fireball'	CBod ECtt EShb GBin LRHS LSou MAsh NLar
	'Firefinch' **new**	NEoE
	'Flame'	MAvo NEoE NLar
	'Flames of Passion' PBR	Widely available
	'Flower of Darkness'	NEoE
	'Furay's Fire' **new**	NEoE
	'Georgeham'	CPla
	'Georgenberg'	CBod CElw CLAP CRos CSam ECtt EPfP EPri GMaP LRHS MBel MCot MNrw MRav NBir NDov NGdn NHol NLar NRHS NWad SBod SPer SPoG SRms SWvt WCAu WGwG WMoo
	'Gimlet' (Cocktails Series)	GBin NLar SCob WHlf
	'Glencoe'	CElw
	'Golden Joy'	CElw LLHF MAvo NEoE WHoo
	'Hannay's'	EBee MAvo MNrw MSpe NEoE SHar SPtp
	'Harvest Moon'	NEoE
	'Hearts in Amber'	NEoE WFar
	'Herterton Lemon'	CElw WCot
	'Herterton Primrose'	CElw CLAP CWCL ECtt EPPr GBuc GCal LLHF LLWG MAvo MSpe NSti WBor WHal WHoo
	'Hilltop Beacon' (d)	CElw EBee LLHF MAvo MHCG NEoE SBri WFar WHoo WPnn
	'Honeydew'	NEoE
*	***hybridum luteum***	NSti SBri
	× ***intermedium***	CBre EPPr GPSL MAvo NEoE NGdn NLar SBri WMoo
	- 'Diane'	MAvo NChi SBri
	- 'Hofrennydd'	NWad
	'Jolly Roger'	EBee NEoE NWad
	'Karlskaer'	CElw CWCL ECtt EPri EWTr EWes EWoo GBin GBuc GQue LHop LPla LRHS LSun MBel MCot MNrw NGdn NLar SBri SPtp WCAu WFar WGwG WMoo WPtf WWtn
	'Lady Stratheden' (d) 🏆H7	Widely available
	'Lemon Delight'	CDor CElw MAvo
	'Lemon Drops'	Widely available

	'Lionel Cox'	CPla CWCL ECtt ELan EPPr EWTr GAbr GCal GCra GMaP LBMP MBNS MBel MCot MRav NBir NBro NChi NGdn NLar SRGP SRms WFar
	'Lipstick Sunset'	NEoE
	'Lisanne'	CElw CSam CWCL IPot MAvo MNrw MSpe NCGa NDov SBri SHar SMHy SPtp
	'Little Lottie'	NEoE
	'Little Twister'	NEoE
	macrophyllum	EBee
	'Maddy Prior'	NEoE
	magellanicum	EWes LEdu NBre NLar
	- PAB 237	LEdu
	'Magic Toybox'	NEoE
	'Mai Tai' PBR	Widely available
	'Mandarin' (d)	CCse GAbr GCal SHar
	'Mango'	EBee NDov
	'Mango Lassi'	CElw GBin MTis NEoE SBri SHar WCAu
	'Marchant's Apricot Sundae'	SBri
	'Marmalade'	ECtt EPri GAbr GJos LLWG LLWP LPla MAsh MAvo MNrw MRav MSpe NEoE NLar SMHy SSut WFar WHrl WKif WMoo WOut
	'McClure's Magic'	NEoE
§	***montanum*** 🏆H5	CRos EBee ECho EDAr GBin GCra GLog LRHS MMuc NBir NRHS NRya NSla SEND SRms XLum
	'Moonlight Serenade'	EBee ECtt EPed GBin GCal LLHF LRHS LSou MAvo NEoE
	'Moorland Sorbet'	NEoE SBri WFar WMoo WPtf
	'Morning Sun'	SBri
	'Mrs J. Bradshaw' (d) 🏆H7	Widely available
	'Mrs W. Moore'	CBre CElw CLAP CWCL EBee ECtt EPPr EShb GAbr GJos IPot MHer MNrw MRav NBir NChi NEoE NLar NPnk NQui SBri SCob SRGP WMoo
	'Nordek'	CElw CMos ECha ECtt GAbr GBuc GCal GQue LRHS MNrw MRav NEgg NGdn SBri SPoG WPtf
	'Norwell Yellow Lamp'	MAvo
	'Octavie'	MAvo
	'Orangeman'	MNrw
	'Peachy Proud'	NEoE
	'Pear Drops'	NEoE
	pentapetalum	see *Sieversia pentapetala*
	'Pink Frills'	CElw CWCL ECtt EPPr EPri EWes GBin GBuc GCra GQue LEdu LLWG MAvo MPnt MRav MTis NCGa NLar SGbt SMHy SPtp WCAu
	'Poco'	CBod CMos EBee ECtt GBin GCal LLHF LRHS MAsh MAvo MNrw NEoE
	'Prairie Dancer'	NEoE
	'Present'	ECtt NBre NCGa NChi NEoE
	'Primrose'	GAbr GJos GQue NEoE NGdn NLar
	'Primrose Cottage'	EBee
	'Prince of Orange' (d)	CElw GAbr LRHS MNrw MRav NBre SBri SWvt WFar WHrl
	'Prinses Juliana'	Widely available
	pseudococcineum	LRHS
	pyrenaicum	EBee NBre NCGa
I	'Rearsby Hybrid'	CElw LLHF MRav NEoE SPlb WHoo
	'Red Wings' (d)	CElw CWCL GBuc GCal GMaP GQue ILea LRHS MAsh MCot MNrw MRav NBir SBri WGwG
§	***reptans***	LLHF
	rhodopeum	EBee

'Rijnstroom'	EPPr MNrw SBri SHar WPtf
'Rise and Shine' new	NEoE
rivale	CArn CBen CBod CHab CRos CWld EAJP ELan EPfP IBoy MCot MHer MHol MMuc MNHC MWts NBro NMir NPer SPlb SRms SWat WFar WHar WMAq WMoo WOut
- 'Album'	Widely available
- 'Apricot'	SBri
- 'Barbra Lawton'	MSpe SBri
- 'Cream Drop'	GJos LLWG MCot MSpe NCGa NChi NEoE SHar
- subsp. ***islandicum***	SBrt
- 'Leonard's Variety'	Widely available
- 'Marika'	CAby CCVN CHid EBee EPri GBin SRGP WMoo WWtn
- 'Marmalade'	CAby CBre CElw CWCL EBee IPot MPnt NChi NEoE SBri
- 'Salmon Bells' new	XEll
- 'Snowflake'	CElw MAvo MSpe NChi NEoE SBri
'Roger's Rebellion'	NEoE WFar
'Rubin'	EBee ECtt GCra IPot NBro NDov WCAu
'Rusty Young'	CBod CMos ECtt EWes GCal LLHF LRHS LSou MAsh MAvo MBel NEoE
'Savanna Sunset'	CMos ECtt EPed EWes GBin GCal LLHF LRHS MCot NEoE WHrl
'Sigiswang'	EWes GJos LEdu MNrw MRav NEoE WCAu
'Son of Poco' new	NEoE
'Spider Muffin'	NEoE
'Stacey's Sunrise'	CBod CMos ECtt EWes GCal LLHF LRHS MAsh MAvo MHCG NEoE SPoG
'Star of Bethlehem'	NEoE
I 'Starker's Magnificum'	MAvo WCot
'Stevie Nicks'	NEoE
'Strawberries and Cream'	NEoE
'Sundrud Star'	NEoE
'Sunrise' (d)	CRos ECrN LRHS SHil
'Sweet Angel Dar'	NEoE
'Tangerine'	EPri MRav MSpe NEoE
'Tango Dream'	LRHS MAvo NEoE
'Tequila Sunrise'	EBee ECtt ELan EWTr IKil ILea LLWG LRHS MAsh MHol MNrw MSpe MTis NDov NHpl SBri SCob SHil SPad
'Tinkerbell'	NEoE
'Tinpenny Orange'	CElw MAvo NEoE WHoo
× ***tirolense***	EBee NBre NCGa NEoE
'Toast of Cumbria'	NEoE
'Toffee Apples'	NEoE
'Totally Tangerine'PBR	Widely available
'Trevor's Lemon'	MAvo
triflorum	CElw CWCL EWes GEdr LEdu MHer MNrw SHar
- SDR 8121 new	GKev
- var. ***campanulatum***	NEoE
- 'Peace Pipe' new	MNrw
'Turbango'	NEoE
'Turbango Twister'	NEoE
'Turnpike Tales'	NEoE
'Turnpike Troubadour'	NEoE
'Tutti Frutti' new	MAvo
urbanum	CArn ENfk SWat WHer WMoo
'Welcome Joy' new	CElw
'Wyn's Wish'	NEoE

Gevuina (*Proteaceae*)

avellana	WPGP

Gilia (*Polemoniaceae*)

achilleifolia	CSpe SPhx
californica	see *Leptodactylon californicum*
tricolor	NPol

Gillenia (*Rosaceae*)

stipulata	CLAP GBin IPot LEdu MNrw SHar SPhx WPGP
trifoliata ♀H7	Widely available
- 'Pink Profusion'	CBot CSpe EBee ECtt EWTr GBin IPot LPla MAvo MBel MHol MSCN NLar SCob SPad SPer STPC WCot WHil

Gilliesia (*Alliaceae*)

graminea new	GKev

Ginkgo (*Ginkgoaceae*)

biloba	Widely available
- B&SWJ 8753	WCru
- 'Anny's Dwarf'	MAsh MBlu NLar SBig
- 'Autumn Gold' (m) ♀H6	CBcs CDul CEnd CMCN EBee ECrN EMOT LLHF MBlu MGos MPkF SBig SLim WMat
- 'Barabits' Fastigiata'	ESwi MBlu SAko SBig
- 'Barabits' Nana'	MBlu SBig
- 'Beijing Gold'	IVic MBlu MPkF SAko SBig SMad WPGP
- 'Broom with Tubes'	SMad
- 'California Sunset'	MBlu SBig
- 'Chase Manhattan'	MPkF
- 'Chotek'	SBig
- 'Chris' Dwarf'	NLar
- 'David'	SBig
- 'Eastern Star' (f)	CAgr
- 'Elsie'	SBig
- 'Everton Broom'	CMac CMen NEgg NLar SBig SBod
- 'Fairmount' (m)	MBlu SBig
- 'Fastigiata' (m)	CMCN EBee EPfP ESwi MBlu SBig
- 'Finger'	SLim
- 'Globosa'	LPar MBlu SBig
- 'Gnome'	ESwi LSRN MPkF SCob
- 'Golden Dragon'	MBlu
- 'Golden Globe'	ESwi MPkF SBig
- 'Gresham'	MPkF
- 'Horizontalis'	MBlu SBig
- 'Jade Butterflies' ♀H6	MBlu MPkF NLar SBig SLim SMad
- 'Jehosaphat'	NLar SBig
- 'Jerry Vercade'	MPkF
- 'King of Dongting' (f)	CAgr ESwi MBlu SBig
- 'Lakeview' (m)	MPkF SBig SCob
- 'Long March'	CAgr
- 'Magyar' new	SBig
- 'Mariken' ♀H6	ELan EPfP ESwi MPkF NLar SBig SCob SLim SPoG
- 'Mayfield' (m)	NLar SBig SMad
- 'McFarland'	CAgr
- 'Menhir'PBR	CBcs EBee ELan EPfP MPkF
- 'Montezuma'	SBig
- 'Nelleke' new	SBig
- 'Obelisk'	NLar
- Ohazuki Group (f)	CAgr SBig
- Pendula Group	CEnd CMCN EBee ESwi MBlu MPkF SBig SGol WMat
- 'Pendula Gruga'	SBig
- 'Pixie'	SBig
- 'Princeton Sentry' (m) ♀H6	EBee IVic LLHF MBlu NLar SBig
- 'Robbie's Twist'	MPkF SBig

- 'Santa Cruz'	SBig
- 'Saratoga' (m) ♀H6	CAgr CBcs CEnd CMCN EBee EPfP ESwi MBlu MPkF NLar SAko SBig SCob SLim WMat
- 'Shangri-La' (m)	MBlu SMad
- 'Sinclair'	MPkF
- 'Thelma'	SLim
- 'Tit'	CEnd CMCN EPfP ESwi LPar MBlu MPkF SBig
- 'Tremonia'	CMCN EPfP MBlu MPkF SAko SBig
- 'Troll' ♀H6	LRHS MAsh MBlu SBig SCoo SLim SMad
- 'Tubifolia'	CMCN ESwi MBlu MPkF NLar SBig SCob SLim
- 'Umbrella'	SBig
- Variegata Group (v)	CBcs ESwi MPkF NLar SBig
- 'W.B.'	MPkF SBig
- 'Weeping Wonder' (f)	SBig
- 'Yellow Mellow' **new**	LRHS

ginseng see *Panax ginseng*

Gladiolus (*Iridaceae*)

'Adi'	WCot
'Akuta' (M/E)	CGrW
alatus	ECho NRog
'Alba' (N)	LRHS
'Alice' (Min)	ERCP
'Amanda Mahy' (N)	GKev LAma NRog
'Amsterdam' (G)	CGrW
angustus L.	CGrW CTal NRog
antakiensis	CPou
'Atom' (S/P)	CAvo CBro CGrW ECho GKev LAma NRog
Barnard hybrids	CGrW
'Beautiful Angel'	CGrW
'Beauty Bride' (L)	CGrW
'Big Boss' (G)	CGrW
'Black Jack'	NNys
'Black Star'	EPfP ERCP
'Blackbird' (S)	CGrW
'Blue Frost' (L)	ERCP SDeJ
'Bonfire' (G)	CGrW
'Break of Dawn'	SDeJ
byzantinus	see *G. communis* subsp. *byzantinus*
callianthus	see *G. murielae*
cardinalis	CPne CPrp EWoo GCal IBlr LEdu SBrt SKHP WCru
carinatus	CGrW NRog
carinatus* × *orchidiflorus	WCot
'Carine' (N)	GKev NRog SDeJ
carmineus	CGrW GKev WCot
carneus	CGrW CTal ECho EPot GBin GKev NRog SDeJ
- 'Georgina'	CGrW
caucasicus **new**	GKev
'Charm' (N/Tub)	CBro GKev LEdu NRog SDeJ
'Charming Beauty' (Tub)	GKev LAma LRHS NRog SDeJ
'Charming Lady' (Tub)	GKev NRog
citrinus	see *G. trichonemifolius*
'Claudia' (N)	CGrW
'Columbine' (P)	SDeJ
× ***colvillii***	IBlr
- 'Albus'	ERCP GKev
- 'The Bride'	CAvo CBro EBee GKev ITim LAma LCro LEdu LOPS LSRN SDeJ SDir
§ ***communis*** subsp. ***byzantinus*** ♀H5	Widely available
'Coral Lace' (L)	SDeJ
crassifolius	CTre
'Cream Perfection' (L)	CGrW SDeJ
'Creamy Yellow' (S)	CGrW
cruentus	CGrW
cunonius	CTal
§ ***dalenii***	CPou CSam CTre GBin GCal IBlr LEdu SMad WCot
- 'Apricot Delight' (v)	IBlr
- 'Boone'	WCot
- 'Citrone Spectrum' (v)	IBlr
§ - subsp. ***dalenii***	CPrp IBlr WCot
- - 'Spinners'	EBee IBlr
- green-flowered	IBlr
- 'Guardsman' (v)	IBlr
- red-flowered	GCal
* - f. ***rubra***	IBlr
'David Hills' (*papilio* hybrid)	CDor CMea NCGa SDys WCot WHal WSHC
'Delirium'	CGrW
'Dion' (M)	CGrW
'Elvira' (N)	GKev LAma NRog
'Esta Bonita' (G)	CGrW
'Extasy'PBR (L)	CGrW
'Far West' (L) **new**	CSut ERCP
'Farandole'	SDeJ
'Fidelio' (L)	SDeJ
'Fiona'	CGrW GKev
'Fiorentina' **new**	ERCP
flanaganii	CBro CPBP CSpe CTre ECho GCal GEdr GKev LLHF NHpl NSla SBrt WAbe
- JCA 261.000	SKHP
'Flevo Dancer' (S)	CGrW
'Flevo Eclips'PBR (G)	CGrW
'Flevo Laguna' (S)	CAvo
'Flevo Souvenir'PBR (L)	CGrW
'Flevo Spirit'	CGrW
'Flevo Sunset'PBR (L)	CGrW
floribundus Jacq.	NRog
- subsp. ***fasciatus***	CGrW
fourcadei	CGrW
'French Silk' (L)	CGrW
'Galaxian'	GKev
× ***gandavensis*** hort.	GBin
garnieri	see *G. dalenii* subsp. *dalenii*
geardii	WCot
(Glamini Series) 'Glamini Luca' **new**	WTor
- 'Glamini Thomas' **new**	WTor
- 'Glamini Tom' **new**	SPad WTor
'Gold Struck' (L)	CGrW
'Good Luck' (N)	CBro
gracilis	CTal WCot
grandis	see *G. liliaceus*
'Green Star' (L)	CGrW ERCP SDeJ
griseus	NRog
gueinzii	CGrW
'Guernsey Glory' (N)	GKev
'Halley' (N)	GKev NRog
'Hansnett'	WCot
'Happy Weekend' (L)	SDeJ
'Holland Pearl' (B)	ERCP SDeJ
'Huron Silk' (L)	CGrW
huttonii	CGrW ECho NRog WCot
huttonii* × *tristis	CPou
huttonii* × *tristis var. ***concolor***	WCot
hyalinus	WCot
'Ibadan'PBR (L)	CGrW
illyricus	GKev SPlb WShi
imbricatus	GKev MHer

	'Imperialis'	IBlr
	'Impressive' (N)	CBro GKev LAma NRog SBod SDeJ
	'Indian Summer'PBR	ERCP
§	***italicus***	CGrW CHid EPfP GKev LCro LOPS LRHS SKHP
	'Jacksonville Gold' (L)	SDeJ
	'Jester' (L)	CSut SDeJ
	'Las Vegas'	CGrW GKev NRog
	'Lemon Drop' (S)	CGrW
	leptosiphon	CGrW
§	***liliaceus***	CGrW NRog WCot
	'Little Vintage'	GKev
	'Loulou' (G)	CGrW
	'Mademoiselle de Paris'	ERCP
	'Match Point' (L)	SDeJ
	meliusculus	NRog
	'Mexico'	CSut SDeJ
	miniatus	NRog WCot
	'Mirella' (N)	CAvo GKev LAma NRog
	'Mon Amour'PBR	CGrW SDeJ
	'Monsieur Piquet' (P)	WCot
§	***murielae*** ♀H3	CAby CAvo CBod CBro CGrW CMea CWld EAJP EPfP ERCP GBin GKev GWyn LCro LOPS LRHS MArt MCot MPie NNys NPnk SCoo SDeJ SHil SPer SPlb SRms WHal
	natalensis	see *G. dalenii*
	'Natan'	WCot
	'Nathalie' (N)	GKev NRog SDeJ
	'Nova Lux' (L)	SDeJ
	'Nymph' (N)	CAvo GKev LAma LCro LEdu LOPS NBir NRog SDeJ
	'Oasis'PBR (G)	CGrW
§	***oppositiflorus***	CTre EBee IBlr LEdu SPlb
	- subsp. ***salmoneus***	see *G. oppositiflorus*
	orchidiflorus	CGrW
	'Oscar' (G)	ERCP
	papilio	Widely available
§	- Purpureoauratus Group	CBro CSam IBlr SRms WSHC
	- yellow-flowered	CMea SMad
	'Passos'PBR	ERCP
	'Peach Blossom' (N)	IBlr WCot
	'Perseus' (P/Min)	ERCP
	'Perth Pearl' (M)	CGrW
	'Peter Pears' (L)	ERCP SDeJ
	'Phyllis M' (L)	CGrW
	Pilbeam hybrids	CGrW WCot
	'Plum Tart' (L)	CBro ERCP LCro LOPS NNys
	'Pop Art'	SDeJ
	primulinus	see *G. dalenii*
	'Prins Claus' (N)	CBro GKev LAma NRog
	'Prinses Margaret Rose' (Min)	SDeJ
	'Priscilla' (L)	SDeJ
	'Purple Flora'	ERCP NNys
	'Purple Mate'	LCro
	'Purple Prince' (M)	CGrW
	purpureoauratus	see *G. papilio* Purpureoauratus Group
	quadrangularis	CGrW
	'Raspberry Swirl' (L/E)	CGrW
	recurvus	CGrW
	'Robinetta' (*recurvus* hybrid) ♀H3	CWCL GKev LAma LCro LOPS LRHS NRog SDeJ
	'Ruby' (*papilio* hybrid)	CAby CAvo CBro CElw CMea CPou CPrp CTal CTca ECha EPri GKev IMou IPot LEdu LSRN MHer NCGa NChi NPnk SMad WAul WCot WHoo WKif WPGP
	'Ruth Ann'	CGrW
	saundersii	GCal LEdu
	scullyi from Ceres Karoo, South Africa	NRog
	segetum	see *G. italicus*
	'Slick Chick' (S)	CGrW
	'Solveiga' (L/E)	CGrW
	'Sophie'PBR	CGrW
	'Spic and Span' (L)	SDeJ
	splendens	CGrW CTal NRog WCot
	stefaniae	CGrW
	'Stiena' (L)	CGrW
	'Terry' (G)	CGrW
	'That's Love' (L)	CSut SDeJ
	'Trader Horn' (G)	CGrW SDeJ
§	***trichonemifolius***	CGrW GKev
	tristis	CAvo CBro CElw CGrW CMea CPne CPou CTal ECho ELon EWoo GBin NRog
	- var. ***concolor***	CGrW CPou CPrp CTre WCot
	'Twister' (L) **new**	CSut
	undulatus	CGrW ECho NRog WCot
	uysiae	CGrW CTal ECho
	vandermerwei	CGrW
	'Vandohia' **new**	ERCP
	'Velvet Eyes' (M)	SDeJ
	venustus	CGrW NRog
	'Violetta' (M)	CGrW SDeJ
	virescens	NRog
	'Volcano'	GKev
	watsonioides	SKHP
	watsonius	NRog
	'Wax Ruffles' (L/E)	CGrW
	'White Prosperity' (L)	CSut ERCP LCro LOPS SDeJ
	woodii	WCot
	'Yellow Gem'	SDeJ
	'Zamora' (L)	CGrW

Glandularia see *Verbena*

Glaucidium (*Ranunculaceae*)

	palmatum ♀H5	EFEx EWld GBuc GEdr GKev WCru
	- 'Album'	see *G. palmatum* var. *leucanthum*
§	- var. ***leucanthum***	EFEx GEdr GKev
	- 'Mikado' **new**	GEdr

Glaucium (*Papaveraceae*)

§	***corniculatum***	CAbP CAby CArn CSpe EBee LRHS SPhx
	flavum	CSpe EBee ECha ELan LRHS MHer MMuc NFav SPav XSen
	- ***aurantiacum***	see *G. flavum* f. *fulvum*
§	- f. ***fulvum***	ECha MMuc MNrw SDix SEND WCot
	- orange-flowered	see *G. flavum* f. *fulvum*
	- red-flowered	see *G. corniculatum*
	phoenicium	see *G. corniculatum*

Glaucosciadium (*Apiaceae*)

	cordifolium	CSpe WCot
	- PAB 9003	LEdu
	- from Hatay, Turkey **new**	WCot

Glebionis (*Asteraceae*)

	coronaria	MNHC SRms
§	***segetum***	CHab

Glechoma (*Lamiaceae*)

	hederacea	GPoy MHer NMir WHer
§	- 'Variegata' (v)	EShb SPer XLum

Gleditsia (*Caesalpiniaceae*)

caspia LEdu
- NJM 13.019 **new** WPGP
japonica ITim NLar
koraiensis LEdu WPGP
- B&SWJ 12569 WCru
triacanthos CDul CWib ESps LEdu SCob SPlb WTSh
- 'Calhoun' CAgr
- 'Emerald Cascade' CEnd EBee
- 'Goofy' SMad
- f. ***inermis*** Spectrum = 'Speczam' MAsh WHar
- - 'Sunburst' Widely available
- 'Millwood' CAgr
- 'Rubylace' CCVT CDul CEnd CLnd CMCN CSBt EBee ECrN ELan EMOT EPfP EWTr IVic LSRN MBlu MGos MRav MSwo SCob SGol SKHP WHar WMat

Globba ✿ (*Zingiberaceae*)

marantina LAma
racemosa var. ***hookeri*** HWJCM 471 WCru
winitii 'Mount Everest' LAma

Globularia (*Plantaginaceae*)

albiflora EPot
alypum SBrt
bellidifolia see *G. meridionalis*
cordifolia ♀H5 CRos ECho EDAr EPot GCrg GEdr LRHS NBir NHpl NRHS NSla SBch
- RCB UA 30 SPad WCot
- 'Alba' NHar
incanescens CPBP SIgm
§ ***meridionalis*** CBod EPot EWes GMaP SIgm WOld
- 'Blue Bonnets' GEdr NHar
- 'Hort's Variety' NSla WAbe
nana see *G. repens*
nudicaulis CMea GEdr IMou
orientalis GKev XSen
punctata SRms
pygmaea see *G. meridionalis*
§ ***repens*** CPBP ECho EPot GEdr LLHF SIgm WAbe
stygia XSen
trichosantha GEdr MMuc SRms XSen
valentina EPot GEdr GKev LLHF
vulgaris XSen

Gloriosa (*Colchicaceae*)

lutea see *G. superba* 'Lutea'
modesta GKev
rothschildiana see *G. superba* 'Rothschildiana'
superba ♀H1c GKev SDeJ
- 'Carsonii' GKev LAma SDeJ
- 'Greenii' GKev LAma SDeJ
§ - 'Lutea' GKev LAma SDeJ SDir
- 'Red Beauty' **new** GKev
§ - 'Rothschildiana' CBcs CGrW GKev LAma LCro LOPS SDeJ SRms WCot
- 'Rothschildiana Orange' GKev SDir
- 'Rothschildiana Salmon' GKev
- 'Simplex' CLak
- 'Sparkling Jip' GKev
- 'Sparkling Orange' GKev
- 'Tricolor' GKev
- 'Verschuurii' CLak

Gloxinia (*Gesneriaceae*)

nematanthodes SBrt
- 'Evita' EShb WCot
sylvatica 'Bolivian Sunset' WDib

Glumicalyx (*Scrophulariaceae*)

flanaganii CTre SPlb
goseloides CTre

Glyceria (*Poaceae*)

aquatica variegata see *G. maxima* var. *variegata*
maxima MMuc MSKA MWLS NPer SEND SPlb
§ - var. ***variegata*** (v) CLet CWat ECha EHoe ELan EPfP EShb EWay GCra GMaP GMcL IBoy LRHS MMuc NGdn NRHS NWsh SCob SEND SPer SRms SVic SWat WMAq WMoo XLum
notata SVic
spectabilis 'Variegata' see *G. maxima* var. *variegata*

Glycyrrhiza (*Papilionaceae*)

echinata CAgr
§ ***glabra*** CAgr CArn CBod CCCN CHby CLau ENfk GPoy MHer MNHC SDix SPlb SRms WJek
glandulifera see *G. glabra*
uralensis CLau ELan GPoy SPhx
yunnanensis CSpe SMHy

Glyptostrobus (*Cupressaceae*)

pensilis CFil SLim WPGP

Gmelina (*Lamiaceae*)

hystrix CCCN

Gnaphalium (*Asteraceae*)

'Fairy Gold' see *Helichrysum thianschanicum* 'Goldkind'
trinerve see *Anaphalis trinervis*

Gomphocarpus ✿ (*Apocynaceae*)

§ ***fruticosus*** SVen

Gompholobium (*Papilionaceae*)

scabrum SPlb

Gomphostigma (*Scrophulariaceae*)

virgatum CAbP CCCN CFis CSpe EPPr EPfP EWld ITim LLWG MHol MPie SBod SEND SMad SPlb WBod WCFE WCot WRHF WTor
- 'White Candy' GBin NLar SVen

Gomphrena (*Amaranthaceae*)

globosa CCCN
pulchella CSpe

Goniolimon (*Plumbaginaceae*)

incanum 'Blue Diamond' NHpl WCot
§ ***tataricum*** MMuc
§ - var. ***angustifolium*** SEND SRms

Goodia (*Papilionaceae*)

lotifolia CCCN

Goodyera (*Orchidaceae*)

biflora EFEx
pubescens EFEx

schlechtendaliana	EFEx

gooseberry see *Ribes uva-crispa*

Gordonia (*Theaceae*)

axillaris	see *Polyspora axillaris*

Gorgonidium (*Araceae*)

intermedium	WCot

granadilla see *Passiflora quadrangularis*

granadilla, purple see *Passiflora edulis*

granadilla, sweet see *Passiflora ligularis*

grape see *Vitis*

grapefruit see *Citrus* × *aurantium* Grapefruit Group

Graptopetalum (*Crassulaceae*)

filiferum	SPlb
§ ***paraguayense***	SVen

× *Graptoveria* (*Crassulaceae*)

'Ghostly'	WCot

Gratiola (*Plantaginaceae*)

officinalis	CArn CBod LLWG LRHS MHer MSKA

Greenovia (*Crassulaceae*)

§ ***aurea***	NMen SPlb
diplocycla 'Gigantea'	SPlb
dodrentalis	SChr

Grevillea (*Proteaceae*)

* ***alba*** **new**	SEle
banksii 'Canberra Hybrid'	see *G.* 'Canberra Gem'
- var. ***forsteri***	SPlb
§ 'Canberra Gem' ♀H4	Widely available
'Clearview David'	CCCN LRHS LSRN MMuc SEND SLim SVen
crithmifolia	SPlb
'Desert Flame'	see *G. rosmarinifolia* 'Desert Flame'
juniperina	CBcs CCCN CLet CMac EPfP LPar SEle SLim SVen
- f. ***sulphurea***	CCCN CTsd ELon EPfP MGil MMuc SEle SPer SPlb WSHC
lanigera 'Mount Tamboritha'	CBcs CCCN CMac EBee EPfP SEle SLim SPoG SVen
- prostrate	MAsh WAbe WGrn WPat
leucopteris	SPlb
'Olympic Flame'	CBcs CCCN CSBt CTsd CWib EBee ELon EPfP LEdu LRHS LSou MGos MMuc SAko SBod SEle SPoG SVen WBor WGrn
paniculata	SPlb
'Pink Lady'	CBcs CCCN ELon EPfP LRHS SAko
'Poorinda Constance'	SEle
'Poorinda Queen' **new**	CCCN
robusta ♀H1c	SPlb
'Robyn Gordon'	CCCN
'Rondeau'	CCCN
rosmarinifolia ♀H4	CBcs CCCN CCht CLet CMac CSBt CTri CTsd CWib ELan EPfP GKin SArc SEle SIgm SLim SLon SPer SPlb WFar
§ - 'Desert Flame'	CBcs
- 'Jenkinsii'	CCCN CMac CSBt EBee EPfP EUJe LSou SEle SLim
§ × ***semperflorens***	CWib EBee LRHS SPlb WGrn
tolminsis	see *G.* × *semperflorens*
victoriae	CBcs CCCN CCht CJun CTsd EBee ECre EPfP IVic LRHS SAko SChF SEle WGrn WPGP
- yellow-flowered	LRHS
williamsonii	CBcs LRHS

Grewia (*Malvaceae*)

occidentalis	LRHS

Greyia (*Melianthaceae*)

sutherlandii	SPlb

Grindelia (*Asteraceae*)

§ ***camporum***	IMou SPlb
chiloensis	CAbb SMad
integrifolia	XLum
robusta	see *G. camporum*
stricta subsp. ***venulosa*** **new**	WHil

Griselinia ✿ (*Griseliniaceae*)

littoralis ♀H4	Widely available
- 'Bantry Bay' (v)	CAbP CBcs CCCN CTsd ECrN EHoe ELan ESwi LRHS MAsh NWad SPer SPoG SWvt WFar
- 'Brodick Gold'	ELon GKin
- 'Dixon's Cream' (v)	CBcs CCCN CDul CMac CSBt EBee EPfP LRHS MRav SGol SLon SVen
- 'Green Favor' **new**	EBee
- Green Horizon = 'Whenuapai'PBR	ELan IBal LRHS SLim SPer STPC
- 'Green Jewel' (v)	CCCN CWib ECrN ESwi NLar
- 'Variegata' (v) ♀H4	Widely available
ruscifolia	LEdu
scandens	CCCN SEND

guava, common see *Psidium guajava*

guava, purple or strawberry see *Psidium littorale* var. *longipes*

Guichenotia (*Sterculiaceae*)

macrantha	SPlb

Gunnera ✿ (*Gunneraceae*)

chilensis	see *G. tinctoria*
cordifolia	LLWG
densiflora	GEdr
dentata	CPla
flavida	CPla
hamiltonii	CPla ECha GAbr MMuc NBir XLum
killipiana B&SWJ 9009	WCru
magellanica	Widely available
- SDR 7035 **new**	GKev
manicata	Widely available
monoica	GAbr LLWG
perpensa	CBcs CBen CCCN EBee EWTr GBin IMou LLWG
prorepens	CMac CPla ECha GAbr NBir
scabra	see *G. tinctoria*
§ ***tinctoria***	CBod CCCN CMac CWib ECha ELan EPfP EWoo IBoy IVic LLWG LRHS LSun MMuc NLar SDix SEND SWat SWvt WBor WFar

Gymnadenia (*Orchidaceae*)

conopsea	ECho EFEx

Gymnocarpium ✿ (*Woodsiaceae*)

	dryopteris ♀H5	CLAP EFer EShb GKev GMaP GWyn ISha WAbe WFib WOut WShi
	- PAB 1757	LEdu
	- PAB 8351 **new**	LEdu
	- 'Plumosum' ♀H7	CBod CKel CLAP CLet CWCL ERod GEdr LEdu LRHS NHar NLar WFib WHal WMoo
	oyamense ♀H5	SKHP
	robertianum	EFer EWld

Gymnocladus (*Caesalpiniaceae*)

	chinensis	WPGP
	dioica	CBcs CDul CLnd CMCN EBee EBtc ELan EPfP EUJe LEdu MBlu SMad SPer WPGP WTSh

Gymnocoronis (*Asteraceae*)

	spilanthoides	LLWG

Gymnospermium (*Berberidaceae*)

§	***albertii***	ECho
	altaicum	ECho

Gynandriris see *Moraea*

Gynerium (*Poaceae*)

	argenteum	see *Cortaderia selloana*

Gynostemma (*Cucurbitaceae*)

	pentaphyllum	CAgr LEdu
	- B&SWJ 570	WCru

Gypsophila (*Caryophyllaceae*)

	aretioides	CRos ECho EPot LHop LRHS NRHS NSla
§	- 'Caucasica'	CPBP ECho LLHF
	- 'Compacta'	see *G. aretioides* 'Caucasica'
	cerastioides	CMea CRos CTri ECho ECtt EDAr EPfP EPot GAbr GCrg LBMP LHop LRHS NGdn NHpl NLar NRHS NSla SPlb SRms SWvt WAbe WHoo WIce XLum
	- 'Rosy Stripe'	GKev
	- silver variegated (v)	MHol
	dubia	see *G. repens* 'Dubia'
	elegans	SVic
	fastigiata 'Silverstar'	CRos LRHS NRHS
	'Festival' (Festival Series)	SGbt
	gracilescens	see *G. tenuifolia*
	'Jolien' (v)	WIce
	muralis 'Garden Bride'	SWvt
	- 'Gypsy Deep Rose'	CRos ELan EPfP LRHS NRHS
	- 'Gypsy Pink' (d)	EPfP SWvt
	nana 'Compacta'	CPBP
	'Pacific Rose'	MRav
	pacifica	WOut
	paniculata	ESps MHol MRav SRms XLum
	- 'Bristol Fairy' (d)	CSBt ECha ELan EPfP EWTr EWoo GMaP GMcL LRHS MBel MJak NLar SCob SHar SPoG SWvt WFar XLum
	- 'Compacta Plena' (d)	CMea ECtt EPfP GMaP LHop MPie MRav NGdn SRms
	- double white-flowered (d)	XLum
	- Festival Star = 'Danfestar'PBR (Festival Series)	GMcL
	- 'Flamingo' (d)	CBcs ECha LHop LRHS NLar SHar SPer SWvt XLum
	- My Pink = 'Dangypink'	EBee
	- 'Pacific Pink'	EBee
	- 'Perfect Alba'	LRHS
	- 'Perfekta'	CBcs SPer
	- 'Pink Star' (d)	ECtt
§	- 'Schneeflocke' (d)	CBod CRos EPfP GMaP LRHS MBel NRHS SRms
	- Snowflake	see *G. paniculata* 'Schneeflocke'
	- Summer Sparkles = 'Esm Chispa'PBR	EBee NPnk
	- White Fire = 'Dangypwhifa'	EBee
	'Pink Festival' (Festival Series) (d)	ECtt EPfP LRHS NRHS SPoG WFar WTor
	repens ♀H5	ECtt GBin GJos SCob SIgm SPlb SWvt WFar XLum
	- dark-pink-flowered **new**	CPBP
	- 'Dorothy Teacher'	CMea CSma CTal ECho ECtt SBch WTor
§	- 'Dubia'	ECha ECho ECtt ELon EPot MHer NLar SRms
	- 'Filou White' **new**	NDov
	- 'Fratensis'	ECho ECtt LLHF WIce
	- Pink Beauty	see *G. repens* 'Rosa Schönheit'
§	- 'Rosa Schönheit'	CMea ECha ECtt EPot NDov SPer XLum
	- 'Rosea'	CTri CWib EAJP EBee ECho ECtt EDAr ELan EPfP EWTr GJos GMaP ITim MHol MMuc NGdn NHpl NSla SBch SCob SEND SPoG SRms SWvt WFar WHoo WIce XLum
	- 'Silver Carpet' (v)	EBee ELan
	- white-flowered	CMea CWib ECho NGdn SWvt
§	'Rosenschleier' (d) ♀H6	CBod CDor CMea EBee ECha ECtt ELan EPfP LCro LHop MBel MRav NCGa NDov NGdn SIgm SRms SRot SWvt WHoo WSHC XLum
I	'Rosenschleier Variegata' (v)	EBee ELan LHop
	'Rosy Veil'	see *G.* 'Rosenschleier'
§	***tenuifolia***	CMea CPBP EPot GMaP ITim NHpl
	Veil of Roses	see *G.* 'Rosenschleier'
	'White Festival'PBR (Festival Series) (d)	EPfP LRHS NRHS SPoG WTor

Gyptis (*Asteraceae*)

	commersonii	LHop

H

Habenaria (*Orchidaceae*)

	radiata	see *Pecteilis radiata*

Haberlea (*Gesneriaceae*)

	ferdinandi-coburgii	CLAP ECho GEdr
	- 'Connie Davidson'	EBee GEdr GKev
	rhodopensis ♀H5	CElw CTal EBee ECho ELan EPPr GEdr NHpl NSla SRms WAbe WCot WThu XLum
	- 'Virginalis'	CElw CLAP ECho GEdr NSla WAbe WThu

Hablitzia (*Amaranthaceae*)

	tamnoides	CAgr LEdu MCoo

Habranthus (*Amaryllidaceae*)

	'Amazing Jumbo'	NRog
	andersonii	see *H. tubispathus*
	brachyandrus	CTal GCal GKev NRog SRms WCot

	caeruleus	NRog
	gracilifolius	ECho NRog
	howardii	ECho
	magnoi	NRog
	martinezii ♀H2	CPBP CTal ECho NRog
	mexicanus	ECho
§	***robustus*** ♀H2	CAby CCCN CTal ECho EPfP EPot GKev LAma LHop NRog
	- 'Russell Manning'	NRog
§	***tubispathus*** ♀H2	CTal ECho GCal GKev NRog SBrt WCot WHil
	- var. ***roseus***	NRog

Hacquetia (*Apiaceae*)

	epipactis ♀H5	Widely available
	- 'Harry Foley' (v)	NWad
§	- 'Thor' (v)	EBee ECha ECho EWes GBin GEdr LLHF NBir NChi SIgm
	- 'Variegata'	see *H. epipactis* 'Thor'

Haemanthus (*Amaryllidaceae*)

	albiflos ♀H2	CPne CPrp CTca ECho ELan EPri EShb GKev LAma LToo SRms
	amarylloides	WCot
	barkerae	WCot
	carneus	ECho WCot
	coccineus ♀H2	CLak ECho EPri WCot
	humilis	CPne ECho WCot
	- subsp. ***hirsutus***	WCot
	kalbreyeri	see *Scadoxus multiflorus* subsp. *multiflorus*
	katherinae	see *Scadoxus multiflorus* subsp. *katherinae*
	natalensis	see *Scadoxus puniceus*
	nortieri	WCot
	pauculifolius	GKev
	pubescens	WCot
	sanguineus	ECho WCot

Hagenia (*Rosaceae*)

	abyssinica	WPGP

Hakea (*Proteaceae*)

	baxteri	SPlb
§	***drupacea***	CTre
	laurina	CTre SPlb
§	***lissosperma***	CBcs EBee EPfP SPlb WPGP
	nodosa	CCCN
	oleifolia	CTre
	platysperma	SPlb
§	***salicifolia***	CBcs CCCN SPlb
	saligna	see *H. salicifolia*
	sericea misapplied	see *H. lissosperma*
	sericea Schrad. & J.C.Wendl.	WCot
	- pink-flowered	SPlb WCot
	suaveolens	see *H. drupacea*
	victoriae	SPlb

Hakonechloa ✿ (*Poaceae*)

	macra ♀H7	Widely available
§	- 'Alboaurea' (v) ♀H7	CBcs CBod CKno CTsd ELan EPfP GMcL LCro LRHS LSRN MGos MMuc NPla NRHS SHil WOld
	- 'Albovariegata' (v)	CAbb CKno EBee EPPr GCal LEdu MAvo SCob SPoG WBor
§	- 'All Gold'	CAby CFil CKno CWCL EBee ECha ECtt EPPr EShb EWes GQue IBoy IKil ITim LBMP LBrs LEdu LRHS MAsh MGos MJak SCob SMad SPad SPoG WCot WPGP
	- 'Aureola' ♀H7	Widely available
	- 'Beni-kaze'	EShb SCob
	- 'Mediovariegata' (v)	EBee ECha EPPr
	- 'Naomi' (v)	EBee SCob
	- 'Nicolas'	CSam EBee ECtt EHoe ELan ELon EPfP EWes GMcL LCro LEdu LLHF LSRN LSou MBel NQui NSti SCob
	- 'Ogon'	see *H. macra* 'All Gold'
	- 'Samurai' (v)	CKno LRHS NRHS
	- 'Stripe It Rich' (v)	CWCL EBee ECtt ELan ESwi EWes SGol
	- 'Variegata'	see *H. macra* 'Alboaurea'

Halenia (*Gentianaceae*)

	elliptica	GKev
	- SDR 7809	GKev

Halesia (*Styracaceae*)

§	***carolina***	Widely available
	- Monticola Group	CAco CBcs CCVT CDul CMCN EBee ELan EPfP IVic LRHS MMuc NLar SPer SWvt WHar WMou
I	- - 'Variegata' (v)	MBlu NLar SSta
	- 'Uconn Wedding Bells'	CJun MBlu SKHP
	- Vestita Group ♀H5	CDul CJun CTho EPfP LRHS MAsh MBlu MGos MRav NLar SPer SSta WPat
	- - 'Rosea'	CJun EPfP MBlu NLar SKHP
	diptera	CBcs MBlu SKHP
	- Magniflora Group	CJun EPfP LRHS MBlu
	macgregorii	CMCN MBlu
	tetraptera	see *H. carolina*

× *Halimiocistus* (*Cistaceae*)

	algarvensis	see *Halimium ocymoides*
§	'Ingwersenii' ♀H4	ECho EDAr ELan EWes SPer SPoG SRms XLum
	revolii misapplied	see × *H. sahucii*
§	***sahucii*** ♀H4	CBcs CBod CSBt CTri ECha ELan EPfP ESps LBMP LRHS MAsh MBNS MRav MSwo NPri SBod SCob SIgm SPer SPoG SRms SWvt XLum
	- Ice Dancer = 'Ebhals'PBR (v)	EBee EPfP MAsh SCob SPer SWvt
	'Susan'	see *Halimium* 'Susan'
§	***wintonensis*** ♀H4	CBcs ELan EPfP LRHS MAsh MMrt MMuc SCob SLon SPer SRms
§	- 'Merrist Wood Cream' ♀H4	CBcs CBod CBot CMac CSBt EBee ELan EPfP EWTr LBrs LRHS LSRN MAsh MGil MRav MSwo NBir SEle SLim SPer SPoG SRkn SWvt WGrn

Halimium (*Cistaceae*)

§	***atriplicifolium***	CAby
§	***calycinum***	CBcs CBod CRos ELan EPfP IVic LRHS MAsh MHtn MMuc SCoo SEND SHil SLim SPer SPoG SWvt WCFE WHar WKif
	commutatum	see *H. calycinum*
	halimifolium misapplied	see *H.* × *pauanum*
§	***lasianthum***	CMac CSBt CWib ELan EPfP LRHS MRav SLim
	- 'Concolor' ♀H4	CWib LRHS MAsh MSwo SWvt
	- subsp. ***formosum***	ELan EPfP LRHS MAsh MMuc SLon
	'Sandling' ♀H4	SPoG SRms
	libanotis misapplied	see *H. calycinum*
§	***ocymoides***	CWib ELan IVic MGil MSwo WKif
§	× ***pauanum***	LRHS MMuc
§	'Susan' ♀H4	EBee ELan EPfP LBrs LRHS MMrt SCoo SLim SPer WAbe
§	***umbellatum***	EPfP
	wintonense	see × *Halimiocistus wintonensis*

Halimodendron (*Papilionaceae*)

halodendron	CBcs CDul MBlu SPer

Halleria (*Stilbaceae*)

lucida	CCCN SEle SPlb SVen

Haloragis (*Haloragaceae*)

erecta	SPlb SVen XLum
- 'Rubra'	WCot
- 'Wellington Bronze'	CBod CSpe EHoe ELan EUJe LEdu LHop SPtp WHer WMoo XLum

Hamamelis ✿ (*Hamamelidaceae*)

'Amethyst'	CJun MBlu MMuc SGol
'Brevipetala'	CEnd CJun
'Danny'	CJun
'Dishi'	CJun
'Doerak'	CJun NLar
'Fire Blaze'	CJun MBlu NLar
'Girard Orange'	LPar
× ***intermedia***	CDul
- 'Advent'	CJun NLar
- 'Andrea'	NLar
- 'Angelly' 🏆H5	CEnd CJun LRHS MBlu NLar
- 'Anne'	LRHS NLar
- 'Aphrodite' 🏆H5	CDul CJun CRos EPfP GMcL LRHS MAsh MBlu MGos MMuc MRav NLar SCob SHil SPer
- 'Arnhem'	NLar
- 'Arnold Promise' 🏆H5	Widely available
- 'Aurora' 🏆H5	CJun CRos EPfP LRHS MBlu NLar SHil
- 'Barmstedt Gold' 🏆H5	CJun CRos EPfP IArd LRHS LSRN MAsh MGos NLar SAko SCob SHil SPer SPoG WPat
- 'Bernstein'	CJun
- 'Carmine Red'	CJun
- 'Copper Beauty'	see *H.* × *intermedia* 'Jelena'
- 'Cyrille'	MMuc
- 'Diane' 🏆H5	Widely available
§ - 'Feuerzauber'	CEnd CSBt CTri LBuc NLar NOrn SCob SPer SWvt
- Fire Cracker	see *H.* × *intermedia* 'Feuerzauber'
- 'Foxy Lady'	CRos LRHS MAsh
- 'Frederic' 🏆H5	CJun EPfP LRHS MAsh
- 'Gimborn's Perfume'	NLar
- 'Gingerbread'	CJun CRos EPfP LLHF LRHS MAsh
- 'Glowing Embers'	CJun LRHS MAsh
- 'Harlow Carr'	LRHS MAsh NLar
- 'Harry' 🏆H5	CJun CRos LRHS LSRN MAsh NLar SHil
- 'Heinrich Bruns'	CJun
§ - 'Jelena' 🏆H5	Widely available
- 'John'	LRHS LSRN MAsh
- 'Kew Sunshine'	LRHS
- 'Limelight'	CJun MBlu MMuc
- 'Livia'	CJun CRos EPfP LRHS MAsh NLar SCoo SHil
- Magic Fire	see *H.* × *intermedia* 'Feuerzauber'
- 'Moonlight'	CJun
- 'Nina'	CRos EPfP LRHS MAsh WPat
- 'Ninotchka'	CJun
- 'Old Copper'	NLar
- 'Orange Beauty'	CBcs CDul CRos LRHS MBlu MGos NOrn SAko SCoo SGol SHil WPGP WPat
- 'Orange Peel'	CDul CJun CRos EPfP LCro LLHF LRHS MAsh NLar SHil SPoG WPat
- 'Ostergold'	CJun NLar
- 'Pallida' 🏆H5	Widely available
- 'Primavera'	CJun CLnd LRHS WPat
- 'Ripe Corn'	CJun EPfP LRHS MAsh
- 'Robert' 🏆H5	CJun CRos EPfP LRHS LSRN MAsh SHil WPat
- 'Rubin' 🏆H5	CJun CRos EPfP GMcL LRHS MAsh MGos NLar SCoo SHil SPer
- 'Rubinstar'	CJun
- 'Ruby Glow'	CBcs CWGN CWib LSRN MGos NEgg NLar NWea SCoo SPer SWvt
- 'Savill Starlight'	CJun
- 'Spanish Spider'	CJun MBlu MMuc NLar
- 'Strawberries and Cream'	CJun MAsh
- 'Sunburst'	CJun CRos LRHS MBlu MGos NLar SGol SHil WPat
- 'Twilight'	CJun NLar
- 'Vesna' 🏆H5	CJun CRos EPfP LRHS MAsh MBlu NLar SCoo SHil WPat
- 'Westerstede'	CJun ESps GMcL LSRN MGos NHol NLar NPla NWea SCob SCoo SEWo SGol SLim WHor
- 'Wiero'	CJun NLar
- 'Zitronenjette'	CJun
japonica 'Pendula'	CJun MBlu
mollis	CBcs CCVT CDul CEnd CHab CMac CNWT CPne CRos CSBt CTri ELan EPfP ESps GKin LCro LPar LRHS MBlu MGos MRav MSwo NEgg NWea SCob SGol SLim SPer SRms SWvt
- 'Boskoop'	CJun
- 'Coombe Wood'	CJun LRHS
- 'Emily'	LRHS MAsh
- 'Goldcrest'	CJun
- 'Imperialis'	CJun LRHS MAsh SPoG
- 'Iwado'	CJun
- 'Jermyns Gold' 🏆H5	CJun CRos EPfP LRHS MAsh SHil
- 'Kort's Yellow'	CJun
- var. ***pallida***	CRos SEWo SWvt
- 'Wisley Supreme' 🏆H5	CJun CRos ELan EPfP LLHF LRHS MAsh MGos SGol SHil WPat
'Rochester'	CJun NLar
vernalis 'Lombarts' Weeping'	NLar
- purple-flowered	MBlu
- 'Quasimodo'	NLar
- 'Sandra'	CBcs CMCN CRos EPfP LRHS MAsh MBlu MGos MRav NLar SLon SPer WPat
virginiana	CAgr GPoy IDee MMuc NWea WBod
- 'Green Thumb' (v)	NLar
- 'Mohonk Red'	CJun
'Yamina'	NLar SGol

Hamelia (*Rubiaceae*)

patens	CCCN

Hanabusaya (*Campanulaceae*)

§ ***asiatica***	SBrt

Haplocarpha (*Asteraceae*)

rueppellii	NHpl SRms SRot

Haplopappus (*Asteraceae*)

coronopifolius	see *H. glutinosus*
§ ***glutinosus***	ECha ECho ECtt EDAr EPot MMuc SEND SPlb SRms
prunelloides	WCot
var. ***mustersii*** F&W 9384	

Hardenbergia (*Papilionaceae*)

comptoniana ♀H3	WCot
violacea ♀H3	CCCN CHll CRHN ELan MHer SEND SLim SPer WCot
- f. ***alba***	CHll SEND
- - 'White Wanderer'	CCCN
- 'Happy Wanderer'	CCCN SChF
- f. ***rosea***	CCCN

Harpephyllum (*Anacardiaceae*)

caffrum (F)	XBlo

Hasteola (*Asteraceae*)

§ ***suaveolens***	LEdu

Hastingsia (*Asparagaceae*)

alba	WSHC

Haworthia ✿ (*Asphodelaceae*)

attenuata	EShb
'Big Band' new	NLos
'Black Major'	LToo
'Black Prince'	EShb SBch
coarctata ♀H2 new	SEND
cooperii var. ***pilifera***	LToo
fasciata	SEND
- 'Concolor' new	NLos
glabrata var. ***concolor***	EShb
'Kermit'	LToo
limifolia	EShb LToo
margaritifera new	NLos
mirabilis var. ***sublineata***	LToo
- var. ***triebneriana***	LToo
pumila ♀H2	SEND
pygmaea new	LToo
reinwardtii ♀H2	LToo
tesselata	see *H. venosa* subsp. *tesselata*
truncata ♀H2	LToo
§ ***venosa*** subsp. ***tesselata*** ♀H2	SEND

hazelnut see *Corylus*

Hebe ✿ (*Plantaginaceae*)

albicans ♀H4	CBcs ELan EPfP ESps GKin GMcL LCro LPot LRHS LSRN MGos MJak MRav NPri NWea SCob SCoo SLim SPer SRms SWvt WHar WOld XLum
- prostrate	see *H. albicans* 'Snow Cover'
* - 'Snow Carpet'	CCCN CLet LRHS
§ - 'Snow Cover'	EWes
- 'Snow Drift'	see *H. albicans* 'Snow Cover'
§ 'Alicia Amherst'	LRHS
'Amanda Cook' (v)	NPer SGol
'Amethyst Mist' new	GMcL
§ 'Amy'	ELon LRHS NPer SPer SWvt
'Amy' variegated (v) new	LRHS
× ***andersonii***	LRHS
§ - 'Andersonii Variegata' (v)	CWib ESps LRHS SRms
- 'Argenteovariegata'	see *H.* × *andersonii* 'Andersonii Variegata'
'Andressa Paula'	CCCN CLet LRHS
anomala misapplied	see *H.* 'Imposter'
§ ***armstrongii***	ECho SCob SEND
'Autumn Glory'	ELan EPfP ESps GMcL LCro LOPS LRHS LSRN MAsh MGos MJak MRav MSwo NBir NPri SCob SGol SPer SPlb SPoG SVen SWvt XLum
'Autumn Joy'	SWvt
azurea	see *H. venustula*
'Azurens'	see *H.* 'Maori Gem'
'Baby Blush'PBR	LRHS
'Baby Boo' (v)	LRHS SCob SLon
'Baby Marie'	CAbP CLet CSBt EBee ECho ELan EPfP GKin GMcL LBMP LBuc LRHS LSRN MSwo NLar NPer SCob SCoo SLim SPoG SRGP SRms SRot SWvt
'Beverley Hills'PBR	CSBt LRHS SCob
'Bicolor Wand'	CCCN CTsd LRHS
bishopiana	SCob
'Black Beauty'	EPfP GMcL LBMP LBuc LRHS MJak NLar SCob
'Black Panther'	ELon GMcL LSou
'Blue Clouds' ♀H4	EBee EPfP LLHF LRHS MSwo NWad SBod SCob SPer WCFE
Blue Elegance = 'Lowgeko'PBR (Garden Beauty Series)	LRHS SLim
§ 'Blue Gem'	CMac GMcL SCob SLim
Blue Haze = 'Lowchi' (Garden Beauty Series)	LRHS
Blue Ice = 'Lowapb' (Garden Beauty Series)	LRHS
'Blue Shamrock'	SWvt
Blue Star = 'Vergeer 1'PBR	EPfP LBuc LRHS MAsh NLar SLon SPoG SRms
'Boscawenii'	WHer
'Bouquet'PBR	LLHF
§ 'Bowles's Hybrid'	CCCN CLet LRHS MRav MSwo SCob SRms
brachysiphon	CTri SCob SEND SPer SRms SVen
brevifolia	LRHS
Bronze Glow = 'Lowglo' (Garden Beauty Series)	EBee LBuc LRHS
'Bronzy Baby'PBR (v)	SPoG
buchananii	ECho MHer NPer
§ - 'Fenwickii'	ECho WHoo
- 'Minima'	ECho
- 'Minor' Hort. NZ	ECho GBin GCrg
'Bullfinch'	LRHS
buxifolia (Benth.) Andersen	see *H. odora*
§ 'Caledonia' ♀H4	CBcs CCCN CWib EPfP LBMP LCro LRHS LSRN MAsh MGos NPer NPri SCob SCoo SLim SPoG SRms SWvt XLum
'Carl Teschner'	see *H.* 'Youngii'
'Carnea Variegata' (v)	EPfP EShb ESps GMcL LRHS SLim SPer SRms WOut
carnosula	SPer
catarractae	see *Parahebe catarractae*
'Celine'	EPfP LRHS
'Champagne'	CCCN EBee EPfP LCro LPot LRHS LSRN MBlu MJak NWad SCob SCoo SLim SRms XLum
Champion = 'Champseiont'PBR	EAEE EBee GMcL LRHS MSwo SCob SCoo
'Charming White'	CChe CLet EAEE LRHS LSRN SCob
chathamica	LRHS
cheesemanii	WAbe
'Christabel'	LRHS
'Clear Skies'PBR	LBuc LLHF LRHS SLim SRms
'Colwall'	ECho
'Conwy Knight'	SRms WAbe
corstorphinensis	LRHS
'County Park'	EWes GAbr GMcL
'Cranleighensis'	CTsd LRHS
cupressoides	GCal LRHS MSCN
- 'Boughton Dome'	CTri ECho MHer WAbe WCFE WHoo WOld
darwiniana misapplied	see *H. glaucophylla*

	'Dazzler' (v)	CAbP
	decumbens	EWes GBin
	'Denise'	LRHS
	'Diamond'	CLet LRHS LSRN SLon SRms
	dieffenbachii	SVen
	diosmifolia	EPfP LRHS
	- 'Wairua Beauty'	LRHS
	'Dorothy Peach'	see *H.* 'Watson's Pink'
	'E.B.Anderson'	see *H.* 'Caledonia'
	'Edington'	SPer WCFE
	'Ellie'	LRHS
	elliptica 'Variegata'	see *H.* 'Silver Queen'
	'Emerald Dome'	see *H.* 'Emerald Gem'
§	'Emerald Gem' ♀H4	CAbP CSma CTri ECho EPfP EShb GMcL GWyn LRHS LSRN MAsh MGos MHer MJak MMuc MSwo NLar NPri SArc SCob SPer SPlb SPoG WFar WHar
	'Emerald Green'	see *H.* 'Emerald Gem'
§	'Eveline'	CSBt CTri GMcL LRHS MJak NBir SBod SLim SPer
	'Eversley Seedling'	see *H.* 'Bowles's Hybrid'
	'Eyecatcher' (v) **new**	EBee
	'Fairfieldii'	WAbe WPat
	'First Light' PBR	LRHS SCob SGol SRms
	'Fragrant Jewel'	CAbP CWib LRHS SEND SLim SPhx
	× ***franciscana***	SBod
	- 'Blue Gem' ambig.	CDul CTsd ELan EPfP LRHS MMuc MRav NBir NPer SCob SEND SGol SPer SPlb SPoG SRms XLum
	- 'Foreness Pink'	SEND
	- 'Lavender Queen'	LRHS
	- lime variegated (v)	SEND
	- 'Purple Tips' misapplied	see *H. speciosa* 'Variegata'
	- 'Variegata'	see *H.* 'Silver Queen'
I	- 'White Gem'	SRms
	- yellow variegated (v)	SPer
	'Frozen Flame' (v)	ELan LBuc LRHS SPoG
	'Galway Bay'	LSou
	(Garden Beauty Series)	EBee LBuc LRHS SLim SRms
	Garden Beauty Blue = 'Cliv' PBR	
	- Garden Beauty Pink = 'Lowink'	LRHS SLim SRms
	- Garden Beauty Purple = 'Nold' PBR	LBuc LCro LRHS SLim
	- Garden Beauty White = 'Lowhi' **new**	LRHS
	(Garden Elegance Series) 'Garden Elegance Blush'	LRHS
	- 'Garden Elegance Pink'	SLim
	- 'Garden Elegance Purple'	SLim
	- 'Garden Elegance Rose'	LRHS SLim
	'Gauntlettii'	see *H.* 'Eveline'
	'Gibby'	LRHS
§	***glaucophylla***	XLum
I	- 'Variegata' (v)	CTri LRHS SCoo SLim SPer WKif
	'Gnome'	LRHS
	'Goethe'	SEND
	'Gold Beauty' (v)	SRms
	'Gold Pixie'	LBuc
	Golden Anniversary = 'Lowag' **new**	LRHS
	'Golden Glow' (v)	EPfP LRHS
	'Golden Nugget'	LRHS
	'Goldrush' PBR (v)	GMcL SPoG
	gracillima	SCob SEle
	'Gran's Favourite'	LRHS LSRN
	'Great Orme' ♀H4	CDul CWib ELan EPfP ESps GBin GLog LRHS LSRN MAsh MGos MJak MMuc MRav MSCN MSwo NPer SBod SCob SEND SLim SPer SPlb SPoG SRms SWvt WBod WCFE WSFF
	'Green Globe'	see *H.* 'Emerald Gem'
	'Greensleeves'	LRHS
	'Hadspen Pink'	LRHS
	'Hagley Park'	LRHS
§	'Hartii'	LRHS MRav SCob
	'Havens Green' **new**	GMcL
	'Heartbreaker' PBR (v)	ELan ESps GMcL LBuc LCro LOPS LRHS MAsh MGos MJak NHpl NPri SCob SCoo SLim SPoG SWvt
	HebeDonna Emma = 'Zassa' PBR	EBee
	HebeDonna Julia = 'Zelma' PBR **new**	EBee
	'Hielan Lassie'	LRHS
	'High Voltage'	MJak
	'Highdownensis'	LRHS
	'Highland Jubilee' **new**	GMcL LRHS
	'Hinderwell'	NPer
	hulkeana	LLHF LRHS MHer SCob WAbe WKif
§	'Imposter'	SRms
	'Inspiration'	LRHS SCob
	'James Stirling'	see *H. ochracea* 'James Stirling'
	'Jane Holden'	LRHS
	'John Collier'	GAbr SEND
§	'Johny Day'	LRHS SCob
	'Judy'	LRHS
	'Karna'	ECrN LPot
	'Karo Golden Esk'	EPfP LRHS
	'Kirkii'	CBar EPfP MSwo NLar SBod SCob XLum
	'Knightshayes'	see *H.* 'Caledonia'
	'La Favorite'	CTsd
	'Lady Ann' PBR (v)	CLet CSBt EPfP ESps GMcL LBuc LRHS LSou MJak NLar SPoG
	'Lady Ardilaun'	see *H.* 'Amy'
	laevis	see ***H. venustula***
	laingii	GCrg
	latifolia	see *H.* 'Blue Gem'
	'Lavender Spray'	see *H.* 'Hartii'
	leiophylla	SVen
	Leopard = 'Lowand' (Garden Beauty Series)	LRHS
	'Lilac Fantasy' **new**	LRHS
	'Lilac Wand'	CTsd
	'Linda'	SEND
	'Lindsayi'	CLet LRHS
	'Liz'	LBuc LRHS
	lyallii	see ***Parahebe lyallii***
	lycopodioides 'Aurea'	see ***H. armstrongii***
	'Lynash'	CLet LRHS
	mackenii	see *H.* 'Emerald Gem'
	macrantha ♀H4	CBod GBin GMcL GWyn LRHS SDix SPer SRms WAbe
	macrocarpa	LRHS
	- var. ***latisepala***	CLet LBuc LRHS SLim
	'Magic Summer' PBR	EBee LBuc LRHS SPoG
§	'Maori Gem'	MRav
	'Margery Fish'	see *H.* 'Primley Gem'
	'Margret' ♀H4	CLet CSBt ECrN EPfP ESps GMcL LRHS LSRN MAsh MBrN MGos MHtn MRav NPri SCob SCoo SLim SPer SPoG SRms
	'Marie Antoinette'	EBee LRHS
	'Marilyn Monroe' PBR	LRHS
	'Marjorie'	CDul CMac ECrN ELan EPfP GBin LRHS LSRN MJak MSwo NLar NPer NWea SCob SPer SPoG SRms SWvt
	'Mauve Queen'	LRHS

	'McKean'	see *H.*'Emerald Gem'
	'Mette'	EAEE
	Midnight Sky = 'Lowten'PBR (Garden Beauty Series)	LBuc LCro LRHS NPri SCoo SLim SPoG
	'Midsummer Beauty' ♀H4	CWCL ECrN EPfP ESps GMcL IBoy LRHS LSRN MGos MJak MMuc MRav NBir SCob SEND SLim SPer SPlb SPoG SRms SWvt WOut WSFF XLum
	'Milmont Emerald'	see *H.* 'Emerald Gem'
§	'Mohawk'PBR	GMcL LRHS
*	'Moppets Hardy'	SPer
§	'Mrs Winder' ♀H4	CCCN CDul CMac ELan EPfP GMcL GWyn LRHS LSRN MAsh MCot MGos MJak MRav MSwo NBes NLar NPer NPri SCob SCoo SGbt SGol SLim SPer SPoG SWvt WFar WHar
	'Nantyderry'	LRHS
§	'Neil's Choice' ♀H4	ELon LRHS
	'New Zealand'	GMcL GWyn XLum
	'Nicola's Blush' ♀H4	CLet CMac ELon EPfP EShb ESps GBin GMcL GWyn LRHS LSRN MCot MMuc MRav NBir NLar SCob SEND SGol SPer SPoG SRGP SRms SWvt WKif
	ochracea	CLet LRHS
§	- 'James Stirling' ♀H4	CBcs CMac CSBt ECho ELan EPfP EShb ESps GKin LRHS LSRN MAsh MGos MJak MMuc MSwo NLar NWad SCob SCoo SPer SPlb SPoG SWvt WFar WHar
	'Oddity'	LRHS
§	***odora***	ELan LHop LRHS MJak MMuc NWea SArc SCob XLum
	- 'New Zealand Gold'	CLet ESps LRHS MAsh MMuc SEND
	- 'Summer Frost'	LRHS
	'Oratia Beauty' ♀H4	LRHS LSRN MMuc MRav NFav NLar SCob SEND
	'Orphan Annie' (v)	LSRN NLar
	'Pacific Paradise'PBR <u>**new**</u>	SPoG
	parviflora misapplied	see *H.*'Bowles's Hybrid'
	- var. ***angustifolia***	see *H. stenophylla*
	- 'Holdsworth'	CBod LRHS
	'Pascal' ♀H4	ELan EPfP ESps GMcL LCro LRHS LSRN MAsh MGos SCoo SLim SLon SPer SPoG SRms SWvt
	'Pastel Blue'	EBee
	Pastel Elegance = 'Lowjap'PBR (Garden Beauty Series)	SLim
	'Patti Dossett'	see *H. speciosa* 'Patti Dossett'
	pauciramosa	SRms
	'Pearl of Paradise'PBR	NWad SPoG
	perfoliata	see *Parahebe perfoliata*
	'Perry's Rubyleaf'	NPer
	'Petra's Pink'	CCCN LRHS SLim
	'Pewter Dome' ♀H4	EPfP GMcL LHop LRHS MGos MRav SCob SDix SRms SWvt XLum
	pimeleoides	GMcL SCob
	- 'Glauca'	NPer SGol
	- 'Quicksilver' ♀H4	CLet CSBt CTri ELan EPfP ESps LRHS LSRN MGos MMuc MRav NBir NPer SBod SCob SCoo SLim SPer SRms WHar XLum
	pinguifolia	NLar SPlb
	- 'Dobson'	LRHS
	- 'Pagei' ♀H5	Widely available
	- 'Sutherlandii'	CBcs CDul ESps GMcL LRHS LSRN MGos MJak NBes NWea SCob SCoo SWvt WFar XLum
	Pink Elegance = 'Lowuni'	LCro
	'Pink Elephant' (v) ♀H4	LBuc LRHS MAsh MJak NLar NPri SLim SPoG
	'Pink Fantasy'	LRHS SCob
	'Pink Goddess'	CLet LRHS SEND
	'Pink Lady'PBR	GMcL SGol SPoG
	'Pink Paradise'PBR	CAbP CLet ELan EPfP GMcL LBuc LRHS MJak NWad SPoG SRms
	'Pink Payne'	see *H.* 'Eveline'
	'Pink Pixie'	LBuc LRHS MAsh SCoo SRms
	'Pink Wand'	CTsd
	'Porlock Purple'	see *Parahebe catarractae* 'Delight'
§	'Primley Gem'	LRHS
I	'Prostrata'	CSBt
	'Purple Emperor'	see *H.* 'Neil's Choice'
	'Purple Paradise'PBR	GMcL SPoG
	'Purple Picture'	ELon
	'Purple Pixie'	see *H.* 'Mohawk'
	'Purple Princess'	LRHS SGol
	'Purple Queen'	EPfP EShb GMcL LRHS MJak SCob
	Purple Shamrock = 'Neprock'PBR (v)	EPfP EUJe GMcL LRHS MAsh NEgg SCoo SLim SPer SPoG SRms SWvt
	'Purple Tips' misapplied	see *H. speciosa* 'Variegata'
	'Rachel'	LRHS LSRN
§	***rakaiensis*** ♀H4	Widely available
	- 'Golden Dome'	see *H. rakaiensis*
	ramosissima	EPot GAbr GBin
	raoulii	SRms WAbe
	Raspberry Ripple = 'Tullyraspb'PBR	ECtt GMcL LBuc
	'Raven'	CLet LRHS
	recurva	CSam CTri EMOT LPot LRHS MCot SCob SRms
	- 'Boughton Silver' ♀H5	CLet LRHS LSRN MMuc SLim
	'Red Edge' ♀H4	Widely available
	'Red Moon'	EBee SCob
	'Red Rum'	LBuc
	'Red Ruth'	see *H.* 'Eveline'
	'Rhubarb and Custard'	LBuc LRHS SCob
	rigidula	LRHS MMuc SEND
	'Rosie'PBR	LBuc LRHS LSRN SCoo SPer SWvt
	'Royal Blue'	LRHS
	'Royal Purple'	see *H.* 'Alicia Amherst'
	salicifolia	CCCN CMac CTca ELan EPfP LRHS MMuc MRav NWad SCob SEND SPer SPlb SRms XLum
	- pale blue-flowered	SEND
	'Sandra Joy'	LRHS
	'Santa Monica' <u>**new**</u>	GMcL
	'Sapphire' ♀H4	EPfP GMcL LRHS MAsh MJak NPri SCob SCoo SLim SRms SWvt
	'Sarana'	LRHS LSRN
	'Shiraz'	LRHS
	'Silver Dollar' (v)	CAbP CCCN CMac GBin GMcL LRHS MJak NEgg NWad SLim SPer SPoG SRms
§	'Silver Queen' (v) ♀H3	CBcs CLet CSBt ECrN ELan EShb GMcL LCro LRHS MAsh MMuc NLar NPer SCob SEND SPer SPoG SRms WOut
	'Silver Swallow'	LRHS SPoG
	'Simon Délaux'	LRHS SEND SPer
I	'Southlandii'	SGol
	'Sparkling Sapphires'	LBuc LRHS SPoG
	speciosa 'Johny Day'	see *H.*'Johny Day'
	- 'La Séduisante'	CTri LRHS SEND SRms
§	- 'Patti Dossett'	LRHS
§	- 'Variegata' (v)	ESps LRHS NPer
	'Spender's Seedling' misapplied	see *H. stenophylla*
	'Spender's Seedling' ambig.	MCot MMuc MSCN SCob

	'Spender's Seedling' Hort.	LRHS MRav SEND SPoG SRms
	'Spring Glory'	LRHS
§	***stenophylla***	EShb EUJe GMcL LRHS LSRN NLar SArc SBod SPer SPlb
	stricta	CLet LRHS SEND
	- var. ***egmontiana***	LRHS
	subalpina	CSBt CWib GMcL
	'Summer Blue'	LRHS MBlu
	'Sunset Boulevard'^{PBR}	LLHF
	'Super Red'	CLet CSBt
	'Sweet Dreams' **new**	EBee LRHS
	'Sweet Kim' (v)	CMac LBuc LRHS SLim SPoG
	topiaria ♀^{H4}	CAbP CLet CMac CSBt CSam ESps GMcL LHop LRHS MBrN MMuc MRav MSwo NBir NFav NLar NWad SCob SCoo SEND SGbt SPer SPoG WHoo WRHF XLum
	- 'Doctor Favier'	LRHS SRms
	townsonii	CLet LRHS SCob
	'Tricolor'	see *H. speciosa* 'Variegata'
	'Twisty'	LRHS
	'Valentino'^{PBR}	SCoo SLim
	'Veitchii'	see *H.* 'Alicia Amherst'
§	***venustula***	LRHS MMuc
	vernicosa ♀^{H4}	CDul CLet EPfP ESps GMcL LRHS MGos MHer NFav NWad SCob SCoo SEle SPer SPlb SPoG SRot SVen SWvt
	'Violet Wand'	CLet LRHS
	'Vogue'	LRHS
	'Waikiki'	see *H.* 'Mrs Winder'
§	'Warley'	LRHS
	'Warley Pink'	CLet LRHS
	'Warleyensis'	see *H.* 'Warley'
§	'Watson's Pink'	LRHS SPer WBod WKif
	'White Gem' (*brachysiphon* hybrid) ♀^{H4}	GMcL GWyn LRHS NPer SEND SPer
	'White Heather'	EPfP LRHS SCob
	'White Paradise'^{PBR}	SPoG
	'Wild Romance'	LBuc LRHS SPoG
	'Willcoxii'	see *H. buchananii* 'Fenwickii'
	'Wingletye' ♀^{H4}	CCCN LRHS XLum
	'Winter Glow'	CCCN LRHS
	'Wiri Blush'	LRHS SLim SWvt
	'Wiri Charm'	CBcs CMac CSBt EBee EPfP LRHS MSwo SCob SEND SLim SPer
	'Wiri Cloud' ♀^{H4}	CBcs CLet CMac EBee EPfP LRHS MMuc MSwo SCob SEND SEle SRms
	'Wiri Dawn' ♀^{H4}	ELan EPfP ESps LBuc LRHS SLim SRms SWvt XLum
	'Wiri Desire'	CCCN LRHS
	'Wiri Gem'	SCob
	'Wiri Image'	CBcs CLet CSBt EAEE EPfP LRHS MRav SEND
	'Wiri Joy'	LRHS SGol
	'Wiri Mist'	CBcs ELan EPfP LPar LRHS MJak SCob XLum
	'Wiri Prince'	CLet LRHS
	'Wiri Splash'	EPfP LRHS SGol
	'Wiri Vision'	CSBt LRHS SEND
	'Wiri Vogue'	LRHS
§	'Youngii' ♀^{H4}	CBcs CMac CSBt CTri ELan EPfP GBin GKin GMcL LOPS LPot LRHS MAsh MHer MJak MMuc MRav NBir NPri SEND SGol SLim SPer SPlb SPoG SRms SWvt WCFE WHoo

Hechtia (*Bromeliaceae*)

sp.	WCot

Hedeoma (*Lamiaceae*)

ciliolata	CPBP WAbe
hyssopifolia	SPhx

Hedera ✿ (*Araliaceae*)

§	***algeriensis***	SArc WFib
	- 'Bellecour'	WFib XLum
§	- 'Gloire de Marengo' (v) ♀^{H5}	Widely available
	- 'Gloire de Marengo' arborescent (v)	GMcL LPar SDix SPer
	- 'Marginomaculata' (v)	EPfP EShb LRHS MAsh SMad SPoG WFib
	- 'Montgomery'	LRHS LSRN NRHS
	- 'Ravensholst' ♀^{H4}	CMac EShb MRav SCob SGol WFib
§	***azorica***	EShb WFib
	- 'Pico'	WFib
	canariensis misapplied	see *H. algeriensis*
	- 'Variegata'	see *H. algeriensis* 'Gloire de Marengo'
	canariensis Willd.	SEND
	-. var. ***azorica***	see *H. azorica*
	- 'Cantabrian'	see *H. maroccana* 'Spanish Canary'
	chinensis	see *H. nepalensis* var. *sinensis*
	- typica	see *H. nepalensis* var. *sinensis*
§	***colchica***	CDul NWea SPer WCFE WFib
	- 'Arborescens'	see *H. colchica* 'Dendroides'
	- 'Batumi'	MBNS WFib
§	- 'Dendroides'	NWea
	- 'Dentata' ♀^{H5}	ESps MRav SGol WFar WFib
	- 'Dentata Aurea'	see *H. colchica* 'Dentata Variegata'
§	- 'Dentata Variegata' (v) ♀^{H5}	Widely available
	- 'My Heart'	see *H. colchica*
	- 'Paddy's Pride'	see *H. colchica* 'Sulphur Heart'
§	- 'Sulphur Heart' (v) ♀^{H5}	Widely available
	- 'Variegata'	see *H. colchica* 'Dentata Variegata'
	cristata	see *H. helix* 'Parsley Crested'
§	***cypria***	WFib
	helix	CCVT CMac CTri ESps LPar NWea SCob WSFF XLum
	- 'Adam' (v)	CWib LSRN NFav WFib
	- 'Amberwaves'	WFib
	- 'Angularis Aurea' ♀^{H5}	WFib
	- 'Anita'	GBin NFav WFib
§	- 'Anna Marie' (v)	SRms WFib
	- 'Anne Borch'	see *H. helix* 'Anna Marie'
	- 'Arborescens'	WSFF
	- 'Ardingly' (v)	WFib
	- 'Atropurpurea'	ELan GBin MMuc WFib
	- var. ***baltica***	WFib
	- 'Bill Archer'	GBin WFib
	- 'Bird's Foot'	see *H. helix* 'Pedata'
	- 'Boskoop'	WFib
	- 'Bredon'	MRav
	- 'Brimstone' (v)	WFib
§	- 'Brokamp'	WFib
	- 'Buttercup' ♀^{H5}	CBcs CDul CMac CTri EHoe ELan EPfP ESps GMcL LRHS LSRN MAsh MGos NBid NLar NPri SDix SEND SPer SPoG SRms SWvt WCFE WFib
	- 'Caecilia' (v) ♀^{H5}	EPfP MSwo SWvt WFib
	- 'Caenwoodiana'	see *H. helix* 'Pedata'
	- 'Caenwoodiana Aurea'	WFib
	- 'Calico' (v)	WFib
	- 'Calypso'	WFib
	- 'Carolina Crinkle'	GBin
	- 'Cathedral Wall'	WFib
§	- 'Cavendishii' (v)	SRms WFib
	- 'Cavendishii Latina' (v)	WCot

§ - 'Ceridwen' (v) ♀H5 SPlb WFib
- 'Cheeky' WFib
- 'Cheltenham Blizzard' (v) CNat
- 'Chester' (v) CKel LRHS WFib
- 'Chicago' CWib WFib
- 'Chicago Variegated' (v) WFib
- 'Chrysophylla' MSwo
- 'Clotted Cream' (v) CRos ECGP ECrN ELon ESps GMcL LRHS MAsh WFib
- 'Cockle Shell' WFib
- 'Colin' GBin
§ - 'Congesta' ♀H5 CMac GCra NBir SRms WFib
- 'Conglomerata' CBcs ELan NBir SRms WFib
- 'Courage' WFib
- 'Crenata' WFib
- 'Crispa' MRav
- 'Cristata' see *H. helix* 'Parsley Crested'
- 'Curleylocks' see *H. helix* 'Manda's Crested'
- 'Curley-Q' see *H. helix* 'Dragon Claw'
- 'Curvaceous' (v) WFib
- 'Cyprus' see *H. cypria*
- 'Dainty Bess' CWib
§ - 'Dealbata' (v) CMac WFib
- 'Deltoidea' see *H. hibernica* 'Deltoidea'
- 'Discolor' see *H. helix* 'Dealbata', *H. helix* 'Minor Marmorata'
§ - 'Donerailensis' MBlu WFib
- 'Don's Papillon' CNat
§ - 'Dragon Claw' WFib
- 'Duckfoot' ♀H5 EShb GBin WCot WFib
- 'Dyinnii' **new** GEdr NLar
- 'Eileen' (v) WFib
- 'Elfenbein' (v) WFib
- 'Erecta' CDul CTca EPPr EPfP GCal IDee LRHS MBlu NHol NWad SDix SMad SPer SPlb SPoG WCFE WFib XLum
- 'Ester' (v) SRGP WHar
§ - 'Eva' (v) WFib
- 'Fantasia' (v) WFib
- 'Feenfinger' WFib
- 'Filigran' WFib
- 'Flashback' (v) WFib
- 'Flavescens' WFib
- 'Fluffy Ruffles' WFib
I - 'Francis Ivy' WFib
- 'Frosty' (v) WFib
- 'Garland' WFib
- 'Gavotte' WFib
- 'Gilded Hawke' WFib
- 'Glache' (v) MRav WFib
- 'Glacier' (v) ♀H5 CBcs CDul CTri CWib ELan EMOT EPfP ESps GMcL LCro LHop LPar LRHS MAsh MGos MJak MMuc MRav MSwo NHol NRHS NWea SCob SEND SLim SPer SPoG SRms SWvt WFib
- 'Glymii' ELan GBin GCal WFib
- 'Gold Harald' see *H. helix* 'Goldchild'
- 'Gold Ripple' NLar SEND
§ - 'Goldchild' (v) ♀H5 CBcs CKel CMac EBee ELon EMOT EPfP EShb ESps EUJe GMcL LCro LPar LRHS MAsh MGos MJak MMuc MRav MSwo NBir NHol NRHS SCob SLim SPer SPoG SWvt WFib WHar
- 'Golden Ann' see *H. helix* 'Ceridwen'
* - 'Golden Arrow' LRHS MAsh
- 'Golden Curl' (v) CMac EPfP LRHS
- 'Golden Ester' see *H. helix* 'Ceridwen'
- 'Golden Girl' WFib
- 'Golden Ingot' (v) ♀H5 ELan WFib
- 'Golden Jytte' (v) WFib
- 'Golden Kolibri' see *H. helix* 'Midas Touch'
- 'Goldfinch' WFib
- 'Goldfinger' WFib
- 'Goldheart' see *H. helix* 'Oro di Bogliasco'
- 'Goldstern' (v) MRav WFib
- 'Gracilis' see *H. hibernica* 'Gracilis'
- 'Green Finger' see *H. helix* 'Très Coupé'
- 'Green Ripple' CBcs CTri ELan EPfP ESps GMcL LRHS MBlu MGos MJak MMuc MSwo MWht NRHS SCob SEND SLim SPer SPlb SRms SWvt WFib
- 'Greenman' WFib
- 'Halebob' WFib
- 'Hamilton' see *H. hibernica* 'Hamilton'
- 'Harald' (v) CTri CWib WFib
* - 'Hazel' (v) WFib
- 'Heise' (v) WFib
- 'Heise Denmark' (v) WFib
- 'Helvig' see *H. helix* 'White Knight'
- 'Henrietta' WFib
- 'Hispanica' see *H. iberica*
- 'Hite's Miniature' see *H. helix* 'Merion Beauty'
- 'Holly' see *H. helix* 'Parsley Crested'
- 'Hullavington' CNat
- 'Imp' see *H. helix* 'Brokamp'
- 'Ingelise' (v) GMcL
- 'Ivalace' CBcs EShb MSwo SRms WFib XLum
- 'Jake' WFib
- 'Jasper' WFib
- 'Jersey Doris' (v) WFib
- 'Jerusalem' see *H. helix* 'Schäfer Three'
- 'Jubilee' (v) WFib
- 'Kaleidoscope' WFib
- 'Kevin' WFib
- 'Kolibri' (v) WFib
- 'Königer's Auslese' WFib
- 'Lalla Rookh' MRav WFib WRHF
- 'Leo Swicegood' WFib
- 'Light Fingers' ELon EPfP LRHS NRHS WFib
- 'Little Diamond' (v) CMac CTri ELan GMcL LRHS SLon SWvt WFib
- 'Little Luzii' WFib
- 'Liz' see *H. helix* 'Eva'
- 'Luzii' (v) WFib
- 'Maculata' see *H. helix* 'Minor Marmorata'
§ - 'Manda's Crested' ♀H5 ELan NLar WFib
- 'Maple Leaf' ♀H5 EShb GBin WFib
- 'Marginata Elegantissima' see *H. helix* 'Tricolor'
- 'Marginata Minor' see *H. helix* 'Cavendishii'
I - 'Marmorata' Fibrex WFib
- 'Mathilde' (v) CKel WFib
- 'Melanie' WFib
- 'Meon' WFib
§ - 'Merion Beauty' WFib
§ - 'Midas Touch' (v) ♀H5 CWib EPfP GMcL WFib
- 'Minikin' (v) WCot
- 'Minima' misapplied see *H. helix* 'Spetchley'
- 'Minima' Hibberd see *H. helix* 'Donerailensis'
- 'Minima' M.Young see *H. helix* 'Congesta'
§ - 'Minor Marmorata' (v) XLum
- 'Minty' (v) WFib
- 'Misty' (v) WFib
- 'Needlepoint' XLum
- 'Niagara Falls' LRHS SPoG
- 'Nigra Aurea' (v) WFib
- 'Obovata' WFib
- 'Oro di Bogliasco' (v) CDul CMac CTri EBee EMOT EPfP GMcL LRHS MMuc MRav MSwo NLar NRHS NWad NWea SCob

		SEND SLim SPer SPlb SRms SWvt WFar WFib
	- 'Ovata'	WFib
§	- 'Parsley Crested' ♀H5	ELan EPfP SGol WFib
	- 'Patent Leather'	WFib
	- 'Pedata'	CDul MSwo WFib
	- 'Perkeo'	WFib
	- 'Peter' (v)	WFib
	- 'Pink 'n' Curly'	WCot WFib
	- 'Pink 'n' Very Curly'	WCot
§	- 'Pittsburgh'	WFib
	- 'Plume d'Or'	WFib
§	- f. ***poetarum***	GCal MBlu WCot WFib
	- - 'Poetica Arborea'	SDix
	- 'Poetica'	see *H. helix* f. *poetarum*
	- 'Raleigh Delight' (v)	WCot
	- 'Ray's Supreme'	see *H. helix* 'Pittsburgh'
	- subsp. ***rhizomatifera***	WFib
	- 'Richard John'	WFib
	- 'Ritterkreuz'	WFib
	- 'Romanze' (v)	WFib
	- 'Russelliana'	WFib
	- 'Sagittifolia' misapplied	see *H. helix* 'Pedata'
	- 'Sagittifolia' Hibberd	CTri EPfP
	- 'Sagittifolia' ambig.	ECrN LRHS MAsh MBlu SPer SPoG
	- 'Sagittifolia Variegata' (v)	WFib WRHF
	- 'Saint Agnes'	LRHS
	- 'Sally' (v)	WFib
	- 'Salt and Pepper'	see *H. helix* 'Minor Marmorata'
§	- 'Schäfer Three' (v)	CWib WFib
	- 'Seabreeze'	WFib
	- 'Shamrock' ♀H5	EPfP WFib
	- 'Shannon'	WFib
	- 'Silver Ferny'	WFib
	- 'Silver King' (v)	WFib
	- 'Silver Queen'	see *H. helix* 'Tricolor'
§	- 'Spetchley' ♀H5	CMac GEdr GKev MRav NLar NPer NWad WFib WHea
	- 'Splashes'	WFib
	- 'Sunrise'	WFib
	- 'Suzanne'	see *H. nepalensis* 'Suzanne'
	- 'Tanja'	WFib
	- 'Teardrop'	WFib
	- 'Telecurl'	WFib
	- 'Temptation' (v)	WFib
	- 'Tenerife' (v)	WFib
	- 'Topazolite' (v)	WFib
§	- 'Très Coupé'	LRHS MMuc SArc SEND
§	- 'Tricolor' (v)	CTri EPfP LRHS WCFE WFib
	- 'Trinity' (v)	WFib
	- 'Tripod'	WFib
	- 'Triton'	WFib
	- 'Troll'	WFib
	- 'Ursula' (v)	WFib
	- 'Very Merry'	WFib
*	- 'Vitifolium'	WFib
§	- 'White Knight' (v) ♀H5	WFib
	- 'White Mein Herz' (v)	WFib
	- 'White Ripple' (v)	WFib
	- 'White Wonder'	LBuc SPoG
	- 'Williamsiana' (v)	WFib
	- 'Winter Purple Vein'	CNat
	- 'Woerneri'	NLar WFib
	- 'Yellow Ripple'	EShb WFib
	- 'Zebra' (v)	WFib
	hibernica	CCVT CDul CSBt EPfP ESps GMcL LBuc LPar LRHS MJak MRav MSwo NWea SCob SEWo SGol SPer SWvt WFib
	- 'Anna Marie'	see *H. helix* 'Anna Marie'
I	- 'Arbori Compact'	WBor
	- 'Betty Allen'	WFib
§	- 'Deltoidea' ♀H5	MWht WCFE WFib
I	- 'Digitata Crûg Gold'	WCru
	- 'Ebony'	WFib
	- 'Glengariff'	WFib
§	- 'Gracilis'	WFib
§	- 'Hamilton'	WFib
	- 'Lobata Major'	SRms
	- 'Palmata'	WFib
	- 'Rona'	WFib
	- 'Sulphurea' (v)	WFib
	- 'Variegata' (v)	WFib
§	***iberica***	WFib
	maderensis	WFib
	maroccana 'Morocco'	WFib
§	- 'Spanish Canary'	WFib
	nepalensis	WFib
	- 'Marble Dragon'	see *H. nepalensis* var. *sinensis* 'Marble Dragon'
§	- var. ***sinensis***	WFib
	- - KWJ 12345	WCru
§	- - 'Marble Dragon'	WFib
§	- 'Suzanne'	WFib
	pastuchovii	EShb WFib
	- from Troödos, Cyprus	see *H. cypria*
	- 'Ann Ala' ♀H5	CFil MBlu WCot WFib WGwG
	- 'Lagocetti'	WFib
§	***rhombea***	WCot WFib
	- 'Japonica'	see *H. rhombea*
I	- f. ***pedunculata*** 'Maculata'	CWib
	- var. ***rhombea*** 'Variegata' (v)	WFib

Hedychium ✿ (*Zingiberaceae*)

	'Anne Bishop'	NLos SEND
	aurantiacum	CBcs CBct CCCN CTsd GKev LAma LEdu NLos SBig XLum
	brevicaule B&SWJ 7171	WCru
	'C.P. Raffill'	see *H.* × *moorei* 'Raffillii'
	chrysoleucum	CCCN
*	'Clarkei'	CCCN CTsd
	coccineum	CDTJ CTsd GKev IKil LTro MNrw SBig
	- B&SWJ 5238	WCru
	- var. ***angustifolium***	CFil WPGP
	- 'Disney'	CDTJ
	- 'Hungphung Stripe' **new**	LEdu WPGP
	- 'Khangkhui Tall Boy' **new**	LEdu WPGP
	- 'Khonoma Silver' **new**	LEdu WPGP
*	- 'Mishmi Form' **new**	GCal
	- 'Shillong Ghost'	LEdu WPGP
	coronarium ♀H1c	CAbb CAvo CBct CCCN CDTJ CFil CTsd EUJe GKev IKil LLWG LTro NLos SBig WPGP XBlo XLum
	- B&SWJ 3745	WCru
	- 'Gold Spot'	CBct CCCN CTsd EUJe GKev LTro NLos SKHP
	- var. ***urophyllum***	see *H. flavum* Roxb.
	densiflorum	CAbb CCCN CDTJ CTsd ECha EUJe GKev IBlr LEdu LOPS NLos SDix WCot WCru WPGP XLum
	- EN 562	CFil
	- LS&H 17393	CFil WPGP
	- 'Assam Orange'	CAvo CCCN CPne CSam CTsd GCal IBlr LEdu MNrw SBig SChr SDix SEND SMad SPlb WCru WPGP
	- pale-flowered	GCal
	- 'Sorung'	CFil LEdu SChr WPGP

	- 'Stephen'	CAvo CBct CCCN CDTJ CFil CPne EBee EUJe LEdu MNrw SChr SPlb WPGP
	'Devon Cream'	CCCN CDTJ LRHS SChr
	'Doctor Moy' (v)	CDTJ EUJe
	ellipticum	CAbb CCCN CDTJ CTsd EUJe GKev LAma LTro MPie NLos SBig XLum
	- B&SWJ 8354	WCru
	- PAB 7867 **new**	LEdu WPGP
§	***flavescens***	CBct CCCN CDTJ CTsd EBee EUJe GKev LAma LOPS NLos SChr
	flavum misapplied	see *H. flavescens*
§	***flavum*** Roxb.	CAbb CBcs IBlr LTro XLum
	- HWJ 604	WCru
	forrestii misapplied	see *H.* 'Helen Dillon'
	gardnerianum 🏆H2	CAbb CPne CTsd EUJe GKev IKil LAma LEdu LOPS LRHS LTro MNrw NLos SArc SChr SDeJ SDir SPlb WCru XLum
	- B&SWJ 12533 **new**	WCru
	'Gold Flame'	EBee
	gracile	EUJe NLos WCru
	greenii	CBcs CBct CCCN CPne CTsd EUJe GKev LEdu LTro MNrw NLos SBig SDir SDix SPlb WBor WCru XLum
	- 'Mhui Fang' **new**	LEdu WPGP
	griffithianum	CCCN CTsd EBee IKil LTro SBig XLum
	- white-flowered	CCCN
§	'Helen Dillon'	CCCN CCse EUJe IBlr SArc WCru WPGP
	'Keneggy'	SVen
	'Luna Moth'	CFil NLos WPGP
	luteum	CTsd
	maximum	CFil NLos SChr SKHP WPGP
	- B&SWJ 8261A	WCru
	- HWJ 810	WCru
§	× ***moorei*** 'Raffillii'	SBig WCru
	'Orange Glow'	CPne
	'Pink V'	NLos
	'Pradhan'	LTro
	'Samsheri'	CCCN SChr
	spicatum	CAbb CAvo CCCN CDTJ CTsd EUJe GCal GKev GPoy IBlr LEdu LTro MNrw MRav NLos WPGP
	- B&SWJ 7231	WCru
	- P. Bon. 57188	CFil WPGP
	- PAB 13.0718 **new**	LEdu
	- from Ciaojiang	SBrt
	- 'Himalayan Lipstick'	GKev
	- 'Huani'	LEdu
	- 'Liberty'	WCru
	- 'Shirui Steps' **new**	LEdu
	- 'Singalila'	WCru
	'St Martin's'	CCCN
	stenopetalum B&SWJ 7155	WCru
	'Tahitian Flame' (v)	EUJe NLos
	'Tai Pink Princess' (Tai Series)	CTsd
	'Tara' 🏆H4	CAbb CBct CPne CSam EUJe IBlr IDee LEdu LRHS MNrw SArc SPlb SPoG WCru WPGP
	tengchongense 'Trum Trom' **new**	WCru
	thyrsiforme	CTsd EUJe GKev LTro SBig WCru XLum
	villosum	CDTJ GCal
	- var. ***tenuiflorum***	WPGP
	- - KWJ 12305	WCru
	wardii	CFil CTsd EUJe WPGP
	yunnanense	LEdu SBig SBrt SPlb WPGP
	- B&SWJ 9717	WCru
	- BWJ 7900	WCru
	- L 633	IBlr
	- from Cally Gardens	GCal

Hedysarum (*Papilionaceae*)

coronarium	CSpe CWCL ELan IBoy SPoG WKif WOut
erythroleucum **new**	CPBP
hedysaroides	IKil SPhx
huetii **new**	CPBP
multijugum	MBlu WSHC
tauricum	SPhx

Heimia (*Lythraceae*)

salicifolia	CArn IMou MGil SBrt

Helenium ✿ (*Asteraceae*)

	'Adios'	MAvo
	'Amber'	EBee ECtt ILea MAvo MSpe
	autumnale	CSBt CTri ESps LPot LSRN MMuc NChi SWvt WFar WHar WMoo WPtf WWtn XLum
	- 'All Gold'	SWvt
I	- 'Cupreum'	SBch
	- 'Fuego' (Mariachi Series)	CWGN EBee ECtt IPot LRHS MMrt WHil WHlf
§	- Helena Series	SWvt WHar
§	- - 'Helena Gold'	EPfP IBoy NBre
	- - 'Helena Rote Töne'	CBod CNec EAJP EPed EPfP LRHS LSun NRHS SPad
	- - 'Helena Yellow'	LRHS NRHS
	- 'Salsa' (Mariachi Series)	EBee IPot LRHS WHil
	- 'Sombrero' (Mariachi Series) **new**	WHlf
	'Baronin Linden'	MAvo MSpe
	'Baudirektor Linne' 🏆H7	ILea LEdu LRHS MAvo MTis SHar
	'Betty' **new**	ECtt MSpe SPoG
	'Biedermeier'	CWCL ECtt LCro LOPS MNrw MSpe SAko
	bigelovii	XLum
	'Blütentisch' misapplied	see *H.* 'Riverton Beauty'
	'Blütentisch' Foerster 🏆H7	CHVG CMea GMaP LRHS MAvo MTis NLar
	'Bressingham Gold'	LRHS MHCG MNrw MSpe WHrl
	'Bruno'	LRHS MArl SHar
	'Butterpat' 🏆H7	CDor ECtt GCra GMaP LRHS MArl MNrw MRav WBod WMoo
	'Can Can'	CBod ECtt ELon LSou MAsh MAvo MHer MTis NGdn SPer WFar WMoo
	'Chelsey'	CMos ECtt ELan EPfP LCro LHop LOPS LPla LRHS LSRN LSou MNrw MPie MRav MSpe NLar NNys NSti SPoG WBor
	'Chipperfield Orange'	CSam EBee ECtt GMaP MArl MNrw NGdn WOld
	'Coppelia'	ECtt LRHS MTis NBir NGdn
	Copper Spray	see *H.* 'Kupfersprudel'
	Dark Beauty	see *H.* 'Dunkle Pracht'
	'Dauerbrenner'	LEdu MAvo MTis SHar
	'Die Blonde'	MAvo SMHy
	'Double Trouble' PBR	CMos CRos EBee ECtt GBin GPSL IBoy IKil LHop LLHF LRHS MBNS MHol MSpe NGdn NHpl NPri NRHS SGbt SPer SPoG WCot WFar
§	'Dunkle Pracht' 🏆H7	EBee ECtt LSRN NLar WCot WFar WOld
	'El Dorado'	EBee ECtt EWoo LEdu MAsh MAvo MBel MSpe MTis NSti WCot WFar

	'Fata Morgana'	ECtt LLHF MTis NBre SCob WCAu
	'Festival'	ECtt
	'Feuersiegel' 🏆H7	CSam ECtt LRHS MAvo MSpe SAko WOld
	'Fiesta'	CSam ECtt MAvo MTis WHlf
	'Flammendes Käthchen'	CSam EBee ECtt EHoe LRHS NCGa SHar SPhx
	'Flammenrad'	CAby CSam EBee SAko
	'Flammenspiel'	ECtt LRHS MNrw NLar
	flexuosum	SPhx
	'Gartensonne' 🏆H7	CSam LPla
	'Gay-go-round'	CSam MAvo MSpe
	'Gelbe Waltraut'	MAvo
	'Gold Doubloons' **new**	EBee
	Gold Fox	see *H.* 'Goldfuchs'
	'Gold Intoxication'	see *H.* 'Goldrausch'
	Golden Youth	see *H.* 'Goldene Jugend'
§	'Goldene Jugend'	CMea ELan MSpe MTis WCot
§	'Goldfuchs'	MSpe WCot
	'Goldkogel'	EBee
§	'Goldlackzwerg'	GBin LRHS MTis
§	'Goldrausch'	CAby CSam EBee ECtt EPfP GBin GCra LSou MNrw MSpe MTis MWat NGdn SAko WFar WMoo WOld
	'Goldreif'	MSpe
	'Goldriese'	MSpe
	'Hartmut Rieger'	CSam MSpe
	'Helena' misapplied	see *H. autumnale* 'Helena Gold'
	'Herbstgold'	MSpe
	hoopesii	see *Hymenoxys hoopesii*
	'Hot Lava'	CNor EBee ECtt GPSL MBel MNrw MSpe SCob
	'Hot Luv'	MSpe WCot
	'Indianersommer'	CDor CWCL ECtt GMaP GWyn ILea LRHS MNrw MSpe NLar WCFE WWtn
	'Jam Tarts'	WCot
	'Julisamt'	LEdu
	'July Sun'	NBir
	'Kanaria'	CAby CDor CHVG EBee ECtt GBin GKev GQue GWyn LHop LRHS MAvo MBel MRav MSpe MTis NEgg NLar SSal
	'Karneol' 🏆H7	LRHS
	'Kleine Aprikose'	MSpe MTis
	'Kleiner Fuchs'	MHer MSpe NLar
	'Kokarde'	IPot MAvo
	'Königstiger'	ECtt GBin LRHS MAvo MHCG MNrw MSpe MTis SAko WFar
	'Kugelsonne'	CSam GBin MSpe NBre SAko
§	'Kupfersprudel'	MAvo MTis SAko
	'Kupferzwerg'	EAJP ELan IPot NBre NNys SAko
	'Lambada'	EBee MTis SMHy
	'Louise Beacock'	MSpe
	'Loysder Wieck'	CKno EBee ECtt EPed MAvo MSpe MTis NGdn
	'Luc'	MAvo MSpe MTis WCot WWtn
§	'Mahagoni'	LEdu MSpe SHar WBod
	'Mahogany'	see *H.* 'Goldlackzwerg'
	Mahogany	see *H.* 'Mahagoni'
	'Mardi Gras'	CMos CRos CWCL ECtt LRHS LSou MAsh MAvo MBel MSpe MTis NPri NRHS SPoG WMoo WSFF WWtn
	'Margot'	CAby CSam MSpe MTis NBre
	'Marion Nickig'	EBee MAvo
	'Meranti'	CMea MAsh MAvo SAko WCot
	'Moerheim Beauty' 🏆H7	Widely available
	'Moth'	MSpe MTis NEgg
	'Oldenburg'	MSpe WCot
	'Patsy'	MAvo
	Pipsqueak = 'Blopip'	LLHF NBre WHar
	'Potter's Wheel'	EBee ECtt EPed LCro LOPS MAsh WWtn
	puberulum	CBod CRos EBee LRHS NBir NRHS SSal
	'Puck'	MSpe
	'Pumilum Magnificum'	ELan EPfP GQue IBoy LEdu LHop LRHS MSpe MTis SMad WFar XLum
	'Ragamuffin'	CSam ECtt MTis WCot
	'Rauchtopas'	CAby EBee GQue GWyn ILea IPot LCro LEdu LOPS LPla MBel MSpe MTis NDov SAko SDix SSal WPGP
	Red and Gold	see *H.* 'Rotgold' Foerster
	'Red Army'	ECtt ELan ELon LEdu LRHS LSou MAsh MAvo MNrw MSpe NGdn NLar SAko SWvt WWtn
	'Red Glory'	MTis
	'Red Jewel'	Widely available
	'Ring of Fire' 🏆H7	SMHy
§	'Riverton Beauty'	CSam ECtt LLHF MNrw MSpe SDix WCot WHoo WWtn
	'Riverton Gem'	CSam ECtt LLHF MHCG MNrw
	'Rotgold' misapplied	see *H. autumnale* Helena Series
§	'Rotgold' Foerster	CBod EBee ECtt SRms WMoo
	'Rouge Foncé'	WCot
	'Rubinzwerg' 🏆H7	Widely available
	'Ruby Charm'	EBee ECtt EPfP MSpe WCot WFar
§	'Ruby Thuesday'	Widely available
	'Ruby Tuesday'	see *H.* 'Ruby Thuesday'
	'Sahin's Early Flowerer' 🏆H7	Widely available
	'Samtjuwel'	MTis
	'Septemberfuchs'	LEdu MCot MTis SPhx
	'Siesta' (Mariachi Series) **new**	LRHS
	'Sonnenwunder'	CSam NBre
	'Sophie zur Linden'	ECtt MSpe MTis WCot
	'Sunshine Superman'	MSpe
	'The Bishop'	CBod CRos EBee ECtt EPfP GCra LBMP LHop LRHS MRav MSpe NHol SCob SGbt SPer SWvt WFar WHar
	'Tie Dye'	CBod EBee ECtt EPfP MAvo MHol MSpe SPoG WFar WTor
	'Tijuana Brass'	EBee ECtt NLar SAko
	'Tip Top'	LRHS
	'Tura'	MSpe
	'Two Faced Fan'	MSpe MTis
	'Vicky'	MAvo MSpe
	'Vivace'	LEdu MSpe WCot
	'Wagon Wheel'	ECtt WCot
	'Waldhorn'	MTis
	'Waltraut' 🏆H7	Widely available
	'Wesergold' 🏆H7	EBee LLHF LPla LRHS LSou MAvo MSpe NDov NLar NSti SPoG
	'Wonnadonga'	GBin MTis
	'Wyndley'	CBcs CDor CHVG CMea CRos ECtt EHoe ELan EPfP GMaP LRHS MHer MRav MSpe MTis NBir NGdn NLar SCob SPer WCAu WFar WHar
	'Zimbelstern'	CCse ECtt EWTr LHop MAvo MCot MPie MSpe MTis NLar SPhx WCot WFar WPGP
	'Zonnedam'	ECtt

Heliamphora (*Sarraceniaceae*)

	heterodoxa	NLos
	× ***nutans*** 🏆H1b	
	nutans	SHmp

Helianthella (*Asteraceae*)

§	***quinquenervis***	CBod EBee ELon GCal LLHF MHer NLar SMad

Helianthemum (*Cistaceae*)

	'Alice Howorth'	ECtt WIce
	'Amabile Plenum' (d)	GBin GCal MAvo
	'Amy Baring' ♀H4	CRos CTri ECho ECtt GCrg LRHS NRHS NWad
	'Annabel' (d)	CRos ECho ECtt GAbr GBin LRHS NRHS NSla
	apenninum	EPPr LLHF MArt SRms XSen
	'Apricot'	CTri ECtt
	'Apricot Blush'	WAbe
	'Baby Buttercup'	CMea
	'Beech Park Red'	CSma CTri ECtt EPot GCrg MHer WAbe WHoo WIce WKif
	'Ben Afflick'	CRos ECho ECtt LHop LRHS NRHS SIgm SRms
	'Ben Alder'	ECtt GAbr MHer
	'Ben Dearg'	CMea ECho ECtt SRms
	'Ben Fhada'	Widely available
	'Ben Heckla'	CRos ECho ECtt GAbr LHop LRHS NRHS SRms XLum
	'Ben Hope'	CRos CTri ECho ECtt ELan EPfP EWoo LRHS MJak NRHS SHil SRGP SRms XLum
§	'Ben Ledi'	CBcs ECho ECtt ELan ELon GAbr GCrg GMaP LHop MAsh MHer MSCN NHol NSla SEND SGbt SPoG SRms SRot WAbe
	'Ben More'	CBcs CRos ECho ECtt ELan EPfP GAbr GJos GMaP LHop LRHS MAsh MRav MSwo NBir NHpl NRHS SEND SHil SIgm SPoG SRGP SRms SRot WHoo WIce
	'Ben Nevis'	CTri ECho ECtt GAbr SRms
	'Ben Vane'	CRos ECho ECtt LRHS NRHS
	'Boughton Double Primrose' (d)	ECtt WAbe WHoo WSHC
	'Bronzeteppich'	EAJP
	'Broughty Beacon'	ECtt
	'Broughty Sunset'	ECtt GAbr
	'Bunbury'	ECtt ELon EPfP GAbr GCrg GJos LRHS NBir NRHS SDix SHil SPoG SRms
	canum subsp. ***balcanicum***	WAbe
	'Captivation'	ECtt GAbr NHol
	'Cerise Queen' (d)	CTri ECha ECho ECtt EPfP ESps GKev LHop MHol MSwo SEND SRms XSen
	chamaecistus	see *H. nummularium*
	'Cheviot'	ECtt NBir SMHy WHoo WSHC XLum
I	'Chloe's Variegata' (v)	EWes
	'Chocolate Blotch'	CRos ECho ECtt GCra LHop LRHS NRHS NWad SEND SRms XSen
	'Cornish Cream'	ECtt GAbr LBee NHol SRms
	croceum	LLHF
	cupreum	ECtt GAbr GKev
	'David'	NHol
	'David Ritchie'	WHoo
	'Diana'	CMea ECtt
	double apricot-flowered (d)	GAbr
	double orange-flowered (d)	LHop
	double primrose-flowered (d)	GAbr
	'Everton Ruby'	see *H.* 'Ben Ledi'
	'Fairy'	ELan EPfP GAbr
§	'Fire Dragon' ♀H4	CMea CRos ECho ECtt ELan EPfP EWoo GAbr GCrg GMaP GQue LRHS NBir NRHS SGbt SIgm SRms WAbe XLum XSen
	'Fireball'	see *H.* 'Mrs C.W. Earle'
	'Firegold' (v)	WAbe
	'Georgeham'	CMea CSam CSma EAJP ECtt ELon GCrg NBir NHol SRms WHoo WRHF WTor XLum
§	'Golden Queen'	ECho ECtt EPfP GAbr MAsh MAvo MHol MSwo
	'Hampstead Orange'	CTri
	'Hartswood Ruby'	GMaP LRHS MBNS MHer NRHS SAko SRms
	'Henfield Brilliant' ♀H4	CHVG CRos CSam CSpe ECho ECtt ELan EPfP EWoo GAbr GCrg LHop LRHS MHol MRav NBir NHol NRHS NSla SDix SIgm SMad SPoG SRms WCot WHil WHoo WSHC XLum
	'Highdown'	SRms
	'Highdown Apricot'	CRos ECho ECtt GCrg LHop LLHF LRHS NHpl NRHS SPoG SRms
	'Honeymoon'	ECtt EPfP GAbr NWad
	'Jubilee' (d) ♀H4	CTri ECho ECtt ELan EShb GJos LHop MAsh MBNS NBir NChi NHol SPoG SRms WKif
	'Karen's Silver'	WAbe
	'Kathleen Druce' (d)	ECtt EWes NWad WHoo
	'Kathleen Mary'	CMea
	'Lawrenson's Pink'	CRos CSma ECho ECtt GAbr GCrg IBoy LHop LPot LRHS MAvo MHol NRHS SAko SRGP SRms
	'Lemon Queen'	ECtt GCrg IBoy WHar
	'Lucy Elizabeth'	ECtt
	lunulatum	CMea ECho LLHF LRHS NRHS NWad SIgm WAbe
	'Mead Sunset'	CMea ECtt
§	'Mrs C.W. Earle' (d) ♀H4	CRos CTri ECho ECtt ELan EPfP LRHS MBNS NRHS NSla SHil SRms
	'Mrs Clay'	see *H.* 'Fire Dragon'
	'Mrs Hays'	ECtt
	'Mrs Lake'	GAbr
	'Mrs Moules'	SRms
	mutabile	SPlb SVic
	'New Moon'	CSma
§	***nummularium***	ECho ENfk GPoy MHer MNHC NMir SRms SVic WAbe WIce WSFF XSen
	- subsp. ***grandiflorum***	LLHF
	oelandicum	NSla NWad SRms WAbe
	- subsp. ***piloselloides***	WAbe
	'Old Gold'	ECtt SRms WAbe
	'Orange Double' (d) **new**	WHil
	'Orange Phoenix' (d)	ECtt MBNS NWad
	'Ovum Supreme'	ECtt NHol
	'Pink Angel' (d)	CSma ECtt GCrg MBNS WAbe
	'Praecox'	CMea CTri ECtt GAbr SRms WHoo
	'Prima Donna'	ELan EPfP
	'Prostrate Orange'	SRms
	'Raspberry Ripple'	CRos CSma ECho ECtt ELan EPfP EPot GCrg LRHS NRHS SPoG SRms XSen
	'Razzle Dazzle' (v)	CBod ECtt NHpl NLar SRms WHil
	'Red Dragon'	EPot GCrg NHpl WAbe
	'Red Orient'	see *H.* 'Supreme'
	'Regenbogen' (d)	ECtt GCal SEND
§	'Rhodanthe Carneum' ♀H4	Widely available
§	'Rosakönigin'	ECtt GAbr MHer NHol WAbe WRHF
	'Rose of Leeswood' (d)	CBod CTri ECtt NEgg SPoG SRms WHoo WKif WSHC XLum
	Rose Queen	see *H.* 'Rosakönigin'
	'Roxburgh Gold'	SRms
	'Saint John's College Yellow'	CRos CSam ECho LRHS NRHS
	'Salmon Queen'	CRos ECho ECtt GAbr LHop LRHS NRHS SEND SRms
*	***scardicum***	CMea
	'Shot Silk'	CSma ECtt EWes SRms

	'Snow Queen'	see *H.* 'The Bride'
	'Sterntaler'	GAbr LLHF SAko SRms
	'Strawberry Fields' **new**	ECtt NSla
	'Sudbury Gem'	CRos CTri ECha ECho ECtt GAbr LRHS NRHS
	'Sulphur Moon'	CRos ECho LRHS NRHS
	'Sulphureum Plenum' (d)	ECtt
	'Sunbeam'	ECtt SRms
§	'Supreme'	ECho ECtt ELan EPfP EWes LHop LPla MHol SAko SRms WCot XSen
	'Tangerine'	ECtt
§	'The Bride' ♀^{H4}	Widely available
	'Tigrinum Plenum' (d)	ECho EWes
	'Tomato Red'	ECtt NSla
	umbellatum	see *Halimium umbellatum*
	'Voltaire'	ECtt LLHF NWad
	'Welsh Flame'	ECtt NHol WAbe
	'Whenday'	CMea
	'Wisley Pink'	see *H.* 'Rhodanthe Carneum'
	'Wisley Primrose' ♀^{H4}	Widely available
	'Wisley Rose'	CRos LRHS NRHS
	'Wisley White'	CTri ECha ECho ECtt ELan EPfP
	'Wisley Yellow'	ECtt ELan
	'Yellow Queen'	see *H.* 'Golden Queen'

Helianthus (*Asteraceae*)

	angustifolius	SDix
	'Anne' **new**	NDov
	atrorubens	LHop MRav MSpe NBro
	'Bitter Chocolate'	LEdu MAvo MSpe WBor WCot WPGP
	'Capenoch Star' ♀^{H7}	CElw ECtt GMaP IBoy LEdu LRHS MBel MRav MSpe MTis NBro NLar SDix SWvt
	'Capenoch Supreme'	ECtt LRHS
	'Carine'	MNrw MTis NLar SMHy WOld
	decapetalus Morning Sun	see *H.* 'Morgensonne'
	'Dorian Roxburgh'	ECtt MAvo MTis WCot
	'Double Whammy' (d)	ECtt MTis
	giganteus	SHar
	- 'Sheila's Sunshine'	CElw EWes GBin LHop LRHS MNrw NDov SAko SHar SMHy SPhx WFar WOld
	grosseserratus	MPie
	'Gullick's Variety' ♀^{H7}	CBre ECtt LLWP NBro NChi NLar SAko SPhx SWvt WFar WOld WWFP XLum
	'Happy Days'	CAby CBre CElw CHVG CSam EBee ECtt ELon EWes GBin LBMP LSou MBel MHol MPie MSpe MTis NCGa NGBl NSti WCot WHoo WMoo WOld WRHF
	'Hazel's Gold'	LRHS
	× ***kellermanii***	EBee MAvo MTis SPhx
§	× ***laetiflorus***	GPSL NLar
	- var. ***rigidus***	see *H. pauciflorus*
§	'Lemon Queen' ♀^{H7}	Widely available
	'Limelight'	see *H.* 'Lemon Queen'
	'Loddon Gold' ♀^{H7}	ECtt ELan EPfP EShb LRHS MBel MRav MSpe MTis NBir SWvt WBor WCot
§	***maximiliani***	CBod ELan ELon LHop MMuc SDix SPhx SPtp
	microcephalus	CSam EBee ELon MMuc NDov WPtf
	'Miss Mellish' ♀^{H7}	EBee ECtt GCal LEdu MSpe SPhx WBor WBrk WCot WHoo
	mollis	CSam SBrt SPav SPhx
	'Monarch' ♀^{H4}	CMea CSam EBee ECtt MBel MMuc MRav MSpe NCGa NLar WCot WFar WHal WHil WOld WTcb
§	'Morgensonne'	MTis WBor WCot
	× ***multiflorus*** 'Meteor'	LRHS NBre SAko
	'O Sole Mio'	WCot WFar
	occidentalis	SMad
	orgyalis	see *H. salicifolius*
§	***pauciflorus***	EBee
	quinquenervis	see *Helianthella quinquenervis*
	'Razzmatazz'	SAko
	rigidus misapplied	see *H.* × *laetiflorus*
	rigidus (Cass.) Desf.	see *H. pauciflorus*
§	***salicifolius***	Widely available
	- 'Low Down'^{PBR}	SWvt
	- 'Table Mountain'^{PBR}	LRHS SAko SWvt WCot
	- very fine-leaved **new**	WCot
	scaberrimus	see *H.* × *laetiflorus*
	'Soleil d'Or'	ECtt WHal
	strumosus	WCot
	'Triomphe de Gand'	LEdu MTis MWat NDov
	tuberosus	CArn EBee GPoy SVic
	- 'Bleu Patate' **new**	LEdu
	- 'Drago' **new**	LEdu
	- 'Dwarf' **new**	LEdu
	- 'Fuseau'	LCro LOPS SVic
	- 'Garnet'	LEdu
	- 'Sakahlinski' **new**	LEdu
	- 'Sugarball'	LEdu

Helichrysum (*Asteraceae*)

	adenocarpum	SPlb
	alveolatum	see *H. splendidum*
	amorginum 'Pink Bud'	MMuc
	- 'Pink Sapphire'^{PBR}	WHlf
	- Ruby Cluster = 'Blorub'^{PBR}	LPla LRHS NPri WCot
	angustifolium from Crete	see *H. microphyllum* (Willd.) Cambess.
§	***arwae***	EPot WAbe
	bellidioides	see *Anaphalioides bellidioides*
	bracteatum	see *Xerochrysum bracteatum*
	'Coco'	see *Xerochrysum bracteatum* 'Coco'
	confertum	SPlb
	coralloides	see *Ozothamnus coralloides*
	'County Park Silver'	see *Ozothamnus* 'County Park Silver'
	'Dargan Hill Monarch'	see *Xerochrysum bracteatum* 'Dargan Hill Monarch'
	'Elmstead'	see *H. stoechas* 'White Barn'
	frigidum	WAbe
	hookeri	see *Ozothamnus hookeri*
§	***hypoleucum***	SDix
	'Icicles'	GBin
	italicum	ECha ECrN ENfk EPfP GBin GMaP GPoy GWyn LPot MHer MMuc MNHC SEND SPoG SRms SVen SVic WHer WJek XLum XSen
	- 'Dartington'	CBod ENfk GBin SRms WJek
I	- 'Glaucum'	CWib
	- 'Korma'^{PBR}	CRos EHoe ELan EPfP ESps GBin LRHS LSou MAsh SLon SPoG SRms
	- subsp. ***microphyllum***	see *H. microphyllum* (Willd.) Cambess.
	- 'Nanum'	see *H. microphyllum* (Willd.) Cambess.
§	- subsp. ***serotinum***	CBcs CRos ECrN EHoe EPfP GPoy LRHS MRav SLim SPer SRms SWvt WRHF XSen
	lanatum	see *H. thianschanicum*
	ledifolium	see *Ozothamnus ledifolius*
	marginatum misapplied	see *H. milfordiae*

	microphyllum ambig.	MMuc SPer SRms
§	***microphyllum*** (Willd.) Cambess.	ENfk MNHC SEND WJek
§	***milfordiae*** ♀H4	EPot ITim SPlb SRms WAbe
	orientale	EPot XSen
	pagophilum	CPBP EPot WAbe
	petiolare ♀H3	EBak ECtt MCot SPer SPoG WHea
	- 'Aureum'	see *H. petiolare* 'Limelight'
	- 'Goring Silver' ♀H3	SPoG
§	- 'Limelight' ♀H3	ECtt MCot NPri SPer SPoG
	- 'Variegatum' (v) ♀H3	ECtt MCot SPoG
	plicatum	WCot
	populifolium misapplied	see *H. hypoleucum*
	rosmarinifolium	see *Ozothamnus rosmarinifolius*
§	'Schwefellicht'	EBee ECha EPfP MRav SPer WSHC
	selago	see *Ozothamnus selago*
	serotinum	see *H. italicum* subsp. *serotinum*
	sessilioides	EPot WAbe
§	***splendidum*** ♀H5	LRHS NBro SKHP SLon XSen
	stoechas	CArn XSen
§	- 'White Barn'	CSpe MAvo WCot XLum
	Sulphur Light	see *H.* 'Schwefellicht'
§	***thianschanicum***	LRHS SRms XLum XSen
	- Golden Baby	see *H. thianschanicum* 'Goldkind'
§	- 'Goldkind'	NBir XLum
	- 'White Wonder'	CRos LRHS
	trilineatum misapplied	see *H. splendidum*
	tumidum	see *Ozothamnus selago* var. *tumidus*
	woodii	see *H. arwae*

Helicodiceros (*Araceae*)

§	***muscivorus***	CAvo CHid WCot

Heliconia ✿ (*Heliconiaceae*)

	caribaea 'Burgundy'	see *H. caribaea* 'Purpurea'
§	- 'Purpurea'	XBlo
	'Golden Torch'	XBlo
	indica 'Spectabilis'	XBlo
	latispatha 'Orange Gyro'	XBlo
*	- 'Red Gyro'	XBlo
	metallica	XBlo
	psittacorum	CCCN
	rostrata	CCCN XBlo
	schiedeana	CHll

Helictotrichon (*Poaceae*)

	pratense	CHab EHoe
§	***sempervirens*** ♀H7	Widely available
I	- 'Pendulum'	CBod CLet EBee GBin MSpe
	- 'Saphirsprudel'	CCse EBee EPfP LRHS MJak NRHS SHil WCot WPGP

Heliophila (*Brassicaceae*)

	coronopifolia	CSpe

Heliopsis (*Asteraceae*)

	Golden Plume	see *H. helianthoides* var. *scabra* 'Goldgefieder'
	helianthoides	EBee LRHS NBre WFar WWtn
	- 'Limelight'	see *Helianthus* 'Lemon Queen'
	- Loraine Sunshine = 'Helhan'PBR (v)	CWGN ECtt GMcL IKil LLWG LSou MHol MMrt MSCN NCou NWsh SMad SPad WCot WFar WRHF
	- var. ***scabra***	NHol SRot WHar
	- - 'Asahi'	CBod ECtt GMaP LCro SAko SMad WHil WHoo
	- - Ballerina	see *H. helianthoides* var. *scabra* 'Spitzentänzerin'
	- - 'Benzinggold' ♀H5	LRHS LSou MRav
	- - 'Bressingham Doubloon' (d)	ECtt
	- - Golden Plume	see *H. helianthoides* var. *scabra* 'Goldgefieder'
§	- - 'Goldgefieder' ♀H5	EBee NBre WFar
	- - Goldgreenheart	see *H. helianthoides* var. *scabra* 'Goldgrünherz'
§	- - 'Goldgrünherz'	LCro
	- - 'Hohlspiegel'	GBin
	- - 'Light of Loddon' ♀H5	LRHS
	- - 'Mars'	EBee
	- - 'Patula'	EBee ECtt
	- - 'Prairie Sunset'PBR	EBee ECtt MSCN SAko
§	- - 'Sommersonne'	CSBt ECtt ELan EPfP GMcL LRHS NGBl NPer SCob SRms
§	- - 'Spitzentänzerin' ♀H5	ECtt
	- - 'Summer Nights'	EBee ELan EPfP EWTr IBoy LCro LOPS MNrw MRav MSpe NSti SPhx WHil
	- - Summer Sun	see *H. helianthoides* var. *scabra* 'Sommersonne'
	- - 'Sunburst' (v)	SPav
	- - 'Venus'	CBod ECtt LRHS LSou
	- - 'Waterperry Gold'	MWat
	- 'Summer Pink' (v)	MHol SPad SPoG WCot WRHF
	- 'Sunstruck' **new**	ECtt
	- 'Tuscan Sun'PBR	CBod EBee ECtt LRHS SCob

Heliotropium ✿ (*Boraginaceae*)

§	***amplexicaule***	SDys
	anchusifolium	see *H. amplexicaule*
§	***arborescens***	CArn ENfk EPfP EShb MCot MHom
	- 'Chatsworth' ♀H1c	CAby CCCN CSpe ECre ECtt MHom
	- 'Dame Alice de Hales'	ECtt MHom
	- 'Gatton Park'	ECtt MHom
	- 'Lord Roberts'	ECtt MHom
	- 'Mary Fox'	ECtt MHom
	- 'Mrs J.W. Lowther'	ECtt MHom
	- 'Netherhall Lilac'	EBee
	- pale lilac-flowered	CSam
	- 'President Garfield'	ECtt MHom
	- 'Princess Marina' ♀H1c	EPfP NLar
	- 'Reva'	ECtt MHom
	- 'The Queen'	ECtt
	- 'The Speaker'	ECtt MHom
	- 'White Lady'	CCCN CSpe ECtt MHom
	- 'White Queen'	ECtt MHom
	- 'Woodcote'	ECtt MHom
	'Butterfly Kisses'	LBuc SPoG
	peruvianum	see *H. arborescens*

Helipterum see *Syncarpha*

Helleborus ✿ (*Ranunculaceae*)

	abruzzicus	MAsh
	- WM 0227	MPhe
	abschasicus	see *H. orientalis* Lam. subsp. *abchasicus*
	'Angel Glow'	EBee LRHS SCob WHil
§	***argutifolius*** ♀H5	Widely available
	- mottled-leaved	see *H. argutifolius* 'Pacific Frost'
§	- 'Pacific Frost' (v)	CPla
	- 'Red Riding Hood'	LRHS
	- 'Silver Lace'	CMil CRos EAEE ELan EPfP GKev IBoy LHop LRHS LSRN MHol NBir NLar NPnk NRHS NWad SKHP SPer SPtp WMoo
	- variegated (v) **new**	GKev
	atrorubens misapplied	see *H. orientalis* Lam. subsp. *abchasicus* Early Purple Group

atrorubens ambig.	EWTr MAsh SCob
atrorubens Waldst. & Kit.	LOPS MRav XEll
- WM 9028 from Slovenia	MPhe
- WM 9805 from Croatia	GBuc MPhe
- spotted form	MPhe
× ***ballardiae***	CLAP EPfP GKev
- 'Candy Love'PBR	CRos EBee LRHS MAvo MHol NLar NRHS SCob
- HGC Camelot = 'Coseh 940'PBR	CRos ECtt EPfP LRHS NRHS SHil
- HGC Champion = 'Coseh 730'PBR	LPre LRHS NRHS
- HGC Joker = 'Coseh 740'PBR	LPre LRHS NRHS
- HGC Maestro = 'Coseh 890'PBR	CRos LRHS SHil
- HGC Merlin = 'Coseh 810'PBR	CRos EBee LRHS NRHS SHil SPoG
- HGC Snow Dance = 'Coseh 800'PBR	CRos EBee LPre LRHS SPoG
'Blue Moon'	IBoy
§ ***bocconei***	MAsh
- WM 1332 from Sicily	MPhe
- WM 1334 from Calabria, Italy	MPhe
- WM 9719 from Italy	MPhe
- WM 9905 from Sicily	MPhe
- subsp. ***bocconei***	see *H. bocconei*
colchicus	see *H. orientalis* Lam. subsp. *abchasicus*
corsicus	see *H. argutifolius*
croaticus	MAsh
- WM 9810	MPhe
cyclophyllus	MAsh MPhe SCob SPer
dumetorum	GBuc GCal GKev MAsh
- WM 1306 from Hungary	MPhe
- WM 1309 from Slovenia	MPhe
- WM 9209	MPhe
- WM 9627 from Croatia	GBuc MPhe
§ × ***ericsmithii***	CLAP CMHG ECha ELon EPfP GBuc LHop LLHF LRHS LSRN LSou MAsh NBir NGdn NLar SCob WHoo WPGP
- 'Bob's Best'	CHid CLAP ECtt EPfP ESwi GMcL MBNS MHol MNrw SEND SKHP SWvt
- HGC Marlon Cream = 'Coseh 980'	LRHS
- HGC Monte Cristo = 'Coseh 860'PBR	CRos LRHS
- HGC Shooting Star = 'Coseh 790'PBR	CRos EBee ECre LRHS NRHS SHil
- 'HGC Silvermoon'PBR	IBoy LRHS NLar
- 'Pirouette'PBR	CLAP EBee ECre EPfP LCro LRHS MAsh SCob
- 'Ruby Glow'	CBcs ECre EPfP LRHS NPnk SCob SPoG WHil
- 'Snow Love'PBR	EBee LBuc LRHS NLar SCob
- 'Winter Moonbeam'PBR	CBod CEnd CLAP ECtt EPfP IKil LBuc LPre LRHS LSRN LSun MAsh MCot MHol SCob SKHP SLon SPoG WCot WHil
- 'Winter Sunshine'PBR	CLAP EPfP ESps LBuc LPre LRHS NPnk SCob SKHP SPoG WHil
foetidus ♀H7	Widely available
- from Italy	IFoB
- 'Chedglow'	CNat
- 'Gold Bullion'	CPla ECtt GBuc MAsh
- 'Harvington Pewter'	CLAP ENun LRHS
- 'Miss Jekyll'	EBee SVic
- 'Ruth'	EWoo MAsh SCob
- 'Sienna'	SCob
- 'Vogezen'	SCob
- Wester Flisk Group	CMea ECtt ELan EPfP GBin GBuc IFoB LHop MAsh NHol NPer NPnk SCob SEND WHar WPGP WWtn
- Wilgenbroek selection	SCob
- 'Yellow Wilgenbroek'	MAsh SCob
Gold Collection	see *Helleborus* with names starting HGC
'Harvington Black' **new**	LRHS
'Harvington Blush Picotee' **new**	LRHS
'Harvington Chocolate' **new**	LRHS
'Harvington Petticoat' **new**	LRHS
'Harvington Rebekah'PBR **new**	ENun LRHS
HGC Cinnamon Snow = 'Coseh 700'PBR	CRos ECre ESwi LRHS NLar NRHS SHil
'HGC Jericho'PBR	IVic
HGC Pink Frost = 'Coseh 710'PBR	CRos ECtt LRHS NRHS
Hillier hybrids anemone-centred, spotted pink	CRos LRHS SHil
- - yellow	CBod CRos LRHS SHil
× ***hybridus***	Widely available
- anemone-centred	CHid CLAP IFoB LEdu LHel MNrw WFar
- 'Apple Blossom'	IFoB WFar
- 'Apricot Blush' (Winter Jewels Series)	CWGN NPnk
- apricot-flowered	CLAP CTal GBuc IFoB WFar
- 'Ashwood Blushing Bride' **new**	MAsh
- 'Ashwood Elegance Pearl'	MAsh
- 'Ashwood Fascination'	MAsh
- Ashwood Garden hybrids	ELan EPfP MAsh MRav SRms
- - anemone-centred	MAsh
- - double-flowered (d)	MAsh
- 'Ashwood Glade'	MAsh
- 'Ashwood Lunar Neon' **new**	MAsh
- 'Ashwood Meadow'	MAsh
- 'Ashwood Moonlight' (d) **new**	MAsh
- 'Ashwood Neon Star' **new**	MAsh
- Ballard's Group	CLAP IBoy LRHS SPer WFar WPnP
- Barnhaven hybrids, anemone-centred	XBar
- - apricot	XBar
- - dark purple **new**	XBar
- - picotee	XBar
- - pink **new**	XBar
- - red and green	XBar
- - slate	XBar
- - spotted	XBar
- - white	XBar
- - yellow	XBar
- 'Black Beauty'	IFoB
- 'Black Knight'	IFoB
- black-flowered	CLAP GBuc GMaP IFoB NChi WFar
- 'Blue Lady' (Lady Series)	CBcs GAbr GMcL IFoB LRHS MBNS NCou NGdn SPer
- 'Blue Metallic Lady' (Lady Series)	CBod CTsd EPed EPfP GKev GMcL IBoy IFoB LCro LRHS MBNS MHol NEgg NGdn NPnk SPer
- Bradfield hybrids	MCot
- - anemone-centred	MCot
- - double-flowered (d)	MCot
- - picotee	MCot

- 'Burgundy' new	CWCL
- Caborn hybrids	LLWP
- 'Cherry Blossom' (Winter Jewels Series)	CWGN NPnk
- 'Cherry Frost'	MAsh
- 'Cinderella'PBR (d)	LRHS
- 'Clare's Purple'	CBod
- 'Cosmos'	CTal MBNS
- cream-flowered	CLAP IFro WFar
- dark picotee	WFar
- dark purple-flowered	IFoB LHel WFar
- dark red-flowered	IFoB LHel WFar
- dark-flowered	WFar
- deep red-flowered	CLAP GBuc MHol NChi WFar
- double (d)	CLAP GBuc IFoB LHop MNrw WFar WHar
- - black-flowered (d)	IFoB WFar
- - pink-flowered (d)	IFoB LHel WFar
- - yellow, cream-speckled (d) new	LRHS NRHS
- - dark purple-flowered (d)	SMad WFar
- - green-flowered (d)	IFoB LHel WFar
- - picotee (d)	CBod GEdr LHel WFar
- - purple-flowered (d)	GEdr LHel WFar
- - red-flowered (d)	LRHS NRHS WFar
- - white-flowered (d)	GEdr IBoy IFoB LHel WFar
- - white picotee (d) new	LRHS
- - yellow-flowered (d)	IBoy IFoB IFro LHel WFar
- 'Double Ellen Picotee' (d)	CWGN IKil NPnk
- 'Double Ellen Pink' (d)	CRos LCro LRHS NPnk NRHS
- 'Double Ellen Purple' (d)	CRos IKil LRHS NRHS
- 'Double Ellen Red' (d)	LRHS NPnk NRHS
- 'Double Ellen White' (d)	CRos CWGN EPfP IKil LCro LOPS LRHS NPnk NRHS
- Double Ladies, mixed (d)	GAbr WCot
- Elizabeth Town anemone-centred	IFro
- - double-flowered (d) new	IFro
- - picotee-centred	IFro
- - red-centred	IFro
- 'Enchantment'	MAsh
- Farmyard anemone-centred	WFar
- - apricot	WFar
- - black	WFar
- - cream	WFar
- - - spotted	WFar
- - dark pink	WFar
- - double apricot (d)	WFar
- - - black (d)	WFar
- - - cream (d)	WFar
- - - - spotted (d)	WFar
- - - pink (d)	WFar
- - - - spotted (d)	WFar
- - - primrose (d)	WFar
- - - - spotted (d)	WFar
- - - red (d)	WFar
- - - slate-grey (d)	WFar
- - - white (d)	WFar
- - - - spotted (d)	WFar
- - green	WFar
- - - spotted	WFar
- - picotee	WFar
- - pink	WFar
- - - spotted	WFar
- - plum	WFar
- - primrose	WFar
- - - dark-eyed	WFar
- - - spotted	WFar
- - red	WFar
- - slate spotted	WFar
- - slate-grey	WFar
- - white	WFar
- - - dark-eyed	WFar
- - - splash	WFar
- - - spotted	WFar
- 'Farmyard Appleblossom'	WFar
- 'Farmyard Woodland'	WFar
- Field of Blooms hybrids	IFoB
- - anemone-centred	IFoB
- - double-flowered (d)	IFoB
- - picotee	IFoB
- 'Gala Queen' (Queen Series)	ELon
- 'Golden Lotus' (d)	CWGN NPnk
- 'Green Ripple'	WFar
- green-flowered	IFoB WFar
- Harvington apricot	CRos ENun LCro LRHS NBir NLar NPri NRHS SKHP SLon
- - double apricot (d)	CRos ENun LRHS NPri NRHS SHeu
- - - blush (d)	ENun
- - - chocolate (d)	CLAP CRos ENun LRHS NPri NRHS SHeu SPoG
- - - cream speckled (d)	ENun
- - - dark purple (d)	CRos LRHS NPri NRHS
- - - green (d)	ENun
- - - pink (d)	CLAP CRos ENun LOPS LRHS NPri NRHS SHeu SKHP SLon SPoG
- - - - speckled (d)	CRos ENun LCro LRHS NPri NRHS SHeu SPoG
- - - purple (d)	CLAP CRos ENun LRHS NBir NLar NPri NRHS SHeu SKHP SPoG
- - - - cascade (d)	CRos ENun LRHS NRHS SHeu SPoG
- - - red (d)	CLAP CRos ENun LCro LOPS LRHS NBir NLar NPri NRHS SLon SPoG
- - - speckled (d)	CRos ENun LCro LRHS NPri NRHS SPoG
- - - white (d)	CLAP CRos ENun LCro LRHS NBir NLar NPri NRHS SHeu SKHP SLon SPoG
- - - yellow (d)	CLAP CRos ENun LRHS NBir NLar NPri NRHS SHeu SKHP SLon SPoG
- - - - speckled (d)	CRos ENun SHeu SPoG
- - - lime-green (d)	CLAP LOPS NPri SHeu
- - dusky	CRos ENun LRHS NRHS
- - lime	CRos LCro LRHS NRHS SPoG
- - picotee	CLAP CRos ENun LCro LRHS NBir NLar NPri NRHS SHeu SKHP SLon SPoG
- - pink	CRos ENun LRHS NLar NPri NRHS SHeu SLon SPoG
- - - speckled	CRos ENun LCro NLar NPri SHeu SLon SPoG
- - red	CRos ENun LCro LOPS LRHS MHer NLar NPri NRHS SLon SPoG
- - smokey	ENun
- - speckled	CRos MHer NPri SHeu SLon
- - white	CRos ENun LCro LOPS LRHS MHer NLar NPri NRHS SKHP SLon SPoG
- - - speckled	ENun LCro LOPS NPri SHeu SKHP SLon SPoG
- - yellow	CRos ENun LRHS MHer NLar NPri NRHS SHeu SKHP SLon SPoG
- - - speckled	CRos ENun LCro LRHS MHer NLar NPri NRHS SHeu SLon SPoG
- - - with maroon eye	ENun
- 'Harvington Shades of the Night'	CRos ENun LCro LRHS MHer NLar NPri NRHS SHeu SKHP SLon SPoG
- 'Harvington Smokey Blues'	CRos LCro NPri SHeu SKHP SLon
- 'Harvington Smokey Double' (d)	NPri SHeu

	- 'Helen Ballard'	SVic
	- Hillier hybrids clear white	CRos LRHS SHil
	- - double pink (d)	CRos
	- - slate	LRHS SHil
	- - spotted, double yellow (d)	CRos EPfP LRHS SHil
	- - - double-pink (d)	EPfP LRHS SHil
	- - - pink	CRos LRHS
	- - - white	CRos LRHS
	- - - yellow **new**	NRHS
	- - anemone-centred	CRos
	- - burgundy	CRos LEdu LRHS SHil SMad
	- 'John Hopkins' **new**	LRHS
	- 'Kingston Cardinal'	MAsh
	- 'Lady in Red'	IBoy
	- Lady Series	IFoB NSum
	- large, pink-flowered	IFoB IFro
	- maroon-flowered	WFar
	- mauve freckled, double (d)	IFro WFar
	- 'Mrs Betty Ranicar' (d)	CBro EPfP IFoB ILea SCob
	- nearly black-flowered	WFar
	- 'Onyx Odyssey'	CWGN NPnk
	- 'Orion'	CTal
	- 'Pale Picotee'	GBuc
	- pale-pink-flowered	GBuc WFar
	- 'Pamina'	IFoB
§	- Party Dress Group (d)	CBod CHid ELon GBin IFoB LSRN NLar SCob WFar
	- - 'Party Dress Pink' (d)	CBod CWCL
	- - 'Party Dress Primrose' (d)	CBod
	- 'Pebworth White'	CTal
	- 'Philip Ballard'	CTal
	- Picotee Group	NLar WFar WHoo
	- 'Picotee'	CLAP GBuc IFoB LHel WFar
	- pink freckled, double (d)	IFro WFar
	- 'Pink Lady' (Lady Series)	CBcs CBod CSBt GMcL GQue IFoB LCro LOPS LRHS NCou NEgg NGdn NPri SPer WHar
	- 'Pink Upstart'	IFoB
	- pink-flowered	CLAP CLet GBuc LHel MBNS SDeJ WHoo
	- pink-red-flowered	LHel WFar
	- plum-flowered	CLAP GBuc MMuc SEND
	- 'Pluto'	CTal WFar
	- 'Pretty Ellen Pink'	CRos GBin LCro LRHS NRHS
	- 'Pretty Ellen Purple'	CRos LRHS NRHS
	- 'Pretty Ellen Red'	CRos LCro
	- 'Pretty Ellen White'	CRos LCro
	- 'Primrose Picotee'	WFar
	- primrose-flowered	CLAP ELan GBuc MCot
	- 'Purity'	MAsh
	- purple-flowered	CLAP WFar
	- Queen Series, dark red-flowered **new**	GBin
	- - double white-flowered (d) **new**	GBin
	- - - yellow-flowered (d) **new**	GBin
	- - picotee **new**	GBin
	- - pink-flowered **new**	GBin
	- - white-flowered **new**	GBin
	- - yellow-flowered **new**	GBin
	- - 'Queen of the Night'	CLAP EPfP IBal
	- red and purple	CBod
	- 'Red Lady' (Lady Series)	CBcs CBod CSBt EPed EPfP GAbr GMcL IBal IFoB LCro LOPS LRHS LSRN MBNS NEgg NHol SPer
	- 'Red Upstart'	IFoB
	- red-flowered	CBod GBuc WFar WHoo
	- 'Sirius'	CTal
	- slaty blue-flowered	CBod CLAP GBuc IFoB LEdu LHel SEND
	- - purple-flowered	GBuc
	- 'Smokey Blue'	ELan IFoB LRHS
	- smokey purple-flowered	LSRN MAsh SGbt
	- SP Charlotte = 'Hlr 140'^{PBR} (Spring Promise Series)	LRHS NRHS SHil
	- SP Elly = 'Hlr 190'^{PBR} (Spring Promise Series) (d)	LRHS NRHS SHil
§	- spotted	CLAP EPfP GBuc IFoB NEgg WCot WFar WHoo
	- - cream	CBod CLAP IFoB NBir WFar
	- - double, pink (d)	GEdr LHel WFar
	- - - white (d)	CBod IFoB LHel WFar
	- - - yellow (d)	IFoB SMad WFar
	- - green	CLAP WFar
	- - ivory	CLAP WFar
	- - light purple	WFar
	- - pink	CBod CLAP CWld IFro LHel LRHS MBNS NBir SEND SHil WFar WHoo
	- - primrose	CLAP ELan EWTr SGbt WFar
	- - white	GBuc IFro LHel MMuc NBir SEND SHil WBor WFar
	- - yellow	LHel SHil WFar
	- 'Stained Glass'	MAsh
	- Sunshine selections	IBal
	- 'Titania'	CTal
	- 'Tricastin'	IBoy
	- 'Tutu'^{PBR}	EPfP LBuc LRHS SCob SPer SPoG SRms WHil
	- 'Ushba'	CLAP IFoB
	- Washfield double-flowered (d)	CWld EPfP LEdu SPer SRkn WBor WHil WRHF
	- - white (d)	IFoB
	- 'White Lady' (Lady Series)	CBcs CBod GAbr GMcL IFoB MBNS NCou NEgg NPri SPer
	- 'White Lady Spotted' (Lady Series)	CBod CLet ELon EPed GMcL GQue LCro LOPS LRHS MHol NEgg NHol SPer
	- white-flowered	GBuc GMaP IFoB LHel WCFE WFar WHoo
	- white-veined	WFar
	- Wilgenbroek hybrids anemone-centred, red	SCob
	- - - white freckled	SCob
	- - apricot	SCob
	- - aubergine with white edge	SCob
	- - black	SCob
	- - dark	SCob
	- - double red	SCob
	- - - picotee	SCob
	- - - slaty blue	SCob
	- - - white	SCob
	- - - white-spotted	SCob
	- - green	SCob
	- - picotee	SCob
	- - red	SCob
	- - slaty blue	SCob
	- - spotted, apricot	SCob
	- - - aubergine	SCob
	- - - pink	SCob
	- - - red	SCob
	- - - yellow	SCob
	- - white	SCob
	- - - with pink edge	SCob
	- yellow freckled, double (d)	IFro

- 'Yellow Lady' (Lady Series)	CBcs CBod CBro CTsd EPed GKev GMcL LCro LRHS MBNS NEgg SPer
- yellow-flowered	GMaP IFoB IKil LHel SEND WFar WHoo
- Zodiac Group	CBod MBNS
'Ice Dance'	LRHS
§ 'Ivory Prince'PBR	EPfP LBuc LRHS MAsh SPoG
'Kiwi Black Velvet'	IBal
liguricus	GKev MAsh
- WM 0230	MPhe
lividus	CBro CLAP CRos CSpe EBee EPfP EWes GKev IFoB LHop LRHS NBir NRHS SDeJ SKHP SRms SWat WAbe
- subsp. ***corsicus***	see *H. argutifolius*
- 'Green Marble' **new**	ELan NPnk
- 'Pink Marble'	EBee ELan
- 'Purple Ear'	EBee LRHS
- 'Purple Marble' **new**	NPnk
- 'Silver Edge'	EPfP
- 'White Marble'	EBee GKev LRHS MAsh SKHP
- white-flowered	GKev
lividus* × *niger **new**	GKev
'Lucy Black'	LRHS
'Marshmallow' **new**	NPnk WCot
'Moonshine'PBR	CLAP CMil EBee MHol NHol NLar NWad SLon WMoo
multifidus	IFoB NBir
- WM 1316	MPhe
- subsp. ***hercegovinus***	SCob XEll
- - WM 0020	MPhe
- - WM 0622	MPhe
- subsp. ***istriacus***	CBro MAsh WCot
- - WM 9322	MPhe
- - WM 9324	MPhe
- subsp. ***multifidus***	MAsh
- - WM 9529	MPhe
- - WM 9833 from Croatia	MPhe
niger	Widely available
- Ashwood marble leaf	MAsh
- Ashwood strain	CLAP MAsh
- Blackthorn Group	CLAP NLar
- 'Christmas Carol'	GMcL LRHS
- 'David'	IVic
- 'Double Fashion'PBR (d)	EPfP LRHS SCob
- double-flowered (d)	CDor MAsh
- 'Eifelturm'	IVic
- 'Harvington Double Petticoat' (d)	ENun
- Harvington hybrids	CLAP CRos ENun LCro LRHS MArt MAsh MHer NPri SPoG
- - double-flowered (d)	CRos LCro LOPS SPoG
- HGC Goldmarie = 'Coseh 2020'PBR **new**	SHil
- 'HGC Jacob'PBR	IVic LBuc LSRN SRms
- 'HGC Jacob Royal'	CRos LRHS NRHS SHil
- HGC Joel = 'Coseh 210'PBR	CRos ECtt LRHS SHil
- HGC Jonas = 'Coseh 220'PBR	CRos ECtt LRHS SHil
- 'HGC Josef Lemper'PBR	IVic LRHS LSRN NLar SRms
- 'HGC Joshua'PBR	CRos IVic LRHS SHil
- HGC Snow Frills = 'Coseh 230'PBR **new**	ECtt LPre SHil
- HGC Wintergold = 'Coseh 2010'PBR	CRos ECtt LPre LRHS SHil
- 'Ivory Prince'	see *H.* 'Ivory Prince'
- marbled leaves	SCob
- 'Marion' (d)	IFoB
- 'Maximus'	CLAP
- pink-flowered	MAsh
- 'Potter's Wheel'	CLAP CRos EPfP LRHS NBir NRHS SCob
- 'Praecox'	CRos EWes LRHS NRHS
- 'Schneeball'	IVic
- Sunset Group	SCob
- 'Wilgenbroek Select'	SCob
× ***nigercors***	ECha ECtt LHop SCob
- double-flowered (d)	LSou
- 'Emma'PBR	CBod CEnd CMil CRos ECtt LRHS LSun MHol NRHS SCob WCot
- 'HGC Green Corsican'	CRos EBee LRHS
- HGC Ice Breaker Fancy = 'Hlr 820'	CRos EBee LRHS NRHS SHil
- HGC Ice Breaker Max = 'Coseh 750'PBR	CRos EBee EPfP LRHS MAsh NRHS SHil
- HGC Ice Breaker Pico = 'Coseh 840'	ECre EPfP SHil
- 'Morning's Pride'PBR	EBee LRHS MMrt
- 'Pink Beauty'	CBod NLar SCob
× ***nigristern***	see *H.* × *ericsmithii*
odorus	GCal IFoB MAsh MPhe SCob XEll XLum
- WM 0312 from Bosnia	MPhe
- WM 9415	MPhe
- WM 9728 from Hungary	MPhe
orientalis misapplied	see *H.* × *hybridus*
orientalis ambig.	CBar CTsd CWCL GKev GMcL MSCN MWat NPri SCob WHar WPtf
orientalis Lam.	CBcs EWes LRHS LSun MPhe MSwo NRHS XLum
§ - subsp. ***abchasicus***	CBro MAsh
§ - - Early Purple Group	CTri GCal MRav SRms
- subsp. ***guttatus*** misapplied	see *H.* × *hybridus* spotted
- subsp. ***guttatus*** (A. Braun & Sauer) B. Mathew	SRkn
- ***olympicus***	see *H. orientalis* Lam. subsp. *orientalis*
§ - subsp. ***orientalis***	GKev
'Pink Beauty'PBR	CBcs CEnd EPfP LPre LRHS NLar SLon SPoG WCot
purpurascens	GBuc GMaP IFoB LCro MAsh MRav MSCN NBir XEll
- WM 0815 from Romania	MPhe
- WM 9211 from Hungary	MPhe
- WM 9412	MPhe
(Rodney Davey Marbled Group) 'Anna's Red'	CRos EPfP GBin LCro LOPS LRHS MAsh MAvo MHol NRHS SDix SPoG WCot
- 'Penny's Pink'	CBcs CMil EPfP GBin LOPS LRHS LSRN MAsh MHol MJak NPnk NRHS SCob SPoG WCot WHil
× ***sahinii*** 'Winterbells'PBR	EBee LCro LRHS
'Silver Dollar'	EBee EPfP GKev GMcL LRHS LSRN NPnk SPer SPoG
(Spring Promise Series) 'SP Bridget'	SHil
- SP Conny = 'Hlr 160' PBR	EPfP LRHS NRHS SHil
- 'SP Frilly Kitty' **new**	SHil
- SP Mary Lou = 'Hlr 150'PBR	LRHS NRHS SHil
- 'SP Rachel' **new**	LRHS NRHS SHil
- 'SP Roxanne'	SHil
- 'SP Sally' **new**	SHil
- 'SP Tiffany' **new**	LRHS NRHS
× ***sternii***	CBcs CRos CSpe CTri ELan ENun EPed EPfP EWTr GKev GMaP LCro LRHS MBel MNrw MWat NEgg NLar NPri SCob SPoG WBrk WMoo WWtn

– Aberconwy strain	MAsh
– 'Ashwood Silver' new	MAsh
– Ashwood strain	MAsh NLar
– Blackthorn Group	ECre ELon EPfP EUJe IFoB LHop LRHS NPnk SWvt
– Blackthorn dwarf strain	CBod
– 'Boughton Beauty'	CLAP CMea ELan GBuc NPnk SCob
– pewter-flowered	CSpe
– 'Tom'	SCob
– 'Wilgenbroek'	SCob
thibetanus	CBro EFEx EWes GKev LAma MAsh MPhe WPnP
torquatus	CBro CTal GBuc MAsh MPhe XEll
– WM 0609 from Montenegro	MPhe
– WM 0617 from Serbia	MPhe
– WM 0620 from Montenegro	MPhe
– WM 9106 from Montenegro	GBuc MPhe
– WM 9820 from Bosnia	MPhe
– Caborn hybrids	LLWP
– 'Dido' (d)	WFar
– double-flowered, from Montenegro (d) WM 0620	MPhe
– – WM 0621	MPhe
– hybrids	CTal IFoB
– Party Dress Group	see *H.* × *hybridus* Party Dress Group
'Verboom Beauty'	CRos LCro LRHS NRHS
vesicarius	MAsh
viridis	GCal GPoy IFoB LRHS MAsh MHer SCob SRms XEll XLum
– WM 0444 from Italy	MPhe
– WM 1303 from Slovenia	MPhe
– WM 9723 from Italy	MPhe
– subsp. ***occidentalis***	CBro GKev MAsh
– – WM 1340 from Germany	MPhe
– – WM 1344 from Spain	MPhe
– – WM 9501 from Wales	MPhe
Walberton's Rosemary = 'Walhero'PBR	CRos EPfP LRHS MAsh NRHS SPoG
'Washfield Queen' (Queen Series)	CWCL
'White Beauty'PBR	EPfP LRHS NLar SCob SPoG WHil

Helminthotheca (*Asteraceae*)

§ ***echioides***	WHer

Helonias (*Melanthiaceae*)

bullata	EBee

Heloniopsis (*Melanthiaceae*)

acutifolia B&SWJ 218	EPot WCru
– B&SWJ 6817	WCru
– B&SWJ 6836	WCru
japonica	see *H. orientalis*
§ ***kawanoi***	EBee SKHP WCot WCru
koreana B&SWJ 4173	WCru
leucantha B&SWJ 11148	WCru
§ ***orientalis***	CBro CLAP CTal ECho GBuc GCal GKev LLHF WCru
– B&SWJ 6278	WCru
– B&SWJ 6327	WCru
– B&SWJ 6380 from Japan	WCru
– from Korea	EPfP SChF SKHP
– var. ***breviscapa***	EPfP GEdr LEdu SChF SMad WCru
– – B&SWJ 5635	WCru
– – B&SWJ 5873	WCru
– – B&SWJ 5938	WCru
– – 'A-so'	LEdu WCru
– 'Dark Single'	GEdr
– var. ***flavida*** B&SWJ 11400	CTal WCru
– – 'Snow White'	GEdr
– variegated (v)	WCru
– var. ***yakusimensis***	see *H. kawanoi*
tubiflora B&SWJ 822	WCot WCru
– 'Temple Blue'	CLAP EBee WCru
umbellata	CTal EBee EPfP LHop SKHP WMoo WSHC
– B&SWJ 1839	CLAP WCru
– B&SWJ 3732	CBct WCru
– B&SWJ 6836	WCru
– B&SWJ 6846	WCru
– B&SWJ 7117	WCru

Helwingia (*Helwingiaceae*)

chinensis	CBcs CCCN EBee ESwi EWld GBin LEdu MPie NLar SBrt SPoG WBor WPGP
– broad-leaved	EBee NLar SChF WPGP
– narrow-leaved	EBee ESwi
himalaica	CFil ESwi SBrt
japonica	CHGN EFEx EWld NLar
– broad-leaved	WPGP

Helxine see *Soleirolia*

Hemerocallis ✿ (*Hemerocallidaceae*)

from Gansu, China	MPhe
'A Bodacious Pattern' new	EStr
'Aabaa'	EWoo
'Aabachee'	CBgR
'Above the Clouds'	EWoo
'Absolute Treasure'	CFwr EStr SBrk
'Absolute Zero'	SBrk SPol
'Adah'	SDay
'Adamas'	CFwr
'Addie Branch Smith'	CWel SDay
'Adeline Goldner'	CFwr
'Adirondack Trust'	CFwr
'Admiral's Braid'	EWoo
'Adorable Tiger'	CFwr
'Adoration'	SPer
'Aerial Display' new	EStr
'Affair d'Amour' new	EStr
'Africa'	SPol
'African Chant'	ELan
'Age of Miracles'	SPol
'Ageless Beauty'	EStr SBrk
'Agnes Elpers'	WAul
'Ahoy Matey' new	EStr
'Ahoya'	CBgR SPol
'Alabama Jubilee'	WNHG
'Alabama Slammer' new	EStr
'Alabama Wildfire'	CFwr
'Alakazam'	EWoo
'Alan'	EAEE ECtt LRHS MRav
'Alaqua'	GBuc MBNS
'Alberene'	CFwr
'Alec Allen'	SBrk SDay
'Alexander the Great'	WHrl
'Alien Encounter'	SPol
'All American Baby'	EStr MBNS MSpe SBrk SPol
'All American Chief' ♀H6	EStr SBrk
'All American Eagle'	SPol
'All American Magic'	SPol
'All American Plum'	CWCL IBoy MBNS MSpe SPol WAul WHrl
'All American Tiger'	SDay
'All American Windmill'	CBgR CFwr EStr EWoo
'All Creation Sings'	CFwr
'All Fired Up'	EStr SBrk SDay SPol

'All I Want for Christmas'	CFwr
'All the Magic'	SDay
'Allegiance'	WNHG
'Alli Sheldon'	ECha
'Alluring Peach'	EStr
'Almost Paradise'	SPol
'Alpine Rhapsody'	SPol
'Alternate Universe'	CFwr
altissima	MNrw SDix SPhx XLum XSen
'Always Afternoon' ♀H6	CBgR CKel EStr EWoo GBuc MBNS MNrw SBrk SPol WCAu WHrl XSen
'Amadeus'	EStr GBuc SCob
'Amazon Amethyst'	WCAu
'Ambassador'	CBgR
'Amber Classic'	ELon
'American Freedom'	EWoo
'American Revolution'	CBgR CBod CCVN CPar CRos CSpe ELon EStr EWoo GBin IPot LLWG LRHS LSun MBNS MHol MWat NChi NRHS SDys SPoG SPol WAul WCot WHrl WMoo WPnP XLum XSen
'Amerstone Amethyst Jewel'	SPol
'Amethyst Island'	CFwr
'Amethyst Squid'	EWoo
'Among Us'	CFwr
'Amy Michelle' (d)	EStr
'Amy's Rainbow' **new**	EStr
'Anatomically Correct'	EWoo
'Andrew Christian'	SPol
'Android'	CFwr
'Andy Candy'	CWel
'Andy Warhol's Hair'	CFwr
'Angel Artistry'	SDay
'Angel Rodgers'	EStr
'Angels Gather Around' **new**	CWel
'Angelus Runaway' **new**	EStr
'Aniakchak'	EWoo
'Ann Kelley'	SBrk
'Anna Warner'	ELon MMuc SEND
'Annabelle's Ghost'	CBgR SPol
'Annie Welch'	ELon EPfP MBNS NBre
'Answering Angels'	CFwr
'Antarctica'	SPol
'Antique Lavender'	WCAu
'Antique Rose'	CKel EStr
'Anzac'	CBro CTsd ECha ECtt IBoy LRHS MBNS NGdn SWvt WMoo
'Apache Bandana'	EWoo
'Apache Beacon'	EWoo
'Apache Uprising'	SDay
'Apollo'	XSen
'Apple Court Chablis'	EStr SPol
'Apple Court Champagne'	SPol
'Apple Court Damson'	EStr SPol
'Apple Court Ruby'	SPol
'Apple Of My Eye'	EWoo
'Apple Swirl'	CFwr EStr SPol
'Applique'	CFwr EStr
'Après Moi'	MBNS
'Apricot Beauty' (d)	MBNS
'Apricot Velvet'	CBgR
'Apricotta'	WCot WPnP
'April Fools'	EStr
'Apron Strings'	CFwr
'Aquadisiac' **new**	CWel
'Aquamarine'	SDay
'Aquarelle'	EStr
'Arabian Magic' **new**	EStr
'Arachnephobia'	EWoo
'Arctic Lace' **new**	CWel
'Arctic Snow' ♀H6	CBgR CBro CMac CRos ECrc ECtt ELon EStr EWoo GKev LRHS MBNS MNrw NNys SBrk SCob SPol WAul WPnP
'Armed and Dangerous'	CFwr
'Arms to Heaven'	CWel EWoo
'Arpeggio'	EStr SDay
'Arriba'	NBro
'Art Gallery Quilling'	EStr
'Arthur Moore'	SDay
'As You Wish'	CFwr
'Asian Artistry'	WNHG
'Asiatic Pheasant'	SPol
'Asterisk' ♀H6	EStr SDay
'Astolat'	EBee
'Astral Voyager'	CFwr
'Aten'	CBgR SBrk SDay
'Athlone'	EWoo
'Atlanta Bouquet'	SDay
'Atlanta Cover Girl'	SDay
'Atlanta Fringe Benefit'	SDay
'Atlas' **new**	WGwG
'Augenstern' **new**	EStr
'August Frost' ♀H6	EStr SDay SPol
'August Morn'	CBgR
'Aunt Wimp'	EWoo
'Authur Vincent'	SPol
'Autumn Jewels'	CFwr CWel EWoo SPol
'Autumn Minaret'	EStr EWoo
'Autumn Prince'	EWoo
'Autumn Red'	CBcs CBgR EStr GKin MBNS MMuc MNrw NBir SEND SPol WCot
'Autumn Wood'	CFwr
'Ava Michelle'	SDay
'Avant Garde'	SPol WCAu
'Avon Crystal Rose'	WNHG
'Awakening Dream'	SDay
'Awakening Spirit'	CFwr
'Awash With Color'	EStr SDay
'Awesome Blossom'	CWel EStr LSou MBNS MNrw SPol
'Awesome Candy'	EWoo
'Aztec Firebird'	CFwr EWoo
'Aztec Furnace'	EStr SDay
'Aztec Gold'	EStr
'Baby Betsy'	EStr
'Baby Blues'	SDay SPol
'Baby Red Eyes'	EStr WFar
'Baja'	WFar
'Bald Eagle'	EStr MNrw
'Bali Hai'	EStr MBNS SRms WHrl
'Bali Watercolor' **new**	EStr
'Ballerina Girl'	EStr
'Bama Bound'	EStr
'Bamboo Blackie'	CBgR EWoo SPol XSen
'Banana Cream Beauty'	SDeJ
'Banana Man'	EStr
'Banbury Cinnamon'	MBNS
'Bandit Man'	EStr
'Banned in Boston'	EWoo
'Barbara Dittmer'	SPol
'Barbara Mitchell'	EStr EWoo GBuc MBNS SDeJ WCAu WNHG XSen
'Barbaresco'	SPol
'Barbarian Princess'	CFwr
'Barbary Corsair'	CWel EStr SDay
'Bark At Me'	CFwr
'Barn Owl' **new**	CWel
'Barnegat Orange Twister'	CFwr
'Baronet's Badge'	SPol
'Baroni'	ECha

'Bas Relief' **new**	EStr
'Bat Masterson' **new**	CWel
'Bat Signal'	EWoo SPol
'Bathsheba'	SPol
'Bayou Bride'	SDay
'Bea'	EStr
'Beat the Barons'	SBrk SPol
'Beautiful Design' **new**	EStr
'Beautiful Edgings'	EStr SBrk SPol
'Beauty to Behold' ♀H6	CWel SBrk SDay
'Becky Lynn'	CWel ECtt EStr MBNS
'Bed of Roses'	EStr
'Before Night Falls'	CFwr
'Beijing'	SDay
'Bela Lugosi'	CBgR CMac CRos ECrc ELon EPfP EStr EWoo GQue LRHS LSRN LSun MBNS MCot MNrw NBro NChi NEgg NQui NRHS SCob SDay SMad SPer SPol WCot WHrl WNHG
'Believe It'	WNHG
'Belly Button Slipknots' **new**	EStr
'Beloved Deceiver' **new**	SDay
'Ben Adams'	SDay
'Ben Bachman' **new**	SBrk
'Ben Webster'	CFwr
'Benchmark'	SDay WHrl
'Bengal Bay'	EWoo
'Bengal Fire'	WNHG
'Berlin Oxblood'	WAul
'Berlin Red'	CBod CWCL CWel ECha ELon MNrw SDay WFar
'Berlin Tallboy'	CWel SBrk SDay WAul
'Berlin Watermelon'	MBNS
'Berliner Premiere'	EStr
'Berry Blitz'	EStr
'Berrylicious'	EPfP
'Bertie Ferris'	CWel EStr EWoo NLar SDay
'Beside Myself'	CFwr
'Bess Ross'	XSen
'Best Kept Secret'	EWoo SPol
'Best Seller'	EStr WCAu
'Bette Davis Eyes'	CBgR CWat EStr SDay SPol
'Betts Allen'	EStr
'Betty Jenkins'	EStr
'Bettylen'	EStr
'Betty's Pick'	EWoo
'Beware the Wizard'	CFwr
'Beyond Borders' **new**	CWel
'Bicolor Beautiful'	CFwr
'Big Apple'	EStr SBrk SDay SPol
'Big Bird'	CWel EStr EWoo MBNS SBrk SDay
'Big Blue'	EStr
'Big City Eye'	CWel MBNS
'Big Kiss' (d)	SPol
'Big Ogeeche' **new**	EStr
'Big Ross'	CFwr
'Big Smile'	CWGN MBNS MNrw SBrk SDeJ
'Big Snowbird'	SDay
'Big Time Happy'	LRHS MBNS SBrk SCob SPoG STPC WHar
'Big World'	CBgR
'Bigcabin Neon Beacon'	CFwr
'Bill Norris'	SPol
'Bird Bath Pink'	SPol
'Birdwing Butterfly'	CWel SPol
'Bite the Bullet'	CFwr
'Bitsy'	ELon SCob WCot WRHF
'Black Adder'	SDay
'Black Ambrosia'	CWel EStr SDay SPol
'Black Arrowhead'	CFwr EStr SPol WCAu

'Black Emanuelle'	IKil LSun MBNS MNrw NLar
'Black Eye'	SDay WNHG
'Black Eyed Stella'	CKel MBNS WCot
'Black Eyed Susan'	ECtt EStr MBNS SBrk
'Black Falcon Ritual'	CFwr
'Black Friar'	EWoo
'Black Ice'	EWoo SPol
'Black Knight'	EWoo NLar SRms
'Black Magic'	CBod CBro CTri EAEE ELan EPfP GBin GKin GMaP LHop LRHS LSRN MHer MRav NBir NEgg NGdn SPer WHer WHrl WMoo WNHG
'Black Plush'	EWoo SPol
'Black Prince'	CBgR EShb EWoo IBoy MBNS NBre NBro WAul
'Black Stockings'	EBee ELon EStr EWes SCob SDeJ
'Blackberries and Cream'	EStr
'Blackberry Candy'	CSam EAEE ECtt GKin MBNS MNrw MSpe NHol NWad SBrk
'Blackberry Sherbert'	WFar
'Blackeye Belle'	EWoo
'Blacky' **new**	EStr
'Blazing Lamp Sticks' **new**	CWel
'Blessed Again'	SDay
'Blessing'	EStr SBrk SPol
'Blizzard Bay'	EStr SDay SPol
'Blonde is Beautiful'	SDay
'Blood Spot'	SDay
'Blue Beat'	CFwr
'Blue Haired Girl' **new**	CWel
'Blue Oasis' **new**	CWel
'Blue Sheen'	CBgR CMac ECtt GMaP MBNS WFar WHlf WMoo WRHF
'Blueberry Breakfast' **new**	WNHG
'Blueberry Candy'	ECtt EStr IBoy ILea MBNS SBrk
'Blueberry Cream'	ELon MBNS MMrt MNrw
'Blueberry Frost'	CBgR
'Blueberry Sundae'	CWat EBee
'Blue-eyed Butterfly'	SPol
'Blushing Belle'	MBNS NBro NEgg
'Blutorange'	CFwr
'Bobby Martin'	CFwr
'Bobby's Lavender Eyes'	EStr
'Bobo Anne'	EStr
'Body Rub'	CFwr
'Bogie and Becall'	SPol
'Bohemian Rhapsody' **new**	EStr
'Bold Courtier'	CBgR
'Bold One'	SPol
'Bold Ruler'	SPol
'Bonanza'	Widely available
'Bone China'	WNHG
'Boney Maroney'	CBgR CFwr EWoo SBrk
'Bonibrae Blue-eyed Baby' **new**	EStr
'Bonnie Boy'	XLum XSen
'Bonnie Holley'	CFwr
'Booger'	SDay
'Boogie my Woogie Baby'	CFwr EWoo
'Booroobin Magic'	EStr EWoo
'Border Baby'	ECtt SBrk
'Border Lord'	EStr EWoo
'Border Music'	EStr
'Borgia Queen'	SDay
'Both Sides Now'	ECtt
'Bourbon Kings'	GNew MBNS MSpe SDeJ WHrl WWtn
'Bowl of Cream' **new**	EStr
'Bowl of Roses'	EStr
'Bradley Bernard'	SPol
'Brass Buckles'	see *H.* 'Puddin'

'Brasstown'	SPol
'Brazilian Orange'	XSen
'Breath of Blue Air' **new**	EStr
'Breed Apart'	CFwr SPol
'Brenda Newbold'	EStr SDay SPol
'Brer Rabbit's Baby'	EWoo
'Bridget'	ELan
'Bright Beacon'	CWel SPol
'Bright Island'	XSen
'Bright Side'	CBgR
'Bright Spangles'	MSpe SDay WAul
'Brilliant Circle'	ECtt
'Bring It On'	CFwr
'Broadway Bold Eyes'	SPol
'Broadway Valentine'	XSen
'Brocaded Gown'	ELan SDay
'Brooklyn Twist'	EStr
'Brother Cal'	CFwr
'Brown Billows'	EWoo
'Brown Exotica'	CFwr
'Brown Witch'	EWoo
'Brown-Eyed Girl'	SPol
'Browns Ferry Royalty' **new**	EStr
'Bruce'	EStr
'Brushed with Bronze'	SPol
'Brutus'	WHrl
'Bubbling Brown Sugar'	EStr MSpe
'Bubbly'	SDay
'Bud Producer'	CBgR SPol
'Buenos Aires'	XSen
'Buffys Doll'	EStr MBNS SDay
'Bug's Hug'	EStr
'Bumble Bee'	ECtt EStr MBNS NBre
'Bumble Bee Boogie'	CFwr
'Bunny Puff'	EStr
'Burgundy Baroness'	EStr
'Burgundy Love' **new**	EStr
'Burlesque'	SDay SPol WCot
'Burning Daylight' 🏆^{H7}	CAby CBgR EAEE EBee ECtt EPfP EStr LRHS MNrw MRav NEgg SCob SPer SRms WAul WCAu WCFE WCot WFar WPtf
'Burning Inheritance'	SDay
'Burnished Ruffles'	EStr
'Bus Stop'	SPol
'Buster Ruster'	CFwr
'Butterfly Charm'	SDay
'Butterpat'	SDay
'Butterscotch'	WFar
'Butterscotch Ruffles'	SDay
'Buzz Bomb'	ECGP ECrc ECtt EStr GKin LRHS LSRN MBNS MCot NEgg NGdn SPer WFar
'By Myself'	XSen
'Byzantine Emperor' **new**	LRHS NRHS
'Caballero'	EStr
'Cabbage Flower'	SDay XSen
'Cabriolet'	XSen
'Cajun Gambler'	EStr
'Cake Plate'	CFwr
'Calgary Stampede'	EStr
'Calico Jack'	EStr SBrk SPad
'Calico Spider'	EStr SBrk SPol XSen
'California Sunshine'	SBrk SPol
'Caliph's Robes'	SDay
'Call Girl'	SDay
'Calypso'	EWoo
'Camden Ballerina'	SDay
'Camden Gold Dollar'	SBrk SDay
'Camelot Green'	WNHG
'Cameroons'	SPol
'Campfire Embers'	EStr
'Canadian Border Patrol'	EStr MBNS MNrw NLar SPer SPol WHrl
'Canary Chaos'	EStr
'Canary Glow'	CTri IBoy WFar
'Canary Wings'	CBgR
'Candide'	SDay
'Candied Popcorn Perfection'	CFwr
'Candor'	SDay
'Candy Cane Dreams'	CFwr
'Canopy of Heaven'	SPol
'Cantique'	SDay SPol
'Cape Breton'	EBee EStr
'Capernaum Cocktail'	SPol
'Capulina'	EWoo
'Cara Mia'	CBgR EStr MBNS NBir SPol WFar
'Caramba'	CBgR
'Cardinal Explosion'	CFwr
'Caribbean Frank League' **new**	SDay
'Caribbean Jack Dolan'	EWoo
'Caribbean Purple Spires'	EStr
'Carlotta'	SDay
'Carmen Marie'	XSen
'Carmine Monarch'	EStr
'Carnival in Mexico'	CFwr
'Carnival Mask'	CFwr
'Carolicolossal'	SDay SPol
'Carolina Cool Down' **new**	EStr
'Carolina Cranberry'	ELan
'Carolina Dynamite'	CFwr
'Carolina Lemon Squeezer' **new**	EStr
'Carolina Low Country'	CFwr
'Carolina Red Bug'	CFwr
'Caroline Taylor'	WHrl
'Carousel Princess'	LRHS
'Carrick Wildon'	CFwr EBee WFar
'Carrot'	SDay
'Cartwheels'	EAEE ECha EPfP EShb EStr GBuc GKin GMaP LRHS MBNS MBel MRav NBro SPer WCAu WFar WMoo
'Carved Initials'	CFwr
'Carved Pumpkin Pie'	CFwr
'Casa des Juan'	CFwr
'Casino Gold'	SDay
'Castile'	SDay
'Castle Pinkney'	CFwr
'Castle Strawberry Delight'	SPol
'Cat Dancer' 🏆^{H6}	EStr
'Catapult Sam'	CFwr
'Catch a Falling Star'	CFwr
'Catherine Neal'	EStr SPol
'Catherine Woodbery'	Widely available
'Cathy Cute Legs'	CFwr
'Cathy's Sunset'	CKel CSam ECtt GKin LRHS LSRN MBNS MSpe NBro NGdn NWad SRGP
'Cause for Pause'	EStr
'Caviar'	SDay
'Cayenne' 🏆^{H6}	SPol
'Cedar Waxwing'	MNrw
'Celery Plate'	CFwr
'Celtic Christmas'	CFwr SPol
'Cenla Crepe Myrtle'	EWoo
'Cerulean Star'	CWel EWoo SPol
'Cerulean Warbler'	EStr

'Challenger'	EWoo
'Chamonix'	XSen
'Chance Encounter'	EStr LRHS MBNS NHol SPol WCAu
'Chang Dynasty'	CFwr
'Changing Latitudes'	SPol WHrl
'Chantilly'	EStr
'Charlene Moore'	SPol
'Charles Johnston'	CBgR CKel EPfP EStr EWoo MBNS SDay
'Charlie Pierce Memorial'	EStr SDay SPol
'Charon the Ferryman'	CFwr SPol
'Chartwell'	EWoo
'Chasing Shadows' **new**	CWel
'Chasing the Sun'	CFwr
'Checkerboard Curls'	CFwr
'Cheerful Note'	WNHG
'Cherokee Patterns'	SPol
'Cherokee Star'	EStr
'Cherokee Vision'	CFwr
'Cherry Cheeks'	CWel ECtt ELan ELon LRHS MBNS MHol MNrw MRav SBrk SPol WCAu WCot WFar WMoo WWtn
'Cherry Eyed Pumpkin' ♀H6	EStr EWoo SBrk SDay SPol WCAu
'Cherry Kiss'	IVic
'Cherry Lace'	XSen
'Cherry Tiger'	EStr MBNS
'Cherry Valentine'	CBcs CWel ELon GWyn MBNS SPad
'Cherrystone'	EStr
'Chesapeake Crablegs'	CFwr
'Chesières Lunar Moth'	CBgR ELon SPol
'Chester Cyclone'	SDay
'Chestnut Mountain' **new**	SDay
'Chevron Spider'	EStr
'Chicago Antique Tapestry'	SDay
'Chicago Apache'	CWel EBee ELon EPfP EStr EWoo LLWG MBNS NBir SBrk SDay SPer SPol
'Chicago Aztec'	ELon
'Chicago Blackout'	ECtt WAul WCot
'Chicago Cherry'	WNHG
'Chicago Fire'	EBee EPfP MBNS SDay
'Chicago Firecracker'	XLum XSen
'Chicago Heirloom'	MBNS WCAu
'Chicago Jewel'	ELon NSti
'Chicago Knobby'	EBee EStr MBNS MNrw SDay
'Chicago Knockout'	ELan EPfP EWoo WAul
'Chicago Mist'	WNHG
'Chicago Peach'	NBir WCAu
'Chicago Petticoats'	WFar
'Chicago Picotee Memories'	EBee MBNS
'Chicago Picotee Promise'	WNHG
'Chicago Princess'	EWoo
'Chicago Queen'	SDay WNHG
'Chicago Rainbow'	CBgR MBNS
'Chicago Royal Crown'	EAEE ECtt
'Chicago Royal Robe'	CWCL ELon GNew MBNS NBid SDay SPer SRms SWat WCot WWtn
'Chicago Silver'	MBNS SDay WAul
'Chicago Star'	WNHG
'Chicago Sugarplum'	SDay
'Chicago Sunrise'	CBgR CRos EAEE ELon GMaP IBoy LRHS MBNS MRav NGdn SBrk SDay SPol SWvt WCot
'Chick Flick' **new**	EStr
'Chicken Coop Madonna' **new**	EStr
'Chief Four Fingers'	EWoo
'Chief Sequoia'	EStr
'Children's Festival'	CMac EAEE ECtt EStr GMaP LRHS MBNS MRav NLar SWvt WFar WMoo
'China Bride'	EStr EWoo SCob SPol
'China Lake'	SDay
'Chinese Autumn'	CWel EStr
'Chinese Cloisonne'	EStr
'Chinese Coral'	EWoo
'Chinese Imp'	NLar SDay
'Chinese New Year'	EStr
'Chinese Temple Flower'	SDay
'Chocolate Candy'	CWGN EPfP IPot MBNS
'Chocolate Splash' **new**	SDay
'Choctaw Chick'	CFwr
'Chokecherry Mountain'	EStr EWoo
'Chorus Line'	SDay SPol WNHG
'Chorus Line Kid'	SPol
'Chosen Ruler' **new**	CWel
'Christina's Pink Parasol'	EStr
'Christine Lynn'	WNHG
'Christine Walser-Hite'	CFwr
'Christmas in Oz'	CFwr
'Christmas Is'	CBgR CMac CPar CWGN CWel EAEE EBee ECtt ELon EStr GBin GKin GMcL LPot LRHS LSou MBNS MBel NHol SPol WAul WCot WHrl XSen
'Christmas Ornament' **new**	EStr
'Christmas Wishes'	EStr
'Château Lafite'	SPol
'Church and Wellesley' (d)	CFwr
'Ciara Marie'	CFwr
'Ciarra Vonnie'	SDay
'Cimarron Knight'	CBgR EWoo SBrk SPol WCAu
'Cinderella Sue'	CFwr
'Cindy's Eye'	EStr WCot
'Cindy's Tie Dye' **new**	CWel
'Cinnamon Sunrise'	EStr
'Circle of Beauty'	SBrk SPol
'Circle of Friends'	CFwr
'Circles and Stripes'	CWel
citrina ♀H6	CBgR CHid CMac EBee EStr EWTr EWoo GKev GNew IBoy IMou LRHS MCot WCot WHrl WRHF XLum XSen
citrina × (× ***ochroleuca***)	WCot
'Civil Law'	SDay
'Civil Rights'	SDay
'Classic Caper'	WNHG
'Classic Edge' **new**	SDay
'Claudine'	ELon
'Claudine's Charm' **new**	CWel
'Cleo'	EWoo WHrl
'Cleopatra'	ELon EWoo SDay SPol
'Clothed in Glory'	CWel EStr EWoo MBNS WCot
'Coach's Hot Lips'	CFwr
'Coburg Fright Wig'	EWoo
'Cocktail Party'	EStr
'Colonel Joe'	EWoo
'Color Flash'	CFwr
'Comanche Eyes'	SDay
'Comet Flash'	SPol
'Coming Up Roses'	CPar ELon
'Concorde Nelson'	CFwr
'Condilla' (d) ♀H6	CWel EStr SDay SPol
'Connie Abel'	CFwr
'Connie Can't Have It'	CFwr
'Conspicua'	CBgR SMHy SPol
'Contessa'	CBro EAEE LRHS
'Cool It'	CKel CWel LHop LLWG MBNS MPie NLar SCob SDeJ WHrl
'Cool Jazz'	SDay SPol
'Cool Summer Breeze'	SPol
'Copper Dawn'	EStr NChi SPol

'Copper Windmill'	CBgR ELon EStr SDay SPol
'Copperhead'	EStr SPol
'Copperhead Road'	CFwr
'Coral Crab'	EWoo
'Coral Eye Shadow'	EWoo
'Coral Mist'	ECrc MBNS NBre
'Coral Sparkler'	WNHG
'Coral Spider'	SPol
'Corky'	CAby CBro ECGP ECha ELan EPfP GBin GBuc GCal GMaP GMcL LPot LRHS LSRN MBel MNrw MSpe NEgg NGdn NLar SCob SDix SPer SPhx SSut WAul WCAu WFar XLum XSen
'Cornwall'	EStr
'Corolla Light'	CFwr
'Corryton Pink'	SPol
'Cosmic Hummingbird'	ECtt EStr LRHS SDay
'Cosmopolitan'	ILea MBNS
'Country Club'	EBee GMaP MBNS SPol
'Country Melody'	SDay
'Court Cavalcade'	SBrk
'Court Magician'	EStr EWoo
'Court Troubadour'	SPol
'Coyote Moon'	EStr SDay
'Craig Green'	CFwr
'Cranberry Baby'	CWel ECtt EStr LRHS WHoo WNHG
'Cranberry Coulis'	CWat MBNS
'Crawleycrow'	XSen
'Crazy Crane'	CFwr
'Crazy Larry'	EStr
'Crazy Mr Jim' **new**	EStr
'Crazy Pierre'	EWoo SPol WHrl XSen
'Cream Drop'	ECtt EPPr GBuc GMaP IBoy LRHS MCot MHer MRav NBro NGdn NLar NSti SCob SPer WAul WCot WFar WHrl WMoo
'Creation'	CFwr EWoo
'Cricket Call'	CFwr
'Crimson Edgings' **new**	CWel
'Crimson Flood'	EWoo
'Crimson Icon'	SDay
'Crimson Pirate'	Widely available
'Crimson Wind'	EStr
'Crintonic Shadowlands'	SPol
'Cripple Creek'	CFwr EStr EWoo
'Croesus'	SRms
'Crooked House'	CFwr
'Cruise Control'	SPol
'Crystal Cupid'	XSen
'Crystal Pinot'	CWel ELon EStr
'Cupid's Gold'	SDay
'Curls'	CBgR MBNS SDay
'Curly Brick Road'	SPol
'Curly Cinnamon Windmill' ♀H6	EStr SDay SPol
'Curly Rosy Posy'	EStr SDay
'Custard Candy' ♀H6	CBod CWCL CWGN ECtt EPfP EStr EWoo GKin MBNS NAst NHol SBrk WCAu WNHG
'Cute As Can Be'	EStr
'Cynthia Mary'	ECtt GKin LHop MBNS SRGP
'Cypriana'	EBee XSen
'Czarina' **new**	EStr
'D.R. McKeithan'	CFwr
'Daddeeo Segrest'	EStr
'Dad's Best White'	EStr
'Daggy'	CWel SBrk
'Daily Dollar'	MBNS NGdn
'Dainty Pink'	WWtn
'Dallas Spider Time'	SDay
'Dallas Star'	EStr SDay SPol WHrl
'Dan Mahony'	EStr MBNS SBrk
'Dan Tau'	CKel SDay
'Dance Among the Stars'	CFwr
'Dance Ballerina Dance'	EBee SDay
'Dance with Somebody' **new**	EStr
'Dancing Crab'	CBgR EWoo SPol
'Dancing in the Rain' **new**	EStr
'Dancing on Ice' **new**	EStr
'Dancing Shiva'	SDay SPol
'Dancing Summerbird'	ELon EStr SBrk SPol
'Daring Deception'	CKel CWel ECtt ELon EPfP LLWG LRHS MBNS MNrw SBrk SCob SPad
'Daring Dilemma'	EStr SPol
'Daring Reflection'	SDay
'Darius'	WNHG
'Dark and Handsome'	MBNS
'Dark Avenger'	MBNS SBrk
'Dark Elf'	SDay
'Dark Magician'	EStr
'Dark Monkey'	CFwr
'Darker Shade'	EStr
'Darla Anita'	SBrk
'Darrell'	SDay
'Date Book'	EWoo
'David Holman'	WNHG
'David Kirchhoff'	EStr SDay
'Davidson Update'	WNHG
'Days of Joy' **new**	CWel
'Dazzling Spider'	CFwr
'De Colores'	EStr
'Dean Corey'	CFwr
'Debary Canary'	CWel EWoo
'Debussy'	EStr EWoo
'Decatur Ballerina'	WNHG
'Decatur Captivation'	WNHG
'Decatur Dictator'	WNHG
'Decatur Elevator'	EWoo
'Decatur Imp'	SDay WHrl
'Decatur Jewel'	WNHG
'Decatur Piecrust'	EStr
'Decatur Rhythm'	WNHG
'Decatur Supreme'	WNHG
'Decatur Treasure Chest'	WNHG
'Deep in My Heart'	CFwr
'Delayed Arrival'	CFwr
'Delicate Design'	SPol
'Delightsome'	SDay
'Deloris Gould'	SDay
'Demetrius'	CWat EStr
'Derrick Cane'	SPol
'Desdemona'	SPol XLum
'Desert Dreams'	WCot
'Desert Icicle'	CWel EStr EWoo SPol
'Designer Gown'	EStr SDay
'Designer Jeans'	EStr SDay SPol
'Designer Rhythm'	EStr
'Desirable Duchess'	EStr
'Destination Y'	XSen
'Destined to See'	CBcs CBro CCVN CPar CWel ECtt ELon EStr LHop LSou MBNS MHol MNrw NBir NBro NEgg SBrk SPad SPer SPol WCot WHrl
'Devil's Footprint'	SPol
'Devon Cream'	SPer
'Devonshire'	SDay
'Diabolique'	EWoo
'Diamond Dust'	CKel ECtt MBNS NLar SPer
'Diamonds and Ringlets'	CFwr

'Diamonds for Divas' **new**	CWel
'Diana Grenfell'	CBgR
'Dick Kitchingman'	CBgR SPol
'Dido'	CTri
'Dipped in Ink'	EStr SPol
'Distant Galaxy'	WCAu
'Distant Star'	EWoo
'Diva's Choice'	SCob
'Divertissment'	CBgR ELon EWoo SDay WHrl
'Dixie Rooster'	CFwr
'Dizzy Miss Lizzy'	CFwr
'Do the Twist'	EWoo
'Doc Holliday'	EStr
'Dominic'	CBgR CPar EWoo IBoy MSpe SDay SPol WCot WMoo
'Don Stevens'	WHrl
'Don's Wild Heather'	EStr
'Don't Know Jack'	CFwr
'Don't Mess with Me'	CFwr
'Dooty Owl'	CFwr
'Dorethe Louise'	CBgR SDay SPol
'Dorothy McDade'	EWoo MNrw
'Dot Paul'	ELan
'Double Action' (d)	SDay SPol
'Double Bold One' (d)	CWel SPol
'Double Charm' (d)	XSen
'Double Coffee' (d)	SPol
'Double Corsage' (d)	SPol
'Double Cream' (d)	WCot
'Double Cutie' (d)	EStr NLar SDay SRms
'Double Delicious' (d)	WCot
'Double Doubloon' (d)	XLum
'Double Dream' (d)	CWld EStr WHrl
'Double Firecracker' (d)	CCVN EBee MBNS MSpe NBro NLar SBrk XSen
'Double Gardenia' (d)	EStr WNHG
'Double Glitter' (d)	XSen
'Double Honey' (d)	EStr
'Double Oh Seven' (d)	ELon SPol
'Double Passion' (d)	MBNS
'Double Peach Schnapps' (d)	SBrk
'Double Pompon' (d)	EStr
'Double Pop Art' (d)	XSen
'Double Red Royal' (d)	EPfP EStr XSen
'Double River Wye' (d)	CBgR CWel ECtt EShb EStr IBoy LRHS MBNS MHer MNrw NGdn SBrk SPol SWat WAul WBrk WCot WFar WHoo WHrl
'Dowager Queen'	WNHG
'Dragon Dreams'	CWel SPol
'Dragon Heart'	EWoo
'Dragon King'	SDay SPol
'Dragon Lore'	EPfP EStr MBNS SBrk
'Dragon's Eye'	CWel EWoo SDay SPol WNHG
'Dragon's Orb'	CKel SDay
'Dream Baby'	NBre
'Dream Catcher'	CFwr EWoo
'Dream Keeper'	CFwr EWoo
'Dresden Doll'	SPer
'Driving Me Wild' **new**	SDay
'Droopy Drawers'	SPol
'Drop Cloth'	EStr
'Druid's Chant'	EWoo
'Drunken Sailor'	CFwr
'Duke of Durham'	EWoo MBNS MSpe
'Duke of Earl'	CBgR
dumortieri	CAgr CBro EBee ECha ELan MCoo MCot MMuc MRav NBid NBir NSti SCob SEND SPer WCot WHrl WWtn XSen
- B&SWJ 1283	WCru
'Dumpy'	EStr
'Dune Buggy'	XSen
'Dune Needlepoint'	EStr SPol WHrl
'Duplex' (d)	XSen
'Dutch Art'	SDay
'Dutch Artist' (d) **new**	EStr
'Dutch Beauty'	WFar
'Dutch Gold'	MHCG MNrw
'Earl of Warwick'	CBgR SPol
'Earlianna'	EStr SPol
'Earnest Yearwood'	SDay
'Earth Angel'	SPol
'Easter Star'	CFwr
'Easy Ned'	ELon EWoo SPol
'Easy Street'	SDay
'Eat Our Wake Pintaheads'	CFwr
'Ed Kirchhoff'	XLum
'Ed Murray'	EStr SBee SDay WAul WCAu WHrl
'Edgar Brown'	MBNS SPol WCot
'Edge Ahead'	CMac EAEE ECtt GKin GMcL LRHS MBNS NHol SBrk SDay WCAu WHrl
'Edge of Darkness'	CKel CWGN EPfP MBNS NSti WFar
'Edge of Frenzy'	CFwr
'Edith Vaughan'	EStr
'Edna Selman'	CFwr
'Edna Spalding'	EAEE LRHS SDay
'Eenie Allegro'	CBro ECtt MBNS SPer
'Eenie Fanfare'	MBNS NBir
'Eenie Weenie'	CBro ECtt ELon EStr GKev IBoy MBNS NBro SRms WOut WWtn
'Eenie Weenie Non-stop'	ECha EPPr
'Eggplant Electricity'	EWoo
'Eggplant Escapade' ♀H6	CBgR EStr MSpe SDay SPol
'Egyptian Ibis'	EWoo MSpe SPol WNHG
'Egyptian Queen'	CBgR
'Eight Miles High'	EStr SBrk
'Eighteen Karat'	EStr
'Einstein'	CFwr
'El Desperado'	CBgR CPar CRos CSam ECtt ELon EPfP EStr EWoo GBuc LRHS LSun MBNS MHol MNrw NEgg NRHS SBrk SPav SPol WCAu WCFE WCot
'El Glorioso'	CWat EStr
'Elaine Farrant'	SDay
'Elaine Strutt'	MBNS MNrw SDay SWvt WCot
'Electric Lemonade' **new**	CWel
'Electric Shocker'	CFwr
'Elegant Candy' ♀H6	CBgR CKel CMac CWel EStr EWoo MBNS SBrk
I 'Elegantissima'	SPol
'Eleonor'	EBee EPfP MBNS WFar
'Elfin Daydream'	SPol
'Elfin Illusion'	EStr
'Elijah Sain'	SPol
'Elizabeth Case'	EStr
'Elizabeth Salter'	CWCL CWel EStr MBNS NLar SPol
'Elmore James'	EWoo
'Eloquent Cay'	CFwr
'Eloquent Silence'	SDay
'Elva White Grow'	SDay
'Elves' Watermark'	SPol
'Emerald Dew'	SDay
'Emerald Eye'	SDay
'Emerald Lady'	SPol
'Emily Anne'	SPol
'Emily's Fiery Horse'	CFwr
'Emperor's Choice'	SDay
'Emperor's Dragon'	EStr SDay
'Enchanted April'	SPol

'Enchanted Forest'	EStr WCAu
'Enchanter's Spell'	SDay
'Enchanting Blessing'	EStr SDay
'Energizer Ty Howard'	CFwr
'English Cameo'	SPol
'Enigma Variations'	SPol
'Entrapment'	ECtt EStr IBoy MBNS SBrk SDeJ WFar
'Envoyé Spécial'	XSen
'Envy Me'	SPol
'Erica Nichole Gonzales'	SDay
'Erin Prairie'	EStr SPol
esculenta	SMad
'Etched Eyes'	CWel EWoo SPol
'Eternal Blessing'	SPol
'Etruscan Tomb'	EStr SPol
'Evelyn Claar'	CMac
'Evelyn Lela Stout'	SDay
'Even Stephen'	SPol
'Evening Enchantment'	EStr SDay
'Evening Gown'	SPol
'Ever So Ruffled'	EStr SDay
'Excellent' **new**	EStr
'Exotic Candy'	SPol
'Exotic Design'	CFwr
'Exotic Love'	SDay
'Exotic Star' **new**	EStr
'Exotic Treasure'	CWel EStr
'Exploded Pumpkin'	EBee EStr
'Eye Catching'	EWoo
'Eye of Round'	CFwr
'Eye of the Hurricane'	EStr
'Eye on America'	CWel EBee SBrk
'Eyelashes'	CFwr
'Eyes Right Jones'	CFwr
'Eyes Wide Shut'	CFwr CWel
'Eye-yi-yi'	SPol
'Ezekiel'	CWel SPol XSen
'Fabergé'	SDay
'Fabergé Easter' **new**	CWel
'Fabulous Prize'	SBrk
'Fairest Love'	EBee MBNS MNrw
'Fairest of Them'	CBgR CWel
'Fairy Charm'	SDay
'Fairy Finery'	SBrk
'Fairy Firecracker'	SPol
'Fairy Summerbird'	SDay SPol
'Fairy Tale Pink'	EStr SDay SPol
'Fairy Wings'	SPer
'Faith Nabor'	SPol
'Falcon'	SPol
'Fall Farewell'	WNHG
'Fall Guy'	SDay
'Fama'	EStr
'Fan Club'	CWel
'Fandango'	SPer
'Fantasia'	EWoo
'Farmer's Daughter'	CBgR EWoo SBrk
'Fashion Police'	CFwr
'Fat Lady Sings'	SPol
'Father James Foster'	EStr
'Father's Day Gift'	CFwr
'Fe, Fi, Foe, Fum'	CFwr
'Feather Down'	SPol
'Fellow'	EStr SPol
'Femme Osage'	EStr SDay
'Feria'	XSen
'Festive Art'	CWel SPol
'Fetish' **new**	CWel
'Fiestaville'	EStr
'Final Exams'	CFwr
'Final Touch'	CBgR EAEE EBee EStr MBNS MSwo NBro SBrk SPol
'Finders Keepers'	EBee EStr
'Fire and Fog'	EStr MBNS
'Fire and Wind'	CFwr
'Fire Bird Suite' **new**	CWel
'Fire Dance'	ELon
'Fire from Heaven'	WHrl
'Fire on the Mountain'	CFwr
'Fire Tree'	CBgR ELon EStr SPol
'Firestorm'	EStr EWoo SPol
'First Formal'	SPer
'First Knight'	CWel EStr SDay
'Fitzasaurus'	CFwr
'Flaming Firebird'	EStr
'Flaming Frolic'	SPol
'Flaming Sword'	WBrk WRHF
'Flamingo Dance'	CFwr
'Flamingo Lipstick'	CFwr
flava	see *H. lilioasphodelus*
'Florentine Silk' **new**	EStr
'Florida Sunshine' (d)	XSen
'Florissant Miss'	EStr
'Flower Basket' (d)	EStr
'Flower Pavilion'	SDay SPol
'Floyd Cove'	SDay
'Fly Catcher'	CBgR
'Flyaway Home'	SPol
'Flying Frisbee'	CFwr
'Flying Saucer'	EWoo
'Fol de Rol'	EWoo
'Fooled Me' ♀H6	CWel EBee ECtt EPfP EStr MBNS MSpe SBrk SDay SPad SPol
'Foolscap'	EWoo
'For the Good Times'	CFwr EWoo
'Forbidden Dreams'	EWoo
'Forest Phantom'	EStr
'Forestlake Ragamuffin'	SPol
'Forever Red'	EStr
'Forgotten Dreams'	EBee MBNS MSpe
forrestii	GKev
'Forsooth'	CBgR
'Forsyth Ace of Hearts'	CBgR
'Forsyth Evening Glow'	EStr
'Forsyth Flamboyant'	CFwr
'Forsyth Frostbound'	SPol
'Forsyth Mint Condition' **new**	CWel
'Forsyth Myra Dolores'	CFwr
'Forsyth Summer Snow' **new**	CWel
'Forsyth White Buds'	EStr
'Forsyth White Sentinel'	CFwr
'Forsyth Wrinkles and Crinkles'	CFwr
'Forty Second Street'	MBNS
'Fox Ears'	EWoo
'Foxhaven Enigma'	CFwr
'Fragrant Bouquet'	EStr
'Fragrant Pastel Cheers'	SDay
'Fragrant Returns' **new**	LEdu SPoG
'Fragrant Treasure'	CWld
'Frances Busby'	CFwr
'Frances Fay'	SPol
'Frances Joiner'	CWel EWoo
'Francis of Assisi'	EWoo
'Francois Verhaert'	EWoo SBrk
'Frank Gladney'	SPol XSen
'Frans Hals'	Widely available
'Fred Ham'	XSen

'Fred Manning'	CFwr
'Free Wheelin''	CWGN EPfP EStr SCob
'French Connection'	SDay
'French Lingerie'	EStr
'French Pavilion'	SDay
'French Porcelain'	SDay
'Fresh Air'	MNrw
'Frilly Bliss'	CFwr
'Fritz Schroer'	CBgR
'Frosted Encore'	SDay
'Frosted Pink Ice'	SPol
'Frosted Vintage Ruffles'	EBee EStr MNrw WCAu
'Frozen Jade'	SDay
'Fuchsia Beauty'	SPol
'Fuchsia Cockatoo'	CFwr
'Fuchsia Four'	SPol
'Full Grown'	EStr
fulva	CTri ELan GPSL LPot MMuc NBir SCob SEND SPol SRms WBrk WHrl XSen
- B&SWJ 8647	WCru
- 'Flore Pleno' (d)	CAvo CMac ECtt ELan GBin LHop MHer MJak MRav MSpe NBir NBro NGdn NSti SMad SPav SPer SRms SWat WBrk WCAu WMoo XSen
- 'Green Kwanso' (d)	CBgR EBee ECGP ECha GMcL ITim LRHS WFar WPnP
- var. ***kwanso*** B&SWJ 6328	WCru
- 'Kwanso' ambig. (d)	EAEE LRHS SBrk
- var. ***littorea***	CMac XLum XSen
- var. ***rosea***	LPla SPol WCot XSen
§ - 'Variegated Kwanso' (d/v)	CBro EBee EWoo GCra MRav NBir SCob SMad WBor WCot WFar WHer WHoo WHrl
- yellow-variegated (v)	WCot
'Fun Fling'	EStr SPol
'Funky Blues' **new**	CWel
'Funky Fuchsia'	SPol
'Future Whispers'	CFwr
'Gadsden Firefly'	CFwr
'Gadsden Goliath'	SPol
'Gadsden Light'	EStr SDay SPol
'Gala Greetings'	XSen
'Galaxy Ranger'	CFwr
'Gale Storm'	SPol WNHG
'Gamma Quadrant' **new**	SBrk
'Garden Crawler'	CBgR
'Garden Portrait'	EWoo SDay SPol
'Garrett Allen' **new**	EStr
'Gay Music'	MBNS
'Gay Octopus'	CBgR SPol WHrl
'Gay Rapture'	SPer
'Gay Troubadour'	EWoo
'Gemini'	SDay
'Geneva Firetruck'	CWel
'Gentle Country Breeze'	SBrk SDay SPol
'Gentle Rose'	EStr SDay
'Gentle Shepherd'	Widely available
'George Cunningham'	EAEE ECtt ELan LRHS MRav NBir SDay SPol WFar
'George David'	WHrl
'George Jets On'	SPol
'Georgette Belden'	EAEE ECGP ECtt GKin LRHS MBNS MSpe NHol SPol
'Georgia Cream' (d)	NLar
'Gerard Deschenes'	CFwr
'German Ballerina'	SPol
'Get All Excited'	ELon SPol
'Giant Moon'	CBgR EAEE ECtt ELan EStr LRHS MBNS SPer SRms WHal
'Giant on the Mountain'	CFwr
'Giddy Go Round'	EWoo SDay SPol
'Ginger Twist'	CFwr EStr
'Gingerbread Man'	MSpe
'Girouette'	XSen
'Give Me Eight'	SPol
'Glacier Bay'	CBgR EWoo MBNS
'Gladys Campbell' (d)	CFwr
'Glass Menagerie'	CFwr
'Glazed Heather Plum'	EStr
'Gleber's Top Cream'	EStr
'Gleeman Song'	CBgR
'Glittering Treasure'	XLum
'Glory in the Sunset'	CFwr
'Glowing Heart'	SDay
'Go Seminoles'	CFwr
'God's Handicraft'	EStr
'Going Bananas'PBR	WCot
'Gold Elephant'	SDay
'Gold Imperial'	NBre
'Golden Bell'	NGdn
'Golden Change'	CFwr
'Golden Chimes'	Widely available
'Golden Compass'	CWel EStr
'Golden Ginkgo'	WNHG
'Golden Marvel'	EWoo
'Golden Prize'	EWoo GQue NGdn SBrk SDay WCot XSen
'Golden Scroll'	SDay
Golden Zebra = 'Malja'PBR (v)	CLet CWGN CWel ELan EPfP GMcL IBoy MRav NSti SRms
'Golliwog'	CBgR EStr
'Gorgeous Smile' **new**	EStr
'Gothic Window'	SDay
'Graal'	XSen
'Grace and Favour'	SDay SPol
'Grace and Grandeur'	EWoo
'Graceful Eye'	SDay
'Graceland'	SDay WHrl
'Grand Masterpiece'	EStr NGdn SDay WFar
'Grand Palais'	CWel SDay
'Grandma Kissed Me'	SPol
'Granite City Towhead'	ELon
'Grape Arbor'	WNHG
'Grape Harvest'	WNHG
'Grape Magic'	MSpe WCot
'Grape Velvet'	CSpe CWel EStr EWoo ILea MHer NSti SDay SPol SRms WCAu WNHG WWtn
'Grapes of Wrath'	EStr
'Green Canary'	SPol
'Green Dolphin Street'	SDay SPol
'Green Dragon'	SDay SPol
'Green Eyed Lady'	SDay
'Green Eyes Wink'	MHol
'Green Flutter'	CBgR EBee EStr EWoo GCal GQue IMou LSRN MBNS NBir NGdn NSti SPhx SPol
'Green Fringe'	SDay
'Green Goddess'	XLum
'Green Lines'	EStr
'Green Mystique'	EBee EStr SBrk
'Green Nautilus'	EStr
'Green Puff'	NBir SDay
'Green Spider'	CBgR SDay
'Green Warrior'	EWoo
'Green Widow'	EWoo SDay
'Greenland'	ECtt EStr
'Grey Witch' ♀H6	SPol
'Greywoods Nautical Nellie'	CFwr
'Groovy Green'	CWel SDay

'Grumbly'	ELan WPnP
'Gryphon Prague Gothic' **new**	EStr
'Guadalajara' (d)	CFwr
'Guardian Angel'	WCFE
'Gwen Leman'	EStr
'Gypsy Cranberry'	SPol
'Gypsy Sweetheart' **new**	WNHG
'Hail Mary'	SDay
'Halloween Costume'	CFwr
'Halloween Masquerade' **new**	CWel
'Halloween Trick' **new**	CWel
'Hamlet'	SDay WNHG
'Happy Apache'	EStr
'Happy Returns'	CBgR CHid CSBt CTri EAEE ECha ELan EPfP EStr EWoo GBin GBuc LPot LRHS LSRN MBNS MBel NGdn NHol SRGP SRms WCAu XLum
'Harbor Blue'	CWel MSpe SDay
'Harrods'	EStr
'Harry Barras'	XLum
'Having Fun'	EStr
'Hawaiian Nights'	EWoo WNHG
'Hawk'	ELon SDay SPol
'Hazel'	EStr
'Heady Wine'	EStr SDay
'Heartbreak Ridge'	CFwr
'Heart's Glee'	XSen
'Heat Wave'	CFwr
'Heavenly Angel Ice'	CFwr EStr
'Heavenly Beginnings'	CFwr EStr
'Heavenly Curls'	SDay SPol
'Heavenly Dragon Fire'	CFwr
'Heavenly Fire Arrow'	CFwr
'Heavenly Flight of Angels'	CFwr EStr
'Heavenly Pink Butterfly'	EStr
'Heavenly Pink Fang'	EStr
'Heavenly Starfire'	CFwr EWoo SPol
'Heavenly Treasure'	SPol
'Heirloom Lace'	SDay WCAu
'Helen Shooter'	EStr
'Helena Seabird'	EStr
'Helix'	EStr SDay
'Helle Berlinerin'	SDay SPol
'Hello Screamer'	CFwr EStr
'Helter Skelter'	SDay SPol
'Henry D. Allnutt' **new**	EStr
'Hen's Teeth'	CFwr
'Her Majesty's Wizard'	CBgR ELan ELon EWoo IMou MBNS SBrk SPol
'Hermitage Newton'	SDay
'Heron's Cove'	EWoo
'Hesperus'	EWoo
'Hexagon'	EStr
'High Profile'	EStr
'High Tor'	ELon EStr GQui SDay SPol WHrl
'Highland Lord' (d)	EBee MBNS SDay WCAu XSen
'Hint of Blue'	SPol
'Hippie Chic'	CFwr
'Holiday Delight'	MBNS WNHG
'Holiday Mood'	ELan
'Holly Dancer' ♀H6	EStr EWoo SPol
'Homeward Bound'	SDay
'Honey Jubilee'	SPol
'Honey Redhead'	SPol
'Honeysuckle Rose' **new**	EStr
'Honor Flight' **new**	EStr
'Hope Diamond'	SDay
'Hornby Castle'	CBro EAEE LRHS

	'Hot Cakes'	EStr
	'Hot Chocolate' PBR	EBee GKev
	'Hot Pepper' **new**	EStr
	'Hot Pink Fury'	EStr
	'Hot Tamales and Red Hots'	EStr
	'Hot Town'	CWel ELan
	'Hot Wheels'	CBgR SBrk
	'Hot Wire'	SDay
	'Hotter than the Fourth of July'	CFwr
	'Houdini'	MSpe WCAu
	'House Music'	XSen
	'House of Bluelights'	SPol
	'House of Orange'	EStr SPol
	'Howlin' Wolf'	CFwr
I	'How's the Weather up There?'	CFwr EWoo
	'Hubbles Buddy'	EWoo
	'Huckleberry Candy'	SPol
	'Humdinger'	EStr SDay WCot
	'Hummingbird'	EStr
	'Hymn'	SDay
	'Hyperion'	CBgR CBod CMac CTri ECha ECtt ELon EShb EStr EWoo GKin GMcL LEdu MHol MMuc MRav MSpe NBid NGdn SDay SEND SPer SWvt WCot WWtn
	'I Luv Lucy'	CFwr
	'Ice Carnival'	CKel ELon EStr MBNS NGdn NLar SCob SPol SWvt
	'Ice Castles'	CTri SDay
	'Icecap'	CBgR WMoo
	'Icy Lemon'	EStr SBrk SDay
	'Ida Duke Miles'	SBrk SDay
	'Ida Munson'	SDay
	'Ida's Magic'	EStr
	'Iditarod'	EStr
	'Ikebana Star'	EStr
	'Illini Jackpot'	SDay
	'Impromptu'	SDay
	'In Depth' (d)	EWoo MBNS NBro NLar WCot WHrl
	'In Her Shoes' **new**	EStr
	'In Search of Angels'	CFwr
	'In Strawberry Time'	WNHG
	'Inchon'	EStr
	'Indian Fandango'	EWoo
	'Indian Fires'	CFwr
	'Indian Giver'	SPol
	'Indian Paintbrush'	ELon EWoo NBir SPol WNHG
	'Indigo Moon'	SPol XSen
	'Inimitable'	CFwr
	'Inky Fingers'	SPol
	'Inner View'	ECtt EStr EWoo MBNS SDay
	'Innocent Blush'	EStr
	'Inspired Word'	SDay
	'Instant Zéro'	XSen
	'Intelligent Design'	CFwr
	'Intertwined Entity'	CFwr
	'Invitation to Immortality'	EWoo
	'Iowa Greenery'	SPol
	'Iridescent Jewel'	SDay
	'Irish Elf'	EBee ELon GBin SDay SHar
	'Irish Handshake'	CFwr
	'Irish Veil' **new**	EStr
	'Iron Gate Glacier'	EBee EStr MBNS SDay XLum
	'Irresistible Charm'	EPfP
	'Isaac'	EStr
	'Isabelle Rose'	SDay
	'Isle of Dreams'	SDay SPol
	'Isleworth'	EWoo

'Isolde'	CBgR EStr
'It's a Zinger' **new**	CWel
'Itsy Bitsy Spider'	CBgR CFwr EWoo
'Ivelyn Brown'	EStr SDay SPol
'Ivory Cloud' (d)	EStr
'Ivory Coast'	SDay
'J.T. Davis' **new**	EStr
'Jabo'	SPol
'Jack Sprat'	CFwr
'Jake Russell'	MBNS
'Jalapeno Pepper'	CFwr
'Jam All Night'	CFwr
'Jamaican Jammin''	SPol
'Jamaican Magic'	CFwr
'Jamaican Me Crazy' ♀H6	CWel SBrk
'Jamaican Midnight' **new**	CWel
'James Clark'	EWoo
'James Marsh'	CBgR EWes EWoo MBNS MNrw MSpe NSti WCAu WCot WFar WNHG
'Jammin' with Jane'	CFwr
'Jane Trimmer' **new**	CWel
'Janet Gordon'	SPol
'Janice Brown'	CKel CWCL ECtt EStr EWoo LRHS LSou MBNS NHol NLar SBrk SDay SPol WHrl
'Janie Wilson' **new**	WNHG
'Jan's Twister'	MNrw SDay SPol WHrl
'Jason Salter'	EStr SDay WAul
'Jay Turman'	SDay
'Jazz at the Wool Club'	CFwr
'Jean'	SDay
'Jean Swann'	EStr MBNS
'Jedi Dot Pierce'	EStr SBrk SDay
'Jelly Dancer'	SPol
'Jellyfish Jealousy' ♀H6	EStr EWoo
'Jenny Wren'	EPPr EWoo MBNS NBro SRGP WAul
'Jersey Breeze'	EStr
'Jersey Jim'	SPol
'Jersey Spider'	EWoo SDay SPol
'Jerusalem'	SBrk SDay
'Jesse James'	SPol
'Jeu de Piste'	XSen
'Jeune Tom'	CBgR
'Jewel Case'	WNHG
'Jim McKinney'	EStr
'Joan Derifield'	EStr
'Joan Senior'	Widely available
'Jockey Club' (d)	ECtt MBNS WHrl
'Joe Marinello'	SPol
'Jogolor'	EStr
'Johanna Klein Strack'	CFwr
'Johnny Come Lately'	EStr SPol
'Joie de Vivre'	EWoo
'Jolly Red Giant'	EWoo
'Jolyene Nichole'	SDay
'Jordan'	LSRN SWvt
'Josephine Marina'	EStr
'Journey to Oz'	EWoo
'Journey's End'	SDay
'Jovial'	EStr SDay
'Joy of Life'	CFwr
'Joyful Participation'	EStr
'Judah'	SBrk SPol
'Judge Roy Bean'	EStr EWoo SPol
'Julie Newmar' ♀H6	CWel
'June Explosion'	CFwr
'June Melody'	WNHG
'June Rose'	EStr
'Jungle Beauty'	CBgR SDay SPol
'Just Celebrate'	SDay
'Just Fabulous' **new**	CWel
'Just Kiss Me'	CWel SPol
'Just My Size'	EBee EStr
'Just Whistle'	EStr
'Justin Brent'	XSen
'Justin George'	SDay SPol
'Kachina Firecracker'	CFwr EWoo
'Kamadeva'	CFwr
'Kangaroo Pouch' **new**	CWel
'Kansas Kitten'	EWoo
'Karateake'	CFwr
'Karen's Curls' ♀H6	EWoo SPol
'Kasia'	WHrl
'Katahdin'	EWoo
'Kate Carpenter'	EStr SDay SPol
'Katherine Harris'	CFwr
'Kathleen Salter'	EStr EWoo SDay
'Kathryn June Wood'	EWoo
'Kathy Macartney'	EWoo
'Kathy's Cat Spooky'	CFwr
'Katie Elizabeth Miller'	SDay
'Kazuq'	SDay
'Keene'	EWoo
'Kelly's Girl'	SPol
'Kempion'	CBgR
'Kent's Favorite Two'	SBrk
'Kenyan Sun'	EWoo
'Kevin Michael Coyne'	SPol
'Key to my Heart'	CBgR
'Killarney Castle'	CFwr
'Killer Purple'	EStr
'Kimberly Sue'	EStr
'Kindly Light'	EWoo SPol
'King George'	EStr
'King Kahuna' (d)	EStr
'King of Anything' **new**	EStr
'King's Gold'	EStr
'King's Throne'	WNHG
'Kipling'	CFwr
'Kirsten My Love'	EStr
'Kiss Me Softly'	SBrk
'Kisses for Cinderella'	CFwr
'Klaatu Barada Nikto'	CFwr
'Knight Returns' **new**	CWel
'Knights in White Satin'	EStr SPol
'Kokopelli'	CFwr
'Krakatoa Lava'	CFwr
'Kristal Sunset'	CFwr CWel
'Kwanso Flore Pleno'	see *H. fulva* 'Green Kwanso'
'Kwanso Flore Pleno Variegata'	see *H. fulva* 'Variegated Kwanso'
'La Fenice'	EStr
'La Peche'	SDay
'Lacy Doily'	EStr LLHF WCAu
'Lacy Marionette'	ELon EWoo SDay SPol
'Lady Betty Fretz'	EBee EStr
'Lady Cynthia'	CKel
'Lady Fermor-Hesketh'	EStr
'Lady Fingers'	CBgR SPol
'Lady Grace' **new**	CWel
'Lady Inara'	EStr
'Lady Liz'	SDay SPol WNHG
'Lady Mischief'	EStr SDay
'Lady Neva' ♀H6	CBgR ELon EWoo SBrk
'Lady Tiger'	WNHG
'Ladybug's Two Moons' (d)	EStr
'Ladykin'	CWel ELon SPol
'Lake Effect'	EWoo
'Lake Norman Spider'	EWoo SPol

'Lamar'	CFwr
'Lambada'	EStr
'Land of Cotton'	XSen
'Land of Enchantment'	CFwr
'Land's End'	EStr
'Lark Song'	EAEE LRHS WFar WHrl
'Last Song'	CFwr CWel
'Laughing Feather'	CFwr EWoo
'Laughing Giraffe'	EStr WCot
'Laughton Tower'	SMHy
'Laura Lambert'	SPol
'Lauradell'	SDay
'Lauren Leah'	SDay
'Laurena'	SPol
'Lavender Blue Baby'	CRos CWel EPfP LRHS NRHS SPer
'Lavender Bonanza'	SDay
'Lavender Cascades'	CFwr
'Lavender Deal'	MNrw WNHG
'Lavender Handlebars'	SDay
'Lavender Illusion'	CWel
'Lavender Light'	EWoo
'Lavender Memories'	EStr SDay
'Lavender Plicata'	SPol
'Lavender Showstopper'	WCAu
'Lavender Silver Cords'	SPol
'Lavender Spider'	CBgR SPol
'Lavender Tonic'	SPol WNHG
'Lavender Tutu'	EStr
'Layers of Gold' (d)	XSen
'Lazy Hazy Days' **new**	EStr
'Ledgewood's Cinnamon Lace'	CFwr
'Ledgewood's Firecracker'	CFwr
'Ledgewood's Gabrielle' **new**	CWel
'Ledgewood's Sunday Dessert' **new**	EStr
'Lee Reinke'	EStr SPol
'Leebea Orange Crush'	SBrk
'Legs Limmer'	CFwr EWoo
'Leila Mantle'	CBgR
'Lemon Bells'	CWat CWel EAEE ECGP ECha EPfP EStr EWoo GKev GKin GMaP LEdu LRHS MBNS NBro NCGa SHar WCAu
'Lemon Custard'	EStr
'Lemon Dessert'	ELon SBrk
'Lemon Fellow'	EWoo
'Lemon Fringed Pastel'	CFwr
'Lemon Madeline'	EStr EWoo
'Lemon Meringue Twist'	EWoo
'Lemonora'	SDay
'Lenox'	SBrk SDay
'Leonard Bernstein'	EStr EWoo SBrk SPol
'Leslie Renee'	CFwr CWel
'Let it Rip'	EWoo SPol
'Let Loose'	CFwr EStr
'Lexington Avenue'	SPol
'Licorice Candy'	CWel SBrk SPol
'Licorice Twist'	CFwr CWel
'Light of the World'	CFwr
'Light the Way'	CBod CRos GBin LLWG LRHS MHol NRHS SPoG WCot
'Light Years Away'	ELon MBNS MNrw
'Lilac Wine'	SCob
§ ***lilioasphodelus***	Widely available
'Lilly Dache'	EStr EWoo
'Lilting Belle'	SPol
'Lilting Lady'	EStr SPol
'Lilting Lavender'	ELon SPol WCAu
'Lime Frost' ♀H6	CBgR CWel EStr SPol
'Lime Painted Lady'	CBgR
'Limetree'	CBgR EStr
'Limited Edition'	EWoo
'Lin Wright'	EWoo
'Linda'	MRav
'Linda Agin'	EWoo
'Lines of Splendor'	EWoo
'Litchfield Plantation' **new**	EStr
'Little Audrey'	EStr
'Little Bee'	NBre
'Little Big Man'	SDay
'Little Bugger'	ELon
'Little Bumble Bee'	CRos LRHS MBNS NRHS WWtn
'Little Business'	MBNS SDay SPol
'Little Cadet'	XLum
'Little Carpet'	MBNS
'Little Cranberry Cove'	GBin
'Little Dart'	ECha
'Little Deeke'	CWel SDay WHrl
'Little Fantastic'	ELon LRHS SDay WWtn
'Little Fat Cat'	EStr
'Little Fat Dazzler'	SPol
'Little Fellow'	EStr MBNS
'Little Girl'	ELon
'Little Grapette'	EPfP ERCP EStr GCra GQue MBNS NLar NSti WAul WCAu WHar
'Little Greenie'	CWel SDay
'Little Gypsy Vagabond'	CBgR CWat EStr SPol
'Little Heavenly Angel'	EStr SPol
'Little Isaac'	EStr
'Little Judy'	SPol
'Little Kiki'	SDay
'Little Lassie'	CBgR
'Little Maggie'	SDay SPol
'Little Men'	WCAu
'Little Miss Manners'	EStr NLar
'Little Missy'	CBgR EPfP MBNS SDay WHoo WNHG
'Little Monica'	SDay
'Little Music Maker' (d)	EStr
'Little Paul' **new**	EStr
'Little Red Hen'	CSam EAEE ECGP GKin LRHS MBNS MSpe NBir NBro NEgg NGdn SDay WFar
'Little Sea Sprite' **new**	CWel
'Little Show Stopper'	EWoo MBNS NBro NLar
'Little Showoff'	SDay
'Little Swain'	SDay
'Little Tawny'	ELon LRHS
'Little Toddler'	SDay
'Little Violet Lace'	SDay
'Little Wart'	CBgR SDay WHrl
'Little Wine Cup'	CBod CMac CSam EAEE ECrc ECtt EPfP EStr GKin GMaP GMcL LRHS MRav NBir NEgg NGdn SPer SPol SRms WAul WMoo
'Little Women'	MBNS SDay
'Little Zinger'	SDay
'Littlest Angel'	SDay
'Littlest Clown'	SDay
'Living in Amsterdam'	EBee EStr
'Liz Schreiner'	CFwr
'Lizard's Purple Fashion'	CFwr
'Lobo Lucy'	ELon EStr
'Lochinvar'	CSam GBuc MRav
'Loco Bo'	EStr
'Lois Burns'	EWoo SDay SPol
'Lonesome Dove'	SPol
'Long John Silver'	ELon EStr
'Long Legged Lap Dancer'	CFwr
'Long Stocking'	EStr EWoo SPol WCot

'Long Tall Sally'	EStr
'Longfields Anwar'	EWoo
'Longfields Bandit'	EWoo
'Longfields Beauty'	EWoo MBNS SBrk
'Longfields × Factor'	EStr
'Longfields Glory'	MBNS MSpe NBre
'Longfields Maxim' (d)	EStr MBNS SDeJ
'Longfields Pride'	EStr IBoy MBNS SBrk SRms WBor
'Longfields Purple Eye'	NLar
'Longfields Think Pink'	EStr
'Longfields Tropica'	MBNS
'Longfields Twins'	MBNS WCot WFar
'Longfields Whoopy'	EPfP SCob
longituba AIK 284	WCot
- B&SWJ 4576	WCru
'Look at Me'	ELan
'Look Lucky'	CFwr
'Loose as a Goose'	CFwr
'Loose Reins'	CFwr
'Lori Goldston'	EWoo MBNS
'Lorita Wadsworth'	CFwr
'Loth Lorien'	CFwr
'Lots of Hoopla'	EStr
'Lotsa Dots'	CFwr
'Lotus Land'	SDay
'Louie the Lip'	CFwr
'Louis Burnes'	SPol
'Louis McHargue'	SDay
'Lourice Abdallah'	EStr
'Love Those Eyes'	CWel EStr
'Lovely Rita' **new**	EStr
'Lovin Up a Storm'	CFwr
'Loving Memories'	SDay
'Lowcountry Gem'	EStr SBrk
'Lucille Lennington'	WNHG
'Lucky Streak'	CFwr
'Lullaby Baby'	CWel ELan GCal MBNS NLar SDay SPol WNHG
'Luna'	SPol
'Luscious Honeydew'	WNHG
'Lusty Lealand'	MBNS SDay
'Luxury Lace'	CAgr EAEE EBee ECtt ELan EPfP EStr GBin GKin LSRN NBir NGdn NHol NWad SPer SPol WFar WHrl WMoo WWtn XLum XSen
'Lycean' **new**	CWel
'Lydia Bechtold'	EStr SDay
'Lyndell's First'	CFwr
'Lyndell's Peach Craze'	CFwr
'Lyndell's Purple Lady'	CFwr
'Lynn Hall'	MBNS NLar
'Lynn's Delight'	EStr
'Mabel Fuller'	CBgR MRav SPer WHrl
'Mabel Nolen' **new**	EStr
'Mable Lewis Nelson'	EStr
'Macbeth'	EStr MBNS
'Mad Max'	EStr EWoo SDay SPol
'Made from Scratch'	CFwr
'Madeline Nettles Eyes'	EBee EStr
'Madge Cayse'	CFwr
'Maestro Puccini'	SDay
'Maggie Fynboe'	CBgR SPol
'Magic Amethyst'	CBgR
'Magic Attraction'	CFwr
'Magic Carpet Ride'	EStr SBrk SPol
'Magic Dancer'	EStr
'Magic Lace'	EStr EWoo
'Magic Masquerade'	SDay
'Magic of Oz'	CWel
'Magical Messenger'	EStr
'Magnificent Eyes'	SPol
'Magnificent Rainbow'	CBcs
'Mahdi'	CFwr
'Mahogany Magic' ♀H6	ELon SBrk
'Majestic Dark Eyes'	EStr
'Malachite Prism'	CWGN EStr
'Malaysian Monarch'	EStr SBrk SDay WNHG
'Malaysian Spice'	WNHG
'Maleny Chantilly Lace'	EStr
'Maleny Debutante'	EStr
'Maleny Kiwi Dazzler' **new**	EStr
'Maleny Mite'	EWoo
'Maleny Piecrust'	EWoo
'Maleny Think Big'	CWel EWoo
'Mallard'	CAby CBgR EAEE ECGP ECtt EStr LLWP LRHS MBNS MRav NBir SPer SWat WCot
'Malmaison Plum'	EStr
'Mama Sohpia'	EStr
'Mambo Maid'	XSen
'Man on Fire'	MBNS WNHG
'Manchurian Apricot'	SDay
'Mandalay Bay Music'	EWoo
'Mansfield Plantation'	CFwr
'Marble Faun'	SDay
'Margaret McWhorter'	SPol
'Margaret Perry'	ECrc MNrw NLar
'Margaret Seawright'	EStr
'Margaret's Blue Diamond' **new**	CWel
'Margo Reed Indeed'	SPol
'Marietta Charmer'	SDay SPol
'Marietta Delight'	EStr
'Marilyn Lee Bock' **new**	CWel
'Marilyn Siwik'	EWoo
'Marion Caldwell'	SPol
'Marion Vaughn'	ECtt ELan EPfP EWoo GBuc GKin GMaP LHop LRHS MBel MRav NSti SBrk SDix SPer SRGP SWvt WCAu WCot WFar WHar WHoo WPtf WSHC
'Mariska'	EStr EWoo SBrk SDay WNHG
'Marked by Lydia'	CFwr ELon SPol
'Marmalade'	EBee EPfP
'Marse Connell'	MSpe
'Martha Adams'	SDay
'Martie Everest'	EWoo
'Martina Verhaert'	CWGN CWel EBee EStr
'Mary Alice Stokes'	EStr
'Mary Ethel Anderson'	EStr EWoo
'Mary Todd'	EBee GMcL MBNS XSen
'Mary's Gold' ♀H6	SBrk SDay SPol
'Masada' **new**	WNHG
'Mask of Time'	EStr
'Masquerade Show'	CFwr
'Mata Hari'	SDay SPol
'Matisse'	SPol
'Mauna Loa'	CSBt ELon EStr GQue MBNS MNrw NLar SDeJ SWvt WAul WCot
'May Colvin'	SBrk
'May May'	CBgR SPol
'Maya Cha Cha'	CFwr
'Mayan Poppy'	EStr
'Meadow Mist'	CBgR ELon WWtn
'Meadow Sprite'	WCot
'Meadowsweet'	EStr
'Medicine Feather'	EWoo
'Medieval Guild'	EStr
'Medusa's Glance'	EWoo
'Meerkat Manor'	CFwr
'Megatrend'	CFwr

'Mema's Dingaling'	EStr
'Mema's Dingbat'	CFwr
'MeMe's Guilty Pleasure' **new**	EStr
'Memories of Oz'	CFwr
'Mephistopheles'	CWel EWoo
'Merry Moppet'	EStr EWoo
'Merry Witch'	EStr
'Metaphor'	SDay XSen
'Michele Coe'	ECtt GKin MBNS NBro NEgg NGdn SDay SRGP WCAu WHrl WMoo
'Mico'	ELon
middendorffii	CMac EBee GMaP MCoo NSti WHrl WThu
'Midnight Dynamite'	MBNS SBrk
'Midnight Love'	EWoo
'Midnight Magic'	EWoo SDay
'Midnight Mantis'	SPol
'Midnight Raider'	EWoo
'Midnight Rambler' **new**	SDay
'Midnight Rendezvous'	EStr
'Mighty Highty Tighty'	CFwr
'Mikado'	CBgR CMac
'Mike Reed'	EStr
'Milady Greensleeves'	EStr EWoo SDay SPol WHrl
'Milanese Mango'	EStr EWoo
'Mildred Mitchell'	CBgR ELon EStr MBNS NLar SBrk SPol
'Military School'	EStr
'Millie Schlumpf'	CWel SPol
'Mimosa Umbrella'	EStr SPol
'Ming Lo'	SDay
'Ming Porcelain'	SBrk SPol WCAu WNHG
'Mini Pearl'	ECtt ELon EStr EWTr LRHS MBNS SDay SPer
'Mini Stella'	CBro ECtt MBNS SDay SHar WFar
miniature hybrids	SRms
'Minnie Wildfire'	EStr SPol
minor	CBro EBee EDAr EPPr EWTr GKev LRHS SRms XSen
- B&SWJ 8841	WCru
'Minstrel's Fire'	CFwr
'Mint Octopus' **new**	CWel
'Miracle Maid'	WNHG
'Miss Jessie'	EStr EWoo SPol WHrl
'Missenden'	CBgR MNrw
'Mississippi Blues' **new**	CWel
'Missouri Beauty'	IBoy MBNS SPol SWvt
'Missouri Memories'	SPol
'Mister Lucky'	CWel
'Misty Twisty'	CFwr
'Molokai' **new**	WHlf
'Moment in the Sun'	CFwr
'Moment of Truth'	EAEE NBre
'Monica Marie'	EStr SDay
'Mont Royal Demitasse'	ELon SPol
'Moon Music' **new**	CWel
'Moon Snow'	SDay
'Moon Witch'	EStr SDay SPol
'Moonlight Masquerade'	CBgR ECtt GBuc MMuc NLar SRms WOut
'Moonlight Mist'	SDay SPol
'Moonlight Orchid'	WHrl
'Moonlit Caress'	CBgR EBee ECtt MBNS NBro
'Moonlit Crystal'	EStr SPol
'Moonlit Masquerade' 🏆H6	CPar CWGN CWel EStr EWoo MBNS MBel MNrw SEND SHar SPer SPol WCAu WHrl
'Moonlit Summerbird'	EStr SDay SPol
'Moontraveller'	WCot
'Moose Man'	CFwr
'Morgen le Fay'	EStr SPol
'Mormon Spider'	EStr SPol
'Morning Sun'	MBNS WCot
'Morocco'	SPol
'Morocco Red'	CBro CCse CTri ELan MHCG
'Morrie Otte'	SPol
'Mosel'	SDay
'Moses' Fire'	ECtt EPfP EStr MBNS MHol NLar WFar
'Mossy Glade'	CBgR
'Mount Echo Sunrise'	EWoo
'Mount Joy'	EStr
'Mountain Lace'	CFwr
'Mountain Laurel'	EAEE ECGP ECtt EStr GKin LRHS MBNS MRav NEgg SPol WFar WGwG
'Moussaka'	CWGN EStr SBrk WCAu WFar
'Move Over Moon'	EStr SDay
'Moving Forward'	CFwr
'Mrs David Hall'	CCse
'Mrs Hugh Johnson'	CChe EShb GCra WHrl
* 'Mrs Lester'	SDay
'Much Ado About Magic' **new**	CWel
'Muddy Waters'	CFwr
'Muffet's Little Friend'	SPol
'Mulberry Charm'	CFwr
'Mulberry Frosted Edge'	EWoo
multiflora	XSen
'Muriel Rhem' **new**	EStr
'Murphy's Law'	EStr
'Muscle Man'	EStr XSen
'Music of the Master' (d)	CFwr
'My Belle'	SDay
'My Darling Clementine'	EStr SDay
'My Friend Floyd'	CFwr
'My Gal Sal' **new**	CWel
'My Heart Belongs to Daddy'	CFwr
'My Hope'	SPol
'My Melinda'	SDay
'Mynelle's Starfish'	CPar SPol WHrl
'Mystical Rainbow'	SBrk SDay
'Nabis'	SDay
'Nacogdoches Lady'	SWvt
nana	GKev
* 'Nana Wallich' **new**	EStr
'Nanuq'	CWel SBrk SDay
'Naomi Ruth'	CWel EStr MBNS
'Nashville'	CBro ELan WHrl
'Nashville Lights'	CBgR EStr SPol
'Nathan Sommers'	EWoo
'Natural Born Charmer' **new**	CWel
'Natural Veil'	SPol
'Nature's Crown' (d)	CFwr CWel
'Navajo Jewel'	EStr
'Navajo Princess'	EBee MBNS MNrw SPol
'Neal Berrey'	EStr SDay SPol
'Ned Cricket'	CFwr
'Ned's Elena'	CFwr
'Nefertiti'	CBgR ELon MBNS NBir SPer WAul WCAu
'Neon Sunshine' **new**	EStr
'Neon Yellow'	EStr
'Never Ending Fantasy'	EStr
'Never Get Away'	EStr
'New Direction'	CFwr EWoo
'New Paradigm' **new**	CWel
'New York Follies'	EStr
'Neyron Rose'	GBuc GKin GQue LRHS MBNS NEgg NGdn WMoo WWtn XLum

'Nick's Faith'	WHrl
'Nicole Joyce'	SPol
'Night Beacon'	CBgR ECtt ELon EStr EWes EWoo GBuc GKin LLWG LPot MBNS MNrw MPie NLar SCob SDay SDeJ SPol WCAu WHrl
'Night Embers'	ECtt EWoo NLar SPer WCAu
'Night Raider'	CBgR EStr SDay WNHG
'Night Whispers' **new**	SPer
'Night Wings'	CWel EWoo
'Nile Crane'	CBgR CWel EStr MBNS MNrw SDay SPer WAul
'Nile Plum'	EStr EWoo SDay SPol
'Nina Winegar'	EStr
'Ninja Throwing Star'	CFwr
'Ninth Millennium'	CFwr
'Nob Hill'	CCse ELon EStr SPol WHrl XLum
'Nona's Garnet Spider'	ELon SPol
'Noonday Dreams'	CFwr
'Nordic Night'	CBgR SDay SPol
'North Wind Dancer' ♀H6	EWoo
'Norton Beauté'	WCot
'Norton Eyed Seedling'	WNHG
'Norton Orange'	EStr
'Nosferatu'	SDay SPol
'Not Forgotten'	WNHG
'Nouveau Riche'	SPol
'Nova'	ELon SBrk SDay
'Novarlis'	CFwr
'Now and Zen' **new**	CWel
'Nowhere to Hide'	EStr
'Nuclear Meltdown'	EWoo
'Nuit Parisienne'	EStr
'Nuka'	XLum
'Nutmeg Elf'	CBgR EWoo SDay SPol
'Nuttin Bugs Me'	CFwr
'Oakes Love'	MNrw
'Ocean Rain'	EStr SDay SPol WNHG
'Octopus Hugs'	SBrk SPol
'Official Curse'	SPol
'Ojo de Dios'	EWoo
'Oke-She-Moke-She-Pop' **new**	EStr
'Oklahoma Kicking Bird'	SDay
'Old San Juan'	EStr
'Old Tangiers' ♀H6	EStr EWoo SBrk WNHG
'Old Time Memories'	CFwr
'Olive Bailey Langdon'	EStr SDay SPol WCot
'Oliver Billingslea'	EWoo
'Olive's Odd One'	EStr
'Olly Olly Oxen Free'	CFwr
'Oloroso'	CBgR
'Olympic Gold'	XSen
'Olympic Showcase'	EStr SBrk
'Omomuki'	CWel SBrk SDay
'On and On'	EStr GBin GQue LHop MBNS
'On Pointe'	CFwr EWoo
'On Silken Thread'	SPol
'On the Border'	CFwr
'On the Fringe'	CFwr
'On the Web'	CFwr
'Once upon a Time'	CFwr
'One Fire'	XSen
'Oodles'	WHrl
'Open Hearth'	EStr SPol WHrl
'Open my Eyes'	EStr EWoo
'Optical Art' **new**	CWel
'Orange Clown'	CFwr
'Orange Dream'	SDay
'Orange Empire' **new**	SDay
'Orange Exotica'	CBgR
'Orange Nassau'	WCAu
'Orange Prelude'	XSen
'Orange Splash'	CFwr
'Orange Velvet'	CFwr SPol
'Orangeman' misapplied	MBNS NGdn
'Orchid Beauty'	WMoo
'Orchid Candy'	EStr EWoo GMcL MBNS NBir SBrk SPol
'Orchid Corsage'	ELon EStr SPol
'Orchid Lady Slipper'	EWoo
'Orchid Moonrise'	EWoo
'Oriental Ruby'	SDay
'Orion's Band'	EWoo
'Orphée'	XSen
'Osterized'	EStr
'Ostrich Plume'	EStr SDay
'Ouachita Beauty'	CBgR SPol
'Our Diane'	EWTr
'Our Kirsten'	EStr SDay
'Out of Darkness'	EWoo
'Outrageous'	CBgR EStr SDay SPol WNHG
'Outrageous Ramona'	WNHG
'Over the Top'	MBNS
'Oy Vey' **new**	EStr
'Paige's Pinata'	EBee EStr MBNS SBrk
'Painted Lady'	WNHG
'Painted Peach'	SPol
'Painted Pink'	SDay
'Painting the Roses Red'	CFwr
'Palace Garden Beauty'	EWoo
'Palace Pagoda' **new**	WNHG
'Pale Moon Windmill'	CFwr
'Panda Bear' **new**	CWel
'Pandora's Box'	CTri CWat EAJP ECtt ELan EStr LLWG LRHS MBNS MMuc MNrw NBir NGdn NLar SBrk SDeJ SPol SWvt WBor WCAu WHoo WMoo
'Panic in Detroit'	CFwr SBrk
'Panther Eyes' **new**	CWel
'Pantherette'	SPol
'Papa Goose' **new**	EStr
'Paper Butterfly'	EStr SDay SPol
'Papilion'	EStr
'Papoose'	XLum
'Paprika Flame'	EStr MHol
'Parade of Peacocks'	CBgR
'Pardon Me'	CBro CWel CWld EAEE ECtt ELan ELon EStr EWoo GKin GMaP LLWG LRHS MBNS MBel NCGa NGdn SDeJ SMad SPol SRGP SWvt WAul WBor WCAu WFar
'Pardon Me Boy'	SPol
'Parfait'	CBgR EStr EWoo SPol WHrl
'Parrot Tattoo' **new**	EStr
'Parson's Robe'	SDay
'Party Queen'	SDay
'Passion for Red'	SDay
'Pastel Ballerina'	SDay
'Pastel Classic'	SPol
'Pastilline'	SPol
'Pat Mercer'	SDay XSen
'Patchwork Puzzle'	CWel EStr EWoo SPol
'Patricia'	MBNS
'Patricia Fay'	XSen
'Patricia Gentzel Wright'	EWoo
'Patricia Snider Memorial'	CFwr
'Patriotic Flavor'	EStr
'Patsy Bickers'	EWoo
'Patsy Jane'	SPol
'Patterns'	SPol

'Patti Neyland'	EStr
'Paul Sain's Prize' **new**	CWel
'Paula Nettles'	CWel EStr
'Peace be Still'	EWoo
'Peach Float'	EWoo
'Peach Jubilee'	EStr SPol
'Peach Magnolia' (d)	EStr
'Peach Whisper' **new**	SDay
'Peach Yum Yum'	CFwr
'Peacock Curls'	EWoo
'Peacock Maiden'	EStr EWoo SPol WHrl XSen
'Pear Ornament'	SDay
'Pearl Jam'	SDay
'Pearl Lewis'	EStr SDay SPol
'Pearl Sherwood'	EWoo
'Penelope Vestey'	CBgR EStr GBuc MBNS NBir SDay SPol SRGP
'Penny Pinsley' (d)	CFwr
'Penny's Worth'	LEdu LRHS MBNS WAul WCot WFar XLum
'Penthouse'	CFwr
'Perfect Pleasure'	MBNS
'Persian Melon Plus'	WCAu
'Persian Ruby'	CWel EStr SBrk SPol
'Persian Shrine'	SPol
'Persimmone'	SPol
'Persimmons Cinnamon and Marmalade'	CFwr
'Petite Ballerina'	SDay
'Photon Torpedo'	CFwr
'Phyllis Cantini'	SPol
'Piano Man'	CWel EStr MBNS WAul WNHG
'Piccadilly Princess'	CWel EStr
'Picket Fences'	CFwr
'Pickin' and Grinnin'' **new**	EStr
'Picotee Rippled Ruffles'	CFwr
'Pinebelt Darkeyes'	CFwr
'Pink Ambrosia'	ECtt EStr EWoo
'Pink Ballerina'	WWtn
'Pink Charm'	CBen CMac EAEE ECha ECtt EPPr GKin GMaP LRHS MBNS NBro SPol
'Pink Circle'	SDay
'Pink Cotton Candy'	EWoo SBrk SDay SPol
'Pink Damask' ♀H7	Widely available
'Pink Dazzler'	WNHG
'Pink Delight'	MPie
'Pink Dream'	CBgR MBNS NBir NBre SPol
'Pink Flirt'	SDay
'Pink Grace'	SPol
'Pink Lady'	MNrw MRav SRms
'Pink Monday'	SDay WNHG
'Pink Pajamas'	CFwr
'Pink Prelude'	MBNS MSpe NBro
'Pink Puff'	MBNS NBir NBre NLar
'Pink Rain Dance'	SPol
'Pink Spider'	SDay
'Pink Stripes'	CFwr EStr
'Pink Sundae'	SBee WHrl
'Pink Super Spider'	EWoo SDay SPol
'Pink Whip Tips'	CFwr
'Pink Windmill'	ELon EWoo SPol
'Pinocchio'	SMHy
'Piping Rock'	CFwr
'Piquante'	SCob
'Pirate Treasure'	EStr MBNS
'Pirate's Patch'	EWoo SBrk SDay SPol WCot
'Pixie Parasol'	WNHG
'Pixie Pinwheel Party' **new**	CWel
'Pixie Pipestone'	SPol
'Pixie Princess'	EStr

'Pizza'	SDay
'Planet Golden Orange Ruffy'	CFwr
'Planet Sunshine'	CFwr
'Plum Beautiful' **new**	EStr
'Plum Beauty'	NLar
'Plum Candy'	EWoo
'Plumburst'	EPfP
'Poetic Dance'	EWoo
'Poinsettia'	EStr
'Point of Honor'	EWoo
'Point of View'	EStr
'Pojo'	EStr SDay
'Pony'	CWat ELon GNew SPol
'Porcelain Pleasure'	SDay
'Possum in a Sack'	CBgR
'Post Time' **new**	EStr
'Prague Spring'	CWel EStr MSpe SDay SPol WHrl
'Prairie Belle'	GKev MBNS NLar SPol
'Prairie Blue Eyes'	ECtt EStr IBoy ILea MBNS NPri SDay SPlb SPol WCot WHrl WWtn
'Prairie Charmer'	MMuc SEND WHrl
'Prairie Moonlight'	EWTr
'Precious Candy' **new**	CWel
'Precious d'Oro'	EBee GQue
'Pretty Miss'	EAEE ECtt EStr EWTr LRHS WGwG
'Preview Party'	WNHG
'Primal Scream' ♀H6	EStr LSun MHol SDay SPoG SPol WCot
'Primrose Mascotte'	NBir
'Prince of Midnight'	SDay
'Prince of Purple'	ELon
'Prince Poppycock' **new**	EStr
'Prince Redbird'	SDay
'Princess Blue Eyes'	SPol
'Princess Lilli'	MBNS
'Princeton Eye Glow'	MSpe SDay
'Princeton Silky'	ELon
'Priscilla's Wish'	SPol
'Prisoner of Time' **new**	CWel
'Prissy Frills'	SPol
'Prize Picotee Deluxe'	SDay SPol
'Prize Picotee Elite'	SDay SPol
'Promising Future'	CFwr
'Protocol'	MSpe SDay SPol
'Proud Mary'	SDay
'Ptarmigan'	CBgR EStr
'Pterodactyl Eye'	EStr
§ 'Puddin'	SDay
'Pueblo Dancer'	EStr
'Pueblo Dreamer'	CFwr EWoo
'Puff the Magic Dragon'	CFwr
'Pug Yarborough'	EStr SPol
'Pullin' Strings' **new**	EStr
'Pumpkin Kid'	CWel SDay SPol
'Pumpkin Pie Spice'	SPol
'Pumpkin Prince'	CFwr
'Pumpkins Gone Wild'	CFwr
'Punxsutawney Phil'	EStr
'Puppet Show'	SDay
'Pure and Simple'	SDay SPol
'Purple Arachne'	SPol
'Purple Bicolor'	WHrl
'Purple Corn Dancer'	WCot
'Purple Grasshopper'	EWoo
'Purple Many Faces'	SPol
'Purple Oddity'	EWoo SPol
'Purple Pinwheel'	EWoo SPol
'Purple Rain'	CWat MBNS MPie SDay SPol SWvt
'Purple Rain Dance'	SPol
'Purple Waters'	EStr MBNS MJak SPol WPnP

'Purpleicious'	NLar
'Pygmy Plum'	SDay XSen
'Pyrotechnics'	EStr
'Quality of Mercy'	SDay
'Queen Charlotte'	EStr
'Queen Empress'	WNHG
'Queen Kathleen'	CFwr
'Queen Lily'	WNHG
'Queen of Can Do'	CFwr
'Queen of May'	MNrw WCot
'Quick Results'	SDay
'Quiet Pink'	SBrk
'Quietly Awesome'	SDay
'Quilt Patch'	EStr SPol
'Quinn Buck'	SDay
'Ra Hansen'	CWel EStr
'Rachael My Love' (d)	XSen
'Racing Stripes'	CFwr
'Radiant Greetings'	XSen
'Radiant Moonbeam' 🏆H6	CBgR EStr
'Radiation Biohazard'	CFwr SPol
'Raging Tiger'	WHrl
'Rags to Riches'	CFwr
'Rain Dance'	EStr
'Rainbow Candy'	CWGN LLHF MBNS SBrk
'Rainbow Drive'	CFwr
'Rainbow Gold'	XSen
'Rainbow Serpent'	CFwr
'Raining Violets'	EWoo
'Rajah'	CBgR CMac EStr MBNS MSpe NBro SCob SPer WHrl
'Randall Moore'	SPol
'Rander's Pride'	EWoo
'Raspberry Beret'	CFwr
'Raspberry Butterflies'	EWoo
'Raspberry Candy'	CBro EStr GCra IBoy MBNS MNrw SBrk SRms WHrl
'Raspberry Griffin'	CFwr
'Raspberry Masquerade'	CFwr
'Raspberry Pixie'	SPol
'Raspberry Wine'	ECha
'Raspberry Winter'	EStr
'Raven Woodsong'	EWoo
'Razzle'	EStr
'Real Life Drama'	EStr
'Real Wind'	EStr SPol
'Red Admiral'	EAEE LRHS
'Red Butterfly'	SPol
'Red Eyed Fantasy'	CFwr
'Red Eyed Shocker'	CFwr
'Red Grace'	EStr
'Red Hill'	EWoo
'Red Pennant'	SDay
'Red Precious' 🏆H7	MNrw SMHy WCot
'Red Rain'	EStr EWoo WHrl XSen
'Red Resplendence'	EWoo
'Red Ribbons'	ELon EWoo SDay SPol
'Red Ruby'	ERCP
'Red Rum'	CBgR EUJe LRHS MSpe MSwo NBro WMoo
'Red Squirrel'	CFwr
'Red Suspenders'	ECtt EStr MBNS
'Red Thrill'	WHrl
'Red Twister'	ELon EStr SBrk SDay SPol
'Red Volunteer'	EStr SBrk SDay SPol
'Redheaded Hussy'	CFwr EStr
'Redneck Red'	CFwr
'Reflections in Time'	EWoo
'Regal Giant'	EStr EWoo
'Regency Dandy'	SDay SPol XSen
'Regency Heights'	EStr
'Reigning Sunshine'	CFwr
'Renee'	MNrw
'Respighi'	EStr SBrk
'Return to Oz'	CFwr
'Return Trip'	SPol
'Revolute'	SDay
'Rhode Island Red'	CFwr
'Rhubarb Wine' **new**	EStr
'Rhythm of Love' **new**	EStr
'Ribbonette'	EBee EStr MBNS
'Ricky Rose'	SDay XSen
'Rigamarole'	SPol
'Riley Barron'	SDay
'Rise of the Phoenix'	EStr
'Roaring Jellyfish'	CFwr
'Robespierre'	SDay
'Rocket Booster'	EStr
'Rocket City'	ELan EStr SPol WNHG
'Rocky Mountain Pals'	CFwr
'Rodeo Sweetheart'	CFwr
'Roger Grounds'	CBgR SPol
'Roll Up Candy'	CFwr CWel
'Rolling Hill'	CFwr
'Rolling Raven'	CFwr
'Roman Toga'	CBgR SDay
'Romanian Rendevous'	CFwr
* 'Romantic Rose'	MBNS NLar WHrl
'Romeo is Bleeding'	EStr
'Romulan Defector' **new**	CWel
'Ron Rousseau'	SPol
'Root Beer'	WCAu WHrl
'Rose Corsage'	EWoo
'Rose Emily'	CBgR EStr SDay SPol
'Rose Fever'	EWoo
'Rose for Charlotte'	SPol
'Rose Tattoo'	EStr
'Rose Victorious'	CFwr
'Roseate Spoonbill'	EWoo
'Roses in Snow'	IBoy MBNS SBrk SPol
'Rosewood Rainbow End'	CWel
'Roswitha'	EStr SPol
'Rosy Lights'	EWoo SPol
'Rosy Polyphemus'	EStr
'Rosy Returns'	CRos EPfP LRHS MBNS NLar NRHS SBrk
'Round Midnight'	SPol
'Royal Braid'	MBNS NLar SBrk SPer WCot
'Royal Butterfly'	CFwr
'Royal Celebration'	WCot
'Royal Crown'	SDay
'Royal Elk'	EWoo
'Royal Emperor'	CFwr
'Royal Eventide'	CFwr XSen
'Royal Flycatcher'	CFwr
'Royal Heritage'	EStr SDay
'Royal Hunter'	CFwr
'Royal Pink Twist'	CFwr
'Royal Robe'	CTri
'Royal Russian Rendezvous'	CFwr
'Royal Saracen'	SDay
'Royal Thornbird'	CBgR
'Royal Trophy'	WNHG
'Royalty'	GCra
'Ruby Corsage'	EStr
'Ruby Sentinel'	SDay
'Ruby Spider' 🏆H6	CWel ELon EStr EWoo SBrk SPol
'Ruby Storm'	CFwr
'Rue Madelaine'	SPol
'Ruffled Apricot'	CKel MBNS SDay WNHG

'Ruffled Carousel'	WNHG
'Ruffled Dude'	EStr
'Ruffled Ivory'	SDay
'Ruffled Lemon Lace'	EStr
'Ruffled Magic'	SDay
'Ruffled Perfection'	EStr
'Rumble Seat Romance'	WNHG
'Russian Easter'	EStr SBrk
'Russian Ragtime'	EStr
'Russian Rhapsody' ♀H6	CKel SDay SPol
'Ruth Oliver'	EStr
'Sabie'	EStr
'Sabine Baur'	CRos EStr LRHS MBNS MNrw NRHS WFar
'Sabra Salina'	EStr EWoo SDay SPol
'Sacred Drummer'	SDay
'Saffron Glow'	SDay
'Sahara Sand Storm'	CWel EStr
'Sahara Song' **new**	EStr
'Saintly'	EWoo
'Sallie Brown'	EStr SDay
'Salmon Pagoda'	EWoo
'Salmon Sheen'	SDay SPer
'Sammy'	EStr SDay WHrl
'Sammy Russell'	Widely available
'Samuel Bell'	EWoo
'San Luis Halloween'	CFwr CWel
'Sandra Elizabeth'	SDay
'Sandra Walker'	WWtn
'Sanford Code Red'	CFwr
'Sanford Star Search'	CFwr
'Santa's Little Helper'	CFwr
'Santiago'	SPol
'Saratoga Belle' **new**	EStr
'Saratoga Pinwheel'	SPol
'Sariah'	SDay
'Satin Glass'	EAEE EBee LRHS
'Satin Glow'	ECha
'Scapes from Hell'	EWoo
'Scarlet Butterfly'	SPol
'Scarlet Flame'	ECha WMoo
'Scarlet Oak'	SBrk
'Scarlet Orbit'	EWoo SDay SPol
'Scarlet Pimpernel'	CFwr
'Scarlet Prince'	WNHG
'Scarlet Ribbons'	EStr SPol
'Scatterbrain'	CFwr CKel SPol
'Schnickel Fritz'	EBee
'School Girl'	EAEE EBee LRHS
'Scorchio' **new**	EStr
'Scorpio'	CBgR MSpe SDay SPol WHrl
'Scout's Honor' (d)	CFwr
'Screaming Demon'	EStr SPol WCot
'Sea Swept Dreams'	SDay
'Seabiscuit'	CFwr
'Seal of Approval'	EBee EStr
'Sebastian'	SDay
'Secret Splendor'	SPol
'Secretary's Sand'	EWoo
'Seductive Fairy Tale'	EStr
'Selma Longlegs' ♀H6	EStr SPol
'Seminole Blood'	SPol
'Seminole Princess'	CFwr
'Seminole Wind'	EWoo SDay SPol
'Semiramide'	CBgR WNHG
'Sentinel Solar Burst' (d)	CFwr
'Serena Lady'	SDay
'Serena Sunburst' ♀H6	CWel EStr SBrk SPol
'Serenade'	EWoo
'Serene Madonna'	ELan ILea
'Serenity Bay'	CFwr
'Serenity Morgan'	CBgR MBNS
'Serge Rigaud'	WHrl
'Sergeant Major'	EWoo
'Shadowed Pink'	WNHG
'Shady Lady'	SDay SPol
'Shaman' Gates	SDay SPol
'Shangri La Truffle'	CFwr
'She Devil'	CFwr EStr
'Shelly Victoria'	SDay
'Sherry Lane Carr'	EStr SDay SPol
'Sherwood Gladiator'	WNHG
'Shibui Splendor'	SPol
'Shimek September Morning'	EStr SPol
'Shinto Etching'	EStr
'Shinto Shrine' **new**	WNHG
* 'Shocker'	EWoo
'Shogun'	MBNS
'Shotgun'	EStr SPol
'Show Amber'	SBrk
'Shuffle the Deck'	CFwr EWoo
'Sidewinder Oh Seven'	CFwr
'Signature Truffle' (d)	CFwr
'Sigudilla'	WNHG
'Silent Sentry'	EStr
'Silken Fairy'	CBgR SDay WWtn
'Silken Touch'	CBgR EStr SPol
'Silly Whimsey' **new**	CWel
'Siloam Amazing Grace'	SDay
'Siloam Angel Blush'	SDay
'Siloam Baby Doll'	SDay
'Siloam Baby Talk'	ELon EStr GBuc NBir SDay WAul WMoo WPnP
'Siloam Bertie Ferris'	MBNS
'Siloam Bo Peep'	SDay
'Siloam Button Box'	MBNS WHrl
'Siloam Bye Lo'	EWoo SDay
'Siloam Cinderella'	SDay SPol
'Siloam David Kirchhoff'	EBee MBNS SDay XSen
'Siloam Doodlebug'	CBgR
'Siloam Double Classic' (d)	EStr SDay SPol
'Siloam Dream Baby'	ELon MBNS
'Siloam Edith Sholar'	CWel
'Siloam Ethel Smith'	SDay SPol
'Siloam Fairy Tale'	SDay
'Siloam Flower Girl'	SDay
'Siloam French Doll'	MBNS NLar
'Siloam French Marble'	SDay
'Siloam Frosted Mint'	SDay SPol
'Siloam Gold Coin'	SDay
'Siloam Grace Stamile'	MBNS SDay
'Siloam Helpmate'	WNHG
'Siloam Joan Senior'	MBNS
'Siloam John Yonski'	SDay
'Siloam June Bug'	CBgR ELan WCot
'Siloam Justine Lee'	MBNS
'Siloam Little Angel'	SPol
'Siloam Little Girl'	CWel ECtt EStr SDay
'Siloam Mama'	SDay
'Siloam Merle Kent'	CWel EWoo SDay SPol WAul
'Siloam Nugget'	EStr
'Siloam Orchid Jewel'	SDay
'Siloam Paul Watts'	EStr GMcL SPol
'Siloam Peewee'	ELon LRHS
'Siloam Pink Glow'	SDay SWat
'Siloam Plum Tree'	SPol
'Siloam Pocket Size'	SDay
'Siloam Queen's Toy'	SPol
'Siloam Red Toy'	SMHy
'Siloam Ribbon Candy'	SDay WNHG

'Siloam Rose Dawn'	SPol
'Siloam Rose Queen'	SDay
'Siloam Ruffled Infant'	SDay
'Siloam Shocker'	EStr
'Siloam Show Girl'	CWGN CWel EStr EWoo GKin MBNS
'Siloam Space Age'	WNHG
'Siloam Spizz'	EStr SDay
'Siloam Tee Tiny'	WAul WWtn
'Siloam Tiny Mite'	SDay WHrl
'Siloam Toddler'	EStr
'Siloam Tom Thumb'	CBgR EStr MBNS
'Siloam Ury Winniford'	CBro CMac GMcL MBNS NLar WHoo WPnP
'Siloam Virginia Henson'	EStr EWoo WWtn
'Silver Ice'	SDay SPol
'Silver Lance'	EStr SDay SPol
'Silver Quasar'	SDay SPol
'Silver Veil'	SDay
'Simmering Elephants'	CFwr
'Simmons Overture'	ECtt EStr
'Simplicity in Motion'	CFwr
'Sinbad Sailor'	NLar
'Singing in the Sunshine'	EWoo
'Sings the Blues'	SBrk
'Sink Into Your Eyes'	EStr WHrl
'Sir Blackstem'	GCal SDay
'Sir Knight'	SPol
'Sir Modred' ♀H6	EStr SPol WHrl WNHG
'Sitting on a Rainbow'	EStr
'Sixth Sense'	ELon MBNS
'Skeezix' (d)	CFwr
'Skeleton Man'	CFwr
'Skinny Dipping'	CFwr
'Skinwalker'	EWoo
'Slapstick'	ELon EStr SDay SPol
'Sleepy'	ECha
'Sleepy Hollow'	EStr
'Slender Lady'	CFwr ELon XSen
'Slipping Into the Abyss'	EStr
'Small Town'	EWoo
'Small World Tornado'	EWoo
'Small World Twister'	CFwr
'Smith Brothers'	SPol
'Smoke Scream'	CFwr
'Smokestack Lightning'	CFwr
'Smoky Mountain Autumn'	EWoo SPol
'Smooch Hollow'	CBgR EStr
'Smuggler's Gold'	ECtt SDay
'Smuggler's Temptation'	SPol
'Snaggle Tooth' **new**	EStr
'Snow Wonder' **new**	CWel
'Snowed In'	EWoo
'Snowy Apparition'	EAEE EBee ECrc ECtt EWTr GBin GKin LHop LRHS MBNS NWad SPol SWvt WCAu
'Snowy Eyes'	CHid GKin MBNS SWat WHrl
'So Excited'	SDay
'So Lovely'	EWoo XLum
'So Many Stars'	CFwr SPol
'Soft Cashmere'	XLum
'Soho Style'	CFwr
'Solid Geometry' **new**	EStr
'Solid Scarlet'	EStr
'Solomon's Robes' **new**	SDay
'Sombrero Way'	SDay
'Someone Special'	EStr SDay SPol
'Somerset Fandango'	CBgR
'Song In My Heart'	EWoo
'Song Sparrow'	CBro
'Soraya Seline'	CBgR
'Sound of Color' **new**	EStr
'South Seas'	EStr
'Southern Prize'	SDay
'Sovereign Queen'	WNHG
'Spacecoast Devil's Eye' **new**	CWel
'Spacecoast Dragon Prince'	EWoo
'Spacecoast Freaky Tiki'	EStr
'Spacecoast Gone Bulldoggin'' **new**	CWel
'Spacecoast Scrambled'	CWel MBNS NLar
'Spacecoast Starburst'	CBcs EStr MBNS WCot
'Spanish Fandango'	EStr SPol
'Spanish Glow'	SPol
'Sparkling Dawn'	EStr
'Sparkling Orange' **new**	SDay
'Special Candy' **new**	CWel
'Spellbound Secret' **new**	CWel
'Spice Hunter'	CFwr
'Spider Breeder'	CBgR ELon EStr
'Spider Man' ♀H6	ELon EStr SDay SPol WCAu XSen
'Spider Miracle'	SDay SPol
'Spider Red'	CWGN EWTr EWoo
'Spider Web'	EStr
'Spilled Milk'	SPol
'Spin Master'	EStr
'Spindazzle'	CBgR SDay SPol
'Spinne in Lachs'	EStr SPol
'Spinneret'	EStr
'Spiny Sea Urchin' **new**	CWel
'Spiral Charmer'	SPol
'Spiral Nebula'	EStr
'Spirit of Sapelo'	EWoo
'Spirited Butterfly' **new**	CWel
'Splittin' Hairs' **new**	EStr
'Spock's Ears'	CFwr
'Spooner'	CBgR
'Spring Willow Song'	EStr SDay
'Springfield Clan'	EStr
'Square Dancer's Curtsy'	CFwr
'Squash Dolly'	EWoo
'Stafford' ♀H7	Widely available
'Staghorn Sumac'	GKin LEdu MBNS NHol WCAu
'Star Asterisk'	CFwr SPol
'Star of Fantasy'	CFwr
'Star of India'	SPol
'Star Poly'	EStr
'Star Spangled'	SPol
'Star Twister'	CFwr
'Stargate Corridor'	SPol
'Starling'	CPar GNew NChi WWtn
'Starman's Quest'	EStr SPol
'Starstruck'	WNHG
'Startle'	ELon EStr MBNS MNrw WCot WHrl
'Startling Creation'	CFwr
'Statuesque'	EWoo
'Steely Blue Eyes'	EStr
'Stella de Oro'	Widely available
'Stella in Purple' **new**	EPfP
'Stella in Red'	EPfP
'Stenciled Impressions' **new**	CWel
'Steve Trimmer'	SPol
'Stinnette'	WCot
'Stippled Starlight'	CFwr
'Stoke Poges'	CBgR CBro EAEE EBee ELon EPPr EPfP EShb EStr GBin LHop LPot MBNS MMuc SPer SWat WHrl
'Stone Beacon'	CFwr
'Stone Island'	CFwr
'Stoplight'	CBgR ELon EStr LRHS SMHy SPol WHrl
'Storm Over Toledo'	CFwr

	'Strasbourg'	CMac
	'Strawberry Candy' ♀H6	CBgR CMac CSBt CWel ECtt ELon EPfP EStr EWoo IBoy ILea MBNS MPie NGdn NLar SBrk SCob SDay SPer WAul WCAu WHoo WHrl WMoo WNHG
	'Strawberry Fields Forever'	EWoo MBNS SPol
I	'Streaker' B. Brown (v)	XSen
	'Street Urchin'	SPol
	'Streets of Heaven'	EWoo
	'Strider Spider'	EStr
	'String Bikini'	EStr
	'String Theory'	CFwr
	'Strutter's Ball'	CBod EStr EWoo MBNS MJak NGdn SPer SPol SWat WAul WCAu WHar WHrl
	'Stupidville USA'	EStr
	'Stu's Old Pink Spider'	CBgR
	'Suburban Golden Eagle'	EStr
	'Sugar Cookie'	EWoo SDay SPol
	'Sugar Plum Jam'	CFwr
	'Summer Dragon'	EStr MBNS
	'Summer Fireworks'	EWoo
	'Summer Interlude'	WMoo
	'Summer Star'	EStr
	'Summer Wine'	Widely available
	'Sunday Gloves'	SPol WNHG
	'Sunday Morning'	EStr SDay
	'Sungold Candy'	CWel EStr
	'Sunray Brilliance'	EWoo
	'Sunrise Sunset Beautiful'	CFwr
	'Sunset Lagoon'	EStr SPol
	'Sunshine Junkie'	CFwr
	'Super Purple'	CKel
	'Superlative'	EStr SPol
	'Susan Pritchard Petit' **new**	CWel
	'Susan Weber'	CWel SPol
	'Suzy Cream Cheese'	CFwr SPol
	'Svengali'	SDay SPol
	'Swallow Tail Kite'	SPol
	'Swan Dance'	SDay
	'Swashbuckler Bay Boy'	CFwr CWel
	'Sweet Charlotte'	SPol
	'Sweet Country Luvin''	EStr
	'Sweet Hot Chocolate'	LRHS MBNS
	'Sweet Pea'	EStr SDay
	'Sweet Sugar Candy'	ECtt EWoo SDeJ
	'Swirling Spider'	CBgR EWoo SPol
	'Tail Feathers'	CFwr
	'Taj Mahal'	ELon EWoo
	'Tammy Faye Eyes'	CFwr
	'Tang'	CHid MBNS
	'Tangerine Tango'	EWoo
	'Tangerine Twist'	EStr SPol
	'Tango Noturno'	SPol
	'Tani'	SDay
	'Taos'	EStr
	'Tar and Feather' **new**	CWel
	'Tarantula'	ELon SPol
	'Taruga'	EWoo SDay
	'Tasmania'	SPer
	'Tchao Pantin'	XSen
	'Teacup Fingers'	CFwr
	'Technical Knockout'	EWoo
	'Techny Peach Lace'	EStr SPol
	'Techny Spider'	EStr SBrk SPol
	'Teenie Girl'	EStr
	'Tejas'	CElw ELon LTro SPer
	'Témoin'	XSen
	'Tennessee Flycatcher'	EStr EWoo SPol
	'Tennessee Williams'	SPol
	'Tennyson'	CFwr
	'Tequila and Lime' **new**	EStr
	'Tequila Mockingbird'	CFwr
	'Tet Set'	WNHG
	'Tetraploid Siloam Red Toy'	SDay
	'Tetraploid Stella de Oro'	SDay
	'Tetrina's Daughter'	CBgR EPfP LRHS
	'Thank Your Lucky Stars' **new**	EStr
	'Thanks a Bunch'	SBrk SPol
	'The Tingler'	CFwr EWoo
	'Thelma Douglas' **new**	EStr
	'Thelma Perry'	LEdu
	'Thermal Overload' **new**	EStr
	'Thin Man'	CFwr
	'Think Pink'	EBee EPfP
	'Third Witch'	CFwr EWoo
	'Thomas Tew'	CFwr CWel
	'Three Diamonds'	SPol
	'Three Times a Lady'	CFwr
	'Thrill Ride'	SPol
	'Thumbelina'	ECha WMoo XLum
§	***thunbergii***	ECha GCal MCoo XLum
	- 'Ovation'	MBNS
	'Thunder and Lightning'	EStr
	'Thundering Ovation'	CWGN
	'Thy True Love'	SDay
	'Tiger Blood' **new**	EStr
	'Tiger Prince'	CFwr
	'Tiger Swirl'	CFwr
	'Tigereye Spider'	EStr EWoo
	'Tigerling'	CWel EStr EWoo SPol
	'Tigger'	EStr SPad SPol WCAu
	'Till I Turn Purple' **new**	EStr
	'Time Lord'	SDay XSen
	'Time to Believe'	SPol
	'Time Together'	EStr
	'Time Window'	EStr
	'Tiny Talisman'	SDay
	'Tiny Temptress'	SDay
	'Tis Midnight'	WNHG
	'Titanic Tower'	CFwr CWel
	'Tixie' **new**	EStr
	'Tom Collins'	SDay
	'Tom Wise'	EStr SBrk SPol
	'Tomorrow's Song'	SPol
	'Tone Poem'	WNHG
	'Tonia Gay'	SDay SPol
	'Toodleloo Kangaroo'	EWoo
	'Tooth'	EStr
	'Toothpick'	EWoo SPol WHrl
	'Tootsie'	SDay
	'Tootsie Rose'	SDay SPol
	'Top Honors'	SPol
	'Topaz Gem'	SPol
	'Topguns Aleah Kaye'	CFwr
	'Topguns Anita Causey' (d)	CFwr
	'Topguns Bandit's Bandana'	CFwr
	'Topguns Butterball' (d)	CFwr
	'Topguns Cactus Jack'	CFwr
	'Topguns Cherokee Dancer'	CFwr
	'Topguns Cherry Limeade'	CFwr
	'Topguns Citrine Dream' (d)	CFwr
	'Topguns Copper Butterflies' (d)	CFwr
	'Topguns Dragonfly Sunset' (d)	CFwr

'Topguns Dream Catcher' (d)	CFwr
'Topguns Eye Popper'	CFwr
'Topguns Grim Reaper'	CFwr
'Topguns Harlequin Ruffles'	CFwr
'Topguns Jennifer Hankins'	CFwr
'Topguns Lemon Ruffles'	CFwr
'Topguns Linda Farris' (d)	CFwr
'Topguns Molten Lava' (d)	CFwr
'Topguns Okie Twister'	CFwr
'Topguns Orange Fizz' (d)	CFwr
'Topguns Orange Marmalade'	CFwr
'Topguns Pawnee Princess'	CFwr
'Topguns Pinwheel'	CFwr
'Topguns Rising Sun' (d)	CFwr
'Topguns Ruffled Amazement' (d)	CFwr
'Topguns Stop 'n' Go'	CFwr
'Topguns Tilt-A-Whirl'	CFwr
'Torpoint'	CBgR MBNS MRav NEgg
'Total Eclipse'	EStr
'Touch of Magic'	EStr
'Towhead'	MRav SDay WCot
'Toyland'	MBNS NBir NGdn NLar SPol
'Trahlyta'	CBgR EStr EWoo SDay SPol WHrl
'Treasure of Love'	EWoo
'Trevi Fountain'	EWoo
'Tribute to Joe' **new**	EStr
'Trog'	EStr
'Trond'	SDay
'Tropical Breeze'	CFwr
'Tropical Depression'	CFwr EWoo
'Tropical Hot Flash' **new**	EStr
'Tropical Passion' **new**	EStr
'Tropical Toy'	SDay
'Tropicana Treat' **new**	EStr
'Troubled Sleep'	EWoo
'Truchas Sunrise'	CFwr EWoo
'True Gertrude Demarest'	WHrl
'True North'	CFwr
'True Pink Beauty'	EWoo
'Truffle Heritage'	CFwr
'Tune the Harp'	EStr SPol
'Tuolumne Fairy Tale'	SPol
'Turkish Tapestry'	CBgR
'Turkish Turban'	SDay SPol
'Turn the Other Cheek'	EStr
'Turtle Island'	EStr
'Tuscawilla Blackout'	SPol XSen
'Tuscawilla Pink Joe' **new**	CWel
'Tuscawilla Princess'	EStr
'Tuscawilla Tigress'	CWel EStr GKin IKil MBNS MNrw MSpe SDay SPol WAul WHrl
'Tutankhamun'	EStr SDay
'Tutti Frutti Truffle'	CFwr
'Tuxedo'	SPol
'Tuxedo Junction' 🏆H6	EStr
'Tuxedo Whiskers'	EStr
'Twenty Third Psalm'	WHal
'Twilight Secrets'	MBNS
'Twilight Swan'	WNHG
'Twirling Wings'	CFwr
'Twist and Shout'	CFwr
'Twist and Spin'	CFwr
'Twist of Lemon'	EWoo SDay
'Two Faces of Love'	SPol
'Tylwyth Teg'	CFwr SPol
'Umbrella Parade'	EStr
'Unchartered Waters'	MBNS SBrk
'Unending Melody'	CFwr
'Unforgetable Fire'	EWoo
'Unique Purple'	SPol
'Uniquely Different'	SPol
'Upper Class Peach'	EStr
'Uptown Girl'	CWel EStr
'Valiant'	EWoo MBNS WHrl
'Valley Monster'	SPol
'Valley Sprite' **new**	EStr
'Vanessa Arden'	SPol
'Vanilla Fluff'	EStr
'Variegated Woottens' (v)	EWoo
'Varsity'	LRHS NBir SPer
'Veins of Truth'	CBgR EBee WCAu
'Velvet Eyes'	EStr
'Velvet Ribbons'	CFwr
'Velvet Shadows'	CBgR SDay
'Vendetta'	WNHG
'Venusian Heat'	CFwr
'Venusian Mirage'	EStr
'Venus's Fire'	CFwr
'Vera Biaglow'	MSpe SDay SPol
'Vermilion Flycatcher' **new**	CWel
'Very Berry Ice'	SPol
'Vespers'	WPnP
vespertina	see *H. thunbergii*
'Vesuvian'	SDay
'Veuve Joyeuse'	XSen
'Vi Simmons'	EStr
'Vicountess Byng'	WWtn
'Victoria Aden'	CBro
'Victoria Elizabeth Barnes'	WNHG
'Victorian Lace'	EWoo
'Victorian Ribbons'	SPol
'Victorian Violet'	SDay
'Video'	SDay
'Vie en Rose'	EStr
'Viewpoint'	SDay
'Vino di Notte'	EStr
'Vintage Bordeaux'	ELan SDay
'Vintage Burgundy'	CBgR WNHG
'Vintage Passion' **new**	EStr
'Vintage Wine' **new**	WNHG
'Violent Thunder'	CFwr EStr
'Violet Hour'	EStr SDay
'Viracocha'	WNHG
'Virgin's Blush'	SPer
'Vision of Love' **new**	EStr
'Vohann'	SDay
'Volcano Queen'	CFwr EPfP EStr
'Voodoo Dancer'	CWel EBee EStr SCob
'Waiting in the Wings'	SBrk SDay
'Walking on Sunshine'	EStr SBrk WCot
'Wally Nance'	CFwr
'Walnut Hill'	EStr
'Walt Disney'	GKin
'War Paint'	EStr SDay
'Warp Drive'	SDay
'Warrior Victorious'	CFwr
'Watch Tower'	CBgR
'Watchyl Christmas Widow'	CFwr
'Watchyl Dancing Spider'	EStr SPol
'Water Witch'	CWat CWel SDay
'Watermelon Man'	CBgR EWoo
'Watership Down'	EWoo
'Watson Park Tempest'	CFwr
'Waxen Splendor' **new**	EStr
'Wayne Johnson'	WNHG
'Wayside Green Imp'	MNrw

'We Love'	EWoo
'Weaver's Art'	SPol
'Web Browser'	CFwr EStr
'Web Dancer'	SPol
'Webster's Pink Wonder'	EStr SBrk SPol
'Wee Willie Winkie'	WNHG
'Wekiwa'	EWoo
'Welchkins'	CWel SDay WAul
'Welfo White Diamond'	SPol
'Westward Wind'	EWoo
'Whammer Jammer'	CFwr
'What a Day for a Daydream'	CFwr
'When I Dream'	EStr
'Which Way Jim'	SDay
'Whichford'	CAby CBgR CBod CBro CSam ECha ECrc ECtt ELan EPfP EWoo GBuc GCal GKin LRHS MBNS SPer SPhx WGwG WHrl WPtf
'Whip City Fancy Free' **new**	EStr
'Whirling Fury'	ELon EWoo
'White Coral'	EAEE LRHS LSRN MBNS NBro
'White Edged Madonna'	WHrl
'White Ensign'	SDay
'White Magician'	EStr
'White Pansy'	SDay
'White Temptation'	EPfP IBoy LRHS NGdn SDay WAul WHoo WNHG XSen
'White Tie Affair'	CWel EWoo SBrk
'White Zone'	EWoo SDay
'Whooperee'	SDay
'Whoopie'	CHid CWld SPad
'Wideyed'	XLum
'Wild about Sherry'	CFwr SPol
'Wild and Wonderful'	EPfP EStr EWoo LSun SBrk WFar
'Wild Child'	CFwr
'Wild Horses'	CRos CWGN CWel EPfP EWes LRHS MNrw NLar NRHS SBrk SCob SMad SPad SPol WHrl
'Wild Mustang'	EStr MBNS MSpe SBrk
'Wild Rose Fandango'	CFwr EWoo
'Wild Winter Wine'	CFwr
'Wildest Dreams'	EWoo
'William Milo Spalding'	EStr
'Willy Nilly'	SPol
'Wilson Spider'	EStr SPol
'Wind Beneath My Sails'	EWoo
'Wind Frills'	NQui SDay SPol XSen
'Wind Master'	CFwr
'Wind Song'	ELon SDay
'Windmill Yellow'	EWoo SDay
'Window Dressing'	EWoo
'Winds of Love'	EWoo
'Wineberry Candy'	EStr EWoo MBNS NLar SDay
'Winged Migration'	CFwr EWoo
'Wings of Chance'	SPol
'Wings on High'	EWoo SPol
'Winnie'	EStr
'Winnie the Pooh'	SDay
'Winsome Lady'	ECGP ECha ECtt GKin MBNS WHrl
'Winter Wolf'	EStr
'Wisest of Wizards'	MBNS SPol WHrl
'Wishing Well'	WCot
'Witch Hazel'	WCAu WWtn
'Witch Stitchery'	EStr SDay
'Witches Brew'	CBgR
'Witches Wink'	EWoo
'Witch's Stick'	CFwr
'Without Warning'	CBgR
'Womanizer' **new**	EStr
'Woodland Spider'	SDay
'Woodside Ruby'	WNHG
'Working with Green' **new**	CWel
'Worth it All'	CFwr
'Wyoming Wildfire'	CBgR
'Xia Xiang'	EWoo SDay
'Xochimilco'	WNHG
'Ya Ya Girl'	EWoo
'Yabba Dabba Doo'	EStr SPol
'Yazoo Green Octopus'	EWoo
'Yazoo Wild Violet'	EStr
'Yellow Angel'	ELon SPol WCot
'Yellow Finch'	CFwr
'Yellow Lollipop'	SDay
'Yellow Mammoth'	SBrk
'Yellow Rain'	WCot
'Yellow Ribbon'	EStr SPol
'Yellow Submarine'	EPfP MBNS SBrk
'Yesterday Memories'	SDay
yezoensis	EBtc
'Yo-rick Yost'	CFwr
'You Angel You'	MBNS
'You Are My Sunshine'	CFwr
'Yum Yum Plum'	EStr SDay
'Yuma'	WNHG
'Zagora'	EStr WCAu
'Zampa'	CBgR EStr SDay
'Zara'	EStr SPer
'Zenobia'	EStr
'Zip Boom Bah'	EStr
'Zuni Mountains'	WNHG
'Zuni Thunderbird'	EWoo

Hepatica ✿ (*Ranunculaceae*)

acutiloba	CBro ECho EPot GBuc GEdr GKev NBir WPnP XEll
- blue-flowered	MAsh
- white-flowered	MAsh
acutiloba* × *nobilis **new**	SPer
americana	ECho ELan EPot GKev MAsh NBir
- 'Ashwood Marble' **new**	MAsh
angulosa	see *H. transsilvanica*
(Forest Series) 'Forest Blue'	EBee
- 'Forest Pink'	EBee ELan EWTr GBin GKev XEll
- 'Forest Purple'	EBee ELan GBin GKev LCro XEll
- 'Forest Red'	CWCL EBee ELan GBin GEdr GKev LCro XEll
- 'Forest White'	EBee ELan GBin GKev LCro XEll
henryi	ECho GEdr GKev MAsh
insularis	GBuc MAsh
maxima	ECho GBuc GEdr MAsh WAbe
× ***media*** 'Ballardii'	GBuc GEdr IBlr LLHF MAsh
- 'Harvington Beauty'	CLAP GEdr IBlr IFoB MAsh NBir WSHC
- 'Millstream Merlin'	GEdr
- 'Violett Prinz' **new**	MAsh
'Miyoshino'	GEdr
§ ***nobilis*** 🏆H5	Widely available
- var. ***asiatica***	MAsh
- - pink-flowered	MAsh
- - purple-flowered	MAsh
- - white-flowered	MAsh NPnk
- blue-flowered	ECho IFoB MAsh NSla WAbe WHoo
- 'Cobalt'	CLAP ECho GEdr NSla
- compact evergreen	MAsh
- 'Cremar'	GEdr MAsh
- dark-blue-flowered	CLAP ITim
- dwarf white-flowered	IFoB
- 'Elkofener Heidi'	GEdr
- 'Gold Band' (v)	GEdr
- var. ***japonica***	EPfP EWes IFoB LHop MAsh NBir NSla
- - 'Akabuku' (1)	GEdr

- - 'Akafuku' (1)	GEdr
- - 'Akane' (1)	GEdr
- - 'Akanezora' (6/d)	GEdr
- - 'Akebono' (9/d)	GEdr
- - 'Anjyu' (9/d)	GEdr
- - 'Asahi' (7/d)	GEdr
- - 'Asahizuru' (6/d)	GEdr
- - 'Benikanzan' (1)	GEdr
- - 'Benikujyaku' (7/d)	GEdr
- - 'Benioiran' (3)	GEdr
- - 'Beniokesa' (9/d)	GEdr
- - 'Benishinjyu' (6/d)	GEdr
- - 'Benisuzume' (1)	GEdr
- - 'Benitaiko' (9/d)	GEdr
- - 'Bojyou' (5A/d)	GEdr
- - 'Daishihou' (9/d)	GEdr
- - 'Dewa' (9/d)	GEdr
- - 'Echigobijin' (1)	GEdr
- - 'Fukujyu' (9/d)	GEdr
- - 'Getsurin' (5A/d)	GEdr
- - 'Gosho-zakura' (5A/d)	GEdr
- - 'Gyousei' (1)	GBuc GEdr
- - 'Hakuji' (1)	GEdr
- - 'Hakurin' (6/d)	GEdr
- - 'Hakusetsu' (9/d)	GEdr
- - 'Haruka' (2)	GEdr
- - 'Harukaze' (5A/d)	GEdr
- - 'Haruno-awajuki' (9/d)	GEdr
- - 'Hatsune' (5/d)	GEdr
- - Herashibe Group (5/d)	GBuc
- - 'Hohobeni' (9/d)	GEdr
- - 'Hokutosei' (7/d)	GEdr
- - 'Hosyun' (1)	GEdr
- - 'Houkan' (9/d)	GEdr
- - 'Isaribi' (1)	GEdr
- - 'Junissen' (6/d)	GEdr
- - 'Kagura' (5A/d)	GEdr
- - 'Kasumino'	GEdr
- - 'Kiko' (9/d)	GEdr
- - 'Kimon' (9/d)	GEdr
- - 'Koshi-no-maboroshi' (7/d)	GEdr
- - 'Kougyoku' (9/d)	GEdr
- - 'Kousei' (9/d)	GEdr
- - 'Kuetsu' (9/d)	GEdr
- - 'Kuukai' (8/d)	GEdr
- - f. ***magna***	MAsh
- - - 'Murasaki-shikibu' (9/d)	GEdr
- - - 'Seizan' (9/d)	GEdr
- - 'Manazuru' (9/d)	GEdr
- - 'Miwaku' (1)	GEdr
- - 'Miyuki' (9/d)	GEdr
- - 'Murasaki-sakama' (9/d)	GEdr
- - 'Odoriko' (9/d)	GEdr
- - 'Okina' (9/d)	GEdr
- - 'Ō-murasaki' (1)	GEdr
- - 'Orihime' (9/d)	GEdr
- - 'Reeka' (1)	GEdr
- - 'Ryokurei' (5A/d)	GEdr
- - 'Ryokusetsu' (9/d)	GEdr
- - 'Ryokuun' (9/d)	GEdr
- - 'Ryougetsu' (1)	GEdr
- - 'Sadobeni' (1)	GEdr
- - 'Saichou' (7/d)	GEdr
- - Sandan Group (7/d)	GEdr
- - 'Sawanemidori' (6/d)	GEdr
- - 'Sayaka' (1)	GEdr
- - 'Seikai' (5A/d)	GEdr
- - 'Senhime' (9/d)	GEdr
- - 'Setsudu' (7/d)	GEdr
- - 'Shihou' (9/d)	GEdr
- - 'Shikouden' (9/d)	GEdr
- - 'Shikouryuu' (9/d)	GEdr
- - 'Shirayuki' (9/d)	GEdr
- - 'Shirin' (9/d)	GEdr
- - 'Shiun' (9/d)	GEdr
- - 'Shoujyouno-homare' (9/d)	GEdr
- - 'Sougetsu' (6/d)	GEdr
- - 'Soushyunka' (9/d)	GEdr
- - 'Subaru' (9/d)	GEdr
- - 'Suien' (9/d)	GEdr
- - 'Syoujyouno-Homare' (9/d)	GEdr
- - 'Tae' (5A/d)	GEdr
- - 'Taeka' (9/d)	GEdr
- - 'Takumi' (9/d)	GEdr
- - 'Tamahime' (8/d)	GEdr
- - 'Tamakujyaku' (6/d)	GEdr
- - 'Tamamushi' (9/d)	GEdr
- - 'Tamao' (1)	GEdr
- - 'Tamasaburou' (1)	GEdr
- - 'Tenjinbai' (1)	GEdr
- - 'Tennyonomai' (6A/d)	GEdr
- - 'Tenzan' (7/d)	GEdr
- - 'Toki' (9/d)	GEdr
- - 'Touen' (9/d)	GEdr
- - 'Touhou' (9/d)	GEdr
- - 'Touryoku' (9/d)	GEdr
- - 'Toyama-chiyoiwai'	GEdr
- - 'Unabara' (9/d)	GEdr
- - 'Usugesyou' (9/d)	GEdr
- - 'Utyuu' (1)	GEdr
- - 'Wakakusa' (9/d)	GEdr
- - 'Yaegoromo' (6/d)	GEdr
- - 'Yahiko' (5/d)	GEdr
- - 'Yahikomurasaki' (1)	GEdr
- - 'Yamahibiki' (9/d)	GEdr
- - 'Yukishino' (2)	GEdr
- - 'Yuunagi' (9/d)	GEdr
- - 'Yuunami' (1)	GEdr
- - 'Yuzuru' (9/d)	GEdr
- large, pale blue-flowered	NSla
- 'Lilac Picotee'	NSla
- mottled leaf	ECho
- patterned leaf	NSla
- pink-flowered	CLAP ECho GAbr MAsh WHoo
- var. ***pubescens***	MAsh
* - var. ***pyrenaica***	GBuc LEdu MAsh NSla WThu
* - - 'Apple Blossom'	GBuc NBir WAbe
* - - white-flowered	NBir
- 'Pyrenean Marbles'	CLAP NBir
- red-flowered	ECho
- var. ***rubra***	CLAP ECho NSla
- 'Rubra Plena' (d)	CElw GEdr MAsh NHar NSla
- violet-flowered	GAbr MAsh
- 'White Sands'	ELan GBin GEdr
- white-flowered	CLAP ECho GAbr MAsh WHoo XEll
'Noubeni'	GEdr
'Oboroyo'	GEdr
'Sakaya'	GEdr
× ***schlyteri*** Ashwood hybrids	MAsh
- 'The Bride' **new**	MAsh
'Stained Glass' **new**	EWld
§ ***transsilvanica*** 🏆H5	CBro CLAP ECho MAsh MCot NPnk WCot WThu
- 'Ada Scott'	GEdr MAsh
- 'Blue Eyes'	ECho GEdr GKev

	- 'Blue Jewel'	CLAP CWCL EBee ECho ELan EPot GBin GEdr GKev LHop MCot MHol WCot WPnP
	- blue-flowered	IBlr IFoB MAsh
	- 'Buis'	CLAP ECha ECho GEdr IFoB ILea MAsh NLar
	- 'Connie Greenfield' **new**	MAvo NSla
	- 'Eisvogel'	ECho GEdr
	- 'Elison Spence' (d)	GEdr IBlr LLHF MCot
	- 'Lilacina'	GEdr MAsh
	- 'Loddon Blue'	GEdr IBlr MAsh
	- pink-flowered	ECho MAsh
	- 'Sieben Bergen'	IBlr
	- 'Supernova' **new**	MAsh
	- white-flowered	ECho GEdr MAsh
	triloba	see *H. nobilis*
	'Umezono'	GEdr
	'Wakana'	GEdr
	yamatutai	GBuc GEdr GKev
	aff. ***yamatutai***	MAsh

Heptacodium (*Caprifoliaceae*)

	jasminoides	see *H. miconioides*
§	***miconioides*** ♀H5	Widely available

Heptapleurum see *Schefflera*

Heptaptera (*Apiaceae*)

triquetra W&B BGA-2	CSpe WCot

Heracleum (*Apiaceae*)

dulce	EBee
sphondylium	WSFF
- 'You're so Vein'	CNat
stevenii	MHol NSti WCot

Herbertia (*Iridaceae*)

§	***lahue***	GKev

Hereroa (*Aizoaceae*)

glenensis	CSma EDAr LRHS NHpl NRHS SPlb

Hermannia (*Malvaceae*)

erodioides	CPBP
flammea	SPlb
stricta	CPBP WAbe

Hermodactylus see *Iris*

Herniaria (*Caryophyllaceae*)

glabra	CArn GPoy

Hertia see *Othonna*

Hesperaloe (*Asparagaceae*)

campanulata	WCot
engelmannii	WCot
funifera white-flowered **new**	WCot
'Lynn's Pink'	WCot
malacophylla	CFil EBee
'Mamulique'	WCot
'New Blue'	WCot
parviflora	EBee LEdu LTro SBig SIgm SPlb XSen
- creamy yellow-flowered	WCot
- 'Rubra'	LRHS

Hesperantha ✿ (*Iridaceae*)

§	***baurii***	CTre GBin GBuc GKev LLHF NHpl WThu
	coccinea	CCVN CMHG CMac CTri CTsd EBee ECho EHoe ELan EPfP EUJe GKev IBlr LSou MBel MSCN MWts NChi NEgg NGdn NHol NLar NPnk SBod SCob SDeJ SRot WFar WMAq XLum
	- f. ***alba***	Widely available
	- 'Anne'	NLar
	- 'Ballyrogan Giant'	CPrp CYeo ECtt GBuc IBlr WFar WHer WSHC
	- 'Big Moma'	CPrp WFar
	- 'Cardinal'	NHol WFar WMoo
	- 'Caroline'	CPrp WFar
	- 'Cindy Towe'	CKno CYeo EAJP LLHF
	- 'Countesse de Vere'	CYeo EBee
	- 'Elburton Glow'	WFar
	- 'Eric's Early' **new**	ETho
	- 'Fenland Daybreak'	Widely available
	- 'Good White'	CYeo NBir NCGa SMHy
	- 'Hilary Gould'	CMea CPrp ECtt GBuc WHal
	- 'Ice Maiden' **new**	SPoG
	- 'Jack Frost'	CYeo EBee WFar WMoo
	- 'Jazz'	CYeo
	- 'Jennifer' ♀H4	CBro CDor CElw CPrp CTri CYeo EBee ECha ECtt ELon EPfP GAbr GBuc LPot LRHS LSou MCot MMuc MRav NLar SRms SWvt WFar WMoo WPnP
	- 'Maiden's Blush'	ECtt ELan LEdu LRHS LSou MCot NLar SRms WFar
§	- 'Major' ♀H4	Widely available
	- 'Marietta'	CYeo
	- 'Mollie Gould'	CPrp CYeo ECtt EHrv ELon GBuc GCra LHop LLWG LRHS LSou MAvo MHer MPie NCGa NHol NPnk SCoo SRms WFar WMoo
	- 'Mrs Hegarty'	Widely available
	- 'November Cheer'	CMac IBlr NBir NLar
	- 'Oregon Sunset'	CPrp CYeo WFar
	- 'Pallida'	CPrp CSam ECtt EHrv ELan MRav NBir WFar
	- 'Pink Marg'	CPrp CYeo ITim WFar
	- 'Pink Princess'	see *H. coccinea* 'Wilfred H. Bryant'
	- pink-flowered	CPne MBel
	- 'Professor Barnard'	CCCN CSpe EBee ECtt ELon EPfP EPri GAbr MBNS NBir NLar SRot WFar WRHF
	- 'Red Arrow'	EWes
	- 'Red Dragon'	CYeo ECtt GBuc LLHF NHol
I	- 'Rosea'	GKev SDeJ
	- 'Salmon Charm'	ECtt GBuc LRHS NCGa WFar WHar WMoo
	- salmon-flowered	CYeo
	- 'Salome'	CPrp CYeo WFar
	- 'Silver Pink'	IBlr
	- 'Snow Drift' **new**	ETho
	- 'Snow Maiden'	CWCL CYeo EBee EWTr GAbr LLHF LRHS MHer
	- 'Strawberry'	CPrp WFar
§	- 'Sunrise' ♀H4	CBcs CBro CCVN CMHG CPrp CSBt CSam EBee ECha EHoe ELan EPfP EPri GAbr GKev IBlr LHop LRHS LSou MCot MHer MRav NBir NGdn NWad SWvt WHoo WKif WMoo
	- 'Tambara'	CCse CPou CPrp CSam ECtt EHrv GAbr GBuc WFar XLum
	- 'Vibrant Scarlet' **new**	WFar
	- 'Viscountess Byng'	CFis CTri CWCL CYeo EBee NBir SPer
§	- 'Wilfred H. Bryant' ♀H4	Widely available

- 'Zeal Salmon'	CBro CElw CPou CYeo ECha ECtt GAbr NBir NCGa WFar
cucullata	CTre ECho NRog
huttonii	ECho GEdr ITim LLHF NBir
mossii	see *H. baurii*
pauciflora	CTre
vaginata	CTre

Hesperis (*Brassicaceae*)

lutea	see *Sisymbrium luteum*
matronalis	Widely available
- ***alba***	see *H. matronalis* var. *albiflora*
§ - var. ***albiflora***	CLau CSpe CTri CWld ELan EPfP EWoo GMaP LCro LOPS LRHS LSun MAvo MCot MNHC NGdn NPnk SIde SPer SPhx SPoG SWat WBrk WHil WMoo
- - 'Alba Plena' (d)	EBee IBoy LRHS MCot NBir WCot
- 'Cally Dwarf' (d)	GCal
- 'Lilacina'	SWat
I - 'Variegata' (v)	WBor
nivea	LEdu

× *Hesperotropsis* see × *Cuprocyparis*

Heteromeles (*Rosaceae*)

arbutifolia	see *H. salicifolia*
§ ***salicifolia***	LEdu

Heteromorpha (*Apiaceae*)

arborescens	SPlb SVen

Heteropolygonatum (*Asparagaceae*)

'Mikinori Ogisu'	EBee
roseolum	CAby

Heterotheca (*Asteraceae*)

mariana	see *Chrysopsis mariana*
subaxillaris	WCot

Heuchera ✿ (*Saxifragaceae*)

'Alan Davidson'	MPnt
'Alison'	MPnt
'Alpine Forest' (Kira Series) **new**	LRHS NRHS
'Amber Waves'PBR	CNor ELan ESps LRHS MJak MPnt NBir SCob SWvt WHar
§ ***americana***	MRav NBir SHeu SWvt WGwG
- var. ***americana***	MPnt
- Dale's strain	GPSL IBoy IFoB LBuc LSun MPnt NLar SHeu SPlb SWvt WRHF
- 'Harry Hay'	EBee EPPr EPri LEdu MPnt SHeu SMHy WPGP WSHC
- 'Marvellous Marble' **new**	MPnt
- 'Ring of Fire'	MPnt SHeu SWvt
'Amethyst Myst'	CLAP CRos ECtt EPfP ESps LHop LRHS LSRN MPnt NPla SCob SHeu SPer
'Apple Crisp'PBR	EBee ECtt LBMP LSou MPnt SCob SHeu SWvt WNPC
'Apple Souffle'	MPnt SHeu
'Apricot'	MPnt WCot
'Apricot Muscat' **new**	WCot
'Autumn Glow' (Seasonal Selection Series) **new**	MPnt SHeu
'Autumn Haze'PBR	MPnt SHeu
'Autumn Leaves'PBR	CAbP CLAP CRos ECtt ELan ESps EUJe EWoo LCro LRHS MPnt MTis NHpl SHeu SPoG SRot SWvt WCot
'Baby's Breath'	ECho MPnt
'Bardot'	MPnt
'Beaujolais'PBR	CAbP CLAP LBrs LRHS MBNS MNrw MPnt NBir SHeu WCot WNPC
'Beauty Colour'	CAbP CLAP CRos ECha ELan EPfP GMaP LHop LRHS LSRN MJak MRav NGdn NWad SHeu SHil SPer SWvt
'Belle Notte'	EBee ECtt MPnt SHeu WNPC
'Berry Marmalade'PBR	EBee ECtt EPfP LSou MAsh MPnt NHpl NWad SCob SHeu SWvt WHar WNPC
'Berry Smoothie'PBR	Widely available
(Big Top Series) 'Big Top Bronze'	EBee SHeu
- 'Big Top Burgundy'	SHeu
- 'Big Top Gold'	MNrw SHeu
'Binoche'PBR	CRos EBee ECtt LRHS MPnt SCob SHeu SHil WCot WTor
'Birkin'	LRHS MPnt
'Black Taffeta'	CRos CWGN EBee EPfP LBMP LRHS MPnt NRHS SHeu SPad
'Blackberry Crisp'PBR	EBee LSou MPnt SHeu WNPC
'Blackberry Jam'	CLAP CRos ECha ELan ELon EUJe GKev GMcL LBMP LRHS MPnt NBir NHol SHeu SHil SWvt
'Blackbird'	ESps GBin MPnt SHeu SWvt
'Blackout'	CAbP CLet ECtt MNrw MPnt NLar SHeu
'Blondie' (Little Cutie Series)	EBee ECtt GBin LRHS MAvo MPnt NPnk SCob SHeu SHil WCot WHlf WHrl
'Blood Red'	LSou MPnt SHeu WNPC
'Blood Vein'	MPnt SHeu
'Blushing Down'	EBee MAsh MPnt
'Bouquet'	MPnt SHeu
bracteata	MPnt XLum
'Bressingham Glow'	MPnt SHeu
Bressingham hybrids	CSBt CWib GJos IFoB NBir SRms
'Bressingham Spire'	MPnt
'Bright and Breezy' (Seasonal Selection Series)	MPnt SCob SHeu
'Bronze Beauty'	CMil ECtt MPnt SAko SHeu WBrk WCot
'Brown Sugar'	ECtt MPnt SHeu
'Brownfinch'	CElw MAvo MPnt SHeu SMHy WCot
'Brownies'	CAbP CLAP ECtt MPie MPnt SHeu WHrl WPtf WWtn
'Burgundy Frost'	MPnt SHeu WBrk
'Café Olé'	ECtt MPnt NLar SCob SHeu WHer WNPC
'Cajun Fire'PBR	CWGN EBee ECtt MPnt SCob SHeu WNPC
'Can-can' ♀H6	CLet CRos CTri ELon EPfP ESps EWoo LRHS MNrw MPnt NBir NLar SCob SHeu SHil SRot SWvt
'Canyon Duet'	MPnt SHeu
'Cappuccino'	EBee ELan EPfP ESps IBoy MPnt MRav SCob SHeu SWvt
'Caramel'PBR	CKno CLAP CMac CRos CWGN EBee ECtt ELan ELon ESps EWoo GMaP LLHF LRHS LSou MNrw NSti SCob SGbt SHeu SHil SPer SPoG SWvt WBrk WCot
'Carmen'	MPnt SHeu
(Carnival Series) 'Carnival Cocomint' **new**	SHeu
- 'Carnival Limeade' **new**	SHeu
- 'Carnival Peach Parfait' **new**	SHeu
- 'Carnival Plum Crazy' **new**	SHeu

- 'Carnival Rosa Granita' **new**	SHeu
'Cascade Dawn'	CLAP EBee MPnt NBir SWvt
'Cassis'	CWGN LSun MPnt SBod SCob SHeu WCot
'Cézanne' (Master Painters Series)	MPnt SHeu
'Champagne Bubbles'	MPnt SHeu
Charles Bloom = 'Chablo'	EBee LRHS MPnt SHeu
'Chatterbox'	MPnt SHeu
'Checkers'	see *H.* 'Quilter's Joy'
'Cherries Jubilee'PBR	CAbP CLAP ELon EPfP GMaP MPnt SHeu SLim WNPC
'Cherry Cola'PBR	CBcs CRos CSBt EBee ECtt EPfP GBin LRHS LSou MAsh MPnt NHpl NLar NPri NSti SCob SHeu SHil SPoG SRkn WNPC WTor
'Chiqui'	MPnt
chlorantha	MPnt
- 'Burnt Sienna'	GCal
'Chocolate Ruffles'PBR	Widely available
'Chocolate Veil'	MPnt
'Christa'	ECtt MPnt SHeu
'Cinnabar Silver'PBR	CLAP CRos ECtt LBMP LRHS MPnt NBir SCob SHeu WHar WNPC
'Circus'PBR	CWGN EBee ECtt MPnt SCob SHeu WTor
'Citronelle'	CRos CWGN ECtt EPfP LRHS MPnt NRHS SCob SHeu SPer SWvt WCot
'City Lights'	SHeu
'Coco' (Little Cutie Series)	CRos EBee ECtt GBin LRHS LSou MPnt NRHS SHeu SHil WNPC
'Color Dream'PBR	MPnt SHeu
coral bells	see *H. sanguinea*
'Coral Bouquet'	MPnt SHeu
'Coral Cloud'	MPnt SHeu
'Corallion'	MPnt
Crème Brûlée = 'Tnheu041' (Dolce Series)	CBcs CRos ECtt EHoe ELan EPfP EShb ESps GMaP LLHF LRHS MGos NBir NHpl NLar NPla SCob SHeu SHil SLim SPer SPoG SRot SWvt
'Crème Caramel'	IFoB MPnt
'Creole Nights'	ECtt MPnt SHeu WNPC
'Crimson Curls'	CLAP CRos ECtt EPfP LBuc LRHS LSou MPnt NRHS SCob SHeu SRms SWvt
'Crispy Curly'	MPnt SHeu
cylindrica	EPfP GKev GWyn MPnt SHeu
- var. ***alpina***	GKev LLHF
- 'Cream'	MPnt
- 'Francis'	MPnt
- 'Greenfinch'	CFis ELan EWTr GKev GLog GMaP GWyn LRHS MPnt MRav NBir SHeu SWat SWvt WHea XLum
- 'Hyperion'	LRHS MPnt SHeu
'Da Vinci' (Master Painters Series)	MPnt SHeu
'Damask'	LRHS MPnt SHeu
'Dark Beauty'PBR	CCVN CLAP CRos ECtt GMcL LBMP LRHS NHpl NWad SCob SHeu SRot WNPC
'Dark Secret'PBR	EBee MPnt SHeu
'Dark Storm' (Seasonal Selection Series)	MPnt SCob SHeu
'David'	MPnt SHeu WBrk
'Delta Dawn'PBR	CBod CRos CSBt CWGN EBee ECtt LBMP LBrs LRHS LSou MAvo MPnt NRHS SCob SHeu SPoG SWvt WNPC WTor
'Dennis Davidson'	see *H.* 'Huntsman'

'Earth Angel'	MPnt SHeu
Ebony and Ivory = 'E and I'PBR	CAbP CLAP EBee EHoe EShb ESps GMaP LHop LRHS LSRN MPnt NBir NWad SCob SRms SRot SWvt
'Eden's Aurora'	MPnt
'Eden's Mystery'	NLar
'Electra'PBR	CBcs CLAP CMea CSpe ECtt EUJe GMcL LBMP LHop LSou MBNS MPnt SCob SHeu SRot SWvt
'Electric Lime'	CLAP ECtt EHoe ELan GBin LHop MPnt NHpl NLar SHeu SPoG WNPC
'Elworthy Rusty'	CElw
'Emperor's Cloak'	GLog LEdu SHeu SPad SWvt WHrl WMoo
'Encore'PBR	ECtt MPnt SHeu
'Fairy Dance'	MPnt
'Fantasia'	SHeu
'Fire Alarm'PBR	CWGN EBee ECtt MPnt SHeu WNPC WTor
'Fire Chief'PBR	CLAP CRos CWGN EAEE EBee ECtt EPfP EShb ESps EUJe EWoo GMcL LBMP LHop LRHS LSou MAvo MPnt NBir NHol NHpl NLar SCob SHeu SHil SPer SPoG SRkn SRot SWvt
'Firebird'	LRHS MPnt
Firefly	see *H.* 'Leuchtkäfer'
'Fireworks'PBR ♀H6	CAbP CCVN ECtt GBin LRHS MBNS MPnt MRav NLar SHeu SPer SRot
'Florist's Choice'	SHeu
'Forever Purple' **new**	MPnt SHeu
'French Quarter'	MPnt SHeu
'Frost' (Little Cutie Series)	EBee ECtt MPnt SHeu SHil WNPC
'Frosted Violet'	see *H.* 'Frosted Violet Dream'
§ 'Frosted Violet Dream'PBR	CLAP ECtt LBMP LSRN LSou MPnt SCob SHeu SWvt WNPC
'Galaxy'PBR	CRos CWGN ECtt GBin LRHS MPnt NRHS SHeu WNPC
'Gauguin' (Master Painters Series)	ECtt MPnt SCob SHeu
'Georgia Peach'PBR	CAbP CLAP CRos CWGN EBee ECtt ELan EPfP ESps LBMP LHop LSou MNrw MPnt NBir NHpl NLar NPla SHeu SRot SWvt WHar
'Georgia Plum'	CRos CWGN ECtt LRHS MPnt NRHS SHeu WNPC
'Ginger Ale'PBR	CLAP CWGN EBee ECha ECtt ELan ELon EPfP ESps EWes GMcL LHop LRHS LSou MBNS MJak MPnt NBir NHol NHpl NLar NPnk NSti NWad SCob SHeu SPer SPoG SWvt WHar
'Ginger Peach'PBR	CLAP CRos ECtt LRHS LSou MPnt NRHS SCob SHeu WNPC
'Ginger Snap'PBR (Little Cutie Series)	LSou MAsh MPnt SHeu WHlf WTor
glabra	MPnt SHeu
glauca	see *H. americana*
'Glitter'	ECtt LRHS MPnt SHeu SHil WNPC
'Gloire d'Orléans'	MPnt XLum
'Gloriana' **new**	LRHS
'Gotham'	ECtt LRHS MPnt SCob SHeu SHil WNPC
'Grape Soda' (Soda Series) **new**	CWGN MPnt SHeu
'Green Ivory'	MPnt SHeu XLum
'Green Sashay'	MPnt SHeu
'Green Spice'	CLAP EAEE EBee ECtt ELan ELon EPed EPfP EShb ESps LBMP LCro LHop LRHS MAvo MJak MPnt MWat NBir NCGa NHol NPla SCob SHeu SHil SPer SPoG SWeb SWvt

'Green Tea' (Kira Series) **new**	LRHS NRHS
grossulariifolia	GMaP
'Guardian Angel'	MPnt SHeu SRGP
'Gypsy Dancer'PBR (Dancer Series)	CLAP EBee MPnt SHeu WNPC
'Hailstorm' (v)	MPnt
hallii	MPnt
Harvest Burgundy = 'Balheubur'	MPnt SHeu
Harvest Silver = 'Balheusil'	EBee MPnt SHeu
'Havana'PBR	ECtt MPnt SHeu
'Helen Dillon' (v)	GMaP MPnt NBir SHeu SRGP SWvt
'Hercules'PBR	ECtt MAsh MPnt SCob SHeu
hispida	MPnt
'Hocus Pocus' **new**	SHeu
'Hollywood'PBR	EBee ECtt ELon EPfP GMcL LBMP MGos MPnt NBir NHol NLar NPri SCob SHeu SPoG SRot
'Hot Stuff' **new**	SHeu
§ 'Huntsman'	LRHS MPnt MRav SHeu
'Iron Maiden' **new**	SHeu
'Jade Gloss'PBR	CLAP EPfP GBin LRHS MPnt SHeu SWvt WNPC
'June Bride'	MPnt
'Kadastra'	MPnt SHeu
'Kassandra'PBR	EBee ECtt MPnt SCob SHeu STPC SWvt
Key Lime Pie = 'Tnheu042'PBR (Dolce Series)	CBcs CMea CWGN ECtt EPfP ESps EUJe GMaP LHop LRHS MGos NBir NHol NHpl SCob SHeu SRms SRot SWvt
'King Kong' **new**	MPnt
Kira Series	MPnt
- 'Kira Arizona' **new**	LRHS MHtn NRHS
- 'Kira Rockies' **new**	LRHS NRHS
'Lady in Red'	NBre
'Lady Romney'	GCal XLum
'Lemon Chiffon'PBR	ECtt MAsh MPnt NHpl SHeu
§ 'Leuchtkäfer'	CBWd CBod CWat EPfP EShb EWTr GMaP GWyn LHop LPot LRHS MHer MMuc MPnt MRav NBir NMir SHeu SPlb SRms WMoo WPtf XLum
Licorice = 'Tnheu044'PBR (Dolce Series)	CBod CRos ECtt ELon ESps EUJe GBin GMcL LRHS MBNS MGos MPnt NBir NHpl NLar NPri NRHS SHeu SHil SLim SPoG SRot SWvt WHoo
'Lime Marmalade'	Widely available
'Lime Rickey'PBR	CWGN ECtt EPfP ESps ETod LBrs LRHS MGos NBir NSti SCob SHeu SWvt WCot
'Lime Ruffles'	LBMP MPnt SHeu WNPC
'Lipstick'PBR	CWGN MPnt SHeu SWvt WNPC
'Little Tinker'	MPnt SHeu
'Lune Rousse'	MPnt SHeu
'Magic Wand' ♀H6	CAbP ELon SHeu
'Magnum'	CMil CWGN IBoy IKil LBrs LHop MPnt SHeu WCot
'Mahogany'PBR	CLAP CRos EPfP EUJe LRHS LSou MJak MPnt NBir NHpl NPri SCob SHeu SHil SLim SWvt WHoo
'Malachite'	CRos EPfP LRHS MPnt NRHS SHeu
'Mango'	ECtt MPnt SHeu
'Marmalade'PBR	Widely available
'Maroon Blush'PBR **new**	SHeu
'Mars'	EPfP LRHS MPnt SHeu
'Mary Rose'	MPnt SHeu
maxima	MPnt
'Mega Caramel' **new**	MPnt SHeu
'Mega Citronelle' **new**	MPnt
'Melting Fire'	CRos GJos GMcL GPSL LRHS MPnt NRHS SHeu WHar WNPC
'Mercury'	SHeu
'Metallic Shimmer' (Fox Series)	MPnt
'Metallica'	SHeu WMoo
micans	see *H. rubescens*
micrantha	GCal MPnt SHeu SRms
- var. ***diversifolia*** misapplied	see *H. villosa*
- 'Martha's Compact'	MPnt
§ - 'Ruffles'	ECha MPnt SHeu
'Midas Touch'	CLAP CWGN EBee MPnt NLar SHeu WNPC
'Midnight Bayou'	CRos EBee ECtt ELan EPfP GBin GMcL LHop LRHS MPnt NHpl NLar NPer SHeu SRot SWvt WNPC
'Midnight Rose'	Widely available
'Midnight Rose Select'	ECtt MPnt NWad SHeu
'Midnight Ruffles'	MPnt SHeu WNPC WWFP
'Milan'PBR	MPnt SCob SHeu WNPC
'Mini Caramel' **new**	MPnt
'Mini Mouse'	MPnt SHeu
'Mint Frost'PBR	ECtt ELan LHop LPot LRHS MPnt NBir SHeu SWvt
'Mint Julep'PBR	CWGN ECtt MPnt SHeu WNPC
'Miracle'PBR	CLAP ECtt EPfP EWoo MPnt SHeu WNPC
'Mocha'PBR	CLAP ECtt MNrw MPnt SHeu SWvt WCot
'Molly Bush' ♀H6	EBee MPnt NCGa SHeu
'Morello'	MPnt SCob SHeu WNPC
'Mother of Pearl'	MPnt SHeu
'Muscat'	ECtt MPnt SHeu
'Mysteria'PBR	LBMP MPnt SHeu WNPC
'Mystic Angel'	ECtt MPnt SHeu
'Neptune'	EShb MAsh MBel MPnt SHeu
'Oakington Jewel'	MPnt
'Obsidian'PBR	Widely available
'Orphée'	MPnt
'Paprika'	CMea CWGN EBee ECtt IKil LBMP LBrs LRHS LSun MPnt SHeu SHil WCot WNPC
'Paris'PBR	CLAP CRos EBee ECtt EPfP GBin LRHS LSRN LSou MGos MPnt NHol NRHS SCob SHeu SHil SPoG WNPC
parishii NNS 93384	MPnt
parvifolia var. ***nivalis***	MPnt
- var. ***utahensis***	MPnt
'Pauline' (Fox Series) **new**	MPnt
'Peach Crisp'PBR	CMos CWGN EBee ECtt LBMP LSou NEoE SCob SHeu SPoG SRkn WNPC
'Peach Flambé'PBR	Widely available
'Peach Melba' **new**	ESps MPnt
'Peach Pie'	MPnt
'Peachy Keen'	SHeu
'Pear Crisp'PBR	CWGN ECtt LSou MPnt SCob SHeu WNPC
'Penelope'	CRos LRHS MAsh MPnt NRHS SHeu
'Peppermint' (Little Cutie Series)	ECtt GBin LRHS MPnt SHeu SHil
'Peppermint Spice'PBR (21st Century Collection Series)	MPnt SHeu
'Persian Carpet'	GMaP LRHS MPnt NBir SHeu SWvt WPtf
(Petite Series) 'Petite Marbled Burgundy'	EHoe LLHF MPnt SHeu SWvt
- 'Petite Pearl Fairy'	CAbP EHoe MPnt SHeu SWvt

	- 'Petite Pink Bouquet'	MPnt SHeu
	'Pewter Moon'	ELan EWTr GMaP MPnt NBir SHeu
	'Pewter Veil'	MPnt SHeu
	'Phoebe's Blush' (Fox Series)	MPnt WNPC
	'Picasso' (Master Painters Series)	ECtt MPnt SHeu
	'Pilley Pink'	SHeu
	'Pilley Pumpkin'	SHeu
	pilosissima	XLum
	'Pink Pearls'	EBee LBrs MPnt SCob SHeu WCot
	'Pinot Bianco'	MPnt SHeu
	'Pinot Gris'[PBR]	CLAP CWGN EBee ECtt MAsh MNrw MPnt SHeu WCot WNPC WTor
	'Pinot Noir'	MPnt SHeu WNPC
	'Pistache'	CAbP ECtt MPnt SHeu WCot WNPC
§	'Pluie de Feu'	GBuc LRHS MPnt MRav SHeu XLum
	'Plum Pudding'[PBR]	Widely available
	'Plum Royale'[PBR]	CLAP CWGN ELan EPfP GBin LRHS MCot MGos MPnt NWad SHeu SPer SWvt
	'Pretty Perinne'[PBR]	EBee MPnt SHeu
	'Pretty Polly'	LRHS MPnt SHeu
	'Pride of Pilley'	SHeu
	'Prince'	CCVN ELan LRHS MBNS MPnt SHeu SWvt
	'Prince of Orange'	SHeu
	'Prince of Silver'	LRHS MPnt SHeu
	pringlei	see *H. rubescens*
	pubescens	MPnt SHeu XLum
	- 'Alba'	MPnt
	pulchella	EDAr GCal GKev GLog LLHF MHer MPnt NLar SHeu SPlb SRms
	'Purple Mountain Majesty'	ECtt
	'Purple Petticoats' ♀H6	CBcs ELan LRHS LSou MGos MHtn MPnt NLar SHeu SLim SPoG SRot
	'Purple Rain Forest' (Kira Series)	SHeu
	'Quick Silver'	LRHS MPnt NBir SWvt
§	'Quilter's Joy'	MPnt
	'Rachel'	CAbP CCVN CLet EAEE EBee ECGP ELan EPfP GBuc GMaP IFoB LRHS LSRN MPnt MRav NBir NGdn SHeu SRGP SWvt XLum
	Rain of Fire	see *H.* 'Pluie de Feu'
	'Raspberry' (Fox Series)	MPnt
	'Raspberry Ice'[PBR]	MPnt SHeu
	'Raspberry Regal' ♀H6	MPnt MRav NBir SHeu SWvt WCot WSHC
	'Rave On'[PBR]	CAbP CCVN CWGN EBee ECtt ELan GBin LHop LRHS LSou MPnt NEgg NHol NLar NWad SCob SHeu SPer SRot SWvt
	'Red Dress'	MPnt SHeu
	'Red Spangles'	LRHS MPnt NBir SHeu
	'Regina' ♀H6	CAbP ECtt EPfP MPnt SCob SHeu SWvt
	'Renoir' (Master Painters Series)	MPnt SHeu
	'Rhapsody'	LRHS
	richardsonii	EBee MPnt SHeu XLum
	'Rickard'	MPnt
	'Rio'[PBR]	ECtt LSou MPnt SCob SHeu WNPC
	'Robert'	MPnt
	'Root Beer'[PBR]	CRos EBee ECtt EPfP LRHS LSou MPnt NHpl NRHS SHeu WNPC
	Rosemary Bloom = 'Heuros'[PBR]	EBee LRHS SHeu
§	***rubescens***	CAbP GAbr NBro WThu
	- var. ***versicolor*** **new**	GKev
	'Ruffles'	see *H. micrantha* 'Ruffles'
	'Sanbrot'	MPnt
§	***sanguinea***	CMac ESps IMou MPnt MRav NBir
	- 'Alba'	LPot MPnt SMHy
	- 'Coral Petite' **new**	LSun
	- 'Frosty' **new**	LRHS
	- 'Geisha's Fan'	CHid ECtt MPnt SHeu SWvt WNPC
	- 'Monet' (v)	EBee ECtt MPnt SHeu
	- var. ***pulchra***	SIgm
	- 'Ruby Bells'	CBod CCVN CSBt ESps GMcL LRHS LSRN MPnt MSCN NLar SHeu WHoo
	- 'Sioux Falls'	GPSL SHeu
	- 'Snow Storm' (v)	ELan MPnt SHeu
	- 'Splendens'	MPnt XLum
	- 'Taff's Joy' (v)	MPnt
	- 'White Cloud' (v)	EBee EPfP EShb MPnt NBre SHeu SRms XLum
	'Sashay' ♀H6	CLAP ELon GBin IBoy LSou MPnt SHeu WNPC
	'Saturn'	MPnt SHeu SWvt WNPC
	'Schneewittchen'	MPnt MRav NSti SCob SHeu
	'Scintillation' ♀H6	MPnt
	'September Morn' (Seasonal Selection Series) **new**	MPnt SHeu
	'Shanghai'[PBR]	CRos EBee ECtt EPfP LHop LRHS LSRN MPnt NRHS SHeu SWvt WNPC WTor
	'Shenandoah Mountain'	MPnt
	'Shere Variety'	LRHS MPnt
	'Silver Dollar'	CWGN EBee MPnt WCot
	'Silver Heart'	EBee MPnt
	'Silver Indiana'	MPnt SHeu
	'Silver Light'[PBR]	MPnt SHeu
	'Silver Lode'[PBR]	MPnt SHeu
	'Silver Scrolls'[PBR]	Widely available
	'Silver Shadows'	MPnt SHeu
	'Silver Streak'	see × *Heucherella* 'Silver Streak'
	'Sioux Falls'	MPnt
	'Slater's Pink' (Fox Series)	MPnt
	'Snow Angel'	CWGN ECtt LRHS LSou MPnt SHeu WCot
	'Snowfire' (v)	MPnt SHeu
	'Southern Comfort'[PBR]	CLAP CWGN EBee ECtt LRHS MBNS MPnt NHol NHpl NLar NPer SHeu SHil SLim SPoG SRot SWvt WCot
	'Sparkler'	MPnt
	'Sparkling Burgundy'	CRos ECtt ELan LRHS MPnt NHpl SHeu SWvt
	'Spellbound'[PBR]	CRos CWGN EBee ECtt EPfP LBMP LRHS MPnt NRHS NSti SCob SHeu SHil SPoG SRkn WNPC
	'Starry Night'	MPnt
	'Steel City'	MPnt SHeu
	'Stormy Seas'	CDor EAEE EBee ELan EPfP EWTr GCra LRHS MPnt MRav NBir SCob SHeu SWvt WPtf
	'Strawberries and Cream' (v)	MPnt SHeu
	'Strawberry Candy'[PBR]	CWGN ELon MPnt NBir NLar NWad SHeu SLim WNPC WWtn
	'Strawberry Swirl'	CElw EPfP EWTr GMaP MPnt MRav NBir SCob SHeu SWvt WNPC
	'Sugar Berry'[PBR] (Little Cutie Series)	EBee ECtt LRHS LSou MPnt NRHS SCob SHeu SHil WCot WHlf
	Sugar Frosting = 'Pwheu0104'[PBR]	CRos EHoe LRHS LSRN MGos MPnt NAst NCou NHol NPri SHeu SHil SRot SWvt

'Sugar Plum'PBR	CRos ECtt ELon EPfP GMcL LBMP LRHS LSRN MBNS MPnt NHpl NPri SCob SHeu SRot WHoo WNPC
'Sunrise' (Seasonal Selection Series)	MPnt SCob SHeu
'Sweet Berry'	MPnt
'Sweet Tart'PBR (Little Cutie Series)	EBee GBin LRHS LSou MPnt NRHS SHeu SHil WCot WTor
'Swirling Fantasy'PBR	EShb MAsh MPnt SHeu
'Tangerine Wave' (Fox Series)	MPnt SHeu WNPC
'Tara'	ECtt MPnt SHeu
'Thomas' (Fox Series)	GBin MPnt SHeu WNPC
'Tiramisu'PBR	CAbP CLAP CWGN ECtt ESps IBoy LHop LRHS MBNS MPnt NBir SHeu SWvt
'Tresahor White'	MPnt
'Van Gogh' (Master Painters Series)	ECtt MPnt SCob SHeu
'Vanilla Spice'	MPnt SHeu
'Veil of Passion'	NBre
'Velvet Night'	EPfP ESps LSou MPnt NBir SHeu SPlb
'Venus'	CWGN ECtt GAbr LSun MBel MMuc MNrw MPnt NSti SHeu SPer WBrk WCFE WCot WHoo WHrl
'Vesuvius'	MPnt SHeu WNPC
'Vienna'PBR (City Series)	GBin MPnt SHeu WNPC
§ ***villosa***	CSam GKev MPnt MRav SVic XLum
- 'Autumn Bride'	MPnt SHeu SMHy
- Bressingham Bronze = 'Absi'PBR	LRHS MPnt SHeu
- 'Chantilly'	MPnt SHeu
- var. ***macrorhiza***	EShb MPnt NBre XLum
- 'Palace Purple'	Widely available
- 'Palace Purple Select'	CMac CTri CWib ETod EUJe GMcL IBoy LSun MCot MJak SLim SWvt WHar
'Virginale'	MPnt
'Vulcano'	EBee WCot
'Walnut' (Fox Series)	GBin MPnt SHeu WNPC
'White Marble'	MPnt SHeu
'White Spires'	EAEE LRHS MPnt SHeu
'White Swirls'	MPnt
'William How'	MPnt
'Winter Joy' (Seasonal Selection Series)	MPnt SCob SHeu
'Winter Red'	CBod LRHS MPnt SHeu
'XXL'	MPnt SCob SHeu
'Zabeliana'	MPnt
'Zipper'	CWGN ECtt MPnt SHeu WNPC

× *Heucherella* ✿ (*Saxifragaceae*)

'Alabama Sunrise'PBR	CHid CLAP CRos ECtt ELan EPfP GMcL IKil LBMP LPre LRHS MAvo MPnt NPer SCob SHeu SHil SPoG SRot SWvt WTor WWFP
alba 'Bridget Bloom'	ECha ELan EPfP EWTr GMaP LPot LRHS MPnt MRav SHeu SPer SRms XLum
§ - 'Rosalie'	ECha EWoo GMcL LRHS MPnt MRav NBir SHeu SPlb WSHC
'Art Deco'	MPnt SHeu
'Berry Fizz'	LBuc MPnt NPnk SHeu SHil SWvt WNPC
'Birthday Cake'	MPnt SHeu
'Blue Ridge'	MPnt
'Brass Lantern'PBR	CRos CSBt CSpe CWGN ECtt EPfP LBMP LRHS LSou MAsh MAvo MBel MJak MPnt NCGa NDov NHol NLar NSti NWad SCob SHeu SHil SRot SWvt WNPC
'Burnished Bronze'PBR	CRos EAEE ECtt EPfP GBin LRHS MPnt NBro NLar NPla NPnk NWad SCob SHeu SPer SRot SWvt
'Buttered Rum'	EBee MPnt NAst SHeu WNPC
'Chocolate Lace'PBR	MPnt SHeu
'Cinnamon Bear'	MPnt SHeu
'Citrus Shock'	EBee MPnt SHeu
'Copper Cascade' (Cascade Series)	MPnt NPnk SHeu WNPC
'Cracked Ice'	EBee MPnt SHeu
'Dayglow Pink'PBR	CDor CLAP ECtt GMaP GMcL LBMP LSRN MPnt NBro NLar SCob SHeu
'Fan Dancer'	CLAP MPnt SHeu
'Fire Frost'	MPnt SHeu WNPC
'Glacier Falls' (Falls Series)	NPnk SHeu WNPC
'Gold Cascade' (Cascade Series)	MPnt
Gold Strike = 'Hertn041'PBR	CLAP ECtt MBNS MPnt SHeu
'Golden Zebra'PBR	CLAP CRos CWGN EBee ELan LRHS MAsh MBNS MNrw MPnt MTis NLar SHeu SHil SWvt
'Great Smokies'	MPnt SHeu
'Gunsmoke'PBR	CLAP CRos ECtt LBMP LRHS LSou MAvo MBel MPnt NRHS NWad SCob SHeu SWvt WNPC
'Heart of Darkness'PBR	MPnt SHeu
'Honey Rose'	LPre MPnt SHeu WNPC
'Infinity' **new**	SHeu
'Kimono'PBR ♀H6	CLAP CMac CRos EAEE ECtt EHoe ELan EPed EPfP EShb GBin GKev GMaP GMcL LPot LRHS LSRN LSou MBel MJak MPnt NBro NLar NSti NWad SCob SHeu SHil SPoG
'Mojito' **new**	MPnt SHeu
'Ninja'	see *Tiarella* 'Ninja'
'Party Time'PBR	SHeu
Pink Whispers = 'Hertn042'PBR	MPnt SHeu
'Quicksilver'	CBcs GMaP MPnt SHeu SWvt
'Redstone Falls'PBR	CWGN ECtt GBin LBMP LBrs LPre LRHS LSou MJak MNrw MPnt NLar NPnk NSti NWad SHeu SHil SPer SPoG SWvt WCot WNPC
'Ring of Fire'	SWvt
§ 'Silver Streak'	MPnt NBro SHeu SWvt
'Solar Eclipse'	EAEE EBee ECtt EShb IBoy LCro LPre LRHS MAvo MJak MPnt NLar NSti NWad SCob SHeu SHil SPer SPoG SWvt WCot WNPC
'Solar Power'PBR	CRos CWGN ECtt EPfP EUJe LRHS LSou MAsh MPnt NLar NWad SCob SHeu SHil SWvt WNPC WTor
'Stoplight'PBR	CAbP CLAP CMac CWGN ECha EPfP GBin GMaP GMcL MGos MJak MPnt MRav NBir NBro NEgg NHol NPla NSti SCob SHeu SHil SPer SRkn SRot SWvt
'Sunrise Falls'PBR (Falls Series)	CWGN EBee LLWG LPre MJak MNrw MPnt NWad SHeu SWvt WNPC
'Sunspot'PBR (v)	CLAP EAEE NBro SHeu WHer
'Sweet Tea'PBR	Widely available
'Tapestry'PBR	CDor CHid CLAP CMos CRos CWCL ECtt ELan EPfP GMaP GMcL LBMP LRHS LSou MBNS MPnt NDov NHol NPnk NSti NWad SCob SHeu SHil SPer SPoG SRkn SRot SWvt
tiarelloides ♀H6	CMac EPfP
'Twilight'	MPnt NPnk SHeu WNPC

§ 'Viking Ship'	CBWd CBod EAEE ECtt MPnt MTPN NBir SHeu
'Yellowstone Falls'PBR	CWGN GBin GMcL LBMP LRHS LSou MJak MPnt NCou NHpl NPnk NWad SCob SHeu SHil SPoG SRot SWvt WNPC

Hexastylis see *Asarum*

Hibanobambusa (*Poaceae*)

tranquillans	CEnt CJng ERod MBrN MMuc MWht SEND
- 'Shiroshima' (v)	CAbb CBod CDTJ CEnt CJng ENBC EPfP ERod EUJe MBrN MJak MMuc MWht SBig SEND

Hibbertia (*Dilleniaceae*)

aspera	CAbb CBcs CCCN CTsd EBee IVic LRHS WCFE WCot WKif WSHC
§ ***cuneiformis***	CCCN
pedunculata	WAbe
procumbens	GEdr WAbe
§ ***scandens*** 🏆H1c	CBcs CCCN CHll CRHN ELan
'Spring Sunshine'	ESwi LHop SEle
tetrandra	see *H. cuneiformis*
volubilis	see *H. scandens*

Hibiscus ✿ (*Malvaceae*)

aculeatus **new**	SBrt
coccineus	SBrt SMad SPlb
'Eruption'	ELon EPfP
'Fireball'PBR	SMad SPoG
Full Blast	see *H.* 'Resi'
hamabo	CCCN
huegelii	see *Alyogyne huegelii*
'Jazzberry Jam'PBR	MNrw
'Kopper King'PBR	MBNS MNrw SMad SPoG
leopoldii	SRms
militaris	SBrt
moscheutos	SBrt SVic XLum
- 'Cranberry Crush'	MNrw
- 'Old Yella'PBR	SMad
'Newbiscus Pink' **new**	CCCN
'Newbiscus Red' **new**	CCCN
'Newbiscus White' **new**	CCCN
paramutabilis	EWes
§ 'Resi'PBR	NPri WMat
rosa-sinensis	EBak SPre
- 'Apple Blossom' **new**	WFib
- 'Arcadian Spring'	WFib
- 'Blues Man'	WFib
- 'Byron Metts'	WFib
- 'Cajun Cocktail'	see *H. rosa-sinensis* 'Jambalaya'
- 'Candy Floss' (d)	WFib
- 'Carmen Keene'	WFib
- 'China Town'	WFib
- 'Cloud Nine'PBR	WFib
- 'Cockatoo'	WFib
- 'Cooperi' (v) 🏆H1b	WFib
- 'Courier Mail'	WFib
- 'Dorothy Brady'	WFib
- 'Enid Lewis' (d)	WFib
- 'Expo'	WFib
- 'Fifth Dimension'	WFib
- 'Gabriel'	WFib
- 'Georgia Peach'	WFib
- 'Gwen Mary'	WFib
- 'Helene'	LSRN
- 'Holly's Pride'	WFib
- 'Hot Bikini'	WFib
§ - 'Jambalaya'	WFib
- 'Jayella'	WFib
- 'June's Joy'	WFib
- 'Key West Thunderhead' (d)	WFib
- 'Lady Flo'	WFib
- 'Lemon Chiffon'	WFib
- 'Linda Pear' (d)	WFib
- 'Madame Dupont'	WFib
- 'Me Oh My Oh'	WFib
- 'Mrs Andreasen' (d)	WFib
- 'Rhinestone'	WFib
- 'Roman Candle'	WFib
- 'Rose Flake' **new**	WFib
- 'Rum Runner'	WFib
- 'Soft Shoulders'	WFib
- 'Spanish Lady'	WFib
- 'Sprinkle Rain'	WFib
- (Sunny City Series) 'Sunny Bary' **new**	CCCN
- - 'Sunny Bordeaux' **new**	CCCN
- - Sunny Cancun = 'Hican'PBR **new**	CCCN
- - Sunny Torino = 'Hirio'PBR **new**	CCCN
- 'Susan Schlueter'	WFib
- 'Tahitian Christmas'	WFib
- 'Tahitian Desert Sands' **new**	WFib
- 'Tarantella'	WFib
- 'The Path'	WFib
- 'Vermillion Queen'	WFib
- 'Weekend'	WFib
- 'White Swan'	WFib
schizopetalus 🏆H1b	WFib
sinosyriacus 'Lilac Queen'	LRHS SKHP WPGP
- 'Ruby Glow'	LRHS LSRN SKHP WPGP
'Summer Storm'PBR	SPad
'Sunny Premiere' **new**	CCCN
syriacus	CCCN ESps
§ - 'America Irene Scott'PBR **new**	SPoG
- 'Aphrodite'	LRHS MAsh
- 'Ardens' (d)	CEnd SPoG WFar
- Blue Bird	see *H. syriacus* 'Oiseau Bleu'
- Blue Chiffon = 'Notwood3'PBR (d) 🏆H5	CSBt LCro SPoG
- China Chiffon = 'Bricutts' (d)	CRos LRHS MAsh MMuc SEND SPoG
- 'Coelestis'	SPer
- 'Diana' 🏆H5	CDul CRos EBee ELon EPfP LRHS LSRN MAsh SCoo SKHP SLon SPer
- 'Dorothy Crane'	EMil LRHS SKHP
- 'Duc de Brabant' (d)	CCCN CSBt MBlu SPer
- 'Elegantissimus'	see *H. syriacus* 'Lady Stanley'
- 'Hamabo' 🏆H5	CBot CDul CRos CSBt CTri EBee ELan ELon EPfP ESps LRHS LSRN MGos MMuc NLar NPri SBod SCoo SEND SGol SLim SPer SPoG SWvt WFar WHar
- 'Helene'	ELan LSRN MBlu
- 'Jeanne d'Arc' (d)	SGol
§ - 'Lady Stanley' (d)	CCCN CMac CSBt LSou SCoo SPer
- Lavender Chiffon = 'Notwoodone'PBR (d) 🏆H5	CRos CSBt EBee ELan ELon EPfP EWes LRHS LSRN MGos MMuc SCoo SEND SPer SPoG WHlf
- 'Leopoldii'	SKHP
- 'Marina'	CCCN ELon EPfP LPar LSou MBlu MRav SGol WFar
- 'Meehanii' misapplied	see *H. syriacus* 'Purpureus Variegatus'

	- 'Meehanii' (v) ♀H5	CEnd CRos EMil EPfP LRHS SCoo SKHP SPer SPoG
	- 'Monstrosus'	MGos NLar
§	- 'Oiseau Bleu' ♀H5	Widely available
	- Pink Chiffon = 'Jwnfour' (d)	WCot
	- Pink Giant = 'Flogi'	CDul CMac ELan EPfP LPar LRHS SPad SPer
	- 'Pinky Spot'	LRHS
	- Purple Pillar = 'Gandini Santiago'PBR	SGol
	- Purple Ruffles = 'Sanchoyo' (d)	EPfP LCro LRHS SPoG
§	- 'Purpureus Variegatus' (v)	CBot CMac LRHS
	- 'Red Heart' ♀H5	CAco CDul CEnd CLet CMac CRos CSBt CTri ELan EPfP ESps LRHS MAsh MGos MMuc SEND SKHP SLim SPad SPer SPoG SRms SWvt WCFE
	- Rosalbane = 'Minrosa'	SGol
	- Russian Violet = 'Floru'	CEnd EPfP LRHS SKHP
	- 'Speciosus'	EBee SPoG WFar
	- Sugar Tip	see *H. syriacus* 'America Irene Scott'
	- 'Totus Albus'	CMac EBee LPar
	- Ultramarine = 'Minultra'PBR	EPfP LRHS NPri SKHP
	- 'Variegatus'	see *H. syriacus* 'Purpureus Variegatus'
	- 'Violet Clair Double' (d)	CMac
	- White Chiffon = 'Notwoodtwo'PBR (d) ♀H5	CSBt EPfP EWes LCro LRHS LSRN MAsh MGos MRav SCoo SPer SPoG
	- 'William R. Smith' ♀H5	CRos LRHS MSwo SPer
	- 'Woodbridge' ♀H5	Widely available
	trionum	CSpe EBtc WKif
	- 'Sunny Day'	ELan

hickory, shagbark see *Carya ovata*

Hieracium (*Asteraceae*)

	aurantiacum	see *Pilosella aurantiaca*
	brunneocroceum	see *Pilosella aurantiaca* subsp. *carpathicola*
	laevigatum subsp. ***nivale***	MMuc
§	***lanatum***	NBir
	maculatum Sm.	see *H. spilophaeum*
	pilosella	see *Pilosella officinarum*
	scullyi	EPPr
§	***spilophaeum***	EHoe MMuc NBid NPer NSti WOut
	- 'Blue Leaf'	WCot
	- 'Leopard'	GPSL NDov
	umbellatum	WOut
	villosum	EHoe WHer
	welwitschii	see *H. lanatum*

Hierochloe (*Poaceae*)

odorata	CBod ELon EPPr GPoy MBNS XLum

Himalayacalamus (*Poaceae*)

	asper	CDTJ ERod
§	***falconeri***	CEnt SDix
§	- 'Damarapa'	CEnt CJng EPfP
§	***hookerianus***	CJng EPfP IMou
	- 'Himalaya Blue'	CDTJ
	porcatus	CJng

× *Hippeasprekelia* (*Amaryllidaceae*)

'Durga Pradhan'	WCot
'Red Beauty'	WCot
'Red Star'	CCCN

Hippeastrum ✿ (*Amaryllidaceae*)

× ***acramannii*** ♀H2	CPne GCal WCot
advenum	see *Rhodophiala advena*
'Amputo'	LAma
'Apple Blossom' ♀H2	GKev LAma SDeJ
'Baby Star'	GKev SDeJ
bifidum	see *Rhodophiala bifida*
'Black Beauty'	LAma
'Black Pearl'	EPfP LCro LOPS
'Bogota'	GKev LCro LOPS
'Bolero'	LAma
'Christmas Gift'	GKev LAma LCro LOPS
'Clown'	LAma
(Diamond Group) 'Bianca'	LAma
- 'Charisma' ♀H2	LAma SDeJ
- 'Fairytale'	SDeJ
- 'Green Magic' ♀H2	GKev LAma NNys
- 'Lemon Lime'	LAma
- 'Picotee'	GKev LAma SDeJ
(Double Diamond Group) 'Alfresco'PBR (d)	LAma
(Double Galaxy Group) 'Blossom Peacock' (d)	LAma
- 'Dancing Queen' (d)	LAma LCro
- 'Double Dragon'PBR (d)	LAma
- 'Lady Jane' (d)	LAma SDeJ
- 'Nymph' (d) **new**	GKev
'Double Record' (d)	SDeJ
'Estella'	LCro LOPS
'Fantasy'	LAma
'Ferrari'	LAma
'Flaming Peacock'	LAma
(Galaxy Group) 'Apricot Parfait' **new**	GKev
- 'Benfica' ♀H2	CSpe LCro
- 'Flamenco Queen'	LAma
- 'Gervase' **new**	GKev
- 'Limona'PBR	LCro LOPS
- 'Orange Souvereign' ♀H2	GKev
- 'Pink Surprise' **new**	GKev
- 'Red Lion' ♀H2	GKev LAma
- 'Rilona'	LAma SDeJ
'Grand Diva'	LAma
'Grandeur'	LAma
'Inca'	LAma
'Jewel' (d)	LAma
× ***johnsonii*** hort. ♀H2	WCot
'La Paz'	LAma
'Liberty'	SDeJ
'Luna' **new**	GKev
'Marilyn'PBR (d)	LAma
'Misty'	LAma
'Mont Blanc'	SDeJ
'Mrs Garfield'	LAma
'Naughty Lady'	LAma
papilio ♀H1c	GKev LAma LCro MMrt SDeJ
'Pink Floyd'	LAma
puniceum	LAma
'Red Peacock' (d)	LAma SDeJ
'Rosario'	LAma
'Royal Velvet'	LAma NNys
'Ruby Meyer'	LAma
'San Antonio Rose'	WCot
'Santiago'	LAma
'Snow Queen'	LCro LOPS
'Sonatini Valentino' **new**	WCot
(Spider Group) 'Chico' ♀H2	GKev
- 'Emerald'	LAma WCot
- 'Evergreen' ♀H2	EPfP

- 'Lima'	LAma
- 'Sumatra' PBR	LCro LOPS
striatum	WCot
'Sweet Surrender'	LAma
'Toughie'	CTal EBee
vittatum	LAma
'White Dazzler'	LAma
yungacense 'Kiara'	XTur

Hippocrepis (*Papilionaceae*)

§ ***comosa***	EDAr SPhx
§ ***emerus***	CBcs CCCN CMHG CMac ELan EPfP MAsh MGil MGos MMuc SBod SEND SNig SVen WSHC

Hippophae (*Elaeagnaceae*)

rhamnoides	Widely available
- (m)	EPom
- 'Askola' (f/F)	CAgr
- 'Dorana' (f/F)	CAgr
- 'Frugna' (f/F)	CAgr NLar
- 'Hergo' (f/F)	CAgr MCoo NLar
- 'Hikul' (m)	CAgr NLar WHor
- 'Juliet' (f/F)	CAgr
- 'Leikora' (f/F) ♀H7	CAgr CDul ELan IVic MBlu MCoo NLar SPer
- Orange Energy = 'Habego' (f/F)	CAgr EPfP MCoo
- 'Pollmix' (m) ♀H7	CAgr ELan IVic MBlu MCoo NLar SPer
- 'Pollmix 3' (m)	MCoo
- 'Sirola' (f/F)	CAgr MCoo
salicifolia	CAgr
- GWJ 9221	WCru

Hippuris (*Plantaginaceae*)

vulgaris	CBen CWat EWay MSKA NPer WMAq XLum

Hirpicium (*Asteraceae*)

armerioides	SPlb

Hoheria ✿ (*Malvaceae*)

'Ace of Spades'	CAbb ELan ELon EPfP LRHS MGil NLar SEND SKHP SMad SPer SWvt WPGP
§ ***angustifolia***	EBee EPfP IDee SVen WPGP
angustifolia* × *sexstylosa	WPGP
'Borde Hill'	CAbb CBcs CDul CJun CMac CTho EBee ELan ELon EPfP EWoo IVic LHop LRHS MAsh MGil SEND SKHP SLim SPer SWvt WCFE WPGP
glabrata	CMac EPfP GBin GGGa IDee NBir SKHP WPGP
'Glory of Amlwch' ♀H4	CAbb CBcs CJun CSam CTho ELan EPfP GGGa GQui LRHS LSRN SChF SKHP SPer SWvt WKif WPGP
'Hill House'	CHII
§ ***lyallii*** ♀H4	CCCN CTho ELan GCra LRHS LSRN SPer SVen
microphylla	see *H. angustifolia*
populnea	CBcs CCCN CTsd IDee
- 'Holbrook'	CSam
sexstylosa	CAbb CBcs CBot CDul CHid CTho CTri ELan EPfP LHop LRHS LSRN MGos NEgg SKHP SPer SPlb SVen SWvt
- 'Crataegifolia'	EBee EWTr MGil NLar
- 'Pendula'	CMac
- 'Stardust' ♀H4	Widely available
'Snow White'	EUJe LRHS SLim SPoG WMat

Holboellia (*Lardizabalaceae*)

angustifolia	NLar WCru
- subsp. ***angustifolia***	LRHS SKHP WCot WCru
- - DJHC 506 new	WCot
- subsp. ***linearifolia*** BWJ 8004	WCru
- subsp. ***obtusa*** DJHC 506	WCru
brachyandra HWJ 1023	WCru
aff. ***chapaensis*** B&SWJ 7250	WCru
coriacea	CBcs CCCN CHII CKel CRHN CTsd ELan EPfP EShb IDee LEdu LRHS MRav NLar SEND SKHP SPer WCFE WCru
- B&SWJ 2818	WCru
latifolia	CBcs CBot CCCN CHII CMac CRHN CRos CTri EBee ELan EPfP LEdu LRHS NLar SAdn SArc SEND SEle SKHP SLim SNig SPer SPoG SWvt WBor WCru WPGP
- HWJCM 008	WCru
- HWJK 2014	WCru
- HWJK 2213	WCru
- SF 95134	EPfP
- subsp. ***chartacea*** DJHC 98442	WCru
- dark-flowered HWJK 2213	WCru
- lanceolate-leaved HWJK 2419	WCru
- pale-flowered HWJK 2213C	WCru

Holcus (*Poaceae*)

lanatus	WSFF
mollis 'Albovariegatus' (v)	CWCL ECha EHoe ELan EMOT EPPr EPfP ESps GMaP GWyn NBid NBro NPer NSti SPlb SRms XLum
- 'White Fog' (v)	CBod EAJP EBee EPPr MMuc NWad

Holmskioldia (*Lamiaceae*)

* ***lutea***	CCCN
sanguinea	CCCN

Holodiscus (*Rosaceae*)

discolor	CBcs CDul ELan EPfP EWes GCal IDee LEdu LRHS MBlu MGil MMuc MRav NLar SKHP SLon SPer SPlb WBor
- var. ***ariifolius***	WSHC

Homalocladium (*Polygonaceae*)

§ ***platycladum***	EShb

Homeria (*Iridaceae*)

breyniana var. ***aurantiaca***	see *Moraea collina*

Homoglossum see *Gladiolus*

Hordeum (*Poaceae*)

jubatum	CKno CSpe CWCL EAJP EHoe EWes LEdu NGdn SEND SPhx
- 'Early Pink'	NDov
secalinum	CHab

Horminum (*Lamiaceae*)

pyrenaicum	ECho MMuc SEND SIgm SRms WMoo
I - f. ***alboviolaceum***	SBrt
- dark-flowered	ECho GCal SBrt

Hornungia (*Brassicaceae*)

alpina	XLum

horseradish see *Armoracia rusticana*

Hosta ✿ (*Asparagaceae*)

AGSJ 302	WCot
'A Many-Splendored Thing'	EMic IBal
'Abana' (v)	IBal
'Abba Dabba Do' (v)	CDor ECtt ELon EMic IBal NEgg NSue
'Abba Showtime'	IBal
'Abby' (v)	EHoe EMic IBal NSue WFar
'Abiqua Ariel'	EMic
'Abiqua Blue Crinkles'	IBal NBir
'Abiqua Blue Edger'	EMic IBal
'Abiqua Blue Madonna'	IBal
'Abiqua Delight' (v)	EMic
'Abiqua Drinking Gourd' ♀H7	CDor ELon EMic GMaP GNew IBal IFoB MHom NEgg NLar NSue SBrk
'Abiqua Elephant Ears'	IBal
'Abiqua Ground Cover'	IBal
'Abiqua Moonbeam' (v)	EMic IBal NGdn
'Abiqua Recluse'	EMic IBal
'Abiqua Trumpet'	EMic IBal LRHS NGdn NLar
'Abraham Lincoln'	IBal
'Academy Mavrodaphne' **new**	EMic
'Ada Reed'	IBal
'Adorable'	IBal
aequinoctiiantha	EMic IBal
'Aksarben'	EMic
'Alabama Gold' **new**	EMic
'Alakazaam' (v)	EMic IBal NSue WFar
'Alan Titchmarsh'	IBal
albomarginata	see *H.* 'Paxton's Original'
§ 'Albomarginata' (*fortunei*) (v)	CBcs CMac GNew IFoB MNrw NBir NGdn SPoG SWvt WFar WMoo
'Alex Summers'	EMic IBal WFar
'All That Jazz' (v)	EMic IBal
'Allan P. McConnell' (v)	EMic GCra IBal LRHS MHom NSue SBrk WHal
'Allegan Emperor' (v)	IBal
'Allegan Fog' (v) ♀H7	EMic EShb IBal IFoB LRHS NHpl NSue SBrk
'Alligator Alley' (v)	EMic IBal
'Alligator Shoes' (v) ♀H7	EMic IBal
'Alpine Aire'	EMic IBal
'Alpine Dream'	IBal
'Alvatine Taylor' (v)	EMic IBal NGdn
'Amanuma'	EMic IBal MHom NSue
'Amazing Grace' (v)	EMic IBal
'Amber Tiara'	EMic IBal SBrk
'American Dream' (v)	EMic IBal LRHS
'American Gothic' (v)	IBal
'American Great Expectations' (v)	IFoB
'American Halo'	EMic IBal NEgg NLar NSti
'American Icon'	EMic IBal
'American Sweetheart'PBR	EMic IBal
'Americana' (v)	IBal
'Amethyst Gem'	IBal NSue
'Amos' **new**	IBal
'Amy Elizabeth' (v)	EMic IBal
'Andorian'	IBal NSue
'Andrew'	EMic
'Andy Murray' (v) **new**	SBrk
'Angel Feathers' (v)	IBal
'Anglo Saxon' (v)	IBal
'Ani Machi' (v) ♀H7	NSue
'Ann Kulpa' (v)	EMic GNew IBal NGdn SBrk
'Annabel Lee'	IBal
'Anne' (v)	IBal LSRN NSue
'Ansly' (v)	IBal
'Antioch' (*fortunei*) (v)	EMic EUJe GLog IBal MRav NLar
'Aoba Tsugaru'	IBal
'Aoki' (*fortunei*)	EMic IBal
'Aphrodite' (*plantaginea*) (d)	EMic EPfP EWTr MBNS MBel NGdn WCot
'Apple Candy' (v) **new**	IBal
'Apple Green'	EMic GKev IBal
'Apple Pie'	IBal
'Aqua Velva'	IBal
'Arc de Triomphe'	EMic IBal NLar
'Arch Duke'	IBal
'Arctic Blast'	EMic IBal
'Arctic Circle' (v) **new**	EMic
'Argentea Variegata' (*undulata*)	see *H. undulata* var. *undulata*
'Aristocrat' (Tardiana Group) (v)	EBee EMic IBal NEgg NGdn
'Asian Pearl' (v)	IBal
'Aspen Gold' (*tokudama* hybrid)	EMic
'Astral Bliss'	IBal
'Atlantis'PBR (v) ♀H7	EMic IBal NGdn NSue
'Atom Smasher'	NSue
'Atomic Elvis'	IBal
'August Beauty'	EMic IBal SBrk
'August Moon'	Widely available
'Aureafolia'	see *H.* 'Starker Yellow Leaf'
'Aureoalba' (*fortunei*)	see *H.* 'Spinners'
'Aureomaculata' (*fortunei*)	see *H. fortunei* var. *albopicta*
'Aureomarginata' ambig. (v)	CLet ESps SCoo
'Aureomarginata' (*montana*) (v) ♀H7	CMac EHoe ELan EMic GCal GMaP IBal MMuc NEgg NGdn NLar NSue WFar
§ 'Aureomarginata' (*ventricosa*) (v) ♀H7	EMic IBal NGdn WFar
'Aureostriata' (*tardiva*)	see *H.* 'Inaho'
'Austin Dickinson' (v)	ECtt EMic IBal LRHS NEgg
'Autumn Frost' (v)	IBal NSue
'Avocado'	ELon EMic IBal NLar NSue
'Awakening Angel' **new**	EMic
'Azure Snow'	IBal
'Azuretini'	IBal
'Babbling Brook'	IBal NSue
'Baby Blue' (Tardiana Group)	EMic
'Baby Blue Eyes'	EMic IBal NSue
'Baby Booties' (v)	IBal NSue
'Baby Bunting' ♀H7	EMic IBal IFoB NBro NLar NSue
'Baby Doll' (v)	IBal
'Bailey's Cream' (v)	IBal
'Baja White'	IBal
'Bali-Hai'	IBal
'Ballerina'	IBal LRHS NSue
'Bam Bam Blue'	IBal
'Banana Muffins'	IBal
'Band of Gold'	EMic IBal
'Banyai's Dancing Girl'	EMic IBal
'Barbara Ann' (v) ♀H7	EBee EMic IBal MHom NGdn SBrk
'Barbara May'	IBal
'Barbara White'	IBal
'Barney Fife'	IBal
'Battle Star' (v)	EMic IBal
'Beach Boy' (v)	IBal MNrw NLar NSue
'Bea's Colossus'	IBal
'Beauty Little Blue'	IBal NSue
'Beauty Substance'	EMic IBal SBrk
'Beckoning'	EMic IBal NSue
'Bedazzled' (v)	IBal
'Bedford Blue'	EMic IBal

'Bedford Rise and Shine' (v)	IBal LRHS
'Bedford Wakey-Wakey'	IBal
'Behemoth'	IBal NSue
'Bell Bottom Blues'	IBal
bella	see *H. crassifolia*
'Bells of Edinburgh'	IBal
'Ben Vernooij' (v)	EMic IBal
'Bennie McRae'	IBal
'Best of Twenty'	IBal NSue
'Betcher's Blue'	EMic IBal
'Betsy King'	CMac MRav NLar
'Bette Davis Eyes'	IBal
'Betty'	IBal NSue
'Biddy's Blue'	IBal
'Big Boy' (*montana*)	IBal LRHS NSue
'Big Daddy' (*sieboldiana* hybrid) (v) ♀H7	Widely available
'Big John' (*sieboldiana*)	IBal
'Big Mama'	EMic IBal MBNS MNrw NGdn NSue
'Big Top'	IBal
'Bigfoot'	IBal
'Biggie'	IBal
'Bill Brinka' (v)	EMic IBal
'Bill Dress's Blue'	EMic
'Birchwood Blue Beauty'	IBal
'Birchwood Gem'	IBal
§ 'Birchwood Parky's Gold'	EBee ECtt EMic EPfP GMaP IBal MBNS NGdn NHol NLar SBrk SCob
'Birchwood Ruffled Queen'	EMic
'Bitsy Gold'	EMic
'Bix Blues'	IBal
'Bizarre'	EMic IBal
'Black Beauty'	IBal
'Black Hills'	EMic IBal NSue
'Blackfoot'	EMic IBal
'Blackjack' (*sieboldiana*)	IBal WFar
'Blaue Venus'	IBal
'Blaze of Glory'	IBal
'Blazing Saddles' (v)	EMic IBal
'Blonde Elf'	EHoe EMic IBal MPnt NEgg NGdn NHol
'Blue Angel' misapplied	see *H. sieboldiana* var. *elegans*
'Blue Angel' (*sieboldiana*) ♀H7	Widely available
'Blue Arrow' ♀H7	IBal LRHS MHol NSue
'Blue Baron'	EMic IBal
'Blue Belle' (Tardiana Group)	EMic IBal NEoE NGdn
'Blue Blush' (Tardiana Group)	EMic IBal NGdn
'Blue Boy'	EMic EWes IBal
'Blue Cadet'	CMac EBee EHoe EMic EPed EShb GBin GQue IBoy IFoB LRHS NBir NGdn NLar NSue NWad SBod SBrk WFar
'Blue Canoe'	IBal
'Blue Cascade'	EMic IBal
'Blue Chip'	EMic IBal
'Blue Circle' PBR	EMic IBal
'Blue Clown'	IBal
'Blue Cup' (*sieboldiana*)	EMic MRav SRms
'Blue Danube' (Tardiana Group)	EMic IBal MHom NEgg
'Blue Diamond' (Tardiana Group)	EMic LRHS NSue WFar
'Blue Dimples' (Tardiana Group)	ECtt EMic IBal
'Blue Dolphin'	IBal
'Blue Edger'	IBal NBir
'Blue Flame'	EMic IBal
'Blue Frost'	IBal
'Blue Haired Lady'	IBal
'Blue Hawaii'	EMic IBal NSue
'Blue Heart' (*sieboldiana*)	ECha EMic IBal
'Blue Ice' (Tardiana Group)	EMic
'Blue Impression'	EMic
'Blue Ivory' (v)	CBod EBee ECtt ELon IBal MAsh NSue SBrk SGol
'Blue Jay' (Tardiana Group)	EMic
'Blue Lady'	EMic IBal
'Blue Lollipop'	NSue
'Blue Mammoth' (*sieboldiana*)	EMic EUJe IBal NEgg NSue
'Blue Maui'	IBal
'Blue Monday'	EMic
'Blue Moon' (Tardiana Group)	EMic ESps GKev IBal NGdn NLar
'Blue Mountains'	IBal LBuc
'Blue Mouse Ears' ♀H7	Widely available
'Blue River' (v)	EMic IBal
'Blue Seer' (*sieboldiana*)	EMic
'Blue Shadows' (*tokudama*) (v)	EMic ESwi GMcL IBal WFar
'Blue Skies' (Tardiana Group)	IBal MHom
'Blue Splendor' (Tardiana Group)	IBal
'Blue Umbrellas' (*sieboldiana* hybrid)	ELan EMic EPfP GMaP GNew IBal LRHS MHom NGdn NLar
'Blue Vision'	EMic IBal
'Blue Wedgwood' (Tardiana Group)	ELan EMic GQue IBal LRHS MHol NGdn
'Blue Wonder'	IBal
'Blue Wu'	IBal
'Blueberry à la Mode'	IBal
'Blueberry Cobbler'	IBal
'Blueberry Muffin'	EMic NSue
'Blueberry Tart'	IBal
'Bluetooth'	IBal
'Bob Deane' (v)	EMic IBal
'Bob Olson' (v)	IBal WFar
'Bobbie Sue' (v)	IBal
'Bobcat'	IBal
'Bogie and Bacall' (v)	IBal
'Bold Edger' (v)	EMic IBal
'Bold Intrigue' (v)	IBal
'Bold Ribbons' (v)	EMic SBrk
'Bolt out of the Blue'	EMic
'Bonanza'	EMic
'Boracay'	IBal
'Border Bandit' (v)	EMic IBal LRHS
'Border Favorite'	EMic
§ 'Borwick Beauty' (*sieboldiana*) (v)	ELon EMic IBal LSou NGdn SPer
'Bottom Line' (v)	IBal
'Bountiful'	EMic IBal
'Boyz Toy'	EMic IBal NSue
'Brandywine'	IBal
'Brave Amherst' (v)	IBal
'Brenda's Beauty' (v)	EMic IBal
'Bressingham Blue'	CAby CRos EBee ECtt GQue IBal LRHS MRav NLar SPer SWvt WFar WMoo
'Bridal Falls' (v) **new**	IBal NSue
'Bridal Veil'	EMic IBal SBrk
'Bridegroom'	EMic IBal
'Bridgeville'	IBal
'Brigadier'	IBal
'Brigham Blue'	IBal
'Bright Glow' (Tardiana Group)	EMic IBal

'Bright Lights' (*tokudama*) (v)	EMic IBal NGdn WFar
'Bright Star' (v) **new**	IBal
'Brim Cup' (v)	CAby CDor CRos EBee ECtt ELon EShb GBuc GMcL IBal LRHS LSou MBNS NBro NGdn SBrk SHil SPer
'Broadway' (v)	EMic IBal
'Bronx Bomber' (v) **new**	IBal
'Brooke'	EMic IBal
'Brother Ronald' (Tardiana Group)	EMic IBal LRHS NEgg
'Brother Stefan'	EMic IBal SBrk
'Brutus'	IBal
'Buckshaw Blue'	EMic IBal NBir NEoE NGdn WHrl
'Bulletproof'	IBal
'Bunchoko'	IBal
'Burke's Dwarf'	IBal
'Cadillac' (v)	EMic
* 'Caerula' (*ventricosa*)	IFoB
'Cally Atom'	EBee GCal IBal
'Cally Colossus'	GCal IBal
I 'Cally Strain' (*nigrescens*)	MHer
'Cally White' (*nigrescens*)	EBee GCal IBal
'Calypso' (v)	EMic IBal NGdn WFar
'Camelot' (Tardiana Group)	IBal LRHS NGdn
'Cameo'	NSue
'Camouflage'	EMic IBal
'Canadian Blue'	EMic IBal NLar NSue
'Candle Wax'	IBal
'Candy Dish'	IBal NSue
'Candy Hearts'	CSam EMic IBal MHom SBrk
capitata B&SWJ 588	WCru
'Captain Kirk' (v) ♀H7	EMic IBal NGdn NSue SBrk
'Captain's Adventure' (v)	EMic IBal NSue WFar
caput-avis	see *H. kikutii* var. *caput-avis*
'Carder Blue'	EMic IBal
'Carnival' (v)	EMic IBal IFoB LRHS NEgg NGdn NHpl SPoG
'Carol' (*fortunei*) (v)	IBal MBel NEgg NGdn NLar NSue SBrk
'Carolina Blue'	IBal
'Carousel' (v)	IBal
'Carrie' (*sieboldii*) (v)	EMic
'Cascades' (v)	EMic IBal NGdn
'Cathedral Windows' (v) ♀H7	EMic IBal NSue SBrk
'Catherine'	ELon GAbr IBal LSun NLar NSue SBrk WFar
'Cat's Eyes' (*venusta*) (v)	IBal ITim NSue
'Cavalcade' (v)	EMic
'Celebration' (v)	ELan EMic IBal
'Celestial'	IBal
'Celtic Dancer'	EMic IBal
'Celtic Uplands'	EMic IBal
'Center of Attention'	EMic IBal NGdn
'Centerfold'	NSue
'Chabo-unazuki' (*kikutii* var. *caput-avis*)	EMic
'Cha Cha Cha'	IBal
'Chain Lightning' (v)	EMic IBal NSue
'Challenger'	EMic
'Chameleon' (v)	EMic
'Champagne Toast' (v) **new**	IBal
'Change of Tradition' (*lancifolia*) (v)	EMic
'Chantilly Lace' (v)	EMic IBal SBrk
'Chariots of Fire' (v)	IBal
'Chartreuse Waves'	IBal
'Chartreuse Wiggles' (*sieboldii*)	EMic IBal NSue
'Cheatin' Heart'	EMic IBal NSue WFar
'Chelsea Babe' (*fortunei*) (v)	IBal
'Cherish' ♀H7	NGdn NHpl NSue WFar
'Cherry Berry' (v)	CBod CWGN ECtt EMic EShb IBal IFoB LRHS MBNS MHol MNrw MPie NBro NEgg NEoE NGdn NLar NWad SCob SHar SHil WFar
'Cherry Tart'	IBal NSue
'Cherub' (v)	EMic IBal LRHS
'Chesapeake Bay'	EMic IBal NSue
'Chesterland Gold'	IBal
'Chief Sitting Bull'	IBal NSue
'Childhood Sweetheart' (v)	IBal
'China Girl'	EMic IBal
'Chinese Gold'	IBal
'Chinese Sunrise' (v) ♀H7	CWCL EMic GBin GMcL GNew GWyn IBal MHom SRms
'Chionea' (v)	IBal
'Chiquita'	IBal
'Chi-town Classic' (v)	IBal
'Chodai Ginba'	IBal
§ 'Chōkō-nishiki' (*montana*) (v)	EMic IBal LRHS NGdn SBrk
'Choo Choo Train'	EMic
'Chopsticks'	EMic
'Christmas Candy'PBR	EMic IBal NSue SBrk
'Christmas Charm' (v)	IBal
'Christmas Cookies'	IBal SBrk
'Christmas Pageant' (v)	EMic IBal
'Christmas Tree' (v) ♀H7	EBee EMic IBal IFoB LRHS NEgg NGdn NLar NSue SBrk WMoo
'Church Mouse'	IBal NSue
'Cinderella'	EMic IBal
'Cinnamon Sticks'	EMic IBal
'Citation' (v)	IBal
'City Lights'	ECtt EMic MHtn NEgg
'City Slicker' (v)	IBal
'Claudia'	IBal
clausa	EMic
- var. ***normalis***	GQui IBal NBir NGdn NLar
'Clear Fork River Valley'	EMic IBal
'Clifford's Forest Fire'	ECtt EMic EUJe IBal LRHS NLar
'Clifford's Stingray' (v)	EMic GNew IBal NSue
'Climax' (v) ♀H7	EMic EPfP IBal IBoy
'Cloudburst'	EMic IBal
'Clovelly'	EMic IBal
'Clown's Collar' (v)	EMic IBal
'Coal Miner'	IBal
'Coconut Custard'	EMic NSue
'Cody'	IBal NSue
'Cold Heart'	EMic IBal
'Collector's Banner'	IBal
'Collector's Choice'	IBal NSue
'Color à la Mode' (v)	IBal
'Color Festival' (v)	CDor EMic IBal LLWG NLar NSue
'Color Glory'	see *H.* 'Borwick Beauty'
'Colored Hulk' (v)	IBal
'Colossal'	EMic IBal
'Columbus Circle' (v)	EMic IBal
'Con Te Partiro' (v)	NSue WFar
'Confused Angel' (v)	IBal
'Cookie Crumbs' (v)	EMic IBal
'Coquette' (v)	EMic GAbr IBal
'Corkscrew'	EMic NSue
'Corn Belt' (v)	EMic IBal
'Corn Muffins'	EMic
'Corryvreckan'	IBal
'Cotillion' (v)	EMic IBal NSue
'Cotton Candy' (v)	NSue
'Count Your Blessings' (v)	EMic IBal

'Country Mouse' (v)	EMic IBal NHpl NSue SBrk WFar
'County Park'	EMic IBal
'Cowrie' (v)	IBal
'Cracker Crumbs' (v) ♀H7	EHoe EMic GEdr GKev IBal ITim LRHS MHom MNrw NHar NHpl NSla NSue SBrk WCot
'Craig's Temptation'	IBal
'Cranberry Wine'	IBal
§ ***crassifolia***	EMic IBal LRHS XLum
'Cream Cheese' (v)	IBal
'Cream Delight' (*undulata*)	see *H. undulata* var. *undulata*
'Crepe Soul' (v)	IBal
'Crepe Suzette' (v)	EMic IBal
'Crested Reef'	EMic
'Crested Surf' (v)	EMic SBrk
'Crinoline Petticoats'	IBal
§ ***crispula*** (v)	EMic EPfP IBal MCot MHom MRav NChi
'Crocodile Socks' (v) **new**	IBal
'Crown Prince' (v)	IBal NGdn
'Crown Royalty'	EMic IBal
§ 'Crowned Imperial' (*fortunei*) (v)	EMic IBal
'Crumb Cake'	NSue
'Crumples' (*sieboldiana*)	IBal
'Crusader' (v) ♀H7	ELon EMic IBal LRHS
'Crystal Chimes'	IBal
'Crystal Dixie'	EMic IBal NSue WFar
'Cumulonimbus'	IBal
'Curlew' (Tardiana Group)	IBal
'Curls'	EMic IBal
'Curly Fries'	EMic IBal NSue
'Curtain Call'	IBal
'Cutting Edge'	EMic IBal
'Cuyahoga' (v)	IBal
'Dab a Green'	IBal
'Dance with Me' (v)	EMic IBal
'Dancing in the Rain' (v)	CWGN EMic GMcL NBro
'Dancing Mouse' (v)	IBal NSue WFar
'Dancing Queen'	EMic IBal
'Dark Shadows'	EMic IBal NGdn NSti WFar
'Dark Star' (v)	EMic IBal NGdn
'Dartmoor Forest'	IBal
'Dawn'	EMic IBal NSue
'Dawn's Early Light'	EMic IBal
'Dax'	IBal
'Daybreak' ♀H7	EMic IBal NBro SBrk
'Day's End' (v)	EMic IBal
'Deane's Dream'	EMic GNew IBal
'Decorata'	EMic
decorata var. ***normalis*** **new**	EMic
'Deep Blue Sea' ♀H7	EMic IBal NSue
'Deep Pockets'	IBal
'Dee's Golden Jewel'	EMic
'Déjà Blu' (v)	EMic IBal SBrk
'Deliverance'	EMic IBal NSue
'Delta Dawn' (v)	EMic IBal NGdn SBrk
'Delta Desire'	IBal
'Desert Mouse'^{PBR} (v)	IBal NSue
'Designer Genes'	EMic IBal SBrk
'Devil's Advocate'	IBal
'Devon Blue' (Tardiana Group)	EMic IBal LRHS
'Devon Desire' (*montana*)	IBal NLar
'Devon Discovery'	IBal
'Devon Giant'	EMic
'Devon Gold'	EMic GAbr IBal
'Devon Green' ♀H7	Widely available
'Devon Mist'	IBal
'Devon Tor'	IBal
'Dew Drop' (v)	EMic
'Dewed Steel'	IBal
'Diamond Tiara' (v)	EMic IBal LRHS NBir NGdn SBrk WWtn
'Diamonds are Forever' (v)	IBal
'Diana Remembered'	EMic GNew IBal NGdn NSue SBrk
'Dick Ward'	EMic IBal
'Dilithium Crystal'	IBal NSue WFar
'Dillie Perkeo'	IBal
'Dilys'	EMic MNrw
'Dimple'	EMic
'Dinky Donna' (v)	EMic IBal NHpl NSue SBrk
'Dinner Jacket'	ELan IBal LRHS SBrk
'Dixie Chick' (v)	EMic IBal LRHS NHpl NSue
'Dixie Chickadee' (v)	NSue
'Dixieland Heat'	IBal
'Doctor Fu Manchu'	IBal
'Domaine de Courson'	EMic IBal NSue WFar
'Don Stevens' (v)	IBal LRHS
'Dorothy'	EMic
'Dorset Blue' (Tardiana Group)	EMic IBal LRHS SHil
'Dorset Charm' (Tardiana Group)	EMic
'Dorset Flair' (Tardiana Group)	EMic IBal
'Doubled Up'	IBal
'Doubloons'	EMic
'Dragon Tails' ♀H7	EMic IBal NHar NHpl NSue SBrk
'Dragon Warrior' (v)	IBal
'Drake's Tail'	IBal NLar
'Dream Queen' (v)	ECtt EMic EWTr GNew IBal
'Dream Weaver' (v) ♀H7	CBod ELon EMic EUJe GNew IBal IFoB IPot LRHS MHom MNrw NBro NEgg NGdn NSue SBrk SPoG WFar
'Dress Blues'	CMac EMic IBal
'Drummer Boy'	EMic IBal
'Duchess' (*nakaiana*) (v)	EMic
'Duke of Cornwall' (v)	IBal
'DuPage Delight' (*sieboldiana*) (v)	EMic IBal NGdn NLar
'Dust Devil' (*fortunei*) (v)	IBal
'Dusty Waters'	IBal
'Eagle's Nest' (v)	IBal
'Early Times'	IBal
'Earth Angel'^{PBR} (v) ♀H7	EBee EMic IBal NGdn NSue
'Ebony Towers'	EMic IBal
'Edge of Night'	EMic IBal
'Edwin Bibby'	EMic
'El Capitan' (v)	EMic IBal IFoB LRHS SBrk
'El Niño'^{PBR} (Tardiana Group) (v) ♀H7	CDor CWGN EMic EPfP IBal LRHS MHom MNrw NBro NGdn NLar SBrk SPoG WFar WHoo
§ 'Elata'	EMic
'Elatior' (*nigrescens*)	IBal LRHS
'Elbridge Gerry' (v)	IBal
'Eldorado'	see *H.* 'Frances Williams'
'Eleanor Lachman' (v)	EMic IBal NSue
'Eleanor Roosevelt'	IBal
'Electrocution' (v)	IBal NSue SBrk
'Elegans'	see *H. sieboldiana* var. *elegans*
'Elephant Burgers' **new**	EMic
'Elisabeth'	EMic IBal LSRN
'Elizabeth Campbell' (*fortunei*) (v)	EMic
'Elkheart Lake'	EMic IBal
'Ellen'	EMic
'Ellerbroek' (*fortunei*) (v)	EMic
'Elsley Runner'	IBal NSue

'Elvis Lives'	EMic IBal LRHS NEgg NEoE NGdn NLar NSue SBrk
'Emerald Carpet'	IBal NSue
'Emerald Charger' (v)	IBal
'Emerald Crown'	EMic IBal
'Emerald Emperor'	IBal
'Emerald Necklace' (v)	EMic IBal
'Emerald Paisley' **new**	IBal
'Emerald Ruff Cut'	EMic IBal
'Emerald Tiara' (v)	CRos EMic IBal LRHS NLar SBrk SHil
'Emeralds and Rubies'	EMic IBal NSue
'Emily Dickinson' (v)	EMic IBal LRHS
'Empress Wu'^{PBR}	CAby CBod CDor EBee ECtt EMic ESwi EUJe GBin IBal IBoy ITim LPla LRHS LSun MBel MHol MSCN NGdn NSue SMad SPoG WCot WFar
'Encore'	IBal
'English Sunrise' (Tardiana Group)	IBal
'Enterprise' (v)	EBee EMic IBal NGdn NSue
'Eola Sapphire'	EMic IBal
'Eos'	IBal NLar
'Eric Smith' (Tardiana Group)	EMic IBal MHom SHar WFar
'Eric Smith Gold'	GKev
'Eric's Gold'	IBal SBrk
'Erie Magic' (v)	EMic IBal
'Eskimo Pie' (v)	WFar
'Essence of Summer'	EMic IBal
'Eternal Flame'	EMic NSue
'Everlasting Love' (v)	IBal
'Excitation'	EMic IBal
'Exotic Presentation' (v)	EMic IBal
'Extasy' (v)	EMic IBal NGdn NSue
'Eye Candy' (v)	IBal SBrk
'Eye Catcher'	EMic
'Eye Declare' (v)	IBal
'Fair Maiden' (v)	NHpl
'Faith'	EMic
'Faithful Heart' (v)	EMic IBal NSue
'Fall Dazzler' (v)	IBal
'Fall Emerald'	EMic
'Fan Dance' (v)	IBal
'Fantabulous' (v)	IBal
'Fantasy Island' (v)	EMic IBal NSue
'Fat Boy'	IBal
'Fatal Attraction'	IBal
'Feather Boa'	EMic IBal IFoB LRHS NHar NSue WFar
'Feng Shui'	IBal
'Fenman's Fascination'	EMic
'Fiesta' (v)	IBal
'Final Summation' (v)	EMic IBal NSue
'Final Victory' (v) **new**	IBal
'Finlandia'	IBal
'Fire and Ice' (v) $\mathbb{Y}^{H7}$	Widely available
'Fire Island' $\mathbb{Y}^{H7}$	EBee ECtt ELan EMic EPfP GBin IBal LRHS MHom MNrw NLar NSue SBrk SPoG WCot
'Fire Opal' (v)	IBal
'Firefly' (v) **new**	IBal
'Fireworks' (v) $\mathbb{Y}^{H7}$	EMic EPfP GBin GEdr GMcL IBal LSun MBNS MBel MHol MNrw NBro NGdn SBrk SDix SMad WCot
'Firn Line' (v)	IBal SBrk
'First Frost' (v) $\mathbb{Y}^{H7}$	EBee EMic EPfP IBal LRHS MNrw NGdn NLar NSue SPoG
'First Love' (*montana*)	EMic IBal
'First Mate' (v)	EMic IBal NSue SBrk
'Five O'Clock Shadow' (v)	IBal
'Five O'Clock Somewhere' (v)	IBal
'Flapjack' (v)	IBal
'Fleet Week'	EMic IBal
'Flemish Angel' (v)	IBal NSue
'Flemish Gold'	IBal
'Flemish Master' (v) **new**	IBal
'Flemish Sky'	EMic IBal IFoB NGdn NLar
'Floradora'	EMic IBal NSue
'Flower Power'	IBal
'Fluted Fountain'	EMic
'Fog Light'	IBal
'Fool's Gold' (*fortunei*)	EMic IBal
'Forbidden Fruit'^{PBR} (v)	IBal NSue SBrk
'Forest Fireworks' (v)	IBal
'Forest Shadows'	IBal
'Formal Attire' (*sieboldiana* hybrid) (v) $\mathbb{Y}^{H7}$	EMic IBal LRHS
'Forncett Frances' (v)	IBal
'Fortis'	see *H. undulata* var. *erromena*
fortunei	EMic ESps GKev GMcL GWyn WFar
§ - var. ***albopicta*** (v)	CSam ECha EHoe ELan EMic EPed EPfP ESps EUJe GMaP GWyn IFoB LEdu LOPS LPot LRHS MJak MRav NEgg NGdn NLar SPer SRms WBrk WFar WHoo WMoo
- - f. ***aurea***	CMac ECha EHoe EMic GMcL MMuc NEgg NLar SRms WFar WHal
- - - dwarf	EMic
§ - var. ***aureomarginata*** (v) $\mathbb{Y}^{H7}$	CSam CTri ECha EHoe ELan ELon EMic EPfP EShb ESps GMaP GMcL GNew IBal LPot LRHS MMuc NGdn NLar SEND SPer SPlb WFar
- var. ***gigantea***	see *H. montana*
- var. ***hyacinthina***	EMic EPfP ESps GNew IBal IBoy LRHS MRav NGdn NLar XLum
- - variegated	see *H.* 'Crowned Imperial'
- var. ***stenantha***	EMic
'Fountain of Youth' (*kikutii*)	IBal
'Fourteen Carats'	EMic IBal
'Fourth of July'	NSue
'Foxfire Palm Sunday' (v)	IBal
'Fragrant Blue'	EMic IBal LRHS NBro NGdn NHpl SPoG XLum
'Fragrant Blue Ribbons' (v)	EMic IBal
'Fragrant Bouquet' (v) $\mathbb{Y}^{H7}$	ECtt ELan EMic GNew IBal LRHS LSRN NEgg NGdn NHol NLar NSue SBrk WFar WHar
'Fragrant Dream'	EBee EMic GBin IBal LRHS NLar SBrk
'Fragrant Fire'	EMic IBal
'Fragrant Gold'	EMic
'Fragrant King'	IBal
'Fragrant Queen'^{PBR} (v)	GNew IBal NSue
'Fragrant Star'	EMic IBal
'Fran Godfrey'	EMic IBal
'Francee' (*fortunei*) (v) $\mathbb{Y}^{H7}$	Widely available
§ 'Frances Williams' (*sieboldiana*) (v) $\mathbb{Y}^{H7}$	Widely available
'Frances Williams Improved' (*sieboldiana*) (v)	EPfP GBuc IFoB
'Francheska' (v)	EMic IBal
'Frank Lloyd Wright'	IBal
'Free Jazz' (v)	IBal
'Fresh' (v)	EMic IBal
'Fried Bananas'	EMic GNew IBal ITim SBrk
'Fried Green Tomatoes'	EMic GNew IBal NLar SBrk
'Friends' (v)	EMic
'Fringe Benefit' (v)	EMic
'Frisian Pride'	EMic IBal
'Frisian Waving Steel'	EMic IBal

	'Frosted Dimples'	EMic GNew IBal
	'Frosted Frolic' (v)	EMic IBal WFar
	'Frosted Jade' (v) ♀H7	EBee EMic EPfP IBal LRHS MMuc NEgg NLar
	'Frosted June'	EMic IBal
	'Frosted Mini Hearts'	IBal NSue
	'Frosted Mouse Ears' PBR	EMic IBal NHpl NSue
	'Frozen Margarita'	EMic IBal NLar
	'Frühlingsgold' (v)	IBal
	'Fruit Punch'	EMic IBal IFoB
	'Fujibotan' (v)	EMic IBal IFoB
	'Fukurin-Fu' (*venusta*) (v) **new**	GEdr
	'Fulda'	EMic IBal
	'Full Moon' **new**	EMic
	'Funky Monkey'	EMic IBal
	'Funny Frolic' (v) **new**	IBal
	'Funny Mouse' (v)	EMic IBal NHpl NSue SBrk WFar
	'Futura' (v)	IBal
	'Gaiety' (v)	ECtt EMic IBal LRHS
	'Gaijin' (v)	EMic IBal NSue
	'Garden Party' (v)	IBal
	'Garnet Prince'	IBal
	'Gay Blade' (v)	IBal
	'Gay Feather' (v)	EMic IFoB
	'Gay Search' (v)	IBal
	'Geisha' (v)	IBal LRHS NEoE NGdn NSue SBrk
	'Geisha Satin Ripples'	IBal
	'Gemstone'	NSue
	'Gene's Joy'	EMic
	'Gentle Giant'	IBal
	'Gentle Spirit' (v)	IBal
	'George M. Dallas' (v)	IBal
	'George Smith' (*sieboldiana*)	EMic IBal
	'Georgia Sweetheart' (v)	IBal
	'Ghost Spirit'	IBal NSue SBrk WFar
	'Ghostmaster' (v)	IBal WFar
	'Giantland Mouse Cheese'	IBal NSue
	'Giantland Sunny Mouse Ears'	IBal NSue
	'Gig Harbor'	IBal
	'Gigantea' (*sieboldiana*)	see *H.* 'Elata'
	'Gilt by Association'	IBal
	'Gilt Edge' (*sieboldiana*) (v)	EMic
	'Gingee'	EMic IBal
	'Ginko Craig' (v) ♀H7	CMac ECha EHoe ELan EMic EPfP GKev GMaP IBal IFoB LRHS MRav NBir NEgg NGdn NLar NSti SBrk SPer SPoG WFar
	'Ginrei'	IBal
	'Ginsu Knife' (v)	EMic IBal
	'Glacial Towers' (v)	IBal
	'Glad Rags' (v)	IBal
	'Glad Tidings'	IBal
	'Glamour'	EMic IBal NSue
	'Glass Hearts'	EMic IBal
	glauca	see *H. sieboldiana* var. *elegans*
	'Glitter'	EMic IBal
	'Glockenspiel'	EMic IBal
I	'Gloriosa' (*fortunei*) (v)	IBal IFoB LRHS NSue
	'Glory'	IBal
	'Glory Hallelujah'	EMic IBal
	'Goddess of Athena' (*decorata*) (v)	IBal
	'Gold Drop' (*venusta* hybrid)	EMic IBal NHol NSue
	'Gold Edger'	CBcs CBod CDor CMac EBee EHoe ELan EMic EPfP EShb GKev GMaP IBal LRHS MMuc MRav NBir NGdn NLar NSti WFar
	'Gold Edger Surprise' (v)	EMic
	'Gold Flush' (*ventricosa*)	EMic
§	'Gold Haze' (*fortunei*)	EMic IBal MHom NBir
	'Gold Leaf' (*fortunei*)	IBal
	'Gold Pressed Latinum'	IBal
	'Gold Regal'	EBee EMic IBal IFoB LRHS MHom WFar
	'Gold Rush'	EMic
	'Gold Standard' (*fortunei*) (v) ♀H7	Widely available
	'Goldbrook' (v)	EMic IBal
	'Goldbrook Galleon'	IBal
	'Goldbrook Gaynor'	IBal
	'Goldbrook Genie'	IBal
	'Goldbrook Glamour' (v)	IBal
	'Goldbrook Gleam' (v)	IBal
	'Goldbrook Glimmer' (Tardiana Group) (v)	IBal LRHS
	'Goldbrook Glory'	EMic IBal
	'Goldbrook Gold'	IBal
	'Goldbrook Good Gracious' (v)	IBal
	'Goldbrook Grace'	IBal
	'Goldbrook Gratis' (v)	IBal
	'Goldbrook Grayling'	EMic IBal LRHS
	'Goldbrook Grebe'	IBal
	'Goldbrook Greengage' (v)	IBal
	'Goldbrook Greenheart'	IBal
	'Golden Age'	see *H.* 'Gold Haze'
	'Golden Fountain'	EMic
	'Golden Gate'	IBal
	'Golden Goal'	IBal
	'Golden Guernsey' (v)	EMic
	'Golden Isle'	EMic IBal
	'Golden Meadows' PBR (*sieboldiana*)	CDor ECtt EMic IBal NGdn NSue WFar
	'Golden Medallion' (*tokudama*)	ECtt EMic LRHS NEgg NGdn WFar
	'Golden Nakaiana'	see *H.* 'Birchwood Parky's Gold'
	'Golden' (*nakaiana*)	see *H.* 'Birchwood Parky's Gold'
	'Golden Needles' (v)	NSue
	'Golden Oriole'	EMic IBal LRHS
	'Golden Prayers' (*tokudama*)	EBee ECtt EHoe ELan GMcL MRav NBir NBro NEgg NGdn NLar WFar WHal WSHC
	'Golden Scepter'	EMic IBal LRHS WFar
	'Golden Sculpture' (*sieboldiana*)	EMic
	'Golden Spades'	EMic NSue
	'Golden Spider'	EMic
	'Golden Sunburst' (*sieboldiana*)	NEgg NGdn NLar XLum
	'Golden Sweetie' **new**	EMic
	'Golden Tiara' (v) ♀H7	Widely available
	'Golden Tusk'	IBal
	'Golden Waffles'	EMic NEgg
	'Goldsmith'	EMic
	'Gone Fishin'' (v)	IBal
	'Gone with the Wind' (v)	IBal
	'Goober'	IBal
	'Good as Gold'	EMic
	'Goodness Gracious' (v)	EMic IBal NSue
	'Gorgeous George'	IBal
	'Gosan' (*tardiva*) **new**	EMic
	'Gosan Leather Strap'	IBal
	'Gosan Mina'	EMic
	'Gosan Shining' **new**	EMic
	gracillima	IBal NRya
	'Granary Gold' (*fortunei*)	MHom
	'Grand Canyon'	EMic
	'Grand Finale'	IBal

'Grand Marquee' (v)	EMic IBal NGdn NLar
'Grand Master'	IBal
'Grand Prize' (v)	EMic IBal NSue
'Grand Rapids'	IBal
'Grand Slam'	IBal
'Grand Tiara' (v)	EMic IBal LRHS NGdn SBrk
'Grand Total'	IBal
'Grant Park'	EMic IBal
'Grape Fizz'	IBal
'Gray Cole' (*sieboldiana*)	EMic IBal ITim
'Great Arrival'	EMic IBal
'Great Escape'PBR (v)	EMic IBal LLWG
'Great Expectations' (*sieboldiana*) (v)	CDor CHid CMac CNor EAEE EMic EPfP IBal IBoy IFoB IVic LRHS LSRN MBNS MHer MNrw NBro NGdn NHpl SBrk SPoG
'Great Lakes Gold'	IBal SBrk
'Green Acres' (*montana*)	EMic GNew IBal LEdu WFar
'Green Angel' (*sieboldiana*)	IBal
'Green Eyes' (*sieboldii*) (v)	IBal NSue
'Green Fountain' (*kikutii*)	EMic IBal
'Green Gold' (*fortunei*) (v)	EMic
'Green Lama'	EMic IBal
'Green Mouse Ears'	EMic IBal NHpl NSue WFar
'Green Piecrust'	EMic
'Green Platter' **new**	EMic
'Green Sheen'	EMic
'Green Velveteen'	IBal
'Green with Envy' (v) ♀H7	EMic IBal LLHF NSue
'Greenie Weenie Bikini' **new**	NSue
'Greensleeves' (v)	IBal
'Grey Ghost'	EMic IBal
'Grey Goose' (Tardiana Group)	EMic
'Groo Bloo'	IBal
'Ground Master' (v)	CMac EBee ECtt ELan EPfP GCra GMaP IBal IFoB MRav NBro NGdn NLar NSti WFar WMoo
'Ground Sulphur'	EMic IBal NSue
'Grover Cleveland'	IBal
'Grünherz'	IBal
'Grunspecht' (Tardiana Group)	IBal
'Guacamole' (v) ♀H7	CAby CBcs CDor ECha ECtt EHoe ELon EMic EPfP GBin GNew IBal LRHS NGdn NLar SBrk SCob SHil SPoG WFar WHar
'Guardian Angel' (*sieboldiana*) ♀H7	EMic IBal NSue
'Gum Drop'	EMic
'Gun Metal Blue'	IBal
'Gunther's Prize' (v)	IBal
'Gunther's Rim' (v)	IBal
'Gypsy Rose' ♀H7	IBal NGdn NLar NSue SBrk WFar
'Hacksaw'	EMic IBal NSue SBrk
'Hadspen Blue' (Tardiana Group) ♀H7	CAby CSBt CWCL EBee ELan EMic EPfP ESps GMaP IBal IBoy LCro LOPS LRHS MBrN MGos MRav NBir NBro NEgg NGdn NHol NLar SHil SPer SPoG
'Hadspen Hawk' (Tardiana Group)	IBal
'Hadspen Heron' (Tardiana Group)	EMic IBal MHom XLum
'Hadspen Honey'	LRHS
'Hadspen Nymphaea'	IBal
'Hadspen Rainbow'	EMic IBal
'Hadspen Samphire'	CRos EMic IBal LRHS MHom NBir NBro
'Hadspen White' (*fortunei*)	EMic IBal NLar
'Haku-chu-han' (*sieboldii*) (v)	EMic NHpl SBrk
'Hakujima' (*sieboldii*)	IBal NSue
'Hakumuo' (v)	IBal
§ 'Halcyon' (Tardiana Group) ♀H7	Widely available
'Halcyon Gold'	ESps
'Half and Half'	EMic IBal NSue
'Hampshire County' (v)	EMic IBal
'Hands Up'PBR (v)	EMic IBal NSue SBrk
'Hanky Panky' (v)	EMic IBal NGdn NSti NSue SBrk WFar
'Hannibal Hamlin' (v)	IBal
'Happily Ever After' (v)	IBal
'Happiness' (Tardiana Group)	EHoe EMic IBal MHom MRav
'Happy Camper' (v)	IBal
'Happy Dayz' (v)	IBal
'Happy Hearts'	EMic
'Happy Valley' (v)	IBal
'Harmony' (Tardiana Group)	EMic
'Harpoon' (v)	EMic
'Harriette Ward'	IBal
'Harry van de Laar'	EMic IBal SBrk
'Harry van Trier'	EMic GBin GWyn SBrk
'Hart's Tongue'	IBal
'Harvest Delight'	EMic
'Harvest Glow'	IBal
'Hawkeye' (v)	IBal
'Hazel'	EMic IBal
'Heart and Soul' (v)	EMic IBal
'Heart Broken'	IBal
'Heart of Chan'	IBal
'Heart Throb'	EMic
'Heartache'	IBal
'Heartleaf'	EMic
'Heart's Content' (v)	IBal
'Heartsong' (v)	EMic IBal LRHS
'Heat Wave'PBR (v)	EMic IBal
'Heavenly Beginnings' (v)	IBal
'Heavy Duty'	IBal
'Heideturm'	IBal
'Helen Doriot' (*sieboldiana*)	EMic
'Helen Field Fischer' (*fortunei*)	IBal NLar
helonioides f. ***albopicta*** misapplied	see *H. rohdeifolia*
'Herifu' (v)	EMic
'Hertha' (v)	EMic
'Hida-no-hana' (*montana*) (v)	IBal
'Hidden Cove' (v)	IBal NSue
'Hidden Treasure' (v)	IBal
'Hideout' (v)	IBal NSue
'High Kicker'	IBal
'High Society' (v)	ELan EPfP IBal IFoB MHom MNrw NGdn NHpl NSue
'High Tide'	IBal
'Hi-ho Silver' (v)	EMic IBal NSue SBrk
'Hilda Wassman' (v)	IBal
'Hillbilly Blues' (v)	NSue
'Hippodrome' (v)	EMic IBal
'Hirao Elite'	EMic IBal
'Hirao Majesty'	IBal
'Hirao Splendor'	GNew
'Hirao Supreme'	EMic IBal
'His Honor' (v)	EMic IBal
'Hoarfrost'	EMic
'Holly's Dazzler'	IBal

'Hollywood Lights' (v)	EMic EPfP IBal NGdn NSue
'Holstein'	see *H.* 'Halcyon'
'Holy Molé' (v)	EMic IBal SBrk
'Holy Mouse Ears'[PBR]	EMic IBal NSue SBrk
'Honey Moon'	EMic IBal
'Honeybells'	CBcs CMac CTri EBee ECha ELan EMic EPfP GBin GNew IBal LEdu LHop MCot MRav NBid NGdn NSti SPer XLum
'Honeysong' (v)	EMic IBal
'Hoosier Dome'	EMic
'Hoosier Harmony' (v)	EMic
'Hope' (v)	IBal NLar
'Hot Air Balloon'	IBal
'Hotcakes'	IBal
'Hotspur' (v)	EMic
'Hudson Bay' (v)	EMic IBal
'Humpback Whale'	IBal
'Hush Puppie'	EMic IBal NHpl NSue WFar
'Hyacintha Variegata' (*fortunei*) (v)	CMac
'Hydon Gleam'	EMic IBal NSue
'Hydon Sunset'	CNor EBee ECtt EMic GCra GEdr IBal LRHS NBir NLar NRya NSti NSue SBrk WHal
hypoleuca	EMic IBal
'Hyuga-urajiro' (v)	EMic IBal WFar
'Ice Cream' (*cathayana*) (v)	IBal LRHS NGdn
'Ice Cube' (v)	IBal NSue
'Ice Prancer'	EMic IBal
'Iced Lemon' (v)	EMic GNew IBal NHpl NSue SBrk WFar
'Illicit Affair'	EMic IBal NHpl NSue SBrk
'Imp' (v)	EMic IBal
§ 'Inaho'	LRHS NSue
'Inca Gold'	IBal NSue
'Incoming'	IBal
'Independence' (v)	EBee EMic IBal NBro NSue SPoG WFar
'Independence Day' (v)	EMic
'Inniswood' (v)	CDor CWCL ECtt EMic IBal MBNS NBro NGdn NLar NSti WFar
'Invincible'	CDor ECtt EMic IBal NBid NEgg NGdn NLar WFar
'Invincible Spirit'	IBal
'Iona' (*fortunei*)	EMic IBal LRHS SBrk
'Irische See' (Tardiana Group)	IBal
'Irish Eyes' (v)	EMic IBal
'Irish Luck'	EMic IBal NSue
'Iron Gate Special' (v)	EMic
'Iron Gate Supreme' (v)	EMic
'Island Charm' (v) ♀H7	GBin IBal LRHS NHar NHpl NLar SCob WFar
'Itty Bitty' (v)	NSue
'Itty Gold' **new**	IBal
'Ivory Coast' (v)	EMic IBal MHol
'Ivory Necklace' (v)	IBal
'Ivory Queen' (v)	EMic IBal
'Iwa Yara Moto'	IBal
'Jack of Diamonds'	IBal
'Jade Cascade'	EMic GBin IBal NBir NEgg NLar SBrk WHal
'Jade Scepter' (*nakaiana*)	EMic
'Janet Day' (v)	EMic
'Janet' (*fortunei*) (v)	EMic NGdn
'Janet's Green Sox'	EMic
'Jason and Katie' (v)	EMic IBal
'Jaws'	EMic IBal NSue
'Jaz'	IBal
'Jennifer' (v) **new**	IBal
'Jennifer Bailey' (v)	IBal
'Jerry Landwehr'	EMic IBal
'Jewel of the Nile' (v)	EMic IBal
'Jimmy Crack Corn'	EMic IBal NEgg NGdn
'Jingle Bells'	IBal
'John Wargo'	IBal
'Johnny Angel'	EMic
'Jolly Green Giant' (*sieboldiana* hybrid)	EMic
'Joseph'	EMic IBal
'Journeyman'	EMic IBal
'Journey's End' (v)	EMic IBal
'Joyce Trott' (v)	EMic
'Joyful' (v)	IBal
'Jubilee' (v)	EMic IBal
'Judy Rocco'	IBal
'Juha' (v)	EMic
'Jules'	IBal
'Julia' (v)	EMic IBal NSue
'Julie Morss'	EMic GMaP IBal MHom NEgg SBrk
'June'[PBR] (Tardiana Group) (v) ♀H7	Widely available
'June Fever'[PBR] (Tardiana Group)	EMic ESwi GBin IBal LLWG NBro NGdn NLar NSue SPoG WFar
'June Spirit' (v)	IBal
'Junka'	SMHy
'Jurassic Park'	EBee EMic EUJe GMcL IBal LLWG LRHS MNrw NLar
'Just So' (v)	EMic IBal
'Justine'[PBR]	EMic IBal NSue
'Kabitan'	see *H. sieboldii* var. *sieboldii* f. *kabitan*
'Kabuki'	IBal
'Kalamazoo' (v)	EMic IBal
'Kaleidochrome' (v)	IBal NSue
'Karin'	EMic IBal
'Katherine Lewis' (Tardiana Group) (v)	EMic IBal LRHS LSRN NHol
'Kath's Gold'	EMic
'Katie Q' (v)	EMic IBal
'Katsuragawa-beni' (v)	EMic IBal
'Kelly'	EMic
'Kelsey'	EMic
'Kenzie' (v)	EMic IBal
'Key Lime Pie'	EMic IBal
'Key West'	EMic
'Kifukurin' (*kikutii*)	see *H.* 'Kifukurin-hyuga'
§ 'Kifukurin-hyuga' (v)	IBal
'Kifukurin-kiyosumi'	IBal
'Kifukurin-ko-mame' (*gracillima*) (v)	EMic NSue
'Kifukurin-otome' (*venusta*) (v)	EMic NSue
'Kifukurin-ubatake' (*pulchella*) (v)	EMic IBal
kikutii	EMic IBal IMou LRHS
§ - var. ***caput-avis***	EMic
§ - var. ***yakusimensis***	EMic GEdr IBal NHar SMad
'Ki-nakafu-otome' (*venusta*)	IBal
'Kinbotan' (*venusta*) (v)	EMic GEdr
'Kinbuchi Tachi' (*rectifolia*) (v)	IBal
'King James'	IBal
'King of Spades'	IBal
'King Tut'	EMic
'Kingfisher' (Tardiana Group)	LRHS
'Kingsize'	IBal
§ 'Kirishima'	EMic NHpl NSue
'Kisuji'	see *H.* 'Mediopicta'

'Kitty Cat'	EMic IBal WFar
'Kiwi Black Magic'	IBal
'Kiwi Blue Baby'	EMic IBal
'Kiwi Blue Ruffles'	IBal
'Kiwi Blue Sky'	IBal
'Kiwi Canoe'	IBal
'Kiwi Cream Edge' (v)	EMic
'Kiwi Forest'	IBal
'Kiwi Full Monty' (v)	CDor EBee EMic IBal NSue SBrk
'Kiwi Gold Rush'	IBal
'Kiwi Hippo'	IBal
'Kiwi Jordan'	IBal
'Kiwi Kaniere Gold'	IBal
'Kiwi Minnie Gold'	IBal ITim
'Kiwi Parasol'	IBal
'Kiwi Skyscraper'	IBal
'Kiwi Sunshine'	IBal
kiyosumiensis	IBal
'Klopping Variegated' (v)	EMic
'Knight's Journey'	IBal
'Knockout' (v)	MBNS MNrw MRav NBro NEgg NGdn NLar
'Komodo Dragon'	EMic IBal SKHP
'Konkubine'	EMic
'Korean Snow'	IBal
'Koriyama' (*sieboldiana*) (v)	EMic
'Krossa Cream Edge' (*sieboldii*) (v)	IBal
'Krossa Regal' 🏆H7	Widely available
'La Donna'	IBal
'Lacy Belle' (v)	CDor CSBt EBee EMic EPfP IBal LRHS NBro NEoE NGdn NSue SBrk WRHF
'Lady Godiva'	IBal
'Lady Guineverre'	EMic IBal
'Lady Helen'	EMic
'Lady in Red'	IBal
'Lady Isobel Barnett' (v) 🏆H7	IBal
laevigata	IBal
'Lake Hitchock'	IBal
'Lake Superior'	IBal
'Lakeside Accolade'	IBal
'Lakeside Alex Andra' (v)	IBal
'Lakeside April Snow' (v)	EMic IBal NGdn
'Lakeside Baby Face' (v)	EMic IBal NHpl NSue
'Lakeside Banana Bay' (v)	IBal NGdn
'Lakeside Beach Bum'	IBal
'Lakeside Beach Captain' (v)	EMic
'Lakeside Black Satin'	EMic WFar
'Lakeside Blue Cherub'	EMic IBal
'Lakeside Breaking News' (v)	EMic IBal
'Lakeside Butter Ball'	IBal
'Lakeside Cha Cha' (v)	EMic IBal SBrk WFar
'Lakeside Cindy Cee' (v)	IBal
'Lakeside Circle O' (v) **new**	IBal
'Lakeside Coal Miner'	EMic IBal NGdn NLar
'Lakeside Color Blue'	IBal
'Lakeside Contender'	IBal
'Lakeside Cupcake' (v)	EMic IBal NGdn NSue
'Lakeside Cupid's Cup' (v)	IBal
'Lakeside Dimpled Darling' (v)	NSue
'Lakeside Dividing Line' (v)	IBal
'Lakeside Doodad' (v)	IBal
'Lakeside Down Sized' (v)	EMic IBal MHom NSue SBrk WFar
'Lakeside Dragonfly' (v)	EBee EMic EPfP EShb IBal LLWG MNrw NGdn NLar NSue SBrk WFar
'Lakeside Elfin Fire'	EMic NSue
'Lakeside Fancy Pants' (v)	IBal
'Lakeside Feather Light' (v)	IBal
'Lakeside Foaming Sea'	IBal
'Lakeside Full Tide'	IBal
'Lakeside Hazy Morn' (v)	IBal
'Lakeside Hoola Hoop' (v)	IBal
'Lakeside Iron Man'	IBal
'Lakeside Jazzy Jane' (v)	IBal
'Lakeside Kaleidoscope'	EMic IBal NGdn SBrk
'Lakeside Keepsake' (v)	IBal
'Lakeside Khum Kaw' **new**	IBal
'Lakeside Legal Tender'	IBal
'Lakeside Lime Time'	IBal
'Lakeside Little Gem'	IBal NSue
'Lakeside Little Tuft' (v)	EMic IBal NSue SBrk
'Lakeside Lollipop'	EMic IBal
'Lakeside Looking Glass'	EMic
'Lakeside Love Affaire'	EMic IBal WFar
'Lakeside Maestro'	IBal NLar
'Lakeside Maverick'	IBal
'Lakeside Meadow Ice' (v)	IBal
'Lakeside Meter Maid' (v)	IBal
'Lakeside Midnight Miss'	IBal
'Lakeside Miss Muffett' (v)	NSue
'Lakeside Missy Little' (v)	IBal
'Lakeside Neat Petite'	IBal NSue
'Lakeside Ninita' (v)	EMic IBal LRHS NSue SBrk
'Lakeside Old Smokey'	IBal
'Lakeside Paisley Print' (v)	EMic IBal NSue
'Lakeside Pebbles'	IBal
'Lakeside Premier'	EMic IBal
'Lakeside Prophecy'	IBal
'Lakeside Prophecy Fulfilled' (v)	IBal
'Lakeside Rhapsody' (v)	EMic IBal
'Lakeside Ring Master' (v)	IBal
'Lakeside Ripples'	IBal
'Lakeside Rocky Top' (v)	IBal
'Lakeside Roy El' (v)	IBal
'Lakeside Sapphire Pleats'	EMic
'Lakeside Sassy Sally'	IBal
'Lakeside Scamp' (v)	EMic NSue
'Lakeside Shadows' (v)	IBal
'Lakeside Shoremaster' (v)	IBal
'Lakeside Slick Chick' (v)	IBal
'Lakeside Sophistication' (v)	IBal
'Lakeside Sparkle Plenty' (v)	IBal
'Lakeside Spellbinder' (v)	IBal LRHS
'Lakeside Spruce Goose' (v)	EMic IBal
'Lakeside Storm Watch'	EMic IBal NSue
'Lakeside Swan Pon' (v)	IBal
'Lakeside Symphony' (v)	EMic
'Lakeside Tee Ki' (v)	IBal
'Lakeside Whizzit' (v)	IBal NSue
'Lakeside Zesty Zeno' (v)	IBal
'Lakeside Zinger' (v)	EMic IBal NSue
lancifolia	CMac EBee ELan EMic GMaP IBal MRav NGdn NSti SPer SRms WKif WSHC WThu
'Last Dance' (v)	IBal
'Laura Lanier'	EMic IBal
'Laura Z'	IBal
'Lavender Doll'	IBal
'Leading Lady' 🏆H7	IBal
'Leather Sheen'	EHoe EMic
'Leatherneck'	IBal
'Lederhosen'	EMic
'Lemon Delight'	EMic IBal LRHS NSue SBrk WFar
'Lemon Frost'	EMic IBal
'Lemon Juice'	EBee

'Lemon Lime'	EMic EWld IBal MHom MNrw NEgg NEoE NSue WCot
'Lemon Meringue'	EMic
'Lemon Twist'	IBal
'Lemonade'	GBin IBal
'Leola Fraim' (v)	EMic IBal LRHS
'Let Me Entertain You'	EMic
'Leviathan'	EMic
'Lewis and Clark'	IBal
'Libby'	EMic IBal
'Liberty'[PBR] (v) ♀H7	CBod CDor CWGN EMic EPfP GMcL IBal NBro NGdn NLar NSue SBrk
'Light of Zetar' **new**	IBal
'Li'l Abner' (v)	IBal
* ***lilacina***	WFar
'Lily Blue Eyes'	EMic
'Lime Fizz'	EMic IBal NHpl NSue SBrk WFar
'Lime Shag' (*sieboldii* f. *spathulata*)	GNew IBal NSue
'Limey Lisa'	EMic IBal NSue
'Linda Sue' (v)	IBal
'Lionheart' (v)	IBal NSue
'Little Aurora' (*tokudama* hybrid)	EMic IBal
'Little Bit'	IBal NSue
'Little Black Scape'	EMic IBal LSRN MHom NEgg NGdn NLar NWad
'Little Blue' (*ventricosa*)	EMic
'Little Bo Beep' (v)	IBal NSue WFar
'Little Boy'	IBal
'Little Caesar' (v)	EMic IBal LRHS NGdn NSue
'Little Devil'	EMic NSue
'Little Doll' (v)	IBal
'Little Jay' (v)	IBal NSue
'Little Maddie'	EMic NSue
'Little Miss Magic'	IBal
'Little Miss Sunshine'	IBal
'Little Razor'	IBal NSue
'Little Red Joy'	EMic IBal NSue
'Little Red Rooster'	EMic IBal NGdn NHpl NLar NSue WFar
'Little Stiffy'	EMic IBal
'Little Sunspot' (v)	EMic NHar
'Little Treasure' (v)	IBal NSue WFar
'Little White Lines' (v)	EHoe EMic GKev IBal NSue
'Little Willie' (v)	NSue
'Little Wonder' (v) ♀H7	EMic NSue
'Living Water'	EMic
'Lizard Lick'	EMic IBal NSue
'Lollapalooza' (v)	IBal
'London Fog' (v)	IBal
'Long Fellow' (v)	IBal
longipes B&SWJ 10806	WCru
longissima var. ***brevifolia***	NSue
'Lost World'	EMic IBal
'Lothar the Giant'	IBal
'Love Pat' ♀H7	ECtt EMic EPfP IBal LSRN MRav NGdn NLar NSue SBrk
'Love Song'	IBal
'Loyalist'[PBR] (v)	EMic IBal LRHS NGdn NLar SPoG WFar
'Lucky Mouse'[PBR] (v)	IBal NSue SBrk
'Lucy Vitols' (v)	EMic IBal
'Lullabye'	EMic
'Luna Moth'	IBal
'Lunar Eclipse' (v)	EMic NEgg
'Machete'	IBal
'Mack the Knife'	EMic IBal NLar WFar
'Maekawa'	EMic IBal
'Magic Fire'[PBR] (v)	EMic EPfP IBal MNrw
'Magic Island'	IBal NSue
'Magica' **new**	IBal
'Majesty'	EMic IBal NGdn
'Major Tom'	IBal
'Majordomo' **new**	EMic
'Malabar' (v)	EMic IBal
'Mama Mia' (v)	EMic EPfP IBal MBNS NBro NGdn NHol NWad WFar
'Mango Salsa'	IBal
'Mango Tango' (v)	EMic IBal
'Manhattan'	EMic
'Maple Leaf' (*sieboldiana*) (v)	EMic
'Maraschino Cherry'	EMic IBal NEgg NGdn
'Mardi Gras' (v)	EMic IBal
'Marge' (*sieboldiana* hybrid)	EMic
'Margie's Angel' (v)	NSue
'Margin of Error' (v)	IBal
'Marginata Alba' misapplied	see *H.* 'Albomarginata' (*fortunei*), ***H. crispula***
'Marilyn'	EMic IBal NSue
'Marilyn Monroe'	EMic IBal NSue
'Marmalade on Toast'	EMic
'Marquis' (*nakaiana* hybrid)	IBal
'Marrakech'	EMic IBal LRHS NSue
'Mary Joe'	EMic
'Mary Marie Ann' (*fortunei*) (v)	EMic IBal
'Masquerade' (v)	EMic LLHF NHar NRya NSue SMHy WFar WHal WThu
'Maui Buttercups'	EMic
'May'	EMic IBal
'Maya' (*fortunei*) (v)	EMic IBal
'Medieval Age' (v)	IBal
§ 'Mediopicta' (*sieboldii*)	EMic IBal
'Mediovariegata' (*undulata*)	see ***H. undulata*** var. ***undulata***
'Medusa' (v)	IBal NGdn NSue SBrk
'Memories of Dorothy'	EMic IBal
'Mesa Fringe' (*montana*)	EMic IBal NLar
'Mid Afternoon'	IBal
'Midas Touch'	NEgg NLar
'Middle Ridge'	EMic
'Midnight at the Oasis' (v)	EMic IBal NSue
'Midnight Ride'	IBal
'Midwest Gold'	MHom
'Midwest Magic' (v)	EMic IBal NLar
'Mighty Mite'	IBal
'Mikawa-no-yuki'	IBal
'Mike Shadrack' (v)	EMic IBal
'Miki'	IBal
'Mildred Seaver' (v)	EMic IBal LRHS MHom
'Millennium'	EMic IBal
I 'Minima Aurea'	IBal
'Minnesota Wild' (v)	IBal
'Minnie Bell' (v)	IBal
'Minnie Klopping'	EMic
minor misapplied f. ***alba***	see *H. sieboldii* var. *alba*
§ ***minor*** Maekawa	GEdr ITim NWad XLum
- B&SWJ 1209 from Korea	WCru
- B&SWJ 8775 from Korea	WCru
- B&SWJ 11103 from Japan	WCru
- from Korea	IBal NSue
'Minor' (*ventricosa*)	see *H. minor* Maekawa
'Mint Julep' (v)	IBal
'Minuet' (v)	IBal
'Minuteman' (*fortunei*) (v) ♀H7	CDor ECtt EMic EPfP EWoo GNew IBal LRHS MAvo MBNS MMuc NFav NGdn NHpl NLar NNys SBrk SEND SPoG WFar

'Minutini'	NSue
'Miss Linda Smith'	EMic IBal
'Miss Ruby'	EMic IBal
'Miss Saigon' (v)	IBal
'Miss Susie'	IBal
'Miss Tokyo' (v)	EMic IBal
'Mississippi Delta'	EMic
'Mister Watson'	EMic IBal
'Misty Waters' (*sieboldiana*)	EMic
'Moerheim' (*fortunei*) (v)	EMic IBal LRHS SBrk WHal
'Mohegan'	EMic
'Moi Marleen'	EMic
'Monster Ears'	IBal
montana	EMic
- B&SWJ 4796	WCru
- B&SWJ 5585	WCru
- f. ***macrophylla***	IBal NSue
aff. ***montana***	WFar
'Moody Blues' (Tardiana Group)	EMic
'Moon Dance' (v)	IBal
'Moon Lily'	EMic
'Moon River' (v)	EMic IBal
'Moon Split' (v)	EPfP IBal NGdn
'Moonbeam'	EMic EShb
'Moongate Flying Saucer'	EMic
'Moonlight' (*fortunei*) (v)	EMic GMaP IBal LRHS NEgg SBrk
'Moonlight Sonata'	EMic IBal
'Moonstruck'PBR (v)	ECtt EMic IBal NSue
'Morning Light'	ECtt EMic EPfP ESps GBin GMcL IBal MBNS NBro NGdn NLar SRkn WFar
'Morning Star' (v)	EMic IBal NSue WFar
'Moscow Blue'	EMic
'Moulin Rouge'	IBal NSue
'Mount Everest'	EMic IBal
'Mount Fuji' (*montana*)	IBal
'Mount Kirishima' (*sieboldii*)	see *H.* 'Kirishima'
'Mount Tom' (v)	EMic IBal
'Mountain Snow' (*montana*) (v)	EMic LRHS
'Mourning Dove' (v)	EMic IBal
'Mr Big'	IBal NGdn WCot
'Mr Blue' **new**	NSue
'Mrs Minky'	EBee EMic LRHS
'Muffie' (v)	EMic
'Munchkin' (*sieboldii*)	LLHF WFar
'My Claire' (v)	IBal
'My Cup of Tea'	IBal
'My Precious' (v) **new**	IBal NSue
'Mystic Mouse'	IBal
'Mystic Star'	IBal NSue
nakaiana	EBee EMic
'Nakaimo'	GBin IBal
'Nana' (*ventricosa*)	see *H. minor* Maekawa
'Nancy'	EMic
§ 'Nancy Lindsay' (*fortunei*)	CDor CTri EMic IBal NGdn NLar
'Nancy Minks'	EMic IBal
'Neat and Tidy'	IBal
'Neat Splash' (v)	CWCL NBir
'Neelix'	IBal
'Nemesis' (v)	IBal
'Neptune'	EMic IBal
'Nesmith's Giant' **new**	EMic
'Niagara Falls' ♀H7	EMic IBal NEgg NGdn NSue SBrk
'Nicola'	EMic IBal MHom NSue
'Night before Christmas' (v) ♀H7	CHid EMic EWTr IBal LRHS MBNS MNrw NBro NEgg NGdn NHol SBrk WHar WHoo
'Night Life'	EMic IBal
nigrescens	EMic IBal LRHS NChi NEgg
'Niko' (v)	IBal
'Nippers'	EMic IBal NSue
'Nokogiryama'	EMic
'None Lovelier' (v)	EMic IBal
'North Hills' (*fortunei*) (v)	EMic IBal MHom NBir NGdn SWvt WFar
'Northern Exposure' (*sieboldiana*) (v)	EMic NGdn NLar SPoG WHar
'Northern Halo' (*sieboldiana*) (v)	CDor
'Norwalk Chartreuse'	IBal
'Nutty Professor' (v)	IBal
'Oberon'	NSue
'Obscura Marginata' (*fortunei*)	see *H. fortunei* var. *aureomarginata*
'Ocean Isle' (v)	IBal
'October Sky'	EMic IBal
'Oder'	EMic IBal
'Ogon Tachi' (*rectifolia*) (v)	EMic IBal
'Ogon-chirifu-hime'	EMic IBal
'Ogon-hime-tokudama'	IBal
'Ogon-koba'	IBal
'Oh Cindy' (v)	EMic IBal
'O'Harra'	EMic NSue
'Old Faithful'	EMic IBal LRHS
'Old Glory'PBR (v)	ECtt EMic IBal
'Olga's Shiny Leaf'	EMic
'Olive Bailey Langdon' (*sieboldiana*) (v)	CDor EMic IBal
'Olive Branch' (v)	EMic IBal
'Olympic Edger'	EMic IBal
'Olympic Glacier' (v)	EMic IBal
'Olympic Gold Medal'	EMic IBal
'Olympic Silver Medal'	EMic IBal
'Olympic Sunrise' (v)	EMic IBal
'Olympic Twilight'	EMic IBal
'On Stage'	see *H.* 'Chōkō-nishiki'
'On the Border' (v)	IBal
'One Iota' (v) **new**	IBal
'One Man's Treasure' ♀H7	EMic IBal MBel NEgg NGdn SBrk
'Ooh La La' (v)	IBal
'Ophir'	EMic IBal
opipara	NEgg
'Ops' (v)	EMic IBal NSue
'Orange Crush' (v)	IBal
'Orange Marmalade' (v) ♀H7	CWGN ECtt EMic EPfP GNew IBal LRHS MNrw NGdn NLar NSue SBrk SCob SPoG
'Orange Star'PBR (v)	EMic IBal
'Oriana' (*fortunei*)	EMic
'Orion's Belt' (v)	IBal
'Over the Waves' **new**	IBal NSue
'Oxheart'	EMic IBal
'Oze' (v)	EMic IBal NSue
pachyscapa	EMic
'Pacific Blue Edger'	EMic NGdn WAul WFar
'Painted Lady' (*sieboldii*) (v)	GKev
'Pamela Lee' (v)	IBal NGdn NSue
'Pandora's Box' (v)	GEdr NHar NHpl NSue WCot WFar
'Papa' (v) **new**	IBal
'Paradigm' (v)	EBee EMic IBal LRHS NGdn NLar
'Paradise Backstage' (v)	EMic IBal
'Paradise Beach'	EMic IBal WFar
'Paradise Blue Sky'	IBal
'Paradise Expectations' (*sieboldiana*) (v)	EMic IBal
'Paradise Glory'	EMic IBal SBrk
'Paradise Gold Line' (*ventricosa*) (v)	IBal

	'Paradise Island'PBR (*sieboldiana*) (v)	EMic EPfP IBal NGdn NSue SBrk
	'Paradise Joyce'PBR	EMic GMcL IBal LRHS NEgg
	'Paradise Ocean'	EMic IBal
	'Paradise on Fire' (v)	EMic IBal
	'Paradise Parade' (v)	IBal
	'Paradise Passion' (v)	IBal
	'Paradise Power'PBR	EMic
	'Paradise Puppet' (*venusta*) ♀H7	EMic GKev IBal NSue SBrk
	'Paradise Red Delight' (*pycnophylla*)	EMic IBal
	'Paradise Sandstorm'	IBal
	'Paradise Standard' (d)	EMic IBal
	'Paradise Sunset'	EMic IBal NHpl NSue SBrk WFar
	'Paradise Sunshine'	EMic IBal
	'Paradise Surprise' (v)	IBal
	'Paradise Tritone' (v)	EMic IBal
	'Parhelion'	EMic
	'Parky's Prize' (v)	IBal
	'Pastures Green'	IBal
	'Pastures New'	EMic MHom NEgg
	'Pathfinder' (v)	EMic IBal WFar
	'Patricia'	EMic
	'Patrician' (v)	EMic IBal
	'Patriot' (v) ♀H7	Widely available
	'Patriot's Fire' (v)	IBal LRHS NRHS
	'Patriot's Green Pride'	IBal
	'Paul's Glory' (v) ♀H7	CDor EMic EPfP GLog GMaP IBal LLWG LRHS MAvo NBir NGdn NNys NSue SBrk SPoG WFar
§	'Paxton's Original' (*sieboldii*) (v)	ESps GKev IFoB
	'Peace' (v)	EMic IBal LRHS
	'Peacock Strut'	IBal
	'Peanut'	IBal NSue
	'Pearl Lake'	EMic IBal MHom NBir NEgg NGdn NHol NLar
	'Peedee Absinth'	EMic
	'Peedee Elfin Bells' (*ventricosa*)	IBal
	'Pelham Blue Tump'	EMic
	'Peppermint Ice' (v)	EMic IBal NGdn
	'Percy'	EMic
	'Permanent Wave'	IBal
	'Perry's True Blue'	EMic IBal SBrk
	'Peter Pan'	EMic IBal NEgg
	'Pete's Dark Satellite'	EMic IBal NSue
	'Pewterware'	EMic IBal
	'Phantom'	IBal
	'Philadelphia'	EMic IBal
	'Phoenix'	EMic IBal NLar
	'Photo Finish' (v)	EMic IBal
	'Phyllis Campbell' (*fortunei*)	see *H.* 'Sharmon'
	'Picta' (*fortunei*)	see *H. fortunei* var. *albopicta*
	'Piecrust Power'	IBal
	'Piedmont Gold'	CHid EHoe EMic GBin IBal LHop LRHS
	'Pilgrim' (v)	CDor EMic IBal LRHS MMuc NBro NEgg NGdn NHpl SBrk SEND WFar
	'Pineapple Poll'	EMic MHom WFar WHoo
	'Pineapple Upside Down Cake' (v)	EMic IBal NBro NLar SBrk
	'Pinky'	IBal
	'Pin-up' (v)	IBal
	'Pistache' (v)	EMic IBal NSue
	'Pixie Vamp' (v)	EMic IBal
	'Pizzazz' (v)	EMic IBal LRHS MHom NGdn NHol NLar WFar
	plantaginea	EMic LEdu LRHS WFar WWtn
	- var. ***grandiflora***	see *H. plantaginea* var. *japonica*
§	- var. ***japonica*** ♀H7	CAby CBot EBee ECha LRHS MNrw MRav SMHy SMad WCFE WFar
	'Platinum Tiara' (v)	EMic IBal NBir
	'Plug Nickel'	EMic IBal NSue
	'Pocketful of Sunshine' (v)	IBal
	'Poker'	IBal
	'Polar Moon' (v)	IBal
	'Pole Cat' (v)	IBal
	'Pooh Bear' (v)	EMic IBal NSue
	'Popcorn'	EMic IBal NSue
	'Popo' ♀H7	EMic IBal NHpl NSue
	'Porter' (*venusta*)	IBal
	'Pot of Gold'	EMic
	'Potomac Pride'	EMic LRHS NEgg
	'Powder Blue' (v)	IBal
	'Powder Keg' (v) **new**	IBal
	'Prairie Sky'	EMic GMcL IBal NGdn NLar WFar
	'Prairie Sunset' (v)	NSue
	'Praying Hands' (v) ♀H7	CDor EBee ECha ECtt ELan EMic EPfP GBin GEdr GKev GNew GWyn IBal IBoy IFoB LRHS LSou MAsh MBNS NEgg NGdn NHpl NLar NSue SBrk SCob SHil WFar
	'Precious Metal'	IBal
	'Prestige and Promise' (v)	EMic IBal
	'Pretty Flamingo'	EMic IBal
	'Prima Donna'	EMic
	'Prince of Wales'	EMic IBal LPla LRHS SPoG
	'Princess Anastasia' (v)	IBal
	'Private Dancer'	IBal
	'Prom Queen' (v)	EMic IBal
	'Proud Sentry'	EMic IBal
	'Punk Rock'	IBal
	'Punky' (v)	EMic IBal
	'Purple Boots'	EMic IBal
	'Purple Dwarf'	EHoe EMic IBal NLar NSue WCru WHal
	'Purple Glory'	EMic
	'Purple Haze'	EMic IBal NGdn SBrk SHar
	'Purple Heart'	CAby EBee ECtt EWoo GNew IBal LCro LPla LRHS NHpl NSti NSue NWad SCob SHar SPoG WCot WNPC
	'Purple Passion'	EMic IBal NSue
	'Purple Profusion'	EMic IBal
	'Purple Python'	IBal
	'Quarter Note' (v)	IBal
	'Queen Josephine' (v)	EMic EPfP GMcL IBal LRHS MBNS MHom NEgg NGdn NHpl SRGP WFar
	'Queen of the Seas'	EMic IBal NSue
	'Quill'	EMic NSue
	'Quilting Bee'	EMic IBal NSue
	'Radiant Edger' (v)	EMic GCra IBal LRHS NHol NSue
	'Rain Dancer'	EMic IBal
	'Rain Forest'	EMic IBal
	'Rainbow's End' (v)	ECtt EMic IBal LLWG NLar NSue
	'Rainforest Sunrise' (v)	ELon EMic IBal LSou NGdn NSue SBrk
	'Randy Rachel' (v)	LRHS
	'Rare Breed' (v)	EMic IBal
	'Rascal' (v)	EMic
	'Raspberries and Cream' (v)	IBal
	'Raspberry Sorbet'	EMic IBal LRHS NSue
	'Raspberry Sundae' (v)	CWGN EBee ECtt EMic IBal MHol NGdn NHpl NSue NWad SCob SPoG WNPC
	'Rebel Heart' (v) **new**	IBal
	'Red Cadet'	EMic IBal SBrk WFar

	Name	Suppliers
	'Red Dog'	EMic NSue
	'Red Dragon'	EMic IBal
	'Red Hot Flash' (v)	EMic IBal
	'Red Hot Poker'	IBal
	'Red Neck Heaven' (*kikutii* var. *caput-avis*)	IBal
	'Red October'	ECtt EMic EPfP EUJe EWTr EWoo GAbr IBal IBoy LEdu LRHS LSou MBNS MHol MPie NEgg NGdn NHpl NLar SBrk SMad WCot WFar
	'Red Salamander'	EMic GNew IBal
	'Red Sox'	IBal
	'Red Stepper'	EMic IBal
	'Red Stilts' **new**	IBal
	'Red Tubes' (*venusta*)	IBal
	'Regal Rhubarb'	EMic IBal
	'Regal Splendor' (v) 𝕐H7	CDor ELan ELon EMic GBin IBal LRHS MHom NBro NGdn NSue SPoG WFar WHoo
	'Regal Supreme' (v)	IBal NSue
	'Regal Tot'	NSue
	'Reginald Kaye'	EMic
	'Rembrandt Blue'	EMic IBal
	'Remember Me'PBR 𝕐H7	CWCL ELan ELon EMic GMcL IBal LSRN MBNS MPnt NEgg NGdn NHol NLar NSue NWad WFar
	'Reptilian'	EMic IBal
	'Resonance' (v)	IBal NGdn NLar
	'Restless Sea'	EMic SBrk
	'Reverend Mac'	IBal
	'Reversed' (*sieboldiana*) (v)	EMic IBal LRHS NBro NGdn WFar WHal
	'Revolution'PBR (v) 𝕐H7	EMic GMcL IBal LSRN NBro NEgg NGdn NLar NSue SBrk WFar
	'Rhapsody' (*fortunei*) (v)	EMic IBal
	'Rhein' (*tardiana*)	IBal
	'Rhinestone Cowboy' (v)	IBal
	'Rhino Hide' (v)	EBee EMic IBal NSue
	'Rhythm and Blues'	IBal NSue
	'Rich Uncle'	IBal
	'Richland Gold' (*fortunei*)	EMic
	'Rim Rock'	EMic IBal
	'Ringtail'	EMic GNew IBal
	'Ripple Effect' (v)	EMic IBal NSue
	'Rippled Honey'	ELan EMic IBal NEoE SBrk
	'Rippling Waves'	EMic
	'Riptide'	EMic NGdn
	'Risa'	IBal
	'Risky Business'PBR (v)	CWGN EBee EMic IBal NLar NSue SBrk
	'Robert Frost' (v)	EMic IBal
	'Robin Hood'	EMic IBal
	'Robin of Loxley'	EMic IBal
	'Robusta' (*fortunei*)	see *H. sieboldiana* var. *elegans*
	'Robyn's Choice' (v)	IBal
	'Rock and Roll'	EMic IBal
	'Rock Island Line' (v)	EMic IBal NSue WFar
	'Rock Princess'	IBal LLHF
	'Rocket's Red Glare'	IBal
§	***rohdeifolia*** (v) B&SWJ 10862	WCru
	- f. ***albopicta***	ELan
	'Roller Coaster Ride'	IBal
	'Ron Damant'	IBal
	'Rootin'-Tootin'' (v)	IBal
	'Roseann Walter' (v)	EMic IBal
	'Rosedale Knox'	IBal
	'Rosedale Lost Dutchman'	IBal
	'Rosedale Melody of Summer' (v)	IBal
	'Rosedale Misty Magic' (v)	IBal
	'Rosedale Richie Valens'	IBal
	'Rosemoor'	IBal
	'Roxsanne'	EMic
	'Roy Klehm' (v)	EMic IBal
	'Royal Charm'	IBal
	'Royal Charmer' (v) **new**	IBal
	'Royal Flush' (v)	IBal
	'Royal Golden Jubilee'	EMic IBal
§	'Royal Standard' 𝕐H7	Widely available
	'Royal Tapestry' (v)	IBal
	'Royal Tiara' (*nakaiana*) (v)	IBal
	'Royalty'	IBal
	'Rubies and Ruffles' (v)	IBal
	'Ruffled Mouse Ears'	NSue
	'Rufus Rider'	IBal
	rupifraga	IBal
	'Rusty Bee'	GNew IBal
	'Ryan's Big One'	EBee EUJe IBal
§	'Sagae' (v) 𝕐H7	EMic EUJe GNew IBal LRHS MHom MNrw NGdn SBrk SDix WAul WFar WHoo
	'Saint Elmo's Fire' (v)	EMic IBal LRHS
	'Saint Fiacre'	EMic
	'Saint John'	IBal
	'Saint Paul'	EMic IBal MNrw NSue SBrk
	'Saishu-jima' (*sieboldii* f. *spathulata*)	EMic GEdr ITim WCru
	'Saishu-yahato-sito' (v)	IBal NSue
	'Salute' (Tardiana Group)	EMic
	'Samurai' (*sieboldiana*) (v)	EMic IBal MRav NBir NBro NEgg NGdn NLar NSue
	'Sandhill Crane' (v)	IBal
	'Sarah Kennedy' (v)	IBal
	'Sara's Sensation' (v)	IBal
	'Satisfaction' (v) 𝕐H7	EMic IBal
	'Sazanami' (*crispula*)	see *H. crispula*
	'Scallion Pancakes'	EMic
	'Scarlet Ribbons' (v)	EMic IBal
	'Schwan'	GBin
	'Scooter' (v)	IBal
	'Sea Current'	IBal
	'Sea Dream' (v)	EMic LRHS NEgg NGdn
	'Sea Fire'	IBal
	'Sea Gulf Stream'	EMic
	'Sea Lotus Leaf'	EMic NLar SBrk
	'Sea Monster'	IBal
	'Sea Nymph' **new**	EMic
	'Sea Sapphire'	IBal
	'Sea Thunder' (v)	EMic IBal LRHS SBrk
	'Sea Yellow Sunrise'	EMic IBal
	'Searing Flame' (v)	IBal
	'Second Wind' (*fortunei*) (v)	EMic
	'Secret Ambition'PBR (v)	EMic IBal
	'Secret Love'	EMic IBal
	'Secret Treasure'PBR (v)	IBal
	'Seducer' (v)	EMic IBal
	'See Saw' (*undulata*)	EMic IBal
	'Semperaurea' (*sieboldiana*)	IBal
	'September Sun' (v)	EMic IBal LRHS
	'Serena' (Tardiana Group)	IBal
	'Serendipity'	EMic GAbr IBal MHom
	'Shade Beauty' (v)	EMic IBal
	'Shade Fanfare' (v)	CDor ECtt EHoe ELan ELon EMic EPfP IBal LRHS MBNS MRav NBir NGdn NLar NSti SPer WFar
	'Shade Finale' (v)	IBal
	'Shade Master'	EMic
	'Shade Parade' (v)	EMic IBal
	'Shady Affair' **new**	EMic

§	'Sharmon' (*fortunei*) (v)	ELon EMic MBNS NEgg NLar
	'Sharp Dressed Man'	IBal SBrk
	'Shazaam'	IBal
	'Sheila West'	EMic IBal
	'Shelleys' (v)	IBal
	'Sherborne Profusion' (Tardiana Group)	EMic IBal
	'Sherborne Songbird' (Tardiana Group)	IBal
	'Sherborne Swallow' (Tardiana Group)	EMic IBal
	'Sherborne Swan' (Tardiana Group)	IBal
	'Sherborne Swift' (Tardiana Group)	EMic IBal LRHS SBrk
	'Shere Khan' (v)	EMic IBal
	'Shimmy Shake'	EMic
	'Shining Tot' 🏆H7	IBal LLHF
	'Shiny Penny' (v)	EMic IBal NSue
	'Shirley Levy'	IBal
	'Shirley Vaughn' (v)	IBal
	'Showboat' (v)	EMic IBal LRHS
	sieboldiana	CAgr CMac CSBt CWat ECha ELan EMic ESps GCra GMaP MRav MSwo NChi SPlb SRms WMoo XLum
§	- var. ***elegans*** 🏆H7	Widely available
	- var. ***mira***	EMic
	- var. ***sieboldiana***	NGdn
	sieboldiana × ***venusta***	NGdn
	sieboldii	GBin MRav
§	- var. ***alba***	IBal
§	- var. ***sieboldii*** f. ***kabitan*** (v)	EMic IBal NGdn NHar NSue SBrk
	- - f. ***shiro-kabitan*** (v)	EMic LRHS
	- f. ***spathulata***	EMic
	'Silberpfeil'	EMic NSue
	'Silk Road' (v)	IBal
	'Silver Bay' 🏆H7	EMic
	'Silver Crown'	see *H.* 'Albomarginata'
	'Silver Halo' (v) **new**	EMic
	'Silver Lance' (v)	EMic IBal
	'Silver Lode' (v)	IBal
	'Silver Moon'	EMic IBal
	'Silver Serenity'	IBal
	'Silver Shadow' (v)	CHid EMic GBin IBal NBir NGdn NWad
	'Silver Spray' (v)	IBal
	'Silver Star' (v)	IBal
	'Silver Threads and Gold Needles' (v)	IBal NHpl NSue
	'Silverado' (v)	IBal
	'Silvery Slugproof' (Tardiana Group)	LRHS
	'Simply Sharon' (v)	IBal
	'Singin' the Blues'	IBal
	'Singing in the Rain' (v)	IBal NSue
	'Sitting Pretty' (v)	IBal
	'Sizzle'	EMic IBal SBrk
	'Sky Dancer'	EMic IBal NSue
	'Sleeping Beauty'	CWGN EMic IBal NGdn
	'Sleeping Star' (v)	IBal
	'Slick Willie'	EMic
	'Slim and Trim'	EMic IBal MHom NHpl NSue
	'Small Parts'	EMic IBal NSue
	'Small Sum'	IBal
	'Smash Hit' (v) **new**	IBal
	'Smiley Face'	NSue
	'Smoke Signals'	IBal
	'Snake Eyes' (v)	CBod MAsh SCob
	'Snow Boy' (v)	EMic IBal NSue

	'Snow Cap' (v)	CDor ECtt EMic IBal NEoE NGdn NLar SPoG WFar
	'Snow Crust' (v)	EMic
	'Snow Flakes' (*sieboldii*)	CMac NBro NEoE NGdn NLar
	'Snow Mouse' (v)	EMic IBal NHpl NSue SBrk WFar
	'Snowden' 🏆H7	ECha GMaP IBal LRHS MWat NBir NGdn SBrk WCru
	'Snowy Lake' (v)	IBal
	'So Sweet' (v)	EBee ECtt EHoe ELan EMic EPfP ESps EWoo GBin GLog IBal LRHS LSun MHom MSwo NBro NGdn NHol SHil SPoG WFar WHar
	'Something Blue'	EMic IBal
	'Something Different' (*fortunei*) (v)	IBal
	'Something Else'	EMic
	'Southern Gold'	EMic
	'Space Odyssey'	IBal
	'Sparkler' (v)	EMic IBal
	'Sparkling Burgundy'	EMic LRHS
	'Sparky' (v)	IBal
	'Spartacus' (v)	EMic IBal NSue
	'Spartan Arrow'	NSue
	'Spartan Glory' (v)	IBal
	'Special Gift'	EMic IBal
	'Spellbound' (v)	IBal
	'Spilt Milk' (*tokudama*) (v) 🏆H7	EBee EMic IBal SBrk SPoG WHoo
	'Spinach Souffle' (v)	IBal
§	'Spinners' (*fortunei*) (v)	ECha EMic IBal
	'Split Decision' **new**	EMic
	'Spock's Ears'	IBal
	'Spring Break' (v)	EMic
	'Spring Fling'	EMic IBal SBrk
	'Spritzer' (v)	EMic MNrw NSue
	'Squash Casserole'	IBal NSue
	'Stained Glass' (v) 🏆H7	CAby CBcs CDor ECtt ELon EMic EPfP GBin IBal LRHS NEgg NGdn NSue SBrk SHil SPoG WFar
	'Stand by Me' (v)	EMic IBal NSue
	'Stand Corrected' (v)	IBal
	'Star Kissed'	IBal
	'Star Light Star Bright'	EMic IBal
	'Starburst' stable (v)	IBal
	'Stardust'	IBal
	'Stargate'	IBal
§	'Starker Yellow Leaf'	EMic
	'Starship' (v)	EMic IBal
	'Steffi' (v)	IBal
	'Step Sister'	EMic IBal
	'Stepping Out' (v)	EMic IBal
	'Stetson' (v)	EMic IBal
	'Stiletto' (v)	EHoe ELon EMic GAbr GBin GCra GEdr GKev IBal LRHS MBNS MHom MNrw NBro NEoE NGdn NHpl NLar NSue SBrk SPoG SWvt WFar WSHC
	'Stimulation'	IBal
	'Stirfry'	EMic SCob
	'Stitch in Time' (v)	IBal
	'Stonewall'	IBal
	'Strawberry Surprise' (v)	EMic IBal
	'Strawberry Yoghurt' **new**	NSue
	'Striker' (v)	IBal NSue
	'Striptease' (*fortunei*) (v) 🏆H7	CMac EMic EPfP GLog IBal LRHS MBNS MNrw NEgg NGdn NHol NLar NSue SBrk WFar
	'Stuck in Time'	IBal
	'Sugar and Cream' (v)	EMic IBal LRHS NGdn
	'Sugar and Spice' (v)	ELon EMic GNew IBal
	'Sugar Daddy'	EMic IBal

'Sultana' (v)	EMic IBal
'Sum and Substance' ♀H7	Widely available
'Sum and Subtle' (v)	EMic IBal
'Sum Cup-o-Joe' (v)	EMic
'Sum it Up' (v)	EMic
'Sum of All' (v)	NSue
'Summer Breeze' (v)	EMic IBal NGdn NSue
'Summer Fragrance'	EBee ECtt EMic GBin IBal LRHS
'Summer Lovin'' (v)	IBal SBrk
'Summer Music' (v) ♀H7	CWCL EMic IBal SBrk
'Summer Serenade' (v)	EMic IBal NGdn
'Summer Squall'	IBal
'Sumsational'	IBal
'Sun Catcher'	EMic
'Sun Power'	EBee ELon EMic LRHS MBNS NBro NLar
'Sun Worshipper'	IBal
'Sundance' (v)	IBal
'Sunlight Child'	IBal NSue
'Sunny Smiles' (v)	EMic
'Sunset Grooves' (v)	IBal
'Sunshine Glory'	EMic IBal
'Super Bowl'	IBal
'Super Nova' (v)	EMic IBal
'Super Sagae'	CDor EMic IBal WFar
'Surfer Girl'	NSue
'Surprised by Joy' (v)	EMic IBal NHpl NSue
'Susy'	IBal
'Sutter's Mill'	IBal
'Suzuki Thumbnail'	EMic
'Swamp Thing' (v)	IBal
'Sweet Bo Beep'	EMic IBal LRHS
'Sweet Bouquet'	EMic
'Sweet Home Chicago' (v)	EBee EMic IBal
'Sweet Innocence' (v)	EMic IBal
'Sweet Marjorie'	IBal
'Sweet Sunshine'	EMic
'Sweet Susan'	EMic LSRN MBNS SPer SWvt
'Sweet Tater Pie'	EMic IBal
'Sweetheart'	EMic
'Sweetie' (v)	EMic IBal LRHS NSue
'Sweetness'	IBal
'Swirling Hearts'	IBal NSue
'Swizzle Sticks'	EMic
'T. Rex'	ELon EMic EUJe IBal NSue WFar
'Tall Boy'	GBin IBal NBir
'Tamborine' (v)	IBal LRHS
'Tango'	EMic IBal
'Tappen Zee' (v)	EMic IBal
Tardiana Group	GWyn MHom NGdn
tardiflora	CFil IBal LRHS
tardiva	EMic NLar
'Tattle Tails'	EMic IBal NHpl NSue SBrk
'Tattoo'PBR (v)	CWGN EMic LSRN MBNS NLar
'Tea at Bettys' ♀H7	EMic IBal NSue
'Tears of Joy'	NSue
'Teaspoon'	EMic IBal NHpl NSue SBrk
'Teatime' (v)	EMic IBal
'Teeny-weeny Bikini' (v)	NSue SBrk WFar
'Templar Gold'	IBal
'Temple Bells'	IBal
'Temptation'	EMic IBal
'Tequila Sunrise'	IBal
'Terpsichore'	EMic
'Terracotta'	MCri
'Terry Wogan'	IBal
'Tet-a-Poo'	IBal
'The King' (v)	IBal
'The Leading Edge' (v)	IBal
'The Queen' (v)	IBal
'The Razor's Edge'	IBal
'The Right One' (v)	IBal
'The Shining'	IBal
'Theo's Blue'	EMic IBal
'Theo's Red'	IBal
'Thomas Hogg'	see *H. undulata* var. *albomarginata*
'Thumb Nail'	EMic IBal NSue
'Thumbelina'	EMic IBal NGdn
'Thunderbolt'PBR (*sieboldiana*)	EMic EUJe IBal MBNS NGdn NLar WFar
tibae	IBal
'Tick Tock' (v)	EMic IBal NSue SBrk
'Tickle Me Pink'	EMic IBal NSue
'Tidewater'	IBal
'Time Tunnel' (*sieboldiana*) (v)	EMic IBal
'Timeless Beauty' (v)	IBal NSue WFar
'Tiny Tears'	GAbr IFoB NSue
'Titanic'PBR	EMic IBal
'Titanium'	IBal
tokudama	EMic IBal LRHS MHom NBir NGdn WFar XLum
§ - f. ***aureo-nebulosa*** (v)	EMic IBal NGdn SRms
'Tokudama Blue'	IBoy
tokudama f. ***flavocircinalis*** (v) ♀H7	EBee ELon EMic EPfP GMaP IBal NBro WFar WHoo
'Tokyo Smog' (v)	NSue
'Toledo'	IBal
'Tom Schmid' (v)	EMic IBal LBMP NSue SBrk
'Tom Thumb'	EMic IBal NSue
'Tongue Twister'	IBal
'Topaz'	IBal
'Torchlight' (v) ♀H7	IBal LRHS MHom NSue
tortifrons	EMic IBal
'Tortilla Chip'	EMic IBal NSue
'Tot Tot'	EMic IBal NSue
'Totally Twisted'	IBal
'Touch of Class'PBR (v) ♀H7	CDor ECtt EMic GMcL IBal NGdn NHol NSue SBrk WFar
'Touchstone' (v)	SBrk SWvt
'Toy Soldier'	EMic IBal NGdn NLar NSue
'Trail's End'	EMic
'Tranquility' (v)	EMic
'Tremors'	EMic IBal
'Trixi' (v)	IBal
'Tropical Dancer'	IBal
'Tropical Storm' (v)	IBal
'True Blue'	EBee ECtt EMic IBal
'Tsugaru Komachi'	EMic
'Tsugaru Komachi Kifukurin' (v)	IBal
'Turnabout' (v)	IBal
'Turning Point'	IBal LRHS
'Twiggie'	EMic
'Twilight' (*fortunei*) (v)	CAby EAEE ECtt ELon EMic EShb IBal LRHS MBNS MHol NEgg NGdn NLar SWvt WFar WHar
'Twilight Time'	IBal LRHS
'Twinkle Toes'	EMic IBal NSue
'Twist of Lemon'	NEgg
'Twist of Lime' (v)	EMic GKev IBal LRHS NGdn NSue SBrk WCot
'Twitter'	IBal
'UFO'	EMic IBal NSue WFar
'Ultramarine'	IBal
'Ultraviolet Light'	IBal
'Ulysses S. Grant'	IBal
'Unchained Melody'	IBal
undulata (v)	WFar

§ - var. ***albomarginata*** (v)	CBcs CMac CSam EMic EPfP ESps GMaP IBoy LRHS LSRN MRav NBid NBir NGdn NLar SCob SDix SPer SRms SWvt WFar XLum
§ - var. ***erromena***	EMic GMaP LRHS WHrl XLum
§ - var. ***undulata*** (v) 🏆^{H7}	EBee ESps GMaP IBal LPot LRHS MCot MRav NEgg NGdn NLar SBrk SCob SPer WHar
- var. ***univittata*** (v)	ECha EMic GKev MHom NBir NEoE WFar WMoo
'Unforgettable'	EMic IBal
'Upper Crust' (v)	IBal
'Uprising' (v)	IBal
'Urajiro' (*hypoleuca*)	IBal
'Urajiro-hachijo' (*longipes* var. *latifolia*)	IBal
'Valentine Lace'	EMic GKev IBal
'Valley's Blue Curaçao' **new**	IBal
'Valley's Cathedral'	IBal
'Valley's Chute the Chute'	EMic IBal
'Valley's Glacier' (v)	EMic IBal MAsh WFar
'Valley's Paparazzi' (v) **new**	IBal
'Valley's Vanilla Sticks'	EMic IBal
'Van Wade' (v)	EMic IBal
'Vanilla Cream' (*cathayana*)	EMic IBal
'Variegata' (*gracillima*)	see *H.* 'Vera Verde'
'Variegata' (*tokudama*)	see *H. tokudama* f. *aureo-nebulosa*
'Variegata' (*undulata*)	see *H. undulata* var. *undulata*
'Variegata' (*ventricosa*)	see *H.* 'Aureomarginata' (*ventricosa*)
'Variegated' (*fluctuans*)	see *H.* 'Sagae'
'Velvet Moon' (v)	EMic IBal
ventricosa 🏆^{H7}	CMac EMic GMcL IBal WFar XLum
- BWJ 8160 from Sichuan	WCru
- var. ***aureomaculata***	EMic NBir WFar
'Venus' (d)	CAby ECtt EMic IBal ITim LEdu MHol NGdn NSue WCot WFar
'Venus Star'	EMic
venusta 🏆^{H7}	EAEE EBee ECho EMic EWld GCra GEdr IBal LRHS MRav NBid NBir NRya SRot WFar WRHF
- B&SWJ 4389	WCru
- dwarf	IBal
- ***yakusimensis***	see *H. kikutii* var. *yakusimensis*
§ 'Vera Verde' (v)	GCra GQui NBir NSue
'Verdi Valentine'	EMic IBal
'Verkade's No 1'	IBal
'Vermont Frost' (v)	IBal NSue
'Verna Jean' (v)	EMic IBal LRHS
'Veronica Lake' (v)	ECtt EMic IBal LRHS NSue WHal
'Vertade's Two' **new**	NSue
'Victor'	IBal
'Victory' 🏆^{H7}	EMic IBal
'Viking Ship'	EMic IBal
'Vilmoriniana'	EMic
'Vim and Vigor'	EMic IBal
'Vina'	IBal
'Virginia Reel' (v) **new**	IBal
'Viridis Marginata'	see *H. sieboldii* var. *sieboldii* f. *kabitan*
'Volcano Island'^{PBR} (v)	EMic IBal NSue SBrk
'Vulcan' (v)	EMic IBal
'Wagtail' (Tardiana Group)	EMic IBal
'Wahoo' (*tokudama*) (v)	IBal
'War Paint' 🏆^{H7}	CBod EMic IBal ITim NSue WFar
'Warwick Comet' (v)	EMic IBal
'Warwick Curtsey' (v)	EMic IBal
'Warwick Edge' (v)	EMic IBal NEgg SBrk
'Warwick Essence'	EMic IBal
'Warwick Sheen'	IBal
'Watermark' (v) **new**	EMic
'Waukon Glass'	EMic IBal
'Waukon Thin Ice'	EMic IBal
'Waukon Water'	EMic IBal
'Waving Winds' (v)	IBal
'Waving Wuffles'	EMic
'Wayne' (v)	EMic
'Wayside Blue'	EMic
'Wayside Perfection'	see *H.* 'Royal Standard'
'Weihenstephan' (*sieboldii*)	EMic IBal
'Well Shaked' (v)	IBal
'Weser'	IBal
'Wheaton Blue'	EMic LRHS
'Wheaton Thunder' (v) **new**	EMic
'Whee' (v)	IBal NSue
'Whirligig' (v)	EMic
'Whirling Dervish' (v)	IBal
'Whirlwind' (*fortunei*) (v) 🏆^{H7}	EBee EMic EPfP GBin GNew IBal LRHS MNrw MRav NBro NEgg NGdn NLar NSue SBrk SPad SPoG SPtp WAul WBor WFar WHoo
'Whirlwind Tour' (v)	IBal
'Whiskey Sour'	IBal
'White Bikini' (v)	IBal NSue
'White Ceiling'	IBal
'White Christmas' (*fortunei*) (v)	NGdn SBrk
'White Christmas' (*undulata*) (v)	EMic
'White Dove' (v)	EMic IBal
'White Edger'	EMic
'White Elephant' (v)	IBal
'White Fairy' (*plantaginea*) (d)	EMic
'White Feather' (*undulata*)	CHid CWGN EBee ELan ELon EPfP LCro LOPS LRHS MNrw NBir NGdn NLar SBrk SMad SPoG WFar
'White Gold'	EMic
'White Knight'	IBal
'White On' (*montana*)	EMic
'White Triumphator' (*rectifolia*)	EMic IBal
'White Trumpets'	EMic
'Wide Brim' (v) 🏆^{H7}	Widely available
'William Lachman' (v)	IBal NLar
'Wily Willy'	IBal
'Wind River Gold'	EMic IBal
'Windsor Gold'	see *H.* 'Nancy Lindsay'
'Winfield Blue'	EMic IBal
'Winfield Gold'	EMic
'Winfield Mist' (v)	IBal
'Winsome' (v)	IBal LRHS NSue SBrk SHil
'Winter Snow' (v)	CDor EMic EUJe IBal LRHS NSue
'Winter Warrior' (v)	EMic IBal
'Wogon' (*sieboldii*)	EMic GKev GMaP ITim
'Wogon's Boy'	EMic LRHS
'Wolverine' (v) 🏆^{H7}	EBee ECtt EHoe EMic LRHS LSou MBNS MHom NGdn NQui NSue SBrk SPoG SWvt WCot WFar
'Woodland Elf' (v)	IBal NSue
'Woolly Mammoth' (v)	IBal
'Woop Woop' (v)	EMic IBal NSue
'World Cup'	IBal
'Worldly Treasure'	IBal
'Wrinkles and Crinkles'	EMic
'Wylde Green Cream'	IBal NGdn
'Xanadu' (v)	IBal
'X-ray' (v)	NSue
'Yakushima-mizu' (*gracillima*)	EMic IBal
'Yankee Blue'	IBal

'Yellow Boa'	EMic IBal NSue
'Yellow Edge' (*fortunei*)	see *H. fortunei* var. *aureomarginata*
'Yellow Edge' (*sieboldiana*)	see *H.* 'Frances Williams'
'Yellow Polka Dot Bikini' (v)	EMic NSue
'Yellow River' (v)	EMic GNew IBal LRHS NGdn NSue SBrk
'Yellow Splash' (v)	EMic LRHS MHom
'Yellow Splash Rim' (v)	EMic
'Yesterday's Memories' (v)	EMic IBal
'Yin' (v)	EMic IBal
yingeri	WPGP WSHC
- B&SWJ 546	LEdu WCru
'Yucca Ducka Do' (v)	EMic IBal
'Zager Blue'	EMic
'Zager Green'	EMic
'Zager White Edge' (*fortunei*) (v)	EMic IBal SBrk
'Zebra Stripes' (v)	IBal
'Zion's Hope'	EMic
'Zodiac' (*fortunei*) (v)	IBal
'Zorro' **new**	IBal
'Zounds'	EBee ECtt EMic EPfP EShb GKev GNew IBal LRHS MRav NGdn NLar NSue SRms WFar

Hottonia (*Primulaceae*)

palustris	MSKA MWts NPer SWat

Houstonia (*Rubiaceae*)

caerulea L.	ECho SRot
- var. ***alba***	EWes SPlb
- 'Millard's Variety'	WIce
michauxii 'Fred Mullard'	EWes GCrg

Houttuynia (*Saururaceae*)

cordata	CAgr ESps GKev GPoy LEdu LLWG LPot SDix SWat WFar WTcb XLum
§ - 'Boo-Boo' (v)	CMac
§ - 'Chameleon' (v)	Widely available
- 'Fantasy' (v)	LLWG
- 'Flame' (v)	CMac EBee GMcL MHol NPla SHil WFar
- 'Flore Pleno' (d)	CBen CMac CWat ECha EPfP MRav MSCN NBir NPer SPer SPlb SRms SWat WPnP WTcb XLum
- 'Joker's Gold'	CMac ECtt ELan EPPr EPfP WFar
- 'Pied Piper' (v)	ELan NBir SPad SPtp
- 'Terry Clarke'	see *H. cordata* 'Boo-Boo'
- 'Tricolor'	see *H. cordata* 'Chameleon'
- Variegata Group (v)	NBro

Hovea (*Papilionaceae*)

celsii	see *H. elliptica*
§ ***elliptica***	SPlb
montana	SPlb

Hovenia (*Rhamnaceae*)

dulcis	CAgr CBcs CPne EBee EPfP ESwi LEdu MBlu NLar
- B&SWJ 11024	WCru
- NJM 11.003	WPGP

Howea (*Arecaceae*)

§ ***belmoreana*** ♀H1b	XBlo
§ ***forsteriana*** ♀H1b	CCCN ETod NLos NPla SPlb XBlo

Hoya (*Apocynaceae*)

§ ***australis***	CBcs
bella	see *H. lanceolata* subsp. *bella*
carnosa ♀H2	CBcs EBak EOHP WWFP
- 'Compacta Regalis' (v)	NPer
- 'Krinkle 8'	NPer
- 'Tricolor' (v)	CCCN NPer
- 'Variegata' (v)	EShb
* ***compacta*** 'Tricolor'	NPer
darwinii misapplied	see *H. australis*
gracilis **new**	CCCN
lacunosa	CCCN
§ ***lanceolata*** subsp. ***bella*** ♀H1c	CBcs CCCN EShb

Huernia (*Apocynaceae*)

keniensis	LToo
schneideriana	LToo

Hugueninia (*Brassicaceae*)

tanacetifolia subsp. ***suffruticosa***	SBrt

Humata (*Davalliaceae*)

tyermannii	CCCN CMen EShb ISha NLos SBrt SPlb WCot WFib
- 'Bunny' **new**	CCCN
- 'Selcka'	CMen

Humea see *Calomeria*

elegans	see *Calomeria amaranthoides*

Humulus ✿ (*Cannabaceae*)

japonicus 'Variegatus' (v)	SGol
lupulus	CBcs EPfP GPoy IKil NLar NMir SCob SIde WHer
- 'Aureus' ♀H6	Widely available
- 'Aureus' (f)	CRHN ELon GCal GKev SPoG WCot
* - ***compactus***	GPoy
- 'Fuggle'	CAgr GPoy SDea
- 'Golden Tassels' (f)	CKel ECrN ELon LRHS MGos MJak MMuc MNHC NLar SBod SEND SGol SNig SPer SPoG WBor
- (Goldings Group) 'Cobbs'	SDea
- - 'Mathons'	CAgr SDea
- 'Hallertauer'	SDea
- 'Northern Brewer' **new**	IPot
- 'Prima Donna'	CAgr CMac LEdu MCoo MMuc NLar SCoo SPer SPoG SWvt
- 'Taff's Variegated' (v)	EWes
- 'Wye Challenger'	CAgr GPoy MHer
- 'Wye Northdown'	CAgr SDea

Hunnemannia (*Papaveraceae*)

fumariifolia	CSpe SBrt

Huodendron (*Styracaceae*)

tibeticum	CBcs CFil

Hutchinsia see *Pritzelago*

rotundifolia	see *Thlaspi cepaeifolium* subsp. *rotundifolium*

Hyacinthella (*Asparagaceae*)

acutiloba	ECho
dalmatica	ECho
glabrescens	WCot
heldreichii	ECho
leucophaea	ECho
millingenii	ECho
pallens	ECho

Hyacinthoides (*Asparagaceae*)

	aristidis	EChoWCot
	- from Algeria	ECho
	'Bakkum Blue' **new**	SDir
	ciliolata	CBro ECho EPot GKev NRog SBch WCot
§	***hispanica***	ECho GKev NBir SEND WCot
	- 'Alba'	ECho GKev LRHS NRHS
	- 'Alba Maxima' **new**	GKev
	- 'Dainty Maid'	ECho GKev WCot
	- 'Excelsior'	GKev
	- 'Miss World'	GKev WCot
	- 'Queen of the Pinks'	GKev WCot
	- 'Rose Queen' **new**	GKev
	- 'Rosea'	ECho GKev
	- 'White City'	ECho GKev WCot
§	***italica*** ♀H4	ECho GKev WCot WShi
	mauritanica	ECho
§	***non-scripta***	Widely available
	- 'Alba'	CAvo ECho GKev MMuc NBir SDir SEND
	- 'Backkum's Blue'	SDir
	- 'Bracteata'	CNat WCot
	- cleistogamous	CNat
	- long-bracteate, white-flowered	WCot
	- 'Rosea'	ECho GKev
	- 'Wavertree'	GKev
	reverchonii	ECho WCot
	- from Spain	ECho GKev WCot
§	***vincentina***	GKev

Hyacinthus ✿ (*Asparagaceae*)

	amethystinus	see *Brimeura amethystina*
	azureus	see *Muscari azureum*
	comosus 'Plumosus'	see *Muscari comosum* 'Plumosum'
	orientalis 'Aida' ♀H4	MGib
	- 'Aiolos'	GKev MGib SDeJ
	- 'Amethyst'	MGib
	- 'Anastasia'	CAvo
	- 'Anna Liza'	SDeJ
	- 'Anna Marie' ♀H4	CBro GKev LAma SDeJ
	- 'Apricot Passion'	ERCP SDeJ SDir
	- 'Blue Eyes'	ERCP MGib SDeJ
	- 'Blue Festival' ♀H4	GKev MGib SDeJ SDir
	- 'Blue Giant'	LAma SDeJ
	- 'Blue Jacket' ♀H4	CBro GKev LAma MGib SCob SDeJ
	- 'Blue Magic'	SDeJ
	- 'Blue Pearl' PBR	GKev LCro LOPS SDeJ
	- 'Blue Star'	LAma
	- 'Blue Tango'	MGib
	- 'Carnegie'	CAvo CBro EPfP ERCP GKev LAma LCro LOPS
	- 'Chestnut Flower' (d)	SDeJ
	- 'China Pink'	GKev LRHS NRHS SDeJ
	- 'City of Haarlem' ♀H4	CBro EPfP GKev LAma LOPS LRHS NRHS SDeJ
	- 'Crystal Palace' (d)	LAma SDeJ SDir
	- 'Dark Dimension' **new**	LAma
	- 'Delft Blue' ♀H4	CAvo CBro EPfP GKev LAma LCro LOPS LRHS NRHS SCob SDeJ SPer WShi
§	- 'Fairly' PBR ♀H4	GKev NNys SDir
	- Fairy White	see *H. orientalis* 'Fairly'
	- 'Fondant'	LAma LRHS NRHS SDeJ
	- 'General Köhler' (d)	LAma SDeJ
	- 'Gipsy Princess'	LAma
	- 'Gipsy Queen' ♀H4	EPfP GKev LAma MGib SCob SDeJ SDir WCot
	- 'Gypsy Princess' **new**	SDir
	- 'Hollyhock' (d) ♀H4	ERCP LAma SCob SDeJ
	- 'Ibis'	MGib SCob SPer
	- 'Jan Bos' ♀H4	GKev LAma LOPS LRHS MGib NRHS SCob SDeJ
	- 'King Codro' (d)	MGib
	- 'Lady Derby'	SDeJ
	- 'L'Innocence' ♀H4	CBro SCob
	- 'Madame Sophie' (d) **new**	MGib
	- 'Marie'	EPfP SPer
	- 'Miss Saigon' ♀H4	CAvo ERCP SDeJ
	- multi-flowered	ERCP SDeJ
	- 'Odysseus'	LAma SDeJ SDir
	- 'Ostara' ♀H4	LAma
	- 'Pacific Ocean' **new**	GKev LAma
	- 'Paul Hermann' ♀H4	GKev MGib SDeJ
	- 'Peter Stuyvesant'	EPfP ERCP LAma LCro LOPS SDeJ
	- 'Pink Elephant' **new**	MGib
	- 'Pink Festival' ♀H4	GKev MGib SDeJ
	- 'Pink Pearl'	EPfP GKev LAma LCro LOPS LRHS NRHS SDeJ
	- 'Pink Royal' (d)	LAma
	- 'Purple Sensation' PBR	GKev
	- 'Red Magic'	SDeJ
	- 'Rosette' (d)	LAma SDeJ
	- 'Royal Navy' (d) ♀H4	ERCP MGib NNys
	- 'Sky Jacket'	GKev LCro LOPS SCob
	- 'Snow Crystal' (d)	ERCP
	- 'Splendid Cornelia'	ERCP GKev SDeJ
	- 'Top Hit'	MGib
	- 'White Festival' ♀H4	CAvo GKev MGib SDeJ
	- 'White Pearl'	CAvo EPfP GKev LAma LCro LOPS LRHS MGib NRHS SCob SDeJ SPer
	- 'Woodstock'	CAvo CBro EPfP ERCP GKev LAma LCro LOPS MGib SCob SDeJ SDir
	- 'Yellow Queen' ♀H4	MGib NNys

Hydrangea ✿ (*Hydrangeaceae*)

	angustipetala	see *H. scandens* subsp. *chinensis* f. *angustipetala*
	anomala subsp. ***anomala*** BWJ 8052 from China	WCru
	- - HWJK 2065 from Nepal	WCru
§	- - 'Winter Glow'	CJun ESwi MRav MTPN SGol WCot WCru WFar
	- subsp. ***glabra*** B&SWJ 6804	WCru
	- - 'Crûg Coral'	WCru
§	- subsp. ***petiolaris*** ♀H5	Widely available
	- - B&SWJ 5996	WCru
	- - B&SWJ 6337	WCru
	- - from Yakushima	CFil
§	- - var. ***cordifolia***	NBro NLar
	- - - B&SWJ 6081	WCru
	- - - B&SWJ 11487	WCru
§	- - - 'Brookside Littleleaf'	NBro NLar WFar
	- - dwarf	see *H. anomala* subsp. *petiolaris* var. *cordifolia*
	- - 'Early Light' (v)	SGbt
	- - 'Firefly' (v)	WPat
	- - var. ***megaphylla*** B&SWJ 4400	WCru
	- - - B&SWJ 8497	WCru
*	- - var. ***minor*** B&SWJ 5991	GEdr WCru
	- - 'Mirranda' (v)	CBcs CRHN ELan EPfP GCal LPar MGos MNHC NBro NLar SGol SPoG SWvt WBor WGrn
§	- - var. ***ovalifolia***	CRHN ESwi GQui LRHS
	- - - B&SWJ 8799	WCru
	- - - B&SWJ 8846	WCru

- - 'Silver Lining'PBR	CRos EBee EPfP LRHS NRHS SPoG
- - 'Summer Snow' (v)	CRos LLHF LRHS NRHS SPoG
- - var. ***tiliifolia***	see *H. anomala* subsp. *petiolaris* var. *ovalifolia*
- - 'Yakushima'	WCru
- subsp. ***quelpartensis***	see *H. anomala* subsp. *petiolaris* var. *ovalifolia*
- 'Winter Surprise'	see *H. anomala* subsp. *anomala* 'Winter Glow'
§ ***arborescens***	CArn LPar MRav WPGP
- 'Annabelle' ♀H6	Widely available
- 'Bounty'	MAsh WPat
§ - subsp. ***discolor***	GBin LEdu WPat
- - 'Sterilis'	CFil GGGa SHyH WPGP WPat
- 'Eco Pink Puff'	WPGP
- 'Emerald Lace' **new**	MBlu
- 'Grandiflora'	CBcs ESps IBoy NBro NEgg WBod WPGP
- 'Hayes Starburst'PBR	CBot CMil CRos CWGN EBee EMil LEdu LHop LLHF LRHS MMrt SGol SHyH SKHP SPoG SWvt WPGP WPat
- 'Hills of Snow'	IVic NLar
- Incrediball = 'Abetwo'PBR	CBcs CLet CRos ELan EPfP GBin LCro LRHS LSRN MBlu NLar SGol SLon SPoG
§ - Invincibelle Spirit = 'Ncha1'	CBcs CBot CLet CRos ELan EPfP GMcL LCro LHop LLHF LOPS LRHS LSRN MBlu NLar SCob SGol SHyH SLon SMDP SMad SPer SPoG SWvt
- 'Invincible Spirit'	see *H. arborescens* Invincibelle Spirit
- 'Picadilly'	NLar
- 'Pink Annabelle'	see *H. arborescens* Invincibelle Spirit
- 'Pink Pincushion'	NBro NLar SAko
- 'Puffed Green'	NLar
- subsp. ***radiata***	CRos EBee LRHS MRav SGol WPGP
- - 'Samantha'	EPfP LLHF LRHS SCob SPoG WPGP
- 'Ryan Gainey'	EUJe LEdu MPkF
- 'Sheep Cloud' **new**	MBlu
- 'Vasterival'	NLar
- 'Visitation'	MMrt
- White Dome = 'Dardom'PBR	NBro
aspera	CMac CTri EUJe SHyH SLon SSta WCru WHar WKif WPGP
- HWJCM 452	WCru
- from Gongshan, China	CFil CMil WPGP
- 'Anthony Bullivant' ♀H5	CBot CTho IArd IDee LRHS MAsh NLar SAko SGol SHyH SKHP SWvt
- 'Bellevue'	IVic WPGP
- Farrell form	CFil
- Hot Chocolate = 'Hpopr012'	CAbb CMil EMil EUJe LCro LOPS LRHS MBlu MGos SCob SGol SHyH SPoG WGrn
- Kawakamii Group	CBot CMil CSpe ESwi LRHS NLar SGol SHyH SKHP SWvt WCru WPGP
- - B&SWJ 3456	WCru
- - B&SWJ 3527	WCru
- - B&SWJ 6702	WCru
- - B&SWJ 6714	WCru
- - B&SWJ 6827	WCru
- - B&SWJ 6996	WCru
- - B&SWJ 7101	WCru
- - 'August Abundance'	WCru
- - 'Formosa'	WCru
- - 'Maurice Mason'	CFil
- - 'September Splendour'	WCru
- Kawakamii Group × ***involucrata***	CFil WPGP
- 'Koki'	LRHS WPGP
- 'Macrophylla' ♀H5	CBot CFil CRos CWib EPfP ESps GCal GKin IVic MGil MGos MRav NLar SHil SHyH SPer SWvt WCru WPGP
- 'Mauvette'	CBot CMil CRos ECre EPfP GKin LRHS MBlu NBro NLar SCob SGol SHyH SPer WCru
- 'Peter Chappell' ♀H5	CMac CMil LRHS NLar SAko SHyH SWvt
- 'Pink Cloud'	CFil
§ - subsp. ***robusta***	LRHS WPGP
- - B&SWJ 13999 **new**	WCru
- - GWJ 9430	WCru
- - WWJ 11888	WCru
- 'Rocklon'	ESwi NLar SGol
- 'Rosthornii'	see *H. aspera* subsp. *robusta*
- 'Sam MacDonald'	CMil EPfP LRHS NLar SKHP WPGP
§ - subsp. ***sargentiana***	Widely available
- - 'La Fosse'	WPGP
- - large-leaved	CFil WCru
- 'Spinners'	NLar
- subsp. ***strigosa***	CDul EPfP LRHS SHyH SWvt WCru WPGP
- - B&SWJ 8201	WCru
- - HWJ 653	WCru
- - HWJ 737	WCru
- - KWJ 12151 from northern Vietnam	WCru
- - 'Gongshan' **new**	WPGP
- aff. subsp. ***strigosa***	CFil
- 'Taiwan Pink'	EPfP IArd NLar SGol
- 'The Ditch'	ESwi NLar
- 'Trelissick Blue Skies'	CFil
§ - Villosa Group	Widely available
- - 'Trelissick'	CFil WPGP
- - 'Velvet and Lace' ♀H5	CJun CRos GMcL LRHS MGos NLar SHil
asterolasia B&SWJ 10481	WCru
§ 'Blue Deckle' (L)	CAbb CMHG CMac LRHS MAsh MGos MRav NBro NLar SDys SGol SHyH WPat
cinerea	see *H. arborescens* subsp. *discolor*
davidii B&SWJ 8307	WCru
- B&SWJ 11692	WCru
- B&SWJ 11717	WCru
- f. ***purpurascens*** KWJ 12233B	WCru
'Dharuma'	GKin LRHS SAko SGol
Early Sensation = 'Bulk'PBR	CBot CLet CRos EPfP EShb ESps ESwi GBin GKin LRHS MSwo SGol SHyH SKHP SMDP SPoG WFar WGrn WMoo
'Garden House Glory'	CFil CMil EBee WPGP
glabrifolia	see *H. scandens* subsp. *chinensis*
glandulosa B&SWJ 4031	WCru
'Glyn Church'	EBee EPfP SAko WPGP
aff. ***gracilis*** B&SWJ 3942	WCru
§ ***heteromalla***	CMCN CMHG CPne GGGa NBro WPGP
- B&SWJ 2142 from India	WCru
- B&SWJ 2602 from Sikkim	WCru
- BWJ 7657 from China	WCru
- GWJ 9337 from Sikkim	WCru
- HWJ 526 from Vietnam	WCru
- HWJ 938 from Vietnam	WCru
- HWJCM 180	WCru

- HWJK 2127 from Nepal	WCru
- KR 9913 from India	WPGP
- SBEC	GGGa
- Bretschneideri Group	EBee EPfP GKin GQui SHyH WCru
- 'Fan Si Pan'	WCru
- 'June Pink'	NLar
- 'Long White'	NLar
- 'Morrey's Form'	NLar WCru
- 'Nepal Beauty'	EBee EPfP ESwi IVic MMrt NLar SGol WPGP
- 'Snowcap'	EPfP ESps GQui IArd LRHS NLar SBrt SHyH SKHP
- f. ***xanthoneura***	CBot
- - NJM 11.009	WPGP
- - 'Wilsonii'	WCru WKif
- 'Yalung Ridge'	WCru
aff. ***heteromalla***	SGol
'Hidcote Pink'	see *H. macrophylla* 'Juno'
hirta	MBlu
- B&SWJ 5000	WCru
- B&SWJ 11022	WCru
indochinensis	ESwi
- B&SWJ 8307	WCru
- WWJ 11609	WCru
integerrima	see *H. serratifolia*
integrifolia B&SWJ 022	WCru
- B&SWJ 6967	NLar WCru
involucrata	CRos LLHF LRHS MMrt SBrt SGol SHil SHyH
- B&SWJ 4790	WCru
- B&SWJ 11578	WCru
- dwarf	CFil WCru
- 'Hortensis' (d)	CBot CMil MRav NLar SMad WBod WCru WKif WPGP WSHC
- var. ***idzuensis***	WCru
- 'Mihara-kokonoe'	SGol WPGP
- 'Multiplex'	CBot WCru
- 'Oshima'	WPGP
- 'Plena' (d)	EBee LRHS MRav NLar SHyH WCru WPGP
- 'Plenissima' (d)	WCru
- 'Sterilis'	CMil WCru
- 'Tokada Yama'	CMil NLar
- 'Viridescens' ♀H4	EBee LLHF LRHS NLar SHyH WCru WPGP
- 'Yohraku-tama' ♀H4	CFil NLar SGol WPGP
- 'Yokudanka' (d)	CBot CMil GQui NLar SAko WPGP
- 'Yoraku' (d)	EBee WCru
kawagoeana	WCru
var. ***grosseserrata*** B&SWJ 11500	
- - B&SWJ 11511	WCru
lobbii	see *H. scandens* subsp. *chinensis*
longifolia B&SWJ 6883	WCru
- CWJ 12413	WCru
longipes	GQui WCru
- var. ***fulvescens*** B&SWJ 8188	WCru
- var. ***longipes***	CFil
luteovenosa	WCru
- B&SWJ 5647	WCru
- B&SWJ 5929	WCru
- B&SWJ 6220	WCru
- B&SWJ 6317	WCru
macrophylla (H)	LRHS
- 'AB Green Shadow'[PBR] (H)	MAsh MMrt SCob SGol
- 'Adria' (H)	NLar SGol
- 'Aduarda'	see *H. macrophylla* 'Mousmée'
- 'All Summer Beauty' (H)	ELon GBin GGGa MAsh SHyH
- Alpen Glow	see *H. macrophylla* 'Alpenglühen'

§ - 'Alpenglühen' (H)	CBcs CSBt IVic LRHS MJak SAko SHyH SLim
- 'Altona' (H) ♀H5	CBcs CCVT EPfP GMcL IArd LCro LOPS LRHS MAsh MGos MRav NBir NLar SHyH SPer WBod
- 'Amethyst' (H/d)	LRHS
- 'Ami Pasquier' (H)	CBcs CMac CSBt CTri ELan EPfP ESps IVic LRHS LSRN MAsh MMuc MRav MSwo NEgg SAko SCob SCoo SHyH SLim SPoG SWvt
- 'Amor' (H)	SCob SGol
* - 'Aureomarginata' (v)	WCot
- 'Ave Maria' (H)	GGGa MAsh
§ - 'Ayesha' (H)	Widely available
- 'Bachstelze' (Teller Series) (L)	IVic MAsh WPGP
- 'Bavaria' (H)	GKin SGol WFar
- 'Beauté Vendômoise' (L)	CMil LRHS NLar SHyH
- 'Bela'[PBR] (H)	EBee LRHS SCob
- 'Benelux' (H)	CBcs MMuc
- 'Bergfink' (Teller Series) (L)	NLar
- Berlin = 'Rabe'[PBR] (City-line Series) (H)	SGol
- 'Bichon' (H)	SGol
- 'Bicolor'	see *H. macrophylla* 'Harlequin'
- Black Steel Series (H) **new**	LRHS NRHS
- - 'Black Steel Zambia' (H)	EPfP LBuc LCro NPri SGol SLon WCot
- - 'Black Steel Zebra' (H)	EBee EPfP LBuc NPri SGol SLon
§ - 'Blauer Prinz' (H)	SHyH
§ - 'Bläuling' (Teller Series) (L) ♀H5	CRos GKin LRHS LSRN SCob SGol SLim
§ - 'Blaumeise' (Teller Series) (L) ♀H5	CFil CMHG EAEE ELon GGGa GMcL LRHS MAsh MGos MRav SCob SCoo SGol SHyH SLim SLon SPoG SWvt WFar WPGP
- 'Blue Bonnet' (H)	CDul EPfP LRHS LSRN MRav SAko SHyH SPer
- Blue Butterfly	see *H. macrophylla* 'Bläuling'
- Blue Prince	see *H. macrophylla* 'Blauer Prinz'
- Blue Sky	see *H. macrophylla* 'Blaumeise'
- Blue Tit	see *H. macrophylla* 'Blaumeise'
- 'Blue Wave'	see *H. macrophylla* 'Mariesii Perfecta'
- 'Bluebird' misapplied	see *H. serrata* 'Bluebird'
- Bluebird	see *H. macrophylla* 'Bläuling'
§ - 'Blushing Bride'[PBR] (H)	ELan GMcL LCro NPri SLon
- 'Bodensee' (H)	CCVT MJak MMuc SCob
- 'Bottstein' (H)	CCVT
- 'Bouquet Rose' (H)	CWib ECtt ESps MJak MMuc NLar SEND SHyH
- 'Brestenburg' (H)	MAsh
- 'Brügg' (H)	LRHS MAsh SAko SGol SHyH SLim SPer
- 'Cameroun' (H) **new**	SGol
- 'Camilla'[PBR] (H)	SGol WFar
- 'Camino' (L)	EPfP
- Cardinal	see *H. macrophylla* 'Kardinal' (Teller Series)
§ - 'Cardinal Red' (H)	ECre NPri WFar
- 'Cendrillon' (H)	EBee LLHF LRHS
- Chique = 'Hbachi'[PBR] (H) **new**	LRHS NRHS
- 'Choco Chic' (L)	SGol
- Clarissa = 'Hba 208901'[PBR] (H) **new**	LRHS
- 'Cocktail' (H)	SGol
- 'Coco' (H)	LRHS
- 'Coco Blanc' (H/d)	SCob SGol

	- Color Fantasy (H)	MBrN
	- 'Cordata'	see *H. arborescens*
	- 'Cotton Candy Two' (L) **new**	EPfP LRHS NRHS
	- 'Dandenong' (L)	GQui
	- 'Dark Angel' (L)	LCro LPar LRHS SGol WHlf
	- 'Dark Angel Purple' (L) **new**	LCro WHlf
	- 'Dart's Romance' (L)	SHyH
	- 'Deep Purple' (L) **new**	WHlf
	- 'Deutschland' (H)	CTri
	- 'Doctor Jean Varnier' (L)	EMil EPfP SHyH
	- Dolce Farfalle = 'Dolfarf' (H)	WCot
	- Dolce Gipsy = 'Dolgip'^{PBR} (L)	CRos EPfP ESwi LRHS MGos SHil
	- Dolce Kiss = 'Dolkis'^{PBR} (L)	CRos EPfP LRHS MGos SGol SHil
	- 'Domotoi'	see *H. macrophylla* 'Setsuka-yae'
	- 'Doris' (H)	SCob SGol SHyH
	- Dragonfly	see *H. macrophylla* 'Libelle'
	- Early Blue = 'Hba 202911'^{PBR} (H)	CRos LRHS SCob SGol SPoG
§	- 'Early Sensation' (Forever & Ever Series) (H)	CMac GKin LBuc LLHF MHol
§	- 'Eisvogel' (L) **new**	SHyH
	- 'Eldorado' (H)	SHyH
	- 'Elégance' (L)	SGol
	- Endless Summer = 'Bailmer' (H)	ELan EPfP LCro NPri SPoG
	- Endless Summer Blushing Bride	see *H. macrophylla* 'Blushing Bride'
	- Endless Summer Twist-n-Shout = 'Piihm-I' (L)	EPfP
§	- 'Enziandom' (H)	CBcs CFil CSBt MAsh
	- Eternity = 'Youmetwo'^{PBR} (H/d)	WCot
	- 'Etoile Violette' (L)	ESwi LRHS
	- 'Europa' (H) 🏆^{H5}	CBcs NLar SHyH
	- Expression = 'Youmesix' (H/d)	LCro SGol
	- 'Fanfare' (H) **new**	SGol
§	- 'Fasan' (Teller Series) (L)	MAsh NBro SDix SGol WHar
	- Firelight	see *H. macrophylla* 'Leuchtfeuer'
	- Fireworks	see *H. macrophylla* 'Hanabi'
	- Fireworks Blue	see *H. macrophylla* 'Jōgasaki'
	- Fireworks Pink	see *H. macrophylla* 'Jōgasaki'
	- Fireworks White	see *H. macrophylla* 'Hanabi'
	- Forever & Ever Together = 'Rie 05' (Forever & Ever Series) (H/d)	SGol SMDP
	- Forever and Ever	see *H. macrophylla* 'Early Sensation'
	- 'Forever Pink' (H)	GGGa MAsh NLar SGol
§	- 'Frau Katsuko' (Lady Series) (H)	SPer
§	- 'Frau Mariko' (Lady Series) (H)	MRav
§	- 'Frau Taiko' (Lady Series) (H)	SPer
	- 'French Cancan' (Teller Series) (L) **new**	SGol
	- 'Freudenstein' (H)	ESwi
	- 'Frillibet' (H)	CAbP MRav NLar
	- 'Ganku Bo Chokens' (H)	WCot
	- 'Gartenbaudirektor Kühnert' (H)	SHyH
§	- 'Générale Vicomtesse de Vibraye' (H) 🏆^{H5}	CBcs CDul CEnd CTri ELan ELon EPfP GBin LRHS MAsh SCob SHyH SLim SPer SPoG WBod WBor
	- Gentian Dome	see *H. macrophylla* 'Enziandom'
	- 'Geoffrey Chadbund'	see *H. macrophylla* 'Möwe'
	- 'Gerda Steiniger' (H)	GMcL SHyH
	- 'Gertrud Glahn' (H)	SHyH
	- 'Gimpel' (Teller Series) (L)	MAsh
§	- Glam Rock = 'Horwack'^{PBR} (H)	SGol
	- 'Glowing Embers' (H)	IArd
	- Goldrush = 'Nehyosh' (L/v)	CDul EBee ESps GMcL LBMP LRHS NHol WCot
	- 'Goliath' (H)	ELon
	- 'Gräfin Cosel' (H)	SGol
§	- 'Grant's Choice' (L)	NBro
	- Great Star = 'Blanc Bleu' (L)	ECrN EPfP LRHS LSRN SLim WFar WPat
	- 'Grünes Gewölbe' (H)	SGol
	- 'Hamburg' (H)	CBcs CTri ECtt EPfP GMcL LRHS SCob SDix SHyH SLim WFar
§	- 'Hanabi' (L/d) 🏆^{H5}	CAbP ECre MBlu NLar SGol
§	- 'Harlequin' (H)	CMac WCot
	- 'Hatfield Rose' (H)	SHyH
	- 'Hatsu-shime' (L)	CMil NLar
	- 'Heinrich Seidel' (H)	CBcs CTri WMoo
	- 'Hercule Poirot' (H) **new**	SGol
	- 'Hobella'^{PBR} (Hovaria Series) (L)	CBcs NPnk WCot WFar
	- 'Hobergine'^{PBR} (Hovaria Series) (H)	SGol
	- 'Holehird Purple' (H)	MAsh
	- 'Homigo'^{PBR} (Hovaria Series) (H)	SGol
	- 'Hopaline'^{PBR} (Hovaria Series) (H) **new**	WPGP
	- 'Hopcorn'^{PBR} (H)	EBee SGol
	- Hot Red = 'Hba 206901'^{PBR} (H)	CRos LRHS
	- 'Hot Red Violet'	LCro LOPS MJak SPoG
	- 'Izu-no-hana' (L/d)	CAbb CBcs CFil CMil ELon EPfP ESwi GBin LHop MBlu NLar SBod SHyH SPoG WBor
	- 'James Grant'	see *H. macrophylla* 'Grant's Choice'
	- 'Jofloma' (H)	ESwi NLar
§	- 'Jōgasaki' (L/d)	CBcs CLAP CMil LRHS MAsh MBlu NLar SDys SHyH WPGP
	- 'Joseph Banks' (H)	CBcs CTri SHyH
§	- 'Juno' (L) **new**	EMil
	- 'Kardinal'	see *H. macrophylla* 'Cardinal Red' (H)
§	- 'Kardinal' (Teller Series) (L) 🏆^{H5}	MAsh SCob SGol SHyH SPoG
	- Kingfisher	see *H. macrophylla* 'Eisvogel'
	- 'King George' (H)	CBar CBcs CDul CRos CSBt ECtt ELon EPfP ESps EUJe GMcL LRHS MGos MMuc NEgg NHol SAdn SAko SCob SGol SHil SHyH SLim SPer SPoG SWvt WFar WHar WMoo
§	- 'Klaveren' (L) 🏆^{H5}	CMil GGGa LRHS MAsh NBro SHyH
	- 'Kluis Superba' (H)	CBcs CTri SHyH
	- 'Koria'^{PBR} (L)	LRHS NPnk
	- 'La France' (H)	CTri IVic LRHS SCob SHyH SLim SPoG
	- 'La Vie en Rose' (H)	SGol
	- 'Lady in Red' (L)	CMil CRos EBee EPfP LRHS SPoG
	- Lady Katsuko	see *H. macrophylla* 'Frau Katsuko'
	- 'Lady Mariko'	see *H. macrophylla* 'Frau Mariko'
	- 'Lady Oshie' (Teller Series) (L)	SGol
	- 'Lady Taiko Blue'	see *H. macrophylla* 'Frau Taiko'
	- 'Lady Taiko Pink'	see *H. macrophylla* 'Frau Taiko'
	- 'Lanarth White' (L) 🏆^{H5}	Widely available
	- 'Lemon Wave' (L/v)	NLar
§	- 'Leuchtfeuer' (H)	ELon GMcL LRHS SGol SHyH WMoo

§	- 'Libelle' (Teller Series) (L) 🏆^{H5}	CBcs CMil ELon EPfP GMcL LPar LRHS MGos MMuc MRav NBir NLar SCob SGol SHyH SLim SPer
	- 'Lilacina'	see *H. macrophylla* 'Mariesii Lilacina'
	- Little Lime	see *H. paniculata* 'Jane'
	- Love = 'Youme H1917' (H/d) **new**	SPer
	- 'Love You Kiss'^{PBR} (Hovaria Series) (L) 🏆^{H5}	CBcs LRHS NLar SCoo SGol SPoG WCot
§	- 'Maculata' (L/v)	ESps GQui WGwG
	- 'Madame A. Riverain' (H)	EPfP NLar SHyH
	- 'Madame Emile Mouillère' (H) 🏆^{H5}	Widely available
	- 'Madame Plumecocq' (H)	LRHS
	- Magical Amethyst = 'Hokomathyst'^{PBR} (H)	EBee SGol
	- Magical Coral = 'Hokomac'^{PBR} (H) **new**	SGol
	- Magical Greenfire = 'Qufu' (H) **new**	SGol
	- Magical Harmony = 'Hortmahar'^{PBR} (H)	NLar
	- Magical Jade = 'Hortmaja'^{PBR} (H)	EPfP MBlu WCot
	- Magical Noblesse = 'Hokomano'^{PBR} (H)	SGol
	- Magical Revolution = 'Hokomarevo' (H)	SGol
	- 'Maréchal Foch' (H)	CTri LRHS NLar
	- 'Mariesii' (L)	CMHG CTri ECrN ELan GBin LPar LRHS MSwo NLar SHyH SPer
§	- 'Mariesii Grandiflora' (L)	EPfP LRHS MMuc NBro SGol SHyH SPer SRms WBod WMoo
§	- 'Mariesii Lilacina' (L) 🏆^{H5}	EPfP MMuc SEND SHyH SPer WMoo
§	- 'Mariesii Perfecta' (L)	Widely available
	- 'Mariesii Variegata' (L/v)	CWib
	- 'Masja' (H)	CBar CBcs CCVT ELon GKin IArd IVic MAsh MGos MMuc MRav MSwo NBro NLar SAko SCob SGol SHyH SLim WBor WMoo
	- 'Mathilde Gütges' (H)	CCVT
	- 'Max Löbner' (H)	SHyH
	- 'Merveille' (H)	NBro
	- 'Merveille Sanguine' (H)	Widely available
	- 'Messalina' (L)	SCob SHyH
	- 'Mini Penny'^{PBR} (H)	SGol
	- Minty Ice = 'Es11' (Flair and Flavour Series) (H) **new**	SGol
	- 'Mirai'^{PBR} (H)	CBcs CMil ELan ESwi LRHS WCot WPGP
	- 'Miss Belgium' (H)	CMac CTri GKin GMcL
§	- 'Mousmée' (L)	SHyH
	- 'Mousseline' (H)	CFil CMil MAsh
§	- 'Möwe' (Teller Series) (L) 🏆^{H5}	CBcs CEnd CMil ECtt ELon EPfP GBin MAsh MMuc MNHC SCob SCoo SDix SEND SGol SHyH SLim SPer SRms SSta WPat
	- Mrs Kumico = 'Kumico' (H)	SGol
	- 'Mrs W.J. Hepburn' (H)	CSBt SPer
§	- 'Nachtigall' (Teller Series) (L) 🏆^{H5}	EPfP IVic MAsh SHyH WPGP WPat
	- 'Nadeshiko-gaku' (L) **new**	SHyH
	- 'Nanping'^{PBR} (Sturdy Series) (L)	NPnk SPoG
	- 'Niedersachsen' (H)	CTri MRav SHyH
	- Nightingale	see *H. macrophylla* 'Nachtigall'
	- 'Nigra' (H)	CBcs CFil CMac CRos CTsd CWib ELan ELon EPfP EWTr GBin IFoB LRHS MAsh MGos MMuc MNHC MRav NBro NLar SAdn SBod SDix SEND SHyH SLim SPer WGrn WGwG
	- 'Nikko Blue' (H)	CBcs CRos EBee ESps GKin LRHS MJak NLar SHyH
	- Nizza = 'Ranice'^{PBR} (City-line Series) (H)	SCob
§	- 'Nymphe' (H)	SCob SHyH
	- 'Oregon Pride' (H)	CFil GGGa MAsh WFar
	- 'Otaksa' (H)	NLar
	- 'Parzifal' (H) 🏆^{H5}	CDul
	- Passion = 'Youmefour' (L)	WCot
	- 'Pax'	see *H. macrophylla* 'Nymphe'
	- 'Pfau' (Teller Series) (L) 🏆^{H5}	CMil ELon GBin MAsh
	- Pheasant	see *H. macrophylla* 'Fasan'
	- 'Pia' (H)	CMac CMil CPla EShb GBin LBMP LRHS MRav SCob SMad SPer SRms
	- Pigeon	see *H. macrophylla* 'Taube'
	- 'Pink Ball' (Black Steel Series) (H) **new**	LPar
	- 'Pink Lollipop' (Flair and Flavour Series) (H) **new**	SGol
	- 'Pirate's Gold' (v)	EHoe WMoo
	- 'Prinses Beatrix' (H)	SHyH
	- 'Quadricolor' (L/v) 🏆^{H5}	CHll CMac CMil CTsd EHoe GCal MGos MHol MRav SAdn SDix SHyH SLim SMDP SPer SPlb SRms WCot WSHC
	- 'Queen Elizabeth' (H)	GKin
	- 'R.F. Felton' (H)	CBcs SHyH
	- 'Red Angel' (H) **new**	SGol
	- 'Red Baron'	see *H. macrophylla* 'Schöne Bautznerin'
	- 'Red Beauty'^{PBR} (H)	LRHS
	- 'Red Red' (H)	MAsh
	- Redbreast	see *H. macrophylla* 'Rotkehlchen'
	- 'Regula' (H)	SHyH
	- 'Renate Steiniger' (H)	EBee MMuc MRav SCob SGol SHyH SLim WMoo
	- Romance = 'Youmenine'^{PBR} (H/d)	GMcL LRHS SCob SGol WCot
	- 'Rosea'	MCri
	- 'Rosita' (H)	EBee MAsh NBir SCob SGol
	- 'Rotdrossel' (Teller Series) (L)	GBin
§	- 'Rotkehlchen' (Teller Series) (L)	EBee GMcL NLar SGol SLim SPlb SWvt
	- 'Rotschwanz' (Teller Series) (L) 🏆^{H5}	CFil CMil ESwi GBin LLHF LRHS MAsh NLar SHyH WBor WPGP WPat
	- 'Rouge Baiser' (H)	SGol
	- 'Royal Red' (H)	LRHS
	- 'Sabrina' (H)	CBcs EBee LLHF LRHS SCob SGol SHil SHyH SRkn
	- 'Saint Claire' (H)	CBcs
	- 'Salsa'	LBMP LLHF SGol SHyH
	- 'Sandra' (Dutch Ladies Series) (L)	CBcs
	- 'Saskia'	SGol
	- Schloss Wackerbarth	see *H. macrophylla* Glam Rock
	- 'Schneeball' (H)	CCVT MAsh SCob SGol
§	- 'Schöne Bautznerin'	CCVT LRHS SAdn SCob SHyH SLim
	- 'Sea Foam' (L)	NLar
	- 'Selina'	CBcs EBee EPfP LBuc LLHF LRHS LSRN SCoo SGol WPat

	- 'Selma'PBR (Dutch Ladies Series) (L)	CBcs SGol SHyH
	- 'Semperflorens' (H)	LRHS
§	- 'Setsuka-yae' (L/d)	CMil
	- 'Shakira' (H)	LLHF SGol
	- 'Shamrock' (L) **new**	SHyH
	- 'Sheila' (Dutch Ladies Series) (L)	CBcs CTsd EPfP LCro LOPS LSRN
	- 'Shin-ozaki' (H)	NLar
	- 'Shooting Star'PBR (L)	LRHS
	- 'Sibilla' (H)	GMcL MJak SGol SHyH SPlb
	- 'Sidashar' (Dutch Ladies Series) (H) **new**	LRHS SPoG
	- 'Sindarella'	GBin
	- Sister Therese	see *H. macrophylla* 'Soeur Thérèse'
	- 'Sita' (L)	LLHF SHyH
§	- 'Soeur Thérèse' (H)	CBar CBcs CSBt EPfP ESps MAsh MMuc NLar SGol SWvt WGwG
	- 'Spike'PBR (H)	LRHS
	- subsp. ***stylosa***	WCru WPGP
*	- 'Sunset' (L)	CBcs
	- 'Superba' (H)	SCob
	- 'Sweet Fantasy' (Hovaria Series) (H)	ELan EPfP SGol
§	- 'Taube' (Teller Series) (L)	CBcs CDul CMHG GMcL GQui MAsh SGol SHyH SLim SWvt
	- 'Teller Pink'	see *H. macrophylla* 'Taube'
	- 'Teller Red'	see *H. macrophylla* 'Rotkehlchen'
	- Teller variegated	see *H. macrophylla* 'Tricolor'
	- Teller Weiss	see *H. macrophylla* 'Libelle'
	- var. ***thunbergii***	see *H. serrata* var. *thunbergii*
	- 'Tivoli' (H)	LRHS SCob WFar
	- 'Tokyo Delight' (L) 🏆H5	CMac LRHS MAsh SDys SHyH
	- 'Tovelit' (H)	SGol
§	- 'Tricolor' (L/v)	CBcs CDul CTri CTsd EBee ELan ELon EShb ESwi LRHS MGos NLar SHyH SLon SPer WFar WMoo
	- 'Variegata'	see *H. macrophylla* 'Maculata'
	- 'Veitchii' (L) 🏆H5	CBcs CDul CMHG CMil CSBt ECre EPfP LPot LRHS MGos MRav MSwo SDix SHyH SPer
	- 'Vicomte de Vibraye'	see *H. macrophylla* 'Générale Vicomtesse de Vibraye'
	- 'Warabe'	see *H. serrata* 'Warabe'
	- Wedding Gown (L/d) **new**	SGol
	- 'Weisse Königin' (H) **new**	SHyH
	- 'Westfalen' (H) 🏆H5	CMac IArd SDix
	- 'White Mop' (H)	CWib
	- 'White Wave'	see *H. macrophylla* 'Mariesii Grandiflora'
	- 'Wudu'PBR (H)	SGol
	- 'Xian'PBR (Sturdy Series) (H) **new**	SGol
	- 'Yola' (H)	NBro SMDP
	- 'Zaza' (Black Steel Series) (H)	EPfP
	- 'Zebra'PBR (H)	ELan ESwi LBuc LCro MHol SCob SMDP WCot WPtf
	- 'Zhuni Hito' (L)	NLar
	- 'Zorro'PBR (L) 🏆H5	CBcs CMil CRos CTsd CWGN EPfP ESwi GGGa GKin GMcL LBMP LRHS MAsh MGos SCob SCoo SHil SHyH SLim SLon SPer SPoG WCot
	- 'Zulu' (H)	ELan
	- 'Zurichsee' **new**	SHyH
	aff. ***mangshanensis*** BWJ 8120	WCru
	Miss Saori = 'H20-2' (H/d) **new**	LCro LRHS NRHS WHlf

	paniculata	CMCN ESps LPar
	- B&SWJ 3556 from Taiwan	WCru WFar
	- B&SWJ 5413 from Japan	WCru
	- B&SWJ 8894 from Japan	WCru
	- from Taiwan	SKHP
	- 'Ammarin'	GQui NLar WPat
	- Angel's Blush	see *H. paniculata* 'Ruby'
	- Baby Lace = 'Piihp-1' **new**	SGol
	- 'Big Ben' 🏆H5	CMil CRos EPfP GGGa GQui LRHS SKHP SPoG
	- Bobo = 'Ilvobo'PBR	MPkF SCob SGol
	- 'Bombshell'PBR	LCro LOPS NLar SCob SGol
	- 'Brussels Lace'	CAbP CAbb CDul CLAP CMil CRos EPfP GBin LEdu LRHS LSRN MRav NLar SCob SGol SHyH SLon SSta WPat
	- 'Burgundy Lace'	CLAP MBlu NLar
	- Candlelight = 'Hpopr013'	SGol
	- 'Chantilly Lace'	CMil CRos EBee GBin LRHS SCob SHyH
	- Confetti = 'Vlasveld 021' **new**	SGol
	- Dart's Little Dot = 'Darlido'PBR	GBin IVic LLHF LSRN NLar SLim WFar WPGP WPat
	- Diamant Rouge = 'Rendia'PBR	LCro LOPS LRHS MPkF SGol
	- Diamantino = 'Ren101'	SGol
	- 'Dolly'	EPfP GQui LRHS LSRN SHyH
	- 'Everest'	CAbP CLAP CRos EPfP EWTr LEdu LRHS NLar SHyH WPat
	- 'Floribunda'	CRos ELan EPfP LRHS WFar
	- 'Grandiflora'	Widely available
	- 'Great Escape'	NLar
	- 'Greenspire'	CRos EPfP LRHS MBlu MRav SHyH WFar
	- 'Harry's Souvenir'	NLar
§	- 'Jane'PBR	LCro LRHS SGol
	- 'Kyushu'	Widely available
	- 'Last Post'	GQui
	- 'Levana'PBR	CMil SGol SHyH
	- 'Limelight'PBR 🏆H5	Widely available
	- Magical Candle = 'Bokraflame'PBR	EPfP LPar SGol WCot
	- Magical Fire = 'Bokraplume'PBR	LRHS NLar SCob SGol
	- Magical Himalaya = 'Kolmahima' **new**	SGol
	- Magical Moonlight = 'Kolmagimo'PBR **new**	ECrN SGol
	- Magical Starlight	see *H. paniculata* Perle d'Automne
	- Magical Vesuvio = 'Kolmavesu' **new**	SGol
	- 'Mathilde'	NLar
	- Mega Mindy = 'Ilvomindy'PBR	CBcs ESwi SCob SGol SKHP
	- 'Mega Pearl'	LSRN NLar
	- 'Melody'	NLar
	- 'Mount Aso'	GQui NBro SGol
	- 'October Bride'	CEnd GQui NLar WPGP
	- 'Papillon'	WPGP WPat
	- 'Pee Wee'	LLHF NLar
§	- Perle d'Automne = 'Degustar' **new**	SGol
	- 'Phantom' 🏆H5	Widely available
	- 'Pink Beauty'PBR (H)	CTri LSRN
	- Pink Diamond = 'Interhydia' 🏆H5	Widely available
	- 'Pink Jewel'	CWib LLHF WPat
	- 'Pink Lady'	NBro SCob SGol SHyH
	- Pinky-Winky = 'Dvppinky'PBR 🏆H5	Widely available

	- Polar Bear = 'Wrhpbb2' **new**	CMil SCob SGol SHyH
	- 'Praecox'	GQui MRav WCru
	- Prim'White = 'Dolprim'	LRHS
	- 'Rosy Morn'	CRos LRHS
§	- 'Ruby'	CBcs LSRN NLar SGol
	- 'Saville Lace'	CMil
	- 'Silver Dollar' 🏆H5	CMil CRos EBee EPfP ESwi IArd LCro LOPS LRHS LSRN SCob SGol SHyH SPoG SWvt WFar
	- 'Starlight Fantasy'	see *H. paniculata* Perle d'Automne
	- Sundae Fraise = 'Rensun'PBR	CMil CWGN EPfP EShb GGGa IBoy LRHS MAsh MGos MPkF SGol WGrn
	- 'Tardiva'	CBcs CTho GKin GQui LCro LRHS MGos MRav NBro SCob SDix SGol SHyH SPer SRms SWvt WFar WPGP WPat
	- 'Tender Rose'	NLar
	- 'Unique'	Widely available
	- Vanille Fraise = 'Renhy'PBR	Widely available
	- 'White Goliath'	GQui NLar
	- 'White Lace'	NLar
	- 'White Lady'	CBcs LRHS
	- 'White Moth'	CAbP CBcs EBee GGGa LEdu LLHF LRHS NBro NLar SAdn SHyH WPat
	- 'Wim's Red'PBR	CBcs CMil ELan ESwi LCro LPar MMrt NLar SCob SGol
	- 'Yuan-Yang'	WCru
	peruviana* × *seemannii	CEnd GKin IArd MJak SSta
	petiolaris	see *H. anomala* subsp. *petiolaris*
	'Preziosa' 🏆H4	Widely available
	quercifolia	Widely available
	- 'Alice'	CJun CRos EBee ELan EPfP ESwi LHop LPre LRHS LSRN MAsh NLar SCob SGol SHyH WPGP
	- 'Alison'	SGol
I	- 'Amethyst' Dirr	CJun NLar SGol
	- 'Applause'	EPfP LRHS NLar SGol
	- 'Back Porch'	NLar SGol
	- 'Burgundy'	CBcs CJun CMil EBee EPfP ESwi IArd IVic LRHS MBlu NLar SAko SGol WPGP
	- 'Flore Pleno'	see *H. quercifolia* Snowflake
	- 'Harmony'	CJun CMil EBee ELan EMil EPfP ESwi LPre LRHS MGos NLar SAko SHil SHyH SKHP SSta WPGP
	- Ice Crystal = 'Hqopr010'PBR	CAbb CMil EBee IVic LBMP LRHS NLar SCob SGol SHyH WHar WPGP
	- 'Lady Anne'	EPfP WPGP
	- 'Little Honey'PBR	NLar SGol
	- Little Honey = 'Brihon'	CAbP IVic LCro LRHS MAsh
	- 'Pee Wee'	CAbP CBcs CJun ELan EMil EPfP LRHS MAsh MPkF SAko SGol SHyH SKHP SLon SMDP SPoG SSta SWvt WPGP
	- 'Sike's Dwarf'	CJun IVic MPkF MRav NLar SCob SGol WPat
	- 'Snow Giant'	CJun
	- Snow Queen = 'Flemygea' 🏆H5	CBcs CDul CRos CTri ELan ELon EPfP EThi IVic LCro LRHS LSRN MAsh MGos MPkF MRav MSwo NLar SCob SGol SHyH SKHP SLim SPer SPoG SWvt WFar WGrn WPGP WPat
	- 'Snowdrift'	CJun CMil
§	- Snowflake = 'Brido' (d) 🏆H5	CAbP CBcs CEnd CMac CMil CRos CWGN ELan EPfP LCro LOPS LRHS MAsh MGos MRav NLar SHyH SIgm SKHP SLon SPer SPoG WCFE WPGP WPat
	- 'Tennessee Clone'	CJun ESwi LRHS NLar SKHP
	sargentiana	see *H. aspera* subsp. *sargentiana*
	scandens	CFil NBro
	- B&SWJ 5448	WCru
	- B&SWJ 5481	WCru
	- B&SWJ 5496	WCru
	- B&SWJ 5523	WCru
	- B&SWJ 5602	WCru
	- B&SWJ 5725	WCru
	- B&SWJ 5893	WCru
	- B&SWJ 6159	WCru
	- B&SWJ 6317	WCru
§	- subsp. ***chinensis*** B&SWJ 1488	WCru
	- - B&SWJ 3214	WCru
	- - B&SWJ 3410 from Taiwan	WCru
	- - B&SWJ 3420	WCru
	- - B&SWJ 3423	WCru
	- - B&SWJ 3487	WCru
	- - B&SWJ 3869	WCru
	- - BWJ 8035	WCru
	- - BWJ 8000 from Sichuan	WCru
§	- - f. ***angustipetala*** B&SWJ 3454	WCru
	- - - B&SWJ 3553	WCru
	- - - B&SWJ 3667	WCru
	- - - B&SWJ 3733	WCru
	- - - B&SWJ 3814	WCru
	- - - B&SWJ 6038 from Yakushima	WCru
	- - - B&SWJ 6041	WCru
	- - - B&SWJ 6056	WCru
	- - - B&SWJ 6787	WCru
	- - - B&SWJ 6802	WCru
	- - - B&SWJ 7121	WCru
	- - - B&SWJ 7128	WCru
§	- - - 'Golden Crane'	SCob WCru
	- - - 'Monlongshou'	see *H. scandens* subsp. *chinensis* f. *angustipetala* 'Golden Crane'
	- - f. ***formosana***	SBrt
	- - - B&SWJ 1488	WCru
	- - - B&SWJ 3271	WCru
	- - - B&SWJ 7058	NLar WCru
	- - - B&SWJ 7097	NLar WCru
	- - f. ***macrosepala*** B&SWJ 3423	ESwi WCru
	- - - B&SWJ 3476	WCru
	- - - CWJ 12441	WCru
	- - f. ***obovatifolia*** B&SWJ 3487b	WCru
	- - - B&SWJ 3683	WCru
	- - - B&SWJ 7121	WCru
	- aff. subsp. ***chinensis*** B&SWJ 3869 from the Philippines	WCru
	- subsp. ***liukiuensis***	WCru
	- - B&SWJ 6022	WCru
	- - B&SWJ 11471	WCru
	- 'Splash' (v)	CMil
	seemannii	Widely available
	- 'Roger Grounds' (v)	WCot
	aff. ***seemannii***	CRos ESps GKin
	Semiola = 'Inovalaur'PBR	EPfP ESwi LLHF LRHS NLar SGol SKHP SLim
	serrata	CTri CWib ESps LPar WKif
	- B&SWJ 6184	WCru
	- B&SWJ 6241	WCru
	- PAB 4757	LEdu

- 'Acuminata'	see *H. serrata* 'Bluebird'
- 'Aigaku' (L)	CFil CMil
- 'Aka Beni-yama'	CLAP GQui
- 'Akabe-yama'	NBro NLar
- 'Akishino-temari'	WPGP
- Amacha Group	SGol
- - 'Amagi-amacha' (L)	CMil GQui NBro NLar
- - 'Ō-amacha' (L)	CMil EBee GQui WPGP
- subsp. ***angustata***	WCru
- 'Ao-yama'	WPGP
- Avelroz = 'Dolmyf'PBR	EPfP LRHS SGol
- 'Belladonna'	GQui NBro
- 'Belle Deckle'	see *H.* 'Blue Deckle'
- 'Beni-gaku' (L)	CFil CLAP CMil CRos ECre LRHS MAsh NBro NLar SCob SGol SHyH
- 'Beni-temari'	NBro
- 'Beni-yama' (L) 🏆H5	CFil CMil GQui
- 'Besshi-temari'	CFil
- 'Bleuet'	LRHS
- 'Blue Billow' (L)	NBro NLar
- Blueberry Cheesecake	see *H. serrata* Tuff Stuff
§ - 'Bluebird' (L) 🏆H5	Widely available
- 'Cap Sizun'	LRHS SChF SGol WPGP
- 'Chiba Cherry-lips'	ESwi WCru
- 'Chiri-san Sue' (d)	CFil WCru
- Cotton Candy	see *H. serrata* Tuff Stuff
- 'Crûg Bicolor' (L)	WCru
- 'Crûg Caerulean' **new**	WCru
- 'Crûg Cobalt' (L)	ESwi GGGa WCru
- 'Crûg Sō Cool' (L)	WCru
- 'Diadem' (L) 🏆H5	CAbb CBot CLAP ELon EPfP GQui LRHS NBro NCGa SHyH
- dwarf white-flowered (L)	WCru
- 'Forget Me Not'	GQui LRHS NBro
- 'Fuji Snowstorm' (v)	CMil
- 'Fuji Waterfall'	see *H. serrata* 'Fuji-no-taki'
§ - 'Fuji-no-taki' (L/d) 🏆H5	CAbP CBot CMil EBee ELon ESwi LLHF NCGa WPGP WWFP
- 'Gaka' **new**	LRHS
- 'Golden Showers' (L)	NBro
- 'Golden Sunlight'PBR (L)	SGol SWvt
- 'Graciosa' (L)	LLHF LRHS WPat
- 'Grayswood' (L) 🏆H5	CBcs CDul CLAP CMac CRos CSBt EPfP GQui LRHS MAsh MRav NBro SCob SDix SGol SHyH SLim SPer WKif WPGP
- 'Hakucho' (L/d)	CMil EBee NBro WPGP
- 'Hallasan' misapplied	see *H. serrata* 'Maiko', 'Spreading Beauty'
- 'Hallasan' R. & J. de Belder (L)	CMil WPGP
- 'Hime-benigaku' (L)	CMil MAsh WFar
- 'Impératrice Eugénie' (L)	GQui NLar
- 'Intermedia' (L)	NBro
- 'Isusai-jaku' (L)	GQui
- 'Kiyosumi' (L) 🏆H5	CEnd CFil CLAP CMil ECre ELon EPfP GQui LRHS NBir NLar SBrt SHyH WBor WCot WCru WPGP WPat
- 'Klaveren'	see *H. macrophylla* 'Klaveren'
- 'Kurenai' (L)	CMil NBro NLar SChF WPGP
- 'Kurohime' (L)	CMil EBee NBro WPGP
- 'Macrosepala' (L)	WPGP
§ - 'Maiko' (L)	IArd
- 'Mikata Yae'	CMil WPGP
- 'Miranda' (L) 🏆H5	CLAP CMil EPfP LRHS MAsh NBro NLar SDys SGol SHyH WFar
- 'Miyama-yae-murasaki' (L/d) 🏆H5	CAbP CFil CLAP CMil ESwi SGol WPGP
- 'Momo-beni-yama'	CMil NBro
- 'Mont Aso'	CBot CMil NLar
- 'Niji' (L)	EBee WPGP
- 'Odoriko-amacha'	CMil EBee LRHS SChF WPGP
- 'Otsu-hime'	NLar
- 'Panachée' (L/v)	SHyH
- 'Pretty Maiden'	see *H. serrata* 'Shichidanka'
§ - 'Prolifera' (L/d)	CMil LLHF WPat
- 'Pulchella'	see *H. serrata* 'Prolifera'
- 'Ramis Pictis' (L)	CBcs GQui NBro NLar SHyH
- 'Rosalba' (L) 🏆H5	CLAP ECre IVic NBro
- 'Santiago'PBR (L)	EPfP SGol WCot
- 'Sapphirine' (L)	GQui
- 'Sekka'	WPGP
§ - 'Shichidanka' (L/d)	CBot CFil CLAP EBee EPfP LLHF LRHS NBro SHyH WPat
- 'Shichidanka-nishiki' (L/d/v)	CLAP ECre ESwi GQui
- 'Shinonome' (L/d)	CMil GQui
- 'Shirahuzi' (L/d) **new**	SGol
- 'Shirofuji' (L/d) 🏆H5	CFil CLAP CMil LLHF MAsh WPat
- 'Shiro-gaku' (L)	CMil MAsh NBro NLar
- 'Shiro-maiko'	WPGP
- 'Shirotae' (L/d)	CFil CMil SGol
- 'Shōjō' 🏆H5	CMil EBee LRHS NBro SGol WPGP WPat
§ - 'Spreading Beauty' (L)	CMil WPGP
- 'Suzukayama-yama'	CMil SChF WPGP
§ - var. ***thunbergii*** (L)	GQui
* - - 'Plena' (L/d)	GQui WCru
- 'Tiara' (L) 🏆H5	CAbb CDul CFil CLAP CMil CRos EPfP GGGa IVic LRHS LSRN MAsh NBir NBro NLar SDix SDys SGol SHyH SLim SPoG WPGP WPat
- 'Tosa-no-akatsuki'	CFil
§ - Tuff Stuff = 'Mak20' (L)	LCro LLHF LRHS SCob SGol SPoG
- 'Veerle' (L)	NBro NLar SGol
- 'Vicomte de Kerlot' **new**	LRHS
§ - 'Warabe'	SGol
- 'Woodlander' (L)	WPat
- 'Yae-no-amacha' (L/d)	CBcs NBro NLar
- subsp. ***yezoensis***	CMil GQui NLar SGol
- - 'Hime-gaku'	CMil
§ ***serratifolia***	IArd IDee SSta WPGP
- HCM 98056	WCru
sikokiana	CLAP
- B&SWJ 5035	WCru
- B&SWJ 5855	WCru
- B&SWJ 11174	WCru
- B&SWJ 11381	WCru
'Silver Slipper'	see *H. macrophylla* 'Ayesha'
tiliifolia	see *H. anomala* subsp. *petiolaris* var. *ovalifolia*
'Victoria' **new**	GMcL
villosa	see *H. aspera* Villosa Group
xanthoneura	see *H. heteromalla*
aff. ***zhewanensis*** MF 93117	WCru

Hydrastis (*Ranunculaceae*)

canadensis	CArn GPoy LEdu

Hydrocharis (*Hydrocharitaceae*)

morsus-ranae	CBen CHab CWat EWay MSKA MWts NPer SWat WPnP

Hydrocleys (*Alismataceae*)

nymphoides	LLWG XBlo

Hydrocotyle (*Araliaceae*)

asiatica	see *Centella asiatica*

sibthorpioides 'Crystal Confetti' (v)	LLWG
vulgaris	CWat

Hydrophyllum (*Boraginaceae*)

canadense	IMou
'Spring Silver'	SKHP
virginianum	LEdu WHal

Hylomecon (*Papaveraceae*)

hylomeconoides	EWld WCru
§ ***japonica***	CAby CLAP EBee ECho ELan EWld GBuc GCra GEdr GKev GLog IMou LEdu LRHS MAvo NBir NHpl NQui NRya WCru WPGP WThu

Hylotelephium see *Sedum*

Hymenanthera see *Melicytus*

Hymenocallis (*Amaryllidaceae*)

'Advance'	GKev LAma
× ***festalis*** 🏆H1c	CCCN GKev LAma LCro LOPS LTro SDeJ SPav WCot
- 'Zwanenburg'	CGrW GKev
harrisiana	CCCN CTca GKev SDeJ
§ ***longipetala***	GKev
'Sulphur Queen' 🏆H1c	CGrW GKev LTro SDeJ SPav

Hymenolepis (*Asteraceae*)

parviflora	see *Athanasia parviflora*

Hymenosporum (*Pittosporaceae*)

flavum	EShb EUJe

Hymenoxys (*Asteraceae*)

grandiflora	see *Tetraneuris grandiflora*
§ ***hoopesii***	CBod CMac ELan EPfP GMaP GMcL GWyn LRHS MHtn MPie NBir NChi NLar NRHS SCob SDix SPer SRms WCot WFar WHar XLum

Hyoscyamus (*Solanaceae*)

niger	GPoy SRms WSFF

Hypericum ✿ (*Hypericaceae*)

aegypticum	ECho MHer SBrt SIgm SPlb WAbe WThu
androsaemum	CArn ECha ELan MHer MMuc MSwo NPer SEND WFar WMoo WOut
§ - 'Albury Purple'	ELan EShb NLar WMoo XLum
- 'Autumn Blaze'	CBcs
- 'Excellent Flair'	NLar
- 'Golden Flair'	MMuc
§ - f. ***variegatum*** 'Mrs Gladis Brabazon' (v)	EShb NBir WCot
athoum	WIce WThu
balearicum	MMuc SBrt XSen
bellum	EBee GCal
buckleyi	WAbe
calycinum	CBcs CBod CDul CMac CTri ECrN ELan ELon EPfP ESps GMcL LBuc MGos MRav NWea SCob SEND SGol SPer SWvt WFar WMoo XLum
- 'Brigadoon' 🏆H5	LRHS MAsh SGol
- Carnival = 'Crowthyp' (v) **new**	SPad
cerastioides	CTri CWib ECho EDAr EWes GCrg MMuc NGdn SIgm SRms WAbe
coris	EWes SRms
cuneatum	see *H. pallens*
× ***cyathiflorum*** 'Gold Cup'	CMac LRHS MAsh
× ***dummeri*** 'Peter Dummer'	EAEE NLar
'Eastleigh Gold'	CMac
'Elite Baby Green'	EPfP
'Elite Mayor'	EPfP
'Elite Sweet Lion'	EPfP
elodes	CWat LLWG
'Fancy Pants' **new**	LEdu
forrestii 🏆H5	MMuc SEND
fragile misapplied	see *H. olympicum* f. ***minus***
Golden Beacon = 'Wilhyp'PBR 🏆H5	CBod CEnd CSpe EBee ESwi GMcL LHop LLWG LRHS LSou LSun MHer MNrw NBir NEgg NWad SBod SEND SPad SPoG WCot
grandiflorum	see *H. kouytchense*
grandifolium	EDAr
henryi L 753	SRms
- subsp. ***hancockii*** NJM 10.092	WPGP
'Hidcote'	see *H.* × *hidcoteense* 'Hidcote'
× ***hidcoteense*** **new**	ESps
§ - 'Hidcote' 🏆H5	Widely available
- 'Hidcote Variegated' (v)	LRHS MAsh SLim SRms
hirsutum	CHab NMir
(Hypearls Series) Hypearls Annelies	CRos LRHS
- Hypearls Ella	CRos LRHS
- Hypearls Jacqueline	CRos LRHS
imbricatum	LLHF SIgm
× ***inodorum*** 'Albury Purple'	see *H. androsaemum* 'Albury Purple'
- 'Autumn Surprise'PBR	ELon NEgg NEoE NWad
- 'Dream'	NLar
- 'Elstead'	ECtt ELan EPfP MRav NLar NWad NWea
- Magical Cherry = 'Kolmcherrip'PBR	ELan EPfP SCob
- Magical Limelight = 'Kolmalimeli'PBR	ELan
- Magical Pumpkin = 'Kolmapuki'	ECrN NEoE
- Magical Sunshine = 'Kolmasun'PBR	CRos LRHS SPer
- Magical Universe = 'Kolmuni'	NEoE SCob
- Magical White Fall = 'Kolmwhifa'PBR	SCob
- Magical White = 'Kolmawhi'PBR	ELan EPfP NEoE SCob SPoG
- 'Rheingold'	MAsh NLar
- 'Ysella'	MRav
japonicum	ECho
kalmianum	SBrt WCot
kamtschaticum	XLum
kazdaghense **new**	EWes
§ ***kouytchense*** 🏆H5	CDul EPfP EWes GQui LRHS MAsh MMuc MRav SEND SPoG SWvt WCFE WCot
lancasteri	EPfP LRHS MAsh SPoG
leschenaultii misapplied	see *H.* 'Rowallane'
'Little Misstery'	IBoy LBuc LRHS NEoE SPoG
maclarenii	EWes
Magical Beauty = 'Kolmbeau'PBR	CRos ELon EPfP LRHS MJak NEoE NLar SCob SPoG
Magical Dream = 'Kolmdream'PBR **new**	SCob
Magical Fall = 'Kolmfa'PBR **new**	SCob

Magical Flame = 'Kolmagif' **new**	SCob
Magical Pink = 'Kolmpin'	SCob
Magical Red = 'Kolmred'	EPfP MJak NEoE NLar SCob SPoG
Magical Red Star = 'Kolmarest'[PBR] **new**	SCob SMad
Magical Sweetheart = 'Kolmsweet' **new**	SCob
Miracle Attraction = 'Alldiablo'[PBR]	CRos LRHS NLar SHil
Miracle Blizz = 'Allblizz'	LRHS SHil
Miracle Blossom = 'Allblossom'[PBR]	CRos LRHS SHil
Miracle Fantasy = 'Hymirfan'	NLar
Miracle Summer = 'Hymirsum'	CRos EPfP LRHS NLar SHil
Miracle Wonder = 'Hymirwon'	CRos LRHS NLar SHil
× ***moserianum*** ♀[H5]	CDul CMac CRos EAEE EMOT EWes LRHS MJak NPer SCob SHil SLon SPer SRms WFar
- 'Daybreak'	LBMP LRHS MAsh NEoE SPoG WRHF
§ - 'Tricolor' (v)	Widely available
- 'Variegatum'	see *H.* × *moserianum* 'Tricolor'
'Mrs Brabazon'	see *H. androsaemum* f. *variegatum* 'Mrs Gladis Brabazon'
olympicum ♀[H5]	CArn CRos CTri EBee ECha ECho ELan GJos LRHS NRHS SCob SEND SPer SRms SWvt WIce XLum XSen
- 'Grandiflorum'	see *H. olympicum* f. *uniflorum*
- f. ***minus***	CTri ECho ECtt MMuc NGdn NHpl SPlb SRms WHrl
§ - - 'Sulphureum'	CBod CRos ECho ELon EWTr EWes LRHS NBir NRHS SPer SRms SWvt WCFE
- - 'Variegatum' (v)	EWes NBir SPoG SWvt
§ - f. ***uniflorum***	ECho MMuc NBro NRya
- - 'Citrinum' ♀[H5]	CMea CSpe ECha ECtt EPfP GBuc MMuc MRav NLar SEND SIgm SRot WAbe WCot WHoo WKif XSen
orientale	EWes GLog
§ ***pallens***	ECho WAbe
perforatum	CArn CBod CHab CHby ENfk EPfP GPoy IRos MHer MMuc MNHC NLar NMir SEND SIde SRms WHer WMoo WSFF
polyphyllum misapplied	see *H. olympicum* f. *minus*
- 'Citrinum'	see *H. olympicum* f. *minus* 'Sulphureum'
- 'Grandiflorum'	see *H. olympicum* f. *uniflorum*
prolificum	MMrt WCFE
pulchrum	SBrt
quadrangulum L.	see *H. tetrapterum*
reptans misapplied	see *H. olympicum* f. *minus*
reptans Hook.f. & Thomson ex Dyer	EWes NWad SBrt
- WJC 13754 **new**	WCru
revolutum PAB 3861	LEdu WPGP
§ 'Rowallane' ♀[H4]	CBot CDul CTri GCal LRHS NLar SDix SWvt
'Sungold'	see *H. kouytchense*
'Sweet Lion'	CMac
§ ***tetrapterum***	CBod CWld LLWG MMuc
trichocaulon	ECho EWes ITim
uralum HWJ 520	WCru

Hypocalyptus (*Papilionaceae*)

sophoroides	SPlb

Hypochaeris (*Asteraceae*)

radicata	CHab NMir

Hypocyrta see *Nematanthus*

Hypoestes (*Acanthaceae*)

aristata	EShb SVen

Hypolepis (*Dennstaedtiaceae*)

millefolium	EBee LEdu LRHS

Hypoxis (*Hypoxidaceae*)

hemerocallidea from Bloemfontein	ECho
hirsuta	CCCN ECho GKev
hygrometrica	ECho IBal WThu
krebsii	ECho
obtusa from Harrismith, South Africa	ECho
parvula	CAby XLum
§ - var. ***albiflora*** 'Hebron Farm Biscuit'	CCCN CTal ECho EWes GEdr NWad SRot WAbe WFar
rigidula from Harrismith, South Africa	ECho
villosa	ECho

Hypsela (*Campanulaceae*)

longiflora	see *H. reniformis*
§ ***reniformis***	CMea ECho GCrg ITim LLWG MSCN NHpl

Hyssopus ✿ (*Lamiaceae*)

from Georgia	EWes
officinalis	CBod CHby CLau CMea CWld ECha ELan ENfk EPfP ESps EWoo GAbr GMaP GPoy MHer MJak MNHC MRav NBir NPri SEND SIde SPer SPlb SPoG SRms SVic WJek XLum
- f. ***albus***	CLau ECha ENfk EPfP GPoy MArt MHer MNHC SPlb SRms WJek XLum XSen
- subsp. ***aristatus***	CBod CLau EBee ELon ENfk EPfP GPoy IMou MHer MNHC SPoG WHoo WJek XLum XSen
- 'Caeruleus' **new**	MArt
- subsp. ***officinalis***	XSen
- 'Roseus'	CLau ECha ENfk EPfP ESps GPoy MArt MHer MHol MNHC SIde SPoG WJek XLum XSen
- white-flowered	CBod

Hystrix (*Poaceae*)

patula	CBod EHoe EPPr EShb ESps LLWP MBel MNrw SPlb XLum

I

Iberis (*Brassicaceae*)

Absolutely Amethyst = 'Ib2401'	ELan ELon GBin LHop LRHS MCot SPoG WHlf WIce
candolleana	see *I. pruitii* Candolleana Group
commutata	see *I. sempervirens*
gibraltarica	CSpe SRms
- 'Betty Swainson' ♀[H4]	CSpe SPhx
jordanii	see *I. pruitii*

'Masterpiece'PBR	CRos ECrN ECtt LRHS NRHS SPoG WCot WHlf
'Pink Ice'	MCot WHlf WIce WTor
§ ***pruitii***	CTal NSla WAbe
§ - Candolleana Group	GEdr
saxatilis	CRos ECho ITim LHop LRHS NRHS SIgm WThu
semperflorens	WCFE
§ ***sempervirens***	CMea CTri CWib ELan EPfP ESps IFoB MAsh MCot MMuc MSCN NBro SEND SIgm SRms WBod WCFE WHar
- 'Appen-Etz'	LRHS MAvo NWad SHil
- 'Elfenreigen'	GCal
- 'Fischbeck'	SRot
- 'Golden Candy'	CTri EHoe NHpl SPoG WCot
- 'Little Gem'	see *I. sempervirens* 'Weisser Zwerg'
- 'Pygmaea'	CTal ECho WHil
- Schneeflocke	see *I. sempervirens* 'Snowflake'
- 'Snow Cushion'	ECho EPfP LSun
§ - 'Snowflake' $\mathbb{Y}^{H5}$	CBod CWCL ECho EPfP EPot ESps GBin GMaP IFoB LHop MBel NCou SPer SPoG SRot SWvt WIce XLum
§ - 'Weisser Zwerg'	CMea ECha ECho ECtt ELan GCrg GEdr GMaP MRav SIgm SRms WHoo WThu
'Snowball'	CBod MHol
umbellata	ECrN

Ichthyoselmis (*Papaveraceae*)

§ ***macrantha***	EPfP EPot GCra IMou LHop WCru WSHC

Idesia (*Salicaceae*)

polycarpa	CBcs CDul CMCN EBee EBtc EPfP IVic LHop SBrt SChF WPGP
- CWJ 12837	WCru

Ilex ✿ (*Aquifoliaceae*)

§ × ***altaclerensis*** 'Belgica Aurea' (f/v) $\mathbb{Y}^{H6}$	CBcs CJun CTho EPfP MSwo NEgg NHol
- 'Camelliifolia' (f) $\mathbb{Y}^{H6}$	CBcs CTho MBlu NEgg SGol
- 'Camelliifolia Variegata' (f/v)	CMac
- 'Golden King' (f/v) $\mathbb{Y}^{H6}$	Widely available
- 'Hendersonii' (f)	NEgg
- 'Hodginsii' (m)	CTri
- 'Howick' (f/v)	CJun
- 'James G. Esson' (f)	CRos LRHS
- 'Lawsoniana' (f/v) $\mathbb{Y}^{H6}$	CDul CJun CMac CRos CSBt CTri EHoe ELan EPfP ESps LRHS MAsh MBlu MJak MMuc NEgg NHol NLar NWea SCob SEND SGol SHil SLim SLon SPer SPoG SRms WHar WPat
- 'Purple Shaft' (f)	CMCN MRav
- 'Ripley Gold' (f/v)	CJun CMac CRos LRHS MAsh MRav NWea
- 'Silver Sentinel'	see *I.* × *altaclerensis* 'Belgica Aurea'
- 'W.J. Bean' (f)	CJun
- 'Wilsonii' (f)	NEgg NLar NWea
aquifolium $\mathbb{Y}^{H6}$	Widely available
- 'Alaska' (f)	CCCN CCVT CDul CJun CMCN CRos EPfP GMcL IBoy LBuc LPar LRHS MAsh NLar NOra NWea SGol SHil SWvt WFar WMat
- 'Amber' (f) $\mathbb{Y}^{H6}$	CJun CTri NLar NWea
- 'Angustifolia' (f)	CJun CRos ESps WCFE
- 'Angustifolia' (m or f)	EPfP LRHS MAsh
§ - 'Argentea Marginata' (f/v) $\mathbb{Y}^{H6}$	Widely available
§ - 'Argentea Marginata Pendula' (f/v)	CMac CRos CTri ELan EPfP LRHS MAsh SPer SRms WFar WPat
- 'Argentea Pendula'	see *I. aquifolium* 'Argentea Marginata Pendula'
- 'Argentea Variegata'	see *I. aquifolium* 'Argentea Marginata'
- 'Atlas' (m)	CBcs LBuc SWvt
- 'Aurea Marginata' (f/v)	CMac EPfP ESps LBuc MGos NOra NWea SCob SEWo WCFE WHar WMat WPat
- 'Aurea Marginata Pendula' (f/v)	WPat
- 'Aurea Regina'	see *I. aquifolium* 'Golden Queen'
- 'Aureomaculata'	NEgg
- 'Aureovariegata Pendula'	see *I. aquifolium* 'Weeping Golden Milkmaid'
- 'Aurifodina' (f)	CJun NEgg
- 'Bacciflava' (f)	CBcs CDul CJun CMac CTho CTri CWib EBee ELan ELon EPfP IArd MBlu MGos MJak MRav NEgg NLar NWea SLim SPer SRms SWvt WCFE WFar
- 'Crassifolia' (f)	CWib EBee SMad
- 'Elegantissima' (m/v)	CJun
- 'Fastigiata Sartori'	NLar
- 'Ferox' (m)	CJun CRos ELan EPfP LRHS NEgg NLar
- 'Ferox Argentea' (m/v) $\mathbb{Y}^{H6}$	Widely available
- 'Ferox Aurea' (m/v)	CJun CRos CWib ELan ELon LRHS MAsh NEgg
§ - 'Flavescens' (f)	MBlu NEgg
- 'Fructu Luteo' (f)	WHar
- 'Glanzzwerg'	SAko
- 'Gold Flash' (f/v)	CJun LRHS NLar
- 'Golden Milkboy' (m/v)	CJun CLnd CMac ELan ESps MAsh SGol WPat
§ - 'Golden Queen' (m/v) $\mathbb{Y}^{H6}$	CWib IBoy NBir SRms WPat
- 'Golden Tears' (f/v)	CJun
- 'Golden van Tol' (f/v)	CBcs CJun CSBt CTri ELan ELon EPfP ESps ETod GMcL IBoy LRHS MAsh MBlu MGos MSwo NEgg NLar SCoo SGol SPer SRms WFar WHar
- 'Green Minaret'	IVic SAko
§ - 'Green Pillar' (f)	CRos LRHS SHil
- 'Green Spire'	see *I. aquifolium* 'Green Pillar'
- 'Handsworth New Silver' (f/v) $\mathbb{Y}^{H6}$	Widely available
- 'Harpune' (f)	IArd SAko
§ - 'Hascombensis'	LHop NWea
- 'Hastata' (m)	CWib IArd IDee
- Heckenzwerg = 'Hachzwerg'PBR	SAko
- 'Ingramii' (m/v)	CJun
- 'J.C. van Tol' (f) $\mathbb{Y}^{H6}$	Widely available
- 'Latispina' (f)	CJun
- 'Lichtenthalii' (f)	CJun IArd IVic NEgg
- 'Madame Briot' (f/v) $\mathbb{Y}^{H6}$	CDul CJun CMac CRos CSam CTri CWib EHoe ELan EMOT EPfP ESps GMcL LBuc LRHS MAsh MRav MSwo NEgg NHol NLar NPri NWea SEND SGol SPer SRms SWvt WFar WHar
- 'Marijo'	CRos LRHS
- 'Monstrosa' (m)	CJun
- moonlight holly	see *I. aquifolium* 'Flavescens'
- 'Myrtifolia' (f)	EBee NEgg SWvt
- 'Myrtifolia' (m)	CJun CMac ELan EPfP NLar SMad
- 'Myrtifolia Aurea' (m/v)	NWea SWvt
- 'Myrtifolia Aurea Maculata' (m/v)	CJun CRos CTri ELan LRHS MAsh MRav NEgg NWea SPoG SWvt WPat

	- 'Northern Lights' (v)	CRos EPfP LRHS MSwo
	- 'Pendula' (f)	MRav NWea
	- 'Pendula Mediopicta'	see *I. aquifolium* 'Weeping Golden Milkmaid'
	- 'Pyramidalis' (f) ♀H6	CBcs CDul CJun CMac CRos CTri ELan GMcL LRHS MAsh MGos MJak NLar NWea SCob SGol SHil SPer SRms WFar
	- 'Pyramidalis Aureomarginata' (f/v)	NLar
	- 'Pyramidalis Fructu Luteo' (f) ♀H6	MAsh
	- 'Recurva' (m)	CJun CMac
	- 'Rubricaulis Aurea' (f/v)	CJun GMcL NEgg NLar
	- 'Scotica' (f)	CJun NWea
	- Siberia = 'Limsi'PBR (f)	IVic NLar
	- 'Silver King'	see *I. aquifolium* 'Silver Queen'
	- 'Silver Lining' (f/v)	CJun
	- 'Silver Milkboy' (f/v)	ELan EPfP MBlu WFar
	- 'Silver Milkmaid' (f/v)	CJun ESps LRHS MAsh MJak MMuc NEgg SLim SWvt
§	- 'Silver Queen' (m/v) ♀H6	CBcs CCVT CDul CEnd CRos CWib EHoe EPfP ESps LRHS MAsh MGos MJak MRav MSwo NBir NEgg NHol NLar NOra NPri NWea SAko SLim SLon SPer SRGP SWvt WHar WMat
	- 'Silver Sentinel'	see *I.* × *altaclerensis* 'Belgica Aurea'
	- 'Silver van Tol' (f/v)	CJun EBee ELan EPfP EWTr GMcL MAsh NEgg NLar NPer NWea SPer WHar
	- 'Somerset Cream' (f/v)	CJun CTri CWib
	- 'Sterntaler'	IVic SAko
*	- 'Variegata' (v)	SArc SWeb
	- 'Victoria' (m)	CJun
§	- 'Weeping Golden Milkmaid' (f/v)	WPat
	- 'White Cream' (m/v)	IVic SAko
	- 'Wichtel'	IVic
	- 'Yellow Star' (f/v)	IVic
	- 'Zig Zag' (f) **new**	CJun
	× ***aquipernyi***	LPar
	- Dragon Lady = 'Meschick' (f) ♀H6	CJun CTho IArd LPar NEgg
	- 'San Jose' (f)	CJun
	× ***attenuata*** 'Sunny Foster' (f/v)	CMCN EPfP MAsh SAko
	× ***beanii***	CJun
§	***bioritsensis***	CMCN CTri
	'Brilliant' (f)	NEgg
	cassine L.	CMCN
	'Clusterberry' (f)	CJun NEgg
	colchica	CMCN IDee SAko
	cornuta	EPfP LPar
	- B&SWJ 8756	WCru
	- 'Anicet Delcambre' (f)	CJun
	- 'Burfordii' (f)	NLar
§	- 'Dazzler' (f)	CJun
	- 'Ira S. Nelson' (f)	CJun IArd SAko
	- 'Mercury' (f) **new**	CJun
	- 'O. Spring' (f/v)	CJun
	crenata	CAco CMCN CTal CTri EPfP GCra LPar MGos NBes NHol NPri NWea SArc SCob STrG SVic WFar
*	- 'Akagi'	WFar
	- 'Aureovariegata'	see *I. crenata* 'Variegata'
	- 'Blondie'PBR (f) **new**	SWeb
	- 'Convexa' (f) ♀H6	CDul CJun CTho EPfP ESps GMcL LPar LRHS MAsh MRav NEgg NWea SCob SHil SPer WMoo WPat
	- 'Convexed Gold' (f/v)	CRos EPfP LRHS NLar NWad SPoG WFar WHar
	- Dark Green = 'Icoprins11'PBR	IBoy LBuc LCro LSRN NWea SPer SVic
	- 'Dwarf Pagoda' (f)	IVic SAko
	- Fastigiata Group	CRos SCob
	- - 'Fastigiata' (f) ♀H6	CAco CRos EPfP LRHS LSRN MAsh MGos NLar SBod SPer SPoG
	- - 'Sky Pencil' (f)	CMCN
	- 'Fructu Luteo'	see *I. crenata* f. *watanabeana*
*	- 'Glory Gem' (f)	CBcs
	- 'Golden Gem' (f/v) ♀H6	CJun CMac CRos CSBt CTri ELan ELon EPfP ESps GMcL IVic LRHS MAsh MGos MSwo NLar NWad NWea SGol SHil SPer SPoG SWvt WFar WPat WThu
	- 'Green Hedger' ♀H6	EPfP LHop LPar MGos
	- 'Helleri' (f)	WPat
	- 'Hetzii' (f)	WMoo
	- 'Kinme'	LPar SWeb
	- 'Luteovariegata'	see *I. crenata* 'Variegata'
	- 'Mariesii' (f)	CMac MBlu SAko
I	- 'Pyramidalis' (f)	CMac MRav NWea
§	- 'Shiro-fukurin' (f/v)	CMCN CRos ELan EPfP LRHS SLon SPoG
	- 'Snowflake'	see *I. crenata* 'Shiro-fukurin'
	- 'Stokes' (m)	MSwo NLar NWad WMoo
§	- 'Variegata' (v)	CMCN CMac CRos EPfP LRHS NLar
§	- f. ***watanabeana*** (f)	WGwG
	'Dazzler'	see *I. cornuta* 'Dazzler'
	dimorphophylla	CMac
	- 'Somerset Pixie' (f)	CJun
	dipyrena	ESwi SAko
	'Doctor Kassab' (f)	CMCN
	'Elegance' (f)	MBlu WFar
	excelsa **new**	CMCN
	fargesii subsp. ***fargesii*** var. ***fargesii*** **new**	GCal
	aff. ***gagnepainiana*** FMWJ 13168 **new**	WCru
	glabra	CJun
	- f. ***leucocarpa*** 'Snow White' (f)	CJun
	'Good Taste' (f)	CJun WFar
	hascombensis	see *I. aquifolium* 'Hascombensis'
	'Hohman'	CJun
	'Indian Chief' (f)	CJun
	× ***koehneana***	CDul
	- 'Chestnut Leaf' (f) ♀H5	CBcs CCVT CJun CLnd CMCN CTho EBtc EWTr LRHS MRav NEgg NLar SDix SSta WFar WGrn
	laevigata	CMCN
	latifolia	CJun CMCN NLar
	'Leonardo' **new**	EBee
*	'Little Diamond'	LSRN
	'Lydia Morris' (f)	CSam
	'Mary Nell' (f)	CJun
	× ***meserveae*** Blue Angel = 'Conang' (f)	CBcs CCCN CDul CMac CTho CWib ELan EPfP ESps EUJe EWTr GMcL IFoB LCro LRHS MMuc MRav NEgg NLar NWea SPer SPoG SRms WFar
	- Blue Bunny = 'Meseal' (f)	IVic SAko
	- 'Blue Girl' (f)	CTri
	- Blue Maid = 'Mesid' (f)	CCCN LCro LPar MGos NEgg NLar
	- Blue Prince = 'Conablu' (m) ♀H6	CBcs CCCN CDul CMCN CMac ELan ESps GMcL LBuc LRHS MBlu MJak MMuc NEgg NHol NLar NWea SCob SLim SPoG WFar
	- Blue Princess = 'Conapri' (f) ♀H6	CBcs CDul CMCN CMac CTho ELan EPfP GBin GMcL LBuc MBlu

	MGos MJak MRav NEgg NLar NWea SCob SCoo SLim SPoG WFar
- 'Casanova'PBR (m/v) new	LCro
- Castle Spire = 'Hachfee'PBR	SLim WFar
- Castle Wall = 'Hecken Star'PBR	EWTr IVic LRHS NLar SLim WFar
- 'Heckenpracht'PBR	IVic WFar
- 'Little Gloss'	SAko
- Little Rascal = 'Mondo' (m)	EBee EPfP LRHS
- 'Little Sensation' new	EBee
myrtifolia	MAsh MRav NHol
'Nellie R. Stevens' (f)	CAco CCVT CJun CTho EBee ECrN ELan EPfP ESps LPar NLar NPri SCob SEWo WMat
opaca	CMCN
perado	NEgg
- subsp. ***azorica***	CFil WPGP
- - B&SWJ 12526	WCru
- subsp. ***perado***	CBcs
- subsp. ***platyphylla***	CBcs CMCN MBlu
pernyi	CJun CMCN CMac CTri LPar LRHS MAsh
- var. ***veitchii***	see *I. bioritsensis*
rotunda	LEdu
rugosa	CMCN
'September Gem' (f)	CJun CMCN NEgg
serrata	CMac CMen
- 'Koshobai'	CMen
- 'Leucocarpa'	CMac CMen
spinigera	CBcs
suaveolens	CMCN
sugerokii var. ***brevipedunculata*** B&SWJ 10856	WCru
'Tanager' (f)	CJun
triflora var. ***kanehirae***	CDul NLar
verticillata	CMCN EBee LRHS WFar
- (f)	CBcs EBtc ELon EPfP MMrt NLar NWea
- (m)	EBtc ELon EPfP MMrt NLar NWea
- f. ***chrysocarpa*** (f)	NLar
- 'Maryland Beauty' (f)	CJun NLar
- 'Southern Gentleman' (m)	CJun MBlu NLar
- 'Winter Gold' (f)	CJun MBlu
- 'Winter Red' (f)	CJun CMCN MBlu
vomitoria	CMCN EBtc
'William Cowgill' (f)	CJun
yunnanensis	GQui IArd

Iliamna see *Sphaeralcea*

Illicium (*Schisandraceae*)

anisatum	CBcs CFil CMac EBee EPfP NLar WPGP WPat WSHC
floridanum	CBcs CPne EPfP LEdu SBrt WPat
- f. ***album***	EPfP
- 'Halley's Comet'	CFil NLar
aff. ***griffithii*** WWJ 11911	WCru
- WWJ 11971	WCru
- WWJ 11974	WCru
henryi	CWib EBee EPfP IVic LRHS NLar WPGP WSHC
aff. ***henryi***	CBcs
lanceolatum	CFil
- KWJ 12245	WCru
majus	CFil
- WWJ 11919	WCru
aff. ***majus***	WCru
- WWJ 12017	WCru
mexicanum	CFil
oligandrum	WPGP
parviflorum	CFil
simonsii	CFil IVic MBlu WPGP
- BWJ 8024	WCru
'Woodland Ruby'	NLar WPGP

Ilysanthes see *Lindernia*

Impatiens (*Balsaminaceae*)

DJHC 98415	WCru
P1961 new	GCal
apiculata	EBee GCal
arguta	CLAP CSam CSpe EShb EWld GCal SBrt WBor WPGP
- 'Alba'	CSpe MPie
auricoma × ***bicaudata***	MPie WDib
balfourii	CPla
bicaudata	CSpe SDix SPlb
congolensis	CCCN
flanaganae	CFil WPGP
forrestii	CLAP
gomphophylla	CDTJ CFil
(Harmony Series) Harmony Orange Star = 'Danhar305'PBR (NG)	ESps
- Harmony Radiance Lilac (NG) new	ESps
insignis new	EBee GCal
keilii	WDib
kerriae B&SWJ 7219	WCru
kilimanjari subsp. ***kilimanjari***	CSpe MPie WCot
kilimanjari × ***pseudoviola***	CSpe MPie WDib
kilimanjari × ***pseudoviola*** pale pink-flowered new	MPie
langbianensis HWJ 1054	WCru
'Little Brother Montgomery'	CHll
macrophylla B&SWJ 10157	WCru
Margenta = 'Danharmgta' (Harmony Series) (NG)	ESps
namchabarwensis	CCCN CSpe MPie
niamniamensis ♀H1b	CHll EBak EShb WDib
- 'Congo Cockatoo'	CDTJ NPer SRms
- 'Golden Cockatoo' (v)	CDTJ CHll EBak EShb
noli-tangere	WSFF
omeiana	CCCN CLAP CMil CSam CSpe EBee EPPr ESwi EWld GCal GEdr GWyn LEdu MNrw MSCN NLar WBod WCru WFar WPGP WPtf
- DJHC 98492	WCru
- 'Ice Storm'	CDTJ EBee GCal GEdr LEdu NLar WCot WCru WPGP
- 'Pink Nerves'	EBee LEdu
- 'Red Leaf' new	GCal
- 'Sango' new	LEdu
- variegated (v)	GEdr
parasitica	WDib
Passion (Harmony Series) (NG) new	ESps
platypetala B&SWJ 9722	WCru
pritzelii 'Sichuan Gold' new	GCal
puberula HWJK 2063	EBee SBrt WCru WPGP
qingchengshanica 'Emei Dawn'	EBee GCal WCru

	repens ♀H1c	MPie WDib
	rothii	CFil GCal WCot
	scabrida	CPla CSpe NSti
§	'Secret Love'	CCCN
	sodenii ♀H1c	CDTJ CHll CSpe EShb GCal SDix WDib
	- 'Madonna'	CSpe
	- 'Robert the Red'	CSpe
	stenantha	SBrt
	tinctoria	CAby CDTJ CFil CHll CSpe EBee GCal GCra SBrt SDix WBod
	- from Cherangani, Kenya	EBee GCal
	tuberosa	WDib
	ugandensis	GCal
	uniflora	EBee SBrt
	Velvetea	see *I.* 'Secret Love'
	walleriana DeZire Series	NPri

Imperata (*Poaceae*)

	cylindrica	CMen XLum
	- 'Red Baron'	see *I. cylindrica* 'Rubra'
§	- 'Rubra'	Widely available

Incarvillea (*Bignoniaceae*)

	arguta	GKev LLHF XLum
	brevipes	see *I. mairei*
	compacta	EBee GKev LLHF
	- BWJ 7620	WCru
	delavayi	CAby CBcs CBod CRos CSBt CTsd CWib ECha ELan EPfP EPot ESps GBuc GKev GMaP IBoy LRHS MGos MSCN NBir NRHS SDeJ SPad SPer SRms SVen SWvt XLum
	- 'Alba'	see *I. delavayi* 'Snowtop'
	- 'Bees' Pink'	CAby EPfP GBuc LPla LRHS
	- dark-pink-flowered **new**	SBrt
	- 'Rose'	CRos LRHS NRHS
§	- 'Snowtop'	CAby EBee ELan EPfP EPot GBin GMaP IBoy LRHS MPie NBir SDeJ SPer SWvt WCot
	cf. ***delavayi***	GMcL
	grandiflora	EBee GKev
	himalayensis 'Frank Ludlow'	EBee GKev
	lutea	EBee GKev
§	***mairei***	CRos CTsd ECho EWld GKev GWyn LRHS NRHS
	- var. ***mairei***	GBuc
	- - f. ***multifoliata***	see *I. zhongdianensis*
	- white-flowered	GKev
	olgae	EPfP
	'Snowdrop'	MSCN
	younghusbandii	EBee GKev
§	***zhongdianensis***	CFis EBee ECho EPot GKev LLHF SBrt SPhx
	- ACE 1600	GBuc
	- BWJ 7692	WCru
	- BWJ 7978	WCru
	- white-flowered	EBee

Indigofera (*Papilionaceae*)

	amblyantha	CBcs CCCN CRos EPfP EWTr LRHS MAsh MBlu NLar SEND SKHP SPlb WSHC
	aff. ***amblyantha***	LSou
	balfouriana BWJ 7851	WCru
	cassioides	WCru
	'Claret Cascade' ♀H5	SKHP WSHC
	dielsiana	CCCN ELan EPfP LRHS
	'Dosua'	SEND
	frutescens	CTre
	gerardiana	see *I. heterantha*
	hancockii	EBee EPfP LRHS SChF SKHP WPGP WSHC
	hebepetala	CHid EBee EPfP SBrt SKHP WPGP WSHC
§	***heterantha*** ♀H5	Widely available
	heterophylla	CCCN
	himalayensis	EBee SKHP
	- Yu 10941	WPGP
	- 'Silk Road'	CCCN CRos ELan EPfP LCro LRHS MBlu MGos NLar SHil SKHP SPoG
	howellii	CHid CMHG EBee SChF SKHP WCru WPGP
	- 'Reginald Cory' ♀H5 **new**	EPfP
	kirilowii	CRos EBee ELan EPfP IVic LRHS NLar SKHP WPGP WSHC
	- var. ***alba***	EPfP LRHS WSHC
§	***pendula***	CCCN CMHG CRos CSpe CWGN ELan EPfP GKev LRHS SBrt SKHP SPoG WKif WPGP WSHC
	- B&SWJ 7741	WCru
	- 'Shangri-La' ♀H5	CBot
	potaninii misapplied	see *I. pendula*
	potaninii ambig.	CBcs CMac LHop SAko WHer
	pseudotinctoria	CCCN SRms
	aff. ***pseudotinctoria***	CCCN
	subverticillata	LRHS WSHC
	szechuensis	LRHS SKHP SMad
	tinctoria	CCCN

Indocalamus (*Poaceae*)

	latifolius	CJng ERod EUJe MMuc MWht
	solidus	see *Bonia solida*
§	***tessellatus*** ♀H4	CAbb CBod CEnt CJng ELon ENBC ERod MWht NGdn SMad WMoo
	- f. ***hamadae***	CJng ERod MWht

Indosasa (*Poaceae*)

	gigantea	ERod

Inula (*Asteraceae*)

	acaulis	WCot
	barbata	GCal
	conyzae	GJos WHer
	dysenterica	see *Pulicaria dysenterica*
	ensifolia	CBcs EBee ELan EPfP EUJe EWTr GAbr LRHS MNHC WHoo XLum
	- 'Compacta'	GCal
	- 'Gold Star'	EBee MBNS MRav NBid NBir WFar
	'Finnish Feathers'	EBee
	glandulosa	see *I. orientalis*
	helenium	CArn CBod CHab CHby CLau ENfk GAbr GPoy IBoy LCro LEdu MHer MNHC NBid NBir NLar NMir SRms WGwG WHer WJek WMoo
	hirta	XLum
	hookeri	Widely available
	- GWJ 9033	WCru
	- 'Mude' **new**	EBee
	macrocephala misapplied	see *I. royleana*
	magnifica	Widely available
	- 'Sonnenstrahl' ♀H7	LEdu NLar SPhx
	oculus-christi	EBee EWes NBre WCot WMoo
§	***orientalis***	EBee EPfP GAbr GJos LRHS LSun NGBl NLar SPad SPer SRms XLum
	racemosa	EBee EPPr EWes GBin GCal LHop LRHS MNrw SPlb WBor
	- 'Sonnenspeer'	NBid NLar WPtf
§	***royleana***	GCal MNrw MRav

salicina	EBee

Inulanthera (*Asteraceae*)

calva	WCot

Iochroma (*Solanaceae*)

§ ***australe*** ♀^{H3}	CBcs CCCN CHll CNor CSpe EBee ELan EWld LSRN MGil SEND SPlb SPoG SPtp SVen WPGP
§ - 'Andean Snow'	CCCN CHll EShb MGil
§ - 'Bill Evans'	EShb
- violet-flowered	SPlb
cyaneum	CCCN CHll ECre SPlb SVen
- purple-flowered	CCCN CHll
gesnerioides 'Coccineum'	CCCN CHll WCot
§ ***grandiflorum***	CCCN CHll SEND
warscewiczii	see *I. grandiflorum*

Ipheion (*Alliaceae*)

'Alberto Castillo' ♀^{H4}	Widely available
'Jessie'	CAby CBro CMea CPrp CRos EBee ECha ECho EPot EWes GBuc GKev LAma LHop LLHF LRHS NHpl NPnk NRHS SCob WBor WCot WRHF WTor
'Judy'	WCot
'Rolf Fiedler' ♀^{H3}	CAvo CBro CPne CPrp CRos CTri EBee ECho ELan EPPr EPfP EPot ERCP EWes GBuc GKev LAma LHop LRHS NPnk NRHS NRya SBch SCob SDeJ SDir WAul WHoo
sellowianum	CAby CPne WCot
sessile	EBee ECho
'Tessa'^{PBR}	EBee ECho EWes GKev LLHF NHpl
§ ***uniflorum***	CBro CPne CTri ECha ECho GKev ITim LAma MNrw SEND SRms WBrk WCot XLum
- f. ***album***	CBro CPrp CRos EBee ECha ECho EPPr EWes GBuc GKev LEdu LRHS NRHS SCob WCot WHil
- 'Charlotte Bishop'	Widely available
- 'Froyle Mill' ♀^{H5}	CAvo CBro CMea CPrp CRos ECho ELon EPPr EPot ERCP EWes GKev LHop LLWP LRHS MNrw NHpl NPnk NRHS SBch SCob SDeJ SDir WCot WHoo WWFP
- subsp. ***tandiliense***	EBee EPPr
- f. ***violaceum***	SCob
- 'Wisley Blue' ♀^{H5}	CBro CMea CPrp CRos CTri EAJP ECha ECho ELan ELon EPPr EPfP EPot ERCP GBuc GKev LAma LHop LLWP LRHS MRav NPnk NRHS NRya SCob SDeJ SDir SRms WCot WHoo

Ipomoea (*Convolvulaceae*)

acuminata	see *I. indica*
alba	CCCN EShb
batatas **new**	CCCN
- 'Blackie'	ESwi
- Bright Ideas Black (Bright Ideas Series)	EShb NPri
- 'Margarita'	ESwi
- (Sweet Caroline Series) 'Sweet Caroline Bronze'^{PBR}	ESwi
- - 'Sweet Caroline Light Green'^{PBR}	EShb
- - 'Sweet Caroline Sweetheart Light Green'^{PBR}	ESwi
- - 'Sweet Caroline Sweetheart Purple'^{PBR}	ESwi
carnea	CCCN
coccinea var. ***hederifolia***	see *I. hederifolia*
§ ***hederifolia***	CCCN
× ***imperialis*** 'Sunrise Serenade'	CCCN
§ ***indica*** ♀^{H1c}	CCCN CHll CRHN EShb SPer
learii	see *I. indica*
§ ***lobata***	CSpe LSou
mauritiana	CCCN
'Milky Way'	CCCN
muellerii	CCCN
× ***multifida***	CSpe
purpurea 'Grandpa Otts'	CWCL
- 'Kniola's Black Night'	CSpe
quamoclit	CSpe
versicolor	see *I. lobata*

Iresine (*Amaranthaceae*)

Blazin' Lime	see *I.* 'Lime'
Blazin' Rose	see *I.* 'Rose'
herbstii ♀^{H1c}	EShb
§ 'Lime'	EUJe
§ 'Rose'	EUJe

Iris ✿ (*Iridaceae*)

'Abbey Chant' (IB)	WCAu XSen
'Abbondanza' (TB)	WCAu
'Abbracciami' (SDB)	SIri
'About Town' (TB)	WCAu
'Acacia Rhumba' (La)	LLWG
'Acoma' (TB)	WCAu
'Action Front' (TB)	CKel CRos EAEE EIri EPfP ESgI EShb EWoo LRHS MGos SDeJ SHil WCAu WGwG
'Actress' (TB)	CKel CRos EAEE EPfP LRHS LSRN LSou MGos SHil WGwG
acutiloba	EPot
- subsp. ***lineolata***	CTal
'Adobe Rose' (TB)	SIri XSen
'Adventuress' (TB)	XSen
'Afternoon Delight' (TB)	EWoo
'Afternoon in Rio' (TB)	WCAu
'Again and Again' (TB)	EWoo
'Agatha Christie' (IB)	WCAu
'Aggressively Forward' (TB)	WCAu
'Aglow Again' (MTB)	SDys
'Agnes James' (CH)	CBro MAvo
'Ahwahnee Princess' (SDB)	EWoo
'Aichi-no-kagayaki' (SpH)	WCot XLum
'Alabaster Unicorn' (TB)	ESgI
albicans ♀^{H5}	CBro CMea CTal ECho GKev LEdu
- 'Blue Pygmy'	CTal
albomarginata	ECho
'Alcazar' (TB)	EWoo GMcL LSRN SWat
'Aldo Ratti' (TB)	ESgI
'Alene's New Love' (SDB)	CTal EWoo
'Alexia' (TB)	CKel
'Alice Harding' (TB)	ESgI
'Alida' (Reticulata)	CBro EBee ECho EPot ERCP GKev LAma LCro LLHF SDeJ WBrk WRHF XEll
'Alien Mist' (TB)	CIri
'Alizes' (TB) ♀^{H7}	CPar ESgI LRHS XSen
'All Night Long' (TB)	EWoo
'Allegiance' (TB)	WCAu
'Amadora' (TB)	EIri
'Amas' (TB)	EWoo

	'Amazing Grace' (TB)	EWoo
	'Ambassadeur' (TB)	EWoo
	'Amber Beauty' (Dut)	GKev
	'Amber Queen' (DB)	CTal ECtt ELan LRHS LSou NBir SDeJ SPer
	'Ambroisie' (TB) 🏆H7	ESgI EWoo
	'Amelia Bedeila' (IB)	SIri
	'American Patriot' (IB)	CKel WCAu
	'Amethyst Flame' (TB)	ECho SRms WCAu
	'Amherst Blue' (IB)	EIri
	'Amherst Bluebeard' (SDB)	ESgI
	'Amherst Caper' (SDB)	EIri ESgI
	'Amphora' (SDB)	CBro
	'Ancient Echoes' (TB)	ESgI
	'Andalou' (TB) 🏆H7	CWCL EWoo XSen
	'Angel Heart' (IB)	EWoo
	'Angel Unawares' (TB)	WCAu
	'Angel Wings' (TB)	CIri
	'Angel's Touch' (TB)	ESgI
	anglica	see *I. latifolia*
	'Ann Dasch' (Sib)	WAul
	'Annabel Jane' (TB)	CKel ELon WCAu
	'Anne Elizabeth' (SDB)	CBro
	'Annemarie Troeger' (Sib) 🏆H7	ELon
	'Annick' (Sib)	EBee LRHS
	'Annikins' (IB)	CKel
	'Antarctique' (IB)	ESgI
	'Antigone' (TB)	EWoo
	'Anvil of Darkness' (TB)	EWoo
	'Aphrodisiac' (TB)	XSen
	aphylla	GBin SBrt WAbe WThu
	- 'Slick'	SDys
	'Apollo' (Dut)	CAvo
	'Appointer' (SpH)	NChi
	'Apricorange' (TB)	CKel WCot
	'Apricot Blaze' (TB)	ESgI
	'Apricot Drops' (MTB) 🏆H7	ESgI WCAu
	'Apricot Frosty' (BB)	WCAu XSen
	'Apricot Silk' (IB)	CCCN CKel IBoy NQui WCot
	'Apricot Topping' (BB)	WCAu
	'Aquamarine'	MHol
	'Arab Chief' (TB)	CKel
*	'Arabic Night' (IB)	WCAu
	'Archie Owen' (Spuria)	WCAu
	'Arctic Age' (TB)	WCAu
	'Arctic Fancy' (IB)	CKel
	'Arctic Fox' (TB)	WCAu
	'Arctic Sunrise' (TB)	ESgI
	'Arctic Wind' (IB)	WCAu
	'Argus Pheasant' (TB)	ESgI
	'Arms Wide Open' (TB)	CIri
	'Around Midnight' (TB)	CRos LRHS NRHS
	'Arpège' (TB)	GWyn XSen
	'Art Deco' (TB)	SIri XSen
	'Art School Angel' (TB)	CIri
	'As de Coeur' (TB)	XSen
	'As You Were' (TB)	CIri
	'Ascension Crown' (TB)	ESgI
	'Ask Alma' (IB)	XSen
	'Astrid Cayeux' (TB)	ESgI
	'Astro Flash' (TB)	ESgI
	'Athaenos' (IB)	CIri
	'Atlantic Crossing' (Sib)	SIri WAul
	'Attention Please' (TB)	CKel ELan
	attica	CBro CPBP ECho GEdr GKev LLHF WCot WThu
	- blue-flowered **new**	GKev
	- lemon-flowered	GKev SBrt WThu
§	***aucheri*** 🏆H4	ECho EPot GKev LLHF
	- 'Olof'	GKev
	- 'Snow White'	GKev
	'Aunt Josephine' (TB)	ESgI
	'Aurelie' (TB)	WViv
	'Austrian Sky' (SDB)	CKel CMac ECtt EPfP LHop LRHS SDeJ WAul WCot
	'Autumn Apricot' (TB)	EWoo
	'Autumn Circus' (TB)	EWoo
	'Autumn Echo' (TB)	ESgI XSen
	'Autumn Encore' (TB)	EWoo GMcL MHer
	'Autumn Leaves' (TB)	WCAu
	'Autumn Princess' (Dut)	GKev
	'Autumn Riesling' (TB)	WCAu
	'Autumn Tryst' (TB)	ESgI WCAu
	'Autumn Wine' (BB)	CIri
	'Avalon Sunset' (TB)	EIri
	'Awesome Blossom' (TB)	ESgI
	'Az Ap' (IB)	ELon WCAu
	babadagica	WAbe
	'Babbling Brook' (TB)	XSen
	'Baby Bengal' (BB)	XSen
	'Baby Blessed' (SDB)	CBro WCAu
	'Baby Prince' (SDB)	ESgI
	'Baby Sister' (Sib)	EBee ELon EWoo GBin GBuc GMcL LRHS LSRN NBro SRGP SWat
	'Bach Toccata' (MTB)	SDys
	'Back in Black' (TB)	CKel
	'Badlands' (TB)	WCAu
	'Baie Rose' (IB)	SIri
	'Bal Masqué' (TB)	EBee ESgI WViv XSen
	'Ballerina Pink' (BB)	WCAu
	'Ballistic' (SDB)	WCAu
	'Ballyhoo' (TB)	WCAu XSen
	'Baltic Star' (TB)	EWoo WCAu
	'Banbury Beauty' (CH) 🏆H4	MAvo NLar
	'Banbury Gem' (CH)	NLar
	'Banbury Ruffles' (SDB)	ESgI LRHS WCAu
	'Bang' (TB)	CKel
	'Bangles' (MTB) 🏆H7	SDys WCAu
	'Banish Misfortune' (Sib)	WAul
	'Banker Dave' (TB)	CIri
	'Bar de Nuit' (TB)	ESgI EWoo
	'Barbara May' (TB)	WCAu
	'Barbara My Love' (TB)	WCAu
	barbatula BWJ 7663	WCru
	'Baria' (SDB)	CTal
	'Batik' (BB)	SIri WCot XSen
	'Battle Star' (TB)	CIri
	'Battlestar Atlantis' (TB)	CIri
	'Bayberry Candle' (TB)	WCAu
	'Be Mine' (TB)	CIri
	'Be My Baby' (BB)	WCAu
	'Beach Girl' (TB)	EWoo
	Beauty Super Mix (Dut) **new**	GKev
	'Bedtime Story' (IB)	SWat XSen
	'Bee's Knees' (SDB) 🏆H7	SIri
	'Before the Storm' (TB)	ELon ESgI LRHS SBee WCAu XSen
	'Being Busy' (SDB)	ESgI
	'Bel Azur' (IB)	ESgI LRHS
	'Belgian Princess' (TB)	WCAu
	'Belle de Nuit' (TB)	EWoo WViv
	'Ben a Factor' (MTB)	ESgI
	'Benbow' (TB)	WMil
	'Benton Apollo' (TB)	EMal
	'Benton Arundel' (TB)	EMal EWoo
	'Benton Bluejohn' (TB)	EMal
	'Benton Caramel' (TB)	EMal EWoo
	'Benton Cordelia' (TB)	EMal EWoo
	'Benton Daphne' (TB)	EMal EWoo

'Benton Dierdre' (TB)	ELon EMal EWoo MNHC SRms
'Benton Evora' (TB)	EMal EWoo
'Benton Farewell' (TB)	EWoo
'Benton Lorna' (TB)	EMal EWoo
'Benton Menace' (TB)	EMal
'Benton Nigel' (TB)	ECha EMal EWoo WCAu
'Benton Nutkin' (TB)	EMal
'Benton Olive' (TB)	EMal EWoo
'Benton Opal' (TB)	EMal
'Benton Pearl' (TB)	EMal
'Benton Primrose' (TB)	EMal EWoo
'Benton Sheila' (TB)	EBee ECha ELon EWoo
'Benton Susan' (TB)	EMal EWoo MMrt
'Beotie' (TB)	EWoo SBee
'Berkeley Gold' (TB)	CKel CLet CSBt ECtt ELan EWes LRHS SCob SDeJ SPer SWat WGwG
'Berlin Bluebird' (Sib)	SMHy
'Berlin Purple Wine' (Sib)	EPri IMou
'Berlin Ruffles' (Sib) ♀H7	CKel EWes EWoo WAul
'Berlin Sky' (Sib)	ESgI EWes
'Berlin Tiger' (SpH) ♀H7	EPPr LCro LLWG MSCN MWts NLar SCob SDix SMHy WMoo
'Bermuda Triangle' (BB)	SDys
'Best Bet' (TB)	ESgI EWoo WCAu
'Bethany Claire' (TB)	ESgI WCAu
'Betty Chatten' (TB)	EPot
'Betty Cooper' (Spuria)	WCAu
'Betty Simon' (TB)	CWCL EWoo XSen
'Beverly Sills' (TB)	CKel CRos CWld EPfP EWoo LCro LRHS LSou MRav SBod SCob SDeJ SRGP WCAu WGwG XSen
'Bewilderbeast' (TB)	XSen
'Bianco' (TB)	WCAu WHil
'Bibury' (SDB) ♀H7	WCAu
'Bickley Cape' (Sib)	GBin
'Big Blue' (Sib)	WFar
'Big Heart' (Sib)	EIri
'Big Squeeze' (TB)	WCAu
biglumis	see *I. lactea*
biliottii	CBro
'Bishop's Robe' (TB)	ESgI EWoo LRHS
'Black as Night' (TB)	XSen
'Black Aura' **new**	NWad
'Black Beauty' (Dut)	EPfP
'Black Bull' (BB) **new**	CIri
'Black Cherry Delight' (SDB)	ESgI
'Black Dragon' (TB)	CBod CCCN CKel CRos GMcL GWyn LRHS NRHS XSen
'Black Flag' (TB)	XSen
'Black Gamecock' (La)	CBod CWCL EBee ECtt ELan LCro MBNS MNrw MSCN MWts NLar SKHP WHar WMAq
'Black Hope' (TB)	CIri EWoo
'Black is Back'	WCAu
'Black Knight' (TB)	LRHS MJak MRav NLar NQui WKif
'Black Magic' (IB)	EWoo
'Black Night' (IB)	NEgg SRGP
'Black Prince' (IB)	SCob
'Black Stallion' (MDB)	ESgI
'Black Swan' (TB)	CKel CLet CMac ECha ECtt ELan EPfP ESgI EShb EUJe EWTr EWoo GCal LCro LRHS LSRN MAvo MNrw NQui SCob SPer SPoG WCot XSen
'Black Tie Affair' (TB)	CKel EAEE ELan EPfP ESgI EWoo IPot LRHS MAsh WCAu XSen
'Blackbeard' (BB) ♀H7	WCAu
'Blackbeard's Ghost' (AB)	WCAu
'Blackberry Tease' (TB)	WCAu
'Blackberry Towers' (TB)	ESgI
'Blackcurrant' (IB)	WCAu
'Blackout' (TB)	ESgI EWoo
'Blast' (IB)	CKel
'Blatant' (TB)	ESgI EWoo WCAu XSen
'Blaue Milchstrasse' (Sib)	GBin
'Blaues Schweben' (Sib) **new**	GBin
'Blazing Light' (TB)	XSen
'Blenheim Royal' (TB)	ESgI WCAu XSen
'Blessed Again' (IB)	EBee
'Blitzen' (IB)	WCAu
'Blowing Bubbles' (TB)	CIri
'Blue Admiral' (TB)	GBin
'Blue Bird' (Sib) **new**	ECtt SPoG
'Blue Boy' (IB)	EWoo
'Blue Burgee' (Sib)	ECha
I 'Blue Butterfly' (Sib)	EBee EPfP NGdn
'Blue Denim' (SDB)	ECho ECtt EPfP GMaP MRav NBir NLar WBor WCAu WCot
'Blue Eyed Brunette' (TB)	WCAu
'Blue Giant' ambig. (Dut)	LLWG
'Blue Gown' (TB)	EWoo
'Blue Hendred' (SDB)	NBir WCAu
'Blue Hill' (Reticulata)	GKev LAma
'Blue Hour' (TB)	WCAu
'Blue King' (Sib)	CDor CHid ELan EPfP GMaP ILea LRHS MRav NBro NGdn SCob SPer WMoo
'Blue Meadow Fly' (Sino-Sib)	LLHF
'Blue Mere' (Sib)	MCot
'Blue Moon' (Sib)	ELon EWTr GBuc GQue IMou MJak MSCN WFar
'Blue Mystery' (J)	LLHF
'Blue Note Blues' (TB)	WCAu
'Blue Note' (Reticulata)	ECho EPfP EPot ERCP GKev LAma LLHF NNys WRHF
'Blue Pigmy' (SDB)	CTal CWat ECtt EPfP LRHS LSou MRav NLar SDeJ SPer
'Blue Reverie' (Sib)	ELon ESgI
'Blue Rhythm' (TB)	CKel ELan ELon EPfP EWoo GBin GMaP GMcL GPSL LCro LRHS MRav SCoo SDeJ SPer WCAu
'Blue Sapphire' (TB)	CBod CKel ESgI WCAu
'Blue Sceptre' (Sib)	IBlr
'Blue Shimmer' (TB)	CMac CSBt EBee ECha ELan EPfP ESgI EShb EWoo LRHS LSRN LSou SDeJ SPer SWat WCAu WGwG
'Blue Splash' (IB)	WCAu
'Blue Staccato' (TB)	WCAu XSen
'Blue Suede Shoes' (TB)	ESgI EWoo LSRN XSen
'Blue Trill' (TB)	WCAu
'Bluebeard's Ghost' (SDB) ♀H7	WCAu
'Bluebird Wine' (TB)	CKel WCAu
'Blue-eyed Susan' (TB)	CIri
'Bob's Fancy'	SDeJ
'Bockingford' (MTB)	SIri
'Bohemian' (TB)	CWCL
'Bold Encounter' (TB)	WCAu
'Bold Pretender' (La)	ECtt ELan ELon EPfP LLWG MBNS MSCN NLar SKHP
'Bold Print' (IB)	CRos EBee ELon IPot LRHS LSRN MGos MHer SHil SPoG WCAu
'Bollinger'	see *I.* 'Hornpipe'
'Bonnie Davenport' (TB)	CIri
'Boo' (SDB)	CPBP CTal EAJP WCAu XSen
'Border Guard' (BB)	WCAu
'Border Happy' (TB)	WCAu
'Bottled Sunshine' (IB)	LRHS

'Bound for Glory' (La)	LLWG
'Bournemouth Ball Gown' (Sib)	WAul
'Bournemouth Beauty' (Sib) 𝕐H7	WAul
'Bouzy Bouzy' (TB)	ESgI XSen
'Bracknell' (Sib)	WAul
bracteata	EBee GBuc
- NNS 04-223	GBuc
'Braggin' Rights' (TB)	CIri
'Braithwaite' (TB)	CKel CRos CWGN ELan EPfP ESgI EShb EWoo LRHS NRHS SDeJ SHil SPer SRms SWat WCAu WGwG
'Brandaris' (TB)	ESgI
'Brannigan' (SDB)	NBir NSti
'Brasero' (TB)	EWoo
'Brasilia' (TB)	NBir
'Brassie' (SDB)	CBro MBNS XSen
'Brave New World' (TB) 𝕐H7	CIri
'Breakers' (TB) 𝕐H7	CKel EWoo WCAu
'Breezy Blue' (SDB)	WCAu
'Brenchley' (IB)	SIri
'Bridal Icing' (TB)	WCAu
'Bride's Halo' (TB)	LSRN WCAu XSen
'Bright Button' (SDB)	CKel ESgI EWoo
'Bright Fire' (TB)	EIri
'Bright Vision' (SDB)	ESgI
'Bright White' (MDB)	CBro CKel ECho
'Bright Yellow' (DB)	MRav
'Brighteyes' (IB)	SRms
'Brindisi' (TB)	XSen
'Brise de Mer' (TB)	XSen
'Bristo Magic' (TB)	XSen
'Bristol Gem' (TB)	XSen
'Broad Shoulders' (TB)	WCAu
'Broadleigh Angela' (CH)	CBro
'Broadleigh Ann' (CH)	CBro
'Broadleigh Carolyn' (CH) 𝕐H5	CBro CElw
'Broadleigh Clare' (CH)	CBro
'Broadleigh Dorothy' (CH)	CBro MAvo
'Broadleigh Eleanor' (CH)	CBro
'Broadleigh Elizabeth' (CH)	CBro
'Broadleigh Emily' (CH)	CBro
'Broadleigh Fenella' (CH)	CBro
'Broadleigh Jean' (CH)	CBro
'Broadleigh Joan' (CH)	CBro
'Broadleigh Lavinia' (CH)	CBro MRav
'Broadleigh Mitre' (CH)	CBro
'Broadleigh Nancy' (CH)	CBro
'Broadleigh Peacock' (CH)	CBro CElw MAvo
'Broadleigh Penny' (CH)	CBro MAvo NLar
'Broadleigh Rose' (CH)	CBro CElw EPri MBrN MRav WSHC
'Broadway Baby' (IB)	ESgI
'Broadway Star' (TB)	CRos LRHS NRHS
'Broken Link' (BB)	CIri
'Bronzaire' (IB)	CKel EIri WCAu WGwG
'Bronze Beauty' (Dut)	ERCP GKev
'Bronze Beauty' (TB)	SDeJ
'Bronze Beauty' van Tubergen (*hoogiana* hybrid)	NBir NNys SDeJ
'Brother Carl' (TB)	XSen
'Brown Chocolate' (TB)	WCAu
'Bruce' (TB)	WCAu
'Brummit's Mauve' (TB)	WCAu
'Bruno' (TB)	LSRN NLar WMil
'Brussels' (TB)	ESgI
bucharica misapplied	see *I. orchioides* Carrière
bucharica ambig.	CAvo ECho ELon LSun MNrw NHpl SDeJ SDix
§ ***bucharica*** Foster 𝕐H5	CBro EPfP EPot GKev LAma
- 'Princess'	ECho
bucharica* × *orchioides	ECho
'Buckwheat' (TB)	EWoo LCro SIri
'Buisson de Roses' (TB)	XSen
bulleyana	CBro ECho GEdr GKev MArt SRms
- BWJ 7912	WCru
- from Dali, Yunnan, China	SBrt
- black-flowered	GKev
- - SDR 1792	EBee
'Bumblebee Deelite' (MTB) 𝕐H7	CJun CKel CTal WCAu
'Bundle of Love' (BB)	WCAu
'Burgermeister' (TB)	XSen
'Burgundy Party' (TB)	XSen
'Burka' (TB)	ESgI
'Burnt Toffee' (TB)	ESgI SIri XSen
'Burst' (TB)	CKel WCAu
'Buto' (TB)	EWoo
'Butter and Cream' (Sib)	MNrw
'Butter and Sugar' (Sib) 𝕐H7	Widely available
'Buttermere' (TB)	SRms
'Butterpat' (IB)	ESgI
'Butterscotch Carpet' (SDB)	WCAu
'Butterscotch Kiss' (TB)	CKel CMac CRos ELan ELon EPfP GMaP LRHS MBNS MGos MRav NBir NLar SHil SPer
'Buzzword' (SDB)	WCAu
'Bye Bye Blues' (TB)	ESgI XSen
'Byzantine Purple' (TB)	EWoo
'Cabaret Royale' (TB)	ESgI XSen
'Cable Car' (TB)	CKel CWCL ESgI EWoo
'Cache of Gold' (SDB)	CTal EWoo
'Caesar' (Sib)	EWoo IBoy SDys SRms
'Caesar's Brother' (Sib)	CHid CKel CRos ELan EPfP EWoo GAbr GBuc LCro LOPS LRHS MGos MSpe NHol NLar NRHS SHil SPer SWat WFar WHar WHoo
'Cajun Rhythm' (TB)	XSen
'Calgary' (TB)	WCAu
'Caliente' (TB)	EWoo MRav WCAu XSen
'California Style' (IB)	XSen
§ Californian hybrids	CElw CMac CPBP GCra NBir WCot
'Calm Stream' (TB)	WCAu
'Calypso Mood' (TB)	XSen
'Cambridge' (Sib) 𝕐H7	CAvo CKel CRos CWld EHoe EIri EPfP GBuc IMou LRHS MAvo NGdn NRHS SWat WAul WFar WHoo
'Cameliard' (TB)	EWoo
'Camelot Rose' (TB)	WCAu XSen
'Cameo Blush' (BB)	XSen
'Cameo Queen' (SDB) 𝕐H7	CIri
'Cameo Wine' (TB)	ESgI MNrw XSen
'Cameroun' (TB)	ESgI EWoo
'Campbellii'	see *I. lutescens* 'Campbellii'
canadensis	see *I. hookeri*
'Canadian Kisses' (SDB)	ESgI
'Canadian Streaker' (TB/v)	WCot
'Canary Bird' (TB)	ESgI
'Candy Rock' (IB)	CIri EWoo WCAu
'Cannington Ochre' (SDB)	CBro
'Canonbury Belle' (Sib)	WAul
'Can't Touch This' (TB)	WCAu
'Cantab' (Reticulata)	CBro CRos ECho EPot ERCP GKev LAma LRHS NRHS SCob SDeJ
'Caprice' (TB)	EWoo
'Capricious Candles' (TB)	CIri
'Captain Indigo' (IB)	ESgI WCAu

	'Captive Sun' (SDB)	CKel CTal EAEE EPfP LRHS MAsh SIri WTor
	'Caramel' (TB)	XSen
	'Cardinal' (TB)	WMil
	'Care to Dance' (TB)	WCAu
	'Careless Sally' (Sib)	WAul
	'Carfax' (TB)	WMil
	'Caribbean Dream' (TB)	XSen
	'Carnaby' (TB)	CKel CRos CWld EPfP ESgI EShb LRHS MRav NRHS SBod SDeJ WCAu WGwG XSen
	'Carnival Time' (TB)	CBod CKel CMac CRos CWGN EBee ECtt EPfP LRHS MCot SHar SHil SPer WHoo XSen
	'Carolina Gold' (TB)	XSen
*	'Caronte' (IB)	ESgI
	'Carriage Trade' (TB)	LRHS
	'Casbah' (TB)	XSen
	'Cascade Rhythm' (TB)	WCAu
	'Cascade Springs' (TB)	XSen
	'Cascade Sprite' (SDB)	SRms
	'Casino Cruiser' (TB)	CIri
	'Casual Joy' (TB)	CIri
	'Catalyst' (TB)	XSen
	'Cat's Eye' (SDB)	CTal ESgI SIri WCAu
	'Catwalk Idol' (La)	LLWG
	caucasica	CMac
	'Cause for Pause' (TB) **new**	CIri
	'Cayenne Capers' (TB)	ESgI
*	'Cedric Morris'	EWes
	'Cee Jay' (IB) ♀H7	EWoo
	'Cee Tee'	EWoo XSen
	'Celebration Song' (TB)	ESgI SIri WCAu XSen
	'Celestial Glory' (TB)	XSen
	'Cerdagne' (TB)	XSen
	'Chalkhill' (SDB)	WCAu
	chamaeiris	see *I. lutescens* subsp. *lutescens*
	'Champagne Elegance' (TB)	EIri EPfP EPri NBir XSen
	'Champagne Encore' (IB)	EWoo
	'Champagne Frost' (TB)	XSen
	'Champagne Waltz' (TB)	SIri XSen
	'Chandler's Choice' (Sib)	EWes
	'Change of Pace' (TB)	ESgI WCAu XSen
	'Chanted' (SDB)	EWoo WCAu XSen
	'Chantilly' (TB)	CBod CHid CKel CLet EAJP EBee ELan EWoo LRHS MRav NBir NGdn NLar SPer SWat
	'Chapeau' (TB)	ESgI WCAu
	'Charlotte's Tutu' (La)	LLWG
	'Charmaine' (TB)	XSen
	'Chartreuse Bounty' (Sib)	EPri EWes GAbr GMaP NLar NSti
	'Chasing Rainbows' (TB)	SDys WCAu
	'Cheap Frills' (TB)	WCAu
	'Cher' (TB)	LSRN
	'Cherished' (TB)	MAvo
	'Cherished One' (La)	LLWG
	'Cherry Blossom Song' (TB)	SIri
	'Cherry Blossom Special' (TB)	CIri
	'Cherry Garden' (SDB)	CBod CBro CKel CMea CPBP CTal CWat EAEE ECho ECtt ELan EPfP EShb EWes GBuc GEdr GMaP LEdu LRHS LSou MBNS MRav NBir NGdn NLar SDeJ WAul WCot WWFP
	'Cherry Twist' (La)	LLWG
	'Cherub's Smile' (TB)	XSen
	'Chicken Little' (MDB)	CBro
	'Chief Moses' (TB)	WCAu
I	'Chieftain' (SDB)	MRav
	'Childhood Sweetheart' (La)	LLWG
	'Chilled Wine' (Sib)	ELon
	'China Dragon' (TB)	XSen
	'Chinese Coral' (TB)	XSen
	'Chinese Treasure' (TB)	XSen
	'Chinook Winds' (TB)	ESgI WCAu
	'Chivalry' (TB)	ESgI
	'Christine Mullins' (Sib)	WBor
	'Christmas Angel' (TB)	WCAu
	Chrysofor Group	CAby
	chrysographes ♀H7	CBWd CBro CHid CLet CMac CTsd CWCL EHoe EPfP EPri EWoo GJos GKev IBoy IKil LRHS MBel MHer MRav NSti SCob SRot
	- BWJ 7930	WCru
I	- 'Black Beauty'	ECho EPfP EWoo
	- 'Black Gold'	EPri MHol
I	- 'Black Knight'	CBot CCse EPfP GBin GBuc GCal GCra LHop MCot NChi NLar SMad SWat WPnP
I	- 'Black Velvet'	GEdr NPnk
	- black-flowered	CAby CBod CFil EBee ELan GAbr GBuc GCal GKev GKin LCro LRHS MNrw NGdn NHpl SCob SPer SPoG WCot WCru WFar WGwG WMoo WPGP WPnP WSHC
	- dark-flowered	GKev GMcL IBoy MSCN WFar
	- 'Goldvein'	CMac
	- hybrid	WFar
	- 'Inshriach'	IMou LEdu WAbe
	- 'Kew Black'	ECho GKev LEdu NBir WHil
	- 'Kilmurry Black'	IKil
	- 'Mandarin Purple'	GCal SPer SWat
§	- 'Rubella'	CAby GCra GKev
	- 'Rubra'	see *I. chrysographes* 'Rubella'
	- yellow-flowered	WFar
	chrysographes × forrestii	NBir
	'Château d'Auvers-sur-Oise' (TB)	SIri WViv
	'Chubby Cheeks' (SDB)	CKel WCAu
	'Church Stoke' (SDB)	WCAu
	'Cimarron Rose' (SDB)	ESgI
	'Cimarron Strip' (TB)	CKel EPfP WCot XSen
	'Cinque Terre' (TB)	WCAu
	'Circle of Light' (TB)	WCAu
	'Circle Round' (Sib)	CSpe
	'Circus Stripes' (TB)	XSen
	'Cirrus Veil' (SDB)	WCAu
	'Citoyen' (TB)	XSen
	'Citronnade' (TB)	ESgI
	'City' (SDB)	SIri
	'City of Paradise' (TB)	ESgI
	'Clairette' (Reticulata)	CRos ECho EPot GKev LAma LRHS MWat NRHS SCob SDeJ
	'Clara Garland' (IB)	WCAu
	'Clarence' (TB)	ESgI EWoo WCAu XSen
	clarkei	ECho
	- B&SWJ 2122	WCru
	- SDR 3819	GKev
	'Class Ring' (TB)	WCAu
	'Classic Look' (TB)	ESgI SIri
	'Classic Navy' (BB)	ESgI
	'Clear Morning Sky' (TB)	GKev
	'Clee Hills' (Sib)	WAul
	'Cleedownton' (Sib)	WAul
	'Clematis' (TB)	CIri WMil
	'Cleo' (TB)	NSti
	'Cleo Murrell' (TB)	ESgI EWoo

	'Cleve Dodge' (Sib)	EPri ESgI EWoo SIri XLum
	'Cliffs of Dover' (TB)	CKel EIri ESgI EWoo GCal MCot SCob SRms
	'Cloudcap' (TB)	SRms
	'Clownerie' (TB)	EWoo WViv
	'Clyde Redmond' (La) 🏆H5	WMAq
	'Coal Face' (TB)	WCAu
	'Coal Seams' (TB)	WCAu
	'Coalignition' (TB)	EWoo WCAu
	'Codicil' (TB)	EIri EWoo XSen
	colchica	LEdu
	'Colette Thurillet' (TB)	XSen
	'Colin's Pale Blue' (Sib)	NCGa SMHy
	collettii	ECho GKev
	'Collingwood Ingram' **new**	WThu
	'Color Carnival' (TB)	ESgI
	'Color Me Blue' (TB)	WCAu
	'Color Splash' (TB)	XSen
	'Color Strokes' (TB)	WCAu
	'Colortart' (TB)	XSen
	'Come to Me' (TB)	CIri
	'Coming Up Roses' (TB)	XSen
	'Con Fuoco' (TB)	XSen
	'Concertina' (IB)	CIri EWoo WCAu
	'Concord Crush' (Sib)	IPot MHol WHil WTor
	confusa 🏆H4	CPla SArc SBig SMad XSen
§	- 'Martyn Rix'	CAbb CAby CBct CHid CMac CPou ELon EPfP GCal IDee LRHS MPie SBrt SEND WGwG
	confusa* × *japonica	WWFP
	'Conjuration' (TB)	EWoo SIri
	'Connection' (TB)	WCAu
	'Constant Wattez' (IB)	CKel ESgI NLar
	'Constantine Bay' (TB)	ESgI
	'Contrast in Styles' (Sib)	CBod ECtt EPri LSou MSCN NQui WFar
	'Cool Satin' (SDB)	CIri
	'Copatonic' (TB)	ESgI WCAu
	'Copper Capers' (TB)	ESgI
	'Copper Classic' (TB)	ELon ESgI LSRN SEND WCAu
	'Coquet Waters' (Sib)	NBid WAul
	'Coquetterie' (TB)	EWoo
	'Coral Point' (TB)	WCAu
	'Coral Splendor' (TB)	WCAu
	'Coral Sunset' (TB)	XSen
	'Cordoba' (TB)	WCAu XSen
	'Coronation Anthem' (Sib)	EPri EWoo WAul
	'Côte d'Or' (TB)	XSen
	'Counting Sheep' (SDB)	SIri
	'Country Kisses' (TB)	WCAu
	'County Town Red' (TB)	SIri
	'Coup de Soleil' (TB)	EWoo
	'Cozy Calico' (TB)	WCAu
	'Cracklin' Burgundy' (TB)	XSen
	'Craithie' (TB)	EMal EWoo
	'Cranapple' (BB) 🏆H7	ESgI SBee WCAu
	'Cranberry Ice' (TB)	ELon EWoo XSen
	'Cranberry Sauce' (TB)	SIri WCAu
	'Cranbrook' (IB) 🏆H7	SIri
	'Cream Beauty' (Dut)	GKev LCro LOPS SDeJ
	'Cream Pixie' (SDB)	WCAu
	'Creative Artistry' (La)	LLWG
	cretensis	see *I. unguicularis* subsp. *cretensis*
	'Crimson King' (IB)	EWoo
	'Crinoline' (TB)	CKel XSen
	'Crispette' (TB)	WCAu
	cristata	EPot GEdr GKev NHar NHpl SMad SRms
	- 'Alba'	CPBP EBee GCal GEdr NHar WThu
	crocea 🏆H7	EBee GBin GKev

	'Croftway Lemon' (TB)	EBee ELon
	'Cross Current' (TB)	WCAu
	'Crowned Heads' (TB)	WCAu XSen
	'Crow's Feet' (BB)	WCAu
	'Crushed Ice' (La)	LLWG
	'Crystal Fountain' (TB)	CIri
	'Crystal Gazer' (TB)	ESgI
	'Crystal Glitters' (TB)	ESgI
	'Cumulus' (TB)	EWoo SIri
	cuniculiformis	ECho WCot
	'Cup Race' (TB)	WCAu XSen
	'Cupid's Arrow' (TB)	WCAu
	'Curlew' (IB)	WCAu
	'Cutie' (IB)	ESgI EWoo WCAu
	'Cyanea' (DB)	ECho
	'Cyclamint' (La)	LLWG
	cycloglossa	ECho GKev
	'Daemon Imp' (MTB)	WCAu
	'Dahdah' (TB)	WCAu
	'Dainty Lace' (La)	LLWG
	'Dakota Smoke' (TB)	EWoo
	'Dale Dennis' (DB)	XSen
	'Dance Ballerina Dance' (Sib)	CHid EBee EPfP EPri MRav NLar WFar WHlf
	'Dance for Joy' (TB)	XSen
	'Dance On' (Reticulata) **new**	LAma
	'Dance the Night Away' (TB)	WCAu
	'Dancer's Veil' (TB)	CKel CMac EBee ECtt ELon ESgI LRHS MArt MRav SPer WCAu
	'Dancing Lilacs' (MTB)	ESgI
	'Dancing Nanou' (Sib)	EBee ECtt
	danfordiae	CBro CRos ECho EPfP EPot GKev LAma LCro LOPS LRHS NHpl NRHS SCob SDeJ
	'Dangerous Mood' (TB)	EWoo
	'Dante's Inferno' (TB)	EWoo
	'Dardanus' (Rc)	ECho EPot ERCP GKev SDeJ WCot
	'Dark Crystal' (SDB)	CTal ESgI EWoo
	'Dark Desire' (Sib)	MRav
	'Dark Drama' (TB)	WCAu
	'Dark Spark' (SDB)	WCAu
	'Dark Vader' (SDB)	CHur CTal ESgI
	'Darkness' (IB)	SIri
	'Darkside' (TB)	XSen
	'Darts' (IB)	CIri
	'Dashing' (TB)	EWoo
	'Dauber's Delight'	CIri
	'Dauber's Surprise' (TB)	CIri
	'Daughter of Stars' (TB)	ESgI
	'Dauntless' (TB)	ESgI EWoo
	'Dawn of Fall' (TB)	ESgI
	'Dawn Waltz' (Sib)	EBee LLWG WFar WHlf
	'Dawning' (TB) 🏆H7	ESgI EWoo
	'Dazzle Time' (TB)	CIri
	'Dazzling' (IB)	WCAu
	'Dazzling Gold' (TB)	ESgI XSen
	'Dear Currier' (Sib)	WAul
	'Dear Delight' (Sib)	EWTr ILea LLHF MSCN NLar WFar
	'Death by Chocolate' (SDB)	CTal ESgI
	'Decadence' (TB)	WCAu
§	***decora***	CTal LLHF
	'Deep Black' (TB)	CKel CPar CRos CSpe CWGN CWld EAJP EBee ELan EPfP ESgI EUJe GMaP LRHS LSRN MBNS MCot MRav MWat NLar NWad SDeJ SHil SPer SPoG SWat WGwG
	'Deep Pacific' (TB)	WCAu
	'Deep Sea Quest' (La)	LLWG
	'Deepening Shadows' (CH)	MAvo

'Deft Touch' (TB)	XSen
delavayi 🏆H7	ECho EWes GMaP WRHF
- SDR 50	GKev
- 'Didcot'	LRHS
'Delirium' (IB)	WCAu
'Delta Blues' (TB)	EWoo SIri
'Delta Butterfly' (La)	WMAq
'Demi-Deuil' (TB)	EWoo
'Demon' (SDB)	CJun XSen
'Demure Illini' (Sib)	MNrw
'Denys Humphry' (TB)	WCAu
'Deputé Nomblot' (TB)	EWoo
'Derwentwater' (TB)	SRms WCAu
'Desert Echo' (TB)	GMcL MHer XSen
'Desert Jewel' (La)	LLWG
'Desert Lullaby' (TB) **new**	EBee
'Desi Brouwer' (IB)	SIri
'Desiris' (TB)	WCAu
'Devil David' (TB)	CIri
'Devil May Care' (IB)	ESgI
'Devilry' (SDB)	CTal EWoo
'Devil's Spoon' (TB)	CIri
'Devonshire Cream' (TB)	WCAu
'Devoted' (SDB)	WCAu
'Dewful' (Sib)	WFar
'Diabolique' (TB) 🏆H7	XSen
'Diamond Ring' (TB)	SDys
§ ***dichotoma***	EWes SBrt
'Disco Jewel' (MTB)	ESgI
'Discovered Treasure' (TB)	WCAu
'Disguise' (TB)	WCAu
'Distant Music' (La)	LLWG
'Ditzy' (SDB)	SIri
'Diversion' (TB)	ESgI
'Dividing Line' (MTB)	WCAu
'Dixie Darling' (TB)	ESgI XSen
'Dixie Pixie' (SDB)	WCAu
'Doctor No' (TB)	CIri
'Dogrose' (TB)	EWoo
'Dolce' (SpH)	WCAu
'Doll Ribbons' (MTB)	EPfP
'Dolly Madison' (TB)	ESgI EWoo
§ ***domestica***	CArn CBro CHll ELan EPfP LRHS SPav SPlb SRms WSHC
- 'Crûg Colossal'	WCru
- 'Freckle Face'	CWCL LSou
- 'Hello Yellow'	WHlf
'Dominion' (TB)	WMil
'Don Juan' (TB)	EWoo
'Doohicky' (IB)	CIri
'Dotted Swiss' (TB)	XSen
'Double Bubble' (TB)	EWoo
'Double Byte' (SDB)	XSen
'Double Click' (TB)	EWoo
'Double Espoir' (TB)	XSen
'Double Lament' (SDB)	CBro
'Double Mini'	EWoo
'Double Shot' (TB)	EWoo
'Double Standards' (Sib)	EBee EPri IPot NLar
'Double Vision' (TB)	EWoo XSen
douglasiana	ECho GCal GKev
- 'Cape Ferrelo'	SKHP
'Dover Beach' (TB)	SIri
'Dover Castle' (BB) 🏆H7	SIri
'Downtown Brown' (TB)	WCAu
'Draco' (TB)	ESgI XSen
'Drake Carne' (TB)	CKel
'Drama Queen' (TB)	WCAu
'Dream Indigo' (IB)	EWoo WCAu XSen
'Dreaming Green' (Sib)	EBee
'Dreaming Orange' (Sib)	ECtt EPri
'Dreaming Rainbows' (TB)	WCAu
'Dreaming Spires' (Sib)	ESgI GBin SIri
'Dreaming Yellow' (Sib)	CAby CAvo CBre CKel CMHG CRos CSam CWld ECha EPfP EPri EShb GBin GBuc GKin LEdu LRHS MMuc MRav NGdn NRHS SBod SPer WAul WGwG WMoo WWtn
'Dreamsicle' (TB)	EWoo
'Dresden Candleglow' (IB)	WCAu
'Drive Me Wild' (TB)	WCAu
'Dualtone' (TB)	CKel
'Dude Ranch' (TB)	WCAu
'Duded Up' (TB)	CIri
'Duke of Bedford' (TB)	WMil
'Dunkler Wein' (Sib)	EWes
'Dunlin' (MDB)	CBro CTal ECho NBir
'Dural White Butterfly' (La)	CBod CHid
'Durham Dream' (TB)	CIri
'Dusky Challenger' (TB)	CKel EBee ESgI EWoo LCro SBee WCAu XSen
'Dusky Evening' (TB)	XSen
'Dutch Chocolate' (TB)	CKel EWes EWoo LCro XSen
Dynamic Duet Mixed (Dut) **new**	GKev
'Dynamite' (TB)	ESgI EWoo XSen
'Dyonisos' (TB)	SIri
'Eagle's Flight' (TB)	XSen
'Earl of Essex' (TB)	WCAu XSen
'Early Frost' (IB)	CKel
'Early Light' (TB) 🏆H7	ESgI WCAu
'Easter' (SDB)	SIri
'Eastertime' (TB)	ESgI EWoo
'Eastman Winds' (La)	LLWG
'Easy' (MTB)	EIri SIri
'Ebony Echo' (TB)	EWoo
'Echo de France' (TB)	CKel ESgI EWoo XSen
'Eden's Paradise Blue' (Sib)	ELon WHar
'Edge of Winter' (TB)	CKel XSen
'Edith Wolford' (TB)	CBod CCCN CKel GMcL GWyn MMrt SCob SRGP XSen
'Edna Grace' (La)	LLWG
'Ed's Blue' (DB)	ELan
'Edward' (Reticulata)	CBro ECho EPfP EPot GKev LAma SDeJ
'Edward of Windsor' (TB)	ELan EWoo GMaP LRHS NLar SCob SRGP
'Ego' (Sib)	CHid ECha ELon EPfP EPri EWoo GBuc SWat WMoo
'Egyptian' (TB)	EWoo
'Eileen Louise' (TB) 🏆H7	WCAu
'El Tovar' (TB)	EWoo
'Eldorado' (TB)	EWoo
'Eleanor Roosevelt' (IB)	EWoo
'Eleanor's Pride' (TB)	ESgI WCAu
'Electrique' (TB)	WCAu
elegantissima	see *I. iberica* subsp. *elegantissima*
'Eliminator' (TB)	CIri
'Elizabeth of England' (TB)	EWoo GKev
'Elizabeth Poldark' (TB)	ESgI XSen
'Ellesmere' (Sib)	NGdn WAul
'Elsa Sass' (TB)	ESgI
'Elsie Petty' (IB)	SIri
'Elvinhall'	CBro
'Emperor' (Sib)	CWat NSti SWat
'Empress of India' (TB)	EWoo
'Encre Bleue' (IB)	ESgI
'Endless Love' (TB)	EIri
'English Charm' (TB)	ESgI WCAu XSen

	'English Cottage' (TB)	CKel ELon GCal LSRN MHer MWat NLar WCAu XSen
	'Ennerdale' (TB)	SRms
	'Enriched' (MTB) ♀H7	SIri WCAu
§	***ensata***	CBcs CBod CBro ELan EPfP GKev LRHS LSun MHer MJak MMuc MNrw NLar SPlb SRms SWat WBor WPnP WWtn
	- 'Activity'	EWTr SHar WFar
	- 'Agrippine'	SKHP
	- 'Alba'	ECha MMuc
I	- 'Amethyst' **new**	IPot
	- 'Aquamarin' **new**	IPot
	- 'Asian Warrior'	WFar
	- 'August Emperor'	MBel
	- 'Azuma-kagami'	EBee ELan MNrw
	- 'Azure'	WFar WMoo
	- 'Barnhawk Sybil'	SKHP
I	- 'Blue King'	NHol
	- 'Caprician Butterfly' ♀H7	EPfP NLar
	- 'Carnival Prince'	WFar WMoo
	- 'Cascade Crest'	SWat WFar
	- 'Center of Interest'	NBir
*	- 'Charm'	LRHS
	- 'Crepe Paper'	WFar
	- 'Cry of Rejoice'	EBee ECho ECtt GMcL SWat
	- 'Crystal Halo' ♀H7	EBee LSun
I	- 'Darling'	ECho EPfP EWTr SWat WFar WMoo
	- 'Dramatic Moment'	GBuc WFar
	- 'Eden's Blush'	EBee
	- 'Eden's Charm'	EPfP
	- 'Eden's Paintbrush'	EShb SPer
	- 'Eden's Purple Glory'	CHid
	- 'Electric Rays'	EBee EWTr IPot WFar
I	- 'Emotion'	CMac EBee WFar
I	- 'Fortune'	CBod EWTr GBin IKil MSCN WHar
	- 'Freckled Geisha'	CMac EBee ELon EPfP IPot NBir NQui WFar
	- 'Frilled Enchantment' ♀H7	IPot WFar
	- 'Galatea Marx'	CBod EBee LEdu WFar
	- 'Gipsy'	CMac EBee
	- 'Gold Bound'	ECtt SKHP
	- 'Gracieuse'	ELan LRHS NLar SWat WCot
	- 'Gusto'	CMac EBee ELon EPfP IPot MNrw SWat WFar
	- 'Harpswell Chantey'	IPot
	- 'Hercule'	CHid NBir
	- Higo white	SPer
	- 'Hoshi-akari'	WFar
	- 'Imperial Velvet'	WFar
*	- 'Innocence'	NLar SWat WFar WMoo
	- 'Iso-no-nami'	EBee WFar
	- 'Jocasta'	EPfP WFar
	- 'Jodlesong'	WFar
	- 'Kalamazoo'	WFar
	- 'Katy Mendez' ♀H7	IPot LLWG NLar
*	- 'Kiyo-zuru'	EPfP
	- 'Kogesho'	EPfP GBuc NLar
	- 'Koh Dom'	SPer
	- 'Kongo-san'	NLar WFar
	- 'Kuma-funjin'	EBee
	- 'Kumo-no-obi'	CMHG EBee GBin GBuc LRHS MCot NHol SPtp SWat WFar
	- 'Lady in Waiting'	EBee ECtt EPfP
	- 'Laughing Lion'	ECtt EWoo IKil WFar WMoo
	- 'Light at Dawn'	CMHG MBel WMoo
	- 'Lilac Blotch'	SPer
I	- 'Loyalty'	ECho EWoo LRHS SHar WFar
	- 'Momogasumi'	ECtt LLWG NQui WHil
	- 'Momozomo'	LLHF
§	- 'Moonlight Waves'	CHid CMHG CMac EBee ELan EPfP GBin GBuc GCra GKin GMaP IPot LRHS MCot MHer MRav NGdn NHol SWat WFar
	- 'Oase'	ECtt
	- 'Ocean Mist'	CHid EBee ECtt GBuc IKil WHar
	- 'Oku-banri'	EBee WFar
	- 'Oriental Eyes'	NGdn
	- pale-mauve-flowered	NBir
	- 'Pin Stripe'	EBee SWat WMoo
	- 'Pink Frost'	EBee ELan EPfP LHop WFar
	- 'Pleasant Earlybird'	WFar
	- 'Pleasant Journey'	ECtt
	- 'Prairie Frost'	EBee
	- 'Prairie Noble'	EBee
	- 'Purple Parasol'	LLWG
	- purple-flowered	SPer
	- 'Queen's Tiara'	ELon IPot LLWG WBor
	- 'Rakka-no-utage'	EBee NLar
	- 'Rebecca Johns'	CRoa
I	- 'Reveille'	SWat
§	- 'Rose Queen' ♀H7	CMac CSam ECha ELan EPfP EWTr GBin GBuc GCra GKin GMaP LRHS MCot MRav MWts NBir NGdn NHol SPer WFar WHar WMoo XLum
	- 'Rowden'	CRoa
	- 'Rowden Amir'	CRoa
	- 'Rowden Autocrat'	CRoa
	- 'Rowden Begum'	CRoa
	- 'Rowden Caesar' **new**	CRoa
	- 'Rowden Caliph'	CRoa
	- 'Rowden Chieftan' **new**	CRoa
	- 'Rowden Consul'	CRoa
	- 'Rowden Czarina' **new**	CRoa
	- 'Rowden Dauphin'	CRoa
	- 'Rowden Dictator'	CRoa
	- 'Rowden Empress'	CRoa
	- 'Rowden King'	CRoa NChi
	- 'Rowden Knight'	CRoa
	- 'Rowden Marquess' **new**	CRoa
	- 'Rowden Mikado'	CRoa NChi
	- 'Rowden Naib'	CRoa
	- 'Rowden Nuncio'	CRoa
	- 'Rowden Prince'	CRoa
	- 'Rowden Queen'	CRoa
	- 'Rowden Sovereign' **new**	CRoa
	- 'Rowden Sultan'	CRoa
	- 'Rowden Tetrarch' **new**	CRoa
I	- 'Royal Banner'	EBee ECtt EWoo LRHS WFar
	- 'Royal Crown'	ECho XLum
I	- 'Ruby King'	LEdu LRHS
	- 'Ruffled Dimity'	EBee IPot
I	- 'Sensation'	CWCL ECho ECtt EWoo GBin IKil IPot MWts NLar SWat
	- 'Snowy Hills'	XLum
	- 'Sorcerer's Triumph'	WFar
	- var. ***spontanea***	SWat
	- - B&SWJ 1103	WCru
	- - B&SWJ 8699	WCru
	- 'Stippled Ripples'	IPot
	- 'Strut and Flourish'	EWoo
	- 'Summer Storm' ♀H7	SPer
	- 'Taketori-hime' (v)	XLum
	- 'Umi-kaze'	NLar
	- 'Variegata' (v) ♀H7	CBod CHid CMac CSpe EBee ECha ELon EPfP GBin GMaP GMcL IBoy LEdu LRHS MMuc NLar NSti SEND SKHP SRms SWat WCot WFar WMoo WPnP WWtn

	- 'Velvety Queen'	ECtt
I	- 'White Ladies'	CSBt EWoo LRHS SWat
	- 'Wine Ruffles'	CMHG LSRN
	- 'Yako-no-tama'	WFar WMoo
	- 'Yedo-yeman'	EBee IMou WFar
	'Épée Violette' (TB)	ESgI
	'Epicenter' (TB)	XSen
	'Eramosa Miss' (BB)	WCAu
	'Eramosa Skies' (SDB)	WCAu
	'Erect' (IB)	CKel
	'Eric the Red' (Sib)	ELon EWoo
	'Erste Sahne' (Sib)	GBin
	'Eternal Bliss' (TB)	SIri
	'Evadne' (TB)	WMil
	'Evening Drama' (TB)	WCAu
	'Evening Gown' (TB)	XSen
	'Ever After' (TB)	EWoo LCro XSen
	'Ever Again' (Sib)	ELon EWoo
	'Everything Plus' (TB)	ESgI XSen
	'Ewen' (Sib)	CDor CHid CPou EWoo GKin GLog GMaP ILea LEdu MNrw NGdn SWat WAul WCot
	'Exotic Isle' (TB)	ESgI XSen
	'Expose' (TB)	WCAu
	'Extra' (BB)	CPBP LLHF
	'Extra Dazzle' (La)	LLWG
	'Extra Innings' (TB)	EWoo
	'Eye Magic' (IB)	CKel XSen
	'Eye of Tiger'	see *I.* 'Tigereye'
	'Eye Shadow' (SDB)	WCAu
	'Eyebright' (SDB) ♀H7	CBro WCAu
	'Fabuleux' (TB)	SIri
	'Face of an Angel' (TB)	WCAu
	'Faenelia Hicks' (La)	WMAq
	'Falconeer' (TB)	CIri
	'Fall Empire' (TB)	EWoo
	'Fall Fiesta' (TB)	XSen
	'Fanciful Whimsy' (IB)	WCAu
	'Fancy Brass' (TB)	SIri
	'Fancy Dress' (TB)	SIri
	'Fanfaron' (TB)	ESgI XSen
	'Farleigh Damson' (SDB)	SIri
	'Fashion Holiday' (IB)	SIri
	'Fashion Lady' (MDB)	CBro ECho
	'Fathom' (IB)	WCAu
	'Feather and Fan' (La)	LLWG
	'Feminine Charm' (TB)	MRav WCAu
	'Festive Skirt' (TB)	CKel WCAu
	'Feu du Ciel' (TB) ♀H7	ESgI EWoo XSen
	'Few Are Chosen' (La)	LLWG
	'Fiddlin' Around' (TB)	WCAu
	'Fiesta Time' (TB)	CWCL XSen
	'Film Festival' (TB)	ESgI
	'Finalist' (TB)	WCAu XSen
	'Fire in the Sky' (IB)	WCAu
	'Firebeard' (TB)	CIri
	'Firebird' (TB)	CRos LRHS NRHS
	'Firebreather' (TB)	MHol SPoG
	'Firebug' (IB)	ESgI XSen
	'Firecracker' (TB)	MRav WCAu
	'First Interstate' (TB)	CWCL ESgI XSen
	'First Movement' (TB)	ESgI
	'First Romance' (SDB)	LSRN
	'First Violet' (TB)	ESgI
	'Fit the Bill' (TB)	EWoo
	'Five Star Admiral' (TB)	XSen
	'Flaming Dragon' (TB)	XSen
	'Flaming Victory' (TB)	XSen
	flavescens	ESgI EWoo WCAu XSen
	'Flavours' (BB)	WCAu
	'Fleece of White' (BB)	WCAu
	'Fleur Collette Louise' (La)	CIri
	'Flight of Butterflies' (Sib)	Widely available
	'Flirting Again' (SDB) ♀H7	CTal SIri
	'Floorshow' (TB)	XSen
§	'Florentina' (IB/TB) ♀H7	CArn CBro CHby ECGP ESgI EWoo GCal GPoy LRHS MRav NBid NBir SEND WCAu WHer XSen
	'Florentine Silk' (TB)	WCAu
	'Floridor' (TB)	EWoo
	'Fluffy Pillows' (TB)	CIri
	'Flumadiddle' (IB)	CBro CTal
	'Flying Solo' (IB)	CIri
	'Flûte Enchantée' (TB)	CIri XSen
	'Focus' (TB)	XSen
	foetidissima ♀H5	Widely available
	- 'Aurea'	WCot
	- ***chinensis***	see *I. foetidissima* var. *citrina*
§	- var. ***citrina***	CBre EPri EWld GAbr GCra GKev LEdu NLar SChr WGwG
	- 'Fructu Albo'	NSti
	- var. ***lutescens***	CHid
	- 'Variegata' (v) ♀H5	CElw ESps EWoo NBir NPer
	'Fogbound' (TB)	WCAu
	'Foggy Dew' (TB)	EAEE EPfP LRHS
	'Fondation Van Gogh' (TB)	XSen
	'Foolish Fancy' (TB)	SIri
	'Footloose' (TB)	SIri XSen
	'For Clive' (TB) **new**	CIri
	'For Richard' (TB)	CIri
	'Fordwich' (SDB)	SIri
	'Forecasting Rain' (SDB)	SIri
	'Foreign Legion' (TB)	EWoo WCAu
	'Foreigner' (TB)	WCAu
	'Forest Light' (SDB)	CBro ESgI
	'Forever Blue' (SDB)	WCAu
	'Forever Gold' (TB)	EWoo XSen
	'Forge Fire' (TB)	ESgI
	formosana	ECho
	- B&SWJ 3076	WCru
	'Forrest Hills' (TB)	EPfP GPSL LRHS
	forrestii ♀H7	CAby CBro CHid CMac ECho EHoe EPfP EWoo GAbr GCal GCra GKev GLog LRHS MMuc NBir SPtp SRot WAbe
	- SDR 5802	GKev
	- SDR 7871	GKev
	'Fort Apache' (TB)	EWes EWoo
	'Fortunata' (TB)	XSen
	'Fortunate Son' (TB)	EWoo WCAu
	'Fourfold Blue' (SpH)	GBin
	'Fourfold Lavender' (Sib)	EWes NLar
	'Fourfold White' (Sib)	ESgI
	'Foxy Lady' (TB)	EWoo
	'Framboise' (TB)	XSen
	'Frances Iva' (TB)	EWoo
	'Francheville' (TB)	EWoo
	'Francina' (TB)	WMil
	'Frank Elder' (Reticulata)	CRos EBee ECho EPot ERCP GKev LAma LLHF LRHS NRHS SDeJ WAbe
	'Freedom Flight' (TB)	CIri
	'French Can Can' (TB)	EWoo SIri
	'French Horn' (TB)	CIri
	'French Rose' (TB)	WCAu
	'Fresno Calypso' (TB)	ESgI WCAu XSen
	'Frison-roche' (TB)	CWCL WViv
	'Frisounette' (TB)	ESgI
	'Fritillary Flight' (IB) ♀H7	CKel
	'From this Moment' (La)	LLWG
	'Frontier Marshall' (TB)	XSen

'Frost and Flame' (TB)	CKel EBee ECtt ELan EWoo GBin LCro LRHS MAsh MRav NBir NLar SDeJ SPer SPoG SWat WGwG
'Frost Echo' (TB)	EWoo
'Frosted Angel' (SDB)	CBro
'Frosted Velvet' (MTB)	WCAu
'Frosty Jewels' (TB)	XSen
'Frosty Moonscape' (TB)	CIri
'Fruit Cocktail' (IB)	XSen
'Full Sun' (Spuria)	EWoo
fulva ♀^{H5}	CSpe EBee EPri EWay GCal LPot MMrt MWts NBir NSti SBrt WCot
- 'Marvell Gold' (La)	CRoa EBee
× ***fulvala*** ♀^{H5}	EWes NBir NSti
- 'Violacea'	LRHS
'Furnaceman' (SDB)	CBro CTal
'Futuriste' (TB)	SIri
'Gai Luron' (TB)	CKel
'Gallant Moment' (TB)	EWoo SIri XSen
'Galway' (IB)	SIri XSen
'Game Plan' (TB)	WCAu
'Gandalf the Grey' (TB)	ESgI
'Garnet Storm Dancer' (La)	LLWG
'Gelbe Mantel' (Sino-Sib)	CHid GKin MSpe NBir NSti
'Gemstone Walls' (TB)	ESgI
'Gentius' (TB)	EWoo
'George' (Reticulata) ♀^{H7}	CAby CAvo CBro CRos CWCL ECho EPfP EPot ERCP GKev LAma LRHS NRHS WBor WBrk WCot WHoo XEll
'Gerald Darby'	see *I.* × *robusta* 'Gerald Darby'
'Germaine Perthuis' (TB)	EWoo
§ ***germanica***	ESps MMuc SEND WCAu WCot WGwG
- var. ***florentina***	see *I.* 'Florentina'
§ - 'Nepalensis'	WCAu
- 'The King'	see *I. germanica* 'Nepalensis'
'Gertrude' (TB)	EWoo
'Ghost Train' (TB)	EWoo SIri
'Giacatollo' (TB)	CIri
'Gingerbread Castle' (TB)	WCAu
'Gingerbread Man' (SDB)	CBro CMea CTal ESgI EWoo MBrN WCAu
'Gingersnap' (TB)	EWoo
'Girly Girl' (TB)	WCAu
'Glacier Gold' (TB)	XSen
'Glacier Point' (TB)	CIri
'Glad Rags' (TB)	XSen
'Gladiator's Gift' (La)	LLWG
'Gladys Austin' (TB)	XSen
'Glas-y-Dorlan' (Sib) **new**	GCal
'Glenthorn' (TB) **new**	SIri
'Glowing Embers' (TB)	ESgI
'Gnu' (TB)	XSen
'Go Between' (TB)	WCAu
'Goddess of Green' (IB)	EWoo
'Godfrey Owen' (TB)	WCAu
'Godsend' (TB)	CIri
'Going Green' (TB)	CIri
'Going Home' (TB) ♀^{H7}	SIri
'Going My Way' (TB)	ESgI EWoo LSou SIri WCAu XSen
'Gold Burst' (TB)	XSen
'Gold Country' (TB)	XSen
'Gold Galore' (TB)	SIri
'Gold of Autumn' (TB)	CKel MArt
'Goldberry' (IB)	WCAu
'Golden Alps' (TB)	SRms WCAu
'Golden Beauty'	GKev SDeJ
'Golden Child' (SDB)	XSen
'Golden Crimping' (Sib)	EWoo
'Golden Edge' (Sib)	ELon EWoo GBin GQue LLWG MBel MWts NLar WFar
'Golden Encore' (TB)	CKel WCAu
'Golden Fireworks' (La)	LLWG
'Golden Folly' (SDB)	CIri
'Golden Forest' (TB)	CBod
'Golden Immortal' (TB)	EWoo
'Golden Panther' (TB)	WCAu
'Golden Violet' (SDB)	ESgI
'Goldfinger' (TB)	GKev
'Good Looking' (TB)	ESgI WCAu
'Good Show' (TB)	ESgI EWoo WCAu XSen
'Good Vibrations' (TB)	SIri XSen
'Goodbye Heart' (TB)	EWoo LSRN
'Gordon' (Reticulata)	CAvo CBro CRos ECho EPfP EPot ERCP GKev LAma LCro LOPS LRHS NRHS SCob
gormanii	see *I. tenax*
'Gossip' (SDB)	CBro
'Got the Melody' (TB)	EWoo WCAu
'Goudhurst' (SDB)	SIri
'Gracchus' (TB)	EWoo WCAu
'Grace Sturtevant' (TB)	WMil
gracilipes	GEdr SBrt
- 'Alba'	GEdr
gracilipes × ***lacustris***	GEdr WAbe
graeberiana	ECho EPot GKev SDeJ
- yellow fall	ECho
graminea ♀^{H7}	CAvo CBro CHid CMac ECho ELan EPfP EPri IFro LLWP NBir NChi NSti WCot XEll
- 'Hort's Variety'	EBee
- var. ***pseudocyperus***	GBin GCal SDys
graminifolia	see *I. kerneriana*
'Granada Gold' (TB)	SRms XSen
'Grand Circle' (TB)	EWoo
'Grand Illusion' (Spuria)	EWoo
'Grand Waltz' (TB)	XSen
'Grandis' (Sib) **new**	GBin
'Granny Jean' (Sib)	CKel
'Grapelet' (MDB)	CPBP WCAu
'Great Lakes' (TB)	ESgI EWoo
'Grecian Skies' (TB)	ESgI
'Green Eyed Lady' (TB)	ESgI
'Green Ice' (TB)	LRHS MRav
'Green Jungle' (TB)	EWoo
'Green Prophecy' (TB)	CKel
'Green Spot' (SDB) ♀^{H7}	CBod CBro CKel CTal EAEE ECha ECho ECtt ELan GBuc LHop LRHS MRav NBir NLar SDeJ SPer WAul WCAu
'Greenstuff' (SDB)	CTal
'Grenade' (TB)	WViv
grey-flowered (Sib)	ELon
'Gringo' (TB)	WCAu
'Grooving' (BB)	ESgI
'Grosser Wein' (Sib) **new**	GBin
'Guatemala' (TB)	WCAu
'Gudrun' (TB)	EWoo
'Guess Who I Am' (TB)	WCAu
'Gull's Wing' (Sib)	EWTr LEdu LLWG MHol NLar NSti
'Gurkha's Dance' (SDB)	SIri
'Gypsy Beauty' (Dut)	CAvo ELan GKev LCro LOPS SDeJ
'Gypsy Jewels' (TB)	CKel ESgI XSen
'Gypsy Romance' (TB) ♀^{H7}	EIri ESgI SIri WCAu
'Gypsy Tart' (SDB)	SIri
'Habit' (TB)	EWoo WCAu
'Hakuna Matata' (AB)	SDys
'Halloween Halo' (TB)	WCAu
halophila	see *I. spuria* subsp. *halophila*

	'Happenstance' (TB)	EWoo WCAu
	'Happy Mood' (IB)	WCAu
	'Harbor Blue' (TB)	CKel CTsd EWoo MWat SWat WCAu
	'Harlow Gold' (IB)	ESgI
	'Harmony' ambig.	SCob SPer
	'Harmony' (IB) **new**	CRos
	'Harmony' (Reticulata)	CAby CAvo CBro ECho EPfP EPot GKev LAma LCro LOPS LRHS MArt MWat NRHS SCob SDeJ WBrk
	'Harpswell Hallelujah' (Sib)	EWoo
	'Harpswell Happiness' (Sib) ♀H7	EBee ELon EPfP EPri GAbr GBin GCra ILea SBch SPer SWat WAul WHlf WMoo
	'Harpswell Haze' (Sib)	ECha
	'Harpswell Velvet' (Sib)	GBin
	'Harriette Halloway' (TB)	CBod CWGN EPfP EShb EWoo LHop LRHS LSRN NLar SHar SRGP WCot
	hartwegii	ECho
	'Harvest King' (TB)	XSen
	'Harvest of Memories' (TB)	CKel ESgI EWoo GMcL GWyn SPoG
	'Haut les Voiles' (TB)	CWCL
	'Haute Couture' (TB)	XSen
	'Haviland' (TB)	XSen
	'Headcorn' (MTB) ♀H7	SIri
	'Headline Banner' (BB)	EWoo WCAu
	'Headway' (Spuria)	WCAu
	'Heartbeat Away' (TB)	CIri
	'Heartbreak Point' (TB)	EWoo
	'Heart's Radiance' (MTB)	SDys
	'Heather Carpet' (SDB)	WCAu
	'Heather Stream' (La)	ELon
	'Heavenly Blue' (Sib)	MWat SPer
	'Heavenly Days' (TB)	WCAu
	'Heavenly Horns' (TB)	CIri
	'Helen Astor' (Sib)	CDor CTri MRav SWat
	'Helen Collingwood' (TB)	ESgI EWoo
	'Helen Dawn' (TB) ♀H7	SIri
	'Helen McGregor' (TB)	EWoo
	'Helen Proctor' (IB)	ESgI WCot XSen
	'Helen Traubel' (TB)	WCAu
	'Helena Terry' (TB)	ESgI
	'Helene C.' (TB)	EWoo WViv XSen
	'Helge' (IB)	ECho SWat
	'Heliotrope Bouquet' (Sib)	EWoo
	'Hellcat' (IB)	EWoo WCAu
	'Hello Darkness' (TB) ♀H7	ESgI EWoo WCAu WCot XSen
	'Hell's Fire' (TB)	ELan ELon EWoo WCAu
	'Hemstitched' (TB)	EBee EWoo MHol
	'Her Majesty' (TB)	EWoo
	'Hercules' (Reticulata)	ECho
	'Here Comes The Sun' (TB)	WCAu
	'Hever Castle' (Kent Castles Series) (BB)	SIri
	'Hey True Blue' (TB)	WCAu
	'High Barbaree' (TB)	EWoo
	'High Blue Sky' (TB)	WCAu
	'High Command' (TB)	CKel WCAu
	'High Impact' (TB)	CIri EWoo
	'High Peak' (TB)	WCAu
	'Highland Mist' (La)	LLWG
	'Hildegarde' (Dut)	SDeJ
	'His Royal Highness' (TB)	WCAu
	histrio	ECho EPot
	- subsp. ***aintabensis***	ECho GKev
	- subsp. ***histrio***	GKev
	histrioides	ECho GKev
	- 'Finola' **new**	ERCP
	- 'Halkis' (Reticulata)	EBee EPot ERCP GKev LAma SDeJ
	- 'Lady Beatrix Stanley'	CAvo CBro CMea CRos ECho EPot ERCP GKev LAma LLHF LRHS NNys NRHS SDeJ WBrk WHoo
	- 'Major'	ECho GKev LAma
	- var. ***sophenensis***	ECho EPot GKev LAma
	'Hoar Edge' (Sib)	NChi WAul
	'Hocus Pocus' (SDB)	CKel CTal CWGN EAEE ECho EPfP EWoo GBuc LRHS LSou WAul
	'Hohe Warte' (Sib) ♀H7	GBin WAul
	'Holden Clough' (SpH) ♀H7	ELan EPfP GBin GCra GMaP GMcL LEdu MMuc MNrw MRav MSpe NBir NChi NGdn NSti NWad WBrk WCAu WFar WSHC
	'Holidaze' (IB) ♀H7	EIri
	'Hollywood Nights' (TB)	EWoo
	'Holtentol'	WCAu
	'Holy Night' (TB)	CKel
	'Honey Glazed' (IB)	ESgI WCAu
	'Honey Mocha Lotta' (Spuria)	EWoo
	'Honey Stars' (La)	LLWG
	'Honeylove' (SDB)	SDys
	'Honeymoon Suite' (TB)	EWoo
	'Honeyplic' (IB) ♀H7	ESgI SIri
	'Honington' (SDB)	WCAu
	'Honky Tonk Blues' (TB)	ESgI LSRN
	'Honorabile' (MTB)	ESgI WCAu
	hoogiana ♀H4	ECho GKev
I	- 'Amazon' **new**	GKev
I	- 'Amphion' **new**	GKev
I	- 'Antiope' **new**	GKev
	- 'Purpurea'	ECho
§	***hookeri***	CFis CPBP CSma CTal ECho ELan GKev GMaP IBoy SBrt WIce WThu
	- SDR 2202	GKev
	'Hopelessly Devoted' (La)	LLWG
	'Hoptoit' (TB)	CIri
	'Horizon Bleu' (TB)	EWoo
	'Horned Rosyred' (TB)	EWoo
§	'Hornpipe' (TB)	WCAu
	'Hortensia Rose' (TB)	SIri
	'Hot and Spicy' (La)	LLWG
	'Hot to Trot' (TB)	ESgI
	'Hottentot' (SDB)	WCAu
	'Howler' (TB)	WCAu
	'Hubbard' (Sib)	EPri LLWG MBel MNrw SPoG SSal WFar WHlf
	'Huckleberry Fudge' (TB)	XSen
	'Hugh Miller' (TB)	WCAu
	'Hula Hands' (IB)	CIri
	'Hypnotizer' (TB)	CIri
	'I Feel Good' (TB)	WCAu
	'I Pink I Can' (TB)	WCAu
	'I Repeat' (TB)	XSen
	'I Seek You' (TB)	ESgI
	iberica	ECho
§	- subsp. ***elegantissima***	ECho
	'Ice'	WCAu
	'Ice and Indigo' (SDB)	WCAu
	'Ice Cave' (TB)	WCAu
	'Ice Dancer' (TB) ♀H7	CKel
	'Ice Etching' (SDB)	WCAu
	'Ice for Brice' (TB)	CIri
	'Ice Wings' (BB)	WCAu
	'Ida' (Reticulata)	ECho LAma
	'Idol' (TB)	EWoo
	'Ila Crawford' (Spuria) ♀H7	XSen
	'Illini Charm' (Sib)	CHid EBee WFar WMoo
	illyrica	see *I. pallida*
	'I'm Back' (TB)	WCAu

	'Immortality' (TB)	CKel CWGN GKev GMcL LRHS SCob WCAu XSen
	'Imperative' (IB)	EWoo SIri WCAu
	'Imperial Opal' (Sib) new	ECtt
I	'Imperial Velvet' (Sib)	ELon EWTr EWoo WFar
	'Impersonator' (TB)	CIri
	'Imprimis' (TB)	EWoo XSen
	'In a Flash' (IB)	WCAu
	'In Love' (TB)	XSen
	'In Town' (TB)	EWoo XSen
	'In Your Dreams' (TB)	CIri
	'Incentive' (TB)	EWoo
	'Incognito Too' (TB)	CIri
*	'Incoscente' (TB)	ESgI
	'Indeed' (IB)	ESgI
	'Indian Chief' (TB)	CBod CCCN CWCL EPfP ESgI EWoo IBoy MCot MRav WCAu
	'Indian Hills' (TB)	EWoo
	'Indian Idyll' (IB)	CKel
	'Indian Jewel' (SDB)	ECho
	'Indiana Sunset' (TB)	CKel
	'Indigo Princess' (TB)	EWoo XSen
	'Infanta' (SDB)	WCAu
	'Inferno' (TB)	EWoo
	'Ink Patterns' (TB)	WCAu
	'Inner Show'	WCAu
	'Innocent Devil' (TB)	CIri
	'Innocent Pink' (TB)	ESgI
	innominata	CRos ECho GKev LRHS NBir NBro NRHS SRms
	- hybrids	CPne
	- yellow-flowered	NRya
	'Inscription' (SDB)	ECho
	'Inside Job' (TB)	WCAu
	'Inspired' (TB)	WCAu
	'Instant Hit' (TB)	WCAu
	'Intermediary' (IB)	WCAu
	'Interpol' (TB)	ESgI EWoo XSen
	'Invicta Daybreak' (IB)	SIri
	'Invicta Garnet' (SDB)	SIri
	'Invicta Gold' (SDB)	SIri
	'Invicta Reprieve' (IB)	SIri
	'Irene' (TB)	WCAu
	'Iriade' (TB)	WCAu
	'Iris Bohnsack' (BB)	WCAu
	'Irisades' (TB)	WCAu
	'Irish Chant' (SDB)	WCAu
	'Irish Gold' (TB)	WCAu
	'Irish Harp' (SDB)	ESgI
	'Irish Jig' (TB)	WCAu
	'Irish Squire' (TB)	WCAu
	'Irish Tune' (TB)	ESgI
	'Iron Eagle' (TB)	CIri
	'Isabelle' (Sib)	LSRN XSen
	'Island Sun' (SDB)	SIri
	'Island Sunset' (TB)	SIri
	'Isoline' (TB)	ESgI
	'It Happens' (TB)	WCAu
	'Italian Ice' (TB)	EIri
	'Italian Velvet' (TB)	EWoo WCAu
	'It's Amazing' (IB)	WCAu
	'Ivory Queen' (Sib)	EWoo
	'J.S. Dijt' (Reticulata)	CAvo CBro CRos ECho EPot ERCP GKev LAma LCro LRHS MGos NRHS SDeJ
	'Jack Attack' (La)	CBod SPoG WHar WMoo
	'Jac-y-do' (Sib)	EWes
	'Jade Mist' (SDB)	ECho
	'Jaguar Blue' (TB)	EWoo
	'Jane Phillips' (TB) ♀H7	Widely available
	'Janet Lane' (BB)	CKel
	'Japanese Pinwheel' new	IPot
	'Japanesque' (MTB)	CIri
	japonica ♀H4	ECho NLar NPer SPlb XLum XSen
	- B&SWJ 8921	WCru
	- 'Ledger'	CAby CHll CMac ECha MRav SEND SMad WWFP
	- 'Monty'	WWFP
	- 'Rudolph Spring'	EBee GCal WSHC WWFP
§	- 'Variegata' (v) ♀H4	CBro CTsd ECha ECho ELan ESwi NPer NSti SArc WWFP XSen
	'Jasper Gem' (MDB)	ECho
	'Jazz Festival' (TB)	EWoo SIri WCAu XSen
	'Jazz Hot' (La)	LLWG
	'Jazzed Up' (TB)	XSen
	'Je l'Adore' (TB)	EWoo
	'Jean Cayeux' (TB)	ESgI EWoo
	'Jean Guymer' (TB)	ESgI
	'Jeanne Price' (TB)	ESgI EWoo LSRN WCAu
	'Jelly Belly' (SDB)	EWoo
	'Jeremy Brian' (SDB)	WCAu
	'Jeremy Jets On' (TB)	CIri
	'Jesse's Song' (TB)	ESgI WCAu XSen
	'Jet Black' (TB)	EWoo
	'Jet-Setter' (TB)	CIri
	'Jeunesse' (TB)	ESgI
	'Jewel Baby' (SDB)	CBro
	'Jeweler's Art' (SDB)	CHur ESgI EWoo
	'Jiansada' (SDB)	CBro
	'Jigsaw' (TB)	XSen
	'Jimmy' (Reticulata) new	GKev
	'Jitterbug' (TB)	WCAu
	'Joanna' (TB)	LSRN NLar
	'John' (IB)	CKel LSRN
	'Joli Coeur' (TB)	EWoo
	'Joyce' (Reticulata)	CBro CRos ECho EPfP EPot GKev LAma LRHS NRHS SDeJ
	'Joyful Skies' (TB)	WCAu
	'Jubilant Spirit' (Spuria)	EWes
	'Jubilation' (TB)	EWoo
	'Jubilee Gem' (TB)	CKel WCAu
	'Judy Mogil' (TB)	CIri
	'Juliet' (TB)	ESgI
	'Jump for Joy' (TB)	CIri
	'Jump Start' (IB)	EWoo WCAu
	'Jumping Jupiter' (TB)	CIri
	'Junaluska' (TB)	EWoo
	'June Prom' (IB)	EAEE LRHS SRGP
	'June Rose' (IB)	CKel
	'Jungle Fires' (TB)	WCAu
	'Jungle Shadows' (BB)	ESgI EWoo MRav NBir WCAu
	'Jurassic Park' (TB)	ESgI EWoo WCAu XSen
	'Just Imagine' (La)	LLWG
	'Just Jennifer' (BB)	WCAu
	'Kabluey' (Sib)	ECtt IPot
	'Kaboom' (Sib)	MHol
	kaempferi	see *I. ensata*
	'Kahuna' (IB)	WCAu
	'Kaint Hardly Believe' (TB)	CIri
	'Karen' (TB)	LSRN
	'Katharine Hodgkin' (Reticulata) ♀H7	Widely available
	'Katharine Hodgkin' dark-flowered (Reticulata)	EPot
	'Katie-Koo' (IB) ♀H7	CKel
	'Katy Petts' (SDB)	ESgI
	'Keeping up Appearances' (TB)	WCAu
	kemaonensis PAB 8473	LEdu
	'Kent Arrival' (Sib)	SIri

	'Kent Blackguard' (IB)	SIri
	'Kent Compote' (IB)	SIri
	'Kent Pride' (TB)	CKel CSBt EAEE ECha ECtt EPfP ESgI EUJe EWoo GBin LRHS MCot MRav SCob SPer SPoG SWat WBod WCAu
	Kenta No Se129 (Sib)	EPri
	'Kentish Icon' (SDB)	SIri
	'Kentish Lad' (IB)	SIri
	'Kentucky Derby' (TB)	XSen
§	***kerneriana*** 🏆H4	CBro EHoe GBuc GKev NBir
	'Kęstutis Genys' (Sib)	WAul
	'Kharput' (IB)	EWoo
	'Kildonan' (TB)	WCAu
	'Kingfisher' (Sib)	WAul
	'King's Jester' (TB)	EWoo
	'Kirkstone' (TB)	WCAu
	kirkwoodii	ECho GKev
	'Kiss of Summer' (TB) 🏆H7	ESgI SDys
	'Kissing Circle' (TB)	ESgI EWoo
	'Kiwi Slices' (SDB)	CWat
	'Knick Knack' (MDB)	CBro CPBP CTal ECho ELan ELon EPfP GMaP LRHS MRav SDeJ SPoG
	korolkowii	CTal ECho
	'Kuh-e-Abr'	GKev LAma LLHF
	'La Meije' (TB)	SIri WViv
	'La Senda' (Spuria)	WCot
	'Lace Legacy' (TB)	EWoo LSRN
	'Laced Cotton' (TB)	WCAu XSen
§	***lactea***	SBrt SMHy XEll XSen
	- CC 7174	GKev
	lacustris	CPBP WAbe WCot XSen
	'Lacy Snowflake' (TB)	GMcL LHop LRHS
	'Lad'	WCAu
	'Lady Belle' (MTB)	ESgI
	'Lady Byng' (TB)	WMil
	'Lady Essex' (TB)	EWoo WCAu
	'Lady Friend' (TB)	WCAu XSen
	'Lady in Red' (SDB)	ESgI WCAu
	'Lady Mohr' (AB)	WCAu
	'Lady of the Night' (BB)	WCAu
	'Lady R' (SDB)	ECho
	'Lady Vanessa' (Sib)	CPou EBee ELon MRav NSti
	laevigata	CRoa CWat ECho ELan EPfP EWay ITim MRav NBro NPer SPer SWat WFar WMAq WMoo WShi
	- var. ***alba***	CRoa ECho LLWG SWat WAbe WMoo
	- 'Atropurpurea'	CRoa LLWG
	- blue-flowered	LLWG
	- 'Colchesterensis'	CRoa CWat EPri EWay NGdn NPer SWat WMAq WMoo
I	- 'Dorothy'	NGdn
	- 'Dorothy Robinson'	ELan EPfP MRav SWat
I	- 'Elegante'	EWay
*	- 'Elgar'	WMAq
	- 'Liam Johns'	LLWG
	- 'Midnight'	see *I. laevigata* 'Weymouth Midnight'
	- 'Monstrosa'	EWay
	- 'Richard Greaney'	CRoa EWay
	- 'Rose Queen'	see *I. ensata* 'Rose Queen'
	- 'Rowden Starlight'	CRoa LLWG
I	- 'Snowdrift'	CRoa CWat EWay LCro MJak NBir NGdn NLar NPer SWat WFar WMAq WMoo
	- 'Variegata' (v) 🏆H7	CBen CBot CRoa CWat EAEE ECha ECho EHoe ELan ELon EPfP EWay LLWG MWts NBro NGdn NPer SPer SWat WMAq WMoo WPnP WWtn
	- 'Violet Garth'	EWay
	- 'Weymouth'	see *I. laevigata* 'Weymouth Blue'
§	- 'Weymouth Blue'	EWay LLWG
§	- 'Weymouth Midnight'	CRoa
	- 'Weymouth Purity'	EWay
	- 'Wychwood Surprise' **new**	CRoa
	laevigata* × *versicolor Tamberg hybrid **new**	LLWG
§	'Lake Niklas' (Sib)	ELon MHol NCGa
	'Lambourn Hills' (TB)	WCAu
	'Lamia' (TB)	CIri
	'Langport Chapter' (IB)	CKel ESgI
	'Langport Chief' (IB)	CKel
	'Langport Claret' (IB)	CKel ESgI
	'Langport Curlew' (IB)	CKel ESgI
	'Langport Duchess' (IB)	ESgI
	'Langport Fairy' (IB)	CKel
	'Langport Flame' (IB)	CKel ESgI MArt
	'Langport Hope' (IB)	CKel
	'Langport Jane' (IB)	CKel
	'Langport Lady' (IB)	CKel
	'Langport Lord' (IB)	ESgI
	'Langport Minstrel' (IB)	CKel ESgI
	'Langport Pearl' (IB)	CKel
	'Langport Pinnacle' (IB)	CKel
	'Langport Smoke' (IB)	CKel
	'Langport Star' (IB)	CKel ESgI
	'Langport Storm' (IB)	CKel EPfP LRHS MRav SDeJ WHoo
	'Langport Sun' (IB)	ESgI
	'Langport Sylvia' (IB)	CKel
	'Langport Violet' (IB)	CKel ESgI
	'Langport Vista' (IB)	CKel
	'Langport Wren' (IB) 🏆H7	CAby CBod CBro CKel CRos EPfP EPri ESgI EShb EWoo GBuc GCal IPot LHop LRHS NBir NGdn NRHS WAul WPtf
	'Langthorns Pink' (Sib)	CCse ELan MRav WAul
	'Lark Rise' (TB) 🏆H7	CKel
	'Larry Gaulter' (TB)	WCAu
	'Larue Boswell' (TB) **new**	EPfP
	'Last Hurrah' (TB)	EWoo
	'Late Liftoff' (TB)	CIri
§	***latifolia***	GKev MMuc SEND WShi
	- ***alba***	WCot
	- 'Duchess of York'	EBee
	- 'Isabella'	SDeJ
	- 'King of the Blues'	CAvo EBee SDeJ SDix
	- 'Mansfield'	MNrw
	- 'Montblanc'	CAvo GKev SDeJ
	- 'Queen of the Blues' (Eng)	GKev SDeJ
	- wild-collected	GCal
	'Latin Lark' (TB)	ESgI
	'Latin Rock' (TB)	WCAu
	'Latino' (IB)	WCAu
	'Laura Jean' (TB)	EWoo
	'Laura Louise' (La)	LLWG SKHP
	'Lavanesque' (TB)	WCAu
	'Lavender Bounty' (Sib)	CHid GBin
	'Lavender Light' (Sib)	WAul
	lazica 🏆H5	CBct CBot CBro CMac CSpe EPPr EPfP EPot EWoo GKev IBlr LRHS MRav NBir NCGa NChi NSti SBrt SEND SPer SPlb WGwG WHil
	- 'Joy Bishop'	CJun
*	- 'Richard Nutt'	CJun ELon WCot WSHC
	- 'Turkish Blue'	IBlr
	'Lazuline'	GKev
	'Legato' (TB)	ESgI
*	'Lemon Beauty' (TB)	LHop
	'Lemon Brocade' (TB)	EWoo WCAu
	'Lemon Flare' (SDB)	EIri MRav SRms

'Lemon Ice' (TB)	CBod CKel EAEE ECha EPfP GBin LRHS SDeJ SPer WHoo
'Lemon Lyric' (TB)	ESgI
'Lemon on Ice' (SDB)	WCAu
'Lemon Pop' (IB)	WCAu
'Lemon Puff' (MDB)	CBro LLHF WCAu
'Lemon Tree' (TB)	WCAu
'Lemon Whip' (IB)	EWoo
'Lena' (SDB)	CBro
'Lenna M' (SDB)	ECho
'Lenora Pearl' (BB)	XSen
'Lent A. Williamson' (TB)	CRos EWoo GMaP LRHS NRHS
'Lenten Prayer' (TB)	EWoo WCAu
'Lenzschnee' (TB)	EWoo
'Leprechaun's Purse' (SDB)	WCAu
'Let's Elope' (IB)	ESgI WCAu
'Licorice Stick' (TB)	XSen
'Life Story' (TB) **new**	EBee
'Light Beam' (TB)	XSen
'Light Cavalry' (IB)	ESgI EWoo
'Light Laughter' (IB)	WCAu
'Light Rebuff' (TB)	EWoo
'Lilac and Lavender' (SDB)	SIri
'Lilac Times'	EWoo
'Lilli-white' (SDB)	CKel CWat ELan ELon EPfP GEdr LRHS MBNS MRav SPoG
'Lilting' (TB)	XSen
'Lime Fizz' (TB)	XSen
'Limeheart' (Sib)	CPou LLHF
'Limelight' (TB)	SRms
'Linda Mary' (Sib)	EWoo
'Linda's Child' (TB)	WCAu
'Lingering Love' (TB)	WCAu
'Lion King' (Dut)	GKev LCro LOPS
'Little Black Belt' (SDB)	EWoo LRHS
'Little Blackfoot' (SDB)	CTal ESgI WCAu WCot
'Little Blue-eyes' (SDB)	ESgI WCAu
'Little Bluets' (SDB)	ESgI
'Little Dandy' (SDB)	ECho
'Little Dogie' (SDB)	ECho
'Little Dream' (SDB)	WCAu
'Little Firecracker' (SDB)	WCAu
'Little Freak' (BB)	CIri
'Little Nutkin' (La)	LLWG
'Little Paul' (MTB)	ESgI
'Little Rosy Wings' (SDB)	CBro CPBP
'Little Shadow' (IB)	MRav SRms
'Little Sheba' (AB)	WCAu
'Little Showoff' (SDB)	ESgI
'Little Tilgates' (CH)	MAvo WCot WSHC
'Living Waters' (TB)	ESgI
'Local Color' (TB)	ESgI EWoo SIri XSen
'Local Hero' (IB)	WCAu
'Lodore' (TB)	SRms
'Logo' (IB)	WCAu
'Lohengrin' (TB)	EWoo
'Lollipop' (SDB)	EAJP ESgI SIri
'London Pride' (TB)	EWoo
longipetala	EPPr NBir
'Looking Forward' (TB)	ESgI
'Loop the Loop' (TB)	CBod CKel CMac CTsd EWoo SPoG SWat
'Loose Valley' (MTB) Υ^{H7}	SIri
'Lord Warden' (TB)	CKel ECtt EPfP LRHS WGwG
'Lorilee' (TB)	ESgI WCAu
'Lost in Love' (TB)	WCAu
'Lost in Space' (BB)	CIri
'Lottie Lou' (TB)	SIri
'Lotus Land' (TB)	WCAu
'Louisa's Song' (TB)	WCAu

Louisiana hybrids	ELan
'Louvois' (TB)	CKel ESgI EWoo NLar
'Love Power' (BB)	WCAu
'Love the Sun' (TB)	ESgI XSen
'Lovely Again' (TB)	CRos GKev LRHS MRav NRHS WCAu
'Lovely Leilani' (TB)	ESgI
'Lovely Señorita' (TB)	WCAu
'Love's Tune' (IB)	CRos EAEE EBee LRHS SRGP SWat
'Low Ho Silver' (IB)	WCAu
'Loyalist' (TB)	CPar EWoo SBee SIri
'Lucy's Gift' (MTB) Υ^{H7}	EAJP SRGP
'Lugano' (TB)	ESgI EWoo
'Lula Marguerite' (TB)	EWoo
'Luli-Ann' (SDB)	CKel
'Lullaby of Spring' (TB)	CKel
'Lullingstone Castle' (Kent Castles Series) (IB)	SIri
'Lumarco' (TB)	EWoo
'Lumière d'Automne' (TB)	XSen
'Lunar Fire' (TB)	CRos LRHS NRHS
'Lure of Gold' (IB)	WCAu
'Lurline' (TB)	WMil
lutescens Υ^{H7}	ECho EPot GCra GKev WAbe
§ - 'Campbellii'	ECho
§ - subsp. ***lutescens***	XSen
'Ma Mie' (IB)	EBee
maackii	GEdr
'Mabel Coday' (Sib)	EPri EWoo
'Mad Magenta' (Sib)	GBin
'Madame Lynn' (Spuria)	EWoo
'Madeira Belle' (TB)	CKel EAEE EPfP ESgI LRHS SHar WCAu WGwG WTor
'Madeleine Frances' (SDB)	SIri
'Magharee' (TB)	ESgI
'Magic Man' (TB)	XSen
'Magic Masquerade' (TB)	WCAu
'Magical Encounter' (TB)	EWoo LCro SIri
magnifica Υ^{H5}	ECho GKev
- 'Agalik'	ECho GKev
- 'Alba'	ECho GKev
* 'Mahogany Mix' (Dut)	GKev
'Maisie Lowe' (TB)	ESgI EWoo
'Majestic' (TB)	WMil
'Majestic Ruler' (TB)	WCAu
'Make a Wish' (TB) **new**	CIri
'Making Eyes' (SDB)	WCAu
'Mambo Italiano' (TB)	WCAu
'Man About Town' (TB)	WCAu
'Mandarin Purple' (Sino-Sib)	NEgg
mandshurica	CPBP
'Mango Entree' (TB)	WCAu
'Mango Smoothy' (BB)	ESgI
'Marcel Turbat' (TB)	SBee
'Marden Beech' (IB)	SIri
'Marden Meadow' (MTB)	SIri
'Margrave' (TB)	EWoo XSen
'Marguérite' (Reticulata/v)	ECho WCAu
'Marilyn Holmes' (Sib)	GLog GQue WCot
'Mariposa Autumn' (TB)	EWoo SIri
'Marksman' (SDB) **new**	CHur
'Marmalade Skies' (BB)	WCAu
'Marsh Marigold' (TB)	WMil
'Martyn Rix'	see *I. confusa* 'Martyn Rix'
'Mary Frances' (TB)	CKel ESgI WCAu XSen
'Mary Geddes' (TB)	EWoo
'Mary McIlroy' (SDB) Υ^{H7}	CBro
'Marybill' (TB) **new**	SIri
'Master Touch' (TB)	EBee ELon XSen
'Masterwork' (TB)	CIri
'Material Girl' (TB)	WCAu

	'Matinata' (TB)	CKel EWoo XSen
	'Matt McNames' (TB)	EWoo
	'Maui Moonlight' (IB) ♀H7	CKel ESgI EWoo NLar WCAu
	'May Melody' (TB)	WCAu
	'Maya Mint' (MDB)	LLHF
	'Meadow Court' (SDB)	CBro CKel CTal WCAu
	'Medallion' (Spuria)	EWoo
	'Medici Prince' (TB)	EWoo WCAu
	'Medway Valley' (MTB) ♀H7	SIri WCAu
	'Megglethorp' (IB)	WCAu
	'Melbreak' (TB)	ESgI
	mellita	see *I. suaveolens*
	'Mellow Yellow' (TB)	CLet
	'Melon Honey' (SDB)	CKel ELon WCAu
	'Melted Butter' (TB)	WCAu
§	'Melton Red Flare' (Sib)	CRos EAJP EBee GBin LRHS LSou MBNS MSpe NRHS
	'Memphis Memory' (Sib)	ELan ELon GCra MHol NLar SPer
	'Men in Black' (TB)	EWoo WCAu
	'Mer du Sud' (TB) ♀H7	EBee EIri ESgI EWoo LCro LRHS WViv XSen
*	'Merebrook Blue Lagoon' (La)	WMAq
	'Merebrook Jemma J' (La)	WMAq
	'Merebrook Purpla' (La)	WMAq
	'Merebrook Rum 'n' Raisin' (La)	WMAq
*	'Merebrook Rusty Red' (La)	WMAq
*	'Merebrook Snowflake' (La)	WMAq
	'Merebrook Sunnyside Up' (La)	WMAq
	'Merebrook Symphony' (La)	WMAq
	'Mescal' (TB)	WCAu
	'Mesmerizer' (TB)	EBee
	mesopotamica	see *I. germanica*
	'Messire Pierre' (BB)	CIri
	'Messy Jessi' (TB)	CIri
	'Metaphor' (TB)	WCAu
	'Mezza Cartuccia' (IB)	ESgI
	'Miami Beach' (TB)	WCAu
	'Midas Mite' (MDB)	LLHF
	'Midhurst White' (TB) **new**	SIri
I	'Midnight Blue' (MDB)	CBro
	'Midnight Caller' (TB)	ESgI EWoo XSen
	'Midnight Majesty' (TB)	EWoo
	'Midnight Oil' (TB)	EWoo
	'Midnight Thunder' (TB)	CIri
	'Midnight Treat' (TB)	WCAu
	'Midsummer Night's Dream' (IB)	CHur ESgI EWoo
	'Mighty Mouse' (MDB)	ELon EWoo
	'Mighty Warrior' (TB)	CIri
	milesii ♀H3	GBin GKev NBir SBrt
	- CC 6839	GKev
	'Millennium Sunrise' (TB)	WCAu
	'Mini Big Horn' (IB)	CIri
	'Mini-Agnes' (SDB)	CBro
	'Minidragon' (SDB) **new**	SIri
	'Minisa' (TB)	ESgI
	'Miss Nellie' (BB)	CKel
	'Miss Sunshine' (SDB)	CPBP
	'Missouri Streams' (Spuria)	EWoo
	missouriensis	CMac
	'Mist Arising' (TB)	CIri
	'Mister Roberts' (SDB)	ESgI
	'Mistress of Camelot' (TB)	SDys
	'Mme Chéreau' (TB)	ESgI EWoo WCAu
	'Moby Grape' (TB)	GKev
	'Mon Prince' (BB)	CIri
	'Monsieur-Monsieur' (TB)	ESgI
	Monspur Group	WCot
	'Moon Journey' (TB)	EWoo
	'Moon Silk' (Sib)	ECtt ELon EPri GBuc LLHF SCob WCot WFar
	'Moonlight Waves'	see *I. ensata* 'Moonlight Waves'
	'Moonlit' (TB)	CIri
	'Moonlit Water' (TB)	WCAu
	'Morning Splendor' (TB)	EWoo
	'Morwell' (TB)	WMil
	'Morwenna' (TB) ♀H7	ESgI
	'Mother Earth' (TB)	ESgI
	'Mountain Lake' (Sib)	EPfP EShb GBin LRHS SPtp SWat WFar WPtf
	'Mountain Violet' (TB)	EWoo
	'Mrs Horace Darwin' (TB)	EWoo SWat
	'Mrs Nate Rudolph' (SDB)	WCAu
	'Mrs Rowe' (Sib)	CPou EIri EPri GBuc LLWP MRav MWat SWat WAul WFar
	'Mrs Tait' (Spuria)	NChi
	'Mrs Valerie West' (TB)	WMil
	'Mrs Wright's Pink'	WCAu
	'Muggles' (SDB)	CHur CTal SIri
	'Mukaddam' (TB)	CIri
	'Murder Mystery' (TB)	WCAu
	'Murmuring Morn' (TB)	WCAu
	'Music' (SDB)	SIri
	'Must Unite' (TB)	WCAu
	'My First Kiss' (Sib)	WAul
	'My Kayla' (SDB)	ESgI
	'My Love' (Sib)	IMou WAul
	'My Seedling' (MDB)	CBro
	'Myra' (SDB)	XSen
	'Mysterieux' (TB)	SIri
	'Mystic' (TB)	WMil
	'Mystic Beauty' (Dut)	GKev SDeJ
	'Mystic Dragon' (TB)	CIri SDys
	'Nada'	WCot
	'Naivasha' (TB)	CKel
	'Nancy Hardy' (MDB)	CBro
	'Naples' (TB)	WCAu
	'Nassak' (TB)	EWoo
	'Natascha' (Reticulata)	ECho EPot GKev LAma SCob SDeJ
	'Natchez Trace' (TB)	CKel EPri LRHS WCot XSen
	'Navajo Code' (TB)	CIri
	'Navajo Jewel' (TB)	ESgI EWoo WCAu XSen
	'Navy Brass' (Sib)	EPri WAul
	'Needlecraft' (TB)	XSen
	'Needlepoint' (TB)	ESgI
	'Negro Modelo' (SDB)	WCAu
	'Neige de Mai' (TB)	ESgI
*	'Nel Jupe' (TB)	LRHS NLar NRHS
	nepalensis	see *I. decora*
	nertschinskia	see *I. sanguinea*
	'Neutron Dance' (TB)	WCAu
	'New Argument' (J)	LLHF
	'New Centurion' (TB)	EWoo XSen
	'New Face' (TB)	WCAu
	'New Flame' (TB)	ESgI
	'New Idea' (MTB)	CBro ESgI WCAu
	'New Leaf' (TB)	WCAu
	'New Perspective' (TB)	CIri
	'New Snow' (TB)	WCAu
	'Next in Line'	EWoo
	'Nibelungen' (TB)	CBro CJun CRos ESgI LRHS NRHS WCAu XSen
	'Night Breeze' (Sib)	EPri
	'Night Edition' (TB)	ESgI EWoo XSen
	'Night Game' (TB)	EWoo XSen

	'Night Owl' (TB)	CKel ELan ELon ESgI GMcL MHer SPoG
	'Night Ruler' (TB)	EWoo WCAu
	'Nights of Gladness' (TB)	ESgI
	nigricans	GKev
	'Nine Lives' (SDB)	WCAu
	'No Down Payment' (TB)	WCAu
	'Noble Lady' (TB)	CIri
	'Noctambule' (TB)	EWoo
	'Noon Siesta' (TB)	ESgI
	'Nordica' (TB)	ESgI
§	× ***norrisii***	EBee
	- 'Butterfly Magic'	EBee
	'North Downs' (BB)	SIri
	'Northern Jewel' (IB)	SIri
	'Northumberland Piper' (TB)	SIri
	'Nottingham Lace' (Sib)	LLHF SWat
	'Nouveau Riche' (TB)	WCAu
	'Now and Forever' (La)	LLWG
	'Now This' (Spuria)	EWoo
	'Oasis Fuzzy Wuzzy' (TB)	CIri
	'Oasis Sydney' (TB)	CIri
	'Oban' (Sib)	GBuc
	'Obligato' (IB)	CKel
	'Obsidian' (TB)	WCAu
	'Ochre Doll' (SDB)	CBro CKel CTal
	ochroleuca	see *I. orientalis* Mill.
	'O'Cool' (IB)	CKel
	'October' (TB)	ESgI
	'October Storm' (IB)	CIri EWoo
	'Oh Happy Day' (La)	LLWG
	'Oh Jamaica' (TB)	WCAu XSen
	'Oh So Cool' (MTB)	ESgI
	'Oklahoma' (TB)	EWoo
	'Oklahoma Centennial' (TB)	WCAu
	'Oktoberfest' (TB)	XSen
	'Ola Kalá' (TB)	CRos GMaP GMcL LRHS MCot MGos NLar SHil SPer WAul WCAu XSen
	'Old Black Magic' (TB)	ESgI EWoo XSen
	'Old Flame' (TB)	XSen
	'Olympiad' (TB)	ESgI XSen
	'Olympic Challenge' (TB)	ESgI MRav WCAu
	'Olympic Torch' (TB)	WCAu
	'Ominous Stranger' (TB)	ESgI MMrt WCAu
	'Once Again' (TB)	EWoo XSen
	'One Desire' (TB)	XSen
	'Open Arms' (TB)	CIri
	'Open Sky' (SDB)	CTal EWoo LRHS SIri XSen
	'Opposing Forces' (TB)	WCAu
	'Orageux' (IB)	CWCL SIri
	'Orange Caper' (SDB)	CMac CPBP CTal EAEE ECtt EPfP ESgI GBuc LRHS LSou MRav WCot
	'Orange Harvest' (TB)	ESgI XSen
	'Orange Order' (TB)	WCAu
	'Orbison' (TB)	CIri
	'Orchidarium' (TB)	CKel
	orchioides misapplied	see *I. bucharica* Foster
§	***orchioides*** Carrière	CAby ECho ELan
	'Oregon Skies' (TB)	ESgI EWoo
	'Oriental Beauty' (Dut)	CAvo GKev LCro LOPS SPer
	'Oriental Beauty' (TB)	SDeJ
	orientalis Thunb.	see *I. sanguinea*
	orientalis ambig.	CAvo EWes MNrw
§	***orientalis*** Mill. ♀^{H7}	GBin GCal GKev WCot WCru XSen
	'Orinoco Flow' (BB) ♀^{H7}	ESgI WCAu
	'Orloff' (TB)	ESgI
	'Oro Antico' (TB)	CIri

	'Orville Fay' (Sib)	WBor WCot
	'Osay Canuc' (TB)	CIri
	'Osborne's Grey' (Sib)	WAul
	'Ostrogoth' (TB)	CIri
	'Ottawa' (Sib)	CPou CWat LPot LRHS MMuc SWat WFar
	'Oulo' (TB)	ESgI XSen
	'Our House' (TB)	ESgI
	'Our Marcus' (TB) **new**	SIri
	'Out of the Dark' (TB)	WCAu
	'Out Yonder' (TB)	WCAu
	'Outrage' (SDB)	CIri
	'Outset' (Sib)	ELon
	'Over Easy' (SDB)	CKel
	'Overjoyed' (TB)	WCAu XSen
	'O'What' (SDB)	ESgI
	'Owyhee Desert' (TB)	WCAu
	'Ozark Maid' (MTB)	SDys
	Pacific Coast hybrids	see *I.* Californian hybrids
	'Pacific Mist' (TB)	WCAu
	'Pacific Panorama' (TB)	XSen
	'Pagan Dance' (TB)	EWoo WCAu
	'Pagan Goddess' (TB)	EWoo
	'Pagan Pink' (TB)	XSen
	'Pagan Princess' (TB)	WCAu
I	'Pageant' (Sib)	WCot
	'Paint It Black' (TB)	EWoo XSen
	'Pale Shades' (IB)	CBro CKel
§	***pallida***	CBro CMac ESgI ESps EWoo GMaP MRav SCob SEND SRms WCAu WTor XSen
§	- 'Argentea Variegata' (TB/v)	Widely available
	- 'Aurea'	see *I. pallida* 'Variegata' Hort.
	- 'Aurea Variegata'	see *I. pallida* 'Variegata' Hort.
	- subsp. ***cengialtii***	XSen
	- var. ***dalmatica***	see *I. pallida* subsp. *pallida*
§	- subsp. ***pallida***	CArn CKel EAEE ECha ELan EPfP GCal LRHS SDix SHar SPer
	- 'Variegata' misapplied	see *I. pallida* 'Argentea Variegata'
§	- 'Variegata' Hort. (v) ♀^{H7}	CBcs CBot CBro CKel CMac CWat ECha ELan EPfP ESgI ESps LRHS MAsh MRav MWat SDix SPer SPlb SRot SWvt WAbe XSen
	'Palm Spring' (Reticulata)	LAma
	'Palm Springs' (IB)	EPot GKev SDeJ
	'Palomino' (TB)	WCAu
	'Pamplemousse' (IB) **new**	SIri
	'Pane e Vino' (TB)	ESgI
	'Panther' (SDB)	WCAu
	'Papillon' (Sib)	CTri ECtt ELan ELon EPri EWoo GWyn LHop LRHS MBel NBir NGdn NSti SCob SDeJ SPer SWat WAul WFar
	'Paprika Fono's' (TB)	WCAu
	'Paradise' (TB)	CKel
	paradoxa	ECho
	'Paris Lights' (TB)	XSen
	'Parisian Dawn' (TB)	WCAu
	'Parisien' (TB)	EIri
	'Parts Plus' (IB)	CIri
	'Party Dress' (TB)	CBod CKel CMac EBee ELan EPfP EShb LRHS MRav NBir NLar NWad SPer SPoG SRms SWat WGwG
	'Party's Over' (TB)	WCAu
	'Passionate Embrace' (TB)	WCAu
	'Patina' (TB)	EIri EWoo LRHS WCAu
	'Patricia Elizabeth Linnegar' (TB)	WCAu
	'Patterdale' (TB)	NBir
	'Paul Black' (TB) ♀^{H7}	WCAu

'Pauline' (Reticulata)	CAvo CBro CRos EPfP EPot ERCP GKev LAma LCro LOPS LRHS MWat NRHS SCob
'Pause' (SDB)	WCAu
'Peaceful Waters' (TB)	XSen
'Peach Eyes' (SDB)	CBro CKel CTal
'Peach Picotee' (TB)	ESgI XSen
'Peaches in Wine' (La)	LLWG
'Peachy Face' (IB)	ESgI XSen
'Pearl Queen' (Sib)	MCot
'Pearls of Autumn' (TB)	WCAu
'Pearly Dawn' (TB)	ECtt SRGP SWat
* 'Pêche Melba' (TB)	XSen
'Peebee and Jay' (MTB)	WCAu
'Peg Edwards' (Sib)	EWoo
'Pelion Hills'	LRHS
'Penny a Pinch' (TB)	CKel
'Pepita' (SDB)	EWoo
'Percheron' (Sib)	EPri ESgI EWoo
'Peresh' (AB)	CTal
'Perfect Interlude' (TB)	EIri XSen
'Perfect Vision' (Sib) ♀H7	CIri
'Performer' (MTB)	EIri
'Perky' (MDB)	CPBP
'Perry's Blue' (Sib)	CAby CBWd CBcs CMac CSBt EBee EPfP EPri ESps GKin GMaP GMcL IKil LCro LRHS MBel MGos MRav MSpe NBir NGdn NPer SPer SRms SWat WFar WWtn
I 'Perry's Favourite' (Sib)	WAul
'Perry's Pigmy' (Sib)	ELon
'Persan' (TB)	EWoo
'Persian Berry' (TB)	WCAu XSen
'Persimmon' misapplied	see *I.* 'Tycoon'
'Persimmon' ambig. (Sib)	CAby CHid CKel CRos ECtt GCra GKin LRHS NRHS SHil SPtp SWat WFar WMoo WPtf
'Petal Pushers' (TB)	CIri
'Peter Hewitt' (Sib) ♀H7	EPri WAul
'Pétillant' (TB)	EWoo
'Petit Tigre' (IB)	EWoo SIri
'Petite Monet' (MTB)	ESgI
'Petite Polka' (SDB)	NLar
'Pharaoh's Daughter' (IB)	EWoo
'Picadee'	CTal EPfP
'Picasso Moon' (TB)	WCAu
'Pigeon' (SDB)	XSen
'Pinewood Amethyst' (CH)	MAvo
'Pinewood Charmer' (CH)	CElw
'Pinewood Sunshine' (CH)	MAvo
'Pink Attraction' (TB)	ESgI XSen
'Pink Bubbles' (BB)	XSen
'Pink Charm' (TB)	CKel EPfP LRHS SDeJ SPlb SPoG
'Pink Confetti' (TB)	EWoo XSen
'Pink Haze' (Sib)	CDor EBee EPfP ESgI
'Pink Horizon' (TB)	XSen
'Pink Kitten' (IB)	WCAu WGwG XSen
'Pink Lavender' (TB)	ELon
'Pink Parfait' (Sib) **new**	MHol WTor
'Pink Pele' (IB)	ESgI
'Pink Pinafore' (TB)	EWoo
'Pink Quartz' (TB)	ESgI
'Pink Reprise' (BB)	EWoo
'Pink Swan' (TB)	XSen
'Pink Taffeta' (TB)	EWoo XSen
'Pinnacle' (TB)	CKel EWoo GCal
'Pioneer' (TB)	WMil
'Pipes of Pan' (TB)	ESgI MRav WCAu
'Pirate Prince' (Sib)	NPer
'Pirate's Quest' (TB)	ESgI EWoo XSen

'Piroska' (TB)	ESgI XSen
* 'Piu Blue' (TB)	ESgI
'Pixie' (DB)	GKev NRHS
'Pixie' (Reticulata) ♀H7	ECho ELan EPot ERCP LAma LRHS SDeJ XEll
planifolia	ECho
'Play With Fire' (TB)	EWoo
'Pleasures of May' (Sib)	EBee ELon LCro
'Pledge Allegiance' (TB)	ESgI EWoo WCAu
'Plickadee' (SDB)	CBro
'Plissée' (Sib) ♀H7	GBin
'Plum Lucky' (SDB)	SIri
'Plum Wine' (SDB)	CKel
'Poem of Ecstasy' (TB)	WCAu
'Pogo' (SDB)	CMac CTal ECho ECtt ELan ELon EPfP EShb GBuc GMaP LRHS LSou MRav NBir SDeJ SRms
'Polvere di Stelle' (TB)	ESgI
'Popsicle' (SDB)	WCAu
'Port of Call' (Spuria)	EWoo
'Pounsley Purple' (Sib)	CPou EPri
'Powder Blue Cadillac' (TB)	WCAu
'Power Point' (TB)	CIri WCAu
'Prairie Sunset' (TB)	EWoo
'Prairie Thunder' (AB)	WCAu
'Presby's Crown Jewel' (TB)	WCAu
'Presence' (TB)	SIri
'Pretender' (TB)	WCAu
Pretty in Blue Mixed (Dut) **new**	GKev
'Pretty Please' (TB)	ESgI
'Primrose Cream' (Sib)	WCot
'Primrose Drift' (TB)	ESgI
'Prince Indigo' (TB)	MRav
'Prince of Burgundy' (IB)	WCAu
'Princess Beatrice' (TB)	WCAu
'Princess Bride' (BB) ♀H7	WCAu
'Princess Caroline de Monaco' (TB) **new**	WViv
'Princess Diana' (SDB)	SIri
'Princess Osra' (TB)	WMil
'Princesse Caroline de Monaco' (TB)	ESgI EWoo
prismatica	GKev
'Private Eye' (TB)	WCAu
'Professor Blaauw' (Dut) ♀H5	CAvo
'Props' (SDB)	CIri
'Prosper Laugier' (IB)	SEND WCAu
'Prospero' (TB)	EWoo
'Protocol' (IB)	CKel
'Proud Tradition' (TB)	ESgI SIri WCAu XSen
'Provençal' (TB)	CKel CPar CWCL ELon ESgI EWoo WCAu XSen
'Prussian Blue' (Sib) ♀H7	GBin SMHy
pseudacorus	Widely available
- B&SWJ 5018 from Japan	WCru
- 'Alba'	MRav MSKA NGdn SWat
- var. ***bastardii***	CBen CRoa CWat ECha ELon EPfP EWay LLWG MSKA NPer SLon SPer SWat WBrk WFar WMoo WPnP WWtn XLum
- 'Clotted Cream' **new**	GLog
- 'Come in Spinner'	LLWG
- cream-flowered	NBir SWat
- 'Crème de la Crème'	ELon EWoo LLWG NLar NSti NWad WFar
- 'Dragonfly Dance'	LLWG
- 'Flore Pleno' (d)	CBen ECho GCra LLWG MSKA NLar NPer WBrk WCot WFar WPnP WWtn

	– giant **new**	CRoa
I	– 'Golden Fleece'	SPer
	– 'Golden Queen'	CRoa EWay LLWG
	– 'Ivory'	LLWG
	– 'Kelis Choice'	LLWG
	– 'Krill'	EBee LLWG
	– 'Mandchurica'	XBlo
	– 'Mini Mart'	LLWG
	– 'Rowden Brimstone' **new**	CRoa
	– 'Roy Davidson' 🏆H7	CBro GCal MWts NLar WCot WFar WWtn
	– 'Spartacus'	EBee
	– 'Sulphur Queen'	GBin NLar WCot
	– 'Sun Cascade'	GBin
	– 'Tiger Brother'	CBro LLWG WBrk
	– 'Turnipseed'	WCot
	– 'Variegata' (v) 🏆H7	Widely available
	'Puddy Tat' (SDB)	WCAu
	'Pulse Rate' (SDB)	CBro
	pumila	CRos ITim LRHS MCot NRHS
	– f. ***atroviolacea***	CKel GEdr WAbe
*	– 'Gelber Mantel'	NBir WFar
	– 'Violacea' (DB)	SRms
	– yellow-flowered	WAbe
	'Pumpin' Iron' (SDB) 🏆H7	CKel CTal ESgI
	'Punk' (MDB)	CIri
	'Pure As Gold' (TB)	CWCL ESgI EWoo WCot XSen
	'Purple Gem' (Reticulata)	CAby CRos ECho EPfP LAma LRHS NRHS
	'Purple Hill' (Reticulata)	LAma
	Purple Lavender Mixed (Dut) **new**	GKev
	'Purple Mere' (Sib)	MHCG
	'Purple Pepper' (TB)	WCAu
	'Purple Ritz' (TB)	WCAu
	'Purple Sensation' (Dut)	ECho SDeJ
	'Purple Study' (MTB)	WCAu
	'Purr for Mints' (TB)	CIri
	'Pussycat Pink' (SDB)	ESgI WCAu
	'Quaker Lady' (TB)	ESgI EWoo SBee SIri WCAu
	'Quantum Leap' (TB)	CIri
	'Quark' (SDB)	CBro CKel
	'Quechee' (TB)	CKel CWld EAEE EAJP EBee EPPr EPfP ESgI EWoo GMaP LBuc LRHS MCot MRav MWat NLar NWad SCob SDeJ SPer SWat WGwG
	'Queen in Calico' (TB)	ESgI WCAu
	'Queen of Angels' (TB)	WCAu
	'Queen of Hearts' (TB)	XSen
	'Queen of May' (TB)	EWoo
	'Queen's Circle' (TB) 🏆H7	WCAu
	'Queen's Prize' (SDB)	SIri
	'Rabbit's Foot' (SDB)	SIri
	'Radiant Apogee' (TB)	EIri
	'Radiant Burst' (IB)	SIri
	'Rain Dance' (SDB) 🏆H7	ESgI
	'Rainbow Candy' (TB)	WCAu
	'Rainbow Etude' (TB)	WCAu
	Rainbow Grand Mixture	SDeJ
	'Rainbow High' (TB)	WCAu
	'Rainbow Rim' (SDB)	ESgI WCAu
	'Rainbow Selection' (TB)	CIri WCAu
	'Rainbow Sky' (TB)	WCAu
	'Rainbow Tour' (TB)	WCAu
	'Rajah' (TB)	CBod CKel CRos ELan ELon EPfP EWoo GMaP LRHS LSRN MRav NRHS SDeJ SPer SPoG WBor
	'Rameses' (TB)	ESgI EWoo WCAu
	'Rancho Rose' (TB)	XSen
	'Rapture in Blue' (TB)	EWoo
	'Rare Edition' (IB)	CKel EWoo MArt NBir XSen
	'Rare Quality' (TB)	XSen
	'Rare Treat' (TB)	XSen
	'Rarer than Rubies' (TB)	WCAu
	'Raspberry Acres' (IB)	MRav WCAu
	'Raspberry Blush' (IB) 🏆H7	CBod CKel CPar EIri EPfP GBin LRHS LSou MRav SWat WAul WGwG WHoo WTor WWFP XSen
	'Raspberry Tiger' (SDB)	WCAu
	'Razoo' (SDB)	CKel CPBP
	'Re La Blanche' (TB)	SIri
	'Reach for the Sky' (TB)	CIri
	'Real Coquette' (SDB)	EWoo SIri
	'Rebecca Perret' (TB)	WCAu
	'Recurring Delight' (TB)	WCAu
	'Red Canyon Glow' (TB)	CIri
	'Red Dazzler' (La)	CIri
	'Red Echo' (La)	CIri
	'Red Ember' (Dut)	ERCP GKev LCro LOPS WRHF
	'Red Flare' (TB)	WFar
	'Red Flash' (TB)	ESgI
	'Red Hawk' (TB)	EWoo
	'Red Heart' (SDB)	ELon ESgI MRav XSen
	'Red Masterpiece' (TB)	EWoo
	'Red Orchid' (IB)	ELan ESgI EWoo LHop LRHS SRms WBod WCAu
	'Red Revival' (TB)	MRav WCAu
	'Red Rum' (TB)	EWes
	'Red Zinger' (IB)	ESgI EWoo LRHS
	'Redelta' (TB)	XSen
	'Redondo' (IB)	EWoo
	'Reflets Safran' (TB)	SIri XSen
	'Regal Surprise' (SpH) 🏆H7	CRoa EWay LLWG
	'Regality' (Sib)	EBee MHer MMuc
	'Regards' (SDB)	CBro XSen
	'Regency Belle' (Sib) 🏆H7	EWoo
	'Regency Buck' (Sib)	EWoo
§	***reichenbachii***	GKev LLHF WAbe
	'Reincarnation' (TB)	CIri EWoo
	'Remembering Vic' (Spuria)	EWoo
	'Renewal' (TB)	EWoo
	'Renown' (TB)	EWoo
	'Repartee' (TB)	XSen
	'Replicator' (SDB)	EWoo
	reticulata	ECho ELan EPfP GKev SDeJ SEND SPer
	– var. ***bakeriana***	ECho GKev LAma LLHF XEll
	– 'Carolina'	CRos GKev LAma LLHF LRHS NRHS
	– 'Fabiola'	CRos EPot ERCP GKev LAma LLHF LRHS NRHS
*	– 'Violet Queen'	ECho
	'Return to Elegance' (TB)	WCAu
	'Réussite' (TB)	EWoo
	'Rhages' (TB)	EWoo
	'Rhapsody' (Reticulata)	ECho EPot ERCP GKev LAma LLHF LRHS NNys NRHS SDeJ
	'Rheinfels' (TB)	EWoo
	'Rheingauperle' (TB)	ESgI EWoo
	'Rhett' (La)	EBee
	'Rhythm' (TB)	CIri
	'Rigamarole' (Sib)	MWts SCob WFar
	'Rikugi-sakura' (Sib)	EBee ELon EPri LLHF NLar WCot
	'Ringo' (TB)	EWoo LSRN MRav WCAu
	'Rings of Saturn' (TB)	CIri
	'Rio Rojo' (TB)	EWoo WCAu
	'Rip City' (TB)	ESgI EWoo SBee
	'Rising Moon' (TB)	EWoo SIri
	'Ritz' (SDB)	EAJP GEdr
	'Rive Gauche' (TB)	ESgI
	'River Avon' (TB)	WCAu

	'Riverbuds' (SDB)	SIri WCAu
	'Riverdance' (Sib)	EWoo
	'Roanoke's Choice' (Sib)	CBro CElw ELon EWes NCGa WFar
	'Roaring Jelly' (Sib)	EPri EWes NLar WCot
	'Rob Cornell' (TB)	ESgI
§	× ***robusta*** 'Dark Aura' ♀H7	MAvo WCot
§	- 'Gerald Darby'	CBod CSpe CWat EBee ELan EPPr EPfP EWTr GBuc LEdu LRHS MCot MHer MHol MNrw NCGa NGdn NLar NSti SCob SDix SWat WBrk WCAu WMoo WPnP WWtn
	- 'Mountain Brook'	CRoa LLWG
*	- 'Purple Fan'	LLWG
	'Rochester Castle' (Kent Castles Series) (IB)	SIri
§	'Rocket' (TB)	EPfP GMaP LBuc LRHS MCot MRav NBir SDeJ SPer
	'Rocket Master' (TB)	ESgI
	'Rocket Randy' (TB)	CIri
	'Rodeo Arena' (TB) **new**	CIri
	'Roku Oji' (Sib)	CIri
	'Roman Carnival' (TB)	EWoo
	'Romance' (TB)	EWoo
	'Romano' (Dut)	GKev
	'Romantic Evening' (TB)	EIri EWoo WCAu XSen
	'Romney Marsh' (IB)	SIri
	'Romola' (TB)	WMil
	'Rosace' (Sib)	EWoo
	'Rosalie Figge' (TB)	ESgI EWoo WCAu WCot
	'Rosé' (TB)	LSRN
	'Rose Queen'	see *I. ensata* 'Rose Queen'
	'Rose Unique' (IB)	EWoo
	'Rose Violet' (TB)	WCAu
	'Rosebud Melody' (Sib) **new**	GBin
	'Rose-Marie' (TB)	EWoo
	'Rosemohr' (TB)	EWoo
	rosenbachiana	ECho
*	- 'Harangon'	ECho
	'Roseplic' (TB)	LRHS
	'Rosette Wine' (TB)	ESgI
	'Rosselline' (Sib)	WAul
	'Rosy Veil' (TB)	EAJP ESgI EWoo
	'Rosy Wings' (TB)	ECho ESgI EWoo
	'Roucoulade' (TB)	SIri
	'Rouge Gorge' (TB)	SIri WViv
	'Rowden Aurelius' (Sib)	WAul
I	'Royal Blue' (Sib)	EBee ECha SWat
	'Royal Crusader' (TB)	CCse EWoo WCAu XSen
	'Royal Elegance' (TB)	SIri
	'Royal Intrigue' (TB)	SIri
	'Royal Satin' (TB)	CHid
	'Royal Summer' (TB)	EWoo
	'Royal Tapestry' (TB)	MAvo
	'Roy's Repeater'	EBee
	'Rubacuori' (TB)	ESgI EWoo
	'Rubistar' (TB)	EWoo
	'Ruby Chimes' (IB)	ESgI WCAu
	'Ruby Contrast' (TB)	WCAu
	'Ruby Eruption' (SDB)	CTal EIri WCAu
	'Ruby Morn' (TB)	WCAu
	'Ruby Wine' (Sib)	EPri LEdu
	rudskyi	see *I. variegata*
	'Ruffled Velvet' (Sib) ♀H7	Widely available
	'Ruffles Plus' (Sib)	EPri
	'Russet Crown' (TB)	CKel
	'Rustic Cedar' (TB)	ESgI
	'Rustle of Spring' (TB)	WCAu
	'Rustler' (TB)	WCAu
	'Rusty Beauty' (Dut)	SDeJ
	'Rusty Magnificence' (TB)	EWoo

	'Ruth Margaret' (TB)	CKel
	'Ruth Rowlands' (TB)	ESgI EWoo
	ruthenica	ECho WCot
	- var. ***nana***	GEdr GKev
	'Sable' (TB)	CKel ELan EPfP ESgI EWoo GMaP LRHS MCot MRav MWat NLar SCob SDeJ SEND SPer WAul WCAu WGwG
	'Sable Night' (TB)	CKel ESgI
	'Safari Sunset' (TB)	WCAu
	'Sailor' (IB)	WCAu
	'Sailor's Dream' (MTB)	WCAu
	'Saint Crispin' (TB)	EBee EPfP EWoo GCra GMaP LRHS MRav SPer SPoG WGwG
	'Salamander Crossing' (Sib) ♀H7	WAul
	'Sally Jane' (TB)	WCAu
	'Salmon Sunset' (Spuria)	EWoo
	'Salonique' (TB)	ESgI EWoo MMrt NLar WCAu
	'Saltwood' (SDB)	CBro ESgI
	'Saltwood Castle' (Kent Castles Series) (IB)	SIri
	'Salzburg Echo' (TB)	WCAu
	'Sam Carne' (TB)	WCAu
	'Samarcande' (TB)	ESgI
	× ***sambucina***	XSen
	'San Diego' (TB)	ESgI
	'San Francisco' (TB)	ESgI EWoo
	'San Gabriel' (TB)	EWoo
	'Sandling Sunset' (TB)	SIri
	'Sandy Caper' (IB)	WCAu
	'Sangreal' (IB)	CRos LRHS NRHS
§	***sanguinea*** ♀H7	CMCN
§	- 'Snow Queen'	CAvo CBcs EBee EHoe ELan EPfP EPri EWoo GBin GWyn IBoy IKil IMou LPot LRHS MMuc NLar NNys NQui NSti SCob SPer SWat WAul WCot WFar WHar WMoo
	'Sapphire Beauty' (Dut)	GKev SDeJ
	'Sapphire Gem' (SDB)	CHur CKel ESgI EWoo LSRN WCAu
	'Sapphire Hills' (TB)	LRHS WCAu XSen
	'Sarah Taylor' (SDB) ♀H7	ECho EWoo
	sari	ECho
	'Sasha Borisovich' (TB)	ESgI
	'Savoir Faire' (Sib)	ECha
	'Scandinavian Girl'	WCAu
	'Scented Wonder' (TB)	WCAu
	'Scent Sational' (Reticulata) **new**	LAma
	schachtii purple-flowered	WAbe
	'Scottish Warrior' (TB)	CIri
	'Scramble' (Sib)	GMcL NEgg WCot
	'Scribe' (MDB)	CBro NBir
	'Sea Fret' (SDB)	CBro
	'Sea of Joy' (TB)	XSen
	'Sea Shadows' (Sib)	EPri ESgI NBir
	'Sea Wisp' (La)	SKHP
	'Seafire' (SDB)	WCAu
	'Seakist' (TB)	WCAu
	'Season Ticket' (IB)	XSen
	'Seastone' (SDB)	WCAu
	'Second Look' (TB)	XSen
	'Second Wind' (TB)	EWoo WCAu
	'Secret Melody' (TB)	XSen
	'Secret Service' (TB)	EWoo
	'Self Evident' (MDB)	LLHF
	'Semola' (SDB)	ESgI
	'Senlac' (TB)	EWoo NLar WMil
	'Señor Frog' (SDB)	ESgI
	serbica	see *I. reichenbachii*

	'Serene Moment' (TB)	SIri
	'Serenity Prayer' (SDB)	WCAu
	setosa ♀H7	CBro CMac CPne CRos CTri CWCL EAJP ECho GBin GCra GKev LRHS MNrw NCGa NHpl NRHS WOld
	- ***alba***	NLar
	- var. ***arctica***	GBuc GKev LEdu
I	- 'Baby Blue'	CRos EPfP LRHS MBNS MJak NRHS
	- subsp. ***canadensis***	see *I. hookeri*
	- dark violet-flowered	EPri
	- var. ***nana***	see *I. hookeri*
	'Seven Hills' (TB)	ESgI
	'Shaker's Prayer' (Sib) ♀H7	EWes GBin MBrN SBch
	'Shakespeare's Sonnet' (SDB)	ESgI
	'Shall We Dance' (Sib) ♀H7	CIri EWes
	'Shampoo' (IB)	SIri WCAu
	'Share the Spirit' (TB)	WCAu
	'Sharp Dressed Man' (TB)	WCAu
	'Shawano' (TB)	EWoo
	'Sheila Ann Germaney' (Reticulata)	CBro CRos ECho EPot ERCP GKev LAma LLHF LRHS NNys NRHS NWad WBrk
	'Shelby Lynne' (TB)	CIri
	'Shelford Giant' (Spuria) ♀H7	NEgg
	'Sherbet Lemon' (IB) ♀H7	WCAu
	'Shifnal'	WCAu
	'Shirley Chandler' (IB) ♀H7	SIri
	'Shirley Pope' (Sib) ♀H7	EWes GBin GBuc LRHS NSti SMHy WFar WMoo
	'Shirley's Choice' (Sib)	EBee EPri SIri
	'Short Distance' (IB)	EWoo SIri
	'Showdown' (Sib)	ECtt GMaP LRHS SWat
	'Shrawley' (Sib)	EWoo WAul
	shrevei	see *I. virginica* var. *shrevei*
	'Shurton Brook' (TB)	CKel
	'Shurton Demon' (TB)	CKel
	'Shurton Inn' (TB)	CKel WCAu
	'Shurton Princess' (TB)	CKel
	sibirica	CAvo CMHG CTsd ESps GAbr GBin GKev LLWP MArt MCot MMuc NChi SCob SPlb SRot WBrk WCFE WFar WGwG WHer WMoo WShi
	- PAB 6119	LEdu
	- 'Niklas Sea'	see *I.* 'Lake Niklas'
	- 'Redflare'	see *I.* 'Melton Red Flare'
	- 'Snow Queen'	see *I. sanguinea* 'Snow Queen'
	'Sibirica Alba'	ECha EPfP EPri LLWP SWat WBrk WFar
	sichuanensis	SPlb
	'Side Effect'	WCAu
	'Sidney Linnegar' (TB)	WCAu
	'Sidney Unknown'	WCAu
	sieboldii	see *I. sanguinea*
	'Sierra Blue' (TB)	ESgI EWoo
	'Sierra Grande' (TB)	SIri XSen
	'Sierra Nevada' (Spuria)	XSen
	'Sign of Leo' (TB)	CKel EWoo XSen
	'Silkirim' (TB)	CKel
	'Silver Edge' (Sib) ♀H7	Widely available
	'Silver Shower' (TB)	EWoo
	'Silverado' (TB)	CKel ESgI EWoo GBin LRHS WCAu
	'Silvery Beauty' (Dut)	ELan GKev LCro LOPS NBir SDeJ
	sindjarensis	see *I. aucheri*
	'Sinfonietta' (La)	LLWG WCot
	'Sing to Me' (TB)	WCAu
	'Sinister Desire' (IB)	EWoo SIri
	sintenisii ♀H5	CBro CPBP ECho GKev LLHF MArt SBrt WAbe XSen

	'Sir Michael' (TB)	ESgI EWoo
	'Siva Siva' (TB)	MRav
	'Sixteen Candles' (IB)	EWoo
	'Sixtine C' (TB)	SIri
	'Skating Party' (TB)	CKel ESgI XSen
	'Sky Beauty' (Dut)	GKev SDeJ
	'Sky Hooks' (TB)	XSen
	'Sky Tracery' (MTB)	SDys
	'Sky Wings' (Sib)	CSam ECha EWoo GQue MArl WMoo
	'Skydancer' (SDB)	WCAu
	'Skyfire' (TB)	ESgI
	'Skylark's Song' (TB)	EIri EWoo
	'Small Sky' (SDB)	CBro
	'Smart' (SDB)	WCAu
	'Smart Aleck' (TB)	ESgI EWoo
	'Smart Girl' (TB)	EIri
	'Smart Move' (TB)	ESgI
	'Smiling Faces' (TB)	WCAu
	'Smith Named Keith' (TB)	CIri
	'Smitten Kitten' (IB)	LSRN WCAu
	'Smokey Salmon' (TB)	CKel
	'Smooth' (SDB)	SDys
	'Snow Fiddler' (MTB)	EWoo
	'Snow Plum' (IB)	SIri
	'Snow Prince' (Sib)	EPri
	'Snow Season' (SDB)	ESgI
	'Snow Shoes' (TB)	CIri
	'Snow Tracery' (TB)	CBod EBee LRHS
	'Snow Troll' (SDB)	WCAu
	'Snowcone' (IB)	EWoo
	'Snowcrest' (Sib)	CBre GBin LRHS MRav MSpe WAul WHoo
	'Snowmound' (TB)	CBod CCCN CKel ESgI EWoo GMcL WCAu
	'Snowy Owl' (TB)	CKel WCAu
	'Snugglebug' (SDB)	CPBP CTal EWoo WCAu
	'Social Event' (TB)	ESgI XSen
	'Soft Blue' (Sib) ♀H7	EPri WAul
	'Soft Rain' (TB)	CIri
	'Soft Return' (TB)	EWoo
	'Solar Fire' (TB)	CIri
	'Solar Fusion' (Spuria)	EWoo
	'Solid Mahogany' (TB)	MRav
	'Soligo' (MDB)	ESgI
	'Solo Flight' (TB)	SDys
	'Somerset Blue' (TB)	CKel
	'Somerset Cider' (TB)	SIri
	'Somerton Dance' (SDB)	CKel
	'Song of Norway' (TB)	EIri EWoo XSen
	'Sonoran Sands' (IB)	SDys
	'Sopra il Vulcano' (BB)	ESgI EWoo
	'Sorbonne' (TB)	WCAu
	'Sordid Lives' (TB)	WCAu
	'Sostenique' (TB)	ESgI
	'Southland' (IB)	EWoo
	'Souvenir de Madame Gaudichau' (TB)	ESgI EWoo
	'Spanish Angel' (TB)	CIri
	'Sparkling Rose' (Sib)	Widely available
	'Sparkling Waters' (TB)	ESgI
	'Spartan' (TB)	EWoo
	'Speck So' (MTB)	WCAu
I	'Speckles' (Sib)	EPPr
	'Spellbreaker' (TB)	EWoo SIri
	'Spice Lord' (TB)	WCAu
	'Spiced Custard' (TB)	EIri ESgI EWoo WCAu
	'Spiced Lemon' (TB)	WCAu
	'Spiced Tiger' (TB)	ESgI
	'Spinning Wheel' (TB)	SIri

	'Spirit of Memphis' (TB)	XSen
	'Splashacata' (TB)	WCAu XSen
	'Splashdown' (Sino-Sib)	SWat
	'Splat' (IB)	CIri
	'Spot of Tea' (MDB)	LLHF
	'Spot On' (Reticulata) **new**	LAma LLHF
	'Spreckles' (TB)	CKel ESgI
	'Spree' (SDB)	WCAu
	'Spring Blush' (MTB) ♀H7	SIri
	'Spring Festival' (TB)	WCAu
	'Spring Kiss' (TB)	SIri
	'Spring Madness' (TB)	WCAu
	'Spring Time' (Reticulata)	ECho GKev LAma LOPS SDeJ
	'Springtime Madonna' (TB) **new**	EBee
	'Spun Gold' (TB)	EWoo
	spuria	CMac CPou
§	- subsp. ***halophila***	GKev
	- subsp. ***notha*** CC 725	WCot
	- subsp. ***ochroleuca***	see *I. orientalis* Mill.
	'Spy' (BB)	WCAu
	'Square Dance Skirt' (TB)	SDys
	'St Louis Blues' (TB)	ESgI XSen
	'Stairway to Heaven' (TB)	ESgI WCAu
	'Stapleford' (SDB)	CBro
	'Staplehurst' (MTB) ♀H7	SIri
	'Star Cluster' (Sib)	WFar
	'Star in the Night' (TB)	WCAu
	'Star Shine' (TB)	ESgI WCAu
	'Starcrest' (TB)	EWoo
	'Stardate' (SDB)	CKel
	'Starheart' (IB)	WCAu
	'Starlette Rose' (TB)	EWoo
	'Starring' (TB)	EWoo
	'Starship' (TB)	XSen
	'Starwoman' (IB) ♀H7	SDys
	'Staten Island' (TB)	ESgI SRms WCAu
	'Stella Polaris' (TB)	ELon
	'Stellar Lights' (TB)	EIri EWoo WCAu
	'Stephen Wilcox' (Sib)	CIri EPri WAul
	'Stepping Out' (TB) ♀H7	CKel CMac CPar EPfP ESgI GBin LRHS SCob SDeJ WCAu WTor
	'Steve' (Sib)	CPar EWes SWat
	'Steve Varner' (Sib)	EPri EWoo IMou
	'Stilo Libero'	WCAu
	'Stinger' (SDB) ♀H7	CIri
	'Stingray' (TB)	ESgI
	'Stitch in Time' (TB)	EIri EWoo WCAu
	'Stockholm' (SDB)	CKel
	stolonifera	ECho GKev
	- 'Zwanenburg Beauty'	ECho GKev
	'Stop the Music' (TB)	XSen
	'Storm Center' (TB)	EWoo
	'Stormy Circle' (SDB)	WCAu
	'Storrington' (TB)	EMal EWoo
	'Strange Brew' (TB)	WCAu
	'Strathmore' (TB)	EMal EWoo
	'Strictly Jazz' (TB)	WCAu
	'Strike it Rich' (TB)	ESgI
	'Striking' (TB)	EWoo
	'Strozzapreti' (TB)	ESgI
	'Strut' (TB)	WCAu
	'Strut your Stuff' (TB)	WCAu
	'Study In Black' (TB)	XSen
	stylosa	see *I. unguicularis*
§	***suaveolens***	CPBP CPou ECho GEdr NHpl NWad
	- var. ***flavescens***	see *I. suaveolens* yellow-flowered
§	- purple-flowered	ECho GCrg GEdr WAbe
	- var. ***violacea***	see *I. suaveolens* purple-flowered
§	- yellow-flowered	ECho GKev WAbe
	'Succès Fou' (TB)	EWoo SIri
	'Sugar' (IB)	NSti WCAu
	'Sugar Magnolia' (TB)	EWoo SIri
	'Sultan's Palace' (TB)	CKel EBee ECho ESgI EWoo LCro LPot LRHS NLar WCAu XSen
	'Summer Holidays' (TB)	XSen
	'Summer Revels' (Sib)	EPri
	'Summer Sky' (Sib)	CBre CSpe LEdu NCGa SWat WAul WCot
	'Summer's Smile' (TB)	EWoo
	'Summertime Blues' (TB)	EWoo
	'Sun Doll' (SDB) ♀H7	CTal
	'Sunblaze' (TB)	WCAu
	'Sunlit Shores' (La)	LLWG
	'Sunny Dawn' (IB)	CKel
	'Sunny Disposition' (TB)	XSen
	'Sunnyside Delight' (TB)	WCAu
	'Sunnyside Up' (TB)	ECho GKev
	'Sunset Skies' (TB)	CWCL
	'Super Model' (TB)	WCAu
	'Superba' (Sib)	WWtn
	'Superstition' (TB) ♀H7	CKel CRos EIri ELan ESgI EWes EWoo LCro LRHS MRav NRHS SCob WCAu XSen
	'Supreme Sultan' (TB)	CWCL ESgI EWoo SBee SCob WCAu XSen
I	'Surprise' (Dut) **new**	GKev
	'Susan Bliss' (TB)	CKel ELan EPfP ESgI EWoo WCAu WMil
	'Sutton Valence' (Sib)	SIri
	'Swain' (TB)	ESgI
	'Swan Ballet' (TB)	ESgI
	'Swank' (Sib)	WAul
	'Swazi Princess' (TB)	ELon ESgI
	'Sweet Kate' (SDB)	WCAu
	'Sweet Lavender' (TB)	WMil
	'Sweet Lena' (TB)	ESgI
	'Sweet Musette' (TB)	WCAu
	'Sweet Surrender' (Sib)	EPri
	'Sweeter than Wine' (TB)	EWoo MRav
	'Swingtown' (TB)	EWoo WCAu
	'Swirling Waters' (La)	LLWG
	'Swiss Majesty' (TB)	WCAu
	'Swizzle' (IB)	XSen
	'Sybil' (TB)	GBin GCra
	'Sylvan' (TB)	XSen
	'Sylvia Murray' (TB)	WCAu
	'Symphony' (Dut)	ECho NBir SDeJ
	'Symphony of Light' (TB)	CIri
	'Syncopation' (TB)	ESgI WCAu XSen
	'Syrian Hills' (TB)	WCAu
	'Tabac Blond' (TB)	EWoo
	'Tact' (IB)	SIri
	'Take Me Away' (TB)	SDys
	'Tall Chief' (TB)	WCAu
	'Tamberg' (Sib)	CKel EBee EWoo
	'Tamerlan' (TB)	EWoo
	'Tan Tingo' (IB)	XSen
	'Tanex'	ECho
	'Tangerine Sky' (TB)	EWoo
	'Tantara' (SDB)	XSen
	'Tantrum' (IB)	WCAu XSen
	'Tanz Nochmal' (Sib)	GBin
	'Tanzanian Tangerine' (TB)	WCAu
	'Tarn Hows' (TB)	ESgI SRms
	'Taubenblau' (Sib)	SAko
	'Teal Velvet' (Sib)	CKel ECha ELon EPfP EPri EWoo GLog LRHS MCot SCob WFar
	'Tealwood' (Sib)	GBin

'Teapot Tempest' (BB)	WCAu
'Teasaucer Hill' (MTB) 𝕐H7	SIri
tectorum	CCse LRHS SChr SDix WCot XLum XSen
- BWJ 8191	WCru
- 'Alba'	WThu XSen
- 'Cruella'	EPfP
- 'Variegata' misapplied	see *I. japonica* 'Variegata'
'Tell Fibs' (SDB)	CBro CTal
'Teller of Tales' (La)	LLWG
'Temper Tantrum' (Sib)	LRHS WHar
'Temple Gold' (TB)	CKel NPer
'Temple Meads' (IB)	ESgI WCAu
'Templecloud' (IB) 𝕐H7	CKel
'Tempting Fate' (TB)	SIri WCAu
§ ***tenax***	EBee ECho GBuc LRHS
'Tenebrae' (TB)	WMil
'Tennison Ridge' (TB)	WCAu
'Teverlae' (Sib)	EBee LRHS
'Thaïs' (TB)	ESgI
'The Black Douglas' (TB)	EWoo
'The Citadel' (TB)	ELon
'The Red Douglas' (TB)	ESgI
'The Rocket'	see *I.* 'Rocket'
'Thelma Perry' (Sib)	EPfP
'Theodolinda' (TB)	EWoo
'Theseus' (AB)	GKev
'Third Charm' (SDB)	CBro
'Third World' (SDB)	CBro
'This and That' (IB)	WCAu
'Thornbird' (TB) 𝕐H7	CIri EIri ESgI EWoo WCAu
'Three Cherries' (MDB)	CPBP ECho SIri
'Three Oaks' (TB) **new**	SBee
'Three Quarters' (Sib)	ELon NChi
'Thriller' (TB)	ESgI EWoo WCAu XSen
thunbergii	see *I. sanguinea*
'Thunder Echo' (TB)	SIri
'Thundering Ovation' (TB)	WCAu
'Tickety Boo' (SDB)	CIri
'Tickle the Ivories' (IB)	CIri
Tiger Mixed (Dut) **new**	GKev
§ 'Tigereye' (Dut)	ERCP GBin GKev LCro SDeJ
'Time to Shine' (SDB)	WCAu
'Time Traveler' (TB)	CIri
'Time Zone' (TB)	WCAu
'Tinkerbell' (SDB)	CBod CPBP CTal EBee EPfP GMaP LRHS NBir SDeJ WTor
'Tishomingo'	EWoo
'Titan's Glory' (TB) 𝕐H7	CKel ESgI EWoo LEdu MRav WCot WHoo
'To the Point' (TB)	CIri
'Tollong'	IKil ILea IMou
'Tom Johnson' (TB) 𝕐H7	EWoo
'Tom Tit' (TB)	WCAu WMil
'Toni Lynn' (MDB)	ECho
'Toots' (SDB)	ECho
'Top Flight' (TB)	CKel ELan LRHS SPer SRms
'Top Gun' (TB)	ESgI
'Topaz Jewel' (TB)	MHol
'Topolino' (TB)	CKel
'Torero' (TB)	EWoo SIri
'Toro Blanco' (IB)	CIri
'Total Eclipse' (TB)	SRms
'Total Recall' (TB)	WCAu
'Totally Cool' (SDB)	LSRN SIri
'Touch of Mahogany' (TB)	WCAu
'Town Flirt' (TB)	WCAu
'Toy Clown' (SDB)	EWoo
'Trails West' (TB)	EWoo
'Trajectory' (SDB)	WCAu
'Trapel' (TB)	ESgI
'Trencavel' (TB)	ESgI
'Trenwith' (TB)	ESgI
'Triffid' (TB)	CIri
'Trillion' (TB)	CIri
'Trim the Velvet' (Sib)	WAul
'Triple Whammy' (TB)	ESgI XSen
'Tripod' (IB)	CIri
'Tristan'	CKel
'Tristram' (TB)	WMil
'Tropic Night' (Sib)	Widely available
'Tropical Delight' (TB)	CIri
'True Charm' (TB)	EWoo
tuberosa	CAby CArn CAvo CBro CHid CTri CWCL ECGP ECha ECho ERCP LAma MHer MPie SDeJ WCot WShi
- BS 348	WCot
- MS 76	WCot
- MS 729	WCot
- MS 731	WCot
- MS 821	WCot
- MS 964	WCot
- PB	WCot
'Tulip Festival' (TB)	CRos LRHS NRHS
'Tumultueux' (TB)	EWoo
'Tut's Gold' (TB)	ESgI WCAu
'Tuxedo' (TB)	XSen
'Twist of Twilight' (La)	LLWG
'Two Sided Coin' (TB)	WCAu
§ 'Tycoon' (Sib)	EShb EWoo GBin GQue LRHS NChi SPer
'Tyland Blue' (TB)	SIri
'Tyrian Dream' (IB)	WCAu
'UFO' (TB)	CIri
'Ultimate' (SDB)	CIri WCAu
'Uncle Charlie' (TB)	WCAu
'Undercurrent' (TB)	WCAu
'Unfinished Business' (TB)	CIri WCAu
§ ***unguicularis***	CAvo CBcs CBro CSBt CTri ECho EIri ELan EPfP EWoo GKev LLHF LLWP LRHS MMuc MNrw MRav NLar SCob SDeJ SPer SPoG SRms WCFE WCot WHil WHoo XSen
- from Karpathos, Greece **new**	GKev
- 'Abington Purple'	CJun EIri
- 'Alba'	CAvo EWoo XSen
§ - subsp. ***cretensis***	ECho GKev SKHP
- 'Diana Clare'	CJun
- 'Kilbroney Marble'	EPri
- 'Marondera'	CAvo CJun
- 'Mary Barnard' 𝕐H5	CAvo CBro CJun CPou EBee ECGP ECho EWoo LRHS MHer NBir WHoo
- 'Oxford Dwarf'	ECho
- 'Stavendale Tiger'	MAvo
§ - 'Walter Butt'	CAvo CJun CMea EBee ECGP EWoo NBir XEll
'Unicorn' (TB)	CIri
'Vague à l'Ame' (TB)	ESgI EWoo
'Val de Loire'	EWoo
'Valda' (Sib)	EBee ELon
'Valerie Joyce'	WCAu
'Vamp' (IB)	CKel EWoo GBin XSen
'Vanilla Mist' (La)	LLWG
'Vanilla Skies' (TB)	WCAu
'Vanity' (TB)	XSen
'Vanity's Child' (TB)	WCAu XSen
§ ***variegata*** 𝕐H7	GBin GKev XSen
- from Podyjí, Moravia **new**	SBrt

	'Vegas Heat' (BB)	CIri
	'Velvet Dusk' (TB)	EWoo
	'Velvet King' (TB)	ESgI
	'Velvet Purple'	XBlo
	'Velvet Smile' (Reticulata) **new**	LAma
	'Venita Faye' (TB)	WCAu
	'Verity Blamey' (TB)	CKel
	versicolor	CArn CBen CRoa CWat GBin GKev GMaP GMcL GPoy MMuc MNHC MWts SEND SPlb SRms SWat WBrk WFar WMAq WMoo WPnP WShi WWtn
	- 'Algonquin'	LLWG
	- 'Between the Lines'	LLWG
	- 'China West Lake'	CRoa LLWG
	- 'Claret Cup'	CPou ILea
	- 'Kermesina'	CWat ECha ELan ESgI GBuc LCro LLWG MMuc MWts NPer NSti SRms SWat WFar WMAq WMoo WPnP
	- 'Mint Fresh'	LLWG
	- 'Mysterious Monique'	CCse CWat EBee LLWG
	- purple-flowered	EWay
	- 'Rosea'	CRoa EWay
	- 'Rowden Anthem' **new**	CRoa
	- 'Rowden Cadenza'	CRoa EWay LLWG
	- 'Rowden Cantata'	CRoa LLWG
	- 'Rowden Concerto'	CRoa LLWG
	- 'Rowden Jingle'	CRoa
	- 'Rowden Melody'	LLWG
	- 'Rowden Pastorale'	LLWG
	- 'Rowden Sonata'	CRoa LLWG
	- 'Tina' **new**	SAko
	'Vi Luihn' (Sib)	ECha ELon WMoo SAko
	'Vibrations' (TB)	ESgI WCAu
	vicaria	ECho
	'Victoria Falls' (TB)	ESgI EWoo MHol
	'Victorian Secret' (Sib)	EBee ELon
	'Viel Schnee' (Sib)	ELon
	'Vigilante' (TB)	EWoo
	'Vin Nouveau' (TB)	XSen
	'Vinho Verde' (IB)	CKel
	'Vino Rosso' (SDB)	ESgI
	'Violet Beauty' (Reticulata)	CRos ECho GKev LAma LRHS NRHS
	'Violet Classic' (TB)	WCAu
	'Violet Fusion' (Spuria)	EWoo
	'Violet Harmony' (TB)	ESgI
	'Violet Icing' (TB)	CKel
	'Violet Rings' (TB)	WCAu
	'Violet Turner' (TB)	MHol
	'Viper' (IB)	CIri EWoo
	virginica	LLWG
	- 'De Luxe'	see *I.* × *robusta* 'Dark Aura'
	- 'Lavender Lustre'	LLWG
	- 'Orchid Purple'	LLWG
	- 'Pale Lavender'	LLWG
	- 'Pink Perfection'	LLWG
	- 'Pond Crown Point'	CRoa
	- 'Pond Lilac Dream'	CRoa
§	- var. ***shrevei***	LLWG
	- 'Slightly Daft'	LLWG
	'Visual Intrigue' (TB)	EWoo
	'Visual Treat' (Sib)	EWoo
	'Vitafire' (TB)	CRos ESgI EWoo LRHS NRHS
	'Vitality' (IB)	ELon ESgI
	'Viva Mexico' (TB)	EWoo
	'Vizier' (TB)	WCAu
	'Voilà' (IB)	CMea ESgI
	'Volts' (SDB)	XSen
	'Volute' (TB)	ESgI
	'Voyage' (SDB)	EWoo XSen
	'Wabash' (TB)	EWoo WCAu XSen
	'Waihi Wedding' (La)	LLWG
	'Wall Street Blues' (Sib)	EWoo
	'Walmer Castle' (Kent Castles Series) (IB)	SIri
	'Walter Butt'	see *I. unguicularis* 'Walter Butt'
	'War Chief' (TB)	EPfP ESgI EWoo MRav WCAu
	'War Sails' (TB)	EWoo SIri WCAu
	warleyensis	ECho EPot GKev
	'Warlsind' (J)	GKev
	'Warrior King' (TB)	EWoo
	'Waters Of Miraba' (BB)	EWoo
	wattii	GCal IKil WGwG
	- KWJ 12172 **new**	WCru
	'Way to Go' (TB)	CIri
	'Wealden Butterfly' (Sib) ♀H7	SIri WAul
	'Wealden Carousel' (Sib)	SIri WAul
	'Wealden Mystery' (Sib)	EPri SIri WAul
	'Wealden Skies' (Sib)	SIri WAul
	'Wealden Spires' (Sib)	WAul
	'Wealden Summer' (Sib)	WAul
	'Wearing Rubies' (TB)	ESgI WCAu
	'Webelos' (SDB)	MRav
	'Wedding Vow' (TB)	EIri
*	'Wedgwood Blue' (Sino-Sib)	GBin
	'Weisse Etagen' (Sib)	ELon
	'Welch's Reward' (MTB)	ESgI
	'Welcome Discovery' (TB)	WCAu
	'Welcome Return' (Sib)	CElw GQue LRHS MMuc SWat WMoo
	'Welfenfürstin' (Sib)	GBin SAko
	'Welfenprinz' (Sib) ♀H7	WAul
	'Well Suited' (SDB)	EWoo
	'Wench' (TB)	EWoo WCAu
	'Westar' (SDB)	CKel CTal EIri
	'Westpointer' (TB)	CIri
	'Westwell' (SDB)	WCAu
	'What a Mixture' (TB)	CIri
	'What Again' (SDB)	XSen
	'What's New' (TB)	WCAu
	'Whee' (SDB)	WCAu
	'Whispering Spirits' (TB)	WCAu
	'White Caucasus' (Reticulata)	EPot GKev LAma LLHF XEll
	'White City' (TB)	CKel EPfP ESgI EWoo GMaP LRHS MCot MRav NPer SCob SDeJ SPer SRms SWat WCAu
	'White Excelsior' (Dut)	ECho
	'White Gem' (SDB)	ESgI EWoo
	'White Knight' (TB)	EBee EPfP ESgI
I	'White Queen' (Sib)	ESgI SWat
	'White Reprise' (TB)	ESgI XSen
I	'White Swan' (Sib)	EPri
	'White Swirl' (Sib)	Widely available
	'White Triangles' (Sib)	ELon EWoo
	'White Umbrella' (La)	ECtt
	'White van Vliet' (Dut)	SDeJ
	'White Wine' (MTB)	WCAu
	'White-Wave' (TB)	XBlo
	'Widow's Veil' (SDB)	ESgI
	'Wild Irish Rose' (TB)	WCAu
	'Wild Jasmine' (TB)	WCAu
	'Wild Missouri' (TB)	EBee
	'Wild Wings' (TB)	EWoo LRHS MCot SGbt WCAu
	willmottiana	ECho
	- 'Alba'	ECho
	wilsonii ♀H7	EBee GKev SBrt WGob

'Windjammer Seas' (TB)	SDys
'Winemaster' (TB)	EWoo SIri
'Winesap' (TB)	ESgI EWoo
'Winged Angel' (IB)	CIri
winogradowii 🏆[H7]	CBro CRos ECho EPot ERCP GKev LAma LLHF LRHS NRHS WAbe XEll
'Winter Olympics' (TB)	CKel ELan EPfP LRHS MRav SPer WGwG WTor
'Winter Pearl' (IB)	EWoo
'Wintry Sky' (TB)	WCAu
'Wise' (SDB)	CTal WCAu
'Wish Upon a Star' (SDB)	WCAu
'Wishful Thinking' (TB)	SIri
'Wisteria Sachet' (IB)	WCAu
'Witch's Wand' (TB)	ESgI EWoo
'Wizard's Return' (SDB)	SIri
'Wonders Never Cease' (TB)	WCAu
'Wondrous' (TB)	ESgI
'Word of Warning' (La)	LLWG
'Wrangler' (IB)	EWoo SIri
'Wrights' Flights' (IB) **new**	CIri
xiphioides	see *I. latifolia*
xiphium var. ***lusitanica***	GKev
'Yankee Consul' (Sib)	EPri
'Yaquina Blue' (TB)	WCAu
'Yellow Flirt' (MTB)	WCAu
'Yeoman' (TB) **new**	WMil
'Yes' (TB)	ESgI
'Yippy Skippy' (SDB)	WCAu
'Yosemite Nights' (TB)	EWoo
'Yosemite Star' (TB)	EWoo
'Youth Dew' (TB)	EWoo
'Zakopane' (Sib)	EWes WAul
'Zantha' (TB)	XSen
'Zero' (SDB)	CHur CKel
'Zweites Hundert' (Sib)	WFar

Isatis (*Brassicaceae*)

tinctoria	CArn CBod CHab CHby ENfk GJos GPoy MHer MNHC SIde SPav SRms WJek WTre

Ismelia (*Asteraceae*)

carinata 'Sunset'	LRHS NRHS

Ismene see *Hymenocallis*

Isodon (*Lamiaceae*)

calycinus	SPlb
§ ***excisus***	EBee IMou SBrt WPGP
longitubus	SBrt
- B&SWJ 11027	WCru
rubescens	IMou WCot

Isolepis (*Cyperaceae*)

§ ***cernua***	CBen CWat EShb LHop LRHS MSKA MWts SCoo SHDw WMAq

Isoloma see *Kohleria*

Isomeris see *Cleome*

Isoplexis see *Digitalis*

Isopogon (*Proteaceae*)

anemonifolius	SPlb
anethifolius	SPlb
formosus **new**	MPkF

Isopyrum (*Ranunculaceae*)

biternatum	LEdu
dicarpon	see *Dichocarpum dicarpon*
nipponicum	WCru WPGP
stoloniferum	WCru
thalictroides	EBee EPot GEdr LEdu LLHF SDys WCot

Isotoma (*Campanulaceae*)

sp.	ESps SWvt
§ ***axillaris***	CSpe NPer SCoo SPer WHea
- 'Fairy Carpet'	CBod NCou NHpl SRms
fluviatilis	NLar

Itea (*Iteaceae*)

ilicifolia 🏆[H5]	Widely available
* - 'Rubrifolia'	CRos ELan LRHS SLon
virginica	CAbP CBcs CMCN ELon ESwi MMuc MRav SLim SLon
§ - 'Henry's Garnet' 🏆[H5]	CAbP CDul CEnd CLet CMCN CMac CRos CSBt ECrN EPfP EUJe GBin LCro LEdu LRHS MGos NLar SBod SCob SEle SHil SLim SPer SPoG SRGP SWvt WPGP
- Little Henry = 'Sprich'[PBR]	CHGN CMac CRos CSBt EBee EPfP IVic LRHS LSRN NLar SCob SMDP
- 'Long Spire'	NLar
- 'Merlot'	MBlu NLar
- 'Sarah Eve'	CMCN NLar SRGP
- 'Saturnalia'	NLar
- Swarthmore form	see *I. virginica* 'Henry's Garnet'
yunnanensis	MBlu NLar WSHC

Itoa (*Salicaceae*)

orientalis	SVen

Ixeris (*Asteraceae*)

stolonifera	XLum

Ixia (*Iridaceae*)

'Blue Bird'	ECho GKev LAma NRog SDeJ
capillaris from Citrusdal	ECho
'Castor'	ECho NRog
curta	ECho
dubia	ECho
'Gemini'	ECho
'Giant'	ECho GKev SDeJ
'Hogarth'	ECho GKev LAma NRog
'Holland Glory'	ECho NRog
'Jesse' **new**	GKev
latifolia var. ***latifolia***	ECho
lutea	ECho
'Mabel'	CWCL ECho GKev NRog WCot
maculata	ECho
'Marquette'	ECho GKev
mixed	SDeJ
paniculata	ECho
- 'Eos'	GKev
'Panorama'	ECho NRog
polystachya var. ***longistylis***	ECho
- var. ***lutea***	ECho
'Rose Emperor'	ECho GKev LAma NRog SDeJ
scillaris	CTre
'Spotlight'	ECho GKev NRog
thomasiae	WCot
trifolia	ECho
'Venus'	CTca CWCL ECho GKev LAma NRog SDeJ
versicolor	ECho

viridiflora	CPne ECho NRog
- var. ***minor***	ECho
'Vulcan'	ECho NRog
'Yellow Emperor'	CTca ECho GKev NRog SDeJ

Ixiolirion (*Ixioliriaceae*)

montanum	ECho
pallasii	see *I. tataricum*
§ ***tataricum***	EBee ECho LAma SDeJ

J

Jaborosa (*Solanaceae*)

integrifolia	EBee LEdu SBrt SVen WPGP XLum

Jacaranda (*Bignoniaceae*)

acutifolia misapplied	see *J. mimosifolia*
§ ***mimosifolia*** 🏆H1c	CBcs CCCN SPlb

Jacobinia see *Justicia*

Jamesbrittenia (*Scrophulariaceae*)

§ ***microphylla***	CPBP
stellata	SPlb

Jamesia (*Hydrangeaceae*)

americana	CBcs CJun CMCN ESwi LLHF NLar SBrt WCru WSHC

Jasione (*Campanulaceae*)

§ ***heldreichii***	NBir SRms
jankae	see *J. heldreichii*
§ ***laevis***	EPfP GAbr SRms WMoo WTcb
§ - 'Blaulicht'	EAJP ECha EPfP LRHS NEgg NLar SPlb WCot WMoo
- Blue Light	see *J. laevis* 'Blaulicht'
montana	MNHC SRms WPnn
perennis	see *J. laevis*

Jasminum ✿ (*Oleaceae*)

CW&T 6374 new	CMCN
affine	see *J. officinale* f. *affine*
angulare 🏆H2	CHll CRHN WFib
azoricum 🏆H2	CBcs CCCN CHll CRHN CTsd CWCL EPfP EShb IDee SEND SPre WFib
beesianum	Widely available
bignoniaceum	WSHC
blinii	see *J. polyanthum*
dispermum	CRHN NLar
§ ***floridum***	EWes
fruticans	CMac ELon LRHS SBrt SEND WCru XSen
- RCB UA 22	WCot
giraldii Diels	see *J. floridum*
grandiflorum misapplied	see *J. officinale* f. *affine*
grandiflorum L. 'De Grasse' 🏆H2	CRHN EShb WFib
humile	MGil SEND WKif
- var. ***glabrum***	see *J. humile* f. *wallichianum*
§ - 'Revolutum' 🏆H5	CBcs CDul CMac CRHN CRos CSBt CWCL CWib EBee ECrN ELan EPfP EShb ESps GCal GMcL LHop LRHS MGos MRav NLar SEND SGbt SLon SPer SPoG SRms SWvt WHar WSHC
§ - f. ***wallichianum***	WCru
B&SWJ 2559	
- - PAB 2534	LEdu
- - PAB 9962 new	LEdu
humile × ***parkeri*** new	SEle
§ ***mesnyi*** 🏆H3	CBcs CCCN CHll CMac CRHN CTri CWib EBak ELan EMOT EPfP EWTr LRHS SBch SEND SPer SVen WSHC
multiflorum	CCCN
multipartitum	CHll
- bushy	CSpe
§ ***nudiflorum*** 🏆H5	Widely available
- 'Argenteum'	see *J. nudiflorum* 'Mystique'
- 'Aureum'	CKel CRos ELan LRHS MAsh MBNS MRav NLar NSti SPer SPoG SRms
§ - 'Mystique' (v)	CRos ELan LRHS MRav NRHS SLon SPoG
officinale	Widely available
- CC 1709	WMoo
§ - f. ***affine***	CBcs CCCN CLet CRHN CRos CTri CWCL CWib ELan EPfP LRHS MAsh MRav NRHS SCoo SDix SLim SRms WHar WPat
§ - 'Argenteovariegatum' (v) 🏆H5	CDul CKel CLet CRos CTsd CWGN CWib EHoe ELan EMOT EPfP ESps LHop LRHS LSRN MAsh MGos MHer MMuc MRav SEND SLim SPer SPoG SWvt WCFE WHar WPat WSHC
- 'Aureovariegatum'	see *J. officinale* 'Aureum'
§ - 'Aureum' (v)	CBcs CKel CMac CRos CTsd CWCL CWib EBee ELan EPfP IBoy LRHS MAsh MHer MJak NBir NPri SCoo SLim SLon SMad SNig SPer SRms
- 'Clotted Cream'	see *J. officinale* 'Devon Cream'
- 'Crûg's Collection'	WCru
§ - 'Devon Cream' PBR	Widely available
- Fiona Sunrise = 'Frojas' PBR 🏆H5	Widely available
- 'Grandiflorum'	see *J. officinale* f. *affine*
- 'Inverleith' 🏆H5	CCCN CKel CMac CRos CWCL EBee ECtt ELan EPfP EWTr LBMP LBrs LHop LRHS MAsh MBNS MGos MRav NRHS SCoo SHil SLim SMad SNig SPad SPer SPoG WGrn WSHC
- 'Sunbeam'	CRos LRHS NPri NRHS
- 'Variegatum'	see *J. officinale* 'Argenteovariegatum'
parkeri	CBcs CCCN CJun CMac CTri EBee ECho ELon EPfP EPot GEdr GMaP LRHS MBNS NLar SEle WPat WThu XEll
- 'Bychan'	WAbe
§ ***polyanthum*** 🏆H2	CBcs CChe CKel CRHN CSBt CTri EBak ELan EPfP ETho IDee SEND SHil SLim SPer SPre SRms WHar
- dark-red-leaved	CCCN EBee ELan EPfP WPGP
primulinum	see *J. mesnyi*
reevesii hort.	see *J. humile* 'Revolutum'
sambac 🏆H2	CArn CBcs CCCN CHll CRHN ELan IDee SPre WFib
- 'Grand Duke of Tuscany' (d)	CCCN SPre
- 'Maid of Orleans' (d)	CCCN EShb SPre
sieboldianum	see *J. nudiflorum*
§ ***simplicifolium*** subsp. ***suavissimum***	CHll CRHN
stenalobium	WFib
× ***stephanense***	Widely available
suavissimum	see *J. simplicifolium* subsp. *suavissimum*

Jatropha (*Euphorbiaceae*)

	cinerea	SPlb
	integerrima	CCCN
	multifida	SPlb
	podagrica 🏆H1a	LToo

Jeffersonia (*Berberidaceae*)

	diphylla	CArn CLAP CRos EBee ECho EPPr EPot EPri GKev LAma LEdu LRHS MNrw NBir NHar NPnk NRHS WAbe WCru WPGP WThu
	dubia	CLAP CRos ECho EPot EWes EWld LEdu LHop LLHF LRHS MNrw NBir NHar NPnk NRHS WAbe WCru WThu XEll
	- 'Alba'	ECho SIgm
	- 'Sunago-fu' (v) **new**	GEdr

jostaberry see *Ribes* × *culverwellii*

Jovellana (*Calceolariaceae*)

	punctata	CBcs CCCN CTsd EBee GCal IBlr SPlb
	- var. ***coerulea***	IBlr
	sinclairii	CHll CPne LLHF
	violacea 🏆H2	CAbb CBcs CBot CCCN CMac CPne CTsd CWib EPfP GCal GMcL IBlr IDee IMou IVic LRHS MGil SEle SMad SVen WBod WPGP

Jovibarba ✿ (*Crassulaceae*)

§	***allionii***	CBod CMea CTri EDAr EPot LBMP MHer MSCN NHpl NMen WHal WHoo
	- 'Oki'	CRos ECho LRHS NMen NRHS SRms
	allionii* × *hirta	CTal MSCN SDys
§	***arenaria***	GAbr NMen XLum
*	***echiniformis***	XLum
	'Emerald Spring'	SFgr
	globiferum subsp. ***hirtum*** 'Blutrot'	SFgr
	- - 'Pascal'	SFgr
§	***heuffelii***	CRos ECho LRHS NHpl NMen NRHS XLum
	- 'Aiolos'	NHol
	- 'Almkroon'	NHol NWad
	- 'Anabokonak'	NMen
	- 'Angel Wings'	NMen WHoo
	- 'Aquarius'	NMen
	- 'Be Mine'	NMen
	- 'Beacon Hill'	NMen
	- 'Belcore'	NMen XLum
	- 'Benjamin'	NMen
	- 'Bermuda'	CMea
	- 'Big Red'	NHol NWad
	- 'Blaze'	NMen
	- 'Bolero'	NMen
	- 'Bora'	NWad
	- 'Brandaris'	SDys
	- 'Brocade'	MSCN NHol NWad
	- 'Bronze Ingot'	NMen WCot
§	- 'Cherry Glow'	NMen
	- 'Chocoleto'	NMen
I	- 'Compacta'	NMen
	- 'Copper King'	NMen
	- 'Elmo's Fire'	NMen
	- 'Eos Moment'	NMen
	- 'Fan Joy'	NMen
	- 'Fandango'	MHom
	- 'Gento'	NMen
	- 'Geronimo'	NHol NMen
	- 'Giuseppi Spiny'	MHom NMen SPlb
	- var. ***glabra***	WHoo
	- - from Anaba Kanak, Bulgaria	MHom NHol NWad
	- - from Haila, Montenegro/Kosovo	NMen
	- - from Jakupica, Macedonia	NMen
	- - from Kapaenianum	NMen
	- - from Ljuboten, Balkans	NMen
	- - from Ošljak, Albania	NMen
	- - from Rhodope, Bulgaria	MHom
	- - from Treska Gorge, Macedonia	NMen
	- 'Gladiator'	NMen
	- 'Gold Rand'	NHol
	- 'Grand Slam'	NMen
	- 'Green Land'	NMen
	- 'Greenstone'	CMea MHom NHol NMen
	- 'Harmony'	NHol
	- 'Henry Correvon'	NMen
	- var. ***heuffelii***	NMen
	- 'Idylle'	NMen
	- 'Ikaros'	NHol
	- 'Inferno'	MHom NMen
§	- 'Inge'	NMen
	- 'Ithaca'	NHol NWad
	- 'Iuno'	NHol NWad
	- 'Jade'	NMen
I	- 'Jovi King'	NMen
	- 'King Sunny'	NMen
	- var. ***kopaonikensis***	MHom NMen
	- 'Lucky Bell'	NMen
	- 'Mary Ann'	MHom NMen
	- 'Miller's Violet'	NMen
	- 'Mink'	NMen
	- 'Minuta'	NMen
	- 'Mystique'	CMea NMen WHoo
	- 'Nannette'	NMen
	- 'Orion'	CMea CTal NMen XLum
	- 'Passat'	NWad
	- var. ***patens***	NMen
	- 'Pink Skies'	NMen
	- 'Pink Star'	NMen NWad
	- 'Prisma'	NMen
	- 'Purple Haze'	XLum
	- 'Purple Heide'	NMen
	- 'Serenade'	NMen
	- 'Silex'	NMen
	- 'Springael's Choice'	NMen
	- 'Sundancer'	NMen
	- 'Sungold'	NHol NWad
	- 'Suntan'	NWad
	- 'Sylvan Memory'	NMen
	- 'Tan'	NMen
	- 'Tancredi'	NMen
	- 'Torrid Zone'	MBrN NMen
	- 'Tuxedo'	NHpl NMen
	- 'Violet'	NMen SDys
	- 'Xanthoheuff'	NMen
	- 'Yodelheuff'	NMen
§	***hirta***	EDAr GAbr GKev NMen XLum
	- from Wintergraben, Austria	SPlb
	- 'Belansky Tatra'	NMen
	- subsp. ***glabrescens*** from High Tatra, Slovakia/Poland	XLum
	- - from Smeryouka, southern Carpathians	NMen

I	– 'Glauca'	SFgr
	– 'Hedgehog'	SFgr
	– var. ***neilreichii***	CRos ECho LRHS MHom NRHS
	– 'Purpurea'	XLum
	preissiana	NMen SFgr
§	***sobolifera***	EDAr GKev NMen SFgr SPlb WHal XLum
	– 'Bronze Globe'	SFgr
	– 'Green Globe'	CRos CTal ECho LRHS NMen NRHS SDys
	– 'Miss Lorraine'	SFgr XLum

Jubaea (*Arecaceae*)

	sp.	ETod
§	***chilensis***	CBcs CPHo ETod SArc SBig SPlb WHor
	spectabilis	see *J. chilensis*

Juglans ✿ (*Juglandaceae*)

§	***ailanthifolia***	CBcs CMCN
	– B&SWJ 11026	WCru
	– var. ***cordiformis***	MRai
	– – 'Brock' (F)	CAgr
	– – 'Campbell Cw3' (F)	CAgr
	– – 'Fodermaier' seedling	CAgr
	– – 'Rhodes' (F)	CAgr
	– – 'Simcoe' (F) **new**	CAgr
	ailanthifolia* × *cinerea	see *J.* × *bixbyi*
§	× ***bixbyi***	CAgr
	cinerea (F)	CBcs
	– 'Beckwith' (F)	CAgr
	– 'Booth' (F) **new**	CAgr
	– 'Booth' seedling (F)	CAgr
	– 'Craxezy' (F)	CAgr
	– 'Kenworthy' seedling (F)	CAgr
	– 'Myjoy' (F)	CAgr
§	***elaeopyren***	WPGP
	hindsii	EBtc
	mandshurica (F)	CBcs
	– B&SWJ 12550 from Korea	WCru
	– BWJ 8097 from China	WCru
	– RWJ 9905 from Taiwan	WCru
	microcarpa	CMCN
	– subsp. ***major***	see *J. elaeopyren*
	microcarpa* × *nigra **new**	EMOT
	nigra (F) ΨH6	CAco CBcs CCVT CDul CHab CLnd CMCN CMac CSBt CTho CWib EBee ECrN ELan EPfP GTwe LCro MAsh MGos NOra NOrn NWea SDea SEND SGol SPer WMat WMou WTSh
	– 'Bicentennial' (F)	CAgr
	– 'Emma Kay' (F)	CAgr
	– 'Laciniata'	EPfP MBlu WPat
	– 'Potsdam' (F) **new**	CAgr
	– 'Thomas' (F)	CAgr
	– 'Weschke' (F)	CAgr
	regia (F)	Widely available
	– 'Axel' (F)	CAgr MCoo WMat
	– 'Broadview' (F) ΨH6	Widely available
	– 'Buccaneer' (F) ΨH6	CAgr CArg CDul CFGn CTho EMOT EPom GTwe NOra SDea SKee WHar WMat
	– 'Chandler' (F)	CAgr
	– 'Corne du Périgord' (F)	CAgr
	– 'Excelsior of Taynton' (F)	CAgr MCoo WMat
	– 'Ferjean' (F)	CAgr
	– 'Fernette'PBR (F)	CAgr NOra WHar WMat
	– 'Fernor' (F)	CAgr WHar WMat
	– 'Franquette' (F)	CAgr EMOT GTwe MCoo NOra WHar WMat
	– 'Hansen' (F)	CAgr
	– 'Hartley' (F)	CAgr
	– 'Laciniata' ΨH6	CDul CMCN ERea WPat
	– 'Lara' (F)	CAgr NOra WMat
	– 'Mayette' (F)	CAgr
	– 'Meylannaise' (F)	CAgr
	– number 16 (F)	CAgr WHar WMat
	– 'Parisienne' (F)	CAgr SGol
	– 'Plovdivski' (F)	CAgr EMOT WHar WMat
	– 'Proslavski' (F)	CAgr CDul WHar WMat
	– 'Purpurea'	CMCN ERea MBlu
	– 'Rita' (F)	CAgr EMOT LBuc
	– 'Ronde de Montignac' (F)	CAgr
	– 'Soleze' (F)	CAgr
	– 'Sychrov' (F)	EMOT WMat
	sieboldiana	see *J. ailanthifolia*
	sigillata	LEdu

jujube see *Ziziphus jujuba*

Juncus (*Juncaceae*)

	articulatus	LLWG XLum
	bulbosus	CNat
	conglomeratus	EWay LLWG
	'Curly Gold Strike' (v)	MSKA
§	***decipiens*** 'Curly-wurly'	CRos EPfP LRHS NRHS NWad SWat
	– 'Spiralis'	see *J. decipiens* 'Curly-wurly'
	effusus	CBen CWat LRHS MSKA MWLS NPer SWat WMAq XLum
	– 'Carman's Japanese'	CKno NSti
	– 'Gold Strike' (v)	EPPr LLWG
§	– f. ***spiralis***	CBen CSpe CWat EHoe EPfP GMaP LBrs LRHS MAsh MJak MWts NBir NRHS SPlb SVic WMAq XLum
	ensifolius	CBen CWat EHoe EWay EWes MMrt MSKA MWts NPer NSti
	filiformis 'Spiralis'	LPot
	inflexus	CBen CWat MMuc MSKA SWat XLum
	– 'Afro'	NBro NWsh SPlb
	pallidus	EPPr GCal
	patens 'Carman's Gray'	CKno CWCL GCal GQue LRHS MMuc NRHS NWad NWsh
	– 'Elk Blue'	CKno
*	***pincei***	GEdr
	subnodulosus	LLWG
	xiphioides	EHoe

Junellia (*Verbenaceae*)

	azorelloides	WAbe
	congesta **new**	WAbe
	erinacea **new**	WAbe
§	***micrantha***	WAbe
	odonnellii	WAbe
§	***succulentifolia***	WAbe
	thymifolia	WAbe

Juniperus ✿ (*Cupressaceae*)

	chinensis	CMen
	– 'Aurea' ΨH6	CBcs CMac ESps SEND
§	– 'Blaauw' ΨH6	CMac CMen SGol SLim
	– 'Blue Alps' ΨH6	CAco EMOT ESps LPar LRHS MGos MMuc NEgg SCob SCoo SEND SGol SLim
	– 'Echiniformis'	CKen
	– 'Expansa Aureospicata' (v)	EMOT EPfP ESps SEND SLim SPoG
§	– 'Expansa Variegata' (v)	CWib EMOT SLim
	– 'Itoigawa'	CMen LPar
§	– 'Kaizuka' ΨH6	LPar SGol WCFE
	– 'Kaizuka Variegata'	see *J. chinensis* 'Variegated Kaizuka'

	- 'Kuriwao Gold'	see *J.* × *pfitzeriana* 'Kuriwao Gold'
§	- 'Parsonsii'	WCFE
	- 'Plumosa Aurea' ♀H6	ESps SLim
	- 'Plumosa Aureovariegata' (v)	CKen
	- 'Pyramidalis' ♀H6	CLet EMOT EPfP ESps GMcL MAsh SCoo
	- 'Pyramidalis Variegata'	see *J. chinensis* 'Variegata'
	- 'San José'	CMen
§	- var. ***sargentii***	CMen
	- 'Shimpaku'	CKen CMen
	- 'Stricta'	CAco CSBt LBee LRHS NOrn SGol SLim
	- 'Stricta Variegata'	see *J. chinensis* 'Variegata'
	- 'Sulphur Spray'	see *J.* × *pfitzeriana* 'Sulphur Spray'
	- 'Torulosa'	see *J. chinensis* 'Kaizuka'
§	- 'Variegata' (v)	ESps
§	- 'Variegated Kaizuka' (v)	EMOT SCoo SLim
	communis	CAco CDul CHab ESps GPoy NWea WTSh
	- 'Arnold'	NLar
	- 'Arnold Sentinel'	CKen
	- 'Barton'	NLar NWad
	- 'Barton Gem'	NWad
	- 'Brien'	CKen
	- 'Brynhyfryd Gold'	CKen
	- 'Compressa' ♀H7	CBcs CKen CLet CMac CSBt CTri CWib EMOT EPfP EPot ESps GEdr GMcL LBee LRHS MAsh MGos MJak NEgg NHol NWea SLim SPer SPoG WIce
	- 'Corielagan'	CKen
	- 'Cracovia'	CKen
	- var. ***depressa***	GPoy SEND SGol
	- 'Depressa Aurea'	CKen CSBt EMOT ESps GMcL LBee
	- 'Depressed Star'	EMOT SPoG
	- 'Effusa'	CKen
	- 'Gelb'	see *J. communis* 'Schneverdingen Goldmachangel'
	- 'Gold Cone'	CKen CLet ELan EMOT EPfP ESps EUJe LBee MAsh MGos SLim SPoG
	- 'Golden Showers'	see *J. communis* 'Schneverdingen Goldmachangel'
	- 'Goldschatz'	CKen EPfP LRHS SLim SPoG
	- 'Green Carpet' ♀H7	CAco CKen ELan EMOT EPfP GKin GMcL LBuc LRHS MAsh MGos NLar SCoo SLim SPoG WCFE
	- 'Haverbeck'	CKen
	- 'Hibernica' ♀H7	CDul CLet CSBt ELan EMOT EPfP ESps GMcL LRHS MGos MJak NWea SLim SPer SPoG
	- 'Hibernica Aurea'	CMac
	- 'Hornibrookii'	NWea SRms
	- 'Kenwith Castle'	CKen
	- 'Pyramidalis'	SPlb
	- 'Rakete'	IVic
	- 'Repanda' ♀H7	CAco CBcs CLet CMac CSBt CWib EMOT EPfP ESps GMcL LRHS MAsh MGos NLar NWea SCoo SGol SLim SPer SPoG
§	- 'Schneverdingen Goldmachangel'	IBoy MAsh
	- 'Sentinel'	ESps WCFE WMou
	- 'Sieben Steinhauser'	CKen
	- 'Silver Mist'	CKen
	- Suecica Group	NWea
	- - 'Suecica Aurea'	GMcL
	- 'Zeal'	CKen
	conferta	see *J. rigida* subsp. *conferta*
	- var. ***maritima***	see *J. taxifolia*

	davurica 'Expansa'	see *J. chinensis* 'Parsonsii'
	- 'Expansa Albopicta'	see *J. chinensis* 'Expansa Variegata'
	- 'Expansa Variegata'	see *J. chinensis* 'Expansa Variegata'
	- 'Leningrad'	NLar
	foetidissima	CMen
	× ***gracilis*** 'Blaauw'	see *J. chinensis* 'Blaauw'
	'Grey Owl' ♀H7	CAco ELan EMOT ESps MMuc NWea SEND SGol SLim
	horizontalis	CLet ESps NWea
§	- 'Andorra Compact'	EPfP
I	- 'Andorra Variegata' (v)	EMOT SCoo
§	- 'Blue Chip'	ELan EPfP ESps GMcL LBee MGos MJak NBir NWea SCoo SPoG
	- 'Blue Moon'	see *J. horizontalis* 'Blue Chip'
	- 'Blue Rug'	see *J. horizontalis* 'Wiltonii'
	- 'Emerald Spreader'	ELan EMOT
	- 'Glacier'	LRHS
	- 'Glauca'	ESps NWea
	- 'Golden Carpet' ♀H7	ELan LBuc LCro NLar
	- 'Grey Pearl'	CKen
	- 'Hughes'	CAco LBee MRav NWea
	- Icee Blue = 'Monber' ♀H7	CKen EPfP GKin MAsh NLar SPoG
	- 'Jade River'	CAco
	- 'Limeglow' ♀H7	ELan EMOT EPfP EUJe GMcL MGos NLar NOrn SCoo SPoG
	- 'Mother Lode'	CKen
	- 'Neumann'	CKen
	- 'Pancake'	NLar
	- 'Plumosa Compacta'	see *J. horizontalis* 'Andorra Compact'
	- 'Prince of Wales'	MAsh NWea
	- 'Prostrata'	IBoy
	- 'Turquoise Spreader'	CSBt NWea SGol
	- 'Villa Marie'	CKen
§	- 'Wiltonii'	CDul NWea
	- 'Youngstown'	SEND
	- 'Yukon Belle'	CKen
	× ***media***	see *J.* × *pfitzeriana*
§	× ***pfitzeriana***	CDul CMac ESps GMcL SCob SGol
	- 'Arctic'	NLar
	- 'Blaauw'	see *J. chinensis* 'Blaauw'
	- 'Blue and Gold' (v)	CKen SPoG
	- 'Blue Cloud'	see *J. virginiana* 'Blue Cloud'
§	- 'Carbery Gold' ♀H7	CBcs CMac CSBt EPfP ESps GKin LBee LRHS MAsh MGos NOrn SCoo SLim SPoG
	- 'Gold Coast'	CKen CSBt ESps LBee MGos SGol SLim
	- Gold Sovereign = 'Blound'	ESps LBee
	- 'Gold Star'	LRHS
	- 'Hetzii'	NLar NWea
	- 'King of Spring'	SLim
§	- 'Kuriwao Gold'	CMac EMOT GKin GMcL MRav SEND SGol
	- 'Mint Julep'	CSBt EPfP ESps GMcL MJak SCob SCoo SGol SLim
	- 'Old Gold' ♀H7	EMOT EPfP ESps GKin GMcL LBee LCro LRHS MGos MJak MMuc NEgg NWea SCoo SEND SGol SLim SPlb WCFE WHar
	- 'Old Gold Carbery'	see *J.* × *pfitzeriana* 'Carbery Gold'
	- 'Pfitzeriana'	see *J.* × *pfitzeriana* 'Wilhelm Pfitzer'
	- 'Pfitzeriana Aurea'	CLet CMac EMOT ESps NWea SCob SGol
	- 'Pfitzeriana Glauca'	CAco ESps
§	- 'Sulphur Spray' ♀H7	CDul CWib ESps LRHS MAsh MMuc SEND SLim WCFE
§	- 'Wilhelm Pfitzer'	NWea
	phoenicea	XSen
§	***pingii*** 'Glassell'	NLar

- 'Hulsdonk Yellow'PBR LRHS MAsh NLar SPoG
§ - var. ***wilsonii*** CKen
procera WPGP
procumbens 'Kishiogima' LRHS NLar
- 'Lighting Spot' NLar
- 'Nana' ♀H7 CKen CLet CMac CSBt EPfP GMcL LBee LRHS MAsh MGos MJak NEgg NHol NLar SCoo SLim SPoG WCFE
recurva 'Castlewellan' NLar WHor
- var. ***coxii*** CDul CMac NHol NLar WCFE
§ - 'Densa' CKen
- 'Nana' see *J. recurva* 'Densa'
rigida CMen
§ - subsp. ***conferta*** CMac EMOT SEND SGol
- - 'All Gold' ♀H6 LRHS SLim SPoG
* - - 'Blue Ice' CKen
- - 'Blue Pacific' CKen CLet EMOT LRHS SGol SPoG
- - 'Blue Tosho' CDul NLar
- - 'Silver Mist' CKen
sabina CArn NWea
- 'Knap Hill' see *J.* × *pfitzeriana* 'Wilhelm Pfitzer'
- 'Skandia' CKen
- 'Tamariscifolia' CBcs CLet CWib ESps GKin GMcL LBee LRHS MAsh MGos MJak NOrn NWea SEND SGol SLim SPoG WCFE
sargentii see *J. chinensis* var. *sargentii*
scopulorum 'Blue Arrow' ♀H7 Widely available
- 'Blue Banff' CKen
- 'Skyrocket' CBcs CCVT CDul CMac CNWT CSBt CWib ECrN EMOT EPfP ESps MGos MJak MRav NWea SCob SGol SPlb WCFE WHar WMou
- 'Springbank' WCFE
- 'Wichita Blue' EPfP IVic
squamata 'Blue Carpet' ♀H7 CBcs CDul CKen CLet CMac CSBt CWib EPfP ESps GMcL LBuc LRHS MAsh MGos MJak NEgg NHol NLar NOrn NWea SCob SEND SGol SLim SPer SPoG WCFE WHar
- 'Blue Spider' LRHS
- 'Blue Star' ♀H7 CJun CKen CLet CMac CSBt ELan EMOT EPfP ESps GMcL IBoy LBee LCro LRHS MAsh MGos MJak NEgg NHol NLar NWad SGol SLim SPer SPoG WCFE
- 'Blue Star Variegated' see *J. squamata* 'Golden Flame'
- 'Blue Swede' see *J. squamata* 'Hunnetorp'
- 'Dream Joy' CKen NLar NWad
- 'Filborna' LBee
- 'Floreant' SLim
- 'Glassell' see *J. pingii* 'Glassell'
§ - 'Golden Flame' (v) CKen
- 'Holger' ♀H7 CLet CMac EPfP ESps GMcL LBee LRHS MAsh MGos MJak NHol NLar SCoo SLim SPoG
§ - 'Hunnetorp' LRHS
- 'Meyeri' ESps GMcL NWea SGol
- 'Wilsonii' see *J. pingii* var. *wilsonii*
§ ***taxifolia*** CSBt
virginiana CAco NWea
§ - 'Blue Cloud' SLim
- 'Frosty Morn' CKen
- 'Glauca' NWea
- 'Golden Spring' CKen
- 'Hillspire' SEND
- Silver Spreader = 'Mona' CKen
- 'Sulphur Spray' see *J.* × *pfitzeriana* 'Sulphur Spray'

Jussiaea see *Ludwigia*

Justicia (*Acanthaceae*)

americana LLWG
aurea EShb
§ ***brandegeeana*** ♀H1b CCCN EShb
- 'Lutea' see *J. brandegeeana* 'Yellow Queen'
- variegated (v) EShb
§ - 'Yellow Queen' EShb
- yellow-flowered EShb
§ ***carnea*** CHll EShb WCot
- 'Alba' CCCN EShb
- dark-leaved CHll EShb
- 'Radiant' SMad
guttata see *J. brandegeeana*
'Penrhosiensis' EShb
pohliana see *J. carnea*
rizzinii ♀H1b CBcs CCCN CHll EUJe LSou MHtn SEle SRot
spicigera CCCN EShb
suberecta see *Dicliptera sericea*

K

Kadsura (*Schisandraceae*)

coccinea B&SWJ 11793 WCru
- FMWJ 13489 WCru
heteroclita FMWJ 13385 WCru
- WWJ 11947 WCru
japonica CBcs
- B&SWJ 1027 WCru
- B&SWJ 4463 from Korea WCru
- B&SWJ 11109 from Japan WCru
- from Japan EPfP WSHC
- 'Fukurin' (v) IDee NLar
- 'Variegata' (v) CCCN EBee EPfP LRHS SEND WSHC
- white fruit CBcs NLar

Kaempferia ✿ (*Zingiberaceae*)

pulchra 'Bronze Peacock' MJak
rotunda CCCN LAma LTro SDir

Kageneckia (*Rosaceae*)

oblonga SPlb

Kalanchoe (*Crassulaceae*)

beharensis ♀H1b CCCN CDTJ ELan EShb WCot
- 'Fang' ♀H1b CDTJ ELan EShb
- 'Rusty' CDTJ CSpe
§ ***delagoensis*** CCCN EShb
fedtschenkoi EShb
- 'Variegata' (v) WCot
hildebrandtii EShb
humilis WCot
laciniata EShb
orgyalis EShb
pinnata EShb
pubescens EShb
pumila ♀H1b EShb SBch
serrata EShb
sexangularis EShb
'Tessa' ♀H1b WCot
thyrsiflora EShb
- 'Bronze Sculpture' CAbb EUJe
- 'Variegata' EShb
tomentosa ♀H1b EShb LAll WCot
tubiflora see *K. delagoensis*

Kalimeris (Asteraceae)

§ ***incisa*** MMuc MRav WBor
- 'Alba' ECha NLar WFar
- 'Blue Star' ECha ECtt MSpe MTis NLar NPnk SCob WCAu WFar WPtf WSHC
- 'Charlotte' EWes LPla MSpe MTis NBre NDov NPnk SAko SPoG
- 'Madiva' CSam EBee IMou LHop NDov NPnk SAko WTor
- 'Nana Blue' EBee NDov

integrifolia MMuc
'Mon Jardin' WCot
§ ***mongolica*** CAby CMac ECGP ECha MMuc SAko SDix WFar WSHC
- 'Antonia' NDov WCot
§ ***pinnatifida*** LRHS
- 'Hortensis' EBee MNrw
§ ***yomena*** 'Shogun' (v) CBod ECha ECtt EHoe ELan EPfP LEdu MNrw MPie MSpe NBir NSti SPer WFar XLum
- 'Variegata' see *K. yomena* 'Shogun'

Kalmia ✿ (Ericaceae)

angustifolia ♀H4 SRms
- f. ***rubra*** ♀H6 CBcs CCCN CDul CRos EBee ELan EPfP LRHS MAsh NLar NPri SPer
I - 'Rubra Nana' CMac
latifolia CBcs ELan EPfP LPar LRHS NPri NWea SPer SWvt WHar
- 'Bandeau' GGGa
- 'Bay State' **new** LRHS
- 'Bridesmaid' NLar
- 'Bullseye' LRHS SAko SPoG
- 'Carousel' CBcs CCCN NLar
- 'Clementine Churchill' CMac
- 'Eskimo' GGGa
- 'Freckles' ♀H6 LRHS MPkF SPoG
- 'Galaxy' GGGa IVic LRHS NLar SAko
- 'Ginkona' GGGa SAko
- 'Heart's Desire' LRHS
- 'Kaleidoscope' GGGa IVic NLar
- 'Little Linda' ♀H6 SAko
- 'Minuet' CBcs CCCN CRos GGGa GMcL IVic LRHS MAsh MLea NLar SPoG SWvt
- 'Mitternacht' GGGa
- 'Moyland' GGGa
- f. ***myrtifolia*** CRos LRHS MLea
- - 'Elf' CRos IVic LRHS MPkF NLar
- 'Nani' GGGa
- 'Nipmuck' MPkF
- 'Olympic Fire' ♀H6 CBcs CRos GGGa GMcL IVic LRHS NLar SWvt WTSh
- 'Olympic Wedding' SPoG
- 'Ostbo Red' CBcs CDul CMac CRos IVic LRHS MLea MMuc MPkF SAko SPoG SWvt
- 'Peppermint' GGGa IVic LRHS NLar
- 'Pink Charm' ♀H6 IVic
- 'Pinkobello' GGGa
- 'Pinwheel' LRHS MJak NLar SAko SPoG
- 'Quinnipiac' MJak
- 'Sarah' CRos LRHS MLea
- 'Snowdrift' LRHS NLar
- 'Starbust' **new** LRHS
- 'Tad' **new** LRHS
- 'You Can' **new** LRHS
polifolia CBcs CCCN LCro NHar SPer WThu
- f. ***leucantha*** NHar WThu

× *Kalmiothamnus* (Ericaceae)

'Haytor' ITim
'Sindelberg' ITim

Kalopanax ✿ (Araliaceae)

pictus see *K. septemlobus*
§ ***septemlobus*** CBcs CDul ELan EPfP MMuc NLar SEND SPtp
- var. ***magnificus*** B&SWJ 10900 WCru
- f. ***maximowiczii*** EPfP IVic MBlu NLar

Keiskea (Lamiaceae)

japonica pink-flowered SBrt

Kelleria (Thymelaeaceae)

dieffenbachii WThu

Kelseya (Rosaceae)

uniflora WAbe

Kennedia (Papilionaceae)

coccinea CCCN SVen
macrophylla CRHN
nigricans CCCN
prostrata SBrt SPlb
rubicunda CCCN CRHN

Kentia (Arecaceae)

belmoreana see *Howea belmoreana*
forsteriana see *Howea forsteriana*

Kentranthus see *Centranthus*

Kerria (Rosaceae)

japonica misapplied single see *K. japonica* 'Simplex'
japonica (L.) DC. CTho ESps
- (d) see *K. japonica* 'Pleniflora'
- 'Albescens' CBot WCot
- 'Buttercup' NLar
- 'Golden Guinea' ♀H5 CMac CRos ELan EPfP ESps GMcL IFro LRHS MAsh MGos MRav SCob SCoo SHil SPer SRms SWvt WFar
- 'Honshu' **new** IArd
§ - 'Picta' (v) CDul CMac CTho CWib EBee ELan MGos MRav MSwo SCob SGol SLim SLon SPer SRms WFar
§ - 'Pleniflora' (d) ♀H5 Widely available
§ - 'Simplex' CDul CMac NWea
- 'Variegata' see *K. japonica* 'Picta'

Khadia (Aizoaceae)

acutipetala CCCN

Kiggelaria (Flacourtiaceae)

africana SVen

Kirengeshoma (Hydrangeaceae)

palmata Widely available
- 'Black Style' **new** EBee
- dwarf WCot
- Koreana Group ♀H7 Widely available

Kitagawia (Apiaceae)

§ ***litoralis*** EBee

Kitaibela (Malvaceae)

vitifolia CSpe ELan EPPr EWoo NBid NSti SEND SPav SPlb WHer WOut

Kitchingia see *Kalanchoe*

kiwi fruit see *Actinidia deliciosa*

Kleinia (*Asteraceae*)

articulata	see *Senecio articulatus*
grantii	CSpe WCot
neriifolia	WCot
repens	see *Senecio serpens*

Knautia (*Caprifoliaceae*)

§ ***arvensis***	CArn CElw CHab CRos CWld EBee EPfP EWoo GCal LCro LRHS MHer MMuc MNHC NLar NMir NRHS SPer SPhx SRms WHer WMoo WOut WSFF
– 'Rachael'	CElw
– white-flowered	SPhx WSHC
dipsacifolia	LPla SHar
'Jardin d'en Face'	CBod EPfP LRHS
§ ***macedonica***	Widely available
– 'Crimson Cushion'	CSpe ECtt LSou
– dark-flowered	IFro
– 'Mars Midget'	CBod CHll CRos CSpe EBee ELan ELon EPfP ESps GCal GQue IBoy LRHS LSou MArt MGos MSpe NLar NRHS SCob SPhx SPoG SWvt WFar WHar WHoo
– Melton pastels	CBod CRos EBee ELan EPfP ESps GJos IBoy LRHS MGos NLar NPer NRHS SPhx SPoG SRkn SRot SWvt WFar WHar
– pink-flowered	CSam
– 'Red Knight'	CBod EBee EPfP ESps GWyn LHop LRHS MBNS SHil WCAu
– red-flowered	CWib
– short	ECtt
– tall, pale-flowered	SPhx
– 'Thunder and Lightning'PBR (v)	CBct CBod CMos CWGN EBee ECtt EPfP EWes IKil ILea LBMP LBuc LRHS MAsh MAvo MHol MNrw MRav NLar SPad SPer SPoG WCot WHil
sarajevensis	MAvo

Knightia (*Proteaceae*)

excelsa	CBcs

Kniphofia ✿ (*Asphodelaceae*)

'Ada'	ELon EWes
albescens	NLos SPlb
'Alcazar'	CBcs CPrp ECtt ELon EPfP GMcL IBoy LCro LOPS MAvo MHer SCob SPer SWvt WCFE WFar
'Ample Dwarf'	ECtt WCot
'Amsterdam'	MWat SHar
angustifolia	SPlb
'Apricot'	LRHS
'Apricot Souffle'	EPri WCot
'Atlanta'	LRHS
'Barton Fever' ♀H6	MAvo WCot
baurii	SPlb
'Bees' Jubilee'	MAvo MNrw NChi
'Bees' Lemon'	Widely available
§ 'Bees' Sunset' ♀H5	CAvo CBWd CPrp CRos CSam EAEE EBee ECha ECtt EUJe GCra LRHS MAvo MBel MNrw MWat SEND SMHy SWvt WAul
'Bees' Yellow'	SBch
'Bitter Chocolate'	WCot
'Border Ballet'	CRos LRHS NBir NGdn NLar NRHS SWat WHar XLum
brachystachya	ELon GAbr SPlb
'Bressingham Comet'	CRos ECtt GKev LEdu LRHS NBir NCGa SHil
Bressingham Sunbeam = 'Bresun'	EBee ECtt LRHS NBir
'Bressingham Yellow'	ECtt
'Brimstone' Bloom ♀H5	CDor CPrp EAEE ECtt EPfP EPri LEdu LHop LRHS MMuc MSpe NBir NPnk SEND SPtp SWvt WFar WGwG
bruceae	EPri SPlb SVen
'Buttercup' ♀H5	CAvo LOPS LSRN
'Butterfly'	EBee
'Candlelight'	EBee ECtt EPri MAvo SAko WSHC
caulescens	Widely available
– LEG 053 **new**	GKev
– 'Coral Breakers'	CBod CPrp ECtt ELon GAbr GBin GCal LRHS MAvo MHol MMuc NEgg NLos SDix SEND SKHP SMad SPer WCot
– 'John May'	CAby CBod CBot EBee ECtt EMFm ESwi MAvo SCob SDix SEND SMad SWvt WCot
– short	ECha
– 'Tiny Girl'	ECtt
'Chichi'	MAvo WCot
'Christmas Cheer'	EBee
citrina	GCra GKev GLog IBoy MBrN NGBl WCot WHar XLum
'C.M. Prichard' misapplied	see *K. rooperi*
'C.M. Prichard' Prichard	WCot
'Cobra'	ECtt GMaP LRHS SAko WAul WCot
'Coral Flame' ♀H5	EBee LRHS
'Coral Sceptre'	WCot
'Creamsicle'PBR (Popsicle Series)	ECtt SCob SHil WCot WHlf
'Dingaan'	EBee ECtt GBin GMcL LTro MBel MNrw MTis NBir NLar WCot
'Dorset Sentry'	CAbb CAby EBee ECtt ELon EPfP EWoo LRHS MBel MGos MNrw NBir NEgg NLar SKHP SMad SPhx WCot WFar
'Drummore Apricot'	CPrp EAEE ECha ECtt ELan EPfP GBin GBuc IBoy LRHS LSRN MAvo NBir NEgg SPtp WCot WFar WGwG
'Early Buttercup'	WFar
'Elvira'PBR	CPne EBee ECtt EUJe GBin LRHS
Ember Glow = 'Tneg'PBR (Glow Series)	CAbb CPne EBee ECtt MNrw SHil
ensifolia	CTca ECtt NGdn SVen XLum
'Erecta'	CPne CTal
'Ernest Mitchell'	WCot
Express hybrids	XLum
'Fiery Fred' ♀H6	CPrp EBee ECGP ECtt ELon EPfP GQue LRHS MAvo MSpe SBod SPtp WAul WCot
Fire Glow = 'Tnfg'PBR (Glow Series)	CMos NCGa NLar SHil
'First Sunrise'PBR	ECtt LRHS MJak NPnk
'Flamenco'	CRos ELon LRHS NGdn NRHS SCob
'Flaming Torch'	EBee ECtt
'Florence Bedecked'	WCot
foliosa Hochst.	LEdu
'Frances Victoria'	WCot
galpinii misapplied	see *K. triangularis* subsp. *triangularis*
galpinii Baker ♀H4	CPne MMuc

	'Gilt Bronze'	WCot
	'Gladness'	MAvo MTis NBir NCGa WCot
	'Goldelse'	EBee LRHS NBir
	'Goldfinch'	CCse CSam
	gracilis	LEdu
	'Grandiflora'	CMac WHar
	'Green and Cream'	MHCG
	'Green Jade'	CAby CBcs CBod CCse CRos EBee ECha ECtt ELan EPfP GBin GBuc LRHS MBel MCot MMuc MNrw MRav NBir NGBl NLar NPri NSti SGbt SKHP SPer SRms WCot WFar
	'Green Jewel'	LRHS
	'H.E. Beale'	WCot
	'Hen and Chickens'	ECtt ESwi MAvo WCot
	hirsuta	EBee LRHS NLos WSHC
	- JCA 3.461.900	SKHP
	- 'Fire Dance'	CRos EAJP LRHS LSun NRHS
	- 'Traffic Lights'	GMcL WHar
	'Ice Queen'	CAvo EBee ECha ECtt ELon EPPr EPri EWTr EWoo GBin GKev MAvo MHer MMuc MNrw MRav MTis NChi NLar SEND SGol SRms SWvt WCot WFar
	ichopensis	LEdu MAvo NLos SVen WPGP
	'Incandesce' ♀H5	EBee MAvo WCot
	'Innocence' ♀H4	EPfP LRHS MAvo
	'Jane Henry'	EBee LEdu
	'Jenny Bloom'	CRos EAEE ECtt ELan ELon EPfP EUJe EWoo GBuc GCal GMaP LEdu LRHS MRav NLar NSti SEND SPtp WAul WCot WFar
	'Jess's Delight'	WCot
	'John Benary'	CBod CPrp CRos EAEE ECtt EPPr GLog GMaP IKil IPot LLWG LRHS MBel NBir NEgg NGdn NLar SEND SPer SPtp WCot WGwG WKif
	'Jonathan' ♀H5	WCot
	laxiflora	EPri NLos WPGP
	'Lemon Popsicle'PBR (Popsicle Series)	CBct CMea CRos CWGN LPre LRHS NAst NPri SCob SHil WFar
	'Light of the World'	see *K. triangularis* subsp. *triangularis* 'Light of the World'
	'Limelight'	EBee ECtt SHil
	linearifolia	CPrp EBee GCra NLos SPlb WCot XLum
	'Little Elf'	MAvo XLum
	'Little Maid'	Widely available
	'Lord Roberts'	MAvo MRav SMad WCot WPGP
	'Luna'	WCot
	macowanii	see *K. triangularis* subsp. *triangularis*
	'Mango Popsicle'PBR (Popsicle Series)	CAbb CMos CPne ECtt EWTr GMcL LRHS LSou MBel NAst NLar NSti SCob SHil SMad WCot WFar WHlf WHoo
	'Mermaiden'	CRos ECtt MAvo MMuc MNrw SEND WCot
	'Minister Verschuur'	EBee ECtt GQue LRHS
	'Modesta'	WSHC
	'Molten Lava'	EBee
	'Moonstone' ♀H5	CPrp CSam EBee ECtt ELon GBin LLHF LSun MAvo MMuc MNrw MTis NLar NSti SEND WCot
	'Mount Etna'	WCot
	multiflora	NLos
	- cream-flowered	NLos
	- 'November Glory'	WCot
	- yellow/orange-flowered	NLos

	'Nancy's Red'	Widely available
	nelsonii Mast.	see *K. triangularis* subsp. *triangularis*
	'New Sensation'	WCot
§	'Nobilis' ♀H6	CAby CLet EBee ECha ECtt ELan ELon EUJe EWoo GAbr GBin GMaP LOPS LRHS LSRN MBel MHol MMuc MNrw NGdn SArc SDix SEND SPoG SWvt WCot
	northiae ♀H4	CBod CBot CHid EBee ELan ELon EPri EUJe EWes GCal LEdu LSun MAvo MMuc MNrw NLos SArc SEND SMad SPlb SPtp SWvt WCot WCru WPGP XLum
	'Orange Vanilla Popsicle'PBR (Popsicle Series)	CAbb CBct CBod CMea CRos ECtt LRHS SCob SHil SMad SPad SPoG WHoo WTor
§	'Painted Lady'	CDor CSam CTri EBee ECtt GMaP MAvo MHol MMuc MNrw NLar SEND SMHy SWvt WCot
	'Papaya Popsicle'PBR (Popsicle Series)	CBct CMea CRos CWGN EBee ECtt ELon LPre LRHS LSou NPri SCob SHil SPoG WFar WHlf
	parviflora	XLum
	pauciflora	CTre WCot
	'Penny Rockets' ♀H6	EBee LRHS
	'Percy's Pride'	Widely available
	'Pfitzeri'	SRms
	'Pineapple Popsicle'PBR (Popsicle Series)	CAbb CRos CWGN ECtt LRHS NAst NLar SCob SHil WHlf
	× ***praecox***	MAvo NLos
	'Primrose Upward' ♀H6	WCot
I	'Primulina' Bloom	EBee LRHS SAko
	'Prince Igor' misapplied	see *K.* 'Nobilis'
	'Prince Igor' Prichard	ECtt NBir
	pumila	LLHF
	'Red Rocket'PBR	EBee EWoo GMcL IBoy LRHS MNrw WCot
	'Redhot Popsicle'PBR (Popsicle Series)	CBod LPre LRHS MHol SHil SPoG WCot
	'Rich Echoes' ♀H5	CAvo CWGN EBee ECGP ECtt ELon ESwi GBin LEdu LLHF MAvo MHol MTis NLar WCot WRHF
	ritualis	SKHP
§	***rooperi*** ♀H5	Widely available
I	- 'Torchlight'	CPne
	'Rosea Superba'	EBee
	'Royal Castle'	CRos GMaP LRHS MJak NBir NGdn NRHS SCob SEND WFar XLum
	'Royal Standard' ♀H5	CBcs CBod CPrp CRos ECtt ELan ELon EPfP GAbr GMaP ILea LCro LOPS LRHS NCGa NLar SCob SPer SPtp SWvt WFar WGwG
	rufa Baker	LEdu MAvo WPGP
	'Safranvogel' ♀H4	EBee ECtt WCot
	'Samuel's Sensation' misapplied	see *K.* 'Painted Lady'
	'Samuel's Sensation' Samuel ♀H5	EBee ECtt LRHS LSun NLar SAko SRGP SWvt WCot
	sarmentosa	NLos SPlb SVen WCot
	'Saturn'	MAvo
	'Sherbet Lemon'	MNrw WCot
	'Shining Sceptre' misapplied	see *K.* 'Bees' Sunset'
	'Springtime'	WCot
	'Star of Baden-Baden'	NBir SEND SMad SSal WCot
	Stark's early perpetual-flowering hybrids	XLum
	'Strawberries and Cream'	CBcs CPrp CTsd EBee ECha ECtt ELon EWld SBod SGbt SWvt
	stricta	XLum

	'Sunningdale Yellow' ♀H6	CCse EAEE ECha ECtt EUJe GMaP ILea MAvo SMHy SRms
	'Tawny King' ♀H5	Widely available
	'Tetbury Torch' PBR	CMos CPrp CWGN EAEE EBee ECtt GBin GQue LRHS MAvo MCot SEND SPtp SWvt WAul
	thomsonii	GCal NGdn
	- 'Kichocheo'	EBee GCal MAvo WCot
	- var. ***snowdenii*** misapplied	see *K. thomsonii* var. *thomsonii*
	- var. ***snowdenii*** ambig.	WPGP XLum
§	- var. ***thomsonii***	SMHy
	- - 'Stern's Trip' ♀H4	EBee
	'Timothy' ♀H5	Widely available
	'Toffee Nosed' ♀H5	Widely available
	'Torchbearer'	WCot
	triangularis	GKev WFar XLum
§	- subsp. ***triangularis***	CBro EPfP GBuc LRHS SCob SMad SRms SVen SWat XLum
§	- - 'Light of the World'	CAby CBcs CBro CDor CMac CPne CPrp CWld EAEE ECtt GAbr LEdu LRHS MHer NBir NLar SCob SPer SPtp SWvt WCot WFar WGrn
	'Tuckii' misapplied	SRms
	typhoides	NBir NLos SPlb
	tysonii	SPlb XLum
	- subsp. ***tysonii***	NLos
	uvaria	CPrp EBee GKev LCro LRHS NBir NLos SCob SPer SRms SVic WCot XLum XSen
	'Vanilla'	EWoo LRHS MMuc NLar SEND
	'Vesta'	EBee LRHS
	'Vincent Lepage'	EBee LHop NLar SAko
	'Wol's Red Seedling'	CAby CSam ECtt ELon EWoo GAbr MCot MNrw NCGa NGdn SBch SEND WCot WGrn WGwG WHoo
	'Wrexham Buttercup' ♀H6	CDor CSam EBee ECtt ELan EUJe GMaP GQue LSRN LSun MAvo MCot MHol MNrw MTis NPri SCob SEND SMad WCot WFar WHal WHoo
	'Yellow Bird'	EBee
	'Yellow Cheer'	WCot
	'Yellow Hammer' Slieve Donard	CSam ECha ELon MMuc SEND

Koeleria (*Poaceae*)

	glauca	CBod CWib ECha EHoe EPfP EShb ESps GMaP GMcL LRHS MBNS MJak NGdn NRHS NWsh SCob SLim SPlb SWvt WFar WHar XSen
	pyramidata	SMea
	vallesiana	EHoe SMea

Koelreuteria (*Sapindaceae*)

	elegans subsp. ***formosana***	CMCN
	paniculata	Widely available
	- 'Beachmaster'	NLar
	- 'Coral Sun' PBR ♀H5	CMHG ELan EPfP EUJe LRHS MBlu MGos NOra NOrn SLim SPoG WCot WMat WMou WPat
	- 'Fastigiata'	CDul EBee EPfP MBlu SCoo WHar WHor
	- 'Rosseels'	EMOT NLar
	- 'September'	EPfP MBlu

Kohleria (*Gesneriaceae*)

	'Ampallang'	WDib
	'An's Nagging Macaws'	WDib
	'Brazil Gem'	WDib
	'Cybele'	WDib
	'Dark Velvet'	WDib
	eriantha ♀H1c	CTsd WDib
	'Flashdance'	WDib
	'Hcy's Jardin de Monet'	WDib
	'Heartland's Blackberry Butterfly'	WDib
	hirsuta	WDib
	'Jester' ♀H1c	WDib
	'Manchu'	WDib
	'Marquis de Sade'	WDib
	'Queen Victoria'	WDib
I	***sciadotydaea*** **new**	WDib
	'Silver Feather'	WDib
§	'Sunrise'	WDib
	'Sunshine'	see *K.* 'Sunrise'
	'Texas Rainbow'	WDib
	warszewiczii ♀H1c	WDib

Kolkwitzia (*Caprifoliaceae*)

	amabilis	CSBt CTri ECGP ELan EPfP ESps GBin GMcL NEgg NWea SCob SGol SPlb SRms WCFE WHar WMoo WRHF WSHC
	- Dream Catcher = 'Maradco'	CMac EPfP MRav NEoE NLar SCob
	- 'Pink Cloud' ♀H5	Widely available

Kosteletzkya (*Malvaceae*)

	virginica	MArt MHol SBrt SPhx

kumquat see *Citrus japonica*

Kunzea (*Myrtaceae*)

	ambigua	EBee IDee SPlb
	- pink-flowered	SEle
	'Badja Carpet'	SEle
	baxteri	CTre CTsd
	ericifolia	SPlb
§	***ericoides***	CTsd GPoy
	parvifolia	SPlb
	pauciflora	SPlb

L

Lablab (*Papilionaceae*)

§	***purpureus***	SHDw
	- 'Ruby Moon'	CSpe

+ *Laburnocytisus* (*Papilionaceae*)

	'Adamii'	CDul CMac EBee ELan EPfP ESwi IVic LSRN MGos MPkF NLar NOrn SAko SPer

Laburnum ✿ (*Papilionaceae*)

	alpinum	NWea SPlb
	- 'Pendulum'	CAco CCVT CDul CLnd ELan EMOT ESps IDee LCro LSRN MAsh MGos MRav NOrn SGol SPer SPoG
§	***anagyroides***	CAco CDul CWib ESps MMuc NWea SEND SRms WBod
	- 'Erect'	WMat
	'Famous Walk'	see *L.* × *watereri* 'Vossii'
	vulgare	see *L. anagyroides*
	× ***watereri***	IBoy
§	- 'Vossii' ♀H6	Widely available
*	- 'Vossii Pendulum'	CCVT

Lachenalia ✿ (*Asparagaceae*)

algoensis ECho
§ ***aloides*** CGrW CPne CTal CTre ECho NRog SDeJ
- var. ***aurea*** see *L. flava*
- var. ***luteola*** see *L. flava*
- 'Nelsonii' see *L.* 'Nelsonii'
- 'Pearsonii' see *L.* 'Pearsonii'
- var. ***quadricolor*** see *L. quadricolor*
- var. ***vanzyliae*** see *L. vanzyliae*
anguinea ECho
arbuthnotiae new CTal
attenuata ECho
bachmanii CTal NRog
barkeriana ECho
bifolia see *L. bulbifera*
bolusii CTal ECho
bowkeri new CTal
§ ***bulbifera*** ♀H2 CPne ECho GKev WCot
- 'George' ♀H2 CTal ECho WCot
capensis ECho
carnosa ECho
comptonii ECho
contaminata ♀H2 CGrW CTal CTre ECho NRog WCot
§ ***corymbosa*** ♀H2 CTal ECho NRog
elegans ECho
- var. ***membranacea*** ECho
- var. ***suaveolens*** ECho NRog
ensifolia ECho LLHF NRog WCot
§ - subsp. ***ensifolia*** ♀H2 ECho
fistulosa CTal ECho
§ ***flava*** ♀H2 CTre ECho NRog SBch WCot
framesii ECho
'Fransie' (African Beauty Series) ECho
gillettii ECho
glaucophylla ECho
hirta ECho
juncifolia ECho NRog
- var. ***juncifolia*** ECho
kliprandensis NRog
lactosa ECho
latimerae CPne ECho WCot
leipoldtii ECho
'Lemon Ripple' (v) WCot
liliiflora CGrW CTal ECho NRog
longibracteata ECho
§ ***longituba*** ♀H3 CTal ECho NRog WCot
marginata ECho
mathewsii ECho NRog
mediana ECho NRog
montana ECho
multifolia ECho
mutabilis ECho
'Namakwa' (African Beauty Series) ♀H1c ECho GKev NRog
namaquensis ECho NRog
namibiensis ECho
nardoubergensis ECho
neilii ECho
§ 'Nelsonii' ECho SBch WCot
nervosa ECho WCot
obscura ECho WCot
orchioides var. ***glaucina*** ECho NRog WCot
orthopetala CTal ECho NRog WCot
pallida ECho NRog
§ ***paucifolia*** ECho
I 'Pearsonii' CTal ECho NRog SPlb
pendula see *L. bulbifera*
polyphylla ECho
pusilla ECho WCot
pustulata ♀H2 ECho NRog WCot
- blue-flowered CGrW ECho NRog
- yellow-flowered ECho NRog
§ ***pygmaea*** new CPBP
§ ***quadricolor*** ♀H2 CGrW CPrp CTsd ECho NRog WCot
reflexa ECho NRog
'Robijn' (African Beauty Series) ECho
'Rolina' (African Beauty Series) ECho
'Romaud' (African Beauty Series) ECho GKev NRog WCot
'Romelia' (African Beauty Series) ECho WCot
'Ronina' (African Beauty Series) ECho GKev NRog WCot
'Rosabeth' (African Beauty Series) ECho GKev NRog WCot
rosea ECho NRog
rubida ECho WCot
'Rupert' (African Beauty Series) ♀H2 GKev NRog WCot
splendida ECho
stayneri CLak
thomasiae ECho
trichophylla ECho
tricolor see *L. aloides*
unicolor ECho NRog WCot
unifolia ECho NRog
§ ***vanzyliae*** ♀H2 NRog WCot
violacea ECho
- var. ***glauca*** ECho
viridiflora ♀H2 ECho NRog
zebrina ECho
zeyheri ECho NRog WCot

Lactuca (*Asteraceae*)

alpina see *Cicerbita alpina*
perennis EPPr EWld WHer
virosa CArn

Lagarostrobos ✿ (*Podocarpaceae*)

§ ***franklinii*** CBcs IDee SAko WPGP
- 'Fota' (f) WThu
- 'Picton Castle' (m) WThu

Lagenaria (*Cucurbitaceae*)

siceraria 'Speckled Swan' SVic

Lagerstroemia (*Lythraceae*)

indica ♀H1c CAco CBod CCCN EPfP MGil SEND SEle SPlb SVen WSHC
- B&SWJ 12660 WCru
- Dynamite = 'Whit II' IDee
- Petite Pinkie = 'Monkie' IDee
- 'Red Imperator' CBcs
- 'Rosea' CBcs LRHS SEND
- 'Rubra' LRHS
subcostata CWJ 12352 WCru
'Tuscarora' new WPGP
'Tuskegee' WPGP

Lagotis (*Plantaginaceae*)

glauca GEdr
takedana new GEdr

Lagunaria (*Malvaceae*)

patersonii CHII LRHS WPGP

Lagurus (*Poaceae*)

ovatus	SAdn

Lamiastrum see *Lamium*

Lamium (*Lamiaceae*)

album	CArn CHab NMir
- 'Friday' (v)	NBir WHer
armenum	WAbe
- subsp. ***sintenisii*** **new**	WAbe
flexuosum	EPPr
§ ***galeobdolon***	CTri CWib CWld EShb MHer SRms WHer WWtn
§ - 'Florentinum' (v)	CMac EBee ECha ELan GMcL MMuc MRav SPer
- 'Hermann's Pride'	CBod EBee EHoe ELan ELon EPfP GKev GMaP LRHS NBir NDov NMir SPer SPoG SRms SWvt WAul WHoo WMoo XLum
- 'Kirkcudbright Dwarf'	EBee EPPr EWes GBin NBre XLum
§ - 'Silberteppich'	ECha MRav XLum
- 'Silver Angel'	XLum
- Silver Carpet	see *L. galeobdolon* 'Silberteppich'
- 'Variegatum'	see *L. galeobdolon* 'Florentinum'
garganicum subsp. ***garganicum***	CCse EWes
- subsp. ***pictum***	see *L. garganicum* subsp. *striatum*
- subsp. ***reniforme***	see *L. garganicum* subsp. *striatum*
§ - subsp. ***striatum***	CDor WAbe
(Lami Series) Lami Blush	CRos LRHS NRHS
- Lami Dark Purple **new**	LRHS NRHS
- Lami Pink	CRos LRHS NRHS
luteum	see *L. galeobdolon*
maculatum	CRos GWyn MMuc SRms WWtn
- 'Album'	ELan EPfP SPer SRms WWtn
- 'Anne Greenaway' (v)	EWes LPot SCob SPoG
§ - 'Aureum'	ECtt EHoe ELan ESps SWvt XLum
- 'Beacon Silver'	CMac CWib EAJP EBee ECha ECtt ELan EPfP EShb ESps GMcL GWyn LCro LPot LRHS MGos MJak MMuc MSCN NBir SCob SPer SPlb SPoG SRGP SRms SWvt WHar XLum
- 'Beedham's White'	NSti
- 'Brightstone Pearl'	EWes EWld MAvo
- 'Cannon's Gold'	CBod ECtt EWes LPot SWvt WMoo
- 'Chequers' ambig.	EBee ELan SPer
- 'Dingle Candy'	MHCG NWad
- 'Elisabeth de Haas' (v)	EWes NBre
- 'Forncett Lustre'	EWes
- 'Ghost'	ECtt EPPr LBuc
- 'Gold Leaf'	see *L. maculatum* 'Aureum'
- Golden Anniversary = 'Dellam'^{PBR} (v)	CBod ELan LSRN NBro SWvt
- 'Golden Nuggets'	see *L. maculatum* 'Aureum'
- 'Golden Wedding'	SRms
- Lami Mega Purple (Lami Series)	EBee
- 'Margery Fish'	SRms
- 'Moonglow'	EBee
- 'Orchid Frost'	CHid EBee EHoe ELon GQue LHop
- Pink Chablis = 'Checkin'^{PBR}	CBod ELon LRHS MHol NCou NLar NRHS
- 'Pink Nancy'	SWvt
- 'Pink Pearls'	CSBt NLar SHar WMoo
- 'Pink Pewter'	EBee ECGP ECha ECtt EHoe ELan EPfP EShb EWoo GMaP GWyn LRHS SCob SPer SPlb SPoG WTor WWtn
- 'Purple Winter'	EPPr
- 'Red Nancy'	ELan ELon LRHS SWvt XLum
§ - 'Roseum'	CWib EBee ELan GWyn MCot MRav NChi SPer WMoo XLum
- 'Shell Pink'	see *L. maculatum* 'Roseum'
- 'Silver Shield'	EWes
- 'Sterling Silver'	CSam
- 'White Nancy'	Widely available
- 'Wootton Pink'	MHCG NBir SWvt
orvala	Widely available
- 'Album'	CLAP EBee ELan EPPr IPot LEdu LHop LPla LRHS MBel NBir NLar SHar WHer
- pink-flowered	CSpe
- 'Silva'	CCVN CLAP EPPr EPfP IPot LEdu LRHS WCot WSHC
purpureum	GJos
sandrasicum	WAbe
'Wisley White' **new**	NBir

Lampranthus (*Aizoaceae*)

aberdeenensis	see *Delosperma aberdeenense*
apricot-flowered	LRHS NRHS
aurantiacus	CBcs
blandus	CBcs CCCN
'Blousey Pink'	SVen
§ ***brownii***	CBcs CCCN ECho ELan EPfP LRHS NRHS SPlb WPnn
deltoides	see *Oscularia deltoides*
edulis	see *Carpobrotus edulis*
'Exposure' **new**	CCCN
glaucus	SEND
multiradiatus	SEND
oscularis	see *Oscularia deltoides*
'Pink'	ELan SPlb WPnn
purple-flowered	CBod SPlb
roseus	CCCN CRos CSma ECho LRHS NRHS
'Salmon Pink'	SPlb WPnn
'Shanklin'	SPlb SVen
spectabilis	CBWd CBcs CCCN CTri GLet SArc WPnn
- orange-flowered	CBod
- purple-flowered	SPlb
- 'Tresco Apricot'	CCCN
- 'Tresco Brilliant'	CBod CCCN CHVG ELon MSCN SEND WPnn
- 'Tresco Fire'	CAbb CCCN CSma ELon SPlb SVen
- 'Tresco Orange'	CCCN WPnn
- 'Tresco Peach'	CCCN
- 'Tresco Purple'	CWCL ELan
- 'Tresco Red'	CCCN ELon EUJe SEND WPnn
- white-flowered	GKev SPlb SVen WPnn
- yellow-flowered	EUJe SVen WPnn
stipulaceus	SPlb

Lamprocapnos (*Papaveraceae*)

§ ***spectabilis*** ♀H7	Widely available
- 'Alba' ♀H7	Widely available
- 'Gold Heart'^{PBR}	CBcs CBod CRos CWGN EBee ECha ECtt EHoe EPfP ESwi GKev GLet GMcL IBoy LHop LRHS MAsh MGos MHol MRav NHpl NLar NSti SCob SPoG WBor WCot WFar WHil
- 'Love Hearts' **new**	MHol
- 'Valentine'	Widely available
- 'White Heart'	GJos

Lamprothyrsus (*Poaceae*)

hieronymi RCB RA K2-2	CAby MAvo WCot WPGP

Lanaria (*Lanariaceae*)

	lanata	CLak

Lancea (*Phrymaceae*)

	tibetica	GEdr

Lantana ✿ (*Verbenaceae*)

	'Calippo Tutti Frutti'	EUJe LSou
	camara	CArn ELan EShb SEle SPhx
	- (Lucky Series) Lucky Peach = 'Balucpea'	SPoG
	- - Lucky Pure Gold = 'Balucpure'PBR	SPoG
	- - Lucky Red Flame = 'Balandimfla'	SPoG
	- - Lucky Sunrise Rose = 'Balandrise'PBR	EPfP SPoG
	- - Lucky White = 'Balucwite'PBR	EPfP SPoG
	- 'Mine d'Or'	EUJe
	- orange-flowered	CCCN
	- pink-flowered	CCCN
	- red-flowered	CCCN
	- white-flowered	CCCN
	'Chapel Hill Gold'PBR	CMan
	'Dallas Red'	CMan
	'Miss Huff'	CMan EBee
§	***montevidensis***	CSam
	'Pink Caprice'	CMan
	sellowiana	see *L. montevidensis*
	'Spreading Sunset'	CMan
	'Sunny Side Up'PBR	CMan

Lapageria ✿ (*Philesiaceae*)

	rosea 🏆H3	CCCN CPne CRHN CTsd SAdn SChF SWvt WPGP
	- var. ***albiflora*** 🏆H3	CRHN SChF
	- 'Beatrix Anderson'	CRHN
	- 'Flesh Pink'	CRHN
	- 'Pink Panther'	CRHN
	- 'Tierra del Fuego'	CRHN

Lapeirousia (*Iridaceae*)

	anceps	ECho
	corymbosa	ECho
	cruenta	see *Freesia laxa*
	divaricata	ECho
	fastigiata	ECho
	laxa	see *Freesia laxa*

Lapsana (*Asteraceae*)

	communis 'Inky'	CNat

Lardizabala (*Lardizabalaceae*)

	biternata	see *L. funaria*
§	***funaria***	CFil CRHN WCru

Larix ✿ (*Pinaceae*)

	decidua	CAco CCVT CDul CMen ECrN ELan EPfP ESps EWTr GMcL IBoy MGos MMuc NEgg NWea SEND SMad SPlb WHar WHed WTSh
	- 'Corley'	CKen
§	- var. ***decidua***	MJak
	- 'Globus'	SLim
	- 'Horstmann Recurved'	NLar
	- 'Krejci'	NLar
	- 'Little Bogle'	CKen MAsh MBlu NEgg NLar
	- 'Lucek' **new**	NLar
	- 'Oberförster Karsten'	CKen NLar
	- 'Pendula'	CMen
	- 'Puli' 🏆H7	LRHS MAsh MBlu NHol NLar NOra SLim SPer WMat
	- 'Raohuil' **new**	NLar
	- 'Roman'	NLar
	× ***eurolepis***	see *L.* × *marschlinsii*
	europaea DC.	see *L. decidua* var. *decidua*
	gmelinii var. ***gmelinii***	CMen
	- 'Tharandt'	CKen SLim
§	***kaempferi***	CAco CCVT CDul CMen ELan EPfP ESps LBuc NEgg NWea SCoo SEWo WTSh
	- 'Bambino'	CKen
	- 'Bingman'	CKen
	- 'Blue Ball'	CKen NLar
	- 'Blue Dwarf' 🏆H7	MAsh
	- 'Blue Rabbit'	CKen NEgg
	- 'Cruwys Morchard'	CKen
	- 'Diana'	CEnd CKen CMen MAsh NEgg NHol NOrn SLim
	- 'Elizabeth Rehder'	CKen
	- 'Grant Haddow'	CKen
	- 'Grey Green Dwarf'	MAsh
	- 'Grey Pearl'	CKen LRHS MAsh
	- 'Hanna's Broom'	SLim
	- 'Hobbit'	CKen NEgg
	- 'Jakobsen'	NLar
*	- 'Jakobsen's Pyramid'	CMen MAsh NOrn WMat
	- 'Lobby Dosser'	CMen NEgg
I	- 'Nana'	CKen CMen NEgg NHol
I	- 'Nana Prostrata'	CKen
	- 'Pendula'	CEnd EPfP SPoG
	- 'Pulii'	EBee
	- 'Stiff Weeper' 🏆H7	LRHS NEgg NLar NOrn SLim
	- 'Varley'	CKen
	- 'Wehlen'	CKen
	- 'Wolterdingen'	CKen NLar
	laricina 'Arethusa Bog'	CKen
	- 'Bear Swamp'	CKen SLim
	- 'Bingman'	CKen
	- 'Blue Sparkler' **new**	NLar
	- 'Hartwig Pine'	CKen
	- 'Newport Beauty'	CKen
	- 'Stubby'	CKen SLim
	leptolepis	see *L. kaempferi*
§	× ***marschlinsii***	CCVT NWea
	- 'Domino'	CKen CMen
	- 'Gail'	CKen
	- 'Julie'	CKen

Laser (*Apiaceae*)

	trilobum	GEdr SPhx
	- PAB 3382	LEdu WPGP

Laserpitium (*Apiaceae*)

	latifolium	EBee
§	***siler***	CArn CSpe IMou MAvo NDov SPhx SPlb WSHC

Lasiagrostis see *Stipa*

Lasiospermum (*Asteraceae*)

	bipinnatum	SPlb

Lastreopsis (*Dryopteridaceae*)

	hispida	ESwi

Lathraea (*Orobanchaceae*)

	clandestina	CAvo

Lathyrus ✿ (*Papilionaceae*)

§	***articulatus***	CSpe
§	***aureus***	CDor CHid CLAP CSpe EBee GBuc GCal IFro MCot MHer MNrw NBid NBir NChi SBrt SKHP WAul WHal WHea
	- 'Cally Variegated' (v)	GCal
	chilensis	GWyn
	chloranthus	SPav
	cirrhosus	EBee WSHC
	clymenum articulatus	see *L. articulatus*
	cyaneus misapplied	see *L. vernus*
	davidii	CFis EWes LEdu SBrt WBor WCot WSHC
	eucosmus	EBee
	fremontii hort.	see *L. laxiflorus*
	grandiflorus 🏆H7	CTri EBee NChi NHpl SDix SMHy WCot
	× ***hammettii*** 'Erewhon'	CHid
	heterophyllus	EBee
	incurvus	SPhx
	inermis	see *L. laxiflorus*
	japonicus	CEls
	- subsp. ***maritimus***	GJos SPhx WCot
	latifolius 🏆H7	CArn CRHN ECrN EPfP ESps GMcL MHer MHol NPer SRms SVic WBor WBrk WCot WFar WHer XLum
§	- 'Albus' 🏆H7	CFlo CTri SPav SRms WKif XLum
	- 'Blushing Bride'	WCot
	- pale pink-flowered	MBel
	- Pink Pearl	see *L. latifolius* 'Rosa Perle'
	- 'Red Pearl'	CBcs CFlo CKel EBee EPfP GAbr LBuc LRHS LSRN NLar SEND SPav SPer SPlb SPoG SWvt WFar
§	- 'Rosa Perle' 🏆H7	CBcs CFlo CKel CLet CRos CTri EBee ECha ESps LCro LHop LRHS LSRN MRav NBir NLar NPer SBod SPer SPoG SWvt WBor WMoo XLum
	- 'Rose Queen'	GJos
	- Weisse Perle	see *L. latifolius* 'White Pearl'
	- 'White Pearl' misapplied	see *L. latifolius* 'Albus'
§	- 'White Pearl' 🏆H7	CBcs CKel CLet CRos EBee ECha EPfP ESps GAbr LBuc LCro LRHS LSRN MBel MHer MRav NBir NLar NPer SPer SPoG SWvt WBor WFar XLum
§	***laxiflorus***	EBee EWld MCot MMuc WHea WMoo WOut WSHC
	- white-flowered **new**	SBrt
	linifolius	EBee NLar SBrt
	montanus	GPoy
	nervosus	CSpe MCot SBee SRms
	neurolobus	SBrt
	niger	CFis CSpe EBee EWld GJos LEdu LHop LSou MCot MHer MMrt
	nissolia	WSFF
	odoratus	SVic
	- 'Alan Titchmarsh' **new**	WHlf
	- 'Anniversary'	MCot
	- 'Beth Chatto'	MCot
	- 'Betty Maiden'	MCot
	- 'Blue Medley'	MCot
	- 'Blue Velvet' **new**	WHlf
	- 'Burlesque' **new**	WHlf
	- 'Burnished Bronze'	MCot
	- 'Charlie's Angel' 🏆H2	LCro LOPS MCot
	- 'Clotted Cream' **new**	NMat
	- 'Cupani'	MNHC SPhx
	- 'Dark Passion'	MCot
	- 'Dawn'	MCot
	- 'Enchanté' **new**	WHlf
	- 'Ethel Grace'	MCot
	- 'Evening Glow' 🏆H2	MCot
I	- 'Fragrantissima' (mixed)	CHid
	- 'George Priestley'	MCot
I	- 'Gwendoline' 🏆H2	LCro LOPS WHlf
	- 'High Scent' 🏆H2	LCro LOPS
	- 'Honey Pink'	MCot
	- 'Honeymoon'	MCot
	- 'Jilly' 🏆H2	MCot
	- 'Karen Louise'	LCro LOPS
	- 'Linda C'	LCro LOPS
	- 'Lord Nelson'	SPhx
	- 'Marion'	MCot
	- 'Marti Caine'	MCot
	- 'Matucana' 🏆H2	CSpe LCro LOPS
	- 'Midnight'	LCro LOPS SPhx
	- 'Milly'	MCot
	- 'Misty Mountain'	MCot
	- 'Mollie Rilstone'	MCot
	- 'Mrs Bernard Jones' 🏆H2	MCot
	- 'Mrs Collier'	SPhx
	- 'Painted Lady'	LCro
	- 'Promise'	MCot
	- 'Restormel'	LCro LOPS MCot
	- 'Richard and Judy'	MCot
	- 'Rose Pearl' **new**	CRos
	- 'Wedding Day' 🏆H2	MCot
	- 'White Frills'	SPhx
	palustris	EBee LLWG SPlb
	pisiformis	EBee
	pratensis	CHab EBee NMir WSFF
	roseus	EBee GCal WHea WSHC
	rotundifolius 🏆H7	CHid GLog SPhx WSHC
	- 'Tillyperone' 🏆H7	EBee GNew SPhx WSHC
	sativus	CHid CSpe ELan MCot
	splendens	SBrt
	subandinus	GBin SPlb
	sulphureus **new**	SBrt
	sylvestris	EBee GJos WBrk
	transsylvanicus	EBee GBin SPhx
	tuberosus	CHid CRHN EBee LEdu WCot WSHC
	'Tubro'	EBee
	venetus	EBee EWes MNrw WSHC
§	***vernus*** 🏆H5	Widely available
	- 'Albiflorus'	MNrw XEll
	- 'Alboroseus' 🏆H5	CDor CLAP CPla ELan EPfP EWTr GBuc GCal GCra IFro LHop MNrw NBir NChi NLar NPnk SPhx SPoG SWat SWvt WCAu WCot WHoo
	- var. ***albus***	CLAP CMea MNrw WCot
	- ***aurantiacus***	see *L. aureus*
	- 'Caeruleus'	CLAP WHoo
*	- 'Cyaneus'	CDor SHar SWat WCot
	- 'Dama Emily'	SHar
	- 'Dama Violetta'	SHar
I	- 'Filifolius'	CSpe MCot
	- 'Flaccidus'	CAby EBee MNrw WCot
*	- 'Gracilis'	EBee LEdu NLar SHar WPGP
I	- 'Gracilis Alboroseus'	SHar
	- 'Little Elf'	SHar
	- 'Madelaine'	WCot
I	- 'Pendulus'	SHar
	- purple-flowered	LRHS MMuc SEND
	- 'Rainbow'	CLAP CRos EPfP LRHS MPie NRHS
	- 'Rosenelfe'	CBcs GBuc LEdu MHer SHar SPhx WCot WHal WHil WSHC

- f. ***roseus***	ECha LRHS MMuc MRav NBir SEND SRms WBrk WCot
- 'Spring Melody'	EBee MRav SHar WCot
- 'Subtle Hints'	SHar WCot
- 'Winter Blush'	SHar

Laurelia (*Atherospermataceae*)

§ ***sempervirens***	WPGP
serrata	see *L. sempervirens*

Laureliopsis (*Atherospermataceae*)

philippiana	CBcs EBee NLar WPGP

Laurentia see *Isotoma*

Laurus (*Lauraceae*)

§ ***azorica***	CBcs
canariensis	see *L. azorica*
nobilis 🏆^{H4}	Widely available
- f. ***angustifolia*** 🏆^{H4}	CJun CMac CTsd LRHS MBlu MHer MMuc MRav NLar SArc SCob SEND SPoG
- 'Aurea' 🏆^{H4}	CBcs CDul CLet CMac EBee ELan ELon EPfP ESps MHer MMuc NLar SCob SEND SLim SLon SMad SWvt WMoo
- clipped pyramid	LSRN
- 'Crispa'	MRav
- variegated (v)	CMac SRms
rotundifolia **new**	CAco

Lavandula ✿ (*Lamiaceae*)

'After Midnight'	see *L.* 'Avonview'
'Alba'	see *L. angustifolia* 'Alba', *L.* × *intermedia* 'Alba'
'Alba' ambig.	CWib SIde SPer
§ ***angustifolia***	Widely available
- 'Alba' misapplied	see *L. angustifolia* 'Blue Mountain White'
§ - 'Alba'	ELan EPfP EWoo GPoy LSRN MHer MRav MSwo SCob SLon SPlb SVen WGwG WJek XSen
- 'Alba Nana'	see *L. angustifolia* 'Nana Alba'
- 'Arctic Snow'	CBcs CRos ENor EPfP LCro LRHS LSRN MHer MSwo NBes NGdn NPri SDow SFai SHil SPer SPoG SRms WLav XSen
- Aromatico Blue = 'Lablusa'^{PBR}	CRos LRHS
- Aromatico Forte Blue = 'Laa20001'	CRos LRHS SPoG
- Aromatico Silver = 'Lasila'	CRos GMcL LRHS
- 'Ashdown Forest'	ELan ENfk MHer MNHC SAdn SBch SCob SDow SFai SPer SRGP SRms WJek WLav XSen
- 'Babelle'	XSen
- 'Backhouse Purple'	SDow
- 'Beechwood Blue' 🏆^{H5}	SCob SDow WLav
- 'Belle Hélène'	XSen
- 'Betty's Blue'	SDow
- Blue Cushion = 'Lavandula Schola'^{PBR}	LCro LOPS LSRN MAsh SFai SPoG SRms WLav
- Blue Ice = 'Dow3'^{PBR}	EAEE ENor MNHC SDow SFai SGol SLim SRms WJek WLav XSen
- 'Blue Lance'	MHol
- 'Blue Mountain'	XSen
§ - 'Blue Mountain White'	CRos LRHS SDow SHil WLav XSen
- 'Blue Rider'	EAEE LRHS WGwG WLav
- Blue Scent = 'Syngablusc'	CRos LRHS
§ - 'Bowles's Early'	WGwG
- 'Bowles's Grey'	see *L. angustifolia* 'Bowles's Early'
- 'Bowles's Variety'	see *L. angustifolia* 'Bowles's Early'
- 'Cedar Blue'	ELan ENfk MHer MHol SDow SHDw SRms WGwG WLav XSen
- 'Coconut Ice'	EMOT WLav XSen
- 'Compacta'	SDow WLav XSen
- 'Crystal Lights'	EMOT
- 'Dursley White'	WLav
- 'Dwarf Blue'	CBod ENfk EPfP ESps LSRN MHed SRms WFar XSen
- 'Elizabeth'	ENor LCro LSRN SCob SDow SFai SPoG SRms WLav XSen
- (Ellagance Series) 'Ellagance Ice'	GMcL LRHS SRms
- - 'Ellagance Pink'	LOPS
- - 'Ellagance Purple'	CRos LOPS LRHS SHil SRms
- - 'Ellagance Sky'	CRos LBMP LOPS LRHS SRms
- 'Essence Purple'	CBod
- 'Felice'^{PBR} **new**	LRHS
- 'Folgate' 🏆^{H5}	CBod ECtt ENfk EPfP MHer MNHC NGdn SDow SRms WHoo WJek WLav XSen
- Garden Beauty = 'Lowmar'^{PBR} (v)	LBuc SPoG XSen
- Granny's Bouquet = 'Lavang38'	EMOT GWyn XSen
- 'Havana'	SPoG XSen
§ - 'Hidcote' 🏆^{H5}	Widely available
- 'Hidcote Pink'	CWCL CWib ESps LBrs LSou MHer MNHC MRav NGdn SCob SDow SPer SRms SWat XSen
- 'Hidcote Superior'	LBMP MArt NGdn
- 'Imperial Gem' 🏆^{H5}	Widely available
- 'Jean Davis'	see *L. angustifolia* 'Rosea'
- 'Lady'	NPer
- 'Lady Ann'	CWCL SDow WLav
- 'Lavenite Petite'^{PBR}	ENor LBMP LLHF LRHS LSRN NLar SDow SFai SHil SPoG SRms WLav XSen
- Little Lady = 'Batlad' 🏆^{H5}	CGar CMea ECtt ENor GMcL LBMP LCro LOPS LRHS LSRN MAsh MNHC MPie MSwo NBes NLar SFai SGol SRms SWvt WGwG WHoo WLav XSen
- Little Lottie = 'Clarmo' 🏆^{H5}	ELon LBrs LSRN MHer SDow SWvt WLav XSen
- 'Loddon Blue'	CRos ENor EPfP LBrs LRHS MAsh SDow SFai SHil SRms WLav XSen
§ - 'Loddon Pink'	CRos ELan ENor EPfP ESps GMaP LRHS MAsh MMuc MRav NGdn SEND SFai SHil SRms WLav XSen
- 'Luberon'	XSen
- 'Lullaby Blue'	SDow
- 'Lumières des Alpes'	XSen
- 'Maillette'	NGdn SDow SRms WLav XSen
- 'Matheronne'	XSen
- 'Melissa'	MHol XSen
- Melissa Lilac = 'Dow4'^{PBR}	CBcs CRos CSBt EAEE EBee ECrN ENfk ENor LBMP LCro LOPS LRHS LSRN MGos MHer MNHC NDov SDow SFai SHil SRkn SRms WLav XSen
- 'Middachten'	XSen
- 'Miss Dawnderry'	SDow
- 'Miss Donnington'	see *L. angustifolia* 'Bowles's Early'
- 'Miss Katherine'^{PBR} 🏆^{H5}	CRos CWCL ECtt ELan ENor EPfP ESps LBMP LRHS MAsh SDow SPoG WLav XSen
- Miss Muffet = 'Scholmis' 🏆^{H5}	LLHF SBch SDow SRms WLav XSen

	- 'Mont Ventoux'	XSen
	- 'Montagne de Lure'	XSen
	- 'Munstead'	Widely available
§	- 'Nana Alba' 🏆H5	CRos ELan ENfk EPfP GMaP GPoy LRHS MAsh MHer SBch SDow SPer SRms SWvt WJek XSen
	- 'Nana Atropurpurea'	SDow XSen
	- 'Nikita'	XSen
	- 'No 9'	SDow
	- 'Pacific Blue'	CRos LRHS SHil XSen
	- 'Perle de Rosée'	XSen
	- 'Peter Pan'	ECtt ELan ESps GBuc LSRN MHer MNHC SDow WLav XSen
	- Platinum Blonde = 'Momparler'PBR	EBee ENor LSou SFai SPoG
	- 'Princess Blue'	ENor LRHS WLav XSen
§	- 'Rosea'	Widely available
	- 'Royal Blue'	LRHS
	- 'Royal Purple'	ENor ESps EWes LSou NGdn SDow SWvt WLav XSen
	- 'Royal Velvet'	SDow
	- 'Saint Jean'	SDow XSen
	- 'Siesta'	XSen
	- 'Silver Blue'	XSen
	- 'Silver Mist'	CBod CMea EPfP GMcL SRms WHer
	- 'Sophie'	XSen
	- 'Thumbelina Leigh'PBR	ENor LBMP MAsh SDow SFai SHil SRms XSen
	- 'Twickel Purple'	CBar CBcs CWCL EAEE EBee ELan ENfk EPfP ESps LBMP LHop LRHS LSRN MHed MHol MNHC SBod SCob SDow SFai SPer SRms SWat SWvt WGwG WLav XSen
	- 'Walberton's Silver Edge'	see *L.* × *intermedia* Walberton's Silver Edge
	aristibracteata	MHer WLav
§	'Avonview'	MHer SDow WHoo WLav
	'Ballerina' 🏆H4	SDow
§	'Bee Brilliant'PBR	ENfk WLav
§	'Bee Cool'PBR	ENfk MHer WLav
§	'Bee Happy'	CWCL ENfk NBir WLav
§	'Bee Pretty'	ENfk
	'Bella Zealand' (Bella Series)	CRos LRHS
	'Blue Star'	EPfP GMcL LRHS MNHC SHil SRms
	'Bouquet of Roses'	CRos LRHS SHil
	buchii var. ***buchii***	SDow SVen WLav
	'Bulls Cross'	WLav
	canariensis	MHer SDow SVen WLav
	× ***chaytoriae*** 'Gorgeous'	SDow
	- 'Helen' **new**	SDow
	- 'Joan Head'	XSen
	- 'Molton Silver'	XSen
	- 'Richard Gray' 🏆H4	LRHS LSRN MHed MHer MNHC NLar SDow SIgm SRms WLav XSen
§	- 'Sawyers' 🏆H4	Widely available
	- 'Silver Sands'	CRos ENor EPfP LBMP LRHS LSou SFai SPoG XSen
	× ***christiana***	ENor LRHS SDow SFai SHDw SVen WJek WLav
	'Cornard Blue'	see *L.* × *chaytoriae* 'Sawyers'
	Crème Brûlée = 'Lavsts10'	LRHS NRHS
	dentata	ENfk GPoy MNHC SEND SRms WJek XSen
§	- var. ***candicans***	MHer MNHC SDow SRms WJek WLav XSen
	- var. ***dentata*** 'Dusky Maiden'	CRos LRHS SDow WLav
	- - 'Ploughman's Blue'	SVen WGwG
	- - f. ***rosea***	SDow
	- - 'Royal Crown' 🏆H3	WLav
	- - Serenity = 'Lavden123'PBR	CRos LRHS
	- 'Harmony'	CRos LRHS
	- silver-leaved	see *L. dentata* var. *candicans*
	'Devonshire Compact'	CSBt EAJP MHol SHil SRms WJek
	'Fathead'	CBcs CBod CRos EBee ECtt ELan EPfP ESps LBMP LRHS LSRN MAsh MGos MHer MNHC NBir NGdn NLar NPri SCob SCoo SDow SFai SGol SPoG WJek WLav
	'Flaming Purple'	SDow
	× ***ginginsii*** 'Goodwin Creek Grey' 🏆H4	MHer SDow SGol SRms WGwG WJek WLav
	'Hazel'	CRos EPfP LRHS
	'Heavenly Blue'	EPfP
	'Helmsdale'PBR	CEnd CRos CSBt ELan ENor EPfP ESps GMaP GMcL IKil LCro LRHS LSRN MAsh MRav NGdn NLar SCob SCoo SFai SGol SLim SPer
	heterophylla misapplied	see *L.* × *heterophylla* Viv. Gaston Allard Group
§	× ***heterophylla*** Viv. Gaston Allard Group	WLav
	- - 'African Pride'	SVen
	'Hidcote Blue'	see *L. angustifolia* 'Hidcote'
	× ***intermedia*** 'Abrialii'	SDow
§	- 'Alba' 🏆H5	CBot CMea MHed MHer MMuc MNHC SCob SEND SVen XSen
	- 'Arabian Night'	see *L.* × *intermedia* 'Impress Purple', 'Sussex'
	- 'Arabian Night' ambig.	SRms
§	- Dutch Group	CSBt CWib ENfk EPfP ESps LRHS MAsh MNHC MRav MSwo SArc SBod SCoo SDow SFai SLim SPer SRms SWat
	- 'Edelweiss'	CBod CRos CSBt CWib ENfk EPfP ESps LRHS MNHC MRav NEgg NGdn NLar SCob SDow SFai SGol SPoG SRms SWvt WLav XSen
	- 'Enigma'	CBar
	- 'Fragrant Memories'	SDow WLav XSen
	- 'Fred Boutin'	SGol
*	- 'Futura'	XSen
	- Goldburg = 'Burgoldeen' (v)	SGol
	- 'Grappenhall' misapplied	see *L.* × *intermedia* 'Enigma', 'Pale Pretender'
	- 'Grey Hedge'	SRms WLav
	- 'Gros Bleu'	SDow SFai WLav XSen
	- 'Grosso'	Widely available
	- (Heavenly Series) 'Heavenly Angel'	ENor SDow SFai
	- - 'Heavenly Night'	ENor SDow SFai SPoG
	- - 'Heavenly Scent'	ENor SDow SFai
	- 'Hidcote Giant' 🏆H5	CRos EPfP GCal LRHS NPer SDow SHil WKif WLav XSen
§	- 'Impress Purple'	SDow WLav XSen
	- 'Lullingstone Castle'	ENfk SDow SRms WJek WLav
	- 'Nizza'	XSen
	- 'Old English' misapplied	see *L.* × *intermedia* 'Seal'
	- 'Old English'	CBod ENfk SDow SRms
	- Old English Group	MMuc MNHC SEND WHoo WJek WLav XSen
	- 'Olympia'	SDow
§	- 'Pale Pretender'	CBod CSBt MHer MRav MSwo SPer SRms WJek XSen
	- 'Provence'	SDow SFai XSen
	- Pure Platinum = 'Niko'	ENor SFai
§	- 'Seal'	ENfk GMaP MNHC SCob SDow SRms WJek XSen

	- 'Super'	XSen
§	- 'Sussex' ♀H5	CBod CFis CRos EPfP LRHS SDow WLav XSen
	- 'Twickel Purple'	CWib ELan EWes NLar SGol SWat WJek
§	- Walberton's Silver Edge = 'Walvera' (v)	CRos EBee EMOT ENor EPfP ESps LBuc LRHS MGos SCoo SDow SFai SPoG SRms XSen
	'Jamboree'	WLav
	'Jean Davis'	see *L. angustifolia* 'Rosea'
	lanata ♀H3	CArn ECha GPoy SRms WJek WLav XSen
§	***latifolia***	CArn XSen
I	'Lavender Lace'	LSRN
	'Loddon Pink'	see *L. angustifolia* 'Loddon Pink'
	'Madrid Blue'	see *L.* 'Bee Happy'
	'Madrid Pink'	see *L.* 'Bee Pretty'
	'Madrid Purple'	see *L.* 'Bee Brilliant'
	'Madrid White'	see *L.* 'Bee Cool'
	'Marshwood'	CTri
	minutolii	SDow
	multifida	MHer WLav
	officinalis	see *L. angustifolia*
	Passionné = 'Lavsts 08'PBR ♀H4	EMOT WLav
	pedunculata	EBee XSen
	- subsp. ***lusitanica***	EPfP LRHS SPoG
	- - Lusi Pink = 'Wijs02'	SFai
§	- subsp. ***pedunculata***	CAby CBar CBod CRos ECha ECrN ENor EPfP LCro LOPS LRHS LSRN MAsh MGos MJak MMuc MNHC MSCN MSwo NGdn SCob SDow SFai SGol SHil SPer SRms SWat WJek
	- - 'James Compton' ♀H3	CRos CWib ECha LRHS MAsh NGdn
	- subsp. ***sampaiana*** 'Purple Emperor'	CRos EPfP LRHS SHil WLav
	pedunculatus subsp. ***lusitanica*** 'Lusi Purple'	SFai SPoG
	pinnata	CRos ENfk ENor EPfP LRHS MHol MNHC SDow SHil
	'Pretty Polly' ♀H4	CAbP CBcs CRos ELan ENor EPfP LRHS MAsh SDow SFai SRkn WJek WLav
	'Pukehou'	EPfP LRHS SCoo SDow WLav
	'Regal Splendour'PBR	CRos CSBt ECrN ELan EMOT ENor EPfP ESps LCro LRHS LSRN MAsh MGos MHer MNHC NPri SCob SCoo SDow SFai SGol SHil SLim SPoG SRms WLav
	Rocky Road = 'Fair09'PBR	ENor LCro SFai WLav
	'Rosea'	see *L. angustifolia* 'Rosea'
	rotundifolia	SDow
	'Silver Edge'	see *L.* × *intermedia* Walberton's Silver Edge
	Silver Sands = 'Fair 14'PBR	EWoo
	'Somerset Mist'	WLav
	spica nom. rejic.	see *L. angustifolia*, *L.* × *intermedia*, *L. latifolia*
	- 'Hidcote Purple'	see *L. angustifolia* 'Hidcote'
	stoechas	CBcs CBod CLet CRos CSBt ECha ELan EPfP ESps GMaP GPoy LBMP LHop LRHS LSRN MArt MJak MNHC MSwo NBes NPri SCob SDow SFai SIgm SPer SPlb SWvt WHar
	- var. ***albiflora***	see *L. stoechas* subsp. *stoechas* f. *leucantha*
	- 'Anouk'PBR	EBee ELan EPfP ESps LRHS SPoG
	- 'Antibes' (Provençal Series)	SRms
	- 'Avignon' (Provençal Series)	SRms
	- (Bella Series) Bella Lavender = 'Bellav'	CRos LRHS NRHS SHil
	- - Bella Peach	CRos LRHS SHil
	- - Bella Rose = 'Belros'	CRos LRHS SHil
	- - Bella Rouge = 'Belrou'	CRos LRHS
	- 'Blueberry Ruffles'PBR (Ruffles Series)	SHil
	- Castilliano Violet	GMcL
	- (Coco Series) Coco Deep Pink	CRos LRHS SHil
	- - Coco Deep Purple	CRos
	- - Coco Deep Rose	CRos
	- - Coco Deep White on Blue	SHil
	- - Coco Deep White on Rose	CRos LRHS
	- - Coco Purple = 'Cocpur' **new**	LRHS NRHS
	- - Coco Rose **new**	LRHS NRHS
	- 'Dark Royalty'PBR	ELan
	- Javelin Blue = 'Jin Bulle' **new**	CRos GMcL LRHS
	- Javelin Compact Rose = 'Labz0001'PBR **new**	GMcL
	- Javelin Upright White Blush = 'Labz0002'PBR **new**	GMcL
	- 'Lace'	LSRN WLav
	- (Little Bee Series) Little Bee Deep Purple = 'Florvendula Deep Purple'	CRos GMcL LRHS
	- - Little Bee Deep Rose = 'Florvendula Deep Rose'	CRos LRHS
	- - Little Bee Lilac = 'Florvendula Lilac'	CRos LRHS
	- subsp. ***luisieri*** 'Tickled Pink'PBR	CWCL
	- 'Night of Passion'	SDow
	- 'Papillon'	see *L. pedunculata* subsp. *pedunculata*
	- subsp. ***pedunculata***	see *L. pedunculata* subsp. *pedunculata*
	- 'Pink Angels'	ELan
	- 'Purley'	SRms
	- Ruffles Series	ENfk
	- 'Silver Anouk'PBR	CBod EPfP LRHS
§	- subsp. ***stoechas*** f. ***leucantha***	CRos CWCL CWib LRHS MSwo SCob SDow SHil
	- - - 'Snowman'	CBcs CRos CSBt EPfP LCro LRHS MAsh MHer SCob SCoo SFai SPoG SWvt
	- - Lilac Wings = 'Prolil'PBR	CRos ENor EPfP LLHF LRHS NLar SCoo SFai SHil WLav
	- - 'Provençal'	CRos LRHS SCob SCoo SHil
	- - 'Purple Wings'	CRos ELan EPfP LRHS MAsh MGos SHil SLim
	- - f. ***rosea*** 'Kew Red'	CBcs CTri CWib EAJP ECrN ENfk ENor LCro LOPS LRHS MGos MHer SDow SFai SRms SWvt WHar WJek WLav
	- 'Sugarberry Ruffles'PBR (Ruffles Series)	ENfk
	- 'Victory'	CRos LRHS SHil SPoG
	- 'With Love'PBR	SDow
	Tiara = 'Fair 10'PBR	CAby CRos CSBt ENfk ENor LCro LOPS LRHS LSRN MGos NLar NPri SCoo SDow SFai SHil SRms WLav
	'Van Gogh'	SDow

	vera misapplied	see *L.* × *intermedia* Dutch Group
	vera DC.	see *L. angustifolia*
	viridis	CBod CLau CPla CRos ELan EPfP LRHS MHer NPer SDow SRms WAbe WJek WLav
	'Whero Iti'	SDow
	'Willow Vale' 🏆H3	CRos ENor EPfP LBMP LCro LRHS MAsh MHer SDow SFai SRms SWvt WJek

Lavatera (*Malvaceae*)

	arborea	CArn SChr SEND WHer
	- 'Rosea'	see *L.* × *clementii* 'Rosea'
	- 'Variegata' (v)	ELan NPer SEND WCot WTou
	bicolor	see *L. maritima*
	cachemiriana	NPer
	Chamallow = 'Inovera'PBR	LRHS LSRN
	× ***clementii*** 'Barnsley'	Widely available
	- 'Barnsley Baby'	CRos EBee ELan GMcL LBMP LBuc LRHS NGdn NLar NPer NPri SEle SHil SPer SRkn SWvt WBor
	- 'Blushing Bride'	CRos EPfP ESps LRHS LSRN MGos NLar SWvt
	- 'Bredon Springs' 🏆H5	CDul CRos CSBt EBee ECha ELon EPfP ESps GMcL LHop LRHS LSRN MAsh MGos MMuc MSwo NGdn SEND SGol SLim SPer SWvt XLum
	- 'Burgundy Wine' 🏆H5	CBcs CRos EBee ELan EPfP ESps EUJe LBMP LRHS MAsh MGos MJak MSwo NBir NEgg NLar NPer NPri SGbt SHil SLim SLon SPer SPoG SWvt WFar WHar
	- 'Candy Floss' 🏆H5	ESps GMcL LRHS MAsh NBir NLar NPer SGol
	- 'Eye Catcher'	IVic LRHS MSwo NLar SPer WHar
	- 'Kew Rose'	ESps LRHS MMuc MNHC MSwo NLar NPer SEND SLim SRms XLum
	- 'Lavender Lady'	LHop NPer SEND
	- 'Lisanne'	ESps LRHS MMuc MSwo SGol
	- 'Mary Hope' 🏆H5	CRos EPfP LRHS MAsh NPri SEle SHil SPoG SWvt
	- Memories = 'Stelav'	LRHS LSRN
§	- 'Pink Frills'	ESps SWvt WCot WFar
	- Red Rum = 'Rigrum'PBR 🏆H5	CMac CRos CSBt EPfP LBuc LLHF LSRN MAsh MGos MHol NEgg NLar NPri SCob SEND SLim SPoG SWvt WFar
§	- 'Rosea' 🏆H5	Widely available
	- 'Ruby Star' **new**	LRHS NRHS SCob
	- 'Songbird' **new**	SCob
§	- 'Wembdon Variegated' (v)	NPer
	'Frederique'	CSBt LBuc LRHS NLar SWvt
	'Grey Beauty'	GMcL LHop LRHS SEle SMad
	'Magenta Magic'	EBee NLar SPoG
§	***maritima*** 🏆H3	CAbP CLet CMac CNec CRos ELan EPfP ESps GMcL LHop LRHS NPri SEND SEle SPer SRkn SWvt WFar WKif WSHC
	- 'Princesse de Lignes'	XLum
	olbia	SDix SPlb SRms WFar
	- 'Lilac Lady'	EBee ECha ECrN ELan LRHS MGos MMuc NLar WFar WKif
	'Peppermint Ice'	see *L. thuringiaca* 'Ice Cool'
	'Pink Frills'	see *L.* × *clementii* 'Pink Frills'
	'Rosea'	see *L.* × *clementii* 'Rosea'
	'Sweet Dreams'PBR	LSou
	thuringiaca	GCal LPla
	- 'First Light'	SPhx
§	- 'Ice Cool'	NLar SCob SWvt WKif
	- 'Saalestrand'	LCro
	'Variegata'	see *L.* × *clementii* 'Wembdon Variegated'
	'White Angel'PBR	GBin NLar
	'White Satin'PBR	NHol

Ledebouria (*Asparagaceae*)

	adlamii	see *L. cooperi*
	concolor misapplied	see *L. socialis*
§	***cooperi***	CTal EAJP ECho EPri EShb GKev LEdu LHop LRHS MPie SBch WBor WPGP XLum
§	***socialis***	ECho LEdu LToo MCot MPie SBch WCot
	violacea	see *L. socialis*

Ledum see *Rhododendron*

Leibnitzia (*Asteraceae*)

	anandria	SBrt

Leiophyllum (*Ericaceae*)

	buxifolium 🏆H5	EPfP WThu
	- subsp. ***hugeri***	GKev

Lembotropis see *Cytisus*

Lemna (*Araceae*)

	gibba	NPer
	minor	CWat MSKA NPer SWat
	polyrrhiza	see *Spirodela polyrrhiza*
	trisulca	CWat EWay MSKA NPer SWat

lemon see *Citrus* × *limon*

lemon, rough see *Citrus* × *taitensis*

lemon balm see *Melissa officinalis*

lemon grass see *Cymbopogon citratus*

lemon verbena see *Aloysia citrodora*

lemonquat see *Citrus* × *japonica* × *C.* × *limon*

Leonotis (*Lamiaceae*)

	leonitis	see *L. ocymifolia*
	leonurus	CBcs CCCN CDTJ CHGN CHll ECre EShb EWes LRHS MSCN SLim SMad SPlb XLum
	- var. ***albiflora***	CCCN
	nepetifolia	CHll
	- var. ***nepetifolia*** 'Staircase'	CCCN SMad SPav
§	***ocymifolia***	CCCN LSou
	- var. ***raineriana***	CHll

Leontice (*Berberidaceae*)

	albertii	see *Gymnospermium albertii*

Leontochir (*Alstroemeriaceae*)

	ovallei	CCCN

Leontodon (*Asteraceae*)

	autumnalis	CHab CWld NMir
	hispidus	CHab NMir
§	***rigens***	CSpe CTal ELan GEdr MHer MMuc NBid NBir SDix WMoo
	- B&SWJ 12527	WCru WSHC
	- 'Girandole'	see *L. rigens*

Leontopodium (*Asteraceae*)

	alpinum	CTri CWib ELan EPfP ESps GAbr MAsh NHpl SPlb SPoG SRms WTor XLum
	- 'Everest'	EDAr
	- 'Matterhorn'	GEdr NLar
	- 'Mignon'	ECho EPfP EWes GMaP WAbe
	- subsp. ***nivale***	GKev WAbe
	coreanum	GKev
	haastioides new	WAbe
	kurilense	SPlb
	muscoides	CPBP
	nanum	CPBP SPlb
§	***ochroleucum*** var. ***campestre***	NLar XLum
	palibinianum	see *L. ochroleucum* var. *campestre*
	pusillum	WAbe
	souliei	MMuc SRot XLum
	stracheyi	GKev

Leonurus (*Lamiaceae*)

	artemisia	see *L. japonicus*
	cardiaca	CArn CBod GPoy MHer MNHC SIde SRms XSen
	- 'Crispa'	SMad
	- 'Grobbebol'	EBee EPPr ESwi WHer
§	***japonicus***	SMad
	macranthus	EFEx
	- var. ***alba***	EFEx
	sibiricus misapplied	see *L. japonicus*
	sibiricus L.	GCal

Leopoldia (*Asparagaceae*)

	comosa	see *Muscari comosum*
	spreitzenhoferi	see *Muscari spreitzenhoferi*
	tenuiflora	see *Muscari tenuiflorum*

Lepechinia (*Lamiaceae*)

	bella	CSpe SDys
	hastata	CCse CFil CSpe MSpe SBrt SIgm WJek

Lepidium (*Brassicaceae*)

	campestre	CHab
	latifolium	CArn ENfk LEdu

Lepidothamnus (*Podocarpaceae*)

§	***laxifolius***	WThu

Lepidozamia (*Zamiaceae*)

	peroffskyana	CBrP

Leptinella (*Asteraceae*)

	atrata subsp. ***luteola***	ELan
	'County Park'	EDAr
	dendyi	EWes GEdr MHer NSla WIce
	dioica	GBin
	hispida	see *Cotula hispida* (DC.) Harv.
§	***minor***	WMoo
§	***pectinata***	ITim
§	***potentillina***	CTal CTri ECha ECho EHoe GBin GEdr MBNS MSCN NLar SRms WMoo WPtf XLum
§	***pyrethrifolia***	ECho EDAr
	reptans	see *L. scariosa*
§	***scariosa***	GAbr
§	***squalida***	ECha ECho GBin NLar NSti WMoo
§	- 'Platt's Black'	CBcs CTal EBee ECha ECho EDAr EHoe ESps EWes GAbr GBin GCrg GKev IBoy LEdu MSCN NHpl NLar SBch SMad SWvt WFar WGwG WMoo WTcb WWFP XLum

Leptocodon (*Campanulaceae*)

	gracilis	EWld
	- HWJK 2155	WCru

Leptodactylon (*Polemoniaceae*)

§	***californicum***	CPBP

Leptodermis (*Rubiaceae*)

	oblonga 'Summer Stars' new	LCro

Leptospermum ✿ (*Myrtaceae*)

	citratum	see *L. petersonii*
	'Copper Sheen'	CBcs
	cunninghamii	see *L. myrtifolium*
	'Electric Red' (Galaxy Series)	CAbb GMcL LRHS SAko SEle
	ericoides	see *Kunzea ericoides*
	flavescens misapplied	see *L. glaucescens*
	flavescens Sm.	see *L. polygalifolium*
§	***glaucescens***	SPlb
§	***grandiflorum***	ELan EPfP SVen WSHC
	grandifolium	LRHS
	'Havering Hardy'	SEle
	humifusum	see *L. rupestre*
	juniperinum	SPlb
	'Karo Pearl Star'	CBcs MPkF
	'Karo Silver Ice'	CBcs
	'Karo Spectrobay'	CBcs
	laevigatum	SVen
§	***lanigerum***	CTri CTsd EPfP SPlb SVen
	- 'Cunninghamii'	see *L. myrtifolium*
	liversidgei	SPlb
§	***myrtifolium***	CBcs CMac CTri CTsd EWes
	nitidum	SPlb
	obovatum	CTsd
§	***petersonii***	MHer
	phylicoides	see *Kunzea ericoides*
	'Pink Cascade'	SEle
§	***polygalifolium***	CBcs SPlb
	prostratum	see *L. rupestre*
	pubescens	see *L. lanigerum*
	'Red Cascade'	SWvt
	rodwayanum	see *L. grandiflorum*
	rotundifolium	SPlb
§	***rupestre***	CTri SPlb SVen WKif WSHC
	scoparium	CArn CTsd GPoy MNHC SPlb SVen WJek
	- 'Adrianne'	CRos EPfP LRHS MRav
	- 'Appleblossom' ♀H3	CEnd EPfP GMcL SAko SEle SGol
	- 'Autumn Glory'	SLim
	- 'Blossom' (d)	CBcs CMac
	- 'Burgundy Queen' (d)	CBcs CMac CSBt EBee EUJe
	- 'Chapmanii'	CMHG WPGP
	- 'Charmer'	EBee
	- 'Coral Candy'	CBcs CEnd
	- 'Crimson Glory' (d)	CSBt
	- 'Elizabeth Jane'	MMuc WFar
	- 'Fred's Red'	MHer
	- 'Gaiety Girl' (d)	CSBt
	- 'Jubilee' (d)	CMac CRos LRHS
	- 'Leonard Wilson' (d)	CTri
	- 'Martini'	CAbb CBcs CCCN CMac CRos CSBt EPfP LRHS MMuc
	- (Nanum Group) 'Kea'	CBcs MHer MRav
	- - 'Kiwi' ♀H3	CAbb CBcs CCCN CLet CRos CSBt EPfP LRHS MAsh MMuc SEle SLim SLon WFar

- - 'Nanum'	CCCN ITim
- - 'Pipit'	ITim
- - 'Tui'	CMac CSBt
- 'Nichollsii' ♀H3	SVen WSHC
- 'Nichollsii Nanum' ♀H3	WAbe WPat WThu
- 'Pink Cascade'	CBcs CMac CTri CWib
- 'Pink Damask'	IVic SWvt
- var. ***prostratum*** misapplied	see *L. rupestre*
- 'Red Damask' (d) ♀H3	Widely available
* - 'Ruby Wedding'	CRos ELan EPfP LRHS LSRN MAsh SLon SPoG
- 'Snow Flurry'	CBcs CRos EPfP LRHS SGol SLim SVen
- 'Sunraysia'	CTsd
- 'Winter Cheer' (d)	CRos EPfP LRHS SGol SHil
- 'Wiri Joan' (d)	CBcs
- 'Wiri Linda'	CBcs CMac
'Silver Sheen' ♀H3	CAbb CCCN CEnd CRos EBee ECre ELan EPfP LHop LRHS MAsh NLar SAko SEle SPer SPoG SVen WPGP WPat

Lespedeza (*Papilionaceae*)

bicolor	CAgr CCCN EBee LRHS MMrt SEND SKHP WCFE WFar WSHC
buergeri	CRos LRHS MMrt NLar WSHC
capitata	SPhx
japonica	SPlb
thunbergii ♀H5	CBcs CBot CHll CLet CRos CWib EBee ELan EPfP IDee IVic LRHS MAsh MBlu MGil SLon SMad SPer SPoG SSta WCFE WPGP WSHC
- subsp. ***formosa***	EBee MMrt
- 'Gibraltar'	WPGP
- 'Summer Beauty'	CBcs
- subsp. ***thunbergii*** 'Albiflora'	ELan LRHS SMad WPGP
- - 'Edo-shibori'	WPGP
- - 'White Fountain'	CRos EPfP LRHS SKHP SPoG
tiliifolia	see *Desmodium elegans*

Lesquerella (*Brassicaceae*)

arctica	WCFE
- var. ***purshii***	GKev

Leucadendron (*Proteaceae*)

argenteum	CCCN CTre SPlb
conicum **new**	CTre
'Cream Delight' **new**	CCCN
daphnoides	SPlb
'Deacon Red'	MPkF
discolor	SPlb
eucalyptifolium	CTre SPlb
galpinii	CTre
- 'Purple Haze' **new**	LRHS
gandogeri	CTre
'Highlights' **new**	CCCN
'Inca Gold' ♀H1c	CBcs CTre
'Jack Harre' **new**	LRHS
laureolum	CCCN CTre
modestum 'Strawberry Fair' **new**	CCCN
'Pisa' **new**	LRHS
'Red Dwarf' **new**	CTre
'Royal Ruby' **new**	LRHS
'Safari Magic' **new**	CCCN
'Safari Sunset' ♀H1c	CBcs CCCN CTre LRHS MPkF
'Safari Sunshine'	CTre
salicifolium	SPlb
salignum	CCCN CTre
- 'Fireglow'	LRHS
sessile	CTre
strobilinum	CTre
'Sundance' **new**	LRHS
tinctum	CTre

Leucaena (*Mimosaceae*)

leucocephala	SPlb

Leucanthemella (*Asteraceae*)

§ ***serotina*** ♀H7	Widely available
- 'Herbststern'	IMou NLar

Leucanthemopsis (*Asteraceae*)

§ ***alpina***	ECho NSla
hosmariensis	see *Rhodanthemum hosmariense*

Leucanthemum ✿ (*Asteraceae*)

'Angel'	ELon MArt NCou NLar
atlanticum	see *Rhodanthemum atlanticum*
catananche	see *Rhodanthemum catananche*
graminifolium	EPfP
hosmariense	see *Rhodanthemum hosmariense*
mawii	see *Rhodanthemum gayanum*
maximum misapplied	see *L. × superbum*
§ ***maximum*** (Ramond) DC.	NBro NPer
- ***uliginosum***	see *Leucanthemella serotina*
nipponicum	see *Nipponanthemum nipponicum*
'Osiris Neige'	ECtt ILea MAvo XLum
paludosum 'Snowland'	CRos LRHS NRHS
'Real Charmer' **new**	LRHS
'Real Galaxy'	CMea LBuc LRHS MTis NRHS
'Sante'	CBod CCVN CRos EBee LCro LRHS MHol NRHS
'Sunshine Peach'	CRos EBee ECho LRHS NRHS SRot
§ × ***superbum***	CMac ESps GAbr IBoy MMuc SDix SEND WBrk
- 'Aglaia' (d)	Widely available
- 'Alaska'	CAni CBod CTsd EAEE EBee ELan EWTr GBin IBoy LHop LRHS LSun MCot NLar SCob SPer SWvt WRHF XLum
- 'Amelia'	EBee LRHS NBre
- 'Andernach'	CAni
- 'Anita Allen' (d)	CAni EBee ECtt WCot
- 'Anna Camilla'	CAni
- 'Antwerp Star'	NBre NLar WBrk
- 'Banana Cream'	CBcs CBod CCVN CRos CWGN EAEE ECtt ELon EUJe LCro LRHS MAsh MHol NLar NPri NRHS SCob SPoG STPC WHoo WTor
- 'Banwell'	CAni
- 'Barbara Bush' (v/d)	SWvt
§ - 'Beauté Nivelloise'	CAni CCVN CElw CWCL CWld EBee ECtt EPfP GWyn IPot LCro LOPS LRHS MSpe NBir NSti SPoG SRms SWat
- 'Becky'	CCse CElw CMac EBee ECha ELan ELon EWes GBin GWyn LLHF LRHS LSRN LSou NEoE NLar SHil SRGP WCAu
- 'Bishopstone'	CAni EBee ECtt ELan LBMP LEdu LLHF MSpe
- 'Bridal Bouquet'PBR	CRos EBee ECtt LRHS NRHS
- 'Brightside'	CRos EBee ELan GQue LRHS MWat WFar WMoo
- Broadway Lights = 'Leumayel'PBR	CRos EBee EPfP EWTr EWoo GBin GMcL IBoy LPot LRHS MRav NBir NRHS SCob WCAu WFar WGrn WTor

- 'Christine Hagemann'	CAni CElw EBee ECtt EWes ILea IPot MAvo MNrw MRav NCGa SHar WBrk WCFE
- 'Cobham Gold' (d)	NBre
- 'Colwall'	CAni
- 'Crazy Daisy'	CAni CBod CChe CTri CWib EAJP ECtt GNew GWyn LRHS NFav SRot SWvt WFar
- 'Devon Mist'	CAni
- 'Droitwich Beauty'	CAni ECtt LLHF MAvo WCFE WHoo
- 'Duchess of Abercorn'	CAni
- 'Dwarf Snow Lady'	LSun NBre NLar
- 'Easton Lady'	CAni
- 'Eclipse'	CAni MAvo
- 'Edgebrook Giant'	CAni SAko WBrk WHil
- 'Edward VII'	CAni
- 'Eisstern'	EBee LEdu MAvo NCGa SHar
- 'Elworthy Sparkler'	CElw MAvo WBrk
- 'Engelina'PBR	CBod EBee NBir NLar SPoG WTor
- 'Esther Read' (d)	EBee ECtt ELan EPfP GBin GMaP LRHS LSRN NBro NEgg NLar SPer SRGP SRms SWat SWvt WBrk WCot WFar
§ - 'Everest'	CAni SRms
- 'Fiona Coghill' (d)	CAni CElw CHVG CWGN EAEE ECtt EPfP GBin GBuc IBoy IKil LRHS LSou MNrw MSpe NBir NEgg NGdn NPnk WCot WHoo
- 'Firnglanz'	CAni GBin MAvo
- 'Flore Pleno' (d)	MMuc SEND SPlb
- Freak! = 'Leuz0001'PBR	CBcs CKno CRos EBee EPfP GBin LRHS NRHS SHar SPoG
- 'Goldfinch'PBR	CMea EBee ECtt ILea LLHF LRHS MTis NAst NHpl NPnk NPri SPoG WCot WHil WTor
- 'Goldrausch'PBR	CBod CCVN CRos EAEE EBee ECtt ELan EPfP IBoy IPot LHop LLHF LRHS LSou MBel MCot MRav NBir NEgg NGdn SCob SGbt SHil SWvt WFar WHil
- 'Gruppenstolz'	CAni SAko
- 'H. Seibert'	CAni MArl MAvo
- 'Harry'	CAni
- 'Highland White Dream'PBR	IKil LRHS
- 'Horace Read' (d)	CAni CDor CElw ECtt NBir SWvt
- 'Ice Star' **new**	EBee
- 'Jennifer Read'	CAni WCFE
§ - 'John Murray' (d)	CAni EWes NBir NWsh WFar
- 'Lacrosse'	CRos EBee LRHS NPnk NRHS SCob SHil WFar
- 'Laspider'	CRos EBee LRHS NPnk NRHS SRot
- 'Little Miss Muffet'	CSBt CWGN EBee ECtt LEdu LLHF LRHS LSou MBNS NCGa
- 'Little Princess'	see *L.* × *superbum* 'Silberprinzesschen'
- 'Majestic'	CAni
- 'Manhattan'	CAni CCse EBee EWes GBin
- 'Margaretchen'	CAni MAvo
- 'Marion Bilsland'	CAni MAvo MSpe NChi WBrk
- 'Mayfield Giant'	CAni CTri
- 'Mount Everest'	see *L.* × *superbum* 'Everest'
- 'Octopus'	CAni WBrk
- 'Old Court'	see *L.* × *superbum* 'Beauté Nivelloise'
- 'Paladin'PBR	EBee ECtt GBin IPot NLar SHar SPoG
- 'Phyllis Smith'	CAni CRos EBee ECtt ELan GBin GNew GWyn LCro LSRN MAvo MCot MHer MPie MRav MSCN MSpe NCGa NGdn SCob SMad WBrk WCAu WCot WMoo
- 'Polaris'	EBee NBre WMoo XLum
- 'Rags and Tatters'	CAni EBee ECtt EWes
- 'Real Dream'	CRos EBee LRHS LSou MTis WFar
- 'Real Galaxy'PBR	LSou MTis
- 'Real Glory'	CBod CRos ECtt ILea LRHS MHol MTis NHpl WFar
- 'Real Neat'	EBee ECtt LRHS LSou MAsh MAvo MHol MTis NHpl SCob SHar
- 'Schwabengruss'	CAni
- 'Shaggy'	see *L.* × *superbum* 'Beauté Nivelloise'
- 'Shapcott Gossamer'	CAby CBod CPou EBee ECtt MTis NGBl SCob WCot
- 'Shapcott Ruffles'	EBee ECtt MTis WCot
- 'Shapcott Summer Clouds'	CBod EBee ECtt ELon MBel MHol MSCN MTis SMad SPoG WCot WRHF
§ - 'Silberprinzesschen'	CAni CRos CSBt ELon EPfP GJos GMaP GMcL GWyn LPot LRHS NRHS SPlb SRms WHar WMoo XLum
- 'Silver Spoon'	EPfP LRHS NRHS
- 'Snehurka'	CAni CRos LLHF LRHS LSou MAvo NRHS WCot WHoo
- 'Snow Lady'	CBod CChe CRos EBee EPfP ESps GMcL GWyn LRHS NPer NRHS SRms WFar WHar
- 'Snow Queen' **new**	GWyn
- 'Snowcap'	CBar CHid ECha EPfP ESps LCro LRHS MBel MRav SPer SPoG SWvt WCAu
- 'Snowdrift'	CAni LBMP NBre NLar WBrk WCot WFar WMoo WTcb
- 'Snowstorm'	MAvo
§ - 'Sonnenschein'	CBar CDor CHVG CRos EBee ECha ECtt ELan EPfP GMaP LHop LRHS LSRN LSou MArl MCot MHer MHol MRav NBir NChi NEgg NGdn NRHS NWsh SPer SRms SWat WCAu
- 'Starburst' (d)	EBee ELan LRHS SRms
- 'Stina'	EBee GBin MAvo XLum
- 'Summer Snowball'	see *L.* × *superbum* 'John Murray'
- 'Sunny Side Up'PBR	CBod CCVN CHVG CRos CWCL EBee ECtt LCro LHop LRHS NLar NPnk SCob SHil SRot WAul WFar
- Sunshine	see *L.* × *superbum* 'Sonnenschein'
- 'T.E. Killin' (d) 🏆H4	CBod EAEE EBee ECha ECtt ELan EPfP EUJe GBin GBuc LCro LRHS LSou MRav MWat SPoG SPtp WFar WHoo
- 'Victorian Secret'PBR	CRos ECtt GBin IPot LBuc LRHS MNrw SCob SHil SMad SPoG WCot WHil WHoo WTor
- Western Star Leo = 'Leuz0002'PBR **new**	CRos LRHS NRHS
- 'White Iceberg' (d)	CAni
- White Mountain = 'Gfleuwhmtn'PBR	CRos LRHS NRHS STPC
- 'White Tutu'	MAvo
- 'Wirral Pride'	CAni CCVN ELon EPfP WBrk
- 'Wirral Supreme' (d) 🏆H5	Widely available
'Tizi-n-Test'	see *Rhodanthemum catananche* 'Tizi-n-Test'
§ ***vulgare***	CArn CBod CHab CMac CWld ENfk EPfP EShb GBin GJos LCro MHer MJak MMuc MNHC NMir SBod SDix SEND SIde SPhx WFar WHer WJek WMoo WOut WSFF WShi XLum XSen

- 'Filigran'	LRHS WFar
- 'Löffelstiel'	SAko
§ - 'Maikönigin'	GWyn SAko XLum
- May Queen	see *L. vulgare* 'Maikönigin'
- 'Sunny'	CBre
'White Knight'	CBod CRos GMcL LRHS NRHS

Leucochrysum (*Asteraceae*)

albicans subsp. ***alpinum***	GKev

Leucocoryne (*Alliaceae*)

alliacea	ECho
'Andes' ♀^{H3}	CCCN ECho GKev NRog
coronata	SPlb
'Dione'	ECho GKev NRog SDeJ
'Double Fantasy'	NRog
hybrids	CGrW ECho
ixioides	ECho
* - ***alba***	ECho NRog
- 'Blue Ocean'	ECho GKev NRog SDeJ
pauciflora	NRog
purpurea ♀^{H3}	CGrW ECho NRog
'Spotlight'	ECho GKev NRog
'Sunny Stripe'	ECho
vittata	NRog
'White Dream'	ECho GKev NRog SDeJ

Leucogenes (*Asteraceae*)

grandiceps	WAbe
leontopodium	EPot NSla WAbe
tarahaoa	EPot

Leucojum ✿ (*Amaryllidaceae*)

aestivum	CAby CBcs CTri EBee ECGP ECho EPfP GKev LAma LHop MCot MMuc MSCN NBir NChi NEgg NHol SDeJ SDir SEND SRms WBod WCFE WCot WFar WHea WRHF WShi
- 'Gravetye Giant' ♀^{H7}	Widely available
- var. ***pulchellum***	CElw
autumnale	see *Acis autumnalis*
roseum	see *Acis rosea*
tingitanum	see *Acis tingitana*
trichophyllum	see *Acis trichophylla*
valentinum	see *Acis valentina*
vernum ♀^{H5}	Widely available
- var. ***vagneri***	CLAP ECha SDys

Leucophysalis (*Solanaceae*)

sinense BWJ 8093	WCru

Leucophyta (*Asteraceae*)

§ ***brownii***	GMcL LTro
- 'Silver Sand'	LSou

Leucopogon (*Ericaceae*)

§ ***colensoi***	WThu
ericoides	GKev
§ ***fraseri***	NHar WThu

× *Leucoraoulia* (*Asteraceae*)

§ ***loganii***	WAbe

Leucosceptrum (*Lamiaceae*)

canum GWJ 9424	WCru
japonicum B&SWJ 10804	WCru
- B&SWJ 10981	WCru
- 'Golden Angel'	GEdr
- 'Silver Angel' (v)	GEdr
stellipilum	IMou
var. ***formosanum***	
- - B&SWJ 1926	WCru
- - RWJ 9907	SBrt WCru
- var. ***tosaense*** B&SWJ 8892	WCru
- 'Variegatum' (v)	GEdr

Leucospermum (*Proteaceae*)

'Carnival Red' **new**	CCCN
conocarpodendron 'Mardi Gras Ribbons'	EBee
cordifolium	CCCN CTre
- 'Carnival Copper' **new**	CCCN
'Fountain'	LRHS
glabrum	SPlb
'Scarlet Ribbon'	CCCN
'Succession' **new**	CCCN
'Tango' **new**	CTre
'Vulkano' **new**	CCCN

Leucostegia (*Davalliaceae*)

immersa PAB 7836 **new**	LEdu

Leucothoe (*Ericaceae*)

axillaris 'Curly Red'^{PBR}	CBod CRos EBee ELan EPfP ESps IVic LPar LRHS MAsh MGos MJak MPkF NLar SHil SLim SLon SPoG SWvt
- Twisting Red = 'Opstal20'^{PBR}	IBoy MBlu
Carinella = 'Zebekot'	CRos EBee LRHS NLar SHil SPoG
davisiae	NLar
§ ***fontanesiana***	CMac GKev
- 'Makijaz'^{PBR} (v)	CRos EPfP LRHS NLar SHil
- 'Rainbow' (v)	CBcs CDul CLet CMac CNec CRos CWib ELan EPfP ESps GMcL LRHS LSou MGos NLar NPri SEle SGbt SGol SHil SLim SPad SPer SPoG SRms SSta SWvt WFar WHar WMoo
- 'Rollissonii' ♀^{H6}	MRav SRms
- Whitewater = 'Howw'^{PBR} (v)	CMac CRos CSBt LRHS MPkF NLar NPri
keiskei Halloween = 'Opstal16' **new**	EBee
- 'Royal Ruby'	CRos ESps GMcL LRHS LSou MGos MJak MPkF NEgg NLar NWad SGbt SGol SHil SLim SPoG WFar WMoo
Lovita = 'Zebonard'	GMcL MRav NLar SCoo
Red Lips = 'Lipsbolwi'^{PBR}	EPfP GMcL IVic LPar
Scarletta = 'Zeblid' ♀^{H6}	Widely available
walteri	see *L. fontanesiana*

Leuzea (*Asteraceae*)

centaureoides	see *Stemmacantha centaureoides*
conifera	WAbe

Levisticum (*Apiaceae*)

officinale	CAgr CArn CBod CHby CLau ENfk EPfP GAbr GPoy LEdu MHer MJak MMuc MNHC NPri SDix SEND SIde SPlb SRms SVic SWat WHer WJek

Lewisia ✿ (*Portulacaceae*)

'Archangel'	NRya
Ashwood Carousel hybrids	CPBP CTri MAsh NHar NRya
Birch strain	CBcs ECho ELan
brachycalyx ♀^{H4}	ECho EWes GCrg LLHF

Brynhyfryd hybrids pink-flowered	GKev
- white-flowered	GKev
- yellow-flowered	GKev
cantelovii	CWCL MAsh
columbiana	CTal ECho MAsh NHpl
- 'Alba'	GKev NRya NSla
- 'Rosea'	GKev MAsh
- subsp. ***rupicola***	ITim MAsh NSla
- subsp. ***wallowensis***	MAsh
congdonii	MAsh
cotyledon ♀^{H4}	CRos CWCL ECho GKev GMaP ITim LLHF LRHS MMuc NFav NHpl NRHS NSla SIgm WIce
- f. ***alba***	CWCL
- - 'Snowstorm'	LLHF
- 'Ashwood Ruby'	MAsh
- Ashwood strain	EPfP EWes LRHS MAsh NHpl SRms WOld
- 'Brannan Bar'	MAsh
- 'Bright Eyes'	GKev
- var. ***cotyledon***	LLHF
- double-flowered (d)	GKev
- var. ***howellii***	LLHF
- hybrid	CRos ECho GKev LHop LRHS NRHS NRya SPoG
- 'John's Special'	MAsh
- magenta-flowered	CWCL ECho GKev
- orange-flowered	CWCL
§ - 'Regenbogen'	MHer MHol WRHF
- rose-pink-flowered	CWCL
- salmon-flowered	CWCL
- Sunset Group ♀^{H4}	CGar ECho EPfP GCrg NHpl NLar WHar
- violet-flowered	GKev
- 'White Splendour'	MAsh
'George Henley'	ECho EPot EWes LLHF MAsh NRya WAbe
glandulosa	NSla
leeana	MAsh
'Little Mango'	CSma EDAr GCrg NSla
'Little Peach'	CPBP CSma ECho ECtt EDAr GBin GKev MAsh NHpl NRya NSla
'Little Plum'	CMea CPBP CSma ECho ECtt EDAr EPot GBin GCrg LRHS MAsh NHpl NLar NRya NSla WHlf WThu
'Little Tutti Frutti' (mixed) **new**	CSma
longipetala	ECho
- 'Little Raspberry' **new**	EDAr
§ ***nevadensis***	CPne CRos ECho EDAr EPot GCrg GKev ITim LRHS NRHS NRya SIgm WThu
I - 'Alba'	NHpl
- ***bernardina***	see *L. nevadensis*
- 'Rosea'	ECho NHpl NRya NSla NWad
oppositifolia	LLHF MAsh
- 'Richeyi'	GKev
'Pinkie'	CPBP GCrg MAsh NHpl
pygmaea	CRos CWCL ECho EWes ITim LRHS MAsh MHer NBir NRHS NRya NSla SPlb XLum
- carmine-flowered	GKev
pygmaea × ***rediviva***	LLHF
Rainbow mixture	see *L. cotyledon* 'Regenbogen'
'Rawreth'	ECho LLHF
rediviva	CPBP GKev LLHF NHpl
- dark pink-flowered **new**	GKev
- white-flowered	GKev
serrata	MAsh
'Trevosia'	MAsh
tweedyi ♀^{H4}	CPBP CRos EAEE ECho EPot LHop LRHS MAsh NHpl NRHS NRya SPlb WAbe WThu
- 'Alba'	LLHF MAsh WAbe
- 'Elliott's Variety'	MAsh
- 'Rosea'	CRos EAEE ECho EPot LHop LRHS MAsh NRHS WAbe
- yellow-flowered	GKev

Leycesteria (*Caprifoliaceae*)

crocothyrsos	CBcs CWib EBee NLar
formosa	Widely available
- from Longstock	SLon
- brown-stemmed	IFoB
- 'Gold Leaf'	GAbr MHer MNHC SPad WBor WFar WPtf
- Golden Lanterns = 'Notbruce'^{PBR} ♀^{H4}	Widely available
- 'Golden Pheasant' (v)	EHoe
- 'Lydia'	LRHS
- 'Purple Rain'	CRos EBee EWes IBoy LRHS MAsh MGos NLar SHil

Leymus (*Poaceae*)

from Falkland Islands	EPPr
§ ***arenarius***	Widely available
cinereus	WCot
hispidus	see *Elymus hispidus*

Lhotzkya see *Calytrix*

Liatris (*Asteraceae*)

aspera	SPhx
cylindracea	SPhx
elegans	EPfP GKev SPlb
ligulistylis	EBee LEdu NDov SPhx
mucronata	NLar NQui
pycnostachya	EBee NLar NQui SAko SRms
scariosa 'Alba'	CBcs SAko
§ ***spicata***	Widely available
- 'Alba'	CBWd CBod CMac CSBt EAJP ECha ELan EPfP ESps GBin GKev LEdu LSRN MSCN NGdn NLar NPri SCob SPer SPlb WHar XLum
- ***callilepis***	see *L. spicata*
- 'Floristan Violett'	CRos CTri EBee EPfP GMaP GMcL LRHS MBel MHer MJak MSpe NDov NEgg NLar NQui SCob SCoo SPlb SPoG SWvt WFar WGwG WMoo WWtn XLum
- 'Floristan Weiss'	CRos CTri EPPr EPfP ERCP GKev GMaP GMcL LRHS MBel MHer MRav NLar NRHS SDeJ SPoG SWvt WFar WHil WMoo WWtn
- Goblin	see *L. spicata* 'Kobold'
§ - 'Kobold'	Widely available
squarrosa	SPhx

Libanotis see *Seseli*

montana	see *Seseli libanotis*

Libertia ✿ (*Iridaceae*)

'Amazing Grace'	EBee GCal
breunioides	see *L. cranwelliae*
chilensis ♀^{H3}	Widely available
- brown-stemmed	IFoB
- Elegans Group	EBee
§ - Formosa Group	CBcs CBod CBro CCVN CElw CHid CLet CTri ECho ELan ESps GCal

	GCra GKev LRHS NChi NSti SArc SCob SPer SPtp SRms SWvt WHer
- Procera Group	CBod CSpe EBee EPfP GBin GCal GLog IVic LEdu LRHS SMad SPlb SPtp WPGP WSHC
§ ***cranwelliae***	WPGP
formosa	see *L. chilensis* Formosa Group
'Grasshopper' **new**	GBin
ixioides	CBcs ECha ECho ILea LEdu MMuc SPtp WPGP
- 'Goldfinger' (v)	CBcs CBct CBod CKno CMac EBee ELan ELon EPfP EShb ESps GMcL IBoy LEdu LLWG LRHS MPkF NHol SHil SKHP SLon SWvt WCot WGrn WHer WMoo
- 'Highlander'	ELon LRHS MHol
- hybrid	SDix
- 'Taupo Blaze'	CBcs CMac EBee EPfP LRHS MRav SLon SPoG
- 'Taupo Sunset'	CBcs CCCN ELon EPfP LRHS MBNS MPkF SWvt
- 'Tricolor'	ECha GEdr MRav WMoo
'Nelson Dwarf'	GCal
peregrinans	CAbb CKno CSpe EBee ECha ECho EHoe ELan EPri GBuc GCal GKev IBoy IFro ILea LEdu LHop LRHS MMuc MRav NBir SEND SKHP SPer SPtp SRkn SWvt WGrn WPGP WPat
- 'Gold Leaf'	CBcs CBod CCCN CTri CTsd ELan EPfP GBuc GMcL LHop LRHS SMad SWvt WFar
- 'Gold Stripe'	CSpe ELan SPad SWvt
'Red Devil' **new**	MHol
sessiliflora	NBir
- 'Ballyrogan Blue'	EBee GKev
- 'Caerulescens'	CBcs CBod CCCN CMac EAJP ECho EPfP LRHS NBir NCGa SMad SPer SPtp WMoo
'Sunset Strain' **new**	IBoy
tricocca misapplied HCM 98.089 **new**	WPGP

Libocedrus (*Cupressaceae*)

chilensis	see *Austrocedrus chilensis*
decurrens	see *Calocedrus decurrens*
plumosa	CBrP

Libonia see *Justicia*

Licuala (*Arecaceae*)

dasyantha	CBlu
mattanensis 'Mapu'	CBlu

Ligularia (*Asteraceae*)

amplexicaulis	GCal
'Bottle Rocket'^{PBR}	NLar
'Britt Marie Crawford'^{PBR} 🏆H6	Widely available
calthifolia	EBee
clivorum	see *L. dentata*
§ ***dentata***	ECtt NBro SRms SWat WBod
- 'Dark Beauty'	IBoy
- 'Desdemona'	Widely available
- 'Enkelrig'	EBee WHar
- 'Franz Feldweber' **new**	EBee
- 'Midnight Lady'	EAJP EHoe ELan ESwi GPSL GWyn MHol NLar
- 'Orange Princess'	NPer
- 'Osiris Café Dark'^{PBR} **new**	SCob
- 'Osiris Fantaisie' (v)	CAbP CMos ECtt EWes GMcL GWyn ILea LLHF MAvo MBel MHol MNrw MWts NLar NPnk NSti SPoG WBor WCot WFar WPnP
- 'Othello'	CBod EBee ECtt EPfP ESps GMcL LRHS NBid NEgg NGdn NWad SCob SWat SWvt WHar
- 'Sommergold'	ECha WFar
- 'Twilight'	CBct ECtt MBNS
dictyoneura	EBee GKev
§ ***fischeri***	ECha LEdu NBre
- B&SWJ 2570	WCru
- B&SWJ 4381	WCru
- B&SWJ 4478	WCru
- B&SWJ 5653	WCru
- B&SWJ 8802	WCru
- CC 7311	GKev
- var. ***megalorhiza*** 'Cheju Charmer'	ELon WCru
'Franz Marc'	GCal
'Garden Confetti' **new**	ECtt MSCN
'Gold Torch'	ECtt NLar
§ 'Gregynog Gold' 🏆H6	ECha ECtt ELan GMaP LRHS MRav NBro NLar
× ***hessei***	GMaP LRHS MMuc SWat WWtn
hodgsonii	CKno EPPr LEdu MRav
- B&SWJ 10855	WCru
intermedia B&SWJ 606a	WCru WSHC
japonica	CLAP ECha GCra LEdu LRHS NLar WWtn
- B&SWJ 2883	WCru
- 'Rising Sun'	NLar WCot WCru
'Laternchen'^{PBR}	ECtt GBin IBal MWts SAko
'Little Rocket'^{PBR}	CBct CBod EBee ECtt EPfP MBNS MPie MWts NBro NGdn NLar SCob SPoG WFar WHil
'Osiris Café Noir'	ECtt ILea NLar SCob WFar WWtn
'Osiris Pistache' (v)	EBee ECtt
× ***palmatiloba***	see *L.* × *yoshizoeana* 'Palmatiloba'
§ ***przewalskii***	Widely available
- SSSE 176	WCot
- 'Dragon Wings'	EWTr GBin MHol NEoE NLar SCob SMad
- 'Dragon's Breath'	ECtt EUJe GBin MHol SCob
- 'Light Fingered'	NBre
sibirica	CSam MArt MMuc NLar SEND WMoo
- B&SWJ 4383	WCru
- B&SWJ 5841	WCru
- var. ***speciosa***	see *L. fischeri*
smithii	see *Senecio smithii*
speciosa	see *L. fischeri*
stenocephala	EBee NBro NLar SCob SWat WWtn XLum
'Sungold'	CMac CSam ECtt LRHS NGdn
tangutica	see *Sinacalia tangutica*
'The Rocket' 🏆H5	Widely available
tussilaginea	see *Farfugium japonicum*
- 'Aureo-maculata'	see *Farfugium japonicum* 'Aureomaculatum'
veitchiana	CBod CSam GCal GKev SWat WWtn
vorobievii	GCal NLar
'Weihenstephan'	GCal LRHS
wilsoniana	LLWG LRHS MMuc MRav SEND SWat WFar WWtn
§ × ***yoshizoeana*** 'Palmatiloba'	ELan ELon EWTr EWes GCal LEdu LRHS MRav SPhx SWat WFar WWtn
'Zepter'	CBct CBod ECtt EShb EUJe GBuc GCal GQue LRHS MBNS MMuc NEgg NHol NLar NWad WCot WWtn

Ligusticum (*Apiaceae*)

	lucidum	EBee EPfP IVic LEdu MAvo NSti SPhx SPtp WBor WCot WFar WPGP
	- subsp. ***lucidum***	CSpe
	mutellina new	LPla
	porteri	CArn
§	***scoticum***	CArn CBod CHid EBee EWes GBin GLog GPoy LEdu LHop LRHS MAvo MHer SDix SPtp SRms WJek WOut WPtf
	- variegated (v)	LEdu WCot

Ligustrum ✿ (*Oleaceae*)

	B&L 12261	WPGP
	chenaultii	see *L. compactum*
§	***compactum***	ETod
§	***delavayanum***	CAco EBee EBtc GKev NPri STrG SWeb WPGP
	ibota	EBtc
	- Musli = 'Muster'PBR (v)	CRos LRHS WCot
	ionandrum	see *L. delavayanum*
	japonicum	CLnd CRos EBar ECrN LPar LRHS LSRN SEND SGol SPer
I	- 'Aureum'	EMOT
	- 'Coriaceum'	see *L. japonicum* 'Rotundifolium'
	- Green Century = 'Melgreen'PBR	LRHS WMat
	- 'Korea Dwarf'	NLar
	- 'Macrophyllum'	EPfP
§	- 'Rotundifolium'	CAbP CBcs CDul EBee ELan EPfP IVic LRHS MAsh MRav NLar SPer SPoG WCFE WCot WFar
§	- 'Silver Star' (v)	NLar SGol
§	- 'Texanum'	ECrN EPfP NLar SArc SWeb WCFE
	- 'Texanum Argenteum'	see *L. japonicum* 'Silver Star'
	- 'Variegatum' (v)	SGol
	lucidum ♀H5	CCVT CDul CSBt CTri ELan ESps EUJe EWTr GCal IDee LPar MRav NLar NWea SArc SCob SEND SGol SPer SWvt
	- 'Curly Wurly'	CRos LRHS SPoG
	- 'Excelsum Superbum' (v) ♀H5	CCVT CJun CLnd CMac CRos EBar ECrN ELan EPfP ESps LHop LPar LRHS LSRN SGol SPoG WCot
	- 'Golden Wax'	CJun MRav
	- 'Tricolor' (v) ♀H5	CJun CRos ELan EPfP LRHS MAsh SPer SPoG SWvt
	obtusifolium var. ***regelianum***	MMuc
	ovalifolium	Widely available
§	- 'Argenteum' (v)	CBcs CCVT CDul CMac CTri CWib ECrN EHoe ELan EMOT EShb ESps GMcL MMuc MRav NEgg SEND SGol SHil SLim SPer SPoG SWvt
	- 'Aureomarginatum'	see *L. ovalifolium* 'Aureum'
§	- 'Aureum' (v) ♀H5	Widely available
	- 'Lemon and Lime' (v)	CBod CRos EBee EHoe ELan EPfP LHop LRHS LSRN MAsh SCob SCoo SHil SWvt
	- 'Variegatum'	see *L. ovalifolium* 'Argenteum'
	quihoui	CBot CTri EBee ECre ELan EPfP IDee LHop LRHS MBlu NLar SDix SEND SKHP SLon SPer
	sempervirens	EPfP
	sinense	CMCN MRav
	- 'Multiflorum'	CWib WFar
	- 'Pendulum'	LRHS
	- 'Variegatum' (v)	LHop MRav SPer
	- 'Wimbei'	WPat
	texanum	see *L. japonicum* 'Texanum'
	tschonoskii	MBlu
	undulatum 'Lemon Lime and Clippers'	CRos EShb LRHS MBNS NLar NPri SCob SDix SLim SPoG WMoo
	'Vicaryi'	CRos ELan EPfP GBin LRHS MGos NEoE SCob SDix SGol SHil SPer WFar
	vulgare	CArg CArn CBcs CCVT CDul CHab CMac CTri ECrN EPfP ESps LBuc MMuc MSwo NBes NWea SCob SEND SEWo SWvt WHed WMat WMou WSFF WTSh
	- 'Lodense'	EBtc

Lilium ✿ (*Liliaceae*)

	'4 You' (Ia-b)	LRHS NRHS
	'Abbeville's Pride' (Ia/b)	SDeJ
	'Acapulco' (VII-/d)	LAma SDeJ
	'Acoustic' (VIIa/b-c) new	LRHS NRHS
	'Adonis' (Ic/d)	GEdr
	African Queen Group (VI-/a) ♀H6	ERCP GKev LAma LCro SCoo SRms
	- 'African Queen' (VIb-c/a)	CBro LOPS MCri SDeJ
	'Altari' (VIIIa-b/b)	CSut SDeJ
	amabile var. ***luteum*** (IXc/d)	MCri
	'Ambergate'	SDeJ
	'Anastasia' (VIIIb-c/b-d)	CSut EPfP GKev LAma SDeJ
	'Annemarie's Dream' (Ia/c)	GKev MAsh SDeJ
	'Apeldoorn' (Ia/b)	MCri
	Apollo (Ia-b)	see *L.* 'Blizzard'
	'Arabian Knight' (IIc/d)	GKev LAma LRHS SDeJ SDir
	'Arena' (VIIa/b)	SCoo
	Asiatic hybrids (I)	LRHS NGdn NRHS
	auratum (IXb/c)	CTsd ECho EFEx EPfP GBuc
	- 'Gold Band'	see *L. auratum* var. *platyphyllum*
	- 'Golden Ray' (IXb/c)	GBuc
§	- var. ***platyphyllum*** (IXb/c)	MCri SDeJ
	- - B&SWJ 4824	WCru
	- - B&SWJ 5041	WCru
	- var. ***virginale*** (IXb/c)	GKev MCri SDeJ
	'Baferrari' (VIIa/b) new	NNys
	'Barbara North' (Ic/d)	GEdr
	'Barbaresco' (VIIa-b/b)	SCoo
	'Belgrado'PBR (VIIa/b-c)	SDeJ
	'Belladonna'PBR (VIIIb-a/b)	SDeJ
	'Belle Epoque' (VIIb/b-c)	SDeJ
	Bellingham Group (IVc/d)	GEdr
	'Bergamo' (VIIb/b)	SCoo SDeJ
	'Beverly Dreams' (VIIIa/a)	ERCP
	'Black Beauty' (VIIIb-c/d)	CTsd GKev LAma LCro LOPS MCri SDeJ
	'Black Dragon'	see *L. leucanthum* var. *centifolium* 'Black Dragon'
§	'Blizzard' (Ia/b)	NBir SDeJ
	'Bonbini' (VIIIa-b/b)	LRHS NRHS
	'Boogie Woogie' (VIIIa-b/b)	SDeJ
	'Bracelet' (VIIIa-b/b)	SDeJ
	'Brasil'PBR (Ia/b) new	GKev
	Brasilia = 'Zora' (VIIa/b-c)	SDeJ
	'Bright Diamond'PBR (VIIIa/b) new	GKev
	Bright Pixie = 'Ceb Bright' (Ia/b)	CBod GKev SDeJ
	'Bright Star' (VIb-c/c)	LAma MCri
	brownii (IXb-c/a)	ECho GKev
	bulbiferum (IXa/b)	ECho GKev
	- var. ***croceum*** (IXa/b)	XEll
	'Butter Pixie'PBR (Ia/b)	CBod GMcL NBir SDeJ
§	***canadense*** (IXc/a)	GBuc GEdr GKev LAma WCru XEll

- var. ***coccineum*** (IXc/a)	GBuc
- var. ***flavum***	see *L. canadense*
'Canberra'^{PBR} (VIIa-b) **new**	GKev
'Cancun' (Ia/b-c)	SDeJ
candidum (IXb/a)	CAvo CBcs CBro CPne CTca CWCL EBee ECha ECho ELan EPot ERCP GKev LAma LSun NRog SDeJ SRms WWFP
carniolicum	see *L. pyrenaicum* subsp. *carniolicum*
'Casa Blanca' (VIIb/b-c) Υ^{H6}	CAvo CBro EPfP GKev LAma LCro LOPS NBir NNys SCoo SDeJ
'Ceb Latte' (Ia/b) **new**	GKev
'Cecil' (VIIIa/b)	IPot SDeJ
cernuum (IXc/d)	ECho LAma SDeJ
* - 'Album'	ECho SDeJ
'Chameleon' (II)	GKev LAma
'Cherubino' (Ia/b) **new**	GKev
'Chill Out' (VIIa/b)	LCro
§ 'Chocolate Canary' (Ic/-)	GKev SDeJ
Citronella Group (Ic/d)	ECho SDeJ
'Claude Shride' (IIc/d)	GEdr GKev LAma LRHS SDeJ SDir
'Cocktail Twins' (Ia/b)	NRHS SDeJ
'Coldplay' (VIIa-b/b-c)	LBuc LRHS NRHS
columbianum (IXc/d)	ECho GBin
- B&SWJ 9564	WCru
'Con Amore' (VIIb/b)	SCoo
'Conca d'Or'^{PBR} (VIIIb/b)	LRHS NRHS SDeJ
'Connecticut King' (Ia/b)	MCri
'Creation' (VIa/b)	SDeJ
'Crimson Pixie' (Ia/b)	CBod CBro GKev GMcL SDeJ
'Crossover' (Ia-b/b-c)	GMcL LRHS NRHS
× ***dalhansonii*** (IIc/d)	CAby WCot
- 'Guinea Gold' (II)	GKev LAma
§ - 'Marhan' (IIc/d)	ECho GBuc
- 'Mrs R.O. Backhouse' (IIc/d)	ECho GEdr GKev SDeJ
- 'Sutton Court' (II)	GBuc GEdr
- Terrace City Group (II) **new**	GKev
'Dark Romance' (VIIb/b) **new**	LRHS NRHS
dauricum var. ***alpinum*** (IXa/b)	MCri
davidii (IXc/d)	ECho GBuc LAma MCri SDeJ WBor WCru
- var. ***unicolor*** (IXc/d)	GBuc
§ - var. ***willmottiae*** (IXc/d)	MCri WCru
'Debby' (VIIIa-b/b-c)	CSut
'Delicate Joy' (Ia/b)	LRHS NRHS
'Diabora' (Ia/b)	GBuc
'Dimension' (Ia/b-c)	LAma LCro LOPS
'Disco' (Ia)	SDeJ
distichum (IXb-c/d) B&SWJ 4465	WCru
- B&SWJ 794	WCru
'Dizzy' (VIIa-b/b-c)	CTsd MCri SDeJ
'Dot to Dot'	LRHS NRHS
duchartrei (IXc/d)	CAby ECho LAma WCru
'Electric' (Ia/b-c)	MCri
'Electric Yellow'	see *L.* 'Yellow Electric'
'Elodie'^{PBR} (Ia/b)	CAvo LAma
'Elusive' (VIIIb/b-d)	GKev SDeJ
'Enchantment' (Ia/b)	SDeJ
'Eros' (Ic/d)	GEdr
'Esta Bonita'^{PBR} (VIIIa-b/b) **new**	SDir
'Eurydike' (Ic/d)	GEdr
'Expression' (VII)	ILea SDeJ
'Eyeliner'^{PBR} (VIIIa/b)	LAma

'Fairy Morning' (IIc/c) **new**	GKev
'Fata Morgana' (Ia/b) Υ^{H6}	LAma MAsh SCoo SDeJ
'Fifty Fifty' (VIIIa/b-c) **new**	GKev
'Fine Romance' **new**	LRHS NRHS
'Fire King' (Ib/d)	SCoo SDeJ SRms
'First Romance' (VIIa/b) **new**	LRHS NRHS
'Fopapo' (Ia-b/c)	SDeJ
'Forever Marjolein' (Ia/b) **new**	GKev
'Forever Marjon' (Ib-a/b-c) **new**	GKev
'Forever Susan' (Ia/b)	ECGP GKev IPot SDeJ
formosanum (IXb/a)	CPne
- short, from high altitude (IXb/a) RWJ 10005	WCru
- var. ***formosanum*** (IXb/a) B&SWJ 1589	WCru
- var. ***pricei*** (IXb/a)	EAJP EBee ECho EDAr ELan EPot GBin GEdr GKev LRHS MHer SHil WIce
- - 'Snow Queen' (Vb/a)	SDeJ
'Friso' (VIIIb/b)	CBro EPfP GKev
'Garden Party' (VIIb/b) Υ^{H6}	GKev SDeJ
'Gaybird' (IIc/c) **new**	GKev LRHS
'Gironde' (Ia/b)	SDeJ
'Gluhwein'^{PBR} (VIIIa-b/b)	LRHS NRHS
Golden Splendor Group (VIb-c/a) Υ^{H6}	GKev LAma MCri SCoo SDeJ
'Golden Stone' (VIIIa-b/b)	GKev SDeJ
'Gran Paradiso' (Ia/b)	MCri SRms
'Grand Cru' (Ia/b)	MCri SDeJ
grayi (IXc/a)	GBuc
'Hannah North' (Ic/d)	GEdr
hansonii (IXb-c/d)	CWCL ECha ECho GBin GBuc GKev LAma MCri SDeJ SDir
- B&SWJ 4309	WCru
- B&SWJ 8506	WCru
- B&SWJ 8528	WCru
- from Aomori, Japan B&SWJ 4756	WCru
hansonii × ***martagon*** (II)	ERCP
henryi (IXc/d) Υ^{H6}	CAvo CBro EBee ECho GKev LAma MCri NNys SCob SDeJ WCru
'Hit Parade' (VII)	SDeJ
'Honeymoon' (VIIIa-b/b)	SDeJ
'Hot Spot' (VII)	LRHS NRHS
'Hotline' (VIIa/b)	LCro
'Ibarra' (Ia/b)	MCri
'Ice Pixie' (Ia/b)	SDeJ
'Ivory Pixie' (Ia/b)	SDeJ
japonicum (IXb/a)	EFEx
'Jo's Choice' (VIa-b/a)	SDeJ
'Josephine' (VIIa/b)	GKev SDeJ
'Joy'	see *L.* 'Le Rêve'
'Karen North' (Ic/d)	GEdr
kelloggii (IXc/d)	GBin
'King Pete' (Ib/b-c)	SDeJ
'Kingdom'^{PBR} (VIIIa/b-c)	SDeJ
'Lady Alice' (VI-/d)	GKev SDeJ
'Ladylike' (Ia/b) **new**	GMcL
'Lake Tulare' (IVc/c-d)	GEdr
§ ***lancifolium*** (IXc/d)	CArn CHid CPne EPot GBin XLum
- B&SWJ 4352	WCru
- var. ***flaviflorum*** (IXc/d)	CBro EBee GBuc GEdr IBoy MCri SDeJ
- 'Flore Pleno' (IXc/d)	CSut EPPr GCal GKev LHop LRHS MHer NBir NRHS SDeJ WCot WCru XLum
* - var. ***forrestii*** (IX)	MCri

	- var. ***fortunei*** (IXc/d)	EPPr GBin GCal SDix
	-- B&SWJ 539	WCru
	- pink-flowered	SDeJ
	- 'Splendens' (IXc/d)	CBro EBee ECho EPfP GBin GKev MCri NBid SDeJ SDir SPhx WCot
	'Landini'^{PBR} (Ia/b)	SDeJ
	'Lankon' (VIIIc/a)	ERCP
	lankongense (IXc/d)	CWCL ECho EPot GBin GBuc GGGa GKev LAma LRHS SDir WCru
	- BWJ 7554	WCru
	- BWJ 7691	WCru
	'Latvia' (Ia/b)	MCri SDeJ
	'Lazy Lady'	see *L.* 'Chocolate Canary'
§	'Le Rêve' (VIIa-b/b)	SDeJ
	ledebourii (IXc/d)	GKev
	leichtlinii (IXc/d)	CAby CAvo CBro EBee ECho EPot GBin GEdr GKev IMou LLHF MCri SDeJ WOld
	- 'Iwashimiza' (IXc/d)	MCri
	'Leslie Woodriff' (VIIIb-c/d)	IPot
	leucanthum (IXb-c/a)	LAma
	- var. ***centifolium*** (IXb-c/a)	MCri WCru
	-- BWJ 8130	WCru
§	-- 'Black Dragon' (IXb-c/a)	MCri
	lijiangense (IXc/d)	GEdr MCri XEll
I	'Linda' (Ia/b)	SDeJ
	'Little John' (VIIa-b/b)	SDeJ
	'Little Kiss' (Ia/d)	SDeJ
	Lollypop = 'Holebibi' (Ia/b)	CSut GBuc GMcL SCoo
	longiflorum (IXb/a)	CTsd EBee ECho MCri SCoo XLum
	- B&SWJ 11376	WCru
	- 'Foliis Variegatis' (Vb/a/v)	MAvo
	- 'Rose'	SDeJ
§	- 'White American' (Vb/a)	ECho EWoo
	- 'White Heaven'^{PBR} (Vb/a)	EPfP LCro LOPS
	lophophorum (IXc/b)	LAma
	'Lovely Girl' (VII-/b)	SDeJ
	'Luxor' (Ia/b)	CTsd NBir
	'Luzia' (VIIa-b/c)	NRHS
	mackliniae (IXc/a) 🏆^{H5}	CPne CWCL ECho EWes GBin GBuc GCal GCra GGGa GKev ITim NBir NHar WAbe WHal WPGP
	- PAB 9327 **new**	LEdu WPGP
	- PAB 9668	LEdu WPGP
	- from Nagaland, India	CPne GGGa
	- deep pink-flowered	GGGa
	'Manitoba Morning' (IIc/c)	GKev LAma LRHS SDir
	'Mapira' (VIIIb/b)	CHid GKev NNys
	'Marco Polo' ambig.	SCoo SDeJ
	'Marhan'	see *L.* × *dalhansonii* 'Marhan'
	'Marie North' (Ic/d)	GEdr
	'Maroon King' (II)	LRHS
	martagon (IXc/d) 🏆^{H7}	CAvo CBro EBee ECha ECho ELan EPot ERCP GBuc GEdr GKev GPoy LAma LCro LRHS NBir NChi NNys SDeJ SRms WAbe WCot WPnP WShi WWFP
	- var. ***albiflorum*** (IXc/d)	GBuc GKev
	- var. ***album*** (IXc/d)	CAvo CBro ECho ELan EPot GBin GKev LAma NBir NChi NNys SDeJ WShi
	- var. ***cattaniae*** (IXc/d)	GBuc GEdr MCri
	- var. ***hirsutum*** (IXc/d)	GEdr
*	- var. ***rubrum***	CBro CWCL
	'Maru' (VIIa/b)	LBuc LRHS NRHS
	'Mascara' (Ia-b/b) **new**	GKev
	medeoloides (IXc/d)	ECho EFEx GBuc
	- B&SWJ 4184	WCru
	- B&SWJ 4363	WCru
	michiganense (IXc/d)	GBuc

	'Miss Feya' (VIIIb/c)	LAma SDeJ SDir
	'Miss France' (VIIb/b-c)	SDeJ
I	'Miss Lily' (VIIIb/b-c)	SDeJ
	'Miss Lucy'^{PBR} (VIIa-b/b-c)	CHid LAma SDeJ
	Miss Rio	see *L.* 'Rio'
	'Mister Job' (VIIIa/c)	SDeJ
	'Mona Lisa' (VIIb/b-c)	LAma LRHS MCri NGdn SDeJ
	monadelphum (IXc/d)	ECho GKev LAma SDeJ
	- pale-flowered **new**	GKev
	'Mont Blanc' (Ia/b-c)	SDeJ
	'Monte Negro' (Ia/b)	MCri
	'Montezuma'^{PBR} (VIIa-b/b)	SDeJ
	'Montreux' (Ia/b-c)	SDeJ
	'Mountain Joy' (Ia)	LRHS NRHS
	'Muscadet'^{PBR} (VIIa-b/b)	GKev LAma SDeJ
	'Must See' (Ia/b) **new**	GKev
§	***nanum*** (IXc/b)	ECho LAma WAbe WHal
	'Navona' (Ia/b)	GKev
	nepalense (IXc/a)	CAby CBcs CBro CHid CWCL ECho EPfP EPot ERCP GBin GBuc GEdr GKev LAma LRHS MCri SDeJ WAbe WCru WPnP XLum
	- B&SWJ 2985	SDir WCru
	'Nerone' (Ia/b)	CHid
	'Netty's Pride' (Ia/b-c)	CAvo CBro CHid ERCP GBuc GKev IPot SDeJ
	'New Wave' (Ia/b)	GMcL SDeJ
	'New Yellow'	LRHS
	'Night Flyer' (Ib-c/b-c)	SDeJ
	nobilissimum (IXa-b/a)	EFEx
	'Nove Cento' (Ia/b)	MCri SDeJ
	'Olivia' (Ia/-)	LAma
	Olympic Group (VI-/a)	MCri
	'Orange County' (Ia/b)	SDeJ
	'Orange Electric' (Ia/b)	SDeJ
	'Orange Marmalade' (IIb/c-d)	LAma LRHS SDeJ SDir
	'Orange Pixie' (Ia/b)	CBod MCri SCoo
	'Orange Twinkle' (Ib-c/b)	SDeJ
	'Orange Twins' (Ia-b)	LRHS NRHS
	'Orania'^{PBR} (VIIIb/b)	GKev SDeJ
	oriental hybrids (VII)	SDeJ
*	Oriental Superb Group	NGdn
§	***oxypetalum*** (IXb-c/b)	CPne ECho
	- var. ***insigne*** (IXb-c/b)	ECho EPot GBin GBuc NHpl WAbe WHal
	'Pan' (Ic/d)	GEdr
	pardalinum (IXc/d) 🏆^{H6}	CAvo CBro CWCL EBee ECho EPot ERCP GKev LTro WBor WCru
	- var. ***giganteum*** (IXc/d)	EPfP MCri MNrw
	- subsp. ***pardalinum*** (IXc/d)	GBuc
§	- subsp. ***vollmeri*** (IXc/d)	GBuc GKev WCru
§	- subsp. ***wigginsii*** (IXc/d)	WCru
	× ***parkmanii*** 'Journey's End' (VIIb/c)	LAma
	- 'Rosy Dimple' (VIIa/b)	SDeJ
	parryi (IXb-c/a)	SDir
	parvum (IXa-b/a)	ECho GBuc
	'Patricia's Pride' (Ia-b/b-c)	SDeJ
	'Peach Butterflies' (Ic/d)	SDeJ
	'Peach Dwarf' (Ia/b-c)	SDeJ
	'Peach Pixie' (Ia/b)	NBir SCoo
	'Pearl Carolina' (Ic/c) **new**	GKev
	'Pearl Jennifer' (Ib-a/c)	GKev SDeJ SDir
	'Pearl Jessica' (Ib-c/b-c)	GKev SDeJ
	'Pearl Justien' (Ia-b/c)	GKev
	'Pearl Loraine' (Ib-c/b-c)	GKev SDeJ
	'Pearl Melanie' (Ib/c) **new**	GKev
	'Pearl Sonja' (Ib/b)	SDeJ

	'Pearl Stacey' (Ib-c/c)	SDeJ
	'Peggy North' (Ic/d)	GEdr
	'Penthouse' (VIIa/b)	LRHS NRHS
	'Pepard Gold' (IIc/d) **new**	GEdr GKev
	philippinense (IXa-b/a)	EWoo LAma WPGP
	'Pimento' (VIIa/b)	SDeJ
	'Pink Blossom' (Ia/b)	LRHS NRHS
	'Pink Expression' (VII)	LRHS NRHS
	'Pink Flavour' (Ic/c)	GKev SDeJ
	'Pink Heart'	LBuc
	'Pink Morning' (IIc/c)	GKev LRHS
	Pink Perfection Group (VIb/a) 🏆H6	CBro ERCP GKev LAma MCri SCoo SDeJ SPer
	'Pink Pixie' PBR (Ia/b)	CBod GKev GMcL NBir SDeJ
	'Pink Planet' (VIa/a)	GKev
	'Pink Romance' (VIIa/b) **new**	LRHS NRHS
	pitkinense (IX)	GBuc
	poilanei misapplied	see *L. primulinum*
	poilanei Gagnep.	see *L. primulinum* var. *poilanei*
	'Precious Joy' (Ia/b)	LRHS NRHS
§	***primulinum*** (IXc/a) HWJ 681	WCru
	- WWJ 11679	WCru
	- var. ***ochraceum*** (IXc/a)	LAma WCru
	- aff. var. ***ochraceum*** (IXc/a) KWJ 12064	WCru
§	- var. ***poilanei***	EBee
	'Proud Bride' (VIIa/b)	NNys
§	***pumilum*** (IXc/d)	EBee ECho EPot GKev LAma SDeJ
	'Purple Eye' (Ia-b/b) **new**	ERCP
	'Purple Prince' (VIIIa-b/a-b)	SDeJ
	'Push Off' (Ia-b)	LRHS NRHS
	pyrenaicum (IXc/d)	CAby ECho GBuc GKev WShi XEll
§	- subsp. ***carniolicum*** (IXc/d)	GKev
	'Red Carpet' (Ia/b)	MCri NBir SDeJ
	'Red County' (Ia/c-b)	SDeJ
	'Red Electric' (Ia/b)	SDeJ
	'Red Eyes' (VIIa/-)	LRHS NRHS
	'Red Flavour' (Ic/b-c)	GKev
	'Red Hot' (VIIIc-d/b)	SDeJ
	'Red Morning' (VIIIa-b/b) **new**	GKev
	'Red Twin' PBR (Ia/b) **new**	GKev MAsh
	'Red Twinkle'	SDeJ
	'Red Velvet' (Ic/d)	CAvo SDeJ
	regale (IXb/a) 🏆H6	CAvo CBro CTca CTsd CWCL EBee ECha ELan EPfP EPot ERCP GBin GKev LAma LCro LRHS MCri NNys SCob SDeJ SDir SPer WCot
	- 'Album' (IXb/a)	CAvo EBee ERCP GBin GKev IMou LAma LCro LOPS LRHS MCri SCob SCoo SDeJ SDir
§	- 'Royal Gold' (IXb/a)	MCri
	'Reinesse' (Ia/b)	SDeJ
	'Releeze' **new**	LRHS NRHS
	'Revelation' PBR (VIIIa/b) **new**	NNys
§	'Rio' (VIIb/b-c)	SCoo
	'Robert Swanson' (VIIIb-c/b)	GKev LAma SDeJ
	'Robina' (VIIIa-b/b-c)	WCot WWFP
	'Rose Arch Fox' (IIc/c-d)	GKev LAma SDir
	Roselily Natalia = 'Dl04544' PBR (VIIa-b/-) **new**	MAsh
	'Rosella's Dream' (Ia/b)	GKev SDeJ
	'Rosemary North' (Ic/d)	GEdr
	'Rosselini' (VIIIa-b/b)	SDeJ
	rosthornii (IXc/d)	EBee LAma WCru
	'Royal Gold'	see *L. regale* 'Royal Gold'
	rubellum (IXb/a)	EFEx
	'Russian Morning' (IIc/c)	GKev LRHS SDir
	'Russian Red' (IIc/d)	LAma
	sachalinense (IXa/b) RBS 0235	EPPr
	'Salinas' (VIIa/b)	GKev SDeJ
	'Salmon Flavour' (Ic/b-c) **new**	GKev
	'Salmon Party' (VIIb/b) **new**	GKev
	'Salmon Tiger'	SDeJ SDir
	'Salmon Twinkle' (Ib-c/c)	SDeJ
	sargentiae (IXb-c/a)	GCal GEdr
	'Satisfaction' (VIIIa-b/-)	SDeJ
	'Scarlet Delight' (VIIb-c/c-d)	GKev SDeJ
	'Scheherazade' (VIIIc/d)	GKev LAma MCri SDeJ
	'Serrada' PBR (VIIIa-b/b)	ILea
	'Set Point' (VIIb/b)	SDeJ
	'Showwinner' (VIIa/b-c) **new**	LRHS NRHS
	'Slate's Morning' (IIc/c) **new**	GKev
	'Slate's Select' (II)	LAma
	'Smoky Mountain' (VIIIc/d)	SDeJ
	'Souvenir' PBR (VIIa-b/b)	NGdn
	speciosum (IXb-c/d) B&SWJ 4847	WCru
	- B&SWJ 4924	WCru
	- var. ***album*** (IXb-c/d)	ECho GKev LEdu NBir NNys SDeJ
	- var. ***gloriosoides*** (IXb-c/d)	LAma
	- var. ***rubrum*** (IXb-c/d)	ECha ECho EPfP LAma LOPS MCri NBir SDeJ SDir SPer SRms
§	- - 'Uchida' (IXb-c/d)	GKev SDeJ
	'Sphinx' (Ia/d)	WCot
	'Spring Pink' (Ia/-)	ERCP GKev SDeJ
	'Spring Romance' (VIIa/b) **new**	LRHS NRHS
	'Stainless Steel' (Ia/b)	SDeJ
	'Star Gazer' (VIIa/c)	CBro EPfP GKev LAma LRHS NRHS SCob SCoo SDeJ
	'Starfighter' (VIIa-b/c)	SDeJ
	'Sterling Star' (Ia/b)	MCri
	'Sulphur King'	WCot
	sulphureum (IXb-c/a)	LAma
	'Sunny Morning' (IIc/d)	LAma LRHS
	superbum (IXc/d)	EBee GBuc GKev LAma WCru WPGP
	'Sweet Lord' (Ia/b)	GKev SDeJ
	'Sweet Surrender' (Ib-c/c-d)	GKev MCri SDeJ
	szovitsianum (IXc/d)	GKev
	'Tailor Made' (Ia/b)	GKev SDeJ
	taliense (IXc/d)	ECho LAma WCru
	'Tarragona' PBR (VIIIb/b)	SDeJ
	tenuifolium	see *L. pumilum*
	Tiger Babies Group (VIIIb-c/c-d)	CAvo GKev
	'Tigeredition' (VIIa-b/b-c)	LCro LOPS
	'Tigerwoods' (VIIa/c)	LCro LOPS
	tigrinum	see *L. lancifolium*
	'Tiny Bee' PBR (Ia-b/b) **new**	MAsh
	'Tiny Dessert' PBR (Ia/b) **new**	MAsh
	'Tiny Dino' PBR (Ia-b/b) **new**	MAsh
	'Tiny Double You' PBR (Ia-b/b) **new**	MAsh
	'Tiny Ghost' PBR (Ia/b-c) **new**	MAsh
	'Tiny Invader' PBR (Ia-b/b-c) **new**	MAsh

'Tiny Nanny'PBR (Ia-b/b-c) new	MAsh
'Tiny Sensation'PBR (Ia-b/b-c) new	MAsh
'Tiny Skyline'PBR (Ia-b/b) new	MAsh
'Tiny Todd' (Ia/b-c) new	MAsh
'Tom Pouce' (VIIa/b)	SDeJ
'Toronto' (Ia-b/b)	SDeJ
'Toscane' (Ia/b-c)	SDeJ
Triumphator = 'Zanlophator'PBR (VIIIb/a-b)	GKev ILea SDeJ
tsingtauense (IXa/c)	GKev LAma MCri SDeJ
- B&SWJ 4263	WCru
- B&SWJ 4698	WCru
- B&SWJ 519	WCru
'Uchida Kanoka'	see *L. speciosum* var. *rubrum* 'Uchida'
'Urandi' (VIIIc/b)	GKev SDeJ
'Val Di Sole'PBR (Ia/b)	SDeJ
'Venezuela' (VIIa-b/b-c)	SDeJ SDir
'Vermeer' (Ia-b/b-c)	ILea
'Visaversa' (VIIIa-b/b)	SDeJ
'Vivaldi' (Ia/b)	SDeJ
vollmeri	see *L. pardalinum* subsp. *vollmeri*
wallichianum (IXb/a)	ECho EPot GKev LAma SDeJ XLum
washingtonianum (IXb/a)	GBin
'White American'	see *L. longiflorum* 'White American'
'White Paradise' (V)	SCoo
'White Planet' (VIa/a)	GKev
'White Present' (Vb/a)	NNys SDeJ
'White Twinkle' (Ia-b/b)	SDeJ
wigginsii	see *L. pardalinum* subsp. *wigginsii*
willmottiae	see *L. davidii* var. *willmottiae*
'Wine Electric' (Ia/c)	SDeJ
xanthellum var. ***luteum*** (IXb-c/d)	WCru
'Yellow Cocotte' (Ia/c) new	GKev
'Yellow County' (Ia/b-c) new	GKev
§ 'Yellow Electric' (Ia/b-c)	SDeJ
'Yellow Eye' (Ia/b)	SDeJ
'Yellow Planet' (VIb-a/a)	GKev
'Yeti' (Ia/b)	SDeJ
'Zulu'	LRHS

lime see *Citrus* × *aurantiifolia*

lime, Philippine see *Citrus* × *microcarpa*

limequat see *Citrus* × *floridana*

Limnanthes (*Limnanthaceae*)

douglasii ♀H7	EPfP MNHC
- subsp. ***rosea***	CSpe

Limonium (*Plumbaginaceae*)

bellidifolium	CFis CMea EDAr ESps
'Blauer Diamant'	EWoo
cosyrense	CMea MHer
dregeanum	WThu
dumosum	see *Goniolimon tataricum* var. *angustifolium*
gmelinii	SPlb
* - subsp. ***hungaricum***	XLum
latifolium	see *L. platyphyllum*
§ ***platyphyllum***	CBod CBot EPfP EWoo GMaP LHop LRHS MBel MHer MMuc MWat SBod SCob SEND SMHy SPer SRms WHar WHoo XSen
- 'Robert Butler'	CBod GCal GQue MRav
- 'Violetta'	CBod EBee ELan EPfP GBin GMcL LRHS MBel MPie SPer SPoG WAul WHoo
sinuatum	SVic
tataricum	see *Goniolimon tataricum*
vulgare	LRHS WHer XSen

Linaria (*Plantaginaceae*)

aeruginea	CPBP
- 'Lindeza Violet'	CSpe
- 'Neon Lights'	CSpe EDAr NGdn SPoG
- subsp. ***nevadensis*** 'Gemstones'	SBch
alpina	CSpe GJos NRya NSla SRms
anticaria 'Antique Silver'	LSou MRav WHil
Blue Lace = 'Yalin'	LSou
cymbalaria	see *Cymbalaria muralis*
§ ***dalmatica***	ECGP ELan EPPr MPie NBid NGBl SPad SPhx WCot WHea WMoo
dalmatica × ***purpurea***	WCot
'Dial Park' new	WCot
× ***dominii*** 'Yuppie Surprise'	CHid NBir
'Florence Lily Sophia Brown'	WCot
genistifolia	WCot
- W&B BGB-6	WCot
- subsp. ***dalmatica***	see *L. dalmatica*
hepaticifolia	see *Cymbalaria hepaticifolia*
* ***lobata alba***	SPlb
origanifolia	see *Chaenorhinum origanifolium*
pallida	see *Cymbalaria pallida*
'Peachy'	CAby CDor CSpe EBee ECtt MHol MPie MSCN MTis SBod SMHy SPad SPoG WCot WHrl WOut WRHF WWFP
pilosa	see *Cymbalaria pilosa*
'Pink Kisses' new	WCot
purpurea	CBod CDor CTri CWld EHoe ELan EPfP ESps IFoB MHer MNHC NBro NPer NPol SEND SPhx SRms WCot WFar WMoo WSFF
- 'Alba'	see *L. purpurea* 'Springside White'
- 'Brown's White Strain'	CBre CSpe EBee EPPr IBoy WCot
- 'Canon Went'	CBod CBre CDor CSpe CTri CWib EBee EHoe ELan EPfP ESps EWoo GJos LRHS MMuc MNHC MSCN NBir NGBl NPol SGbt SHil SPer SPhx SRms SWvt WFar WKif WMoo
- 'Freefolk Piccolo'	SHar
- pink-flowered	CSpe
- 'Poached Egg' new	CMea MAvo
- 'Radcliffe Innocence'	see *L. purpurea* 'Springside White'
§ - 'Springside White'	CBod CDor GJos LRHS NBir NGdn SBch SPhx WFar
repens	WCot WHer
× ***sepium***	WCot
triornithophora	SPlb WKif WMoo
- 'Pink Budgies'	EBee LSou
- purple-flowered	WMoo
- 'Rosea'	CSpe
vulgaris	CHab CWld EDAr EPfP MHer MNHC NMir SRms WHer WMoo
- f. ***peloria***	CPBP

Lindelofia (*Boraginaceae*)

anchusoides misapplied	see *L. longiflora*
anchusoides (Lindl.) Lehm.	EPPr NBid
§ ***longiflora***	GCal GCra GPSL WHea WSHC

Lindera (Lauraceae)

aggregata	CBcs WPGP
angustifolia FMWJ 13156	WCru
benzoin	CBcs CRos EPfP LRHS MBlu NLar
erythrocarpa	EPfP
- B&SWJ 6271	WCru
- B&SWJ 8730	WCru
metcalfiana	WCru
var. ***dictyophylla*** KWJ 12312	
obtusiloba ♀H5	CAbP MBlu WPGP
- B&SWJ 8723	WCru
- B&SWJ 11054	WCru
- B&SWJ 12555 from Korea	WCru
praecox	EPfP
- B&SWJ 10802	WCru
- B&SWJ 10953 from north Japan	WCru
- B&SWJ 11125 from south Japan	WCru
reflexa	NLar
sericea B&SWJ 11123	WCru
- B&SWJ 11141	WCru
- var. ***lancea*** B&SWJ 11071	WCru
- - B&SWJ 11118	WCru
strychnifolia	EPfP
tonkinensis FMWJ 13123	WCru
triloba B&SWJ 5570	WCru
- B&SWJ 11121	WCru
- B&SWJ 11466	WCru
umbellata B&SWJ 10881	WCru
- var. ***membranacea*** B&SWJ 6227	WCru
- - B&SWJ 10837	WCru

Lindernia (Linderniaceae)

grandiflora	CBod ESwi LLWG WTor

Linnaea (Caprifoliaceae)

borealis	EPot NSla WAbe XEll
- subsp. ***americana***	NHar WAbe

Linum (Linaceae)

arboreum ♀H4	GKev LLHF NBir WThu
boissieri	LLHF
campanulatum	WThu
flavum	XSen
- 'Compactum'	CMea LLHF NSla SRms
'Gemmell's Hybrid' ♀H4	ECho EPot EWes GCrg NBir WAbe WThu
grandiflorum 'Bright Eyes'	CSpe
- 'Rubrum'	CSpe
hypericifolium	SPhx
kingii var. ***sedoides***	WAbe
monogynum	LLHF
narbonense	CCse MArt SIgm SPhx
- 'Heavenly Blue'	NCGa
§ ***perenne***	CBod ECha ELan ENfk EPfP ESps GMaP LSun MHer MNHC SCob SIde SPer SPoG WJek WSHC
- 'Album'	EBee ECha ELan EPfP
- subsp. ***alpinum*** 'Alice Blue'	WAbe
§ - 'Blau Saphir'	GQue MBel NHol
- Blue Sapphire	see *L. perenne* 'Blau Saphir'
- 'Nanum Sapphire'	see *L. perenne* 'Blau Saphir'
sibiricum	see *L. perenne*
suffruticosum subsp. ***salsoloides***	SBrt
- - 'Nanum'	WThu
- 'Spanish Sun' **new**	CPBP
tenuifolium	NSla
uninerve	WAbe
usitatissimum	MHer
- 'Blue Dress'	SPhx

Lippia (Verbenaceae)

sp.	SWvt
canescens	see *Phyla nodiflora* var. *canescens*
chamaedrifolia	see *Verbena peruviana*
citriodora	see *Aloysia citrodora*
dulcis	CArn ENfk
nodiflora	see *Phyla nodiflora*
repens	see *Phyla nodiflora*

Liquidambar ✿ (Hamamelidaceae)

acalycina	CDul CJun EBee EBtc ELan EMOT EPfP NLar NOra SBir SCoo SGol SLim SSta WMat WPGP WPat
- 'Burgundy Flush' ♀H6	CJun NLar SBir SSta
- 'Spinners'	CRos ELan LRHS SBir SPoG
formosana	CDul CMCN CMac IArd MHid SBir SGol SSta WPGP
- 'Afterglow'	CJun NLar
- 'Ellen'	CJun NLar
- Monticola Group	CJun SLim SSta
orientalis	CDul CJun CLnd CMCN EBtc EPfP LLHF SBir SSta WPat
- 'M. Foster'	NLar
styraciflua	Widely available
- 'Andrew Hewson'	CAbP CJun CLnd CRos EBee EPfP IVic LRHS MAsh MBlu SBir SSta WPat
- 'Anja'	CJun MBlu SBir SSta WPat
- 'Anneke'	CJun SBir SSta
- 'Aurea'	see *L. styraciflua* 'Variegata' Overeynder
- 'Aurea Variegata'	see *L. styraciflua* 'Variegata' Overeynder
- 'Aurora'	CJun SBir
- 'Burgundy'	CJun CLnd LLHF MBlu SBir SSta WPat
I - 'Corky'	SSta
- 'Elstead Mill'	CAbP
- 'Emerald Sentinel'	CJun SSta
- 'Festeri'	CEnd SBir SSta
- 'Festival'	CJun MBlu SGol
- 'Frosty' (v)	CJun SBir SSta
- 'Globe'	see *L. styraciflua* 'Gum Ball'
- 'Gold Beacon'	MPkF NLar
- 'Golden Sun' PBR	NLar
- 'Golden Treasure' (v)	CDul CJun CLnd CMCN CRos LRHS MAsh MGos SBir SGol SReu SSta
- 'Goldmember'	CJun SSta
- 'Granary Sunset'	SBir SSta
§ - 'Gum Ball'	CCVT CEnd CJun CLnd CMCN EBee ELon EPfP EWes LLHF NLar SBir SCob SLim SSta SWvt WPat
- Happidaze = 'Hapdell'	CJun NLar SBir WPat
- 'Jennifer Carol'	NLar SBir SSta
- 'Kia'	CAbP CEnd CJun LLHF SBir
- 'Lane Roberts' ♀H6	Widely available
- 'Lynn'	SBir SSta
- 'Manon' (v)	CJun SPoG
- 'Midwest Sunset'	CJun EBee MBlu NLar SBir WPat
- 'Moonbeam' (v)	CJun SBir SCob SLim SSta WPat
- 'Moraine'	CJun ESwi
- 'Naree'	CJun NLar SSta WPat
- 'Nina'	SSta

	- 'Nyewood'	SBir
	- 'Oconee'	CEnd EPfP LEdu LLHF MAsh NLar SSta WPat
	- 'Paarl' (v)	CJun CLnd EMOT SGol
	- 'Palo Alto' 🏆^{H6}	CEnd CJun EMOT LLHF MAsh MBlu SAko SBir SCoo SLim SMad SSta WMat WPGP WPat
	- 'Parasol'	CAbP CAco CEnd CJun CLnd EBtc SBir SSta
	- 'Pendula'	CJun CLnd MBlu SBir SSta WPat
	- 'Penwood' 🏆^{H6}	CJun NLar SBir SSta WPat
	- 'Red Sunset'	SSta
	- 'Rotundiloba'	CJun CMCN EPfP LEdu LLHF LRHS MAsh MBlu SSta WPGP WPat
	- 'Savill Torch'	CJun SBir SSta
	- 'Schock's Gold'	CJun MAsh NLar SSta WPat
§	- 'Silver King' (v)	CJun CLnd CMCN CMac EBee MAsh MGos MPkF NLar SCoo SGol SHil SLim SPoG SReu SSta WPat
	- 'Simone'	SBir SGol SSta
	- 'Slender Silhouette' 🏆^{H6}	Widely available
	- 'Stared'	CDul CEnd CJun CLnd EBee EBtc EMOT EPfP GQue MBlu MGos NOra SBir SCoo SLim SSta WMat WMou WPGP WPat
	- 'Thea'	CAbP CJun CLnd CRos EBee EPfP LRHS MAsh MBlu SBir SSta WPat
	- 'Variegata' misapplied	see *L. styraciflua* 'Silver King'
§	- 'Variegata' Overeynder (v)	CJun CLnd CMac CRos EBee ELan EMOT ESps LRHS SBir SLim SSta
	- 'White Star' (v)	CJun
	- 'Woorby Rose'	CJun NLar SBir
	- 'Worplesdon' 🏆^{H6}	Widely available

Liriodendron (*Magnoliaceae*)

	'Chapel Hill'	MBlu NLar WPat
	chinense 🏆^{H6}	CBcs CDul CMCN EBee EPfP MBlu MPhe SGol WPGP
	chinense* × *tulipifera	NOrn WPGP
	'Doc Deforce's Delight'	MBlu NLar
	tulipifera 🏆^{H6}	Widely available
	- 'Aureomarginatum' (v) 🏆^{H6}	CBcs CCVT CDul CEnd CLet CMCN CTho EBee ECrN ELan EMOT EPfP ESps IDee LHop LLHF MBlu MGos MSwo NEgg NLar SCob SGol SPer SPoG SSta WHar WMat WMou WPat
	- 'Fastigiatum'	CDul CEnd CLnd CMCN CTho EBee ECrN ELan EMOT EPfP ESps MAsh MBlu MGos NLar SGol SPer WPat
	- 'Glen Gold'	CEnd MBlu NLar
	- 'Purgatory'	MBlu
	- 'Roodhaan'	ESwi MBlu NLar
	- 'Rotundiloba'	MBlu
	- 'Snow Bird' (v)	WMat

Liriope ✿ (*Asparagaceae*)

	'Big Blue'	see *L. muscari* 'Big Blue'
§	***exiliflora***	CLAP
	- 'Ariaka-janshige' (v)	LRHS
	- Silvery Sunproof misapplied	see *L. spicata* 'Gin-ryu', *L. muscari* 'Variegata'
§	***gigantea***	CLAP
	graminifolia misapplied	see *L. muscari*
	hyacinthifolia	see *Reineckea carnea*
	'Majestic'	CBct CLAP MHer WHoo
	minor	CMac
§	***muscari*** 🏆^{H5}	Widely available
	- B&SWJ 561	WCru
	- 'Alba'	see *L. muscari* 'Monroe White'
	- Amethyst = 'Liptp'	CBod WMoo
§	- 'Big Blue'	CAbb CBct CDul CLAP CMac EAEE EBee ECtt ELan ELon EPPr EPfP EPri EShb EWoo GBin LHop LPar LRHS LSRN MJak MRav MSwo NLar SArc SCob SGol SPoG SWvt WMoo
	- 'Christmas Tree'	EBee EPPr WHoo WMoo
	- 'Evergreen Giant'	see *L. gigantea*
	- 'Gold-banded' (v)	CBct CLAP EBee EPfP GWyn LHop LRHS SCob
	- 'Goldfinger'	EBee SMad
	- 'Ingwersen'	CBod CKno EBee ECho ELon EPPr EPfP EWTr EWoo SCob XLum
	- Isabella = 'Lirf'	EBee EPPr
	- 'John Burch' (v)	CBct CLAP ELon NLar WGob WGrn
	- 'Lilac Wonder'	EPPr LRHS SCob
	- 'Majestic' misapplied	see *L. exiliflora*
	- 'Moneymaker'	EPPr GBin GKev MNrw SCob XEll
§	- 'Monroe White'	CBct CBro CDor CLAP CMac EBee ELan EPfP EShb EWoo LCro LOPS MJak MRav NBid NLar SCob SPer SWvt
	- 'Okina' (v)	CBro CKno EBee ELon GEdr LHop LLWG MNrw MSCN NGBl NLar NSti SMad SPer WCot
	- 'Purple Passion'	EBee SCob
	- 'Royal Purple'	CBct CLAP EAJP EBee ECtt ELon EPfP EWoo LRHS NLar SCob SPer SPoG WGrn WMoo
	- 'Silver Ribbon'	CBro CLAP EPfP LSRN MGos
	- 'Superba'	WCot
§	- 'Variegata' (v)	CBod CLAP EBee ECho ELan EWes LEdu LRHS MJak NBir SPer SWvt WMoo
	- variegated, white-flowered (v)	ECho
	- 'Webster Wideleaf'	EBee WCot
	platyphylla	see *L. muscari*
	Pure Blonde = 'Lirblonde'	ESwi
	spicata	CBod EBee ECho EWoo GCal XLum
	- B&SWJ 8821	WCru
	- 'Alba'	ECho MRav
§	- 'Gin-ryu' (v)	CBct CLAP CMac EAEE ELan EPfP EShb EWes LEdu LPot MRav SCob SGol SPer WMoo XLum
	- 'Silver Dragon'	see *L. spicata* 'Gin-ryu'

Listera (*Orchidaceae*)

	ovata	WHer

Litchi (*Sapindaceae*)

	chinensis	CCCN

Lithocarpus ✿ (*Fagaceae*)

	densiflorus	CMCN
	- var. ***echinoides***	CMCN
	edulis	CFil SArc SKHP
§	***glaber***	CFil

Lithodora (*Boraginaceae*)

§	***diffusa***	ECho SGol SRot
	- 'Alba'	CSma CTri CWCL ECho NCou SPoG
	- 'Compacta'	CSma SRot WAbe
§	- 'Grace Ward' 🏆^{H5}	CBod CWCL ECtt ELan EPfP GCrg MHol MMuc NWad
§	- 'Heavenly Blue' 🏆^{H5}	Widely available
	- 'Inverleith'	ECho
	- 'Pete's Favourite'	NWad WAbe
	- 'Picos'	CMea ECho EPot NLar NSla NWad SBrt SIgm WAbe WThu

- 'Star'^{PBR} — CHid CWCL ELan ELon EPfP GLog LRHS NHpl NLar NRHS SCoo SPer SPoG SRot SWvt WFar WHil WIce
- 'White Star' — WIce

× *intermedia* — see *Moltkia* × *intermedia*
§ ***oleifolia*** 🏆H4 — ECho LLHF LRHS NBir NRHS
rosmarinifolia — WCFE
zahnii — ECho EWld LLHF LRHS NRHS SVen
- 'Azure-ness' — MCot SBch SChF WAbe
- compact — SIgm

Lithophragma (*Saxifragaceae*)

parviflorum — EWes

Lithospermum (*Boraginaceae*)

diffusum — see *Lithodora diffusa*
doerfleri — see *Moltkia doerfleri*
'Grace Ward' — see *Lithodora diffusa* 'Grace Ward'
'Heavenly Blue' — see *Lithodora diffusa* 'Heavenly Blue'
officinale — GPoy NMir
oleifolium — see *Lithodora oleifolia*
purpureocaeruleum — see *Buglossoides purpurocaerulea*

Litsea (*Lauraceae*)

PAB 13.047 **new** — WPGP
cubeba FMWJ 13011 — WCru
glauca — see *Neolitsea sericea*
japonica — SVen

Littonia (*Colchicaceae*)

modesta — CPne CRHN ECho LAma

Livistona (*Arecaceae*)

chinensis 🏆H1c — CPHo NLos SBig SChr
decora — LTro
jenkinsiana — NLos
rotundifolia **new** — NLos

Loasa (*Loasaceae*)

acanthifolia — GCal
triphylla var. ***volcanica*** — EBee EWes

Lobelia ✿ (*Campanulaceae*)

angustifolia — SBee
'Bordervale' — WBor
bridgesii — CDTJ CFil EWes GCal LRHS WKif WMoo WPGP
§ ***cardinalis*** 🏆H3 — CMac ELon GMaP LCro NGBl NLar NPer SPlb SRms SWat SWvt WBod WFar WHil WMAq
- 'Bee's Flame' — CLet CNor CWGN EAEE ECtt GBuc IKil LRHS MRav MSpe NEgg NGdn SPtp SRkn WWtn
- 'Black Truffle' — CAbb EBee SPad
§ - 'Elmfeuer' — CBod CMHG CWCL ECtt EHoe EWoo IBoy NLar NPri SPlb SPoG SWvt WHar XLum
- 'Illumination' — ELon
§ - 'Queen Victoria' 🏆H3 — Widely available
- 'Russian Princess' misapplied — CBot CRos CWCL CWld EPfP ESps IBoy LRHS MHol MSCN NAst NGdn NRHS SPoG SRkn SWvt WFar WHar

chinensis — LLWG
'Cinnabar Deep Red' — see *L.* × *speciosa* 'Fan Tiefrot'
'Cinnabar Rose' — see *L.* × *speciosa* 'Fan Zinnoberrosa'
Compliment Blue — see *L.* × *speciosa* 'Kompliment Blau'
Compliment Deep Red — see *L.* × *speciosa* 'Kompliment Tiefrot'
Compliment Purple — see *L.* × *speciosa* 'Kompliment Purpur'
Compliment Scarlet — see *L.* × *speciosa* 'Kompliment Scharlach'
'Compton Pink' — CBod CBot EAEE ECtt ELan EShb EWes IPot LBuc LRHS NGBl SCob
davidii PAB 8547 — LEdu
Elizabeth Strangman selection — CSpe NDov
erinus Blue Star = 'Wesstar'^{PBR} — LSou
- 'Cambridge Blue' — ESps
- 'Crystal Palace' — ESps NPri
- (Fountain Series) 'Fountain Blue' — ESps NPri
- - 'Fountain White' — ESps NPri
- 'Kathleen Mallard' (d) — CCCN SWvt
- Purple Star = 'Wespurstar'^{PBR} — LSou
- Riviera Series — NPri
- 'Sapphire' — ESps NPri
- 'String of Pearls' — ESps
- Super Star = 'Weslosu'^{PBR} (Star Series) — LSou
- (Waterfall Series) Waterfall Blue = 'Balobwablu'^{PBR} — LBMP
- - Waterfall White Sparkle = 'Balobwaspar' — LBMP

excelsa — GCal MTPN SBrt SEND
- B&SWJ 9513 — WCru

Fan Deep Red — see *L.* × *speciosa* 'Fan Tiefrot'
Fan Deep Rose — see *L.* × *speciosa* 'Fan Orchidrosa'
Fan Salmon — see *L.* × *speciosa* 'Fan Lachs'
'Flamingo' — see *L.* × *speciosa* 'Pink Flamingo'
fulgens — see *L. cardinalis*
- Saint Elmo's Fire — see *L. cardinalis* 'Elmfeuer'

× ***gerardii*** — see *L.* × *speciosa*
gibberoa — CDTJ
'Gladys Lindley' — LRHS
'Hadspen Purple' — see *L.* × *speciosa* 'Hadspen Purple'
inflata — GPoy
Laguna Trailing Blue = 'Lob Bule' **new** — ESps
Laguna Trailing Dark Blue = 'Loblamoubl'^{PBR} **new** — ESps
Laguna Trailing Violet = 'Tec Travio' **new** — ESps
Laguna Trailing White = 'Lobtrawi' **new** — ESps
Laguna White = 'Lobwhi'^{PBR} **new** — ESps
laxiflora — CBot CFis CHll WBod
- B&SWJ 9064 — WCru
- var. ***angustifolia*** — CAby CDTJ CSam CTre CWCL EWld GCal LRHS SMHy SRms

linnaeoides — SPlb
§ ***montana*** — EWld
- B&SWJ 8220 — WCru

pedunculata — see *Pratia pedunculata*
'Queen Victoria' — see *L. cardinalis* 'Queen Victoria'
sessilifolia — LLWG MArt
- B&SWJ 8875 — WCru

siphilitica — Widely available
- 'Alba' — CLet CSam EBee EPfP GCal MArt SBch SRms SWat SWvt WBor WFar WHrl WMoo WShi
- f. ***albiflora*** — LEdu
- blue-flowered — CSpe NCGa SWat SWvt
- 'Rosea' — MNrw

§ × ***speciosa*** — ESps IKil SVic SWat WMoo XLum

- 'Butterfly Blue'	CNor LRHS SGbt
- 'Butterfly Rose'	SRot
- 'Cherry Ripe'	LLHF
- 'Cranberry Crush'	CAbb LRHS
- Crimson Princess = 'Gencrim' (Princess Series) **new**	SPoG
- 'Dark Crusader'	CMea EBee ECtt ELan EPfP LRHS MSpe NDov SWat
- Fan Series	MRav
- - 'Fan Blau'	CBod ELan EPfP LPot LRHS MCot MHol NRHS SCob SPer WHar WMoo WTor
- - 'Fan Burgundy'	EPfP ESps EWoo LRHS MCot MHer MHol NGdn NLar NRHS SCob SPer
§ - - 'Fan Lachs'	CWCL EPfP LRHS MHer MSCN NRHS SPer WMoo WTor
§ - - 'Fan Orchidrosa' ♀H5	EPfP LRHS NRHS SRot
- - 'Fan Scharlach' ♀H5	EPfP LRHS NLar SPoG SRot SWvt WTor
§ - - 'Fan Tiefrot' ♀H5	LRHS NRHS SRms SWvt WBor WMoo
§ - - 'Fan Zinnoberrosa' ♀H5	SRms SRot SWvt WMoo
- 'Grape Knee-high'	LLHF
§ - 'Hadspen Purple'PBR	CAby CBod CBot CMHG CMac CMos CSpe CWGN EBee ECtt ELan EPfP IBoy IPot LHop LOPS LRHS LSRN MCot MRav NCGa NDov NPnk SHar SRms SWat SWvt
- 'Kimbridge Beet'	CMac
§ - (Kompliment Series) 'Kompliment Blau'	SWvt
§ - - 'Kompliment Purpur'	MMuc MNrw SWvt
§ - - 'Kompliment Scharlach' ♀H5	CAby CWat EPfP MNrw NPer SWvt
§ - - 'Kompliment Tiefrot'	EPfP LRHS MMuc MNrw SWvt
- 'Monet Moment'	EBee ECtt EWes ILea SBee SWvt
- 'Pauline'	ECtt
- 'Pink Elephant' ♀H3	ECtt GCra SHar WCFE
§ - 'Pink Flamingo'	ELan WMoo
- Rose Princess = 'Genross' (Princess Series) **new**	EWTr LRHS SPoG
- 'Ruby Slippers'	EBee ELan EPfP
- 'Russian Princess' purple-flowered	CBod EAEE ECtt EHoe ELan EWTr EWoo IBoy LHop LSou MBel MCot MHer MPie MSpe NCGa NDov NGBl NHol NPnk SPer SPtp WFar WHar
- Scarlet Princess **new** = 'Genlet' (Princess Series)	LRHS
- 'Sparkling Burgundy'	LRHS
- 'Sparkling Ruby'	EPfP IKil LBuc MCot SWvt WMoo
- 'Tania'	Widely available
§ - 'Vedrariensis'	CBod CMac CSam CSpe CWib EAJP ECtt ELan EPfP GBuc MBel MCot MHer MMuc MNrw NGBl SPer SRms SWvt WCFE WFar WHoo XLum
- 'Will Scarlet'	LRHS NRHS
spicata	SBrt
'Starship Scarlet' **new**	MHol
'Tania's Sister'	WCot WGrn
treadwellii	see *Pratia angulata* 'Treadwellii'
tupa	Widely available
- JCA 12527	IBlr
- Archibald's form	GCra WPGP
urens	CFil
valida	SWvt
- 'True Blue'	CWGN SWvt
vedrariensis	see *L.* × *speciosa* 'Vedrariensis'
Waterfall Light Lavender = 'Balwalila'PBR (Waterfall Series)	LBMP
wollastonii	SPlb

Lobostemon (*Boraginaceae*)

belliformis	CTre

Lobularia (*Brassicaceae*)

maritima Easter Bonnet Series	NPri
- 'Snow Crystals'	NPri
Snow Princess = 'Inlbusnopr'PBR	NPri

Loeselia (*Polemoniaceae*)

mexicana	CHll

loganberry see *Rubus* × *loganobaccus*

Lomandra (*Asparagaceae*)

filiformis Savanna Blue = 'Lmf500'	ESwi LSou
hystrix	SPlb
longifolia	GCal LEdu SPlb
- Nyalla = 'Lm400'PBR	LHop
- Tanika = 'Lm300'PBR	ESwi GBin

Lomaria see *Blechnum*

Lomatia (*Proteaceae*)

dentata	LRHS MGil MRav
ferruginea	CBcs CCCN CDTJ CTsd EPfP MPkF SArc SKHP WCru WPGP
fraseri	CCCN EBee EPfP LRHS SPoG
hirsuta	MGil SKHP
longifolia	see *L. myricoides*
§ ***myricoides***	CBcs CBct CCCN CTsd EBee ELan EPfP IDee LRHS MAsh NLar SAko SKHP SLon SPer
silaifolia	LRHS
tinctoria	CBcs CTre EPfP LRHS MAsh SAko WBod

Lomatium (*Apiaceae*)

columbianum	SIgm
grayi	SPhx

Lonicera ✿ (*Caprifoliaceae*)

KR 291	ELon
KR 10106	WPGP
§ ***acuminata***	CMCN LRHS
- B&SWJ 3480	WCru
- B&SWJ 6743	CRHN WCru
- B&SWJ 6815	WCru
- var. ***acuminata***	WCot
aff. ***acuminata*** NJM 11.033	WPGP
albertii	CDul EBee EPfP MBNS NLar SEND
alseuosmoides	CBcs CDul CRHN EBee EWTr LEdu LRHS MMuc NLar SEND SKHP SLon SPoG WCru WPGP WSHC
× ***americana*** misapplied	see *L.* × *italica*
americana ambig.	ESps
§ ***americana*** (Mill.) K. Koch	CBcs CFlo EPfP ETho LEdu MJak MMuc MSwo NLar NWea SEND SKHP SLim SRms WBor WSHC
§ × ***brownii*** 'Dropmore Scarlet'	Widely available
- 'Fuchsioides' misapplied	see *L.* × ***brownii*** 'Dropmore Scarlet'

	- 'Fuchsioides' K. Koch	SNig WSHC
	caerulea	CWld EPom IDee LRHS MNHC MRav SCob SDea SPoG SRms SVic WBor WHar
	- var. ***altaica***	LEdu
	- 'Atut'	NLar
	- 'Balalaika'	CAgr MCoo
	- 'Duet'	NLar
	- var. ***edulis***	CAgr CWld EPfP EWTr LBuc LEdu MCoo MNHC SDea SEle WMat
	- - 'Blue Moon'	CAgr
	- 'Eisbar'	CAgr
	- 'Kalinka'	CAgr
	- var. ***kamtschatica***	CAgr EBee EPom LCro LOPS NLar WPGP
	- - 'Fialka'PBR	NLar
	- - 'Larisa' **new**	LEdu WPGP
	- - 'Maries' **new**	LEdu WPGP
	- - 'Morena'PBR	EPom GGGa
	- - 'Nimfa'	GGGa
	- - 'Rebecca' **new**	LEdu WPGP
	- - 'Ruth' **new**	LEdu WPGP
	- - 'Sinoglaska' **new**	NLar
	- - 'Wojtek' **new**	NLar
	- 'Kirke'	GBin NLar
*	- var. ***longifolia***	NLar
§	***caprifolium***	CAco CArn CFlo CRHN ECrN ELan EPfP LRHS NLar SPer WCot
	- 'Anna Fletcher'	CRHN WCFE
	- 'Cornish Cream'	SGol
	- f. ***pauciflora***	see *L.* × *italica*
	- 'Spring Bouquet'	LRHS
	Caprilia Ever = 'Inov42'PBR	CKel EBee MJak
	'Celestial'	EPfP LRHS SPoG
	chaetocarpa	CEnd WSHC
	'Clavey's Dwarf'	EPPr GKin LLHF
	crassifolia	GEdr IDee NLar SBrt WSHC
	- 'Little Honey'	EPPr MBNS MMrt MPie MRav NLar NPnk SPoG
	deflexicalyx	CMCN EPfP NLar
	demissa	EPfP
	'Early Cream'	see *L. caprifolium*
	'Elegant'	LBuc SArc SCob
	elisae	CAbP CBcs CBot CMac CWld EBee EPfP EWTr GBin IDee IMou LLHF MMuc NLar SEle SMad SSta WCot WSHC
	etrusca	MRav XSen
	- 'Donald Waterer'	CFlo CRHN EPfP LRHS LSRN NLar WFar
	- 'Michael Rosse'	CBot ELan IArd MBNS NLar SKHP
	- 'Superba' ♀H5	CFlo CRHN EBee ELan EPfP EWTr LRHS NLar SEND SLim SNig SPer WSHC
	'Fire Cracker'	NLar SLon
	flexuosa	see *L. japonica* var. *repens*
	fragrantissima	Widely available
	giraldii misapplied	see *L. acuminata*
	giraldii Rehder	CBot CRHN WSHC
	glabrata	NLar SCoo
	- B&SWJ 2150	WCru
	'Golden Trumpet'	CWGN EPfP LSRN
	grata	see *L.* × *americana* (Mill.) K. Koch
	× ***heckrottii***	CRHN CSBt NLar SNig
§	- 'American Beauty'	CKel LCro
	- 'Gold Flame' misapplied	see *L.* × *heckrottii* 'American Beauty'
	- 'Gold Flame' ambig.	CFlo ESps GKin LSRN NLar SCob
	- 'Gold Flame' hort. ♀H5	CDul CMac CRos CWld EBee ELan EMOT EPfP ETho LBuc LCro LRHS MAsh MJak MMuc MRav NRHS SEND SLim SNig SPer SPoG SRms SWvt WFar WMoo WSHC
	hemsleyana	CBot
§	***henryi***	Widely available
	- B&SWJ 8109	WCru
	- 'Copper Beauty'PBR	Widely available
	- var. ***subcoriacea***	see *L. henryi*
	hildebrandiana ♀H2	CCCN CFil CHll CRHN SKHP
	hispidula	SBrt
	'Honey Baby'PBR	ELon EPfP NHol NWad
	implexa	CMCN CRHN
	involucrata	CHll CMCN CWib EPPr LHop MBNS MBlu MMuc NChi SEND SPer WCFE
	- var. ***ledebourii***	CBcs ELan EPfP LLHF LRHS MGil MMrt MRav NLar SKHP
	- - 'Vian'	NLar
	- 'Orange Dwarf'	SKHP
	- f. ***serotina*** **new**	CAco
§	× ***italica***	CRHN CTri EBee ECrN LRHS MBNS MJak MSwo NPer SCoo SKHP SPer
§	- Harlequin = 'Sherlite'PBR (v)	CKel CMac EPfP ESps GMcL LHop LRHS MJak SLim SPlb SRms SWvt
	japonica	CMen ESps IBoy WFar
§	- 'Aureoreticulata' (v) ♀H5	CDul CMac CWib ECrN EHoe ELan EMOT EPfP EShb LRHS MJak MRav NPer SGol SPer SRms WFar
	- 'Cream Cascade'	EWoo MSwo NLar SCoo SGol
	- 'Dart's Acumen'	CRHN
	- 'Dart's World'	CKel CWld EBee LPre MHtn NLar
	- 'Halliana'	Widely available
	- 'Hall's Prolific' ♀H5	CDul CKel CRos CSBt ECrN ELan EPfP ESps EWTr LBMP LBrs LBuc LCro LRHS LSRN MAsh MBlu MGos MRav MSwo NRHS SCob SGol SLim SNig SPad SPoG SWvt WFar WHar
§	- 'Horwood Gem' (v)	ECtt NLar SCoo SLim
	- 'Maskerade' (v)	LLHF NBro NLar
	- 'Mint Crisp'PBR (v)	Widely available
	- 'Peter Adams'	see *L. japonica* 'Horwood Gem'
	- 'Princess Kate'	ELan LPre NLar NPri
	- 'Purple Queen' **new**	EBee
	- 'Red World'	WPat
§	- var. ***repens*** ♀H5	CDul CKel CMac CSBt CTri ECrN ECtt ELan EPfP LRHS MRav MSwo NLar NRHS SCoo SGol SLim SLon SNig SPad SPer SRms WMoo
	- 'Variegata'	see *L. japonica* 'Aureoreticulata'
	korolkowii	CBot CFil EPPr EWTr LLHF MBNS MMuc NBir NLar SEND WCFE WSHC
	- 'Blue Velvet'	CAgr MCoo NLar
	- 'Mayberry Farm' **new**	MCoo
	- var. ***zabelii*** misapplied	see *L. tatarica* 'Zabelii'
	lanceolata BWJ 7935	WCru
	'Lemon Beauty' (v)	Widely available
	maackii	CBot CHll CMCN EPPr EPfP MRav NLar WCFE
	- f. ***podocarpa***	MMuc
*	***macgregorii***	CMCN
	macrantha B&SWJ 11687	WCru
	- WWJ 11606	WCru
	'Mandarin' ♀H5	CRHN ELan LCro MBlu MJak NLar SCoo SGol SWvt WCot WPat WSHC
	maximowiczii var. ***sachalinensis***	NLar
	morrowii 'Ullung do' **new**	CMCN
	myrtillus	NLar
	nitida	CAco CArg CBar CBcs CCVT CDul CLet CMac CMen CSBt CTri ECrN EPfP ESps GMcL NBes NWea SCob

	SEWo SGol SPer WHar WHed WMat WTSh
- 'Baggesen's Gold' 🏆H5	Widely available
- Edmée Gold = 'Briloni'	MAsh
- 'Ernest Wilson'	EPPr
- 'Fertilis'	SPer
- 'Golden Glow' **new**	NEoE
- 'Lemon Queen'	CWib ELan MMuc MSwo SEND
§ - 'Maigrün'	CBar CBcs CCVT CDul EAEE EPfP EShb GMcL LRHS MSwo NEoE SCob SHil SPer SWvt WFar
- Maygreen	see *L. nitida* 'Maigrün'
- 'Red Tips'	EHoe EShb NLar SCob SCoo WMoo
- 'Silver Beauty' (v)	CDul CMac CWib ECrN EHoe ESps GMcL LHop MGos MSwo SCob SPer SPlb SRms SWvt WFar WMoo
- 'Tidy Tips'	NEoE SCob
- 'Twiggy' (v)	CSBt EDAr EHoe EUJe GMcL LHop LRHS MAsh NHol NLar NWad WGrn
periclymenum	CArn CCVT CDul CTri CWld ECrN ESps GJos GPoy LPar MHer MRav NMir NWea SCob SPlb WPnn WSFF
- 'Belgica' misapplied	see *L.* × *italica*
- 'Belgica'	Widely available
- 'Belgica Select'	EWoo
- Chic et Choc = 'Inov205'	WCot
* - 'Cream Cascade'	GMcL
- 'Florida'	see *L. periclymenum* 'Serotina'
- 'Fragrant Cloud'	ETho LBuc
- 'Graham Thomas' 🏆H5	Widely available
- 'Harlequin'	see *L.* × *italica* Harlequin
- 'Heaven Scent'	CFlo ETho LBuc LCro LSRN NLar WFar WPnn
- 'Honeybush'	CJun CWGN CWld LBMP MAsh MGos NHol NWad SLim WFar WMoo
- 'La Gasnérie'	SLim
- 'Munster'	WSHC
- 'Purple Queen'	CChe
- 'Red Gables'	CRHN ELon LSRN MBNS NLar SCoo SLim SWvt WCot WKif WPat
- 'Rhubarb and Custard' **new**	LCro
- 'Scentsation'PBR	CFlo CKel CMac CSBt CWCL CWGN ELan EPfP GBin LBMP LRHS MAsh MJak NCGa NLar NRHS SCoo SLon SPoG SRkn
- 'Serotina' 🏆H5	Widely available
- 'Sweet Sue'	CFlo CKel CRHN CRos ELan ELon EPfP EWTr LRHS LSRN MAsh MBNS MGos MSwo NEgg NLar NRHS SCoo SNig SPoG SWvt WFar WMoo
pileata	Widely available
- 'Moss Green'	CBod EShb
- 'Silver Lining' (v)	WCFE
pilosa (Kunth) Willd. ex Kunth	CRHN
- F&M 207	CFil WPGP
- - F&M 256	CFil WPGP
prolifera	NLar
× ***purpusii***	CHll CMac CRHN CTri CWib EBee ECrN ESps LSRN MBNS SCob SRms WCFE WFar WSHC
- 'Spring Romance'	CMac
- 'Winter Beauty' 🏆H5	Widely available
ramosissima	NLar
reticulata 'Silver'	NLar
saccata	EPfP
sempervirens	CBot CRHN CSBt IDee MBNS MRav WHar WSHC
- 'Cedar Lane'	LRHS
- 'Dropmore Scarlet'	see *L.* × *brownii* 'Dropmore Scarlet'
- 'Leo'	CWGN
- f. ***sulphurea***	CBot WSHC
- - 'John Clayton'	EPfP LRHS SKHP
setifera 'Daphnis'	CJun
similis var. ***delavayi*** 🏆H5	CBot CFlo CKel CRHN CWGN ELan EMOT EPfP ESps ETho GMcL LBMP LPar LRHS MAsh MNHC MRav NEgg NRHS SDix SEND SRms SWvt WCot WCru WSHC
'Simonet'	CWCL EBee NLar WCot
splendida	WSHC
'Spring Purple' **new**	LCro
standishii	CTri WFar
- var. ***lancifolia*** 'Budapest'	CBot ELan ELon EPfP IArd LEdu LLHF LRHS MAsh MBlu MRav NLar WFar WPat
subaequalis	CFil CRHN
- Og 93.329	SKHP WPGP WSHC
Sweet Isabel = 'Genbel'PBR	EPfP LRHS NRHS
syringantha	CArn CBcs CRHN CWld ECrN ELan EPfP EWTr IDee LHop MMuc MNrw MRav NEgg NEoE NLar NWad SBod SDix SEND SEle SPer WCFE WFar WPat WSHC
- 'Grandiflora'	CBot GQui
tatarica	CBot CHll CMCN CWib MRav
- 'Alba'	EPPr
- 'Arnold Red'	CBcs ELan EPPr EPfP MBlu MHer NLar SEND
- 'Hack's Red'	CBot CMCN CWib EPPr EPfP EWTr LEdu LHop LRHS MMuc NLar SCoo SKHP SPer SPoG SVen SWvt WBor WCot WGrn
- 'Rosea'	EPPr
§ - 'Zabelii'	MNrw
× ***tellmanniana*** 🏆H5	Widely available
- 'Joan Sayers'	SCoo SLim WCFE
- 'Pharaoh's Trumpet'	LRHS SLon
thibetica	CBot MBlu
tomentella B&SWJ 2654	WCru
tragophylla 🏆H5	CBot CKel CSBt ELan EWTr IDee IMou LEdu LRHS MBNS MMuc MRav NLar SCoo SEND SLim SPer SWvt WSHC
- 'Maurice Foster'	CRHN EBee ELan EWTr NLar WSHC
turczaninowii	LLHF
webbiana	ELan
× ***xylosteoides***	NLar
xylosteum	CArn EBtc EPPr MMuc NLar SSta

Lophomyrtus ✿ (*Myrtaceae*)

§ ***bullata*** 🏆H2	CDTJ GMcL SPer
× ***ralphii*** 'Black Pearl'	CMac CRos EShb ESps LRHS MPkF SCoo SEle SGbt SHil SLim SPoG WFar WGrn
- 'Gloriosa' (v)	CCCN
- 'Kathryn'	CBcs CTsd ELan LRHS MPkF NLar SRGP
- 'Krinkly'	SVen
- 'Little Star' (v)	CBcs LRHS SEle WPat
- Logan's form (v)	CBcs EBee LRHS MGil NLar
- 'Magic Dragon'PBR (v)	EBee ELan LCro LRHS SEle SGbt SHil SPoG
- 'Multicolor' (v)	CBcs EBee ELan EPfP LRHS MRav SLim SVen
- 'Pixie'	CBcs LRHS MAsh SEle SLim SPoG SVen
- 'Red Dragon'	CAbP CBcs CMac ELan ESps LRHS LSou MAsh SLim WFar
- 'Wild Cherry'	LRHS

Lophosoria ✿ (*Dicksoniaceae*)

	quadripinnata	CDTJ NLos SBig

Lophospermum (*Plantaginaceae*)

	'Cream Delight'	CCCN
§	***erubescens*** 🏆H2	CRHN SBch
	- 'Bridal Bouquet'	CPla
	Lofos Wine Red = 'Sunasaro'	EShb
§	'Magic Dragon'	CPla MPkF SEND SLim WBor
§	'Red Dragon'	CCCN CPla SBch
§	***scandens***	CCCN

loquat see *Eriobotrya japonica*

Loropetalum (*Hamamelidaceae*)

	chinense	CWib SEle
§	- 'Chang Nian Hong' **new**	LCro
	- Ever Red	see *L. chinense* 'Chang Nian Hong'
	- 'Ming Dynasty'	CAbP MAsh SEle SSta WFar
	- var. ***rubrum***	CWib
	- - 'Blush'	CBcs GMcL SEle SGol
	- - 'Daybreak's Flame'	CBcs EBee MGil SEle SGol SSta
	- - 'Fire Dance'	CAbP CBcs CBct CCCN CLet CTsd CWib CWld EPfP EShb EUJe LCro LPar LRHS MAsh MGos MMuc MNHC SEle SHil SPad SPoG SRkn SWvt WCot WFar WPat
	- - 'Fire Glow'	LRHS
	- 'Snowdance'	CAbP
	- 'Tang Dynasty'	CBct EBee ESwi WFar

Lotononis (*Papilionaceae*)

	galpinii	SBrt

Lotus (*Papilionaceae*)

	berthelotii	CCCN CDTJ ECtt LPot MCot
	- deep red-flowered 🏆H1c	SWvt
	berthelotii* × *maculatus 🏆H1c	CCCN MSCN
	corniculatus	CArn CHab CWld GJos MCoo MHer MMuc MNHC NMir SEND SIde SRms WSFF
	formosissimus	EBee
	germanicus	SPhx
	hirsutus 🏆H4	CBod CChe CWib ECha EHoe ELan EPfP LBMP LHop LPot MAsh MCot MRav SEND SIgm SLon SPer SPhx SPlb SPoG SRms SWvt WIce XLum XSen
	- 'Brimstone' (v)	CWib LHop MRav SPer SPoG SWvt XSen
	- Little Boy Blue = 'Lisbob'PBR	CLet CSBt EPfP LBMP LRHS
	- 'Lois'	LRHS SPoG
	jacobaeus	LHop MCot
	maritimus	XLum
	mearnsii	SPlb
	pedunculatus	CHab MCoo NMir WSFF
	pentaphyllus	XSen
	tetragonolobus	SPhx SVic WSFF

lovage see *Levisticum officinale*

Loxostigma (*Gesneriaceae*)

	kurzii GWJ 9342	WCru

Ludwigia (*Onagraceae*)

	natans **new**	XBlo

Luffa (*Cucurbitaceae*)

	aegyptiaca	SVic

Luma ✿ (*Myrtaceae*)

§	***apiculata*** 🏆H4	Widely available
§	- 'Glanleam Gold' (v)	Widely available
	- 'Nana'	LEdu WJek
	- 'Penlee'	SRms WJek
	- 'Rainbow's Gold' (v)	EShb
	- 'Saint Hilary' (v)	CBcs CLet EPfP LRHS SRms WJek
	- 'Variegata' (v)	CTri WFar
§	***chequen***	CBcs CBod CSBt EShb LEdu MHer NLar SRms WJek WPGP

Lunaria (*Brassicaceae*)

§	***annua***	CWCL EWoo MNHC SIde SWat WCot WSFF
	- var. ***albiflora*** 🏆H7	LSun NBir SEND SWat WCot WTou
I	- - 'Alba Variegata' (v) 🏆H7	CSpe IBoy MNHC NPnk WBor WBrk
	- 'Chedglow'	CNat LEdu
	- 'Corfu Blue'	CSpe EWes MAvo SPtp WCot
	- 'Cynthia'	CNat
	- 'Munstead Purple' 🏆H7	CSpe
	- 'Nettleton'	CNat
	- purple-leaved	CMea MAvo
	- 'Ruth'	CNat LEdu WCot
	- 'The Optimist' **new**	CNat
	- 'Variegata' (v)	CNat NBir SWat WCot
	biennis	see *L. annua*
	rediviva 🏆H7	CSpe ECGP ECha EPPr GAbr GBin GCal GCra GMaP IBlr IBoy IFro LEdu LRHS MBel MMuc MNHC MWat NBid NChi NPer NSti SEND SHil WCot WFar WHil WPGP
	- 'Partway White'	CFis CMil WCot

Lunathyrium (*Woodsiaceae*)

	petersenii	ISha
	pycnosorum	ISha

Lupinus ✿ (*Papilionaceae*)

	albifrons	EBee
	arboreus 🏆H4	Widely available
	- blue and white-flowered	SCob WFar
	- 'Blue Boy'	ELan LRHS LSRN SWvt
	- blue-flowered	CRos CWCL CWld GPSL LRHS NLar SBod SCob SPer SPlb SPoG SWvt WFar WOut
	- 'Chelsea Blue'	EPfP LRHS
	- cream-flowered	SCob
	- 'Snow Queen'	CWCL LRHS SCob SPoG SWvt
	- 'Sulphur Yellow'	SWvt
	- white-flowered	CSpe CWld EWTr SCob SPlb
	- yellow and blue-flowered	IBoy NBir SRkn WFar
	- yellow-flowered	CLet CWld ELan IBoy SCob SWvt
	arcticus	EBee
	argenteus	GKev
	'Beefeater'	CWCL ELan IBoy LBuc LLHF LRHS NPri SPoG
	'Bishop's Tipple'	EWes
	'Blossom'PBR	CWCL CWGN LLHF LRHS NPri NRHS SPoG
	caespitosus	see *L. lepidus* var. *utahensis*
	(Camelot Series) 'Camelot Blue'	EPfP GMcL WTor
	- 'Camelot Red' **new**	WTor
	- 'Camelot Rose' **new**	GMcL
	- 'Camelot White' **new**	GMcL WTor

- 'Camelot Yellow' **new**	GMcL
'Cashmere Cream'	CWCL EBee LRHS NAst NPri NRHS SPoG
'Chameleon'	LBuc LRHS NRHS
chamissonis	CPla CSpe CWCL ELan EWes LHop LRHS NRHS SIgm SPer WKif
'Chandelier' (Band of Nobles Series)	Widely available
'Desert Sun'PBR	CRos CWCL LRHS NAst NRHS
Dwarf Gallery hybrids	IBoy
'Dwarf Lulu'	see *L.* 'Lulu'
Gallery Series	CBod CSBt IBoy SCoo SPlb WFar
- 'Gallery Blue'	CRos ECtt ELan EPfP IBoy LCro LOPS LRHS LSRN MHol NLar NPri NRHS SCoo SPer SPoG WFar
- 'Gallery Pink'	CRos ELan EPfP ESps IBoy LRHS NLar NPri NRHS SCoo SPer SPoG WFar
- 'Gallery Red'	CRos ECtt ELan EPfP IBoy LRHS MHol NLar NPri NRHS SCoo SPer SPoG WFar
- 'Gallery Rose'	IBoy LSRN SPoG WFar
- 'Gallery White'	CRos ELan EPfP IBoy LRHS NLar NPri NRHS SCoo SPer SPoG WFar
- 'Gallery Yellow'	CRos ECtt ELan EPfP ESps IBoy LRHS NLar NPri NRHS SPer SPoG WFar
'Gladiator'PBR	CWCL EBee ECtt EPfP EWes LLHF LRHS LSou MNrw NAst SPoG
'Heathcliffe Blue'	WOut
'Judy Harper'	ECtt ELan GBin LRHS
'Jupiter'	CWCL EBee GBin NLar NRHS SPoG
'King Canute'	CWCL NAst NPri
latifolius subsp. ***parishii***	EBee
'Le Gentilhomme' (Band of Nobles Series)	MCot
§ ***lepidus*** var. ***utahensis***	SPlb
§ 'Lulu'	EPfP IBoy LRHS SGbt SPer SPoG SWvt WHar
luteus	GJos
'Magic Lantern' **new**	CWCL
'Manhattan Lights'PBR	CChe CRos CWCL CWGN EPfP EWTr EWes EWoo IBoy ILea IPot LLHF LRHS NAst NLar NPri SPoG
'Masterpiece'PBR	CWCL EWoo GBin IBoy ILea IPot LLHF LRHS LSRN LSou MCot NPri SPoG
Minarette Group	CTri LRHS MAsh MNrw NRHS SRms
montanus	CHid
'Morello Cherry'	CWCL SHar
'My Castle' (Band of Nobles Series)	Widely available
'Neptune'	CWCL
'Noble Maiden' (Band of Nobles Series)	Widely available
nootkatensis	GLog
oreophilus	GJos
'Pam Ayres'	ECtt GBin LRHS
'Persian Slipper'PBR	CEnd CWCL CWGN ECtt EPfP EWes EWoo IBoy IPot LBuc LCro LLHF LOPS LRHS LSRN MCot NAst NPri SPoG
'Polar Princess'	CWCL ECtt ELan EWes GBin LRHS NPri NRHS SPoG SWat
polyphyllus var. ***burkei***	EBee
'Purple Swirl'	CWCL EBee ECtt LRHS NAst NRHS SPoG
'Rachel de Thame'	CWCL CWGN EBee LRHS NAst NPri
'Red Arrow'	CWCL
'Red Rum'PBR	CEnd CWCL CWGN EWoo LBuc LRHS LSRN MNrw NLar NPri SPoG
'Rote Flamme'	ELon EWes LBMP SCob WOut
Russell hybrids	CSBt EPfP GMcL IBoy MHer MMuc SPlb SRms SVic SWvt WFar WHar
'Saffron'PBR	CEnd CWCL EWoo LBuc LRHS LSRN NPri SPoG
'Salmon Star'PBR	CWCL IBoy LRHS MNrw NAst NLar NRHS SPoG
'Sand Pink'	EWes
sericatus	EBee
'Silver Fleece'	CCCN CHid
sparsiflorus	GJos
'Tequila Flame'PBR	CWCL LBuc LLHF LRHS LSou SPoG
'Terracotta'	IBoy LRHS LSou NPri
texensis	CSpe
'The Chatelaine' (Band of Nobles Series)	Widely available
'The Governor' (Band of Nobles Series)	Widely available
'The Page' (Band of Nobles Series)	Widely available
'Thundercloud'	EBee
'Towering Inferno'	CEnd CRos CWCL ECtt EWTr EWes IBoy LBuc LRHS NAst NLar NPri SPoG
'Tutti Frutti'	CBot GJos IBoy WHar
variicolor	SIgm
Woodfield hybrids	LRHS

Luzula (*Juncaceae*)

alpinopilosa	EPPr
× ***borreri*** 'Botany Bay' (v)	GBin
'Engel'	EPPr EWes
forsteri	IMou
luzuloides 'Schneehäschen'	WSHC
maxima	see *L. sylvatica*
nivalis	GAbr
nivea	Widely available
pedemontana	SMea
pilosa	GCal
- 'Grünfink'	EBee
- 'Igel'	CBod CKno EBee EShb LEdu NBid SCob
purpureosplendens	LEdu
§ ***sylvatica***	ELan EPPr EWoo GBin GMcL LRHS MMuc MRav NBro NLar NMir NRHS SCob SEND SPer WHer WShi XLum
- from Tatra Mountains, Slovakia	EPPr
- 'A. Rutherford'	see *L. sylvatica* 'Taggart's Cream'
- 'Aurea'	CBot CKno ECha EPPr EWoo LRHS MJak MMuc MRav NBid NRHS NSti NWsh SEND WCot WFar WGrn WMoo WPtf
- 'Aureomarginata'	see *L. sylvatica* 'Marginata'
I - 'Auslese'	EPPr EPfP WMoo
- 'Bromel'	EPPr
- 'Hohe Tatra'	CBod CSpe EHoe EPPr EWes GBin GMaP LEdu MBNS NGdn SCob SPoG
§ - 'Marginata' (v)	CKno EBee ECha EHoe ELon EPPr EWoo GBin GMaP LRHS LSun MAvo MBNS MMuc MRav NBid NGdn NLar NSti SArc SCob SEND WCot WHoo WMoo
- 'Mariusz'	EPPr
* - f. ***nova***	ELon EPPr
- 'Solar Flair'	GBin
- 'Starmaker'	CBod

§ - 'Taggart's Cream' (v) CRos EHoe GCal LRHS NBid NHol NRHS NWad WMoo
- 'Tauernpass' EPPr GCal LRHS
- 'Thierry's Cream' (v) WCot
- 'Wäldler' EPPr
ulophylla GCrg GEdr SIgm SPlb WAbe WThu

Luzuriaga (*Luzuriagaceae*)

polyphylla CTal
- HCM 98202 WCru
radicans CCCN GEdr IMou WCru WSHC
- RH 0602 WCru

Lychnis (*Caryophyllaceae*)

alpina CMac ECho EDAr NGdn WFar WIce XLum
- 'Alba' GKev
- 'Rosea' NBir
- 'Snow Flurry' EDAr GKev
§ × ***arkwrightii*** ECha LRHS
- 'Orange Zwerg' SGbt
- Scarlet O'Hara = 'Pmoore05'PBR EBee
- 'Vesuvius' CBcs CMac EBee NBir SDix SPer SRms
chalcedonica 🏆H7 Widely available
- var. ***albiflora*** EPfP MBel NBro WCAu WHrl WMoo
- 'Carnea' EBee EPPr LRHS MBNS NGdn SPhx
- 'Dusky Salmon' WHrl WOut
- 'Flore Pleno' (d) EShb GCal NChi WCot
- 'Pinkie' MMuc NFav NLar NWad
- 'Rauhreif' NLar SPhx WHer
- 'Rosea' EPfP ESps NBir WHrl WMoo
* - 'Salmonea' EPPr GPSL NBir SRms
cognata CTal IMou
- B&SWJ 4234 WCru
§ ***coronaria*** 🏆H7 Widely available
- MESE 356 MAvo SPhx
- 'Abbotswood Rose' see *L.* × *walkeri* 'Abbotswood Rose'
- 'Alba' 🏆H7 Widely available
- 'Angel's Blush' NBir NLar SPav SRkn
- Atrosanguinea Group CBod CBre EPfP ESps GMaP GMcL IBlr LRHS MBel MHol MRav MSpe NEgg NGdn NSti NWad SPer WCAu WGwG WTor
- 'Blood Red' CSpe EBee LEdu LRHS
- 'Cerise' MArl NBir
- Gardeners' World = 'Blych' (d) CBod CElw CSpe EBee ECtt ELon EMFm EWes IKil LCro LOPS LRHS LSou MBNS MBel MHol MPie NSti SPer SRkn WBrk WCot
- Oculata Group CSpe CTsd EBee ELan EPfP LEdu LPot SPav SPlb WFar WKif WMoo
coronata CTsd
§ - var. ***sieboldii*** SBrt SPhx
dioica see *Silene dioica*
flos-cuculi Widely available
- var. ***albiflora*** CBre CElw CSam CWld EWoo MSKA NBro NLar WHer WMoo
- var. ***congesta*** WAbe
- Jenny = 'Lychjen'PBR (d) CDor EBee ECtt ELan EPfP GQue LBMP LEdu LLWG LRHS MBNS MBel MHol MNrw NSti SCob SHil SPoG SRkn WBor WCot WHer
- 'Little Robin' LLWG
- 'Nana' ECho NGdn NLar WTor
- 'Petite Jenny' (d) **new** WCot
- 'White Robin' Widely available
flos-jovis 🏆H5 ECha EPfP GJos LRHS NBir NRHS SRms WMoo XLum
- 'Hort's Variety' EBee LRHS NBir NSti
- 'Minor' see *L. flos-jovis* 'Nana'
§ - 'Nana' MSCN SBch
- 'Peggy' EBee LRHS NBre NGdn NLar
× ***haageana*** MPie SRms
- 'Lengai Red' **new** GMcL
- 'Lumina Bronze Leaf Red' LRHS NRHS
'Hill Grounds' CElw EBee ECtt WCot WSHC
miqueliana WMoo
'Molten Lava' ELan EPfP LRHS NRHS WHar
nivalis **new** WAbe
§ ***viscaria*** CArn CWld ECha GCra GJos GPSL WMoo
- 'Alba' ECha NBre NGBl XLum
- ***alpina*** see *L. viscaria*
§ - subsp. ***atropurpurea*** CFis EWes GJos LRHS LSou MArt MPie SEND SRms WHrl WMoo
- 'Feuer' EWes GJos NGBl SPhx WMoo WTcb
- 'Firebird' EWes
- 'Plena' (d) NBir SRkn WHil
- 'Schnee' GJos NLar
- 'Snowbird' CTsd
- 'Splendens' LPot MBel WFar XLum
- 'Splendens Plena' (d) 🏆H5 XLum
§ × ***walkeri*** 'Abbotswood Rose' 🏆H7 IBlr MJak
§ ***yunnanensis*** EBee NSti SPhx
- ***alba*** see *L. yunnanensis*

Lycianthes (*Solanaceae*)

biflora FMWJ 13059 WCru
§ ***rantonnetii*** 🏆H1c CBcs CCCN CHll ELan EUJe SEND SPoG WBor WKif
- 'Variegata' (v) CHll MSCN WCot

Lycium (*Solanaceae*)

afrum SVen
barbarum CAgr CBcs CCCN CSBt EPom LCro LEdu LOPS LRHS MCoo MJak NLar SCob SDea SEND SPre SVic SWvt WHar
- 'Big Lifeberry' CAgr LEdu
- 'Number 1 Lifeberry' CAgr
- 'Sweet Lifeberry' CAgr LEdu
chinense IBoy NQui

Lycopodium (*Lycopodiaceae*)

clavatum GPoy

Lycopsis see *Anchusa*

Lycopus (*Lamiaceae*)

europaeus CArn CHab EBee GPoy LLWG MMuc WGwG

Lycoris (*Amaryllidaceae*)

albiflora NRog
aurea CPne CTsd ECho ERCP GKev LAma LTro NRog SDeJ
caldwellii NRog
chinensis NRog
haywardii NRog
houdyshelii NRog
longituba NRog
radiata CAby CCCN CPne CTsd ECho GKev LAma SDeJ
rosea NRog
sanguinea NRog
sprengeri NRog

Lygeum (*Poaceae*)

spartum	XSen

Lygodium (*Lygodiaceae*)

japonicum	ISha WFib

Lygos see *Retama*

Lyonia (*Ericaceae*)

villosa	CPne

Lyonothamnus (*Rosaceae*)

floribundus subsp. ***aspleniifolius***	CCCN EBee EUJe SArc WPGP

Lysichiton (*Araceae*)

americanus	Widely available
camtschatcensis 🏆H7	CBcs CBen CFwr CLAP CTsd CWat ECha EPfP EUJe GBin GBuc LLWG LRHS NPer SMad SPer SWat SWvt WPnP WShi XLum
× ***hortensis***	ECha

Lysiloma (*Mimosaceae*)

watsonii	SPlb

Lysimachia (*Primulaceae*)

albescens	SPad XLum
§ ***atropurpurea***	CSpe EAJP EBee EHoe ELan EPfP GJos GPSL LRHS SPer
- 'Beaujolais'	CBWd CMos CWld IBoy IPot LCro LRHS LSRN MGos MHol MNHC SCob SPoG SPtp STPC WHar WHil
- 'Geronimo'	CSpe
barystachys 🏆H7	CSam LEdu MBel MRav SHar WCot XLum
- PAB 8755 **new**	LEdu
- 'Huntingbrook'	LEdu MAvo WPGP WWtn
Candela = 'Innlyscand'	CBod CMos CSpe ECtt GWyn LRHS LSou MHol MMuc NPnk WCot WHil WMoo WTor
candida	WCot
ciliata	CMHG CMac ECha ELan GMaP LRHS MNrw NBir NGdn NLar SWat
§ - 'Firecracker' 🏆H7	Widely available
- 'Purpurea'	see *L. ciliata* 'Firecracker'
clethroides 🏆H7	Widely available
- 'Geisha' (v)	EBee WCot
- 'Lady Jane'	CLet MAvo MNrw SRms
- 'Leigong Storm'	WPGP
§ ***congestiflora***	NPer
- 'Golden Falls'	CTsd
- 'Midnight Sun'PBR	CCCN ECtt
- 'Outback Sunset'PBR (v)	ECtt
- 'Persian Carpet'	WCot
- 'Persian Chocolate'	WCot WFar
'Elisabeth'PBR	EBee WBod
ephemerum 🏆H6	Widely available
fortunei	XEll XLum
japonica var. ***minutissima***	SRot
lichiangensis	EBee GKev GPSL IMou LRHS NBir WMoo
lyssii	see *L. congestiflora*
minoricensis	XLum
nemorum	CWld IMou
- 'Lola Playle'PBR	WCot
- 'Pale Star'	CBre EBee
nummularia	CSBt CTri CWat EPfP GPoy NBir SWat WBrk
- 'Aurea' 🏆H5	CMac CSBt CTri ECha ECtt EHoe ELan EPfP ESps GAbr LPot MHer MJak MMuc MRav NBid NBir NBro NFav NLar NMir SEND SPer SPoG SRms SWvt WMoo WWtn XLum
paridiformis var. ***stenophylla***	GBin SPtp
punctata misapplied	see *L. verticillaris*
punctata L.	CSBt ECha EPfP ESps GMaP MHer MRav NBro NMir NPer SCob SEND SPer SPlb SRms SWat WBrk WCAu WFar WHar WHlf WMAq WMoo
§ - 'Alexander' (v)	Widely available
- 'Gaulthier Brousse'	MHCG WCot
- Golden Alexander = 'Walgoldalex'PBR (v)	CBod CChe CLet ELon LBMP LRHS MBNS NHol NLar NPnk WMoo
- 'Golden Glory' (v)	WCot
- 'Hometown Hero'	EBee NLar
- 'Ivy Maclean' (v)	SWvt
- 'Variegata'	see *L. punctata* 'Alexander'
- ***verticillata***	see *L. verticillaris*
'Purpurea'	see *L. atropurpurea*
Snow Candles = 'L9902'	CCVN EBee NPnk
thyrsiflora	CWat EBee EWay NPer SWat WCot WMAq
§ ***verticillaris***	CBod CTri WCot
vulgaris	CArn CHab GBin LLWG MSKA WMoo
- subsp. ***davurica***	WCot
- - B&SWJ 8632	WCru

Lysionotus (*Gesneriaceae*)

gamosepalus B&SWJ 7241	WCru
kwangsiensis HWJ 625	WCru
'Lavender Lady'	EBee NCGa
pauciflorus	WAbe
- B&SWJ 303	WCru
- B&SWJ 335	WCru
- HWJ 643 from Vietnam	WCru
- HWJ 811 from Vietnam	WCru
- dwarf B&SWJ 189	WCru
serratus HWJK 2426	WCru

Lythrum (*Lythraceae*)

alatum	NDov
anceps	NBre NLar
'Rose Dream'	NWad
salicaria	CArn CBen CHab CWat CWld ENfk GJos MCot MHer MMuc MNHC MWLS MWts NBro SEND SPlb SRms SWat WBrk WHer WHil WMoo WPnP WSFF WShi WWtn XLum
- 'Augenweide'	XLum
- 'Blush' 🏆H7	Widely available
§ - 'Feuerkerze' 🏆H7	CAby CBod CMea EBee ECtt ELan ELon EPed EPfP GBin LBMP LHop LRHS LSou MBel MCot MRav MSpe NBir NEgg NHol NSti SCob SPer WFar WWtn
- Firecandle	see *L. salicaria* 'Feuerkerze'
- 'Happy'	ELon
- 'Lady Sackville'	EBee ECtt ELon EPPr GMaP IKil IPot MCot MTis NLar WSHC
- 'Little Robert'	ECtt IBoy LBMP
- 'Morden Pink'	CBod EBee MMuc NLar SEND SPhx XLum
- 'Prichard's Variety'	EBee
- 'Red Beauty'	LSun
- 'Robert'	Widely available

- 'Robin'	CBod CRos ECtt GJos LLHF LRHS MHol NPri NRHS SGbt SRot SWvt
- 'Rose'	ELan NBir SWvt
- 'Stichflamme'	ELon SBee
- 'Swirl'	ECtt ELon EPfP IKil ILea LLWG MTis NDov NLar SHar WHoo
- 'The Beacon'	EBee NLar SPad SRms
- 'Zigeunerblut'	CKno ECtt ELon EPPr GQue MRav NLar SWat WHil XLum
virgatum	CMHG ESps NDov SMHy SPhx WCFE WMoo WOut WSHC
- 'Dropmore Purple'	Widely available
- 'Helene'	IMou NDov
- 'Rose Queen'	ECtt ESps IPot MRav SMHy
- 'Rosy Gem'	EBee EPfP ESps GJos GMaP IBoy LRHS NBro SRms SWvt WHar
- 'The Rocket'	CAby CBod CSam CTri EPPr EPfP EShb GCal GQue LRHS MPie MRav NBro NDov SPer SWvt WFar WPnP

M

Maackia (*Papilionaceae*)

amurensis	CBcs CDul CHGN CMCN ELan EPfP IVic LRHS NLar
hupehensis	MBlu NLar

mace, English see *Achillea ageratum*

Macfadyena (*Bignoniaceae*)

§ ***unguis-cati*** ♀H2	CCCN CRHN

Machaerina (*Cyperaceae*)

rubiginosa 'Variegata' (v)	EWay LLWG

Machilus see *Persea*

Mackaya (*Acanthaceae*)

§ ***bella*** ♀H1b	CHII EShb

Macleaya (*Papaveraceae*)

cordata misapplied	see *M.* × *kewensis*
§ ***cordata*** (Willd.) R. Br. ♀H6	EBee LHop LRHS LSun MHol NBir SEND SPer SPlb SRms WMoo XLum
§ × ***kewensis***	EBee SCob SHil
- 'Flamingo' ♀H6	CMos EBee ECha ECtt GBin GBuc GQue GWyn LRHS MBNS MPie SPer SWvt WWtn
§ ***microcarpa***	IBoy MHol SWat
- 'Kelway's Coral Plume' ♀H6	CBcs CBod CMac EBee ECtt ELan EPed EPfP EWoo GBin GMaP GMcL LCro LRHS LSRN MAvo MRav NBid NBro NEgg NLar NPri SDix SPer SPoG SWvt WBor WCot WWtn
- 'Spetchley Ruby'	EBee GBin MRav NLar SPhx WCot XLum

Maclura (*Moraceae*)

pomifera	CArn CBcs CMCN IDee IVic LEdu MBlu SPlb
- 'Cannonball' <u>**new**</u>	LRHS SAko
- 'Naughty Boy'	NLar
- 'Pretty Woman'	NLar
tricuspidata	LRHS
- B&SWJ 12755	WCru

Macrodiervilla see *Weigela*

Macrozamia (*Zamiaceae*)

communis	CBrP
dyeri	see *M. riedlei*
lucida	CBrP
moorei	CBrP
§ ***riedlei***	CBrP

Maddenia (*Rosaceae*)

hypoleuca	MBlu NLar

Maesa (*Primulaceae*)

japonica CWJ 12371	WCru

Magnolia ✿ (*Magnoliaceae*)

acuminata	CBcs CMCN
- 'Blue Opal'	CBcs CJun
* - 'Kinju'	CEnd CJun
- 'Koban Dori'	CBcs CJun
- 'Moegi Dori'	NLar
- 'Patriot'	CMCN SKHP
- 'Patriot' × (× ***brooklynensis*** 'Yellow Bird')	IDee LPar MAsh
- 'Seiju'	CJun
- var. ***subcordata*** 'Miss Honeybee'	CBcs CJun
- - 'Mister Yellowjacket'	CJun
acuminata × 'Elizabeth'	ERea
'Advance'	CBcs CJun
'Albatross'	CBcs CEnd ERea WPGP
'Alex'	CJun
'Alixeed'	CJun
'Amber'	CJun
'Ambrosia'	CJun
amoena	CBcs CTho
- 'Multiogeca'	CWib
'Angelica'	CJun
'Anilou'	CJun
'Anna'	CJun
'Anne Rosse'	SAko SKHP WPGP
'Anticipation'	CBcs CEnd CJun CMHG SAko WPGP
'Apollo'	CBcs CJun IVic LSRN SAko SKHP WPGP
'Apricot Brandy'	LRHS
'Archangel'	CJun
ashei	see *M. macrophylla* subsp. *ashei*
'Asian Artistry'	CJun
'Athene' ♀H5	CBcs CEnd CJun CMHG IVic LMil SAko WPGP
'Atlas'	CBcs CEnd CJun CTho ERea SAko WPGP
'Aurora'	CBcs CJun
'Banana Split'	LMil LRHS MAsh
'Betty'	CBcs CDul CMac ELon EMOT ESps LRHS LSRN LSou MBlu MGos NLar NPla SKHP SLim SSta
'Big Dude'	CBcs CEnd CJun EPfP ERea LRHS SAko SCob
biondii	CBcs IMou MBlu NLar
'Black Beauty'	CBcs CJun LRHS WHor
'Black Swan'	WPGP
Black Tulip = 'Jurmag1'PBR	CBcs ELan EPfP ERea IVic LBuc LCro LMil LRHS MAsh MGos NLar SCoo SKHP SLon SPer WHor WPGP
'Blackbird'	LRHS
'Blushing Belle'	CJun SAko
'Brenda'	CJun
'Brixton Belle'	CBcs WPGP
× ***brooklynensis*** 'Evamaria'	CTho LRHS

- 'Golden Joy'	CJun LRHS MPkF
- 'Hattie Carthan'	CBcs CJun
- 'Woodsman'	CBcs NLar NOra WMat
- 'Yellow Bird'	CBcs CDul CEnd CJun CMCN CMHG CRos CTho EPfP ERea IArd LMil LPar LRHS LSRN MAsh MBlu MGos NLar NOrn SCob SHil SKHP SPoG WMat
'Burgundy Star'	ERea SPer SWeb
'Butterbowl'	CJun
'Butterflies'	CBcs CDul CJun CTho CTsd ELan EMOT EPfP LMil LPar LRHS LSRN MBlu MGos NLar NOra SAko SGol SKHP SPer SSta WFar WMat
'Caerhays Belle' ♀H5	CBcs CJun IVic LMil LRHS NLar SAko SKHP WPGP
'Caerhays Surprise' ♀H5	CBcs CEnd CJun LRHS SKHP WPGP
campbellii	CBcs CMCN EPfP LRHS SKHP
- Alba Group	WPGP
- - 'Chyverton'	WPGP
- - 'Sir Harold Hillier'	CJun WPGP
- - 'Strybing White'	EBee WPGP
- 'Ambrose Congreve'	WPGP
- 'Betty Jessel'	CBcs CJun CMHG WPGP
- 'Darjeeling' ♀H4	CBcs CJun IVic LRHS SKHP WPGP
- 'John Gallagher'	SKHP
- 'Lionel de Rothschild'	EBee WPGP
- subsp. ***mollicomata***	EPfP SAko
- - 'Lanarth'	CBcs WPGP
- - 'Peter Borlase'	WPGP
- 'Queen Caroline'	WPGP
- (Raffillii Group) 'Charles Raffill'	CBcs CDul ELan EPfP IDee IMou LRHS SAko WHor
- - 'Kew's Surprise'	CBcs WPGP
- 'Sidbury'	WHor
campbellii* × *sprengeri	WPGP
'Candy Cane'	CJun ERea
'Carlos'	CBcs CJun
cathcartii B&SWJ 11802	WCru
- HWJ 874	WCru
cavaleriei var. ***platypetala***	CBcs
caveana NJM 13.044 **new**	WPGP
'Cecil Nice'	CBcs
Chameleon	see *M.* 'Chang Hua'
§ 'Chang Hua'	CJun
chapensis	CBcs SKHP
'Charles Coates'	CBcs CJun EPfP NLar SAko WPGP
'Charming Lady' **new**	CJun
chevalieri B&SWJ 11802	WCru
- DJHV 06037	WCru
- HWJ 621	WCru
China Town = 'Jing Ning'	CJun
'Columnar Pink'	NLar
compressa	CBcs
'Coral Lake'	CJun LMil SKHP
'Cornish Chough'	WPGP
crassifolia hort.	see *M. fansipanensis*
'Crescendo' **new**	CJun
'Crystal Chalice'	CJun
'Cup Cake'	CJun
'Curlew'	WPGP
'Curly Locks'	CJun
cylindrica misapplied	see *M.* 'Pegasus'
cylindrica ambig.	CBcs CMCN
cylindrica E.H.Wilson	EPfP LRHS
- 'Bjuv'	CJun
'Daphne' ♀H6	CBcs CJun CMHG EPfP ERea IVic LMil LRHS LSRN MAsh NLar SAko SCob SKHP SPoG WPGP
'Darrell Dean'	CJun ERea

'David Clulow' ♀H5	CBcs CJun ERea SAko SKHP WPGP
dawsoniana	CBcs CTho EPfP IDee IMou
- 'Barbara Cook'	CJun
- 'Chyverton Red'	CBcs WPGP
- 'Valley Splendour'	CJun
'Daybreak' ♀H6	CBcs CJun ERea LMil LRHS MBlu MRav NOra SGol SSta WMat WPGP
dealbata	see *M. macrophylla* subsp. *dealbata*
'Deborah'	CJun
decidua	CBcs SKHP
delavayi	CBcs CBrP CDul CFil CMCN CTho EBee EPfP ERea EUJe LRHS SArc SBig SMad WPGP
'Delia Williams'	WPGP
§ ***denudata*** ♀H6	CBcs CDul CMCN CTho CWib EPfP LMil MBlu SEWo
- 'Double Diamond'	CBcs CJun
- Festirose = 'Minfor' **new**	LRHS
- 'Forrest's Pink'	CBcs LRHS
- Fragrant Cloud = 'Dan Xin'	CBcs CJun CWib WHar
- 'Gere'	CBcs CJun
- 'Ghost Ship'	CJun
- late-flowered	see *M. denudata* 'Sleeping Beauty'
§ - 'Sleeping Beauty'	ERea
- Yellow River = 'Fei Huang'	CBcs CEnd CJun CWib MJak NOra WHor WMat
doltsopa	CBcs CCCN LRHS SKHP SSta WPGP
- NJM 12.028	WPGP
- NJM 12.047	WPGP
- 'Silver Cloud'	CBcs
'Early Rose'	CJun
'Eleanor May'	CJun
'Elegance'	CJun
'Elisa Odenwald'	CJun
'Elizabeth' ♀H6	CBcs CJun CMCN CTho ELan EPfP ERea ESps IArd LCro LMil LPar LRHS LSRN MAsh MBlu MGos NLar SKHP SPer SPoG SWvt WMat
'Eskimo'	CJun SKHP
'Eternal Flames'	NLar
'F.J. Williams'	CBcs WPGP
Fairy Blush = 'Micjur01'	EPfP LCro MGos
Fairy Cream = 'Micjur02' **new**	LCro
Fairy Magnolia White = 'Micjur05' **new**	LCro
§ ***fansipanensis*** FMWJ 13054 **new**	WCru
- FMWJ 13163	WCru
'Felicity'	CJun
Felix Jury = 'Jurmag2' PBR	CBcs ELan EPfP ERea LCro SAko
figo	CBcs CCCN CFil EBee ELan EPfP EShb LRHS MMuc SKHP SSta WBod WPGP
figo* × *laevifolia	SKHP
'Fireglow'	CJun CTho
'Flamingo'	CJun
floribunda NJM 09.179	WPGP
- WWJ 11874	WCru
- WWJ 11996	WCru
- WWJ 12003	WCru
- WWJ 12011	WCru
- 'Furry Uok'	WPGP
- aff. var. ***tonkinensis*** DJH V06 105	WCru
§ ***foveolata***	CWib
- B&SWJ 11749	WCru
- WWJ 11929	WCru
- WWJ 11955	WCru
'Frank Gladney'	CJun ERea

	'Frank's Masterpiece'	CJun ERea SAko SKHP
	fraseri	SKHP
	- var. ***pyramidata***	SKHP
	'Galaxy' ♀H6	CBcs CDul CEnd CJun CMHG CMac ELon EPfP ERea IArd IDee LMil LPar LRHS MAsh MGos MMuc NLar NOrn SAko SEWo SLim SPoG SSta WMat WMou
	garrettii	CPne
	'Genie' PBR	CBcs LRHS NLar SCob SWeb WPGP
	'George Henry Kern' ♀H6	CBcs CDul CLnd CRos CTho EMOT EPfP IArd LPar LRHS MGos MJak MMuc NEgg NLar NPri SEND SHil
	'Gladys Carlson'	CJun
	globosa	CBcs LRHS SPoG
	- from Yunnan, China	GCal
	'Gold Crown'	CJun LMil LRHS SPoG
	'Gold Cup'	LRHS
	'Gold Star' ♀H6	CBcs CDul CEnd CJun CMHG CTho EBee EPfP LMil LRHS MGos NLar NOra SAko SKHP SPoG WMat WPGP
	'Golden Endeavour'	CBcs CJun
	'Golden Gala'	CJun
	'Golden Gift'	CJun LMil LRHS MAsh WPGP
	'Golden Pond'	CJun SPoG
	'Golden Rain'	CJun
	'Golden Sun'	CBcs CJun IArd
	'Goldfinch'	CJun
I	× ***gotoburgensis*** Chollipo clone	WPGP
	grandiflora	CMCN CWib EBee EMOT EPfP ESps ESwi ETod LCro LEdu LPar LSRN MGos MMuc MRav NEgg NLar NOrn NPri SArc SCob SEWo WTSh
	- Alta = 'Tmgh' PBR **new**	LRHS
	- 'Blanchard'	CBcs CJun LRHS NLar
	- 'Bracken's Brown Beauty'	CMCN
	- 'Charles Dickens'	CJun SVen
	- 'Edith Bogue'	CBcs EUJe LRHS NEgg NLar
	- 'Exmouth'	Widely available
	- 'Ferruginea'	CBcs CJun EPfP NLar SGol
	- 'Flore Pleno' (d)	SGol
	- 'François Treyve'	EPfP LRHS LSRN
	- 'Galissonnière'	CAco CBcs CCVT ECrN EPfP ERea ESps ETod LRHS MGos NPri SCob SEND SGol SKHP SWvt
	- 'Goliath'	CBcs CDul ELan EPfP LRHS NPri SEWo SKHP SPer
	- 'Harold Poole'	CJun
	- 'Kay Parris' ♀H5	CJun EPfP LMil LRHS MAsh SKHP SPoG
	- 'Little Gem'	CBcs CJun ELan EPfP EUJe LRHS SGol SPoG
	- 'Mainstreet'	CJun LRHS
	- 'Monlia'	CJun
	- 'Nannetensis'	CJun LRHS
	- 'November Fox' **new**	LRHS
	- 'Overton'	CJun
	- 'Russet'	CJun
	- 'Saint Mary'	CJun
	- 'Samuel Sommer'	CJun
	- 'Symmes Select'	CJun
	- 'Treyvei'	CJun
	- 'Victoria' ♀H5	CDul CJun CTho ELan ELon EPfP LMil LRHS LSRN MAsh MBlu MGos NLar SReu SSta
	'Green Bee'	CBcs CJun LRHS
	'Hawk'	CBcs EBee WPGP
	'Heaven Scent' ♀H5	Widely available
	'Helen Fogg'	CJun
	heptapeta	see *M. denudata*
	'Honey Flower'	CJun
	'Honey Liz'	CBcs LMil LRHS SKHP SPoG
	Honey Tulip = 'Jurmag5'	CBcs LCro SPer SWeb
§	'Hong Yun'	CJun
	'Hot Flash'	CBcs CJun
	'Hot Lips'	CJun
	hypoleuca	see *M. obovata* Thunb.
	'Ian's Red'	CBcs CJun EBee IVic LRHS SCob WMat WPGP
§	***insignis***	CBcs LEdu SKHP WPGP
	- B&SWJ 11810	WCru
	- NJM 12.040	WPGP
	- WWJ 11854	WCru
	insignis × ***yuyuanensis***	WPGP
	'Iolanthe'	CBcs CEnd CJun CMCN CMHG CTho ELan EPfP ERea IVic MAsh MGos NOrn WPGP
	'Iufer'	CJun
	'J.C. Williams'	CBcs CJun CTho IVic LRHS WPGP
	'Jack Fogg'	MPkF SKHP
	'Jane'	CJun CMac ELan EPfP LMil LRHS MAsh MGos MRav NOrn
	'Janet'	SKHP
	'Jersey Belle'	CJun
	'Joe McDaniel'	CBcs CJun ERea IArd NLar SAko SKHP
	'John Congreve'	WPGP
	'Joli Pompom'	CBcs CJun LRHS
	'Judy Zuk'	CBcs ERea LMil LRHS SKHP SPoG
	× ***kewensis*** 'Wada's Memory'	see *M. salicifolia* 'Wada's Memory'
	'Kinikuuso'	EBee
	kobus	CBcs CCVT CDul CLnd CMCN CNWT CTho CTsd EPfP ERea ESps GKin MBlu NLar NWea SCob SEWo WBod WMou
	- B&SWJ 12751	WCru
	- 'Esveld Select'	CJun LRHS
	- 'Janaki Ammal'	CJun SAko
§	- 'Norman Gould'	CJun CMCN EPfP NPla
	- 'Octopus'	CJun
	- pink-flowered	CBcs CJun
	- 'White Elegance'	CJun
	'Kunming' **new**	LRHS
	laevifolia	CHid CJun CMCN CTho EBee EPfP LRHS SChF SKHP WPGP WSHC
	- 'Cascade'	SKHP
	- 'Gail's Favourite'	EPfP LMil LRHS MAsh SKHP
	- 'Kh-Achteraan' **new**	LRHS
	- 'Mini Mouse'	LRHS MAsh SKHP
	- 'Velvet and Cream'	IVic
	- 'Willow Leaf'	SKHP
	'Laura Saylor'	CJun
	'Leda'	CBcs CJun ERea SSta WPGP
	'Legacy'	CJun SKHP WPGP
	'Legend'	CJun EPfP
	'Lennarth Jonsson'	CJun
§	***liliiflora***	LPar
	- 'Darkest Purple'	CJun LPar
§	- 'Nigra' ♀H6	Widely available
	- 'Raven'	EBee LMil LRHS SKHP WPGP
	liliiflora × ***stellata*** **new**	LPar
*	'Limelight'	CBcs CJun EBee EPfP NLar NOra WMat WPGP
	× ***loebneri***	LPar
	- 'Ballerina'	CBcs
	- 'Donna' ♀H6	CBcs CJun EPfP LMil LRHS LSRN MAsh SKHP

- 'Encore'	CJun
- 'Green Mist'	CJun LRHS
- 'Leonard Messel' ♀H6	Widely available
- 'Lesley Jane'	CJun
- 'Mag's Pirouette' ♀H6	CBcs CJun EBee EMil EPfP LLHF LMil LRHS SAko SKHP SLim SPoG
- 'Merrill' ♀H6	CBcs CDul CJun CLnd CMCN CMac CNWT CTho CWib ELan EMOT EPfP ERea ESps LMil LRHS MAsh MGos MRav NEgg NLar SEND SGol SHil SKHP SPer SReu SSta
- 'Neil McEacharn'	CJun
- 'Pink Cloud'	CJun
- 'Powder Puff'	CBcs CJun
- 'Raspberry Fun'	CJun IArd
- 'Snowdrift'	CJun
- 'Star Bright'	CJun
- 'Two Stones'	SKHP
- 'White Stardust'	CJun
- 'Wildcat' ♀H6	CBcs CJun LRHS SAko SHil SKHP
- 'Willow Wood'	CJun
'Lois' ♀H6	CBcs CJun EPfP ERea GGGa LMil LRHS LSRN SKHP WPGP
'Lombardy Rose'	NLar
'Longsleeper'	LRHS
'Lotus'	CBcs CJun WPGP
'Lucy Carlson'	CJun
macrophylla	CBcs CBrP CFil CMac EPfP IDee LRHS MBlu MPkF NLar SKHP WPGP
§ - subsp. ***ashei***	CFil CMCN IDee SKHP WPGP
- subsp. ***ashei*** × ***virginiana***	CJun WPGP
§ - subsp. ***dealbata***	CFil
macrophylla × ***macrophylla*** subsp. ***ashei***	SKHP
macrophylla × ***sieboldii***	CJun LPar
'Malin'	CJun
'Manchu Fan'	CBcs CJun EPfP IArd IVic LRHS LSRN SKHP WPGP
§ 'March Til Frost'	CBcs CJun EBee SKHP WPGP
'Margaret Helen'	CBcs CJun CMHG WPGP
'Marj Gossler'	CJun
'Marjorie Congreve'	WPGP
'Mark Jury'	SKHP
martinii	CBcs SKHP
'Mary Bee'	SKHP
'Mary Nell'	CJun
'Maryland'	CJun GGGa SKHP
maudiae	CBcs EPfP NLar SKHP
'Maxine Merrill'	CBcs CJun SAko
'May to Frost'	see *M.* 'March Til Frost'
'Milky Way' ♀H5	CDul CJun CMHG CTho EPfP ERea LMil MGos SKHP WPGP
'Mister Yellowjacket'	CJun
'Moondance'	CJun
'Morning Calm'	SKHP
'Nimbus'	CJun ERea LRHS SKHP WPGP
nitida	CBcs CFil
obovata Diels	see *M. officinalis*
§ ***obovata*** Thunb.	CBcs CJun CMCN CTho EPfP NLar SBig WMou WPGP
- B&SWJ 10821 **new**	WCru
- B&SWJ 12626	WCru
- pink-flowered **new**	WPGP
obovata × ***sargentiana*** var. ***robusta***	WPGP
§ ***officinalis***	CBcs EPfP NLar
- var. ***biloba***	CBcs MBlu NLar WPGP
'Old Port'	CBcs
'Olivia'	CJun LRHS WPGP
'Peaches 'n' Cream' **new**	CJun
'Peachy'	CBcs CJun LRHS
§ 'Pegasus' ♀H6	CBcs CEnd CJun LMil SKHP SSta
'Peppermint Stick'	CBcs CTsd LRHS WMat
'Peter Dummer'	LMil
'Peter Smithers'	CJun
'Petit Chicon'	CBcs
'Phelan Bright'	CJun EBee SAko WPGP
'Phillip Tregunna'	CBcs CTho SKHP WPGP
'Phil's Masterpiece'	CJun
'Pickard's Garnet'	CBcs
'Pickard's Stardust'	EPfP
'Pickard's Sundew'	see *M.* × *soulangeana* 'Sundew'
'Piet van Veen'	CJun
'Pink Delight'	CJun
'Pink Goblet'	LRHS
'Pink Surprise'	CJun
'Pinkie'	CJun LSRN
'Porcelain Dove'	CBcs CJun LMil LRHS SKHP WPGP
'Princess Margaret'	CBcs CJun
'Pristine'	EPfP LMil LRHS
× ***proctoriana***	CAbP CBcs EBee LMil LRHS MMuc SKHP WPGP
- 'Robert's Dream'	CJun LRHS MAsh SSta
- 'Slavin's No 44'	CJun
'Purple Breeze'	MBlu NLar SAko
'Purple Globe'	CJun EBee SKHP
'Purple Platter'	CBcs
'Purple Sensation'	CBcs CJun WPGP
quinquepeta	see *M. liliiflora*
'Randy'	CBcs
'Raspberry Ice'	CBcs CMHG CMac CTho EPfP LMil LRHS MAsh SRms WFar
'Raspberry Swirl'	SSta
'Rebecca's Perfume'	LRHS WMat
'Red as Red'	CBcs LRHS
'Red Baron'	CJun
'Red Lion'	CBcs CJun
'Ricki'	CJun CLet LSRN MBlu
'Roseanne'	CJunx
rostrata	CBcs CFil EBee IArd IMou SKHP WPGP
'Rouged Alabaster'	CBcs
'Royal Crown'	CBcs EMil EPfP IArd LRHS MRav
'Royal Flush'	NEgg
'Ruby'	CJun
salicifolia	CBcs CMCN MMuc
- var. ***concolor***	CJun
- 'Garden House Upright'	EBee
- 'Jermyns'	CJun
- 'Louisa Fete'	CJun
* - 'Rosea'	CJun
- upright	WPGP
- 'Van Veen'	CJun
§ - 'Wada's Memory' ♀H6	CAbP CDul CHid CJun CMCN CTho ELan EMil EPfP ERea LMil LRHS MAsh MBlu MMuc NPri SKHP SPer SSta WFar WMat
- 'Windsor Beauty'	CJun ERea SSta
sapaensis FMWJ 13315	WCru
- FMWJ 13330	WCru
- HWJ 533	WCru
- NJM 09.168	WPGP
'Sarah Coe'	WMat
sargentiana	SSta
- 'Broadleas'	CJun
- var. ***robusta***	CBcs CLnd CMCN CTsd EPfP MMuc
- - 'Blood Moon'	CBcs CJun EBee WPGP
- - 'Multipetal'	WPGP

- - 'Trengwainton Glory'	ERea
'Satisfaction'	CJun LCro NLar
'Sayonara' 🏆H5	CJun ERea LRHS
'Schmetterling'	see *M.* × *soulangeana* 'Pickard's Schmetterling'
'Sentinel'	WMat
'Serene'	CBcs CEnd CJun CMHG EPfP LMil LRHS
Shirazz = 'Vulden'	CBcs CJun EPfP LMil LRHS NLar SCob SKHP WPGP
sieboldii	Widely available
- B&SWJ 4127	WCru
- 'Colossus' 🏆H6	CJun IArd MBlu SAko SKHP WPGP
- 'Genesis'	CJun NLar
- 'Genesis' × ***tripetala***	CJun
- 'Genesis' × ***virginiana***	CJun
- 'Michiko Renge' (d)	CJun
- 'Min Pyong-gal'	CJun
- 'Pride of Norway'	CJun
- subsp. ***sieboldii*** B&SWJ 12553 from Korea	WCru
- subsp. ***sinensis***	CBcs CJun CMCN CTho ELan LPar WPGP
I - - 'Grandiflora'	CJun WPGP
- 'White Flounces' (d) **new**	NLar
'Sir Harold Hillier'	CBcs WPGP
'Sleeping Beauty'	SKHP
'Snow Goose'	CJun
'Solar Flair'	CBcs CJun IArd LRHS NLar SKHP
× ***soulangeana***	Widely available
- 'Alba Superba'	CBcs CBot CTri EMOT EPfP ESps LCro LMil LPar LRHS MBlu MRav NLar SLim WFar
- 'Alexandrina'	CBcs EPfP MBlu NLar
- 'André Leroy'	EPfP LRHS
- 'Beugnon'	IArd
- 'Brozzonii' 🏆H5	CMac EPfP GCra LMil LRHS SSta
- 'Cleopatra'	CBcs
- 'Fukuju'	CJun
- 'Just Jean'	EBee
- 'Lennei'	CBcs CMCN CMac CSBt CTho EMOT EPfP ESps IArd LPar LRHS MGos MRav NLar NOrn SHil SPer SRms WFar
- 'Lennei Alba'	CMCN CMac ELan IArd LPar MBlu NOra SPer WFar WMat
- 'Lennei Alba' × ***sprengeri*** var. ***diva***	LPar
- 'Nigra'	see *M. liliiflora* 'Nigra'
- 'Pickard's Opal'	CMCN
- 'Pickard's Ruby'	CBcs
§ - 'Pickard's Schmetterling' 🏆H5	CBcs EPfP LMil LRHS MAsh
- 'Pickard's Snow Queen'	CJun
- 'Pickard's Sundew'	see *M.* × *soulangeana* 'Sundew'
- 'Picture'	CMac CTri
- 'Purpliana'	NPri
- Red Lucky	see *M.* 'Hong Yun'
- 'Rubra' misapplied	see *M.* × *soulangeana* 'Rustica Rubra'
§ - 'Rustica Rubra'	CBcs CDul CLnd CMCN CMac CTri ELan EPfP LMil LRHS LSRN MAsh NLar SGol SRms WFar WHar
- 'San José'	CJun LMil LRHS MAsh
- 'Speciosa'	SSta
§ - 'Sundew'	EPfP ERea GMcL
- 'Superba'	CMac LPar
- 'Verbanica'	EPfP LMil LRHS MAsh
'Spectrum' 🏆H6	CBcs CEnd CJun EPfP ERea IArd IDee IMou LMil LRHS MBlu MGos SAko SKHP SPoG SSta

sprengeri	CTsd CWib
- from Guizhou, China	WPGP
- var. ***diva***	CBcs CEnd SKHP WPGP
- - 'Burncoose' 🏆H6	CBcs
- - 'Copeland Court' 🏆H6	CJun LMil WPGP
- - 'Dark Diva'	CJun
- - 'Diva'	LRHS SAko WPGP
- - 'Eric Savill' 🏆H6	CBcs CJun ERea IVic SKHP WPGP
- - 'Lanhydrock'	CJun LRHS SKHP WPGP
- - 'Marwood Spring'	CMHG ERea SKHP WPGP
- - 'Westonbirt'	WPGP
- var. ***sprengeri***	SKHP
'Spring Rite'	CBcs CJun SKHP
'Star Wars' 🏆H5	CBcs CCVT CDul CEnd CJun CTho ELan EPfP ERea GGGa LMil LRHS MAsh MGos NLar NOra NOrn SAko SKHP SPoG SSta WMat WPGP
'Stellar Acclaim'	CBcs CJun LMil
stellata	Widely available
- 'Centennial' 🏆H6	CJun CTho
- 'Chrysanthemumiflora'	CJun ERea SKHP
- 'Dawn'	CJun
- 'Jane Platt' 🏆H6	CBcs CJun ELan EPfP ERea LMil LRHS MGos SKHP SPoG SSta WPGP
- f. ***keiskei***	CEnd CJun MGos NHol SKHP
- 'Kikuzaki'	CJun
- 'King Rose'	CBcs CJun CTsd EPfP LRHS MAsh SPer
- 'Massey'	CJun
- 'Norman Gould'	see *M. kobus* 'Norman Gould'
- 'Rosea'	CDul CJun CLet CMCN CTho ELan ELon EPfP ESps GMcL LMil LPar MGos MRav MSwo NEgg NLar NOrn NPri SCob SKHP SWeb
- 'Rosea Massey'	CJun WFar
- 'Royal Star' 🏆H6	Widely available
- 'Scented Silver'	CJun LRHS MAsh SKHP SPoG
- 'Shi-banchi Rosea'	CJun
- 'Water Lily'	CBcs CBot CJun CMCN CRos CTho ELan ELon EPfP LRHS LSRN MAsh MBlu MGos NEgg SHil SKHP SPer SPoG SSta WFar WHor WPGP
- 'Wisley Stardust'	LRHS
'Summer Solstice'	CBcs CJun WPGP
'Sun Ray'	CJun
'Sunburst'	CBcs CJun SRms
'Sundance'	CBcs CJun IArd MBlu NLar
'Sunrise'	CBcs CDul
'Sunsation'	CBcs CJun ERea
'Sunset Swirl' **new**	CJun
'Sunspire'	CJun ERea NLar
'Suntown'	CJun
'Susan' 🏆H6	Widely available
'Susanna van Veen'	CBcs CEnd CJun WPGP
'Swedish Star'	CJun
'Sweet Merlot'	CBcs CJun LRHS
'Sweet Valentine'	CBcs CJun GMcL WPGP
'Sweetheart' 🏆H5	CBcs CJun
'Sybille'	CMCN WPGP
× ***thompsoniana***	CBcs CMCN
- 'Olmenhof'	IArd IDee
'Thousand Butterflies'	CJun
'Tina Durio'	CBcs SKHP WMat
'Todd Gresham'	CJun
'Todd's Forty Niner'	CBcs CJun
'Touch of Pink'	CBcs
'Tranquility'	CBcs CJun SKHP
'Trewidden Belle'	CEnd
tripetala	CBcs CMCN CTho ELan EPfP LRHS MBlu NLar SBig SKHP SMad SSta

- 'Bloomfield'	CJun
- 'Petite'	SKHP
'Ultimate Yellow'	CJun NLar
× ***veitchii***	CBcs EPfP
- 'Columbus'	CJun ERea LRHS SKHP WPGP
- 'Peter Veitch'	CTho
virginiana	CBcs CJun CMCN EPfP NLar SBig SKHP
- 'Aiken County'	SKHP
- var. ***australis*** 'Green Shadow'	SGol
- - 'Satellite'	NLar
- 'Havener'	SKHP
- Moonglow = 'Jim Wilson'	CBcs CJun EPfP MBlu
'Vulcan'	CBcs CEnd CJun CMCN ELan EPfP LRHS NLar NOrn SCoo
× ***watsonii***	see *M.* × *wieseneri*
'Wedding Vows' **new**	CJun
'White Mystery'	CJun
§ × ***wieseneri***	CBcs CJun CMCN CMHG EPfP ERea LRHS MBlu SKHP SPer SPoG WPGP
- 'Aashild Kalleberg'	CBcs CJun SKHP WPGP
- 'Lupo Osti'	SKHP
wilsonii ♀H6	CBcs CCVT CDul CJun CMCN CTho CTri EBee ELan EPfP IArd IDee LCro LOPS LRHS MBlu MGos MMuc MNrw NLar SBrt SEND SKHP WHar WPGP WSHC
- 'Gwen Baker'	CEnd CJun
- 'Highdownensis'	EBee
'Yaeko'	CBcs
'Yellow Fever'	CBcs CJun CTho EBee WPGP
'Yellow Garland'	CJun
'Yellow Lantern' ♀H6	CAbP CBcs CEnd CJun EBee ELan EPfP GGGa LMil LRHS LSRN MAsh MBlu SPoG SSta WPGP
'Yellow Sea'	CJun SKHP
Yuchelia No. 1	CBcs WPGP
yunnanensis	CBcs CCCN MPkF
zenii	CBcs CMCN IArd
- 'Pink Parchment'	CJun

× *Mahoberberis* (*Berberidaceae*)

aquisargentii	CMac EBee EMil EPfP IVic LRHS MMuc MRav NLar SCob SEND SKHP WFar
'Dart's Desire'	NLar
miethkeana	SRms

Mahonia ✿ (*Berberidaceae*)

§ ***aquifolium***	CAco CAgr CBcs CDul EAEE ECrN ESps GMcL GPoy MGos MMuc MRav NWea SCob SEND SGol SPer SPlb SWvt WHar WHed
- 'Apollo' ♀H5	CBcs CRos CSBt CWib ELan ELon EPfP ESps GMcL LCro LHop LRHS LSRN MAsh MBlu MGos MJak MRav NLar SCob SCoo SPer SPoG SWvt WFar
- 'Atropurpurea'	CMac CSBt CTsd ELan EPfP LRHS MRav NLar SPer
- 'Cosmo Crawl'	CRos LRHS
- 'Fascicularis'	see *M.* × *wagneri* 'Pinnacle'
- 'Moseri'	WPat
- 'Smaragd'	CMac CRos ELan EPfP LRHS LSRN MBlu MGos MRav NLar SCob
- 'Versicolor'	MBlu
'Arthur Menzies'	CRos LRHS
§ ***bealei***	CAco CBcs CBod CDul CFil CRos CSBt CTho EBee ELan ELon EPfP ESps GMcL LRHS MAsh MGos MRav MSwo NEgg NLar NPer NPla SCob SCoo SGol SKHP SLim SWvt
Blackfoot = 'Bokrafoot' PBR	CRos ELan EPfP LRHS MAsh SLon
bodinieri	WPGP
- Og 93.033 **new**	WPGP
chochoco	CFil SKHP
conferta	CFil
confusa × ***gracilipes***	SKHP
§ ***duclouxiana***	CFil
eurybracteata	CFil IArd LRHS SKHP WCru WPGP
- subsp. ***ganpinensis*** **new**	WPGP
- - 'Soft Caress'	CBcs CRos EBee ELan EPfP EUJe EWTr IDee LCro LOPS LRHS MGos MPkF NLar NLos SCob SCoo SHil SMad SPoG SWvt WCot
- 'Minganpi' PBR	LSRN
- 'Sweet Winter'	LRHS SWvt
eutriphylla misapplied	see *M. trifolia*
fargesii	see *M. sheridaniana*
fortunei	CBcs CFil
- 'Winter Prince'	NLar WSHC
fremontii	SBrt
gracilipes	CFil EPfP EWes GCal IDee IMou MBlu NLar SBrt SChF SKHP SMad WCru WPGP WPat
gracilis	CFil
haematocarpa	SIgm
hartwegii **new**	CFil
huiliensis	see *M. sheridaniana*
japonica ♀H5	Widely available
- 'Gold Dust'	CMac MBlu
- 'Hiemalis'	see *M. japonica* 'Hivernant'
§ - 'Hivernant'	EAEE NWea
lanceolata	CFil EBee WPGP
leschenaultii B&SWJ 9535	WCru
× ***lindsayae***	CFil WPGP
- 'Cantab' ♀H4	CFil EBee EPfP SChF SMad WPGP
lomariifolia	see *M. oiwakensis* subsp. *lomariifolia*
longibracteata	GKin
mairei	see *M. duclouxiana*
× ***media***	ESps LPar
- 'Buckland' ♀H4	CBcs CDul CMac CRos CTho EPfP ESps SCob SPer SRms WPat
- 'Charity'	Widely available
- 'Lionel Fortescue' ♀H4	CBcs CMac CRos CSBt CTho EBee ELan EMOT EPfP ESps GKin LHop LRHS MAsh NEgg SCob SKHP SPer SWvt WHor
- 'Winter Sun' ♀H4	Widely available
moranensis	CFil EBee SMad
- T 292	WPGP
napaulensis	CFil
- 'Maharajah'	IArd IDee IMou NLar
nervosa	CBcs CMac EBee EPfP MBlu NLar SKHP WCru WPGP
- B&SWJ 9562	WCru
- B&SWJ 13580 **new**	WCru
nevinii	SBrt
nitens	EBee WCru WPGP
- 'Cabaret' PBR ♀H4	CBcs CRos CSBt EBee EPfP LCro LLHF LOPS LRHS MAsh MBlu MGos MJak SCob SHil SPoG SWvt
* ***nitida***	SKHP
oiwakensis	WPGP
- B&SWJ 371	WCru
- B&SWJ 3660	WCru

§	- subsp. ***lomariifolia*** ♀H4	CFil CRos EPfP EWes LRHS SArc SKHP
	- - var. ***tenuifoliola***	CFil
	pallida	CFil SKHP WPGP
	- from Tamazunchale, Mexico	CFil
	- from Zimapan, Mexico	CFil
	'Pan's Peculiar'	WPGP
	pinnata misapplied	see *M.* × *wagneri* 'Pinnacle'
	pinnata (Lag.) Fedde 'Ken S. Howard'	NLar WPGP
	repens	NLar
	- 'Rotundifolia'	SPlb
	× ***savilliana***	CFil NLar WPGP
	- 'Commissioner'	CWib
§	***sheridaniana***	CFil
	Sioux = 'Bokrasio'PBR	CRos LRHS MAsh SPoG
§	***trifolia***	CFil GCal LRHS SKHP
	- EKB 4618 new	WPGP
	trifoliolata var. ***glauca***	CEnd CFil CJun SKHP
	× ***wagneri***	SWvt
	- 'Aldenhamensis'	NLar
	- 'Fireflame'	GCal
	- 'Hastings' Elegant'	NLar
§	- 'Pinnacle' ♀H5	ELan EPfP LRHS MAsh MBlu NLar SPer SPoG SWvt
	- 'Sunset'	MBlu NLar
	- 'Undulata'	LRHS MBlu SRms
	- 'Vicaryi'	NLar

Maianthemum (*Asparagaceae*)

	amoenum B&SWJ 10390	WCru
	atropurpureum	WCru
	bicolor	CTal LEdu SWat
	bifolium	CAvo CBct CHid CTal ECho GCra GLog GMaP LEdu MAvo MMuc MNrw NBro NPnk SRms WCru XLum
§	- subsp. ***kamtschaticum***	CAvo CLAP ECha EPPr LEdu MAvo NLar NRya WCot WPGP
	- - B&SWJ 4360	GKev WCru
	- - CD&R 2300	WCru
	- - var. ***pumilum***	EBee GCal LEdu WCru
	canadense	EAJP EBee ECho EPot GBuc GCal GKev LEdu MNrw NBid WCru
	chasmanthum	see *M. bifolium* subsp. *kamtschaticum*
	comaltepecense B&SWJ 10215	WCru
	dilatatum	see *M. bifolium* subsp. *kamtschaticum*
	flexuosum	LEdu
	- B&SWJ 9069	WCru
	- B&SWJ 9079	WCru
	- B&SWJ 9150	WCru
	aff. ***flexuosum*** B&SWJ 9026	WCru
	- B&SWJ 9055	WCru
	formosanum B&SWJ 349	EPPr WCru
	forrestii	WCru
	fuscum	GEdr WCru
	- PAB 7749	LEdu
	- var. ***cordatum***	WCru
	gigas B&SWJ 10470	WCru
	henryi	ECho EHrv GEdr GKev LEdu WCru WPGP
	- BWJ 7616	WCru
	japonicum	CTal EHrv LEdu
	- B&SWJ 1179	WCru
	- B&SWJ 4714	WCru
	- B&SWJ 7306	WCru
	oleraceum	CBct GEdr GKev LEdu LRHS
	- B&SWJ 2148	WCru
	- purple-flowered	GEdr
	paniculatum	EBee LEdu
	- B&SWJ 9137	WCru
	- B&SWJ 9140	WCru
	- purple-flowered B&SWJ 9139	WCru
	pendent, B&SWJ 10305 from Guatemala	WCru
	purpureum	GEdr GKev
	- G-W&P 150	EPPr
	racemosum ♀H7	Widely available
	- subsp. ***amplexicaule***	GCal ILea
	- - 'Emily Moody'	CBct CPou EBee EPPr EPfP SChF SKHP WCot WPGP
	- dwarf	ECho
	- 'Major'	LRHS
	aff. ***salvinii***	CBct CTal
	- B&SWJ 9000	WCru
	- B&SWJ 9088	WCru
	- B&SWJ 10402	WCru
	scilloideum	CTal
	- B&SWJ 10407	WCru
*	- var. ***roseum*** B&SWJ 10335	WCru
	stellatum	CBct CSam CTal EBee ECha ECho EPPr EPfP GBuc GEdr ILea LEdu LHop LRHS MBel NChi NLar NPnk WCru XLum
	szechuanicum	WCru
	tatsienense	CBct EHrv GEdr LEdu WCru

Maihuenia (*Cactaceae*)

	poeppigii	CCac SPlb
	- F&W 9670	WCot

Maihueniopsis (*Cactaceae*)

	darwinii	SPlb
	- LB 347	CCac
§	***glomerata*** TG 63	CCac

Maireana (*Amaranthaceae*)

	georgei	SPlb

Mallotus (*Euphorbiaceae*)

	japonicus	WPGP

Malotigena (*Aizoaceae*)

§	***frantiskae-niederlovae***	CCCN CPBP CSma CTal ECho EDAr EPot GEdr GKev NHpl SMad WAbe WHal WIce XLum
	- 'Album'	see *M. frantiskae-niederlovae* 'White Nugget'
	- 'Gold Nugget' ♀H3	CRos EAEE ECho ESps LRHS NRHS
	- white-flowered	see *M. frantiskae-niederlovae* 'White Nugget'
§	- 'White Nugget'	CCCN CRos CSma CTal EDAr EPot EWes GEdr LRHS NHpl NRHS WAbe WIce

Malus ✿ (*Rosaceae*)

§	'Adirondack' ♀H6	CLnd EBee EMOT EPfP MAsh MMuc NLar NOra NPri SCoo SPoG WJas WMat
	'Admiration'	see *M.* 'Adirondack'
	× ***adstringens*** 'Hopa'	CAgr CDul CLnd
	- 'Simcoe'	EBee EMOT
	'Aldenhamensis'	see *M.* × *purpurea* 'Aldenhamensis'
	'Allow Super' (D)	WMat
	'Amberina'	CLnd

baccata	CDul CLnd CMCN CTho GTwe MMuc NWea SCoo SEND SPlb
- var. ***mandshurica***	CTho
aff. ***baccata***	NWea
(Ballerina Series) 'Ballerina Bolero' (D)	WMat
- 'Ballerina Polka' (D)	EMOT WMat
- 'Ballerina Samba' (D)	LCro WMat
'Barbara'	WMat
§ ***bhutanica***	CDul CLnd
- 'Mandarin'	SCoo
'Bramley 20' (C)	WMat
brevipes	CLnd LRHS SCoo
- 'Wedding Bouquet' ♀H6	EBee EMOT EPfP ERea LBuc LCro LSRN MAsh NLar NOra SPer WMat WMou
'Butterball' ♀H6	CDul CLnd CNWT CSBt CTho CTsd ECrN EMOT EPfP ERea ESps NOra NWea SCoo SLim SPer SPoG SVic WHar WJas WMat WMou WWct
'Candymint Sargent'	CLnd ERea NOra SLim
'Captain Tom' (C/D)	WMat
'Cave Hill'	CLnd
'Cheal's Scarlet'	CHab
* 'Cheal's Weeping'	CAco CLnd CMac EMOT MJak NEgg WMou
Coccinella = 'Courtarou'	SGol
'Comtesse de Paris' ♀H6	CDul CLnd EBee EPfP LRHS MAsh MBlu NLar NOra NOrn WMat
Coralburst = 'Coralcole'	ERea MAsh NOra WMat
coronaria var. ***dasycalyx*** 'Charlottae' (d)	CDul CLnd EWTr SPer
- 'Elk River'	EPfP MAsh NOra SCoo WMat
'Cowichan'	ECrN
'Crimson Brilliant'	CLnd
'Crittenden'	EPfP MAsh MRav
'Dartmouth'	CDul CHab CLnd CSBt CTri
'Directeur Moerlands'	CArg CCVT CEnd CSBt ECrN EMOT EPfP LRHS MMuc NOra NOrn SCoo SEND SPer SWvt WHar WMat
domestica '1400 Ke'PBR (F)	SBdl
- 'Acklam Russet' (D)	CHab GTwd SKee
- 'Acme' (D)	ECrN SDea SKee
- 'Adams's Pearmain' (D)	CHab CTho CTri ECrN ERea GTwd GTwe MAsh NOra SBdl SCob SDea SKee WHar WMat WWct
- 'Admiral'PBR (D)	ECrN ERea
- 'Akane' (D)	SDea
- 'Akerö' (D)	GTwd
- 'Alderman' (C)	GTwd
- 'Alfriston' (C)	CAgr CHab GTwd SKee WMat
§ - 'Alkmene' (D) ♀H6	CAgr ECrN NOra SDea
- 'All Doer' (C/D/Cider)	EMOT
- 'Allen's Everlasting' (D)	SDea
- 'Allington Pippin' (D)	CHab CSBt CTho CTri ECrN ERea GTwd MGos NOra SDea SKee WHar WMat
- Ambassy = 'Dalil'PBR (D)	EBee
- 'American Mother'	see *M. domestica* 'Mother'
- 'Ananas Reinette' (D)	CHab ECrN SKee
- 'Anna Boelens' (D)	SDea
- 'Annie Elizabeth' (C)	CAgr CDul CHab CWib ECrN EMOT ERea ESps GTwd GTwe IArd MGos MRai NOra SDea SKee SVic WHar WJas WMat WWct
- 'Anniversary' (D)	SDea
- 'Api' (D)	EMOT ERea LSRN NOra NWea SCob SKee WHar WMat
- 'Api Noir' (D)	SKee
- 'Ard Cairn Russet' (D)	ECrN IArd SDea SKee
- 'Aromatic Russet' (D)	SKee
- 'Arthur Turner' (C) ♀H6	CCVT CHab CTri ECrN EMOT EPom ERea ESps GTwd GTwe LBuc MWat NOra SBdl SDea SKee SPer WHar WJas WMat
- 'Ashmead's Kernel' (D) ♀H6	Widely available
- 'Ashton Bitter' (Cider)	CHab CTri GTwe
- 'Askham Pippin' (F)	MCoo
- 'Autumn Harvest' (C/D)	GTwd
- 'Autumn Pearmain' (D)	SDea WHar
- 'Baker's Delicious' (D)	EBee ECrN ERea NOra SDea SKee WHar WMat
- 'Ballyvaughan Seedling' (D)	IArd
- 'Balsam'	see *M. domestica* 'Green Balsam'
- 'Banana Pippin' (F)	CEnd
- 'Banns' (D)	ECrN ERea
- 'Bardsey' (D)	CAgr CArg CHab EPom ERea NOra SKee WGwG WHar WMat
- 'Barnack Beauty' (D)	CHab GTwd LEdu NOra SKee
- 'Barnack Orange' (D)	GTwd
- 'Baron Ward' (C)	CHab
- 'Baron Wood' (C)	SKee
- 'Bascombe's Mystery' (D)	SKee
- 'Baxter's Pearmain' (D)	ECrN SDea SKee
- 'Beauty of Bath' (D)	CAgr CArg CCVT CDul CHab CLnd CTho CTri CWib ECrN ELan EMOT EPom ERea ESps EWTr GTwd GTwe LBuc MRav NOra SBdl SDea SKee SPer WHar WJas WMat WWct
- 'Beauty of Hants' (C/D)	ECrN SKee
- 'Beauty of Kent' (C)	GTwd SDea SKee
- 'Beauty of Moray' (C)	GTwd SKee
- 'Beeley Pippin' (D)	SDea SKee
- 'Bell Apple' (Cider/C)	CTho
- 'Belle de Boskoop' (C/D) ♀H6	CAgr CHab ECrN GTwe MCoo NOra SBdl SCob SDea SKee
- 'Belledge Pippin' (C/D)	GTwd SBdl
- 'Belvoir Seedling' (C/D)	MRai SKee
- 'Bembridge Beauty' (F)	CHab SDea
- 'Ben's Red' (D)	CAgr CEnd CFGn CTho SKee WMat
- 'Bess Pool' (D)	CHab GTwd MCoo SBdl SDea
- 'Bewley Down Pippin'	see *M. domestica* 'Crimson King' (Cider/C)
- 'Bickington Grey' (Cider)	CTho
- 'Billy Down Pippin' (F)	CTho
- 'Bismarck' (C)	SKee
- 'Black Dabinett' (Cider)	CEnd CTho ERea WMat
- 'Blenheim Orange' (C/D) ♀H6	Widely available
- 'Blood of the Boyne' (D)	IArd
- 'Bloody Ploughman' (D)	CHab ECrN ERea ESps GQue GTwd GTwe NOra NPri SBdl SKee SLon WHar WMat
- 'Blue Moon' (D)	LRHS
- 'Blue Pearmain' (D)	SDea SKee
- Bolero	see *M. domestica* 'Tuscan'
- 'Bonum' (D/C)	WMat
- 'Boston Russet'	see *M. domestica* 'Roxbury Russet'
- 'Bountiful' (C)	CAgr CDul CLnd CMac CSBt CTri CWib ECrN EMOT EPom ESps GTwd GTwe LRHS LSRN MAsh MRav NOra SBdl SDea SKee WHar WMat WWct
- 'Bow Hill Pippin' (C)	GTwd SKee
- 'Braddick's Nonpareil' (D)	SKee

- 'Bradley's Beauty' (C/D)	NWea
- 'Braeburn' (D)	CAgr CDul CLnd CSBt CSut CTri CTsd ECrN EMOT EPom ERea ESps LBuc LEdu LRHS MWat NOra SBdl SCob SDea SEND SEWo SFrt SKee SPer WHar WJas WMat
- 'Braeburn Hillwell' (D)	EPom NOra
- 'Braintree Seedling' (D)	ECrN
- 'Bramley's Seedling' (C) ♀H6	Widely available
- 'Bramley's Seedling' clone 20 (F)	CFGn CTsd ERea LSRN MAsh MWat NLar NOra SBdl SCoo SDea SKee SLim SPoG WHar WWct
- 'Bread Fruit' (C/D)	CEnd CFGn
- 'Brenchley Pippin' (D)	SBdl
- 'Bright Future' (D)	EPom NOra WMat WWct
- 'Brith Mawr' (C)	WGwG
- 'Broad-eyed Pippin' (C)	SKee
- 'Broadholme Beauty' (C)	EPom MAsh NOra WHar WMat
- 'Brookes's' (D)	SKee WHar
- 'Brown Crofton' (D)	IArd
- 'Brown Snout' (Cider)	CTho SFrt
- 'Brownlee's Russet' (D)	CAgr CHab CTho CTri GTwd MCoo NEgg NOra NWea SDea SKee WHar WMat
- 'Brown's Apple' (Cider)	CAgr CHab CTri ECrN ERea GTwe MRai NOra SBdl SFrt WMat
- 'Broxwood Foxwhelp' (Cider)	SFrt
- 'Burley Grove'	SBdl
- 'Burr Knot' (C)	SKee
- 'Burrowhill Early' (Cider)	WMat
- 'Bushey Grove' (C)	SDea
- 'Byfleet Seedling' (C)	SKee
- 'Calville Blanc d'Hiver' (D)	NOra SBdl SKee
- 'Cambusnethan Pippin' (D)	GTwd SKee
- 'Camelot' (Cider/C)	EMOT
§ - 'Captain Broad' (Cider/D)	CEnd CTho
- 'Captain Kidd' (D)	EPom ERea NOra SKee WHar
- 'Caravel' (D)	GTwd
- 'Carlisle Codlin' (C)	GTwd NLar NOra NWea SDea WMat
- 'Caroline' (D)	ECrN ERea
- 'Carswell's Honeydew' (D)	SKee
- 'Catherine' (C)	ECrN
- 'Catshead' (C)	CAgr CHab CTri CTsd ECrN GTwd IArd NOra SDea SKee WHar WMat WWct
- 'Cellini' (C)	NOra SDea
- 'Cevaal' (D)	WWct
- 'Channel Beauty' (D)	WGwG
- 'Charles Ross' (C/D) ♀H6	Widely available
- 'Charlotte'PBR (C)	ECrN EMOT SDea SKee
- 'Cheddar Cross' (D)	CAgr CCVT CTri ECrN SKee
- 'Chelmsford Wonder' (C)	ECrN SKee
- 'Chisel Jersey' (Cider)	CAgr CTri MRai NOra SFrt SKee
- 'Chivers Delight' (D)	CAgr ECrN EMOT EPom ERea GTwd GTwe LRHS MCoo NOra SDea SKee WHar WJas
- 'Christmas Pearmain' (D)	CAgr CTho ECrN GTwe MRai SDea SKee WMat
- 'Christmas Pippin' (D)	CArg EPom ERea LBuc LCro LPre LRHS MCoo MWat NLar NOra SBdl WMat
- 'Cider Lady's Finger' (Cider)	SKee
- 'Cissy' (D)	WGwG

- 'Claygate Pearmain' (D)	CAgr CHab CTho CTri ECrN ERea GTwe MCoo NOra SDea SKee SVic WHar WMat
- 'Cleeve' (D)	SKee
- 'Clopton Red' (D)	ECrN SKee
- 'Clydeside' (C)	GTwd
- 'Cobra' (F)	CAgr LBuc MAsh MCoo NOra SKee SPoG WHar WJas WMat
- 'Cockle Pippin' (D)	CAgr MRai SDea SKee
- 'Cockpit' (C)	CHab GTwd NWea SKee
- 'Coleman's Seedling' (Cider)	CTho
- 'Collogett Pippin' (C/Cider)	CEnd CTho CTsd
- 'Colonel Vaughan' (C/D)	SKee
- 'Colonel Yate' (D)	SKee
- 'Cornish Aromatic' (D)	CAgr CDul CFGn CTho CTri CTsd GTwe NOra SBdl SDea SKee WHar WMat
- 'Cornish Gilliflower' (D)	CAgr CEnd CHab CTho CTsd EBee ECrN MCoo NOra SBdl SDea SKee WHar WMat
- 'Cornish Honeypin' (D)	CEnd SKee
- 'Cornish Longstem' (D)	CAgr CEnd
- 'Cornish Mother' (D)	CEnd CTho CTsd
- 'Cornish Pine' (D)	CEnd SDea SKee
- 'Coronation' (D)	CHab SDea SKee
- 'Costard' (C)	CHab
- 'Cottenham Seedling' (C)	SKee
- 'Coul Blush' (D)	GTwd GTwe SKee WMat
- 'Court of Wick' (D)	CAgr CDul CHab CTho CTri ECrN GTwd NOra SVic WHar WMat
- 'Court Pendu Plat' (D)	CAgr CArg CHab GQue GTwd LEdu MAsh MWat NOra NWea SBdl SDea SKee WHar WJas WMat WWct
- 'Court Royal' (Cider)	SKee
- 'Cow Apple' (C)	SBdl
- 'Cox Cymraeg' (D)	WGwG
- 'Cox's Orange Pippin' (D)	Widely available
- 'Cox's Pomona' (C)	GTwd SDea WHar
- 'Cox's Rouge de Flandres' (D)	SKee
- 'Cox's Selfing' (D)	CDul CMac CSBt CTri CWib EPfP ESps GTwe LBuc MAsh MGos NLar SDea SKee SPer SPoG WHar WJas WMat WWct
- 'Crawley Beauty' (C)	CAgr CHab GTwd GTwe SDea SKee WHar WMat
- 'Crawley Reinette' (D)	CHab
- 'Crimson Beauty of Bath' (D)	CAgr
- 'Crimson Bramley' (C)	IArd
- 'Crimson Cox' (D)	SDea
§ - 'Crimson King' (Cider/C)	CAgr MRai SFrt
- 'Crimson King' (D)	CAgr CHab CTri
- 'Crimson Peasgood' (C)	ECrN SKee
- 'Crimson Queening' (D)	WHar
- 'Crimson Victoria' (Cider)	CTho
- Crispin	see *M. domestica* 'Mutsu'
- 'Croen Mochyn' (D)	WGwG
§ - 'Crowngold' (D)	EPom SBdl
- 'Cutler Grieve' (D)	GTwd SDea
- 'Dabinett' (Cider)	CAgr CArg CFGn CHab CTho CTri EMOT EPom ERea GTwd GTwe LBuc LRHS MRai NOra SBdl SDea SFrt SKee WHar WMat WWct
- 'D'Arcy Spice' (D)	CAgr ECrN EPfP ERea GQue MCoo MWat NOra SDea SFrt SKee WHar WMat WWct
- 'Dawn' (D)	SKee

	- 'Deacon's Blushing Beauty' (C/D)	SDea
	- 'Deacon's Millennium' (D)	SDea
	- 'Decio' (D)	SKee
	- 'Devon Crimson Queen' (D)	CTho
	- 'Devonshire Buckland' (C)	CEnd CTho
	- 'Devonshire Crimson Queen' (D)	SDea
	- 'Devonshire Quarrenden' (D)	CAgr CDul CHab CTho CTsd ERea GTwd NOra SBdl SDea SKee SVic WHar WMat
	- 'Diamond' (D)	WGwG
	- 'Discovery' (D) 🏆H6	Widely available
	- 'Discovery NFT' (D)	SBdl
	- 'Doctor Harvey' (C)	ECrN ERea SKee
	- 'Doctor Kidd's Orange Red'	see *M. domestica* 'Kidd's Orange Red'
	- 'Doddin' (D)	WWct
	- 'Domino' (C)	MCoo
	- 'Don's Delight' (C)	CTho WMat
	- 'Downton Pippin' (D)	CHab WHar
	- 'Duchess of Oldenburg' (C)	GTwd NOra
	- 'Duchess's Favourite' (D)	SKee
	- 'Duck's Bill' (D)	SKee
	- 'Duke of Cornwall' (C)	CTho
	- 'Duke of Devonshire' (D)	CSBt CTri GTwd SDea SKee
	- 'Dumeller's Seedling'	see *M. domestica* 'Dummellor's Seedling'
§	- 'Dummellor's Seedling' (C) 🏆H6	CHab CTri GTwd MCoo NOra SBdl SDea SKee WHar
	- 'Dunkerton Late Sweet' (Cider)	CCVT CHab EMOT LBuc WMat
	- 'Dunn's Seedling' (D)	SDea
§	- 'Dutch Codlin' (C)	MRai
	- 'Early Blenheim' (D/C)	CEnd
	- 'Early Bower' (D)	CEnd
	- 'Early Julyan' (C)	GTwd SKee
	- 'Early Victoria'	see *M. domestica* 'Emneth Early'
	- Early Windsor	see *M. domestica* 'Alkmene'
	- 'Early Worcester'	see *M. domestica* 'Tydeman's Early Worcester'
	- 'East Lothian Pippin' (C)	GTwd SKee
	- 'Easter Orange' (D)	SKee
	- 'Ecklinville' (C)	SBdl SDea
	- 'Eden' (F)	WMat
	- 'Edith Hopwood' (D)	ECrN
	- 'Edward VII' (C) 🏆H6	CHab EMOT MAsh NOra SBdl SDea SKee WHar WMat WWct
	- 'Egremont Russet' (D) 🏆H6	Widely available
	- 'Ellis' Bitter' (Cider)	EMOT GTwe SKee SVic
	- 'Ellison's Orange' (D) 🏆H6	Widely available
	- 'Elmore Pippin' (D)	SBdl
	- 'Elstar' (D) 🏆H6	CCVT CLnd ECrN EMOT EPom NOra SDea SKee WHar
	- 'Elton Beauty' (D)	SDea
§	- 'Emneth Early' (C) 🏆H6	CAgr CHab CLnd ECrN ERea EWTr GTwd GTwe NOra SDea SKee WJas WMat WWct
	- 'Empire' (D)	NOra SKee
	- 'Encore' (C)	SDea SKee
	- 'Endsleigh Beauty' (D)	CEnd
	- 'English Codlin' (C)	CTho CTri ERea
	- 'Epicure'	see *M. domestica* 'Laxton's Epicure'
	- 'Ernie's Russet' (D)	SDea
	- 'Eros' (D)	ECrN
	- 'Essex Pippin' (D)	ECrN
	- 'Evening Gold' (C)	SDea
	- 'Eve's Delight' (D)	SDea
	- 'Excelsior' (C)	ECrN
	- 'Exeter Cross' (D)	CSBt ECrN GTwd SDea
	- 'Fair Maid of Devon' (Cider)	CAgr CDul CEnd CTho GTwd WMat
	- 'Falstaff'^{PBR} (D)	CAgr CDul CTri ECrN EPfP EPom ESps GTwe LSRN MGos NOra SCob SCoo SDea SPer WHar
	- 'Fameuse' (D)	NOra
	- 'Farmer's Glory' (D)	CAgr CTho WMat
	- 'Fearn's Pippin' (D)	SKee
	- 'Fiessers Erstling' (C)	SBdl
	- 'Fiesta'^{PBR} (D) 🏆H6	Widely available
	- 'Fillbarrel' (Cider)	CHab
	- 'Fillingham Pippin' (C)	CHab
	- 'Firedance' (D)	LRHS
	- 'Firmgold' (D)	SDea
	- 'First and Last' (D)	NOra WMat
	- 'Flame' (D)	ECrN
	- 'Flamenco'	see *M. domestica* 'Obelisk'
§	- 'Flower of Kent' (C)	CHab EPom MAsh NOra NWea SBdl SDea SKee WMat
	- 'Flower of the Town' (D)	CHab SBdl SKee
	- 'Forge' (D)	CAgr CHab SDea SKee
	- 'Fortune'	see *M. domestica* 'Laxton's Fortune'
	- 'Forty Shilling' (D)	GTwd
	- 'Foxwhelp' (Cider)	CHab GTwd NWea SKee
	- 'Francis' (D)	ECrN
	- 'Frederick' (Cider)	WMat
	- 'French Codlin'	see *M. domestica* 'Dutch Codlin'
	- 'French Crab' (C)	SDea
	- 'Freyberg' (D)	NOra SKee
	- 'Fuji' (D)	NOra SDea SKee
	- 'Gala' (D)	CSBt EBee EPom ESps NOra SCob SCoo SDea SKee WHar WMat
	- 'Galaxy'^{PBR} (D)	NOra
	- 'Galloway Pippin' (C)	GTwd GTwe NLar NOra SKee WMat
	- 'Garden Fountain' (D)	LRHS
	- 'Gascoyne's Scarlet' (C/D)	GTwd SBdl SDea SKee WHar
	- 'Gavin' (D)	CAgr SDea SKee
	- 'Genesis II' (C/D)	SDea
	- 'Genet Moyle' (C/Cider)	CTri GTwd MCoo WHar WMat
	- 'George Carpenter' (D)	CTri SDea SKee
	- 'George Cave' (D)	CDul CTho ECrN EMOT ESps GTwe IArd MCoo NOra SDea SEND SFrt SKee WHar WJas
	- 'George Neal' (C)	CAgr SDea SKee
	- 'Gibbon's Russet' (D)	IArd
	- 'Gladstone' (D)	CAgr GTwd NOra SKee WHar WMat WWct
	- 'Glansevin' (D)	WGwG
§	- 'Glass Apple' (C/D)	CEnd CTho
	- 'Gloria Mundi' (C)	SDea
	- 'Gloster '69' (D)	CLnd SDea SKee
	- 'Gloucester Cross' (D)	SKee
	- 'Golden Ball' (Cider)	CTho
	- 'Golden Bittersweet' (D)	CAgr CTho WMat
	- 'Golden Delicious' (D) 🏆H6	CCVT CDul CMac CSBt CWib EBee ECrN ELan EMOT EPom ESps LBuc MJak MMuc NOra SCob SDea SEND SEWo SKee SVic WHar WMat
	- 'Golden Gate' (D)	LRHS
	- 'Golden Glow' (C)	SDea
	- 'Golden Harvey' (D)	CAgr
	- 'Golden Jubilee' (F)	CEnd
	- 'Golden Knob' (D)	CTri GTwd SKee
	- 'Golden Noble' (C) 🏆H6	CAgr CDul CTri ECrN EMOT ERea GTwd GTwe IArd MCoo NOra SBdl SDea SKee

- 'Golden Nugget' (D) CAgr SKee
- 'Golden Pippin' (C) CAgr NOra WHar WMat
- 'Golden Reinette' (D) SKee
- 'Golden Russet' (D) CAgr ECrN NOra SDea SKee WHar
- 'Golden Spire' (C) CHab MCoo NOra SDea SKee WHar
- 'Gooseberry' (C) SKee
- 'Grandpa Ailes' (D) CTho
- 'Grandpa Buxton' (C) CHab
- 'Granny Smith' (D) CBcs CDul CWib ECrN EMOT ESps IBoy LSRN NOra SBdl SDea SKee SPer SVic WHar WMat
- 'Gravenstein' (D) CHab GTwd NOra SDea SKee
- § 'Green Balsam' (D) CHab CTri
- 'Green Harvey' (D/C) SKee
- 'Green Roland' (C/D) ECrN ERea
- 'Greenfinch' (D) LRHS
- 'Greensleeves'PBR (D) ℽH6 CAgr CDul CMac CTri CWib EBee ECrN EMOT EPfP EPom ESps GTwd GTwe MAsh MGos MMuc NLar NOra SBdl SCob SDea SEND SKee SLim SPer WHar WJas WMat WWct
- 'Greenup's Pippin' (D) CHab GTwd
- 'Grenadier' (C) ℽH6 CAgr CHab CLnd CTri ECrN EMOT EPom GTwd GTwe IBoy MGos MJak MMuc NLar NOra NWea SBdl SCob SDea SEND SKee SLon SPer WHar WJas WMat
- 'Guillevic' (Cider) CHab NWea
- 'Gwell Na Mil' (D) WGwG
- 'Halstow Natural' (Cider) CAgr
- 'Hambledon Deux Ans' (C) SDea
- 'Hangy Down' (Cider) WMat
- 'Harling Hero' (D) ECrN
- § 'Harry Master's Jersey' (Cider) CAgr CFGn CTho CTri EPom NOra SBdl SDea SKee WHar WMat WWct
- 'Harry Pring' (D) SKee
- 'Harvey' (C) SDea SKee
- 'Hawthornden' (C) CHab GTwd GTwe
- 'Hector MacDonald' (C) GTwd
- 'Hereford Cross' (D) SKee
- 'Herefordshire Beefing' (C) SKee
- 'Herefordshire Redstreak' (Cider) CAgr CArg CDul EMOT EPom LBuc NOra SBdl WHar WMat
- 'Herefordshire Russet'PBR (D) CFGn EMOT EPom ERea LBuc LPre LRHS MAsh MCoo NLar NOra SBdl SKee SPer WHar WJas WMat WWct
- 'Herring's Pippin' (C/D) CTri SDea SKee
- 'High View Pippin' (D) SKee
- 'Histon Favourite' (D) SKee
- 'Hoary Morning' (C) CTho ECrN SDea
- 'Hocking's Green' (C/D) CAgr CEnd CTho CTsd
- 'Holland Pippin' (C) SKee WHar
- 'Hollow Core' (C) CAgr
- 'Holstein' (D) NOra SBdl SDea SKee WHar
- 'Honey Pippin' (D) ECrN SKee
- § 'Honeygold' (D) CEnd
- 'Hood's Supreme' (D) GTwd
- 'Hormead Pearmain' (C) SKee
- 'Horneburger Pfannkuchen' (C) SKee
- 'Horsford Prolific' (D) ECrN
- 'Horsham Russet' (D) EWTr
- 'Houblon' (D) SKee
- 'Howgate Wonder' (C) ℽH6 Widely available
- 'Hubbard's Pearmain' (D) ECrN SKee
- 'Hunter's Majestic' (D/C) ECrN
- 'Hutton Square' (D) GTwd
- 'Idared' (D) CWib ECrN NOra SBdl SDea SKee SVic WHar WMat
- 'Improved Dove' (Cider) MRai
- 'Improved Keswick' (C/D) CEnd
- 'Improved Lambrook Pippin' (Cider) CTri
- 'Ingall's Pippin' (D) SKee
- 'Ingall's Red' (D) SKee
- 'Ingrid Marie' (D) NWea SBdl SDea SKee
- 'Irish Peach' (D) CAgr CFGn CHab CTri ECrN ERea ESps GTwe IArd MCoo NOra SDea SKee WHar WMat
- 'Isaac Newton's Tree' see *M. domestica* 'Flower of Kent'
- 'Isle of Wight Pippin' (D) SDea
- 'Isle of Wight Russet' (D) SDea
- 'Jackson's' see *M. domestica* 'Crimson King' (Cider/C)
- 'James Grieve' (D) ℽH6 Widely available
- 'Jerseymac' (D) SDea
- 'Jester' (D) ECrN SDea SKee
- 'Joaneting' (D) CAgr CHab
- 'John Broad' see *M. domestica* 'Captain Broad'
- 'John Standish' (D) CAgr CTri ERea SDea SKee
- 'John Toucher's' see *M. domestica* 'Crimson King' (Cider/C)
- 'Johnny Andrews' (Cider) CAgr
- 'Johnny Voun' (D) CEnd CTho
- 'Jonagold' (D) ℽH6 CLnd CTri CWib ECrN ELan EMOT EPom ESps GTwe IArd IBoy NLar NOra SDea SKee SPer WWct
- 'Jonagold Crowngold' see *M. domestica* 'Crowngold'
- § 'Jonagored'PBR (D) NOra SDea WHar WMat
- 'Jonathan' (D) NOra SDea SKee
- 'Jordan's Weeping' (C) SDea
- 'Josephine' (D) SDea
- 'Jubilee' see *M. domestica* 'Royal Jubilee'
- 'Julie's Late Golden' (F) CTri
- 'Jumbo' (C/D) CLnd EMOT MAsh MCoo NOra SKee WHar WJas WMat
- 'Jupiter'PBR (D) ℽH6 CAgr CSBt CTri CWib ECrN EMOT ESps EWTr GTwe LSRN MJak MRav NLar NOra SBdl SDea SKee SLon WHar WJas WMat
- 'Kapai Red Jonathan' (D) SDea
- 'Karmijn de Sonnaville' (D) MRai NOra SDea SKee
- § 'Katja' (D) Widely available
- Katy see *M. domestica* 'Katja'
- 'Kemp' SDea
- 'Kenneth' (D) WGwG
- 'Kent' (D) ℽH6 ECrN SDea SKee
- 'Kentish Quarrenden' (D) SKee
- 'Kerry Pippin' (D) IArd SKee
- 'Keswick Codlin' (C) CHab ECrN ERea GQue GTwd GTwe MCoo NEgg NLar NOra NWea SBdl SDea SKee WHar WJas WMat
- § 'Kidd's Orange Red' (D) ℽH6 CAgr CDul CMac CTri ECrN EMOT EPfP EPom ESps GTwe LBuc LRHS MWat NOra SBdl SDea SFrt SKee SLon WHar WMat WWct
- 'Kim' (C/D) GTwd
- 'King Byerd' (C/D) CEnd CTho
- 'King Charles' Pearmain' (D) SKee
- 'King Coffee' (D) WHar
- 'King Luscious' (D) SDea
- § 'King of the Pippins' (D) ℽH6 CFGn CHab CLnd CTri ECrN EPom ESps GTwd GTwe MCoo NOra SDea SKee SVic WHar

- 'King Russet' (D) ♀H6	SDea
- 'King's Acre Pippin' (D)	NOra SDea SKee WHar WMat
- 'Kingston Bitter' (Cider)	CTho
- 'Kingston Black' (Cider/C)	CAgr CArg CDul CEnd CHab CTho CTri EMOT EPom GTwd GTwe LBuc MGos NOra SBdl SDea SFrt SKee WMat
- 'Knobby Russet' (D)	SBdl SKee
- 'Lady Henniker' (C)	CDul CEnd CHab ECrN GTwd SDea SKee WHar
- 'Lady Isabel' (D)	SKee
- 'Lady Lambourne' (C/D)	CHab
- 'Lady of the Lake' (D)	GTwd
- 'Lady of the Wemyss' (C)	GTwd SKee
- 'Lady Sudeley' (D)	CEnd CHab GTwd SDea SKee
- 'Lady's Finger' (C/D)	CEnd
- 'Lady's Finger of Lancaster' (C/D)	CHab
- 'Lady's Finger of Offaly' (D)	IArd SDea
- 'Lamb Abbey Pearmain' (D)	SKee
- 'Lambourne Pippin' (F)	CTho
- 'Lamb's Seedling' (D)	GTwd
- 'Lane's Prince Albert' (C) ♀H6	CAgr CHab CLnd CSBt CTri ECrN EMOT EPfP GTwe MGos MRav MWat NOra NWea SCoo SDea SKee SVic WHar WJas WMat
- 'Langley Pippin' (D)	SDea
§ - 'Langworthy' (Cider)	SKee
- 'Lass o' Gowrie' (C)	GTwd SKee
§ - 'Laxton's Epicure' (D) ♀H6	CAgr CHab ECrN EMOT ESps SDea SKee WHar
§ - 'Laxton's Fortune' (D) ♀H6	CArg CDul CHab CMac CSBt CTri CWib ECrN ESps GTwd GTwe IArd NOra SBdl SDea SKee WHar WJas WMat WWct
- 'Laxton's Pearmain' (D)	MCoo
- 'Laxton's Royalty' (D)	SDea
§ - 'Laxton's Superb' (D)	Widely available
- 'Leicester Burton'	see *M. domestica* 'Dutch Codlin'
- 'Lemon Pippin' (C)	EBee ECrN ELan NOra SDea SKee WHar
- 'Lemon Queen' (D)	GTwd
- 'Liberty' (D)	SDea
- 'Liddel's Seedling' (C/D)	GTwd
- 'Limelight' (D) ♀	EBee EMOT ERea ESps GTwd LPre MAsh MCoo NLar NOra SBdl SCoo SKee WHar WMat
- 'Linda' (D)	SKee
- 'Link Wonder' (F)	CEnd
- 'Little Pax' (D) **new**	EPom MCoo
- 'Lobo' (D)	GTwd
- 'Lodgemore Nonpareil' (D)	SKee
- 'Lodi' (C)	SDea
- 'London Pearmain' (D)	ECrN
- 'London Pippin' (C)	CAgr SKee
- 'Longkeeper' (D)	CAgr CEnd
- 'Lord Burghley' (D)	SDea
- 'Lord Derby' (C)	CAgr CDul CHab CLnd CMac CTho CWib ECrN EMOT EPom ESps EWTr GTwe MRav NOra SBdl SDea SEND SKee SPer SVic WHar WMat WWct
- 'Lord Grosvenor' (C)	WHar
- 'Lord Hindlip' (D)	CHab NOra SDea SKee WMat WWct
- 'Lord Lambourne' (D) ♀H6	Widely available
- 'Lord of the Isles' (Cider)	CAgr
- 'Lord Rosebery' (D)	GTwd
- 'Lord Stradbroke' (C)	ECrN
- 'Lord Suffield' (C)	CTri ECrN
- 'Lough Tree of Wexford' (D)	IArd
- 'Love Beauty' (D)	GTwd
- 'Lucombe's Pine' (D)	CAgr CEnd CTho ECrN SVic
- 'Lucombe's Seedling' (D)	CTho
- 'Lynn's Pippin' (D)	ECrN SKee
- 'Mabbott's Pearmain' (D)	SDea
- 'Machen' (D)	WGwG
- 'Maclean's Favourite' (D)	ECrN
- 'Madresfield Court' (D)	SDea SKee WWct
- 'Magdalene' (D) **new**	SKee
- 'Maggie Sinclair' (D)	GTwd
- 'Major' (Cider)	CAgr GTwd MRai SFrt WMat
- 'Maldon Wonder' (D)	ECrN
- 'Malling Kent' (D)	SDea SFrt
- 'Maltster' (D)	MCoo SKee
- 'Manaccan Primrose' (C/D)	CEnd CFGn
- 'Mank's Codlin' (C)	GTwd
- 'Mannington's Pearmain' (D)	WMat
- 'Marged Nicolas' (D)	WGwG
- 'Margil' (D)	SDea SKee WHar
- 'Markham Pippin' (D)	MCoo
- 'Marriage-maker' (D)	MRai SKee
- 'Martin's Custard' (C) **new**	MRai
- 'Mary's Apple' (F) **new**	SDea
- 'Maxton' (D)	ECrN
- 'May Queen' (D)	SDea SKee WWct
- 'Maypole'PBR (D)	SDea
- 'McIntosh' (D)	NOra SKee
- 'Médaille d'Or' (Cider)	SFrt SKee WMat
- 'Melba' (D)	GTwd
- 'Melon' (D)	SDea
- 'Melrose' (D)	ECrN SKee
- 'Merchant Apple' (D)	CTri
- 'Mère de Ménage' (C)	SDea SKee WHar
- 'Meridian'PBR (D)	CAgr ECrN LSRN MCoo NOra SDea WMat
- 'Merton Beauty' (D)	SBdl SKee
- 'Merton Champion'	SBdl
- 'Merton Charm' (D)	SKee
- 'Merton Knave' (D)	SDea
- 'Merton Pearmain' (D)	SBdl
- 'Merton Prolific' (D)	SBdl
- 'Merton Russet' (D)	SBdl SCob SDea SKee
- 'Merton Worcester' (D)	ECrN SDea SKee
- 'Michaelmas Red' (D)	GTwe SKee
- 'Michelin' (Cider)	CAgr CTri GTwe LBuc MGos MRai NOra SBdl SDea SKee WHar WMat WWct
- Miel d'Or	see *M. domestica* 'Honeygold'
- 'Miller's Seedling' (D)	NOra SBdl SKee
- 'Millicent Barnes' (D)	SDea
- 'Mingan' (D) **new**	MRai
- 'Minshull Crab' (C)	SKee
- 'Mollie's Delicious' (D)	SKee
- 'Monarch' (C)	CAgr CTri ECrN EPom GTwd GTwe SDea SKee
- 'Monmouthshire Green' (D)	WGwG
- 'Montfort' (D)	ECrN
- 'Morgan's Sweet' (C/Cider)	CEnd CHab CTho CTri NOra SBdl SDea SKee WMat
- 'Moss's Seedling' (D)	SDea
§ - 'Mother' (D) ♀H6	CAgr CDul CEnd CTri ECrN GTwe MRai SDea SKee

§	- 'Mutsu' (C/D)	CLnd CTri ECrN EMOT MRav NOra SDea SKee SPer WMat
	- 'Mylor Pike' (D)	CEnd
	- 'Nancy Jackson' (C)	CHab GTwd
	- 'Nanny' (D)	SKee
	- 'Nant Gwrtheyrn' (D)	WGwG
	- 'Nettlestone Pippin' (D)	SDea
	- 'New Bess Pool' (D) **new**	GTwd
	- 'Newton Wonder' (C)	CAgr CDul CHab CSBt CTho CTri CWib ECrN EMOT EPom ERea ESps EWTr GTwe MCoo MGos NOra SBdl SDea SFrt SKee WHar WJas WMat WWct
	- 'Newtown Pippin' (D)	SDea
	- 'Nine Square' (D)	CTho
	- 'Nittany Red' (D)	SDea
	- 'Nolan Pippin' (D)	ECrN SBdl
	- 'Nonpareil' (D)	WHar
	- 'Norfolk Beauty' (C)	ECrN ERea
	- 'Norfolk Beefing' (C)	CHab ECrN ERea EWTr NOra SDea SKee WMat
	- 'Norfolk Royal' (D)	ECrN ERea GTwe NOra SDea SKee
	- 'Norfolk Royal Russet' (D)	ECrN ERea GTwd NOra SBdl SFrt SKee WMat
	- 'Norfolk Summer Broadend' (C)	ECrN
	- 'Norfolk Winter Coleman' (C)	ERea SKee
	- 'Northern Greening' (C)	WHar
§	- 'Northwood' (Cider)	CTho WMat
	- 'Nottingham Pippin' (D)	SBdl
	- 'Nutmeg Pippin' (D)	ECrN SDea
	- Nuvar Cheerfull Gold (D)	SKee
	- Nuvar Freckles (D)	SKee
	- Nuvar Golden Elf (D)	SKee
	- Nuvar Golden Hills (D)	SKee
	- 'Oaken Pin' (D)	CEnd CTho
§	- 'Obelisk'PBR (D)	EMOT MAsh NOra SDea SKee WMat
	- 'Old Pearmain' (D)	SDea WHar
	- 'Old Somerset Russet' (D)	CTho
	- 'Onibury Pippin' (D)	WHar
	- 'Opalescent' (D)	CEnd
	- 'Orin' (D)	SKee
	- 'Orleans Reinette' (D)	CAgr CLnd CSut CTri CWib ECrN EMOT EPom ESps EWTr GTwe LBuc MWat NOra SDea SFrt SKee WHar WJas WMat WWct
	- 'Oslin' (D)	GTwd GTwe SKee WMat
	- 'Otava'PBR (C/D)	SKee
	- 'Owen Thomas' (D)	SKee
	- 'Oxford Conquest' (D)	SKee
	- 'Paignton Marigold' (Cider)	CTho
	- 'Palmer's Rosey' (D)	SKee
	- 'Payhembury' (C/Cider)	CAgr CTri
	- 'Peacemaker' (D)	SKee
	- 'Pear Apple' (D)	CAgr CEnd CFGn CTho MRai
	- 'Pearl' (D)	NOra SDea WMat
	- 'Peasgood's Nonsuch' (C) 🏆H6	CAgr CHab CLnd ECrN EPom ERea GTwd GTwe IArd LSRN MAsh NOra SBdl SDea SFrt SKee SLon WMat
	- 'Pendragon' (D)	CEnd CTho
	- 'Peter Lock' (C/D)	CAgr CEnd CTho SKee
	- 'Peter's Pippin' (D)	SDea
	- 'Peter's Seedling' (D)	SDea
	- 'Pethyre' (Cider)	CCVT
	- 'Pig Aderyn' (C)	CHab WGwG
	- 'Pig y Colomen' (C)	WGwG
	- 'Pig's Nose Pippin' (D)	CEnd CTsd SKee
	- 'Pig's Nose Pippin' Type III (D)	CAgr
	- 'Pig's Snout' (Cider/C/D)	CEnd MRai
	- 'Pine Apple Russet of Devon' (D)	CEnd
	- 'Pine Golden Pippin' (D)	GTwd
	- 'Pineapple Russet' (C/D)	CAgr ERea MAsh
	- 'Pinova'PBR (D)	CAgr EPom WHar
	- 'Pitmaston Pine Apple' (D)	CArg CHab CTho CTri ECrN EMOT ERea ESps GTwd MCoo MWat NOra SBdl SCob SDea SFrt SKee SLon WHar WMat WWct
	- 'Pitmaston Russet Nonpareil' (D)	SKee
	- 'Pixie' (D) 🏆H6	CSBt CWib EMOT EPom GTwe MWat NOra SCob SDea SKee SLon WHar WWct
	- 'Plum Vite' (D)	CAgr CTri
	- 'Plymouth Cross' (D)	GTwd
	- 'Plympton Pippin' (C)	CEnd CTho CTri
	- Polka = 'Trajan'PBR (D)	NOra SDea SKee
	- 'Polly' (C/D)	MRai
	- 'Polly Prosser' (D)	SKee
	- 'Polly Whitehair' (C/D)	SDea
	- 'Pomeroy of Somerset' (D)	CHab CTho CTri SKee
	- 'Ponsford' (C)	CAgr CTho WMat
	- 'Port Allen Russet' (C/D)	GTwd
	- 'Port Wine'	see *M. domestica* 'Harry Master's Jersey'
	- 'Porter's Perfection' (Cider)	NOra
	- 'Pott's Seedling' (C)	SKee
	- 'Prince Charles' (D)	MRai SBdl
	- 'Princesse' (F)	CLnd ECrN SDea SKee
	- 'Profit' (F)	CTho
	- 'Pumpkin Sunset'	SBdl
	- 'Quarry Apple' (C)	CTho
	- 'Queen' (C)	CAgr ECrN SKee WHar
	- 'Queen Cox' (D)	CLnd CSut CTri CWib ECrN EPom ERea LSRN NOra SDea SKee SLon SWvt WHar WMat WTSh
	- 'Queens' (D)	CEnd
	- 'Rajka'PBR (D)	GQue NOra SKee WWct
	- 'Red Alkmene'	see *M. domestica* 'Red Windsor'
	- 'Red Belle de Boskoop' (D)	CAgr
	- 'Red Bramley' (C)	CDul CWib ECrN
	- 'Red Charles Ross' (C/D)	SDea
	- 'Red Delicious'	see *M. domestica* 'Starking'
	- 'Red Devil' (D)	CAgr CLnd CMac CTri ECrN EMOT EPom ESps GTwd GTwe LRHS MAsh MRav MWat NLar NOra NPri SBdl SCob SCoo SDea SEWo SKee SLim SLon WHar WJas WMat WWct
	- 'Red Ellison' (D)	CTri ECrN ERea GTwe SDea
	- 'Red Falstaff'PBR (D) 🏆H6	CAgr CCVT CDul CMac CTri EBee ECrN EMOT EPfP ERea ESps GKin LBuc LRHS LSRN MAsh MCoo NLar NOra NPri SBdl SFrt SKee SLim SLon SPer SPoG WHar WMat WWct
	- 'Red Fuji' (D)	SDea
	- 'Red James Grieve' (D)	LSRN SDea
	- 'Red Joaneting' (D)	SKee WHar
	- 'Red Jonagold'	see *M. domestica* 'Jonagored'
	- 'Red Jonathan' (D)	SDea
	- 'Red Miller's seedling' (D)	ECrN SDea
	- 'Red Pixie' (D)	GQue LRHS MCoo WMat
	- 'Red Rattler' (D)	CTri
	- 'Red Sauce' (C)	SKee
	- 'Red Victoria' (C)	GTwe

§	- 'Red Windsor' (D)	CArg CDul CLnd CMac EBee EMOT EPom ERea ESps LBuc LPre LRHS NLar NOra SBdl SCoo SKee SLim SPoG WHar WJas WMat
	- 'Redcoat Grieve' (D)	SDea
	- 'Redsleeves' (D)	CAgr CLnd ECrN EMOT GTwd GTwe NOra SDea SKee
	- 'Reine de Pommes' (Cider)	MRai
	- 'Reine des Reinettes'	see *M. domestica* 'King of the Pippins'
	- 'Reinette Descardre' (D)	SVic
	- 'Reinette Rouge Etoilée' (D)	SDea
	- 'Resi'^{PBR} (C/D)	WWct
	- 'Reverend Greeves' (C)	SDea
	- 'Reverend McCormick' (D)	CTho
	- 'Reverend W. Wilks' (C)	CAgr CHab CSBt CTri ECrN EMOT EPom ESps EWTr GTwd MAsh NOra SBdl SDea SFrt SKee WHar WJas WMat WWct
	- 'Ribston Pippin' (D) 🏆^{H6}	CDul CTho CTri CWib ECrN EMOT ERea ESps GTwd GTwe LBuc MCoo MRav MWat NOra NPri NWea SBdl SDea SFrt SKee SLon WHar WJas WMat WWct
	- 'Rival' (D)	CAgr SDea SKee
	- 'Rivers' Nonsuch' (D)	CHab
	- 'Rock' (C)	GTwd
	- 'Rome Beauty' (D)	SDea
	- 'Rosemary Russet' (D) 🏆^{H6}	CAgr CHab CTho EBee ERea ESps GTwd MCoo NOra SBdl SDea SFrt SKee SLon WHar WMat WWct
	- 'Rosette' (D)	EPom LBuc LPre LRHS MAsh NLar NOra WMat
	- 'Ross Nonpareil' (D)	CAgr IArd NOra SDea WHar WMat
	- 'Rosy Blenheim' (D)	ECrN SKee
	- 'Rough Pippin' (D)	CEnd
	- 'Roundway Magnum Bonum' (C/D)	CAgr CTho SDea
§	- 'Roxbury Russet' (D)	SKee
	- 'Royal Gala' (D)	CMac ECrN EMOT EPom LBuc MRav SBdl SCob SDea SLon
§	- 'Royal Jubilee' (C)	SKee
	- 'Royal Russet' (C)	CAgr CEnd CTri ECrN SDea
	- 'Royal Somerset' (C/Cider)	CTho CTri WMat
	- Rubinette = 'Rafzubin' (D)	ECrN NOra SDea SKee
	- Rubinette Rosso = 'Rafzubex'^{PBR} (D)	NOra WMat
	- 'Rubinola'^{PBR} (D)	SKee WWct
	- 'Ruby' Thorrington (D)	ECrN
	- 'Saint Cecilia' (D)	CHab SDea WGwG
§	- 'Saint Edmund's Pippin' (D) 🏆^{H6}	CHab CTho ECrN ELan EPfP ERea GTwd GTwe MCoo NOra SDea SFrt SKee
	- 'Saint Edmund's Russet'	see *M. domestica* 'Saint Edmund's Pippin'
	- 'Saltcote Pippin' (D)	SKee WMat
	- 'Sam Young' (D)	CAgr
	- 'Samba' (C/D)	LCro LOPS
	- 'Sandew' (C/D) **new**	SKee
	- 'Sandlands' (D)	SDea
	- 'Sandlin Duchess' (D)	NOra WMat
	- 'Sandringham' (C)	ECrN SKee
	- 'Sanspareil' (D)	CAgr
	- 'Santana'^{PBR} (D)	NOra WMat
	- 'Saturn' (D)	CAgr CCVT CTri ERea ESps MRai NOra SBdl SDea SKee WHar WMat WWct
	- 'Saw Pits' (D)	CAgr CEnd MRai
	- 'Scarlet Crofton' (D)	IArd SKee
	- 'Scarlet Nonpareil' (D)	SDea SKee
	- 'Scarlet Pearmain' (D)	GTwd
	- 'Scarlet Pimpernel' (D)	SKee
	- 'Scotch Bridget' (C)	CArg CHab GQue GTwd NBid NOra SCoo SKee WHar WMat WWct
	- 'Scotch Dumpling' (C)	GBin GKin GQue GTwd GTwe MCoo NOra WHar WMat
	- 'Scotia' (C/D)	GTwd
	- 'Scrumptious'^{PBR} (D) 🏆^{H6}	Widely available
	- 'Seaton House' (C)	GTwd
	- 'Sharleston Pippin' (D)	SBdl SKee
	- 'Sheep's Nose' (C)	CHab IArd SBdl SDea SKee
	- 'Shenandoah' (C)	SKee
	- 'Sidney Strake' (C)	CAgr CEnd
	- 'Sir Isaac Newton's'	see *M. domestica* 'Flower of Kent'
	- 'Sir John Thornycroft' (D)	SDea
	- 'Sisson's Worksop Newtown' (D)	MCoo SKee
	- 'Slack Ma Girdle' (Cider)	NOra SKee WMat
	- 'Smart's Prince Arthur' (C)	CHab SDea SKee
	- 'Smoothie' (C/D)	SBdl
	- 'Snell's Glass Apple'	see *M. domestica* 'Glass Apple'
	- 'Somerset Lasting' (C)	CTri
	- 'Somerset Redstreak' (Cider)	CAgr CHab CTri GTwe NOra SBdl WHar WMat
	- 'Sops in Wine' (Cider/D)	CTho CTsd ECrN NOra SKee SVic WMat
	- 'Sour Bay' (Cider)	CAgr
	- 'Sour Natural'	see *M. domestica* 'Langworthy'
	- 'Sowman's Seedling' (C)	GTwd
	- 'Spartan' (D)	Widely available
	- 'Spencer' (D)	CTri ECrN GTwd
	- 'Spotted Dick' (Cider)	CTho
	- 'Stamford Pippin' (D)	SDea
	- 'Stanway Seedling' (C)	ECrN
	- 'Star of Devon' (D)	CEnd SDea SKee
	- 'Stark' (D)	SDea
§	- 'Starking' (D)	ECrN NOra SKee
	- 'Stark's Earliest' (D)	SVic
	- 'Steyne Seedling' (D)	SDea
	- 'Stibbert' (D) **new**	SKee
	- 'Stirling Castle' (C)	CAgr GQue GTwd NOra SKee WMat
	- 'Stobo Castle' (C)	GTwd SKee
	- 'Stoke Edith Pippin' (D)	SBdl WHar
	- 'Stoke Red' (Cider)	NOra SFrt SKee WMat
	- 'Striped Beefing' (C)	ECrN ERea SKee
	- 'Sturmer Pippin' (D)	CSBt CTri ECrN GTwe MWat NOra SBdl SDea SKee WHar WWct
	- 'Summerred' (D)	ECrN SDea
	- 'Sunburn' (D)	ECrN
	- 'Sunnydale' (D/C)	SDea
	- 'Sunrise'^{PBR} (D)	EMOT ESps NOra SCob SKee WHar
	- 'Sunset' (D) 🏆^{H6}	Widely available
	- 'Suntan' (D)	CWib ECrN ESps EWTr MWat NOra SDea SKee
	- 'Superb'	see *M. domestica* 'Laxton's Superb'
	- 'Sussex Mother' (C/D)	CHab
	- 'Sweet Alford' (Cider)	CTho SBdl WMat WWct
	- 'Sweet Bay' (Cider)	CAgr
	- 'Sweet Caroline' (D)	SDea
	- 'Sweet Cleave' (Cider)	CTho
	- 'Sweet Coppin' (Cider)	CTri MRai WMat
	- 'Sweet Lilibet'	see *M. domestica* 'Red Windsor'
	- 'Sweet Pethyre' (C) **new**	EMOT
	- 'Sweet Sixteen' (D) **new**	MRai
	- 'Sweet Society' (D)	EMOT LRHS MAsh NOra SKee WHar WJas WMat

	- 'Sweetings' **new**	MRai
	- 'Sylvia' (D)	GTwd MRai
	- 'Tamar Beauty' (D)	CEnd
	- 'Tan Harvey' (Cider)	CEnd
	- 'Taunton Cross' (D)	CAgr WMat
	- 'Taylor's' (Cider)	CAgr SDea
	- 'Ten Commandments' (Cider/D)	SBdl SDea WWct
	- Tentation = 'Delblush'^{PBR} (D)	SDea
	- 'The Rattler' (Cider)	CEnd
	- 'Thomas Jeffrey' (D)	GTwd
	- 'Thomas Rivers' (C)	SDea
	- 'Thorle Pippin' (D)	GTwd SKee
	- 'Thorpe's Peach' (D) **new**	SKee
	- 'Thurso' (D)	GTwd
	- Tickled Pink = 'Baya Marisa' (C/D)	EPom ERea LRHS NLar NOra SPer SPoG WMat
	- 'Tidicombe Seedling' (D)	CTho WMat
	- 'Tom Putt' (C)	CAgr CArg CCVT CDul CHab CTho CTri CWib ECrN ESps GTwe LBuc NOra SBdl SDea SKee WHar WJas WMat WWct
	- 'Tommy Knight' (D)	CAgr CEnd
	- 'Topaz'^{PBR} (D)	SKee
	- 'Totnes Apple' (D)	CTho
	- 'Tower of Glamis' (C)	CHab GQue GTwd GTwe SKee
	- 'Tregonna King' (C/D)	CTho CTsd
	- 'Tremlett's Bitter' (Cider)	CAgr CHab CTho MRai NOra SBdl SDea SVic WMat
	- 'Trwyn Mochyn' (C)	WGwG
§	- 'Tuscan'^{PBR} (D)	EMOT SDea SKee
§	- 'Tydeman's Early Worcester' (D)	CAgr CDul CHab CLnd CWib ECrN GTwe SBdl SDea SKee WWct
	- 'Tydeman's Late Orange' (D)	CHab CTri ECrN ESps EWTr GTwe MCoo NOra NWea SBdl SDea SFrt SKee WHar WMat
	- 'Upton Pyne' (C/D)	CTho SDea
	- 'Veitch's Perfection' (C/D)	CTho WMat
	- 'Venus Pippin' (C/D)	CEnd
	- 'Vicar of Beighton' (D)	ECrN
	- 'Vicary's Late Keeper' (C)	CTho
	- 'Vickey's Delight' (D)	NWea SDea
	- 'Vista-bella' (D)	ECrN EMOT SDea SKee
	- 'Wagener' (D)	ECrN SDea
	- Waltz = 'Telamon'^{PBR} (D)	EMOT SDea
	- 'Warden' (D)	GTwd
	- 'Warner's King' (C) 🏆H6	CTri GTwd NOra SBdl SDea SKee WHar
	- 'Warrior' (F)	CTho
	- 'Wealthy' (D)	SDea
	- 'Weight' (C)	GTwd
	- 'Wellington' (C)	see *M. domestica* 'Dummellor's Seedling'
	- 'Wellington' (Cider)	CAgr
	- 'Welsh Russet' (D)	SDea
	- 'Werrington Wonder' (F)	CEnd
	- 'West View Seedling' (D)	ECrN
	- 'White Melrose' (C)	GQue GTwd GTwe NOra SDea SKee WMat
	- 'White Transparent' (C/D)	SDea SKee
	- 'Whitpot Sweet' (Cider)	CEnd
	- 'William Crump' (D)	CDul CHab CTho ECrN NOra SDea WHar WMat WWct
	- 'Willoughby' (D)	MCoo
	- 'Winston' (D) 🏆H6	CAgr CCVT CLnd CMac CTri ECrN ESps MCoo NWea SDea SKee SVic WHar WWct
	- 'Winter Banana' (D)	CHab ECrN GQue LEdu NOra SDea SVic WHar WMat

	- 'Winter Gem' (D)	CAgr CArg CCVT CDul CLnd ECrN EPom ERea ESps LBuc NOra SBdl SCob SDea SKee WHar WJas WMat
	- 'Winter Peach' (D/C)	CAgr ECrN
	- 'Winter Pearmain' (D)	WHar
	- 'Winter Quarrenden' (D)	SDea
	- 'Winter Queening' (D/C)	SDea
	- 'Winter Red' (F)	CEnd
	- 'Woodbine'	see *M. domestica* 'Northwood'
	- 'Woodford' (C)	ECrN
	- 'Woolbrook Pippin' (D)	CAgr CEnd CTho WMat
	- 'Woolbrook Russet' (C)	CEnd ECrN
	- 'Worcester Pearmain' (D) 🏆H6	Widely available
	- 'Wormsley Pippin' (D)	ECrN
	- 'Wyatt's Seedling'	see *M. domestica* 'Langworthy'
	- 'Wyken Pippin' (D)	ECrN SDea SKee WWct
	- 'Yarlington Mill' (Cider)	CAgr CHab CTri MRai NOra SBdl SDea SFrt SKee SVic WMat WWct
	- 'Yellow Ingestrie' (D)	CHab ERea GTwd MCoo NOra WHar WMat WWct
	- 'Yorkshire Greening' (C)	CHab GTwd NOra SBdl WHar
	- 'Zabergäu Renette' (D)	NOra
	'Donald Wyman'	CLnd EPfP MAsh NLar NOra SCoo WMat
§	'Echtermeyer'	CTri SDea
	'Evelyn'	CLnd WMat
§	'Evereste' 🏆H6	Widely available
	florentina	CTho EPfP
	- 'Rosemoor'	CLnd EBee
	- 'Skopje'	EPfP
	floribunda 🏆H6	Widely available
	fusca	CLnd
	'Gardener's Gold'	CEnd CTho
	× ***gloriosa*** 'Oekonomierat Echtermeyer'	see *M.* 'Echtermeyer'
	'Golden Gem'	CLnd EMOT EPfP GQue MAsh NOra NOrn SEWo SKee WMat
	'Golden Hornet'	see *M.* × *zumi* 'Golden Hornet'
	'Gorgeous'	Widely available
	'Harry Baker'	CCVT CDul CEnd CLnd CMac ECrN EMil EPfP EPom ERea LRHS LSRN MAsh MBlu MRav NOra SCoo SLim SPer SPoG WHar WJas WMat WMou WWct
	× ***hartwigii***	CLnd
	'Hillieri'	see *M.* × *scheideckeri* 'Hillieri'
	'Honeycrisp'^{PBR}	CFGn NOra WHar WMat
	'Hornsea Herring' (D/C)	LEdu
	hupehensis 🏆H6	CDul CEnd CLnd CMCN CSBt CTho CTri EBee EPfP ESps EWTr IMou LHop MBlu MGos MRav NLar NOra NWea SDix SPer WMat WMou WTSh
	'Hyde Hall Spire'	SCoo
	'Indian Magic'	CLnd EBee ESps LRHS MAsh NLar NOra WMat
	'Indian Summer'	CLnd
	Jelly King = 'Mattfru' 🏆H6	CLnd EBee ECrN EMOT EPfP EPom LBuc LRHS LSRN MAsh NLar NOra NWea SPer SPoG WHCr WHar WMat WMou
	'John Downie' (C)	Widely available
	'Kaido'	see *M.* × *micromalus*
	kansuensis	CLnd
	'Lady Northcliffe'	CDul CLnd
	'Laura' 🏆H6	CDul CFGn CLnd CMac EMOT EPfP EPom ERea LRHS LSRN MAsh NLar NOra SCoo SKee SLim SLon SPer SPoG WHar WJas WMat
	'Lisa'	CLnd

'Louisa'	CLnd EBee EPfP NOra NWea SCoo SGol SLim WMat
× ***magdeburgensis***	CCVT CDul CLnd CSBt
'Mariri Red' (D)	WMat
'Mary Potter'	CLnd
§ × ***micromalus***	CLnd NLar
× ***moerlandsii***	CLnd
- 'Liset'	CDul CEnd CLnd CSBt CWib EBee ECrN EMOT ESps LHop MRav NEgg NOra SCoo WFar
§ - 'Profusion'	CBcs CDul CTri EBee ECrN ELan EMOT ESps EWTr LCro LOPS LRHS MGos MJak MRav MSwo NOra NPri NWea SCob SEND SGol SPer SWvt WJas
'Mokum'	CLnd
'Molten Lava'	CLnd MAsh
'Montreal Beauty'	CLnd WJas
niedzwetzkyana	CLnd CTho
Nuvar Carnival	SKee
Nuvar Marble	EBee NOra NOrn SKee WMat
Perpetu	see *M.* 'Evereste'
'Pink Mushroom'	EMOT
'Pink Perfection'	CEnd ECrN NOra NPri NWea WHar WMat
'Pond Red'	CLnd
'Prairifire'	CDul CLnd EMOT LRHS MAsh NOra NPri SCoo SLim SLon SPoG WMat WMou
prattii	CLnd CTho EBee EPfP GLog
- 'Pourpre Noir'	CLnd
'Princeton Cardinal' ♀^{H6}	CLnd CMac EPfP MAsh SCoo SLim WHar
'Professor Sprenger'	see *M.* × *zumi* 'Professor Sprenger'
'Profusion'	see *M.* × *moerlandsii* 'Profusion'
prunifolia	MBlu
- var. ***rinkii***	CLnd
§ × ***purpurea*** 'Aldenhamensis'	CLnd SDea WHar
- 'Eleyi'	CLnd CNWT EPfP NWea
- 'Lemoinei'	CDul
- 'Neville Copeman'	CCVT CDul EMOT EPom EWTr WJas
- 'Pendula'	see *M.* 'Echtermeyer'
'R.J. Fulcher'	CLnd CTho
'Ralph Shay'	CLnd
'Red Ace'	CDul
'Red Barron'	CLnd
'Red Glow'	CDul ECrN MAsh WJas
'Red Jade'	see *M.* × *scheideckeri* 'Red Jade'
§ 'Red Jonaprince'^{PBR}	WMat
Red Obelisk = 'Dvp Obel'	CLnd LBuc LRHS NOra SCoo SPoG WMat
'Red Peacock'	CLnd
'Red Prince'	see *M.* 'Red Jonaprince'
'Robinson'	CLnd
§ × ***robusta***	CLnd EMOT ESps GTwe LSRN NWea SLon
- 'Dolgo'	CLnd CSBt EMOT EPom ERea LCro MBlu NOra SCoo SKee WHar WMat WMou
- 'Red Sentinel' ♀^{H6}	Widely available
- 'Red Siberian'	SDea SPer
- 'Yellow Siberian'	CLnd
'Rosehip'	CFGn CLnd EBee EMOT LBuc LCro NLar NOra NOrn WMat
'Royal Beauty'	CDul CLnd CWib EMOT EPfP ESps LRHS MAsh MGos MJak MSwo NOra NOrn NPri SCoo SLon SPer WHar WMat WMou
'Royalty'	Widely available
'Rudolph'	CCVT CDul CLnd CNWT EBar EBee ECrN EMOT ESps GKin LBuc LHop LSRN MAsh MGos MMuc NOra NOrn NPri SCoo SEWo SLim SPer SPoG WJas WMat
'Ruth Ann'	CLnd
sargentii	CDul CLnd CTho EWTr NOra NWea
- 'Candy Mint'	WMat
- 'Tina'	CLnd LRHS MAsh NOra WMat
'Satin Cloud'	CLnd
§ × ***scheideckeri*** 'Hillieri'	CDul CLnd MBlu
§ - 'Red Jade'	CDul CLnd CMac CTri CWib EBee ECrN ELan EMOT ESps EWTr MGos MJak MMuc MRav MSwo NOrn NWea SPer WHar WJas
Siberian crab	see *M.* × *robusta*
sieboldii	see *M. toringo*
sieversii	CDul
sikkimensis B&SWJ 2431	WCru
'Silver Drift'	CLnd
'Simon'	WMat
'Snowcloud'	CDul CLnd ECrN EMOT ESps MAsh NOrn SLim
'Snowdrift'	CLnd
'Street Parade'	CLnd
× ***sublobata***	CLnd
Sugar Tyme = 'Sutyzam'	CLnd
'Sun Rival' ♀^{H6}	CCVT CDul CEnd CLnd CMac CSBt EMOT EPfP ESps LRHS MAsh MBlu MRav NOra NOrn SCoo SEWo SLim SPoG WHar WJas WMat
sylvestris	CAco CArg CCVT CDul CHab CLnd CPer ECrN EPfP LBuc MJak MMuc MRav NBes NWea SEND SEWo SPer SPre WHar WHed WMou WTSh
- 'Red Jewell' **new**	LRHS
'Tinsley Quince' (D)	WMat
§ ***toringo***	CTho ECrN EPfP LEdu NOra WSHC
I - var. ***arborescens***	CLnd CTho
- 'Browers'	CNWT
- 'Scarlett' ♀^{H6}	CDul CLnd EMOT EPfP IArd LRHS LSRN NLar NOra NWea SCoo SEWo SLim SPoG WHar WMat WMou
- 'Wintergold'	EWTr MMuc
- 'Wooster'	CLnd
toringoides	see *M. bhutanica*
transitoria ♀^{H6}	CDul CEnd CLnd CMac CTho EBee ECrN ELan EMOT EPfP ESps EWTr GKin LRHS MAsh MBlu MRav NLar NOra NWea SCoo SLau SPer WMat WMou WPGP
- 'Thornhayes Tansy'	CDul CTho EBee NOra SLim SPoG WMat
trilobata	CDul CTho EBee ELan EPfP ESps GKin LHop MBlu MGos MMuc SCoo SEND
- 'Guardsman'	EMOT EPfP MBlu NPri WMat WMou
tschonoskii	CDul CLnd CMCN CMac CTri CWib ELan EMOT ESps EWTr GTwe LRHS MBlu MGos MJak MMuc NOrn NWea SEND SPer SWvt WJas WMou WTSh
'Van Eseltine'	CAgr CMac CSBt CWib EBee ECrN EMOT EPfP MAsh MMuc SPer WHar WJas
'Veitch's Scarlet'	CDul CHab CSBt LEdu
Velvet Pillar = 'Velvetcole'	SPer SPoG
Weeping Candied Apple = 'Weepcanzam'	CLnd

'White Angel'	CLnd EWTr
'White Star'	CCVT CDul CLnd CSBt EBee ECrN EMOT NOra SEWo SLon WHar WMat
'Winter Gold'	CDul SGol
'Wisley Crab'	CLnd EMOT ESps SDea SLon WMou
yunnanensis	EPfP
- var. ***veitchii***	CTho
× ***zumi*** new	GLog
- var. ***calocarpa***	CLnd
§ - 'Golden Hornet'	Widely available
§ - 'Professor Sprenger'	CLnd CSam EPfP NOra SCoo

Malva (*Malvaceae*)

alcea	CAgr
- var. ***fastigiata***	CMac EPPr LRHS NBro SMad SPer SRms WOut
bicolor	see *Lavatera maritima*
'Gibbortello'	NCou
moschata	CAgr CBcs CBod CFGn EAJP EBee ECha ELan ENfk EPfP ESps GAbr GPoy MHer MMuc MNHC NLar NMir NWad SIde SPer SPlb SRms SWat WHar WHer WJek WMoo WOut
§ - f. ***alba*** ♀^{H5}	Widely available
- 'Appleblossom'	ELon EWTr
- 'Romney Marsh'	see *Althaea officinalis* 'Romney Marsh'
- 'Rosea'	EPfP GMaP GMcL LRHS NPer NRHS SPoG SWvt WHar
- 'Snow White'	see *M. moschata* f. *alba*
pusilla	CCCN
sylvestris	CArn CBod SRms SWat WJek WMoo
- 'Blue Fountain'^{PBR}	SAko
- 'Brave Heart'	SPav SWvt
- Marina = 'Dema'^{PBR}	NLar SAko
- var. ***mauritiana***	LCro MArt MSpe NPer SMad WMoo
- - 'Bibor Felho'	CSpe EBee
- - 'Mystic Merlin'	SPav
- - 'Primley Blue'	ECtt ELan EPfP GMaP ILea LRHS MRav NPer
- - 'Zebrina'	EPfP IFro MSpe NGBl NPer SAko SMad SWvt WMoo
- 'Perry's Blue'	NPer
- 'Windsor Castle'	MPie

Malvastrum (*Malvaceae*)

× ***hypomadarum***	see *Anisodontea* × *hypomadara* (Sprague) D.M. Bates

Malvaviscus (*Malvaceae*)

arboreus	CHll

mandarin see *Citrus reticulata* Mandarin Group

mandarin, Cleopatra see *Citrus reticulata*

Mandevilla ✿ (*Apocynaceae*)

§ × ***amabilis***	CCCN
- 'Alice du Pont' ♀^{H1c}	CBcs CCCN CMan ELan EShb SPre
- 'Passion Pink' (Parfait Series) (d)	IDee
× ***amoena***	see *M.* × *amabilis*
'Audrey'^{PBR} (Vogue Series)	CWGN LSou
boliviensis ♀^{H1c}	CCCN CMan CRHN
'Ginger' (Vogue Series)	CAbb CWGN LHop LSou
§ ***laxa*** ♀^{H1c}	CBot CCCN CHGN CHll CMan CRHN CSam CSpe ELan SBrt SVen WSHC
(Rio Series) Rio Deep Red = 'Fisrix Dered'^{PBR}	CCCN
- Rio Pink = 'Fisrix Pinka'^{PBR}	CCCN
- Rio White = 'Fisrix Whit'^{PBR}	CMan
'Ruby' (Vogue Series)	CAbb CWGN LSou
sanderi	CCCN EShb SPre
- 'Pink of Hint'	CMan
- 'Rosea'	CCCN
- (Sundaville Series) Sundaville Pretty Red = 'Sunmanderemi'^{PBR}	CMan
- - Sundaville Red Star = 'Sunparasuji'^{PBR}	CMan
splendens ♀^{H1c}	CBcs CCCN CHll CMan
suaveolens	see *M. laxa*
Sundaville Series	CCCN
- Sundaville Cosmos Crimson King = 'Sunmandecrikin'^{PBR}	CMan
- Sundaville Cosmos Pink = 'Sunmandecos'^{PBR}	CMan
- Sundaville Cosmos White = 'Sunmandeho'^{PBR}	CMan
- Sundaville Cream Pink = 'Sunparapibra'^{PBR}	CMan
- Sundaville Dark Red = 'Sunparabeni'^{PBR}	CMan EBee
- Sundaville Pretty Rose = 'Sunparaprero'^{PBR}	CMan
- Sundaville Red = 'Sunmandecrim'^{PBR}	CMan

Mandragora (*Solanaceae*)

autumnalis	GEdr WSFF
§ ***officinarum***	GCal GEdr GPoy

Manettia (*Rubiaceae*)

inflata	see *M. luteorubra*
§ ***luteorubra***	CCCN

Manfreda see *Agave*

maculosa	see *Agave maculosa*
sileri	see *Agave sileri*
undulata	see *Agave undulata*
variegata	see *Agave variegata*
virginica	see *Agave virginica*

× *Mangave* see *Agave*

Mangifera (*Anacardiaceae*)

indica (F)	CCCN SPre

Manglietia see *Magnolia*

yunnanensis	see *Magnolia insignis*

mango see *Mangifera indica*

Manihot (*Euphorbiaceae*)

carthaginensis	SPlb

Mantisalca (*Asteraceae*)

salmantica	WCot

Mantisia (*Zingiberaceae*)

saltatoria PAB 4208	LEdu WPGP

Maranta (*Marantaceae*)

leuconeura var. ***erythroneura*** ♀^{H1b}	XBlo
- var. ***kerchoveana*** ♀^{H1b}	XBlo

Marchantia (*Marchantiaceae*)

	polymorpha	CArn

Margyricarpus (*Rosaceae*)

§	***pinnatus***	EWld SIgm
	setosus	see *M. pinnatus*

Mariscus see *Cyperus*

marjoram, pot see *Origanum onites*

marjoram, sweet see *Origanum majorana*

marjoram, wild, or oregano see *Origanum vulgare*

Marrubium (*Lamiaceae*)

§	***bourgaei*** var. ***bourgaei*** 'All Hallows Green'	ECha ECtt LRHS MRav NEgg
	candidissimum	see *M. incanum*
*	***cylleneum*** 'Velvetissimum'	WCot XSen
§	***incanum***	SEND WCot XSen
	lutescens	XSen
	supinum	SEND WHea
	vulgare	CArn CBod ENfk GPoy MHer MNHC SIde SRms WJek

Marsdenia (*Apocynaceae*)

	formosana CWJ 12354	WCru
	oreophila	CRHN GCal LRHS SKHP WPGP WSHC

Marshallia (*Asteraceae*)

	grandiflora	EBee
	trinerva	ELon

Marsilea (*Marsileaceae*)

	mutica	EWay
	quadrifolia	EWay
	- variegated (v)	LLWG
*	***schelpiana***	XBlo

Masdevallia ✿ (*Orchidaceae*)

	coccinea new	NLos

Massonia (*Asparagaceae*)

	depressa ♀H2	CTal NRog SChF
	echinata	LSou NRog SChF WCot
	pustulata ♀H2	EUJe NRog SChF WCot

Mathiasella (*Apiaceae*)

	bupleuroides	CFis LSou
	- 'Green Dream'	CAbP CAby CAvo CBcs CBod CBre CSpe EBee ECtt ELan EWld EWoo GBin ILea LCro LRHS MAvo MBel MHol MNrw NPnk NSti SCob SDix SPoG WCot

Matricaria (*Asteraceae*)

	chamomilla	see *M. recutita*
	maritima	see *Tripleurospermum maritimum*
	parthenium	see *Tanacetum parthenium*
§	***recutita***	ESps GPoy MNHC
	tchihatchewii	XLum XSen
	'White Star'	EPfP

Matteuccia ✿ (*Onocleaceae*)

	orientalis ♀H5	CBod CDTJ CKel CLAP CLet CTal CWCL ECha EFer ERod GCal GMaP LEdu LRHS MMuc NBid NLar SEND WMoo WPnP XLum
	pensylvanica	CLAP
	struthiopteris ♀H4	Widely available
	- 'Jumbo'	CCCN CLAP GBin ISha LRHS
	- 'The King'	WCot

Matthiola (*Brassicaceae*)

	fruticulosa 'Alba'	CAby EPfP WPGP
	- subsp. ***perennis***	NSti WHal
	incana	CBod LRHS MArl SVic WKif
	- ***alba***	CHid CWld EBee ECha ELan LRHS LSou MAvo MPie NCGa NCou NPnk SEND SPad SPav WCot WRHF
	- purple-flowered	CSpe CWld SEND
	- 'Vintage' (mixed)	NPri
	scapifera	CPBP
	sinuata	CWld
	white-flowered perennial	CMea CSpe NPer

Maurandella (*Plantaginaceae*)

§	***antirrhiniflora***	MArt

Maurandya (*Plantaginaceae*)

§	***barclayana***	CSpe IDee WHea
	erubescens	see *Lophospermum erubescens*
	lophantha	see *Lophospermum scandens*
	lophospermum	see *Lophospermum scandens*
	'Magic Dragon'	see *Lophospermum* 'Magic Dragon'
	'Red Dragon'	see *Lophospermum* 'Red Dragon'

Maytenus (*Celastraceae*)

	boaria	CBcs CMCN IArd IDee LEdu MGos SAko SArc SEND WPat
	disticha (Hook.f.) Urb.	LEdu
	magellanica	WPGP

Mazus (*Phrymaceae*)

	miquelii	EBee
	reptans	CBod ECho ECtt GEdr MSKA NLar NPer NQui WBor WRHF XLum
	- 'Albus'	CBod ECho ECtt LLWG NLar SPlb
	- 'Blue'	LLWG

Mecardonia (*Plantaginaceae*)

	'Goldflake'	CCCN

Meconopsis ✿ (*Papaveraceae*)

§	***baileyi*** ♀H4	CBcs CBod CSBt CTri EBee ELan EPfP GBuc GCra GGGa GKev GKin GMcL IBoy ITim LCro LOPS LRHS MBel NBir NEgg NSum SPoG WFar WMoo WSFF
*	- var. ***alba***	EBee ELan GCal GCra GGGa GKev IMou LRHS NSum
	- 'Hensol Violet'	CBod CPne EBee GBuc GCra GEdr GGGa GKev GMcL NSum WHlf
	- violet-flowered	ITim
	Ballyrogan form	GEdr
	× ***beamishii***	GKev
	betonicifolia misapplied	see *M. baileyi*
	'Cally Purple'	GCal
	cambrica	CCCN CMac CTri EBee EHrv ELan EWoo LEdu MMuc WBrk WCot WFar WHer
	- 'Anne Greenaway' (d)	WCot
	- var. ***aurantiaca***	WCot
	- double-flowered (d)	WCot
	- double-flowered, orange (d)	NBir WCot
§	- 'Frances Perry'	GCal WCot

- 'Muriel Brown' (d)	WCot
- 'Rubra'	see *M. cambrica* 'Frances Perry'
chelidoniifolia	CAby GCra LRHS NBid WCru
× ***cookei***	EBee GKev NHpl NSum
- 'Old Rose'	GBuc GEdr GGGa GMaP NHar
'Edrom' **new**	GEdr
'Evelyn'	GEdr
Fertile Blue Group	ITim
- 'Blue Ice'	see *M.* (Fertile Blue Group) 'Lingholm'
- 'Cally Lingholm'	GCal
- 'Lingholm'	Widely available
- 'Louise'	GEdr GMaP
- 'Mop-head' ♀H5	GEdr GKev GMaP
§ George Sherriff Group	GCal GCra MArl NBir
- 'Ascreavie'	GBuc GEdr GKev GMaP
- 'Barney's Blue'	GEdr GMaP
- 'Branklyn' ambig.	GEdr WPGP
- 'Dalemain' ♀H5	GBuc GEdr GMaP
- 'Huntfield'	EBee GEdr GGGa GKev GMaP
- 'Jimmy Bayne'	GEdr GMaP
- 'Susan's Reward' ♀H5	GEdr GMaP
grandis misapplied	see *M.* George Sherriff Group
grandis ambig.	CPla ITim NEgg
- GS 600	see *M.* George Sherriff Group
- 'Alba'	ITim
- 'Burgundy' **new**	GWyn
horridula	GCra
- var. ***racemosa***	see *M. racemosa* var. *racemosa*
(Infertile Blue Group) 'Bobby Masterton' ♀H5	GCra GEdr GKev GMaP
- 'Bryan Conway'	GEdr
- 'Crarae'	GEdr GGGa
- 'Crewdson Hybrid'	GBuc GCal GEdr GMaP
- 'Cruickshank'	GKev
- 'Dawyck'	see *M.* (Infertile Blue Group) 'Slieve Donard'
- 'Maggie Sharp'	GEdr
- 'Mrs Jebb' ♀H5	GBuc GCra GEdr GGGa GMaP
- 'P.C. Abildgaard' ♀H5	GEdr GGGa GMaP
§ - 'Slieve Donard' ♀H5	ENun GBuc GCal GCra GEdr GGGa GKev GMaP LRHS
integrifolia	CCCN
'Inverewe' ♀	GEdr
'Keillour' ♀H5	GEdr GKev
'Marit' ♀H5	GEdr GKev GMaP
'Mervyn Kessell' **new**	GEdr
'Mildred' **new**	GEdr
napaulensis misapplied	CPne EBee GCra GKev ITim LHop
- pink-flowered	LCro LOPS
napaulensis DC. B&SWJ 13952 **new**	WCru
- from Solukhumbu, Nepal	GCra
nudicaulis	see *Papaver nudicaule*
paniculata	CDor EBee GCra GGGa
- B&SWJ 13922 **new**	WCru
- from Ghunsa, Nepal	CSma
- ginger foliage	CHid
pseudointegrifolia	GGGa GKev
punicea	GKev NHpl
- 'Sichuan Silk' **new**	NHpl
quintuplinervia ♀H5	CLAP GCra GEdr GKev NHar NHpl NSla
- Farrer's form	GEdr
- 'Kaye's Compact'	GEdr
§ ***racemosa*** var. ***racemosa***	EWld GKev
× ***sarsonsii***	GKev
× ***sheldonii*** misapplied (fertile)	see *M.* Fertile Blue Group
× ***sheldonii*** misapplied (sterile)	see *M.* Infertile Blue Group
× ***sheldonii*** ambig.	CBcs CWCL GAbr GMcL LRHS NBir NLar NPer
'Stewart Annand'	GEdr GMaP
'Strathspey'	GEdr
superba	GGGa GKev
villosa	GCra GGGa
wallichii misapplied	see *M. wallichii* Hook.
§ ***wallichii*** Hook.	GGGa
'Willie Duncan'	GEdr GMaP

Medicago (*Papilionaceae*)

arborea	SEND SPlb
lupulina	CHab
sativa	WHer WSFF

Medinilla (*Melastomataceae*)

magnifica ♀H1a	CCCN

medlar see *Mespilus germanica*

Meehania (*Lamiaceae*)

cordata	EBee
urticifolia	EPPr GCal GEdr WSHC
- B&SWJ 1210	WCru
- 'Japanblau'	IMou

Megaskepasma (*Acanthaceae*)

erythrochlamys	SVen

Melaleuca (*Myrtaceae*)

acuminata	SPlb
alternifolia	CAby CBcs CCCN CTsd EShb GPoy MHer SPlb SVen
armillaris	CCCN CTsd IDee SEND SPlb
cuticularis	SPlb
decussata	SPlb
§ ***diosmatifolia***	CBcs
diosmifolia	CTre
ericifolia	CTri CTsd SEND SPlb
erubescens	see *M. diosmatifolia*
fulgens	SPlb
gibbosa	ELan IDee IVic LSou SEND SVen
hypericifolia	SPlb SVen
linariifolia	CCCN SPlb
nesophila	SPlb
pungens	SPlb
pustulata	SVen
squamea	CTsd SEND SPlb
squarrosa	IDee SPlb SVen
thymifolia	SPlb
trichophylla	SPlb
wilsonii	IDee

Melandrium see *Vaccaria*

rubrum	see *Silene dioica*

Melanoselinum (*Apiaceae*)

§ ***decipiens***	CArn CSpe IBoy IMou LEdu LRHS MHer SDix WCru WJek WPGP

Melanoseris (*Asteraceae*)

taliensis BWJ 7891	WCru

Melasphaerula (*Iridaceae*)

graminea	see *M. ramosa*
§ ***ramosa***	ECho GKev NRog

Melia (*Meliaceae*)

§ ***azedarach***	CArn CBcs CCCN EShb SBrt SPlb
- var. ***japonica***	see *M. azedarach*

Melianthus (*Melianthaceae*)

	comosus	CDTJ ELan EPri ESwi EWes NLar NLos SCoo SPlb
	dregeanus subsp. ***insignis***	NLos
	major ♀H3	Widely available
	minor	CHid
	pectinatus	NLos
	villosus	CHGN EBee EWes NLos SPad SPlb

Melica (*Poaceae*)

	altissima 'Alba'	IKil LRHS SPhx
	- 'Atropurpurea'	CBod ECha EHoe LEdu LHop LLWP LRHS MNrw NRHS SEND SPlb WHea WMoo
	ciliata	EAJP EHoe EPPr EPfP WPtf XLum
	nutans	CWCL EAJP EHoe EPPr EShb GMaP MAsh NWsh SMHy WCot
	transsilvanica 'Red Spire'	CWib SGol SHDw SMea WMoo XLum
	uniflora	IMou NWsh
	- f. ***albida***	CKno EAJP ECha EHoe GCal LLWP LRHS MRav NRHS SMHy WCot WSHC
	- 'Variegata' (v)	CBre ECha EHoe EShb GCal MAvo WCot WMoo

Melicytus (*Violaceae*)

	sp.	WSHC
	alpinus	WThu
	crassifolius	WSHC
	obovatus	NLar
	ramiflorus	CDul

Melilotus (*Papilionaceae*)

	officinalis	CArn CHab GPoy SIde WHer
	- subsp. ***albus***	CArn

Meliosma (*Sabiaceae*)

	dilleniifolia subsp. ***cuneifolia***	CBcs EBee SBrt WPGP
	- subsp. ***flexuosa***	CBcs
	- subsp. ***tenuis***	CBcs
	simplicifolia subsp. ***pungens***	CBcs
	veitchiorum	CBcs NLar SAko WPGP

Melissa ✿ (*Lamiaceae*)

	officinalis	CBod CHab CLau CPbn CTri ENfk GJos GMaP GPoy LEdu LPot MArt MHer MMuc MNHC NBir SEND SIde SPlb SRms SVic WBor WJek XLum
	- 'All Gold'	CBre CLau CPbn ECha EHoe ELan ENfk NBid SPer SPoG SRms
§	- 'Aurea' (v)	CArn CBod CLau ELan ESps GCra GMaP GPoy MHer MMuc MNHC MRav NBid NBir NBro SEND SIde SPer SPoG SRms WHea WJek WMoo
*	- 'Compacta'	CPbn GPoy
	- 'Lemona'	CAgr
	- 'Lime Balm'	CPbn
	- 'Quedlinburger Niederliegende'	CPbn
	- 'Variegata' misapplied	see *M. officinalis* 'Aurea'

Melittis (*Lamiaceae*)

	melissophyllum	CAby CLAP GAbr IMou LEdu LRHS LSou MAvo MHol MNrw MPie MPnt MRav SHar WCot WOut WRHF
	- subsp. ***albida***	CBct LEdu SCob WCot
	- pink-flowered	CLAP LEdu WBor WCot
	- 'Royal Velvet Distinction'[PBR]	CBct CBod CMos EBee GEdr LBMP LLWG LRHS MHol MRav MSCN NHpl NPnk SCob SHar SHil SPad SPoG WCot WHil WPtf

Melothria (*Cucurbitaceae*)

	scabra new	SVic

Menispermum (*Menispermaceae*)

	canadense	CTri GPoy
	dauricum	NLar

Mentha ✿ (*Lamiaceae*)

	from Jamaica	CArn
	angustifolia Corb.	see *M.* × *villosa*
	angustifolia Host	see *M. arvensis*
	angustifolia ambig.	CPbn
	aquatica	CArn CBen CBod CHab CPbn CWat GPoy LEdu MHer MJak MWLS MWts NMir NPer NPol SIde SPlb SRms SVic SWat WHer WMAq WMoo WPnP WSFF XLum
§	- var. ***crispa***	CPbn
	- krause minze	see *M. aquatica* var. *crispa*
	- 'Mandeliensis'	CPbn
§	***arvensis***	CArn CPbn MHer SIde
	- 'Banana'	CBod CPbn ENfk LEdu MHer MNHC SIde SRms SVic WJek
	- 'Lemon' new	LEdu
	- var. ***piperascens***	CBod LEdu MHer SIde SRms WJek
§	- - 'Sayakaze'	CArn CLau
	- 'Thai' new	ENfk
	- var. ***villosa***	CPbn
	asiatica	CLau CPbn MHer
	'Berries and Cream'	CBod ENfk LEdu LLWP MHer SRms WJek
	'Betty's Slovakian'	CPbn
	Bowles's mint	see *M.* × *villosa* var. *alopecuroides* Bowles's mint
*	***brevifolia***	CPbn
	cervina	CArn CBen CPbn CWat LEdu MHer MSKA MWts SIde SRms SWat WJek XLum
*	- ***alba***	CPbn ENfk LLWG MHer MSKA MWts SRms WJek WMAq
I	'Chocolate Peppermint'	ENfk LEdu LLWG NBir NLar
	citrata	see *M.* × *piperita* f. *citrata*
	'Clarissa's Millennium'	CPbn
	cordifolia	see *M.* × *villosa*
	corsica	see *M. requienii*
	crispa L. (1753)	see *M. spicata* var. *crispa*
	crispa L. (1763)	see *M. aquatica* var. *crispa*
	crispa ambig. × (× ***piperita***)	CArn CPbn MJak
	cucumber mint	CPbn
	'Dionysus'	CPbn
	× ***dumetorum***	CPbn
	- wine mint	CPbn
	'Eau de Cologne'	see *M.* × *piperita* f. *citrata*
	eucalyptus mint	CPbn MHer
	gattefossei	CArn
	× ***gentilis***	see *M.* × *gracilis*
§	× ***gracilis***	CArn CBod CLau CPbn ENfk GAbr NLar NPri SIde SVic
	- 'Aurea'	see *M.* × *gracilis* 'Variegata'
§	- 'Variegata' (v)	CLau CPbn ECha GPoy LEdu MCot MHer MNHC NPri SPlb SRms WHer WJek XLum
	haplocalyx	CArn CLau

	'Herbert McHale'	LEdu
*	'Hillary's Sweet Lemon'	CLau CPbn ENfk MHer SIde
*	***hopwoodiana*** **new**	SIde
	'Julia's Sweet Citrus'	CPbn MHer
	lavender mint	CBod CLau GPoy LEdu MHer MNHC SRms WJek
§	***longifolia***	CLau CPbn ENfk LEdu MMuc SEND SPlb SRms
	- Buddleia Mint Group	CArn CLau CPbn EBee ENfk GAbr LEdu MHer MRav NSti SIde WJek XLum
	- - variegated (v)	CBod LEdu WJek
	- dwarf	CPbn
	- 'Lake Van' **new**	LEdu
	- subsp. ***schimperi***	LEdu SRms WJek
	- silver-leaved	CArn CLau CPbn GAbr LEdu MHer MNHC SEND SRms WJek
*	- 'Variegata' (v)	CPbn GAbr SRms
	Nile Valley mint	CArn CLau LEdu SHDw SIde SRms WJek
	× ***piperita***	CArn CHby CLau CPbn CWld ECha EHoe GJos GPoy LCro MHer MJak MNHC NPri SPlb SVic
	- 'Black Mitcham'	CArn CPbn SIde
	- black peppermint	CAgr CBod CHby CPbn ENfk EPfP GAbr LEdu LLWG MMuc MNHC NBir NLar SEND SRms WJek
§	- f. ***citrata***	CArn CBod CHby CLau CPbn CTri ECha ENfk GAbr GJos GMaP GPoy LEdu LLWG MHer MNHC MRav NBir NLar NPer NPri SHDw SIde SPlb SRms SVic WJek
	- - from Portugal	CPbn
*	- - 'Basil'	CBod CLau CPbn GAbr GLog LEdu MHer MNHC MRav SHDw SIde SRms SVic WGwG WJek
	- - 'Bergamot'	CPbn SRms
	- - 'Chocolate'	CArn CBod CLau CPbn ENfk EPfP GJos LBMP LEdu LLWP MHer MNHC NPer SHDw SIde SPlb SRms SVic WJek XLum
	- - 'Grapefruit'	CBod CPbn GLog LSou MHer MNHC NWad SRms WJek
	- - 'Kumin' **new**	LEdu
	- - 'Lime'	CPbn ENfk GAbr GLog LEdu LLWP MHer SHDw SIde SPlb SRms SVic WJek
	- - 'Orange'	CPbn ENfk LEdu LLWP MHer MMuc MNHC NPer SRms WJek
	- - 'Reverchonii'	CPbn
	- - 'Swiss Ricola'	MHer
	- 'Crispa'	NPol
	- 'Logee's' (v)	CPbn WJek
	- 'Milly Mitcham'	CPbn
	- f. ***officinalis***	CLau CPbn SIde
	- var. ***ouweneellii*** Belgian mint	CPbn
	- 'Persephone'	CPbn
	- var. ***piperita*** 'Agnes' **new**	SIde
	- 'Priluskaja' **new**	SIde
	- 'Reine Rouge'	CPbn SIde
	- 'Strawberry'	ENfk
	- 'Swiss'	CBod LEdu MNHC NLar WHer WJek
I	- Swiss mint	CArn CPbn ENfk
*	- white-flowered	CArn CPbn
	'Polynesian Mint'	CPbn
	pulegium	CArn CBod CHby CPbn CTri ENfk GPoy LEdu LLWG MHer MMuc MNHC MWts SIde SPlb SRms SVic WHer WJek WSFF
	- 'Upright'	CArn CBod CPbn ENfk GPoy MHer SHDw SIde SRms WJek
§	***requienii***	CArn CBod CPbn CTri ECho ENfk GAbr GCal GPoy ITim LEdu MHer MNHC NBir NRya NWad SDix SIde SPlb SRms WGwG WJek WTou XEll
	rotundifolia misapplied	see *M. suaveolens*
	rotundifolia (L.) Huds.	see *M.* × *villosa*
	rubra var. ***raripila***	see *M.* × *smithiana*
	'Russian' curled leaf	CPbn
	'Russian' plain leaf	CPbn
	'Sayakaze'	see *M. arvensis* var. *piperascens* 'Sayakaze'
§	× ***smithiana***	CArn CLau CPbn ENfk GPoy LEdu MHer MNHC MRav NBir SRms WJek
	- 'Capel Ulo' (v)	CLau
	'South of France'	CPbn
§	***spicata***	CAgr CArn CBod CLau CPbn CTri CTsd ENfk GJos GKev GPoy LBMP LPot MCot MHer MJak MMuc MNHC NPol NPri SEND SPlb SRms WHer WJek XLum
	- Algerian fruity	CPbn LEdu
	- 'Austrian'	CPbn
*	- 'Brundall'	CLau CPbn SIde
	- 'Canaries'	CPbn
	- 'Cretan' **new**	LEdu
*	- var. ***crispa***	CArn CLau CPbn ECha ENfk LEdu LHop LPot MHer MMuc MNHC NRya SIde SPlb SRms WJek
	- - 'Moroccan'	CArn CLau CPbn ENfk GAbr GJos GLog GPoy LEdu MHer MNHC NLar NPri SHDw SIde SRms SVic WJek
	- - 'Persian'	CPbn
	- 'Crispula'	GAbr XLum
	- 'Erdbeere' **new**	SIde
	- 'Guernsey'	CPbn SHDw SIde SRms
	- 'Irish'	CPbn
	- 'Kentucky Colonel'	CPbn LEdu
	- 'Mexican'	CArn CPbn
	- 'Newbourne'	CLau CPbn SRms
	- 'Nile Valley' **new**	LEdu
	- 'Pharaoh'	CArn CPbn
	- 'Rhodos'	CPbn
	- 'Russian'	CArn LEdu MHer SIde
	- 'Small Dole' (v)	SHDw
	- 'Spanish'	LEdu NLar SRms
	- 'Spanish Furry'	CPbn MHer
	- 'Spanish Pointed'	CLau CPbn WJek
	- 'Tashkent'	CArn CHby CLau CPbn ENfk LEdu LLWP MHer MNHC SHDw SIde SRms WGwG WHer WJek
	- subsp. ***tomentosa***	CPbn
*	- 'Variegata' (v)	CPbn SHDw
	- 'Verte Blanche'	CPbn
I	'Strawberry Mint'	LEdu WJek
§	***suaveolens***	CAgr CArn CBod CHby CLau CPbn ENfk GJos GMaP GPoy LBMP MHer MNHC SIde SPlb SRms SVic WJek WSFF
*	- 'Grapefruit'	LEdu
	- 'Jokka'	CPbn
*	- 'Mobillei'	CPbn
*	- 'Pineapple'	CBod ENfk GLog WJek
	- subsp. ***timija***	CLau CPbn LEdu MHer WJek

	- 'Variegata' (v)	CArn CLau CPbn CTri ECha EHoe GJos GMaP GPoy LEdu MCot MHer MMuc MNHC MRav NChi NPri SIde SPlb SRms SVic WHer XLum
	'Sweet Pear'	MHer
	sylvestris L.	see *M. longifolia*
I	'Tangerine Mint'	LEdu
*	***verona***	CPbn
	× ***verticillata***	WJek
§	× ***villosa***	CArn CPbn MMuc SEND SRms
§	- var. ***alopecuroides*** Bowles's mint	CBre CLau CPbn GPoy LEdu MHer MNHC NBir NLar NSti SRms SWat WHer WJek
	- 'Jack Green'	LEdu
	viridis	see *M. spicata*

Menyanthes (*Menyanthaceae*)

trifoliata	CBen CWat EWay GPoy LLWG MMuc MSKA MWts NPer WHal WMAq WSFF WWtn XLum

Menziesia (*Ericaceae*)

alba	see *Daboecia cantabrica* f. *alba*
ciliicalyx lasiophylla	see *Rhododendron multiflorum* var. *purpureum*
ferruginea	see *Rhododendron menziesii*

Mercurialis (*Euphorbiaceae*)

perennis	GPoy WHer WSFF WShi

Merendera (*Colchicaceae*)

	attica	NRog
	eichleri	see *M. trigyna*
	filifolia	NRog
§	***montana***	EPot GKev NRog
	- 'Norman Barratt'	WCot
	pyrenaica	see *M. montana*
	raddeana	see *M. trigyna*
	sobolifera	ECho NRog WCot
§	***trigyna***	NRog

Mertensia (*Boraginaceae*)

	ciliata	CCse SWat
	franciscana	GCal
	lanceolata	EBee GKev
§	***maritima***	CSpe ECho EPot EWes EWld GKev GPoy LEdu LRHS NBir SPlb WHoo
	- subsp. ***asiatica***	see *M. maritima*
	pterocarpa	see *M. sibirica*
	pulmonarioides	see *M. virginica*
§	***sibirica***	CSpe SPlb
§	***virginica*** ♀H4	CBro CLAP CMos CWCL EBee ECho ECtt EHrv ELan EPfP EPot EWTr GKev IFro LAma LEdu LHop LRHS MBel MNrw MPie MSCN NBir NLar NPnk NSti SDir SRms WFar
	viridis	SPlb

Merwilla (*Asparagaceae*)

§	***plumbea***	WCot

Merxmuellera (*Poaceae*)

cincta	see *Danthonia cincta*

Mesembryanthemum (*Aizoaceae*)

brownii	see *Lampranthus brownii*
crystallinum	NPri

Mespilus ✿ (*Rosaceae*)

'Flanders Giant' (F)	WMat
germanica (F)	CBcs CDul CHab CLnd CMCN CTri ECrN ELan ESps IDee NLar NWea SLon WFar
- var. ***apyrena*** (F)	WMat
- 'Brabant Giant'	SAko
- 'Bredase Reus' (F)	SKee
- 'Dutch' (F)	SDea SKee
- 'Iranian' (F)	SKee
- 'Large Russian' (F)	CAgr
- 'Macrocarpa' (F)	SKee
- 'Monstrous' (F)	SDea
- 'Nottingham' (F) ♀H6	Widely available
- 'Royal' (F)	CAgr CFGn ERea LCro LOPS LRHS MCoo MRai NOra SCoo SKee WHar WMat
- 'Westerveld' (F)	CLnd EPom SKee

Metapanax ✿ (*Araliaceae*)

davidii	CFil WPGP
delavayi	SBig

Metaplexis (*Apocynaceae*)

japonica	SBrt

Metasequoia ✿ (*Cupressaceae*)

	glyptostroboides	Widely available
	- 'Chubby'PBR	EPfP NLar
	- 'Emerald Feathers'	SLim
	- 'Fastigiata'	see *M. glyptostroboides* 'National'
	- Gold Rush = 'Golden Oji' ♀H7	Widely available
	- 'Golden Dawn'	NLar
	- 'Hamlet's Broom'	SLim
	- 'Little Creamy'	NLar
	- 'Little Giant'	MBlu
	- 'Matthaei Broom'	MBlu SLim
	- 'McCracken's White' (v)	NLar
	- 'Miss Grace'	MAsh NLar
§	- 'National'	MBlu
	- 'Royal Air'	NLar
	- 'Sheridan Spire'	CEnd MBlu
	- 'Waasland'	MBlu
	- 'White Spot' (v)	MBlu SLim

Metrosideros (*Myrtaceae*)

	carminea	CCCN
§	***excelsa***	CHll ECre ESwi
	- 'Parnell'	CBcs CCCN
	- 'Vibrance'	CCCN
	kermadecensis 'Twisty' (v)	CBcs
	- 'Variegata' (v)	CBcs
	lucida	see *M. umbellata*
	robusta	CBcs CCCN SPlb
	- ***aureovariegata*** (v)	CCCN EShb
§	'Springfire'	CCCN
	'Thomasii'	see *M.* 'Springfire'
	tomentosa	see *M. excelsa*
§	***umbellata***	CBcs CCCN CTsd
	- 'Gold Nugget'	CCCN LSou SLim
	- Moonlight = 'Lowmoo'	CCCN LSou SLim

Meum (*Apiaceae*)

athamanticum	CArn CSpe EBee GCal GPoy LEdu LRHS MAvo MRav SIgm SMHy SPhx WHil WSHC

Michauxia (*Campanulaceae*)

campanuloides	CSpe EBee GJos
tchihatchewii	CDTJ CSpe LEdu NGBl

Michelia see *Magnolia*

fulgens — see *Magnolia foveolata*

Microbiota (*Cupressaceae*)

decussata ♀H5 — CBcs CMac CSBt ECho ESps GMcL IDee LBee LRHS MGos NHol NWea
- 'Jakobsen' — CKen
- 'Trompenburg' — CKen

Microcachrys ✿ (*Podocarpaceae*)

tetragona — IDee WThu

Microglossa (*Asteraceae*)

albescens — see *Aster albescens*

Microlepia (*Dennstaedtiaceae*)

strigosa — CCCN CLAP EBee ISha LRHS
- 'MacFaddeniae' — EBee ISha LRHS

Micromeria (*Lamiaceae*)

sp. — SRms
corsica — see *Acinos corsicus*
fruticosa — WJek
juliana — XLum
rupestris — see *M. thymifolia*
§ ***thymifolia*** — SPlb

Microseris (*Asteraceae*)

ringens hort. — see *Leontodon rigens*

Microsorum (*Polypodiaceae*)

diversifolium — see *Phymatosorus diversifolius*
musifolium — NLos
punctatum Green Flame = 'Vp005' **new** — NLos

Microtropis (*Celastraceae*)

petelotii HWJ 719 — WCru

Mikania (*Asteraceae*)

araucana — LSou

Milium (*Poaceae*)

effusum 'Aureum' ♀H7 — Widely available
- 'Yaffle' (v) — CBod CBre CKno EPPr EShb LEdu WPnP

Millettia (*Papilionaceae*)

pachycarpa **new** — CMen

Mimetes (*Proteaceae*)

chrysanthus — SPlb
cucullatus **new** — CTre
- 'Crackerjack Red' **new** — CCCN

Mimosa (*Mimosaceae*)

pudica ♀H1c — CCCN CDTJ SPlb

Mimulus (*Phrymaceae*)

'Andean Nymph' — see *M. naiandinus*
§ ***aurantiacus*** ♀H2 — CMac CSpe CTri EBak ECtt EShb IDee LHop LPot MGil NPer SPlb WBod
- 'Primrose' **new** — MGil
× ***bartonianus*** — see *M.* × *harrisonii*
× ***burnetii*** — ECho SRms
cardinalis ♀H1c — EBee ELan EPfP EWes GKev MSKA NBir WBor WMoo
- gold-flowered — EBee
- 'Red Dragon' — CBod CFis WHrl
cardinalis × ***lewisii*** — EWes
cupreus 'Whitecroft Scarlet' ♀H5 — GCrg SRms
eastwoodiae — GKev
'Eleanor' — ECtt
glutinosus — see *M. aurantiacus*
- ***atrosanguineus*** — see *M. puniceus*
- ***luteus*** — see *M. aurantiacus*
§ ***guttatus*** — NMir NPer SRms WMoo WPnP
§ × ***harrisonii*** — EWes LSou
'Highland Orange' — EPfP GWyn MAsh SPlb SPoG WIce
'Highland Pink' — EPfP GWyn MAsh NHpl SPlb SPoG
'Highland Red' ♀H5 — EPfP GMaP GWyn MAsh NHpl SPlb SPoG SRms WIce
'Highland Yellow' — GMaP GWyn NHpl SPlb SPoG WIce
hose-in-hose (d) — NPer
langsdorffii — see *M. guttatus*
lewisii ♀H1c — EBee EWes MNrw SRms
'Lothian Fire' — CWat
luteus — CBen CWat GAbr LLWG NPer WBrk WMAq XLum
- 'Variegatus' ambig. (v) — NPer
* 'Major Bees' — MJak
'Malibu Orange' — EPfP
'Maximus' (mixed) — NPri
moschatus — EBee LLWG
§ ***naiandinus*** ♀H4 — EWes SPlb
- 'Mega' **new** — GKev
'Orange Glow' — LLWG
orange hose-in-hose (d) — NBir
§ 'Orkney Gold' (d) — ECtt
'Popacatapetl' — CSpe
primuloides — ECho EWes GCrg SPlb
§ ***puniceus*** — CTri LHop SRkn
ringens — CBen CWat EBee MSKA NBir NPer SPlb SRms WMAq WMoo
'Threave Variegated' (v) — EBee
'Vortex' — LSou
'Vortex Hot Spot' — LSou
'Vortex Orange Glow' — LSou
'Wisley Red' — ECho SRms
yellow hose-in-hose — see *M.* 'Orkney Gold'

Mina see *Ipomoea*

mint, apple see *Mentha suaveolens*

mint, Bowles's see *Mentha* × *villosa* var. *alopecuroides*

mint, curly see *Mentha spicata* var. *crispa*

mint, eau-de-Cologne see *Mentha* × *piperita* f. *citrata*

mint, ginger see *Mentha* × *gracilis*

mint, horse or long-leaved see *Mentha longifolia*

mint (pennyroyal) see *Mentha pulegium*

mint (peppermint) see *Mentha* × *piperita*

mint, round-leaved see *Mentha suaveolens*

mint (spearmint) see *Mentha spicata*

Minuartia (*Caryophyllaceae*)

capillacea — ECho
laricifolia — MMuc XSen

parnassica	see *M. stellata*
§ ***stellata***	EPot
§ ***verna***	ECho EDAr
- subsp. ***caespitosa***	CTri ECho
- - 'Aurea'	see *Sagina subulata* var. *glabrata* 'Aurea'

Mirabilis (*Nyctaginaceae*)

dichotoma	EShb
jalapa	CArn EPfP GKev LAma LEdu SDir SRms
- 'Buttermilk'	CCCN
longiflora	EShb SBrt
multiflora	EBee SBrt
nyctaginea	SPhx

Miscanthus (*Poaceae*)

capensis	SPlb
chejuensis B&SWJ 8803	WCru
'Dronning Ingrid'	CKno EPPr IMou MNrw NDov XLum
'Elfin'	CKno
flavidus	XLum
floridulus misapplied	see *M.* × *giganteus*
floridulus ambig.	MMuc MNrw NLos SCob SPlb XLum
floridulus (Labill.) Warb. ex K. Schum. & Lauterb. HWJ 522	WCru
§ × ***giganteus***	CKno EHoe EHrv ELon EPPr EUJe GCal GKev GMcL GQue IBoy LTro MAsh MNrw NLos NWsh SCob SDys SMad SSal SVic WCot XLum
- 'Aksel Olsen'	SAko
- 'Gilt Edge' (v)	CKno EPPr
- 'Gotemba' (v)	EPPr EWes
nepalensis	CAby CBot CElw CHVG CKno CSam EBee ECha ECre EHoe EPed EUJe EWes EWoo GCal LEdu LRHS LSun MAvo MNrw NDov NLos NRHS NWsh SDix SPlb WPGP
- NJM 09.141	WPGP
- 'Shikola'	EMFm WCru
oligostachyus	CChe IMou SDys
§ - 'Afrika'	EPPr GBin IMou MAvo MNrw WPGP
I - 'Nanus Variegatus' (v)	CKno EHoe LEdu SAko WCot WPGP
'Purpurascens'	CBod CBot CKno CWCL ECha EHoe EPPr EPed IBoy LPot LRHS LSRN MNrw NLos NRHS SAko SCob SGol SPer WMoo XLum
sacchariflorus misapplied	see *M.* × *giganteus*
sacchariflorus ambig.	CBcs CDul CKno ECha ELan EPfP LRHS MBrN NGdn NRHS SPer WMoo
sacchariflorus (Maxim.) Hack.	LEdu
sinensis	CTri EPed ESps LEdu LPar WFar WHar WMoo XSen
- 'Abundance'	CKno CRos EPfP LRHS MMuc NRHS
- 'Adagio'	CBod CKno EAEE EHoe ELon EPPr EShb EWoo GBin GQue ILea LRHS MNrw NRHS NWad NWsh SCob SHDw SMHy SMad SMea WCot XLum
- 'Afrika'	see *M. oligostachyus* 'Afrika'
- 'Aldebaran'	EBee IMou MNrw
- 'Andante'	CKno
- 'Aperitif' **new**	EBee
- 'Arabesque'	EMFm EPPr XLum
- 'Augustfeder'	EPPr MAvo SMea XLum
- 'Autumn Light'	EPPr SMea XLum
- 'Barney Campbell' **new**	NWsh
- 'Blütenwunder'	EPPr XLum
- 'Bogenlampe'	GBin
- 'China' 🏆	CKno CPar CRos EAEE EHoe ELon EPPr EShb EWes IPot LEdu LRHS MAsh MAvo MNrw NPnk NRHS NWsh SDys SHDw SRms SWat WMoo
- 'Cindy'	CKno
- var. ***condensatus***	LEdu LSou SMHy
- - NJM 11.021	WPGP
- - 'Cabaret' (v)	CBod CKno EAEE EHoe EPPr EUJe GMaP GMcL ILea LBMP LEdu LHop LPar LRHS LSRN MMuc MNrw NRHS NWsh SEND SHDw WCot WHal WMoo WPGP XLum
- - 'Central Park'	see *M. sinensis* var. *condensatus* 'Cosmo Revert'
§ - - 'Cosmo Revert'	EPPr LEdu NWsh WPGP
- - 'Cosmopolitan' (v) 🏆H5	Widely available
- - 'Emerald Giant'	see *M. sinensis* var. *condensatus* 'Cosmo Revert'
- - 'Laigong'	LEdu
- 'David'	ELon EPPr LEdu MBNS MSpe XLum
- 'Dixieland' (v)	CKno ELan ELon EPPr EWes IFoB IMou LEdu
- 'Dreadlocks'	EBee EPPr GBin MAvo
- 'Dresdner Rotgold' **new**	SAko
- 'Dresdner Silbersprudel'	SAko
- 'Emmanuel Lepage'	CKno EPPr XLum
- 'Etincelle'	CKno EPPr EWes ILea
- 'Federriese'	GBin
- 'Ferner Osten' 🏆H7	Widely available
- 'Feuergold'	SAko
- 'Flamingo' 🏆H6	Widely available
- 'Flammenmeer'	SAko
- 'Gearmella'	EPPr
- 'Gewitterwolke' 🏆H6	EPPr EWes SMHy XLum
- 'Ghana' 🏆H6	CSpe EBee ELon EPPr GBin GQue IMou LEdu MAvo MNrw SDys SMHy SSut XLum
- 'Giraffe'	CDTJ CKno EWes LEdu XLum
- 'Gnome'	CKno EAEE EHoe EPPr EShb EUJe IMou LRHS MAsh
- 'Gold Bar'^{PBR} (v)	CBod CChe CDul CKno CLet CWGN EAEE ECha EHoe ELon EPfP EUJe GMcL LBrs LRHS LSRN LSou MAsh MBNS NGdn NRHS NWad SEle SGol SPad SPer WMoo
- 'Gold Breeze' **new**	LRHS NRHS
- 'Gold und Silber' 🏆H6	XLum
- 'Goldfeder' (v)	EMFm XLum
- 'Goliath'	CKno EHoe ELan ELon EPPr GBin GLog GQue LBMP LEdu MBNS NLos XLum
- 'Gracillimus'	Widely available
- 'Graziella'	CBod CEnd CKno CLet CSam CWCL CWib EHoe EPPr EPed EPfP GBin LBMP LRHS NGdn NLar NRHS SHil SPer SRms WBor WMoo WPGP XSen
- 'Grosse Fontäne' 🏆H6	EHoe ELan EPPr GBin LEdu LRHS LSRN NWsh SMHy SMad WCot WMoo XLum
- 'Gutenberg Gold'	XLum
- 'Haiku'	CKno EPPr LEdu XLum

	- 'Helga Reich'	EWes
	- 'Hercules'	EBee EPPr MAvo XLum
	- 'Hermann Müssel'	CBWd CKno EBee EPPr EWes IMou LEdu LRHS NLos NRHS SMHy SMea XLum
§	- 'Hinjo' (v)	CDul EAEE ECha EHoe ELon GBin GBuc LRHS LSou MSpe NGdn NWsh SPoG WCot
I	- 'Jubilaris' (v)	EBee EMFm EPPr EWes
	- 'Juli'	EPPr LRHS NRHS
	- 'Kaskade' ♀H6	CKno CPar EHoe EPPr EUJe GBin LEdu LRHS MMuc NDov NLar NRHS SMad WMoo
	- 'Kirk Alexander' (v)	EPPr
	- 'Kleine Fontäne' ♀H6	Widely available
	- 'Kleine Silberspinne' ♀H6	Widely available
	- 'Korea'	EPPr
	- 'Krater'	EBee EHoe EPPr ILea LRHS MBrN NRHS SDys SMea SWat XLum
	- 'Kupferberg'	XLum
	- 'Kupferzwerg'	EPPr
§	- 'Little Kitten'	CKno EPPr EPed LEdu SMad SMea WMoo XLum
	- Little Nicky	see *M. sinensis* 'Hinjo'
	- 'Little Zebra' PBR (v)	EBee EPfP GMaP LHop LSRN MGos NLar NLos SCob SEle SMad SRms
	- 'Malepartus'	Widely available
	- 'Memory'	EPPr
	- 'Morning Light' (v) ♀H6	Widely available
	- 'Nippon'	EAEE EHoe EPPr GBin IPot LEdu LRHS NGdn NRHS NWsh SCob SDys SPer XLum
	- 'Nishidake'	EPPr XLum
	- 'November Sunset'	EPPr EWes XLum
	- 'Overdam'	IFoB NGdn
	- 'Poseidon'	EPPr MAvo SDys SMad XLum
	- 'Positano'	CKno XLum
	- 'Professor Richard Hansen'	CKno EPPr EWes SMHy XLum
	- 'Pünktchen' (v)	EAEE ECha EHoe EPPr GBin LEdu LRHS MAsh MSpe NRHS SCob SHDw SMHy SMad SRms WMoo XLum
	- 'Purple Fall'	CBot CPar CSpe EWes GBin IPot LRHS LSou MAvo MNrw NRHS STPC
	- 'Red Chief'	EBee EPPr EWes GQue IMou IPot MAvo NDov NLar SCob
	- 'Red Meister'	CKno CRos EPfP LRHS MAsh NRHS
	- 'Red Star'	SRms
	- 'Red Tower'	EWes
	- 'Red Wine'	GBin MNrw
	- 'Roland'	CKno EHoe EPPr SMad XLum
	- 'Rosi' **new**	GBin
	- 'Roterpfeil'	EPPr
	- 'Rotfeder'	EPPr
	- 'Rotfuchs'	EBee LLWP MAvo XLum
	- 'Rotsilber'	CBWd CBod CKno CMos CSpe CWib ECha EHoe EPPr GMaP IArd LRHS MJak MMuc NDov NRHS NWsh WHoo WMoo XLum
	- 'Samurai'	EPPr GMaP GQue MAvo MNrw
	- 'Sarabande' ♀H6	EHoe EPPr GQue NLar SMHy WMoo
	- 'Septemberrot' ♀H6	CKno EPPr LEdu MMuc SCob SEND
	- 'Serim' **new**	EPPr
§	- 'Silberfeder' ♀H6	Widely available
	- 'Silberpfeil' (v)	NWsh
	- 'Silberspinne'	CCse EBee EPPr GBin IBoy ILea LEdu LRHS MWat NLos NRHS SCob SHil SMHy SMea SPlb XLum
	- 'Silberturm'	EPPr XLum
	- Silver Feather	see *M. sinensis* 'Silberfeder'
	- 'Silver Sceptre'	MAvo SMHy
	- 'Silver Stripe'	EPPr EWoo MAvo
	- 'Sioux'	EBee EHoe EPPr EShb EUJe GBin GQue LRHS MAvo MBNS NRHS SPer
	- 'Sirene'	EAEE EHoe EPPr GQue MBNS MMuc MSpe NBir
	- 'Spätgrün'	EPPr SAko
	- 'Starlight'	CKno
	- 'Strictus' (v) ♀H6	Widely available
	- 'Super Stripe' (v)	EPPr IMou
	- 'Taiwan'	EBee EPPr
	- 'Tiger Cub' (v)	CWCL EPPr EWes
	- 'Undine' ♀H6	CBWd CKno CMea ECha EHoe ELan EPPr EPfP LEdu MBel MBrN MMuc NWsh WMoo XLum
	- 'Variegatus' (v)	Widely available
	- 'Verneigung'	GBin
	- 'Vorläufer'	EPPr GBin
	- 'Werner Neufliess' **new**	SAko
	- 'Westacre Wine'	EWes
	- 'Wetterfahne'	EPPr LEdu
§	- 'Yaku-jima'	CBod CSam ECha EPPr LHop MMuc NLos SCob SMea
	- 'Yakushima Dwarf'	Widely available
	- 'Zebrinus' (v) ♀H6	Widely available
	- 'Zwergelefant'	EBee MAvo SMHy XLum
	tinctorius 'Nanus Variegatus' misapplied	see *M. oligostachyus* 'Nanus Variegatus'
	transmorrisonensis	CKno EHoe ELan EPPr EUJe LEdu LRHS MAvo NDov NLos NRHS NWsh WCot
	yakushimensis	see *M. sinensis* 'Little Kitten', *M. sinensis* 'Yaku-jima'

Mitchella (*Rubiaceae*)

	repens	CBcs EBee LEdu MNrw WCru
	undulata B&SWJ 10928	WCru
*	- f. ***quelpartensis*** B&SWJ 4402	WCru

Mitella (*Saxifragaceae*)

acerina B&SWJ 11029	EWld WCru
breweri	CHid CMac ECha GCal GLog MRav NSti WBor WMoo WOut WPnP
caulescens	ECha NBro
diphylla	MHer
formosana B&SWJ 125	EPPr WCru
furusei var. ***subramosa*** B&SWJ 11097	WCru
× ***inami*** B&SWJ 11122	WCru
japonica B&SWJ 4971	WCru
kiusiana	CLAP
- B&SWJ 5888	WCru
makinoi	CLAP MAvo
- B&SWJ 4992	WCru
pauciflora B&SWJ 6361	WCru
pentandra	EBee
stylosa B&SWJ 5669	WCru
yoshinagae B&SWJ 4893	CHid EBee EPPr WCru WMoo

Mitraria (*Gesneriaceae*)

coccinea	CBcs CCCN CHll CMac CTsd CWib ECho ELan ESps GEdr GKev IDee LSou MBlu NLar SLim SLon SPer SPlb WBod
- Clark's form	EUJe LRHS NLar
- 'Lago Puyehue'	CAbb CBcs CCCN EPfP LRHS MAsh SPlb SPoG SVen SWvt WSHC WThu

- 'Lake Caburgua'	CCCN CSpe EBee ELon EWld GCal IArd NLar WHor

Modiolastrum (*Malvaceae*)

lateritium	CHll CRHN CSpe CTri ELan EPri LHop LRHS MAvo MNHC NBir SPhx SPoG SRms WBod WHal WHar WSHC WWFP XLum

Moehringia (*Caryophyllaceae*)

muscosa	WCot

Moenchia (*Caryophyllaceae*)

mantica	WCot

Molinia ✿ (*Poaceae*)

altissima	see *M. caerulea* subsp. *arundinacea*
'Autumn Charm'	CKno
caerulea	CKno CRos CWib EPPr LRHS MAsh MBlu NRHS
§ - subsp. ***arundinacea***	CKno CSpe CWCL ECha EPPr SSut XLum
- - 'Automne Bronze'	EPPr
- - 'Bergfreund'	CKno CSam EBee EHoe EPPr EPed GBin LHop MAvo NWsh SMHy
- - 'Breeze'	CKno
- - 'Cordoba'	CKno EBee EPPr GBin GQue IPot MAvo NDov SMHy SPhx WMoo XLum
- - 'Fontäne'	CSam EHoe EPPr GQue MAsh MAvo NWsh SPhx
- - 'Granada'	EPPr
- - 'JS Mostenveld' (v) **new**	GBin
- - 'JS Witches Broom' **new**	GBin
- - 'JS Yellow Pipe' **new**	GBin
- - 'Karl Foerster'	Widely available
- - 'Les Ponts de Cé'	EPPr
- - 'Liebreiz'	EPPr
- - 'Skyracer'	CBWd CCVN CChe CKno EBee EHoe ELan ELon EPPr EUJe GBin GCal GLog GMaP GQue LRHS MAsh MAvo MNrw NRHS SMHy SMad SPhx WCot WGrn WMoo
- - 'Staefa'	EHoe
- - 'Sunbeam'	EPPr
- - 'Tears of Joy'	EPPr
- - 'Transparent'	Widely available
- - 'Windsaule'	CKno EPPr MAvo NDov SPhx
- - 'Windspiel'	Widely available
- - 'Zuneigung'	CKno CSam EPPr LRHS MAvo NRHS SPhx
- subsp. ***caerulea***	EPPr
- - 'Carmarthen' (v)	EHoe EPPr LRHS NRHS
- - 'Claerwen' (v)	ECha EPPr MAvo SPhx WMoo
- - 'Coneyhill Gold' (v)	EPPr
- - 'Dark Defender'	EPPr SPhx
- - 'Dauerstrahl'	CKno EBee EPPr GCal GQue MAsh MNrw NDov
- - 'Edith Dudszus'	CBWd CBod CKno CMea EAEE ECha EHoe ELan ELon EPPr EPed GBin GQue LHop LRHS MBel MBrN NCGa NDov NGdn NHol NRHS SCob SPer SPhx WGrn WMoo
- - 'Heidebraut'	CBod EAEE EBee EHoe EHrv EPPr EWoo GBin GMaP GQue IBoy LOPS LRHS MBel MRav NCGa NDov NRHS NWsh SCob SPhx WMoo XSen
- - 'Heidezwerg'	EBee EPPr GBin
- - 'Igel'	EBee GBin NDov
- - 'Moorflamme'	CSam EPPr MAvo SPhx
- - 'Moorhexe'	Widely available
- - 'Overdam'	EPPr
- - 'Poul Petersen'	CKno EBee EPPr GBin LCro MBel NDov SPhx
- - 'Rotschopf'	EBee
- - 'Strahlenquelle'	CBod CSam ELan EPPr GBin GQue LRHS MSpe NDov NHol NWsh
- - 'Variegata' (v) ♀^{H7}	Widely available
- 'Showers of Gold'	SPhx
litoralis	see *M. caerulea* subsp. *arundinacea*

Molopospermum (*Apiaceae*)

peloponnesiacum	CAby CSpe EBee GCal IMou LEdu NDov SBrt SDix SMHy SPhx WCru WPGP WPtf WSHC

Moltkia (*Boraginaceae*)

§ ***doerfleri***	EBee GCal LHop NBir NChi SBrt WSHC
§ × ***intermedia*** ♀^{H5}	CMea CRos LRHS NRHS SBch SBrt SIgm WAbe WThu
petraea	ECho LHop LLHF LRHS NRHS WAbe

Moluccella (*Lamiaceae*)

laevis	CSpe LCro SPhx SVic

Monadenium (*Euphorbiaceae*)

capitatum	LToo
magnificum	LToo
schubei	LToo

Monanthes (*Crassulaceae*)

laxiflora	WCot
pallens	WCot

Monarda ✿ (*Lamiaceae*)

'Adam'	GBuc GCal LSRN MRav NLar WSHC
'Aquarius'	CBod EAEE EPPr EPed EWoo GQue IBoy IKil LRHS MSpe NDov WFar XLum
austromontana	see *M. citriodora* subsp. *austromontana*
§ 'Balance'	EBee ECtt MMrt MRav NBro NDov NGdn SHar WSHC XLum
'Beauty of Cobham' ♀^{H4}	Widely available
'Bergamo' **new**	MHol
§ 'Blaustrumpf'	CElw EAJP ECtt EPfP EWes EWoo LRHS NLar SPer WHea WSHC XLum
Blue Stocking	see *M.* 'Blaustrumpf'
Bowman	see *M.* 'Sagittarius'
bradburyana	CBWd GJos LPla MMuc MNrw SAko SBrt SPhx
- 'Ozark' **new**	SAko
'Cambridge Scarlet'	Widely available
'Capricorn'	XLum
citriodora	GPoy MNHC NSti SIde SRms
§ - subsp. ***austromontana***	NBir
- - 'Bee's Favourite'	IKil
'Comanche'	EWes NLar
'Croftway Pink'	Widely available
didyma	CBod CNec ENfk EPfP ESps NBro SRms SVic SWat WHar WJek
- 'Alba'	NLar
- 'Balmy Purple' **new**	MHol
- 'Coral Reef'	EWes LRHS
- 'Cranberry Lace'^{PBR}	CBot CRos EBee ECtt EPfP LRHS MSCN NLar NRHS SHil SPoG

- 'Duddiscombe'	CSam
- 'Pardon my Pink' **new**	NPnk
- 'Pink Lace' PBR	CBot CRos ECtt IBoy LRHS LSou LSun MHol MNrw NDov NHol NLar NRHS SCob SHil SPoG WHil WMoo
- 'Sugar Lace' PBR	LRHS NLar NRHS
'Earl Grey'	CBod EBee ECtt GAbr MSpe NDov SCoo
'Elsie's Lavender'	EBee EPfP LRHS NDov NLar
'Elworthy'	CElw WWFP
§ 'Feuerschopf'	EBee
'Fireball' PBR	Widely available
Firecrown	see *M.* 'Feuerschopf'
§ 'Fishes'	CMac EAEE EBee ECtt EHrv ELan EPPr EWes EWoo IKil LEdu LRHS LSou MRav MSpe NDov NGdn NLar SGbt SPoG SWvt WPtf
fistulosa	CBod CHby CMac CMea GJos MArt MMuc MNHC SRms WJek WMoo XLum
- var. ***menthifolia*** 'Mohikaner'	NDov SAko
'Gardenview Scarlet' ♀H4	CBot CElw CRos CSam CWCL EAEE ECtt EWes GCra GQue IBoy IKil LCro LEdu LRHS MCot MMuc MNrw MPie MWat NDov NFav NHol NSti SSut SWvt WCot WHoo
Gemini	see *M.* 'Twins'
'Gewitterwolke'	CSam MNrw NDov
'Hartswood Wine'	ECtt EWes LEdu
'Heidelerche'	EBee
'Jacob Cline'	EAJP ECtt EPPr EWes GBin GWyn IPot LPla LRHS MBel MNrw MSpe NBre NCGa NLar SGbt SHar SMHy SPhx WBor WMoo XLum
'Kardinal'	GBin LRHS MTis NDov NLar XLum
'Lambada'	GJos
'Lederstrumpf' **new**	EBee
Libra	see *M.* 'Balance'
'Loddon Crown'	CTsd CWld ECtt ELon GQue LPla LRHS MTis NHol NLar SHar SIde WFar WSHC
'Mahogany'	EAEE EBee ECtt ELan EPed ESps EWTr GBuc GMaP GQue IBoy IKil IPot LRHS MCot MNrw MRav MSpe MTis NSti SCob SPer SPhx XLum
'Marshall's Delight' ♀H4	CBod CWCL EAEE EBee ECtt EWes GQue IBoy LRHS MNrw MRav NDov NLar NRHS SWvt WHoo
'Melissa'	EBee LSRN NBre NLar WSHC
menthifolia	SRms
'Mohawk'	EAEE ECtt EHrv EPPr EPed EPfP ESps GMcL GQue ILea LRHS MPie MRav MSpe NDov NGdn SDix SPoG WPtf XLum
'Mrs Perry'	EWes
'Neon'	NDov SPhx
'On Parade'	CElw CSam CWCL CWld EAEE ECtt GPSL LEdu LPla LRHS MMrt MTis NDov NGdn
'Othello'	NDov
'Ou Charm'	EBee EWes NLar
Panorama Series	SPlb WMoo
- 'Panorama Red Shades'	CWib EPfP MNHC WCFE WMoo
Petite Delight = 'Acpetdel'	ELan LSou NLar SPad XLum
'Petite Wonder'	EBee
'Pink Supreme' PBR	CBct CBod CRos ECtt ELan ELon GMcL LEdu LRHS LSou MSpe NDov NLar NRHS SCoo SHil WHil WMoo WTor
'Pink Tourmaline'	NDov
Pisces	see *M.* 'Fishes'
'Poyntzfield Pink'	GPoy LEdu LPla
Prairie Night	see *M.* 'Prärienacht'
§ 'Prärienacht'	Widely available
punctata	GJos MMuc MNHC SWat
'Purple Ann'	XLum
'Purple Lace' **new**	NDov
'Purple Tower'	EWes
'Raspberry Wine'	CBod EAEE EBee ECtt EPPr EWes LEdu LRHS WMoo WPGP
'Ruby Glow'	CSam EHrv GMcL GWyn LRHS LSRN MMrt
§ 'Sagittarius'	EAEE EBee LRHS MBNS MMrt MSpe NGdn NSti
'Saxon Purple'	LPla NDov NLar XLum
§ 'Schneewittchen'	CBWd CBod EAJP EBee ECha ECtt EHrv ELan EPfP IBoy LCro LRHS MRav MTis NHol NLar NSti SCob SCoo SCbt SIde SPer SPoG SWvt WCAu WHar WHlf XLum
'Scorpion'	CBWd EBee ECtt EHrv ELan EPPr EPfP EWTr GBin GMcL IBoy LCro LEdu LRHS MRav NBir NDov NEgg NGdn NLar NSti SBod SWvt WCAu WSHC XLum
'Shelley'	ECha
'Sioux'	EHrv EWes
'Snow Maiden'	see *M.* 'Schneewittchen'
'Snow Queen'	EBee ECtt EWTr LRHS MBel MPie NDov
Snow White	see *M.* 'Schneewittchen'
'Squaw' ♀H4	Widely available
'Talud' ♀H4	MNrw NDov
§ 'Twins'	CWCL GKev LSRN NLar SWvt WSHC
'Vintage Wine'	CElw CWCL MMuc NDov
'Violacea'	NHol
'Violet Queen' ♀H4	CBod CWCL EAEE EBee ECtt ELan EWes GQue LEdu LRHS MAvo MBel MCot MSpe NEoE SCoo WFar WPtf
'Violette'	EBee
'Westacre Purple'	EBee EPPr EWes

Monardella (*Lamiaceae*)

macrantha subsp. ***hallii***	CPBP
nana subsp. ***arida***	CPBP
odoratissima	MHer

Monochoria (*Pontederiaceae*)

§ ***hastata***	LLWG MSKA

Monstera (*Araceae*)

deliciosa (F) ♀H1b	XBlo

Montbretia see *Crocosmia*

Montia (*Portulacaceae*)

perfoliata	see *Claytonia perfoliata*
sibirica	see *Claytonia sibirica*

Moraea (*Iridaceae*)

algoensis	WCot
alticola	CPne ECho GBin GCal GKev SPlb
§ ***aristata***	CTal NRog
atropunctata	NRog
§ ***bellendenii***	NRog WCot
bipartita	NRog WCot
ciliata	NRog WCot
citrina	ECho

§ ***collina***	ECho GKev NRog
elegans	ECho
flaccida	ECho
§ ***fugax***	WCot
gawleri	WCot
gigandra	NRog WCot
glaucopsis	see *M. aristata*
huttonii	CCCN CFis CSpe CTre CTsd EPri GAbr MHer SBrt SMad WCot WKif WSHC
incurva	ECho
iridioides	see *Dietes iridioides*
longifolia Sweet	see *M. fugax*
longifolia (Jacq.) Pers.	MHol
loubseri	NRog
lugubris	NRog
lurida	CTal WCot
macrocarpa	NRog
mediterranea	GKev
neglecta	ECho
ochroleuca	ECho GKev NRog
pavonia var. ***lutea***	see *M. bellendenii*
polystachya	CGrW ECho NRog
setifolia	ECho
sisyrinchium	ECho GKev
- purple-flowered	ECho
spathacea	see *M. spathulata*
§ ***spathulata***	EBee ECho GCal GKev WCot
thomsonii	NRog
tricolor	ECho
tricuspidata	NRog
tripetala	NRog
tulbaghensis	NRog
vegeta	CTal ECho NRog WCot
villosa	CTal ECho NRog

Morella (*Myricaceae*)

californica	CAgr
pensylvanica	CAgr CArn CDul IVic NLar

Moricandia (*Brassicaceae*)

moricandioides	WCot

Morina (*Caprifoliaceae*)

* ***afghanica***	GAbr
alba	GCra
bulleyana	see *M. nepatensis* var. *delavayi*
longifolia	Widely available
§ ***nepatensis*** var. ***delavayi***	GKev
persica	EWes
polyphylla	GPoy

Morinda (*Rubiaceae*)

umbellata WWJ 11688	WCru

Morisia (*Brassicaceae*)

hypogaea	see *M. monanthos*
§ ***monanthos***	CPla CTsd GCrg GEdr LRHS SRot
- 'Fred Hemingway'	ELan EPot LRHS NSla WAbe

Morus ✿ (*Moraceae*)

§ ***alba***	CArn CBcs CCVT CDul CHab CLnd CMCN CWib ECrN ELan EMOT EPfP ERea ESps LBuc LHop MRav SDea SPre SVic WFar WHar WTSh
- 'Baby Doll' **new**	CBot
- 'Black Tabor'	CAgr
- 'Issai'	GKev MGos
- 'Laciniata'	ELan
- 'Macrophylla'	CMCN MBlu
- 'Pakistan' (F)	CAgr ERea
- 'Paradise'	CAgr WMat
- 'Pendula'	CAgr CDul CEnd CMCN CMac CTri ECrN ELan ESps MBlu NOra NPri SCoo SLim SPoG SWvt WMat
- 'Platanifolia'	CLnd MBlu
- 'San Martin'	ERea
- var. ***tatarica***	CAgr LEdu NLar
'Capsrum' (F)	CAgr WMat
'Carmen' (F)	CAgr WMat
cathayana **new**	WPGP
'Illinois Everbearing' (F)	CAgr ERea WMat
'Italian' (F)	CAgr WMat
'Ivory' (F)	CAgr WMat
kagayamae	see *M. alba*
latifolia 'Spirata'	NLar
nigra (F)	Widely available
§ - 'Chelsea' (F) ♀H6	CDul CEnd CTho CTri ECrN EPfP EPom ERea GTwe IVic LRHS MGos NOra NWea SCoo SEWo SKee SLim SPer SPoG WHar WMat
- 'Izvor' (F)	CAgr
- 'Jerusalem' (F) ♀H6	MCoo NOra WHar WMat
- 'King James'	see *M. nigra* 'Chelsea'
- 'Large Black' (F)	EPom
- 'Repsime' (F)	CAgr
- 'Sham Dudu' (F)	CAgr
rubra	NLar
- 'Nana'	NLar
'Wellington' (F)	CCVT CEnd CLnd EMOT GTwe LCro LOPS LRHS LSRN NOra WMat

Mosla (*Lamiaceae*)

dianthera	EWld GCal MAvo

Muehlenbeckia (*Polygonaceae*)

astonii	EBee LRHS WPGP
axillaris misapplied	see *M. complexa*
§ ***axillaris*** (Hook. f.) Endl.	CBcs CTri EShb GBin SBig XLum
§ ***complexa***	CBcs CFlo CMac CTri CWib EBee EPfP EShb ETod EUJe LRHS MBlu MGil NQui SAdn SArc SCob SEND SLim SLon SNig SPer SPoG SWvt WCFE WPGP WSHC XLum
- 'Nana'	see *M. axillaris* (Hook. f.) Endl.
- small-leaved	EUJe
- 'Spotlight'[PBR] (v)	EShb
- var. ***trilobata***	CBcs EShb ESwi EUJe SSta XLum
platyclados	see *Homalocladium platycladum*

Muhlenbergia (*Poaceae*)

capillaris	EBee SDix SHDw SMad WCot
dumosa	CKno SMad WCot WPGP
japonica 'Cream Delight' (v)	EHoe
lindheimeri	CKno SDix SMea WCot
mexicana	SRms
rigens	CKno XLum

Mukdenia (*Saxifragaceae*)

acanthifolia	GCal LEdu WPGP
rossii	CAby CLAP CTal EHrv ELon EWTr GBin GCal IFro LEdu LPla LRHS MBel MNrw NBid NCGa NLar NPnk WCru WOld WPGP WSHC WThu XLum
- from Japan	GCal
- from Korea **new**	GCal
- 'Crimson Fans'	see *M. rossii* 'Karasuba'
- dwarf	CLAP CTal GCal MNrw

§	– 'Karasuba'	Widely available
	– 'Shishiba'	LEdu NPnk

mulberry see *Morus*

Murraya (*Rutaceae*)

	exotica	see *M. paniculata*
	koenigii	EOHP GPoy SCit SPre SVen WJek WSFF
§	***paniculata***	EShb

Musa ✿ (*Musaceae*)

	from Yunnan, China	see *M. itinerans* 'Yunnan'
§	***acuminata***	IDee
§	– 'Dwarf Cavendish' (AAA Group) (F) ♀H1b	CBct CTsd ELan LHop NLos NPla XBlo
	– 'Siam Ruby' (AA Group) (F)	NLos
	– 'Williams' (AAA Group) (F)	XBlo
	– 'Zebrina' ♀H1b	CDTJ LRHS NLos XBlo
	basjoo ♀H2	CAbb CAby CBcs CHll CSBt ELan EPfP EUJe LCro LEdu LTro MGos MMuc NLos NPla SArc SChr SEND SMad SPlb SPoG SSal
I	– 'Rubra'	CCCN ESwi
	'Cavendish Super Dwarf'	NLos XBlo
	cavendishii	see *M. acuminata* 'Dwarf Cavendish'
§	***coccinea*** ♀H1b	XBlo
	ensete	see *Ensete ventricosum*
	hookeri	see *M. sikkimensis*
	itinerans	NLos
	– var. ***xishuangbannaensis*** 'Mekong Giant'	EUJe
§	– 'Yunnan'	NLos
	lasiocarpa ♀H1c	CDTJ CHll ESwi EUJe LTro MGos MPkF NLos NPla SBig SPlb
	nana misapplied	see *M. acuminata* 'Dwarf Cavendish'
	nana Lour.	see *M. acuminata*
	ornata ♀H1b	CCCN XBlo
	× ***paradisiaca*** 'Ney Poovan' (AB Group) (F)	CCCN
§	***sikkimensis*** ♀H1c	CDTJ EUJe LTro NLos SBig SPlb XBlo
	– 'Red Tiger'	CCCN CDTJ NLos
	uranoscopus misapplied	see *M. coccinea*
	velutina ♀H1b	CCCN NLos SBig

Muscari ✿ (*Asparagaceae*)

	adilii	NRog
	'Aleyna'	ECho NRog
	ambrosiacum	see *M. muscarimi*
	anatolicum	ECho NRog WCot
	armeniacum ♀H5	CBro CRos CTri ECho GKev GWyn LCro LOPS LPot LRHS MMuc NRHS NRog SCob SDir SEND SPer SRms WCot WShi
	– PAB 6748	LEdu
	– 'Album'	SCob
	– 'Argaei Album'	ECho GKev NRog
	– 'Artist'	GKev NRog
	– 'Atlantic'	CRos ECho EPfP GKev LRHS NRHS NRog
	– 'Blue Pearl'	ECho NRog
	– 'Blue Spike' (d)	CBro ECho GKev LAma NBir NEgg NRog SDeJ SDir WGwG
	– 'Cantab'	ECho SDeJ XLum
	– 'Christmas Pearl' ♀H4	ECho GKev NNys NPnk NRog WCot
	– 'Cupido'	GKev
	– 'Dark Eyes'	ECho EPfP GKev IBoy SCob SDir
	– 'Early Giant'	ECho SDeJ
	– 'Fantasy Creation'	ECho GKev NRog SDeJ
	– 'Gül'	WCot
	– 'Heavenly Blue'	ECho
	– 'Icicle'	WHil
	– 'Lady Blu'	GKev LRHS
	– 'New Creation'	ECho
	– 'Peppermint'	CAvo CRos ECho ERCP GKev LAma LRHS SDir WBor
	– 'Saffier' ♀H5	ECho GKev LAma NRog WCot WHil
	– 'Siberian Tiger'	EPot GKev WTor
	– 'Touch of Snow' **new**	GKev
	– 'Valerie Finnis'	CAby CAvo CBre CBro CTca ECho EPPr EPfP EPot ERCP EShb GKev LRHS NLar NPnk SCob SDeJ SDir SMad SPhx WBrk WCot
	aucheri ♀H5	ECho NRya
*	– var. ***bicolor***	WCot
	– 'Blue Magic'	CAvo ECho EPot ERCP GKev LAma NRog SDeJ
	– 'Ocean Magic'	CAvo CBro ECho GKev LAma NHpl NLar NPnk
§	– 'Tubergenianum'	ECho
	– 'White Magic'	CAvo CBro ECho ERCP GKev LAma LRHS NHpl SCob SDeJ WBor WBrk
§	***azureum*** ♀H5	CAvo CBro CTca ECho ELan ERCP GKev GMaP LAma LPot LRHS NLar NRog SPhx WCot
	– 'Album'	ECho GKev LAma MBel NRog SPhx WCot
	– 'Bling Bling'	CBro ECho ERCP GKev LAma LRHS
	'Baby's Breath'	see *M.* 'Jenny Robinson'
	'Big Smile'	GKev NRog WCot WRHF
	'Blue Dream'	ECho
	'Blue Eyes'	ECho WCot
	'Blue Star'	ECho
	botryoides	CAvo ECho LAma NRog SCob WCot
	– 'Album'	CAvo CBro CTca CTri ECho EPfP GKev LAma LCro LOPS NRog SCob SDeJ SRms WCot WShi
	bourgaei	ECho GKev WCot
	caucasicum	ECho WCot
	chalusicum	see *M. pseudomuscari*
	coeleste	GKev
	commutatum	ECho GKev
§	***comosum***	CBro ECho ERCP GKev MCot NEgg NRog SDir WCot
	– 'Monstrosum'	see *M. comosum* 'Plumosum'
	– 'Pinard'	ECho
§	– 'Plumosum'	ECho ELan EPfP GKev LAma NRog SCob SDeJ WCot
	dionysicum	ECho
	– HOA 8965	ECho
	discolor	ECho GKev NRog
	inconstrictum	ECho
	'Ivor's Pink'	WCot
§	'Jenny Robinson' ♀H5	ECho EHrv GKev IFoB LAma LRHS MArt NPnk SDys SMad WCot
	'Joyce Spirit' **new**	GKev LAma LRHS
	latifolium ♀H5	CAby CBro CRos CTca ECho EPfP ERCP GKev LAma LCro LRHS MWat NEgg NLar NNys NRHS NRog SCob SDeJ SDir WBor WCot
*	– 'Blue Angels'	NBir
	macbeathianum	WCot
§	***macrocarpum***	CBro CTal CTca ECha ECho EPot LAma NRog

– 'Golden Fragrance' PBR	CAby CAvo CBro CHid ECho EPot ERCP GKev IFoB LAma MCot MNrw NPnk NRog SDeJ WHil
'Marieke' **new**	GKev
'Memory of Gary Fisher' **new**	WCot
'Morgenhimmel' **new**	GKev
moschatum	see *M. muscarimi*
'Mount Hood'	CBro ECho ERCP GKev MBel NPnk SCob SDeJ
'Mountain Lady' **new**	GKev
§ ***muscarimi***	CAvo CBro CTca ECho GKev IFoB LAma NRog SDeJ WCot
– var. ***flavum***	see *M. macrocarpum*
§ ***neglectum***	ECho GKev LAma MMuc NLar NRog SEND WCot WShi
pallens	ECho GKev NRog
paradoxum	see *Bellevalia paradoxa*
parviflorum	ECho WCot
'Pink Sunrise'	CBro ECho EPot ERCP EWTr GKev NHpl SCob
'Pink Surprise' **new**	LAma
§ ***pseudomuscari*** ♀H5	ECho GKev WCot
racemosum	see *M. neglectum*
'Rosy Sunrise'	MArt WCot
'Sky Blue'	ECho GKev WCot
§ ***spreitzenhoferi***	NRog
'Superstar'	ECho GKev
§ ***tenuiflorum***	ECho WCot
aff. ***tenuiflorum*** JCA 0.691.251	WCot
tubergenianum	see *M. aucheri* 'Tubergenianum'
'Venus'	GKev NPnk SDir WCot
verticillaris **new**	GKev
'White Beauty'	ECho GKev
'Winter Amethyst'	WCot

Muscarimia (*Asparagaceae*)

ambrosiacum	see *Muscari muscarimi*
macrocarpum	see *Muscari macrocarpum*

Musella see *Musa*

Mussaenda (*Rubiaceae*)

'Tropic Snow'	CCCN

Mutisia (*Asteraceae*)

oligodon	GKev

Myoporum (*Scrophulariaceae*)

acuminatum	see *M. tenuifolium*
laetum	IDee SPlb SVen
parvifolium	EBee
§ ***tenuifolium***	SPlb SVen

Myosotidium (*Boraginaceae*)

§ ***hortensia***	CAbb CAby CBcs CBct CSpe ECre EPot ETod EUJe EWes EWoo GBin GCal GKev IBoy IKil LEdu LRHS WBor
– 'True Blue'	CHid
– white-flowered	IKil
nobile	see *M. hortensia*

Myosotis (*Boraginaceae*)

from Eyre Mountains, New Zealand	EPot
capitata	GEdr
decumbens	GEdr
dissitiflora 'Elegantissima' (v) **new**	CNat
glabrescens **new**	EPot
'Malmesbury'	CNat
My Oh My = 'Myomark' PBR	LSou
palustris	see *M. scorpioides*
pulvinaris	CPBP SPlb
§ ***scorpioides***	CBen CHab CWCL CWat MMuc MNrw MSKA MWLS MWts NMir SCoo SPlb SRms SWat WBrk WMAq WMoo WPnP WRHF XLum
– 'Alba'	MSKA MWts NPnk
– 'Ice Pearl'	ECha
– Maytime = 'Blaqua' (v)	LLWG NBir
– 'Mermaid'	CBen CWat ECha EWay LLWG SDix SWat WPtf
– 'Pinkie'	CWat LLWG SWat
– 'Snowflakes'	CWat EWay SWat
– variegated (v)	MSKA
sylvatica	LCro MMuc NMir
– (Sylva Series) 'Bluesylva'	LRHS SPhx
– – 'Rosylva'	CWCL
– 'Ultramarine'	WMoo
– 'Victoria Indigo-blue' (Victoria Series)	CWCL EPfP
traversii	SBch

Myrica (*Myricaceae*)

gale	CAgr GPoy IVic NLar SWat WGwG

Myricaria (*Tamaricaceae*)

germanica	NLar

Myriophyllum (*Haloragaceae*)

propinquum	LLWG
spicatum	MSKA MWts WMAq
verticillatum	CWat EWay MSKA SCoo

Myrrhis (*Apiaceae*)

odorata	CArn CBre CHby CLau CMac CSpe ECha ENfk GBin GPoy IFro LHop LRHS MHer MMuc MNHC NPri SCob SDix SIde SPad SPer SRms SWvt WHlf WJek WPGP WSFF WWFP
– 'Forncett Chevron'	LEdu

Myrsine (*Primulaceae*)

africana	CBcs CFil CWib EShb MHer
australis	SVen
divaricata	SVen

Myrteola (*Myrtaceae*)

§ ***nummularia***	GAbr ITim NHar WAbe WThu

Myrtus ✿ (*Myrtaceae*)

apiculata misapplied	see *Luma apiculata*
bullata	see *Lophomyrtus bullata*
chequen	see *Luma chequen*
communis ♀H4	Widely available
– 'Flore Pleno' (d)	MHer
– 'Jenny Reitenbach'	see *M. communis* subsp. *tarentina*
– 'Merion'	WJek
– 'Microphylla'	see *M. communis* subsp. *tarentina*
– 'Nana'	see *M. communis* subsp. *tarentina*
– 'Pyewood Park'	SRms WJek
§ – subsp. ***tarentina*** ♀H4	Widely available
– – 'Compacta'	SCoo SLon
– – 'Microphylla Variegata' (v)	CBcs EShb LRHS MHer MNHC SPer SRms WHar WJek
I – – 'Variegata' (v)	CBod CLet EPfP
– 'Tricolor'	see *M. communis* 'Variegata'

§ - 'Variegata' (v) — CArn CBot CLet CMCN CMac CSBt CTri CWib CWld ELan ELon ENfk EPfP EShb LEdu LHop LRHS MGil MHer MSwo NLar SEND SGbt SLon SPer SPoG WCFE WJek WSHC
'Glanleam Gold' — see *Luma apiculata* 'Glanleam Gold'
lechleriana — see *Amomyrtus luma*
luma — see *Luma apiculata*
nummularia — see *Myrteola nummularia*
ugni — see *Ugni molinae*

N

Nabalus (*Asteraceae*)

albus — see *Prenanthes alba*

Nandina (*Berberidaceae*)

Blush Pink = 'Aka'PBR — CMac LRHS SCob SPoG
domestica — Widely available
- B&SWJ 4923 — LPar WCru
- B&SWJ 11113 — LPar WCru
- 'Filamentosa' — EBee EPfP NLar SCob
- 'Fire Power' — Widely available
- Flirt = 'Murasaki'PBR — LRHS SCob
- 'Gulf Stream' — LBuc LRHS MGos NLar
- 'Harbour Dwarf' — CEnd LRHS NLar WFar
- 'Lemon-Lime' **new** — LCro
- var. ***leucocarpa*** — CMCN NLar
- 'Nana' — see *N. domestica* 'Pygmaea'
- Plum Passion = 'Monum' — CRos EPfP LCro LRHS MAsh MGos SCob SPoG
§ - 'Pygmaea' — CMen SGol
- 'Richmond' 🏆H5 — CBcs CBot CDul CRos EBee ELan EPfP LRHS MAsh MGos NLar NPri SCob SHil SLim SPer SPoG SWvt WFar
- 'Seika'PBR — CBot CMac CRos EBee ELan EPfP EUJe LCro LPar LRHS LSou MGos MHtn MPkF SCob SHil SMad SPoG
- Sienna Sunrise = 'Monfar' — LCro LOPS
- 'Sunset'PBR — EBee LSRN NLar SCob
- 'Tuscan Flame' **new** — LRHS
- 'Wood's Dwarf' — CBcs MPkF NLar

Nannorrhops (*Arecaceae*)

arabica — see *N. ritchieana*
§ ***ritchieana*** — LTro SPlb

Napaea (*Malvaceae*)

dioica — SPhx WCot

Narcissus ✿ (*Amaryllidaceae*)

'Abalone' (2) — CQua
'Abba' (4) 🏆H6 — CFen CQua
'Abbey Road' (5) — CQua
'Aberfoyle' (2) 🏆H6 — CQua
'Abstract' (11a) — CQua
'Accent' (2) — CQua GKev
'Accomplice' (3) — IRhd
'Achduart' (3) — CQua
'Achentoul' (4) — CQua
'Achnasheen' (3) — CQua
'Acropolis' (4) — CQua GKev SDeJ
'Actaea' (9) 🏆H6 — CBro CFen CQua GBin GKev LCro LOPS NNys SCob SDeJ SDir
'Acumen' (2) — CQua
'Admiration' (8) — CQua
'Adorable Lass' (6) — CQua
'Ad-Rem' (2) — CFen
'Adversane' (3) — CQua
'Advocat' (3) — CQua
'Aflame' (3) — CFen
'African Sunset' (3) — IRhd
'After All' (3) — CFen
'Agnes Mace' (2) — IRhd
'Ahwahnee' (2) — CQua IRhd
'Ainley' (2) — CQua
'Aintree' (3) — CQua
'Aircastle' (3) — CQua
'Airtime' (2) — IRhd
'Akepa' (5) — CQua
'Akita' (2) **new** — GKev
'Albatross' (3) — CQua GCro WShi
'Albus Plenus Odoratus' — see *N. poeticus* 'Plenus' ambig.
'Alex Jones' (2) — CQua
'Alice Knights' (1) — GCro
'All Rounder' (3) — IRhd
'Alpine Winter' (1) — IRhd
'Alto' (2) — IRhd
'Altruist' (3) — CQua ERCP SDeJ
'Altun Ha' (2) — CQua IRhd MGib
'Amabilis' (3) — GCro
'Amadeus Mozart' (2) — CQua
'Amazing Grace' (2) — CQua IRhd
'Amber Castle' (2) — CQua
'Ambergate' (2) — CQua GKev LAma SDeJ SDir
'Ambergris Caye' (1) — CQua
'American Dream' (1) — CQua
'American Goldfinch' (7) — CQua
'American Heritage' (1) — CQua
'American Robin' (6) — CQua
'Amstel' (4) — CQua
'Andalusia' (6) — CQua
'Andrew's Choice' (7) 🏆H6 — CQua
'Angel' (3) — CQua
'Angel Face' (3) — CQua IRhd
'Angel Wings' — see *N.* 'Celtic Wings'
'Angel's Breath' (5) 🏆H6 — CQua
Angel's tears — see *N. triandrus* subsp. *triandrus* var. *triandrus*
'Angel's Whisper' (5) — CQua
'Angel's Wings' (2) — CQua
'Angels Wood' (2) — IRhd
'Angkor' (4) — CQua MGib
'An-gof' (7) — CQua
'Animal Crackers' (2) — CQua
'Ann Sonia' (4) — IRhd
'Anna Panna' (3) — IRhd
'Annequin' (3) — CQua
'Apollo Gold' (10) — CQua ECho NHpl
'Apotheose' (4) — CFen SDeJ
'Apricot' (1) — CBro GCro
'Apricot Whirl' (11a) — CQua GKev
'April Dawn' (2) — IRhd
'April Love' (1) — CQua
'April Snow' (2) — CQua
'Ara' (6) — CQua
'Aranjuez' (2) — CFen CQua
'Arctic Gem' (3) — CQua
'Arctic Gold' (1) 🏆H6 — CQua LAma
'Ard Righ' (1) — GCro
'Areley Kings' (2) — CQua
'Argent' (4) — CQua GCro
'Argosy' (1) — CQua
'Arid Plains' (3) — IRhd
'Ariel'PBR (8) — GKev

'Ark Royal' (1)	CFen
'Arkle' (1) ♀H6	CQua GKev SDeJ
'Arleston' (2)	CQua IRhd
'Armada' (2)	CFen CQua
'Armidale' (3)	CQua IRhd
'Armoury' (4)	CQua
'Arndilly' (2)	CQua
'Arpege' (2)	CQua
'Arthurian' (1)	IRhd
'Articol' (11a)	CQua
'Arwenack' (11a)	CQua
'Ashland' (2)	IRhd
'Ashmore' (2)	CQua IRhd
'Ashton Wold' (2)	CQua
'Asila' (2)	IRhd
'Assertion' (2)	IRhd
§ ***assoanus*** (13)	ECho EPot GCal LLHF WCot
'Astropink' (11a)	CQua
§ ***asturiensis*** (13)	GKev LLHF SEND
– giant	see *N. asturiensis* 'Wavertree'
§ – 'Wavertree' (1)	CQua LLHF
'Atholl Palace' (4)	MGib
'Atlas Gold'	see *N. romieuxii* 'Atlas Gold'
'Atricilla' (11a)	IRhd
'Auchranie' (2)	IRhd
'Audubon' (2)	CQua GKev SDeJ
'Aunt Betty' (1)	CQua
'Auntie Eileen' (2)	CQua
§ ***aureus*** (13)	CQua
'Auspicious' (2)	IRhd
'Autocrat' (2)	GCro
'Autumn Habit' (3)	IRhd
'Avalanche' (8) ♀H4	CFen CQua EPfP GKev LCro LOPS SDeJ
'Avalanche of Gold' (8)	CQua
'Avalon' (2)	CQua ERCP GKev
'Avon Mill' (1)	MGib
'Baby Boomer' (7)	ERCP GKev LAma
'Baby Moon' (7)	CAby CFen CQua CTca EPfP EPot ERCP GKev LAma SDeJ
'Back Flash' (2)	CQua
'Badanloch' (3)	CQua
'Badbury Rings' (3) ♀H6	CQua IRhd
'Bailey' (2)	IRhd
'Bala' (4)	CQua
'Balalaika' (2)	CQua
'Baldock' (4)	CQua
'Ballydorn' (9)	IRhd
'Ballygarvey' (1)	CQua
'Ballyrobert' (1)	CQua
'Balvenie' (2)	CQua
'Bandesara' (3)	CQua
'Bandit' (2)	CQua IRhd
'Banker' (2)	CQua IRhd
'Banstead Village' (2)	CQua
'Bantam' (2) ♀H6	CBro CQua GKev SDeJ
'Barbara Hunt' (7)	CQua
'Barbary Gold' (2)	CQua
'Barn Dance' (3)	CQua
'Barnesgold' (1)	IRhd
'Barnham' (1)	CQua
'Barnsdale Wood' (2)	CQua
'Barnum' (1) ♀H6	IRhd
'Barrett Browning' (3)	GKev SDeJ
'Barrii' (3)	CQua
'Bath's Flame' (3)	CAvo CQua GCro GKev WShi
'Bear Springs' (4)	IRhd
'Bear's Gold' (4)	CQua
'Beaulieu' (1)	CQua
'Beautiful Dream' (3)	CQua
'Beauvallon' (4)	SDeJ
'Bebop' (7)	CBro
'Bedruthan' (2)	CQua
'Beersheba' (1)	CQua GCro GKev
'Belbroughton' (2)	CQua
'Belcanto' (11a)	CQua GKev SDeJ
'Belisana' (2)	SDeJ
'Bell Rock' (1) ♀H6	CQua
'Bell Song' (7)	CBro CFen CMea CQua GKev LSou SDeJ WShi
'Bella Estrella' (11a)	ERCP GKev
'Bells of Joy' (5)	IRhd
'Belzone' (2)	CQua
'Ben Aligin' (1)	IRhd
'Ben Hee' (2)	CQua IRhd
'Berceuse' (2)	CQua
'Bere Ferrers' (4)	CQua
'Bergerac' (11a)	CQua
'Berlin' (2)	GKev
'Bernardino' (2)	CQua GCro
'Beryl' (6)	CQua GKev WShi
'Best Friend' (3)	CQua
'Best Seller' (1)	SPer
'Bethal' (3)	CQua
'Bethan-Sîan' (2)	CQua
'Betsy MacDonald' (6)	CQua
'Biffo' (4)	CQua
'Big Gun' (2) **new**	GKev
Biggar Bountiful (2)	GCro
'Bikini Beach' (2)	IRhd
'Bilbo' (6)	CBro CQua
'Billy Graham' (2)	CQua
'Binkie' (2)	CQua SPer
'Birchwood' (3)	CQua
'Birma' (3)	LAma SDeJ
'Birthday Girl' (2)	IRhd
'Bishops Light' (2)	CQua
'Bittern' (12)	CQua GKev SDeJ
'Blackstone' (2)	CQua
'Blair Athol' (2)	CQua
'Blakey' (2)	CQua
'Blarney' (3)	CQua
'Blisland' (9)	CQua
'Blossom' (4)	CQua
'Blossom Lady' (4)	CQua
'Blue Danube' (1)	CQua IRhd
'Blushing Maiden' (4)	CQua
'Bob Spotts' (2)	CQua
'Bobbysoxer' (7)	CBro CQua
'Bobolink' (2)	CQua
'Boconnoc' (2)	CQua
'Bodelva' (2)	CQua
'Bodwannick' (2)	CQua
'Bolton' (7)	GCro
'Bombay' (2)	CFen
'Bon Viveur' (11a)	IRhd
'Bonython' (1)	GCro
'Border Beauty' (2) ♀H6	CQua
'Bosbigal' (11a)	CQua
'Boscastle' (7)	CQua
'Boscoppa' (11a)	CQua
'Boslowick' (11a) ♀H6	CQua
'Bosmeor' (2)	CQua
'Bossa Nova' (3)	CQua
'Bossiney' (11a)	CQua
'Bosvale' (11a)	CQua
'Bosvigo' (11a)	CQua
'Boughton Park' (1)	MGib
'Boulder Bay' (2) ♀H6	IRhd
'Bouzouki' (2)	IRhd

'Boyne Bridge' (1)	IRhd
'Brackenhurst' (2)	SDeJ
'Brahms' (2)	CFen
'Brandaris' (11a)	CQua
'Bravoure' (1) ♀H6	CQua GBin GKev SDeJ
'Breezand Tristar' (11a) ♀H6 **new**	CBro
'Brentswood' (8)	CQua
'Brian's Favorite' (2)	CQua
'Bridal Crown' (4) ♀H6	CFen EPfP GKev LAma LCro LOPS LRHS NNys
'Brideshead' (2)	CFen
'Bright Flame' (2)	CQua
'Bright Spangles' (8)	IRhd
'Bright Spot' (8)	CQua
Brighterwell (2/3) **new**	GCro
'Brightling' (2) **new**	GCro
'Brilliancy' (3)	CQua GCro
'Brindaleena' (2)	IRhd
'Brindle Pink' (2)	IRhd
'Broadland' (2)	CQua
'Broadwalk Beauty' (2)	MGib
'Broadway Star' (11b)	LAma NNys SDeJ
'Broadway Village' (2)	CQua
'Brodick' (3)	CQua
'Bronzewing' (1)	IRhd
'Brooke Ager' (2) ♀H6	IRhd
'Broomhill' (2) ♀H6	CQua
'Broughshane' (1)	CQua GKev
broussonetii (13)	CFil GKev
- from Morocco	WPGP
'Brunswick' (2)	CFen GCro SDeJ
'Bryanston' (2) ♀H6	CQua
'Buckshead' (4)	CQua
'Budock Water' (2)	CQua
'Bugle Major' (2)	CQua
bulbocodium (13) ♀H4	CBro CRos GKev LCro LEdu LOPS LRHS NRHS SRms
§ - subsp. ***bulbocodium*** (13)	CBro MGib
§ - - var. ***citrinus*** (13)	CRos ENun GBuc LRHS NRHS
- - - 'Bayonne' **new**	CPne
- - var. ***conspicuus*** (13)	CAby CBro CQua CTca ECho ERCP GKev LAma MPie NNys SDeJ WCot WHea WShi XLum
* - - var. ***filifolius*** (13)	CBro
- - var. ***nivalis*** (13)	ECho EPot GKev
§ - Golden Bells Group (10)	CHid CQua CRos CTri CWCL ECho EPfP EPot GBin GKev LRHS MPie NHol NNys NPnk NRHS SCob SDeJ
- 'Ice Warrior' (10)	SKHP
- var. ***mesatlanticus***	see *N. romieuxii* subsp. *romieuxii* var. *mesatlanticus*
- subsp. ***obesus*** (13)	ECho GKev WAbe WCot
§ - - 'Diamond Ring' (10)	CQua ECho EPot GKev LAma MNrw SDir
- subsp. ***praecox*** (13)	ECho LRHS NRHS
- - var. ***paucinervis*** (13)	ECho GKev
- subsp. ***tananicus***	see *N. cantabricus* subsp. *tananicus*
- subsp. ***vulgaris***	see *N. bulbocodium* subsp. *bulbocodium*
'Bunclody' (2)	CQua
'Bunting' (7) ♀H6	CQua
'Burning Bush' (3)	IRhd
'Burning Ring' (3)	IRhd
'Burravoe' (1)	CQua
'Burt House' (2)	IRhd
'Busselton' (3)	IRhd
'Bute Park' (4)	CQua
'Butter and Eggs' (4)	GCro GKev
'Butterscotch' (2)	CQua
'Cabernet' (2)	IRhd
'Cacatua' (11a)	IRhd
'Cadgwith' (2)	CQua
'Cairngorm' (2)	SDeJ
'Cairntoul' (3)	CQua
'Calamansack' (2)	CQua
'Calgary' (4)	CQua GKev
'California Rose' (4)	CQua IRhd
'Camaraderie' (2)	IRhd
'Camelot' (2) ♀H6	CFen CQua SDeJ
'Cameo Angel' (2)	CQua
'Cameo Baron' (2)	CQua
'Cameo Frills' (2)	CQua
'Cameo Gem' (1)	CQua
'Cameo King' (2)	CQua
'Cameo Marie' (3)	CQua
'Camilla Duchess of Cornwall' (2)	CFen CQua
'Camoro' (10)	EPot
'Campernelli' (7)	CQua
'Campernelli Plenus'	see *N.* 'Double Campernelle'
'Campion' (9)	CQua IRhd MGib
'Canaliculatus' (8)	CFen CQua CTri ECho EPfP ERCP GKev LAma LCro LOPS LRHS NRHS SCob SDeJ SPer
canaliculatus Gussone	see *N. tazetta* subsp. *lacticolor*
canariensis (13)	CQua
'Canary' (7)	CQua
'Canarybird' (8)	CQua GKev
'Canasta' (11a)	CQua
'Candlepower' (1)	CQua
'Canisp' (2)	CQua
'Cantabile' (9) ♀H6	CQua MGib
cantabricus (13)	CPne CQua ECho
- subsp. ***cantabricus*** (13)	CFil EPot GKev
- - var. ***foliosus*** (13) ♀H4	CFil ECho GKev WAbe
- - var. ***kesticus*** (13)	MGib
- - var. ***petunioides*** (13)	GKev
- subsp. ***monophyllus*** (13)	MGib
§ - subsp. ***tananicus*** (13)	ECho
'Cantatrice' (1)	CQua
'Canterbury' (5)	CQua
'Canticle' (9)	IRhd
'Capax Plenus'	see *N.* 'Eystettensis'
'Cape Cornwall' (2)	CQua MGib
'Cape Helles' (3)	IRhd
'Cape Point' (2)	CQua IRhd
'Capisco' (3)	CQua
'Carbineer' (2)	CQua GCro SDeJ
'Cardiff' (2)	CFen CQua
'Cargreen' (9)	CQua
'Carib Gipsy' (2) ♀H6	CQua
'Caribbean Snow' (2)	CQua MGib
'Carlton' (2) ♀H6	CFen CQua EPfP GKev LAma LCro LOPS SCob SDeJ
'Carn Brea' (3)	CQua
'Carnearny' (3)	CQua
'Carnkeeran' (2)	CQua
'Carnkief' (2)	CQua
'Carnyorth' (11a)	CQua
'Carole Lombard' (3)	CQua
'Carolina Dale' (2)	IRhd
'Carra' (8)	CQua
'Carwinion' (2)	CQua
'Casiah' (2)	CQua
'Cassandra' (9)	GCro
'Cassata' (11a)	GKev LAma NBir SDeJ

'Cassopolis' (2)	CQua
'Castanets' (8)	CQua IRhd
'Casterbridge' (2)	CQua
'Castle Rings' (4)	CQua
'Castlerock' (2)	CFen
'Catalyst' (2)	IRhd
'Cataract' (1)	IRhd
'Catistock' (2)	CQua
'Causeway Gem' (6)	IRhd
'Causeway Ringer' (3)	IRhd
'Causeway Sunset' (2)	IRhd MGib
'Causeway Sunshine' (1)	IRhd
'Causeway Torch' (2)	IRhd
'Causeway Winner' (2)	IRhd
'Cavalli King' (4)	CQua
'Cavalryman' (3)	IRhd
'Caye Chapel' (3)	CQua
'Cazique' (6)	CQua
× ***cazorlanus*** (13)	EPot
'Cedar Hills' (3)	CQua
'Cedric Morris' (1)	CHid CLAP CQua ECha EWoo GBuc
'Celestial Fire' (2)	CQua
'Celtic Gold' (2)	CQua
§ 'Celtic Wings' (5)	IRhd
'Centenary Gold' (2)	CQua
'Centrefold' (3)	CQua
'Cernuus Plenus' (4)	GCro
'Cha-cha' (6)	CBro CQua
'Changing Colors' (11a)	GKev SDeJ
'Chanson' (1) ♀H6	CQua IRhd MGib
'Chanterelle' (11a)	GKev LAma SDeJ
'Charity May' (6)	CQua
'Charleston' (2)	CQua
'Charlie Connor' (1)	CQua MGib
Charlotte van Plemp (1)	GCro
'Chasseur' (2)	IRhd
'Chaste' (1)	CQua IRhd
'Chat' (7)	CQua
'Cheer Leader' (3)	CQua
'Cheerfulness' (4) ♀H6	CAvo CFen CQua ESps GKev LAma LCro LOPS NNys NPer SDeJ
'Cheesewring' (3)	CQua
'Cheetah' (1)	IRhd
'Chelsea Girl' (2)	CQua
'Cheltenham' (2)	CQua
'Chérie' (7)	CQua
'Cherish' (2)	CQua
'Cherry Glow' (3)	IRhd
'Cherry Ice' (2)	CQua
'Cherrygardens' (2)	CQua IRhd
'Chesapeake Bay' (1)	CQua
'Chesterton' (9) ♀H6	CQua
'Chickadee' (6)	CQua
'Chicken Hill' (1)	CQua
'Chickerell' (3)	CQua
'Chief Inspector' (1)	CQua IRhd
'Chiffon' (2)	CFen
'Chiloquin' (1)	CQua
'China Doll' (2)	CQua MGib
'China Gold' (10)	CQua GKev
'Chinchilla' (2)	CQua
'Chingah' (1)	IRhd
'Chinita' (8)	CQua
'Chipper' (5)	CQua
'Chit Chat' (7) ♀H4	CQua LLHF MGib SDeJ SPlb
'Chiva' (7)	GKev LLHF
'Chobe River' (1)	CQua IRhd
'Chortle' (3)	IRhd
'Chromacolor' (2) ♀H6	GKev
'Chukar' (4) ♀H6	IRhd
'Churchfield Bells' (5)	CQua
'Churston Ferrers' (4)	CQua
'Chy Noweth' (2)	CQua
'Cinder Hill' (2)	IRhd
'Cisticola' (3)	CQua IRhd
citrinus	see *N. bulbocodium* subsp. *bulbocodium* var. *citrinus*
'Citron' (3)	CQua
'Citronita' (3)	CQua
'Citrus Souffle' (4)	IRhd
'Clare' (7)	CQua MGib
'Classic Gold' (10) ♀H6	CQua GKev
'Claverley' (2)	CQua MGib
'Clean Sweep' (3)	IRhd
'Cloth of Gold' (8)	CQua
'Cloud Nine' (2)	CBro
'Clouded Yellow' (2)	CQua MGib
'Clouds Hill' (4)	CQua
'Clouds Rest' (2)	IRhd
'Clovelly Ayr' (9)	CQua
'Codlins and Cream'	see *N.* 'Sulphur Phoenix'
'Coker's Frome' (9)	CQua
'Coldbrook' (2)	CQua
'Colin's Joy' (2)	CQua
'Coliseum' (2)	IRhd
'Colleen Bawn' (1)	CQua WShi
'Colley Gate' (3)	CQua
'Colliford' (2)	CQua
'Colorama' (11a)	CQua
'Colorful' (2)	IRhd
'Colville' (9)	CQua
'Comal' (1)	CQua
'Come to Good' (2)	CQua
'Compressus'	see *N.* × *intermedius* 'Compressus'
'Compton Court' (3)	IRhd
'Conestoga' (2)	CQua IRhd
'Congress' (11a)	CQua
'Conowingo' (11a)	CQua
'Conspicuus' ambig.	LAma
'Conspicuus' (3)	CAvo GCro GKev WShi
'Content' (1)	CQua
'Contralto' (2)	IRhd
'Cool Autumn' (2)	CQua
'Cool Crystal' (3)	CQua
'Cool Evening' (11a)	CQua IRhd
'Cool Flame' (2) **new**	GKev
'Cool Shades' (2)	CQua
'Coolmaghery' (2)	IRhd
'Coombe Creek' (6)	CQua
'Copperdale' (2)	MGib
'Copperfield' (2)	CQua
'Cora Ann' (7)	CBro
'Coral Ribbon' (2) **new**	GKev
'Corbiere' (1)	CQua IRhd MGib
'Corbridge' (2)	CQua
'Corby Candle' (2)	CQua MGib
'Corky's Song' (2)	CQua
'Cornish Chuckles' (12) ♀H6	CBro CFen CQua
'Cornish King' (2) **new**	GKev
'Cornish Pride' (2)	CFen
'Cornish Sun' (2)	CQua
'Cornish Vanguard' (2) ♀H6	CFen CQua
'Cornsilk' (11a)	CQua
'Corofin' (3)	CQua
'Corozal' (3)	CQua
'Corroboree' (2)	IRhd
'Cosine' (11a)	IRhd
'Cotinga' (6)	CBro CQua GKev SDeJ

'Countdown' (2)	CQua
'Court Martial' (2)	CFen
'Coverack Glory' (2)	CQua
'Crackington' (4) 🏆H6	CQua IRhd
'Cragford' (8)	SDeJ
'Craig Stiel' (2)	CQua
'Creag Dubh' (2)	CQua
'Creed' (6)	CQua
'Crenver' (3)	CQua
'Crevenagh' (2)	IRhd
'Crewenna' (1)	CQua
'Crill' (7)	CQua
'Crimson Chalice' (3)	CQua IRhd
'Cristobal' (1)	CQua
'Croesus' (2)	CQua GCro GKev
'Crofty' (6)	CQua
'Croila' (2)	CQua
'Crowndale' (4)	CQua IRhd MGib
'Crugmeer' (11a)	CQua
'Cryptic' (1)	CQua IRhd
'Crystal Star' (2)	CQua
cuatrecasasii	GKev
var. ***segimonensis*** (13)	
'Cudden Point' (2)	CQua
'Cul Beag' (3)	CQua
'Culmination' (2)	CQua
'Cultured Pearl' (2)	CQua IRhd
'Cum Laude' (11a)	ERCP SDeJ
'Curlew' (7) 🏆H6	CQua GKev LCro LOPS SDeJ WShi
'Curly' (2)	GKev SDeJ
'Cuscarne' (8)	CQua
cyclamineus (13) 🏆H6	CAvo CBro CFil CRos CWCL ECho ENun GKev LEdu LLHF LRHS NRHS SKHP SRms
'Cyclope' (1)	CQua
'Cynosure' (2)	GCro
cypri (13)	CQua
'Cyros' (1)	CQua
'Dailmanach' (2)	CQua IRhd
'Dailmystic' (2)	IRhd
'Dainty Miss' (7)	CQua
'Daisy Schäffer' (2)	GCro
'Dallas' (3)	CFen CQua
'Dalmeny' (2)	CQua
'Dambuster' (4)	IRhd
'Damson' (2)	CQua
'Dan du Plessis' (8)	CFen CQua
'Dancing Queen' (2)	IRhd
'Dardanelles' (2)	IRhd
'Darlow Dale' (2)	IRhd
'Dateline' (3)	CQua
'David Alexander' (1)	CQua
'David Mills' (2)	CQua
'Dawn Brooker' (2)	CQua
'Dawn Call' (2)	IRhd
'Dawn Cloud' (2)	CQua
'Dawn Run' (2)	IRhd
'Dawn Sky' (2)	CQua
'Daydream' (2)	CQua
'Daymark' (8)	CQua
'Daymer Bay' (1)	CFen
'Dayton Lake' (2)	CQua
'De Lacey' (11a)	CQua
'Dean' (2)	CQua
'Debutante' (2)	CQua
'December Bride' (11a)	CQua
'Decision' (2)	IRhd
'Defence Corps' (1)	IRhd
'Del Rey' (1)	CQua
'Delia' (6)	IRhd

'Dell Chapel' (3)	CQua
'Delnashaugh' (4)	CQua ERCP GKev LAma NHol SDeJ
'Delos' (3)	CQua
'Delta' (11a)	CQua
'Delta Flight' (6)	IRhd
'Demand' (2)	CQua
'Demeanour' (3)	IRhd
'Demmo' (2)	CQua IRhd MGib
'Dena' (3)	IRhd
'Denali' (1)	CQua IRhd
'Derek Tangye' (2)	CQua
'Derringer' (7)	CAvo
'Descant' (1)	IRhd
'Desdemona' (2) 🏆H6	CQua SDeJ
'Desert Bells' (7)	CQua
'Desert Orchid' (2)	CQua
'Dewy Dell' (3)	IRhd
'Diamond Ring'	see *N. bulbocodium* subsp. *obesus* 'Diamond Ring'
'Dick Wilden' (4)	GKev SDeJ
'Dickcissel' (7) 🏆H6	CQua ERCP GKev
'Dignitary' (2)	IRhd
'Dimity' (3)	CQua
'Dimple' (9)	CQua
'Dinkie' (3)	CBro
'Discreet' (2)	IRhd
'Dispatch Box' (1) 🏆H6	IRhd
'Disquiet' (1)	CQua IRhd
'Diversity' (11a)	IRhd
'Doctor Hugh' (3) 🏆H6	CQua IRhd
'Doctor Jazz' (2)	CQua
'Doctor Who' (4)	CQua
'Dolcoath' (2)	CQua
'Doombar' (1)	CQua
'Dorchester' (4)	CQua IRhd
'Dorneywood' (1)	IRhd
§ 'Double Campernelle' (4)	CQua GKev SDeJ WShi
double pheasant eye	see *N. poeticus* 'Plenus' ambig.
double Roman	see *N.* 'Romanus'
'Double White' (4)	CQua
'Doubleday' (4)	IRhd
'Doublet' (4)	CQua
'Doubtful' (3)	CQua
'Dove Song' (2)	IRhd
'Dove Wings' (6)	CQua
'Dover Boy' (11a)	CQua
'Dover Cliffs' (2)	CQua
'Downfield' (4)	IRhd
'Downing College' (2)	CQua
'Downlands' (3)	CQua
'Dragon Run' (2)	CQua
'Drama Queen' (11a)	IRhd
'Draycote Water' (3)	MGib
'Dream Catcher' (2)	IRhd
Dream Torte (1)	GCro
'Dreamlight' (3)	CQua
dubius (13)	ECho EPot GKev
'Duiker' (6)	IRhd
'Duke of Windsor' (2)	CFen
'Dunadry Inn' (4)	IRhd
'Dunchurch' (2)	MGib
'Dunkeld' (2)	CQua GCro
'Dunkery' (4)	CQua IRhd MGib
'Dunley Hall' (3)	CQua IRhd
'Dunskey' (3)	CQua
'Dupli Kate' (4)	IRhd
'Dusky Lad' (2)	IRhd
'Dusky Maiden' (2)	IRhd
'Dutch Delight' (2)	IRhd

'Dutch Lemon Drops' (5) ♀H6	CMea CQua EPot
'Dutch Master' (1) ♀H6	CFen CQua ESps GKev LAma LCro LOPS SCob SDeJ
'Early Bird' (3)	EPot
'Early Bride' (2)	CFen CQua
'Early Flame' (2)	CFen
'Early Splendour' (8)	CQua
'Earthlight' (3)	CQua
'Eastbrook Beauty' (2)	MGib
'Eastbrook Moonlight' (2)	MGib
'Eastbrook Snowflake' (3)	MGib
'Easter Moon' (2)	CQua LCro
'Eastern Dawn' (2)	CFen CQua SDeJ
'Eastern Promise' (2)	CQua
'Eaton Song' (12) ♀H6	CQua
'Ebony' (1)	CQua
'Eddy Canzony' (2)	CFen CQua
'Eden Gold' (2)	CFen
'Edenderry' (1)	IRhd
'Edgbaston' (2)	CQua
'Edge Grove' (2)	CQua
'Edinburgh' (11a) **new**	GKev
'Editor' (2)	IRhd
'Edward Buxton' (3)	CFen CQua GCro
'Egard' (11a)	CQua
'Egmont King' (2)	CQua
'Eira Hibbert' (3)	CQua
'Eland' (7)	CQua
'Elburton' (2)	CQua
'Electrus' (11a)	IRhd
'Elegance' (2)	CAvo CQua
elegans (13)	ECho
'Elegant Queen' (2)	IRhd
'Elf' (2)	CQua
'Elfin Gold' (6)	CQua
'Elizabeth Ann' (6)	CQua
'Elka' (1) ♀H6	CAby CAvo CBro CQua ERCP GKev LLHF MGib NNys SDir WShi
'Elmbridge' (1)	IRhd
'Elphin' (4)	CQua
'Elrond' (2)	CQua
'Elven Lady' (2)	CQua
'Elvira' (8)	CQua WShi
'Emcys' (6)	GKev LLHF
'Emerald City' (3)	IRhd
'Emerald Pink' (3)	CQua
'Emily' (2)	CQua
'Eminent' (3)	CQua
'Emperor' (1)	CQua
'Empress' (1)	GCro
'Empress of Ireland' (1)	CQua IRhd
'English Caye' (1)	CQua IRhd
'Ensemble' (4)	CQua
'Epona' (3)	CQua
'Erin' (3)	CQua
'Erlicheer' (4)	CQua GKev SDeJ
'Estrella' (3)	CQua
'Estremadura' (2)	CQua
'Ethereal Beauty' (2)	IRhd
'Ethos' (1)	IRhd
§ ***eugeniae*** (13)	CFil GKev MGib WCot
'Euryalus' (1)	CQua
'Evangeline' (3)	GCro
'Eve Robertson' (2)	CQua
'Evelyn Roberts' (11a)	CQua
'Evening' (2)	CQua
'Evesham' (3)	CQua IRhd MGib
'Exotic Beauty' (4)	CQua GKev
'Eyeglass' (3)	CQua

'Eyelet' (3)	CQua
'Eyrie' (3)	CQua
§ 'Eystettensis' (4)	IBlr
'Fair Prospect' (2)	CQua
'Fairgreen' (3)	CFen
'Fairlawns' (3)	CQua
'Fairmile' (3)	CQua
'Fairy Chimes' (5)	CQua
'Fairy Footsteps' (3)	CQua
'Fairy Island' (3)	CQua
'Fairy Magic' (2)	IRhd
'Fairy Tale' (3)	CQua
I 'Faith' (1)	SDeJ
'Falaise' (4)	CQua
'Falconet' (8) ♀H6	CQua GKev SDeJ
'Falmouth Bay' (3)	CQua
'Falstaff' (2)	CQua
'Far Country' (2)	CQua
I 'Fashion' (11b)	CQua
'Fashion Model' (2)	IRhd
'Fastidious' (2)	CQua
'February Gold' (6) ♀H6	CAvo CBro CQua CTri EPfP EPot ERCP ESps GCro GKev LAma LCro LOPS LRHS NBir NRHS SDeJ SRms WShi
'February Silver' (1)	CBro CQua EPot ERCP GKev LAma SDeJ
'Feeling Lucky' (2)	CQua
'Felindre' (9)	EPot
'Feline Queen' (1)	IRhd
'Feock' (3)	CQua
'Ferial Wendy' (2)	CFen
fernandesii (13)	ECho WAbe WCot WThu
– var. ***cordubensis*** (13)	CBro CFil CQua ECho LLHF MGib
– var. ***fernandesii*** (13)	MGib
'Ferndown' (3)	CQua IRhd
'Fertile Crescent' (7)	CQua
'Ffitch's Ffolly' (2)	CQua
'Fiery Maiden' (2)	CFen CQua
'Filoli' (1)	CQua
'Filskit' (2)	CQua
'Finchcocks' (2)	CQua
'Fine Gold' (1)	CQua
'Fine Romance' (2)	CQua MGib
'Fine Trim' (2)	IRhd
'Finedon Feast' (2)	MGib
'Fineshade' (1)	MGib
'Finland' (2)	CFen CQua NNys
Fintry Beauty (2)	GCro
'Fiona Linford' (3)	IRhd
'Fiona MacKillop' (2)	CQua IRhd
'Fire-Blade' (2)	CQua
'Firebrand' (3)	CQua
'Firefighter' (3)	IRhd
'Firehills' (2)	CQua
'Firetail' (3)	CQua GCro GKev WShi
'First Born' (6)	CQua
'First Hope' (6)	CFen
'Flambards Village' (4)	CQua
'Fletching' (1)	CQua IRhd
'Flirt' (6)	CQua
'Flomay' (7)	CQua
'Flor d'Luna' (2)	MGib
'Flower Drift' (4)	GKev
'Flower Record' (2)	LAma
'Flusher' (2)	CQua
'Flycatcher' (7)	CQua
'Flying Colours' (4)	IRhd
'Flying High' (3)	CQua
'Foff's Way' (1)	CQua

'Folkestone Girl' (11a)	CQua
'Forfar' (3) **new**	GCro
'Forge Mill' (2)	CQua
'Forged Gold' (2)	IRhd
'Fortissimo' (2)	GKev SDeJ SPer
'Fortune' (2)	CQua LAma SDeJ
'Fossie' (4)	CQua
'Foundling' (6)	CQua
'Fowey' (3)	CFen
'Foxfire' (2)	CQua
'Foxhunter' (2)	CQua
'Fragrant Breeze' (2)	CQua GKev NNys SDeJ
'Fragrant Rose' (2)	CQua ERCP GKev
'Frances Delight' (11a)	CQua
'Francolin' (1)	IRhd
'Frank' (9)	IRhd
'Frank Miles' (2)	CQua
'Freedom Rings' (2)	CQua
'Freedom Stars' (11a) 🏆H6	IRhd
'Fresco' (11a)	IRhd
'Fresh Lime' (1)	CQua MGib
'Fresno' (3)	IRhd
'Frigid' (3)	CQua
'Front Royal' (2)	CQua
'Frosted Pink' (2)	IRhd
'Frostkist' (6)	CBro CQua
'Frozen Jade' (1)	CQua
'Fruit Cup' (7)	GKev LCro SDeJ
'Fuco' (1)	CQua
'Full House' (4)	GKev SDeJ
'Fulwell' (4)	CQua
'Furbelow' (4)	CQua
'Furnace Creek' (2)	IRhd
'Fynbos' (3)	IRhd
'Gabriella Rose' (4)	CQua
gaditanus (13)	CBro
gaditanus* × *rupicola* subsp. *watieri (13)	ECho GKev
'Gambas' (1)	CQua
'Gamebird' (1)	CQua IRhd
'Ganilly' (2)	CFen
'Garden Club of America' (2)	MGib
'Garden News' (3)	IRhd
'Garden Opera' (7) 🏆H6	CFen
'Garden Treasure' (2)	IRhd
'Gatecrasher' (1)	IRhd
'Gay Kybo' (4) 🏆H6	CQua
'Gay Song' (4)	CQua
'Gay Time' (4)	CFen SDeJ
gayi (13)	CQua WShi
'Geevor' (4)	CQua
'Gellymill' (2)	CQua
'Gemini Girl' (2)	CQua
'Gentle Giant' (2)	SDeJ
'Geometrics' (2)	IRhd
'George Leak' (2)	CFen CQua
'Georgia Moon' (2)	CFen
'Georgie Girl' (6)	IRhd
'Georgie May' (2)	CQua
'Geranium' (8) 🏆H6	CBro CFen CQua EPfP ERCP ESps GKev LAma LCro LOPS SDeJ SDir SPer WShi
'Gettysburg' (2)	CQua
'Gigantic Star' (2)	SDeJ
'Gillan' (11a)	CQua
'Gin and Lime' (1)	CQua
'Gipsy Moon' (2)	CQua MGib
'Gipsy Queen' (1)	CBro CQua EPot LLHF WShi
'Gironde' (11)	CQua
'Glacier' (1)	CQua
'Glapthorne' (2)	CQua
'Glasnevin' (2)	CQua IRhd
'Glasney' (3)	CQua
'Glen Cassley' (3)	CQua
'Glen Clova' (2)	CQua
'Glendermott' (2)	CQua
'Glendurgan' (2)	CQua
'Glenfarclas' (1)	CQua
'Glenside' (2)	CQua
'Glissando' (2)	CQua IRhd
'Gloria Townsin' (4)	CQua
'Gloriosus' (8)	CQua
'Glorious' (8)	CQua
'Glory of Lisse' (9)	WShi
'Glover's Reef' (1)	CQua
'Glowing Phoenix' (4)	CQua GCro
'Glowing Red' (4)	CQua
'Goblet' (1)	SDeJ
'Goff's Caye' (2)	IRhd
'Golant' (2)	CQua
'Gold Bond' (2)	CQua IRhd
'Gold Cache' (11a)	CQua
'Gold Charm' (2)	CQua
'Gold Convention' (2) 🏆H6	CQua IRhd MGib
'Gold Ingot' (2) 🏆H6	IRhd
'Gold Medallion' (1)	CQua
'Gold Top' (2)	CQua
'Golden Amber' (2)	CQua
'Golden Anniversary' (2)	CFen CQua
'Golden Aura' (2) 🏆H6	CQua
'Golden Bear' (4)	CQua
'Golden Bells'	see *N. bulbocodium* Golden Bells Group
'Golden Cheer' (2)	CFen CQua
'Golden Cycle' (6)	CQua
'Golden Dawn' (8) 🏆H4	CFen CQua EPfP GKev SDeJ
'Golden Ducat' (4)	CFen CQua LAma NBir SDeJ
'Golden Flute' (2)	IRhd
'Golden Gamble' (11a)	IRhd
'Golden Harvest' (1)	CQua ESps LAma NPer
'Golden Incense' (7)	CQua
'Golden Jewel' (2) 🏆H6	CQua
'Golden Joy' (2)	CQua MGib
'Golden Lady' (1)	CQua
'Golden Lion' (1)	CFen
'Golden Marvel' (1)	CQua
'Golden Mary' (3)	GCro
'Golden Orbit' (4)	CQua
'Golden Peak' (1)	IRhd
'Golden Perfection' (7)	CQua
'Golden Phoenix' (4)	CQua WShi
'Golden Rain' (4)	CQua
'Golden Rapture' (1)	CQua
'Golden Sheen' (2)	CQua
'Golden Splash' (11a)	IRhd
'Golden Spur' (1)	CQua GCro GKev LAma
'Golden Torch' (2)	CQua
'Golden Twins' (7)	CQua
'Golden Vale' (1)	CQua
'Goldfinger' (1) 🏆H6	CQua IRhd MGib SDeJ
'Goldhanger' (2)	CQua IRhd MGib
'Golitha Falls' (2)	CQua
'Good Fella' (2)	CQua
'Good Intentions' (2)	IRhd
'Good Measure' (2)	CQua
'Good Success' (11a)	CQua
'Goonbell' (2)	CQua
'Goose Green' (3)	GKev
'Gorran' (3)	CQua

'Gossmoor' (4)	CQua
'Grafton Brook' (1)	MGib
'Grafton Gold' (2)	MGib
'Grand Monarque'	see *N. tazetta* subsp. *lacticolor* 'Grand Monarque'
'Grand Opening' (4)	IRhd
'Grand Primo' (8)	LCro LOPS
'Grand Primo Citronière' (8)	CQua
'Grand Prospect' (2)	CQua
'Grand Soleil d'Or' (8)	CQua GKev LAma LCro LOPS SDeJ
'Great Expectations' (2)	CQua
'Great Warley' (2)	GCro
'Greatwood' (1)	CQua
'Greek Surprise' (4)	IRhd
'Green Howard' (3)	CQua
'Green Island' (2)	CFen SDeJ
'Green Lawns' (9)	CQua
'Green Lodge' (9)	IRhd
'Green Pearl' (3)	GKev XEll
'Greenhithe Village' (3)	MGib
'Greenodd' (3)	CQua
'Greenpark' (9)	IRhd
'Grenoble' (2)	CQua
'Gresham' (4)	CQua
'Gribben Head' (4)	CQua
'Groundkeeper' (3)	IRhd
'Guiding Spirit' (4)	CQua
'Gulliver' (3)	CQua
'Gunwalloe' (11a)	CQua
'Guy Wilson' (2)	CQua MGib
'Gwawr' (2)	CQua
'Gwendoline Rae' (3)	CQua
'Gwenllian' (3)	CQua
'Gwennap' (1)	CQua
'Gwinear' (2)	CQua
'Habit' (1)	IRhd
'Hacienda' (1)	CQua
'Half Moon Caye' (2)	CQua
'Halley's Comet' (3)	CQua IRhd
'Halloon' (3)	CQua
'Halzephron' (2)	CQua
'Hambledon' (2) ♀H6	CQua
'Hampton Court' (2)	CQua IRhd
'Hannah Jesse' (7)	CQua
'Happy Dreams' (2)	IRhd
'Happy Fellow' (2)	CQua
'Happy Valley' (2)	IRhd
'Harbour View' (2)	IRhd
'Harmony Bells' (5)	CQua
'Harp Music' (2)	IRhd
'Harpers Ferry' (1)	CQua
Hartland's Irving (1)	GCro
'Hartlebury' (3)	CQua
'Harvard' (2)	CQua
* 'Hat' (10)	EPot
'Havelock' (2)	GCro
'Hawangi' (3)	IRhd
'Hawera' (5) ♀H6	CAvo CBro CFen CQua CTca CTri EPfP EPot ERCP GKev LAma LCro LEdu LOPS LPot LRHS MPie NNys NPnk SDeJ SPer WShi
'Heamoor' (4) ♀H6	CQua
hedraeanthus (13)	EPot
'Helford Dawn' (2)	CQua
'Helford Sunset' (2)	CQua
'Helios' (2)	CQua GCro
hellenicus	see *N. poeticus* var. *hellenicus*
'Hello Gorgeous' (11a) new	IRhd
henriquesii	see *N. jonquilla* var. *henriquesii*
'Henry Irving' (1)	CQua GCro
'Hero' (1)	CQua
'Heslington' (3)	CQua
'Hexameter' (9)	CQua
'Hexworthy' (3)	CQua
'Hibernian' (4)	IRhd
'Hicks Mill' (1)	CQua
'High Life' (2)	CFen
'High Society' (2) ♀H6	CQua GKev LCro LOPS SDeJ
'Highfield Beauty' (8) ♀H6	CQua
'Highgrove' (1)	CQua
'Highlite' (2)	CQua
'Hilda's Pink' (2)	CQua
'Hill Head' (9)	IRhd
'Hillstar' (7) ♀H6	CQua GKev SDeJ
'Hindenburg' (1)	CQua
hispanicus (13)	CQua ECho GKev
'Hocus Pocus' (3)	IRhd
'Holly Berry' (2)	CFen
'Hollywood' (2)	CFen
'Holme Fen' (2)	CQua
'Home Fires' (2)	CFen CQua
'Homestead' (2) ♀H6	IRhd
'Honey Pink' (2)	CQua
'Honeybird' (1)	CQua
'Honeybourne' (2)	CQua MGib
'Honeyorange' (2)	IRhd
'Hoopoe' (8) ♀H6	CQua GKev
'Hope House' (2)	IRhd
'Horace' (9)	CQua GCro
'Horn of Plenty' (5)	CQua
'Hornpipe' (1)	IRhd
'Hors d'Oeuvre' (1)	CBro
'Hospodar' (2)	CQua GCro
'Hot Affair' (2)	IRhd
'Hot Date' (3)	IRhd
'Hot Gossip' (2)	CFen CQua
'Hot Lava' (2)	IRhd
'Hotspur' (2)	CQua
Howick's Half Nelson (2)	GCro
'Hugh Town' (8)	CQua
'Hugus' (7)	CQua
'Hullabaloo' (2)	IRhd
humilis misapplied	see *N. pseudonarcissus* subsp. *pseudonarcissus* var. *humilis*
'Hummingbird' (6)	EPot
'Hunting Caye' (2)	CQua
'Huntley Down' (1)	CQua
'Hyperbole' (2)	IRhd
'Ice Dancer' (2)	CQua IRhd
'Ice Diamond' (4)	CQua
'Ice Emerald' (3)	IRhd
'Ice Follies' (2) ♀H6	CFen CQua EPfP ESps GKev LAma LCro LOPS NBir SCob SDeJ
'Ice King' (4)	GKev NBir SDeJ
'Ice Wings' (5) ♀H6	CAvo CBro CFen CQua EPot GKev MGib NPnk SDeJ WShi
'Idless' (1)	CQua
'Idol' (7)	CBro CQua ECho EPot GKev
'Immaculate' (2)	CQua
'Impeccable' (2)	IRhd
'Inara' (4)	CQua
'Inca' (6)	CQua
'Inchbonnie' (2)	CQua
× ***incomparabilis*** (13)	MMuc SEND
'Independence Day' (4)	CQua
'Indian Maid' (7) ♀H6	CQua IRhd
'Indian Ruler' (2)	CFen
'Indora' (4)	CQua
'Inglescombe' (4)	GKev WShi

	'Inner Glow' (2)	IRhd
	'Innisidgen' (8)	CQua
	'Innovator' (4)	CQua GKev
	'Innuendo' (2)	IRhd
	'Inny River' (1)	IRhd
	'Insulinde' (4)	CQua
	'Interim' (2)	CFen CQua SDeJ
	× ***intermedius*** (13)	CBro CQua MGib WAbe
§	- 'Compressus' (8)	CBro CQua WShi
	'Intrigue' (7) $\mathbb{Y}^{H6}$	CQua GKev SPer
	'Invercassley' (3)	CQua
	'Inverpolly' (2)	CQua
	'Ipi Tombi' (2)	GKev
	'Irene Copeland' (4)	CQua GKev
	'Irish Cream' (3)	CQua
	'Irish Fire' (2)	CQua
	'Irish Light' (2)	CQua
	'Irish Linen' (3)	CQua
	'Irish Minstrel' (2) $\mathbb{Y}^{H6}$	CFen CQua
	'Irish Rum' (2)	CQua
	'Irish Trip' (7)	IRhd
	'Irish Wedding' (2)	CQua
	'Isambard' (4)	CQua
	'Island Pride' (8)	CQua
	'Ita' (2)	IRhd
	italicus (13) **new**	GKev
	'Itsy Bitsy Splitsy' (11a)	IRhd
	'Itzim' (6) $\mathbb{Y}^{H6}$	CBro CQua GKev SDeJ
	'Jabberwocky' (11a)	CQua
	'Jack Snipe' (6) $\mathbb{Y}^{H6}$	CAby CBro CQua EPfP EPot ERCP ESps GKev LAma LCro LRHS NHol SCob SDeJ WShi XEll
	'Jack Wood' (11a)	CQua IRhd
	'Jackadee' (2)	IRhd
	'Jacob Maurer' (6)	CQua
	'Jake' (3)	IRhd
	'Jamage' (8)	CQua
	'Jamaica Inn' (4)	CQua
	'Jambo' (2)	CQua
	'Jamboree' (2)	CQua
	'Jamestown' (3)	NPnk
	'Jammin' (3)	IRhd
	'Janelle' (3)	CQua
	'Janet's Gold' (2)	IRhd
	'Jantje' (11a)	CQua
	'Jauno' (1)	IRhd
	'Javelin' (2)	CQua
	'Jeanine' (2)	CQua
	'Jeanne Bicknell' (4)	CQua
	'Jeannie Tangye' (2)	CQua
	'Jenny' (6) $\mathbb{Y}^{H6}$	CBro CMea CQua EPot ERCP ESps GKev LAma LCro LOPS NBir SDeJ WShi
	'Jenny Out' (7) $\mathbb{Y}^{H6}$	CFen
	'Jersey Lace' (2)	CQua
	'Jersey Roundabout' (4)	CQua
	'Jersey Star' (4)	CQua
	'Jersey Torch' (4)	CQua
	'Jetfire' (6) $\mathbb{Y}^{H6}$	CQua EPfP EPot ERCP ESps GKev LAma LCro LOPS LPot LRHS LSou NHol NRHS SCob SDeJ WShi
	'Jim Lad' (2)	ECho
	'Jimmy Noone' (1)	CQua
	'Jim's Gold' (2)	CQua
	'Jodi' (11b)	IRhd
	'Jodi's Sister' (11a)	IRhd
	'Johanna' (5)	CBro
	'John Daniel' (4)	CQua
	'John Evelyn' (2)	GCro
	'John Lanyon' (3)	CQua
	'John's Delight' (3)	CQua
	'Joke Fulmer' (2)	CFen
	'Jolly Good' (2)	IRhd
	jonquilla (13)	CBro CQua ECho EPot GKev LAma WShi
	- 'Flore Pleno' (4)	ECho
§	- var. ***henriquesii*** (13)	CFil CQua ECho EPot GKev MGib
	- var. ***jonquilla*** (13)	MGib
	'Joppa' (7)	CQua
	'Joy Bishop'	see *N. romieuxii* 'Joy Bishop'
	'Joybell' (6)	CQua
	'Juanita' (2)	CFen NNys NPer SDeJ
	'Jules Verne' (2)	CQua
	'Julia Jane'	see *N. romieuxii* 'Julia Jane'
	'Jumblie' (12) $\mathbb{Y}^{H6}$	CBro EPfP EPot LAma LRHS NRHS SDeJ
	'Jumbo Gold' (1)	CTri
	juncifolius Req. ex Lag.	see *N. assoanus*
	'June Allyson' (2)	CFen
	'June Lake' (2)	CQua IRhd
	'Kabani' (9)	CQua
	'Kaka Point' (2)	IRhd
	'Kamau' (9)	IRhd
	'Kamms' (1)	CQua
	'Kamura' (2)	CQua
	'Kantzeewai' (2) **new**	IRhd
	'Karamudli' (1)	CQua
	'Kate Davies' (2)	CQua
	'Katherine Jenkins' (7) $\mathbb{Y}^{H6}$	CQua
	'Kathy A' (5)	IRhd
	'Kathy's Clown' (6)	CQua
	'Katie Heath' (5)	ERCP GKev SDeJ
	'Katrina Rea' (6)	CQua
	'Kaydee' (6) $\mathbb{Y}^{H6}$	CQua GKev IFro IRhd SDeJ
	'Kea' (6)	CQua
	'Keats' (4)	CQua
	'Kebaya' (2)	CQua
	'Kedron' (7)	ERCP GKev
	'Kelly Bray' (1)	CQua
	'Ken Sunshine Johnson' (2)	CQua
	'Kernow' (2)	CQua
	'Kholmes' (10)	MGib
	'Kidling' (7)	CQua
	'Killara' (8)	CQua
	'Killearnan' (9)	CQua
	'Killigrew' (2)	CQua
	'Killivose' (3)	CQua
	'Kiltonga' (2)	IRhd
	'Kilworth' (2)	CQua
	'Kimmeridge' (3)	CQua
	'King Alfred' (1)	CQua EPfP LCro LOPS SDeJ SPer
	'Kingham' (1)	CQua
	'Kinglet' (7)	CQua
	'King's Grove' (1)	CQua
	'Kings Pipe' (2)	CQua
	'Kingscourt' (1)	CQua
	'Kingsleigh' (1)	IRhd
	'Kingsmill Lake' (2)	CQua
	'Kiss Me' (1) **new**	GKev
	'Kissproof' (2)	GKev SDeJ
	'Kit Hill' (7)	CQua
	'Kitten' (6)	CQua
	'Kiwi Magic' (4)	CQua IRhd
	'Kiwi Sunset' (4)	CQua IRhd
	'Knight of Saint John' (2)	CFen
	'Knightsbridge' (1)	CQua
	'Knocklayde' (3)	CQua
	'Knowing Look' (3)	IRhd
	'Kokopelli' (7) $\mathbb{Y}^{H6}$	CAvo CBro CQua EPfP GKev MGib SDeJ

'Korora Bay' (1)	IRhd
'Kuantan' (3)	MGib
'La Belle' (7)	LLHF SDeJ
'La Riante' (3)	GCro
'Ladies' Choice' (7)	IRhd
'Lady Ann' (2)	IRhd
'Lady Be Good' (2)	CQua
'Lady Diana' (2)	CQua IRhd
'Lady Eve' (11a)	IRhd
'Lady Godiva' (3)	GCro
'Lady Hilaria' (2)	CQua
'Lady Margaret Boscawen' (2)	CQua GCro
'Lady Marina Cowdray' (1)	CFen
Lady Mary's Gwyther (2)	GCro
'Lady Moore' (3)	GCro
'Lady Sainsbury' (2)	CFen
'Lady Serena' (9)	CQua
'Lady's Favorite' (7)	IRhd
'Lake Alabaster' (2)	CQua
'Lake District' (2)	IRhd
'Lalique' (3)	CQua
'Lamanva' (2)	CQua
'Lamlash' (2)	IRhd
'Lanarth' (7)	GCro
'Lancaster' (3)	CFen CQua
'Landewednack Lady' (4)	CQua
'Langarth' (11a)	CQua
'Lapwing' (5)	IRhd
'Larkhill' (2)	CQua
'Larkwhistle' (6)	SDeJ
'Las Vegas' (1)	GKev SDeJ
'Latchley Meadows' (2)	CQua
'Laura Webb' (4)	CQua
'Laurelbank' (2)	IRhd
'Lauren' (3)	IRhd
'Laurens Koster' (8)	CQua GKev
'Lava Flow' (3)	IRhd
'Lavender Lass' (6)	CQua
'Lavender Mist' (2)	CQua MGib
'Lazy River' (1)	MGib
'Leading Light' (2)	CQua
'Lee Moor' (1)	CQua
'Leedsii' (3)	CQua
'Lemma' (3)	IRhd
'Lemon Beauty' (11b)	CQua GKev SDeJ
'Lemon Brook' (2)	CQua
'Lemon Cocktail' (1)	IRhd
'Lemon Cycla' (6)	CQua
'Lemon Drizzle' (2)	CQua
'Lemon Drops' (5)	CQua EPot ERCP GKev SDeJ SPhx
'Lemon Haze' (2)	CQua
'Lemon Shake' (1) **new**	GKev
'Lemon Silk' (6)	CBro CQua
'Lemonade' (3)	CQua
'Lennymore' (2)	CQua IRhd MGib
'Lewis George' (1)	CQua
'Lezant' (3)	CQua
'Libby' (2)	IRhd
'Liberty Bells' (5)	CQua LAma
'Liebeslied' (3)	CQua
'Lieke'	EPfP EPot ERCP GKev LCro LOPS NNys SDeJ
'Life' (7)	CQua
'Lifeline' (1)	IRhd
'Lighthouse' (3)	CQua
'Lighthouse Reef' (1)	CQua IRhd MGib
'Lilac Charm' (6)	CQua IRhd MGib
'Lilac Hue' (6)	CBro
'Lilac Mist' (2)	CQua IRhd

'Lilliput' ambig.	CQua
'Lima's Green Goddess' (8)	IRhd
'Lima's Shooting Stars' (12)	IRhd
'Limbo' (2)	CQua
'Limequilla' (7)	CQua IRhd
'Limpopo' (3)	IRhd
'Lincolnshire Lady' (3)	CQua
'Lindsay Joy' (2)	CQua
'Lisburn' (3)	IRhd
'Lisnamulligan' (3)	IRhd
'Little Alice' (4)	IRhd
'Little Beauty' (1)	CBro CQua LAma
'Little Becky' (12)	MGib
'Little Dancer' (1)	CBro CQua
'Little Dianne' (8)	IRhd
'Little Dorr' (4)	IRhd
'Little Flik' (12)	CQua ECho
'Little Jewel' (3)	CQua
'Little Karoo' (3)	IRhd
'Little Meg' (7)	CQua
'Little Oliver' (7)	EPfP GKev
'Little Rusky' (7)	CBro CQua
'Little Sentry' (7)	CBro CQua
'Little Soldier' (10)	CQua
'Little Spell' (1)	ECho
'Little Tyke' (2)	CQua
'Little Witch' (6)	CBro CQua GCro GKev LAma SCob SDeJ SPhx WShi
'Littlefield' (7)	CQua
'Livelands' (1)	CQua
'Liverpool Festival' (2)	CQua MGib
'Living Colour' (3)	CQua
'Lizard Beacon' (2)	CQua
'Lobularis'	see *N. lobularis* (Haw.) Schult. & Schult. f.
lobularis misapplied	see *N. nanus*
§ ***lobularis*** (Haw.) Schult. & Schult. f.	CAby CAvo CBro CQua CTca CTri ECho EPot ERCP GKev LCro NNys SCob SDeJ
'Loch Alsh' (3)	CQua IRhd
'Loch Assynt' (3)	CQua
'Loch Brora' (2)	CQua
'Loch Coire' (3)	CQua
'Loch Fada' (2)	CQua
'Loch Fyne' (2)	GCro
'Loch Hope' (2)	CQua
'Loch Leven' (2)	CQua
'Loch Loyal' (2)	CQua
'Loch Lundie' (2)	CQua
'Loch Maberry' (2)	CQua
'Loch Naver' (2)	CQua
'Loch Owskeich' (2)	CFen CQua
'Logan Rock' (7)	CQua
'Longitude' (1)	IRhd
'Lord Grey' (1)	GCro
'Lordship' (1)	CQua
'Lorikeet' (1)	CQua GKev
'Lostwithiel' (2)	CQua
'Lothario' (2)	EPfP LAma
'Lough Gowna' (1)	IRhd
'Louise de Coligny' (2)	ERCP
'Loveday' (2)	CFen
'Lowin' (1)	CFen
'Lubaantun' (1)	CQua
'Lucie Nottingham' (4)	CQua
'Lucifer' (2)	CAvo CQua GCro GKev WShi
'Lucky Chance' (11a)	IRhd
'Lundy Light' (2)	CQua
'Lutana' (2)	IRhd
'Lyme Bay' (1)	IRhd

'Lynher' (2)	CQua
'Lyrebird' (3)	CQua
'Lyric' (9)	CQua
'Lysander' (2)	CQua
MacEwan (2)	GCro
'Madam Speaker' (4)	CQua MGib
'Madame Plemp' (1)	GCro
'Madison' (4)	CQua GKev
Maggie Maybe (2)	GCro
'Magic Moment' (3)	CQua
'Magician' (2)	CQua
'Magna Carta' (2)	CQua
'Magnificence' (1)	CFen CQua GCro
'Maker's Mark' (1)	CQua
'Mallee' (11a) ♀H6	GKev IRhd MGib
'Malpas' (3)	CQua
'Malvern City' (1)	CFen CQua
'Mamma Mia' (4)	IRhd
'Manaccan' (1)	CQua MGib
'Mangaweka' (6)	CQua
'Manly' (4) ♀H6	CQua ERCP GKev
'Manon Lescaut' (2)	GKev
'Mantle' (2)	CQua
'Margaret Herbert' (7)	CQua
'Maria Pia' (11a)	IRhd
'Marie Curie Diamond' (7) ♀H6	CFen CQua
'Marieke' (1)	LAma SDeJ
'Marilyn Anne' (2)	CQua
'Marjorie Hine' (2)	CQua
'Marjorie Treveal' (4)	CQua
'Market Merry' (3)	GCro
'Marlborough' (2)	CQua
'Marlborough Freya' (2)	CQua
'Marshfire' (2)	CQua
'Martha Washington' (8)	CQua
'Martinette' (8)	CAvo CFen CQua GKev SDeJ
'Martinsville' (8)	CQua
marvieri	see *N. rupicola* subsp. *marvieri*
'Mary Bohannon' (2)	GKev
'Mary Copeland' (4)	CQua GCro
'Mary Kate' (2)	CQua
'Mary Lou' (6)	IRhd
'Mary Moore' (2)	CQua
'Mary Rosina' (4)	CQua
'Mary Veronica' (3)	CQua
'Marzo' (7)	IRhd
'Masked Light' (2)	CFen
'Matador' (8)	CFen CQua IRhd
'Mawla' (1)	CQua
'Max' (11a)	CQua
'Maximus Superbus' (1)	CQua
'Maya Dynasty' (2)	CQua
Maybole Elegance (2)	GCro
'Mayor's Choice' (11a)	CQua
'Maywood' (11a)	CQua
'Mazzard' (4)	CQua
'Media Girl' (2)	IRhd
× ***medioluteus*** (13)	CBro CQua GCro WShi
'Medway Gold' (7)	CQua
'Melancholy' (1)	CQua
'Melbury' (2)	CQua
'Meldrum' (1)	CQua
'Melen' (2)	CFen
'Melodia d'Amore' (2) **new**	GKev
'Memento' (1)	CQua
'Menabilly' (4)	CQua
'Mên-an-Tol' (2)	CQua
'Menehay' (11a) ♀H6	CQua
'Mer d'Or' (1)	IRhd
'Merlin' (3) ♀H6	CFen CQua LAma SDeJ
'Merry Bells' (5)	CQua
'Merrymeet' (4)	CQua
'Mersing' (3)	CQua
'Merthan' (9)	CQua
'Midas Touch' (1)	CQua
'Midget'	see *N. nanus* 'Midget'
Midtown Aerolite (2)	GCro
Midtown Alfie (1)	GCro
Midtown Amber (2)	GCro
Midtown Brigadier (2)	GCro
Midtown Laurie (1)	GCro
Midtown Noble (1)	GCro
Midtown Ruckle (1)	GCro
'Mike Pollock' (8)	CFen CQua
'Milan' (9)	CQua GCro
'Mill Grove' (2)	MGib
'Millennium Gold' (1)	CQua
'Millennium Sunrise' (2)	CQua
'Millennium Sunset' (2)	CQua
'Milly's Magic' (2)	CQua
'Minard' (4)	CQua
Minicycla Group (6)	ECho
minimus misapplied	see *N. asturiensis*
'Minnow' (8) ♀H4	CAvo CBro CFen CHid CQua ECho EPfP EPot ERCP ESps GKev LAma LCro LOPS LPot LRHS NBir NRHS SCob SDeJ SPer
'Minnowlet' (11a)	CQua
minor (13) ♀H5	CBro CPne CQua ECha ECho EPot GCro GKev WShi
- 'Douglasbank' (1)	LLHF
- 'Little Gem' (1) ♀H6	CBro CQua CTri GKev LAma SDeJ SPhx
- var. ***pumilus*** 'Plenus'	see *N.* 'Rip van Winkle'
- Ulster form (13)	IBlr
'Minor' (Nelsonii Group) (2) **new**	GCro
'Mint Julep' (3) ♀H6	SDeJ
'Mirar' (2)	CQua
Misleeding (2)	GCro
'Misquote' (1)	CQua
'Miss Diddles' (7)	CQua
'Miss Klein' (7)	LLHF
'Miss Muffit' (1)	CQua
'Miss Primm' (2)	IRhd
'Mission Bells' (5) ♀H6	CQua IRhd
'Mission Impossible' (11a)	CQua
'Mist of Avalon' (4)	CQua
'Misty Glen' (2) ♀H6	CQua EPfP GKev MGib SDeJ
'Mite' (6) ♀H6	CAvo CBro CQua ECho EPot GKev LAma LLHF NHpl
'Mithrel' (11a)	CQua
'Mitimoto' (10)	ECho
'Mitylene' (2)	CQua GCro
'Mitzy' (6)	LLHF
'Modern Art' (2)	CQua GKev SDeJ
'Modulation' (2)	MGib SDeJ
'Monal' (2) **new**	GKev
'Mondragon' (11a)	CQua GKev
'Mongleath' (2)	CQua
'Monks Wood' (1)	CQua
'Monksilver' (3)	CQua
'Monmouthshire' (2)	CQua
'Montclair' (2)	CQua
'Montego' (3)	CQua
'Monterrico' (4)	CFen
'Montroig' (2)	IRhd
'Moon Dream' (1)	CQua
'Moon Ranger' (3)	CQua

'Moon Shadow' (3)	CQua IRhd
'Moon Valley' (2)	IRhd
'Moonstruck' (1)	CQua
'Morab' (1)	CQua
'Moralee' (4)	CQua IRhd
'Morval' (2)	CQua
moschatus (13) ♀H6	CBro CQua ECho EPot GKev MGib WShi
'Mother Duck' (6)	LAma
'Motmot'	CQua
'Mount Fuji' (2)	CQua
'Mount Hood' (1) ♀H6	EPfP GKev LAma NBir SDeJ SPer
'Mountain Poet' (9)	CQua
'Mousehole' (3)	CQua
'Movie Star' (2)	IRhd
'Mowser' (7)	CQua
'Mr Sweet' (2)	CQua
'Mrs Langtry' (2)	CQua GKev WShi
'Mrs R.O. Backhouse' (2)	CQua GCro WShi
'Muiranna' (1) **new**	IRhd
'Mullion' (3)	CQua
'Mulroy Bay' (1)	CQua IRhd
'Murlough' (9)	CQua
'Muscadet' (2)	CFen CQua
'My Story' (4) ♀H6	SDeJ
'My Sunshine' (2)	CQua
'My Sweetheart' (3)	CQua
'My Word' (2)	CFen
'Mystic' ambig. (3)	CQua
'Mzungu' (2) **new**	IRhd
'Namraj' (2)	CQua
'Nancegollan' (7)	CBro CQua
'Nangiles' (4)	CQua
'Nanpee' (7)	CQua
'Nanpusker' (2)	CFen
'Nansidwell' (2)	CQua
'Nanstallon' (1)	CQua
'Nantucket Red' (3) **new**	IRhd
§ ***nanus*** (13)	CQua CWCL ECho GBuc
§ - 'Midget' (1)	CBro CQua ECho EPot ERCP GKev LAma NHpl SKHP
'Nare Celebration' (2)	CFen
'Narrative' (2)	IRhd
'Navarre' Buckland (2)	CFil
'Navigator' (2) **new**	IRhd
'Nederburg' (1)	IRhd
'Nelly' ambig.	CQua
'Nessa' (7)	CQua
'Nether Barr' (2)	CQua
nevadensis (13)	SKHP
'New Hope' (3)	CQua
'New Life' (3)	CQua
'New Penny' (3)	CQua IRhd
'New World' (2)	CQua
'New-Baby' (7)	CQua ERCP GKev SDeJ
'Newcomer' (3)	CQua
'Nickelodeon' (8)	CQua
'Night Music' (4)	CQua IRhd
'Nightcap' (1)	CQua
'Nightflight' (1)	MGib
'Niphetos' (2)	GCro
'Nirvana' (7)	CBro
'Niveth' (5)	CAvo CFen CQua GCro LCro LOPS
§ ***nobilis*** (13)	CQua EPot GKev
- var. ***leonensis*** (13)	CFil
'Nonchalant' (3)	CQua IRhd
'Norma Jean' (2)	CQua
'North Rim' (2)	CQua
'Noss Mayo' (6)	CQua
'Notre Dame' (2) ♀H6	CQua IRhd

'Nuage' (2)	CFen
'Numen Rose' (2)	IRhd
Nylon Group (10)	CBro ECho EPot EPri
- yellow-flowered (10)	ECho
'Nynja' (2)	CQua
'Oadby' (1)	CQua
'Obdam' (4)	GKev SDeJ
'Obsession' (2)	CQua
obvallaris (13) ♀H6	CAvo CBro CFen CQua CTca ECho EPot ERCP GBuc GCro GKev LCro NNys SDeJ SPhx WHer WShi
'Ocarino' (4)	CFen CQua
'Ocean Blue' (2)	IRhd
'Odd Job' (12)	CQua
× ***odorus*** (13)	CQua GKev WShi
- 'Plenus' (4)	CQua ERCP
'Oh Wow' (3)	IRhd
old pheasant's eye	see *N. poeticus* var. *recurvus*
'Olympic Medal' (1)	IRhd
'Ombersley' (1)	CQua MGib
'Omri' (8) **new**	GKev
'Oops' (2)	IRhd
'Orange Phoenix' (4)	CQua WShi
'Orange Progress' (2) **new**	GKev
'Orange Queen' (3)	GKev
'Orange Supreme' (2)	CQua
'Orange Tint' (2)	CQua
'Orange Walk' (3)	CQua IRhd
'Orangery' (11a)	GKev LAma SDeJ
'Orbital Pink' (3)	IRhd
'Orchard Place' (3)	CQua
'Oregon Pioneer' (2)	IRhd
'Orkney' (2)	CQua
'Ormeau' (2)	CQua
'Ornatus' (9)	CQua GCro GKev
'Oryx' (7) ♀H6	CQua
'Osmington' (2)	CQua
'Ouma' (1)	CQua
'Outline' (2)	IRhd
'Ouzel' (6)	CQua
'Owyhee' (2)	CQua
'Oxford Gold' (10) ♀H6	CAvo CQua GKev MGib
'Oykel' (3)	CQua
'Oz' (12)	LLHF
pachybolbus (13)	CQua ECho
'Pacific Coast' (8) ♀H6	CQua LCro LLHF LOPS MGib
'Pacific Mist' (11a)	CQua
'Pacific Rim' (2)	CQua IRhd
'Pacific Waves' (3)	CQua
'Painted Desert' (3)	CQua
'Palace Pink' (2)	IRhd
'Pale Sunlight' (2)	CQua
'Palheiro' (2)	MGib
pallidiflorus (13)	ECha
- var. ***pallidiflorus*** (13) **new**	GKev
'Palmares' (11a)	CQua SDeJ
'Pamela Hubble' (2)	CQua
'Pamela Joan' (2)	CQua
'Pampaluna' (11a)	CQua IRhd
'Panache' (1)	CQua
panizzianus (13)	CFil CQua
'Panorama Pink' (3)	IRhd
'Pantaloon' (4) **new**	IRhd
'Paper White'	see *N. papyraceus*
'Paper White Grandiflorus' (8)	CQua EPfP SDeJ SPer
'Papillon Blanc' (11b)	ERCP GKev NNys
'Papua' (4)	CFen CQua
§ ***papyraceus*** (13)	CFil CQua GKev NNys

- subsp. ***polyanthos*** new	GKev
- 'Ziva' (8)	CAvo GKev LCro LOPS SDeJ
'Paradigm' (4)	IRhd
'Paramour' (4)	IRhd
'Parcpat' (7)	CBro CQua
'Parisienne' (11a)	GKev SDeJ
'Park Springs' (3)	CQua
'Parkdene' (2)	CQua
'Partisan' (2)	IRhd
'Party Time' (2)	IRhd
'Passionale' (2) $\mathbb{Y}^{H6}$	CQua EPfP LAma NBir
'Pastiche' (2)	CQua
'Pat Brown' (2)	CQua
'Pat Redman' (3)	CQua
'Patabundy' (2)	CQua
'Pathos' (3)	IRhd
'Patois' (9)	CBro CQua IRhd
'Patrick Hacket' (1) $\mathbb{Y}^{H6}$	CFen CQua
'Pay Day' (1)	CQua
'Peach Prince' (4)	CQua
'Pearl Wedding' (3)	CQua
'Pearlshell' (11a)	CQua
'Peeping Jenny' (6)	ERCP NNys
'Peeping Tom' (6) $\mathbb{Y}^{H6}$	CBro CQua ERCP GKev LAma SDeJ SRms
'Peggy's Gift' (3)	IRhd
'Pelynt' (3)	CQua
'Pemboa' (1)	CQua
'Pencrebar' (4)	CQua EPot GKev LAma LRHS MPie NHol NRHS SDeJ WShi
'Pend Oreille' (3)	CQua
'Pengarth' (2)	CQua
'Penjerrick' (9)	CQua
'Penkivel' (2) $\mathbb{Y}^{H6}$	CQua
'Pennance Mill' (2)	CQua
'Pennine Way' (1)	CQua
'Penny Perowne' (7)	CQua
'Pennyfield' (2)	CQua
'Penpol' (7)	CBro CFen CQua
'Penril' (6)	CQua
'Penselwood' (2)	CQua
'Penstraze' (7)	CQua
'Pentewan' (2)	CQua GCro
'Pentille' (1)	CQua
'Pentire' (11a)	CQua
'Penvale' (7)	CQua
'Peppercorn' (6)	CQua
'Percuil' (6)	CQua
'Perdredda' (3)	CQua
perez-chiscanoi (13)	CFil SKHP
'Perimeter' (3)	CQua
'Peripheral Pink' (2)	CQua
'Perlax' (11a)	CQua
'Perpetuation' (7)	CQua
'Personable' (2)	CQua
'Petanca' (5)	IRhd
'Peter Chown' (11a)	CQua
'Petit Four' (4)	GKev LAma SDeJ
'Petrel' (5)	CBro CQua ERCP GKev SDeJ WShi
'Phantom' (11a)	CQua
'Phil's Gift' (1)	CQua
'Phinda' (2)	IRhd
'Phoenician' (2)	CQua
'Picatou' (3)	IRhd
'Picket Post' (3)	IRhd
'Picoblanco' (2)	CBro CQua
'Pinafore' (2)	EPfP
Pineapple Plemp (1)	GCro
'Pineapple Prince' (2) $\mathbb{Y}^{H6}$	CQua
'Pink Angel' (7)	CQua

'Pink Champagne' (4)	CQua
'Pink Charm' (2)	CQua GKev NBir SDeJ
'Pink China' (2)	CQua
'Pink Formal' (11a)	CQua
'Pink Gilt' (2)	IRhd
'Pink Glacier' (11a)	CQua
'Pink Holly' (11a)	CQua
'Pink Ice' (2)	CQua
'Pink Pageant' (4)	CQua
'Pink Paradise' (4)	CQua
'Pink Parasol' (1)	GKev SDeJ
'Pink Silk' (1)	CQua GKev SDeJ
'Pink Smiles' (2)	CFen
'Pink Surprise' (2)	CQua
'Pink Tango' (11a)	CQua
'Pinza' (2) $\mathbb{Y}^{H6}$	CQua SDeJ
'Pipe Major' (2)	CQua NNys
'Pipers Barn' (7)	CQua
'Piper's Gold' (1)	CQua
'Pipestone' (2)	CQua
'Pipit' (7)	CAvo CBro CFen CQua EPfP EPot ERCP GKev LAma LPot LRHS NBir SDeJ WShi
'Piraeus' (4)	IRhd
'Pismo Beach' (2)	CQua
'Pistachio' (1) $\mathbb{Y}^{H6}$	GKev
'Pitchroy' (2)	CQua
'Pitt's Diamond' (3)	CQua
'Pixie's Sister' (7) $\mathbb{Y}^{H6}$	CQua LLHF
'Pledge' (1)	CQua
'Plymouth Hoe' (1)	CQua
§ ***poeticus*** var. ***hellenicus*** (13)	CBro CQua GCro IRhd
- old pheasant's eye	see *N. poeticus* var. *recurvus*
- var. ***physaloides*** (13)	CFil CQua ECho GKev
- 'Plenus' misapplied	see *N. poeticus* 'Spalding Double White', *N.* 'Tamar Double White'
§ - 'Plenus' ambig. (4)	CAby CBro CQua ERCP GKev GQui SDeJ WShi
§ - var. ***recurvus*** (13) $\mathbb{Y}^{H6}$	CAby CAvo CBro CFen CQua CTca ECho EPfP ERCP GCro GKev LAma LCro MGib NBir NNys SCob SDeJ SEND SPer SPhx WShi
§ - 'Spalding Double White' (4)	CQua EPot
- white-flowered (13)	SDeJ
'Poetry in Motion' (9)	IRhd
'Poet's Way' (9)	CQua IRhd
'Pol Crocan' (2)	CQua IRhd
'Pol Dornie' (2)	CQua
'Pol Voulin' (2)	CQua IRhd MGib
'Polar Ice' (3)	CFen CQua GKev LAma SDeJ
'Polbathic' (2)	CQua
'Polgoon' (2)	CFen
'Polgooth' (2)	CQua
'Polindra' (2)	GCro
'Polly's Pearl' (8)	CQua
'Polmenor' (2)	CQua
'Polnesk' (7)	GCro
'Polonaise' (2)	CQua
'Polruan' (7)	CQua
'Poltreen' (4)	CQua
'Polwheveral' (2)	CQua
'Polyphant' (2)	CQua
'Pomona' (3)	GCro
'Pooka' (3)	CQua IRhd
Poolewe Pintuck (2)	GCro
'Popeye' (4)	EPfP
'Poppy's Choice' (4)	CQua
'Pops Legacy' (1)	CQua
'Porthchapel' (7)	CQua

'Portloe Bay' (3)	CQua
'Portrait' (2)	CQua
'Portrush' (3)	CQua
'Potential' (1)	CQua
'Powerstock' (2)	IRhd
'Praecox' (9)	CBro MGib
'Prairie Fire' (3)	CQua IRhd
'Pratincole' (3)	IRhd
'Preamble' (1)	CQua
I 'Precocious' (2) ♀H6	CQua GKev SDeJ
'Predator' (1)	IRhd MGib
'Premiere' (2)	CQua
'Presidential Pink' (2)	CQua
'Pretty Baby' (3)	CQua
'Pride of Cornwall' (8)	CQua
'Primegold' (2)	CFen
'Primrose Beauty' (4)	CFen CQua NNys
'Princeps' (1)	CQua GCro GKev
'Princess Alexandra' (6)	CFen
'Princess Diana' (6)	CFen
'Printal' (11a)	SDeJ
'Priorsford' (2)	IRhd
'Prism' (2)	CQua
'Problem Child' (2)	IRhd
'Probus' (1)	CQua
'Professor Einstein' (2)	EPfP GKev SDeJ
'Prologue' (1)	CQua
'Prom Dance' (11a) **new**	GKev
'Prototype' (6)	IRhd LAma
'Proud Fellow' (1)	IRhd
'Proverbial Pink' (2)	IRhd
pseudonarcissus (13)	CHab CQua CWld GCro MMuc WHer WShi
- JMH 8271 **new**	GKev
- subsp. ***eugeniae***	see *N. eugeniae*
- subsp. ***nobilis***	see *N. nobilis*
- var. ***porrigens*** (13) **new**	GCro
- subsp. ***pseudonarcissus*** double-flowered (4)	CQua
§ - - var. ***humilis*** (13)	ECho
'Ptolemy' (1)	CFen
'Pueblo' (7)	CQua GKev LRHS NNys SDeJ
'Pukenui' (4)	CQua
'Pulsar' (2)	IRhd
pumilus ambig. (13)	CQua ECho LLHF SDeJ
'Punchline' (7) ♀H6	CQua
'Punter' (2)	CQua IRhd
'Puppet' (5)	CQua EPfP GKev
'Purbeck' (3) ♀H6	CQua IRhd
'Quail' (7) ♀H6	CFen CQua CTca EPfP ESps GKev LAma LSou SDeJ
'Quasar' (2) ♀H6	CQua
Queen Anne's double daffodil	see *N.* 'Eystettensis'
'Queen Fiona' (1)	IRhd
'Queen Juliana' (1)	CQua
'Queen Mum' (1)	CQua
'Queen of Spain' (5)	CQua GKev
'Queen of the North' (3)	GCro
'Queen's Guard' (1)	IRhd
'Queensland' (2)	CFen
'Quetta' (3) **new**	GCro
'Quick Step' (7)	CQua
'Quiet Hero' (3)	IRhd
'Quiet Magic' (2)	IRhd
'Quiet Man' (1)	IRhd
'Radiant Gem' (8)	CQua
radiiflorus (13)	EPot
- var. ***poetarum*** (13)	CBro CQua
- var. ***radiiflorus*** (13)	GCro
- var. ***stellaris*** (13) **new**	GCro

'Radjel' (4)	CQua
'Rainbow' (2) ♀H6	CQua
'Raj' (2)	CQua
'Rame Head' (1)	CQua
'Rameses' (2)	CQua MGib
'Raoul Wallenberg' (2)	GKev
'Rapid Stride' (6)	IRhd
'Rapture' (6) ♀H6	CBro CQua ERCP GKev IRhd MGib NNys WShi
'Rashee' (1)	CQua
'Raspberry Ring' (2)	CQua
'Rathowen Gold' (1)	CQua
'Ravenhill' (3)	CQua
'Rebekah' (4)	CQua
'Recital' (2)	CQua
'Red Devon' (2)	CFen GKev LCro LOPS SDeJ
'Red Era' (3)	CQua
'Red Mantle' (2)	CQua
'Red Marvel' (3)	CFen
'Red Reed' (1)	IRhd
'Red Socks' (6)	CQua
'Redwell Beauty' (3) **new**	MGib
'Refrain' (2)	CQua
'Regal Bliss' (2)	CQua
'Reggae' (6) ♀H6	CBro CQua GKev SDeJ
'Rembrandt' (1)	CFen CQua
'Rendezvous Caye' (2)	CQua
'Renovator' (1)	CQua
'Repertoire' (3)	IRhd
'Replete' (4)	CQua GKev
requienii	see *N. assoanus*
'Resistasol' (1)	IRhd
'Resolute' (2)	GCro
'Reverse Image' (11a)	CQua
'Rheban Red' (2)	IRhd MGib
'Ribald' (2)	IRhd
'Richard Lionheart' (2) **new**	GKev
'Ridgecrest' (3)	CQua
rifanus	see *N. romieuxii* subsp. *romieuxii* var. *rifanus*
'Rijnveld's Early Sensation' (1) ♀H6	CAvo CBro CFen CMea CQua ECha ERCP GKev LCro NNys SDeJ
'Rikki' (7)	CBro CQua
'Rima' (1)	CQua
'Rimmon' (3)	CQua
'Rimski' (2)	IRhd
'Ring Fence' (3)	IRhd
'Ring Flash' (2)	IRhd
'Ringing Bells' (5)	CQua
'Ringleader' (2)	CQua
'Rio Rondo' (2)	IRhd
§ 'Rip van Winkle' (4)	CAby CBro CFen CQua CTca EPfP EPot ERCP ESps GCro GKev LAma LRHS NHol NHpl NRHS SCob SDeJ WShi
'Rippling Waters' (5)	CQua LAma
'Rising Star' (7) ♀H6	IRhd
'Rival' (6)	CQua
'River Dance' (2)	IRhd
'River Queen' (2)	CQua IRhd
'Roberta' (1)	CFen
'Roberta Watrous' (7)	IRhd
'Rockall' (3)	CQua
'Rocoza' (2)	IRhd
'Roger' (6)	CQua
'Rogue' (2)	CBro
'Romance' (2) ♀H6	LAma
§ 'Romanus' (4)	CAvo CQua
romieuxii (13) ♀H4	CBro ECho EPri GCal ITim LRHS NRHS WCot

	JCA 805	CFil EPot
	- SF 370	WCot
	- subsp. ***albidus*** (13)	ECho
	- - var. ***albidus*** (13)	MGib
§	- - var. ***zaianicus*** (13)	ECho MGib
	- - - SB&L 82	WCot
§	- 'Atlas Gold' (10)	ECho
§	- 'Joy Bishop' (10)	ECho EPot
§	- 'Julia Jane' (10)	CQua ECho EPot GKev
*	- subsp. ***pallidus*** SB&L 237	WCot
§	- subsp. ***romieuxii*** var. ***mesatlanticus*** (13)	ECho EPot
§	- - var. ***rifanus*** (13)	ECho MGib
	- - B 8929	WCot
	- - var. ***romieuxii***	MGib
§	- 'Treble Chance' (10)	EPot
	'Rongoiti Gem' (4)	CQua
	'Rosannor Gold' (11a)	CQua
	'Roscarrick' (6)	CQua
	'Rose of May' (4)	CQua WShi
	'Rose of Tralee' (2)	CQua
	'Rose Royale' (2)	CQua
	'Rose Villa' (2)	CQua
	'Rosemary Pearson' (2)	CQua
	'Rosemerryn' (2)	CQua
	'Rosemoor Gold' (7) ♀H6	CBro CFen CQua
	'Rosemullion' (4)	CQua
	'Rosevine' (3)	CQua
	'Round Oak' (1)	CQua
	'Rowell Fair' (2)	MGib
	'Roxton' (4)	IRhd
	'Royal Armour' (1)	CFen
	'Royal Ballet' (2)	CQua
	'Royal China' (2)	MGib
	'Royal Connection' (8)	CQua
	'Royal Marine' (2)	CQua IRhd
	'Royal Princess' (3)	CQua ERCP GKev MGib
	'Royal Regiment' (2)	CQua
	'Rubh Mor' (2)	CQua
	'Ruby Red' (2)	CQua
	'Ruby Rose' (4)	IRhd
	'Ruby Wedding' (2)	IRhd
	'Rubythroat' (2)	CQua
	'Ruddy Duck' (2)	IRhd
	'Ruddy Rascal' (2)	IRhd
	'Rugulosus' (7)	CBro CQua GCro
	'Runkerry' (4)	IRhd
	rupicola (13)	CBro CQua ECho LLHF NSla WCot
§	- subsp. ***marvieri*** (13)	MGib
§	- subsp. ***watieri*** (13)	CBro CQua ECho EPot LLHF MGib NHpl
	'Rustom Pasha' (2)	CQua GCro
	'Rytha' (2)	CQua
	'Saberwing' (5)	CQua
	'Sabine Hay' (3)	CQua EPot ERCP GKev
	'Sabrosa' (7) ♀H4	CBro CQua GKev LLHF MGib
	'Sacajawea' (2)	CFen
	'Sacré Coeur' (2)	IRhd
	'Saffron Strand' (3)	IRhd
	'Sagana' (9)	CQua
	'Sagitta' (1) ♀H6	GKev
	'Sailboat' (7) ♀H6	CAvo CBro CQua GKev LCro SPer
	'Saint Agnes' (8)	CQua
	'Saint Budock' (1)	CQua
	'Saint Day' (5)	CQua
	'Saint Dilpe' (2)	CQua
	'Saint Keverne' (2) ♀H6	CFen CQua GCro SDeJ
	'Saint Keyne' (8)	CQua
	'Saint Louie Louie' (6) **new**	IRhd
	'Saint Olaf' (3)	GCro

'Saint Patrick's Day' (2)	CFen CQua LAma SDeJ
'Saint Peter' (4)	CFen CQua
'Saint Petroc' (9)	CQua
'Saint Piran' (7)	CQua
'Salakee' (2)	CQua
'Salcey Forest' (1)	CQua
'Salome' (2) ♀H6	CQua LAma LCro LOPS NBir NPer SCob SDeJ
'Salute' (2)	CQua
'Samantha' (4)	CQua
'Samsara' (3)	IRhd
'Sandra's Diamond' (3)	CQua
'Sandycove' (2)	CQua IRhd
'Sandymount' (2)	CQua
'Santa Claus' (4)	CQua
'Sarah Dear' (2)	CQua
'Sarah Markillie' (11a)	CQua
'Sargeant's Caye' (1)	CQua IRhd MGib
'Satchmo' (1)	CQua
'Satin Blanc' (7)	IRhd
'Satsuma' (1)	CQua
'Saturn' (3)	CQua
'Savoir Faire' (2)	IRhd
'Saxby' (11a)	CQua
scaberulus (13)	ECho
'Scarlet Chord' (2)	CQua
'Scarlet Elegance' (2)	CQua
'Scarlet Gem' (8)	SDeJ
'Scarlet Tanager' (2)	IRhd
'Scarlett O'Hara' (2)	CFen
'Scented Breeze' (2)	IRhd
'Scilly White' (8)	CFen CQua WShi
'Scorrier' (2)	CQua
'Scrumpy' (2)	CQua
'Sea Dream' (3)	CQua
'Sea Green' (9)	CQua
'Sea Legend' (2)	CQua
'Sea Moon' (2)	IRhd
'Sea Princess' (3)	GKev SDeJ
'Sea Shanty' (2)	IRhd
'Seagull' (3)	CQua GKev LAma WShi
'Sealing Wax' (2)	CFen CQua MGib
'Season's Greetings' (7)	IRhd
'Segovia' (3) ♀H6	CAvo CBro CQua EPot GKev LAma MGib NNys SDeJ
'Sempre Avanti' (2)	LAma SDeJ
'Seraglio' (3)	CQua
'Serena Beach' (4)	IRhd
'Serena Lodge' (4) ♀H6	CQua IRhd
serotinus (13)	ECho EPot
'Sextant' (6)	CQua
'Shangani' (2)	IRhd
'Sharnden' (1)	MGib
'Sheelagh Rowan' (2)	CQua IRhd MGib
'Sheelagh's Party' (2) **new**	MGib
'Sheer Joy' (6)	CQua
'Shepherd's Hey' (7)	CQua SDeJ
'Sherborne' (4) ♀H6	CQua
'Sherpa' (1)	CQua IRhd
'Sheskin' (2)	IRhd
'Shindig' (2)	IRhd
'Shining Light' (2)	CQua
'Shockwave' (2)	CQua
'Shrimp Boat' (11a)	IRhd
'Sidley' (3)	CQua IRhd
'Sidney Torch' (2)	CFen
'Signet Ring' (3)	IRhd
'Signorina' (2)	IRhd
'Silent Valley' (1)	IRhd
'Silk Cut' (2)	CQua

'Silkwood' (3)	IRhd
'Silver Bells' (5)	IRhd
'Silver Chimes' (8)	CAvo CBro CFen CQua GKev LAma LCro LOPS NBir SDeJ
'Silver Convention' (1)	CQua MGib
'Silver Crystal' (3)	IRhd
'Silver Kiwi' (2)	CQua
'Silver Moon' (2)	CFen
'Silver Plate' (11a)	CQua
'Silver Sabre' (2)	IRhd
'Silver Smiles' (7)	GKev SPhx
'Silver Surf' (2)	CQua IRhd
'Silversmith' (2)	CQua
'Silverthorne' (3)	CQua
'Silverwood' (3)	CQua IRhd
'Singing Pub' (3)	IRhd
'Sinopel' (3)	GKev LAma SDeJ
'Sir Samuel' (2)	CQua
'Sir Watkin' (2)	CQua GCro GKev
'Sir Winston Churchill' (4) ♀H6	CQua EPfP ESps GKev LAma LCro LOPS SCob SDeJ SPer
'Sirius' (2)	GCro
'Sissy' (6)	CQua
'Skerry' (2)	CQua
'Skilliwidden' (2) ♀H6	CQua
'Skookum' (3)	CQua
'Skywalker' (2)	IRhd
'Slieveboy' (1)	CQua
'Slim Whitman' (2)	GKev
'Slipstream' (6)	IRhd
'Small Fry' (1)	CQua
'Small Talk' (1) ♀H6	CQua LLHF
'Smarple' (10)	MGib
'Smiling Twin' (11a)	GKev
'Smokey Bear' (4)	CQua
'Smooth Sails' (3)	CQua
'Snipe' (6)	CAvo CQua GKev WShi
'Snook' (6)	CQua
'Snoopie' (6)	CQua
'Snow Bunting' (7)	CBro
'Snow Frills' (2)	CQua
'Snowball' (4) **new**	GKev
'Snowcrest' (3)	CQua
'Snowshill' (2)	CQua
'Snowy Canyon' (4)	IRhd
'Soft Focus' (2)	IRhd
'Solar Eclipse' (2)	IRhd
'Solar System' (3)	IRhd
'Solar Tan' (3)	CQua
'Soleil d'Or' (8)	CQua
'Solera' (2)	IRhd
'Solferique' (2)	CQua
'Soloist' (2)	IRhd
'Solveig's Song' (12)	EPot WAbe
'Sonata' (9)	CQua
'Songket' (2)	CQua
'Sophia' (2)	CQua
'Sophie Girl' (2)	GKev
'Sophie's Choice' (4)	CAvo GKev
'Soprano' (2)	CQua IRhd MGib
'Sorbet' (11b)	GKev
'Sorcerer' (3)	CQua
'South Street' (2)	CQua
'Southease' (2)	CQua
'Southern Gem' (2)	GCro
'Spaniards Inn' (4)	CQua
'Sparkling Tarts' (8)	CQua
'Sparnon' (11a)	CQua
'Spartan Gold' (2)	IRhd
'Special Envoy' (2)	CQua
'Speenogue' (1)	IRhd
'Spellbinder' (1)	CQua SDeJ
'Spencer Tracy' (2)	CFen CQua
'Sperrin Gold' (1)	IRhd
'Spin Doctor' (3)	IRhd
'Spirit of Rame' (3)	CQua
'Split Vote' (11a)	IRhd
'Spoirot' (10) ♀H6	CAby CQua ECho ERCP GBin GBuc GKev LEdu MGib MNrw NPnk SDeJ
'Sportsman' (2)	CQua
'Spring Dawn' (2)	EPfP LCro SPer
'Spring Morn' (2)	CQua IRhd
'Spring Sunshine' (12) **new**	GKev
'Spun Honey' (4)	CQua
'Stadium' (2)	CFen LAma
'Stainless' (2)	GKev SPhx
'Standard Value' (1)	CFen
'Stann Creek' (1)	CQua
'Stanway' (3)	CQua MGib
'Star Glow' (2)	CQua
'Star Quality' (3)	IRhd
'Starfire' (7)	CQua
'Starlight Sensation' (4) **new**	GKev
'State Express' (2)	CQua IRhd
'Steenbok' (3)	IRhd
'Stella' (2)	CQua GCro GKev WShi
'Stellar Glow' (3)	IRhd
'Stenalees' (6)	CQua
'Step Child' (6)	CQua
'Step Forward' (7)	CQua
'Steren' (7)	CQua
'Stilton' (9)	CQua
'Stinger' (2)	CQua
'Stint' (5) ♀H6	CQua GKev SDeJ WCot
'Stocken' (7)	CBro CQua ECho EPri WAbe
'Stoke Charity' (2)	CQua
'Stoke Doyle' (2)	CQua MGib
'Stonham Gold' (2)	CQua
'Stormy Weather' (1)	CQua
'Stratosphere' (7) ♀H6	CQua SDeJ
'Strines' (2) ♀H6	CQua MGib
'Suave' (3)	CQua
'Subtle Shades' (2)	IRhd
'Sugar and Spice' (3)	CQua
'Sugar Cups' (8)	CQua
'Sugar Loaf' (4)	CQua
'Sugar Rose' (6)	CQua
'Sugarbush' (7)	WShi
'Suisgill' (4)	CQua
'Sukey' (6)	CQua
§ 'Sulphur Phoenix' (4)	CQua WShi
Sulphur Star (2)	GCro
'Summer Solstice' (3)	IRhd
'Sumo Jewel' (6)	CQua
'Sun Disc' (7) ♀H6	CBro CFen CQua CTri ECho GKev LAma LCro LOPS MGib MPie SCob SDeJ SPer WShi
'Sunbeam Valley' (1)	MGib
'Sunday Chimes' (5)	CQua
'Sundial' (7)	CBro LAma
'Sunlight Sensation' (4) **new**	GKev
'Sunny Girlfriend' (11a)	SDeJ
'Sunnyside Up' (11a) ♀H6	SDeJ
'Sunrise' (3)	CQua
'Sunstroke' (2)	CQua
'Suntory' (3)	CQua
'Suntrap' (2)	IRhd
'Surfside' (6) ♀H6	CQua GKev SDeJ
'Surprise Packet' (2)	IRhd
'Surrey' (2)	CQua IRhd

	'Suzie Dee' (6)	IRhd
	'Suzie's Sister' (6)	IRhd
	'Suzy' (7) 🏆H6	CBro CFen GKev SDeJ
	'Swaledale' (2)	CQua
	'Swallow' (6)	CQua SDeJ
	'Swallow Wing' (6)	IRhd
	'Swan of Avon' (1)	CQua
	'Swanpool' (3)	CQua
	'Sweet Blanche' (7)	CQua
	'Sweet Lorraine' (2)	CQua
	'Sweet Love' (7) **new**	GKev NNys
	'Sweet Memory' (2)	CQua
	'Sweet Smiles' (7) **new**	GKev
	'Sweet Sue' (3)	CQua
	'Sweetness' (7) 🏆H6	CAvo CBro CFen CQua GCro GKev LAma LCro LOPS WShi
	'Swift Arrow' (6) 🏆H6	CQua
	'Swing Wing' (6)	CQua
	'Swoop' (6)	GKev SDeJ
	'Sydling' (5)	CQua
	'Taffeta' (10)	EPri
	'Tahiti' (4) 🏆H6	CFen CQua GKev LAma LCro LOPS SCob SDeJ
	× ***taitii*** (13)	WShi
	'Talgarth' (2)	CQua
	'Talskiddy' (6)	CQua
§	'Tamar Double White' (4)	CBro CFil CQua
	'Tamar Fire' (4) 🏆H6	CQua
	'Tamar Lad' (2)	CQua
	'Tamar Lass' (3)	CQua
	'Tamar Snow' (2)	CQua
	'Tamara' (2)	CFen CQua
	'Tangent' (2)	CQua
	'Tangerine Tango' (4)	IRhd
	'Tao' (3)	CQua
	'Tasgem' (4)	CQua
	'Taslass' (4)	CQua
	tazetta (13)	CQua ECho
	- subsp. ***aureus***	see *N. aureus*
§	- subsp. ***lacticolor*** (13)	CFil CQua ERCP GKev SDeJ
§	- - 'Grand Monarque' (8)	CBro CQua
	- subsp. ***ochroleucus*** (13)	CQua
*	- var. ***odoratus***	CQua WShi
	- subsp. ***tazetta***	CQua
	'Teal' (1)	CQua
	'Tehidy' (3)	CQua
§	'Telamonius Plenus' (4)	CBro CQua GBin GCro GKev SEND WShi
	'Temba' (1)	IRhd
	'Temple Cloud' (4)	IRhd
	Tequila Sunrise Group (12)	IRhd
	'Terminator' (2)	CQua IRhd
	'Terracotta' (2)	CQua
	'Terrapin' (3)	IRhd
	'Terwegen' (4)	CFen
	'Tête-à-tête' (12) 🏆H6	CAvo CBro CFen CQua CTca CWCL EPfP EPot ERCP ESps GAbr GKev LAma LCro LOPS LPot LRHS LSou NHpl NRHS SCob SDeJ SPer
	'Thalia' (5)	CAvo CBro CQua CTca EPfP ERCP ESps GKev IFro LAma LCro LOPS LPot NBir NHol NNys SCob SDeJ SPer SPhx WShi
	'The Alliance' (6) 🏆H6	CBro CQua
	'The Caley' (2)	CQua
	'The First' (1) **new**	GCro
	'The Grange' (1)	CQua
	'The Mount' (2)	IRhd
	'Therapia' (3)	GCro
	'Thistin' (1)	IRhd

	'Thomas Kinkade' (2)	CQua
	'Thoughtful' (5)	CBro CQua
	'Three Oaks' (1)	CQua
	'Three Trees' (1)	IRhd
	'Tibet' (2)	CFen CQua
	'Tickled Pink' (11a)	IRhd
	'Tideford' (2)	CQua
	'Tidy Tippet' (2)	IRhd
	'Tiercel' (1)	CQua
	'Tiffany Jade' (3)	CQua
	'Tiger Moth' (6)	CQua
	'Timolin' (3)	CQua
	'Tingdene' (2)	MGib
	'Tinhay' (7)	CQua
	'Tiritomba' (11a)	CQua
	'Tittle-tattle' (7)	CFen CQua
	'Toby' (2)	SDeJ
	'Top Hit' (11a)	CQua
	'Topolino' (1) 🏆H6	CAvo CBro CFen CQua EPot ERCP GKev IFro LAma LCro LOPS LRHS NRHS SCob
	'Topsy Turvy' (4)	CQua
	'Toreador' ambig. (3)	CFen
	'Toretta' (3)	IRhd
	'Torianne' (2) 🏆H6	CQua
	Torosay Elegance (2)	GCro
	'Torr Head' (9)	IRhd
	'Torridon' (2)	CQua
	'Toto' (12) 🏆H6	CAvo CBro CQua ECho ERCP GKev SDeJ SPhx
	'Tracey' (6)	CQua IRhd LAma
	'Transmitter' (4)	CQua
	'Treasure Hunt' (2)	IRhd
	'Trebah' (2) 🏆H6	CQua
	'Treble Chance'	see *N. romieuxii* 'Treble Chance'
	'Treble Two' (7)	CQua
	'Trecara' (3)	CQua
	'Tregarrick' (2)	CQua
	'Treglisson' (2)	CFen
	'Trelawney Gold' (2)	CFen CQua
	'Trelissick' (7)	CQua
	'Tremelling' (2)	CFen
	'Tremough Dale' (11a)	CQua
	'Trena' (6) 🏆H6	CQua ERCP GKev MGib
	'Trendy Trail' (3)	IRhd
	'Trentagh' (3)	IRhd
	'Trenwith' (1)	CQua
	'Trepolo' (11b)	ERCP SDeJ
	'Tresamble' (5)	CBro CQua EPfP GCro GKev LAma NBir NNys SDeJ
	'Tresham Gold' (2)	MGib
	'Tresserve' (1) **new**	GCro
	'Trevaunance' (6)	CQua
	'Treverva' (6)	CQua
	'Treviddo' (2)	CQua
	'Trevithian' (7)	CBro CQua GCro GKev LAma SDeJ
	'Trewarvas' (2)	CQua
	'Trewirgie' (6)	GCro
	triandrus var. ***albus***	see *N. triandrus* subsp. *triandrus* var. *triandrus*
§	- subsp. ***triandrus*** var. ***triandrus*** (13)	GBin
	'Tricollet' (11a)	GKev SDeJ
	'Trident' (3)	CQua
	'Trielfin' (5)	IRhd
	'Trigonometry' (11a) 🏆H6	CQua IRhd
	'Tripartite' (11a) 🏆H6	CFen CQua GKev IRhd MGib SDeJ
	'Triple Crown' (3) 🏆H6	CQua IRhd
	'Tristram' (2)	CQua
	'Tropic Isle' (4)	CQua

'Tropical Heat' (2)	IRhd
'Trousseau' (1)	CFen CQua
'Tru' (3)	CQua
'Truculent' (3)	CQua
'Trueblood' (3)	IRhd
'Trumpet Warrior' (1) 🏆^{H6}	CQua IRhd MGib
'Tryst' (2)	CQua
'Tudor Minstrel' (2)	CQua
'Tuesday's Child' (5) 🏆^{H6}	CQua
'Turncoat' (6)	CQua
'Tutankhamun' (2)	CQua
'Twicer' (2)	CQua IRhd
'Twilight Zone' (2)	IRhd
'Twink' (4)	CQua GCro
'Twinkling Yellow' (7) 🏆^{H6}	CBro GKev MGib
Tyndrum Flame (3)	GCro
'Tyrone Gold' (1) 🏆^{H6}	CQua IRhd
'Tyrree' (1)	IRhd
'Tywara' (1)	CQua
'Ulster Bank' (3)	CQua
'Ulster Bride' (4)	CQua
'Ultimus' (2)	CQua
'Uncle Duncan' (1)	CQua
'Unique' (4) 🏆^{H6}	CQua GKev LAma SDeJ
'Unsurpassable' (1)	CFen CQua GCro LAma
'Upalong' (12)	CQua
'Upshot' (3)	CQua
'Urchin' (2)	IRhd
'Utiku' (6)	CQua
'Val d'Incles' (3)	CQua IRhd
'Valdrome' (11a)	CQua
'Valediction' (3)	CQua
'Valinor' (2)	CQua
'Van Sion'	see *N.* 'Telamonius Plenus'
'Vanellus' (11a) 🏆^{H6}	IRhd
'Vanilla Peach' (11a)	SDeJ
'Vantage' (2)	CQua
'Vaticaan' (1)	SDeJ
'Velocity' (6)	GKev LAma MGib
'Vendell' (3)	IRhd
'Verdant Sparks' (7)	IRhd
'Verdin' (7)	CQua
'Verdoy' (2)	IRhd
'Verger' (3)	LAma SDeJ
'Vernal Prince' (3) 🏆^{H6}	CQua
'Verona' (3) 🏆^{H6}	CQua
'Verran Rose' (2)	IRhd
'Vers Libre' (9)	CQua
'Version' (2)	IRhd
'Victoria' (1)	CQua GKev
'Video Kid' (2)	IRhd
'Viking' (1) 🏆^{H6}	CQua
'Village Green' (3)	IRhd
'Vineland' (6)	CQua
'Violetta' (2)	CQua
'Virginia Waters' (3)	CQua MGib
'Viva Diva' (3)	IRhd
'Volare' (2)	CQua
'Volcanic Rim' (3)	IRhd
'Vulcan' (2)	CQua
'W.P. Milner' (1)	CAby CAvo CBro CQua EPfP EPot ERCP GKev LAma SDeJ SPhx WShi
'Walden Pond' (3)	CQua
'Waldorf Astoria' (4)	CQua
'Walton' (7)	CQua
'Waltz' (11a)	CQua
'War Dance' (3)	IRhd
'Warbler' (6) 🏆^{H6}	CQua GKev LAma SDeJ WHea
'Warleggan' (2)	CFen
'Warm Day' (2)	IRhd
'Warm Welcome' (2)	IRhd
'Warmington' (3)	CQua
'Warmwell' (3)	IRhd
'Watamu' (3)	IRhd
'Waterperry' (7)	CBro GKev LAma
'Watership Down' (2)	CQua IRhd
'Watersmeet' (4)	CQua
watieri	see *N. rupicola* subsp. *watieri*
'Wave' (4)	CQua GKev
'Wavelength' (3)	IRhd
'Wavertree'	see *N. asturiensis* 'Wavertree'
'Waxwing' (5)	CQua MGib
'Wayward Lad' (3)	IRhd
'Wee Bee' (1)	CQua
'Welcome' (2)	CFen CQua
'Welland Vale' (1)	MGib
'Welsh Rugby Union' (1)	CQua
'Welsh Warrior' (1)	CQua
'Wendron' (1)	CFen
'West Post' (3)	IRhd
'Westward' (4)	CQua
'Whang-hi' (6)	CQua
'Wheal Bush' (4)	CQua
'Wheal Coates' (7) 🏆^{H6}	CQua
'Wheal Jane' (2)	CQua
'Wheal Kitty' (7)	CQua
'Wheal Rose' (4)	CQua
'Wheatear' (6) 🏆^{H6}	CQua IRhd
'Whetstone' (1)	CQua
'Whipcord' (7) 🏆^{H6}	CQua IRhd
'Whisky Galore' (2)	CQua
'Whisky Mac' (2)	CQua
'White Convention' (1)	IRhd
'White Empress' (1)	CQua
'White Giant' (1)	GKev
'White Lady' (3)	CAvo CQua GCro GKev LAma WShi
'White Lion' (4) 🏆^{H6}	CFen CQua ESps LAma SDeJ
'White Marvel' (4)	CQua GKev
'White Medal' (4)	GKev SDeJ
'White Nile' (2)	CQua GCro
'White Star' (1)	IRhd
'White Tea' (2)	CQua IRhd MGib
'White Tie' (3)	CQua
'Whitewell' (2)	GCro
'Wicklow Hills' (3)	CQua
'Widgeon' (2)	CQua
'Wild Honey' (2)	CQua
'Wild Rover' (1)	IRhd
'Will Scarlett' (2)	CQua GCro
willkommii (13)	CBro CQua ECho EPot GKev
'Wimbledon County Girl' (2) 🏆^{H6}	CQua
'Winholm Jenni' (3)	CQua
'Winifred van Graven' (3)	CFen CQua
'Winter Waltz' (6)	CQua
'Wisley' (6) 🏆^{H6}	ERCP
'Witch Doctor' (3)	CQua
Woodcroft Beauty (2)	GCro
Woodcroft Gold (2)	GCro
'Woodland Prince' (3)	CQua
'Woodland Star' (3)	CQua
'Woodley Vale' (2)	CQua
'Woolsthorpe' (2)	CQua
'World Class' (5)	CQua
'Xit' (3)	CAvo CBro CQua
'Xunantunich' (2)	CQua
'Yellow Belles' (5)	IRhd
'Yellow Cheerfulness' (4) 🏆^{H6}	CQua EPfP GKev LAma LCro LOPS SCob SDeJ SPer
'Yellow River' (1) 🏆^{H6}	LAma

'Yellow Triumphator' (1) CFen
'Yellow Xit' (3) CQua GKev
'York Minster' (1) CQua
'Young American' (1) CQua
'Young Blood' (2) CQua IRhd
'Your Grace' (2) CQua
'Yummy Mummy' (2) IRhd
'Yum-Yum' (3) IRhd
zaianicus see *N. romieuxii* subsp. *albidus* var. *zaianicus*
'Zekiah' (1) CQua
'Zion Canyon' (2) CQua
'Zoë's Pink' (3) CQua
'Zwynner' (2) IRhd

Nardostachys (*Caprifoliaceae*)

grandiflora GPoy

Nassauvia (*Asteraceae*)

darwinii WAbe
gaudichaudii SPlb WAbe
lagascae WAbe

Nassella (*Poaceae*)

neesiana SPhx
tenuissima see *Stipa tenuissima*
trichotoma CAby CKno EHoe LPla SPer WHal
- 'Palomino' CRos LRHS NRHS

Nasturtium (*Brassicaceae*)

'Banana Split' CCCN ELan
officinale MSKA SVic SWat

Natal plum see *Carissa macrocarpa*

nectarine see *Prunus persica* var. *nectarina*

Nectaroscordum (*Alliaceae*)

sp. SDir
§ ***siculum*** CAvo CBre CBro CSpe CTri EAJP ECho ELan EPfP ERCP GCra GKev LCro LEdu LLWP LRHS MBel NBir NChi NSti SCob SDeJ SPer SPoG WBor
§ - subsp. ***bulgaricum*** CAby CBro CTca CWCL EBee ECha EHrv EPfP EPot GKev IBlr IBoy LRHS MNrw SPhx WBrk WCot WPnP XEll XLum
tripedale CAvo CBro ECho EPot GKev

Neillia (*Rosaceae*)

affinis CDul EBee EPfP GCal IDee LLHF LRHS MGil MMuc NBid NLar SLon SPad SWvt WPat
longiracemosa see *N. thibetica*
sinensis NLar
§ ***thibetica*** Widely available
thyrsiflora PAB 3267 LEdu
- var. ***tunkinensis*** HWJ 505 WCru

Nelumbo (*Nelumbonaceae*)

'Beautiful Dancer' LLWG
'Carolina Queen' LLWG
'Emerald Daybreak' (d) LLWG
'First Lady' **new** LLWG
'High Noon' LLWG
lutea LLWG XBlo
'Momo Botan' LLWG
'Mrs Perry D. Slocum' LLWG
nucifera XBlo
- 'Alba Striata' LLWG
- 'Chawan Basu' LLWG
- 'Hindu' LLWG
'Penelope' LLWG
'Perry's Giant Sunburst' LLWG
'Pink 'n' Yellow' EWay
'Pink Pretty Princess Payton' LLWG
'Russian Red' LLWG
'The President' LLWG
'Wa Ba Sabie' LLWG
'Wann Shou Hing' LLWG

Nematanthus (*Gesneriaceae*)

'Apres' WDib
'Black Magic' WDib
'Christmas Holly' WDib
'Freckles' WDib
§ ***gregarius*** ♀H1c WDib
§ - 'Golden West' (v) WDib
- 'Variegatus' see *N. gregarius* 'Golden West'
'Lemon and Lime' WDib
radicans see *N. gregarius*
'Tropicana' ♀H1c WDib

Nemesia (*Scrophulariaceae*)

§ Amelie = 'Fleurame'PBR CRos EPfP LBuc SPoG
Berries and Cream = 'Fleurbac'PBR CRos ECtt EPfP LBuc LRHS LSou SPoG
Blue Lagoon = 'Pengoon'PBR (Maritana Series) EBee NPri SCoo
'Blueberry Ripple' LSou
'Bluebird' see *N.* Bluebird = 'Hubbird', 'Fleurie Blue'
§ Bluebird = 'Hubbird'PBR CHll
Candy Girl = 'Pencand' (Maritana Series) SCoo
Ciruela = 'Innemsunci'PBR **new** NPri
§ ***denticulata*** ♀H3 CBar ELon EWoo LHop LRHS MHer NEgg SCoo WHlf
- 'Confetti' see *N. denticulata*
Elph Dark Blue (Elph Series) WCot
'Fleurie Blue' CRos EPfP LBuc SPoG
Framboise = 'Fleurfram'PBR CRos EPfP LBuc SPoG
fruticans Benth. ELon
Honey Girl = 'Penhon' (Maritana Series) SCoo
Ice Pink = 'Fleuripi' EPfP
'Innocence' ♀H3 SCoo
(Karoo Series) Karoo Blue = 'Innkablue'PBR SCoo
- Karoo Soft Blue = 'Innkarsofb'PBR CWGN MCot
- Karoo Violet Ice = 'Innemkavic'PBR MCot NPri
Lagoon White see *N.* Pure Lagoon
Maritana Sky Lagoon = 'Pensky' (Maritana Series) SCoo
'Mirabelle' CRos EPfP LBuc SPoG
Myrtille = 'Fleurmyr'PBR CRos EPfP LBuc SPoG
Opal Innocence see *N.* Amelie
Pink Lagoon = 'Penpink' (Maritana Series) **new** EBee
Provençal Dusky Blue = 'Fleurpdblu'PBR EPfP
Provençal Dusky Pink = 'Fleurpdpnk'PBR EPfP

§ Pure Lagoon = 'Penpur'PBR	EBee
Raspberries and Cream = 'Fleurrac'	CRos EPfP LBuc LRHS SPoG
'Sugar Almond'	CMac
'Sugar Plum'	LRHS
'Sundrops'	NPri
(Sunsatia Series) Sunsatia Blackberry = 'Inuppink'PBR	SCoo
- Sunsatia Cherry on Ice	NPri SPoG
- Sunsatia Cranberry = 'Intraired'PBR	SCoo
- Sunsatia Lemon = 'Intraigold'PBR	SCoo
- Sunsatia Peach = 'Inupcream'	CWGN SCoo
- Sunsatia Raspberry	LSou
(Sunsatia Plus Series) Sunsatia Plus Papaya = 'Innemnewpa'	NPri
- Sunsatia Pomelo = 'Innemsunpo'PBR	NPri
'Sweet Lady'	LBMP LSou NPri
sylvatica	CSpe
(Utopia Series) 'Utopia Lavender'	EBee
- 'Utopia Painted Face'	ENor
'Vanilla Lady'	ECtt LBMP LSou NPri
Vanilla Mist = 'Grega'	LRHS LSou
'Wisley Vanilla'	CRos EPfP LBuc LRHS NRHS SPoG

Nemophila (*Boraginaceae*)

menziesii 'Penny Black'	CSpe SPer

Neodypsis (*Arecaceae*)

decaryi	see *Dypsis decaryi*

Neolitsea (*Lauraceae*)

glauca	see *N. sericea*
polycarpa B&SWJ 11705	WCru
- KWJ 12309	WCru
§ ***sericea***	CBcs CCCN EBee LEdu WPGP
- CWJ 12800 **new**	WCru

Neomarica (*Iridaceae*)

caerulea	WCot

Neopanax ✿ (*Araliaceae*)

§ ***arboreus***	CDTJ CTsd EBee LEdu SBig
§ ***laetus*** ♀H3	EBee LEdu SArc SBig WPGP

Neoregelia ✿ (*Bromeliaceae*)

carolinae (Meyendorffii Group) 'Meyendorffii'	XBlo
'Chiquita Linda'	NLos
'Dr Oeser'	NLos
'Fireball'	NLos
'Hannibal Lector' × ***punctatissima*** var. ***rubra***	NLos
'Hojo Rojo'	XBlo
'Marconfos'	XBlo
'Red on Green'	NLos
'Scarlet Charlotte'	NLos
'Spicy'	NLos
'Zuleica'	NLos

Neoshirakia (*Euphorbiaceae*)

japonica	MBlu WPGP
- B&SWJ 8744	WCru

Neottianthe (*Orchidaceae*)

cucullata	EFEx

Nepenthes ✿ (*Nepenthaceae*)

alata	NLos
alata × ***ventricosa*** ♀H1b	SHmp
albomarginata	NLos
aristolochioides × ***spectabilis***	NLos
'Black Beauty' **new**	NLos
'Bloody Mary'PBR **new**	SHmp
bongso	NLos SHmp
bongso × ***inermis***	NLos
boschiana × ***densiflora***	NLos
burbidgeae	NLos
burbidgeae × ***robcantleyi*** **new**	SHmp
× ***burkei***	NLos
× ***burkei*** × ***hamata*** **new**	SHmp
× ***burkei*** × ***singalana*** **new**	SHmp
chaniana × (***clipeata*** × ***eymae***)	NLos
chaniana × ***veitchii***	NLos
clipeata × ***eymae***	NLos
copelandii	NLos
(***copelandii*** × ***truncata***) × ***spathulata***	SHmp
densiflora	NLos SHmp
densiflora × ***spectabilis***	NLos
diatas	NLos SHmp
dubia × ***singalana*** **new**	SHmp
dubia × ***spathulata*** **new**	SHmp
eymae	NLos
fusca	NLos SHmp
fusca × ***maxima***	SHmp
glabrata	NLos
glabrata × ***spathulata*** **new**	SHmp
gracillima	NLos
× ***hookeriana*** ♀H1a	NLos SHmp
inermis	NLos
inermis × ***singalana***	NLos
inermis × ***ventricosa***	NLos
jacquelineae × ***spectabilis*** **new**	SHmp
'Lady Pauline' ♀H1b	NLos
'Linda'PBR **new**	SHmp
'Louisa' **new**	SHmp
lowii	NLos
macfarlanei	SHmp
maxima	NLos
maxima × (× ***mixta***)	SHmp
maxima × ***talangensis***	SHmp
mikei	NLos
mira × ***spathulata***	NLos SHmp
mira × ***spectabilis***	NLos
muluensis × ***lowii***	NLos
ovata	NLos SHmp
ovata × ***ventricosa*** **new**	SHmp
petiolata × ***veitchii*** **new**	SHmp
pilosa	NLos
pilosa × ***veitchii***	NLos
platychila × ***spathulata*** **new**	SHmp
platychila × ***veitchii***	NLos
rajah	NLos
ramispina	NLos SHmp
'Rebecca Soper' ♀H1b	SHmp

	robcantleyi **new**	SHmp
	robcantleyi* × *spathulata **new**	SHmp
	robcantleyi* × *talangensis **new**	SHmp
	sanguinea	NLos SHmp
	sibuyanensis	SHmp
	sibuyanensis* × *spectabilis	NLos
	sibuyanensis* × *ventricosa	NLos
	singalana	NLos SHmp
	spectabilis	NLos SHmp
	spectabilis* × *talangensis	NLos
	talangensis	NLos SHmp
	talangensis* × *veitchii	SHmp
	tobaica	NLos SHmp
	truncata	NLos
	- highland form	SHmp
	- 'King of Spades' × ***truncata*** 'Queen of Hearts'	SHmp
	veitchii	NLos
	ventricosa	SHmp

Nepeta ✿ (*Lamiaceae*)

	from China	EWes
	'Blue Beauty'	see *N. sibirica* 'Souvenir d'André Chaudron'
	'Blue Dragon'	ECtt EPed GBin GPSL GQue GWyn LRHS LSou MPie MSpe MTis NCGa NDov NLar SBee SPoG WHoo
	bucharica	GBuc
*	***buddlejifolium***	NLar
*	- 'Gold Splash'	NLar
	camphorata	SRms
	cataria	CArn CBod CLau CTri CWld ENfk GJos GPoy MHer MNHC NBro NLar SIde SRms SVic WJek WMoo
§	- 'Citriodora'	CBod ENfk GPoy SPhx SRms WJek
	'Chettle Blue'	MAvo
	citriodora Dum.	see *N. cataria* 'Citriodora'
	clarkei	EPPr GMaP MArt MRav MTis SWat WMoo
	'Dropmore'	EBee GWyn MTis
	'Early Bird'	EBee
§	× ***faassenii*** ♀H7	Widely available
	- 'Alba'	EBee ECtt ELan EPfP LPot LRHS NLar WJek
	- 'Blauknirps'	EBee
	- 'Blue Wonder'	EBee ELan EPfP LRHS MTis
	- 'Gletschereis' **new**	EBee
	- 'Kit Cat'	CRos CSpe ECtt GBin GBuc GCal GWyn IBoy LHop LRHS LSRN MAsh MTis NCGa NDov NRHS SAko WCAu WCFE WHoo WSHC
	- 'Limelight'	IBoy MTis SPoG
	- 'Senior'	XLum
	glechoma 'Variegata'	see *Glechoma hederacea* 'Variegata'
	govaniana	Widely available
	grandiflora	CDor MRav NBre SIde WHrl
	- 'Blue Danube'	EBee GBin GWyn MTis XLum
	- 'Blue Elf'	NDov
	- 'Bramdean' ♀H6	CBod CDor CMea EBee ECtt EPfP EWes GBin GWyn LBMP LHop LRHS MCot MHer MRav MTis NRHS SPhx SRms WCAu WCot XLum
	- 'Dawn to Dusk'	Widely available
	- 'Pool Bank'	EBee ECtt EWes MAvo MTis SIde XLum
	- 'Summer Magic'	CBod CRos EBee ECha GBin LRHS NDov NRHS SCob SHar WTor
	- 'Wild Cat'	EPfP MAvo MTis SPhx
	- 'Zinser's Giant'	EBee SAko
	hederacea 'Variegata'	see *Glechoma hederacea* 'Variegata'
	'Hill Grounds'	MAvo WCot
	italica	SHar
	'Joanna Reed' **new**	GBin
	Junior Walker = 'Novanepjun'	CKno LCro LHop MAsh NDov SCob
	kubanica	CBWd CSpe EBee IMou MRav SBee SMHy SPhx WCot
	'Lamendi'	NDov
	latifolia 'Super Cat'	EBee ELan EPfP
§	'Leeds Castle'	CBod EBee ECGP ECtt EPed LRHS MAvo MTis NCGa NGdn NSti SHar SPer SPoG WHal WTor
	'Limelight'	NLar
	longipes hort.	see *N.* 'Leeds Castle'
	macrantha	see *N. sibirica*
	manchuriensis 'Manchu Blue' **new**	EBee
	'Maurice'	NDov SMHy
	mussinii misapplied	see *N.* × *faassenii*
	mussinii Spreng.	see *N. racemosa*
	nervosa	CSpe ECha ELan EPfP NBro NLar NSti SBrt SPer WHar WHea WJek WSHC
	- 'Blue Carpet'	CRos CSpe LRHS NEgg NRHS
	- 'Blue Moon'	CWld EBee EPfP EWes GAbr IBoy LRHS LSou MBNS MHol MMrt MPie MSCN NDov NQui SRms
	- 'Forncett Select'	CSam MRav NBre
	- 'Pink Cat'	CBod CMea EPfP LRHS MArt MSCN NLar NRHS WFar
	- 'Schneehäschen'	SAko
§	***nuda***	ECha ECrN EWes LPla MRav SHar SMHy
	- 'Accent'	EBee
	- subsp. ***albiflora***	ECha
*	- 'Grandiflora'	NBre WMoo
	- 'Isis'	NDov
	- 'Purple Cat'	EBee EPfP LHop LLHF NDov
	- 'Romany Dusk'	LEdu
	- 'Snow Cat'	SPhx
	pannonica	see *N. nuda*
	parnassica	EPPr EWTr GLog GQue MArt MBel MCot MHol MMuc MTis WHrl WMoo WPtf
	phyllochlamys	CBot CPBP SRms
	'Pink Candy'	SRms
§	***prattii***	CBod MMuc MWat NLar SEND
	'Purple Haze' PBR	CMea ECtt NLar
§	***racemosa*** ♀H7	CHby CLau CMac CNec CPbn EPfP GWyn LRHS MCot MNHC MSCN SCob SIde WMoo
	- RCB AM 3	WCot
	- ***alba***	CBod EAJP XLum
	- 'Amelia'	CBWd CBod EBee EPfP MAsh MHer MSpe WTor
	- 'Grog'	CWld EWTr GBin GWyn LRHS MTis NLar SPoG
	- 'Little Titch'	CBod EBee ECha ECtt EPfP GBuc GWyn LRHS LSRN MAsh MCot NGdn NLar SCob SWat
	- 'Odeur Citron' **new**	SAko
	- 'Snowflake'	CBcs CMea CRos ECtt ELan ELon EPfP EShb EWTr GMaP GPSL GWyn LRHS MAvo MTis NBir SCob SPer SPoG SWvt WCAu WTor

	- 'Superba'	NBre
	- 'Toria'	IMou MAvo MTis NDov
	- 'Walker's Low' 🏆H7	Widely available
*	'Rae Crug'	ECtt EWes
	reichenbachiana	see *N. racemosa*
§	***sibirica***	ECha ELan EPfP LRHS MMuc NBid NBro NLar SRkn WCot WJek XLum
§	- 'Souvenir d'André Chaudron' 🏆H6	CAby CBod CMea CSam CWCL EBee EHrv ELan EPfP EWTr GBuc GCal GMaP IPot LHop LRHS LSou MCot MRav MTis NLar SCob SPer SPoG WHea
	'Six Hills Giant'	Widely available
	'Six Hills Gold'	CAby CDor EBee LBuc LPre MArt SCob SPoG WTor
	stewartiana	LLHF MRav WMoo
	subsessilis	CAby CBod CCVN CMHG ECtt EHrv ELan EPfP GLog GMaP IBoy IKil LCro LRHS MBel MCot MRav MSpe NBid NBir NGdn NLar NSti NWad SCob SPhx SRms WCru
	- 'Blue Dreams'	ELon GWyn MArt MHol MNHC NLar SCob SHar SPhx SRkn WHar XLum
	- 'Candy Cat'	ELan IBoy LPot MTis NBre NLar
	- 'Cool Cat'	EBee ELan EPfP LSRN NBre NLar
	- 'Laufen'	IPot
	- Nimbus = 'Yanim'	MHol MPnt NFav
	- 'Pink Dreams'	CBod EAJP EBee ELan EPfP GJos GWyn LRHS MHer SCob SHar XLum
	- pink-flowered	ECha EPPr SPhx
	- 'Sweet Dreams'	CBod EPfP GJos LCro LHop LRHS MRav MSpe MTis NLar NSti XLum
	- 'Washfield'	LHop NLar SAko
	transcaucasica	SDix
	- 'Blue Infinity'	CNor MSCN WMoo
	tuberosa	CArn CBod CWld EBee ECha WCot WMoo WTcb XSen
	'Veluws Blauwtje'	NLar
	'Veluwse Wakel'	IMou
	wilsonii new	GBin
	yunnanensis	EBee EPPr IPot MPie SPhx WOut WPGP

Nephrolepis (*Lomariopsidaceae*)

cordifolia	NLos
exaltata 'Verona'	WCot
falcata	NLos
- f. ***furcans***	NLos

Nerine ✿ (*Amaryllidaceae*)

	'Afterglow'	ECho LAma LRHS WCot
	'Alresford'	ECho
	alta	see *N. undulata* Alta Group
	'Ancilla'	ECho
	'Angelico'	ECho
	angustifolia	WAbe
	'Atlanta'	ECho
	'Audrey Clarke'	CPne
	'Aurora'	ECho WCot
	'Bach'	ECho
	'Baghdad'	ECho WCot
	'Belladonna'	CWCL WCot
	'Bennett-Poë'	WCot
	'Berlioz'	ECho WCot
	'Beth Chatto'	ECho
	'Blanchefleur'	CTal WCot
	bowdenii 🏆H5	Widely available
	- 'Alba' misapplied	see *N. bowdenii* 'Pallida'
	- 'Alba' ambig.	CPrp CTca EBee ECho ELan EPot ERCP SCoo SHil SMHy
	- 'Alba'	CBro CWCL ECha EPri GKev IBal LAma LRHS MNrw SCob SDeJ WFar
	- 'Albivetta'	EBee ECho EPri GKev IBal LAma MNrw NNys
	- 'Blanca Perla'	EBee GKev LAma WCot
	- 'Castlewellan'	IBlr
	- 'Codora'	see *N.* 'Codora'
	- 'E.B. Anderson'	WCot
	- 'Elegance Red'	CBro
	- 'Ella K'	CBod ECho EPfP EPot EPri ERCP GKev IBal LAma MNrw SPer WHil
	- 'Eric Smith'	WCot
	- 'Gletsjer'	GKev LAma WCot
	- Irish clone	WCot
	- 'Isabel'	CAby CBro CPrp CTsd ECha ECho ELan EPot EPri ERCP EWes GKev IBal LAma WBor WCot WHil WHoo
	- 'Kathleen Pollock'	WCot
	- 'Linda Vista'	WCot
	- 'Manina'	CCse
	- 'Marjorie'	EMal
	- 'Mark Fenwick'	CBro WCot
	- 'Marnie Rogerson'	CBro CPne SMHy WCot
§	- 'Mollie Cowie' (v)	CCse CPrp GCal IBlr WCot WCru
	- 'Mount Stewart'	CPne IBlr WCot
	- 'Nikita'	CPne ECho EPri ERCP GKev IBal LAma LRHS MNrw SCob SDeJ SHil WCot
	- 'Ostara'	CBod CPrp ELan EPot EPri GKev IBal LAma LRHS MNrw WCot WFar
§	- 'Pallida'	LRHS
	- 'Patricia'	EPot EPri GKev IBal LAma MNrw
	- 'Pink Frostwork'	EPri WCot
	- 'Pink Surprise'	CAvo EPri WCot
§	- 'Quinton Wells'	CTca WCot
	- 'Richard Blakeway-Phillips'	WCot WHil
	- 'Robert Smith'	WCot
	- 'Rowie'	CPrp EPri LRHS
	- 'Sheila Owen'	WCot
	- 'Stam 63'	EPot GKev IBal LAma WHil
	- 'Stefanie'	CAby ELan EPri GKev IBal LAma SDeJ
	- Ted Allen No 2	WCot
	- 'Variegata'	see *N. bowdenii* 'Mollie Cowie'
	- 'Vesta K'	EPot EPri GKev IBal LAma LRHS
	- 'Wellsii'	see *N. bowdenii* 'Quinton Wells'
	'Brahms'	ECho
	'Canasta'	WCot
	'Cardinal'	ECho
	'Caryatid'	WCot WFar
	'Catherine'	CPne WCot
	'Catkin'	CPne WCot
	'Clent Charm'	WCot
§	'Codora'	CCCN ECho EPfP SPer WCot WFar
	'Corlette'	WCot
	corusca 'Major'	see *N. sarniensis* var. *corusca*
	'Cranfield'	WCot
	crispa	see *N. undulata* Crispa Group
	'Cynthia Chance'	ECho WCot
	'Daphne'	ECho
	'Diana Oliver'	CPne WCot
	'Doris Vos'	WCot
	'Elegance' new	LRHS
	'Elspeth'	WCot
	'Exbury Red'	WCot
	filamentosa misapplied	see *N. filifolia* Baker
	filamentosa ambig.	CBro ECho
	filamentosa W.F. Barker	CTal

§	***filifolia*** Baker	EChoWAbe
	'Firelight'	CPne
	flexuosa	see *N. undulata* Flexuosa Group
	gaberonensis	WAbe
	'Gaiety'	WCot
	'George'	ECho
	'Glacier'	EBee LRHS MNrw
	gracilis	ECho WCot
	'Grania'	ECho
	'Hamlet'	CPne
	'Hanley Castle'	ECho
	'Harlequin'	WCot
	'Helena'	ECho
	'Hera'	CBro
	'Hertha Berg'	WCot
*	***hirsuta***	ECho GKev WCot
	'Hotspur'	ECho
	humilis ♀H2	ECho
	- from Franschhoek, South Africa	CTal
	- Breachiae Group	CTal
	- Peersii Group from Toorwaterpoort, South Africa	CTal
	huttoniae	ECho
	'Iman'	WCot
	'Isabella' new	NNys
	'Isobel'	LEdu LRHS XEll
	'Janet'	ECho WCot
	'Jenny Wren'	ECho WCot
I	'Judith' Norris	ECho
	'King Leopold'	ECho WCot WFar
	'King of the Belgians'	ECho LAma LRHS
	'Kinn McIntosh'	EPri WCot
	'Koko'	ECho
	'Koriba'	ECho
	krigei	ECho WCot XEll
	'Kyle'	WCot
	'Kyrie'	ECho
	'La Reine'	ECho
	'Lady Cynthia Colville'	WCot
	'Lady Downe'	WCot
	'Lady Eleanor Keane'	ECho WCot
	'Lady Havelock-Allen'	WCot
	'Lady Llewellyn'	ECho WCot
	'Lady St Aldwyn'	WCot
	'Lambourne'	WCot
	laticoma	WCot
	'Lavant'	ECho
	'Lawlord'	WCot
	'Leila Hughes'	WCot
	'Lucinda'	WCot
	'Lyndhurst Salmon'	ECho WCot
	'Malvern'	WCot
	'Maria'	WCot
	'Mars'	CTal
	masoniorum ♀H2	CTal ECho GKev SBch WAbe
	'Miss E. Cator'	CPne CTal WCot
	'Miss Florence Brown'	WCot
	'Miss Frances Clarke'	WCot
	'Monet'	ECho
	'Mr John' new	CPne GKev LAma LRHS WCot
	'Mrs C. Goldsmith'	ECho
	'Mrs Cooper'	WCot
	'Mrs Dent Brocklehurst'	WCot
	'Murilla'	ECho
	'Mystic'	ECho
	'Natasha'	ECho
	'Nena'	WCot
	'November Cheer'	ECho LAma
	'Oberon'	WCot
	'Ophelia'	WCot
	'Orange Flame'	ECho
	'Paragon'	ECho
	peersii	WCot
	'Pink Triumph'	CAbP CBcs CTsd EBee ECho ELan EPot ERCP EShb GKev IBal LAma LRHS SDeJ SPer WCot WHoo
	'Plymouth'	CTal ECho
	pudica	CTal
	- pink-flowered	WCot
	pusilla	CLak
	'Quivotina'	WCot
	'Red Pimpernel'	ECho LAma
	'Regina'	WCot
	'Rembrandt'	ECho WCot
	'Rose Princess'	WCot
	'Rotherside'	CTal
	'Rushmere Star'	CTal ECho SChr WCot
	'Ruth'	WCot WFar
	sarniensis	CBro CPne ECha EPot EPri SKHP WCot
	- 'Anne Baring'	ECho
*	- 'Borde Hill White'	WCot
§	- var. ***corusca***	LAma
	- - 'Major'	ECho MPie SChr WCot
	- var. ***curvifolia*** new	CBro
	- - f. ***fothergillii***	ECho WCot
	- 'Mottistone'	WCot
	- 'Pink Petticoat'	CTal
	- 'Salmon Star'	LRHS
	- var. ***sarniensis***	GKev
	- 'Shell Pink'	CTal
	'Sidney Smee'	CTal
	'Snowflake'	MAsh WCot
	'Stephanie'	CCCN CPne CTca ECho EShb LAma LEdu MNrw WCot WHoo
	'Susan Norris'	WCot
	'Tweedledee'	WCot
	undulata	CAby CCCN CPne CTal CTca ECha ECho EHrv EPri GCal GKev IBal LAma LRHS MPie SDeJ SPer
§	- Alta Group	WCot
§	- Crispa Group	CBod EPfP WFar
§	- Flexuosa Group	ECho EWoo MRav
	- - 'Alba' ♀H3	CBro CPne EBee ECha ECho EPri GKev LRHS MRav WAbe WCot
	× ***versicolor*** 'Mansellii'	CBro SKHP
	'Vicky'	WCot
	'Virgo'	ECho LAma
	'Winter Sun'	LRHS
	'Wolsey'	CPne ECho
	'Wombe'	ECho
	'Zeal Giant' ♀H3	CAvo CBro CPne EPri GCal WCot
	'Zeal Grilse'	CPne WCot
	'Zeal Purple Stripe'	WCot
	'Zennor'	ECho WCot

Nerium (*Apocynaceae*)

	oleander L.	CAbb CArn CBcs CHll CTri EBak ELan EShb ESps MHtn SPer SPlb SPoG
	- 'Album'	CTri
	- 'Album Maximum'	CCCN
	- 'Album Plenum' (d)	XSen
	- 'Alsace'	SEND
*	- 'Atlas'	XSen
*	- 'Barcelona'	SEND
	- 'Cavalaire' (d)	XSen
*	- 'Claudia'	SEND

- 'Commandant Barthélemy' (d) XSen
- 'Flavescens Plenum' (d) EShb XSen
- 'Hardy Red' XSen
- 'Isle of Capri' CCCN
- 'Italia' XSen
- 'Jannoch' XSen
- 'Louis Pouget' (d) XSen
- 'Madame Allen' (d) EShb
- 'Margaritha' SEND XSen
- * - 'Maurin des Maures' CCCN
- 'Minouche' SEND
- 'Professeur Granel' (d) EShb
- 'Provence' (d) XSen
- 'Red Beauty' XSen
- salmon-flowered SEND
- 'Soleil Levant' XSen
- 'Splendens Giganteum' (d) EShb
- 'Tito Poggi' XSen
- 'Variegatum' (v) ♀H2 CHll ELan EShb
- 'Villa Romaine' XSen
- white-flowered SEND

Neviusia (*Rosaceae*)

alabamensis CJun NLar

Nicandra (*Solanaceae*)

physalodes CHby ELan ENfk NBir SEle WBod WSFF
- 'Splash of Cream' (v) CCCN
- 'Violacea' CSpe GLog SRms SWvt

Nicotiana ✿ (*Solanaceae*)

alata CBod CSpe EPfP GDun LCro WSFF
glauca CCCN CDTJ CHll GDun SPlb
glutinosa new GDun
'Hopleys' CSpe
knightiana CDTJ CSpe GDun
langsdorffii ♀H2 CSpe GDun SPav SPhx
- 'Cream Splash' (v) CPla
- 'Hot Chocolate' CSpe
'Lime Green' CSpe ELan
mutabilis CSpe GDun LEdu SDys SPhx
'Perfume Deep Purple' (Perfume Series) CSpe
quadrivalvis new GDun
rustica GDun
× ***sanderae*** Cuba Series NPri
- 'Cuba Deep Lime' NPri
solanifolia GDun SPlb
suaveolens GDun SPhx
sylvestris ♀H2 CBod CDTJ CSpe ELan EPfP GDun MMuc NPri SDys SEND SPav SPhx SPoG SWvt WTou
tabacum GDun
'Tinkerbell' CSpe

Nidularium (*Bromeliaceae*)

correia-araujoi NLos
innocentii XBlo

Nierembergia (*Solanaceae*)

frutescens see *N. scoparia*
§ ***repens*** EBee ECho NLar WCot XLum
rivularis see *N. repens*
§ ***scoparia*** CSpe

Nigella (*Ranunculaceae*)

damascena CWCL LCro MNHC SPhx
'Miss Jekyll' ♀H7
- 'Miss Jekyll Alba' ♀H7 CSpe
- 'Oxford Blue' LCro
- Persian Jewels Group SVic
hispanica L. SPhx
papillosa 'African Bride' CSpe MNHC
- 'Midnight' CSpe

Nigritella see *Gymnadenia*

Niphidium (*Polypodiaceae*)

crassifolium EShb

Nipponanthemum (*Asteraceae*)

§ ***nipponicum*** CBod EBee GBin GCal GWyn IVic LRHS MMuc NLar NSti SAko SPoG SRms WHil XLum
- 'Homa-giku' NWad

Noccaea see *Thlaspi*

Nolina (*Asparagaceae*)

bigelovii WCot XSen
* ***brevifolia*** CFil
durangensis CFil EUJe
hibernica CFil LTro
lindheimeriana WCot
microcarpa WCot XSen
nelsonii CFil LTro NLos SPlb
texana WCot XSen

Nomocharis (*Liliaceae*)

aperta ECho EHrv GBuc GCal GCra GGGa LAma LRHS NHar SDir WAbe WCru
- ACE 2271 EHrv
farreri CPne
× ***finlayorum*** LLHF
mairei see *N. pardanthina*
meleagrina EPot LAma LRHS NHpl SDir
nana see *Lilium nanum*
oxypetala see *Lilium oxypetalum*
§ ***pardanthina*** GBuc
- CLD 1490 GBuc
- f. ***punctulata*** GBuc GGGa
saluenensis GGGa

Nonea (*Boraginaceae*)

lutea LSou NSti WHal

Nothochelone see *Penstemon*

Nothofagus ✿ (*Nothofagaceae*)

antarctica CBcs CDul CMCN CNWT CTho EBee ELan EPfP EWTr GKin IVic MAsh MBlu MGos NOra NWea SAko SWvt WHar WMat
betuloides CMCN GBin IArd SAko SPlb
cunninghamii CBcs CBrP IArd IDee SAko SPlb
dombeyi ♀H5 CBcs CFil CMCN EPfP GBin IArd IDee IVic MBlu SAko SArc SWvt WPGP
fusca IArd SAko WPGP
glauca IVic
menziesii IDee WPGP
moorei WPGP
obliqua CMCN GAbr IVic SPlb

Notholaena see *Cheilanthes*

Notholirion (*Liliaceae*)

bulbuliferum EBee ECho GBin GCra GKev

	campanulatum	EBee ECho GKev
	macrophyllum	EBee ECho GBin GKev
	thomsonianum	CTal ECho GKev

Nothoscordum (*Alliaceae*)

	bivalve	ECho IMou
	dialystemon	ECho EPot LLHF NHpl NPnk WAbe
	montevidense	ECho GKev WCot
	neriniflorum	see *Allium neriniflorum*
	ostenii	ECho WCot
	strictum	ECho

Nuphar (*Nymphaeaceae*)

	japonica	LLWG
	lutea	CBen CHab LCro MSKA SWat
	- subsp. ***advena***	LLWG
	pumila	LLWG

Nuytsia (*Loranthaceae*)

	floribunda	SPlb

Nylandtia (*Polygalaceae*)

	spinosa	SPlb

Nymphaea ✿ (*Nymphaeaceae*)

	alba (H)	CBen CHab CWat GQue LCro MSKA MWts NBir SVic SWat WMAq WPnP
	'Alba Plenissima' (H)	EWay
	'Albatros' misapplied	see *N.* 'Hermine'
§	'Albatros' Latour-Marliac (H)	CWat LLWG MSKA NPer SWat WPnP
	'Albatross'	see *N.* 'Albatros' Latour-Marliac, *N.* 'Hermine'
*	'Albida'	WMAq XBlo
	'Almost Black' (H)	CBen EWay LLWG MSKA
	'Amabilis' (H)	CBen EWay SWat WMAq
	'American Star' (H)	SWat
	'Andreana' (H)	EWay LLWG MSKA
	'Anna Epple' (H)	LLWG
	'Arc-en-ciel' (H)	CBen EWay LLWG SWat WMAq
	'Atropurpurea' (H)	EWay LLWG MSKA NPer SWat WMAq
	'Attraction' (H)	CBen EWay MSKA MWts NPer SVic SWat WMAq XBlo XLum
	'Augustus McCray' (H)	LLWG
	'Aurora' (H)	CWat GQue LCro MWts SVic SWat WMAq
	'Barbara Davies' (H)	EWay LLWG MSKA
	'Barbara Dobbins' (H)	CBen EWay LLWG MSKA
	'Bateau' (H)	CBen LLWG
	'Berit Strawn' (H)	EWay
	'Bernice Ikins' (H)	LLWG
	'Betsy Sakata' (H)	EWay
	'Black Princess' (H)	EWay LCro LLWG
	'Blue Beauty' (T/D)	LLWG
	'Brakeleyi Rosea' (H)	MSKA WMAq
	'Burgundy Princess' (H)	CWat EWay LLWG MSKA MWts NPer
	candida (H)	CBen MSKA MWts NPer WMAq
	'Candidissima' (H)	CBen MWts SWat
§	***capensis*** (T/D)	LLWG XBlo
	'Carolina Sunset' (H)	EWay LLWG
	'Caroliniana Nivea' (H)	CBen
	'Caroliniana Perfecta' (H)	CBen MSKA SWat
	'Celebration' (H)	EWay LLWG
	'Charlene Strawn' (H)	EWay LLWG WMAq
	'Charles de Meurville' (H)	CBen LLWG MSKA NPer SVic WMAq WPnP
	'Château le Rouge' (H)	CBen LLWG
	'Cliff Tiffany' (H) **new**	CBen
	'Clyde Ikins' (H)	EWay LLWG MSKA
	'Colonel A.J. Welch' (H)	CBen MSKA NPer SWat WMAq
	'Colorado' (H)	CBen EWay LLWG MSKA NPer
	colorata	see *N. capensis*
	'Colossea' (H)	CBen CWat MSKA NPer WPnP
	'Comanche' (H)	CBen EWay MSKA NPer WMAq
	'Conqueror' (H)	CBen LLWG MSKA NPer SVic SWat
	'Dallas' (H)	LLWG
§	'Darwin' (H)	CWat MSKA MWts NPer SLon SWat WMAq WPnP
	'David' (H)	CBen EWay LLWG
	'Debbie June' (H)	LLWG
	'Denver' (H)	EWay LLWG MSKA
	'Ellisiana' (H)	CBen LLWG MSKA NPer SWat
	'Escarboucle' (H) 🏆H7	CBen CWat EWay LLWG MSKA NPer SVic SWat WMAq WPnP XBlo
§	'Fabiola' (H)	LLWG MSKA NPer WMAq
	'Fantasy' **new**	LLWG
	'Fiesta' (H)	CBen MSKA
	'Fire Crest' (H)	CBen GQue LLWG NPer SVic SWat WMAq
	'Florida Sunset' (H)	EWay
	'Fritz Junge' (H)	CBen
	'Froebelii' (H)	CBen CWat EWay MSKA NPer SWat WMAq
	'Fulva' (H)	LLWG
	'Galatée' (H)	CBen MSKA
	'Geisha Girl' (H)	MSKA
	'Georgia Peach' (H)	EWay LLWG MSKA
	'Gladstoniana' (H) 🏆H7	CBen MSKA NPer SWat WMAq
	'Gloire du Temple-sur-Lot' (H)	CBen EWay LLWG NPer SWat WMAq
	'Gloriosa' (H)	CBen LLWG NPer SWat
	'Gold Medal' (H)	CBen EWay LLWG MSKA
	'Gonnère' (H) 🏆H7	CBen CWat EWay MSKA MWts NPer SLon SWat WMAq WPnP
	'Graziella' (H)	MSKA WMAq
	'Gypsy' (H)	EWay LLWG
	'Hal Miller' (H)	LLWG
	'Hassell' (H)	LLWG
	'Hazorea Dagan White' (H)	EWay LLWG
	'Helen Fowler' (H)	WMAq
	× ***helvola***	see *N.* 'Pygmaea Helvola'
§	'Hermine' (H)	CBen MSKA NPer SWat WMAq
	'Hidden Violet' (H)	LLWG
§	'Highlight'	EWay LLWG
	'Hilite'	see *N.* 'Highlight'
	'Hollandia' misapplied	see *N.* 'Darwin'
	'Hollandia' Koster (H)	SWat
	'Indiana' (H)	CBen MSKA NPer WMAq
	'Inner Light' (H)	EWay LLWG MSKA
	'J.C.N. Forestier' (H)	CBen
	'James Brydon' (H) 🏆H7	CBen CWat EWay MSKA MWts NPer SLon SVic SWat WMAq WPnP
	'Jean de Lamarsalle' (H)	LLWG MSKA
	'Jerusalem Dawn' (H)	LLWG MSKA
	'Joey Tomocik' (H)	CBen CWat EWay LLWG MSKA WMAq WPnP
	'Lactea' (H)	CBen LLWG
	'Laura Strawn' (H)	EWay
	'Laydekeri Fulgens' (H)	CBen EWay LLWG MSKA SWat WMAq
	'Laydekeri Lilacea' (H)	CBen SWat WMAq
	'Laydekeri Purpurata' (H)	EWay SWat
	'Laydekeri Rosea' misapplied	see *N.* 'Laydekeri Rosea Prolifera'
§	'Laydekeri Rosea Prolifera' (H)	CBen EWay
	'Lemon Mist' (H)	LLWG
	'Lily Pons' (H)	CBen EWay LLWG
	'Liou' (H)	CBen LLWG MSKA
	'Little Sue' (H)	EWay LLWG MSKA
	'Livingstone' (H)	LLWG

	'Lucida' (H)	CBen MSKA SWat WMAq
	'Madame Bory Latour-Marliac' (H)	CBen
	'Madame Wilfon Gonnère' (H)	CBen CWat EWay MSKA MWts NPer SVic SWat WMAq
	'Mangkala Ubol' (H)	CBen
	'Marliacea Albida' (H)	CBen CWat EWay LCro LLWG MSKA MWts NPer SWat WMAq WPnP XBlo XLum
	'Marliacea Carnea' (H)	CBen LCro MSKA MWts NPer SWat WMAq
§	'Marliacea Chromatella' (H) ♀H7	CBen CWat EWay GQue MSKA MWts SVic SWat WMAq XBlo XLum
	'Marliacea Rosea' (H)	CBen MSKA SWat WMAq XBlo XLum
	'Martha' (H)	EWay
	'Mary' (H)	EWay LLWG
	'Masaniello' (H)	CBen MSKA SWat WMAq
	'Maurice Laydeker' (H)	CBen LLWG
	'Maxima'	see *N.* 'Odorata Maxima'
	'Mayla' (H)	CBen EWay LLWG MSKA NPer
§	'Météor' (H)	CBen EWay MSKA WMAq
	mexicana	LLWG
	'Millennium Pink'	MSKA
	'Moorei' (H)	CBen MSKA SWat WMAq
	'Mrs Richmond' misapplied	see *N.* 'Fabiola'
	'Mrs Richmond' Latour-Marliac (H)	CBen SWat XBlo
	'Munkala Ubon' (H)	LLWG
	'Murillo' (H)	EWay
	'Neptune' (H)	LLWG
	'Newchapel Beauty'	WMAq
	'Newton' (H)	CBen CWat EWay LLWG MSKA SWat WMAq
	'Nigel' (H)	EWay LLWG MSKA SWat
	'Norma Gedye' (H)	CBen CWat MSKA SWat WMAq
§	***odorata*** (H)	CBen MSKA WMAq
§	- var. ***minor*** (H)	CBen EWay MSKA SWat WMAq
	- 'Pumila'	see *N. odorata* var. *minor*
	- subsp. ***tuberosa*** (H)	CBen
	'Odorata Alba'	see *N. odorata*
	'Odorata Juliana' (H)	EWay
§	'Odorata Maxima' (H)	WMAq
	'Odorata Sulphurea' (H)	SWat
§	'Odorata Sulphurea Grandiflora' (H)	SWat XBlo
§	'Odorata Turicensis' (H)	MSKA
	'Odorata William B. Shaw'	see *N.* 'W.B. Shaw'
	'Pam Bennett' (H)	CBen LLWG
	'Panama Pacific' (T/D)	LLWG XBlo
	'Patio Joe'	EWay LLWG MSKA
	'Paul Hariot' (H)	CWat EWay LLWG MSKA NPer SWat WMAq WPnP
	'Peace Lily' (H)	EWay LLWG MSKA
	'Peach Glow' (H)	EWay LLWG MSKA
	'Peaches and Cream' (H)	EWay LLWG MSKA
	Pearl of the Pool (H)	SWat
	'Perry's Baby Red' (H)	CBen CWat EWay LLWG MSKA MWts NPer WMAq
	'Perry's Double White' (H)	EWay NPer WPnP
	'Perry's Double Yellow' (H)	LLWG MSKA
	'Perry's Dwarf Red' (H)	LLWG MSKA
	'Perry's Fire Opal' (H)	EWay LLWG NPer
	'Perry's Orange Sunset' (H)	LLWG MSKA
	'Perry's Pink' (H)	SWat WMAq
	'Perry's Red Bicolor' (H)	LLWG
	'Perry's Red Glow' (H)	LLWG MSKA
	'Perry's Red Star' (H)	EWay MSKA
	'Perry's White Star' (H)	LLWG
	'Perry's Yellow Sensation'	see *N.* 'Yellow Sensation'
	'Peter Slocum' (H)	CBen EWay SWat
	'Phoebus' (H)	CBen SWat
	'Picciola' (H)	LLWG
	'Pink Domino' (H)	MSKA
	'Pink Grapefruit' (H)	LLWG XBlo
	'Pink Opal' (H)	CBen CWat EWay LLWG
	'Pink Peony' (H)	EWay MSKA
	'Pink Pumpkin' (H)	EWay LLWG MSKA
	'Pink Sensation' (H)	CBen EWay LLWG MSKA NPer SLon SWat WMAq
	'Pink Sparkle' (H)	EWay LLWG
	'Pink Starlet' (H)	EWay
	'Pink Sunrise' (H)	EWay MSKA
	'Pinwaree' (H) **new**	LLWG
	'Pöstlingberg' (H)	LLWG MSKA
	'Princess Elizabeth' (H)	LLWG SVic
	'Pygmaea Alba'	see *N. tetragona*
§	'Pygmaea Helvola' (H) ♀H7	CBen CWat EWay LCro LOPS MSKA MWts NPer SLon SVic SWat WMAq WPnP
	'Pygmaea Rubis' (H)	SWat WMAq
	'Pygmaea Rubra' (H)	CBen CWat EWay LCro LLWG MSKA MWts NPer SVic WMAq WPnP
	'Queen of Siam' (T/D) **new**	LLWG
	'Radiant Red' (H)	LLWG
	'Ray Davies' (H)	CBen LLWG
	'Red Cup' (T/N)	LLWG
	'Red Paradise' (H)	LLWG MSKA
	'Red Spider' (H)	CWat EWay LLWG MSKA NPer SVic
	'Reflected Flame' (H)	EWay LLWG
	'Rembrandt' misapplied	see *N.* 'Météor'
	'René Gérard' (H)	CBen GQue MSKA MWts NPer SWat WMAq WPnP
	'Robinsonii' (H)	CBen
	'Rosanna Supreme' (H)	LLWG SWat
	'Rose Arey' (H)	CBen EWay LCro LLWG MSKA NPer SWat WMAq
	'Rose Magnolia' (H)	CWat SWat
	'Rosennymphe' (H)	CBen MSKA NPer SWat WMAq WPnP
	'Rosy Morn' (H)	CBen LLWG MSKA
	'Seignouretti' (H)	LLWG
	'Shady Lady' (H)	LLWG MSKA MWts
	'Siam Purple 1' (H) **new**	LLWG
	'Siam Purple 2' (H) **new**	LLWG
	'Sioux' (H)	CBen MSKA NPer SVic WMAq XBlo
	'Sirius' (H)	CBen LLWG MSKA SWat
	'Snow Princess' (H)	EWay
	'Solfatare' (H)	EWay LLWG
	'Splendida' (H)	WMAq
	'Starbright' (H)	EWay LLWG
	'Starburst' (H)	LLWG MSKA
	'Steven Strawn' (H)	LLWG
	'Sultan' (H)	MSKA
	'Sunny Pink' (H)	CBen EWay LLWG MSKA
	'Sunrise'	see *N.* 'Odorata Sulphurea Grandiflora'
	'Superba' (H)	CBen
	'Tan-khwan' (H)	LLWG
§	***tetragona*** (H)	CWat EWay LCro NPer WMAq WPnP
	- 'Alba'	see *N. tetragona*
	'Texas Dawn' (H)	CBen CWat EWay LLWG MSKA SLon WMAq
	'Thomas O'Brian' (H)	LLWG
	'Tuberosa Flavescens'	see *N.* 'Marliacea Chromatella'
	'Tuberosa Richardsonii' (H)	CBen MSKA NPer
	'Turicensis'	see *N.* 'Odorata Turicensis'
	'Venusta' (H)	EWay
	'Vésuve' (H)	LLWG MSKA SWat

	'Virginalis' (H)	CBen LLWG MSKA NPer SWat WMAq
	'Virginia' (H)	LLWG
§	'W.B. Shaw' (H)	CBen MSKA NPer SWat WMAq
	'Walter Pagels' (H)	EWay LLWG MWts WMAq
	'Wanvisa' (H)	CBen LLWG
	'Weymouth Red' (H)	CBen
	'White Sultan' (H)	CWat LLWG MSKA
	'William Doogue' (H)	MSKA
	'William Falconer' (H)	CBen MSKA NPer SWat
	'Wow' (H)	MSKA
	'Yellow Princess' (H)	EWay
	'Yellow Queen' (H)	MSKA
§	'Yellow Sensation' (H)	CBen
	'Yul Ling' (H)	EWay LLWG
	'Zeus'	MSKA
	'Ziyu' (H)	EWay

Nymphoides (*Menyanthaceae*)

	indica	XBlo
	peltata	CBen CBod CHab CWat EWay MSKA NPer SVic WMAq WPnP XLum

Nyssa ✿ (*Nyssaceae*)

	aquatica	CBcs MBlu
	leptophylla	NLar SBir WPGP
	shweliensis FMWJ 13122	WCru
	sinensis	CAbP CBcs CDul CLet CMCN CMac CTho ELan EPfP IDee LRHS MAsh MBlu MPkF NLar SBir SPer
	- 'Jim Russell' ♀H5	SAko SBir WPGP
	- Nymans form	CRos LRHS SBir
	- 'Select'	ESwi
	sylvatica	Widely available
	- 'Autumn Cascades'	EBee ELan EPfP LRHS MAsh MBlu SBir SSta
	- var. ***biflora***	SSta
	- Bulk's form	SSta
	- 'Haymen's Red'	see *N. sylvatica* Red Rage
	- 'Inferno' **new**	EBee
	- 'Isabel Grace'	EPfP LRHS MAsh SBir
	- 'Jermyns Flame'	CAbP CRos EPfP LRHS MAsh NLar SBir
	- Jolly = 'Yiping' (v)	MPkF
	- 'Lakeside Weeper'	EBee LRHS SBir
	- 'Miss Scarlet' (f)	NLar SBir SSta
	- 'Pendula'	SBir
§	- Red Rage = 'Haymanred'	EPfP LRHS MAsh MPkF SBir
	- 'Red Red Wine'	EPfP IVic NLar SBir WPGP
	- 'Sheffield Park'	CAbP LRHS MAsh SBir SLim SPer
	- 'Valley Scorcher'	NLar
	- 'Wildfire'	LRHS MPkF SBir SGol
	- 'Windsor'	EPfP LRHS MAsh NLar SBir
	- 'Wisley Bonfire' (m) ♀H6	CAbP CBct CRos EBee ELan EPfP LRHS MAsh NLar NWea SBir SChF SMad SPoG SSta WPGP
	ursina	CBcs

O

Oakesiella see *Uvularia*

Ochagavia (*Bromeliaceae*)

	carnea	WCot
	- RCB RA S-2	LSou
	elegans	WCot
§	***litoralis***	CPne SArc SMad WCot
*	***rosea***	SPlb

Ochna (*Ochnaceae*)

	serrulata	CCCN

Ocimum (*Lamiaceae*)

	'African Blue'	CBod CLau CSpe ENfk GPoy LSou MHer SPoG SRms
§	× ***africanum***	ENfk MNHC SHDw WJek
	- 'Lime'	ENfk MNHC
	- Pesto Perpetuo = 'Perpetuo'PBR (v)	ENfk SRms
	- 'Siam Queen'	CLau MHer SRms WJek
	- 'Spicy Globe'	CLau
§	***americanum***	WJek
	- 'Meng Luk'	see *O. americanum*
	basilicum	CLau GPoy NPri SIde SRms SWat WJek
	- 'Anise'	see *O. basilicum* 'Horapha'
	- 'Ararat'	CLau
	- ***camphorata***	see *O. kilimandscharicum*
	- 'Cinnamon'	CLau ENfk MNHC SHDw SRms WJek
	- 'Dark Opal'	ENfk MNHC SHDw SRms
	- 'Gecofure'	CLau
	- 'Genovese'	CLau MHer MNHC
	- 'Genovese Special Select'	CLau
	- 'Glycyrrhiza'	see *O. basilicum* 'Horapha'
	- 'Green Ruffles'	CLau EPfP WJek
	- 'Holy'	see *O. tenuiflorum*
§	- 'Horapha'	CLau ENfk MHer MNHC SIde WJek
*	- 'Horapha Nanum'	ENfk SRms WJek
	- 'Magic Michael'	CLau
	- 'Magic Mountain'	SPoG
	- 'Magic White'	SPoG
	- 'Mexican'	CLau
	- 'Mrs Burns' Lemon' ♀H1c	WJek
	- 'Napoletano'	CBod CLau ENfk SIde SWat WJek
	- 'New Guinea'	CLau
	- 'Osmin'PBR	CLau
	- 'Pistou'	CLau
	- 'Purple Delight'	CLau
	- var. ***purpurascens***	SIde
	- - 'Purple Ruffles'	ENfk EPfP SIde SWat WJek
	- - 'Red Rubin'	WJek
	- var. ***purpurascens*** × ***kilimandscharicum***	CSpe GPoy
	- 'Queenette'	CLau
	- 'Sweet Genovese'	SVic
	- 'Thai'	see *O. basilicum* 'Horapha'
	- 'Wild Magic'PBR **new**	SHil
	canum	see *O. americanum*
	× ***citriodorum***	see *O.* × *africanum*
	gratissimum	CLau
§	***kilimandscharicum***	CLau GPoy
	minimum	CLau ENfk MHer MNHC SIde SRms WJek
	sanctum	see *O. tenuiflorum*
	'Spice'	CLau ENfk MNHC
§	***tenuiflorum***	CLau GPoy MNHC SHDw SIde SPre WJek

Odontonema (*Acanthaceae*)

	schomburgkianum	CCCN
	tubaeforme	CCCN

Oemleria (*Rosaceae*)

	cerasiformis	CBcs CHGN CJun CTri EBtc EPfP LEdu LRHS MMuc WBod WCot WGwG WSHC

Oenanthe (*Apiaceae*)

	fistulosa	LLWG MSKA
	javanica	LEdu
	- 'Flamingo' (v)	CBod CWat EBee ELan EWay GCal LEdu MSKA MWts NBro WMAq XLum
	lachenalii	LLWG
	pimpinelloides	CHab LLWG

Oenothera ✿ (*Onagraceae*)

§	***acaulis***	CSpe GBin MNrw WCot
§	- 'Aurea'	XLum
	- 'Lutea'	see *O. acaulis* 'Aurea'
	'Apricot Delight'	CWld NPnk SGbt SIde SPad WHar WMoo
§	***biennis***	CFis ELan ENfk GAbr GPoy MHer MNHC NBro SIde SPhx SRms WBrk WHea WHer WJek WSFF
	'Blood Orange'	GEdr
	childsii	see *O. speciosa*
	cinaeus	see *O. fruticosa* subsp. *glauca*
	'Colin Porter'	WMoo
	'Crown Imperial'	CMac LEdu LSou MArl NHol SHar SLon
	Crown of Gold = 'Lishal'	LLHF LRHS
§	***elata*** subsp. ***hookeri***	EWes NBre
	erythrosepala	see *O. glazioviana*
	'Finlay's Fancy'	WCru
§	***fruticosa***	NLar SPlb
	- 'African Sun' PBR	ECtt SRot
	- 'Camel' (v)	MNrw NEoE XLum
	- Fireworks	see *O. fruticosa* 'Fyrverkeri'
§	- 'Fyrverkeri'	CBcs CMea ECtt ELan GMaP GMcL GWyn LEdu LHop LRHS MRav SCob SPer SWvt XLum
§	- subsp. ***glauca***	CElw CFis EPfP MHer SRms
	- - 'Erica Robin' (v)	CChe ECtt EHoe GBin LRHS LSou MAvo MNrw MRav NEgg NGdn SMad SRot SWvt WCot WHoo
	- - 'Longest Day'	MBrN
	- - Solstice	see *O. fruticosa* subsp. *glauca* 'Sonnenwende'
§	- - 'Sonnenwende'	CBre CElw LRHS NEoE NLar WMoo XLum
	- Highlight	see *O. fruticosa* 'Hoheslicht'
§	- 'Hoheslicht'	EBee
	- 'Lady Brookeborough'	MRav
	- 'Michelle Ploeger'	NBre
	- 'Silberblatt' (v)	EBee
	- 'Yellow River'	CElw EBee
	- 'Youngii'	EPfP LEdu MMuc SEND
	'Give-me-Sunshine'	SLon WMoo
	glabra Miller	see *O. biennis*
§	***glazioviana***	GBin NBir
	'Gold Dream'	LSou
	hookeri	see *O. elata* subsp. *hookeri*
	kunthiana	CBod ECha WMoo
	- 'Glowing Magenta'	SPoG
	lamarckiana	see *O. glazioviana*
	Lemon Drop = 'Innoeno131' PBR	LRHS
	'Lemon Sunset'	CCVN EHoe LSou WHar WMoo WRHF
	linearis	see *O. fruticosa*
§	***macrocarpa*** ♀H5	Widely available
	- subsp. ***fremontii*** 'Shimmer'	SMad
	- - 'Silver Wings'	LHop SMad SPhx
	- subsp. ***incana***	CSpe SPhx WHoo
	- - 'Silver Blade' **new**	LLHF
	missouriensis	see *O. macrocarpa*
	oakesiana	SPhx
	odorata misapplied	see *O. stricta*
	odorata Hook. & Arn.	see *O. biennis*
	odorata Jacquin	XLum
	- cream-flowered	CSpe
	organensis	EBee MNrw
	pallida	GJos
§	***perennis***	MPie SRms WThu XLum
	pumila	see *O. perennis*
	rosea	XLum
	serrulata	see *Calylophus serrulatus*
	'Silky Orchid'	CElw
§	***speciosa***	GCal MMuc SEND SPhx SRms XLum
*	- 'Alba'	EBee EWes
	- var. ***childsii***	see *O. speciosa*
	- 'Pink Petticoats'	ECha LSun NPer
	- 'Rosea'	SPlb
	- 'Siskiyou'	CBcs CBod ECtt EPfP EWoo LBMP LEdu LRHS MNrw NRHS SCob SCoo SPer SPoG WGwG WHil XLum
	- Twilight = 'Turner01' PBR (v)	CAbb ECtt LHop LRHS LSou NEoE NHol SCob SHar
§	***stricta***	CMea GCal MNrw WGwG
	- 'Sulphurea'	CDor CMea EAJP ECGP ELan GCal IFro LRHS NPer SPhx
	'Summer Sun'	CBod GMcL LRHS SPoG
	'Sunny Delight'	CBod ECtt LBuc MHol
	taraxacifolia	see *O. acaulis*
	tetragona	see *O. fruticosa* subsp. *glauca*
	- var. ***fraseri***	see *O. fruticosa* subsp. *glauca*
	versicolor 'Sunset Boulevard'	CSpe CTsd EAJP ESps GCal LRHS MMuc WMoo XLum

Olea (*Oleaceae*)

	europaea (F)	Widely available
	- 'Arbequina' (F)	ETod SBig
§	- 'Cipressino' (F)	ESwi ETod SBig
	- 'El Greco' (F)	CBcs
	- 'Fastigiata'	EBee LRHS NPri
	- 'Frantoio' (F)	ETod SBig
	- 'Hojiblanca' (F)	EBee SBig
	- 'Leccino' (F)	ETod SBig
	- 'Manzanillo' (F)	ETod
	- 'Maurino' (F)	SBig
	- 'Peace'	CDoy
	- 'Pendolino' (F)	SBig
	- 'Picual' (F)	ETod SBig
	- 'Pyramidalis'	see *O. europaea* 'Cipressino'

Olearia ✿ (*Asteraceae*)

	algida	GBin
	arborescens 'Moondance' (v)	MMrt SAko SCob SEND
	avicenniifolia	CMac IVic
	canescens	CPne
	× ***capillaris***	CBcs EBee
	chathamica	IVic
§	***cheesemanii***	GMcL NLar NWad SVen
	- compact **new**	LRHS
	erubescens	LRHS
	erubescens × ***ilicifolia***	SVen
	fragrantissima	GBin
	gunniana	see *O. phlogopappa*
	× ***haastii***	Widely available
§	'Henry Travers'	CCCN EPfP GCal IVic SAko SVen
	ilicifolia	CTsd EPfP IVic LRHS MAsh

insignis	see *Pachystegia insignis*
lacunosa	IDee WHor
lepidophylla	NLar
macrodonta ♀H4	Widely available
- 'Major'	CCCN NLar SCob
- 'Minor'	CCCN CMac ELan EPfP GCal IVic SPlb
× ***mollis*** (Kirk) Cockayne	CMac EBee LRHS WKif
- 'Zennorensis' ♀H3	CBcs CCCN IVic
nummularifolia	CBcs CCCN CTri CTsd EBee ELan EPfP GBin GKin IVic LRHS NLar SBod SPer SVen SWvt
odorata	CPne
× ***oleifolia*** 'Waikariensis'	GKin IVic LRHS MAsh SEND SLon WCFE
paniculata	CCCN CTri CTsd EPfP IVic LRHS MMuc SAko SEND SVen
§ ***phlogopappa***	CTri SVen WKif WSHC
- 'Comber's Blue'	CBcs CCCN ELan EPfP GKin IVic LRHS MMuc SAko SCob SLim SPer WGrn
§ - 'Comber's Pink'	CBcs CBod CCCN CHid ELan ELon EPfP GKin LBMP LRHS MAsh MMuc MSCN NPer SAko SCob SEle SLim SPer SPoG WGrn WKif WSHC
- 'Rosea'	see *O. phlogopappa* 'Comber's Pink'
I - var. ***subrepanda*** (DC.) J.H. Willis	GBin
ramulosa	CCCN
- 'Blue Stars'	CMac LRHS SRms
rani misapplied	see *O. cheesemanii*
rani Druce	CPne
× ***scilloniensis*** misapplied	see *O. stellulata* DC.
× ***scilloniensis*** ambig.	CBcs EWld GMcL LRHS MAsh MGil SCob SPoG
× ***scilloniensis*** Dorrien-Smith ♀H3	CCCN MMuc SEND
- 'Master Michael' ♀H3	CCCN CTri ELon EWld IVic LRHS MNHC NLar SPer SPoG WCFE WGrn WSHC
semidentata misapplied	see *O.* 'Henry Travers'
solandri	CBod CCCN CMac EHoe IDee LRHS NLar SDix SEND
- 'Aurea'	CBcs
'Stardust'	LRHS SPlb SVen
stellulata misapplied	see *O. phlogopappa*
§ ***stellulata*** DC.	CMac CSBt CWib EPfP MAsh SDix SLim SPer
traversii	CBcs CBod CCCN CSBt CTsd EPfP LRHS NWea SAko SEND SLim WHer
- 'Tweedledee' (v)	SEND
- 'Tweedledum' (v)	CBod CCCN CWib EHoe
- 'Variegata' (v)	CBcs
virgata	CCCN NLar
- var. ***laxiflora***	WHer
- var. ***lineata***	MMuc NLar SEND WHer WSHC
- - 'Dartonii'	CBcs CTsd GBin LRHS NLar SPlb SVen

Oligoneuron see *Solidago*

Oligostachyum (*Poaceae*)

lubricum	see *Semiarundinaria lubrica*

olive see *Olea europaea*

Olsynium (*Iridaceae*)

biflorum	GEdr
§ ***douglasii*** ♀H5	CBro ECho EPot LLHF NHpl NRya NSla
- 'Album'	EBee ECho ELon EPot LLHF MNrw NHar NRya NSla WWFP
- var. ***inflatum***	EWes
§ ***junceum***	CSpe SPlb
trinerve B&SWJ 10459	WCru

Omphalodes ✿ (*Boraginaceae*)

'Blue Eyes'	EBee ELon GBin MHol WCot
cappadocica ♀H5	CMac EPfP EPot EWld GBin IFoB LEdu NBro NPer SRms SWat WBrk
- 'Cherry Ingram' ♀H5	Widely available
- 'Lilac Mist'	EBee GBuc MRav NPnk SRms SWvt
- 'Starry Eyes'	Widely available
§ ***linifolia*** ♀H3	CSpe GBin GWyn LCro MCot SPhx
- ***alba***	see *O. linifolia*
nitida	CSpe EWld GWyn IMou LLHF MMuc MNrw NQui
verna	CBod CTri EBee ECha ECho ELan EPPr EPfP EWTr GAbr GEdr GJos GMaP GWyn LHop LLWP LRHS MCot MNrw NChi NLar SCob SPer SPlb SPoG SWat WBod WCAu WFar
- 'Alba'	Widely available
- 'Elfenauge'	EBee GMaP IMou NBir NLar WCot
- ***grandiflora***	WCot

Oncostema see *Scilla*

onion see *Allium cepa*

Onixotis (*Colchicaceae*)

stricta	CLak WCot

Onobrychis (*Papilionaceae*)

viciifolia	CWld SPhx

Onoclea ✿ (*Onocleaceae*)

sensibilis ♀H6	Widely available
- copper-leaved	CJun EPfP WPGP
- 'Rotstiel'	EBee

Ononis (*Papilionaceae*)

cristata	WAbe
spinosa	IMou MHer

Onopordum (*Asteraceae*)

acanthium	CAby CDor ECha ELan ENfk GAbr GMaP GPoy LEdu LRHS LSun MWat NBid NChi NGBl NSti SHar SIde SPhx WHea
algeriense	EBee
arabicum	see *O. nervosum*
bracteatum	EBee
illyricum	WCot
§ ***nervosum*** ♀H7	CSpe SEND

Onosma (*Boraginaceae*)

alborosea	ECha ECre ELan GCal GCra SEND WKif
echioides	SIgm
nana	CTal EPot WAbe WOld

Onychium ✿ (*Pteridaceae*)

contiguum	WCot
japonicum	EBee EFer ISha LEdu LRHS MRav NLos SPlb WAbe WCot

Ophiopogon ✿ (*Asparagaceae*)

BWJ 8244 from Vietnam	WCru
from India	GCal

	'Black Dragon'	see *O. planiscapus* 'Nigrescens'
	bodinieri	CBct EShb EWes LEdu
	- B&L 12505	CLAP EBee EPPr
	caulescens B&SWJ 11813	WCru
	- B&SWJ 8230	WCru
	aff. ***caulescens*** B&SWJ 11287	WCru
	- HWJ 590	WCru
	chingii	EBee EPPr EWes GCal LEdu WCot
*	- 'Crispum'	EBee
	clavatus KWJ 12267	WCru
	formosanus B&SWJ 3659	WCru
	'Gin-ryu'	see *Liriope spicata* 'Gin-ryu'
	graminifolius	see *Liriope muscari*
	'Hosoba Kokuryu'	CAbb EShb GBin LLHF NEoE
	intermedius	CBct CSpe EPPr EShb WCot
	- GWJ 9387	WCru
§	- 'Argenteomarginatus' (v)	EWes
	- 'Variegatus'	see *O. intermedius* 'Argenteomarginatus'
§	***jaburan***	CMac EBee LEdu NPnk WMoo WPtf
	- 'Variegatus'	see *O. jaburan* 'Vittatus'
§	- 'Vittatus' (v)	ELan EWes LEdu MPkF WCot
	japonicus	CMac CTsd EBee ECho EPPr EShb GPoy LEdu LTro SCob SGol XLum XSen
	- B&SWJ 1871	WCru
	- 'Albus'	CLAP ECho EPri
	- 'Compactus'	WPGP
	- 'Gyoku-Ryu'	EBee GCal
	- 'Kigimafukiduma'	CMac MRav NGdn SGol SPad
	- 'Kyoto'	EPPr ESwi
	- 'Lengteng Giant' new	LEdu
	- 'Minor'	CKno ELon EPPr NLar SCob WPGP XLum
	- 'Nanus Variegatus' (v)	EBee
	- 'Nippon'	ECho EHoe EPPr NGdn
	- 'Silver Dragon' (v)	EPPr WCFE
*	- 'Tama-ryu Number Two'	ECho EPPr
*	- 'Variegatus' (v)	CDTJ CMac ECho LEdu
	aff. ***latifolius*** KWJ 12031	WCru
	parviflorus GWJ 9387	WCru
	- HWJK 2093	WCru
	planiscapus	CKno CMHG CSpe ECha ECho EPPr NBro SPad SPtp WMoo
*	- 'Albovariegatus' (v)	WFar
	- 'Black Beard'	CKno EAEE EUJe EWTr GWyn LRHS MAsh SHar WFar
	- 'Black Needle'	EBee
	- 'Black Smaragd'	EBee
	- 'Green Dragon'	CRos LRHS NRHS
	- f. ***leucanthus***	EPPr WCot
	- 'Little Tabby' (v)	CFil CLAP CMil EBee ECho ESwi WCot WGrn WHal WSHC
§	- 'Nigrescens' ♀H5	Widely available
	scaber B&SWJ 1842	ESwi WCru
	- B&SWJ 3655	WCru
	'Spring Gold'	EShb

Oplopanax (*Araliaceae*)

horridus	CArn
- B&SWJ 9551	WCru
japonicus	WCru

Opopanax (*Apiaceae*)

chironium	CArn SDix SPhx
- PAB 845	LEdu WPGP

Opuntia (*Cactaceae*)

	angustata	see *O. phaeacantha*
	arenaria SB 964 from El Paso County, Texas	CCac
	atrispina DJF 1020	CCac
	aurea	CCac
	- red-flowered, from St George, Utah	CCac
	aureispina SB 1002	CCac
	basilaris	CCac
	- SB 1819 from Yucca Valley, California	CCac
	- SB 1976 from Silver Peak, Nevada	CCac
	- from Tonopah, Nevada	CCac
	- 'Berlin'	CCac
	bentonii from Galveston, Texas	CCac
	'Budapest'	CCac
	camanchica	see *O. phaeacantha*
	chisosensis SB 992 from Brewster County, Texas	CCac
	chlorotica	CCac
	- NNS 99-262	WCot
	- 'Kurt'	CCac
	'Claude Arno'	CCac
	× ***columbiana*** from Wishram, Washington State	CCac
	- 'Smithwick'	CCac
	compressa	see *O. humifusa*
	cylindrarticulata	see *Cumulopuntia boliviana* subsp. *dactylifera*
	cymochila	see *O. tortispina*
	echinocarpa	see *Cylindropuntia echinocarpa*
	elata	SChr
§	***engelmannii***	CCac SChr
	- from Beeville, Texas	CCac
	- from Carrizozo, New Mexico	CCac
	- var. ***engelmannii*** DJF 1400	CCac
	- - 'Natural Bridge'	CCac
*	- f. ***inerme***	CCac
*	- var. ***sandia*** HK 1809	CCac
	erinacea var. ***utahensis***	see *O. polyacantha* var. *erinacea*
§	***ficus-indica***	CCac SPlb WCot
	fragilis	CCac SKHP SPlb XSen
	- from Black Canyon, Gunnison, Colorado	CCac
	glomerata	see *Maihueniopsis glomerata*
§	***humifusa***	CCac CDTJ LTro SChr XLum XSen
	- from Monmouth County, New Jersey	CCac
	- 'Louisiana'	CCac
	joconostle	see *O. ficus-indica*
	lindheimeri	see *O. engelmannii*
	linguiformis	see *O. engelmannii*
	mackensenii	see *O. macrorhiza*
	macrocentra	CCac
	- SB 103 from Rincon, New Mexico	CCac
	- SB 911 from Orogrande, New Mexico	CCac
	- SB 994 from Eddy County, New Mexico	CCac
§	***macrorhiza***	CCac
	- DJF 720 from Kenton, Oklahoma	CCac
	- DJF 1299 from Reagan County, Texas	CCac
	- DJF 86512 from Huerfano County, Colorado	CCac

- 'Apricot'	CCac
- 'Viola'	CCac
megapotamica BKN 124 from La Cumbrecita, Argentina	CCac
monacantha	SEND
orbiculata from Seymour, Texas	CCac
§ ***phaeacantha***	CCac SChr
- DJF 162	CCac
- DJF 913	CCac
- DJF 970.18 from Fremont County, Colorado	CCac
- DJF 1139 from Albuquerque, New Mexico	CCac
- SB 1070 from Larimer County	CCac
- from White Canyon, Wayne County, Utah	CCac
* - var. ***albispina*** from Mohave County, Arizona MUG 177	CCac
- 'Judge'	CCac
- var. ***major*** DJF 1138	CCac
- - DJF 1139 from Albuquerque, New Mexico	CCac
- - SB 1092 from Santa Fe, New Mexico	CCac
- - SB 1763 from Manzano Mountains, New Mexico	CCac
- 'Minor'	CCac
- 'Pueblitos'	CCac
- 'Salmonea'	CCac
- 'Sunrise'	CCac
phaeacantha × pottsii	CCac
pisciformis	CCac
pollardii	see *O. humifusa*
polyacantha	CCac SChr SPlb
- SB 912	CCac
- SB 928 from Wyoming	CCac
- SB 1911 from Lybrook, New Mexico	CCac
- SB 1765 from Manzano Mountains, New Mexico	CCac
- from Alberta, Canada	CCac
- from Bicknell, Utah	CCac
- from Blind Valley, Millard County, Utah	CCac
- from Chaffee County, Colorado	CCac
* - from Januskowetz, Canada	CCac
- from North Dakota	CCac
- from Trout Creek Pass, Colorado	CCac
- from Wyoming	CCac
- 'Carmin'	XSen
- 'Crystal Tide'	CCac
* - ***eranthemum***	CCac
§ - var. ***erinacea***	CCac LTro SChr WCot
- - from St. George, Utah	CCac
- - from Torrey, Utah	CCac
- - from Yucca Valley, California	CCac
§ - var. ***hystricina***	CCac
- - DJF 1001	CCac
- - DJF 1338	CCac
- - DJF 1339 from Belen, New Mexico	CCac
- - SB 478	CCac
- - SB 485 from Marble Canyon, Arizona	CCac
- - 'Cactusmannia'	CCac
- - 'Hagen Miniature'	CCac
- - 'Halblech'	CCac
- - 'Hamm'	CCac
- - 'Heather'	CCac
- - 'Heidelberg'	CCac
- - 'Thornless Judge'	CCac
- 'Linz'	CCac
* - 'Nigra'	CCac
- 'Oettingen'	CCac
- var. ***polyacantha***	CCac
- - from Laguna Pueblo, New Mexico	CCac
- 'Rom'	CCac
- 'Wibke'	CCac
pottsii DJF 1394 from Hildago County, New Mexico	CCac
- DJF 1441	CCac LTro
- DJF 1447	CCac
- from Albuquerque, New Mexico	CCac
- 'Bochum'	CCac
* - var. ***montana*** DJF 667	CCac
rhodantha	see *O. polyacantha* var. *hystricina*
salmiana new	SEND
* ***sandiana***	CCac
- DJF 475A	CCac
sanguinocula DJF 801	CCac
santarita	CCac
spinosior	see *Cylindropuntia spinosior*
stenopetala HK 1985	CCac
stricta	CCac LTro
'Super Rutila 2'	CCac
tardospina	see *O. engelmannii*
§ ***tortispina*** DJF 1139.38	CCac
- from Gaza County, Colorado	CCac

orange, sour or Seville see *Citrus × aurantium* Sour Orange Group

orange, sweet see *Citrus × aurantium* Sweet Orange Group

Orbexilum (*Papilionaceae*)

pedunculatum var. ***psoralioides***	SBrt SPhx

Orchis (*Orchidaceae*)

anthropophora	EFEx
elata	see *Dactylorhiza elata*
foliosa	see *Dactylorhiza foliosa*
fuchsii	see *Dactylorhiza fuchsii*
maculata	see *Dactylorhiza maculata*
maderensis	see *Dactylorhiza foliosa*
majalis	see *Dactylorhiza majalis*
§ ***mascula***	ECho WHer

oregano see *Origanum vulgare*

Oreocharis (*Gesneriaceae*)

aurea B&SWJ 11718	WCru

Oreomyrrhis (*Apiaceae*)

argentea	CSpe EBee SPhx

Oreopanax ✿ (*Araliaceae*)

capitatus	CFil

floribundus see *O. incisus*
§ ***incisus*** B&SWJ 10669 **new** WCru
xalapensis B&SWJ 10444 WCru

Oreopteris ✿ (*Thelypteridaceae*)

§ ***limbosperma*** EFer

Oreostemma (*Compositae*)

§ ***alpigenum*** WHil
- var. ***alpigenum*** LLHF
- var. ***haydenii*** LLHF

Origanum ✿ (*Lamiaceae*)

from Kalamata SEND
acutidens XSen
amanum ♀H3 CPBP ECho EPot EWes NBir NSla SBch WAbe
- var. ***album*** ECho WAbe
'Amethyst Falls' XSen
'Barbara Tingey' CTal ECho EPot EWes ITim MNrw SIgm SRms WCFE
'Bristol Cross' CTal EBee ECtt EPot LEdu MAsh MHer SIde WTor XSen
'Buckland' ECho ECtt ELon EPot WAbe
caespitosum see *O. vulgare* 'Nanum'
§ ***calcaratum*** ECho LLHF
creticum see *O. vulgare* subsp. *hirtum*
dictamnus ECho EPot GPoy LLHF MHer SIgm WAbe WJek WOld XEll XSen
'Dingle Fairy' CPBP CWCL ECtt EPot EWes MHer NBir SBch SIde SRot SWvt WMoo XSen
ehrenbergii XSen
'Emma Stanley' CPBP WAbe
'Frank Tingey' ECho LLHF
'French' SRms
'Gold Splash' EPfP SIde WMoo
'Golden Narrow' EBee LRHS
heracleoticum L. see *O. vulgare* subsp. *hirtum*
'Hot and Spicy' CPbn ENfk LBMP LEdu SRms WJek XSen
'Ingolstadt' (v) SPhx
'Jekka's Beauty' WJek
'Kent Beauty' ♀H4 CMea CSpe CWCL EBee ECho ECtt ELan EPfP EPot GBuc IMou IPot LBMP LRHS LSou MBel MHer NBir SPhx SWvt WAbe WHea WHoo WJek WKif WSHC WTor XSen
'Kent Beauty Variegated' (v) ECho
laevigatum ♀H7 ECho ELan MHer NBro NPer SIde WCot WKif WMoo WSHC XSen
I - 'Aromaticum' IMou
- dwarf SIgm
- 'Herrenhausen' ♀H7 Widely available
- 'Hopleys' CBod CDor CMea CTri EAJP EBee ECha EHrv ELan EPfP LEdu LHop LRHS MCot MHer MHol MMuc MRav MWat NBir NLar SEND SPer SPhx SRms WHea WHoo WSHC XSen
- 'Purple Charm' EDAr SRms
majorana CArn CHab CLau CPbn ENfk GPoy LBMP MHer MNHC SIde SRms SVic SWat WJek
I - 'Aureum' GKev
- Pagoda Bells = 'Lizbell'[PBR] CBod SIde XSen
'Marchants Seedling' SPhx
microphyllum CArn
minutiflorum ECho LLHF
'Norton Gold' CBre ECha ECtt MHer NPer SIde
'Nymphenburg' LSou XSen
onites CBod CHby CLau ENfk LBMP LEdu MHer MNHC SIde SPlb SRms WJek
'Pilgrim' XSen
'Rosenkuppel' ♀H7 CBod CDor CMea EBee ECha ECtt ELan EPPr LHop LOPS MHer NDov NLar SBch SPer SPhx SPlb SWvt WCAu WJek WMoo XSen
'Rotkugel' WCFE XSen
rotundifolium ♀H4 CMea ECho ELan ELon LEdu MHer NBir SBch WThu
scabrum EPot
subsp. ***pulchrum***
- - 'Newleaze' SBch
'Teddy' EBee
tournefortii see *O. calcaratum*
vulgare CArn CHab CMea CPbn CTsd CWld ESps GJos GMaP GPoy LBMP MArt MHer MJak MMuc MNHC NBro NMir NPol NPri SEND SIde SPlb SRms SVic WHer WJek WSFF XLum
- from Israel CLau
- 'Acorn Bank' CArn CBod ECtt ENfk EWes LEdu MNHC NLar SIde SPoG SRms WHer WJek
- var. ***album*** CLau MArt
- 'Aureum' ♀H6 Widely available
- 'Aureum Crispum' CBod CLau ECha ENfk GBin GPoy GWyn NBid SIde SRms SWat WJek
- 'Compactum' CArn CBod CMea EBee ECha ECtt ENfk GCal GPoy LEdu MHer MNHC NBir NSla SIde SPlb SRms SWat WAbe WJek XLum XSen
- 'Country Cream' (v) CBod CElw CLau CPbn EBee ECtt EHoe ENfk EPfP ESps EWes LBMP LPot MHer MNHC NBir NGdn NPri SPer SPoG SRms SRot SWat WCFE
- var. ***formosanum*** B&SWJ 3180 WCru
§ - 'Gold Tip' (v) CBod CLau CMea ENfk GJos MCot MHer MHol MNHC SIde SPlb SRms SWat WHer WJek
- 'Golden Shine' EHoe EWes SIde
§ - subsp. ***hirtum*** CArn CHby CPbn GPoy SPlb WJek XSen
- - 'Greek' CBod CLau ENfk LEdu MHer MNHC SRms
§ - 'Nanum' LHop SRms WJek XSen
- 'Nyamba' GPoy
- 'Pink Mist' MNrw WHoo
- 'Polyphant' (v) CPbn LSou NBir SHar SRms WJek XSen
- 'Thumble's Variety' CBod CMea EAEE EBee ECha ECtt EHoe EPfP GCal LHop LRHS MAsh MHer MRav SWat SWvt WCFE WMoo XLum XSen
- 'Tomintoul' GPoy
- 'Variegatum' see *O. vulgare* 'Gold Tip'
- 'White Charm' CBod CPbn EBee NWad SIde
'Z'Attar' WJek

Orixa (*Rutaceae*)

japonica NLar WPGP
- 'Variegata' (v) LRHS NLar

Orlaya (*Apiaceae*)

grandiflora CAvo CBre CSam CSpe LCro LEdu LRHS MCot NPnk SBch SPhx WCot WHal WTor

Ornithogalum (*Asparagaceae*)

algeriense	ECho GKev
arabicum	CBro CCCN ECho GKev LAma SDeJ
arcuatum	WCot
arianum	ECho
atticum new	GKev
balansae	see *O. oligophyllum*
caudatum	see *O. longibracteatum*
chionophilum	ECho
creticum new	GKev
cuspidatum	ECho GKev
dubium ♀H2	CTal ECho ELan
- hybrids	CGrW GKev
fimbriatum	ECho GKev
- 'Ai-Petri' new	CTal
- 'Oreanda' new	CTal
lanceolatum	CTal ECho GKev WCot
§ ***longibracteatum***	ECho GKev SChr WHer
magnum	CAvo CBro CWCL EBee ECho EPot ERCP GBin GBuc GKev MCot MNrw SDeJ WCot XEll
- 'Saguramo'	GKev
montanum	GKev
'Mount Everest'	GKev
'Mount Fuji'	GKev
multifolium from Loeriesfontein, South Africa	ECho
'Namib Gold'	EUJe GKev SDeJ
nanum	see *O. sigmoideum*
narbonense	ECho GKev
nutans ♀H4	CAvo CBro CHid CWCL EBee ECho EPot GBuc GKev LAma LRHS MMuc MNrw NBir NNys SDeJ SEND WHea
§ ***oligophyllum***	ECho EPot GKev MNrw
§ ***orthophyllum***	ECho
ponticum	ECho WCot
- 'Sochi'	EBee ECho GKev
pyramidale	EBee ECho MNrw
- short	SMHy
pyrenaicum	CAvo CSpe ECha SRms WCot WShi XEll
reverchonii	EBee ECho ERCP GKev
saundersiae	ECho EUJe GKev
sibthorpii	see *O. sigmoideum*
§ ***sigmoideum***	EBee
sintenisii	CTal EBee ECho GKev
tenuifolium	see *O. orthophyllum*
thyrsoides ♀H2	CCCN ECho GKev LAma LCro LOPS LRHS SDeJ
ulophyllum	ECho
umbellatum	CAvo CHab CTri EBee ECho GKev GPoy LAma LHop MCot MMuc MNrw SDeJ SEND SRms WHil WShi

Ornithoglossum (*Colchicaceae*)

viride	CLak

Orontium (*Araceae*)

aquaticum	CBen CWat EWay LLWG MSKA MWts NPer SWat WMAq

Orostachys (*Crassulaceae*)

furusei	WHal
iwarenge	CBod LHop SPlb
§ ***spinosa***	ECho EDAr EWes GKev LRHS NRHS SPlb WAbe WCot

Orthophytum (*Bromeliaceae*)

gurkenii	WCot

Orthrosanthus (*Iridaceae*)

chimboracensis	CPou
JCA 13743	
laxus	CBod CWCL EAJP ECre LLHF NBir SMad WMoo
multiflorus	CBro CTre EBee EPri IKil
polystachyus	CAby CCVN CTsd MPie WHea WSHC

Orychophragmus (*Brassicaceae*)

violaceus	CCCN

Oryzopsis (*Poaceae*)

hymenoides 'Rimrock'	SPhx
lessoniana	see *Anemanthele lessoniana*
miliacea	CSpe EHoe EPPr MAvo NSti SBee SDix SEND SMHy WCot WHea WPGP WSHC WWtn
paradoxa	EPPr

Oscularia (*Aizoaceae*)

§ ***deltoides*** ♀H2	CCCN EShb LAll MSCN SVen

Osmanthus (*Oleaceae*)

armatus	CAbP CBcs CMac EBee EPfP IDee LRHS NLar SEND SGol
× ***burkwoodii*** ♀H5	Widely available
§ ***decorus***	CBcs CHll CMac CTri EBee ELan EPfP MGos MRav NLar NWea SBrt SGol SPer
- 'Angustifolius'	NLar
delavayi ♀H5	Widely available
- 'Frank Knight'	LRHS MAsh
- 'George Gardner'	CMac
- 'Latifolius'	CJun LRHS MAsh SLon SPoG SWvt
- 'Pearly Gates'	LRHS
forrestii	see *O. yunnanensis*
× ***fortunei***	CBcs CBot EBee EPfP LLHF LPar LRHS SEND WPat
fragrans	CBcs IDee LPar SLon SWvt
- f. ***aurantiacus***	SCob
§ ***heterophyllus***	CBcs CDul CMac EBee ECrN ELan EPfP ESps GMcL LPar MGos MRav NLar SCob SGol SPer SRms SSta SWeb
§ - all gold	ELan EMil EPfP LRHS SPer SPoG
- 'Argenteomarginatus'	see *O. heterophyllus* 'Variegatus'
§ - 'Aureomarginatus' (v)	CBcs CMHG CTsd EHoe ELon SCob SLon WCFE
- 'Aureus' misapplied	see *O. heterophyllus* all gold
- 'Aureus' Rehder	see *O. heterophyllus* 'Aureomarginatus'
§ - 'Goshiki' (v) ♀H5	Widely available
- 'Gulftide'	CDul CRos EPfP LRHS MAsh MGos MJak NLar SPoG
- 'Kembu' (v)	NLar
- 'Myrtifolius'	CMac NLar
- 'Ōgon'	EPfP NLar
- 'Purple Shaft' ♀H5	CAbP ELan EPfP LRHS MAsh
- 'Purpureus'	CBcs CDul CMHG CMac CTsd CWib EBee ELon MGos MRav MSwo NLar SCob SCoo SEND SGol SLon SPer
- 'Rotundifolius'	CMac NLar
- 'Sasaba' new	IArd
- Tricolor	see *O. heterophyllus* 'Goshiki'
§ - 'Variegatus' (v) ♀H5	Widely available
ilicifolius	see *O. heterophyllus*
serrulatus	CBot EPfP LRHS

suavis	NLar
§ ***yunnanensis*** ♀^{H5}	CBcs CBot CMCN EBee EPfP MBlu MRav NLar SArc WPGP WSHC

× *Osmarea* see *Osmanthus*

Osmaronia see *Oemleria*

Osmorhiza (*Apiaceae*)

aristata B&SWJ 1607	WCru
chilensis	WCru

Osmunda ✿ (*Osmundaceae*)

sp.	CCCN
asiatica	EBee WCru
cinnamomea ♀^{H7}	CAby CBod CCCN CKel CLAP CWCL EBee EUJe EWes ISha LEdu LRHS MMuc NBro NLar
claytoniana	CLAP CLet EBee EFer ISha LRHS NBro NLar WCot XLum
japonica	CHid CLAP EBee ISha NBro
regalis ♀^{H6}	Widely available
- from southern USA	CLAP
- 'Cristata' ♀^{H6}	CLAP ELan LRHS NBid SWvt WFib
- 'Purpurascens'	Widely available
- var. ***spectabilis***	CCCN CLAP GBin ISha LRHS
- 'Undulata'	WFib

Osteospermum (*Asteraceae*)

'African Queen'	see *O.* 'Nairobi Purple'
Banana Symphony = 'Sekiin47' (Symphony Series)	CCCN
barberae misapplied	see *O. jucundum*
'Blue Streak'	CCCN CMac
'Buttermilk'	CCCN ELan
'Cannington John'	CCCN
'Cannington Joyce'	CCCN
'Cannington Roy'	CBcs CCCN CEnd CMac CSam CSma EBee ECtt ELan ELon EPfP EWoo GAbr LRHS NPri WFar
caulescens misapplied	see *O.* 'White Pim'
ecklonis	CBcs CCCN CDTJ CHll CTri NBro NGdn WPnn
- var. ***prostratum***	see *O.* 'White Pim'
Flower Power Double Series (d)	LBuc SPoG
- Flowerpower Double Pink = 'Kleoe10180'^{PBR} (d) **new**	SPoG
'Giles Gilbey' (v)	CCCN MBNS
'Gold Sparkler' (v)	SEND
'Gweek Variegated' (v)	CCCN
'Helen Dimond'	LRHS
'Hopleys' ♀^{H3}	SEND
'Iced Gem'	LBuc LRHS
'In the Pink'	LCro LOPS WNPC
'Irish'	ECtt EPot LSou SIgm WIce
§ ***jucundum*** ♀^{H3}	CCht CMea CTri CWCL ECha LRHS LSRN MMuc NBir NFav NPer SEND SPlb SRms WBod WIce WThu
- 'Blackthorn Seedling' ♀^{H3}	CCCN CMea CWGN ECha IVic NFav
- var. ***compactum***	CBod CChe CMac CPrp CTsd CWCL ELan ELon EPfP EWoo GLog GMaP LRHS LSRN MAvo MSpe NPer NPri SPer SPoG SWvt WBrk WHil WWFP
- 'Elliott's Form'	WHoo
- 'Nanum'	EDAr
'Keia' (Springstar Series)	CCCN
§ 'Lady Leitrim' ♀^{H3}	CBar CBod CCCN CChe CCht CPrp CSma CWCL CWGN ECha ECtt ELan ELon EPfP GCra GLog LHop LRHS LSRN MAvo MSpe NPer NPri SPad SPer SPoG SWvt WHil WHoo
'Lisa Traxler' **new**	SVen
Milk Symphony = 'Seiremi' (Symphony Series)	CCCN
'Mirach' (Springstar Series)	CWCL
§ 'Nairobi Purple'	CBcs CBod CCCN CChe CCht CPrp EBee ECtt ELan MHol NPri SEND SSut SWvt WBor WBrk WFar WHil WHoo
Nasinga Cream = 'Aknam'^{PBR} (Cape Daisy Series)	CCCN
Orange Symphony = 'Seimora'^{PBR} (Symphony Series)	CBcs CCCN
'Pale Face'	see *O.* 'Lady Leitrim'
'Peggyi'	see *O.* 'Nairobi Purple'
'Pink Gem'	EDAr
'Pink Whirls'	CCCN
'Port Wine'	see *O.* 'Nairobi Purple'
'Silver Sparkler' (v)	CCCN CDTJ ELan MHer SVen
'Snow Pixie'	CBod CWGN EBee ECtt EDAr ELan ELon EWoo LCro LOPS SPoG SWvt WIce
'Sparkler'	CCCN
'Stardust'^{PBR}	ECtt LBuc LRHS NPer NRHS SCoo SPoG
(Sunny Series) 'Sunny Bronze' **new**	CSpe
- 'Sunny Mary'^{PBR}	SPoG
- 'Sunny Xena'^{PBR} **new**	SPoG
I 'Superbum'	EBee MHol WFar
'Tauranga'	see *O.* 'Whirlygig'
'Tresco Peggy'	see *O.* 'Nairobi Purple'
'Tresco Pink'	CCCN
'Tresco Purple'	see *O.* 'Nairobi Purple'
'Weetwood' ♀^{H3}	CCCN CEnd CPrp ECtt ELan EPot EWld EWoo GLog LHop LRHS MHer SWvt WFar WTor
§ 'Whirlygig'	CCCN ELan
§ 'White Pim' ♀^{H3}	CDTJ CHll NPer SDix SEND
'Wine Purple'	see *O.* 'Nairobi Purple'
'Wisley Pink'	NEgg
'Zaurak' (Springstar Series)	CCCN
'Zulu' (Cape Daisy Series)	CCCN

Ostrowskia (*Campanulaceae*)

magnifica	EPot GKev

Ostrya (*Betulaceae*)

carpinifolia	CBcs CCVT CDul CLnd CMCN CTho CWib EBee ELan EMOT EPfP LRHS MBlu MMuc NLar NOra NWea SEND SGol SWvt WMat WTSh
japonica	CDul CMCN

Otatea (*Poaceae*)

aztecorum	ERod

Othonna (*Asteraceae*)

cheirifolia	CCCN CMea EWes NBir SEND SIgm XLum XSen
coronopifolia	SVen

Othonnopsis see *Othonna*

Ourisia (*Plantaginaceae*)

× ***bitternensis*** 'Cliftonville Canary'	WAbe
- 'Cliftonville Crimson'	WAbe
- 'Cliftonville Damask'	WAbe
- 'Cliftonville Ling'	WAbe
- 'Cliftonville Old Rose'	WAbe
- 'Cliftonville Pink'	WAbe
- 'Cliftonville Roset'	WAbe
caespitosa	GAbr
- var. ***gracilis***	GKev MHol
coccinea	CTal EWes GAbr GBin GKev MAvo NBir NHpl WHal
'Loch Ewe'	CTal GAbr GKev
macrocarpa	GKev
macrophylla	NWad
microphylla	WAbe
- f. ***alba***	WAbe
- 'Hollowcliffe'	WAbe
modesta	GBin
polyantha 'Cliftonville Scarlet'	WAbe
ruelloides	GKev
'Snowflake' ♀^{H5}	GAbr GKev IMou NHpl

Oxalis (*Oxalidaceae*)

from Mount Stewart	WMoo
acetosella	GAbr GPoy MHer MMrt MMuc NMir NQui WHer WShi
- var. ***rosea***	IFro IMou
- var. ***subpurpurascens***	WCot
adenodes	NRog
adenophylla ♀^{H4}	CTri ECho ELan EPot GBin GKev GMaP LAma LHop LRHS MJak MPie NEgg NFav NHol NHpl NLar NRHS SDeJ SPer SPoG SRms
adenophylla × ***enneaphylla***	see *O.* 'Matthew Forrest'
'Anne Christie'	CPBP NSla
anomala	ECho
arenaria F&W 10584	WCot
§ ***articulata***	GBuc NPer SEND XLum
- 'Alba'	WCot XLum
- f. ***crassipes*** 'Alba'	WCot
- 'Festival'	ECho GKev
§ - subsp. ***rubra***	SDeJ
bowiei	EBee ECho EPot WCot
- 'Amarantha'	ECho GKev
brasiliensis	ECho GKev
compressa	NRog
convexula	NRog
'Dark Eye'	EPot
dentata 'Pot of Gold'	GKev
deppei	see *O. tetraphylla*
§ ***depressa***	CTri ECho EPot EWes GKev LLHF NBir SDeJ SRms
'Double Trouble' (d) **new**	GKev
eckloniana	ECho
- var. ***sonderi***	ECho NRog
enneaphylla ♀^{H4}	CElw ECho ELon GBin GEdr LHop LLHF LRHS NRHS NRya
- F&W 2715	CPBP
- 'Alba'	CElw CPBP ECho NRya NSla
- subsp. ***ibari***	ECho EPPr GEdr NRya NSla
- 'Minutifolia'	NRya
* - 'Minutifolia Rosea'	CPBP
- 'Rosea'	CElw ECho EPot GKev LLHF NLar NRya NSla
- 'Sheffield Swan'	CPBP GEdr LLHF NHar NSla SIgm WAbe
- 'Ute'	GEdr NRya
fabifolia	ECho
'Fanny'	ECho GKev
flava	ECho NRog SChr
- white-flowered **new**	GKev
floribunda misapplied	see *O. articulata*
fourcadei	ECho NRog
foveolata	NRog
gracilis	ECho GKev
griffithii 'Pink Charm'	GEdr
- 'Snowflake'	GEdr
'Gwen McBride'	CPBP GEdr WAbe
hedysaroides misapplied	see *O. spiralis* subsp. *vulcanicola*
hedysaroides Kunth	CCCN
'Hemswell Knight'	CPBP
hirta	EPot GKev SBch
- 'Gothenburg'	ECho EPri GKev NRog
imbricata	ECho LLHF NRog
inops	see *O. depressa*
'Ione Hecker' ♀^{H4}	ECho EPot GCrg GEdr GKev ITim NHar NHpl NLar NRya WOld
'Irish Mist' (v)	ECho
* ***karroica***	ECho NHpl WCot
§ ***laciniata***	CPBP ECho
- hybrid	GEdr NHar
lactea double-flowered	see *O. magellanica* 'Nelson'
lasiandra	CCCN ECho GKev
§ ***latifolia***	ECho LLHF
magellanica	CTri ECho GAbr IMou SPlb WMoo
- 'Flore Pleno'	see *O. magellanica* 'Nelson'
§ - 'Nelson' (d)	EBee ECho EWTr GBin NBir NPer WMoo WPtf
magnifica **new**	GKev
massoniana ♀^{H2}	ECho WAbe WCot
§ 'Matthew Forrest'	CPBP WCot
§ ***megalorrhiza***	SChr
melanosticta	ECho EPot GEdr GKev LLHF NRog SDeJ WCot
§ - 'Ken Aslet' ♀^{H2} **new**	GKev NHpl SDeJ
monophylla	ECho
namaquana	ECho
obtusa	ECho EPot GKev MPie
- apricot-flowered	WCot
oregana	CHid CMac ECho ELon EWld GBuc GCal SPhx WCot WCru WPGP
- 'Bob Haszeldine'	GEdr
- 'Klamath Ruby'	WSHC
- f. ***smalliana***	EBee GEdr IMou LHop WCot WCru
perdicaria	ECho EPot EWes GKev LHop LRHS NRHS NRog WAbe
- 'Citrino'	WAbe
polyphylla	ECho
§ ***purpurea***	ECho
- 'Ken Aslet'	see *O. melanosticta* 'Ken Aslet'
- yellow-flowered	ECho
regnellii	see *O. triangularis* subsp. *papilionacea*
'Ridgeway Jewel'	CPBP
'Ridgeway Sapphire'	CPBP
rosea misapplied	see *O. articulata* subsp. ***rubra***
semiloba	ECho GCal NCGa
Slack Top hybrids	NSla
'Slack's 53'	NSla
'Snipe'	NSla
speciosa	see *O. purpurea*
§ ***spiralis*** subsp. ***vulcanicola***	CCCN GCal LSou

- - 'Burgundy'	NPri
- - 'Sunset Velvet'	CSpe WCot
squamata	LLHF
squamoso-radicosa	see *O. laciniata*
succulenta Barnéoud	see *O. megalorrhiza*
succulenta ambig.	CHll
'Sunny'	ECho GKev
'Sweet Sue'	CPBP
§ ***tetraphylla***	ECho GKev NPer
- 'Alba'	ECho
- 'Iron Cross'	CCVN CHid ECho GKev LAma MPie NBir SDeJ SPlb
'Tina'	CPBP
triangularis	CCCN ECho NBir NPer
- 'Birgit'	ECho GKev SDeJ
- Burgundy Wine = 'JR Oxburwi' (Xalis Series)	CWGN NPer
- 'Cupido'	ECho
- 'Marmer' (v)	GKev
- 'Mijke'	ECho GKev
§ - subsp. ***papilionacea*** 🏆H2	ECho GKev LAma
- - 'Atropurpurea'	CSpe LHop SDeJ
- subsp. ***triangularis***	CHid ECho EUJe GKev MBel WWFP
tuberosa	EPfP GPoy LEdu SPoG
- 'Amarillo' **new**	LEdu
- 'Baumi Golden' **new**	LEdu
- 'Mexican Red' **new**	LEdu
- 'Polar Bere'	LEdu
- scarlet-flowered, white-eye	LEdu
'Ute'	CPBP NSla SIgm
valdiviensis	NWad
versicolor 🏆H2	ECho EPot GKev NBir NRog SDeJ WCot WHil XEll
- 'Golden Cape' **new**	GKev
vespertilionis Zucc.	see *O. latifolia*
virginea	NRog
I 'Waverley Hybrid'	GCrg GKev LLHF
zeekoevleyensis	NRog

Oxycoccus see *Vaccinium*

Oxydendrum ✿ (*Ericaceae*)

arboreum	CAbP CBcs CBct CDul CEnd CMCN EBee EPfP IArd IVic LRHS MAsh MBlu MMuc NLar SAko SPer SSta WBor WHar WHor

Oxypetalum (*Apocynaceae*)

caeruleum	see *Tweedia coerulea*

Oxyria (*Polygonaceae*)

digyna	CAgr

Oxytropis (*Papilionaceae*)

campestris	EBee
- var. ***gracilis*** **new**	GKev
hailarensis var. ***chankaensis***	CPBP
lambertii	CPBP
podocarpa	SPlb
purpurea	SPlb
sajanensis	CPBP

Ozothamnus (*Asteraceae*)

§ ***coralloides***	ITim WAbe WCot WThu
§ 'County Park Silver'	EBee EWes GCrg GEdr GKev
§ ***hookeri***	CBcs EBee MBrN SVen WCFE WJek WPGP WPat
§ ***ledifolius***	CBcs ELan EPfP GMcL LRHS SBrt SPer WSHC
§ ***rosmarinifolius***	CBcs CRos CTsd ELan EPfP EWld GMcL LRHS MAsh MSwo SPer SVen WPnn
- 'Silver Jubilee'	CBcs CCht CSBt ECrN ECre ELan EPfP GCal GMcL LRHS MAsh MMuc MRav MSwo SLon SPer SPlb SRkn
§ ***selago***	ELan WCot
- 'Major'	SPlb
§ - var. ***tumidus***	EBee ITim WThu
'Threave Seedling'	CCht EBee ELan IVic LRHS MAsh SPer

P

Pachyphragma (*Brassicaceae*)

§ ***macrophyllum***	EBee ECGP ECha EHrv ELon EWTr GCal IBlr IMou LEdu MMuc MRav NLar NSti SDix WCot WCru WPGP WSHC

Pachyphytum (*Crassulaceae*)

oviferum 🏆H2	WCot

Pachypodium (*Apocynaceae*)

bispinosum	LToo
lamerei 🏆H1a	EUJe LToo SPlb
lealii subsp. ***saundersii***	LToo
succulentum	LToo

Pachysandra (*Buxaceae*)

axillaris	EBee EPPr GCal SKHP WCot
- BWJ 8032	WCru
- 'Crûg's Cover'	EWld SMad WCru
procumbens	EHrv IMou LHop NLar SKHP WCot
- 'Angola' (v)	WCot
stylosa	MRav
terminalis	Widely available
- 'Green Carpet'	Widely available
- 'Green Sheen' 🏆H5	ECha EPfP ESwi EWTr LRHS
- 'Silver Edge' (v)	EBee
- 'Variegata' (v) 🏆H5	Widely available

Pachystachys (*Acanthaceae*)

lutea 🏆H1b	CCCN

Pachystegia (*Asteraceae*)

§ ***insignis***	CPne LRHS MPkF SBrt SLim

Paederota (*Plantaginaceae*)

§ ***bonarota***	EPot GKev WAbe
lutea	GEdr WAbe

Paeonia ✿ (*Paeoniaceae*)

'Ace of Hearts'	GBin
'Age of Gold' (S)	XGra
albiflora	see *P. lactiflora*
'America'	CKel GBin NCGa
anomala	GKev MPhe NLar SIgm WCot
arietina	see *P. mascula* subsp. *arietina*
'Armani' **new**	LRHS NCGa
'Athena'	GBin LRHS NRHS
'Avant Garde'	GBin
'Bai Xue Ta' (S)	NTPC
banatica	see *P. officinalis* subsp. *banatica*

§ 'Bartzella' (d) ♀H5	CKel ELan ELon GBin ILea LMea LRHS NRHS WCAu WCot WHil XGra
beresowskii	GKev
'Black Pirate' (S) ♀H5	CKel
'Blaze'	CKel EWoo GMaP ILea LRHS NCGa NRHS WCAu WCot
'Border Charm'	CKel ILea XGra
'Boreas' (S)	XGra
'Bridal Icing'	GBin WCAu
'Bride's Dream'	GBin
'Brightness'	XGra
broteroi	SKHP WThu
'Buckeye Belle' (d)	CKel EBee ELan EPfP EWTr EWoo GBin GMaP GMcL IBoy ILea LCro LMea LRHS LSRN NCGa SCob SPer SPoG SWat WCAu WCot XGra
'Burma Joy'	XGra
'Burma Midnight'	GBin
'Callie's Memory'	CKel ELon GBin ILea NCGa WCAu WHil
cambessedesii ♀H3	CBro CRos CTal EPot GBin GEdr GKev LHop LRHS NBir NRHS NSla WAbe WCot WKif
cambessedesii* × *mlokosewitschii	CRos LRHS NRHS
'Cameo Lullaby'	GBin
'Canary Brilliant' PBR	CKel GBin ILea XGra
'Carol'	ILea WCAu
caucasica	see *P. mascula* subsp. *mascula*
× ***chamaeleon***	LPla SKHP
'Cherry Ruffles'	WCAu
'Chocolate Soldier'	CKel WCAu
'Chu E Huang' (S)	LPar
'Claire de Lune'	CHur CKel GBin ILea LRHS WCAu WCot WTor
'Color Magnet'	GBin XGra
'Command Performance'	GBin
'Convoy' (d)	GBin
'Copper Kettle'	CKel ILea
'Cora Louise'	CKel ELan ELon ILea LMea LRHS WCAu XGra
'Coral Charm' ♀H7	CHur CKel EPfP GBin GMaP IBoy ILea LCro LMea LRHS LSRN MMrt NCGa NLar NNys NPnk SCob SDeJ SKHP WCAu WCot WHil XGra
'Coral Fay'	GBin
'Coral 'n' Gold'	NPnk
'Coral Sunset'	CHur CKel CWCL GBin IBoy ILea LCro LMea MAvo NCGa SCob SDeJ WCAu XGra
'Coral Supreme'	GBin WCot
corallina	see *P. mascula* subsp. *mascula*
coriacea	GBin GKev
- var. ***atlantica***	CBro
'Court Jester'	CKel ELan ILea
Crimson Red	see *P. suffruticosa* 'Hu Hong'
'Cutie'	GBin WCAu
'Cytherea'	GBin LRHS WCAu WCot XGra
'Dancing Butterflies'	see *P. lactiflora* 'Zi Yu Nu'
'Dao Jin' (S) **new**	LMea
'Daredevil' (S)	GBin
daurica misapplied	see *P. mascula* subsp. *triternata*
- subsp. ***coriifolia*** RCB UA 12	WCot
'Dawn Glow'	GBin
decomposita	MPhe
decora	see *P. peregrina*
delavayi (S)	CBcs CKel CPne CRos CTho CTsd ELan EPfP GCal GKev GMaP LCro LHop LPar LRHS MAsh MGos MMuc NBir NEgg SDix SEND SKHP SPer SPoG SRms WBod WCot

- BWJ 7775	WCru
- from China (S)	MPhe
§ - var. ***angustiloba*** f. ***angustiloba*** (S)	GBin GKev SCob
- copper-flowered **new**	LPar
§ - var. ***delavayi*** f. ***lutea*** (S)	CCVT CDul CHVG CJun CTho EPfP EUJe GBin GKev GLog IBoy IFro LEdu LRHS MAsh MGos NBir NEgg SCob SLon SMad SPoG SRms WBod WHar WHoo
- - f. ***lutea*** × 'Right Royal'	XGra
- - f. ***lutea*** × 'Tria'	XGra
- var. ***lutea***	see *P. delavayi* var. *delavayi* f. *lutea*
- 'Mrs Colville' (S)	GCal
- 'Mrs Sarson' (S)	SWat
- Potaninii Group	see *P. delavayi* var. *angustiloba* f. *angustiloba*
- 'Tapestry' (S)	CSpe
delavayi* × *suffruticosa	LSRN
'Diana Parks'	GBin ILea NCGa NLar XGra
'Don Richardson'	WCAu
Drizzling Rain Cloud	see *P. suffruticosa* 'Shiguregumo'
'Early Bird'	GBin
'Early Glow'	WCAu XGra
'Early Scout'	CHur EBee ELon GBin LRHS NRHS SCob SHil XGra
'Early Windflower'	WCAu
'Eden's Perfume'	CBod ELon EPfP IKil
'Eliza Lundy' (d)	GBin WCAu XGra
'Ember's Wish' **new**	NCGa
emodi	CKel GBin GKev LRHS WCAu WCot
'Etched Salmon'	CHur CKel GBin NCGa
'Eventide'	WCAu
'Fairy Princess'	GBin XGra
'Feng Dan Bai' (S)	NTPC
'Firelight'	WCAu
'First Arrival'	CKel GBin ILea WCAu
'First Dutch Yellow'	see *P.* 'Garden Treasure'
'Flame'	EBee EPfP GMaP ILea LRHS MNrw NCGa NRHS NSti SDeJ WCot XGra
'Fragrant Pink Imp'	GBin
'Fuchsia Cuddles'	XGra
§ Gansu Group (S)	CKel GKev MPhe NTPC
- 'Bai Bi Fen Xia' (S)	MPhe
- 'Bai Bi Lan Xia' (S)	MPhe
- 'Bei Ji Xiong' (S)	MPhe
- 'Bing Shan Xue Lian' (S)	MPhe
- 'Bing Xin Zi' (S)	MPhe NTPC
- 'Cheng Xin' (S)	MPhe
- 'Dan Feng Ling Kong' (S) **new**	NTPC
- 'Dan Feng Zhan Chi' (S)	NTPC
- 'Dan Feng Zhu' (S)	MPhe
- 'Dian Jin Bai Yan Wei' (S)	MPhe
- 'Er Long Nao Hai' (S)	MPhe
- 'Fen Die' (S)	NTPC
- 'Fen Guan Yu Zhu' (S)	NTPC
- 'Fen He' (S)	MPhe
- 'Fen Jin Yu' (S)	NTPC
- 'Fen Jin Yu Zhu' (S)	MPhe
- 'Fen Lou Dan Xia' (S)	MPhe
- 'Fen Mian Tao Sai' (S)	MPhe
- 'Feng Xian' (S)	MPhe
- 'Gan Lan Yu' (S) **new**	NTPC
- 'Gu Cheng Xiang Hui' (S)	MPhe
- 'Guan Yu Zhu' (S) **new**	NTPC
- 'Guang Hui Li Cheng' (S)	MPhe
- 'Gui Fu Ren' (S)	MPhe

	- 'Han Hai Bing Xin' (S)	MPhe
	- 'He Hua Deng' (S)	MPhe
	- 'He Ping Lian' (S)	MPhe
	- 'Hei Bai Fen Ming' (S)	MPhe
	- 'Hei Fa Nü Lang' (S)	MPhe
	- 'Hei Feng Die' (S)	MPhe NTPC
	- 'Hei Hai Feng Yun' (S) **new**	IPot
	- 'Hei Tian E' (S)	MPhe
	- 'Hei Xuan Feng' (S)	MPhe
	- 'Hei Yuan Shuai' (S)	MPhe
	- 'Hei Zhen Zhu' (S)	LPar MPhe
	- 'Hong Hai Qing Long' (S)	MPhe
	- 'Hong Lian' (S)	MPhe NTPC
	- 'Hong Xia Ying Xue' (S)	MPhe
	- 'Huang He' (S)	MPhe
	- 'Huang Lian' (S)	MPhe
	- 'Hui He' (S)	MPhe
	- 'Jiao Rong' (S)	MPhe
	- 'Jin Bo Dan Yang' (S)	MPhe
	- 'Jin Cheng Ming Yue' (S)	MPhe
	- 'Ju Hua Fen' (S)	MPhe
	- 'Lan Hai Yiu Bo' (S)	MPhe
	- 'Lan He' (S)	MPhe
	- 'Lan He Qi Ming' (S) **new**	NTPC
	- 'Lan Mo Shuang Hui' (S)	MPhe
	- 'Lan Tian Meng' (S)	MPhe
	- 'Lan Xian Nü' (S)	MPhe
	- 'Lan Yu San Cai' (S)	MPhe NTPC
	- 'Lan Zhen Zhu' (S)	MPhe
	- 'Li Xiang' (S)	MPhe
	- 'Lian Chun' (S)	MPhe
	- 'Long Dan Fan' (S)	MPhe
	- 'Long Yuan Hong' (S)	MPhe
	- 'Long Yuan Xia Nu' (S)	MPhe
	- 'Mei Gui Sa Jin' (S)	MPhe
	- 'Mo Guan Yu Zhu' (S)	MPhe
	- 'Mo Hai Yin Bo' (S)	MPhe
	- 'Mo Hai Yin Zhou' (S)	MPhe
	- 'Pan Pan' (S)	MPhe
	- 'Ren Mian Tao Hua' (S)	NTPC
	- 'Ri Yue Tong Hui' (S)	MPhe
	- 'San Hua Nu' (S)	MPhe
	- 'Shen Guang Yu Lu' (S)	MPhe
	- 'Shu Sheng Peng Mo' (S)	MPhe
	- 'Tao Hua Nu' (S)	MPhe
	- 'Tian Shan Ri Chu' (S)	MPhe
	- 'Tie Mian Wu Si' (S)	MPhe
	- 'Tong Xin Tong De' (S)	MPhe
	- 'Wu Kong Xiu Xing' (S)	MPhe
	- 'Xiang Lu Zi Yan' (S)	MPhe
	- 'Xiao Xue' (S)	MPhe
	- 'Xiong Mao' (S)	MPhe NTPC
	- 'Xue Hai Bing Xin' (S)	MPhe NTPC
	- 'Xue Hai Dan Xin' (S)	NTPC
	- 'Xue Li Cang Jin' (S)	MPhe
	- 'Xue Lian' (S)	MPhe NTPC
	- 'Xue Shan Fei Cai' (S) **new**	NTPC
	- 'Xue Yuan Yu Hui' (S)	MPhe NTPC
	- 'Yan Chun' (S)	MPhe
	- 'Yan Wei Bai' (S)	MPhe
	- 'Ye Guang Bei' (S)	MPhe
	- 'Yi Du Chun Qiu' (S) **new**	NTPC
	- 'Yin Yang Shan' (S)	MPhe
	- 'Yu Ban Xiu Qiu' (S)	MPhe
	- 'Yu Guan Lan Dai' (S)	MPhe
	- 'Yu Lou Cang Jiao' (S)	MPhe
	- 'Yu Lu Lian Dan' (S)	MPhe
	- 'Yu Rong Dan Xin' (S)	MPhe
	- 'Yu Shi Zi' (S)	MPhe
	- 'Yuan Yang Pu' (S)	MPhe

	- 'Zhu Sha Hong' (S) **new**	IPot
	- 'Zi Ban Bai' (S)	IPot NTPC
	- 'Zi Die Ying Feng' (S)	MPhe NTPC
	- 'Zi Hai Yin Bo' (S)	MPhe
	- 'Zi Lou Xiang Jin' (S)	MPhe
	- 'Zi Yan' (S)	MPhe NTPC
	- 'Zong Ban Bai' (S)	MPhe NTPC
	- 'Zui Fei' (S)	MPhe
	Gansu Mudan Group	see *P.* Gansu Group
	'Garden Peace'	WCAu
§	'Garden Treasure'	CKel LRHS NRHS SDeJ WCAu WHil XGra
	'Going Bananas' **new**	CKel
	'Golden Bowl'	CKel GBin
	'Golden Dream'	see *P.* 'Bartzella'
	'Golden Isles'	CKel
	'Golden Thunder'	CKel
	'Happy'	GBin
	'Hei Hua Kui'	see *P. suffruticosa* 'Hei Hua Kui'
	'Henry Bockstoce' (d)	ELon GBin ILea NLar SHar WCAu XGra
	'Hephestos' (S)	XGra
	'Hillary'	CKel GBin ILea WCAu
	'Ho-gioku'	GBin
	'Hong Bao Shi' (S)	NTPC
	'Honor'	WCAu
	'Hua Er Qiao' (S)	LMea
	'Huo Lian Jin Dan' (S)	NTPC
	'Icarus' (S)	XGra
	'Iphigenia' (S)	XGra
	japonica misapplied	see *P. lactiflora*
	'Jay Cee'	GBin
	'Jin Ge' (S)	LPar NTPC WKif
	jishanensis	MPhe
	'Joseph Rock'	see *P. rockii*
	'Joyce Ellen'	NLar
	'Julia Rose'	CKel GBin ILea LMea LRHS NCGa WCAu WHil XGra
	kavachensis	GKev
	kesrouanensis	GKev
	'Kinkaku'	see *P.* × *lemoinei* 'Souvenir de Maxime Cornu'
	'Kinko'	see *P.* × *lemoinei* 'Alice Harding'
	'Kinshi'	see *P.* × *lemoinei* 'Chromatella'
	'Koikagura'	CKel
	'Kokamon'	CKel
	'La Donna' (d) **new**	GBin
§	***lactiflora***	ESps GCal MPhe
	- from East Russia	GCal
	- 'Abalone Pearl'	GBin XGra
	- 'Adolphe Rousseau'	CKel ILea LCro LOPS LRHS WCAu
	- 'Agida'	GBin LRHS MRav WGwG
	- ***alba***	MBel
	- 'Albert Crousse'	CBcs CKel GBin MRav NBir SWat
	- 'Albâtre'	CKel
	- 'Alertie' (d)	GBin
	- 'Alice Harding'	CKel GBin WCAu
	- 'Amabilis' (d)	ILea
	- 'Amalia Olson' (d)	XGra
	- 'Amibilis'	ELon WCAu
	- 'Angel Cheeks'	CKel GBin LCro LMea LOPS NCGa NLar WCAu
	- 'Ann Cousins' **new**	GMcL
	- 'Antwerpen'	LRHS
	- 'Argentine'	CKel
	- 'Asa Gray'	CKel
	- 'Auguste Dessert'	CKel WCAu WCFE
§	- 'Augustin d'Hour'	CKel ILea SHar WGwG
	- 'Aureole'	MRav
	- 'Avalanche'	EPfP GBin ILea LRHS NLar NRHS

- 'Avalon' (d) WCAu XGra
- 'Ballerina' MRav
- 'Balliol' **new** EPfP
- 'Barbara' GBin WCAu
- 'Baroness Schröder' CKel GBin WCAu XGra
- 'Barrington Belle' EBee EPfP LRHS MBel NRHS SHil WFar WHoo WTor
- 'Bess Bockstoce' WCAu
- 'Bessie' GBin
- 'Best Man' EBee NGdn
- 'Bev' GBin
- 'Big Ben' CKel EWTr GBin ILea LRHS NLar
- 'Black Beauty' EBee GBin IPot LRHS NRHS SCob WHil
- 'Blitz Tort' XGra
- 'Bluebird' IBoy
- 'Blush Queen' CKel GBin
- 'Border Gem' LRHS MRav
- 'Bouchela' NSti
- 'Boule de Neige' GBin LHop
- 'Bouquet Perfect' GBin LMea NRHS WCAu
- 'Bowl of Beauty' ♀H7 Widely available
- 'Bowl of Cream' (d) CKel GBin LRHS SWat SWvt WCAu XGra
- 'Break o' Day' WCAu
- 'Bridal Gown' GBin
- 'Bridal Veil' CKel
- 'Bunker Hill' CKel ELon GBin IBoy ILea LRHS SPer SWvt WCAu WGwG
- 'Butter Bowl' GBin WCAu
- 'Candidissima' GBin
- 'Candy Stripe' (d) **new** GBin
- 'Catherine Fontijn' CHur CKel GBin ILea WCAu
- 'Celebrity' CWCL LMea SCob
- 'Charles Burgess' CKel ELon GBin ILea MSCN NCGa SCob WCAu
- 'Charlie's White' CKel GBin ILea LRHS NCGa NLar SDeJ XGra
- 'Cheddar Charm' GBin
- 'Cheddar Supreme' GBin
- 'Cherry Hill' GBin
- 'Chiffon Parfait' GBin XGra
- 'Circus Circus' XGra
- 'Claire Dubois' CKel
- 'Class Act' (d) **new** GBin
- 'Cora Stubbs' GBin NCGa SHil SPer WCAu WTor
- 'Corinne Wersan' GBin
- 'Cornelia Shaylor' CKel WCAu
- 'Couronne d'Or' GBin ILea
- 'Cream Puff' WCAu
- 'Crimson Glory' CKel
- 'Crinkles Linens' GBin
- 'Daisy Coronet' XGra
- 'Dawn Pink' CBod EBee EPfP SPer
- 'Daystar' MRav
- 'Dayton' WCAu
- 'Dinner Plate' CKel GBin NCGa SHar SPer WCAu
- 'Do Tell' CKel CWCL EBee ELon EPfP GBin MMrt NCGa SPer WCAu WTor
- 'Docteur H. Barnsby' CKel
- 'Doctor Alexander Fleming' (d) CKel CRos EBee GBin ILea LRHS MBNS MHol MNrw NBir NRHS SDeJ SHil SRot SWat SWvt WCAu WFar WHar
- 'Don Juan' CKel
- 'Doreen' CKel EBee GBin LMea SHar WCAu
- 'Doris Cooper' WCAu
- 'Drumline' SDeJ
- 'Duchesse de Nemours' ♀H7 Widely available
- 'Duchesse d'Orléans' GBin
- 'Edulis Superba' ELan GBin GKev ILea LEdu LRHS MBNS MRav NPer SHar SHil SPer WCAu WTor
- 'Elaine' MRav
- 'Elizabeth Queen of the Belgians' (d) XGra
- 'Elsa Sass' GBin ILea NCGa WCAu XGra
- 'Embraceable Pink' GBin
- 'Emma Klehm' (d) CKel GBin ILea LSRN WCAu XGra
- 'Emperor's Buttons' XGra
- 'Evelyn Tibbets' GBin
- 'Fairy's Petticoat' CKel GBin WCAu
- 'Fancy Nancy' GBin
- 'Félix Crousse' ♀H7 CBcs CBod CGar CKel CTri ELan ELon GBin GMaP IBoy ILea LRHS LSRN MBNS MRav NBir NLar NPri SDeJ SHil SPer SWat WCAu WFar
- 'Felix Supreme' GBin XGra
- 'Festiva Maxima' ♀H7 CHur CKel CSBt CTri EBee ELan EPfP EWoo GBin GKev ILea LCro LMea LOPS LRHS LSun NBir NEgg NLar NPri SPer SPoG SRkn SRot SWat SWvt WCAu WFar
- 'Festiva Supreme' GBin
- 'Fiona' (d) WCAu
- 'Firebelle' WCAu
- 'Florence Ellis' WCAu
- 'Florence Nicholls' CKel ELan GBin ILea XGra
- 'Foxtrot' GBin XGra
- 'François Ortegat' **new** LMea
- 'Fuchsia Dragonfly' GBin
- 'Garden Lace' SDeJ WCAu
- 'Gardenia' CKel GBin IBoy LMea LRHS NRHS SDeJ WCAu WCot XGra
- 'Gay Paree' CKel CWCL GBin IBoy ILea MRav NCGa SCob SHar WCAu WTor
- 'Gayborder June' GMcL
- 'Général Joffre' MRav
- 'Général MacMahon' see *P. lactiflora* 'Augustin d'Hour'
- 'Germaine Bigot' CKel MRav WCAu
- 'Gertrude Allen' GBin
- 'Gilbert Barthelot' EBee WCAu
- 'Gladys McArthur' GBin
- 'Gleam of Light' CKel
- 'Globe of Light' CKel
- 'Go-Daigo' GBin
- 'Goldilocks' GBin WCAu
- 'Great Sport' MRav
- 'Green Halo' GBin
- 'Green Lotus' XGra
- 'Grover Cleveland' CHur
- 'Hakodate' CKel
- 'Hansina Brand' (d) GBin
- 'Helen Hayes' WCAu
- 'Hermione' CKel GBin XGra
- 'Honey Gold' CKel GBin SPoG WCAu XGra
- 'Hot Chocolate' GBin WCAu XGra
- 'Immaculée' CKel CWCL EBee GBin IBoy IKil ILea LCro LHop LRHS MMrt MRav NCGa SCob SPoG XGra
- 'Inspecteur Lavergne' CKel CRos EBee EPfP GBin IBoy ILea LRHS NGdn NRHS SGol SPer WCAu WCot WHar XGra
- 'Institeur Doriat' CKel LRHS WCAu
- 'Ivory Inspirations' XGra
- 'Jacorma' ILea LRHS NCGa
- 'Jadwigha' CHur EBee ILea IPot
- 'James Kelway' CKel

	- 'Jan van Leeuwen'	CHur CKel EBee ELon EPfP EWTr GBin GMaP LCro LOPS LRHS NCGa SPer WCAu WCot WTor XGra
	- 'Jappensha-ikhu'	GBin
	- 'Jeanne d'Arc'	CKel
	- 'Joker'	GBin
	- 'Joseph Christie' (d)	EBee
	- 'June Rose'	GBin
	- 'Kansas'	CHur CKel CWCL EBee ELan EPfP GBin GMcL IBoy ILea LRHS MHol NBir NGdn NLar NRHS SPoG WCAu WCot WFar
	- 'Karen Gray'	WCAu
	- 'Karl Rosenfield'	Widely available
	- 'Katherine Havemeyer'	XGra
	- 'Kelway's Betty'	CKel
	- 'Kelway's Glorious'	CKel EPfP GBin ILea LRHS MBNS MRav NLar WGwG
	- 'Kelway's Lovely Lady'	CKel
	- 'Kelway's Majestic'	MRav
	- 'Kelway's Supreme'	SWat
§	- 'Koningin Wilhelmina'	EBee EPfP MNrw
	- 'Krekler's Red'	WCAu
	- 'Krinkled White'	CKel EBee ELon EPfP EWTr EWoo GBin GKev GMaP ILea LMea LRHS MRav NCGa NLar NRHS NSti SDeJ SHil SKHP SPoG WCAu WHar XGra
	- 'La Belle Hélène'	CKel
	- 'Lady Alexandra Duff' ♀H7	CKel ELon EWTr GBin ILea LRHS MRav NBir NGdn SWvt WCAu XGra
	- 'Lady Orchid'	EPfP WCAu
	- 'Lancaster Imp'	GBin
	- 'Largo'	WCAu
	- 'Laura Dessert' ♀H7	CKel GBin IBoy ILea LCro LRHS NCGa NLar WCAu XGra
	- 'Laura Shaylor'	WCAu
	- 'Lavender Lotus'	XGra
	- 'L'Éclatante'	LRHS WGwG
§	- 'L'Étincelante'	GBin
	- 'Liebchen'	WCAu
	- 'Lilac Times'	CKel
	- 'Little Medicineman'	EBee SHil XGra
	- 'Little Pink Lullaby'	GBin
	- 'Lois Kelsey'	WCAu
	- 'Longfellow'	CKel
	- 'Lord Kitchener'	CKel EPfP GBin LRHS WGwG
	- 'Louis van Houtte'	ILea NEgg
	- 'Love's Touch' (d)	GBin
	- 'Lowell Thomas'	GBin WCAu
	- 'Lucky'	XGra
	- 'Ma Petite Cherie' (d)	GBin WCAu XGra
	- 'Madame Calot'	EBee LMea LRHS NRHS WCAu XGra
	- 'Madame Emile Debatène'	CKel EBee MBNS WCAu WFar WHar XGra
	- 'Madame Gaudichau'	WCot
	- 'Madelon'	CKel
	- 'Maestro'	GBin XGra
	- 'Magenta Glow'	XGra
	- 'Magenta Moon'	WCAu
	- 'Mammoth Rose' (d) **new**	GBin
	- 'Margaret Clark'	WCAu
	- 'Margaret Truman'	WCAu
	- 'Marie Lemoine'	CKel ELan GBin ILea LRHS WCAu XGra
	- 'Marietta Sisson'	WCAu
	- 'Mary Elizabeth'	XGra
	- 'Midnight Sun'	WCAu
	- 'Mikado'	CHur
	- 'Mischief'	MRav WCAu

	- 'Miss America' ♀H7	EPfP GBin LMea NCGa WCAu XGra
	- 'Miss Eckhart'	CKel
	- 'Miss Mary'	EWTr
	- 'Mister Ed'	GBin WCAu
	- 'Mistral'	CKel
	- 'Monsieur Jules Elie' ♀H7	CKel EBee ELan EPfP EWoo GBin IBoy ILea LCro LMea LRHS NGdn NLar SHar SPer WCAu WHar WHoo
	- 'Monsieur Martin Cahuzac'	CKel ILea LRHS
	- 'Moon of Nippon'	CRos GMcL IKil ILea LRHS NRHS WCAu
	- 'Moon River'	EPfP GBin WCAu WHoo
	- 'Moonstone'	CKel SCob
	- 'Morning Kiss'	NCGa
	- 'Mother's Choice'	CKel EWoo GBin LSRN NGdn NLar SHar WCAu WCot
	- 'Mr G.F. Hemerik'	CKel GBin IBoy WCAu WCot XGra
	- 'Mrs Franklin D. Roosevelt'	XGra
	- 'Mrs Livingston Farrand'	GBin
	- 'My Pal Rudy'	GBin
	- 'Myrtle Gentry'	CKel GBin WCAu
	- 'Nancy Nicholls'	WCAu
	- 'Nancy Nora'	SPer
	- 'Nellie Shaylor' (d)	GBin ILea NCGa
	- 'Neomy Demay'	CKel NCGa
	- 'Neon'	GBin ILea LRHS
	- 'Nice Gal'	GBin WCAu
	- 'Nick Shaylor'	GBin WCAu XGra
	- 'Nippon Beauty'	CKel EBee GBin GMcL IKil ILea LRHS NCGa NLar SCob SDeJ SKHP WCAu WCot WFar WTor
	- 'Noémie Demay'	LRHS
	- 'Norma Volz'	WCAu XGra
	- 'Nymphe'	CKel EBee ILea MRav NLar SDeJ WCAu
	- 'Paul M. Wild'	CKel ILea NLar WCAu
I	- 'Peaches and Cream' (d) **new**	LMea
*	- 'Pecher'	CBod EPfP LRHS NLar NPer WHar WHil
	- 'Peter Brand'	CKel EBee ELan GBin LSRN NLar SCob WTor
	- 'Petite Elegance' (d)	GBin
	- 'Petite Porcelain'	GBin WCAu XGra
	- 'Philippe Rivoire'	CKel GBin WCAu
	- 'Picotee'	WCAu
	- 'Pietertje Vriend Wagenaar' (d) **new**	GBin
	- 'Pillow Cases'	WCAu
	- 'Pillow Talk'	CKel CRos EBee GBin ILea LRHS NRHS SPoG WCAu
	- 'Pink Cameo'	WFar
	- 'Pink Delight'	GBin
	- 'Pink Giant'	GBin
	- 'Pink Jitterburg'	XGra
	- 'Pink Parfait'	ILea NCGa NLar SHil SPer
	- 'Pink Princess'	GBin
	- 'Pink Spinners'	XGra
	- 'Plink Platters' (d) **new**	GBin
	- 'Port Royale'	GBin
	- 'President Franklin D. Roosevelt'	LRHS SWat
	- 'President Lincoln'	WCAu
	- 'Président Poincaré'	MRav SWat
	- 'President Taft'	see *P. lactiflora* 'Reine Hortense'
	- 'Primevère'	CKel GMcL ILea LRHS NBir NCGa NSti SCob SPer WFar
	- 'Princess Bride'	GBin
	- 'Princess Margaret'	WCAu

- 'Purple Spider'	EBee MHol
- 'Queen of Sheba'	WCAu
- 'Queen Wilhelmina'	see *P. lactiflora* 'Koningin Wilhelmina'
- 'Raoul Dessert'	WCAu
- 'Raspberry Sundae'	CKel CRos ELan ELon GBin ILea LMea LRHS MRav NLar NRHS SPer SPoG WCAu WCot
- 'Ray Payton'	GBin
- 'Red Emperor'	WCAu
- 'Red Queen' **new**	GBin
- Red Sarah Bernhardt	CKel EPfP GBin SDeJ
- 'Red Satin'	WCAu
§ - 'Reine Hortense'	CKel LRHS MRav
- 'Renato'	LSun WHar XGra
- 'Riches and Fame'	LRHS
- 'Roland'	WCAu
- 'Ruth Cobb'	WCAu
- 'Salmon Dream'	CKel GBin
- 'Santa Fe'	CBod CKel EBee EPfP ILea NLar WCAu
- 'Sarah Bernhardt' 🏆H7	Widely available
- 'Sea Shell'	GBin GMaP IKil ILea WCAu XGra
- 'Sebastiaan Maas'	EBee
- 'Serene Pastel'	GBin WCAu
- 'Shawnee Chief'	GBin
- 'Shirley Temple' (d)	Widely available
- 'Silver Flare'	see *P. lactiflora* 'L'Étincelante'
- 'Silver Rose'	GBin
- 'Sir Ernest Shackleton' (d)	MRav
- 'Soft Salmon Joy'	GBin WCAu XGra
- 'Solange'	CKel IKil ILea LRHS NLar SPer WCAu
- 'Sorbet'	CHur CKel EBee ELon EPfP IKil ILea LHop LMea LRHS MHol NBir NLar NPer SMad WCAu WFar
- 'Springfield' (d)	XGra
- 'Summer Carnival'	XGra
- 'Super Gal'	WCAu
- 'Suzanne Krekler'	WCAu
- 'Svarte Petter'	NCGa
- 'Sweet Sixteen'	WCAu
- 'Sword Dance'	CKel CRos ELon GBin GMcL IBoy ILea LRHS NRHS SDeJ SHil XGra
- 'Taff'	EBee
- 'Tamate-boko'	WCAu
- 'The Fawn'	CHur GBin
- 'The Mighty Mo'	GBin
- 'The Nymph'	LRHS NBir
- 'Theatrical' (d)	WCAu
- 'Thérèse'	WCAu
- 'Tom Eckhardt'	CKel GBin SPer WCAu
- 'Top Brass'	CKel ILea LMea MRav NLar WCAu
- 'Top Hat' **new**	LMea
- 'Topeka Garnet'	XGra
- 'Twitterpated'	ELon
- 'Unique'	CKel ELan ILea
- 'Victoire de la Marne'	CKel ILea
- 'Victoria Blush' (d)	WCAu
- 'Vivid Rose'	GBin WCAu
- 'Vogue'	CKel EBee EPfP LRHS MRav SWvt WCAu
- 'W.F. Turner'	CKel
- 'Walter Faxon'	GBin
- 'Waltz'	GBin
- 'Westerner'	GBin WCAu
- 'White Cap'	CKel GBin ILea NCGa WCAu
- 'White Imp'	WCAu
- 'White Sands'	GBin
- 'White Sarah Bernhardt'	SPer

- 'White Wings'	CBcs CKel CTri ELan EPfP EWTr GBin GMaP ILea LRHS MBel NCGa NLar NSti SPer SWat SWvt WCot
- 'Whitleyi Major' 🏆H7	WCot
- 'Wilbur Wright'	CKel GBin
- 'Wine Red'	GBin
- 'Wladyslawa'	GBin LRHS NLar SHar WCot
§ - 'Zi Yu Nu'	LRHS LSRN NRHS
- 'Zuzu'	GBin WCAu
lactifolia 'Hari-ai-nin' **new**	ILea
'Lafayette Escadrille' (S)	XGra
× ***lagodechiana***	GKev LEdu
'Lan Yue Liang' **new**	LMea
'Late Windflower'	CKel GBin GCra GKev LPla WCAu
'Le Printemps' **new**	GBin LMea
'Leda' (S)	GBin XGra
'Legion of Honour'	GBin
× ***lemoinei*** (S)	WHal
§ - 'Alice Harding' (S)	CKel
§ - 'Chromatella' (S)	CKel
- 'High Noon' (S) 🏆H5	CKel LRHS MPhe SKHP SWat
- 'Marchioness' (S)	CKel
§ - 'Souvenir de Maxime Cornu' (S)	CKel LRHS SKHP
'Lemon Chiffon'	GBin
'Lemon Dream' PBR	CKel NCGa XGra
lithophila	see *P. tenuifolia* subsp. *lithophila*
lobata 'Fire King'	see *P. peregrina*
'Lollipop' (d)	ELan ILea
'London' **new**	LRHS NRHS
'Lorelei' (d) **new**	GBin
'Lovebirds'	WCAu
'Lovely Rose'	WCAu
ludlowii (S)	Widely available
ludlowii × ***suffruticosa*** 'Hakuojisi' **new**	LRHS
lutea	see *P. delavayi* var. *delavayi* f. *lutea*
'Mackinac Grand'	GBin
macrophylla	MPhe
'Madrid' **new**	LRHS NRHS
'Magenta Gem'	GBin XGra
'Mai Fleuri'	WCAu
mairei	GGGa GKev MPhe
'Many Happy Returns'	CKel GBin ILea
mascula	CBro GEdr GKev GLog IMou LHop LLHF NBir
§ - subsp. ***arietina***	CSpe GKev
- 'Immaculata'	MHol
§ - subsp. ***mascula***	GKev
§ - subsp. ***russoi***	CTal GKev LPla WThu
§ - subsp. ***triternata***	EPot GKev WCot
'May Apple'	WCAu XGra
'Merry Mayshine'	GBin XGra
'Mikuhino-akebono'	CKel SDeJ
mlokosewitschii 🏆H7	CBot CBro CFil CJun CMea CTal EBee ECha ECho ELan ENun EPot GBin GEdr GKev ILea LHop LRHS MNrw NBir NEgg SDix SLon SWvt WAbe WCot WHoo WKif WPat
- hybrids	EBee GKev
mollis	see *P. officinalis* subsp. *villosa*
'Montezuma'	GBin XGra
'Moonrise'	CKel GBin WCAu
'Morning Lilac'	CKel
'Murad of Hershey Bar' (S)	GBin XGra
'My Love'	GBin WCAu XGra
'Nike' (d)	XGra
'Normie' (d)	WCAu
'Norwegian Blush'	CKel
'Nosegay'	GBin WCAu

'Nova'	CKel GBin
obovata 🏆H5	GKev LLHF MPhe
- var. ***alba*** 🏆H5	CPne GEdr GKev LLHF
- var. ***willmottiae***	MPhe
officinalis	CArn GCra GKev MCot
- WM 9821 from Slovenia	MPhe
- from NW Croatia	LEdu
- 'Alba Plena' (d)	CKel CPou CRos EBee GKev GMaP LMea LRHS MRav NEgg NLar NRHS SPer SWvt WCAu WFar WHil WTor
- 'Anemoniflora Rosea' 🏆H7	EBee EPfP LRHS SPer SWvt WCAu
§ - subsp. ***banatica***	GKev MPhe
- 'Mutabilis Plena' (d)	IBlr
- subsp. ***officinalis*** **new**	GKev
- 'Rosea Plena' (d) 🏆H7	EBee ECtt EPfP GKev GMaP LRHS NEgg SCob SPer SWat SWvt WCAu WFar XGra
- 'Rubra Plena' (d) 🏆H7	Widely available
§ - subsp. ***villosa***	ELan LRHS SEND
'Old Faithful'	GBin XGra
'Old Rose Dandy'	CKel GBin
'Oriental Gold'	CKel
ostii (S)	CKel MPhe SKHP
§ - 'Feng Dan Bai' (S)	CKel MPhe
'Pageant'	XGra
'Paladin'	GBin
papaveracea	see *P. suffruticosa*
'Paris' **new**	LRHS NRHS
'Pastel Splendor'	CKel ELan ILea NCGa XGra
'Pastelegance' (d) **new**	GBin
'Paula Fay'	CKel EBee EPfP GBin GMaP ILea IMou MRav SDeJ WCAu XGra
Peony with the Purple Roots	see *P. suffruticosa* 'Shou An Hong'
§ ***peregrina***	CBro CKel ECho GEdr GKev LEdu MPhe SKHP WCot
- 'Fire King'	CKel ILea
§ - 'Otto Froebel' 🏆H7	CKel EPot GBin GCra GEdr NLar WCAu WCot
- 'Rosabella' **new**	LMea LRHS NRHS
- 'Sunshine'	see *P. peregrina* 'Otto Froebel'
'Picotee'	GBin WCAu
'Pink Hawaiian Coral'	CKel EBee GBin ILea MMrt NCGa NLar WTor XGra
'Pink Tea Cup'	XGra
potaninii	see *P. delavayi* var. *angustiloba* f. *angustiloba*
'Prairie Charm'	CKel XGra
'Prairie Moon'	CKel GBin NLar WCAu
qiui	MPhe
'Raspberry Charm'	XGra
'Red Charm'	CHur CKel CWCL EBee EPfP EWoo GBin IBoy IKil ILea LRHS NCGa WCAu WFar WTor
'Red Grace' (d) **new**	GBin
'Red Magic'	EBee EPfP WFar
'Red Red Rose'	GBin WCAu XGra
'Renown' (S)	CKel
'Requiem'	WCAu
'Ri Yue Jin' (S) **new**	LMea
§ ***rockii*** (S)	CKel CSpe EPfP EWoo GBin MPhe
- from Tianshui, Gansu	MPhe
- from Wenshian, Gansu	MPhe
- hybrid	see *P.* Gansu Group
- subsp. ***linyanshanii*** (S)	GKev MPhe
'Roman Gold'	CKel
romanica	see *P. peregrina*
'Rome' **new**	LRHS NRHS
'Rooster Reveille' (d)	XGra
'Rosedale'	WCAu XGra
'Roselette'	GBin LRHS NCGa WCAu
'Rubyette'	XGra
russoi	see *P. mascula* subsp. *russoi*
'Salmon Beauty' (d)	WCAu
'Salmon Chiffon'	GBin XGra
'Scarlet Heaven'	CKel GBin ILea
'Scarlet O'Hara'	CBod EWoo GBin SPer WCAu WCot XGra
'Scrumdidleumptious' (d) **new**	XGra
'Seeing Blue' **new**	NCGa
'Sequestered Sunshine'	CKel
'Serenade'	WCAu
Shandong Red Lotus	see *P. suffruticosa* 'Lu He Hong'
'Shimano-fuji'	CKel
'Shining Light'	NCGa SCob
'Show Girl'	GBin NCGa WCAu XGra
'Showanohokori'	CKel
'Simply Red' **new**	CKel
sinensis	see *P. lactiflora*
'Singing in the Rain'	CKel ILea
× ***smouthii***	GEdr
'Sonoma Kaleidoscope'	CKel ILea
'Soshi'	GBin LRHS NLar SHar
'Stardust'	WCAu
'Starlight'	CKel GBin LCro LOPS LRHS MMrt NCGa WCAu WCot WTor
§ ***suffruticosa*** (S)	CWib ELan GKev MGos
- 'Akashigata' (S)	CKel
- 'Alice Palmer' (S)	CKel
- 'Bai Yuan Hong Xia' (S)	LMea
- Bird of Rimpo	see *P. suffruticosa* 'Rimpo'
- Black Dragon Brocade	see *P. suffruticosa* 'Kokuryū-nishiki'
- Black Flower Chief	see *P. suffruticosa* 'Hei Hua Kui'
- Brocade of the Naniwa	see *P. suffruticosa* 'Naniwa-nishiki'
- 'Cardinal Vaughan' (S)	CKel
- Charming Age	see *P. suffruticosa* 'Howki'
- 'Chu Wu' (S)	LMea NTPC
- 'Dou Lu' (S)	NTPC
- Double Cherry	see *P. suffruticosa* 'Yae-zakura'
- 'Duchess of Kent' (S)	CKel
- 'Duchess of Marlborough' (S)	CKel
- Eternal Camellias	see *P. suffruticosa* 'Yachiyo-tsubaki'
- Flight of Cranes	see *P. suffruticosa* 'Renkaku'
- Floral Rivalry	see *P. suffruticosa* 'Hana-kisoi'
- Fragrant Jade	see *P.* 'Xiang Yu'
- 'Gekkyu-den'	LRHS
- 'Godaishu' (S)	CKel LRHS SKHP
- 'Guan Shi Mo Yu' (S)	LPar
- 'Guardian of the Monastery' (S)	XGra
- 'Hai Huang' (S)	LPar NTPC WKif
§ - 'Hakuo-jisi' (S/d)	CKel LRHS
§ - 'Hana-daijin' (S)	LRHS
§ - 'Hana-kisoi' (S)	CKel LRHS
- 'Hei Hai Sa Jin' (S)	NTPC
§ - 'Hei Hua Kui' (S)	NTPC
§ - 'Howki' (S)	LRHS
§ - 'Hu Hong' (S)	LPar
§ - 'Huang Hua Kui' (S)	NTPC
- 'Iso-no-nami' (S) **new**	LRHS
- Jewel in the Lotus	see *P. suffruticosa* 'Tama-fuyo'
- Jewelled Screen	see *P. suffruticosa* 'Tama-sudare'
- 'Jin Zhi'	LRHS NTPC
- 'Jitsugetsu-nishiki' (S)	CKel
- 'Joseph Rock'	see *P. rockii*
- Kamada Brocade	see *P. suffruticosa* 'Kamada-nishiki'
§ - 'Kamada-fuji' (S)	LRHS
§ - 'Kamada-nishiki' (S)	CKel

§	- 'Kaow' (S)	CKel
	- King of Flowers	see *P. suffruticosa* 'Kaow'
	- King of White Lions	see *P. suffruticosa* 'Hakuo-jisi'
	- 'Kinkaku'	see *P.* × *lemoinei* 'Souvenir de Maxime Cornu'
	- 'Kinshi'	see *P.* × *lemoinei* 'Alice Harding'
	- 'Kokucho' (S)	CKel
§	- 'Kokuryū-nishiki' (S)	CKel SKHP
	- 'Koshino-yuki' (S)	CKel LRHS
	- 'Lan Bao Shi' (S)	NTPC
§	- 'Lu He Hong' (S)	LPar
	- Magnificent Flower	see *P. suffruticosa* 'Hana-daijin'
	- 'Mo Sa Jin' (S)	NTPC
	- 'Montrose' (S)	CKel
*	- 'Mrs Shirley Fry' (S)	CKel
	- 'Mrs William Kelway' (S)	CKel
§	- 'Naniwa-nishiki' (S)	CKel
	- 'Nigata Akashigata' (S)	CKel
	- Pride of Taisho	see *P. suffruticosa* 'Taisho-no-hokori'
	- 'Reine Elisabeth' (S)	CKel
§	- 'Renkaku' (S)	CKel LRHS SKHP
§	- 'Rimpo' (S)	CKel SKHP XGra
	- 'Rou Fu Rong' (S)	LMea LPar
	- 'Seidai'	LRHS
§	- 'Shiguregumo' (S)	CKel
	- 'Shimadaigin' (S)	CKel LRHS
	- 'Shimane-chōjuraku' (S)	CKel LRHS
	- 'Shimane-hakugan' (S)	CKel
	- 'Shimane-seidai' (S)	CKel
	- 'Shimanishiki' (S)	CKel SKHP
	- 'Shin Shima Kagayaki' (S)	CKel LRHS
	- 'Shin-fusōtsukasa' (S) **new**	LRHS
	- 'Shintoyen' (S)	CKel
§	- 'Shou An Hong' (S)	NTPC
	- Snowy Pagoda = 'Xue Ta'	CKel LPar
	- 'Sumi-no-ichi' (S)	CKel
	- 'Superb' (S)	CKel
§	- 'Taisho-no-hokori' (S)	CKel
§	- 'Taiyo' (S)	CKel LRHS SKHP
§	- 'Tama-fuyo' (S)	CKel
§	- 'Tama-sudare' (S)	CKel
	- The Sun	see *P. suffruticosa* 'Taiyo'
	- 'Toichi Ruby' (S)	XGra
	- Wisteria at Kamada	see *P. suffruticosa* 'Kamada-fuji'
	- 'Wu Long Peng Sheng' (S)	CKel LPar
	- 'Xue Ying Tao Hua' (S)	LMea
§	- 'Yachiyo-tsubaki' (S)	CKel LRHS SKHP
§	- 'Yae-zakura' (S)	LRHS
	- yellow-flowered (S) **new**	GMcL
	- 'Yin Hong Qiao Dui' (S)	CKel LMea NTPC
	- 'Yoshinogawa' (S)	CKel
	- 'Yu Ban Bai' (S)	MPhe NTPC
	- 'Yu Pan Sheng Yan' (S)	NTPC
	- 'Zhao Fen' (S)	NPer
	suffruticosa × 'Ezra Pound' (S)	XGra
	suffruticosa × ***suffruticosa*** 'Hinode-sekai' (S)	XGra
	'Sunny Girl'	WCAu
	'Sunshine'	see *P. peregrina* 'Otto Froebel'
	'Taiheko'	CKel
	'Tango'	WCAu
	'Ten' i'	CKel
	tenuifolia	CAby CBro CJun EBee GBin GCal GEdr GKev ILea LLHF MAvo SKHP SMad WCot
	- RCB UA 11	WCot
	- subsp. ***biebersteiniana***	GKev
§	- subsp. ***lithophila***	GKev MPhe
	- 'Maiko' **new**	GKev
	- 'Rosea'	GBin
	'Terpsichore' (S)	XGra
	turcica	GKev
	veitchii	CKel EPot GCal GKev GMaP NBid NLar WCot WPGP WPat WWFP
	- from China	MPhe
	- pale-flowered	GCal
	- var. ***woodwardii***	CJun ECho GCra GKev LLHF LPla NWad WCot WHoo WThu
	'Vesuvian'	CKel
	'Viking Full Moon'	CKel
	White Phoenix	see *P. ostii* 'Feng Dan Bai'
	'White Towers'	EBee EPfP NCGa WFar
	'Whopper'	GBin XGra
	'Wine Angel'	GBin
	wittmanniana	GBin GCal GEdr WCot
	- PAB 3673	LEdu
§	'Xiang Yu' (S)	LMea
	'Xin Ri Yue' (S) **new**	LMea
	'Yellow Crown'	CKel
	'Yellow Emperor'	CKel
	Yellow Flower of Summer	see *P. suffruticosa* 'Huang Hua Kui'
	'Yellow Gem'	CKel GBin
	'Yellow Waterlily' **new**	CKel
	'Yokohama'	GBin
I	'Zephyrus' (S)	XGra

Paesia (*Dennstaedtiaceae*)

	scaberula	CFil CLAP NBir

Paliurus (*Rhamnaceae*)

	spina-christi	CArn CBcs

Pallenis (*Asteraceae*)

§	***maritima***	CCCN

Panax (*Araliaceae*)

	ginseng	GPoy
	japonicus	WCru
	- BWJ 7932	WCru

Pancratium (*Amaryllidaceae*)

	illyricum	XEll
	maritimum	ECho GKev NRog SDeJ

Pandorea (*Bignoniaceae*)

	jasminoides 🏆H1c	CCCN CHll CRHN CTri EBak EShb
	- 'Alba'	CRHN SPer
§	- 'Charisma' (v)	CBcs CCCN CHll EPfP EShb LSou SEND SPer
	- 'Lady Di'	CCCN
	- 'Rosea'	CCCN
	- 'Rosea Superba' 🏆H1c	CBcs CRHN LHop SEND SPer
	- 'Variegata'	see *P. jasminoides* 'Charisma'
	lindleyana	see *Clytostoma calystegioides*
	pandorana	CHll CRHN MGil SLim
	- 'Golden Showers'	CBcs CCCN CRHN MRav SEND

Panicum (*Poaceae*)

	amarum 'Dewey Blue'	EPPr IPot SMHy
	bulbosum	CKno EHoe EPPr
	clandestinum	EHoe EPPr EWes IMou LRHS MMuc NRHS SEND SMea
§	'Fibre Optics'	CSpe
	miliaceum	LRHS NRHS
	- 'Purple Majesty'	CWib
	- 'Violaceum'	SPhx
	oligosanthes var. ***scribnerianum***	SPhx

virgatum	CKno XLum
- 'Blue Tower'	CKno ELon EPPr LRHS NRHS SMea XLum
- 'Cardinal'	EBee EPPr MNrw WHoo
- 'Cloud Nine'	CKno EPPr EPed LRHS MAvo WHal WRHF
- 'Dallas Blues'	CBWd CBod CKno CSpe EBee ECha EHoe EPPr EPed EShb EWes LHop LRHS MAvo MSpe NSti SCob SHDw SMHy SPer SPoG WMoo XLum
- 'Emerald Chief'	LRHS
- 'Farbende Auslese'	MAvo
- 'Hänse Herms'	CBod CKno EHoe ELon EPPr EPed LRHS NLar NRHS SMea WFar
- 'Heavy Metal'	Widely available
- 'Heiliger Hain'	EPPr MAvo WCot
- 'Külsenmoor' **new**	EBee
I - 'Kupferhirse'	EPPr MAvo
- 'Kurt Bluemel'	EBee SAko
- 'Nican'	EPPr
- 'Northwind'	CKno CRos EBee EHoe EPPr EPfP GBin LRHS MAvo NRHS SCob SHDw SMHy SMad WFar
- 'Prairie Sky'	CBod CKno CRos EAEE EBee EHoe ELon EPPr EUJe EWoo GMaP LEdu LHop LRHS MAsh MAvo MMuc NBro NLar NRHS NWsh SCob SGbt SMHy SMad SMea WMoo
- 'Purple Haze'	CKno EHoe EPPr LRHS MAvo NRHS
- 'Red Cloud'	CKno MAvo SMHy
- 'Rehbraun'	EBee EHoe EPPr EPfP LCro LEdu LHop LOPS LRHS MJak NRHS XLum
- 'Rotstrahlbusch'	CKno CWib EBee EHoe EPPr EWoo GMaP LSun MAvo SPer WCot WMoo XLum XSen
- 'Rubrum'	EHoe ELan EPPr ESps MAvo WMoo
- 'Shenandoah'	Widely available
- 'Squaw'	CBod CKno CMac CWib EAEE EAJP EHoe EPPr EPfP EShb EWoo GMcL LRHS MAvo MJak MMuc NDov NRHS NWsh SEND SMad SPer WCot WFar WMoo XSen
- 'Straight Cloud'	EPPr
- 'Strictum'	EHoe EPPr EWes GQue LEdu SBee SCob SMHy SPer SPhx WMoo
I - 'Strictum Compactum'	CBod
- 'Warrior'	CBWd CBod CKno EAEE EAJP EHoe EHrv ELan ELon EPPr EPau EPfP LHop LRHS MAsh NRHS NWsh SCob SDix SPer WFar
- 'Wood's Variegated' (v)	WCot

Papaver ✿ (*Papaveraceae*)

alboroseum	LLHF LRHS NRHS
'Alpha Centauri' (SPS)	SWat
alpinum	CSpe ESps LRHS MAsh NGdn NRHS SWat
atlanticum	NBro NGdn SPlb
- 'Flore Pleno' (d)	CSpe IFro NBro NGdn
bracteatum	see *P. orientale* var. *bracteatum*
'Bright Star' (SPS)	SWat
burseri	SRot
commutatum 🏆H5	CSpe ELan SPhx SWat
- 'Ladybird' 🏆H5	CBot CCVN CRos GAbr SPoG SVic
corona-sancti-stephani	SWat
dubium	CSpe LRHS SPhx
- subsp. ***lecoqii***	SPhx
- - 'Albiflorum' **new**	LRHS
'Eccentric Silk' (SPS)	SWat
§ 'Fire Ball' (d)	NBid NBro SWat
glaucum	LRHS SPhx
'Heartbeat' (SPS)	CBcs CSpe EBee EPfP IPot LRHS MBel MHol MNrw NCou SDix SPoG SWat WCot WFar WRHF
heldreichii	see *P. pilosum* subsp. *spicatum*
hybridum 'Flore Pleno' (d)	SWat
'Jacinth' (SPS)	SWat
lateritium	CHid CPou SRms
- 'Nanum Flore Pleno'	see *P.* 'Fire Ball'
'Lauffeuer'	CSam SWat
'Matador' PBR 🏆H7	EBee IKil LRHS NLar WCot
'Medallion' (SPS)	EPri LRHS SWat
§ ***miyabeanum***	CSpe ELan LRHS NRHS SRot
- ***tatewakii***	see *P. miyabeanum*
'Moondance'	LRHS
nanum 'Flore Pleno'	see *P.* 'Fire Ball'
§ ***nudicaule***	SVic
- Champagne Bubbles Group	CSBt SWat
- Garden Gnome Group	see *P. nudicaule* Gartenzwerg Group
§ - Gartenzwerg Group 🏆H7	CSpe EPfP LRHS NGdn SHil SPlb SPoG SRot SWvt WHar WRHF
- 'Kelmscott Giant'	SVic
- orange-flowered	LRHS
- 'Pacino'	CSBt EAJP LRHS NLar
- 'Party Fun' (mixed)	CSpe EAJP
- 'Solar Fire Orange' 🏆H7	EUJe
- 'Summer Breeze Orange' 🏆H7	NPri
- 'Summer Breeze Yellow'	NPri
- (Wonderland Series) 'Wonderland Pink Shades'	NPri
- - 'Wonderland White'	NPri
orientale	CBcs CTsd EPfP ESps SRms SVic SWat WBod WHar
- 'Abu Hassan'	IPot
- 'Aglaja' 🏆H7	CBcs CElw CKno ECtt LRHS MPie NEgg NGdn SPad SWat WCot
- 'Aladin'	SWat
- 'Ali Baba'	GCra
- 'Alison'	SWat
- 'Allegro'	CMac CSBt EAJP EBee EPfP EWoo GMaP IBoy LRHS MBNS MRav NGdn SCob SHil SPer SPlb SPoG SVic SWat SWvt WFar
- 'Aslahan'	MRav SWat
- 'Atrosanguineum'	SWat
- 'Avebury Crimson'	SWat
- 'Baby Kiss' PBR	ECtt SWat WFar
- 'Beauty Queen'	ECha MRav NGdn
- 'Big Jim'	SWat
- 'Black and White' 🏆H7	ELan MRav NEgg SWat
- 'Blackberry Queen'	SWat
- 'Blickfang'	SWat
- 'Bolero'	CElw CWCL ECtt EPri NLar
- 'Bonfire'	SCob
- 'Bonfire Red'	SWat
§ - var. ***bracteatum***	NBir SWat
- 'Brilliant'	CRos EPfP ESps IBoy LRHS NGdn NRHS SWat WFar WMoo
- 'Brooklyn' (New York Series)	EBee ECtt LRHS LSRN MAvo SWat
- 'Burning Heart'	CWGN ECtt EPri IBoy LRHS SWat
- 'Carmen' PBR	ECtt

*	- 'Carneum'	LRHS NRHS SPoG
	- 'Carnival'	SWat
	- 'Cedar Hill'	EPri EWes MRav
	- 'Cedric Morris' ♀H7	ECha MRav SWat
	- 'Central Park' (New York Series)	ILea LRHS SWat WFar WHar WHoo
I	- 'Charming' pink-flowered	CMac ECtt SPhx SWat
	- 'Charming' red-flowered	LRHS
	- 'Clochard'	CElw ECtt WCot
	- 'Coral Reef'	EPfP MHer WHar WMoo WRHF
	- 'Curlilocks'	ELan GMcL IBoy LRHS MRav SRms SWvt WFar
*	- 'Diana'	SWat
	- 'Double Pleasure'	ECtt
	- double red shades (d)	EAJP NGdn
	- 'Doubloon' (d)	SWat WFar
	- 'Dwarf Allegro Vivace'	LRHS NRHS
	- 'Effendi' ♀H7	SWat
	- 'Elam Pink'	WCot
	- 'Erste Zuneigung'	SWat
	- 'Eskimo Pie'	SWat
	- 'Fancy Feathers'PBR	ECtt WHil
	- 'Fatima'	SWat
	- 'Feuerzwerg'	SWat
	- 'Fiesta'	ELon SWat
	- 'Firefly'PBR	SWat
	- 'Flamenco'	EBee IBoy SWat WFar
	- 'Flamingo'	IBoy
*	- 'Flore Pleno' (d)	NGdn
	- 'Forncett Summer'	EAJP ECtt MAvo MRav NLar SPer SWat WCot
	- 'Frosty' (v)	SHar
	- 'Fruit Punch'	MNHC WHar
	- 'Garden Glory'	ECtt LSRN MArl SWat
	- 'Glowing Embers'	ECtt SWat
	- Goliath Group	ELan MRav NBro SCob SDix SRms SWat WFar
	- - 'Beauty of Livermere'	Widely available
§	- - 'Beauty of Livermere' clonal	ECtt WCot
	- 'Graue Witwe'	EBee
	- 'Guardsman'	see *P. orientale* (Goliath Group) 'Beauty of Livermere' clonal
	- 'Harlem' (New York Series)	CElw CWCL EBee ELon EPfP MAvo MSCN SPer SWat
	- 'Harvest Moon' (d)	ECtt NPer SWat WHal
	- 'Indian Chief'	EPri LRHS MRav NPer WFar
	- 'Inferno'PBR	ECtt
	- 'John III' ♀H7	SPhx
	- 'John Metcalf'	ECtt MRav
	- 'Juliane'	ECha SWat
	- 'Karine' ♀H7	ECha ELan EPPr IBoy LHop LRHS SDix SWat
	- 'Khedive' (d) ♀H7	SWat
	- 'King Kong'	ECtt MAsh SPer SWat WCot WFar
	- 'Kleine Tänzerin'	GMcL MRav WFar
	- 'Kollebloem'	SWat
	- 'Lady Frederick Moore'	SWat
	- 'Lady Roscoe'	SWat
	- 'Ladybird'	EPfP LRHS NRHS
	- 'Laffeuer'	SPhx
	- 'Lauren's Lilac'	LSRN SWat
	- 'Leuchtfeuer' ♀H7	SWat
	- 'Lighthouse' ♀H7	SWat WCAu
	- 'Lilac Girl'	SWat
	- 'Little Candyfloss'PBR	SWat
	- 'Little Patty Plum'PBR	EPfP SPad
	- 'Louvre' (Parisienne Series)	SWat WFar
	- 'Maiden's Blush'	ECtt SWat
	- 'Mandarin'PBR	MHol WCot
	- 'Manhattan' (New York Series)	CElw CSam CSpe ECtt EPfP EWes LOPS LRHS MNrw NPnk NSti SGbt SWat WFar WHar WHoo
	- 'Marcus Perry'	EWes LRHS NGdn SWat
	- 'Marlene'	GBin IBoy ILea IPot LRHS SWat
	- 'Mary Finnan'	SWat
	- 'May Queen' (d)	ECtt ELon EWes IBlr MRav SWat WCot WFar WPnn
	- 'May Sadler'	SWat
	- 'Midnight'	SWat
	- 'Miss Piggy'PBR	EBee ECtt IKil NLar SGbt SPoG WCot WFar
	- 'Mrs H.G. Stobart'	SWat
	- 'Mrs Marrow's Plum'	see *P. orientale* 'Patty's Plum'
	- 'Mrs Perry'	CMea ECtt ELan GMcL IFro LRHS NGdn NPer SGbt SRms SWat WBrk WFar
	- 'Nanum Flore Pleno'	see *P.* 'Fire Ball'
	- 'Orange Glow'	WMoo
	- 'Orangeade Maison'	SWat
	- 'Oriana'	SWat
	- 'Papillon'PBR	CBcs CBod LRHS MPie NLar WCot WHar
	- 'Paradiso'PBR	EPfP
§	- 'Patty's Plum'	Widely available
	- 'Perry's White'	CBcs CBod EBee ECtt ELan EPfP EWoo GMaP GMcL IBoy LHop LRHS MRav SPoG SRkn SWat SWvt
	- 'Peter Pan'	SWat
	- 'Petticoat'	ECtt SWat
	- 'Picotée'	CBcs ECtt ELan ESps GMcL LRHS MRav NEgg NLar SPoG SRot SWat SWvt WFar WMoo
	- 'Pink Panda'	SWat
	- 'Pink Pearl'PBR	SWat WCot
	- 'Pink Ruffles'PBR	ECtt LCro LRHS SGbt SPoG SWat WFar
	- 'Pinnacle'	EPri SWat WFar
	- 'Pizzicato'	CWib EPfP IBoy NPer SWat WFar WHar WMoo
	- 'Place Pigalle' (Parisienne Series)	ECtt EPfP SWat
	- 'Plum Pudding'	CHid
	- 'Prince of Orange'	SWat SWvt
	- Princess Victoria Louise	see *P. orientale* 'Prinzessin Victoria Louise'
	- 'Prinz Eugen'	SWat WFar
§	- 'Prinzessin Victoria Louise'	CDor CRos EAJP ELan EPfP IBoy LRHS MMuc NGdn NPri NRHS SEND SHil SPoG SWat WBrk WHar
	- 'Prospero'	SWat
	- 'Queen Alexandra'	IBoy MArt NGdn
	- 'Raspberry Queen'	CMac ECtt ELan EPfP EPri GMaP IBoy IPot MArl MBel MRav NChi SWat WHal
	- 'Raspberry Ruffles'	SWat
	- 'Rembrandt'	MJak SWat WCot
	- 'Rosenpokal'	SWat
	- 'Roter Zwerg'	ECha SWat
	- 'Royal Chocolate Distinction'	CElw CSpe EBee ECtt ELan EPPr EPfP LRHS LSRN NSti SWat WFar
	- 'Royal Wedding'	Widely available
	- 'Ruffled Patty'PBR	ECtt EPfP LCro SGbt SWat WCot
	- 'Ruffled Princess of Orange'PBR	SWat
*	- 'Saffron'	SWat
	- 'Salmon Glow' (d)	SWat WFar
	- 'Salome'	SWat
	- 'Scarlet King'	CMac SWat
	- scarlet-flowered	MMuc SEND

	- 'Scarlett O'Hara'PBR (d)	ECtt EPfP SWat WFar
*	- 'Silberosa'	IPot
	- 'Sindbad'	SWat
	- 'Snow Goose'	CBod CDor CSpe CWGN EBee ECtt ESwi IPot LRHS LSun MBel MNrw NLar NPri SWat WCot WHoo
	- 'Springtime'	MRav SWat
	- Stormtorch	see *P. orientale* 'Sturmfackel'
§	- 'Sturmfackel'	SWat
	- 'Sultana'	CSam EPri MArl SWat
	- 'Sunset'PBR	SWat
	- 'The Promise'	SWat
	- 'Tiffany'	CMac ECtt LSRN MAvo NEgg SWat
	- 'Türkenlouis'	ECtt GCra GMaP GMcL IBoy LRHS MRav NGdn SWat WBrk WFar WHil
	- 'Turkish Delight'	EHrv EWoo GCra ILea LRHS MRav NBir SWat SWvt
	- 'Victoria Dreyfuss'	SWat
	- 'Violetta'	SWat
	- 'Walking Fire'	MNrw
	- 'Watermelon'	EWoo GMcL SWat
	- 'White Ruffles'PBR	EWTr IKil SGbt SWat
	- 'Wunderkind'	SWat
	pilosum	SWat
§	- subsp. ***spicatum***	CSpe ECha LHop NBir WHer WMoo
	'Rhapsody in Red' (SPS)	SWat
	rhoeas	CHab GPoy LCro MNHC SVic WJek
	- Angels' Choir Group (d)	SWat
	- 'Bridal White'	SPhx
	- 'Flanders' **new**	LRHS NRHS
	- Mother of Pearl Group	CSpe LRHS SPhx SWat
	- Shirley Group	CWCL
	rupifragum	ECha MMuc SBee WCot WPnn
	- 'Double Tangerine Gem'	see *P. rupifragum* 'Flore Pleno'
§	- 'Flore Pleno' (d)	CLet CSpe EAJP GBin NChi SVic WBrk WMoo
	- 'Tangerine Dream'	GPSL
	'Serena' (SPS)	SWat
	'Shasta' (SPS)	EBee LRHS SWat WFar
	'Snow White' (SPS)	EBee SWat
	somniferum	CLau ENfk GPoy SVic SWat
	- 'Blackcurrant Fizz' (d)	LCro SPhx
	- 'Boudoir Babe' (d)	CSpe
	- 'Double Shiraz' (d)	LRHS
	- (Laciniatum Group) 'Danebrog'	CBot
	- 'Lauren's Grape'	CSpe LCro MArt SPhx
	- Paeoniiflorum Group (d)	SWat
	- - 'Black Beauty' (d)	CSpe SDeJ SVic SWat
	- - 'Black Paeony' (d)	CBot LCro LRHS SPhx
	- - 'Schwarzer Drachen' (d)	LRHS
	- 'Pink Chiffon' (d)	SWat
	- 'Ragged Red' (d)	CSpe
	- single white-flowered	CSpe
	- 'White Cloud' (d)	CSpe SWat
	'Tequila Sunrise' (SPS)	MAvo SWat
	'The Falklands' (SPS)	SWat
	trinifolium	CSpe GCal MMuc WCot
	'Vesuvius' (SPS)	SWat
	'Water Melon'	EPri

papaya (pawpaw) see *Carica papaya*

Parabenzoin see *Lindera*

Paracaryum (*Boraginaceae*)

racemosum	CPBP SIgm

Parachampionella see *Strobilanthes*

Paradisea (*Asparagaceae*)

	liliastrum misapplied	see *P. lusitanica*
	liliastrum (L.) Bertol. ♀H5	CHid EBee ECho EPri GCal LRHS NBid NChi WPtf
	- 'Major'	EBee ECho GKev ITim
§	***lusitanica***	CAvo CMHG CSam CSpe CTca EBee ECho ECtt EPot EPri GBin GCal GKev IBlr IBoy LEdu MCot MHol WCot WPGP WRHF XEll

Parahebe (*Plantaginaceae*)

	'Angela'	MSCN
	× ***bidwillii***	GBin GCrg GJos MHer NHar SRms SRot
	- 'Kea'	ECho SRot
§	***catarractae***	CTri CWib EBee EPfP GAbr ITim NBir SRms WKif
	- 'Avalanche'PBR	GBin GMaP SCob WNPC
	- blue-flowered	SPer
§	- 'Delight' ♀H4	EWes GMaP GQue LHop MHer NPer SDix SRot
	- subsp. ***diffusa***	NPer SRot
	- 'Miss Willmott'	SPer SPlb
	- 'Porlock'	CMea GKev GWyn SRot WHoo WTor
	- 'Porlock Purple'	see *P. catarractae* 'Delight'
	- 'Rosea'	ECho MAsh SRms
	- white-flowered	CBot CSpe SRms
	- 'Whittallii' **new**	GBin
§	***formosa***	SPlb SVen
	'Greencourt'	see *P. catarractae* 'Delight'
	'Jean'	GBin
	'Kenty Pink'	MMuc
	linifolia	CTri
	- 'Blue Skies'	EPot GBin GCrg
§	***lyallii***	EBee ECho EPfP GMaP MCot MHer MMuc MRav MSwo NQui SPlb SRms WKif
	- 'Julie-Anne' ♀H4	GCal
	- 'Rosea'	CTri
	- 'Snowcap'	MRav SPlb
	'Mervyn'	CNor CTri
§	***perfoliata***	CBot CDor CMea EBee ECha ECre ELan EPri GAbr GCal GMaP LEdu LHop LRHS MAsh MCot MNrw MRav NChi SBrt SDix SEND SPer SRms XLum
	'Snow Clouds'	CMea EBee EPfP EWoo GKev MMuc NHpl SBch SDix SRot WTor

Parajubaea (*Arecaceae*)

torallyi **new**	LRHS

Parakmeria see *Magnolia*

Paramongaia (*Amaryllidaceae*)

weberbaueri	CPne

Paranomus (*Proteaceae*)

reflexus	SPlb

Paraquilegia (*Ranunculaceae*)

§	***anemonoides***	GKev WAbe
	grandiflora	see *P. anemonoides*

Parasenecio (*Asteraceae*)

delphiniifolius B&SWJ 5789	WCru
- B&SWJ 10885	WCru

- B&SWJ 11189	WCru WSHC
- B&SWJ 11415	WCru
farfarifolius	WCru
- var. ***acerinus*** B&SWJ 11549	WCru
- - B&SWJ 11554	WCru
- var. ***bulbifer***	WCru
hastatus	see *P. maximowiczianus* var. ***farfarifolius***
kiusianus B&SWJ 11460	WCru
§ ***maximowiczianus*** B&SWJ 11468	WCru
mortonii GWJ 9419	WCru
- HWJK 2214	WCru
tebakoensis B&SWJ 11167	WCru
- B&SWJ 11536	WCru

Paraserianthes (*Mimosaceae*)

distachya	see *P. lophantha*
§ ***lophantha*** ♀H2	EBak SPlb

Parasyringa see *Ligustrum*

Parathelypteris (*Thelypteridaceae*)

§ ***novae-boracensis***	ISha NLos

× *Pardancanda* (*Iridaceae*)

norrisii	see *Iris* × *norrisii*

Pardanthopsis (*Iridaceae*)

dichotoma	see *Iris dichotoma*

Parietaria (*Urticaceae*)

judaica	CArn GPoy WHer WSFF

Paris ✿ (*Melanthiaceae*)

chinensis	WCru
- B&SWJ 265 from Taiwan	WCru
delavayi	WCru
fargesii	ECho GKev LAma SDir WCru
- var. ***brevipetalata***	WCru
- var. ***petiolata***	WCru
forrestii	WCru
incompleta	CArn CLAP GCal LEdu MAvo WCru
japonica	GEdr GKev LAma WCru
lancifolia B&SWJ 3044 from Taiwan	WCru
mairei	WCru
polyphylla	CBro ECho GBin GEdr GKev LAma LRHS MNrw NBid NHpl NLar NWad SDir SDix SKHP WCru WPnP
- B&SWJ 2125	WCru
- HWJCM 475	WCru
- var. ***polyphylla*** **new**	GKev
- var. ***stenophylla***	EBee GKev LAma WCru
- var. ***yunnanensis***	ECho GEdr
* - - ***alba***	GCal
quadrifolia	CLAP CSpe EBee ECho EPfP GBin GCal GEdr GKev GPoy LEdu MAvo MNrw NLar SKHP SPhx WCru WHer WPGP WPnP WShi
- SDR 2828	GKev
tetraphylla	WCru
thibetica	EBee ECho GKev LRHS NBid NWad SDir SKHP WCru
- var. ***apetala***	WCru
- var. ***thibetica***	GEdr
verticillata	LAma WCru
- 'Ryokutei' (d)	WCru

Parnassia (*Celastraceae*)

SDR 5128	EBee
foliosa	GEdr
gansuensis SDR 5128 **new**	GKev
nubicola	GKev
palustris	WHer
- var. ***izuinsularis***	GEdr
- var. ***yakushimensis***	GEdr

Parochetus (*Papilionaceae*)

communis ambig.	MSCN NPer
- subsp. ***africanus*** ♀H2	CHid
- subsp. ***communis*** from Himalaya	GCra
* - 'Blue Gem'	CCCN

Paronychia (*Caryophyllaceae*)

sp.	SIgm
§ ***capitata***	CTri SRms WHoo
kapela	SPlb XSen
§ - subsp. ***serpyllifolia***	XLum
- var. ***serpyllifolia*** 'Binsted Gold' (v)	XLum
nivea	see *P. capitata*
serpyllifolia	see *P. kapela* subsp. *serpyllifolia*

Parrotia ✿ (*Hamamelidaceae*)

persica	Widely available
- PAB 13.046 **new**	LEdu
- 'Bella'	CJun EMOT MBlu
- 'Biltmore'	CJun NLar SSta
- 'Burgundy'	CJun EPfP NLar
- fastigiate	CJun
- 'Felicie'	CJun EPfP LPre NLar
- 'Het Plantsoen'	NLar
- 'Jodrell Bank'	CJun LRHS MBlu NLar SBir
§ - 'Lamplighter' (v)	CJun
- 'Pendula'	CJun CMCN EPfP MBlu SSta
- 'Persian Carpet'	NLar
- 'Summer Bronze'	CJun LRHS LSRN MAsh SBir
- 'Vanessa' ♀H6	CBcs CJun CMCN CMac CRos EBee EPfP ESps EWes GKin IArd LRHS MAsh MBlu NLar SAko SBir SGol SSta WMou
- 'Variegata'	see *P. persica* 'Lamplighter'
subaequalis	CBcs CDul CJun EBee LRHS NLar WPGP

Parrotiopsis (*Hamamelidaceae*)

jacquemontiana	CBcs CJun GBin IVic MBlu NLar

parsley see *Petroselinum crispum*

Parthenium (*Asteraceae*)

integrifolium	CArn GPoy IMou SPhx WCot

Parthenocissus (*Vitaceae*)

§ ***henryana*** ♀H5	Widely available
himalayana	CBcs
- 'Purpurea'	see *P. himalayana* var. *rubrifolia*
§ - var. ***rubrifolia***	CBcs CMac CRHN CRos CWCL ELan EUJe GBin LRHS MAsh MRav SEND SLim SLon SPtp WCru
inserta misapplied	see *P. quinquefolia*
inserta ambig.	CMac CTsd NLar
laetevirens	NLar
§ ***quinquefolia***	Widely available
- var. ***engelmannii***	CBcs EMOT EShb LBuc SCob WCFE
- 'Guy's Garnet'	WCru

- Red Wall = 'Troki' ETho LPar LRHS NRHS
- Star Showers = 'Monham' (v) EBee EPfP NLar
- 'Yellow Wall'PBR ETho LRHS NRHS
semicordata B&SWJ 6551 WCru
striata see *Cissus striata*
thomsonii see *Cayratia thomsonii*
§ ***tricuspidata*** CCVT CDul EBee EPfP IBoy MAsh MGos SArc SCob SGol SPer
- 'Beverley Brook' CRHN ELon LPre LSRN NLar SNig SPer SRms
- 'Crûg Compact' WCru
- 'Fenway Park' CFlo CKel EBee ELan LRHS MRav NLar
- 'Green Spring' CBcs ELan IArd LPre MGos NLar
- 'Lowii' CMac CRos EBee EPfP LPre LRHS MBlu MRav NLar NRHS SLon SNig
- 'Purpurea' CKel
- 'Robusta' EMOT GMcL
§ - 'Veitchii' ♀H5 Widely available

Pasithea (*Hemerocallidaceae*)

caerulea CAbP CPne EBee EPri ESwi LHop MBel MHol MSCN NGBl SBrt WCot WPGP

Paspalum (*Poaceae*)

glaucifolium MNrw
quadrifarium RCB RA S-5 WCot

Passiflora ✿ (*Passifloraceae*)

actinia CCCN CRHN SPlb
'Adularia' CCCN
alata (F) ♀H1a CCCN
× ***alatocaerulea*** see *P.* × *belotii*
× ***allardii*** CCCN
ambigua CCCN
§ 'Amethyst' ♀H3 CBcs CCCN CFlo CKel CRHN CSBt LHop LSRN NLos SArc SPoG
amethystina misapplied see *P.* 'Amethyst'
§ ***amethystina*** Mikan ECre LRHS
'Anastasia' CCCN
'Andy' CCCN
'Anemona' CCCN
'Angelo Blu' CCCN
'Annika' CCCN
antioquiensis misapplied see *P.* × *exoniensis*
antioquiensis ambig. CBcs CCCN CTsd
antioquiensis H. Karst. ♀H2 CHll CRHN
'Ariane' CCCN
× ***atropurpurea*** CCCN
§ ***aurantia*** CCCN
banksii see *P. aurantia*
§ × ***belotii*** CCCN
- 'Impératrice Eugénie' see *P.* × *belotii*
- 'Perfume Passion'PBR CCCN WHlf
'Betty Myles Young' CCCN CKel CRHN LRHS NRHS
'Blue Bird' CCCN
'Blue Bouquet' new CCCN
'Blue Crown' CCCN
'Blue Moon' CCCN
'Blue Stripper' CCCN
'Blue Velvet' CCCN
'Byron Beauty' CCCN
'Byte' CCCN
§ ***caerulea*** ♀H4 Widely available
- 'Chinensis' CCCN
- 'Clear Sky'PBR CCCN CFlo CKel EBee ELan EPfP EUJe LRHS NLar NRHS SNig
- 'Constance Eliott' ♀H4 CAgr CBcs CCCN CFlo CKel CMac CRHN CRos CSBt CWib ELan EPfP ESps LBMP LCro LRHS MAsh MGos MHer NLar NLos NRHS SCob SGol SNig SPer SWvt
- 'Pierre Pomié' CCCN
- ***rubra*** CSBt
- 'White Lightning' CCCN CFlo CKel ELan EMOT LRHS NPri NRHS SHil SLim SPoG SWvt
× ***caeruleoracemosa*** see *P.* × *violacea*
× ***caponii*** CCCN
- 'John Innes' CCCN
'Celine' CCCN
chinensis see *P. caerulea*
citrifolia CCCN
citrina CCCN
* ***classica*** × ***coccinea*** CCCN ELan
× ***colvillii*** CCCN CHll
'Coordination' CCCN
§ ***coriacea*** CCCN
'Crimson Tears' CCCN
'Daylight' CCCN
'Debby' CCCN
× ***decaisneana*** (F) CCCN
'Divertido' CCCN
Eden = 'Hil Pas Eden' ♀H3 CCCN CFlo CKel SCoo SRkn
edulis (F) CBcs CCCN CLau NLos SPre SVic
- 'Byte' (F) new CCCN
§ - f. ***edulis*** (F) CCCN
- f. ***flavicarpa*** (F) CCCN
- 'Norfolk' (F) CCCN
- 'Parati' (F) CCCN
'Elizabeth' (F) CCCN
'Empress Eugenie' see *P.* × *belotii*
'Evatoria' CCCN
§ × ***exoniensis*** ♀H2 CCCN CHll CRHN CSBt ECre
'Fairylights' CCCN
'Fantasma' CCCN
'Fata Confetto' CCCN
'Fledermouse' CCCN
'Flying V' CCCN
'Grand Duchess' CCCN
gritensis CCCN
'Guglielmo Betto' CCCN
'Heidi' CCCN
'Hetty Nicolaas' CCCN
'Hildegard' CCCN
'Hill House' CHll
incarnata (F) CCCN GPoy SPlb
'Incense' (F) ♀H2 CCCN SPlb
'Inspiration' CCCN
'Jara' CCCN
'Jelly Joker' CCCN
'Justine Lyons' CCCN CKel LRHS NRHS
karwinskii CCCN
× ***kewensis*** CCCN
'Lady Margaret' CCCN
'Lambiekins' CCCN CKel LRHS NRHS
§ ***ligularis*** (F) CCCN
'Lilac Lady' see *P.* × *violacea* 'Tresederi'
'Livie' CCCN
lowei see *P. ligularis*
lutea CCCN
'Luzmarina' CCCN
'Manapany' CCCN
manicata (F) CCCN
'Maria' CCCN
'Marijke' CCCN
'Mary Jane' CCCN
I ***matthewsii*** 'Alba' CRHN

'Mavis Mastics'	see *P.* × *violacea* 'Tresederi'
mayana	see *P. caerulea*
membranacea (F)	CCCN
'Michael'	CCCN
'Minai'	CCCN
'Mini Lamb'	CCCN
mixta (F)	CCCN
- clone 2	CCCN
- red-flowered	CCCN
mollissima misapplied	see *P. tarminiana*
mollissima ambig. (F)	CBcs CCCN SPlb
mollissima (Kunth) L.H. Bailey (F) 🏆^{H2}	CRHN
'Monika Fischer'	CCCN
mucronata	CCCN
murucuja	CCCN
'New Incense'	CCCN
'Nightshift'	CCCN
obtusifolia	see *P. coriacea*
onychina	see *P. amethystina* Mikan
'Panda'	CCCN
'Party Animal'	CCCN CKel LRHS NRHS
'Pink Festival'	CCCN
'Pink Nightmare'	CCCN
'Pink Passion'^{PBR}	CCCN ELan
'Pinky'	CCCN
× ***piresiae***	CCCN
'Poppet'	CCCN CKel LRHS NRHS
'Precioso'	CCCN
'Pura Vida'	CCCN
'Purple Companion'	CCCN
'Purple Haze'	CCCN CKel CWib LCro LRHS NLos NRHS
'Purple Passion'	see *P. edulis* f. *edulis*
'Purple Pendulum'	CCCN
'Purple Rain'	CCCN
quadrangularis (F) 🏆^{H1a}	CCCN CHll
quinquangularis	CCCN
racemosa 🏆^{H1b}	CCCN
- 'Buzios'	CCCN
'Red Inca'	CCCN
reitzii	CCCN
riparia	CCCN
rubra	CCCN SLim
sexocellata	see *P. coriacea*
'Silly Cow'	CCCN CKel LRHS NRHS
'Silvie'	CCCN
'Simply Red'	CCCN
'Smythiana'	CBot
'Star of Bristol' 🏆^{H2}	CKel SLim
'Star of Kingston'	CCCN
'Star of Surbiton'	CCCN LRHS NRHS
'Sunburst'	CCCN
'Surprise'	CCCN
§ ***tarminiana*** (F)	CCCN CRHN CSBt
- white-flowered	CCCN
'Temptation'	CCCN
× ***tresederi***	see *P.* × *violacea* 'Tresederi'
trifasciata	CCCN
tucumanensis tetraploid	CCCN
tulae	CCCN
venusta	CCCN
§ × ***violacea*** 🏆^{H2}	CBcs CCCN CRHN EBee
- 'Eynsford Gem'	CCCN
- 'Lilac Lady'	see *P.* × *violacea* 'Tresederi'
- 'Sabin'	CCCN
§ - 'Tresederi'	CCCN ELan WFar
- 'Twin Star'	CCCN
- 'Victoria'	CCCN CSBt EBee LSou LTro
vitifolia (F)	CCCN
- 'Innocentiae'	CCCN
'White Queen'	CCCN
'White Surprise'	CCCN
'White Wedding'	CCCN CKel
'Wilgen Heintje'	CCCN
'Wilgen Marieke'	CCCN
'Winterland'	CCCN

passion fruit see *Passiflora*

passion fruit, banana see *Passiflora mollissima* (Kunth) L.H. Bailey

Pastinaca (*Apiaceae*)

sativa	CHab SVic

Patersonia (*Iridaceae*)

occidentalis	LRHS SPlb

Patrinia ✿ (*Caprifoliaceae*)

gibbosa	CSam CSpe CTal ECtt GEdr MMrt MMuc NLar NPnk SPhx WFar WMoo WPnP
- B&SWJ 874	WCru
aff. ***punctiflora***	NDov
rupestris B&SWJ 12654	WCru
scabiosifolia	CBWd CElw CHll CKno CSpe ECha ECtt EWld GJos MAvo MHer NBir NLar NPnk SDix SPhx WFar WHoo WMoo WTcb
- B&SWJ 8740	WCru
- 'Nagoya'	MNrw
triloba	CPla CSpe CTal ECho GCal GEdr LRHS LSou MMrt NPnk WFar WMoo
* - 'Minor'	ECho ECtt
- var. ***palmata***	EBee GKev LHop NPnk WMoo
villosa	EBee GJos IMou NGdn NPnk

Paulownia (*Paulowniaceae*)

catalpifolia	NLar SAko
elongata	NLar
fortunei	IVic MBlu SAko SPlb
- Fast Blue = 'Minfast' 🏆^{H5}	CHGN ESwi LSRN SGol
kawakamii	EBee EPfP SChF WBod WPGP
- RWJ 9909	WCru
'Purple Spendour'	SAko
tomentosa 🏆^{H5}	Widely available
- W 769 **new**	WPGP
- 'Coreana'	CHll WCru
undulate-leaved, from Taiwan	CMCN

Pavonia (*Malvaceae*)

multiflora ambig.	CCCN
strictiflora	CCCN
* ***volubilis***	CCCN

pawpaw (false banana) see *Asimina triloba*

pawpaw (papaya) see *Carica papaya*

peach see *Prunus persica*

pear see *Pyrus communis*

pear, Asian see *Pyrus pyrifolia*

pecan see *Carya illinoinensis*

Pecteilis (*Orchidaceae*)

§	***radiata***	GKev
*	- 'Variegata' **new**	GKev

Pedicularis (*Orobanchaceae*)

SDR 7872	GKev
SDR 7920	GKev
SDR 7926	GKev

Peganum (*Nitrariaceae*)

harmala	SBrt

Pelargonium ✿ (*Geraniaceae*)

	'A.M. Mayne' (Z/d)	WFib
	'Abba' (Z/d)	WFib
	'Abbie Hillier' (R)	WFib
	abrotanifolium (Sc)	ENfk EWoo MHer SVen WFib WGwG
	acetosum	EWoo GCal MHer SPhx WFib
	'Ada Green' (R)	WFib
	'Adam's Quilt' (Z/C)	LAll
	'Ainsdale Beauty' (Z)	WFib
	alchemilloides	WFib
	'Alcyone' (Dw/d)	LAll
	'Alde' (Min)	LAll
	'Aldwyck' (R) ♀H1c	WFib
	'Alex Kitson' (Z)	WFib
	'Algenon' (Min/d)	WFib
I	'Alice' (Min)	WFib
	'Alison March' (Dw/Z/v/d) **new**	WFib
	'Allesley Shadow' (Dw/d)	WFib
	alpinum	MHer
	'Alta Bell' (R)	ELan
	'Always' (Z/d)	LAll
	'Amari' (R)	WFib
	'Ambrose' (Min/d)	LAll WFib
	Amelit = 'Pacameli'PBR (I/d)	MCot SSea
	'American Prince of Orange' (Sc)	SPet
	Ameta = 'Pacmeta'PBR (Z)	SSea
	'Amethyst' (R)	LAll SCoo WFib
	'Angel Eyes Blueberry' (A)	LSou
	(Angeleyes Series) Angeleyes Bicolor = 'Pacbicolor'PBR (A)	MCot
	- Angeleyes Orange = 'Paccrio'PBR (A)	EWoo WCot
	- Angeleyes Randy (A)	SSea
	- Angeleyes Viola = 'Pacviola'PBR (A)	LSou
	'Angelique' (Dw/d)	LAll WFib
	'Ann Hoystead' (R) ♀H1c	WFib
	'Annsbrook Beauty' (A/C)	SPet WFib
	'Antoine Crozy' (Z × I/d)	WFib
	'Apache' (Z/d)	WFib
	appendiculatum	CLak MHer
	'Apple Betty' (Sc)	EWoo WFib
	'Apple Blossom Rosebud' (Z/d) ♀H1c	ECtt EShb LAll MHer WFib
	'Apricot' (Dw/v)	LAll
	'Apricot Fool' (U/Sc) **new**	WFib
	'Apricot Glace' (U/Sc) **new**	WFib
	'April Hamilton' (I)	CWCL LCro WFib
	'April Showers' (A)	WFib
	'Arctic Frost'	WFib
§	'Arctic Star' (Z/St) ♀H1c	CSpe WBrk WFib
	'Ardens' ♀H1c	CSpe CTre EBee EWoo LAll LCro LSou MCot MHer SBod SCob SDix SWvt WCot WFib WWFP
	'Ardwick Cinnamon' (Sc)	CCht ENfk EWoo LAll MHer SPet WFib
	'Arnside Fringed Aztec' (R)	MHer WFib
	'Ashby' (U/Sc) ♀H1c	CWCL ENfk EWoo LAll MHer SBch SPet
	'Ashfield Blaze' (Z/d)	LAll
	'Ashfield Jubilee' (Z/C)	LAll
	'Ashfield Serenade' (Z) ♀H1c	WFib
	'Askham Fringed Aztec' (R) ♀H1c	WFib
	asperum Ehr. ex Willd.	see *P.* 'Graveolens'
	'Athabasca' (Min)	LAll
	'Atlantic Burgundy'	CWCL
§	'Atomic Snowflake' (Sc/v)	ENfk LAll MNHC SPet WFib
	'Atrium' (U)	MHer WFib
	'Attar of Roses' (Sc) ♀H1c	CArn ECtt ENfk EWoo LAll LCro MCot MHer MNHC NCou NPri SBch SIde SPet SPoG WBrk WFib WGwG
	'Aurora' (Z/d)	LAll
	australe	EWoo MCot MHer SBch SVen WFib
	'Australian Bute' (R)	LAll
	'Australian Mystery' (R/Dec) ♀H1c	CSpe WFib
	'Aztec' (R) ♀H1c	LAll WFib
	'Baby Bird's Egg' (Min)	WFib
	'Baby Brocade' (Min/d)	LAll
	'Baby Harry' (Dw/v)	WFib
	'Balcon Imperial'	see *P.* 'Roi des Balcons Impérial'
	'Balcon Lilas'	see *P.* 'Roi des Balcons Lilas'
	'Balcon Rouge'	see *P.* 'Roi des Balcons Impérial'
	'Balcon Royale'	see *P.* 'Roi des Balcons Impérial'
	'Balcony Red' (I)	ECtt
	'Ballerina' (R)	see *P.* 'Carisbrooke'
I	'Ballerina' (Min)	WFib
	'Banstead Village' (Z)	LAll
	'Barbara Eldridge' (Z) **new**	WFib
§	'Barbe Bleu' (I/d) ♀H1c	LCro WFib
	barklyi	WFib
	'Bath Beauty' (Dw)	CSpe
	'Beacon Hill' (Min)	LAll
	'Beatrice Cottington' (I/d)	WFib
	'Beauty of Eastbourne' misapplied	see *P.* 'Lachskönigin'
	'Belinda Adams' (Min/d) ♀H1c	LAll
	Belladonna = 'Fisopa' (I/d)	SCoo
	'Bembridge' (Z/St/d)	WFib
	'Ben Matt' (R)	WFib
	'Berkswell Carnival' (A)	ELan
	'Berkswell Jester' (A)	LAll
	'Berkswell Lace' (A)	MHer
	'Beromünster' (Dec)	EWoo MHer WFib
	'Bert Pearce' (R)	WFib
	'Beryl Gibbons' (Z/d)	LAll
	'Beryl Reid' (R)	WFib
	'Betty' (Z/d)	LAll
	'Betty Catchpole' (Z)	EWoo
	betulinum	CTre WFib
	'Betwixt' (Z/v)	WFib
	'Biedermeier' (R)	LAll
	'Big Apple' (Sc)	EWoo
	'Bird Dancer' (Dw/St) ♀H1c	CSpe LAll MHer MNHC WBrk
	'Birdbush Eleanor' (Birdbush Series) (Z)	WFib
	'Birthday Girl' (R)	WFib
	'Bitter Lemon' (Sc)	ECtt WFib
	'Black Butterfly'	see *P.* 'Brown's Butterfly'
	'Black Knight' (R)	ECtt EWoo MHer

	Name	Suppliers
	'Black Knight' (A)	SPet
	'Black Pearl' (Z/d)	LAll
	'Black Prince' (R/Dec)	EWoo WFib
	'Black Velvet' (R)	EWoo LAll MCot
	'Black Vesuvius'	see *P.* 'Red Black Vesuvius'
	'Blackcurrant Sundae'	LAll
	'Blackcurrant Yhu' (Dec)	MPtG
	Blanche Roche = 'Guitoblanc' (I/d)	LAll LSou MCot MHer SCoo SSea
§	'Blandfordianum' (Sc)	EWoo MHer
I	'Blandfordianum Album' (Sc) **new**	WFib
	'Blandfordianum Roseum' (Sc)	EWoo MHer WFib
	'Blazonry' (Z/v)	WFib
	(Blizzard Series) Blizzard Blue = 'Fisrain'PBR (I)	SCoo
	- Blizzard Dark Red = 'Fisblizdark' (I)	CWCL EWoo
	- Blizzard Red = 'Fizzard' (I)	SCoo
	- Blizzard White = 'Fisbliz'PBR (I)	SCoo
	'Blue Beard'	see *P.* 'Barbe Bleu'
	Blue Sybil = 'Pacblusy'PBR (I/d)	LSou
	'Bob Newing' (Min/St)	WFib
	'Bobberstone' (Z/St)	LAll WFib
	'Bold Ann' (Dw/Z/d) **new**	WFib
	'Bold Appleblossom' (Z)	WFib
	'Bold Bridesmaid' (Dw/d) **new**	WFib
	'Bold Carmine' (Z/d)	LAll
	'Bold Carousel' (Z/d)	WFib
	'Bold Cherie' (Dw/d) **new**	WFib
	'Bold Cherub' (Z/d)	WFib
	'Bold Cyclamen' (Dw/d) **new**	WFib
	'Bold Debonair' (Dw/d) **new**	WFib
	'Bold Dove' (Dw) **new**	WFib
	'Bold Flame' (Z/d)	WFib
	'Bold Gem' (Z/d)	WFib
	'Bold Limelight' (Z/d)	WFib
	'Bold Minstrel' (Z/d)	WFib
	'Bold Moonlight'	WFib
	'Bold Pixie' (Dw/d)	WFib
	'Bold Princess' (Z/d)	WFib
	'Bold Special' (Z)	WFib
	'Bold Spirit' (Z) **new**	WFib
	'Bold Sunset' (Z/d) 🏆H1c	WFib
	'Bolero' (U) 🏆H1c	LAll WFib
	'Bon Bon' (Min/St)	WFib
	'Bonito' (I/d)	LAll
	'Bontrosai'PBR (Sc)	MCot
	'Bornholm' (d)	LAll
	'Bosham' (R)	WFib
	'Both's Snowflake' (Sc/v)	WFib
	bowkeri	WFib
	'Brackenwood' (Dw/d) 🏆H1c	LAll
	'Bramford' (Dw)	LAll
	Bravo = 'Fisbravo' (Z/d)	WFib
	'Break o' Day' (R)	LAll
	'Brenda' (Min/d)	WFib
	'Brenda Hyatt' (Dw/d)	LAll WFib
	'Brian West' (Min/St/C)	WFib
	'Brian West Butterfly' (Z/St) 🏆H1c	WFib
	'Bright Eyes' ambig. (Dw)	WFib
	'Brightstone' (Z/d)	ECtt WFib
	'Brilliant' (Dec)	ENfk SPet WFib
	'Brilliantine' (Sc)	ENfk EWoo MHer WFib
	'Britannia' (R)	WFib
	'Brixworth Charmer' (Z/v)	LAll
	'Brixworth Pearl' (Z)	WFib
	'Broadway' (Min)	LAll
	'Brook's Purple'	see *P.* 'Royal Purple'
	'Brookside Flamenco' (Dw/d)	LAll WFib
	'Brookside Primrose' (Min/C/d)	WFib
	'Brookside Serenade' (Dw)	WFib
§	'Brown's Butterfly' (R)	ECtt EWoo WFib
	'Brunswick' (Sc)	EWoo MHer WFib
	'Burnaby' (Min/d)	LAll
	'Bushfire' (R) 🏆H1c	EWoo WFib
	'Butley' (Min)	LAll
	Butterfly = 'Fisam'PBR (I)	SCoo
	'Butterfly Lorele' (Z/d)	LAll
	caespitosum	MHer
	caffrum	WFib
	'Cal'	see *P.* 'Salmon Irene'
	'California Brilliant' (U)	MHer
	'Calignon' (Z/St)	WFib
	'Caligula' (Min/d)	LAll
	'Cameo' (Dw/d)	LAll WFib
	'Camisole' (Dw/d)	LAll
	'Can-can' (I/d)	WFib
	canescens	see *P.* 'Blandfordianum'
	'Cape Town' (Dw/Z/v)	WFib
	capitatum	ENfk WFib
	'Capri' (Sc)	WFib
	'Captain Starlight' (A) 🏆H1c	EWoo LAll MHer SPet WFib
	'Carefree' (U) 🏆H1c	WFib
§	'Carisbrooke' (R) 🏆H1c	WFib
	'Carmel' (Z)	WFib
	carnosum	MHer
	'Carol Gibbons' (Z/d) 🏆H1c	LAll
	'Carole Munroe' (Z/d)	WFib
	'Caroline Schmidt' (Z/d/v)	LAll MCot WBrk WFib
	'Carolyn Hardy' (Z/d)	WFib
	Cascade Lilac	see *P.* 'Roi des Balcons Lilas'
	caucalifolium subsp. ***caucalifolium***	MHer
	- subsp. ***convolvulifolium***	WFib
	'Celebration' (Z/d)	WFib
	'Cézanne' (R)	LAll MCot
	'Charity' (Sc) 🏆H1c	ENfk LAll MCot MHer SPet WFib
	'Charlotte Bronte' (Dw/v)	WFib
	'Charmay Snowflurry' (Sc/v) **new**	WFib
	'Chavarri Hermanos' (Z/d) **new**	WFib
	'Chelsea Gem' (Z/d/v) 🏆H1c	LAll WFib
	'Chelsea Morning' (Z/d)	WFib
	'Cherry' (Min)	WFib
	'Cherry Orchard' (R)	WFib
	'Chew Magna' (R)	WFib
	'Chieko' (Min/d)	WFib
§	'Chocolate Peppermint' (Sc)	ECtt ELan ENfk EWoo MCot MHer SEND SPet WFib
	'Chocolate Tomentosum'	see *P.* 'Chocolate Peppermint'
	'Chocolate Twist' (St/C)	LAll
	'Choun Cho' (I)	LCro
	'Chrissie' (R)	WFib
	'Christopher Ley' (Z)	LAll
	'Cindy' (Dw/d)	WFib
	'Citriodorum' (Sc) 🏆H1c	ELan MCot MHer WFib
	'Citronella' (Sc)	WFib

	'Clara Read' (Dw)	LAll
	'Claret Rock Unique' (U)	EWoo WFib
	'Clatterbridge' (Dw/d) ♀H1c	LAll
	'Clorinda' (U/Sc)	ENfk EWoo LAll MCot MHer MNHC NWad SPet WFib
	'Clown' (R)	WFib
	'Coddenham' (Dw/d)	WFib
	'Cola Bottles'	NPer SPet SPoG WFib
§	'Colonel Baden-Powell' (I/d)	WFib
	'Colwell' (Min/d)	WFib
	'Concolor Lace'	see *P.* 'Shottesham Pet'
	'Contrast' (Z/C/v)	LAll SCoo SPoG WFib
	'Cook's Peachblossom'	LAll WFib
	'Copthorne' (U/Sc) ♀H1c	EWoo MCot MHer SPet WFib
	cordifolium	GCal WFib
	- var. ***rubrocinctum***	MHer
	coriandrifolium	see *P. myrrhifolium* var. *coriandrifolium*
	'Cornell' (I/d)	WFib
	cortusifolium	MHer
	'Cotta Lilac Queen' (I/d)	LAll
	'Cottenham Glamour' (A) ♀H1c	MHer
	'Cottenham Jubilee' (A)	MHer
	'Cottenham Surprise' (A) ♀H1c	MPtG SPet
	'Cottenham Wonder' (A) ♀H1c	SPet
	'Cottontail' (Min)	LAll
	cotyledonis	WFib
	'Countess of Scarborough'	see *P.* 'Lady Scarborough'
	'Cover Girl' (Z/d)	WFib
	'Covina' (R)	WFib
	'Cramdon Red' (Dw)	WFib
	'Crampel's Master' (Z)	LAll
	'Creamery' (d)	WFib
	'Creamy Nutmeg' (Sc/v)	ENfk EShb EWoo MHer NWad SEND
	'Creeting St Mary' (Min)	LAll
	'Creeting St Peter' (Min)	LAll
	'Crimson Unique' (U) ♀H1c	CSpe ELan ENfk EWoo MCot MHer WFib
§	***crispum*** (Sc)	GPoy
	- 'Cy's Sunburst' (v)	MHer WFib
§	- 'Golden Well Sweep' (Sc/v)	WFib
	- 'Major' (Sc)	WFib
	- 'Peach Cream' (Sc/v)	ENfk WFib
	- 'Variegatum' (Sc/v) ♀H1c	ENfk GBin GPoy LAll MHer SBch SIde SPet WCot WFib
	crithmifolium	MHer
	'Crock O Day' (I/d)	LAll
	'Crocodile' (I/C/d) ♀H1c	ECtt ELan MHer MNHC NWad WFib
	'Crowfoot Rose' (Sc)	WFib
	'Crystal Palace Gem' (Z/v)	LAll WFib
	cucullatum	WFib
	- 'Flore Pleno' (d)	MHer WFib
	- subsp. ***strigifolium***	EWoo
	'Cupid' (Min/Dw/d)	WFib
§	'Czar' (Z/C)	SCoo
	'Dainty Maid' (Sc)	ENfk
	'Dale Queen' (Z)	WFib
	'Dame Anna Neagle' (Dw/d)	LAll
	'Dark Red Irene' (Z/d)	LAll WFib
	'Dark Secret' (R)	CSpe WFib
	'Dark Venus' (R)	WFib
	'David John' (Dw/d)	LAll
	'Davina' (Min/d)	WFib
	'Deacon Arlon' (Dw/d)	LAll
	'Deacon Avalon' (Dw/d)	WFib
	'Deacon Barbecue' (Z/d)	LAll WFib
	'Deacon Birthday' (Z/d)	LAll
	'Deacon Bonanza' (Z/d)	LAll WFib
	'Deacon Clarion' (Z/d)	LAll WFib
	'Deacon Constancy' (Z/d)	LAll
	'Deacon Coral Reef' (Z/d)	LAll WFib
	'Deacon Fireball' (Z/d)	LAll WFib
	'Deacon Gala' (Z/d)	LAll WFib
	'Deacon Golden Bonanza' (Z/C/d)	WFib
	'Deacon Golden Lilac Mist' (Z/C/d)	WFib
	'Deacon Jubilant' (Z/d)	LAll
	'Deacon Lilac Mist' (Z/d)	WFib
	'Deacon Mandarin' (Z/d)	WFib
	'Deacon Minuet' (Z/d)	LAll WFib
	'Deacon Peacock' (Z/C/d)	WFib
	'Deacon Picotee' (Z/d)	LAll WFib
	'Deacon Regalia' (Z/d)	LAll
	'Deacon Romance' (Z/d)	LAll
§	'Deacon Summertime' (Z/d)	LAll WFib
	'Deacon Sunburst' (Z/d)	LAll
	'Deacon Suntan' (Z/d)	LAll
	'Deacon Trousseau' (Z/d)	LAll
	'Deborah Miliken' (Z/d) ♀H1c	WFib
	'Decora Impérial' (I)	LAll
	'Decora Lavender'	see *P.* 'Decora Lilas'
§	'Decora Lilas' (I)	ECtt
	'Decora Mauve'	see *P.* 'Decora Lilas'
	'Decora Pink'	see *P.* 'Decora Rouge'
	'Decora Red'	see *P.* 'Decora Rouge'
§	'Decora Rose' (I)	ECtt
§	'Decora Rouge' (I)	ECtt
	'Deerwood Darling' (Min/v/d)	WFib
	'Deerwood Lavender Lad' (Sc)	ENfk EWoo MHer WFib
	'Deerwood Lavender Lass'	MCot MHer
	'Deerwood Pink Puff' (St/d)	WFib
	'Delightful' (R)	WFib
	'Delli' (R) ♀H1c	CWCL MHer NPer WFib
	'Denebola' (Min/d)	LAll
	denticulatum	MHer
§	- 'Filicifolium' (Sc)	ELan ENfk EPri LAll MCot MHer WFib
	'Diana Palmer' (Z/d)	LAll
	'Diane' (Min/d)	LAll
	'Dibbinsdale' (Z) ♀H1c	LAll
	dichondrifolium (Sc)	LAll WFib
	'Didi' (Min)	LAll
	'Display' ambig. (Dw/v)	WFib
	'Distinction' (Z)	LAll SPoG WFib
	'Dodd's Super Double' (Z/d)	WFib
	'Dolly Varden' (Z/v) ♀H1c	LAll WFib
	'Don's Helen Bainbridge' (Z/C)	WFib
	'Don's Richard A. Costain' (Z/C)	WFib
	'Don's Silver Wedding'	LAll
	'Don's Stokesley Gem' (Z/C)	WFib
	'Don's Swanland Girl' (Min)	LAll
	'Doris Hancock' (R)	WFib
	'Dorothy Baker' (R) **new**	WFib

'Double Pink' (R/d) WFib
'Dovedale' (Dw/C) WFib
'Downlands' (Z/d) WFib
'Dragon's Breath' (Z/St) LAll
'Dresden White' (Dw) WFib
'Duchess of Devonshire' (U) WFib
'Duke of Buckingham' (Z/d) LAll
'Duke of Devonshire' (Z/d) LAll
'Duke of Edinburgh' see *P.* 'Hederinum Variegatum'
'Dunkery Beacon' (R) WFib
§ 'Dwarf Miriam Baisey' (Min) LAll
'Dwarf Miriam Read' see *P.* 'Dwarf Miriam Baisey'
'E. Dabner' (Z/d) WFib
'East Sussex' (Dw/C) LAll
echinatum EWoo MHer
- 'Album' EWoo WFib
'Eclipse' (Dw/d) LAll
'Eden Gem' (Min/d) LAll WFib
'Edith Stern' (Dw/d) LAll
'Edmond Lachenal' (Z/d) WFib
'Eileen Postle' (R) ♀H1c WFib
'Elaine Ward' (R) **new** WFib
Elbe Silver = 'Pensil' (I) ♀H1c SCoo
'Electra' (Z/d) LAll
'Elizabeth Read' (Dw) LAll
'Ella Jane' (Z/d) **new** WFib
'Ellen Gray' (v) LAll
'Elmsett' (Dw/C/d) LAll WFib
'Els' (Dw/St) WBrk
'Els' (1870) LAll
'Elsi' (I × Z/d/v) LAll WFib
'Elsie Gillam' (St) WFib
'Embassy' (Min) WFib
Emilia = 'Pactina'PBR SSea
'Emma Hössle' see *P.* 'Frau Emma Hössle'
'Emma Jane Read' (Dw/d) WFib
'Emma Louise' (Z) WFib
'Encore' (Z/d/v) LAll
endlicherianum MHer WAbe WCot
'Endsleigh' (Sc) WFib
'Erwarton' (Min/d) LAll
'Escapade' (Min/d) LAll
'Eskay Gold' (A) WFib
'Eskay Jewel' (A) WFib
'Eskay Ruby' (A) MHer
'Eskay Sugar Candy' (A) WFib
'Eskay Verglo' (A) WFib
Evening Glow = 'Bergpalais'PBR SSea
'Evka'PBR (I/v) SCoo
exstipulatum EWoo MHer SVen
'Fair Ellen' (Sc) LAll MHer WFib
'Fairlee' (DwI) WFib
'Fairy Lights' (Dw/St) LAll
'Fairy Orchid' (A) WFib
'Fallen Angel' (Z/St) LAll
'Fandango' (Z/St) LAll WFib
'Fanny Eden' (R) EWoo WFib
'Fantasia' white-flowered (Dw/d) ♀H1c WFib
'Fareham' (R) ♀H1c WFib
'Faye Brawner' (Z/St) LAll
'Feuerriese' (Z) LAll
'Fiat Queen' (Z/d) WFib
'Fieldings Unique' (U) EWoo SPet
'Fiery Sunrise' (R) WFib
'Fifth Avenue' (R) WFib
'Filicifolium' see *P. denticulatum* 'Filicifolium'
'Fir Trees Catkins' (A) MHer
'Fir Trees Echoes of Pink' (A) EWoo
'Fir Trees Ellie' **new** MPtG
'Fir Trees Fiesta' (R) MPtG
'Fir Trees Mark' (R/Dec/v) MPtG
'Fir Trees Muffin' (Sc) MPtG
'Fir Trees Pearl Anniversary' (Z/C) **new** WFib
'Fir Trees Silver Wedding' (Z/C/d) WFib
'Firebrand' (Z/d) LAll
'First Blush' (R) WFib
First Yellow = 'Pacyell'PBR WFib
'Fleur d'Amour' (R) WFib
'Fleurette' (Min/d) LAll
'Fleurisse' (Z) WFib
'Floria Moore' (Dec) EWoo
(Flower Fairy Series) Flower Fairy Berry = 'Sweberry'PBR (Z) SSea
- Flower Fairy Rose = 'Swero'PBR (Z) LSou
- Flower Fairy Velvet = 'Swevel'PBR (Z) SSea
- Flower Fairy White Splash = 'Swewhi'PBR (Z) LSou SSea
'Flowton' (Dw/d) LAll
Foxy = 'Pacfox'PBR (Z) LSou
fragrans ENfk LAll SPet
Fragrans Group (Sc) EWoo GPoy MCot MHer WFib WGwG
§ - 'Fragrans Variegatum' (Sc/v) ♀H1c SPet SPoG WFib
- 'Snowy Nutmeg' see *P.* (Fragrans Group) 'Fragrans Variegatum'
'Fraiche Beauté' (Z/d) WFib
'Francis Gibbon' (Z/d) WFib
'Francis Parrett' (Min/d) ♀H1c WFib
'Frank Headley' (Z/v) ♀H1c EShb LAll MCot NPer SCoo WFib WOld
§ 'Frau Emma Hössle' (Dw/d) LAll WFib
'Freak of Nature' (Z/v) LAll MHer WFib
'Frensham' (Sc) ENfk MHer WFib
'Freshwater' (St/C) WFib
'Friary Wood' (Z/C/d) WFib
'Friesdorf' (Dw/Fr) MCot MHer WBrk WFib
'Fringed Apple' (Sc) WFib
'Fringed Aztec' (R) ♀H1c CWCL MHer WFib
'Frosty' misapplied see *P.* 'Variegated Kleine Liebling'
'Frosty Petit Pierre' see *P.* 'Variegated Kleine Liebling'
'Frou Frou' LAll
frutetorum MHer
fruticosum EWoo WFib
fulgidum EWoo LAll MCot MHer WFib
'Gabriel' (A) EWoo
'Galilee' (I/d) LAll
Galleria Sunrise = 'Sunrise' (R) LAll
'Galway Star' (Sc/v) ♀H1c MHer WFib
'Ganther' (Dec) WFib
'Garland' (Dw/d) LAll
'Garland' (R) WFib
'Garnet Rosebud' (Min/d) LAll WFib
'Garnet Wings' (R) WFib
'Gartendirektor Herman' (Dec) ♀H1c ELan EWoo WFib

	'Gaudy' (Z)	WFib
	'Gemini' (Z/St/d) 🏆H1c	CWCL WFib
	'Gemma' (R)	LAll
	'Gemstone' (Sc) 🏆H1c	ENfk MHer SPet WFib
	'Genie' (Z/d)	LAll WFib
	'Gentle Georgia' (R)	WFib
	'Georgia' (R)	WFib
	'Georgia Peach' (R)	WFib
	'Georgina Blythe' (R) 🏆H1c	WFib
	'Gerald Wells' (Min)	LAll
	'Giant Butterfly' (R)	WFib
	gibbosum	CSpe EWoo MHer WFib
	'Glacis'PBR (Quality Series) (Z/d)	LSou SSea
	'Gladys Evelyn' (Z/d)	WFib
	'Gladys Weller' (Z/d) 🏆H1c	WFib
	glaucum	see *P. lanceolatum*
	'Gleam' (Z/d)	LAll
§	***glutinosum***	WFib
	'Goblin' (Min/d)	LAll
	Golden Angel	see *P.* 'Sarah Don'
	'Golden Brilliantissimum' (Z/v)	WFib
	'Golden Chalice' (Min/v)	WFib
	'Golden Clorinda' (U/Sc/C)	SEND SPet WFib
	'Golden Ears' (Dw/St/C) 🏆H1c	NPer WFib
	'Golden Edinburgh' (I/v)	WFib
	'Golden Harry Hieover' (Z/C)	LAll
	'Golden Lilac Gem' (I/d)	WFib
	'Golden Princess' (Min/C)	WFib
	'Golden Square' (Dw/St)	WFib
	'Golden Staphs' (Z/St/C)	LAll MHer
	'Golden Stardust' (Z/St)	LAll
	'Golden Tears' (MinI/C/d)	ECtt
	'Golden Well Sweep'	see *P. crispum* 'Golden Well Sweep'
	'Goldstone Copper' (Min/d)	LAll
	'Good Vibrations'	LAll
	'Gooseberry Leaf'	see *P. grossularioides*
	'Grace Thomas' (Sc) 🏆H1c	MHer WFib
	'Grace Wells' (Min)	WFib
	'Grand Slam' (R) 🏆H1c	WFib
	grandiflorum	EWoo MCot MHer WFib
	graveolens L'Hér.	see *P.* 'Graveolens'
	graveolens ambig.	SEND
	graveolens *sensu* J.J.A. van der Walt	SBch WFib
§	'Graveolens' (Sc)	ENfk GPoy LAll MHer SVen WBrk WFib
	'Graveolens Minor' (Sc)	EWoo
	'Great Blakenham' (Min)	LAll
	'Great Bricett' (Dw/d)	LAll
	'Great Glemham Lemon' (Sc)	EWoo
	'Green Eyes' (I/d)	MHer
	'Greetings' (Min/v)	LAll WFib
§	'Grenadier' (Z)	LAll
	'Grey Lady Plymouth' (Sc/v)	LCro MCot MHer WFib
	'Grey Sprite' (Min/v)	WFib
§	***grossularioides***	MHer
§	'Hannaford Star' (Z/St)	WFib
	'Hansen's Wild Spice' (Sc)	WFib
	'Happy Appleblossom' (Z/v/d)	LAll
	'Happy Thought' (Z/v) 🏆H1c	LAll MCot SCoo WFib
	'Harbour Lights' (R)	WFib
	'Harewood Slam' (R)	WFib
	'Harlequin Pretty Girl' (I × Z/d)	LAll WFib
	'Harlequin Rosie O'Day' (I)	WFib
	'Harvard' (I/d)	WFib
	'Hazel' (R)	WFib
	'Hazel Cherry' (R)	WFib
	'Hazel Glory' (R)	WFib
	'Hazel Gypsy' (R)	WFib
	'Hazel Peach' (R)	WFib
	'Hazel Star' (R)	WFib
§	'Hederinum Variegatum' (I/v)	ECtt WFib
	'Helen Bainbridge' (Z/C)	LAll
	'Helen Christine' (Z/St)	MHer WFib
	'Hemley' (Sc)	LAll
	'Henry Weller' (A) 🏆H1c	WFib
	'Hermanus Show' (Sc)	WFib
	'Hermione' (Z/d)	WFib
	'Highfields Always' (Z/d)	LAll
	'Highfields Appleblossom' (Z)	LAll
	'Highfields Attracta' (Z/d)	WFib
	'Highfields Ballerina' (Z/d)	LAll
	'Highfields Candy Floss' (Z/d)	LAll WFib
	'Highfields Charisma' (Z/d)	LAll
	'Highfields Choice' (Z) 🏆H1c	LAll WFib
	'Highfields Contessa' (Z/d)	LAll
	'Highfields Dazzler' (Z)	LAll
	'Highfields Delight' (Z)	WFib
	'Highfields Fancy' (Z/d)	LAll
	'Highfields Festival' (Z/d) 🏆H1c	LAll WFib
	'Highfields Flair' (Z/d)	LAll WFib
	'Highfields Melody' (Z/d)	WFib
	'Highfields Orange' (Z)	LAll
	'Highfields Pink' (Z)	LAll WFib
	'Highfields Pride' (Z)	LAll WFib
	'Highfields Prima Donna' (Z/d)	LAll
	'Highfields Salmon' (Z/d)	LAll
	'Highfields Serenade' (Z)	LAll
	'Highfields Snowdrift' (Z)	WFib
	'Highfields Sugar Candy' (Z/d)	LAll
	'Highfields Supreme' (Z)	LAll
	'Highfields Symphony' (Z)	LAll WFib
	'Highfields Vogue' (Z)	LAll WFib
	'Hilda's Memory' (Dw/Z/d) **new**	WFib
	'Hills of Snow' (Z/v)	LAll MHer WFib
	'Hindoo' (R × U) 🏆H1c	EWoo WFib
	'Hintlesham' (Min)	LAll
	hispidum	MHer
	'Hitcham' (Min/d)	WFib
	'Holbrook' (Dw/C/d)	WFib
	'Holt Beauty'	EWoo
	'Honeywood Lindy' (R)	WFib
	'Honeywood Suzanne' (Min/Fr)	LAll
	'Honneas' (Dw)	LAll
	Hot Spot Ria = 'Ria'PBR (Z)	LAll
	'Hula' (R × U)	EWoo WFib
	'Ian Read' (Min/d)	LAll
	'Ibiza' (Dw/C)	LAll
	'Ice Cap' (Min)	LAll
	'Icecrystal'PBR (Sweetheart Series) (Z/d)	SSea

	Name	Suppliers
	'Icing Sugar' (I/d)	WFib
	ignescens	EWoo WFib
	'Immaculatum' (Z)	WFib
	'Imperial Butterfly' (A/Sc) ♀H1c	ENfk SPet WFib
	incrassatum	MHer
	ionidiflorum	CSpe EShb MCot MHer MNHC
	'Irene' (Z/d)	WFib
	'Irene Toyon' (Z)	WFib
	'Islington Peppermint' (Sc)	SPet WFib
	'Ivalo' (Z/d)	WFib
	'Ivory Snow' (Z/d/v)	WFib
	'Jacey' (Z/d)	LAll
	'Jack of Hearts' (I × Z/d)	WFib
	'Jack Phillips' (Z/d) new	WFib
§	'Jackie' (I/d)	LAll WFib
	'Jackie Davies' (R)	EWoo
	'Jackie Gall'	see *P.* 'Jackie'
	'Jackie Totlis' (Z/St)	WFib
	'Jackpot Wild Rose' (Z/d)	WFib
	'Jacqui Caws' (Dw)	LAll
	'Jane Innes' (I/d) new	WFib
	'Janet Hofman' (Z/d)	WFib
	'Janet James'	LAll
	'Janet Kerrigan' (Min/d)	WFib
	'Jayne' (Min/d)	LAll
	'Jayne Eyre' (Min/d)	WFib
	'Jean Bart' (I)	LAll
§	'Jeanne d'Arc' (I/d)	WFib
	'Jer'Rey' (A)	EWoo WFib
	'Jessel's Unique' (U)	SPet
	'Jessica'	LAll
	'Jip's Bishops Wood' (Dw/d) new	WFib
	'Jip's Desert Poppy' (Z/Min)	WFib
	'Jip's Eleanor Renton' (Dw/d)	WFib
	'Jip's Freda Burgess' (Z/C/d)	LAll
	'Jip's Little Lady' (Dw) new	WFib
	'Jip's Pippin' (Dw) new	WFib
	'Jip's Proud Sentinel' (Dw/d)	WFib
	'Jip's Sky Gipsy' (Dw) new	WFib
	'Jip's Twilight' (Dw) new	WFib
	'Joan Fontaine' (Z)	WFib
	'Joan Morf' (R) ♀H1c	EWoo WFib
	'Joan of Arc'	see *P.* 'Jeanne d'Arc'
	'John Squires' (Z/C/d)	LAll
	'John's Angela'	LAll
	'Joy' (R) ♀H1c	CSpe WFib
	'Judith Thorp' (R)	LAll
	'Julie Smith' (R)	WFib
	'Juniper' (Sc)	WFib
	'Just Beth' (Z/C/d)	WFib
	'Just Jip' (Dw/Z) new	WFib
	'Just Joss' (Dw/d)	WFib
	'Just William' (Min/C/d)	WFib
	'Kamahl' (R)	WFib
	'Karen' (Dw/C)	LSou
	'Karl Hagele' (Z/d)	WFib
	'Karmin Ball'	WFib
	'Karrooense'	see *P. quercifolium*
	'Katie' (R)	EWoo
	'Katie Hillier' (R)	WFib
	'Kaufman's Bonfire' (R) new	WFib
	'Keepsake' (Min/d)	LAll WFib
	'Kenny's Double' (Z/d)	ECtt WFib
	'Kerensa' (Min/d)	WFib
	'Kesgrave' (Min/d)	WFib
	'Kewense' (Z)	EShb WFib
	'Key's Unique' (U)	WFib
	'King Edmund' (R) ♀H1c	WFib
	'King of Denmark' (Z/d)	LAll WFib
	'King Solomon' (R)	WFib
	'King's Ransom' (R)	WFib
§	'Kleine Liebling' (Min)	WFib
	'Kyra' (Min/d)	LAll
	'La France' (I/d) ♀H1c	LAll LCro WFib
	'La Paloma' (R)	WFib
§	'Lachskönigin' (I/d)	WFib
	'Lady Alice of Valencia'	see *P.* 'Grenadier'
	'Lady Ilchester' (Z/d)	WFib
	'Lady Love Song' (R)	WFib
	'Lady Mary' (Sc)	EWoo MHer WFib
	'Lady Mavis Pilkington' (Z/d)	WFib
	'Lady Plymouth' (Sc/v) ♀H1c	CSpe ELan ENfk EPfP EWoo GLog LAll MCot MHer NWad SEND SPet WFib WGwG
§	'Lady Scarborough' (Sc)	ENfk EWoo MHer WFib
	laevigatum	MHer
	'Lancastrian' (Z/d)	WFib
§	***lanceolatum***	MHer
	'Lara Ballerina' ♀H1c	SPet
	'Lara Beacon'	EWoo
	'Lara Candy Dancer' (Sc) ♀H1c	SPet WFib
	'Lara Jester' (Sc)	ENfk EWoo WFib
	'Lara Rajah' (R)	EWoo
	'Lara Starshine' (Sc) ♀H1c	ENfk EWoo MHer SPet WFib
	'Lara Waltz' (R/d)	WFib
	'Laurel Hayward' (R)	WFib
	'Lauren Alexandra' (Z/d)	WFib
	'Lavender Grand Slam' (R) ♀H1c	LAll
	'Lavender Lindy' (Sc)	EWoo WCot WFib
	'Lavender Sensation' (R)	WFib
	'Lawrenceanum'	LCro WFib
	laxum	WFib
	'L'Élégante' (I/v) ♀H1c	EWoo LAll MCot MHer WFib
	'Lemon Air' (Sc)	WFib
	'Lemon Crisp'	see *P. crispum*
	'Lemon Fancy' (Sc) ♀H1c	LAll MHer NWad SPet WFib
	'Lemon Kiss' (Sc)	CSpe EWoo WFib
	'Lemon Meringue' (Sc)	WFib
	'Leslie William Burrows'	EWoo
	'Letitia' (A)	ENfk
	Lila Compakt-Cascade	see *P.* 'Decora Lilas'
	Lilac Cascade	see *P.* 'Roi des Balcons Lilas'
	'Lilac Gem' (Min/I/d)	ENfk
	'Lilian Pottinger' (Sc) ♀H1c	ENfk EWoo MHer WFib
	'Lilian Woodberry' (Z)	WFib
	'Limoneum' (Sc)	ENfk MHer WFib
	'Lincolnshire Lady' (R)	ECtt
	'Lipstick' (St)	WFib
	'Lisa Jo' (St/v/Dw/d)	WFib
	'Little Alice' (Dw/d) ♀H1c	LAll WFib
	'Little Gem' (Sc)	ENfk MHer WFib
	'Little Jip' (Z/d/v) ♀H1c	LAll WFib
	'Little Spikey' (St/Min/d)	WFib
	'Lizzie Hillier' (R)	WFib
	longifolium	WBod
	'Lord Baden-Powell'	see *P.* 'Colonel Baden-Powell'
	'Lord Bute' (R) ♀H1c	CSpe ECtt EWoo LCro MCot MHer NPer SPet SVen WBod WFib WGwG
	'Lord de Ramsey'	see *P.* 'Tip Top Duet'
	'Lord Roberts' (Z)	WFib

'Lotusland' (Dw/St/C) ♀H1c	WFib
'Love Song' (R/v)	WFib
'Lucy Gunnett' (Z/d/v) ♀H1c	WFib
'Lyewood Bonanza' (R)	CWCL WFib
'Mabel Grey' (Sc) ♀H1c	CSpe ENfk EWoo LAll MHer MNHC NPer SPet WFib
§ 'Madame Auguste Nonin' (U/Sc)	ENfk LAll MHer SPet WFib
'Madame Crousse' (I/d) ♀H1c	EWoo WFib
'Madame Layal' (A) ♀H1c	MHer WFib
'Madame Margot'	see *P.* 'Hederinum Variegatum'
'Madame Salleron' (Min/v)	LAll LSou
'Magda' (Z/d)	LAll
magenteum	MHer
'Magnum' (R)	WFib
'Mandarin' (R)	LAll
'Mangles' Variegated' (Z/v)	WFib
'Maple Leaf' (Sc)	EWoo
'Maréchal MacMahon' (Z/C)	ENfk
'Margaret Soley' (R) ♀H1c	WFib
'Margaret Thorp'	LAll
'Margaret Waite' (R)	WFib
'Margery Stimpson' (Min/d)	WFib
'Marie Rudlin' (R)	LAll
'Marie Thomas' (Sc)	SBch
Marimba = 'Fisrimba' PBR	SCoo
'Marion Saunders' (Dec)	WFib
'Mariquita' (R)	WFib
'Mark' (Dw/d)	WFib
'Marmalade' (Min/d)	LAll
'Marquis of Bute' (R/v)	MHer SPet
'Martha Parmer' (Min)	LAll
'Martin Parrett' (Min/d)	WFib
'Mary Harrison' (Z/d)	WFib
'Maureen' (Min)	LAll
I 'Maureen' Hoddinott (Z/d)	MHer
'Mauve Beauty' (I/d)	WFib
'Maxime Kovalevski' (Z)	WFib
'Maxine Colley' (Z/d/v)	LAll
'May Day' (R)	WFib
'May Magic' (R)	WFib
'Meadowside Dark and Dainty' (St)	WFib
'Meadowside Fancy' (Z/d/C)	LAll
'Meadowside Mahogany' (Z/C)	LAll
'Meadowside Midnight' (St/C)	WFib
'Meadowside Orange' (Z/d)	LAll
'Medley' (Min/d)	WFib
Melosilver = 'Penber' (Tempo Series) (Z/d/v)	LAll
'Memento' (Min/d)	LAll WFib
'Mendip' (R)	WFib
'Mendip Candy Floss' (R)	WFib
'Mendip Royale' (R) **new**	WFib
'Meon Maid' (R)	WFib
'Mere Casino' (Z)	WFib
'Mexican Beauty' (I)	WFib
'Mexicana'	see *P.* 'Rouletta'
'Mexicanerin'	see *P.* 'Rouletta'
'Michael' (A) ♀H1c	MHer SPet
'Michelle West' (Min)	WFib
Millennium Dawn (Dw)	LAll
'Millfield Gem' (I/d)	WFib
'Millfield Rose' (I/d)	EWoo LAll
'Mini-Czech' (Min/St)	ECtt LAll WBrk
'Minnie' (Z/d/St)	WBrk
'Minstrel Boy' (R)	EWoo WFib
'Minx' (Min/d)	WFib
'Miriam Basey'	see *P.* 'Dwarf Miriam Baisey'
'Miss Burdett Coutts' (Z/v)	MHer WFib
'Miss McKinsey' (Z/St/d)	LAll
'Miss Muffett' (Min/d)	WFib
§ 'Miss Stapleton'	EWoo LCro MHer WFib
'Misterioso' (R)	EWoo WFib
'Misty Morning' (R)	EWoo WFib
'Mixed Blessings' (Min/C)	LAll
'Modesty' (Z/d)	WFib
'Mohawk' (R)	LAll WFib
'Mole'	see *P.* 'The Mole'
'Molly' (A)	ENfk
'Monsieur Ninon' misapplied	see *P.* 'Madame Auguste Nonin'
§ 'Monsieur Ninon' (U)	WFib
'Mont Blanc' (Z/v)	LAll WFib
'Montague Garabaldi Smith' (R)	WFib
'Moon Maiden' (A)	EWoo WFib
Moonlight Violino (Moonlight Series) (Z)	SSea
'Moor' (Min/d)	LAll
'More's Victory' (U/Sc)	WFib
Morning Sun = 'Pacmorsu' PBR (Green Leaf Series) (Z)	LAll
'Morval' (Dw/C/d) ♀H1c	LAll WFib
'Morwenna' (R)	LAll MHer WCot WFib
'Mosaic Gay Baby' (I/v/d)	WFib
'Mosaic Red' (Z)	LAll
'Mr Henry Cox' (Z/v) ♀H1c	LAll MHer WFib
'Mr Wren' (Z)	ELan LAll WFib
'Mrs Cannell' (Z)	WFib
'Mrs Farren' (Z/v)	MCot
'Mrs G.H. Smith' (A) ♀H1c	SPet WFib
'Mrs Kingsbury' (U)	WFib
'Mrs Martin' (I/d)	WFib
'Mrs McKenzie' (Z/St)	WFib
'Mrs Parker' (Z/d/v)	LAll WFib
'Mrs Pollock' (Z/v)	ELan LAll MCot NEgg SCoo WBrk WFib
'Mrs Quilter' (Z/C) ♀H1c	ECtt LAll WBrk WFib
'Mrs Salter Bevis' (Z/Ca/d)	LAll
'Mrs W.A.R. Clifton' (I/d)	WFib
multibracteatum	WFib
multiradiatum **new**	WFib
mutans	WFib
§ 'Mutzel' (I/v)	LAll
'My Chance' (Dec)	WFib
§ ***myrrhifolium*** var. ***coriandrifolium***	MHer WFib
'Mystery' (U) ♀H1c	LCro WFib
'Narina' (I)	SCoo
'Needham Market' (A)	ENfk SPet
'Neil Jameson' (Z/v)	LAll
'Nellie Nuttall' (Z)	WFib
Neona = 'Pacneon' PBR (Z)	SSea
'Nervous Mabel' (Sc) ♀H1c	MHer WFib
'Nettlestead' (Dw)	LAll
'New Gypsy' (R)	CWCL
'Newbridge' (St/Min/d)	LAll
'Newchurch' (Z/St) **new**	WFib
'Nicor Star' (Min)	WFib
'Night' (I)	EWoo
'Noel' (Z/Ca/d)	LAll
'Noele Gordon' (Z/d)	LAll WFib
'Occold Embers' (Dw/C)	LAll
'Occold Shield' (Dw/C/d) ♀H1c	LAll MHer NEgg WBrk WFib

'Occold Tangerine' (Z)	WFib
'Occold Volcano' (Dw/C/d)	WFib
odoratissimum	ENfk EWoo GPoy LAll MHer SPet
(Sc) 🏆H1c	WFib
'Odyssey' (Min)	WFib
'Old Spice' (Sc/v)	ENfk MCot WFib
'Oldbury Duet' (A/v) 🏆H1c	MHer SPet
'Olivia' (R)	WFib
'Opera House' (R)	WFib
'Orange Fizz' (Sc) 🏆H1c	CCht EWoo MHer SPet WFib
'Orange Imp' (Dw/d)	LAll
'Orange Parfait' (R)	WFib
'Orange Splash' (Z)	LAll
'Orangeade' (Dw/d)	LAll WFib
'Orangesonne' (Z/d)	LAll
'Orchid Clorinda' (Sc)	WFib
'Orchid Paloma' (Dw/d)	WFib
'Orion' (Min/d)	WFib
'Orsett' (Sc) 🏆H1c	GLog LAll
otaviense	WFib
'Our Flynn' (Z/St)	WFib
'Our Gynette' (Dec)	EWoo LAll
'Our Henry' (Dw/d) **new**	WFib
PAC cultivars	see under selling name
'Pagoda' (Z/St/d)	LAll MHer WFib
'Paisley Red' (Z/d)	WFib
'Pamela Vaughan' (Z/St)	WFib
'Pampered Lady' (A)	SPet
panduriforme	WFib
papilionaceum	ELan EWoo MCot MHer SSal WFib
'Parisienne' (R)	EWoo WFib
'Party Dress' (Z/d)	WFib
'Pat Hannam' (St)	WFib
'Paton's Unique'	ELan ENfk EWoo LAll MCot MHer
(U/Sc) 🏆H1c	SPet SVen WCot WFib
'Patricia Andrea' (T) 🏆H1c	LAll NPer WFib
patulum	WFib
'Paul Crampel' (Z)	EWoo MCot MHer WFib
'Paul West' (Min/d)	LAll SBch
'Pauline Harris' (R)	WFib
'Peace' (Min/C)	WFib
'Pegasus' (Min)	LAll
'Peggy Franklin' (Min)	LAll
'Peggy Sue' (R)	LAll
PELFI cultivars	see under selling name
peltatum	WFib
'Penny' (Z/d)	WFib
'Penny Lane' (Z)	WFib
'Pensby' (Dw)	WFib
'Penve'PBR (Quality Series)	SSea
(Z/d)	
'Peppermint Lace' (Sc)	EWoo
'Peppermint Scented Rose'	MSCN
(Sc)	
'Perfect' (Z)	WFib
'Pershore Princess'	WBrk
'Peter Beard' (Dw/d)	LAll
'Peter Godwin' (R)	WFib
'Peter's Choice' (R)	WFib
'Petit Pierre'	see *P.* 'Kleine Liebling'
'Petite Blanche' (Dw/d)	LAll
'Phyllis Richardson' (R/d)	LAll WFib
'Phyllis Variegated' (U/v)	ECtt ENfk EWoo LAll MHer SPet
	WCot WFib
'Pink Aurore' (U)	WFib
'Pink Bonanza' (R)	WFib
'Pink Capitatum'	see *P.* 'Pink Capricorn'
§ 'Pink Capricorn' (Sc)	ENfk EWoo LAll LCro NPri WFib
'Pink Champagne' (Sc)	MHer
'Pink Dolly Varden' (Z/v)	WFib

'Pink Fondant' (Min/d)	WFib
'Pink Gay Baby'	see *P.* 'Sugar Baby'
'Pink Happy Thought' (Z/v)	LAll WFib
'Pink Hindoo' (Dec)	EWoo
'Pink Needles' (Min/St)	WFib
'Pink Pandora' (T) **new**	WFib
'Pink Pet' (U)	ECtt
'Pink Rambler' (Z/d)	WFib
'Pink Rosebud' (Z/d)	WFib
'Playboy Blush' (Dw)	LAll
'Playmate' (Min/St)	WFib
'Plum Rambler' (Z/d)	ECtt EShb WBrk WFib
'Polka' (U) 🏆H1c	EWoo SPet WFib
Polka (Z/d)	LAll
'Pompeii' (R)	WFib
'Porchfield' (Min/St)	WBrk
praemorsum	WFib
Precision Bright Red	NPri
(Precision Series)	
'Preseli Lottie' (Z/d) **new**	WFib
'Preston Park' (Z/C)	WFib
'Pretty Polly' (Sc)	WFib
'Prim' (Dw/St/d)	WFib
'Prince of Orange'	ENfk EWoo GPoy MCot MHer NPri
(Sc) 🏆H1c	SIde SPet WFib
'Princeanum' (Sc) 🏆H1c	WFib
'Princess Abigail' (Dw/d)	WFib
'Princess Alexandra' (Z/d/v)	LAll
'Princess Josephine' (R)	WFib
'Princess of Balcon'	see *P.* 'Roi des Balcons Lilas'
'Princess of Wales' (R)	LAll WFib
'Princess Virginia' (R/v)	WFib
'Priory Salmon' (St/d)	EShb
'Priory Star' (St/Min/d)	WFib
pseudoglutinosum	WFib
'Pulsar Salmon Splash'	LRHS NRHS
(Pulsar Series) (Z) **new**	
'Purple Rogue' (R)	WFib
Purple Sybil	SSea
= 'Pacpursyb'PBR	
'Purple Unique' (U/Sc)	ENfk EWoo MCot MHer SPet SVen
	WFib
'Pygmalion' (Z/d/v)	WFib
'Quantock' (R)	WFib
'Quantock Angelique' (A)	SPet
'Quantock Butterfly' (A)	SPet
'Quantock Candy' (A) 🏆H1c	ELan EWoo SPet
'Quantock Clare' (A)	SPet
'Quantock Double	MPtG
Diamond' **new**	
'Quantock Kennedy' **new**	MPtG
'Quantock Kirsty' (A) 🏆H1c	EWoo SPet
'Quantock Marjorie'	SPet
(A) 🏆H1c	
'Quantock Matty' (A) 🏆H1c	MPtG
'Quantock Perfection' (A)	MPtG SPet WFib
'Quantock Sally' (A/d)	SPet
'Quantock Ultimate'	SPet
(A) 🏆H1c	
'Queen Esther' (Z/d/St)	LAll
'Queen of Denmark' (Z/d)	LAll WFib
'Queen of Hearts' (I × Z/d)	WFib
'Queen of the Lemons'	EWoo
quercifolium (Sc)	ECtt ELan GPoy WFib
quinquelobatum	WFib
radens (Sc)	ENfk WFib
'Radula' (Sc) 🏆H1c	ELan LAll MHer SPet WFib
'Radula Roseum' (Sc)	EWoo WFib
'Ragamuffin' (Dw/d)	LAll
'Rager's Star' (Dw)	LAll

(Rainbow Series) Rainbow Neon = 'Genraineon' (I) SSea
- Rainbow White = 'Genrawhite' (I) SSea
'Raspberry Sundae' (R) LAll
'Ray Bidwell' (Min) WFib
'Red Admiral' (Min/d/v) LAll
§ 'Red Black Vesuvius' (Min/C) MHer WFib
'Red Cascade' (I) ♀H1c LAll WFib
'Red Ice' (Min/d) LAll
'Red Pandora' (Z) ♀H1c LAll WFib
'Red Pimpernel' (Z/T) **new** WFib
'Red Pimpernella' LAll
'Red Rambler' (Z/d) LAll WBrk WFib
'Red Robin' (R) ENfk WCot
'Red Silver Cascade' see *P.* 'Mutzel'
'Red Spider' (Dw/Ca) WFib
'Red Startel' (Z/St/d) WFib
'Red Susan Pearce' (R) WFib
'Red Witch' (Dw/St/d) LAll MHer WBrk WFib
§ Red-Mini-Cascade = 'Rotemica' (I) LAll
'Redondo' (Dw/d) EWoo LAll
'Reflections' (Z/d) WFib
'Regina' (Z/d) LAll WFib
'Rembrandt' (R) LAll WFib
'Renate Parsley' ♀H1c LCro MHer WFib
reniforme GPoy MHer WFib
'Reunion Rose' (Sc) **new** WFib
'Richard Collins' (St) LAll
'Richard Gibbs' (Sc) ENfk MHer
'Richard Key' (Z/d/C) WFib
'Rietje van der Lee' (A) ENfk WFib
'Rigel' (Min/d) LAll
'Rimfire' (R) ♀H1c CWCL EWoo LAll LCro MHer NWad WFib
'Rio Grande' (I/d) LAll MHer WFib
'Rober's Lemon Rose' (Sc) ENfk MHer SEND SPet WBrk WFib
'Rober's Salmon Coral' (Dw/d) LAll
'Robert Fish' (Z/C) SCoo
'Robert McElwain' (Z/d) WFib
'Robin' (Sc) LAll
'Robin's Unique' (U) WFib
'Robyn Hannah' (St/d) MHer
'Rogue' (R) WFib
§ 'Roi des Balcons Impérial' (I) SSea
§ 'Roi des Balcons Lilas' (I) LAll SSea
'Roller's Echo' (A) WFib
'Roller's Pathfinder' (I/d/v) LAll
'Roller's Pioneer' (I/v) ENfk EWoo LAll
'Roller's Satinique' (U) MHer
'Rollison's Unique' (U) MHer WFib
'Romeo' (R) EWoo LAll
'Rosa della Sera' (St) LAll
'Rose Bengal' (A) ENfk
'Rose Eye' (Dw) **new** WFib
'Rose of Amsterdam' (Min/d) WFib
'Rose Paton's Unique' (U/Sc) LAll
'Rose Silver Cascade' (I) LAll MCot MHer
'Rosebud Supreme' (Z/d) WFib
'Rosina Read' (Dw/d) LAll
'Rosita' (Dw/d) LAll
'Rosmaroy' (R) WFib
'Rosy Dawn' (Min/d) LAll WFib
'Rote Mini-cascade' see *P.* Red-Mini-Cascade
§ 'Rouletta' (I/d) WFib
'Royal Ascot' (R) EWoo SPet
'Royal Norfolk' (Min/d) ♀H1c LAll
'Royal Oak' (Sc) ♀H1c ENfk LAll MCot MHer MNHC NWad SPet SPoG SVen WFib
§ 'Royal Purple' (Z/d) WFib
(Royal Series) Royal Candy Cane = 'Klep01028' (I) SSea
- Royal Lavender = 'Klepp07196'PBR (I) SSea
- Royal Magenta = 'Klepp10206' (I) SSea
- Royal Red = 'Kleroder'PBR (I) SSea
'Royal Sovereign' (R) **new** WFib
'Royal Surprise' (R) ♀H1c EWoo
'Ruben' (d) LSou
'Ruby' (Min/d) WFib
'Ruffled Velvet' (R) EWoo
'Rushmere' (Dw/d) WFib
'Rushmoor Golden Rosebud' (Z) WFib
'Rushmoor Mrs Eve Scott' (Z/d) WFib
Sailing = 'Klesail' SSea
'Saint Elmo's Fire' (St/Min/d) MHer WFib
'Salmon Beauty' (Dw/d) WFib
§ 'Salmon Irene' (Z/d) WFib
Salmon Princess = 'Pacsalpri'PBR LSou
'Salmon Queen' see *P.* 'Lachskönigin'
Salmon Queen = 'Pacsalque'PBR (Z) SSea
'Salmon Slam' (R) LAll
salmoneum WFib
'Samantha' (R) WFib
'Samantha Stamp' (Dw/C/d) WFib
Samelia = 'Pensam'PBR (Dark Line Series) (Z/d) SSea
'Sammi Brougham' (Dw/Z) WFib
'Sancho Panza' (Dec) CSpe WFib
'Sandra Lorraine' (I/d) WFib
Sangria Nova = 'Gendana'PBR (Z) SSea
'Sanguineum' CSpe
'Santa Maria' (Z/d) LAll
§ 'Sarah Don' (A/v) ECtt WFib
'Sarah Jane' (Sc) WFib
'Sassa'PBR (Quality Series) (Z/d) SSea
'Saxifragoides' WFib
'Scarlet Gem' (Z/St) WBrk WFib
'Scarlet Pet' (U) ♀H1c ENfk SPet
'Scarlet Rambler' (Z/d) EShb WFib
'Scarlet Unique' (U) EWoo MCot WFib
schizopetalum MHer WFib
'Schottii' ♀H1c CTre EWoo LCro MHer WFib
'Scottow Star' (Z/C) WFib
'Seaview Silver' (Min/St) WFib
'Seaview Sparkler' (Z/St) WFib
'Seeley's Pansy' (A) EWoo MHer
'Sefton' (R) ♀H1c WFib
'Shannon' EWoo WFib
'Shaun Jacobs' (Min/d) LAll
'Shimmer' (Z/d) LAll
§ 'Shottesham Pet' (Sc) ECtt ENfk EWoo MHer NWad SPet
sidoides ♀H1c CSpe CTre EAJP EWoo GPoy LAll LCro LHop MCot MHer SBch SChr

	SDix SMHy SPhx SPlb SVen WBod WFib WHer WKif
- black-flowered	CTca SBrt
- 'Sloe Gin Fizz'	CSpe
'Sil Falko'PBR (I)	LSou
'Sil Linus'PBR (Z)	LSou
'Sil Malaika'PBR (I)	LSou
'Sil Pia'PBR (I)	LSou
'Sil Tomke'PBR (I)	LSou
'Silky'	LAll
'Silver Blazon' (Z/Dw/C/v)	WFib
'Silver Delight' (v/d)	WFib
'Silver Kewense' (Dw/v)	WFib
'Silver Snow' (Min/St/d)	WFib
'Silver Wings' (Z/v)	LAll
'Simplicity' (Z)	LAll
'Skelly's Pride' (Z)	LAll WFib
'Skies of Italy' (Z/C/d)	WFib
'Snow Flurry' (Sc)	WFib
'Snowbaby' (Min/d)	WFib
'Snowdrift' (I/d)	LAll WFib
'Snowflake' (Min)	see *P.* 'Atomic Snowflake'
'Snowstorm' (Z)	WFib
'Sofie'	see *P.* 'Decora Rose'
'Solferino' (A)	ENfk
Solo = 'Guillio' (Z/I)	LAll
'Something Else' (Z/St/d)	LAll
'Something Special' (Z/d) ♀H1c	LAll WFib
Sophie Casade	see *P.* 'Decora Rose'
'Sophie Dumaresque' (Z/v) ♀H1c	WFib
'Sophie Emma' (Z)	WFib
'Sophie Marion' (Dw/Z)	WFib
'South American Bronze' (R) ♀H1c	WFib
'South American Delight' (R)	LAll
'Southern Peach' (Min/d)	LAll
'Southern Rosina' (Dw)	WFib
'Souvenir de Prue'	EWoo
'Spanish Angel' (A) ♀H1c	CWCL MHer SPet WFib
'Sparkler' (Z)	LAll
'Spellbound' (R)	WFib
'Spital Dam' (Dw/d)	LAll WFib
'Spitfire' (Z/Ca/d/v)	LAll WFib
§ 'Splendide' ♀H1c	CSpe CTre MHer SWvt WFib
'Spot-on-bonanza' (R) ♀H1c	WFib
'Springfield Black' (R)	LAll MCot
'Springtime' (Z/d)	WFib
'Stadt Bern' (Z/C)	LAll
× ***stapletoniae***	see *P.* 'Miss Stapleton'
'Star Flecks' (St) ♀H1c	LAll
'Startel Salmon' (Z/St)	MHer
'Stella Vernante'	LAll
'Stellar Arctic Star'	see *P.* 'Arctic Star'
'Stellar Hannaford Star'	see *P.* 'Hannaford Star'
'Stenbury' (Dw/d)	LAll
'Stewart Meehan' (R)	WFib
'Stolen Kisses' (Min/D)	LAll
'Strawberry Fayre' (Dw/St)	WFib
'Stringer's Souvenir' (Dw/d/v)	LAll
§ 'Sugar Baby' (DwI)	LAll MHer WFib
'Summer Cloud' (Z/d)	WFib
'Summertime' (Z/d)	see *P.* 'Deacon Summertime'
'Sun Rocket' (Dw/d)	WFib
'Sundridge Moonlight' (Z/C)	WFib
'Sundridge Surprise' (Z)	WFib
Sunflair Rose = 'Genrose' (Sunflair Series) (I/d)	LAll
'Sunraysia' (Z/St)	WFib
'Sunset Snow' (R)	LAll WFib
'Sunspot Petit Pierre' (Min/v)	WFib
'Sunstar' (Min/d)	WFib
'Supernova' (Z/St/d)	WFib
'Surcouf' (I)	WFib
(Survivor Series) Survivor Scarlet (Z)	LBMP
- Survivor White (Z)	LBMP
'Susan Hillier' (R)	WFib
'Susan Payne' (Dw/d)	LAll MHer
'Susan Pearce' (R)	LAll
'Susie' (Z/C) **new**	WFib
'Susie 'Q'' (Z/C)	LAll
'Sussex Gem' (Min/d)	LAll WFib
'Swainham Mellow Yellow' (Z)	LAll
'Swanland Lace' (I/d/v)	WFib
'Swedish Angel' (A)	WFib
'Sweet Mimosa' (Sc) ♀H1c	ELan ENfk EWoo LAll MCot MHer SBch SPet WFib WGwG
'Sweet Sixteen' (R)	WFib
'Sweet Sue' (Min)	LAll
'Swiss Star' (Z/St)	LAll
'Sybil Holmes' (I/d)	WFib
'Tamie' (Dw/d)	LAll
'Tammy' (Dw/d)	LAll WFib
'Tangerine' (Min/Ca/d)	LAll
'Tara Caws' (Z)	WFib
tetragonum	EWoo MHer WFib
'The Boar' (Fr) ♀H1c	EShb EWoo MCot WFib
'The Culm' (A)	WFib
'The Czar'	see *P.* 'Czar'
'The Joker' (I/d)	WFib
'The Kenn-Lad' (A)	EWoo
'The Marchioness of Bute' (R)	LAll MHer SPet WFib
§ 'The Mole' (A)	WFib
'The Tamar' (A)	EWoo MHer
'The Yar' (Z/St)	WFib
'Thomas Earle' (Z)	WFib
'Timothy Clifford' (Min/d)	LAll
'Tinker West' (Z/St/Dw)	WFib
§ 'Tip Top Duet' (A) ♀H1c	EWoo MHer WFib
'Tirley Garth' (A)	WFib
tomentosum (Sc) ♀H1c	CSpe CTre ENfk EWoo GLog GPoy LAll LCro MCot MHer NWad SPet SSal WFib WHea
- 'Chocolate'	see *P.* 'Chocolate Peppermint'
Tommy = 'Pactommy' (I)	SSea
tongaense	WFib
'Topscore' (Z/d)	WFib
'Tornado' (R) ♀H1c	LCro WFib
'Torrento' (Sc)	MHer SPet WFib
'Tortoiseshell' (R)	WFib
'Toscana Okka' (Toscana Series) (I)	LSou
'Tracy' (Min/d)	LAll
transvaalense	CTre
Trend Dark Red = 'Gentreak'PBR (Z)	LAll
tricolor misapplied	see *P.* 'Splendide'
tricolor Curt.	CTre
tricuspidatum	EWoo WCot WFib
trifidum	EWoo WFib
'Triomphe de Nancy' (Z/d)	WFib
triste	EWoo MHer WFib

'Trudie' (Dw/Fr) LAll MHer WFib
'Turkish Coffee' (R) WFib
'Turkish Delight' (Dw/C) WFib
'Turtle's Surprise' (Z/d/v) WBrk
'Turtle's White' (R) LAll
'Two Dees' (Dw/d) LAll WFib
'Tyabb Princess' (R) EWoo
'Uncle Ernie' (Z/C) LAll
'Unique Aurore' (U) MHer
'Unique Mons Ninon' see *P.* 'Monsieur Ninon'
'Urchin' (Min/St) WFib
'Ursula Key' (Z/c) WFib
'Ursula's Choice' (A) WFib
'Val Merrick' (Dw/St) WFib
'Valentine' (Z/C) WFib
'Vancouver Centennial' (Dw/St/C) 🏆H1c LAll MCot MHer NEgg SCoo SSea WFib
'Vandersea' (Sc) EWoo MCot
'Variegated Attar of Roses' (Sc/v) NWad
'Variegated Clorinda' (Sc/v) WFib
'Variegated Fragrans' see *P.* (Fragrans Group) 'Fragrans Variegatum'
§ 'Variegated Kleine Liebling' (Min/v) WFib
'Variegated Petit Pierre' (Min/v) MHer WFib
'Vectis Blaze' (I) EWoo
'Vectis Cascade' (I) EWoo
'Vectis Glitter' (Z/St) 🏆H1c LAll WBrk WFib
'Vectis Imp' (Min/Z) LAll
'Vectis Pink' (Dw/St) WFib
'Vectis Purple' (Z/d) WFib
'Vectis Spider' (Dw/St) LAll
'Vectis Starbright' (Dw/St) LAll WFib
'Vectis Volcano' (Z/St) WFib
'Venus' (Min/d) LAll
'Vicki' (R) EWoo
'Vicki Town' (R) WFib
'Vicky Claire' (R) EWoo WFib
Vicky = 'Pacvicky'PBR (I) SSea
Victor = 'Pacvi' (Quality Series) (Z/d) LSou
'Village Hill Oak' (Sc) LAll
Ville de Dresden = 'Pendresd'PBR (I) EWoo
'Vina' (Dw/C/d) WFib
violareum misapplied see *P.* 'Splendide'
'Viscossisimum' (Sc) MHer
viscosum see *P. glutinosum*
'Vivat Regina' (Z/d) WFib
'Voodoo' (U) 🏆H1c CSpe ECtt EWoo MCot MHer SPet WCot WFib
'Wallis Friesdorf' (Dw/C/d) WFib
'Wantirna' (Z/v) 🏆H1c LAll
'Warrenorth Coral' (Z/C/d) WFib
'Waveney' (Min) LAll
'Wedding Royale' (Dw/d) LAll WFib
'Welling' (Sc) ENfk MHer SPet WFib
'Wendy Jane' (Dw/d) WFib
'Wendy Read' (Dw/d) LAll WFib
'Westdale Appleblossom' (Z/C/d) LAll WFib
'Westside' (Z/d) MHer WFib
'Westwood' (Z/St) WFib
'Whisper' (R) EWoo WFib
'White Bird's Egg' (Z) WFib
'White Boar' (Fr) CSpe EShb EWoo WFib
'White Bonanza' (R) WFib
'White Butterfly' (Z/C) LAll
'White Chiffon' (R) LAll
'White Eggshell' (Min) WFib
'White Feather' (Z/St) MHer
'White Unique' (U) SBch SPet WFib
'Wild Spice' (Sc) LAll
'Wilhelm Kolle' (Z) WFib
'Wilhelm Langath' (Z/v) EShb SCoo WBrk
'Willa' (Dec) WFib
'Winford Festival' LAll
'Winnie Read' (Dw/d) LAll
'Wirral Moonlight' (Z/C/d) **new** WFib
'Wolverton' (Z) WFib
'Wootton's Unique' (U) EWoo
'Wychwood' (A/Sc) EWoo
'Yale' (I/d) 🏆H1c WFib
'Yan le Grounch' (Z/C) WFib
'Yhu' (R) WFib
'York Florist' (Z/d/v) LAll
'Yvonne' (Z) WFib
'Zena' (Dw) LAll
'Zinc' (Z/d) WFib
zonale WFib
'Zulu King' (R) WFib
'Zulu Warrior' (R) WFib

Peliosanthes (*Asparagaceae*)

arisanensis B&SWJ 3639 WCru
caesia B&SWJ 5183 WCru
teta subsp. ***humilis*** RWJ 10044 WCru

Pellaea (*Pteridaceae*)

atropurpurea NLos
falcata EShb ISha NLos
ovata SPlb
paradoxa 'Glowstar' ISha
rotundifolia 🏆H1b CLAP ISha LCro LLWG LRHS NLos WBor WCot

Peltandra (*Araceae*)

undulata see *P. virginica* (L.) Schott
§ ***virginica*** (L.) Schott EWay NPer SWat
- 'Snow Splash' (v) EWay

Peltaria (*Brassicaceae*)

alliacea CSpe LEdu WCot
* ***dumulosa*** WCot

Peltiphyllum see *Darmera*

Peltoboykinia (*Saxifragaceae*)

§ ***tellimoides*** CElw CLAP EBee GCal GKev NBir WMoo WPnP
watanabei CLAP CSpe CWld EBee ESwi GEdr GPSL IMou LEdu MAvo MMrt MSCN NLar SPad WCru WMoo WPnP

Pennellianthus see *Penstemon*

Pennisetum ✿ (*Poaceae*)

× ***advena*** 'Chelsea' **new** SHDw
- 'Fireworks'PBR (v) EBee EPfP LPar LRHS MAsh NRHS SCob SWvt
- 'Knightsbridge' **new** SHDw
- 'Leopard' **new** SHDw
- 'Mayfair' **new** SHDw
§ - 'Rubrum' 🏆H2 CBcs CKno CMea EShb LRHS MAsh NWsh SCoo SHDw SMad SRot SWvt

§ ***alopecuroides***	CBcs CBod CRos CWCL EAEE ECha EHoe EPed EPfP GMcL LRHS LSou MJak MSpe NGdn NRHS SCob SLim SPer SPlb SWat SWvt WBod WHar XLum XSen
– B&SWJ 11434	WCru
– Autumn Wizard	see *P. alopecuroides* 'Herbstzauber'
– 'Black Beauty'	CSpe MAvo SMHy SSut WHoo
– 'Cassian's Choice'	CKno EHoe EWes IBoy ILea NCGa SHar SSal
– 'Caudatum'	CKno
– 'Dark Desire'	CKno LRHS NRHS
– 'Foxtrot'	EPPr
– 'Gelbstiel'	CKno LRHS NRHS
– 'Goldstrich'	XSen
– 'Hameln'	Widely available
§ – 'Herbstzauber'	CBod CKno EHoe LHop NLar XLum
– 'Little Bunny'	CBod CKno CMea EBee EHoe ELan ELon EPfP EShb ESps EUJe GCal GMcL IVic LRHS LSRN NDov NGdn NRHS SCob SMea SWvt XSen
– 'Little Honey' (v)	CKno NLar XLum XSen
– 'Magic'	CBod EBee ELon
– 'Moudry'	CBod CKno EBee EHoe ELon EPed EPfP EUJe LHop LRHS MAvo NLar NSti SHDw XLum
– 'National Arboretum'	EBee
– 'Piglet'^{PBR} **new**	EBee
– 'Red Head'	CAbP CBWd CKno CMea EBee ELon EPfP EUJe EWes LRHS LSou LSun MAvo NRHS NSti WCot
– f. ***viridescens***	CKno ELan EPPr EShb EUJe LEdu LRHS NDov NRHS SCob SMad SPhx WPtf XLum
– 'Weserbergland'	CKno EBee EHoe ELon
– 'Woodside'	CKno EHoe EPed ESps LEdu SMad XLum
caffrum	WCot
clandestinum	EShb
compressum	see *P. alopecuroides*
'Fairy Tails'	CBWd CKno CRos EPPr EPfP LPla LRHS MAsh NDov NRHS SMHy SPoG
flaccidum	EPPr
glaucum 'Purple Baron'	MAsh
– 'Purple Majesty'	CSpe SWvt
incomptum	EHoe XLum
longistylum misapplied	see *P. villosum*
macrourum	CBWd CBod CCVN CKno CSam CSpe ECha EHoe ELon LEdu LHop LRHS MArt MAvo MNrw MSpe NDov NRHS NWsh SEND SMHy SMad SPtp WPGP
– 'Short Stuff'	CKno
massaicum 'Red Bunny Tails'	CChe LRHS
– 'Red Buttons'	see *P. thunbergii* 'Red Buttons'
orientale 🏆^{H5}	CAby CKno CSpe ECha EHoe EPfP ESps EWoo LHop LRHS LSun MRav NBir NRHS NWsh SEND SPer SPtp SRkn SWvt WBod WCot WHoo WKif XLum
– 'Karley Rose'^{PBR}	CKno CPar CSpe EHoe EPed EWes EWoo IBoy IPot LEdu LHop LRHS MAvo NDov NRHS SCob SHil SMad SWvt
I – 'Robustum'	EBee EPPr MAvo WPGP
– 'Shogun'	CKno CRos CSam EPPr EPfP LRHS NRHS SMHy
– 'Tall Tails'	CBod EHoe EPPr EWes EWoo LRHS NDov NRHS SMea XLum
'Paul's Giant'	CKno XLum
rueppellii	see *P. setaceum*
§ ***setaceum*** 🏆^{H6}	EPfP LCro LPar NWsh SHDw SWvt WCot
– 'Rubrum'	see *P.* × *advena* 'Rubrum'
– 'Sky Rocket'^{PBR} (v)	LPre LRHS NRHS
– 'Summer Samba'	EBee LRHS NRHS
thunbergii	CAby CBod GKev LRHS NRHS
§ – 'Red Buttons'	CBWd CKno CRos EBee EHoe ELon EPfP EShb LCro LEdu LRHS MAsh MAvo MGos NRHS SHDw SMHy SMea SPhx SPoG SSut WHea WHoo
Vertigo = 'Tift-8'	CBod EBee NCou
§ ***villosum*** 🏆^{H3}	CAby CBod CCVN CKno CMac CSpe EAJP ECha EHoe ELan EPPr EPfP EShb EUJe LEdu LHop LOPS LRHS LSRN NRHS SEND SHil SMad SMea SPer SPhx XLum XSen
– 'Cream Falls'	CBod

pennyroyal see *Mentha pulegium*

Penstemon ✿ (*Plantaginaceae*)

'Abbotsmerry'	CWCL ECtt EPfP LLHF MBNS MCot NLar SLon
albertinus	see *P. humilis*
§ 'Alice Hindley' 🏆^{H4}	CBar CBcs CNec CSpe CTri CWCL EAJP ELan EPfP LHop LLWP LRHS LSRN MCot MRav MWat NBir SBod SCob SLon SPoG SRGP SRms SWvt WAvo WCFE WCot WHoo WKif XLum
alpinus	EDAr GWyn
'Amy Gray'	WAvo
§ 'Andenken an Friedrich Hahn' 🏆^{H5}	Widely available
'Apple Blossom' misapplied	see *P.* 'Thorn'
'Apple Blossom' 🏆^{H3}	Widely available
'Arabesque Appleblossom' **new**	LRHS NRHS
'Arabesque Pink' **new**	LRHS NRHS
'Arabesque Red' **new**	LRHS NRHS
'Arabesque Violet' **new**	LRHS NRHS
aridus	GEdr
arizonicus	see *P. whippleanus*
'Ashton'	WAvo
attenuatus subsp. ***militaris***	SPlb
'Audrey Cooper'	CChe CMac MBNS
'Axe Valley Penny Mitchell'	ECtt
'Axe Valley Suzie'	CAby
azureus	GKev
'Barbara Barker'	see *P.* 'Beech Park'
§ ***barbatus***	CFis SPer SRms SSut WTcb
– 'Coccineus'	CAby CSpe EAJP GBin MBNS XLum
– 'Iron Maiden'	LRHS
– 'Jingle Bells'	IFro
– orange-flowered	SPlb
– 'Peter Catt'	CMea
– Pinacolada Series	LRHS NRHS
– – 'Pinacolada Blue'	LRHS NRHS
– – 'Pinacolada Dark Rose'	LRHS NRHS
– – 'Pinacolada Rosy Red'	LRHS NRHS
– – 'Pinacolada White'	LRHS NRHS
– var. ***praecox***	MBNS SRot
– – f. ***nanus*** 'Rondo'	EAJP LRHS
'Beckford'	CWCL LLHF MBNS

§	'Beech Park' ♀H3	ELan EPfP EWes LRHS
	'Bisham Seedling'	see *P.* 'White Bedder'
	'Blackbird'	Widely available
	'Blue Riding Hood'PBR (Riding Hood Series)	LCro LRHS NRHS SPoG
	'Blue Spring' misapplied	see *P. heterophyllus* 'Blue Spring'
	'Blueberry Fudge' (Ice Cream Series)	LSou LSun
	'Blueberry Taffy'PBR	ECtt NCGa
	'Bodnant'	LLHF MBNS WAvo WBod WHoo WHrl
	bradburii	see *P. grandiflorus*
	'Bredon'	MBNS WAvo
	'Bubblegum' (Ice Cream Series)	CAby LSun
	'Burford Purple'	see *P.* 'Burgundy'
	'Burford Seedling'	see *P.* 'Burgundy'
	'Burford White'	see *P.* 'White Bedder'
§	'Burgundy'	CBod CMac CWCL ECtt ESps GMaP LLWP LRHS NBir NPer SPer SRms WAvo XLum
	californicus	SBrt
§	***campanulatus***	EPot EWes LRHS NRHS SRms
	- PC&H 148	SDys
	- ***pulchellus***	see *P. campanulatus*
	- 'Roseus' misapplied	see *P. kunthii*
	'Candy Pink'	see *P.* 'Old Candy Pink'
	cardwellii	EWes
	'Castle Forbes'	GMaP MBNS SRms
	'Cathedral Rose'	ELan EPfP LRHS
	'Catherine de la Mare'	see *P. heterophyllus* 'Catherine de la Mare'
	'Centra'	MBNS
	centranthifolius	EBee SIgm
	'Charles Rudd'	CWCL ECtt ELan ELon EPfP LSRN MBNS NLar SRms SWvt WHrl
§	'Cherry' ♀H3	ECtt ESps MBNS SHar WHea
	'Cherry Ripe' misapplied	see *P.* 'Cherry'
§	'Chester Scarlet' ♀H3	ECtt MBNS SDix WCFE WKif
	'Choirboy'	EWes
	clutei	LLHF
	cobaea	CSpe GLog SBrt
	'Comberton'	MBNS WAvo
	confertus	CTri EBee ECho EPot SBrt
	- RCB/MO A-7	WCot
	'Connie's Pink' ♀H4	MBNS SRms WAvo
	'Coral Sea'	WFar
	'Cottage Garden Red'	see *P.* 'Windsor Red'
§	'Countess of Dalkeith'	ECtt ELan GBin LLWP MCot MRav SHar SRms SWvt WAvo WCFE
	crandallii	EPot
	cristatus	see *P. eriantherus*
*	***cyananthus*** var. ***utahensis***	WCot
	aff. ***cyananthus***	SBrt
	cyaneus	GKev
	'Dark Towers'PBR	CAbb CMos CSpe ECtt EPfP EUJe IPot LRHS MNrw MSCN NHpl NRHS SLon SPad SPoG WCot WHil WHlf
	davidsonii	ECho EWes GCrg GEdr NSla SIgm WOld
	- var. ***davidsonii***	WAbe
	- var. ***menziesii***	EPot GCrg GEdr LLHF NHar NWad
	'Microphyllus'	WAbe
	- var. ***praeteritus***	GEdr
	- 'Silverwells'	GEdr
	'Dazzler'	SWvt
	'Delfts Blue Riding Hood'PBR (Riding Hood Series)	CSpe EBee LCro LRHS
	'Devonshire Cream'	CWCL MBNS
	diffusus	see *P. serrulatus*
	digitalis	MBNS NFav
§	- 'Husker Red'	Widely available
	- 'Isa' **new**	WCot
	- 'Mystica'	EBee LRHS NRHS
	- 'Purpureus'	see *P. digitalis* 'Husker Red'
	- 'Ruby Tuesday'	EWes
	- white-flowered	EBee
	discolor pale lavender-flowered	NBir
§	'Drinkstone Red'	EHrv MBNS SDix SDys
	'Drinkwater Red'	see *P.* 'Drinkstone Red'
	eatonii	GKev
	(Elgar Series) 'Elgar Crown of India'	WCot
	- 'Elgar Enigma'	WCot
	- 'Elgar Firefly'	NCGa WCot
	- 'Elgar Light of Life'	WCot
	- 'Elgar Nimrod'	WCot
	'Ellenbank Amethyst'	SDys
	'Ellwood Red Phoenix'	MBNS
	'Elmley'	MBNS WAvo
§	***eriantherus***	LLHF SPlb
	- var. ***redactus***	CPBP
	Etna = 'Yatna' (Volcano Series)	CRos ECtt EPfP EUJe GMcL LAll LRHS MBNS SRms
	euglaucus	EBee GKev LLHF MMuc
	- NNS 07-397	GKev
§	'Evelyn' ♀H4	CLet CTri ECha ELan EPfP ESps IBoy LRHS LSRN MBNS MCot MHer MRav SPer SPoG SRGP SRms SWvt WAvo WBod WKif XLum
	'Fanny's Blush'	SWvt
	'Firebird'	see *P.* 'Schoenholzeri'
	'Flame'	MBNS WAvo
	'Flamingo'	CWCL ELon EPfP EWes GBin LRHS MBNS NLar SGbt SRms SWvt
§	***fruticosus***	MAsh MMuc
	var. ***scouleri*** ♀H5	
	- - 'Albus' ♀H5	CSpe WAbe
	- - 'Amethyst'	SRms WAbe
	- var. ***serratus*** 'Holly'	SIgm
	Fujiyama = 'Yayama'PBR	CBod CWGN ECtt EPfP LAll LHop LRHS SLon SPad SRms SWvt
	'Garden Red'	see *P.* 'Windsor Red'
	'Garnet'	see *P.* 'Andenken an Friedrich Hahn'
	gentianoides B&SWJ 10271	WCru
	'Geoff Hamilton'	CWCL ECtt LSRN MBNS NLar SLon SPoG WAvo
	'George Elrick'	LLHF WHoo
§	'George Home' ♀H3	EWes GBin MBNS SRms
	'George Moon'	SPad
	'Gilchrist'	ECtt SLon
	glaber	EWld LHop LLWP SPlb WKif
	- 'Roundway Snowflake'	SHar SPhx
	globosus	SBrt
	'Gloire des Quatre Rues'	XLum
§	***grandiflorus***	EPfP
	- 'Prairie Snow'	EBee
	'Grape Taffy'PBR **new**	LBMP
	hallii	EPot EWes SBrt
	hartwegii 'Albus'	LHop SHar SIgm SRms
	- 'Picotee Red'	CWCL LRHS
§	***heterophyllus***	LRHS MNrw MSCN NBir NGBl SRkn SRms WHea
	- 'Blue Gem'	CElw CTri
§	- 'Blue Spring'	CSpe EPfP LRHS MRav NRHS SPoG WBod

§	- 'Catherine de la Mare' $\mathbb{Y}^{H4}$	EBee ELan EWoo GBin LHop LRHS LSRN MWat NBir SBod SCob SHar SPer SWvt WKif XLum
	- 'Electric Blue'	CKno MHol SLon
	- 'Heavenly Blue'	Widely available
	- 'Jeanette'	CMea WHoo WTor
	- 'Margarita Bop'	EBee
	- 'True Blue'	see *P. heterophyllus*
	- 'Züriblau'	EBee SPlb
§	'Hewell Pink Bedder' $\mathbb{Y}^{H4}$	CBod EPfP EWoo GBin GBuc GPSL LPot LRHS MBNS MRav NCGa NCou NRHS SPtp SRms SWvt
	'Hewitt's Pink'	SLon
	hidalgensis	WCot
	'Hidcote Pink' $\mathbb{Y}^{H3}$	Widely available
	'Hidcote Purple'	SHar WHoo XLum
	'Hidcote White'	LPot MHer SWvt
	'Hillview Pink'	SLon XLum
§	***hirsutus***	EBee XLum
	- 'Blue Foam' **new**	GWyn
	- var. ***pygmaeus***	CMea CPBP ECho EDAr MHer NHpl NRya SBrt SHil SPlb WHoo
*	- - f. ***albus***	EBee ECho WHoo
	- - 'Purpureus'	WAbe
	'Hopleys Variegated' (v)	SWvt
	'Hot Pink Riding Hood'^{PBR} (Riding Hood Series)	EBee LCro LRHS NRHS SPoG
§	***humilis***	SBrt
	'James Bowden'	MBNS
	'John Booth'	MBNS
	'John Nash' misapplied	see *P.* 'Alice Hindley'
	'John Nash'	SRms
	'John Spedan Lewis'	SLon
	'Juicy Grape' (Ice Cream Series)	LAll LSun
	'June'	see *P.* 'Pennington Gem'
	'Jupiter' **new**	XLum
	'Kate Gilchrist'	SLon
	Kilimanjaro = 'Yajaro' (Volcano Series)	EPfP LRHS SLon SRms WFar
	'King George V'	Widely available
	'Knight's Purple'	ECtt
§	***kunthii***	MAsh
§	***laetus*** subsp. ***roezlii***	ECho EPot GCrg
	'Lavender Riding Hood' (Riding Hood Series)	LRHS NRHS
§	'Le Phare'	XLum
	'Lilac and Burgundy'	MBNS SRms SWvt
	'Lilac Frost'	LLHF MMuc SRGP WMoo
	'Lilliput'	ENor GBin
	linarioides	SBrt
	- 'Marilyn Ross'	ECtt
	'Lord Home'	see *P.* 'George Home'
	'Lucinda Gilchrist'	SLon
	lyallii	ELan GAbr GKev GWyn MPie SRms WCot
	'Lynette'	MBNS SBch
	'Macpenny's Pink'	CMac MBNS WAvo XLum
	'Madame Golding'	MBNS XLum
	'Marble Riding Hood'^{PBR} (Riding Hood Series)	LRHS NRHS
	'Margery Fish' $\mathbb{Y}^{H3}$	CFis ECtt EWes
	'Maurice Gibbs' $\mathbb{Y}^{H3}$	CBcs ECtt EPfP ESps EWes LHop LSRN MBNS MBel SRms
	'Melting Candy' (Ice Cream Series)	LSun WCot
	mensarum	CFis
	Mexicali hybrids	LRHS NRHS
	'Carillo Purple' (Carillo Series) **new**	
	- 'Carillo Red' (Carillo Series) **new**	LRHS NRHS
	× ***mexicanus*** 'Sunburst Amethyst'	NFav SPhx SRms XLum
	- 'Sunburst Ruby'	CPla NFav SLon
	'Midnight'	ECtt ELan EWTr GBin LPot MBNS MRav MSwo SEND SHar SWvt WCFE XLum
	'Modesty'	MBNS SRms
	'Mother of Pearl'	CBcs EHrv ELan EPfP EShb ESps GBin GMaP LHop LRHS LSRN MBNS MCot MSwo MWat SHar SRms SWvt
	'Mrs Miller'	MBNS
	'Mrs Morse'	see *P.* 'Chester Scarlet'
	'Mrs Oliver'	EWes
	multiflorus	EBee
§	'Myddelton Gem'	MWat SRms
	'Myddelton Red'	see *P.* 'Myddelton Gem'
	newberryi $\mathbb{Y}^{H5}$	GCrg
	- f. ***humilior***	EPot
§	- subsp. ***sonomensis***	GCrg SRms WAbe
	'Newbury Gem'	MBNS SHar SWvt
	'Oaklea Red'	GBin
§	'Old Candy Pink'	SWvt
	'Osprey' $\mathbb{Y}^{H3}$	CMac CMea CWCL ECtt ELan EPfP ESps GBin LRHS MBNS NBir SRms SWvt
	ovatus	CMac EBee ELan SPhx SRms WKif
	'Overbury'	ECtt SRms WAvo
	'Papal Purple'	MAsh MBNS MHer NBir SHar SPhx SRms XLum
	'Patio Wine'	MBel WAvo
	'Peace'	GBin MBNS
§	'Pennington Gem' $\mathbb{Y}^{H3}$	ELan MHer NBir SHar SRms SWvt WBod
	(Pensham Series) 'Pensham Amelia Jane'	CAby CNec CRos CWGN ECtt ELon EPfP GMcL GWyn LAll LHop LRHS LSRN LSou MBNS MTis NLar NPri SHil SLon SPer SRms SWvt WCot WHil
	- 'Pensham Arctic Fox'	CSpe ECtt LRHS SLon
	- 'Pensham Arctic Sunset'	WHrl
	- 'Pensham Avonbelle'	MBNS SRms
	- 'Pensham Bilberry Ice'	LSun MBNS SWvt
	- 'Pensham Blackberry Ice'	CLet ECtt LAll LSou MBNS SLon SRms
	- 'Pensham Blueberry Ice'	ECtt LSou MBNS SWvt
	- 'Pensham Capricorn Moon'	ECtt
	- 'Pensham Charlotte Louise'	ECtt ELon LAll LRHS SRms
	- 'Pensham Czar'	Widely available
	- 'Pensham Dorothy Wilson'	CRos LRHS NRHS
	- 'Pensham Eleanor Young'	CRos ECtt EPfP LAll LRHS LSou MBNS NRHS SLon SPoG SPtp SWvt
	- 'Pensham Freshwater Pearl'	SRms WHoo
	- 'Pensham Great Expectations'	ECtt
	- 'Pensham Jessica Mai'	ECtt LRHS LSou SHil SPer SRms SWvt WHil
	- 'Pensham Just Jayne'	ECtt ELon EPfP LAll LRHS LSRN MBNS SLon SRms SWvt WHoo XLum
	- 'Pensham Kay Burton'	EPfP
	- 'Pensham Laura'	CAby CBod CNec CSam CWGN ECtt EPfP LAll LCro LOPS LRHS LSRN LSun MAsh MBNS MBel NPri SHil SLon SPad SWvt WBor WHoo
	- 'Pensham Loganberry Ice'	LSou MBNS SLon

- 'Pensham Miss Wilson'	SRms
- 'Pensham Plum Jerkum'	CAby CRos CWGN ECrN ECtt ELon EPfP GMcL LAll LHop LRHS LSou MBNS MCot MHer MPie NLar NPri SCob SDix SHil SLon SPad SPer SWvt WHil WHoo
- 'Pensham Princess'	ECtt
- 'Pensham Raspberry Ice'	CLet CRos MBNS SLon
- 'Pensham Son of Raven'	WAvo
- 'Pensham Tayberry Ice'	CRos ECtt MBNS SLon
- 'Pensham Ted's Purple'	WCFE
- 'Pensham Victoria Plum'	CElw EShb SHar WHoo
- 'Pensham Wedding Bells'	SRms
- 'Pensham Wedding Day'	CBod CSpe CWCL ECrN ELan EPfP GMcL LAll LRHS LSRN LSou MBNS MCot MSCN SCob SLon SPer SPtp WHoo
- 'Pensham Westminster Belle'	ECtt MTis WHil
'Pershore Anniversary'	WAvo
'Pershore Carnival'	SRms WAvo WHrl
'Pershore Fanfare'	WAvo WHrl
'Pershore Festival'	WAvo
'Pershore Pink Necklace'	CWCL ECtt SRms SWvt WAvo
'Phare'	see *P.* 'Le Phare'
(Phoenix Series) Phoenix Appleblossom 09 = 'Peni Ablos09'	CRos LRHS NRHS SHil
- Phoenix Lavender = 'Peni Laver'	CRos LRHS NRHS SHil
- Phoenix Magenta 09 = 'Peni Mag09'	CRos LRHS NRHS SHil
- Phoenix Pink 09 = 'Peni Pina09'PBR	CRos
- Phoenix Pink = 'Pheni Pinka' **new**	LRHS NRHS
- Phoenix Red = 'Pheni Reeda'PBR	CRos LRHS SHil
- Phoenix Rose = 'Penharros'PBR	LRHS NRHS SHil
- Phoenix Violet 09 = 'Peni Vio09'PBR	CRos EPfP LRHS NRHS SHil
'Phyllis'	see *P.* 'Evelyn'
pinifolius ♀H4	CMea CTri EBee ECho ELon EPot EUJe GCrg ITim LHop LRHS MBel MMuc NHar NRHS WAbe WHoo WThu
- 'Mersea Yellow'	CMea ECho ELan EPfP EPot GCrg GKev ITim LHop LRHS MHer MMuc NHar NLar NRHS SIgm SLon SPlb WAbe XLum
- 'Wisley Flame' ♀H4	EPfP EPot EWes GCrg MBNS MHer MSCN NHpl SCob SIgm
'Pink Bedder'	see *P.* 'Hewell Pink Bedder', 'Sutton's Pink Bedder'
'Pink Endurance'	MBNS WHal
'Port Wine' ♀H3	CMea CTri ELon EPfP GMaP LHop LPot LRHS MCot MWat NBir SPoG SWvt WAvo WKif
'Prairie Twilight'PBR	WHlf
'Precious Gem'	WHlf
'Pretty Petticoat'	IPot LRHS NRHS
procerus var. ***brachyanthus***	GKev
§ - var. ***formosus***	WAbe
- 'Hawkeye'	CPBP
§ - 'Roy Davidson' ♀H5	CMea ECho EPot NHar WAbe
- var. ***tolmiei***	EPot GCal GEdr MPie WAbe
pubescens	see *P. hirsutus*
pulchellus Greene	see *P. procerus* var. *formosus*
pulchellus Lindl.	see *P. campanulatus*
'Purple and White'	see *P.* 'Countess of Dalkeith'
'Purple Bedder'	CBod CMac CRos ELan EPfP GBin LRHS LSRN MWat NBir NRHS SHil SPoG SPtp SRkn SRms SWvt XLum
'Purple Passion'	CElw EBee EHrv ELan EPfP EWes EWoo LRHS SCob
'Purple Riding Hood'PBR (Riding Hood Series)	EBee LCro LRHS NRHS SPoG
'Purple Sea'	MHol WFar
'Purpureus Albus'	see *P.* 'Countess of Dalkeith'
'Raspberry Ripple' (Ice Cream Series)	LSou LSun
'Raven' ♀H3	Widely available
'Razzle Dazzle'	SPlb WCot
'Red Knight'	MBNS
'Red Riding Hood'PBR (Riding Hood Series)	EPfP LCro LRHS NRHS
'Red Rocks'	GBin WCot
'Red Sea'	MHol WFar
'Rich Purple'	MBNS SPlb XLum
'Rich Ruby' ♀H3	CAby CFis CWCL EHrv ELan EPfP EWes LLWP LRHS MSCN NBir SBee SHar SPlb SPtp SWvt WCAu XLum
richardsonii var. ***richardsonii***	SBrt
roezlii Regel	see *P. laetus* subsp. *roezlii*
roezlii ambig.	MAsh
'Ron Sidwell'	WAvo
'Rosy Blush'	MBNS SPlb
'Roy Davidson'	see *P. procerus* 'Roy Davidson'
'Royal White'	see *P.* 'White Bedder'
'Rubicundus' ♀H4	CWCL ELan EPfP GBin LRHS LSRN MBNS SLon SWvt WBor WHil
'Ruby' misapplied	see *P.* 'Schoenholzeri'
'Ruby Candle'	ECtt LRHS NRHS
rupicola ♀H5	EPot LHop
- 'Conwy Lilac'	SRms WAbe
- 'Conwy Rose'	EPot GCrg WAbe WThu
'Russian River'	ECtt EPfP ESps LRHS SPlb SWvt XLum
rydbergii	SBrt SPlb
'Samsong'	WCFE
§ 'Schoenholzeri' ♀H4	Widely available
scouleri	see *P. fruticosus* var. *scouleri*
§ ***serrulatus***	EWes GKev XLum
- 'Albus'	MArt
'Sherbourne Blue'	WAvo WCot
'Sissinghurst Pink'	see *P.* 'Evelyn'
'Six Hills'	EPot SDys WAbe WOld
'Skyline'	EPfP
smallii	CAby CFis EPPr EPfP EWes GBin LRHS LSRN MHer NRHS SPhx
'Snow Storm'	see *P.* 'White Bedder'
'Snowflake'	see *P.* 'White Bedder'
sonomensis	see *P. newberryi* subsp. *sonomensis*
'Sour Grapes' misapplied	see *P.* 'Stapleford Gem'
'Sour Grapes' ambig.	CAby CBcs CBod EHoe EHrv EWoo IBoy LAll LPot MBel MHtn MJak NGdn SBod SCob SHil WBod WCAu
§ 'Sour Grapes' M. Fish ♀H4	CMac CRos CWCL CWld EBee ECha ELan EPfP EShb ESps GBin GMaP IBoy LCro LEdu LOPS LRHS LSRN MHer MSwo NLar NRHS SEND SHar SPer SPtp WHar WHea WHil WKif
'Southgate Gem'	GKev GMcL GWyn MBNS MHCG MWat SRms SWvt WAvo
'Souvenir d'Adrian Regnier'	MBNS MHCG

'Souvenir d'André Torres' misapplied	see *P.*'Chester Scarlet'
§ 'Stapleford Gem' ♀H3	CFis CMac CWCL ELan GBuc LBMP LRHS MBel MRav SHar SRms SWvt WHar WHoo
aff. 'Stapleford Gem'	NCGa
'Storm'	WHlf
'Strawberries and Cream' (Ice Cream Series)	CWCL EBee ELon LAll LSun MTis NLar SCob SRkn WBor WCot WHil
strictus	EBee EPPr MBNS NFav SBrt
§ 'Sutton's Pink Bedder'	MBNS
'Sweet Cherry' (Ice Cream Series)	ECtt LSou LSun WCot
tall, pink-flowered	see *P.* 'Welsh Dawn'
teucrioides	CPBP EPot
'The Juggler'	ECtt MBNS SWvt
§ 'Thorn'	ECtt ESps LRHS MJak MWat NBir SPhx SRms SWvt WAvo WHrl
'Threave Pink'	ECtt LLWP MRav SHar SWvt WAvo
'Thundercloud'	ECtt WAvo
'Torquay Gem'	MBNS
'True Sour Grapes'	see *P.*'Sour Grapes' M. Fish
'Tubular Bells Purple'	CWCL
uintahensis	SBrt
'Vanilla' (Ice Cream Series)	LSun
'Vanilla Plum' (Ice Cream Series)	LSou LSun WHil
venustus purple-flowered	SBrt
Vesuvius = 'Yasius' (Volcano Series)	CRos EPfP LRHS SLon SRms WCAu WFar
virens	CPBP EBee EPot
virgatus	EBee
- 'Blue Buckle'	LRHS SPlb WFar
'Watermelon Taffy' (Taffy Series)	ECtt
§ 'Welsh Dawn'	MBNS
§ ***whippleanus***	LRHS MMuc SPlb
- black-flowered **new**	SBrt
- 'Chocolate Drop'	WHlf
§ 'White Bedder' ♀H3	Widely available
'Whitethroat' Sidwell	MBNS
I 'Whitethroat' purple-flowered	WCot
'Willy's Purple'	ECtt
§ 'Windsor Red'	CTri ECtt EPfP LRHS MBNS SCob SLon SRms SWvt WAvo WCot
'Winter Star' **new**	NAst
'Woodpecker'	ECtt IPot MBNS SRms WAvo

Pentaglottis (*Boraginaceae*)

§ ***sempervirens***	EPfP SRms WSFF

Pentapanax see *Aralia*

Pentapterygium see *Agapetes*

Pentas (*Rubiaceae*)

lanceolata	CCCN EShb

Penthorum (*Saxifragaceae*)

sedoides	LLWG

pepino see *Solanum muricatum*

peppermint see *Mentha* × *piperita*

Pereskia (*Cactaceae*)

aculeata 'Godseffiana' (v) **new**	WCot
grandifolia **new**	CCCN

Perezia (*Asteraceae*)

recurvata	EPot

Pericallis (*Asteraceae*)

× ***hybrida*** Senetti Series	NPer NPri SPoG
- - Senetti Blue Bicolor = 'Sunseneribuba'PBR	MGos SPoG
- - Senetti Blue = 'Sunsenebu'PBR	SPoG
- - Senetti Magenta Bicolor = 'Sunsenereba'PBR	MGos SPoG
- - Senetti Magenta = 'Sunsenere'PBR	SPoG
§ ***lanata*** (L'Hér.) B. Nord.	CHll EShb
- Kew form	CSpe

Perilla (*Lamiaceae*)

§ ***frutescens*** var. ***crispa***	CSpe SHDw
- green-leaved	CLau
- var. ***japonica***	GPoy
- var. ***nankinensis***	see *P. frutescens* var. *crispa*
- var. ***purpurascens***	CLau WJek

Periploca (*Apocynaceae*)

graeca	CBcs EBee SNig

Pernettya see *Gaultheria*

Perovskia (*Lamiaceae*)

abrotanoides	XLum
atriplicifolia	CArn CBot CDul CMea ELan LRHS LSun MGil MHer MNHC NSti WKif XSen
- 'Blue Shadow'	EWTr LRHS NLar
'Blue Haze'	GCal
'Blue Spire' ♀H5	Widely available
'Filigran'	CWld EBee ELan EPed GBin GBuc LRHS LSou NLar SBod SMad SPad SPoG WGrn WGwG WPat XSen
'Hybrida'	GCal LRHS
Lacey Blue = 'Lisslitt'PBR	ECrN EPfP LPla LRHS MAsh NLar NRHS SCob SWvt WHil
'Little Spire'PBR	CBar CBod CMac CRos CSBt CSpe EHoe ELon EPfP EUJe EWes EWoo GMaP GMcL GQue IBoy LBMP LCro LRHS LSRN MAsh NBid NDov NLar SCob SGol SPer SPoG SRkn WHil
'Longin'	LRHS XLum
Silvery Blue = 'Lissvery' **new**	LRHS NRHS

Persea (*Lauraceae*)

americana	CCCN
indica	CCCN
- B&SWJ 12535	WCru
japonica B&SWJ 8410	WCru
- B&SWJ 12789	WCru
thunbergii	CBcs CFil
- B&SWJ 12747	WCru

Persicaria (*Polygonaceae*)

B&SWJ 11268 from Sumatra	WCru
§ ***affinis***	CBcs CSBt EAEE EHrv GAbr LSun MArt MSCN NBro SCob SWat WFar WMoo WTcb
- 'Darjeeling Red' ♀H5	Widely available
- 'Dimity'	see *P. affinis* 'Superba'
- 'Donald Lowndes' ♀H5	Widely available

	- 'Kabouter'	GBin NLar SCob WBor
§	- 'Superba' ♀H5	Widely available
	alata	see *P. nepalensis*
	alpina	CBct CBot CSpe EBee ECha EHoe EHrv EPPr GBin GMaP GMcL IPot LEdu LRHS MAvo MHol MRav NDov NLos SDix SMad WCot WMoo WPnP WTcb WWtn
	amphibia	GBin LLWG MSKA SWat XLum
§	***amplexicaulis***	CBre CKno ELan EWes GMaP MBel MCot MHer WBor WFar WMoo WRHF WWtn XLum
	- 'Alba'	Widely available
	- 'Anouk'	EBee
	- 'Atrosanguinea'	CKno CMac CTri ECha ELan GLog LRHS MMuc MRav MSpe NBir NLar SEND SPer SRms SWat SWvt WFar WOld XLum
	- 'Betty Brandt'	GBin GWyn
	- 'Blackfield'PBR	CBcs CBct CKno CMos CSpe EBee ECha ECtt ELon EWes GBin GMaP GQue IBoy IKil IPot LRHS MBNS MBel MHol MNrw MSpe NDov NLar SCob WCot
	- 'Blush Clent'	WHoo
	- 'Clent Charm'	MHCG NChi WOut
	- 'Cottesbrooke Gold'	ECtt MAvo
	- deep-pink-flowered **new**	MAvo
	- 'Dikke Floskes'	CBct CKno EBee ELon GBin MHol WCot
	- 'Early Pink Lady'	WMoo
	- 'Eastfield' (v)	WCot
	- 'Fascination'	MAvo WCot
	- 'Fat Domino'PBR	CBct CKno EBee ECtt EHoe GBin GQue IKil ILea IPot LPla MBel MHol MNrw NCou NDov NLar SAko SCob WCAu WCot
	- 'Firedance'	CAby CKno ECtt EHoe ELon EPPr GBin GQue IPot MSpe NDov SMHy SPhx SWat WCot WFar
	- 'Firetail'	Widely available
	- 'Golden Arrow' (v)	CBct ECtt ELon GBin LRHS MHtn NEoE SCob SHar SHil SPoG WHil WMoo
	- 'High Society'	CKno GBin WCAu
	- 'Inverleith'	CBct CBre CKno EBee ECGP ECha ECtt ELon EPPr GBin GBuc GMaP GMcL GQue LRHS MAvo MBel MHer MMuc MSpe NBir SCob WCAu WHar WMoo WOut WPGP WPnP
I	- 'Jo and Guido's Form'	CHVG ELon NLar WCAu WFar
	- 'JS Caliente'PBR	CHVG CKno ECGP ECtt ELon GBin GQue LRHS LSun MArt MSCN NBir SCob WCot WPnP
	- 'JS Delgado'	CKno CMos EBee GBin MNrw
	- 'Lisan'	EBee GBin
	- Orange Field = 'Orangofield'PBR	CBct CKno EBee ECtt ELon EPPr EWoo GBin GQue IKil LHop LRHS MBel MHol MJak MNrw MSCN NCGa NDov NLar NPnk SAko SCob SHil WBor WCAu WMoo
	- var. ***pendula***	EBee GBin GQue NBir SMHy WFar WMoo
	- - HWJK 2255	WCru
	- 'Pink Elephant'	see *P.* 'Pink Elephant'
	- 'Pink Knot'	LRHS
	- 'Pink Lady'	ECGP MPie
	- 'Rosea'	Widely available
	- 'Rowden Gem'	GBin IPot WMoo WOut
	- 'Rubie's Pink'	ECha
	- 'Sangre'	GBin
	- 'September Spires'	NDov
	- 'Seven Oaks Village'	GBin SCob
	- 'Summer Dance'	CKno EBee ECtt EPPr GQue SMHy
	- Taurus = 'Blotau'	CElw CHVG CKno CSam ECha ECtt ELon EPPr GBuc GQue IPot LRHS NCGa NLar NPnk NSti SCob SMHy WFar WHil WHoo WPGP
	- 'White Eastfield'	SPhx
	aff. ***amplexicaulis*** 'Guizhou Bronze' **new**	LEdu
§	***bistorta***	CArn GBin GPoy MArt MHer MMuc NBir NLar SEND SRms SWat WFar WOut
	- subsp. ***carnea***	EBee ECha EHoe ELon EPPr GBin LRHS MBNS MMuc NBir NBro NDov NPnk WCot WMoo WTcb WWtn
	- 'Hohe Tatra'	EBee EPPr GMaP LRHS MBel MHol NDov SPoG WCot WFar
	- 'JS Calor'PBR	EBee GQue
	- 'Superba' ♀H7	Widely available
	campanulata	CBod CElw ECha ECtt EHoe GAbr GMaP IFro LPot MAvo MMuc MRav NEgg NSti SEND SPer WFar WMoo WOut WTcb WWtn
	- Alba Group	CElw MPie WMoo
	- 'Madame Jigard'	GBin
	- 'Rosenrot'	CBre ILea NBir SAko SWat WOld
	- 'Southcombe White'	GBin
§	***capitata***	LLWG XLum
	- 'Pink Bubbles'	EHoe NBir SWvt
	chinensis B&SWJ 11268	WCru
	emodi	GKev
	× ***fennica*** 'Johanniswolke'	EBee GBin IPot
*	***hydropiper*** var. ***rubra***	WJek
	'Indian Summer'	GCal LPla
*	***kahil***	GBin WCot
*	***macrophylla***	EBee
	- CC 5790	GKev
	microcephala	EWes MHer
	- 'Dragon's Eye'PBR	EBee WNPC
	- 'Red Dragon'PBR	Widely available
	milletii	CAby EBee GBuc LRHS NDov WCru
§	***mollis***	WPGP
	neofiliformis	EShb WTcb
§	***nepalensis***	EPPr EShb IMou MTPN
	'October Pink'	CSam SMHy
§	***odorata***	CArn CLau ENfk GPoy MHer MNHC SHDw SRms WJek WTre
	orientalis	CSpe
§	'Pink Elephant'	CBot CKno CMos CSam EPPr GBin GQue MNrw NDov NLar SCob STPC WFar WHoo WTcb
	polystachya	see *P. wallichii*
	'Red Baron'	EPPr
§	***runcinata***	EBee MMuc NBir WMoo WWtn
	- 'Purple Fantasy'	CBod CBot EBee IKil LHop LPla MAvo MHol MSpe NSti SCob SDix SMad SPoG WHil WMoo WNPC WTcb
	scoparia	see *Polygonum scoparium*
	'Silver Dragon'PBR **new**	WCot
	sphaerostachya Meisn.	see *P. macrophylla*
	tenuicaulis	CBre EHrv GBin SBch SBrt WCru WMoo WWtn
§	***tinctoria***	WSFF
§	***vacciniifolia*** ♀H5	Widely available
§	***virginiana***	EPPr GCal LEdu LSun SDix WMoo WWtn

- 'Alba' EPPr
- var. ***filiformis*** CBod CBot CSam CSpe ELan LBMP MBel MPie SBrt SPoG SRkn SWvt WAul WCot
- - 'Ballet' WCot
- - 'Batwings' ESwi LRHS SPtp
- - 'Compton's Red' CSam ECha ECtt EShb EUJe LHop MAvo NLos SBrt WAul WCot
- - 'Lance Corporal' CMac EHoe EPPr EShb EUJe GBin LPot MAvo NLar SPhx
- - 'Moorland Moss' WMoo
- Variegated Group (v) ECha EShb MBNS WCot WMoo
- - 'Painter's Palette' (v) CBod CMac ECha ECtt EHoe ELan EPPr EShb EUJe GBuc GMcL LRHS MHol MRav NBid NSti SDix SMad SPer SWvt WAul WCot WCru WMoo XLum

§ ***wallichii*** CSpe MMuc SDix SEND SWat WCot WMoo WTcb WWtn XLum

§ ***weyrichii*** EPPr GCal NBir NBro NLar WFar WMoo WWtn XLum

persimmon see *Diospyros virginiana*

persimmon, Japanese see *Diospyros kaki*

Petalostemon see *Dalea*

Petamenes see *Gladiolus*

Petasites (*Asteraceae*)

albus GPoy MHer NLar NSti
fragrans LLWG SWat WHer XLum
§ ***frigidus*** var. ***palmatus*** NLar
- - JLS 86317CLOR SMad
- - 'Golden Palms' CHid EHrv EUJe WBor
hybridus EBee MSKA SWat
- 'Variegatus' (v) XLum
japonicus CAgr CBcs GPoy
- var. ***giganteus*** CHid ECha EPfP EUJe LEdu MBel SWat WCru
§ - - 'Nishiki-buki' (v) CMac EBee ECha EPPr EUJe EWld GQue LEdu MHer MSKA NBir NSti SMad WBor WFar XLum
- - 'Variegatus' see *P. japonicus* var. *giganteus* 'Nishiki-buki'
- f. ***purpureus*** EPPr
palmatus see *P. frigidus* var. *palmatus*
paradoxus EWld LEdu LPot MBel WCot WPGP

Petrea (*Verbenaceae*)

volubilis CCCN CHII

Petrocallis (*Brassicaceae*)

lagascae see *P. pyrenaica*
§ ***pyrenaica*** GEdr WAbe
- white-flowered WAbe

Petrocoptis (*Caryophyllaceae*)

pyrenaica SRms

Petrocosmea (*Gesneriaceae*)

barbata WDib
begoniifolia WAbe WDib
coerulea **new** WDib
§ ***cryptica*** CTal WAbe WDib
- 'Yumebutai' WDib
flaccida **new** WDib
'Fluffer Nutter' WDib
forrestii CTal WAbe WDib
grandiflora WAbe WDib
- 'Crème de Crûg' WCru
'Ht-2' WDib
iodioides WDib
kerrii WCot WDib
'Keystone's Angora' WDib
'Keystone's Bantam' WDib
'Keystone's Barnswallow' WDib
'Keystone's Belmont' WDib
'Keystone's Blue Jay' **new** WDib
'Keystone's Magic' **new** WDib
martini CTal
mengliangensis WDib
minor CPBP WDib
'Momo' **new** WDib
parryorum WDib
'Paul Kroll' **new** WDib
'Rosemary Platz' WDib
rosettifolia misapplied see *P. cryptica*
sericea WAbe WDib

Petromarula (*Campanulaceae*)

pinnata EBee

Petrophytum (*Rosaceae*)

caespitosum CMea SIgm WAbe
cinerascens GEdr
§ ***hendersonii*** WAbe

Petrorhagia (*Caryophyllaceae*)

'Pink Starlets' EPfP LHop
saxifraga ♀H4 CSpe ECho EPPr GLog NLar SRms WMoo XLum

Petroselinum (*Apiaceae*)

§ ***crispum*** ENfk GPoy LPot MJak MNHC NPol NPri SIde SPoG SRms WJek
- 'Bravour' ♀H4 CLau MHer
- 'Champion Moss Curled' SVic
- 'Darki' CLau
- French CLau ENfk MHer MNHC NPri SPoG SRms WJek
- 'Italian' see *P. crispum* var. *neapolitanum* plain-leaved
- 'Moss Curled' ♀H4 SRms
§ - var. ***neapolitanum*** plain-leaved CLau ENfk SIde SPoG SRms SVic
§ - var. ***tuberosum*** MNHC SIde SRms SVic
hortense see *P. crispum*
tuberosum see *P. crispum* var. *tuberosum*

Petteria (*Papilionaceae*)

ramentacea EBtc

Petunia (*Solanaceae*)

'Baby Duck Yellow' NPri
Black Satin = 'Dueswebsa'PBR (Sweetunia Series) LBMP
Black Velvet Improved LBMP NPri
Blueberry Ice (Sweetunia Series) LBMP
Candyfloss = 'Kercan'PBR (Tumbelina Series) (d) LSou NPri
Caramello (Sweetunia Series) LBMP
(Cascadias Series) Cascadias Bicolor Pastel = 'Dancasbipas' NPri
- Cascadias Rim Magenta LBMP NPri

- Cascadias Rim Violet NPri
Cherry Ripple = 'Kerripcherry'PBR (Tumbelina Series) (d) LSou
'Corona Amethyst' (Corona Series) NPri
Daddy Series CWCL
(Easy Wave Series) Easy Wave Blue = 'Pas320593' NPri
- Easy Wave Burgundy Star = 'Pas760702' NPri
- Easy Wave Coral Reef = 'Pas481972' NPri
- Easy Wave Neon Rose = 'Pas760700' NPri
- Easy Wave Plum Vein = 'Pas739163' NPri
- Easy Wave Violet = 'Pas760717' **new** NPri
- Easy Wave White = 'Pas760712' NPri
exserta CSpe EBee
Famous Lilac Picotee = 'Kleph08152' (Famous Series) LBMP
(Fanfare Series) 'Fanfare Appleblossom' LBMP
- 'Fanfare Crème de Cassis' LBMP
- 'Fanfare Hot Rose' NPri
- 'Fanfare Red' LBMP
- 'Fanfare Royal Purple' LBMP
- 'Fanfare White' LBMP
- 'Fanfare Yellow' LBMP
Grape Ice = 'Dueswegrice'PBR (Sweetunia Series) LBMP
Hot Rod Red = 'Dueswehotre'PBR (Sweetunia Series) LBMP
Inga (Tumbelina Series) (d) LSou
Joanna (Tumbelina Series) LSou
Littletunia Pink = 'Danlittun1'PBR (Littletunia Series) **new** NPri
Melissa = 'Kermelis'PBR (Tumbelina Series) (d) LSou
patagonica ECho SPlb WAbe
Priscilla = 'Kerpril'PBR (Tumbelina Series) (d) LSou NPri
'Purple Flash' (Designer Series) LBMP NPri
Soft Pink Morning (Sweetunia Series) LBMP
Sun Spun Orange = 'Balspunor' **new** NPri
Supercascade Series CWCL
Supertunia Pretty Much Picasso = 'Bhtun31501'PBR (Supertunia Series) NPri
(Surfinia Series) Surfinia Blue Picotee LSou
- Surfinia Blue = 'Sunblu' LBMP LSou NPri
- Surfinia Blue Vein = 'Sunsolos'PBR ESps
- Surfinia Giant Purple = 'Sunlapur'PBR LBMP
- Surfinia Hot Pink 06 = 'Sunrovein'PBR LBMP
- Surfinia Hot Pink = 'Marrose' LSou
- Surfinia Hot Red = 'Sunhore'PBR LBMP
- Surfinia Lime = 'Keiyeul'PBR ESps
- Surfinia Purple = 'Shihi Brilliant' LSou NPri
- Surfinia Sky Blue = 'Keilavbu'PBR NPri
- Surfinia Sweet Pink = 'Sunsurfmomo'PBR LSou NPri
- Surfinia Vanilla = 'Sunvanilla'PBR LSou
- Surfinia White = 'Kesupite' ESps
- Surfinia Yellow Dream **new** NPri
(Surprise Series) Surprise Lime LBMP
- Surprise Marine = 'Duesurmar'PBR LBMP
- Surprise White = 'Duesurimwi'PBR LBMP
Sweet Sunshine Burgundy = 'Kleph09191' (Sweet Sunshine Series) LBMP
Victoria = 'Kervic'PBR (Tumbelina Series) LSou

Peucedanum (*Apiaceae*)

* ***aromaticum*** IMou
baicalense **new** EBee
litorale see *Kitagawia litoralis*
longifolium **new** WCot
officinale GBin LRHS SPlb SPtp
ostruthium GPoy LEdu WPtf
- 'Daphnis' (v) CSpe EBee LEdu MAvo MNrw MSCN NChi NEoE NLar WCFE WCot WHrl WSHC XLum
rablense **new** NDov
verticillare CArn CSam CSpe EBee GAbr GBin IMou LEdu LPla LRHS MBel MSpe SDix SKHP SPhx WCot WSHC

Peumus (*Monimiaceae*)

boldus IDee

Phacelia (*Boraginaceae*)

bolanderi EBee EWld GEdr
californica EBee
tanacetifolia WSFF

Phaedranassa (*Amaryllidaceae*)

BKBlount 2623 WCot
carmiolii WCot
dubia NRog WCot
glauciflora NRog
tunguraguae NRog
viridiflora ECho NRog WCot

Phaedranthus see *Distictis*

Phaenocoma (*Asteraceae*)

prolifera SPlb

Phaenosperma (*Poaceae*)

globosa CSam CSpe EBee ECha EHoe EPPr EShb GQue NLos NWsh WCot WPGP XLum

Phaiophleps see *Olsynium*

nigricans	see *Sisyrinchium striatum*

Phalaris (*Poaceae*)

	arundinacea	LPot MBNS MSKA MWLS SCob SPlb SSal SVic SWat
	- 'Elegantissima'	see *P. arundinacea* var. *picta* 'Picta'
	- var. ***picta***	CBen CDul CTri CWib ESps MJak MSKA NBir NPer WFar XLum XSen
	- - 'Arctic Sun' (v)	CKno EBee ELon EPPr ESps GBin LLWG LRHS NEoE SEND SPoG
	- - 'Aureovariegata' (v)	CBcs MRav NPer SWat WMoo XLum
	- - 'Feesey' (v) Y^{H7}	Widely available
	- - 'Luteopicta' (v)	EPPr MMuc XLum
§	- - 'Picta' (v)	ELan EPfP GBin LRHS MMuc NRHS SEND SPer SWat WMoo
	- - 'Streamlined' (v)	EPPr NWsh
	- - 'Tricolor' (v)	EHoe

Phanerophlebia ✿ (*Dryopteridaceae*)

caryotidea	see *Cyrtomium caryotideum*
falcata	see *Cyrtomium falcatum*
fortunei	see *Cyrtomium fortunei*

Pharbitis see *Ipomoea*

Pharnaceum (*Molluginaceae*)

orange-flowered new	SBrt

Phaseolus (*Papilionaceae*)

caracalla	see *Vigna caracalla*
coccineus 'Polestar' new	SVic

Phedimus see *Sedum*

Phegopteris (*Thelypteridaceae*)

§	***connectilis***	EFer NHar
	decursive-pinnata	CLAP EBee LRHS MMuc SEND WFib WPnP
	hexagonoptera	NLos

Phellodendron (*Rutaceae*)

amurense	CBcs CCCN CDul CMCN EBee ELan EPfP EWTr GBin IVic MBlu SEND WBor
- B&SWJ 11000	WCru
japonicum B&SWJ 11175	WCru
sachalinense	LEdu

Phemeranthus (*Portulacaceae*)

sediformis	GKev

Phenakospermum (*Strelitziaceae*)

guianense	XBlo

Pherosphaera ✿ (*Podocarpaceae*)

fitzgeraldii	CKen WThu

Philadelphus ✿ (*Hydrangeaceae*)

	SDR 4862	GKev
	SDR 4945	GKev
	SDR 4946	GKev
	SDR 5111	GKev
	affinis	CFil
	'Atlas' (v)	NLar
	'Avalanche'	MMuc NLar SPer SRms
	'Beauclerk' Y^{H6}	CBod CCCN CDul CLet CRos CTri EBee ECrN EPfP EWTr GQui IVic LRHS MGos MMuc MRav NLar NWea SCob SKHP SLim SMad SPer SRms SWvt WHar
	'Belle Étoile' Y^{H6}	Widely available
	'Bialy Karzel'	NLar
	'Bicolore'	NLar WAvo WHar
	'Bouquet Blanc'	MRav NLar SRms WCFE
	brachybotrys	MRav
	'Buckley's Quill' (d)	CWld EBee EPfP EWes LRHS MRav SGol SWvt WGrn
	'Burfordensis'	CBot MMuc MRav SEND
	calcicola	CFil
	caucasicus	CFil
	coronarius	CBcs CDul EPfP ESps LBuc MRav NWea SPer
	- 'Aureus' Y^{H6}	Widely available
	- 'Bowles's Variety'	see *P. coronarius* 'Variegatus'
§	- 'Variegatus' (v) Y^{H6}	Widely available
	coulteri	CFil SBrt WPGP
	'Coupe d'Argent'	MRav
	'Dainty Lady'	GBin SLon
	'Dame Blanche' (d)	EPfP EWTr LSou MRav NLar
	delavayi	CFil EPfP EWTr GBin LEdu LLHF NLar SDix SKHP SPer WPGP
	- var. ***calvescens***	LRHS MRav
	- - BWJ 8005	WCru
	- f. ***melanocalyx***	EPfP GCra MRav SChF WPGP
	- - B&L 12168	CFil EBee WPGP
	- - 'Nyman's Variety' Y^{H6}	CBot CFil CTho SKHP WKif WPGP
	aff. ***delavayi***	SBrt
	'Enchantement' (d)	MRav SDix
	'Erectus'	CSBt CWib EBee ELon EPfP EWTr LRHS MRav NLar SKHP SLim SPer SPoG WAvo WPat
	'Étoile Rose'	WAvo WMoo
	'Falconeri'	MRav
	'Frosty Morn' (d)	CBcs EPfP EWTr LEdu LRHS MBlu MMuc MRav NLar SEND SPer SPoG
	incanus B&SWJ 8616	WCru
§	'Innocence' (v) Y^{H6}	CBot CMac CRos CTsd CWld EHoe ELan EPfP LRHS MAsh MGos MMuc MRav MSwo NEoE SEND SGol SKHP SLim SPad SPer SPoG SRms WFar WPat WSHC
	'Innocence Variegatus'	see *P.* 'Innocence'
§	***insignis***	MRav
	karwinskianus	CFil
	- F&M 152	WPGP
	'Lemoinei'	CBcs CBod CDul CTri CWld ESps GMcL MGos NWea SCob SGol WGrn WHar
	'Lemon Hill'	NLar
	lewisii 'Snow Velvet'	EPfP LLHF LRHS MMrt
	'Limestone'	MRav
	maculatus	CFil WPat
	- 'Mexican Jewel'	CBcs CFil EBee ELon GBin NLar SKHP SMad SPad WGob WKif WPGP WPat WSHC
	- 'Scented Storm'	CMHG WPGP
	- 'Sweet Clare' Y^{H5}	CRos EPfP LCro LRHS SHil
	maculatus × mexicanus	CFil
	madrensis	LHop MRav
	- F&M 326	CFil WPGP
	'Manteau d'Hermine' (d) Y^{H6}	Widely available
	'Marjorie'	NLar
	mexicanus	CFil GCal
	- B&SWJ 10253	WCru
	- 'Rose Syringa'	CFil SKHP WPGP WPat
	mexicanus × palmeri	EBee WPGP

microphyllus	CBot CDul CMCN CTho CTri EBee ELan ELon EPfP ESps EWTr GBin LRHS MAsh MGos MRav SKHP SLon SPer SPoG WFar WSHC
- var. ***occidentalis***	NLar
'Miniature Snowflake' (d)	MAsh WPat
'Minnesota Snowflake' (d)	CBcs CSpe EPfP EWes LRHS LSRN MMuc MRav NLar SEND SGol SPoG WFar
'Mont Blanc'	CBcs GKin MRav NLar
'Mrs E.L. Robinson' (d)	CMac CRos CWld ELon EPfP GLog LLHF LRHS MAsh MGos NEgg NLar SHil WAvo WCFE
myrtoides B&SWJ 10436	WCru
'Natchez' (d)	CMac EAEE ELon EWTr LEdu LLHF NLar SCob SMad
'Oeil de Pourpre'	MRav
palmeri	CFil WPGP
'Patricia'	WAvo
pekinensis	NLar
'Perryhill'	MRav
'Polar Star'	ELon NLar WKif
purpurascens	CBot CJun EBee EPfP EWes GLog GQui LLHF MGos MMrt MRav NLar SChF SKHP WPGP
- BWJ 7540	WCru
'Purpureomaculatus'	ELon LLHF MAsh MRav WPGP
sargentianus	CFil
satsumi	NLar
- B&SWJ 10811	WCru
- B&SWJ 11004	WCru
schrenkii	CFil EBee NLar
- B&SWJ 8465	EBee ESwi WCru
sericanthus	NLar
§ 'Silberregen' ♀H6	CDul CMac CSam CWld EBee ELon EPfP EWTr GBin LRHS MAsh MGos MMuc MRav NEoE NGdn NLar SEND SGol SMad SPoG SRms SWvt WBod WGrn
Silver Showers	see *P.* 'Silberregen'
'Snowbelle' (d)	CCCN EPfP ESps LBMP LRHS MAsh NGdn NLar NPri SKHP SPoG SWvt WBor
'Snowflake'	WMoo
'Snowgoose'	LRHS
'Souvenir de Billiard'	see *P. insignis*
'Starbright'PBR	CCCN EPfP LRHS MAsh SCob
subcanus L 524	CFil
'Sybille' ♀H6	CBot CMac CTho CWld ECrN EPfP LHop LRHS MAsh MRav MSwo SDix SKHP SRms WKif WPat
tomentosus AC 3678	MHid
- B&SWJ 2707	WCru
- GWJ 9215	WCru
'Velléda'	WAvo
'Virginal' (d)	Widely available
× ***virginalis*** new	EWTr
'Voie Lactée'	EWTr MRav NLar
White Icicle = 'Bialy Sopel'	CCCN
White Rock = 'Pekphil' ♀H6	CBot CMac EBee EPfP IVic LLHF LRHS LSRN MRav NLar SKHP SLim SPer
'Yellow Cab'	LRHS
'Yellow Hill'	CMac EPfP LRHS NLar SKHP

Philesia (*Philesiaceae*)

buxifolia	see *P. magellanica*
§ ***magellanica***	CFil CRHN GGGa ITim MGil SBrt SIgm WCru WSHC
- 'Rosea'	CRHN CWib EPfP

Phillyrea (*Oleaceae*)

angustifolia	CBcs CDul CFil CHll CMCN CTho EBee ELan ELon EPfP EUJe IVic LRHS MGos MRav NLar SBig SEND SPer WPGP WPat WSHC XSen
- f. ***rosmarinifolia***	CCCN CDul ELan
- - 'French Fries'	EBee EPfP WPGP
decora	see *Osmanthus decorus*
§ ***latifolia***	CBcs CDul CFil CTho CTsd EBee ELan EPfP EUJe LRHS NLar SArc SEND WPGP XSen
media	see *P. latifolia*

Philodendron (*Araceae*)

'Angra dos Reis'	see *P. cordatum*
§ ***angustisectum*** ♀H1b	XBlo
'Atom' new	NLos
bipinnatifidum ♀H1c	NLos SEND XBlo
corcovadense	XBlo
§ ***cordatum***	XBlo
elegans	see *P. angustisectum*
erubescens 'Imperial Red'	NLos
- 'Red Emerald'	XBlo
'Imperial Green' new	NLos
* ***radiatum*** var. ***pseudoradiatum*** 'Simmonds'	XBlo
* ***rubrum***	XBlo
scandens 'Green Emerald'	XBlo
- 'Mica'	XBlo
tripartitum	XBlo
xanadu	NLos XBlo

Philotheca (*Rutaceae*)

§ ***myoporoides***	LRHS MPkF

Phlebodium (*Polypodiaceae*)

§ ***aureum*** ♀H1b	CSpe WCot
- var. ***areolatum***	EShb
- 'Blue Star'	ISha NLos
- 'Mandaianum'	ISha NLos
pseudoaureum	EBee ISha LRHS WCot

Phleum (*Poaceae*)

phleoides	EHoe LRHS NRHS
pratense	EHoe NMir WSFF

Phlomis ✿ (*Lamiaceae*)

NJM 10.020	WPGP
PAB 13.132 new	LEdu
alpina	SPlb
* ***anatolica***	LRHS NLar SKHP
- 'Lloyd's Variety'	see *P. grandiflora* 'Lloyd's Silver'
angustifolia	LRHS XSen
anisodonta white-flowered	XSen
armeniaca	XSen
atropurpurea BWJ 7922	WCru
bourgaei	XSen
bovei subsp. ***maroccana***	SEND WHal XLum XSen
breviflora HWJCM 250	WCru
capitata	XSen
cashmeriana	CBod CSpe EBee ECha EHoe EWTr GCal GJos LRHS LSou MArt MHol SKHP SMad SPhx WCFE
chrysophylla ♀H4	CAbP ECha ELan EPfP LRHS MAsh MRav NLar SDix SKHP SPer WCFE XSen
cretica	SVen
crinita	XSen

	× ***cytherea***	XSen
	'Edward Bowles'	CBot CDul ECha EPfP GBin LRHS LSRN MRav NLar SEND SIgm SKHP SWvt XSen
	fruticosa ♀H4	Widely available
	grandiflora	MMuc SEND XSen
	- NJM 10.014	WPGP
§	- 'Lloyd's Silver' ♀H5	CSam ELan GBin LRHS MAsh NLar SPer
	herba-venti	XSen
	italica	Widely available
	- 'Pink Glory'	CMac
	lanata	CAbP CRos ELan EPfP LRHS SBrt SCob WCFE WSHC XSen
	- 'Pygmy'	XSen
	'Le Sud'	WCot XSen
	leucophracta	SVen
	longifolia	CRos EBee EPfP LRHS MNrw SBrt SEND SKHP SPer WGrn WPGP XSen
	- var. ***bailanica*** ♀H4	CBot CSam EPfP LRHS NRHS SKHP XLum
	- var. ***longifolia***	SKHP
	lunariifolia	XSen
	lychnitis	SIgm XSen
	lycia	LRHS XSen
	- NJM 10.016	WPGP
	macrophylla	SPhx
	× ***margaritae***	XSen
	monocephala	XSen
	nissolei	XSen
	purpurea	CAbP ELan EPfP LRHS MAsh MMuc NBir SEND WCot XSen
I	- 'Alba'	CBot EPfP EWTr GBin GMaP LRHS MMrt SKHP XSen
	- subsp. ***caballeroi***	XSen
§	***russeliana*** ♀H7	Widely available
	- PAB 7444 **new**	LEdu
	- 'Dappled Shade' (v)	WCot
	samia Boiss.	see *P. russeliana*
	samia L.	CBod CKno CMac EWoo LHop LRHS MMrt MMuc NBir NGdn NLar SAko SBrt SEND SKHP WPtf XSen
	sieheana	XSen
	taurica	EPfP MMuc SEND SPhx
	× ***termessi***	XSen
	tuberosa	CArn CBWd CBcs CBod CKno CMac CPou EHoe EPfP LEdu LRHS LSRN MArt MMuc NGdn SDix SPhx WCFE WPtf XLum XSen
	- 'Amazone' ♀H5	CBod CKno ECha EHrv EPfP GBin GMaP LCro LPla MBel MRav NBid NDov NPnk NSti SCob SMad SPer WCot WFar WHil WSHC
	- 'Bronze Flamingo'	CKno EPfP GBin GJos LRHS MBel MNrw MPnt MRav NLar SBee SKHP SPoG
	viscosa misapplied	see *P. russeliana*

Phlox ✿ (*Polemoniaceae*)

	Adessa White (Adessa Series)	EBee
	adsurgens 'Red Buttes'	ECho
	- 'Wagon Wheel'	ECho ECtt EPot EWes GBuc GCrg LHop LRHS NHar NHpl NRHS SPlb SRms SRot WIce
	amplifolia	MSpe WCot XLum
	- 'Winnetou'	IPot SAko
	× ***arendsii*** 'Andrew'	WCot
	- 'Anja'	SAko
	- 'Autumn's Pink Explosion'	WCot
	- 'Babyface'	ELon NGdn
	- 'Casablanca'	NDov
	- 'Dylan'	WCot
	- 'Eyecatcher'	NBro
	- 'Gary'	WCot
	- 'Hesperis'	EBee ECha ELon GBin GQue LRHS MAvo MSpe MTis NDov NLar SPhx WCAu
	- 'Luc's Lilac' ♀H7	CBWd ECtt EPPr LLHF MCot MSpe NBro NEgg NGdn NSti SDix SGbt SPhx WAul WCot
	- 'Miss Jessica' (Spring Pearl Series)	MSpe
§	- 'Miss Jill' (Spring Pearl Series)	EBee ELan EPfP IPot LCro LOPS WCot
§	- 'Miss Karen' (Spring Pearl Series)	EBee ELan NBro
§	- 'Miss Margie' (Spring Pearl Series)	LEdu
§	- 'Miss Mary' (Spring Pearl Series) ♀H7	ECtt ELan EPfP IBoy LRHS MMrt MSCN MSpe NCGa SRkn
§	- 'Miss Wilma' (Spring Pearl Series)	EBee ELan EPfP
	- 'Paul'	MNrw WCot
	- 'Ping Pong'	SGbt
	- 'Pink Attraction'	NBro
	- 'Purple Star'	EPfP
	- 'Utopia' ♀H7	EBee ELon IMou NDov SPhx WCot
	austromontana	CTal NWad
	bifida	ECho
	- 'Alba'	ECho LLHF
	- blue-flowered	ECho
	- 'Colvin's White'	ECho
	- 'Frohnleiten'	NHar
	- 'Minima Colvin'	ECho
	- 'Ralph Haywood'	CPBP CWCL ECtt EPot
	- 'Thefi'	ECtt
	borealis	see *P. sibirica* subsp. *borealis*
	caespitosa	CMea ECho EWes
	- subsp. ***pulvinata***	see *P. pulvinata*
	- 'Zigeunerblut'	CMea ECtt EPot GCrg ITim NWad SIgm WAbe WHal
	canadensis	see *P. divaricata*
	carolina 'Bill Baker' ♀H5	CSam ECha ECtt EPPr EPfP GMaP IKil MNrw NBir NGdn NSti SIgm WCAu WKif WPtf WSHC XLum
	- 'Magnificence'	EBee EWes LHop SBod SMad SPhx SPlb WCot WSHC
	- 'Miss Lingard' ♀H5	CBod CSam EAEE EAJP ECtt ELon LRHS LSou MCot MMuc MRav MWat NBir NGdn NLar NSti SBee WCot
	'Charles Ricardo'	CSam
	'Chattahoochee'	see *P. divaricata* subsp. *laphamii* 'Chattahoochee'
	colubrina **new**	GKev
	'Daniel's Cushion'	see *P. subulata* 'McDaniel's Cushion'
	diffusa	EPot
§	***divaricata*** ♀H4	EWTr IBoy SPlb
	- 'Blue Dreams'	ECtt ESps MNrw WFar
	- 'Blue Perfume'	CAby EBee ECtt LCro NBro
	- 'Charles'	XLum
	- 'Clouds of Perfume'	CAby CBod CRos CWCL EAEE EAJP ECtt EPfP GBuc GEdr GMaP ILea LCro LOPS LRHS LSou MSCN MSpe NDov NEgg NHpl NLar NPnk NRHS SAko SGbt SPoG SWvt WAul WFar
	- 'Dirigo Ice'	ECho LHop LRHS NRHS SAko

- 'Eco Texas Purple'	MSCN
- 'Fuller's White'	CWCL
- subsp. ***laphamii***	EBee EWes
§ - - 'Chattahoochee' ♀H4	Widely available
- 'May Breeze'	EAJP ECho ECtt EHrv GMaP LHop LRHS MNrw MSCN NPnk SHar WSHC
- 'Plum Perfect'	ECtt
- 'White Perfume'	CMos CWCL EBee EWes IBoy ILea LRHS LSou NBro NLar NRHS SHar WFar WTor XLum
douglasii	SRms
- 'Apollo'	CTri ECho ECtt EPot
- 'Boothman's Variety' ♀H5	ECho ECtt ELan GCrg ITim SRms
- 'Crackerjack' ♀H5	CBod CMea CTri ECho ECtt EDAr ELan ELon EPot EUJe GAbr GCrg GKev GMaP ITim LRHS MAsh MHer MHol NBir NEgg NHol NHpl NRHS NSla SPoG WIce
- 'Eva'	ECho ECtt EDAr ELon GCrg GMaP ITim LHop LRHS LSRN MAsh MHol NBir NHpl NLar NRHS NSla NWad SBch
- 'Georg Arends'	ECtt GJos
- 'Ice Mountain'	CBod CMea ECho ECtt ELan EPot NEgg NHol NWad SPoG SRot
- 'Iceberg' ♀H5	ECho GJos
- 'J.A. Hibberson'	EPot GCrg NWad
- 'Lilac Cloud'	ECho ECtt EDAr GJos
- Lilac Queen	see *P. douglasii* 'Lilakönigin'
§ - 'Lilakönigin'	CTri
- 'Napoleon'	ECho ECtt EPot ITim NWad
- 'Ochsenblut'	CSma ECho EPot GEdr LLHF LRHS NHar NLar NRHS NWad SIgm
- 'Red Admiral' ♀H5	ECho ECtt ELan EPfP EWes GJos GMaP MHol NWad WCFE
- 'Rose Cushion'	ECho EDAr EWes GCrg
- 'Rose Queen'	ECho ESps
- 'Rosea'	ECho EDAr ELan MMuc NHpl
- 'Silver Rose'	ECho
- 'Sprite'	SRms
- 'Tycoon'	see *P. subulata* 'Tamaongalei'
- 'Violet Queen'	ECho
- 'Waterloo'	ECho ECtt EPot LRHS NRHS
I - 'White Admiral'	CTri ECho ECtt ELan GBin LHop LRHS LSRN MHol NRHS
drummondii 'Grammy Pink and White'	NPri
I - 'Phlox of Sheep'	CWCL
'Flare'	see *P. paniculata* 'Neon Flare'
glaberrima 'Morris Berd'	EBee MAvo WSHC
hendersonii	WAbe
idahoensis	SPhx
'Jeff's Pink'	ECtt
'Kelly's Eye' ♀H5	ECho ECtt EPot GCrg LRHS NBir NHar NRHS SPoG
kelseyi 'Lemhi Purple'	CPBP ECho EPot WAbe
- 'Rosette'	ECho NWad
Light Pink Flame = 'Bareleven' PBR	ECtt EPfP SPoG
Lilac Flame = 'Barten' PBR	EPfP WHil
longifolia subsp. ***brevifolia***	CPBP WAbe
maculata	ESps
- 'Alba'	SAko WAul
- 'Alpha' ♀H6	CBot CMea CSam CWCL EBee ECha ECtt EPfP EWoo GBuc GCra GMaP ILea LEdu LRHS LSou MWat NCGa NLar SGbt SKHP SPer SWvt WFar WSHC XLum

- Avalanche	see *P. maculata* 'Schneelawine'
- 'Delta'	EBee EPPr GBuc LRHS NLar SAko SGbt SPer SRkn SWvt
- 'Natascha' ♀H7	Widely available
- 'Omega' ♀H6	CBod CMac EAEE EBee ECtt EWoo GBuc GMcL ILea LEdu LSou MCot MMuc MNrw MPie NGdn NLar NPnk SGbt SKHP SPer SWvt WFar
- 'Princess Sturdza' ♀H6	SDix
- 'Reine du Jour'	CSam IVic NDov SPhx
- 'Rosalinde'	ECtt GBin GBuc LRHS LSou MCot MRav NLar NPnk SAko SWvt WSHC
§ - 'Schneelawine'	LRHS SPlb
'Matineus'	SPhx
'Millstream'	see *P. × procumbens* 'Millstream'
'Millstream Blue'	EPfP
'Minnie Pearl'	EWes LPla MAvo MPie NDov SKHP WCot
nivalis 'Jill Alexander'	SBch
paniculata	ESps GCra NBid NDov SDix WCot
- 'A.E. Amos'	ELon
- 'Aida'	EBee
- var. ***alba***	SDix WCAu WCot
- 'Alba Grandiflora' ♀H7	GMaP MAvo MNrw WCot
- 'Amethyst' misapplied	see *P. paniculata* 'Lilac Time'
- 'Amethyst' Foerster	CWld ELon GBin GQue LRHS MRav MSpe MTis NBir NCGa NLar SWat WMoo
- 'André' **new**	LRHS
- 'Anne'	CSam MSpe
- 'Argus' **new**	MTis
- 'Auslese D. Bach'	CSam
- 'Balmoral'	CMac EBee ECtt GAbr GCra MSpe NEgg NSti SWat SWvt
- 'Barnwell'	SWat
- 'Becky Towe' PBR (v) ♀H7	ECtt LLHF MHer MHol MNrw NEgg NHol SDix WCot
- 'Blauer Morgen'	XLum
- 'Blue Boy'	EBee ECtt ELan ELon EPfP GMaP LRHS NBir NBro NEgg SKHP SRms SWvt WFar
- 'Blue Evening'	LCro LOPS MCot MSpe
- 'Blue Ice'	NBro
- 'Blue Paradise'	Widely available
- 'Blushing Bride'	SRms
- 'Border Gem'	CAby CBcs CMac ECtt ELon EShb LRHS MCot MRav MSpe MTis NChi SDix SWat SWvt WBrk WCot WHrl
- 'Bosvigo Pink' **new**	MAvo
- 'Branklyn'	GCra
- 'Brigadier'	CBod CTri EBee ECtt ELan ELon GMaP LRHS MCot MSpe NEgg NGdn SPer SRms WFar
- 'Bright Eyes'	Widely available
- 'Burgi'	SDix
- 'Candy Floss'	ELon
- 'Cardinal'	MTis NDov
- 'Caroline van den Berg'	SRms
- 'Cecil Hanbury'	WSHC
- 'Charlotte'	MSpe
- 'Cherry Red'	WMoo
- 'Chintz'	MRav SRms
- 'Cinderella'	ECtt
- 'Cleopatra' **new**	SPad WHlf
- Compact Lilac	see *P. paniculata* Sweet Summer Favourite
- Compact Rose White	see *P. paniculata* Sweet Summer Candy
§ - 'Cool of the Evening'	WKif

	- Coral Flame = 'Barsixtytwo'PBR (Flame Series)	CBod CBot CMac ELon EUJe LBMP LSou NLar SCob SRkn WHil
	- 'Cosmopolitan'PBR	MNrw NLar SHil WFar WHar
	- Count Zeppelin	see *P. paniculata* 'Graf Zeppelin'
	- 'Danielle' ♀H7	LRHS SHar WHil
	- 'Darwin's Choice'	see *P. paniculata* 'Norah Leigh'
	- 'David' ♀H7	Widely available
	- 'David's Lavender' ♀H7	ELon LRHS
	- 'Delilah'PBR	CWGN ECtt NHpl
	- 'Discovery'	EHrv EShb EWes LRHS MCot MRav MSpe NEgg SHar SWat WFar
	- 'Doghouse Pink'	SDix
	- 'Dresden China'	SHar SWat
	- 'Duchess of York'	MAvo MSpe SDix
§	- 'Düsterlohe'	CSam EBee ECtt ELon GBin GBuc GQue GWyn IPot LPla LRHS MRav MSpe MTis NBir NCGa NDov NLar SAko SPer SWat WCot WHar XLum
	- 'Eclaireur' misapplied	see *P. paniculata* 'Düsterlohe'
	- 'Eclaireur' Lemoine	MAvo SWat
	- 'Eden's Flash'	CElw ECtt MPie MSpe
	- 'Eden's Smile'	ECtt MSpe
	- 'Elisabeth' (v)	EPfP LSRN NWad
	- 'Elizabeth Arden'	ECtt ELon MSpe MTis SWat
	- 'Elizabeth Campbell'	GCal LRHS
	- 'Ending Blue'	MAvo
	- 'Etoile de Paris'	see *P. paniculata* 'Toits de Paris' Symons-Jeune
	- 'Europa'	EBee ECtt ELan MCot NBir NGdn NLar SPer
	- 'Eva Cullum' ♀H7	CBod CSam EBee ECtt EHrv ELan ELon EPfP ESps GCra GMaP LCro LOPS LRHS MArl MCot MSpe MTis NCGa NHpl NRHS SAko SDix SPer SWat WCot
	- 'Eva Foerster' ♀H7	GWyn XLum
	- 'Eventide'	CMac CSam ECtt EPfP GQue LRHS MArl MCot MNrw MRav MSpe MWat SPer SWat WFar WHrl
	- 'Ferris Wheel'	EBee ECtt
	- 'Flamingo' ♀H7	EBee ECtt LRHS MSpe NAst SWvt XLum
	- 'Fondant Fancy'PBR	NLar SHil SPoG WFar
	- 'Franz Schubert' ♀H7	CSam ECtt ELan EPfP ESps EWoo GBin GCra GWyn LCro LRHS MAvo MCot MSpe NBir NChi NGdn NLar NRHS NSti SPer SWat SWvt WCot WFar WKif
	- 'Fujiyama'	see *P. paniculata* 'Mount Fuji'
	- 'Glow' **new**	MSpe
	- 'Goldmine'PBR (v)	CAby CBod EBee LRHS MHol MNrw NHpl SMad SPoG WCot
§	- 'Graf Zeppelin'	ECtt MSpe MTis NHol SRms XLum
	- 'Grenadine Dream'PBR ♀H7	CWGN EBee ELon LRHS MNrw NHpl SPoG WCot
	- 'Grey Lady' ♀H7	MNrw
	- 'Harlequin' (v)	CMac CWGN ECha ECtt ELon GMaP MHol NBro NEgg NSti SPer WCot
	- 'Herbstwalzer' **new**	IPot
	- 'Ice Cream'	ELon
	- 'Irene Mast'	CSam
	- 'Iris'	MNrw SRms WCot
	- 'Jade'	CAby CBod EBee ECtt ELon EWTr EWoo GBin LRHS MCot MHol MNrw MSpe NLar NPnk NSti SHil WCot
	- 'Jeff's Blue'	EBee ELon WCot
	- 'Judy'	GBin LSRN MAvo
§	- 'Juliglut'	SWat WCot
	- July Glow	see *P. paniculata* 'Juliglut'
	- 'Junior Bouquet'	MHol NLar
	- 'Junior Dream'	NLar
	- 'Katarina'	CElw
	- 'Katherine'	IPot LRHS MSpe NLar WHar
	- 'Katja'PBR	CNor ELon IPot
	- 'Kirchenfürst'	CElw LCro LRHS MSpe MTis NAst NBir SAko SHil
	- 'Kirmesländler'	ECtt EWTr GBin IPot MTis NLar SAko SWat
	- 'Lads Pink'	SDix
	- 'Lady Clare'	SRms
	- 'Landhochzeit'	GBin
	- 'Laura'	see *P. paniculata* 'Uspekh'
§	- 'Lavendelwolke'	GBin GCal LRHS MSpe MTis NBir NLar SWat WCot
	- Lavender Cloud	see *P. paniculata* 'Lavendelwolke'
	- 'Le Mahdi' ♀H7	LCro NLar SRms SWat WBor
	- 'Lichtblick' **new**	MSpe
	- 'Lichtspel'	EBee NDov SPhx
§	- 'Lilac Time'	CElw EBee ECtt EPfP EWTr GKev LRHS LSRN MMuc MTis NLar SPer SWat SWvt
	- 'Little Boy'	CElw ELon MNrw NLar SGbt
	- 'Little Laura'	CElw ECtt EWTr LSRN MNrw MSpe NLar NWad SPoG WCot WHoo
	- 'Little Princess'	ELon NLar
	- 'Little Sara'	NDov
	- 'Lizzy'PBR	NLar
	- 'Logan Black'	GCal MSpe SDix SHar
	- 'Long Border Mauve'	SDix
	- Magical Dream	see *P. paniculata* Sweet Summer Dream
	- Magical Favorite	see *P. paniculata* Sweet Summer Favourite
	- Magical Surprise	see *P. paniculata* Sweet Summer Surprise
	- 'Manoir d'Hézèques'	WCot
	- 'Mardi Gras' **new**	EBee
	- 'Mary Christine' (v)	LRHS NBid
	- 'Maude Stella Dagley'	MSpe
	- 'Mia Ruys'	MArl
	- 'Mike's Favourite'	EBee
	- 'Milly van Hoboken'	WKif
	- 'Miss Holland'	ELon NGdn SGbt XLum
	- 'Miss Jill'	see *P.* × *arendsii* 'Miss Jill'
	- 'Miss Karen'	see *P.* × *arendsii* 'Miss Karen'
	- 'Miss Kelly'	EHrv ELon EShb MSpe NLar WHoo
	- 'Miss Margie'	see *P.* × *arendsii* 'Miss Margie'
	- 'Miss Mary'	see *P.* × *arendsii* 'Miss Mary'
	- 'Miss Pepper' ♀H7	CLet CWCL ECtt ELon EWoo LRHS MMuc MSpe NGdn NLar WBor
	- 'Miss Universe'	ELon
	- 'Miss Wilma'	see *P.* × *arendsii* 'Miss Wilma'
	- 'Monica Lynden-Bell' ♀H7	CAby CBWd CDor CWGN ELon EWoo GBin GMaP LRHS MBel MHol MMuc MNrw MPie MRav MSpe NBid NChi NLar NSti SBod SGbt SKHP SPoG WAul WCot WHoo WKif WPtf WSHC
	- 'Monte Cristallo'	GBin GWyn MSpe
	- 'Mother of Pearl' ♀H7	ESps IPot LRHS MSpe MWat NEgg
§	- 'Mount Fuji'	Widely available
	- 'Mount Fujiyama'	see *P. paniculata* 'Mount Fuji'
	- 'Mrs A.E. Jeans'	SRms
	- 'Mystique Black'	EBee WPtf
	- 'Nadia'PBR	LRHS
	- 'Natural Feelings'PBR (Feelings Series)	NLar

§	- 'Neon Flare' (Neon Series)	CWGN ECtt
	- 'Newbird'	EBee ECtt EPfP IBoy LRHS MSpe SRms
	- 'Nicky'	see *P. paniculata* 'Düsterlohe'
	- 'Nirvana'	CSam
§	- 'Norah Leigh' (v) ♀H7	CElw CMac CWGN ECha ECtt EHoe EHrv ELan ELon EWes GCal GCra GMcL IFoB LBMP LHop LRHS MHer MHol MWat NPer NSti NWad SPer SPoG SRms SWvt WCFE WCot WPtf
	- 'Orange Perfection'	see *P. paniculata* 'Prince of Orange'
	- 'Othello'	CBod CSam ECGP ECtt ELon MSpe NGdn NSti WHoo
	- 'Otley Choice'	CSam EBee ECtt GBin GWyn LRHS MRav NCGa NSti SDix SWat WHrl
	- 'Otley Purple'	MHer MSpe NRHS
	- 'P.D. Williams'	WCot
	- 'Pallas Athene'	IPot
	- 'Pastorale'	WCot
	- (Peacock Series) Peacock Cherry Red ♀H7	GMcL LRHS NRHS WCFE WTor
	- - Peacock Lilac ♀H7	EPfP GMcL LRHS
	- - Peacock Neon Purple ♀H7	LRHS NRHS WMoo
	- - Peacock Purple Bicolor	GMcL LRHS
	- - Peacock White ♀H7	GMcL LRHS NRHS WTor
	- 'Peppermint Twist'	CNor CWGN EBee ELon GKev LRHS LSou MHol MNrw NEgg NLar NRHS SPad SWvt WCot WFar WHil
	- 'Picasso'	ECtt MSpe
	- 'Pina Colada' PBR	CWGN EBee ECtt ELon NPri SPoG WFar
	- Pink Eye Flame = 'Barthirtyfive' PBR ♀H7	EPfP LBMP LSou SCob SKHP SPoG SRkn
	- 'Pink Lady' PBR	ELon SHil WFar
	- 'Pink Posie' (v)	WCot
	- Pink Red Eye Flame = 'Barthirtyfour'	EPfP LSou SPoG
	- 'Pinky Hill'	WCot WHar
	- 'Popeye'	IPot WCot
	- 'Prime Minister'	ELon
§	- 'Prince of Orange' ♀H7	CBcs CBod CSBt CSam EBee ECtt ELon EPfP GMcL IBoy LPla LRHS MAvo MCot MJak MRav MSpe MWat NAst NEgg NLar NRHS NWad SGbt SPer SWvt WBor WCot XLum
	- 'Prospero' ♀H7	CSam CSpe MRav NBid SWat
	- Purple Eye Flame = 'Barthirtythree' PBR ♀H7	LLHF LRHS LSou SKHP SRkn SWvt WFar
	- 'Purple Kiss' PBR	CWGN ECtt LSou MHol NHpl NPri SHil WFar
	- 'Purple Paradise' **new**	LRHS NRHS
	- 'Rainbow'	ELon NLar
	- 'Rectory Pink'	MSpe
	- 'Red Caribbean'	ECtt LSou NPri SHil
	- 'Red Feelings' (Feelings Series)	CBod LRHS
	- 'Red Flame'	CWGN CWld EBee ECtt EPfP GBin LRHS LSou MHol MNrw NLar SAko SKHP SRkn WFar
	- 'Red Riding Hood'	see *P. × arendsii* 'Miss Mary'
I	- 'Reddish Hesperis'	MAvo
	- 'Rembrandt'	ELon EPfP EWoo GBin LCro LOPS XLum
	- 'Rijnstroom'	CBcs ECha ECtt ELon GMcL MArl NAst NLar SCob WBrk
	- 'Robert Poore'	ECtt ELon
	- 'Roberta' **new**	LCro
	- 'Rosa Goliath'	CSam
	- 'Rosa Pastell' ♀H7	CAby CBod CDor CEnd CSpe ECGP ECtt EHrv ELon EWoo GBin GQue IPot LRHS MAvo MHol MPie MTis NBid NDov NLar SPer SPoG WAul WCot
	- 'Rosanne'	IPot
	- 'Rowie'	NBid
	- 'Sandringham'	EHrv LRHS MArl MRav MSpe NBir SPer SWvt
§	- 'Schneerausch'	SPhx
	- 'Septemberglut'	EBee EPfP LRHS NLar SHil
	- 'Shockwave' (v)	WCot
	- 'Skylight'	LSRN NBro SDix
	- Snowdrift	see *P. paniculata* 'Schneerausch'
	- 'Speed Limit 45'	WCot
	- 'Starfire' ♀H7	Widely available
I	- 'Stars and Stripes'	LRHS
	- 'Steeple Bumpstead'	WCot
I	- 'Stellata'	EBee LRHS
	- 'Sternhimmel'	MSpe MTis
	- 'Strawberry Daiquiri' PBR	WFar WHil
§	- (Sweet Summer Series) Sweet Summer Candy = 'Ditosdre' PBR	WTor
§	- - Sweet Summer Dream = 'Ditomdre' PBR	IKil MAvo
	- - Sweet Summer Fantasy = 'Ditopur' PBR	IKil WTor
§	- - Sweet Summer Favourite = 'Ditomfav' PBR ♀H7	WCAu
	- - Sweet Summer Queen = 'Ditoran' PBR	IKil
§	- - Sweet Summer Surprise = 'Ditomsur' PBR	ECtt WCAu
	- - Sweet Summer Wine = 'Ditowine' PBR	ECtt IKil
	- 'Swizzle'	CWGN ECtt LCro NPri SHil WBor WFar
	- 'Tatjana' PBR **new**	IPot
	- 'Tenor'	CMac CTri CWCL ECtt ELon EPfP GBin GBuc IBoy LEdu LRHS MCot MJak NLar SCob SWvt WCAu WSHC
	- 'Tequila Sunrise' PBR	EBee ECtt MNrw
	- 'The King' ♀H7	EBee ECtt MAvo MSpe NBro NLar SWat WSHC
	- 'Tiara' PBR (d)	EBee ECtt LRHS MPie SWvt WCot
	- 'Toits de Paris' misapplied	see *P. paniculata* 'Cool of the Evening'
§	- 'Toits de Paris' Symons-Jeune	WSHC
	- 'Twister'	EBee MNrw WFar
§	- 'Uspekh' ♀H7	Widely available
	- 'Valentina' PBR	IPot
	- 'Van Gogh'	CCse
	- 'Velvet Flame' ♀H7	EPfP LSou SKHP
	- 'Vintage Wine'	MNrw
	- 'Volcano Betty'	GBin
	- 'Watermelon Punch'	ECtt NLar NPri SHil WFar
	- 'Wendy House'	ECtt LEdu MNrw NHol WRHF
	- 'Wenn Schon Denn Schon'	EBee
	- 'White Admiral' ♀H7	CBcs CElw EBee ECtt EHrv ELan ELon EPfP EWoo GBin GCra GKev GMaP IBoy LRHS MHer MSpe MWat NEgg NNys SCob SPer SPhx SRms SWat SWvt WCAu WSHC XLum
	- White Flame = 'Bartwentynine' PBR ♀H7	CDor CMea CWGN ECtt EPfP IPot LBMP LCro LOPS LRHS LSou NLar SCob SKHP SWvt WCot

	- 'Wilhelm Kesselring'	EBee ECtt ELon LRHS MTis WBor
	- 'Willow Lodge' new	SHar
	- 'Windsor'	EBee ECtt EPfP EWTr MSpe NEgg NHol SRms SWvt
	- 'Younique White' (Paparazzi Series)	LEdu MNrw
	Paparazzi Angelina	LRHS SHil
	- Paparazzi Britney = 'Ppphl0604' new	LRHS NRHS
	- Paparazzi Gaga = 'Ppphl07301' new	LRHS NRHS
	'Peppermint Candy'	WFar
	'Petticoat'	CMea CPBP CSma ECtt SIgm WIce
	Pink Flame = 'Bartwelve'PBR	CMea EPfP LLHF LRHS LSou NLar SCob SRkn WHil
	'Pride of Rochester'	ECho ECtt LHop LRHS NRHS
§	× ***procumbens*** 'Millstream' ♀H5	ECtt
	- 'Variegata' (v)	EBee ECha ECho ECtt SRot
§	***pulvinata***	SPlb WAbe
	Purple Flame = 'Barfourteen'PBR	CBod EPfP GWyn LBMP LRHS LSou SCob SRkn WFar
	× ***rugelii***	EWld
	'Sherbet Cocktail'PBR	CWGN EBee MSCN NHol WPtf
§	***sibirica*** subsp. ***borealis***	EDAr
	'Sileniflora'	EPot
	'Special Purple Star' (Adessa Series)	EBee
	stolonifera	MNrw
I	- 'Alba'	EBee EPfP
	- 'Ariane'	ECha ECtt LSou MCot
	- 'Blue Ridge' ♀H5	EBee ECha ECtt EPfP EWld LRHS LSRN MHol MRav SIgm SRms WHar
	- 'Fran's Purple'	ECtt EWld MNrw NBro WCFE WTor
	- 'Home Fires'	EBee ECho ECtt EPfP LEdu LRHS MNrw NBro SPlb
	- 'Janusz' new	NWad
	- 'Montrose Tricolor' (v)	NBro
	- 'Pink Ridge'	XLum
	- 'Purpurea'	EBee EPfP LEdu LSou WPGP
	subulata	ESps
	- 'Alexander's Surprise'	CMea ECho ECtt EDAr EPfP EPot LRHS MAsh NBir NRHS SIgm
	- 'Amazing Grace'	CTri CWCL ECho EDAr EPfP EWes GJos IPot LHop LRHS NRHS NSla NWad SPoG WHoo WIce
	- 'Apple Blossom'	ECho NHol SPoG SRms
	- 'Atropurpurea'	ECho EDAr EPfP SPoG XLum
	- 'Bavaria'	CMea ECho ECtt EPfP GJos IPot LLHF LRHS MBel NRHS WIce
	- Beauty of Ronsdorf	see *P. subulata* 'Ronsdorfer Schöne'
	- 'Blue Eyes'	see *P. subulata* 'Oakington Blue Eyes'
	- 'Bonita'	ECho ECtt GCrg GJos LRHS MAsh NRHS WHoo WIce
	- 'Bressingham Blue Eyes'	see *P. subulata* 'Oakington Blue Eyes'
	- 'Candy Stripe'	see *P. subulata* 'Tamaongalei'
	- 'Cavaldes White'	ECtt
	- 'Coral Eye'	ECtt
	- 'Daisy Hill'	XLum
	- 'Drumm'	see *P. subulata* 'Tamaongalei'
	- Early Spring Purple = 'Barseventyfour'PBR new	LRHS NRHS
	- 'Emerald Cushion'	CTri ECho ECtt EDAr ELon EPfP LRHS NHol NHpl NLar NSla SGbt WCFE WTor XLum
	- 'Emerald Cushion Blue'	CTri EAJP ECho ECtt EPfP LRHS MAsh MHCG MHol NBir NRHS SPlb SPoG WAbe
	- 'Fort Hill'	ECtt
	- 'G.F. Wilson'	see *P. subulata* 'Lilacina'
	- 'Holly'	EPot ITim NHol NWad
	- 'Kimono'	see *P. subulata* 'Tamaongalei'
§	- 'Lilacina'	CMea ECha ECho MAsh WIce
§	- 'Maischnee'	CTri ECho ECtt MAsh SPlb
	- 'Marjorie'	ECho ECtt GJos MHer NBir SPoG
	- May Snow	see *P. subulata* 'Maischnee'
§	- 'McDaniel's Cushion' ♀H5	CBod EAJP ECha ECho ECtt EDAr ELan ELon EPfP EPot ESps EUJe GJos GMaP LHop LRHS MAsh MMuc MSCN NHar NLar NRHS SEND SPlb SPoG WCFE WHoo WIce
	- 'Mikado'	see *P. subulata* 'Tamaongalei'
	- 'Millstream Daphne'	ECho ECtt
	- 'Moonlight'	ECho SIgm
	- 'Nettleton Variation' (v)	ECho ECtt EDAr ELon EPot EWes GCrg GKev LHop LRHS MMuc NRHS SPoG WHoo
§	- 'Oakington Blue Eyes'	CTri SRms
	- 'Purple Beauty'	CMea ECho ECtt GJos GMaP LHop LLHF LRHS NHar NRHS NWad SIgm SPoG WCFE WHoo WSHC XLum
	- 'Red Wings' ♀H5	ECho ECtt EPfP ESps SRms
§	- 'Ronsdorfer Schöne'	EPfP LLHF MSCN NBir
	- 'Samson'	ECho GJos LSRN WOld
	- 'Scarlet Flame'	CMea ECho ECtt EDAr ELon EPfP EPot GJos MAsh NHol NHpl WHoo WIce
	- 'Snow Queen'	see *P. subulata* 'Maischnee'
	- 'Snowflake'	GCrg
§	- 'Tamaongalei'	CBod CMea CTri ECho ECtt EDAr ELon EWes GKev GMaP LBMP LRHS MHol MMuc NRHS NWad SIgm WCFE WIce XLum
	- 'Temiskaming'	CTri ECho ECtt EDAr EWes LHop LRHS MBel NRHS SRms WSHC
	- 'White Delight'	CMea ECho ECtt ELon EPfP ESps GJos SPoG
	- 'Winifred'	NEgg
	Sweet Summer Sensation = 'Ditosse'PBR (Sweet Summer Series)	IKil
	'Tiny Bugles'	SIgm
	Violet Flame = 'Barsixtyone'PBR	CBod CMea EPfP EUJe GAbr LPla LRHS LSun MAvo MHol NLar SCob SPer SPoG WBor WCot WHil WRHF
	White Eye Flame = 'Barsixty'PBR	CBod CBot CMea CWGN EPfP IPot LBMP LRHS NLar SCob
	'White Kimono'	ECho LRHS NRHS
	'Zwergenteppich'	EPfP LRHS NRHS

Phoenix (*Arecaceae*)

	canariensis ♀H1c	CBcs CWib EPfP ESps EUJe IVic MMuc SArc SEND SPlb SPoG
	dactylifera (F)	LTro SBig
	loureiroi new	LRHS
	- var. ***pedunculata*** from Kashmir	LTro
	reclinata	XBlo
	roebelenii ♀H1b	CDTJ NLos SBig
	- 'Multistem'	XBlo
	theophrasti	CPHo LRHS LTro

Phormium ✿ (*Hemerocallidaceae*)

§	'Alison Blackman'PBR	CBcs EBee EMOT EPfP ESps EUJe IVic LRHS LSRN MAsh MGos MJak NLar SCob SCoo SEND SHil SPoG SWvt
	'Amazing Red'	SCob

	'Apricot Queen' (v)	CAbb CBcs CCCN CSBt CWib EMOT EPfP ESps GMcL IBoy LCro LRHS LSRN MGos NLar SCob SEND SHil SPer SPoG
	Back in Black = 'Seilack'PBR	CLet EUJe LRHS SCob SHil WFar
	'Black Adder'PBR	CBcs CBot EBee EPfP GMcL IBoy ILea LBuc LPar LRHS LSRN MAsh MJak SCob SEND SPer SPoG
	'Black Rage'	CBcs EPfP LRHS NLos
	Black Velvet = 'Seivel'PBR	CSpe EUJe IBoy LRHS MHtn MSwo NPla SHil
	'Bronze Baby'	CBcs CCCN CMea CNec CSBt EHoe ELan ELon EMOT EPfP ESps LCro LRHS LSRN MGos MSwo NLar SCob SLim SPer SPoG SWvt
	'Buckland Ruby'	EBee
	'Chocolate Fingers'	CBcs
	'Chocomint'PBR	LRHS
	colensoi	see *P. cookianum*
§	***cookianum***	LPar SArc SCob
	- 'Alpinum Purpureum'	see *P. tenax* 'Nanum Purpureum'
	- subsp. ***hookeri*** 'Cream Delight' (v) ♀H4	CAbb CBcs CCCN CEnd CLet CSBt EMOT EPfP ESps EUJe GMcL IBoy LRHS LSRN MAsh MGos MSwo NFav SCob SCoo SGol SHil SPer SWvt WGrn
	- - 'Tricolor' (v) ♀H4	Widely available
	'Crimson Devil'	CBcs LRHS SHil SLim
	Dark Avocado = 'Westado'PBR	MAsh SLim
	'Dark Delight'	CBcs LTro
	'Dazzler' (v)	ESps
	'Duet' (v) ♀H3	CBcs CCCN EBee EPfP ESps MMuc SEND SWvt WHar
	'Dusky Chief'	CSBt EPfP NLar
	'Evening Glow' (v)	CBcs CCCN ELan ELon EMOT EPfP ESps GMcL LCro LRHS LSRN LTro MGos NLar SCob SEND SHil SPoG SWvt WGrn
	'Firebird'	ELon LRHS LSRN SHil SWvt
	'Flamingo' (v)	CBcs CCCN CDTJ CNec ELan ELon EMOT EPfP GMcL LRHS LSou MGos MHol NLar SCob SLim SPer SPoG
	'Gold Ray' (v)	CBcs EBee EPfP EUJe GMcL LRHS MJak NLos SCob SCoo SHil SWvt WHil
	'Gold Sword' (v)	CCCN CSBt EPfP ESps GMcL LRHS NEgg SCob
	'Golden Alison'	see *P.* 'Alison Blackman'
	'Green Sword'	CBcs CCCN
	'Jack Spratt' (v)	EHoe SWvt WHar
	'Jessie'	NLos
	'Jester' (v)	Widely available
	'Limelight'	SEND SWvt
§	'Maori Chief' (v)	CSBt EMOT EPfP ESps LRHS SWvt WFar
	'Maori Eclipse'	GMcL
§	'Maori Maiden' (v)	CCCN CDul CTri ELon EPfP GMcL LRHS MSwo SWvt
§	'Maori Queen' (v)	CBcs CCCN CChe CDTJ ELon EPfP ESps EUJe ILea LCro LRHS MGos MSwo SCob SCoo SEND SHil SPer SPoG SWvt
§	'Maori Sunrise' (v)	CBcs CCCN ELon GMcL IArd LCro LOPS LRHS LSRN MGos SCob SCoo SLim SPer SWvt
	'Margaret Jones'PBR	CBcs CCCN LSRN SLim
	'Moonraker'PBR	CBcs MHol
	'Pink Jester'	GMcL
	'Pink Panther' (v)	CAbb CBcs CCCN CDul CWib ELan ELon EMOT EPfP ESps LRHS LSRN MGos NLar NPla SCob SHil SPoG
	'Pink Stripe' (v)	CBcs CChe CNec CSBt EPfP GMcL LCro LRHS MAsh MGos MJak SCob SHil SPoG SWvt
	'Platt's Black'	CBcs CCCN EMOT EPfP ESps GMcL IBoy LCro LRHS LSRN MGos MJak MSwo NBir NLar NPla SCob SHil SLim SPer SPoG SWvt WFar WGrn
	'Rainbow Chief'	see *P.* 'Maori Chief'
	'Rainbow Glossy'	NLos
	'Rainbow Maiden'	see *P.* 'Maori Maiden'
	'Rainbow Queen'	see *P.* 'Maori Queen'
	'Rainbow Sunrise'	see *P.* 'Maori Sunrise'
I	'Rubrum'	SEND
	'Sundowner' (v) ♀H3	CBcs CCCN CDul CLet CSBt CTsd EBee ELan EMOT EPfP ESps GMcL LCro LRHS MAsh MGos MJak MMuc NBir NEgg NLar SCob SCoo SEND SHil SLim SPer SPoG SWvt WGrn
	'Sunset' (v)	CBcs CCCN CSBt SWvt
	'Surfer' (v)	CBcs WGrn
	'Surfer Bronze'	CBcs CCCN
	'Surfer Green'	CCCN NLos
	'Sussex Velvet'	SCoo SLim
	tenax	Widely available
	- 'All Black'	LRHS MGos SCoo SHil
	- 'Bronze'	CTsd SWvt
	- 'Chocolate Dream'	IBoy
	- 'Co-ordination'	CBcs CCCN EMOT
	- dwarf	CSpe
	- 'Joker' (v)	CBcs CMea ELon NLar NLos
*	- ***lineatum***	SEND
§	- 'Nanum Purpureum'	SArc
	- Purpureum Group ♀H4	CBar CDul CLet CWib EBee ELan ELon EPfP ESps GMcL IBoy LPar LRHS MJak MMuc MSwo NLar SCob SEND SGol SHil SLim SLon SPer SPlb WFar XLum
	- 'Thumbelina'	CCCN
	- 'Tiny Tiger'	EPfP
	- 'Variegatum' (v) ♀H5	CDTJ CDul CLet EBee EPfP GMcL LPar MGos MJak MMuc SArc SCob SEND SPer SRms
	- 'Veneer'PBR	NLos
	- 'Yellow Queen'	WFar
	variegated (v)	SCob
	'Yellow Wave' (v) ♀H4	Widely available

Photinia ✿ (*Rosaceae*)

	arbutifolia	see *Heteromeles salicifolia*
	beauverdiana var. ***notabilis***	CJun EPfP NLar
	davidiana	CMCN CMac CTri ELan EPfP GMcL IDee MGil MRav NLar SCob SRms SVen
	- PAB 8097 **new**	LEdu
	- 'Palette' (v)	CBcs CDul CMac CWib EBee EHoe ELan ELon EPfP ESps GMcL LHop LRHS MAsh MGos MMuc MSwo NEgg NLar SCob SGol SPer SPoG SRms SWvt WFar WMat WMoo
	- var. ***undulata*** 'Fructu Luteo'	CAbP MMuc MRav SEND
	- - 'Prostrata'	CMac CTri MRav NLar
	× ***fraseri***	LPar WTSh
I	- 'Atropurpurea Nana'	EPfP MGos
	- 'Birmingham'	CMac EWes

	- 'Canivily' ♀H5	CEnd CRos ESps IVic LRHS MGos MPkF NLar SGol SHil
	- Cracklin' Red = 'Parred'PBR	WMoo
	- 'Goldstar'	MPkF
*	- 'Ilexifolium'	ESwi
	- 'Little Red Robin'	Widely available
	- 'Louise' (v)	CSBt EBee GMcL LBuc LRHS MGos SHil SPoG
	- Magical Volcano = 'Kolmavoca'	LCro NLar SGol
	- Pink Marble = 'Cassini' (v) ♀H5	Widely available
	- 'Red Robin' ♀H5	Widely available
	- 'Red Select'	WPat
	- 'Robusta'	CMac EPfP LRHS SWvt
I	- 'Robusta Compacta'	LSRN
	glabra	SArc
§	- 'Parfait' (v)	CAbP CMac EBee LRHS MAsh SLon
	- 'Pink Lady'	see *P. glabra* 'Parfait'
	- 'Rubens'	EPfP LRHS MAsh MRav
	- 'Variegata'	see *P. glabra* 'Parfait'
	integrifolia HWJ 946	WCru
	lasiogyna	CMCN
	lucida	WCru
	microphylla B&SWJ 11837	WCru
	- HWJ 564	WCru
	niitakayamensis	MHid
	- CWJ 12435	WCru
	'Redstart'	CAbP CMac EBee ELan EPfP LRHS MMuc NLar SLon SPer SWvt WFar WMoo
§	***serratifolia***	CAbP CBcs CBot CDul CMCN ELan EPfP NLar SArc SBrt SEND SPer WFar WPGP
	- Curly Fantasy = 'Kolcurl'PBR	IVic LRHS MRav NLar
	- 'Jenny'	LRHS NLar WFar
	serrulata	see *P. serratifolia*
	Super Hedge = 'Branpara'PBR	GBin LRHS LSou MSwo WFar
	'Super Red'	CSBt NLar
	villosa	CAbP CTho EPfP MHid WPat
	- B&SWJ 8665	WCru
	- var. ***coreana*** B&SWJ 8789	WCru
	- var. ***laevis***	EBee EPfP WPGP
	- - B&SWJ 8877	WCru
	- f. ***maximowicziana***	CJun NLar
*	- var. ***zollingeri*** B&SWJ 8903	WCru

Phragmites (*Poaceae*)

	sp.	CHab
	from Sichuan, China	EPPr
§	***australis***	CBen CHab CWat MMuc MSKA MWLS NMir SVic SWat WMAq WPnP XLum
	- subsp. ***australis*** var. ***striatopictus***	EPPr
	- - 'Variegatus' (v)	CBen CKno CWat EBee EPPr EShb LLWG MMuc MPie NBir SEND SMad WWtn XLum
	- subsp. ***humilis***	CHab
	- subsp. ***pseudodonax***	EPPr
	communis	see *P. australis*
	karka 'Candy Stripe' (v)	CBen EPPr MSKA

Phuopsis (*Rubiaceae*)

§	***stylosa***	CBod CHVG CTri CWld EBee ECha ELan EPPr EPfP GAbr GMaP IFoB LSou MHer MMuc MSpe NBid NBir NBro NChi NSti SEND SPoG SRms SWvt WMoo WTcb XLum
	- 'Purpurea'	EBee ECGP MNrw MRav NChi NDov

Phycella (*Amaryllidaceae*)

	cyrtanthoides	WCot

Phygelius (*Scrophulariaceae*)

	aequalis	MRav WMoo
	- ***albus***	see *P. aequalis* 'Yellow Trumpet'
	- 'Aureus'	see *P. aequalis* 'Yellow Trumpet'
	- 'Cream Trumpet'	see *P. aequalis* 'Yellow Trumpet'
	- 'Indian Chief'	see *P.* × *rectus* 'African Queen'
	- 'Sani Pass'	ELon GMaP MHer SCob SPlb
	- 'Trewidden Pink' ♀H5	CLet CWib EBee ELan ELon GBin LHop MHer MSCN SWvt WMoo XLum
§	- 'Yellow Trumpet' ♀H5	CSBt CTca CWib ELan ELon EPfP ESps GKev GMaP GMcL IBoy LSRN MAsh MMuc SEND SGbt SLim SWvt WMoo
	Candy Drops Cream = 'Kerphycrem'PBR (Candy Drops Series)	NGBl SCob
	capensis	CHll CWib ELan GCra GMcL MHer SRms WOut WRHF
	'Golden Gate'	see *P. aequalis* 'Yellow Trumpet'
	Logan form	GBin
	'Midas Touch'	NLar
	New Sensation = 'Blaphy'PBR	EPfP GMcL MRav SCob SWvt
	'Passionate'PBR	NLar
§	× ***rectus*** 'African Queen' ♀H5	EBee ELan EPfP ESps LPot MMuc MRav MSwo NBir NGdn SEND SPlb SWvt WKif XLum
	- 'Bridgetown Beauty'	GCal
	- (Candy Drops Series) Candy Drops Deep Rose = 'Kerphyros'PBR	NGBl
	- - Candy Drops Red = 'Kerphyrouge'PBR	GMcL
	- 'Devil's Tears' ♀H5	CBcs ELan ESps LPot LRHS MMuc NEgg SCob SEND SLim SWvt WHar WMoo
	- 'Ivory Twist'	ELon LHop
	- 'Jodie Southon'	ELon LSou SDys WCot
	- 'Moonraker'	CAby CBcs CHll CRos CTri ELan ELon EPfP GBin GWyn LRHS MAsh MHer MRav NGdn NLar SCob SEND SPer SPlb SRms WHil WKif XLum
	- 'Salmon Leap' ♀H5	CBcs CTri ELan EPfP GBuc LRHS LSRN MBNS MGos MMuc MRav NEgg NFav SCob SEND SLim SPlb SWvt
	- Somerford Funfair Series	IBoy
	- - Somerford Funfair Apricot = 'Yapapr'	SWvt
	- - Somerford Funfair Coral = 'Yapcor'PBR	EBee EPfP LPot LRHS MAsh NCou NLar SBod SCob SLim SRkn SWvt
	- - Somerford Funfair Cream = 'Yapcre'PBR	EPfP LRHS NLar SLim SWvt
	- - Somerford Funfair Orange = 'Yapor'PBR	EPfP LRHS MAsh NLar SLim SPoG SWvt
	- - Somerford Funfair Wine = 'Yapwin'	CAby CBot CChe CDul ELan EPfP LPot LRHS MAsh MBNS NPri SCob SLim SPer SPoG SWvt
	- - Somerford Funfair Yellow = 'Yapyel'PBR	EPfP LRHS MAsh SLim SPoG SWvt

§	- 'Winchester Fanfare'	CLet CSBt ELan GBin GMcL GWyn LRHS MGos MRav SCob SEND SLim SWvt WKif
	- 'Winton Fanfare'	see *P.* × *rectus* 'Winchester Fanfare'
	'Rory'^{PBR}	SRms
	Snow Queen = 'Crosnoque'^{PBR} (Croftway Series)	SCob

Phyla (*Verbenaceae*)

	lanceolata	LLWG
§	***nodiflora***	ECha MHer SRms WJek XSen
	- 'Alba'	MMuc SEND
§	- var. ***canescens***	XLum
	- var. ***rosea*** new	SRot

Phylica (*Rhamnaceae*)

pubescens	CTre

Phyllanthus (*Phyllanthaceae*)

angustifolius new	EPed

× *Phylliopsis* (*Ericaceae*)

'Coppelia' Υ^{H5}	EPot ITim NHar
'Crinoline'	NHar
hillieri 'Askival'	EPot WThu
- 'Pinocchio'	GEdr NHar WThu
- 'Sugar Plum'	CCCN GEdr LRHS NHar SWvt WThu
'Hobgoblin'	ITim
'Mermaid'	EPot ITim NHar WThu
'Sprite'	ITim
'Swanhilde'	WThu

Phyllitis see *Asplenium*

scolopendrium	see *Asplenium scolopendrium*

Phyllocladus ✿ (*Podocarpaceae*)

trichomanoides var. ***alpinus***	CDul NWad WThu

Phyllodoce (*Ericaceae*)

	aleutica	ECho GKev NHar NLar SRms WThu
§	- subsp. ***glanduliflora*** 'Flora Slack'	WThu
	- - white-flowered	see *P. aleutica* subsp. *glanduliflora* 'Flora Slack'
	caerulea Υ^{H5}	ECho
	- ***japonica***	see *P. nipponica*
	- 'Murray Lyon'	NHar WThu
	- 'W.M. Buchanan's Peach Seedling'	NHar
	empetriformis	ECho SRms WThu
§	***nipponica***	NHar WThu
	'Peach'	NLar WThu
	tsugifolia	NLar

Phyllostachys ✿ (*Poaceae*)

	angusta	ERod MWht SBig
	arcana	CJng
	- 'Luteosulcata'	CEnt CFil CJng ERod MMuc MWht
§	***atrovaginata***	CJng ERod SGol
	aurea Υ^{H5}	Widely available
	- 'Albovariegata' (v)	CJng CRos ENBC EPfP ERod LRHS MWht NRHS SPoG
	- 'Flavescens Inversa'	CJng ERod MWht
	- 'Holochrysa'	CDTJ CFil CJng CJun ERod MMuc MWht NLar
	- 'Koi'	CDTJ CEnt CJng ERod MWht SBig SGol
	aureocaulis	see *P. aureosulcata* f. *aureocaulis*, *P. vivax* f. *aureocaulis*
	aureosulcata	CJng CWib ERod LPar MWht WMoo
	- f. ***alata***	see *P. aureosulcata* f. *pekinensis*
§	- f. ***aureocaulis***	Widely available
	- 'Harbin'	ERod
	- 'Harbin Inversa'	ERod
	- 'Lama Tempel'	CDTJ CFil CJun
§	- f. ***pekinensis***	SBig
	- f. ***spectabilis*** Υ^{H5}	Widely available
	bambusoides	CDTJ CJng ERod SBig SDix
	- 'Allgold'	see *P. bambusoides* 'Holochrysa'
	- 'Castillonii' Υ^{H5}	CBcs CEnt CJng ENBC ERod EUJe EWes LEdu MMuc MWht NLar SBig SDix SEND
	- 'Castillonii Inversa'	CJng ENBC ERod LEdu MWht WPGP
	- 'Castillonii Inversa Variegata' (v)	CJng
	- 'Castillonii Variegata' (v)	ERod
§	- 'Holochrysa' Υ^{H5}	CDTJ CEnt CJng ERod MMuc MWht SEND WPGP
	- 'Kawadana' (v)	CJng ERod
	- f. ***lacrima-deae***	CDTJ
	- 'Marliacea'	CJng ERod SBig
	- 'Sulphurea'	see *P. bambusoides* 'Holochrysa'
	- 'Tanakae'	CDTJ SBig
	- 'Violascens'	SBig
	bissetii Υ^{H5}	Widely available
	congesta misapplied	see *P. atrovaginata*
	decora	CJng ERod MMuc MWht
	dulcis	CEnt CFGn CJng EPfP ERod MWht SBig
§	***edulis***	CAgr CBlu CJng ELon ERod SArc SBig SPlb
	- 'Bicolor'	CJng
§	- 'Heterocycla'	XBlo
	- f. ***pubescens***	see *P. edulis*
	fimbriligula	CJng
	flexuosa	CBcs CEnt CJng MWht SGol
	glauca	EPfP ERod LCro MWht SBig
	- f. ***yunzhu***	CJng ERod MWht
	heteroclada	CBlu CEnt CJng
	- 'Solid Stem' misapplied	see *P. purpurata* 'Straight Stem'
	heterocycla	see *P. edulis* 'Heterocycla'
	- var. ***pubescens***	see *P. edulis*
	humilis	CEnt CJng ENBC ERod EUJe MMuc MWht SBig
	incarnata	CJng
	iridescens Υ^{H5}	CJng ERod ETod MWht SBig
	lithophila	ERod
	makinoi	ERod
	mannii	ERod MWht
	nidularia	CJng ERod SBig
	nigra Υ^{H5}	Widely available
	- 'Boryana'	CCVT CEnd CEnt CJng EPfP ERod EUJe MGos MMuc MWht SBig SEND SWvt WMoo
	- 'Hale'	MWht
	- f. ***henonis*** Υ^{H5}	CJng ENBC ERod MMuc MWht NLar SBig SEND SGol WPGP
	- 'Megurochiku'	CJng ERod MWht
	- f. ***nigra***	CFil
	- f. ***punctata***	CJng ENBC ERod MAvo MMuc SEND WMoo
	- 'Tosaensis'	ERod
	nuda	CJng ERod MWht
	- f. ***localis***	ERod MWht
	parvifolia	CEnt CJng ERod MWht
	platyglossa	ERod

praecox	CJng
- f. ***viridisulcata***	CJng ERod
prominens	ERod
propinqua	CJng ERod MWht
§ ***purpurata*** 'Straight Stem'	MWht
rubicunda	CJng
rubromarginata	CEnt CJng ERod MMuc MWht
'Shanghai 3'	ERod
stimulosa	CJng ERod MWht
sulphurea 'Houzeau'	ERod MMuc SEND
§ - f. ***sulphurea***	CJng ERod
- 'Sulphurea'	see *P. sulphurea* f. *sulphurea*
§ - f. ***viridis***	ERod SBig
violascens	CAgr CEnt CJng ERod EUJe MWht SBig
viridiglaucescens	CAgr CDTJ CJng ERod ETod MBrN MMuc MWht SBig SEND
viridis	see *P. sulphurea* f. *viridis*
vivax	CJng ENBC EPfP ERod EUJe MMuc MWht NLar SBig
§ - f. ***aureocaulis*** ♀H5	CAbb CAgr CBcs CCVT CDul CEnd CEnt CJng ENBC EPfP ERod ETod EUJe IBoy LCro LEdu LRHS LSRN MGos MMuc MWht NLar SBig SCob SEND SGol WPGP
- - 'Huangwenzhu'	CDTJ CJng ENBC ERod EUJe MWht
- 'Katrin'	LEdu
* - 'Sulphurea'	XBlo

× *Phyllothamnus* (*Ericaceae*)

erectus	WThu

Phymatosorus (*Polypodiaceae*)

§ ***diversifolius***	WPGP

Phymosia (*Malvaceae*)

§ ***umbellata***	WPGP

Phyodina see *Callisia*

Physalis (*Solanaceae*)

alkekengi ♀H7	CTri EPfP ESps LPot NBir NLar NPnk SWvt
- var. ***franchetii***	CBcs CBod CMac CSBt EBee ECha ELan EPfP LCro LRHS MBel MHer MNrw NBir NBro NEgg SMad SPer SPoG SRms WFar WOld WTcb
- - dwarf	LRHS NLar
- - 'Gigantea'	CWld ECGP LSun NLar SPlb WFar
- - 'Gnome'	see *P. alkekengi* var. *franchetii* 'Zwerg'
- - 'Variegata' (v)	EWes LEdu SEND WPGP
§ - - 'Zwerg'	EBee GMcL LRHS NRHS
- 'Halloween King'	EBee LRHS NLar NRHS SPoG
- 'Halloween Queen'	LRHS NLar NRHS SPoG WHil
campanula B&SWJ 10409	WCru
edulis	see *P. peruviana*
§ ***peruviana*** (F)	CCCN SHDw SPlb SVic

Physaria (*Brassicaceae*)

alpina	SPlb
saximontana	GKev

Physocarpus (*Rosaceae*)

capitatus 'Tilden Park'	SGol
'Korona'	WFar
Little Devil	see *P. opulifolius* 'Donna May'
'Midnight'	GBin LRHS NEoE WHar WMoo
opulifolius Amber Jubilee = 'Jefam'PBR	ELan EPfP LCro
- 'Angel Gold'	CNec EBee ELan LRHS MAsh NPri SPoG
- 'Burning Embers'	SRms
- 'Chameleon'	EMil GBin LBuc NEoE SPoG WMoo
- Coppertina	see *P. opulifolius* Diable D'Or
- 'Dart's Gold' ♀H7	Widely available
§ - Diable D'Or = 'Mindia'PBR	CBar CRos EPfP IBoy LCro LRHS LSRN MAsh MBlu MGos MPkF NEgg NLar NOra NPla SGbt SGol SHil WCot WMoo
- 'Diabolo'PBR ♀H7	Widely available
§ - 'Donna May'PBR	ELan EPfP EShb NEoE SCob
§ - Lady in Red = 'Tuilad'PBR ♀H7	Widely available
- Little Angel = 'Hoogi016' **new**	LCro
§ - 'Luteus'	CWib MRav WMoo
- 'Nugget'	CRos LRHS
- 'Red Baron'	EBee GMcL LHop
- Ruby Spice	see *P. opulifolius* Lady in Red
- Summer Moon = 'Tuimon' **new**	NEoE WMoo
- Summer Wine = 'Seward'PBR	EPfP EWes LHop LRHS MAsh
ribesifolius 'Aureus'	see *P. opulifolius* 'Luteus'

Physoplexis (*Campanulaceae*)

§ ***comosa*** ♀H5	CPBP EPot WAbe

Physostegia (*Lamiaceae*)

angustifolia	GQui NBre
I 'Aquatica'	LLWG
§ ***virginiana***	CBod CSBt CTri GMaP LHop MBel SRms SWat WCFE WOld
- 'Alba'	CBod CNec CSBt CTri EAJP EBee EHrv ELon GAbr GJos GMaP LEdu LSun MArt NChi SBod SDix SPlb XLum
§ - 'Crown of Snow'	EBee EPfP GMcL GWyn MHer MRav SPoG SWvt WHar WMoo
- 'Crystal Peek White'	CBod EBee
- 'Miss Manners'	CMac ECGP ECtt LRHS MPie NBre NCGa NGdn NLar
- 'Olympic Gold' (v)	NWad
- 'Pink Manners'	STPC
- 'Red Beauty'	WTcb
- 'Rose Crown'	SPer
- 'Rose Queen'	CTri NBre NChi WFar WTcb
- 'Rosea'	CNec EPfP GJos GPSL GWyn IFoB LSun MMuc NGdn SHar SPad SPoG SWvt WHar WHrl
- Schneekrone	see *P. virginiana* 'Crown of Snow'
- 'Snow Queen'	see *P. virginiana* 'Summer Snow'
§ - var. ***speciosa*** 'Bouquet Rose'	CBod CMac EBee ECha EHrv EPfP LEdu LRHS MRav NBir NLar SGbt SPer SWvt WCAu WHar WMoo WRHF XLum
- - Rose Bouquet	see *P. virginiana* var. *speciosa* 'Bouquet Rose'
- - 'Variegata' (v)	CBod CMac EBee ECtt EHoe EHrv ELan ELon EPfP GLog LHop MRav NBir NGdn NHol SPer SPoG SRms SWat WCAu WCot WFar XLum
§ - 'Summer Snow' ♀H7	CBcs ECha ELan EPfP EWoo LHop LRHS NGBl NLar SPer SRms SWat WCAu WCot
- 'Summer Spire'	EHrv
- 'Vivid' ♀H7	CBod CMac ECha ELan ELon EPfP LRHS MHer MNrw MPie MRav NCGa NEgg NGBl NHol NLar SDix

	SPer SPlb SRms WCot WGwG WHil WWtn XLum

Phyteuma (*Campanulaceae*)

balbisii	see *P. cordatum*
betonicifolium	EPPr
charmelii	GEdr WHoo
comosum	see *Physoplexis comosa*
§ ***cordatum***	GJos
halleri	see *P. ovatum*
hemisphaericum	ECho GEdr GJos NSla
humile	WThu
nigrum	ECho GEdr LLHF NBid WBor WCot
orbiculare	GEdr GJos
§ ***ovatum***	SPlb
scheuchzeri	CWld EBee ECho EPfP EWld GEdr GWyn MMrt SMad SPad SRms WCot WIce WRHF WTcb XLum
spicatum	GEdr GJos NBro
- subsp. ***coeruleum***	GJos

Phytolacca (*Phytolaccaceae*)

acinosa	EWld SBrt SWat WHil
- HWJ 647	WCru
§ ***americana***	CAby CArn CLet EBee ELan EPfP ESwi EUJe GPoy MBNS MHer MPie NChi NLos SIde SRms SWat WHlf
- B&SWJ 8817A	WCru
- 'Silberstein' (v)	EBee ESwi MBNS MHol NLos WHer
- 'Variegata' (v)	CLet
bogotensis	WCru
clavigera	see *P. polyandra*
decandra	see *P. americana*
dioica	CArn SPlb
esculenta	LEdu SEND
icosandra B&SWJ 8988	WCru
- Purpurascens Group B&SWJ 11251	GCal SRms WCru
japonica B&SWJ 3005	NBid WCru
- B&SWJ 3522	WCru
octandra B&SWJ 9514	WCru
§ ***polyandra***	NBid NBro SRms
rivinoides B&SWJ 10264	WCru
rugosa B&SWJ 10263	WCru

Picea ✿ (*Pinaceae*)

§ ***abies***	CAco CCVT CDul CLnd CMac CSBt CTho CTri CWib EPfP ESps GMcL IBoy LBuc LRHS MJak MMuc NEgg NWea SCoo SEND SPoG WHar WHed WMou WTSh
- 'Acrocona' ♀^{H7}	LRHS NLar
- 'Archer'	CKen
- 'Aurea'	ELan
- 'Barus'	NLar
- 'Brunn' **new**	NLar
- 'Capitata'	CKen
- 'Clanbrassiliana' ♀^{H7}	CKen ELan LRHS NWad
- Columnaris Group	NEgg
I - 'Congesta'	CKen
- 'Crippsii'	CKen
I - 'Cruenta'	CKen SLim
- 'Cupressina'	CKen
- 'Diffusa'	CKen NLar
- 'Dumpy'	CKen NHol
- 'Excelsa'	see *P. abies*
- 'Fahndrich'	CKen CMen
- 'Formanek'	CMen
- 'Four Winds'	CKen
- 'Frohburg'	CKen LRHS NEgg
- 'Gold Drift'	NLar
- 'Gregoryana'	CKen
- 'Heartland Gem'	CKen
- 'Horace Wilson'	CKen CMen
- 'Humilis'	CKen
- 'Hystrix'	CMen NLar NWad
- 'Inversa' ♀^{H7}	CKen MBlu SLim
- 'J.W. Daisy's White'	see *P. glauca* var. *albertiana* 'J.W. Daisy's White'
- 'Jana'	CKen NLar
- 'Jermyns Broom No. 1'	CKen
- 'Kral'	CKen
- 'Little Gem' ♀^{H7}	CKen CMen ELan ESps EUJe GEdr LRHS MAsh MGos NHol NLar NWad NWea SCoo SLim
- 'Marcel'	CKen
- 'Mini Kalous'	CKen
- 'Nana Compacta'	CKen CMen MAsh
- 'Nidiformis' ♀^{H7}	CKen CMac CMen CSBt CTri ESps EUJe GMcL IBoy LPot LRHS MGos NWea SGol SRms
- 'Norrköping'	CKen
- 'Ohlendorffii'	CKen GMcL
- 'Pachyphylla'	CKen
- 'Pseudomaxwellii'	LRHS
- 'Pumila'	WCFE
- 'Pusch'	CKen CMen NLar SLim
- 'Pygmaea'	CKen LPar NWad
- 'Reflexa'	NEgg
- 'Remontii'	NWea
- 'Rydal' ♀^{H7}	CBcs CDul CKen LRHS MAsh NEgg NLar
- 'Saint Mary's Broom'	NEgg
- 'Spring Fire'	CKen
- 'Tompa'	NLar
- 'Typner'	CKen NLar
- 'Vermont Gold'	CKen NLar
- 'Walter Bron'	NLar
- Will's Dwarf	see *P. abies* 'Wills Zwerg'
§ - 'Wills Zwerg'	ELan SGol
§ ***alcoquiana*** var. ***alcoquiana***	NWea SLim
- var. ***reflexa***	MPkF
asperata 'Mongolei' **new**	NLar
bicolor	see *P. alcoquiana* var. *alcoquiana*
I - 'Prostrata'	NEgg
breweriana ♀^{H6}	CDul CMac CTho EPfP GKin IDee LEdu LRHS MBlu MGos MJak NEgg NLar NWea SLim SSta WCFE WTSh
- 'Kohout's Dwarf'	CKen NLar
chihuahuana	SLim
engelmannii	CDul NWea
- 'Bush's Lace'	NLar
- 'Compact'	SLim
- subsp. ***engelmannii***	CKen
- 'Jasper'	CKen NLar
- 'Lace'	SLim
glauca	LPar NWea SWvt
- var. ***albertiana*** **new**	LPar
- - Alberta Blue = 'Haal'PBR	CKen LRHS
- - 'Alberta Globe' ♀^{H7}	ESps EUJe GEdr GKin GMcL LRHS MAsh MGos NEgg NHol NWad SCoo SPoG
- - 'Conica' ♀^{H7}	CBcs CMac CMea CSBt EPfP ESps EUJe GMcL IBoy LBrs LCro LOPS LPar LRHS MAsh MGos MJak MMuc NEgg NHol NOrn NWad NWea SEND SGol SPer SPoG SRms SWvt WCFE
- - 'Gnome'	CKen

§	- - 'J.W. Daisy's White' ♀H7	CBcs CKen ELan EPfP ESps GKin LRHS MAsh MGos MJak NHol NLar NWad NWea SCoo SLim SPoG
	- - 'Laurin' ♀H7	CKen NWad SLim
	- - 'Lilliput'	CKen NLar NWad NWea SPoG
	- - 'Piccolo'	CBcs CKen NEgg NLar NWad SLim
	- - 'Sander's Blue'	CAco CKen EPfP GKin LRHS SPoG
	- - 'Tiny'	CKen NWad
	- 'Arneson's Blue Variegated' (v)	CKen MAsh SLim
	- 'Biesenthaler Frühling'	CKen SLim
	- 'Blue Planet'	CKen IVic
	- 'Coerulea'	NEgg
	- 'Cy's Wonder'	CKen
	- 'Dendroforma Gold'	CKen
	- 'Echiniformis' ♀H7	CKen ESps GMcL LRHS NLar
	- 'Goldilocks'	CKen
§	- 'Nana'	CKen
	- 'Pendula'	CKen SLim
	- 'Pixie'	CKen
	- 'Pixie Dust'	CKen
	- 'Rainbow's End' (v)	CKen NLar
	- 'Sleeping Giant'	NLar
	- 'Spring Surprise'	CKen
	- 'Zuckerhut'	LRHS
	glehnii 'Sasanosei'	CKen
	- 'Shimezusei'	CKen
	jezoensis	CKen CMen NWea
	- 'Aurea'	SLim
	- subsp. ***hondoensis***	CMen
	- 'Marianbad'	CKen
	- 'Mariánské Làzně' **new**	NLar
	- 'Yatsabusa'	CKen CMen
	koraiensis	CDul NWea
	kosteri 'Glauca'	see *P. pungens* 'Koster'
	koyamae 'Bedgebury Blue'	SLim
	- 'Bedgebury Cascade'	SLim
	likiangensis	CDul CMCN EBtc EPfP
	- var. ***balfouriana***	see *P. likiangensis* var. *rubescens*
§	- var. ***rubescens***	SLim WHor
	mariana	EPfP NWea
	- 'Austria Broom'	CKen
	- 'Bill Archer'	NWad
	- 'Blue Teardrop'	CKen
	- 'Fastigiata'	CKen
	- 'Nana' ♀H7	CKen CMac CMen EPfP GEdr GMcL MAsh MGos MMuc NHol NWad NWea SCoo SLim SPoG
I	- 'Pygmaea'	CKen NWad
	meyeri	CTho EPfP
	morrisonicola	CKen
	obovata var. ***coerulea***	EPfP
	omorika ♀H7	CBcs CCVT CDul CJun CMCN CMac CTho EPfP ESps MMuc NWea SEND SEWo WCFE WHar WMou
I	- 'Aurea'	ESps
	- 'Berliner's Weeper' witches' broom **new**	NLar
	- 'de Ruyter'	IVic NEgg
	- 'Frohnleiten'	CKen
	- 'Frondenberg'	CKen
	- 'Halone'	CKen
	- 'Karel'	CKen
	- 'Minimax'	CKen
	- 'Nana' ♀H7	LRHS NEgg SLim WCFE
	- 'Pendula' ♀H7	MBlu SLim SSta
	- 'Pendula Bruns'	MBlu SLim SMad
	- 'Pimoko'	CKen NEgg NLar SLim
	- 'Pimpf'	IVic
	- 'Pygmy'	CKen

	- 'Schneverdingen'	CKen
	- 'Tijn'	CKen SLim
	- 'Treblitsch'	CKen NLar SLim
	- 'Tremonia'	NLar
	orientalis ♀H7	CDul IDee WThu
	- 'Aurea' (v) ♀H7	ELan MJak SMad
	- 'Aureospicata'	CTho MAsh MBlu NEgg SLim
	- 'Bergman's Gem'	CKen
	- 'Golden Start'	NEgg NLar SLim
	- 'Juwel'	CKen NLar
	- 'Kenwith'	CKen
	- 'Mount Vernon'	CKen NLar
	- Nana Group	GKin
	- 'Professor Langner'	CKen NLar
	- 'Shadow's Broom'	CKen CMen NEgg
	- 'Skylands' ♀H7	CKen ELan MAsh NEgg NLar SLim
	- 'Tom Thumb'	CKen NLar
	- 'Wittboldt'	CKen
	pungens	CCVT ESps LPar
	- 'Blaukissen'	CKen
	- 'Blue Diamond'	LRHS MJak SPoG
	- 'Blue Pearl'	CKen NLar
	- 'Donna's Rainbow'	NLar
	- 'Edith' ♀H7	CDul CKen ESps GMcL NEgg NLar NOra NOrn SEWo SLim WMat
	- 'Erich Frahm'	CAco CCVT GMcL MAsh NLar NOra SPoG WMat
	- 'Fat Albert' ♀H7	CCVT LRHS NEgg NWea SLim SPoG
	- 'Frieda'	NLar SLim
	- Glauca Group	CAco CCVT CDul CMac EWTr LPar MMuc NWea SCoo SEND SPoG WHar WMou WTSh
	- - 'Glauca Procumbens'	CKen NWea
§	- - 'Glauca Prostrata'	SLim
I	- - 'Globosa' ♀H7	CBcs CCVT CKen CSBt EPfP ESps GMcL LPar LRHS MAsh NEgg NHol NWea SCoo SLim SPoG WCFE
	- - 'Hoopsii' ♀H7	CAco CDul EPfP ESps GKin GMcL IVic LPar LRHS MAsh MGos MJak NEgg NLar NOrn NWea SLim SPoG SWvt WMat
	- - 'Iseli Fastigiate'	CCVT GKin GMcL MAsh NEgg SCoo SLim SPoG
§	- - 'Koster'	EPfP ESps LPar MAsh NWea SPoG
	- - 'Moerheimii'	CDul
	- - 'Oldenburg'	NEgg NWea SLim
	- 'Glauca Globosa'	see *P. pungens* (Glauca Group) 'Globosa'
	- 'Globe'	CKen CMen LPar
	- 'Gloria'	CKen SLim
	- 'Koster Fastigiata'	GMcL
	- 'Lucky Strike'	CKen NLar
	- 'Maigold' (v)	CKen IVic NLar SLim
	- 'Montgomery'	CKen
	- 'Mrs Cesarini'	CKen NLar SLim
	- 'Nimetz'	CKen
	- 'Prostrata'	see *P. pungens* (Glauca Group) 'Glauca Prostrata'
	- 'Ruby Teardrops' **new**	NLar
	- 'Saint Mary's Broom'	CKen
	- 'Snowkiss'	NEgg
	- 'The Blues'	CKen
	- 'Thuem'	NEgg
	- 'Waldbrunn'	CKen NLar SLim
	- 'Wendy'	CKen
	- 'Yvette'	NLar
	purpurea	EPfP LRHS
	retroflexa	NWea
	schrenkiana	CMCN
	sitchensis	CAco CDul MAsh MMuc NWea WTSh

	- 'Harwood Silver'	SLim
	- 'Nana'	NLar
	- 'Papoose'	GMcL SLim
	- 'Pévé Wiesje'	NLar
	- 'Silberzwerg'	CKen NLar SLim
	- 'Strypemonde'	CKen NEgg
	- 'Tenas'	CKen SPoG
	smithiana	CDul CTho EPfP
	- 'Sunray'	SLim
	wilsonii	CKen NLar

Picrasma (*Simaroubaceae*)

	ailanthoides	see *P. quassioides*
§	***quassioides***	CMCN EBee EPfP WPGP

Picris (*Asteraceae*)

echioides	see *Helminthotheca echioides*

Picrorhiza (*Plantaginaceae*)

kurrooa	GPoy LEdu

Pieris (*Ericaceae*)

	'Balls of Fire'	CMac
	'Bert Chandler'	CMac GKin
	'Firecrest' ♀H5	NLar
	'Flaming Silver' (v) ♀H5	Widely available
	'Forest Flame' ♀H5	Widely available
	formosa B&SWJ 2257	WCru
	- var. ***forrestii***	CWib
	- - 'Jermyns'	CMac MRav
	- - 'Wakehurst' ♀H5	CAbP CDul CMac CTri EPfP GKin LMil LRHS MAsh MGos MMuc MRav NWea SCob SPer WHor
	Havila = 'Mouwsvila' (v)	CMac MAsh NWad
	japonica	CMac ESps LPar
	- 'Astrid'	IVic
	- 'Bisbee Dwarf'	WThu
	- 'Bonfire' ♀H5	CCCN CRos ELan GMcL IVic LRHS LSou MGos MMuc NLar SCob SHil SLim SPoG
	- 'Carnaval' (v) ♀H5	Widely available
	- 'Cavatine' ♀H5	IVic
§	- 'Christmas Cheer'	CMac EPfP LRHS LSRN WMoo
	- 'Cupido'	IVic MAsh NLar SLim WBod WFar
	- 'Debutante' ♀H5	CBcs CRos CWib ELan ESps GKin GMcL IVic LRHS MAsh MGos NLar SAko SCob SCoo SWvt WFar WHlf
	- 'Don'	see *P. japonica* 'Pygmaea'
	- 'Dorothy Wyckoff'	LSRN MAsh SSta
	- 'Erik' **new**	IArd SAko
	- 'Flaming Star'	SWvt
	- 'Flamingo'	CMac
I	- 'Katsura'PBR	Widely available
	- 'Little Heath' (v)	Widely available
	- 'Little Heath Green'	CMac ELon ESps GKin IBoy MAsh MGos MMuc NEgg SCob SPer SPoG SWvt WFar WMoo
	- 'Minor'	GKev NWad WFar WThu
	- 'Mountain Fire' ♀H5	Widely available
	- 'Passion'PBR	CBcs CEnd CRos CSBt EBee EPfP GMcL IVic LCro LRHS LSRN NLar SAko SCob SPer
	- 'Pink Delight' ♀H5	CNec CRos EMOT ESps LRHS LSRN MRav SRms
	- 'Prelude' ♀H5	CRos CSBt LMil LRHS MAsh NLar WAbe
	- 'Purity' ♀H5	CBcs CMac CNec EMOT MAsh MGos NEgg NLar SArc SLim SPer SWvt WFar WHar
§	- 'Pygmaea'	NWad WThu
	- 'Ralto'PBR	CRos LRHS MRav NLar SHil SPoG
	- Ralto Rose = 'Opstal10'	MPkF
	- Red Mill = 'Zebris'	CEnd IVic LSou SLim SPer
	- 'Rondo'	IVic
	- 'Rosalinda'	MAsh
	- 'Sarabande' ♀H5	IVic LRHS MAsh MMuc MPkF SCob SHil
	- 'Scarlett O'Hara'	CSBt NLar
	- Taiwanensis Group	GKin NLar SRms WFar
	- 'Temple Bells'	CSBt
	- 'Valley Rose'	CSBt ELan GKin IVic NLar
	- 'Valley Valentine' ♀H5	CBcs CLet CMac CRos CSBt CWib EPfP ESps GMcL IVic LCro LMil LRHS LSRN MAsh MGos MJak MMuc MPkF NHpl SAko SCob SCoo SHil SLim SPer SPoG SWvt
	- 'Variegata' misapplied	see *P. japonica* 'White Rim'
	- 'Variegata' ambig.	GMcL LMil SCob
	- 'Variegata' (Carrière) Bean (v)	EPfP LRHS MRav
	- 'Wada's Pink'	see *P. japonica* 'Christmas Cheer'
	- 'White Pearl'	CMac EPfP IVic MAsh
§	- 'White Rim' (v)	CDul CMac SPlb
	- 'William Buchanan'	GBin NWad WThu
	- var. ***yakushimensis***	NLar
	nana	WThu
	'Tilford'	CMac

Pilea (*Urticaceae*)

libanensis	EShb

Pileostegia (*Hydrangeaceae*)

viburnoides	CBcs CBot CMac CRHN CRos EBee ELan EPfP EUJe GCal LHop LRHS MGos MMuc MRav NLar NRHS SArc SDix SEND SLon SPer SPoG SSta WCot WPGP WPat WSHC
- B&SWJ 3565	WCru
- B&SWJ 3570 from Taiwan	WCru
- B&SWJ 7132	WCru

Pilgerodendron (*Cupressaceae*)

uviferum **new**	CBcs

Pilosella (*Asteraceae*)

§	***aurantiaca***	CArn ELan IRos LEdu LPot LRHS MHer MNHC NBid SIde SPhx SRms WCot WHer WMoo WOut WSFF
§	- subsp. ***carpathicola***	MMuc SEND
§	***officinarum***	NRya
	tardans	CFis

Pilularia (*Marsileaceae*)

globulifera	MSKA

Pimelea (*Thymelaeaceae*)

	coarctata	see *P. prostrata*
	drupacea	IDee SAko
	ferruginea	SVen
	oreophila	WThu
§	***prostrata***	CTri EPot
	tomentosa	LRHS

Pimpinella (*Apiaceae*)

anisum	SVic
major	LEdu
- 'Rosea'	Widely available
minima rosea	NDov
saxifraga	CHab WSFF
siifolia **new**	WHil

tripartita	MAvo
- PAB 6112	LEdu WPGP

pineapple see *Ananas comosus*

Pinellia (*Araceae*)

cordata	CAby ECho GKev LEdu WCot WCru XLum
pedatisecta	GKev LTro MRav WCot
pinnatisecta	see *P. tripartita*
ternata	EBee ECho EWld GEdr NLar WCot
- B&SWJ 3532	WCru
§ ***tripartita***	ECho GKev LTro WCot
- B&SWJ 1102	WCru
- 'Dragon Tails' (v)	SKHP
- 'Purple Face'	WCru

Pinguicula (*Lentibulariaceae*)

ehlersiae	EFEx SPlb
esseriana ♀H1c	EFEx
grandiflora ♀H4	ECho EECP EFEx EWld GKev NLos NRya
longifolia subsp. ***longifolia***	EFEx
moranensis var. ***caudata***	EFEx
- ***moreana***	EFEx
- ***superba***	EFEx
'Tina'	NLos
vulgaris	EFEx WHer
'Weser' ♀H1c	NLos

pinkcurrant see *Ribes rubrum* (P)

Pinus ✿ (*Pinaceae*)

albicaulis 'Flinck'	CKen
- 'Nana'	see *P. albicaulis* 'Noble's Dwarf'
- 'No 3'	CKen
§ - 'Noble's Dwarf'	CKen
aristata ambig.	LRHS
aristata Engelm.	CAco CDul CMCN CMen WHor
- 'Bashful'	CKen
- 'Cecilia'	CKen
- 'Kohout's Mini'	CKen
- 'Rich Broom' **new**	NLar
- 'Sherwood Compact'	CKen MAsh
- 'So Tight'	CKen
- 'Timberline' **new**	NLar
armandii	CAco CDul CMCN EPfP LRHS
austriaca	see *P. nigra* subsp. *nigra*
ayacahuite	CKen CPne
- var. ***veitchii***	CTho EBee WPGP
balfouriana dwarf	CKen
banksiana	CDul NWea
- 'Chippewa'	CKen
I - 'Compacta'	CKen
- 'Neponset'	CKen
- 'Schneverdingen'	CKen NEgg NLar
bhutanica	WPGP
bungeana	CDul CMCN EPfP MBlu
- 'Diamant'	CKen NLar
- 'June's Broom'	CKen
cembra	CAgr CDul EPfP MJak NWea
- 'Aurea'	see *P. cembra* 'Aureovariegata'
§ - 'Aureovariegata' (v)	SLim
- 'Barnhourie'	CKen
- 'Blue Mound'	CKen
- 'Compacta Glauca'	NLar
- 'Frieda' **new**	NLar
- 'Inverleith'	CKen
- 'Jermyns'	CKen
- 'King's Dwarf'	CKen
- 'Ortler'	CKen NLar
- 'Stoderzinken 8' **new**	NLar
- 'Stricta'	CKen
- witches' broom	CKen
cembroides NJM 09.022A	WPGP
- 'Fancy Nancy' **new**	CKen
contorta	CBcs CDul IBoy NWea SPlb
- 'Asher'	CKen
- 'Chief Joseph' ♀H7	CKen MAsh NLar SLim
- 'Frisian Gold'	NLar
- var. ***latifolia***	CDul
- 'Spaan's Dwarf'	CKen SLim
- 'Taylor's Sunburst'	CKen NLar
coulteri	CAco EPfP SKHP
densiflora	CAco EBtc EUJe LPar
- 'Alice Verkade' ♀H7	CMen LPar LRHS NEgg NLar
- 'Golden Ghost'	NLar
- 'Jim Cross'	CKen
- 'Low Glow'	CKen NEgg NLar SBod SLim SPoG
- 'Oculus-draconis' (v)	NLar SLim
- 'Pendula'	CKen MBlu NEgg SLim
I - 'Pygmaea'	WHor
- 'Pygmy'	EUJe
- 'Umbraculifera'	CMen CNWT GKin SSta
× ***densithunbergii*** 'Jane Kluis' ♀H7	CMen NLar SLim SPoG
edulis	CMCN EGFP
- 'Juno'	CKen
elliottii var. ***densa***	CKen
fenzeliana	CKen
flexilis	EGFP
- 'Cheyenne'	NLar
- 'Cow Creek' **new**	NLar
- 'Firmament'	NLar NOra SLim WMat
- 'Glenmore Dwarf'	CKen
- 'Lil Wolf' **new**	NLar
- 'Nana'	CKen
I - 'Pygmaea'	NLar
- 'Ririe'	CKen MAsh
- 'Tara Mae'	NLar
- 'Tarryall'	CKen
- 'Vanderwolf's Pyramid'	NLar
- WB No 1	CKen
- WB No 2	CKen
greggii	CDul EBtc
griffithii McClell.	see *P. wallichiana*
halepensis	SEND
§ ***heldreichii***	CDul EPfP GKin NOra NWea SLim WMat
- 'Aureospicata'	NLar
- 'Compact Gem' ♀H7	CKen EUJe GMcL LRHS NEgg SLim
- 'Dolce Dorme'	CKen
- 'Green Pyramid'	NLar
- 'Groen'	CKen
- var. ***leucodermis***	see *P. heldreichii*
- 'Malink'	CKen EUJe IVic SAko SLim
- 'Ottocek'	CKen
- 'Pygmy'	CKen
- 'Satellit' ♀H7	CKen GMcL MAsh NEgg NLar SLim
- 'Schmidtii'	see *P. heldreichii* 'Smidtii'
§ - 'Smidtii' ♀H7	CKen CMen EUJe LRHS NEgg NLar NWad SAko SLim SPoG
- 'Zwerg Schneverdingen'	CKen SLim
× ***holfordiana***	WPGP
jeffreyi	CAco CMCN CTho
- 'Joppi'	CKen NLar SLim
koraiensis	GKin LEdu SLim
- 'Bergman'	CKen
- 'Blue Ball'	CKen NLar
- 'Dragon Eye'	CKen SLim

- 'Jack Corbit'	CKen
- 'Shibamichi' (v)	CKen
- 'Silveray'	NLar
- 'Silvergrey'	CKen
- 'Spring Grove'	CKen NLar
- 'Winton'	CKen NLar
leucodermis	see *P. heldreichii*
monophylla	EBtc
- 'Wrinkle'	NLar
montezumae Lamb.	CAco SArc
- 'Sheffield Park'	SLim
monticola 'Ondulata'	NLar
- 'Pendula'	CKen
- 'Pygmy'	see *P. monticola* 'Raraflora'
§ - 'Raraflora'	CKen
- 'Strobicola'	EPfP
- 'Windsor Dwarf'	CKen
mugo	CArn CBcs CDul EPfP ESps LPar MAsh MGos MJak NWea SCob SHil
- 'Allgäu'	CKen
- 'Alpen Hexe' **new**	NLar
- 'Benjamin'	CKen LRHS NLar SAko
- 'Bisley Green'	NLar
- 'Bonita'	LRHS
- 'Brownie'	CKen
- 'Carsten' ♀H7	CKen ELan EPfP GMcL LPar LRHS MAsh NEgg NLar SCoo SLim SPoG
- 'Chameleon'	NLar
- 'Corley's Mat'	CKen
- 'Devon Gem'	NEgg
- 'Dezember Gold'	IVic NLar SLim
- 'Flanders Belle'	SLim
- 'Gnom'	CDul ELan ESps GKin LRHS MAsh MGos NEgg SCoo
- 'Gold Star'	CMen SLim
- 'Golden Glow'	NLar SLim SPoG
- 'Hesse'	GMcL SCoo
- 'Hoersholm'	CKen
- 'Hulk'	CKen
- 'Humpy' ♀H7	CKen CMen ESps MAsh NEgg SCoo SLim
- 'Ironsides'	CKen NLar
- 'Jacobsen'	CKen NLar SLim
- 'Janovsky'	CKen
- 'Kamila'	NLar
- 'Kissen' ♀H7	CKen EPfP NHol SLim
- Klostergrun	see *P. mugo* 'Klosterkötter'
§ - 'Klosterkötter'	LRHS
- 'Kobold'	NEgg
- 'Krauskopf'	CKen
- 'Laarheide'	SPoG
- 'Laurin'	CKen
- 'March'	CKen
- 'Mini Mops'	CKen
- 'Minikin'	CKen
- 'Mops' ♀H7	CDul CMen EPfP ESps GMcL LRHS MAsh MBlu MGos NEgg NWea SCob SCoo SLim SPoG SSta
- 'Mops Midget'	CMen MAsh NEgg
- var. ***mughus***	see *P. mugo* subsp. *mugo*
§ - subsp. ***mugo***	CAco GMcL LPar NWea SCob SGol
- - 'Milky Way' **new**	CKen
- 'Mumpitz'	CKen LRHS
- 'Northern Lights'	CKen
- 'Ophir' ♀H7	CBcs CDul CKen CMen ELan EPfP LRHS MAsh MGos NEgg SCob SCoo SLim SPoG SSta
- 'Pal Maleter' (v)	SCoo SLim SPoG
- 'Paul's Dwarf'	CKen
- 'Picobello'	LRHS MAsh NHol NLar SLim
- 'Piggelmee'	CKen IVic
- 'Pincushion'	LRHS NLar
- Pumilio Group	CAco EAEE EPfP ESps GQue LPar LRHS MGos MMuc NLar NWea SEND WMoo
- var. ***rostrata***	see *P. mugo* subsp. *uncinata*
- subsp. ***rotundata*** 'Ježek'	CKen MAsh NLar
- 'Rushmore'	CKen
- 'Ruze'	LRHS NLar
- 'Sherwood Compact'	SLim
- 'Spaan'	CKen
- 'Sunshine' (v)	CKen
- 'Suzi'	CKen
- 'Suzy Hexe'	NWad
- 'Trompenburg'	NEgg
- 'Tuffet'	CKen LRHS NHol SLim
- 'Uelzen'	CKen
§ - subsp. ***uncinata***	CDul NWea
- - 'Adam'	NLar
- - 'Etschtal'	CKen
- - 'Grüne Welle'	CKen NLar SLim
- - 'Heideperle'	NLar
- - 'Kostelnicek'	CKen NLar
- - 'Leuco-like'	CKen
- - 'Offenpass'	CKen
- - 'Paradekissen'	CKen NLar
- - 'Süsse Perle'	CKen
- 'Varella'	CKen NLar SCoo SLim
- 'White Tip'	CKen
- 'Winter Gold'	ELan EPfP EUJe LPar LRHS MGos MJak NHol SSta
- 'Winter Sun'	LRHS MAsh
- 'Winzig'	CKen
- 'Yellow Tip' (v)	NHol
- 'Zundert'	CKen SPoG
- 'Zwergkugel'	CKen
muricata	EBtc NWea
nigra	CBcs CDul CLnd CMac CTri EMOT EPfP ESps EUJe MAsh MGos MRav SGol WMou
- var. ***austriaca***	see *P. nigra* subsp. *nigra*
- 'Bambino'	CKen
- 'Black Prince' ♀H7	CKen EUJe NEgg NOra SLim WMat
- 'Bobo'	CKen
- var. ***calabrica***	see *P. nigra* subsp. *laricio*
- 'Cebennensis Nana'	CKen
- var. ***corsicana***	see *P. nigra* subsp. *laricio*
- 'Frank'	CKen NLar
- 'Globosa'	ESps
- 'Green Tower'	LRHS
- 'Hornibrookiana'	CKen
- 'Komet'	IVic NLar SLim
§ - subsp. ***laricio***	CAco CCVT CDul CMac CNWT ECrN IVic MMuc NWea SEND
- - 'Aurea'	MBlu
- - 'Bobby McGregor'	CKen
- - 'Globosa Viridis'	NEgg
- - 'Goldfinger'	NLar
- - 'Pygmaea'	CKen NEgg
- - 'Wurstle'	CKen
- 'Lucia' **new**	NLar
- subsp. ***maritima***	see *P. nigra* subsp. *laricio*
- 'Moran' **new**	NLar
- 'Moseri'	CKen NEgg NLar
- 'Nana'	LRHS
§ - subsp. ***nigra***	CCVT CLnd CNWT CTho GMcL LRHS MMuc NWea SCob SEND SEWo SGol WHed
- - 'Birte'	CKen
- - 'Bright Eyes'	MAsh NEgg SLim

- - 'Schovenhorst'	CKen
- - 'Skyborn'	CKen
- - 'Strypemonde'	CKen NEgg
- - 'Yaffle Hill'	CKen
- 'Obelisk'	CKen
- 'Oregon Green'	CKen NLar
- 'Pierrick Bregéon' PBR	LRHS
- 'Richard'	CKen SLim
- 'Spielberg'	SAko
oocarpa	EBtc
palustris	IVic SKHP
parviflora	LPar NEgg SPlb
- 'Aaba-jo'	CKen
- 'Adcock's Dwarf' 🏆H7	CKen NEgg SLim
- 'Al Fordham'	CKen
- 'Aoi'	CKen CMen NLar
- 'Ara-kawa'	CKen CMen
- 'Atco-goyo'	CKen
- Azuma-goyo Group	CKen CMen LRHS
I - 'Baasch's Form'	CKen NLar
- 'Bergman'	MAsh
- 'Betsy' **new**	NLar
- 'Blue Angel'	LRHS MBlu
- 'Blue Giant'	CDul IArd MBlu SAko
- 'Bonnie Bergman' 🏆H7	CKen EPfP LRHS NHol
- 'Catherine Elizabeth'	CKen NLar
- 'Chikusa Goten'	IArd SAko
- 'Dai-ho'	CKen
- 'Daisetsusan'	CKen
- 'Dougal'	CKen
- 'Floppy Joe'	NLar
- 'Fukai' (v)	CKen NHol NLar
- 'Fukiju'	CKen
- Fukushima-goyo Group	CKen CMen
- 'Fuku-zu-mi'	CKen IVic
- 'Fu-shiro'	CKen
- 'Gemstar' **new**	CKen
- 'Gimborn's Ideal'	IVic
- 'Gin-sho-chuba'	CKen
- Glauca Group	CAco LRHS MAsh MBlu NEgg SGol SKHP
- - 'Glauca' 🏆H7 **new**	CAco GMcL
I - 'Glauca Nana'	CKen
- 'Goykuri'	CKen
- 'Green Wave'	CKen
- 'Gyok-kasen'	CKen
- 'Gyo-ko-haku'	CKen
- 'Gyokusen Sämling'	CKen NLar
- 'Gyo-ku-sui'	CKen CMen
- 'H2'	CKen
- 'Hagaromo Seedling'	CKen CMen
- 'Hakko'	CKen
- 'Hatchichi'	CKen
- 'Ha-tzumari'	NLar
- 'Hobbit'	NWad
- 'Ibo-can'	CKen CMen
- 'Ichi-no-se'	CKen
- 'Iri-fune'	CKen
- Ishizuchi-goyo Group	CKen NLar
- 'Jade Tiers'	LRHS
- 'Jim's Mini Curls'	CKen
- 'Ka-ho'	CKen
- 'Kanrico'	CKen
- 'Kanzan'	CKen
- 'Kin-po'	CKen
- 'Kiyomatsu'	CKen LRHS
- 'Kobe'	CKen
- 'Kokonoe'	CKen CMen
- 'Kokuho'	CKen
- 'Kusu-dama'	CKen
- 'Little Hedgehog' **new**	CKen
- 'Lorraine'	CKen
- 'Masami'	CKen
- 'Meiko'	CKen CMen
- 'Michinoku'	CKen
- 'Momo-yama'	CKen NLar
- 'Myo-jo'	CKen
- Nasu-goyo Group	CKen
- 'Negishi' 🏆H7	CKen CMen LRHS MAsh NEgg SLim
- 'Ogon-goyo'	CKen
- 'Ogon-janome'	CKen MAsh NEgg SLim
- 'Ossorio Dwarf'	CKen
- var. ***pentaphylla***	IVic
- 'Regenhold'	CKen
- 'Richard Lee'	CKen MAsh
- 'Ryo-ku-ho'	CKen
- 'Ryu-ju'	CKen IArd NLar
- 'Sa-dai-jin'	CKen
- 'San-bo'	CKen
§ - 'Saphir'	CKen SAko
- 'Schoon's Bonsai'	LRHS NHol NLar
- 'Setsugekka'	CKen
- 'Shika-shima'	CKen
- Shikoku-goyo Group	LRHS
- 'Shimada'	CKen
- 'Shin Sen'	LRHS NLar
- 'Shin Sho'	LRHS
- Shiobara-goyo Group	CKen
- 'Shizukagoten'	CKen SLim
- 'Shu-re'	CKen NLar
- 'Sieryoden'	CKen
- 'Smout'	CKen
- 'Tani-mano-uki'	CKen
- 'Tempelhof'	CAco NOrn
- 'Tenysu-kazu'	CKen LRHS MAsh NLar
- 'Tokyo Dwarf'	CKen
- 'Walker's Dwarf'	CKen
- 'Watnong'	CKen
- 'Zelkova'	CMen
- 'Zui-sho'	CKen
patula 🏆H4	CBcs CCCN CHll EPfP EUJe IDee IVic SArc SBig SCoo SMad SPlb SPoG WMat WPGP
peuce	CDul EPfP GMcL NWea
- 'Arnold Dwarf'	CKen NLar
- 'Cesarini'	CKen NLar
- 'Daniel'	CKen
- 'Thessaloniki Broom'	CKen
pinaster	CBcs CDul CLnd EPfP ESps IVic MMuc SEND
pinea 🏆H5	CAco CAgr CArn CCVT CDul CLnd CTho EPfP ETod EUJe IDee IVic LPar MGos MMuc SArc SCoo SEND SEWo SGol SPlb WPGP
- 'Queensway'	CKen
ponderosa	CDul CMCN EGFP EPfP LRHS NWea
- var. ***scopulorum***	NWea
pumila	ESps
- 'Buchanan'	CKen
- 'Draijer's Dwarf'	SLim
- 'Dwarf Blue'	LRHS NHol NLar
- 'Glauca' 🏆H7	CKen MAsh
- 'Globe'	MAsh SLim
- 'Jeddeloh'	CKen
- 'Pinocchio'	CKen
- 'Säntis'	CKen
- 'Saphir'	see *P. parviflora* 'Saphir'
pungens	CDul

	radiata	CAco CBcs CCVT CDul CLet CLnd CMac CNWT CTho CTri ECrN ELan EPfP ESps EUJe MMuc NWea SArc SBod SCoo WMat
	- Aurea Group	ELan NEgg SCoo SLim SPoG WMat
	- - 'Aurea' Υ^{H5} **new**	NOra
	- 'Bodnant'	CKen
	- 'Isca'	CKen
	- 'Marshwood' (v)	CKen SLim
	- 'Nana'	NLar
	resinosa 'Don Smith'	CKen
	- 'Joel's Broom'	CKen
	- 'Quinobequin'	CKen
	sabineana	CMCN
	× ***schwerinii***	CKen
	- 'Wiethorst' Υ^{H7}	CKen LRHS SLim WHar WMat
	sibirica 'Blue Smoke'	CKen
	- 'Mariko'	CKen
	strobiformis	EGFP
	- 'Coronado'	CKen
	- 'Loma Linda'	CKen SLim
	strobus	CAco CBcs CCVT CDul CMen EPfP ESps LPar LRHS MGos MMuc NWea SEND
§	- 'Alba'	SLim
	- 'Amelia's Dwarf'	CKen
	- 'Angel Falls'	CKen NLar
	- 'Anna Fiele'	CKen NEgg
	- 'Bennett Fastigiate' **new**	NLar
	- 'Bergman's Mini'	CKen SLim
	- 'Bergman's Pendula Broom'	CKen
I	- 'Bergman's Sport of Prostrata'	CKen
	- 'Beth'	CKen
	- 'Bloomer's Dark Globe'	CKen
	- 'Blue Covers' **new**	NLar
	- 'Blue Shag' Υ^{H7}	CAco LRHS NLar NWad SCoo SLim
	- 'Brevifolia'	CKen
	- 'Cesarini'	CKen
	- 'Densa'	CKen
	- 'Ed's Broom'	CKen
	- 'Elf' **new**	NLar
	- 'Elkins Dwarf'	CKen NEgg
	- 'Fastigiata'	CDul CKen SAko
	- 'Golden Showers'	NLar
	- 'Green Curls'	CKen
	- 'Green Twist'	CKen NLar
	- 'Greg'	CKen NLar
	- 'Hershey'	CKen
	- 'Hillside Gem'	CKen
	- 'Horsford'	CKen NLar SLim
	- 'Horsford Sister'	CKen
	- 'Jamaican Curls'	CKen
	- 'Julian Pott'	CKen
	- 'Julian's Dwarf'	CKen
	- 'Krügers Lilliput'	LRHS NLar NWad SLim
	- 'Little Suzy' **new**	NLar
	- 'Louie'	CKen MAsh NLar
	- 'Mary Butler'	CKen
	- 'Merrimack'	CKen
	- 'Minima' Υ^{H7}	CDul CKen LRHS MBlu NEgg NWea SLim SPoG
	- 'Minuta'	CKen LRHS
§	- Nana Group	NEgg SEWo
	- 'Nana'	see *P. strobus* Nana Group
	- 'Nana Compacta'	LRHS NEgg
	- 'Niagara Falls'	CKen
	- 'Nivea'	see *P. strobus* 'Alba'
	- 'Northway Broom'	CKen
	- 'Pacific Sunrise'	NLar
	- 'Paul Waxman'	NLar
	- 'Pendula'	CKen LRHS MBlu
I	- 'Pendula Broom'	CKen
	- 'Prostrata'	SLim
	- 'Pygmaea'	LRHS
	- 'Radiata'	CTri ESps GMcL
I	- 'Radiata Aurea'	NEgg
	- 'Reinshaus'	CKen
	- 'Sayville'	CKen
	- 'Sea Urchin'	CKen LRHS MAsh NLar SLim
	- 'Secrest'	LRHS NLar
	- 'Stowe Pillar'	NLar SLim
	- 'Tiny Kurls'	CKen MAsh
	- 'Torulosa'	MBlu
	- 'Uncatena'	CKen
	- 'Verkade's Broom'	CKen NEgg
	- 'White Mountain'	EUJe MBlu NLar SLim
	sylvestris	Widely available
	- 'Abergeldie'	CKen
	- 'Albyns' **new**	NLar
	- 'Alderly Edge'	CMen
	- 'Andorra'	CKen
	- 'Argentea Compacta'	LRHS
	- Aurea Group	CDul CKen CMac CMen ELan MAsh MBlu MJak NEgg NWea SLim SSta WMat
	- 'Avondene'	CKen
	- 'Bergfield'	CMen
	- 'Beuvronensis' Υ^{H7}	CMen NEgg SLim
	- 'Buchanan's Gold'	CKen
	- 'Burghfield'	CMen
	- 'Chantry Blue'	CMen CNWT GMcL MAsh MGos NEgg NLar NOra SCoo SLim SPoG WMat
	- 'Clumber Blue'	CKen
	- 'Dereham'	CKen NLar
	- 'Doone Valley'	CKen NEgg
	- 'Edwin Hillier'	CMen NEgg NOra SLim WMat WPGP
	- Fastigiata Group	CDul CEnd CKen CMac CMen LPar LRHS SCoo SLim WCFE
	- 'Frensham' Υ^{H7}	CKen MAsh
	- 'Gold Coin' Υ^{H7}	CDul CKen EPfP MAsh NEgg NLar NWad SPoG
	- 'Gold Medal'	CKen SLim
	- 'Grand Rapids'	CKen
	- 'Green Penguin' **new**	NLar
	- 'Gwydyr Castle'	CKen
	- 'Hillside Creeper'	CKen
	- 'Humble Pie'	CKen
	- 'Jeremy'	CKen NEgg
	- 'John Boy'	CMen
	- 'Kelpie'	SLim
	- 'Kenwith'	CKen
	- 'Lakeside Dwarf'	CMen
	- 'Lodge Hill'	CMen MAsh NEgg SLim
	- 'Longmoor'	CKen
	- 'Martham'	CKen CMen
	- 'Mitsch Weeping'	CKen
	- Nana Group	LPar
	- 'Nana' misapplied	see *P. sylvestris* 'Watereri'
	- 'Nana Compacta'	CMen SWeb
§	- 'Nisbet's Gem'	CKen CMen NLar
	- 'Padworth'	CMen
	- 'Perkeo'	NLar
	- 'Piskowitz'	CKen
	- 'Pixie'	CKen
I	- 'Prostrata'	NEgg SLim
	- 'Repens'	CKen
	- 'Saint George'	CKen

	- 'Sandringham'	NLar
	- 'Saxatilis'	CKen CMen
	- subsp. ***scotica***	NWea
	- 'Scott's Dwarf'	see *P. sylvestris* 'Nisbet's Gem'
	- 'Sentinel'	CKen
	- 'Skjak I'	CKen
	- 'Skjak II'	CKen
	- 'Spaan's Slow Column'	CKen SLim
	- var. ***sylvestris*** new	LPar
	- 'Tage'	CKen
	- 'Tanya'	CKen
	- 'Tilhead'	CKen
	- 'Treasure'	CKen
	- 'Trefrew Quarry'	CKen
	- 'Troll Guld'	CKen NLar
	- 'Umbraculifera'	NEgg
	- 'Vargguld'	CKen
§	- 'Watereri'	CNWT GMcL IDee LPar LRHS MJak NLar SCob SCoo
	- 'Westonbirt'	CKen CMen MAsh
	- 'Wintergold'	LPar NEgg SPer
	- 'Wittichenau'	CKen
	tabuliformis	CAco CMCN
	taeda	EPfP
	taiwanensis	CDul EPfP
	thunbergii	CAco CDul CLnd CMCN CMen ELan IDee MMuc
	- 'Akame'	CKen CMen
	- 'Akame Yatsabusa'	CMen
	- 'Aocha-matsu' (v)	CKen CMen
	- 'Arakawa-sho'	CKen CMen
	- 'Banshosho'	CKen CMen
	- 'Beni-kujaku'	CKen CMen
	- 'Compacta'	CKen CMen
	- var. ***corticosa*** 'Fuji'	CMen
	- - 'Iihara'	CMen
	- 'Dainagon'	CKen CMen
	- 'Eechee-nee'	CKen
	- 'Hayabusa'	CMen
	- 'Iwai'	CMen
	- 'Janome' (v)	CMen
	- 'Katsuga'	CMen
	- 'Kotobuki'	CKen CMen NLar
	- 'Koyosho'	CMen
	- 'Kujaku'	CKen CMen
	- 'Kyokko'	CKen CMen
	- 'Kyushu'	CKen CMen
	- 'Mikawa'	CMen MBlu
	- 'Miyajuna'	CKen CMen
	- 'Nishiki-ne'	CKen CMen
	- 'Nishiki-tsusaka'	CMen
	- 'Ogi-matsu'	CKen
	- 'Ōgon'	CMen NLar SLim
	- 'Porky'	CKen CMen
§	- 'Sayonara' ♀H7	CMen MAsh NEgg NLar
	- 'Senryu'	CKen CMen
	- 'Shinsho'	CKen CMen
	- 'Shio-guro'	CKen CMen
	- 'Suchiro'	NEgg
	- 'Suchiro Yatabusa'	CKen CMen
	- 'Sunsho'	CKen CMen
	- 'Taihei'	CKen CMen
I	- 'Thunderhead' ♀H7	CKen CMen NLar SLim
	- 'W.B.'	CKen
	- 'Yatsubusa'	see *P. thunbergii* 'Sayonara'
	- 'Ye-i-kan'	CKen
	- 'Yoshimura'	CMen
	- 'Yumaki'	CKen CMen
	uncinata	see *P. mugo* subsp. *uncinata*
	virginiana 'Wate's Golden'	CKen NLar
§	***wallichiana*** ♀H6	Widely available
	- 'Densa Hill'	LRHS SLim
	- 'Frosty'	CKen
	- 'Nana' ♀H6	CKen LRHS NLar SCoo SLim
	- 'Umbraculifera'	MAsh
	- var. ***wallichiana***	EUJe
	- 'Zebrina' (v)	MBlu NHol NLar
	yunnanensis	LRHS

Piper (*Piperaceae*)

	auritum	GPoy LEdu
	betle	GPoy
	heydei B&SWJ 10445	WCru
	methysticum	GPoy

Piptanthus (*Papilionaceae*)

	forrestii	see *P. nepalensis*
	laburnifolius	see *P. nepalensis*
§	***nepalensis***	CBcs CDul CSBt CSpe EBee ELan EPfP LHop LRHS MGil MGos MPie NBid NLar SBrt SPer SRms WPat
	aff. ***nepalensis***	SWvt

Pistacia (*Anacardiaceae*)

	atlantica	XSen
	chinensis	CBcs EBee EBtc EPfP WPGP
	lentiscus	CArn CBcs EUJe LRHS SEND SVen XSen
	terebinthus	XSen
	- NJM 11.004	WPGP
	vera new	CTsd

Pistia (*Araceae*)

	stratiotes	MSKA NPer SCoo

Pitavia (*Rutaceae*)

	punctata	IArd SAko

Pitcairnia (*Bromeliaceae*)

	bergii	CHll
	heterophylla	WCot
	recurvata	WCot
	ringens	WCot

Pittosporum ✿ (*Pittosporaceae*)

	adaphniphylloides	CBcs
	anomalum	CCCN CTsd ELon SEle
	'Arundel Green' (f) ♀H4	CRos ELon EPfP ESps ETod LRHS LSRN MAsh SCob SHil SLim SPer SWvt
	bicolor	CPne GQui WPGP
	buchananii	SVen
	'Collaig Silver'	EPfP LPre LRHS MAsh SLim
	coriaceum new	CBrP
	crassifolium	CBcs CCCN CTsd
	- 'Variegatum' (v)	CBcs CCCN WPat
	'Crinkles' (f)	SVen
	daphniphylloides	EBee ELan WPGP
	- B&SWJ 6789	WCru
	- CWJ 12404	WCru
	- RWJ 9913	WCru
	eugenioides	CMCN CSam SEND
	- 'Platinum' (v)	CCCN ELan
	- 'Variegatum' (v) ♀H4	CBcs CCCN CDul CLet CMac ELan EPfP ESps EUJe GQui IArd LHop LRHS MGos NLar SAko SCob SEND SHil SKHP SLim SVen
	'Garnettii' (v) ♀H4	Widely available
	glabratum B&SWJ 11685	WCru

heterophyllum	ECrN ELan EPfP EWes LRHS MMrt SEND
– variegated (v)	CCCN EBtc EPfP LRHS WSHC
'Holbrook' (v)	CSam
illicioides var. ***angustifolium***	WPGP
– – B&SWJ 6771	WCru
– – RWJ 9846	WCru
– var. ***illicioides*** B&SWJ 6712	WCru
– – PAB 9004	LEdu WPGP
× ***intermedium***	CWib SWvt
– 'Craxten' (f)	CCCN
'Nanum Variegatum'	see *P. tobira* 'Variegatum'
oblongilimbum DJHV 06137	WCru
'Oliver Twist'	ETod LRHS LSRN MAsh SCob SCoo
omeiense	EWes SKHP
– VdL 80626	WPGP
ralphii	CCCN CMCN CTsd
– 'Green Globe'	SKHP
– 'Variegatum' (v)	CCCN LRHS SKHP WPGP
'Saundersii' (v)	SCoo
'Tadina Gold'	ETod
tenuifolium	Widely available
– 'Abbotsbury Gold' (f/v)	CAbb CBcs CBod CCCN CLet CMac CNec CTri EHoe ELan EPfP ESps ETod EWes GMcL IBoy LBMP LPar LRHS MAsh MGos MSwo SCob SEND SGbt SGol SHil SLim SPer SWvt
– 'Atropurpureum'	CBcs ELan ETod
– 'Brockhill Compact'	CCCN LRHS SAko SLim
– 'Cornish Mist'	CTsd
– 'County Park'	CCCN EUJe
– 'County Park Dwarf'	MAsh
§ – 'Eila Keightley' (v)	CMHG
– 'Elizabeth' (m/v)	CAbP CBcs CMac CNec CRos EHoe EPfP ETod EUJe EWTr GMcL IArd IBoy LRHS LSRN LSou MAsh MGos MRav MSwo SCob SCoo SEND SHil SLim SPoG
– Emerald Dome = 'Minpitto'PBR **new**	SArc
– 'French Lace'	CBcs CCCN ELan GMcL WFar
– 'Gold Star'	CBcs CChe EHoe ELan EPfP ESps LBMP LPar LRHS MAsh MGos SBod SCob SCoo SEND SEle SLim SPer SPoG SWvt WMoo
– 'Golden King'	CCCN CMac CSBt EPfP ESps LRHS MAsh MGos SHil SLim SPoG SRms
– 'Golf Ball'PBR	CBcs CRos EPfP EUJe GBin LCro LRHS LSRN MGos SCob SGbt SHil
– 'Green Thumb'	CMac
– 'Irene Paterson' (m/v) ♀H4	Widely available
– 'James Stirling'	CCCN SEND
– 'John Flanagan'	see *P. tenuifolium* 'Margaret Turnbull'
– 'Limelight' (v)	CBcs CCCN CSBt EBtc EPfP EUJe LHop LPre LRHS LSRN SLim SPoG
– 'Loxhill Gold'	CCCN IArd LRHS SGol SHil
§ – 'Margaret Turnbull' (v)	ELan EPfP EWes GKin LHop LRHS MGos SGol SHil
– 'Marjory Channon' (v)	ELan EPfP LRHS
– 'Moonlight' (v)	CBcs LRHS MRav SCob
– 'Mountain Green'	CMac
– 'Nutty's Leprechaun'	CCCN
– 'Pompom'	CCCN IVic LRHS
– 'Purpureum' (m)	CCCN CMac CSBt CSam CTri EPfP EUJe EWoo GBin LRHS LSRN MAsh MMuc NEgg SCob SEND SHil SLim SPer SPoG SRms WFar WSHC
– 'Silver Magic' (v)	CBcs EPfP ESps GMcL LRHS SCob SEle SRkn
– 'Silver Queen' (f/v) ♀H4	Widely available
– 'Silver Sheen' (m)	CBcs CJun CLet CMac LRHS
– 'Stevens Island'	CBcs
– 'Stirling Gold' (f/v)	EWes
– 'Sunburst'	see *P. tenuifolium* 'Eila Keightley'
– 'Tandara Gold' (v)	CBcs CCCN CLet CMac CSBt ELan ELon EPfP ESps ETod GMcL LBMP LRHS MAsh MGos SCob SCoo SLim SPoG WCot
– 'Tiki' (m)	CCCN
– 'Tom Thumb' ♀H4	Widely available
– 'Tresederi' (f/m)	CCCN CTsd
– 'Variegatum' (m/v)	CBcs CLet CSBt ELon ETod GMcL LCro LRHS LSRN MGos MSwo SArc SCob SGbt SHil SLim SPer SWvt
– 'Victoria' (v)	CBcs CCCN LRHS LSRN SHil SLim
– 'Warnham Gold' (m) ♀H3	CBcs CCCN CMac CWib EBee ELan EPfP ESps GKin IVic LRHS MAsh MGos SHil SLim SPer SPoG SVen
– 'Wendle Channon' (m/v)	CBcs CCCN CMHG CMac CSBt EHoe EPfP ETod GMcL LBMP LRHS MAsh SGol SLim WSHC
– 'Wrinkled Blue'	CBcs CRos EPfP ETod LRHS MAsh MRav MSwo SPoG
tobira ♀H3	Widely available
– B&SWJ 12758	WCru
* – 'Nanum'	CAco CBcs CCCN CLet CMac EAEE ELan EPfP ETod EUJe LCro LHop LPar LRHS MGos SCob SLim SPer SPoG
§ – 'Variegatum' (v) ♀H4	CBcs CCCN CDul CLet CMac CWib ELan EPfP EUJe IVic LHop LRHS LSRN MGos NLar SArc SCob SEND SKHP SLim SLon SPer SPoG WSHC
'Trim's Hedger'	CBod CTho
truncatum	CCCN EPfP SKHP
viridiflorum	EShb

Pityrogramma (*Pteridaceae*)

trifoliata	WCot

Plagianthus (*Malvaceae*)

betulinus	see *P. regius*
lyallii	see *Hoheria lyallii*
§ ***regius***	CBcs

Plagiorhegma see *Jeffersonia*

Plantago (*Plantaginaceae*)

coronopus	CAgr
holosteum	GKev
lanceolata	CAgr CArn CHab WSFF
major	CArn GPoy WSFF
– 'Atropurpurea'	see *P. major* 'Rubrifolia'
– 'Bowles's Variety'	see *P. major* 'Rosularis'
– 'Brenda'	CNat
– 'Everywhere I Glow'	CNat
§ – 'Rosularis'	CBre CFis CSpe EBee LEdu NBro SPav SRms WHer
§ – 'Rubrifolia'	CBod CHid CSpe EShb LLWG MHer MMuc NBid NBro NChi SHar SSal WMoo WPGP WSFF XLum
– 'Tony Lewis'	CNat
media	CHab MHer
nivalis	GEdr
rosea	see *P. major* 'Rosularis'
triandra 'Wanaka'	IMou

Platanthera (*Orchidaceae*)

hologlottis	EFEx
metabifolia	EFEx

Platanus ✿ (*Platanaceae*)

× ***acerifolia***	see *P.* × *hispanica*
§ × ***hispanica*** ♀H6	CBcs CCVT CDul CLnd CMCN EBee ECrN ELan EMOT EPfP ESps LPar MGos MMuc NWea SArc SCob SEND SEWo SGol SPer WMat WMou WTSh
- 'Bloodgood'	CTho
- 'Pyramidalis'	ECrN
orientalis	CCVT CDul CLnd CMCN CTho EPfP ESps SCob WPGP
- PAB 346	LEdu
- 'Cuneata'	ECrN
§ - f. ***digitata*** ♀H6	CCVT CDul CLnd CMCN CTho EBee EPfP ERod WMou
- var. ***insularis***	WPGP
- 'Laciniata'	see *P. orientalis* f. *digitata*
- 'Minaret'	CDul WMou
- 'Mirkovec'	EPfP IArd

Platycarya (*Juglandaceae*)

strobilacea	LEdu SBrt

Platycerium (*Polypodiaceae*)

alcicorne misapplied	see *P. bifurcatum*
§ ***bifurcatum*** ♀H1b	CCCN NLos XBlo
- 'Netherlands'	NLos
'Dawboy' **new**	NLos
ellisii	NLos
grande hort.	see *P. superbum*
hillii	NLos
'Lemoinei'	NLos
'Mount Kitshakood' **new**	NLos
ridleyi **new**	NLos
§ ***superbum*** ♀H1b	CCCN NLos
willinckii **new**	NLos

Platycladus (*Cupressaceae*)

orientalis 'Aurea' **new**	LPar
§ - 'Aurea Nana' ♀H6	CKen CLet CMac CSBt CWib ELan EMOT EPfP GMcL LBee LRHS MAsh MGos MJak NWad NWea SGol SLim SPoG WCFE
- 'Autumn Glow'	CKen
- 'Beverleyensis'	NLar
- 'Conspicua'	CKen CSBt CWib EMOT
- 'Elegantissima'	LRHS
- 'Flame'	LRHS
- 'Franky Boy' ♀H6	NLar SLim SPoG
- 'Golden Pygmy'	CKen
- 'Kenwith'	CKen
- 'Meldensis'	CTri
- 'Minima Glauca'	CKen
I - 'Pyramidalis Aurea'	ESps LBee
- 'Rosedalis'	CKen CSBt EMOT EPfP ESps LBee MAsh
- 'Sanderi'	WCFE
- 'Shirley Chilcott'	MAsh
- 'Southport'	LBee LRHS
- 'Summer Cream'	CKen

Platycodon ✿ (*Campanulaceae*)

grandiflorus ♀H5	CTri CTsd ECha ECho EPfP GKev LHop MHer SRms WHar WHoo
- 'Albus'	CBod ECho EPfP SPer SWvt WHar
- Apoyama Group ♀H5	WHoo WThu
- - 'Fairy Snow'	WHoo
- (Astra Series) 'Astra Blue'	EPfP LHop LRHS NRHS SPoG SRot
- - 'Astra Double Lavender' **new**	LRHS NRHS
- - 'Astra Pink'	LRHS NRHS SPoG
- - 'Astra White'	SPoG
- 'Blue Pearl'	WHoo
- 'Fuji Blue'	ELon WHoo XLum
- 'Fuji Pink'	ECho ELan LHop MRav SWvt WHoo XLum
- 'Fuji White'	ELan ELon WHoo
- 'Hakone'	MRav WHoo
- 'Hakone Blue'	EPfP NBre
- 'Hakone Double Blue' (d)	ELan SRms
- 'Hakone White'	EPfP GKev MRav WRHF
- 'Mariesii' ♀H5	CAby CBod CSBt EAEE ELon EPfP IBoy MMuc MNHC MRav NBir NEgg SEND SPer SPlb SRms SWvt WAul WHoo
- Mother of Pearl	see *P. grandiflorus* 'Perlmutterschale'
§ - 'Perlmutterschale'	EBee MRav
- 'Pink Star'	EBee
- 'Sentimental Blue'	CWib XLum
- 'Shell Pink'	see *P. grandiflorus* 'Perlmutterschale'
- 'Willy'	XLum
- 'Zwerg'	NBre

Platycrater (*Hydrangeaceae*)

arguta	EBee WCru WPGP
- B&SWJ 6266	WCru

Plectranthus (*Lamiaceae*)

ambiguus	EGeo SSal
- 'Manguzuku' ♀H1c	SSal
- 'Nico'	EGeo
amboinicus	EGeo LAll MNHC SSal WJek
- 'Variegatus' (v)	EGeo
- 'Well Sweep Wedgewood' (v)	EGeo SSal
argentatus ♀H1c	CBcs CPne CSpe CTsd EGeo EUJe EWld GCal IDee MCot MPie SDix SRkn SSal WHea WKif
- 'Hill House' (v)	CHll CPne EShb MPie SSal
- 'Silver Shield'	EShb MPie SSal
australis misapplied	see *P. verticillatus*
barbatus	EGeo SSal
- 'Vicki'	CPne
behrii	see *P. fruticosus*
Blue Angel = 'Edelblau' (Cape Angels Series)	EGeo SSal
caninus	ETho SPoG
ciliatus	EGeo EShb SRkn SSal
- 'Easy Gold' (v) ♀H1c	EGeo SSal
- 'Richard'	CPne SSal
- 'Sasha' (v)	CCCN CHll ECtt EShb EUJe SSal
'Cloud Nine'	SSal
coleoides 'Marginatus'	see *P. forsteri* 'Marginatus'
- 'Variegatus'	see *P. madagascariensis* 'Variegated Mintleaf'
Cuban oregano	SSal
'Dzoukou Choc' **new**	SSal
ecklonii	SSal
- 'Medley Wood'	SSal
ernstii	EGeo EWld
- blue-flowered **new**	SSal
excisus	see *Isodon excisus*
forskohlii	SSal

§ ***forsteri*** 'Marginatus'	EGeo SSal
'Frills'	CPne SSal
§ ***fruticosus***	CPne CTre SSal
- 'Behr's Pride'	EGeo SSal
- blue-flowered **new**	EGeo
- 'James' 🏆H1c	EGeo
hadiensis	EGeo SSal
var. ***tomentosus***	
- - 'Carnegie'	EGeo SSal
- - green-leaved	EGeo SSal
- - 'Penge' (v)	EGeo SSal
madagascariensis	EGeo SSal
- 'Lothlorien' (v)	EGeo SSal
§ - 'Variegated Mintleaf' (v) 🏆H1c	MNHC SRms SSal
'Marble Ruffles'	EGeo SSal
menthol-scented, large-leaved	EGeo SSal
menthol-scented, small-leaved	SSal
Mona Lavender = 'Plepalila'PBR 🏆H1c	EGeo
mutabilis	EGeo SSal
neochilus	CSpe
§ ***oertendahlii*** 🏆H1c	CTre EBak EGeo SSal
- silver-leaved	SSal
- 'Uvongo' 🏆H1c	CPne
ornatus	EGeo NPla SSal
- variegated (v)	SSal
parviflorus Blue Spires = 'Limplep1' (v)	CPne
prostratus	EGeo
purpuratus 🏆H1c	EGeo SSal
rotundifolius	LEdu
saccatus	EGeo
subsp. ***longitubus***	
- subsp. ***pondoensis***	SSal
sinensis	LRHS
spicatus	EGeo SSal
strigosus	SSal
Swedish ivy	see *P. oertendahlii, P. verticillatus*
venteri	EGeo
§ ***verticillatus***	EGeo EWld SSal
- 'Barberton'	EGeo
- 'Pink Surprise'	SSal
Vick's plant	EGeo SSal
zuluensis	CArn CPne CTre EGeo EUJe EWld SDix SRkn SSal WBor

Pleioblastus (*Poaceae*)

akebono	see *P. argenteostriatus* 'Akebono'
§ ***argenteostriatus*** 'Akebono'	ERod
§ - 'Okinadake' (v)	MWht
§ - f. ***pumilus***	EHoe ERod GMaP MMuc MWht NLar SPlb
auricomus	see *P. viridistriatus*
- 'Vagans'	see *Sasaella ramosa*
chino	see *P. argenteostriatus* 'Okinadake'
var. ***argenteostriatus***	
- f. ***elegantissimus***	CEnt CJng EPfP ERod EShb MMuc SBig SEND WMoo
- var. ***hisauchii***	CJng ERod MWht
fortunei	see *P. variegatus* 'Fortunei'
'Gauntlettii'	see *P. argenteostriatus* f. *pumilus*
glaber 'Albostriatus'	see *Sasaella masamuneana* 'Albostriata'
§ ***hindsii***	ERod
§ ***humilis***	ENBC
- var. ***pumilus***	see *P. argenteostriatus* f. *pumilus*
linearis	CJng ERod LRHS MWht NRHS SBig WMoo
§ ***pygmaeus***	CDul CTri CTsd EHoe ELan ENBC GKev GMcL MBrN MJak SCob SGol SRms WMoo
§ - 'Distichus'	CEnt ENBC MJak WMoo
* - var. ***pygmaeus*** 'Mini'	MMuc SEND WCot
§ ***simonii***	LRHS MMuc MWht NRHS SEND SPoG XBlo
- 'Variegatus' (v)	CBcs LRHS NRHS SPer SPoG
§ ***variegatus*** (v) 🏆H4	CBcs CDul CEnt CJng EHoe ELan ELon ENBC EPfP LEdu LPot LRHS MBrN MJak MWht NRHS SArc SCob SDix SLim SPlb SWvt WMoo XBlo
§ - 'Fortunei' (v)	CTsd GMcL MMuc NLar SEND SGol
- 'Tsuboii' (v)	CAbb CDTJ CJng ERod GMcL MBrN MJak SGol WMoo
§ ***viridistriatus*** 🏆H5	Widely available
- f. ***variegatus*** (v)	CTsd SWvt WMoo

Pleione (*Orchidaceae*)

sp.	NDav SDir
Alishan gx 'Merlin'	LYaf
- 'Mother's Day'	GEdr LYaf
- 'Mount Fuji'	LYaf
Anstice Harris gx	LYaf
Asama gx 'Red Grouse'	GEdr LYaf
Askia gx	GEdr
aurita	GEdr GKev LYaf SDir
× ***barbarae***	GKev IFoB LYaf
Barcena gx	LYaf
Berapi gx 'Purple Sandpiper'	LEdu LYaf WPGP
Brigadoon gx 'Stonechat'	LEdu WPGP
Britannia gx 'Doreen'	LEdu LYaf WPGP
§ ***bulbocodioides***	CFil EPot GEdr GKev LYaf
- 'New Forest'	GEdr
§ - 'Yunnan'	GEdr GKev IFoB
Burnsall gx	GEdr
Captain Hook gx	LYaf
Caroli gx 'Cape Robin'	LYaf
chunii	EFEx GEdr GKev LAma LYaf
Confirmation gx	LYaf
Eastfield gx 'Purple Emperor'	LYaf
Eiger gx	LYaf
El Pico gx 'Pheasant'	LYaf
Erebus gx 'Redpoll'	GEdr
formosana 🏆H3	CFil CPne ECho EFEx EPot GKev LAma LCro LEdu LOPS LRHS MHer NHpl SDir WFar WPGP
- Alba Group	ECho GKev WFar
- - 'Claire'	IFoB LEdu LYaf WPGP
- - 'Snow Bunting'	LEdu LYaf WPGP
- 'Blush of Dawn'	NHpl
- 'Cairngorm'	GKev IFoB
- 'Greenhill'	LYaf
- Hyb 8001	IFoB
- 'Iris'	IFoB
- 'Pitlochry'	LYaf
- (Pricei Group) 'Oriental Grace'	IFoB LYaf
- - 'Oriental Splendour'	LYaf
- 'Snow Cap'	ECho
- 'Snow White'	CFil LEdu LYaf WPGP
forrestii	ECho EFEx EPot GKev LAma NHpl
Fuego gx	GKev IFoB
Gerry Mundey gx	GEdr
- 'Tinney's Firs'	LYaf
Glacier Peak gx	LYaf
§ ***grandiflora***	GKev

Harlequin gx 'Norman'	LYaf
Hekla gx	IFoB
- 'Locking Stumps'	GEdr
- 'Partridge'	GEdr
- 'Partridge' × **Zeus Weinstein gx**	GEdr
hookeriana	GKev
humilis	GKev LYaf SDir
- orange-red-flowered	GKev
- purple-flowered	GKev
Irazu gx	IFoB
- 'Cheryl'	GEdr
Jake Butterfield gx	LYaf
Jorullo gx 'Long-tailed Tit'	GEdr LYaf
Katmai gx 'Crossbill' **new**	LYaf
Keith Rattray gx 'Kelty'	LYaf
Kenya gx 'Bald Eagle'	LYaf
Krakatoa gx 'Wheatear'	LYaf
Lascar gx 'Dipper'	LYaf
- 'Purple Finch'	LYaf
Lhasa gx 'Blushes'	LYaf
limprichtii 🏆H3	ECho EFEx GKev IFoB LEdu LYaf
Lyn Butterfield gx	LYaf
maculata	EFEx GKev
Mageik gx 'Black Kite'	LYaf
Mandalay gx 'Purple Rain'	LYaf
- 'Strawberry Fields'	LYaf
Marco Polo gx	GKev
Marion Johnson gx 'Bubs'	LYaf
- 'Whinchat' **new**	LYaf
Mauna Loa gx	LYaf
- 'Glossy Starling'	LYaf
Mawenzi gx	LYaf
Michael Butterfield gx	LYaf
Novarupta gx 'Raven'	LYaf
Orinoco gx 'Gemini'	GEdr
Orizaba gx	GEdr
- 'Fish Eagle'	LYaf
Pelee gx 'Cape Weaver'	LYaf
pinkepankii	see *P. grandiflora*
Piton gx	EPot LYaf
§ ***pleionoides***	GKev LYaf
pogonioides misapplied	see *P. pleionoides*
pogonioides (Rolfe) Rolfe	see *P. bulbocodioides*
praecox	GKev
Quizapu gx 'Peregrine'	LYaf
Rakata gx	IFoB
- 'Locking Stumps'	EPot GEdr
- 'Redwing'	LYaf
- 'Shot Silk'	GEdr LYaf
- 'Skylark'	LEdu WPGP
Red Colobus gx	LYaf
'Rossini'	ECho GKev
Salek gx 'Eagle Owl'	LYaf
Santa Maria gx 'Nightjar'	LYaf
Santorini gx	LYaf
- 'Yellow Wagtail'	LYaf
saxicola	GKev LYaf
scopulorum	EFEx LYaf
Semeru gx **new**	LYaf
Shantung gx	EPot LAma NHpl SDir
- 'Double Cream'	LYaf
- 'Ducat'	LYaf
- 'Gerry Mundey'	LYaf
- 'Muriel Harberd' 🏆H3	GEdr
- 'Ridgeway'	LYaf
Shasta gx	LYaf
Sinope gx	LYaf
Sirena gx	LYaf
Sorea gx	GEdr GKev
Soufrière gx	GEdr
speciosa Ames & Schltr.	see *P. pleionoides*
Steve James gx 'Plum Perfect' **new**	LYaf
Stromboli gx 'Fireball'	CFil EPot LEdu WPGP
Taal gx 'Red-tailed Hawk'	LYaf
× ***taliensis***	LYaf
Tibesti gx	LYaf
Toff gx	LYaf
Tolima gx 'Moorhen'	LEdu LYaf WPGP
Tongariro gx	CPBP ECho EPot GEdr GKev LCro LEdu LOPS WPGP
Ueli Wackernagel gx 'Pearl'	GKev LYaf
'Verdi'	ECho GKev
Versailles gx 'Bucklebury'	GEdr LEdu WPGP
- 'Muriel Turner'	GEdr
Vesuvius gx	GKev
- 'Leopard'	LYaf
- 'Phoenix'	EPot LYaf
- 'Tawny Owl'	GEdr
'Vivaldi'	ECho GKev
Volcanello gx 'Honey Buzzard'	GEdr LYaf
- 'Song Thrush'	LYaf
Whakari gx	LYaf
- 'Mountain Pipit' **new**	LYaf
Wharfedale gx 'Pine Warbler'	LYaf
yunnanensis misapplied	see *P. bulbocodioides* 'Yunnan'
yunnanensis ambig.	GEdr GKev LAma
Zeus Weinstein gx	IFoB LYaf

Pleomele see *Dracaena*

Pleurospermum (*Apiaceae*)

sp.	CSpe
SDR 7941	GKev
SDR 7985	EBee GKev
from Nepal	WCot
benthamii B&SWJ 2988	WCru
camtschaticum B&SWJ 12627	WCru
yunnanense BWJ 7952A	WCru

plum see *Prunus domestica*

Plumbago (*Plumbaginaceae*)

§ ***auriculata*** 🏆H2	CBcs CCCN CSBt CTri CWCL EBak ELan EPfP EPri EShb EUJe MGil MHtn MRav SEND SPer SPoG SRms WFib
- f. ***alba*** 🏆H2	CBcs CCCN CRHN EPfP EShb IDee SEND
- 'Crystal Waters'	CCCN CSam EShb
- dark blue-flowered	CRHN CSpe
- (Escapade Series) 'Escapade Blue'	CWGN EShb SPre
- - 'Escapade White'	EShb
capensis	see *P. auriculata*
larpentiae	see *Ceratostigma plumbaginoides*

Plumeria (*Apocynaceae*)

sp.	WSFF
rubra 🏆H1b	CCCN XBlo
- 'Golden Glow'	XBlo
- 'Velvet Red'	XBlo

Pneumatopteris (*Thelypteridaceae*)

pennigera	NLos

Poa (*Poaceae*)

alpina	SMea XLum
chaixii	EHoe EPPr
cita	IMou
colensoi	EHoe
glauca	EShb
labillardierei	CKno CWCL EBee ECha EHoe EPPr IMou LRHS MAvo MBel MMuc NRHS SEND XLum
pratensis	CHab

Podalyria (*Papilionaceae*)

calyptrata	SPlb
sericea	SPlb

Podanthus (*Asteraceae*)

ovatifolius	SVen

Podocarpus ✿ (*Podocarpaceae*)

acutifolius	CBcs
alpinus R. Br. ex Hook. f.	CDul
andinus	see *Prumnopitys andina*
'Autumn Shades' (m)	NLar
'Blaze' (f)	CBcs LEdu SLim
chilinus	see *P. salignus*
'Chocolate Box' (f)	ELan MAsh NLar SLim
'County Park Fire'[PBR] (f) ♀[H6]	CBcs EMOT EPfP ESwi MAsh MGos NHol NLar SCoo SLim SWvt
cunninghamii 'Roro' (m)	CBcs
dacrydioides	see *Dacrycarpus dacrydioides*
'Flame'	EMOT MAsh NLar SLim
'Guardsman'	LRHS
henkelii	CBcs
lawrencei	CBcs
- 'Blue Gem' (f)	CJun EPfP ESps LRHS MAsh MMuc SCoo SLim WThu
- 'Purple King'	NLar
- 'Red Tip'	NLar
macrophyllus	ESps SArc WPGP
- 'Aureus'	CBcs
'Maori Prince' (m)	NLar
matudae	CFil
nivalis	CBcs CDul CMac SRms WThu
- 'Bronze'	GCal
- 'Jack's Pass' (m)	EMOT
- 'Kilworth Cream' (v) ♀[H6]	CBcs EMOT ESwi LRHS NHol SLim SWvt
- 'Otari' (m)	MAsh NLar
nubigenus	CMCN
'Red Embers' (f)	EMOT ESwi SCoo SLim
§ ***salignus*** ♀[H5]	CBcs CTsd EPfP EUJe IDee SArc SLim WPGP WSHC WThu
totara	CBcs CBrP LEdu
- 'Aureus'	CBcs LRHS
'Young Rusty' (f)	CBcs LRHS MAsh

Podophyllum (*Berberidaceae*)

Chen Yi D-106 **new**	WCot
aurantiocaule	EBee GGGa
- subsp. ***aurantiocaule***	GBin GEdr
§ ***delavayi***	CBct ECho GEdr GKev SDir SKHP
difforme	CBct CLAP ECho GKev LEdu SDir SKHP
emodi	see *Sinopodophyllum hexandrum* var. *emodi*
- var. ***chinense***	see *Sinopodophyllum hexandrum* var. *chinense*
hexandrum	see *Sinopodophyllum hexandrum*
- var. ***chinense***	see *Sinopodophyllum hexandrum* var. *chinense*
'Kaleidoscope' (v)	CBct CLAP EBee ECtt ELan ESwi EUJe GEdr MHol NHpl NLar SKHP SPoG WCot
peltatum	CAby CArn CBct CBro CHid CLAP CWCL EBee ECho EHrv EPfP EWld GBin GEdr GKev GMcL GPoy ILea LAma LEdu NHar NLar NSti SMad SPhx WBor WCot WCru WPGP WPnP
pleianthum	CAby CBct CLAP ECho GCal GEdr WCru
- B&SWJ 282 from Taiwan	WCru
- short	WCru
* ***tsayuensis***	GEdr
veitchii	see *P. delavayi*
versipelle	LEdu SKHP WCru
- 'Spotty Dotty'[PBR] (v)	CBct CGar CLAP ECtt ELan EPot ESwi EUJe EWTr GEdr IBoy IKil LEdu LPla MAvo MHol MMrt MNrw NAst NBir NHpl NLar NPnk NSti SHeu SKHP SMad SPoG WCot WPnP
- subsp. ***versipelle*** **new**	GKev

Podranea (*Bignoniaceae*)

§ ***ricasoliana*** ♀[H1c]	EShb SPoG WBor

Pogonatherum (*Poaceae*)

* ***distichum***	XBlo

Pogonia (*Orchidaceae*)

sp.	NDav

Pogostemon (*Lamiaceae*)

from An Veleniki Herb Farm, Pennsylvania	CArn
§ ***cablin***	EOHP GPoy
patchouly	see *P. cablin*

Polemonium ✿ (*Polemoniaceae*)

ambervicsii	see *P. pauciflorum* subsp. *hinckleyi*
'Apricot Beauty'	see *P. carneum* 'Apricot Delight'
archibaldiae ♀[H5]	MArt NBir SRms WSHC
'Blue Pearl'	CBod EBee ELan EPfP EWld GJos GMcL LRHS MAsh MHol NBro NGdn NLar NRHS SPer WFar WGwG
§ ***boreale***	EWld GBin NPol SWvt WMoo
- 'Heavenly Habit'	GJos LRHS NGdn NRHS
brandegeei misapplied	see *P. pauciflorum*
§ ***brandegeei*** Greene	CCVN GKev WTcb
- subsp. ***mellitum***	see *P. brandegeei* Greene
§ ***caeruleum***	Widely available
- subsp. ***amygdalinum***	see *P. occidentale*
- 'Azuro' **new**	LRHS NRHS
- 'Bambino Blue'	CBod EWoo SWvt WHar
- Brise d'Anjou = 'Blanjou'[PBR] (v)	CMac CWCL ECtt ELan EPfP EShb EWes GMcL IBoy LRHS MAsh NBir NGdn NPol NRHS SCob SMad SPer SWvt WWtn
- subsp. ***caeruleum***	GKev
- - f. ***album***	CBre CSBt CWCL EBee ECha EHrv ELan EPfP EWTr EWoo GAbr GBin GKev GMcL LRHS MArt MBNS MBel MHer MRav NBro NGBl SGbt SPer SPoG SRms WMoo
- - - 'White Pearl' **new**	GWyn
I - f. ***dissectum***	NPol

	- 'Filigree Clouds'	MArt NLar
	- 'Filigree Skies'	MArt NGdn NLar
§	- subsp. ***himalayanum***	CSpe GAbr WMoo
	- - CC 7325	EWld
	- 'Humile'	see *P.* 'Northern Lights'
	- 'Idylle'	NPol
	- 'Larch Cottage' (v)	NPol
	- 'Pam' (v)	NPol
	- 'Sky Blue'	MBel WRHF WWtn
	- 'Snow and Sapphires' (v)	CWGN EBee ECtt MPnt NPer NPol SWvt
	- 'Southern Skies'	NPol
	- subsp. ***vulgare***	NPol
	- white-flowered	GJos IBoy MMuc
	carneum	CTri EBee ECha EWTr LRHS NPol WMoo
§	- 'Apricot Delight'	GJos MNHC MNrw NGdn NPol SGbt WPtf WWtn
	cashmerianum	see *P. caeruleum* subsp. *himalayanum*
	chartaceum	LLHF
	'Churchills'	CBre EBee NPol WSHC
	'Dawn Flight'	NPol
	'Eastbury Purple'	CElw NPol
	'Elworthy Amethyst'	CElw EBee NPol
	eximium	ECho LLHF
	flavum	see *P. foliosissimum* var. *flavum*
	foliosissimum misapplied	see *P. archibaldiae*
	foliosissimum A. Gray	NPol
	- var. ***albiflorum***	see *P. foliosissimum* var. *alpinum*
§	- var. ***alpinum***	NPol
	- 'Cottage Cream'	LEdu NPol WCot
§	- var. ***flavum***	NPol
	- var. ***foliosissimum***	NPol
	- 'Scottish Garden'	NPol
	- 'White Spirit'	NPol
	'Glebe Cottage Lilac'	CDor EBee GCra NBir NPol
	'Glebe Cottage Violet'	NPol
	'Hannah Billcliffe'	CElw ECtt EWes MBrN NPol WFar
	'Heaven Scent'PBR	EBee ECtt ESps NDov NLar WGrn
	'Heavenly Blue'	IBoy
§	'Hopleys'	GCal LHop MBNS MNrw
	× ***jacobaea***	EPPr EWes WCot
	'Katie Daley'	see *P.* 'Hopleys'
	'Lambrook Mauve'	Widely available
	'Mary Mottram'	NPol
	mellitum	see *P. brandegeei* Greene
	'North Tyne'	NChi NPol NWad
§	'Northern Lights'	Widely available
	'Norwell Mauve'	MNrw NPol
§	***occidentale***	NPol
§	***pauciflorum***	ECtt ELan EWld IFro LPot NBir SBee WHea WMoo
§	- subsp. ***hinckleyi***	GKev NPol NQui
§	- subsp. ***pauciflorum***	NPol
	- silver-leaved	see *P. pauciflorum* subsp. *pauciflorum*
	- 'Sulphur Trumpets'	SWvt WRHF
	- subsp. ***typicum***	see *P. pauciflorum* subsp. *pauciflorum*
	'Pink Beauty'	EBee ECtt ELan EPfP GBuc NGdn NPol WWtn
	pulchellum Salisb.	see *P. reptans*
	pulchellum Turcz.	see *P. caeruleum*
	pulcherrimum misapplied	see *P. boreale*
	- 'Tricolor'	see *P. boreale*
	pulcherrimum Hook.	ECho NBro
	- subsp. ***pulcherrimum***	LLHF
§	***reptans***	CArn GPoy MHer NBro NPol SRms WMoo
	- 'Album'	see *P. reptans* 'Virginia White'
	- 'Blue Ice'	NPol
	- 'Firmament'	EBee
*	- 'Sky Blue'	NBro
	- 'Stairway to Heaven'PBR (v)	Widely available
	- 'Touch of Class'PBR (v)	CWGN CWld MAsh MHol NLar SPoG
§	- 'Virginia White'	CBre CElw EWes MAvo MTis NChi NPol SBch
	- 'White Pearl'	MHol
	'Ribby'	NPol
	× ***richardsonii*** misapplied	see *P.* 'Northern Lights'
	× ***richardsonii*** Graham	see *P. boreale*
	'Sapphire'	CBre LRHS
	'Sonia's Bluebell'	CElw CWCL ECtt EPPr EWTr EWes EWld MNrw MPie NDov NLar NPol NSti SBch
	'Sunnyside Storm'	NPol
	'Theddingworth'	NPol
	viscosum	GKev LLHF NPol SPlb
	- f. ***leucanthum***	NPol
	yezoense	NBre NPol
	- var. ***hidakanum***	NPol
	- - Bressingham Purple = 'Polbress'	CAby CBod CMos CWCL CWld EBee ELan ELon EPfP EWes EWoo GMaP IKil LBMP LRHS MAsh MBNS MBel NHol NLar NPol NPri NRHS NSti NWad SGbt SHil SPer SPoG WCAu
	- - 'Halfway to Paradise'	CMos SCob
	- - 'Purple Rain'	Widely available

Polianthes (*Asparagaceae*)

elongata	WCot
tuberosa	CBcs CCCN ECho GKev LCro LOPS SPer XLum
- 'Cinderella' **new**	GKev WHil
- 'Golden Harvest' **new**	GKev
- 'Pink Sapphire' **new**	GKev WHil
- 'Sensation' **new**	GKev
- 'Super Gold' **new**	GKev
- 'The Pearl' (d)	ECho GKev LAma SDeJ WCot XLum
- 'Yellow Baby' **new**	GKev WHil

Poliomintha (*Lamiaceae*)

bustamanta	NBir SPhx
incana	CArn

Poliothyrsis (*Salicaceae*)

sinensis	CBcs EPfP IArd SAko

Pollia (*Commelinaceae*)

japonica	ESwi EWes SBrt WCot

Polygala (*Polygalaceae*)

	'Africana'PBR	CTre
	africana 'Nana' **new**	LRHS
	calcarea Bulley's form	EPot
	- 'Lillet' ♀H5	EPot GEdr LHop LLHF LRHS NRHS WAbe
	chamaebuxus ♀H5	GKev LLHF MAsh MGos NLar NSla SRms WIce WThu
I	- ***alba***	LBee NLar WAbe
§	- var. ***grandiflora*** ♀H5	CBcs EPfP EPot GAbr GEdr GKev GMcL IVic LBee LHop MAsh MGil MGos NBir NHpl NSla SPlb SPoG WAbe WIce
	- 'Loibl'	EPot
	- 'Purpurea'	see *P. chamaebuxus* var. *grandiflora*

	- 'Rhodoptera'	see *P. chamaebuxus* var. *grandiflora*
§	× ***dalmaisiana*** ♀H2	CAbb CCCN CRHN CSpe CTsd CWGN EBee ECre ELan GBin LRHS SEND WAbe WCFE
	'Dolomite'	GEdr
	myrtifolia ♀H2	CCCN CTre ELan GBin GFai IDee MGos SAdn SPlb
	- Bibi Pink = 'Polylap'	SAdn
	- 'Grandiflora'	see *P.* × *dalmaisiana*
	'Purple Passion'	CCCN LRHS
	virgata	CCCN

Polygonatum ✿ (*Asparagaceae*)

	Og 94047	LEdu
	SBQE 310	LEdu MAvo
	acuminatifolium 'Ogon'	EBee
	altelobatum B&SWJ 286	WCru
	- B&SWJ 1886	WCru
	arisanense B&SWJ 271	WCru
	- B&SWJ 3839	WCru
§	***biflorum***	CBod CHid CPou EBee ECho ECtt ELan EPfP EWTr GBin GKev GMaP IBal ILea LRHS MAvo MSCN NLar NWad SMad SPhx SPoG SWvt WCru WFar WPnP XLum
	- dwarf	LRHS
	canaliculatum	see *P. biflorum*
	cathcartii B&SWJ 2429	WCru
	- yellow-flowered B&SWJ 2412	WCru
	cirrhifolium	CBro CCse EBee ECho EPot GEdr GKev LEdu LRHS MAvo MNrw NHpl NWad SKHP WCru WPGP
	- ARGS 320	EPPr
	- from China	WCru
	commutatum	see *P. biflorum*
	'Corsley'	CPou
	cryptanthum	GKev WCru
	curvistylum	CAby CAvo CBct CLAP CTal EHrv EPPr EWld GEdr GKev IFoB ILea IMou LEdu MAvo NCGa NLar NRya SPhx WCru WSHC
	cyrtonema misapplied	see *Disporopsis pernyi*
	cyrtonema Hua	WCru
	- B&SWJ 271	LEdu
*	***desoulavyi*** var. ***yezoense*** B&SWJ 764	WCru
	falcatum misapplied	see *P. humile*
	falcatum A. Gray	EBee NHpl NRya
	- B&SWJ 1077	EHrv WCru
	- B&SWJ 5054	WCru
	- 'Shikoku Silver'	MAvo WCru
	- 'Variegatum'	see *P. odoratum* var. *pluriflorum* 'Variegatum'
	'Falcon'	see *P. humile*
	filipes	EHrv EPPr WCru
	fuscum	WCru
	geminiflorum	CBct CLAP WCru WFar
	- McB 2448	GEdr
	giganteum	see *P. biflorum*
	'Golden Gift'	CBct
§	***graminifolium***	CAby CBct CLAP CPBP CTal ECho EPPr GKev WCru WThu
	- G-W&P 803	ECho
§	***hirtum***	CAby CBct CLAP ECho EPPr IFoB LEdu LRHS WCru
	- BM 7012	ECho
	- 'Robustum'	ECho WCru
	hookeri	CAby CBct CSpe CTal ECho EHrv EPPr EWld GBin GEdr GKev GMaP ITim LEdu LRHS NBid NCGa NHpl NLar NRya NSla NWad SPhx WAbe WCru WFar
§	***humile***	Widely available
I	- 'Variegatum' (v)	CMac
§	× ***hybridum*** ♀H7	Widely available
	- 'Bere'	LEdu WPGP
	- 'Betberg'	CBct CLAP ECha EHrv ELon EPPr IFoB IMou LEdu MAvo NBir WCot
	- 'Flore Pleno' (d)	WHer
	- 'Nanum'	CBct CHid MRav WCot
§	- 'Striatum' (v)	Widely available
	- 'Variegatum'	see *P.* × *hybridum* 'Striatum'
	- 'Wakehurst'	EHrv LEdu
	- 'Weihenstephan'	GCal IPot LEdu
	- 'Welsh Gold' (v)	CAvo EBee
	inflatum	ECho GEdr WCru
	- B&SWJ 922	WCru
	involucratum	ECho WCru
	- B&SWJ 4285	WCru
	japonicum	see *P. odoratum*
	kansuense	ECho
	kingianum yellow-flowered B&SWJ 6545	WCru
	- - B&SWJ 6562	WCru
	'Langthorn's Variegated' (v)	ELan
	lasianthum	ECho SMHy WCru
	- B&SWJ 671	WCru
	latifolium	see *P. hirtum*
	maximowiczii	EBee EPPr WCru WPGP
	mengtzense f. ***mengtzense*** HWJ 588 **new**	WCru
	- - HWJ 861	LEdu WCru
	- f. ***tonkinense*** B&SWJ 8246	LEdu WCru
	- - HWJ 551	WCru
	- - HWJ 567	WCru
	- - HWJ 573	WCru
	'Multifide'	EBee GKev
	multiflorum misapplied	see *P.* × *hybridum*
	multiflorum L.	Widely available
	- CC 4572	WCot
	- 'Flore Pleno' (d)	WFar
	- ***giganteum*** hort.	see *P. biflorum*
	- 'Ramosissima'	SMHy WCru
	- var. ***ramosum***	LEdu
*	***nanum*** 'Variegatum' (v)	CBcs ECho
	nodosum	WCru
§	***odoratum***	CAvo CBct CBro CTal CTsd EBee ECho EHrv EPfP GMaP LEdu NBid NLar NPnk NRya SCob WCru
	- RBG 93-101	EBee
	- 'Byakko' (v)	GEdr
§	- dwarf	CTal ECho LEdu
	- 'Flatmate'	LEdu WCru
	- 'Flore Pleno' (d)	CLAP ECho EHrv GKev LEdu MHer WCot WHoo
	- 'Grace Barker'	see *P.* × *hybridum* 'Striatum'
	- 'Koryu'	GEdr
	- 'Leigong Stripe' **new**	LEdu
	- var. ***odoratum***	GKev
	- var. ***pluriflorum***	GKev
§	- - 'Variegatum' (v)	Widely available
	- 'Red Stem'	CTal ECho EHrv LEdu WCru
	- 'Silver Wings' (v)	CBct CLAP ECha EHrv IPot NBir NLar
	- var. ***thunbergii***	WCru
	- - 'Variegatum' (v)	CWld
	- 'Ussuriland'	EBee EPPr GCal LEdu MAvo
	- 'Ussuriland Roundleaf'	GCal LEdu MAvo

	officinale	see *P. odoratum*
	oppositifolium B&SWJ 2537	WCru
§	***orientale***	CBct CLAP ECho GKev
	pluriflorum	see *P. graminifolium*
	polyanthemum	see *P. orientale*
	prattii	CTal ECho GKev ILea WCru
	- CLD 325	LEdu
	pubescens	CBct ECho EHrv LEdu WCru WThu
	pumilum	see *P. odoratum* dwarf
	punctatum ambig.	CBct GEdr LEdu NBid WPGP
	punctatum Royle ex Kunth B&SWJ 2395	CBct WCru
	racemosum	CBct IMou
	roseum	CLAP EPPr GKev LLHF MAvo WCru
	sewerzowii	EPPr
	sibiricum	CBct GEdr WCru WFar
	- DJHC 600	EBee LEdu WPGP
	singalilense	EBee GKev WCru
	stenanthum	ECho
	- B&SWJ 5727	LEdu WCru
	- B&SWJ 11425	WCru
	stenophyllum	IMou WCru
	stewartianum	CLAP EBee EPPr ILea MAvo NRya
	tessellatum PAB 8336	LEdu
	aff. ***tessellatum*** B&SWJ 9752	WCru
	verticillatum	CBct CBro CHid CTal EBee ECha EPPr EPfP GEdr IFoB LEdu LRHS MNrw MRav SKHP SMad WCru WFar WPGP WWtn
	- B&SWJ 2147	WCru
	- CLD 1308	EPPr
	- PAB 2455	LEdu
	- 'Giant One'	IMou MAvo XEll
	- 'Himalayan Giant'	CHid ECho EPPr MAvo WPnP
	- 'Krynica'	LEdu WPGP
*	- 'Roseum'	CAvo
	- 'Rubrum'	CAby CBct CLAP EBee EHrv EPPr GEdr GKev ILea LEdu LHop LRHS NBid NChi NLar NPnk WCot WCru WHoo
	- 'Serbian Dwarf'	CBct CHid CTal ECho GEdr GKev LEdu WPGP
	aff. ***verticillatum***	CSpe IFoB
	aff. ***wardii*** B&SWJ 6599	WCru
	yunnanense	CBct LEdu
	zanlanscianense	CBct EBee ECho EHrv LEdu WCru

Polygonum (*Polygonaceae*)

	affine	see *Persicaria affinis*
	amplexicaule	see *Persicaria amplexicaulis*
	aubertii	see *Fallopia baldschuanica*
	baldschuanicum	see *Fallopia baldschuanica*
	bistorta	see *Persicaria bistorta*
	capitatum	see *Persicaria capitata*
	compactum	see *Fallopia japonica* var. *compacta*
	equisetiforme misapplied	see *P. scoparium*
	filiforme	see *Persicaria virginiana*
	molle	see *Persicaria mollis*
	multiflorum	see *Fallopia multiflora*
	odoratum	see *Persicaria odorata*
	polystachyum	see *Persicaria wallichii*
	runciforme	see *Persicaria runcinata*
§	***scoparium***	EHoe EPPr ESwi EWes SDys SVen WOld XLum
	tinctorium	see *Persicaria tinctoria*
	vacciniifolium	see *Persicaria vacciniifolia*
	weyrichii	see *Persicaria weyrichii*

Polylepis (*Rosaceae*)

	australis	CPne IDee IMou LEdu SAko SMad
	- tall	WPGP

Polypodium ✿ (*Polypodiaceae*)

	appalachianum	SKHP
	aureum	see *Phlebodium aureum*
	- 'Glaucum'	CSpe WCot
	australe	see *P. cambricum*
	calirhiza 'Sarah Lyman'	SKHP
§	***cambricum***	EFer WCot WFib
	- GG 20131 **new**	SMHy
	- 'Barrowii'	CLAP WAbe WFib WGwG
	- 'Bob's Choice' **new**	WCot
I	- 'Cambricum' ♀H7	CLAP GCal WAbe
	- 'Conwy'	WFib
	- 'Cristatum'	CLAP WFib
	- (Cristatum Group) 'Grandiceps Forster'	CLAP
	- - 'Grandiceps Fox' ♀H7	MRav WFib
	- 'Hornet'	WFib
	- 'Macrostachyon'	CLAP GBin NBid WFib
	- 'Oakleyae'	EWld SMHy WCot
	- 'Omnilacerum Oxford'	CLAP
	- 'Prestonii'	WCot WFib
	- Pulcherrimum Group	CLAP SDys
	- - 'Pulcherrimum Addison'	EBee GBin LEdu WCot WFib WPGP
	- - 'Pulchritudine'	CLAP LLWG WCot
	- 'Richard Kayse' ♀H7	CLAP EWes SMHy WAbe WCot WFib WPGP
	- Semilacerum Group	EFer
	- - 'Carew Lane'	WFib
	- - 'Falcatum O'Kelly'	WCot
	- - 'Robustum'	WFib
	- 'Whilharris' ♀H7	CLAP SMHy
I	× ***coughlinii*** bifid	WFib
	glycyrrhiza	CLAP GPoy SKHP WFib
	- bifid	see *P.* × *coughlinii* bifid
	- 'Lawrence Crocker' **new**	WCot
	- 'Longicaudatum' ♀H7	CLAP EFer EShb WCot WFib
	- 'Malahatense' (sterile)	EBee WCot WPGP
	interjectum	CLAP EFer EShb MRav WCot
	- 'Cornubiense' ♀H7	CLAP ECGP EWld NBid NBir SMHy
	- 'Glomeratum Mullins'	WFib
	macaronesicum	WCot
	× ***mantoniae***	WFib
	- 'Bifidograndiceps'	NBid WFib
	scouleri	CFil CLAP EFer ISha LRHS MRav NBro WCot WPGP
	vulgare	Widely available
	- 'Bifidocristatum'	see *P. vulgare* 'Bifidomultifidum'
	- 'Bifidomulticeps'	WCot
§	- 'Bifidomultifidum'	CLAP CWCL ELon EPed EPfP GBin GCal GEdr ISha LLWP MGos MRav NLar SEND WCot WMoo
*	- 'Congestum Cristatum'	SRms
	- 'Cornubiense Grandiceps'	GCal SRms
*	- 'Cornubiense Multifidum'	EBee WCot
	- 'Elegantissimum'	NBid WFib
	- 'Parsley'	WCot
	- 'Trichomanoides Backhouse'	CLAP GCal WAbe WFib
	'Whitley Giant'	CAby CBod EBee ECtt ESwi GBin GEdr ISha ITim LEdu LLWG LPla LSun MArt MMuc MPie NBid NCou SEND SMad WCot

Polypompholyx see *Utricularia*

Polyspora (*Theaceae*)

§	***axillaris***	CBcs CCCN CHll EBee
	- CWJ 12363	WCru
	longicarpa DJHV 06041	WCru
	- WWJ 11604	WCru
	speciosa B&SWJ 11708 from Vietnam	WCru
	- B&SWJ 11750	WCru WSHC
	- WWJ 11934	WCru

Polystichum ✿ (*Dryopteridaceae*)

	acrostichoides	CDTJ CLAP EBee ERod GBin LEdu LRHS MMuc NBro NLar WPGP XLum
	aculeatum 🏆H7	CBod CLAP CLet ECha EFer ELan ERod EShb GBin GMaP GMcL LCro LEdu LHop LRHS MGos MMuc NBid NEgg NLar SCob SRms SWvt WFib WMoo XLum
	- 'Cristatum Wollaston'	WCot
I	- Densum Group	EFer GMcL
	- 'Portia'	WFib
	braunii	CBcs CDor CLet CMac CWCL EPfP GMaP IKil LRHS NBid NBro NLar SPoG WFib WPnP XLum
	caryotideum	see *Cyrtomium caryotideum*
	× ***dycei*** 🏆H6	ISha LRHS NLos
	falcatum	see *Cyrtomium falcatum*
	fortunei	see *Cyrtomium fortunei*
	imbricans	CLAP
	interjectum	MRav
	luctuosum	ISha
	makinoi	CCCN CLAP GBin ISha LLWG LRHS NBid NBro NEgg SPlb WFib WMoo
	mayebarae	EBee ISha
	munitum 🏆H7	Widely available
	neolobatum	WFib
	- BWJ 8182	WCru
	nepalense	NLos
	polyblepharum 🏆H7	Widely available
	- 'Jade'	CMac EBee LRHS
	prescottianum	GCra
	proliferum misapplied	see *P. setiferum* Acutilobum Group
	proliferum ambig.	GMcL
	proliferum (R. Br.) C. Presl	CLAP SBig WFib WPGP
*	- ***plumosum***	SPad SWvt
	richardii	SBig
	rigens	CBod CLAP CWCL EFer EMOT ISha LRHS LSou NBro NLar SRms SRot WFib
	setiferum 🏆H7	Widely available
§	- Acutilobum Group	CBod CLAP ECha EMOT GMaP IBoy LLWG LRHS NLos SCob SDix SPer SRms WMoo WPGP XLum
	- Congestum Group	CDor CKel ELon EMOT GBin NBro NCGa NEgg NHol NLar SMad SPer SRms WFib WPat
	- - 'Congestum'	CLAP CLet CWCL ELan EMOT EPPr EPfP EPot ERod IKil ISha LBMP LHop LRHS MRav NBir NEgg NGdn NHol SPad SPoG SPtp WMoo XLum
	- 'Cristatopinnulum'	CFil NHar WPGP
	- Cristatum Group	CLAP SRms
	- (Decompositum Group) 'Proliferum'	CWCL EBee
	- Divisilobum Group 🏆H7	CLAP EFer ELan MCot MGos SRms WAbe WFar WFib WHoo WPGP
	- - 'Caernarfon'	CFil CLAP
	- - 'Dahlem'	CFil CLAP CLet EBee ECha ECtt EFer ELan ELon EMOT EPfP EUJe GMaP LRHS LSRN NBid NEgg SPer WFib WMoo WPat WPtf XLum
	- - 'Divisilobum Densum' 🏆H7	CLAP EPfP MRav NBir
	- - 'Divisilobum Grandiceps'	CFil
	- - 'Divisilobum Iveryanum' 🏆H7	CFil CLAP EFer SRms WFib
	- - 'Divisilobum Laxum'	CFil CLAP EBee
§	- - 'Divisilobum Wollaston'	CDTJ CFil CKel CLAP CLet CTal CWCL ECtt ELon IBal ISha LLWG LRHS MBel MGos MRav NBid NLar SBod SHil WCot WMoo
	- - 'Herrenhausen'	Widely available
	- - 'Madame Patti'	CFil
	- - 'Mrs Goffey'	CFil
	- - 'Proliferum' **new**	EUJe
	- Foliosum Group	CLAP EFer
	- 'Gabeljurgel' **new**	CFil
	- 'Gracile'	MRav NBir
	- 'Grandiceps'	CLAP EFer
	- 'Grandiceps Jentsch' **new**	CFil
	- 'Hamlet'	WFib
	- 'Helena'	WFib
	- 'Hirondelle'	SRms
	- Lineare Group	WFib
	- Multilobum Group	CLAP SRms WFib
	- 'Nantes'	CFil
	- 'Othello'	CFil WFib
	- Perserratum Group	NBid WFib
	- 'Plumo-Densum'	see *P. setiferum* Plumosomultilobum Group
	- 'Plumosodensum'	see *P. setiferum* Plumosomultilobum Group
	- Plumosodivisilobum Group	CLAP ECha NBid NBro SMHy WAbe WFib WRHF
	- - 'Baldwinii'	CLAP WFib
	- - 'Bland'	WFib
§	- Plumosomultilobum Group	CDor CFil CLAP CWCL EAJP EBee EPfP GEdr ISha LCro LPla MCot MGos NBir NLar SMad WCot WFib WHoo WMoo WPat
I	- - 'Plumosomultilobum Densum'	CAby CBod CHVG ECtt EPed EUJe LRHS MBel SBod SCob WCot
	- Plumosum Group	CLAP CMac CSpe CTal EFer ELon LLWG MJak SArc SRot
	- - dwarf	CSBt
*	- ***plumosum grande*** 'Moly'	SRms
	- Proliferum Group	see *P. setiferum* Acutilobum Group
	- 'Proliferum Wollaston'	see *P. setiferum* (Divisilobum Group) 'Divisilobum Wollaston'
	- 'Pulcherrimum Bevis' 🏆H6	CAby CFil CHid CLAP CSpe EBee ELon ESwi IKil ISha ITim MAvo MCot MMuc MPie NGdn SArc SDix SEND SWvt WCot WFib WPGP WPat
	- (Pulcherrimum Group) 'Pulcherrimum'	ISha
	- (Rotundatum Group) 'Cristatum'	CLAP ISha
	- 'Seestern' **new**	CFil
	- 'Smith's Cruciate'	CFil CLAP MRav WFib
	- 'Wakeleyanum'	EFer SRms
	tsussimense 🏆H6	Widely available
	vestitum	SBig

Polyxena (*Asparagaceae*)

*	***brevifolia***	ECho
	corymbosa	see *Lachenalia corymbosa*
	ensifolia var. ***ensifolia***	see *Lachenalia ensifolia* subsp. *ensifolia*

longituba	see *Lachenalia longituba*
odorata	see *Lachenalia ensifolia* subsp. *ensifolia*
paucifolia	see *Lachenalia paucifolia*
pygmaea	see *Lachenalia pygmaea*

pomegranate see *Punica granatum*

Poncirus see *Citrus*

Ponerorchis (*Orchidaceae*)

graminifolia	GKev LAma
- purple-on-white-flowered	ECho GKev
- red point	ECho GKev
- white-flowered	GKev

Pontederia (*Pontederiaceae*)

cordata 🏆H5	CBen CWat EPfP EWay LCro MSKA MWts NPer SCoo SPlb SWat WMAq WPnP XLum
- f. ***albiflora***	CWat EPfP EWay MWts XLum
- 'Blue Spires'	MSKA
§ - var. ***lancifolia***	CBen EWay LLWG MNrw MSKA MWts NPer SWat
- pink-flowered	LLWG
dilatata	see *Monochoria hastata*
lanceolata	see *P. cordata* var. *lancifolia*

Populus ✿ (*Salicaceae*)

× ***acuminata***	WMou
alba	CBcs CCVT CDul CLnd CMac CTho CTri CWib ECrN EPfP ESps LBuc NOrn NWea SCob SEND SEWo SGol SPer WHed WMou WTSh
- 'Bolleana'	see *P. alba* 'Pyramidalis'
§ - 'Pyramidalis'	SRms WMou
§ - 'Raket'	CCVT CLnd CTho ECrN ELan NWea SPer
- 'Richardii'	CLet EBtc EGFP WCot WMou
- Rocket	see *P. alba* 'Raket'
§ 'Balsam Spire' (f)	CDul CTho NWea WHed WMou
§ ***balsamifera***	CCVT CLnd CSBt CTri ECrN SPer WCot
- 'Vita Sackville West'	MBlu
× ***canadensis***	EWld
§ - 'Aurea' 🏆H6	CDul CTho CWib ECrN SPer WMat WMou
- 'Columbia'	WMou
- 'Eugenei' (m)	WMou
- 'Robusta' (m)	CCVT CDul CLnd CTri NWea WHed WMou
- 'Serotina' (m)	WMou
× ***canescens***	CLnd
- 'Tower'	WMat
deltoides 'Fuego'	SGol
- 'Purple Tower' PBR	CEnd EBee ELan EPfP MBlu MMuc NOra SLim SMad SPoG WHar
× ***generosa*** 'Beaupré'	WMou
glauca new	IArd WPGP
- KR 3993 new	WPGP
× ***jackii*** 'Aurora' (f/v)	CBcs CCVT CDul CLnd CMac CSBt CTsd GMcL LBuc LPot MGos MMuc NPri NWea SGol SPer WHar WMou
lasiocarpa	CBcs CLnd CMCN CTho EPfP IArd IDee MBlu SGol SMad WMou WPGP WPat
- (m/f) new	WPGP
nigra	CHab CMac CTho CTri CTsd ESps NOrn NWea SCob WSFF
- (f)	ECrN MMuc SEND
- (m)	MMuc SEND
- subsp. ***betulifolia***	CCVT CDul CHab CLnd NWea WHed WMou
- - (f)	EBtc WMou
- - (m)	EBtc WMou
§ - 'Italica' (m) 🏆H6	CCVT CDul CLnd CMac CSBt CTho CTri CWib ECrN ELan ESps LBuc MGos NWea SEND SEWo SPer WHed WMou
- 'Pyramidalis'	see *P. nigra* 'Italica'
purdomii	WPGP
'Serotina Aurea'	see *P.* × *canadensis* 'Aurea'
simonii 'Fastigiata'	WMou
szechuanica	WMou
§ - var. ***tibetica***	WMou
tacamahaca	see *P. balsamifera*
'Tacatricho 32'	see *P.* 'Balsam Spire'
tremula	CAco CCVT CDul CHab CLnd CMac CTho CTri CWib ECrN ELan ESps EWTr GQue LBuc MJak MMuc NWea SCob SEWo SPer WHar WHed WMou WSFF WTSh
§ - 'Erecta' 🏆H7	CDul CEnd CTho MBlu MMuc SEND WMat
- 'Erecta' × ***tremuloides***	NOrn
- 'Fastigiata'	see *P. tremula* 'Erecta'
- 'Pendula' (m)	CEnd CTho ECrN
trichocarpa	CDul SPer
- 'Fritzi Pauley' (f)	CDul CTho WMou
violascens	see *P. szechuanica* var. *tibetica*
× ***wilsocarpa*** 'Beloni'	WPGP WPat
wilsonii	WPGP
yunnanensis	WMou

Porophyllum (*Asteraceae*)

ruderale	CLau WJek

Portulaca (*Portulacaceae*)

grandiflora	SVic
oleracea	ENfk SVic WJek WTre
- var. ***aurea***	MNHC WJek

Potamogeton (*Potamogetonaceae*)

crispus	CWat MSKA WDra WMAq WSFF
malainus	LLWG
natans	LLWG MSKA WDra WSFF XLum
schweinfurthii new	XBlo

Potentilla ✿ (*Rosaceae*)

alba	CTri ECha ECho ELan ESps GCal LPot MRav NChi NSti NWad SPer WSHC
alchemilloides	CMac
ambigua	see *P. cuneata*
ancistrifolia var. ***dickinsii***	GEdr
andicola	EBee
anserina	CAgr MHer NMir WHer XLum
- 'Golden Treasure' (v)	EBee WHer
anserinoides	WMoo
arbuscula misapplied	see *P. fruticosa* (Sulphurascens Group) 'Elizabeth'
- 'Beesii'	see *P. fruticosa* 'Beesii'
'Arc-en-ciel'	Widely available
argentea	SPlb WFar XLum
arguta	EBee
argyrophylla	see *P. atrosanguinea* var. *argyrophylla*
atrosanguinea	Widely available
§ - var. ***argyrophylla***	CSam CWCL EBee ECha ELan EPfP GCal GKev GPSL ITim MMuc MRav

		NBir NBro NChi NLar SEND SMad SRms WMoo XLum
	- - 'Golden Starlit'	EDAr IBoy SVic
§	- - 'Scarlet Starlit'	CAby CDor EDAr EPfP IBoy LRHS LSun NCou SVic
	- 'Fireball' (d)	EPfP GJos
	- var. ***leucochroa***	see *P. atrosanguinea* var. *argyrophylla*
*	- 'Sundermannii'	GJos LLHF SBrt
	aurea	ECho ECtt EPfP GBin
	- 'Aurantiaca'	NLar
§	- 'Goldklumpen'	ECtt MRav NEoE
	- 'Plena' (d)	NRya
	'Blazeaway'	CBod ECtt GCal LRHS MArl MAvo MBNS NEoE NGdn WCot
	calabra	ECha EWes SPhx WHer
	caulescens	SBrt
§	***cinerea***	CTri ECho LLHF
	clusiana	CPBP
§	***crantzii***	CMea SRms
	- 'Nana'	see *P. crantzii* 'Pygmaea'
§	- 'Pygmaea'	ECho ECtt NBir
§	***cuneata*** 🏆^{H5}	ECho GAbr GKev MMuc
	davurica 'Abbotswood'	see *P. fruticosa* 'Abbotswood'
	delavayi	MNrw
	dombeyi	IMou
	'Emilie' (d)	CSpe CWCL ECtt GBuc GCal GMcL IKil MBNS MBel MCot MNrw NEoE NLar SWvt WBor WCot
§	***erecta***	GPoy MNHC
	eriocarpa	CPBP ECho EPot GCrg NSla WAbe WIce
	'Esta Ann'	CAby CBod CMac ECtt GBuc LHop LRHS MArl MBNS MNrw NLar SRGP
	'Etna'	CWCL ECtt ELan GBuc GCal LRHS MNrw NBir NCou NLar WHrl WMoo WPtf
	'Everest'	see *P. fruticosa* 'Mount Everest'
	'Fireflame'	NLar WMoo
	fissa	MNrw NBir NLar SPhx
	'Flambeau' (d)	CWCL ECtt EShb GBuc GKin ILea IPot LRHS MArl MAvo MRav MSpe NCGa NGdn NLar NSti WMoo XEll
	'Flamenco'	CSam CTri ECtt LRHS MArl MAvo MBNS MNrw MRav NBir NCGa WFar WMoo
	fragariiformis	see *P. megalantha*
	fruticosa	ESps LBuc NWea
§	- 'Abbotswood' 🏆^{H7}	Widely available
	- 'Abbotswood Silver' (v)	WMoo
	- 'Annette'	MBrN NEoE NLar WRHF
	- 'Apple Blossom'	CWib
	- var. ***arbuscula*** hort.	see *P. fruticosa* (Sulphurascens Group) 'Elizabeth'
	- 'Argentea Nana'	see *P. fruticosa* 'Beesii'
	- 'Baby Bethan'^{PBR} (d)	LLHF
§	- 'Beesii'	EPfP LRHS MAsh SIgm
	- 'Bewerley Surprise'	WFar
	- 'Bo-Peep'	CEnd LRHS
	- 'Chelsea Star' 🏆^{H7}	CMac CRos LRHS LSRN MAsh SHil SPoG
	- 'Chilo' (v)	WMoo
	- 'Clotted Cream'	CRos SGbt
	- var. ***dahurica*** 'Hersii'	see *P. fruticosa* 'Snowflake'
	- Danny Boy = 'Lissdan'^{PBR}	LCro LRHS MAsh NEoE SLon SPoG
	- 'Daphne'	NWad
	- 'Dart's Golddigger'	CTri NWad
	- 'Daydawn'	CBcs CBod CDul CMac CTri ELan EPfP ESps GMcL LHop LRHS MAsh MMuc MRav MSwo NBir NEgg NLar NWad SGol SLim SPer SWvt WMoo
	- 'Farreri'	see *P. fruticosa* 'Gold Drop'
	- 'Floppy Disc'	ELan
	- 'Glenroy Pinkie'	MRav
§	- 'Gold Drop'	CMac NHol
	- 'Golden Dwarf'	WMoo
	- 'Goldfinger'	CAco CBod CChe CMac CSBt EBee ELan EMOT EPfP ESps GMcL IBoy LHop LRHS MAsh MGos MJak MMuc MRav MSwo NEgg SCob SCoo SEND SLim SPer SPlb SPoG WMoo
	- Goldkugel	see *P. fruticosa* 'Gold Drop'
	- 'Goldstar'	CRos ESps IArd LRHS NPri SCob SEND SLim SLon SRms WFar
	- 'Goldteppich'	LBuc
	- 'Grace Darling'	ECrN ELan EPfP EWes NBir NEgg SRGP SWvt WMoo WRHF
	- 'Groneland' 🏆^{H7}	CRos ELan EPfP LRHS MAsh SCoo SPoG
	- 'Haytor's Orange'	CWib
	- 'Hopleys Orange' 🏆^{H7}	CRos CSBt ELon EPfP ESps EWes LHop LRHS NHol NPri SCob SGbt SGol SHil SRms WFar WMoo
	- 'Hurstbourne'	NEoE
	- 'Jackman's Variety' 🏆^{H7}	CLet CWib EPfP IBoy LRHS MAsh SCob SRms
	- 'Katherine Dykes'	CDul CTri CWib EPfP ESps GKin GMcL LBMP LRHS LSRN MAsh NEgg NWea SCob SCoo SGbt SLim SPer SRms WFar WMoo
	- 'King Cup' 🏆^{H7}	EPfP LRHS MAsh
§	- 'Klondike'	CBcs CSBt NWea
	- 'Kobold'	CDul GMcL LRHS NLar SHil
	- 'Lemon and Lime'	see *P. fruticosa* 'Limelight'
§	- 'Limelight' 🏆^{H7}	CRos CSBt ELan EPfP GKin LHop LRHS MAsh MRav MSwo NEoE NWad SHil SPer SRms
	- 'Lovely Pink'	see *P. fruticosa* 'Pink Beauty'
§	- 'Maanelys'	CSBt ELan NWea SPer WMoo
	- 'Macpenny's Cream'	CMac
§	- 'Manchu'	CMac MRav SCob SPer WCFE
	- Mango Tango = 'Uman'^{PBR}	CRos CSBt EBee EMOT EMil EPfP LHop LRHS LSRN MAsh NLar SPoG WFar
§	- Marian Red Robin = 'Marrob'^{PBR} 🏆^{H7}	CLet CWib ELan EPfP GKin GMcL IBoy LCro LRHS MAsh MRav MSwo NPri NWea SCoo SLim SLon SPer SPoG SWvt
	- 'McKay's White'	NLar
	- 'Medicine Wheel Mountain' 🏆^{H7}	CRos ELan EWes IArd LRHS MAsh MPkF MRav NLar NWad SCob SCoo SGol SHil SLim SPer SPoG
	- Moonlight	see *P. fruticosa* 'Maanelys'
§	- 'Mount Everest'	CTri GMcL MMuc NWea SEND SLon
	- 'Nana Argentea'	see *P. fruticosa* 'Beesii'
	- 'New Dawn'	CBcs EMOT GKin
	- 'Orangeade'	CRos EPfP LRHS MAsh NLar SCoo SPoG
*	- 'Peachy Proud'	NEoE
§	- 'Pink Beauty'^{PBR} 🏆^{H7}	Widely available
	- Pink Paradise = 'Kupinpa'^{PBR}	NCGa
	- 'Pink Pearl'	WMoo
	- 'Pink Queen'	NLar
	- 'Pink Whisper'	NEoE
	- 'Pretty Polly'	ELan ESps LRHS MSwo NHol NLar NWad WFar WMoo

	- 'Primrose Beauty' 🏆^{H7}	Widely available
§	- Princess = 'Blink'	CAco CBcs CDul EBee ELan EPfP ESps GMcL LRHS MAsh MJak MRav SCob SCoo SGol SLim SRms WFar WMoo
	- 'Red Ace'	Widely available
	- 'Red Lady'^{PBR}	EMOT EPfP LRHS NHol SCob SHil SPoG WMoo
	- Red Robin	see *P. fruticosa* Marian Red Robin
	- 'Red Surprise'	WFar
	- Rhodocalyx Group	GCal
	- 'Royal Flush'	NWad
	- 'Setting Sun'	LBuc
	- 'Snowbird'	EBee NEoE SLim WFar
§	- 'Snowflake'	CBcs WMoo
	- 'Sommerflor' 🏆^{H7}	CAco EPfP LRHS MAsh
	- 'Sophie's Blush'	MRav
§	- (Sulphurascens Group) 'Elizabeth'	CBcs CDul CWib ECrN ELan EPfP ESps LBMP LRHS LSRN MGos MJak MMuc MSwo NHol NWea SCob SGol SLim SPer SRms SWvt WCFE WFar WHar WMoo
	- - 'Longacre Variety'	CMac CTri IArd MSwo NLar NWea
	- 'Summer Dawn'	LBuc
	- 'Sunset'	CBcs CMac CWib ELan GKin LSRN MJak NBir NWea SCob SCoo SHil SLim SRms WFar WMoo
	- 'Tangerine'	Widely available
	- 'Tilford Cream'	CRos CSBt CTri ECrN ELan EPfP ESps GKin IBoy LRHS LSRN MJak MRav MSwo NBir NEgg NHol SCob SGbt SGol SLim SPer SRms WCFE WFar WMoo
	- 'Tom Conway'	CMac NLar
	- var. ***veitchii***	CSBt
	- 'Vilmoriniana'	CTri ELan EMil EPfP ESps GCal LRHS MAsh MRav NLar SPer SPoG SWvt WSHC
	- 'Whirligig'	CMac
	- 'White Lady'^{PBR}	MPkF
	- 'Wickwar Beauty'	CWib
	- 'William Purdom'	WHar
	- 'Yellow Bird' 🏆^{H7}	LRHS MAsh
	'Gibson's Scarlet' 🏆^{H7}	Widely available
§	***glandulosa*** subsp. ***nevadensis***	CTri ECho EWld MAsh SRms
	'Gloire de Nancy' (d)	EBee GBuc IKil MAvo MRav NBir NChi NLar
	'Gold Clogs'	see *P. aurea* 'Goldklumpen'
	'Herzblut'	NLar
	hippiana	EBee
	× ***hopwoodiana***	CMea CSpe CWCL EAJP EBee ECha ECtt ELan EPPr GCal GMaP IKil ILea LHop MNrw MRav NBir NChi NDov NLar SCob SPer WCAu WFar WMoo WPtf
	× ***hybrida*** 'Jean Jabber'	EBee GLog MAvo MRav NEoE NLar SRGP WHea
	'Jack Elliot'	NEoE
	kurdica	GJos XLum
	'Lemon Me' new	IRob
	'Light My Fire'	EBee ECtt LLHF MBNS MNrw
§	'Majland'	EBee
	'Mandshurica'	see *P. fruticosa* 'Manchu'
	'Maynard's'	see *P.* 'Majland'
§	***megalantha***	CBcs CBro CLet EAJP ECtt EDAr ELan EPfP EPri GCal GCra LEdu LHop LRHS MBNS MNrw MRav NBir NBro SGbt SPer SRms SRot WHea WMoo XLum

	- 'Gold Sovereign'	EBee EPfP LRHS NEoE NLar
	'Melton Fire'	EAJP EPfP GJos GKin GPSL GQue MNrw NBir WHrl WMoo WPnP
	micrantha 'Purple Haze'	LEdu
	- 'Purple Heart'	WPGP
	'Monarch's Velvet'	see *P. thurberi* 'Monarch's Velvet'
	'Monsieur Rouillard' (d)	CElw CMac CSam CSpe ECtt GCra IPot LRHS MArl MCot MNrw MRav NGdn NLar WHoo WHrl
	'Mont d'Or'	EBee MRav NLar
	nepalensis	EHoe LRHS NBro NChi XLum
	- 'Helen Jane'	GBin GBuc GJos IBoy LEdu MArt MHer NBir NHol NWad SMad SPad WFar WHrl WKif WMoo WOut WPtf WWFP
§	- 'Miss Willmott'	Widely available
	- 'Ron McBeath'	CDor CKno CLet CWCL ECtt ELan EPfP GBin GCra ITim MAvo MRav MSCN NHol NLar NSti SGol SPer SRGP SRkn SWvt WGwG WHoo WMoo WPtf
	- 'Roxana'	ELan GJos MRav NBro SRGP WMoo
	- 'Shogran'	GJos GQue LRHS NHol NLar WPtf
§	***neumanniana***	MAsh NBir
	- 'Goldrausch'	IMou MRav XLum
§	- 'Nana'	ECho ECtt EPot GCrg MHer NRya NWad SPlb SRms WHoo WIce WMoo XLum
	nevadensis	see *P. glandulosa* subsp. *nevadensis*
	nitida	MAsh SRms WAbe
	- 'Alba'	ECho EPot
	- 'Rubra'	CMea CPBP ECho EDAr GCrg GEdr NBir NHar SRms WAbe
	nivalis	ECho
	palustris	CWat EBee EWay LLWG MWts NLar NMir WMoo XLum
	parvifolia 'Klondike'	see *P. fruticosa* 'Klondike'
	pedata	LLWP NChi XLum
	peduncularis CC 5717	GKev
	'Pink Panther'	see *P. fruticosa* Princess
	aff. ***polyphylla*** CHP&W 314	GKev
	porphyrantha	GEdr LLHF SBrt SIgm
	pyrenaica Ramond ex DC.	MMuc
	recta	GJos MMuc WTou XLum
	- 'Alba'	GMaP NEgg
	- 'Citrina'	see *P. recta* var. *sulphurea*
	- 'Macrantha'	see *P. recta* 'Warrenii'
§	- var. ***sulphurea***	CAby CMea EAJP ELon EWoo GAbr GJos GWyn MCot MNrw NBir NLar NSti NWad SPhx SRkn WBrk WCAu WHal WHea WHoo WHrl WMoo XLum
§	- 'Warrenii'	CSBt EPfP GJos GMaP LRHS MRav NBir NEgg SHar SPer SRms WHal WHar WHrl WMoo XLum
	'Roxanne' (d)	LRHS MHer
	rupestris	CMea ECha EPPr GCal LSun MHer NSti WCAu WFar WHal WHea WMoo WOut
	× ***russelliana***	LRHS NRHS
	'Scarlet Starlet'	see *P. atrosanguinea* var. *argyrophylla* 'Scarlet Starlit'
	speciosa	EWes WMoo
	sterilis	CHid WHer WSFF
*	***sundermanii***	WHrl
	tabernaemontani	see *P. neumanniana*
	thurberi	CMea LRHS MCot NLar SPhx WHrl WMoo XLum
§	- 'Monarch's Velvet'	Widely available
	tommasiniana	see *P. cinerea*

	× ***tonguei*** ♀H5	Widely available
	tormentilla	see *P. erecta*
	tridentata	see *Sibbaldiopsis tridentata*
	'Twinkling Star'	EBee MSCN WPtf
	verna misapplied	see *P. neumanniana*
	- 'Pygmaea'	see *P. neumanniana* 'Nana'
	'Versicolor Plena' (d)	NLar
	villosa	see *P. crantzii*
	'Volcan'	CAby CWCL ECtt EWes GBuc IKil IPot MAvo NChi SMHy WHal
	'White Queen'	GLog MRav SHar
	'William Rollisson' ♀H6	Widely available
	willmottiae	see *P. nepalensis* 'Miss Willmott'
	'Yellow Queen'	CMac CTri GKin GMaP LPot LRHS MNrw MRav NLar SBod SPer WCAu

Poterium see *Sanguisorba*

	sanguisorba	see *Sanguisorba minor*

Prangos (*Apiaceae*)

	ferulacea	WCot

Pratia (*Campanulaceae*)

§	***angulata*** 'Treadwellii'	ECha ECtt GEdr SPlb WHal
	montana	see *Lobelia montana*
§	***pedunculata***	CTri ECha ECho ECtt EDAr ELan EPfP EWTr GAbr LLWG LSun NHpl SIgm SPlb SRms SRot WMoo WPtf
I	- 'Alba'	CBod EWes NHpl
	- 'County Park'	CMea CSpe CTri ECha ECho ECtt EDAr ELan ELon EWTr GAbr LLWG LRHS MSCN NDov NHpl SPlb SPoG SRms SRot WBor WIce WMoo XLum
	- 'White Stars'	ECho LLWG

Prenanthes (*Asteraceae*)

§	***alba***	SBrt

Preslia see *Mentha*

Primula ✿ (*Primulaceae*)

	KR KRW 56/380 new	EPot
	(Si)	MAsh
	acaulis	see *P. vulgaris*
	'Adrian Jones' (Au)	IPen ITim NWad
	agleniana (Cy)	IPen
	- var. ***alba*** new	GKev
	'Alan Robb' (Pr/Prim/d)	ECtt NGdn
	albenensis (Au)	IPen
	'Alexina' (*allionii* hybrid) (Au)	GKev MFie NHar
	algida (Al)	ECho
§	***allionii*** (Au)	GKev IPen NSum WAbe
	- HNG 12	IPen ITim
	- 'Agnes' (Au)	IPen ITim MFie
	- 'Aire Waves'	see *P.* × *loiseleurii* 'Aire Waves'
	- 'Alan Burrow' (Au)	IPen
	- var. ***alba*** (Au)	IPen MFie
	- 'Allen Charm' (Au) new	ITim
	- 'Allen Moonbeam' (Au)	GAgs ITim MFie
	- 'Allen Queen' (Au)	IPen
	- 'Andrew' (Au)	IPen
	- 'Anna Griffith' (Au)	CPBP CTal IPen MFie WAbe WHil
	- 'Anne' (Au)	EPot IPen
	- 'Aphrodite' (Au)	IPen NHar
	- 'Apple Blossom' (Au)	CLet NHpl
	- 'Archer' (Au)	IPen ITim NWad
	- 'Ares' (Au)	NHar
	- 'Aries Violet' (Au)	IPen ITim NHar
	- 'Austen' (Au)	MFie
	- 'Avalanche' (Au)	IPen
	- 'Beryl' (Au)	IPen
	- 'Biddy' (Au)	IPen
	- 'Bill Martin' (Au)	IPen ITim NWad
	- 'Blood Flake' (Au)	IPen ITim
	- 'Broadwell No 4' (Au)	CPBP
	- 'Cherry' (Au)	WAbe
	- 'Chivalry' (Au)	CPBP WAbe
	- 'Circe's Flute' (Au)	NHar
	- 'Cissie' (Au)	CPBP IPen ITim
	- 'Claude Flight' (Au)	IPen MFie
	- 'Crowsley Variety' (Au)	ITim
	- 'Crusader' (Au)	CTal WAbe
	- 'Crystal' (Au)	CPBP MFie
	- 'Daniel Burrow' (Au)	IPen
	- 'David Burrow' (Au)	IPen
	- 'David Philbey' (Au)	CPBP IPen
§	- 'Edinburgh' (Au)	IPen NWad
	- 'Edrom' (Au)	IPen NWad
	- 'Ekli Weib' (Au)	IPen
	- 'Elizabeth Baker' (Au)	IPen ITim MFie
	- 'Elizabeth Burrow' (Au)	IPen ITim WAbe
	- 'Elizabeth Earle' (Au)	IPen ITim
	- 'Elliott's Large'	see *P. allionii* 'Edinburgh'
	- 'Elliott's Variety'	see *P. allionii* 'Edinburgh'
	- 'Emily Jane' (Au)	IPen
	- 'Eureka' (Au)	CPBP EPot LLHF WAbe
	- 'Eveline Burrow' (Au)	CPBP WAbe
	- 'Fanfare' (Au)	IPen MAsh NHar NWad
	- 'Flute' (Au)	IPen
I	- 'Forma' (Au) new	XBar
	- 'Frank Barker' (Au)	IPen NWad
	- 'Gabriele' (Au)	MFie
	- 'Gavin Brown' (Au)	IPen
	- 'Gilderdale Glow' (Au)	CPBP IPen MFie
	- 'Giuseppi's Form'	see *P. allionii* 'Mrs Dyas'
	- 'Grace Burrow' (Au)	IPen
	- 'Grandiflora' (Au)	ITim
	- 'Hannah' (Au)	EPot IPen
	- 'Hartside 6' (Au)	IPen ITim NHar
	- 'Hartside 12' (Au)	IPen
	- 'Hazey' (Au)	ITim
	- 'Hemswell' (Au)	NHpl
	- 'Herald' (Au)	ITim
	- 'Hocker Edge' (Au)	ITim MFie NWad
	- 'Horwood' (Au)	ITim
	- 'Huntsman' (Au)	MFie
	- 'Hythe Dorothy' (Au)	IPen
	- 'Imp' (Au)	IPen
	- Ingwersen's form (Au)	MFie NWad
	- 'Io 2' (Au)	NHar
	- 'Ion's Amethyst' (Au)	NHar
	- 'Isobel' (Au)	IPen LLHF
	- 'Jacqueline' (Au)	IPen
	- 'James' (Au)	IPen
	- 'Jan' (Au)	IPen
	- 'Jenny' (Au)	IPen
	- 'Joe Elliott' (Au)	IPen ITim
	- 'Joseph Collins' (Au)	IPen
	- 'Judy Burrow' new	CPBP
	- 'Julia' (Au)	IPen
	- 'Kate Evans' (Au)	IPen
§	- 'Kath Dryden' (Au)	IPen
§	- 'Ken's Seedling' (Au)	IPen MFie
	- KRW	see *P. allionii* 'Ken's Seedling'
	- 'Laura Louise' (Au)	IPen
	- 'Lepus' (Au)	IPen WAbe
	- 'Lindisfarne' (Au)	IPen
	- 'Lindum Prima' (Au)	IPen
	- 'Lindum Whisper' (Au)	LLHF

- Lismore 81/19/2 (Au)	MFie
- Lismore 81/19/3 **new**	MFie
- Lismore 87/3/2 (Au)	MFie
- 'Little O' (Au)	NWad
- 'Louise' (Au)	IPen
- 'Lucy' (Au)	IPen NHar
- 'Malcolm' (Au)	IPen ITim
- 'Margaret Earle' (Au)	IPen
- 'Marion' (Au)	IPen XBar
- 'Marjorie Wooster' (Au)	CPBP IPen MFie XBar
- 'Martin' (Au)	IPen ITim
- 'Mary Anne' (Au)	WAbe
- 'Mary Berry' (Au)	CPBP IPen MFie NWad
- 'Maurice Dryden' (Au)	IPen
- 'Megan' (Au)	IPen
- 'Molly' (Au)	IPen
§ - 'Mrs Dyas' (Au)	IPen MFie NWad
- 'Neon' (Au)	CPBP IPen
- 'Neptune's Wave' (Au)	NHar
- 'New Dawn' (Au)	ITim MFie NHar
- 'Pale Venus' (Au)	IPen NHar
- 'Peace' (Au)	MFie
- 'Peggy Wilson' (Au)	EPot EWld IPen NWad WThu
- 'Pennine Pink' (Au)	CPBP IPen
- 'Perkie' (Au)	IPen
- 'Phoebe's Moon' (Au)	IPen ITim NHar
- 'Pinkie' (Au)	CPBP IPen WAbe
- 'Praecox' (Au)	IPen
- 'Quip' (Au)	IPen
- RAH form	MFie
- 'Raymond Wooster' (Au)	IPen NWad
- 'Roger Bevan' (Au)	IPen
- 'Saint Dalmas' (Au)	IPen
- 'Scimitar' (Au)	IPen MFie NWad
- 'Serendipity' (Au)	IPen
- 'Snowflake' (Au)	CPBP IPen
- 'Stanton House' (Au)	MFie
- 'Stephen' (Au)	IPen MFie
- 'Steven Burrow' **new**	CPBP
- 'Tranquillity' (Au)	CPBP CTal ITim NHar NWad
- 'Travellers' (Au)	IPen
- 'Viscountess Byng' (Au)	IPen ITim
- white-flowered, thrum-eyed (Au)	IPen
- 'William Earle' (Au)	CPBP CTal IPen ITim XBar
allionii* × *auricula misapplied 'Old Red Dusty Miller' (Au)	ECho NWad XBar
- 'Blairside Yellow' (Au)	CPBP ECho IPen NSum WThu
allionii* × *clusiana (Au)	ECho
allionii* × *hirsuta (Au)	NWad
allionii × 'Lismore Jewel' (Au)	CPBP
allionii × 'Lismore Treasure' (Au)	ITim NHpl
allionii* × *pedemontana	see *P.* × *sendtneri*
allionii* × *pubescens (Au)	ECho NHpl
allionii* × *pubescens 'Harlow Car' (Au)	ITim
allionii × 'Snow Ruffles' (Au)	IPen ITim
allionii × 'White Linda Pope' (Au)	IPen MFie NHar NHpl NWad
alpicola (Si) ♀H7	CAby CLAP CPne CTsd CWCL EPot GAbr GKev IPen MFie NBid NBro NGdn NSum NWad SEND XBar
- var. ***alba*** (Si)	CPla CSta GAbr GBuc GKev IPen NBid
§ - var. ***alpicola*** (Si)	CLAP EBee GBuc GCra GKev IPen

- hybrids (Si)	NHpl WMoo
- 'Kevock Sky' (Si)	CWCL GKev
- 'La Luna' (Si)	CSta MMuc
- var. ***luna***	see *P. alpicola* var. *alpicola*
- mixed (Si)	ECho GKev MFie
- var. ***violacea*** (Si)	CCVN CLAP CPla CSta EWld GAbr GCra GKev IPen MArt MMuc MNrw NBid NCGa WHil
- - wine-red-flowered (Si)	CWCL GKev
'Altaica'	see *P. elatior* subsp. *meyeri*
altaica grandiflora	see *P. elatior* subsp. *meyeri*
amethystina subsp. ***brevifolia*** (Am)	GKev
amoena	see *P. elatior* subsp. *meyeri*
'Amy Smith'	GAbr
angustifolia (Pa)	LLHF
anisodora	see *P. wilsonii* var. *anisodora*
× ***anisodoxa*** 'Kevock Surprise' **new**	GKev
'Annemijne'	GEdr WCot
apoclita (Mu)	GKev LLHF WHil
× ***arctotis***	see *P.* × *pubescens*
'Arduaine' (Pe)	LLHF
aurantiaca (Pf)	CPla EBee EPot EWld GKev IPen NHpl
- SDR 7874 **new**	GKev
aureata (Pe)	IPen
I ***auricula*** '1-2-3' (Au)	EBee
auricula ambig. (Au)	NSla WHoo
auricula L. (Au) ♀H5	EDAr GKev IPen LRHS MFie NBro NRHS SPer SPlb SPoG WRHF
- SDR 5705 **new**	GKev
- SDR 6960 **new**	GKev
auricula misapplied (Au)	ECha LRHS NRHS
- A74 (Au)	SEND
- K85 (Au/S)	SPop
- '2nd Vic' (Au/S)	SPop
- 'A.C. Hadfield' (Au)	MFie
- 'Abdor' (Au/St)	SPop
- 'Abrigde' (Au/d)	WAln
- 'Abundance' (Au/A)	EWoo NDro SPop WCre
- 'Achates' (Au/A)	IPen WAln
- 'Admiral' (Au/A)	WAln
- 'Adrian' (Au/A)	EWoo GAgs IPen MFie NDro SPop WCre WHil XBar
- 'Adrian's Cross' (Au/A)	EWoo
- 'Adrienne' (Au/A)	SPop
- 'Adrienne Ruan' (Au/A)	NDro WAln
- 'After Glow' (Au/St)	SPop
- 'Aga Khan' (Au/A)	WAln
- 'Agamemnon' (Au/A)	EWoo IPen LLHF MFie NDro SPop
- 'Airy Fairy' (Au/S)	SPop
- 'Alamo' (Au/A)	MFie SPop WCre
- 'Alan Ball' (Au)	WAln
- 'Alan Ravenscroft' (Au/A)	MFie SPop WHil
- 'Albert Bailey' (Au/d)	EWoo GAbr GAgs IPen ITim MFie NDro SPop WCre WHil
- 'Albury' (Au/d)	IPen WCre
- 'Alchemist' (Au/S)	IPen SPop WAln WCre
- 'Alexandra Georgina' (Au/A)	MFie SPop WAln
- 'Alf' (Au/A)	IPen MFie NDro NSum SPop WHil
- 'Alfred Charles' (Au/A)	SPop WAln
- 'Alfred Niblett' (Au/S)	GAgs IPen
- 'Alice' (Au/d)	IPen
- 'Alice Haysom' (Au/S)	ELan EWoo GAbr GAgs IPen ITim MAsh NDro SPop WCre WHil XBar
- 'Alicia' (Au/A)	EWoo GAbr GAgs MFie NDro NSum SPop WCre XBar
- 'Alison' (Au/S)	GAgs NDro

- 'Alison Jane' (Au/A) GAgs IPen MFie SPop WCre WHil XBar
- 'Alison Rose' (Au/B) NDro
- 'Alison Telford' (Au/A) WHil
- 'Allard' (Au/A) WAln
- 'Allegro' (Au/A) WAln
- 'Allensford' (Au/A) WCre
- 'Alloway' (Au/d) WAln
- 'Almand' (Au/d) WAln
- 'Almondbury' (Au/S) NDro SPop
- alpine mixed (Au/A) EPfP SRms
- 'Amanda' (Au/d) **new** SPop
- 'Amazon' (Au/St) SPop
- 'Amber Light' (Au/S) SPop WAln
- 'Amethyst' (Au/S) GAgs WAln
- 'Amicable' (Au/A) EWoo GAgs IPen MFie NDro NSum SPop WCre WHil
- 'Amore' (Au/St) SPop WAln
- 'Ancient Order' (Au/A) IPen WAln
- 'Ancient Society' (Au/A) EWoo GAbr GAgs IPen MFie NSum NWad SPop WHil
- 'Andrea Julie' (Au/A) GAgs IPen NDro SPop WCre WHil
- 'Andrew Hunter' (Au/A) IPen MFie NDro NSum SPop WCre
- 'Andy Cole' (Au/A) EWoo IPen NDro SPop WAln WCre
- 'Angel Eyes' (Au/St) IPen NDro SPop WHil
- 'Angel Islington' (Au/S) NDro
- 'Angela Gould' (Au) EWoo MFie NDro SPop WHil
- 'Angela Grace' (Au/d) XBar
- 'Angela Short' (Au/St) IPen SPop WAln
- 'Angostura' (Au/d) EWoo GAgs IPen SPop WCre
- 'Ann Brookes' (Au/d) WAln
- 'Ann Taylor' (Au/A) GAgs IPen WAln
- 'Anne Hyatt' (Au/d) GAbr NDro SPop
- 'Anne Swithinbank' (Au/d) IPen WAln
- 'Annette' (Au/B) **new** NDro
- 'Annie Tustin' (Au/S) SPop
- 'Ansells' (Au/S) SPop WAln
- 'Antoc' (Au/S) EWoo SPop
- 'Anwar Sadat' (Au/A) EWoo GAbr GAgs MFie NDro NSum WCre WHil
- 'Apple Blossom' (Au/B) NDro WHil
- 'Applecross' (Au/A) GAgs IPen NDro NHpl NSum SPop WCre WHil
- 'Apricot Truffle' (Au/d) SPop
- 'April Moon' (Au/S) GAbr GAgs MFie NDro SPop WCre WHil
- 'April Tiger' (Au/St) EWoo WAln
- 'Aquarius' (Au/d) SPop
- 'Arab Prince' (Au/A) WAln
- 'Arab Queen' (Au/A) WAln
- 'Arabian Night' (Au/A) WAln
- 'Arapaho' (Au/A) SPop WAln
- 'Arctic Fox' (Au) MFie WAln WHil
- 'Argentine' (Au/S) SPop XBar
- 'Argus' (Au/A) EWoo GAgs IPen LSun MFie NSum NWad SPop WCre WHil XBar
- 'Arlene' (Au/A) WAln
- 'Art Deco' (Au/B) WAln
- 'Arthur Delbridge' (Au/A) MFie NDro SPop WHil
- 'Arundel Cross' (Au) IPen
- 'Arundell' (Au/S/St) EBee GAgs IPen ITim MFie NDro NSum SPop WCre WHil XBar
- 'Arwen' (Au/A) IPen MFie SPop
- 'Ascot Gavotte' (Au/S) NDro WAln
- 'Ashcliffe Gem' (Au/A) GAgs IPen NDro WAln
- 'Astolat' (Au/S) EBee EWoo GAgs IPen NDro NHpl SPop WCre WHil XBar
- 'Athene' (Au/S) IPen ITim NDro SPop WAln
- 'Atlantic' (Au/S) NDro NEgg
- 'Aubergine' (Au/B) NDro SPop

I – 'Aubergine' (Au/d) **new** SPop
- 'Audacity' (Au/d) IPen MFie NDro WAln
- 'Audrey' (Au/S) SPop
- 'Aurora' (Au/A) EDAr MFie NSum WAln WCre
- 'Austin' (Au/A) IPen SPop WAln
- 'Autumn Fire' (Au/A) EWoo GAbr GAgs SPop WCre
- 'Autumn Glow' (Au/d) SPop
- 'Aviemore' (Au/A) WCre
- 'Avon Angel' (Au/d) SPop
- 'Avon Bunny' (Au/d) SPop
- 'Avon Buster' (Au/d) **new** SPop
- 'Avon Carrier' (Au/d) SPop
- 'Avon Citronella' (Au) EWoo SPop
- 'Avon Eclipse' (Au/d) SPop
- 'Avon Elegance' (Au/d) SPop
- 'Avon Khaki' (Au/d) SPop
- 'Avon Tan' (d) GAbr GAgs WCre
- 'Avon Toro' (Au/d) SPop
- 'Avon Twist' (Au/d) EWoo SPop
- 'Avondale' (Au/B) **new** NDro
- 'Avril' (Au/A) IPen NDro SPop WAln WHil
- 'Avril Hunter' (Au/A) GAgs IPen ITim MFie MHer NDro NSum WCre WHil XBar
- 'Awesome' (Au/St) SPop
- 'Aztec' (Au/d) WAln
- 'Baby Blue' (AU) NDro
- 'Bacchante' (Au/d) SPop WAln
- 'Bacchus' (Au/A) GAgs MFie NDro SPop WHil
- 'Baggage' (Au) EWoo GAgs IPen MAsh NDro SPop WCre WHil
- 'Bailey Boy' (Au/B) NDro
- 'Baker's Boy' (Au/d) **new** SPop
- 'Balbithan' (Au/B) EWoo
- 'Ballynahinch' (Au) ITim
- 'Baltic Amber' (Au) EWoo GAgs MFie NDro SPop WAln WCre WHil
- 'Bank Error' (Au/S) IPen NDro SPop WAln
- 'Barbara Mason' (Au) WAln
- 'Barbara Weinz' (Au/S) WAln
- 'Barbarella' (Au/S) IPen MFie NDro SPop WCre
- Barnhaven Border hybrids (Au/B) XBar
- Barnhaven doubles (Au/d) GAbr NSum XBar
- 'Barnhaven Gold' (Au) IPen
- 'Barr Beacon' (Au/A) IPen ITim NDro
- 'Basilio' (Au/S) NDro WAln
- 'Basuto' (Au/A) EWoo GAgs IPen ITim MFie NDro SPop WCre WHil
- 'Beatrice' (Au/A) CTri EWoo GAgs IPen MFie NDro NHpl SPop WCre WHil WIce XBar
- 'Beauty of Bath' (Au/S) WAln
- 'Beckminster' (Au/A) WAln
- 'Bedford Lad' (Au/A) NDro WCre
- 'Beechen Green' (Au/S) EWoo IPen ITim MAsh NDro SPop WCre
- 'Behold' (Au) WAln WCre
- 'Belgravia Gold' (Au/B) NDro WCre
- 'Bella' (Au/d) WAln
- 'Bellamy Pride' (Au/B) GAbr IPen MAsh NDro SPop WCre
- 'Belle Zana' (Au/S) EWoo GAgs IPen MFie NDro SPop WCre
- 'Bellini' (Au/d) **new** XBar
- 'Ben Lawers' (Au/S) SPop
- 'Ben Wyves' (Au/S) IPen SPop WCre
- 'Bendigo' (Au/S) EWoo NDro SPop WAln WCre
- 'Bengal Rose' (Au/S) SPop
- 'Benno' (Au/St) EWoo
- 'Benny Green' (Au/S) IPen MFie NDro SPop WCre
- 'Beppi' (Au) WHil
- 'Bessie' (Au/d) XBar

– 'Best Wishes' (Au/F)	WAln
– 'Bethan McSparron' (Au/B)	NDro
– 'Betty Stewart' (Au/A)	WAln
– 'Bewitched' (Au/A)	MFie NDro WAln
– 'Bilbao' (Au/A)	WAln
– 'Bilbo Baggins' (Au/A)	MAsh NDro SPop WAln
– 'Bill Bailey' (Au/d)	EWoo GAbr GAgs NDro WCre
– 'Bilton' (Au/S)	SPop WCre
– 'Bingley Folk' (Au/B)	NDro SPop
– 'Bisto' (Au/S)	SPop WAln
– 'Bitterne Beauty' (Au/d)	IPen SPop
– 'Bitterne Bounty' (Au/d)	SPop
– 'Bitterne Buttercup' (Au/d)	SPop
– 'Bitterne Delight' (Au/d) new	SPop
– 'Bitterne Primrose' (Au/d)	SPop
– 'Bizarre' (Au)	GAgs WCre
– 'Black Adder' (Au/S)	IPen SPop WAln
– 'Black Diamond' (Au/d)	MFie SPop WHil
– 'Black Ice' (Au/S)	WAln
– 'Black Jack'PBR (Au/d)	EBee ECtt GBin MHol NHpl NLar WTor
– 'Black Knight' (Au/d)	SPop
– 'Blackfield' (Au/S)	SPop
– 'Blackhill' (Au/S)	ITim MFie NHpl SPop
– 'Blackpool Rock' (Au/St)	CWCL MFie SPop WAln WCre XBar
– 'Blairside Yellow' (Au/B)	ECho LLHF NDro NSla
– 'Blakeney' (Au/d)	MFie NDro
– 'Blossom' (Au/A)	MFie SPop
– 'Blossom Dearie' (Au/St)	SPop
– 'Blue Bonnet' (Au/A/d)	EWoo GAbr GAgs MFie NDro WAln WCre
– 'Blue Boy' (Au/S)	WAln WHil
– 'Blue Chip' (Au/S)	EWoo IPen MFie NDro SPop WCre WHil
– 'Blue Cliff' (Au/S)	IPen SPop WAln
– 'Blue Denim' (Au/S)	IPen
– 'Blue Fire' (Au/S)	MFie SPop
– 'Blue Frills' (Au)	NDro WAln
– 'Blue Heaven' (Au/A)	EWoo IPen NDro SPop WCre
– 'Blue Jean' (Au/S)	GAbr GAgs IPen MFie NDro SPop WCre
– 'Blue Lace' (Au)	WAln
– 'Blue Merle' (Au/B)	NDro
– 'Blue Mist' (Au/B)	NDro
– 'Blue Night' (Au/B)	GAgs ITim
– 'Blue Nile' (Au/S)	SPop WCre
– 'Blue Ridge' (Au/A)	WAln
– 'Blue Skies' (Au/St)	SPop
– 'Blue Steel' (Au/S)	WAln
– 'Blue Veil' (Au/S)	SPop
– 'Blue Velvet' (Au/B)	EWoo GAbr IPen LLHF MFie NDro NHpl SBch SPop WCre WHil
– 'Blue Wave' (Au/d)	MFie SPop
– 'Blue Waves' (Au/B) new	NDro
– 'Blue Yodeler' (Au/A)	MFie NDro NSum SPop WCre WHil
– 'Blue Yonder' (Au/S)	ITim WAln
– 'Blush Baby' (Au/St)	EWTr EWoo GAbr GAgs NDro NSum NWad SPop WCre WHil XBar
– 'Blusher' (Au/St)	WAln
– 'Blyth Spirit' (Au/A)	NDro SPop WAln WCre
– 'Bob Dingley' (Au/A)	IPen SPop
– 'Bob Lancashire' (Au/S)	IPen ITim MFie NDro SPop WHil XBar
– 'Bokay' (Au/d)	WAln
– 'Bold Tartan' (Au/St)	IPen NDro SPop WAln
– 'Bolero' (Au/A)	SPop WAln
– 'Bollin Tiger' (Au/St)	WAln
– 'Bonafide' (Au/d)	SPop WAln WCre
– 'Bonanza' (Au/S)	SPop WAln
– 'Bookham Firefly' (Au/A)	GAbr GAgs IPen MFie NDro SPop WCre WHil
– 'Border Bandit' (Au/B)	GAbr MFie NDro SPop WAln
– 'Border Beauty' (Au/St)	NDro
– 'Border Blue' (Au/B)	NDro WAln
– 'Border Patrol' (Au/B)	ITim WAln
– 'Border Tawny' (Au/B)	NDro
– 'Boromir' (Au/A)	EWoo MFie NDro SPop WAln
– 'Bournebrook' (Au/A)	WAln
– 'Bowen's Blue' (Au/B)	EWoo NDro SPop
– 'Boy Blue' (Au/S)	NDro
– 'Bradford City' (Au/A)	CFis CWCL EBee GAgs NDro SPop WHil XBar
– 'Bradmore Bluebell' (Au)	GAbr NDro
– 'Bramley Rose' (Au/B)	SPop
– 'Bran' (Au/B)	NDro
– 'Brandaris' (Au/A)	WAln
– 'Branno' (Au/S)	WAln
– 'Branston' (Au/d)	XBar
– 'Brass Dog' (Au/S)	WAln
– 'Brasso' (Au)	IPen MAsh MFie NDro SPop WAln
– 'Brazen Hussy' (Au/d)	MFie WAln
– 'Brazil' (Au/S)	CTal EBee GAbr GAgs IPen NDro SPop WCre WHil
– 'Brazos River' (Au/A)	EWoo GAgs IPen MFie NDro SPop WHil
– 'Breckland Joy' (Au/A)	NDro WAln
– 'Brenda's Choice' (Au/A)	EWoo GAgs IPen MFie NDro NSum SPop WCre
– 'Brentford Bees' (Au/St)	WAln
– 'Brickmaker' (Au/d) new	SPop
– 'Bright Eyes' (Au/A)	IPen MFie WCre
– 'Bright Ginger' (Au/S)	EWoo NDro SPop WAln WCre
– 'Brimstone and Treacle' (Au/d)	SPop WAln
– 'Broad Gold' (Au/A)	MFie NDro SPop WCre
– 'Broadwell Gold' (Au/B)	NDro NSum SPop WCre
– 'Brocade' (Au/St)	WCre
– 'Brompton' (Au/S)	SPop
– 'Brookfield' (Au/S)	GAbr IPen MFie NDro NHpl SPop WCre WHil
– 'Broughton' (Au/S)	NDro SPop
– 'Brown Ben' (Au)	EWoo IPen MFie SPop WCre WHil
– 'Brown Bess' (Au/A)	GAbr GAgs IPen ITim MFie WCre WHil
– 'Brown Sugar' (Au/d)	SPop
– 'Brown Tan Double' (Au/d)	EWoo GAgs
– 'Brownie' (Au/B)	EWoo GAbr GAgs NBir NDro NSum SPop WCre WHil XBar
– 'Brownie Point' (Au/B)	NDro
– 'Bucks Green' (Au/S)	GAbr NDro SPop
– 'Bunty' (Au/A)	MFie
– 'Buoyance' (Au/A)	WAln
– 'Burnished Gold' (Au/d)	WAln
– 'Bush Baby' (Au/B)	NDro
– 'Buttercup' (Au/d)	SPop
– 'Buttermere' (Au/d)	WAln WCre
– 'Butternut' (Au/S)	WAln
– 'Butterwick' (Au/A)	EWoo GAbr GAgs IPen MFie NDro NEgg SPop WCre XBar
– 'C.F. Hill' (Au/A)	NDro
– 'C.G. Haysom' (Au/S)	GAbr NDro SPop WCre WHil
– 'C.W. Needham' (Au/A)	GAgs IPen ITim MFie NDro SPop WCre XBar
– 'Cadiz Bay' (Au/d)	WAln
– 'Café au Lait' (Au/A)	XBar
– 'Callisto' (Au/d)	SPop
– 'Calypso' (Au/d)	NDro SPop WAln

– 'Cambodunum' (Au/A)	IPen MFie NDro NSum SPop WCre WHil
– 'Camelot' (Au/d)	EWoo MFie NBro NDro SPop WCre WHil
– 'Cameo' (Au/A)	GAgs NHpl
– 'Cameo Beauty' (Au/d)	EWoo NDro SPop
– 'Camilla' (Au/A)	WAln
– 'Candida' (Au/d)	IPen SPop
– 'Candy Stripe' (Au/St)	GAgs SPop
– 'Cappela' (Au/d)	WAln
– 'Caramel' (Au/A)	GAgs IPen WAln
– 'Cardinal Red' (Au/d)	NDro SPop
– 'Cardington' (Au/A)	WAln
– 'Carioca' (Au/A)	WAln
– 'Carl Andrew' (Au/S)	WAln
– 'Carmel' (Au/d)	EWoo MAsh SPop WAln WCre
– 'Carnaval' (Au/B) **new**	XBar
– 'Carne' (Au/D) **new**	NDro
– 'Carnival' (Au/A)	WAln
– 'Carole' (Au/A)	MFie SPop WHil
– 'Carousel' (Au/B) **new**	NDro
– 'Carreras' (Au)	MFie NDro
– 'Carsa Wakes' (Au/d)	NDro SPop WAln
– 'Carzon' (Au/A)	NDro
– 'Catherine Wheel' (Au/St)	SPop WAln
– 'Cathy McKay' (Au/B) **new**	NDro
– 'Catta Ha' (Au/d)	NDro
– 'Celtic One' (Au/St)	NDro SPop
– 'Ceri Nicolle' (Au/B)	NDro
– 'Chadwick End' (Au/S)	WAln
– 'Chaffinch' (Au/S)	EWoo GAbr GAgs IPen NDro SPop
– 'Chamois' (Au/B)	EWoo GAbr IPen MFie NDro WCre WHil
– 'Chanel' (Au/S)	EWoo SPop WAln WCre
– 'Chantilly Cream' (Au/d)	WAln
– 'Charles Bronson' (Au/d)	GAgs MFie NDro SPop WAln
– 'Charles Rennie' (Au/B)	EWoo ITim MFie NDro SPop
– 'Charlie's Aunt' (Au/A)	NDro WAln
– 'Charlotte Brookes' (Au/d)	SPop WAln
– 'Checkmate' (Au)	EWoo MFie SPop WAln
– 'Cheeky' (Au/d)	SPop
– 'Chelsea Bridge' (Au/A)	EWoo GAgs IPen MFie NDro SPop WCre WHil
– 'Cheops' (Au/A)	GAgs IPen MFie NDro NEgg NSum WCre XBar
– 'Cherry' (Au/S)	GAgs IPen SPop WCre
– 'Cherry Picker' (Au/A)	GAgs MFie NDro SPop WCre
– 'Cheyenne' (Au/S)	EWoo GAbr GAgs MFie NDro SPop WCre
– 'Chiffon' (Au/S)	EWoo GAbr GAgs IPen NDro NSum SPop WCre
– 'Chiquita' (Au/d)	EWoo SPop WCre
– 'Chirichua' (Au/S)	WAln
– 'Chloë' (Au/S)	IPen MFie NHpl SPop
– 'Chloris' (Au/S)	MFie SPop
– 'Choir Boy' (Au/A)	WAln
– 'Chorister' (Au/S)	EBee GAgs IPen ITim MFie NDro NSum SPop WCre WHil
– 'Chyne' (Au)	EWoo
– 'Cicero' (Au/A)	MFie SPop WAln
– 'Cinders' (Au/St)	SPop
– 'Cindy' (Au/A)	NDro
– 'Cinnamon' (Au/d)	EWoo GAgs ITim MFie NDro SPop WCre WHil
– 'Cinnamon' (Au/S)	GAbr
– 'Ciribiribin' (Au/A)	WAln
– 'Citron-Ella' (Au/d)	MFie SPop
– 'Clara' (Au/d)	SPop
– 'Clare' (Au/S)	IPen MFie NDro SPop WCre
– 'Classic' (Au/A)	WAln
– 'Classy Stripe' (Au/St) **new**	ITim
– 'Clatter-Ha' (Au/d)	NSum SPop WCre WHil
– 'Claud Wilson' (Au/St)	SPop WAln WCre
– 'Claudia Taylor' (Au)	EWoo SPop
– 'Cleft Stick' (Au)	IPen
– 'Clipper' (Au/S)	SPop WAln
– 'Cloth of Gold' (Au/A)	NDro WCre
– 'Clotted Cream' (Au/B)	NDro
– 'Cloud Nine' (Au/S)	WCre
– 'Clouded Yellow' (Au/S)	SPop WHil
– 'Cloudy Bay' (Au)	NDro WCot
– 'Cloverdale' (Au/d)	WAln
– 'Clunie' (Au/S)	IPen NDro WCre
– 'Clunie II' (Au/S)	GAgs IPen
– 'Cobden Meadows' (Au/A)	SPop WAln WCre
– 'Cockle' (Au/S)	SPop
– 'Cocoa' (Au/d)	XBar
– 'Coffee' (Au/S)	IPen ITim MFie NDro SPop XBar
– 'Colbury' (Au/S)	NDro SPop WCre XBar
– 'Colonel Champney' (Au/S)	EWoo NDro SPop
– 'Comet' (Au/S)	IPen NDro NSum
– 'Confederate' (Au/S)	WAln
– 'Connaught Court' (Au/A)	EWoo IPen LLHF NDro WCre
– 'Conquistador' (Au/A)	IPen NDro WAln
– 'Conservative' (Au/S)	EWoo IPen NDro
– 'Consett' (Au/S)	EWoo GAgs IPen MFie SPop WHil
– 'Cooks Hill' (Au/d)	WAln
– 'Cooper's Gold' (Au/B)	NDro
– 'Coop's Green' (Au/S)	EWoo
– 'Copper King' (Au/B)	WAln
– 'Coppi' (Au/A)	EWoo IPen NDro SPop
– 'Coral' (Au/S)	GAgs ITim SPop
– 'Coral Sea' (Au/S)	SPop
– 'Corn Dolly' (Au/S)	SPop
– 'Cornish Cream' (Au/B)	IPen NDro
– 'Cornmeal' (Au/S)	GAgs MFie NDro SPop WAln WHil
– 'Corntime' (Au/S)	IPen SPop WAln WCre
– 'Corona' (Au/S)	WAln
– 'Corporal Jones' (Au/S)	SPop WCre
– 'Corporal Kate' (Au/St)	WAln
– 'Corrie Files' (Au/d)	MFie SPop WAln
– 'Cortez Silver' (Au/S)	SPop WAln
– 'Cortina' (Au/S)	ECho EWoo GAbr GAgs IPen ITim MFie NDro SPop WHil
– 'Country Maid' (Au/A)	WAln
– 'County Park Red' (Au/B)	NDro
– 'Coventry Street' (Au/S)	MAsh MFie NDro NSum SPop WCre
– 'Crackley Tagetes' (Au/d)	ECho
– 'Crackling Rosie' (A/d)	WAln
– 'Craig Nordie' (Au/B)	NDro
– 'Craig Vaughan' (Au/A)	MFie NDro NSum SPop XBar
– 'Cranborne' (Au/A)	SPop WAln
– 'Crecy' (Au/A)	SPop WAln WHil
– 'Cressida' (Au/d)	SPop
– 'Crimple' (Au/S)	NDro SPop WAln WHil
– 'Crimson Black' (Au/B)	SPop
– 'Crimson Glow' (Au/d)	EWoo GAgs ITim LCro LOPS MAsh MFie NDro NSum SPop WHil
– 'Crimson Maid' (Au/d) **new**	SPop
– 'Crinoline' (Au/S)	NDro SPop
– 'Cuckoo Fair' (Au/S)	EWoo GAbr GAgs IPen NDro SPop WCre
– 'Cuddles' (Au/A)	EWoo MFie NDro WAln WCre
– 'Curry Blend' (Au/B)	GAbr IPen NDro SPop WHil
– 'Cutie Pie' (Au/St)	IPen SPop WCre
– 'Cuttlefish' (Au/St)	SPop
– 'Cyrn Las' (Au/St)	SPop
– 'Daftie Green' (Au/S)	EWoo GAgs IPen NDro WCre
– 'Dakota' (Au/S)	EWoo SPop

– 'Dales Red' (Au/B) EWoo GAgs IPen MAsh MFie NDro NHpl NSum SPop WHil
– 'Damerham' (Au/A) SPop
– 'Dan Tiger' (Au/St) EWoo MFie SPop WAln WHil
– 'Daniel' (Au/A) EWoo NDro SPop WAln
– 'Daniel T. Taylor' (Au/A) NDro WAln
– 'Daphnis' (Au/S) SPop WAln
– 'Darent Tiger' (Au/St) SPop XBar
– 'Dark Eyes' (Au/d) EWoo GAgs MFie NDro NSum SPop WHil
– 'Dark Lady' (Au/A) WAln
– 'Dark Red' (Au/S) IPen
– 'Darth Vader' (Au/d) XBar
– 'David Beckham' (Au/d) NDro SPop WAln
– 'Day by Day' (Au/St) SPop
– 'Decaff' (Au/St) WAln
– 'Deckchair' (Au/St) MFie NDro SPop
– 'Dedham' (Au/d) WAln
– 'Del Boy' (Au/A) SPop WAln
– 'Delicious' (Au/St) SPop
– 'Delilah' (Au/d) GAbr ITim MAsh MFie NDro NSum SPop
– 'Denise' (Au/S) WAln
– 'Denna Snuffer' (Au/d) GAbr MFie NDro
– 'Derrill' (Au/B) NDro SPop
– 'Devon Cream' (Au/d) ECho GAgs IPen MFie NDro SPop WCre
– 'Diamond' (Au/d) WAln
– 'Diamond Dust' (Au/B) **new** NDro
– 'Diane' (Au/A) IPen MFie
– 'Dick Rogers' (Au/B) NDro
– 'Dido' (Au/B) XBar
– 'Digby' (Au/d) NDro WAln
– 'Digit' (Au/d) NDro WAln
– 'Dilemma' (Au/A) SPop
– 'Dill' (Au/A) IPen MFie NDro NSum SPop WHil
– 'Dilly Dilly' (Au/A) GAbr MFie NDro SPop
– 'Divint Dunch' (Au/A) IPen LLHF MFie NDro SPop WCre
– 'Doctor Duthie' (Au/S) SPop WAln
– 'Doctor Lennon's White' (Au/B) GAbr IPen MFie MHer NDro SPop WCre WHil
– 'Doctor Woolhead' (Au/S) SPop
– 'Dolly' (Au/B) NDro
– 'Dolly Viney' (Au/d) WAln
– 'Don Carlos' (Au/d) XBar
– 'Donhead' (Au/A) ITim MFie NDro SPop WCre WHil
– 'Donn' (Au/d) SPop WAln WCre
– 'Donna Clancy' (Au/S) WCre
– 'Dorado' (Au/d) SPop WAln
– 'Doreen Stephens' (Au/A) GAgs NDro
– 'Doris Jean' (Au/A) MFie NDro
– 'Dorothy' (Au/S) WAln
– 'Doublet' (Au/d) ECho GAgs IPen MFie NDro NSum SPop WCre WHil
– 'Doubloon' (Au/d) ECho XBar
– 'Doublure' (Au/d) EWoo GAbr NDro SPop WCre WHil
– 'Douglas Bader' (Au/A) GAgs ITim MFie NDro NSum SPop WCre WHil
– 'Douglas Black' (Au/S) EWoo GAbr GAgs IPen MFie NDro SPop WCre WHil
– 'Douglas Green' (Au/S) EWoo IPen NDro WCre
– 'Douglas Red' (Au/A) IPen
– 'Douglas White' (Au/S) MFie SPop
– 'Dovedale' (Au/S) NDro SPop WAln
– 'Dowager' (Au/A) MFie
– Downtown Doubles (Au/d) SPop
– 'Doyen' (Au/d) EWoo IPen ITim MFie NDro NHpl WAln WCre WHil
– 'Dragon's Hoard' (Au/A) WAln
– 'Drax' (Au/A) SPop WAln
– 'Dream' (Au/St) SPop
– 'Dreamweaver' (Au/S) **new** SPop
– 'Dubarii' (Au/A) MFie NDro WAln
– 'Duchess of Malfi' (Au/S) SPop WAln
– 'Duchess of York' (Au) LLHF
– 'Duke of Edinburgh' (Au/B) NDro WAln
– 'Dusky Girl' (Au/A) NDro WAln
– 'Dusky Maiden' (Au/A) EWoo GAbr GAgs MFie NDro NPnk NSum SPop WCre WHil
– 'Dusky Yellow' (Au/B) ECho NDro
– 'Dusty Miller' (Au/B) EBee ECho LRHS NBir
– 'Eastern Promise' (Au/A) EWoo GAgs MFie NDro NSum SPop WHil
– 'Eaton Dawn' (Au/S) MFie SPop
– 'Ed Spivey' (Au/A) NDro WCre
– 'Eddy Gordon' (Au/A) IPen WAln
– 'Eden Alexander' (Au/B) MFie NDro
– 'Eden Amethyst' (Au/B) NDro
– 'Eden Blue Star' (Au/B) EWoo GAbr NDro NSum SPop
– 'Eden Bonanza' (Au/B) **new** SPop
– 'Eden Bramley' (Au/B) **new** NDro
– 'Eden Carmine' (Au/B) MFie MHer NDro SPop
– 'Eden Cynthia' (Au/B) IPen MFie SPop
– 'Eden Dark Eyes' (Au/B) **new** SPop
– 'Eden David' (Au/B) MFie NDro SPop
– 'Eden Ensign' (Au/B) SPop
– 'Eden Fanfare' (Au/B) NDro
– 'Eden Goldfinch' (Au/B) GAbr IPen MAsh NDro SPop
– 'Eden Grace' (Au/B) SPop
– 'Eden Greenfinch' (Au/B) EWoo MFie NDro SPop WCre
– 'Eden Lilactime' (Au/B) NDro SPop
– 'Eden Moonlight' (Au/B) MFie SPop WAln WCre WHil
– 'Eden Rhiann' (Au/B) **new** NDro SPop
– 'Eden Sunrise' (Au/B) NDro
– 'Edinburgh' (Au/A) WAln
– 'Edith Allen' (Au/A) WAln
– 'Edith Major' (Au/d) MFie NDro SPop
– 'Edith Mather' (Au/S) WAln
– 'Edward Sweeney' (Au/S) WAln
– 'Eggborough' (Au/A) SPop
– 'Eglinton' (Au) NDro NSum SPop WCre
– 'Eileen K' (Au/S) NDro
– 'El Zoco' (Au/S) SPop
– 'Elara' (Au/d) SPop
– 'Elegance' (Au/S) SPop
– 'Elf Star' (Au/A) NSum SPop WAln
– 'Eli Jenkins' (Au) WAln
– 'Elizabeth Ann' (Au/A) NDro SPop
– 'Ellen Thompson' (Au/A) EWoo GAbr IPen MFie NDro SPop WCre WHil XBar
– 'Ellie May' (Au/S) **new** XBar
– 'Elsie' (Au/A) WCre
– 'Elsie May' (Au/A) EWoo IPen ITim MFie NDro SPop WCre
– 'Elsinore' (Au/S) IPen SPop WCre
– 'Emberglow' (Au/d) WAln
– 'Embley' (Au/S) NDro NHpl SPop WCre
– 'Emery Down' (Au/S) NDro SPop WCre
– 'Emily' (Au/d) IPen
– 'Emma Louise' (Au) IPen
– 'Emmett Smith' (Au/A) NBro NDro SPop WAln
– 'Ems Blue' (Au/B) WAln
– 'Ems Choice' (Au/B) WAln
– 'Ems Funny Face' (Au/B) **new** NDro
– 'Enigma' (Au/S) SPop WAln
– 'Enlightened' (Au/A) MFie NDro
– 'Envy' (Au/S) MFie WAln

- 'Erica' (Au/A) GAbr IPen MFie NDro NSum SPop WCre WHil XBar
- 'Erjon' (Au/S) MFie NDro SPop
- 'Error' (Au/S) WAln
- 'Eschman Starflower' (Au/S) WHil
- 'Esso' (Au/S) NDro WAln
- 'Ethel' (Au) NDro
- 'Ethel Wild' (Au/d) SPop
- 'Ethel Wilkes' (Au/d) WAln
- 'Etna' (Au/S) WAln
- 'Ettrick' (Au/S) WAln
- 'Europa' (Au/d) SPop
- 'Eve Guest' (Au/A) EWoo NDro SPop WAln
- 'Eventide' (Au/S) GAgs SPop
- 'Everest Blue' (Au/S) EWoo GAbr GAgs ITim NDro SPop WCre XBar
- 'Everest Flush' (Au/S) WAln
- 'Excalibur' (Au/d) EWoo GAgs NDro NSum SPop WCre
- 'Exhibition Blau' (Exhibition Series) (Au/B) IBoy WHil
- 'Eye Candy' (Au/St) SPop
- 'Eyeopener' (Au/A) IPen MFie NDro NSum SPop WHil
- 'Fabuloso' (Au/St) EWoo NDro SPop WCre
- 'Fairy' (Au/A) WAln
- 'Fairy Light' (Au/S) SPop WAln
- 'Fairy Moon' (Au/S) IPen WAln
- 'Fairy Queen' (Au/S) WAln
- 'Falcon' (Au/S) SPop WAln
- 'Faliraki Fanciful' (Au) EWoo
- 'Faloonside' (Au) IPen
- 'Falstaff' (Au/d) WAln
- 'Fanciful' (Au/S) EWoo MFie NDro SPop WHil XBar
- 'Fancy Free' (Au) SPop
- 'Fancy Pants' (Au/S) NDro SPop
- 'Fandancer' (Au/A) WAln
- 'Fandango' WCre
- 'Fanfare' (Au/S) EWoo MFie NDro SPop WHil
- 'Fanny Meerbeck' (Au/S) GAbr IPen MFie NDro SPop WHil
- 'Fantasia' (Au/d) SPop WAln
- 'Faro' (Au/S) NDro SPop WCre
- 'Favourite' (Au/S) EWoo GAbr GAgs IPen ITim MAsh MFie NDro SPop WCre WHil XBar
- 'Fearless' (Au/S) WAln
- 'Fen Tiger' (Au/St) SPop WAln
- 'Fenby' (Au/S) EWoo SPop
- 'Fennay' (Au/S) EWoo NSum WAln
- 'Ferrybridge' (Au/A) IPen NDro WAln
- 'Fiddler's Green' (Au/d) EWoo GAbr IPen NDro SPop WCot WCre XBar
- 'Figaro' (Au/S) EWoo MFie NDro SPop WCre
- 'Figurine' (Au/d) WAln
- 'Finchfield' (Au/A) GAbr IPen MFie NDro WAln WCre
- 'Finlay Thomas' (Au/S) **new** SPop
- 'Finley' (Au/B) NDro
- 'Firecracker' (Au) IPen WAln
- 'Firenze' (Au/A) MFie SPop
- 'Firsby' (Au/d) EWoo MFie NDro SPop WHil
- 'First Green' (Au/St) SPop
- 'First Lady' (Au/A) IPen SPop WAln WCre
- 'First Light' (Au/B) NDro SPop
- 'Fishtoft' (Au/d) MFie SPop
- 'Fitzroy' (Au/d) EWoo SPop
- 'Fleecy' (Au/S) SPop
- 'Fleet Street' (Au/S) GAgs MFie NDro SPop
- 'Fleminghouse' (Au/S) GAbr NDro SPop WCre
- 'Florence Brown' (Au/S) IPen
- 'Fluffy Duckling' (Au/S) SPop
- 'For You' (Au/St) SPop
- 'Foreign Affairs' (Au/S) SPop
- 'Forest Beech' (Au/d) SPop
- 'Forest Bordeaux' (Au/d) SPop
- 'Forest Bracken' (Au/d) SPop
- 'Forest Burgundy' (Au/d) GAgs SPop
- 'Forest Burnt Gold' (Au/d) SPop
- 'Forest Cappuccino' (Au/d) EWoo GAgs SPop
- 'Forest Coffee' (Au/D) **new** NDro
- 'Forest Duet' (Au/d) EWoo NDro SPop
- 'Forest Fire' (Au/d) EWoo GAbr MFie NSum SPop
- 'Forest Glade' (Au/d) SPop
- 'Forest Gorse' (Au/d) SPop WCre
- 'Forest Heath' (Au/d) **new** SPop
- 'Forest Lemon' (Au/d) EWoo MFie SPop WCre
- 'Forest Lime' (Au/d) SPop
- 'Forest Pecan' (Au/d) **new** SPop
- 'Forest Pines' (Au/S) SPop WAln
- 'Forest Purple Plum' (Au/D) **new** NDro
- 'Forest Shade' (Au/d) SPop
- 'Forest Sunburst' (Au/d) SPop
- 'Forest Sunlight' (Au/d) SPop
- 'Forest Sunshine' (Au/d) SPop
- 'Forest Twilight' (Au/d) EWoo MFie SPop WCre
- 'Foundling' (Au) **new** ITim
- 'Foxfire' (Au/A) WAln
- 'Fradley' (Au/A) IPen MFie NDro WAln WCre WHil
- 'Françoise' (Au/d) XBar
- 'Frank Bailey' (Au/d) EWoo MFie SPop WAln
- 'Frank Crosland' (Au/A) MFie NDro NSum SPop WCre WHil
- 'Frank Faulkner' (Au/A) WAln
- 'Frank Jenning' (Au/A) NDro WAln
- 'Frank Taylor' (Au/S) EWoo
- 'Fred Booley' (Au/d) EWoo GAbr IPen LLHF MFie NDro NSum SPop WHil XBar
- 'Fred Livesley' (Au/A) WAln
- 'Freestyle' (Au/B) WAln
- 'Fresco' (Au/A) SPop WAln
- 'Freya' (Au/S) NDro SPop
- 'Friskney' (Au/d) EWoo SPop WAln
- 'Frittenden Yellow' (Au/B) GAbr SPop
- 'Frosty' (Au/S) EWoo NDro SPop WCre
- 'Fuller's Red' (Au/S) ITim NDro SPop WCre WHil
- 'Funny Valentine' (Au/d) EWoo IPen MFie NDro NSum SPop WCre WHil
- 'Fuzzy' (Au/St) WAln
- 'G.L. Taylor' (Au/A) IPen NDro
- 'Gaia' (Au/d) EWoo SPop WCre
- 'Gail Atkinson' (Au/A) SPop WAln
- 'Galatea' (Au/S) SPop WAln
- 'Galator' (Au/A) WAln
- 'Galen' (Au/A) GAbr SPop WCre
- 'Ganymede' (Au/d) SPop WAln
- 'Gary Pallister' (Au/A) SPop WAln WCre
- 'Gas Lane' (Au/A) **new** SPop
- 'Gateshead' (Au/S) WCre
- 'Gavin Ward' (Au/S) WAln
- 'Gay Crusader' (Au/A) GAbr IPen MFie NDro NSum SPop WCre WHil
- 'Gazza' (Au/A) WAln
- 'Gee Cross' (Au/A) IPen MFie NDro NSum WCre
- 'Geldersome Green' (Au/S) NDro SPop
- 'Geldersome Green No. 2' (Au/S) **new** ITim
- 'Gemini' (Au/S) NDro
- 'General Champney' (Au) WCre
- 'Generosity' (Au/A) GAgs MFie NDro NSum WCre WHil
- 'Geoffrey Bick' (Au/A) SPop
- 'Geordie' (Au/A) WAln
- 'George Edge' (Au/B) NDro

- 'George Harrison' (Au/B) NDro SPop
- 'George Jennings' (Au/A) MFie NDro SPop
- 'George Swinford's Leathercoat' (Au/B) GAbr NDro
- 'Geronimo' (Au/S) GAbr IPen MAsh MFie NDro SPop WCre
- 'Gimli' (Au/A) WAln
- 'Girl Guide' (Au/S) WHil
- 'Gizabroon' (Au/S) CFis EWoo GAbr GAgs MFie NDro NEgg NLar SPop WCre WHil XBar
- 'Glasnost' (Au/S) WAln
- 'Glazebrook' (Au/S) SPop
- 'Gleam' (Au/S) CTal CWCL EBee ECho EDAr GAgs IPen LLHF MFie NDro NSum SPop WCre WHil XBar
- 'Glencoe' (Au/S) EWoo GAgs NDro SPop
- 'Gleneagles' (Au/S) EWoo IPen NDro SPop WAln WCre
- 'Glenelg' (Au/S) EWoo GAbr ITim MFie NDro NSum SPop WCre WHil XBar
- 'Glenluce' (Au/S) EWoo GAgs NDro SPop
- 'Gloire de Dijon' (Au/S) XBar
- 'Gnome' (Au/B) GAbr GAgs IPen NDro
- 'Goeblii' (Au/B) MFie NDro SPop WHil
- 'Gold Seal' (Au/d) SPop
- 'Gold Seam' (Au/A) EWoo MFie WAln WHil
- 'Golden Boy' (Au/A) MFie NDro NSum SPop WAln
- 'Golden Chartreuse' (Au/d) EWoo GAbr NDro SPop
- 'Golden Fleece' (Au/S) EWoo GAbr MAsh MFie NDro SPop WCre
- 'Golden Girl' (Au/A) WAln
- 'Golden Glory' (Au/A) GAgs NDro WAln
- 'Golden Harvest' (Au/A) SPop
- 'Golden Hill' (Au/S) ITim
- 'Golden Hind' (Au/d) EWoo GAbr GAgs MFie NDro NSum SPop
- 'Golden Splendour' (Au/d) EWoo GAgs IPen ITim MFie NDro NSum SPop WCre WHil
- 'Golden Wedding' (Au/A) GAgs IPen MFie NDro SPop WAln WCre WHil
- 'Goldie' (Au/S) GAgs NDro
- 'Goldwin' (Au/A) NDro NSum
- 'Gollum' (Au/A) MFie NDro SPop WAln
- 'Good Report' (Au/A) MAsh MFie NDro NSum SPop WHil
- 'Goody Goody' (Au/St) NDro SPop
- 'Googie' (Au/d) SPop
- 'Gordon Files' (Au/S) WAln
- 'Gorey' (Au/A) IPen MFie NDro WCre WHil
- 'Gorgeous George' (Au/St) SPop
- 'Grabley' (Au/S) EWoo NDro SPop WCre
- 'Grace' (Au/S) WAln
- 'Grace Ellen' (Au/S) WAln
- 'Grand Slam' (Au/D) MFie
- 'Grandad's Favourite' (Au/B) EWoo NDro SPop
- 'Grasmere' (Au/D) **new** NDro
- 'Green Abundance' (Au/B) EWoo
- 'Green Café' (Au/S) SPop
- 'Green Finger' (Au/S) EWoo MFie SPop
- 'Green Frill' (Au) NDro
- 'Green Goddess' (Au/St) EWoo WAln
- 'Green Heart' (Au/S) EWoo SPop
- 'Green Isle' (Au/S) EWoo IPen MFie NDro SPop WCre XBar
- 'Green Jacket' (Au/S) IPen SPop WCre
- 'Green Lane' (Au/S) XBar
- 'Green Meadows' (Au/S) GAgs SPop WAln
- 'Green Mouse' (Au/S) WAln
- 'Green Mustard' (Au/S) NDro SPop
- 'Green Parrot' (Au/S) EWoo GAbr NDro SPop WCre WHil
- 'Green Shank' (Au/S) EWoo IPen NDro SPop WHil
- 'Green Woodpecker' (Au/S) IPen
- 'Greenfield's Fancy' (Au) EBee
- 'Greenfinch' (Au/S) EWoo
- 'Greenfinger' (Au/S) WAln
- 'Greenheart' (Au/S) SPop
- 'Greenpeace' (Au/S) EWoo GAbr GAgs SPop WAln WCre XBar
- 'Greswolde' (Au/d) EWoo MFie SPop WAln
- 'Greta' (Au/S) CWCL ECho EWoo GAgs IPen MFie NDro SPop WCre WHil
- 'Gretna Green' (Au/S) EWoo SPop
- 'Grey Bonnet' (Au/S) SPop WAln
- 'Grey Cloud' (Au/B) NDro
- 'Grey Dawn' (Au/S) WAln
- 'Grey Edge' (Au) ECho
- 'Grey Friar' (Au/S) SPop WAln
- 'Grey Hawk' (Au/S) IPen NDro SPop WAln
- 'Grey Lady' (Au/S) WAln
- 'Grey Ladywood' (Au/d) SPop
- 'Grey Lag' (Au/S) NSum SPop XBar
- 'Grey Monarch' (Au/S) GAbr IPen MFie SPop WAln WCre WHil
- 'Grey Owl' (Au/S) NDro SPop WAln
- 'Grey Ridge' (Au/S) WAln
- 'Grey Shrike' (Au/S) SPop WAln
- 'Grizedale' (Au/S) SPop
- 'Groupie' (Au/St) SPop
- 'Grüner Veltliner' (Au/S) SPop WCre
- 'Guinea' (Au/S) CTal EWoo GAbr IPen ITim MFie NDro SPop WCre
- 'Gwai Loh' (Au) NDro
- 'Gwen' (Au/A) MFie NDro SPop WAln WCre XBar
- 'Gwen Baker' (Au/d) IPen MFie NDro SPop WAln WCre
- 'Gwenda' (Au/A) NDro SPop WAln WHil
- 'Gypsy Boy' (Au/A) **new** WAln
- 'Gypsy Rose Lee' (Au/A) MFie
- 'H Old Gold' (Au/S) NDro
- 'Habanera' (Au/A) MFie NDro NSum SPop WCre
- 'Haffner' (Au/S) IPen NDro SPop
- 'Hallmark' (Au/A) EWoo MFie NDro WAln
- 'Handsome Lass' (Au/St) EWoo GAgs IPen MFie NDro SPop WAln WCre
- 'Hannah' (Au/A) WAln
- 'Harlequin' (Au/B) NDro
- 'Harmony' (Au/B) EWoo MFie NBro NDro NSum XBar
- 'Harry Hotspur' (Au/A) GAgs IPen MFie NDro NSum SPop WCre WHil
- 'Harry 'O'' (Au/S) MFie NDro SPop WCre
- 'Harthorpeburn' (Au/B) NDro
- 'Harvest Glow' (Au/S) IPen NDro SPop WHil
- 'Harvest Gold' (Au/S) NDro WCre
- 'Havana' (Au/d) SPop WAln
- 'Hawkwood' (Au/S) EBee GAgs IPen MFie NDro NEgg WCre WHil XBar
- 'Hazel' (Au/B) MFie NDro WCre
- 'Hazel' (Au/A) IPen ITim MFie NDro SPop WHil
- 'Headdress' (Au/S) EWoo GAbr GAgs IPen MFie SPop
- 'Heady' (Au/A) CWCL EWoo GAgs MFie NDro WCre WHil XBar
- 'Heart of Gold' (Au/A) MFie NDro SPop WAln
- 'Hearts of Oak' (Au/A) WAln
- 'Heaven Scent' (Au) NDro WHil
- 'Hebers' (Au) NDro SPop WAln
- 'Helen' (Au/S) GAbr IPen MFie NDro SPop WCre WHil
- 'Helen Barter' (Au/S) NDro NSum SPop WCre WHil
- 'Helen Ruane' (Au/d) EBee EWoo GAgs GKev SPop WCre
- 'Helena' (Au/S) IPen MFie NDro SPop WAln WCre WHil XBar

- 'Helena Brown' (Au/S)	SPop WAln
- 'Helena Dean' (Au/d)	SPop WAln
- 'Helluinn' (Au/d)	SPop
- 'Henry's Bane' (Au/St)	SPop
- 'Her Nibs' (Au/St)	MAsh SPop WCre
- 'Hermia' (Au/A)	MFie SPop WHil
- 'Hetty Woolf' (Au/S)	GAbr ITim NDro SPop WCre
- 'Hew Dalrymple' (Au/S)	NDro SPop WAln
- 'High Hopes' (Au)	WAln
- 'Highland Park' (Au/A)	NDro SPop
- 'Hillhook' (Au/A)	NSum WAln
- 'Hillview Hermes' (Au/S)	WHil
- Hillview selection (Au)	WHil
- 'Hinton Admiral' (Au/S)	EWoo GAgs IPen NDro SPop WCre WHil XBar
- 'Hinton Fields' (Au/S)	EBee EShb EWTr GAbr GAgs IPen MFie NDro NEgg SPop WCre WHil
- 'Hobby Horse' (Au)	EWoo GAgs ITim
- 'Holyrood' (Au/S)	EWoo GAbr IPen ITim NDro NHpl SPop WAln XBar
- 'Honey' (Au/d)	GAbr NBro NDro NEgg NSum SPop
- 'Honeydawn' (Au/B)	NDro
- 'Hopleys Coffee' (Au/d)	EWoo GAbr NDro SPop WAln WCre
- 'Hopton Gem' (Au/B)	NDro
- 'Hot Chocolate' (Au/d)	SPop
- 'Howard Telford' (Au/A)	MFie SPop
- 'Hughie' (Au/A)	WAln
- 'Humphrey' (Au/S)	WAln
- 'Hurstwood Midnight' (Au)	MFie WAln XBar
- 'Iago' (Au/S)	NDro SPop WAln
- 'Ian Greville' (Au/A)	IPen MFie NDro SPop
- 'Ibis' (Au/A)	NDro WAln WCre
- 'Ice Cap' (Au/d)	SPop
- 'Ice Maiden' (Au/A)	EWoo GAbr IPen MFie NDro NSum SPop WCre WHil
- 'Icon' (Au/St)	SPop
- 'Ida' (Au/A)	IPen
- 'Idmiston' (Au/S)	EWoo GAgs IPen NDro SPop WCre WHil XBar
- 'Ilona' (Au/d)	SPop
- 'Imari Stripe' (Au/St)	WHil
- 'Immaculate' (Au/A)	GAgs MFie NDro NSum SPop WCre WHil
- 'Impassioned' (Au/A)	MFie SPop WCre XBar
- 'Impeccable' (Au/A)	IPen MFie
- 'Imperturbable' (Au/A)	IPen MFie NDro SPop
- 'Indian Love Call' (Au/A)	GAbr GAgs IPen ITim MFie NDro SPop WCre WHil
- 'Innsworth' (Au/A)	SPop WAln
- 'Iris Scott' (Au/A)	ITim NDro
- 'Isabel' (Au/S)	WAln
- 'Isabella' (Au/A)	NDro WAln
- 'Jac' (Au/S)	SPop
- 'Jack Dean' (Au/A)	EWoo GAgs MFie SPop WCre WHil XBar
- 'Jack Horner' (Au)	WAln
- 'Jack Redfern' (Au/A)	NDro
- 'Jaffa' (Au/A)	EWoo NDro NSum WAln WCre
- 'James Arnot' (Au/S)	GAbr IPen NDro SPop WCre XBar
- 'James Watham' (Au/S)	WAln
- 'James Wattam' (Au/S) **new**	NDro
- 'Jane' (Au/S)	WAln
- 'Jane Myers' (Au/d)	WAln WHil
- 'Janet' (Au)	ECho
- 'Janet Watts' (Au)	GAgs WCre
- 'Janie Hill' (Au/A)	MFie SPop WCre XBar
- 'Jealous Lover' (Au/St)	SPop
- 'Jean Fielder' (Au/A)	NDro SPop WAln
- 'Jean Jacques' (Au/A)	NDro WAln
- 'Jean Jacques' (Au/d)	XBar
- 'Jean Walker' (Au/B)	SPop
- 'Jeanne' (Au/A)	EWoo MFie
- 'Jeannie Jingles' (Au/St) **new**	SPop
- 'Jeannie Telford' (Au/A)	MFie NDro SPop WCre
- 'Jeff Scruton' (Au/A)	SPop WAln
- 'Jenny' (Au/A)	EWoo IPen MFie NDro NRya SPop WCre
- 'Jersey Bounce' (Au/A)	EWoo ITim NDro WCre
- 'Jesmond' (Au/S)	SPop WAln
- 'Jessie' (Au/d)	EWoo
- 'Jilting Jessie' (Au/St)	GAgs IPen NDro SPop
- 'Joan Butler' (Au)	WAln
- 'Joan Curtis' (Au/d)	SPop
- 'Joan Elliott' (Au/A)	GAbr
- 'Joanne' (Au/A)	EWoo GAgs MFie NDro SPop WCre
- 'Joe Perks' (Au/A)	EWoo GAgs IPen ITim MFie NDro SPop WCre WHil XBar
- 'Joel' (Au/S)	EWoo GAgs IPen ITim MFie NDro SPop WCre
- 'Johann Bach' (Au/B)	EWoo NDro SPop
- 'John Stewart' (Au/A)	MFie SPop
- 'John Wayne' (Au/A)	EWoo GAbr MFie NDro SPop WCre WHil
- 'John Woolf' (Au/S)	NDro
- 'Jonathon' (Au/A)	EWoo NDro WAln
- 'Jorvik' (Au/S)	MFie SPop WCre
- 'Joy' (Au/A)	IPen LLHF MFie NDro NSum NWad SPop WCre WHil
- 'Joyce' (Au/A)	EWoo GAbr IPen MFie NDro NSum SPop WHil XBar
- 'Judith Borman' (Au/d)	NDro
- 'Julia' (Au/S)	NDro SPop WAln
- 'Julia Jane' (Au/B)	NDro WCre
- 'Julie Nuttall' (Au/B)	EWoo GAbr GAgs NDro NSum NWad SPop WHil
- 'June' (Au/A)	NDro NSum SPop
- 'Jungfrau' (Au/d)	MFie NDro SPop WAln
- 'Jupiter' (Au/S)	NDro SPop WAln
- 'Jupp' (Au)	EBee EWTr GAgs
- 'Jura' (Au/A)	WAln
- 'Just Steven' (Au/A)	SPop WAln
- 'Justin Case' (Au/B)	WAln
- 'K S' (Au/S)	NDro
- 'Karen Cordrey' (Au/S)	EBee ECho EWoo GAgs IPen ITim MFie NDro NSum SPop WHil
- 'Karen McDonald' (Au/A)	MFie NDro SPop
- 'Kate Haywood' (Au/B)	NDro WCre WHil
- 'Kath Dryden'	see *P. allionii* 'Kath Dryden'
- 'Kelso' (Au/A)	MFie
- 'Ken Chilton' (Au/A)	EWoo GAgs MFie NDro SPop WCre WHil
- 'Kenco' (Au/d)	SPop
- 'Kentucky Blues' (Au/d)	IPen MFie NDro SPop WAln
- 'Kercup' (Au/A)	EWoo MFie SPop WCre
- 'Kerry' (Au/A)	EBee GAgs WAln
- 'Kersey' (Au/S)	SPop
- 'Kevin' (Au/A)	SPop WAln
- 'Kevin Keegan' (Au/A)	MFie NDro NSum SPop WHil
- 'Key West' (Au/A)	NDro SPop WAln
- 'Khachaturian' (Au/A)	MFie NDro WAln
- 'Kilby' (Au/A)	GAgs NDro NSum SPop
- 'Kim' (Au/A)	IPen MFie NDro SPop WCre WHil
- 'Kimberworth Boy' (Au/A)	NDro WAln
- 'Kincraig' (Au/S)	SPop WAln
- 'King George' (Au/d)	MFie WAln WHil
- 'King Kong' (Au)	WAln
- 'Kingcup' (Au/A)	GAbr GAgs MFie NDro SPop WCre
- 'Kingfisher' (Au/A)	EWoo GAgs IPen MFie NDro SPop
- 'Kingpin' (Au/St)	NDro

– 'Kintail' (Au/A)	MFie
– 'Kiowa' (Au/S)	SPop WCre
– 'Kirklands' (Au/d)	EWoo ITim MFie NDro SPop WCre WHil
– 'Kitterford Cross' (Au/B) **new**	NDro
– 'Knights' (Au/S)	SPop
– 'Kohinoor' (Au)	MFie WHil
– 'Königin der Nacht' (Au/St)	EWoo MFie NDro SPop WCre WHil
– 'Lady Daresbury' (Au/A)	MFie NDro SPop WCre WHil
– 'Lady Day' (Au/d)	SPop WAln
– 'Lady Diana' (Au/S)	EWoo IPen NDro
– 'Lady Emma Monson' (Au/S)	EWoo NDro SPop
– 'Lady Joyful' (Au/S)	WCre
– 'Lady of the Vale' (Au/A)	NDro SPop WAln
– 'Lady Penelope' (Au/S)	WAln
– 'Lady Zoë' (Au/S)	EWoo LLHF MAsh MFie NDro SPop WCre
– 'Laguna' (Au/d)	SPop
– 'Lambert's Gold' (Au)	GAbr SPop
– 'Lambrook Gold' (Au/B)	NDro
– 'Lamplugh' (Au/d)	IPen NSum SPop WHil
– 'Lancelot' (Au/d)	EWoo SPop
– 'Landy' (Au/A)	MFie NDro SPop WCre
– 'Langley Park' (Au/A)	IPen MFie NDro SPop WCre WHil
– 'Laphroaigh' (Au/S)	WAln
– 'Laptop' (Au/St)	SPop WCre
– 'Lara' (Au/A)	MFie NDro SPop WCre
– 'Laredo' (Au/A)	EWoo WAln
– 'Larry' (Au/A)	EWoo GAgs LLHF MFie NDro SPop WCre XBar
– 'Late Romantic' (Au)	CBod ECtt GAbr GBin MHol NHpl NLar WIce WTor
– 'Lavender and Old Lace' (Au/d)	SPop
– 'Lavender Lady' (Au/B)	IPen NDro NEgg WAln
– 'Lavender Ridge' (Au/B)	WAln
– 'Lavenham' (Au/S)	SPop WAln
– 'Laverock' (Au/S)	NBir NBro NEgg WCre
– 'Laverock Fancy' (Au/S)	EWoo GAgs IPen NDro XBar
– 'Lazy River' (Au/A)	EWoo NDro WAln
– 'Leather Jacket' (Au)	GAbr WCre
– 'Leathercoat' (Au)	EWoo SPop
– 'Lechistan' (Au/S)	GAgs IPen MAsh NDro SPop WCre WHil
– 'Lee' (Au/A)	IPen MFie NDro WAln WCre
– 'Lee Clark' (Au/A)	MFie NDro WAln
– 'Lee Paul' (Au/A)	EWoo GAgs IPen MFie NDro NSum SPop WCre WHil
– 'Lee Sharpe' (Au/A)	EWoo IPen MFie NDro NSum SPop WAln
– 'Legolas' (Au/A)	SPop WAln
– 'Leicester Square' (Au/S) **new**	NDro
– 'Lemmy Getatem' (Au/d)	IPen
– 'Lemon Drizzle' (Au/S)	WAln
– 'Lemon Drop' (Au/S)	EWoo GAgs IPen ITim MFie NBro NDro SPop WCre
– 'Lemon Ice' (Au/S)	IPen WAln
– 'Lemon Ridge' (Au/B)	WAln
– 'Lemon Sherbet' (Au/B)	EWoo GAbr GAgs IPen NDro SPop WHil
– 'Lemon Zest' (Au/d)	WAln
– 'Lemonade' (Au)	GAgs
– 'Leona' (Au/d)	SPop
– 'Lepton Jubilee' (Au/S)	EWoo GAbr NDro WAln
– 'Leroy Brown' (Au/A)	WAln
– 'Lester' (Au/d)	MFie SPop WAln
– 'Leverton' (Au/d)	EWoo SPop
– 'Lewis Telford' (Au/A)	SPop
– 'Lich' (Au/S)	NDro
– 'Lichfield' (Au/A/d)	EWoo IPen SPop WCre
– 'Light Fantastic' (Au/S)	NDro SPop
– 'Light Hearted' (Au/A)	MFie NDro XBar
– 'Light Music' (Au/d)	WAln
– 'Likely Lad' (Au/St)	EWoo SPop
– 'Lila' (Au/S)	NDro SPop WAln WCre
– 'Lilac Domino' (Au/S)	GAgs IPen MFie NDro NEgg SPop WCre WHil
– 'Lilac Ladywood' (Au/d)	MFie SPop
– 'Lilac Mist' (Au/d) **new**	XBar
– 'Lillian Hill' (Au/A)	EWoo MFie WAln
– 'Lillibet' (Au/A)	NDro
– 'Lima' (Au/d)	IPen SPop WAln
– 'Limaki' (Au/d)	SPop
– 'Lime 'n' Lemon' (Au)	ITim NDro
– 'Lime Ridge' (Au)	WAln
– 'Limelight' (Au/A)	EWoo IPen SPop
– 'Limelight' (Au/S)	IPen NDro SPop
– 'Lincoln Biscuit' (Au/d)	SPop
– 'Lincoln Bullion' (Au/d)	EWoo MAsh NDro SPop WCre XBar
– 'Lincoln Charm' (Au/d)	GAbr SPop
– 'Lincoln Chestnut' (Au/d)	EWoo NDro SPop WCre XBar
– 'Lincoln Consort' (Au/d)	SPop
– 'Lincoln Cuckoo' (Au/d) **new**	NDro
– 'Lincoln Elf' (Au/d)	SPop
– 'Lincoln Gem' (Au/d)	SPop
– 'Lincoln Glow' (Au/d)	SPop
– 'Lincoln Halo' (Au/d)	SPop
– 'Lincoln Imperial' (Au/d)	NDro SPop
– 'Lincoln Major' (Au/d)	SPop
– 'Lincoln Melody' (Au/St/d) **new**	XBar
– 'Lincoln Poacher' (Au/d) **new**	NDro
– 'Lincoln Pride' (Au/d)	SPop
– 'Lincoln Storm' (Au/d)	SPop
– 'Lincoln Whisper' (Au/d)	NDro
– 'Linda' (Au/A)	SPop WAln
– 'Lindley' (Au/S)	GAgs NDro SPop
– 'Lindsey Moreno' (Au/S)	WAln
– 'Ling' (Au/A)	GAbr MFie NDro SPop WCre
– 'Linnet' (Au/B)	NDro
– 'Lintz' (Au/B)	MFie NDro SPop WCre
– 'Linze 2' (Au/S)	NDro
– 'Lisa' (Au/A)	EWoo GAbr GAgs IPen MFie SPop WCre WHil
– 'Lisa Clara' (Au/S)	EWoo GAbr GAgs IPen MAsh MFie NDro NHpl SPop WCre
– 'Lisa's Smile' (Au/S)	EWoo MFie NDro SPop WHil
– 'Little Bo Peep' (Au)	WAln
– 'Little Rosetta' (Au/d)	GAbr GAgs MFie NDro NSum WCre WHil
– 'Lizzie Files' (Au/A)	SPop WAln
– 'Lockyer's Gem' (Au/B/St)	IPen NDro NEgg
– 'Lolita' (Au/St)	EWoo GAgs SPop WHil
– 'Lord Saye and Sele' (Au/St)	CWCL EWoo GAbr GAgs IPen MAsh MFie NCGa NDro NEgg NSum NWad SPop WCre WHil XBar
– 'Lothlorien' (Au/A)	WAln
– 'Louis' (Au/d)	XBar
– 'Louisa Woolhead' (Au/d)	EWoo SPop
– 'Louise Jordan' (Au/A)	NDro
– 'Love Nest' (Au/S)	SPop
– 'Lovebird' (Au/S)	EWoo GAbr MFie NDro NHpl SPop WCre WHil XBar
– 'Lucia' (Au/B)	XBar
– 'Lucky Sport' (Au/B)	WAln

- 'Lucky Strike' (Au) WAln
- 'Lucy Locket' (Au/B) EWTr GAbr IPen ITim NDro NEgg NSum WCre
- 'Ludlow' (Au/S) GAbr SPop WCre
- 'Lune Tiger' (Au/St) SPop
- 'Lupy Minstrel' (Au/S) IPen MFie NDro SPop WAln WCre
- 'Lusty Lad' (Au/St) SPop
- 'Lyn' (Au/A) WCre
- 'Lynn' (Au/A) WAln
- 'Lynn Cooper' (Au) EWoo SPop
- 'MacWatt's Blue' (Au/B) GAbr IPen NDro SPop WCre WHil
- 'Macy the Cat' (Au) WHil
- 'Madelaine Palmer' (Au/d) SPop
- 'Maggie' (Au/S) EWoo NDro NSum SPop WCre
- 'Magnolia' (Au/B) WCre
- 'Maizie' (Au/S) WCre
- 'Mamba' (Au/S) **new** SPop
- 'Mandarin' (Au/A) GAbr GAgs MFie NDro NSum SPop WCre WHil XBar
- 'Mandy' (Au/S) MFie
- 'Manka' (Au/S) SPop
- 'Mardi Gras' (Au/d) WAln
- 'Margaret' (Au/S) EWoo GAbr
- 'Margaret Faulkner' (Au/A) MFie SPop WCre
- 'Margaret Irene' (Au/A) IPen SPop WCre
- 'Margaret Martin' (Au/S) IPen ITim MFie NDro SPop WCre
- 'Margery Thompson' (Au/d) SPop
- 'Margot' (Au/S) **new** WAln
- 'Margot Fonteyn' (Au/A) EWoo GAbr IPen MFie SPop WHil
- 'Mariandl' (Au/A) EBee
- 'Marie Crousse' (Au/d) CFis CMea GMaP IPen ITim MFie NDro SPop WCot WCre WHil
- 'Marie Pierre' (Au/d) XBar
- 'Marion Howard Spring' (Au/A) MFie WCre
- 'Marion Tiger' (Au/St) NDro SPop WAln
- 'Mark' (Au/A) GAgs IPen MFie NBro NDro SPop WCre
- 'Marmalade' (Au/d) **new** SPop
- 'Marmion' (Au/S) EWoo GAgs IPen ITim MFie NDro SPop WCre WHil XBar
- 'Martha Livesley' (Au/A) WAln
- 'Martha's Choice' (Au/A) WAln
- 'Martin Fish' (Au) WCre
- 'Martin Luther King' (Au/S) EWoo NDro SPop WCre WHil XBar
- 'Mary' (Au/d) GAbr NDro SPop WAln
- 'Mary Poppins' (Au/S) MFie NDro
- 'Mary Taylor' (Au/S) WAln
- 'Mary Zach' (Au/S) EWoo MFie NDro SPop WAln WHil
- 'Matthew Yates' (Au/d) EBee GAbr GAgs IPen ITim MFie NDro NHpl SPop WCot WCre WHil
- 'Mattie' (Au/d) **new** GAgs
- 'Maureen Millward' (Au/A) IPen MFie SPop
- 'May' (Au/A) EWoo NDro NSum WCre
- 'May Be' (Au/B) WAln
- 'May Booley' (Au/d) SPop
- 'Mazetta Stripe' (Au/S/St) GAbr GAgs MFie NBro NDro SPop WCre
- 'Meadow Sweet' (Au/S) WAln
- 'Meadowlark' (Au/A) EWoo ITim MFie SPop WHil
- 'Meg' (Au/d) **new** SPop
- 'Megan' (Au/d) SPop WAln
- 'Mehta' (Au/A) IPen NDro SPop WAln
- 'Mellifluous' (Au) GAgs MFie WCre WHil
- 'Melody' (Au/S) IPen NDro SPop
- 'Menin' (Au/d) SPop
- 'Mere Green' (Au/S) EWoo WAln
- 'Mere Peppermint' (Au) EWoo WAln
- 'Merlin' (Au/S) IPen MFie NSum
- 'Merlin Stripe' (Au/St) CWCL EBee IPen NDro SPop WCre WHil XBar
- 'Mermaid' (Au/d) GAbr IPen
- 'Merridale' (Au/A) GAbr MFie SPop WCre
- 'Mersey Tiger' (Au/S) EWoo GAbr GAgs ITim MFie NDro NSum SPop WHil
- 'Metis' (Au/d) SPop
- 'Mexicano' (Au/A) WAln
- 'Michael' (Au/S) MFie SPop WAln WHil
- 'Michael Wattam' (Au/S) NDro SPop WAln
- 'Mick' (Au/A) MFie WCre WHil
- 'Midland Marvel' (Au/St) SPop
- 'Midnight' (Au/A) WAln
- 'Mikado' (Au/S) IPen MFie NSum SPop WCre WHil XBar
- 'Milkmaid' (Au/A) MFie NSla WMAq
- 'Millicent' (Au/A) MFie NDro NSum WCre WHil
- 'Millicent Betsy' (Au/d) **new** SPop
- 'Millie Redfern' (Au/d) SPop
- 'Minley' (Au/S) EWoo GAbr GAgs MFie NBir NDro NEgg SPop WCre WIce
- 'Minotaur' (Au/A) SPop
- 'Minstead' (Au/S) SPop
- 'Minstrel' (Au/S) ITim MFie NDro SPop WCre
- 'Minty' (Au/St) SPop
- 'Mipsie Miranda' (Au/d) SPop
- 'Mirabella Bay' (Au/A) WAln
- 'Miranda' (Au/d) SPop
- 'Mirandinha' (Au/A) NDro
- 'Miriam' (Au/A) EWoo SPop WAln
- 'Mish Mish' (Au/d) GAbr NDro WHil
- 'Miss Bluey' (Au/d) EWoo NDro SPop WAln XBar
- 'Miss Jones' (Au/St) SPop
- 'Miss Muffet' (Au/S) WAln
- 'Miss Newman' (Au/A) NSum SPop
- 'Miss Otis' (Au/S) **new** SPop
- 'Miss Pinky' (Au) EWoo NDro SPop WCre
- 'Mist' (Au/S) WAln
- 'Mojave' (Au/S) EWoo GAbr GAgs IPen ITim MFie NDro NEgg NHpl NSum SPop WCre WHil XBar
- 'Mollie Langford' (Au/A) MFie NDro SPop WCre WHil
- 'Mondeo' (Au/A) WAln
- 'Monet' (Au/S) WAln
- 'Moneymoon' (Au/S) EWoo GAbr IPen NDro SPop WCre WHil
- 'Monica' (Au/A) MFie
- 'Monk' (Au/S) EWoo MFie SPop WAln WCre XBar
- 'Monmouth Star' (Au/St) SPop WHil
- 'Moon Fairy' (Au/S) NDro SPop WAln WCre
- 'Moondance' (Au/d) WAln
- 'Moonglow' (Au/S) EWoo GAbr NDro
- 'Moonlight' (Au/S) WAln
- 'Moonrise' (Au/S) EWoo MFie NDro
- 'Moonriver' (Au/A) EWoo SPop WCre WHil
- 'Moonshine' (Au/d) SPop WAln
- 'Moonshot' (Au/d) **new** NDro SPop
- 'Moonstone' (Au/d) SPop WAln
- 'Morello' (Au/d) XBar
- 'Morning Glory' (Au/B) WAln
- 'Morven' (Au) GAbr
- 'Moscow' (Au/S) SPop
- 'Moselle' (Au/S) MFie NDro SPop WAln
- 'Mossy Vale' (Au/S) SPop
- 'Mr A' (Au/S) EWoo GAgs NDro WHil
- 'Mr Bojangles' (Au/d) MFie WAln
- 'Mr Greenfingers' (Au) WCre
- 'Mrs Cairn's Blue' (Au/B) NDro
- 'Mrs Dargan' (Au/d) NDro

– 'Mrs J.H. Watson' (Au) WCre
– 'Mrs L. Hearn' (Au/A) EWoo IPen ITim MFie NDro SPop WCre
– 'Mrs R. Bolton' (Au/A) WCre WHil
– 'Mrs Robinson' (Au/St) SPop
– 'Mrs Wilson' (Au) GAbr
– 'Muriel James' (Au/A) SPop
– 'Murray Lakes' (Au/A) EWoo NDro SPop WAln
– 'Mustard Sauce' (Au/B) NDro
– 'My Buddy' (Au/St) SPop WCre
– 'My Delight' (Au/d) SPop
– 'My Fair Lady' (Au/A) MFie NDro SPop
– 'My Friend' (Au/B) NDro SPop
– 'Myfanwy' (Au/B) WAln
– 'Myodeboots' (Au/A) SPop
– 'Myrtle Park' (Au/A) WAln
– 'Mystery' (Au) GAbr
– 'Nancy Dalgetty' (Au/B) NDro SPop
– 'Nantenan' (Au/S) GAbr MFie NDro SPop WCre
– 'Neat and Tidy' (Au/S) CTal EWoo GAbr GAgs ITim MFie NDro SPop WCre
– 'Nefertiti' (Au/A) EWoo IPen MFie NDro SPop WCre WHil
– 'Nessun Dorma' (Au/A) EWoo NDro WAln
– 'Neville Telford' (Au/S) GAbr IPen MFie NDro SPop WCre WHil
– 'Newbottle' (Au/S) SPop WAln WHil
– 'Newsboy' (Au/A) WAln
– 'Newton Harcourt' (Au/A) SPop WHil
– 'Nicholas Loakes' (Au/S) WAln
– 'Nick Drake' (Au/d) SPop
– 'Nickity' (Au/A) EWoo GAbr GAgs IPen ITim MFie NDro NSum SPop WCre WHil XBar
– 'Nicola Jane' (Au/A) EWoo GAgs SPop WAln
– 'Nigel' (Au/d) GAbr MFie NDro
– 'Night and Day' (Au/St) SPop WAln WCre
– 'Night Dance' (Au/S) WCre
– 'Nightwink' (Au/S) WAln
– 'Nil Amber' (Au) GAbr SPop
– 'Nina' (Au/A) NDro SPop WAln
– 'Nita' (Au/d) SPop WAln
– 'No 21' (Au/S) NDro SPop
– 'No Deal' (Au/S) SPop WCre
– 'Nocturne' (Au/S) EWoo IPen NBro NDro NSum SPop WCre
– 'Noelle' (Au/S) EBee EWoo GAgs IPen
– 'Nona' (Au/d) EWoo MFie NDro NSum SPop
– 'Nonchalance' (Au/A) MFie NDro NSum SPop WHil
– 'Norma' (Au/A) EWoo MFie NDro SPop
– 'Northern Lights' (Au/S) GAbr NDro WAln
– 'Nureyev' (Au/A) EWoo SPop
– 'Nymph' (Au/d) EWoo GAbr GAgs MFie NDro SPop WCre WHil
– 'Oakenshield' (Au/A) **new** WAln
– 'Oakie' (Au/S) SPop WAln
– 'Oban' (Au/S) MFie NDro SPop XBar
– 'Odette' (Au) IPen MFie SPop
– 'O'er the Moon' (Au/S) WAln
– 'Oikos' (Au/B) NDro SPop
– 'Ol' Blue Eyes' (Au/St) SPop WAln
– 'Old Black Isle Dusty Miller' (Au/B) NDro
– 'Old Buffer' (Au/St) SPop
– 'Old Clove Red' (Au/B) EWoo GAbr IPen MFie NDro NSum WCre WHil
– 'Old Cottage Blue' (Au/B) GAbr NDro
– 'Old England' (Au/S) EWoo GAbr MFie NDro SPop WCre
– 'Old Gold' (Au/S) GAbr IPen NDro SPop WCre
– 'Old Gold Double' (Au/d) EWoo
– 'Old Gold Dusty Miller' (Au/B) NDro
– 'Old Irish Blue' (Au/B) IPen ITim NDro NEgg WCre
– 'Old Irish Green' (Au/B) EWoo GAbr NDro NSum
– 'Old Irish Scented' (Au/B) CTal EWoo GAbr IPen MFie NBro NDro
– 'Old Irish Yellow' (Au/B) NDro NEgg NHpl
– 'Old Mustard' (Au/B) NDro SBch SIgm SMHy WCre
– 'Old Pink Dusty Miller' (Au/B) GAbr IPen NDro
§ – 'Old Purple Dusty Miller' (Au/B) GAbr
– 'Old Red' (Au) GAgs
– 'Old Red Dusty Miller' (Au/B) GAbr LLHF NDro NSum SPop WHil
– 'Old Red Elvet' (Au/S) GAbr SPop WCre
– 'Old Smokey' (Au/A) EWoo MFie NDro SPop WHil XBar
– 'Old Suffolk Bronze' (Au/B) GAbr GAgs ITim NDro WCre WHil
– 'Old Tall Purple Dusty Miller' (Au/B) WCre
– 'Old Timer' (Au/S) SPop
– 'Old White Dusty Miller' (Au/B) **new** NDro
– 'Old Yellow Dusty Miller' (Au/B) CTal EWes EWoo GAbr IPen NBro NDro NWad WCre WHil
– 'Old-Fashioned' (Au/B) NDro
– 'Oldfield' (Au/d) SPop
– 'Olivia' (Au/d) SPop
– 'Olton' (Au/A) IPen MFie WCre XBar
– 'Onyx' (Au/B) WAln
– 'Optimist' (Au/St) EWoo GAgs IPen NDro SPop
– 'Opus One' (Au/A) EWoo WAln
– 'Orb' (Au/S) IPen MFie NDro SPop WCre WHil
– 'Ordvic' (Au/S) NDro WAln
– 'Orlando' (Au/S) MFie NDro SPop WAln
– 'Orwell Tiger' (Au/St) EWoo GAgs IPen MFie NDro SPop WCre
– 'Osbaston Bullseye' (Au/St) SPop
– 'Osborne Green' (Au/B) GAbr GAgs GBin SPop WCre WHil
– 'Osorno' (Au/d) SPop
– 'Ossett Sapphire' (Au/A) NDro SPop
– 'Otto Dix' (Au/A) SPop WAln
– 'Our Sophie' (Au/B) NDro
– 'Overdale' (Au/A) NDro NSum SPop WAln
– 'Oyster' (Au/B) NDro WAln
– 'Paddlin' Madeleine' (Au/A) EWoo NDro WAln
– 'Pageboy' (Au/A) WAln
– 'Paleface' (Au/A) EWoo GAgs IPen MFie NDro NSum SPop WCre
– 'Pam Tiger' (Au/St) WAln
– 'Panache' (Au/S) WAln
– 'Pang Tiger' (Au/St) EWoo SPop WAln
– 'Papageno' (Au/St) WAln
– 'Paphos' (Au/d) IPen SPop
– 'Paradise Yellow' (Au/B) EWoo GAbr MFie NDro NEgg SPop WCre
– 'Paragon' (Au/A) IPen MFie WCre WHil
– 'Parakeet' (Au/S) WAln
– 'Paris' (Au/S) WAln
– 'Party Animal' (Au/St) SPop
– 'Party Time' (Au/S) IPen SPop WCre
– 'Pass Me By' (Au) IPen
– 'Passchendaele' (Au/d) SPop WCre
– 'Passing Cloud' (Au/d) WAln
– 'Pastiche' (Au/A) WCre
– 'Pastures New' (Au) SPop WAln
– 'Pat' (Au/S) SPop
– 'Pat Barnard' (Au) IPen
– 'Pat Mooney' (Au/d) NDro

– 'Patience' (Au/S)	NDro WHil
– 'Patricia Barras' (Au/S)	EWoo WAln
– 'Pauline' (Au/A)	EWoo MFie SPop
– 'Pavarotti' (Au/A)	ITim NDro NSum SPop
– 'Peewit' (Au/S)	WAln
– 'Pegasus' (Au/d)	EWoo NDro SPop
– 'Peggy' (Au/A)	ITim NSum WHil
– 'People's Choice' (Au/d)	SPop
– 'Pequod' (Au/A)	MFie NDro NSum SPop
– 'Perdito' (Au/S)	WAln
– 'Perirot' (Au) **new**	ITim
– 'Perito Moreno' (Au/d)	SPop
– 'Persephone' (Au/B) **new**	NDro
– 'Perseus' (Au/S)	WAln
– 'Phantom' (Au/d)	EWoo SPop WAln
– 'Pharaoh' (Au/A)	CWCL EWoo GAgs MFie NDro SPop WCre XBar
– 'Phoenix' (Au/A)	WAln
– 'Phyllis Douglas' (Au/A)	EWoo GAgs IPen MFie NDro NEgg SPop WCre WHil
– 'Piccadilly' (Au/S)	MAsh MFie NDro SPop
– 'Piccalilli' (Au/d) **new**	XBar
– 'Pierot' (Au/A)	GAgs IPen MFie NDro NSum SPop WCre XBar
– 'Piers Telford' (Au/A)	CTal EBee EWoo GAbr GAgs IPen MFie NDro NEgg NSum SBch SPop WCre WHil XBar
– 'Piglet' (Au/d)	GAbr NDro SPop
– 'Pikey' (Au/S)	NDro SPop
– 'Pimlico' (Au/S)	SPop
– 'Pimroagh' (Au/A)	EWoo SPop
– 'Pink Floyd' (Au/A)	SPop
– 'Pink Fondant' (Au/d)	GAbr NDro
– 'Pink Hint' (Au/B)	NDro SPop
– 'Pink Lady' (Au/A)	GAbr GAgs MFie NBro NSum SPop WHil
– 'Pink Lilac' (Au/A/S)	NDro
– 'Pink Triumph' (Au)	NDro WHil
– 'Pinkerton' (Au/d)	EWoo SPop WAln
– 'Pinkie Dawn' (Au/B)	IPen NDro WCre
– 'Pinky' (Au/d)	WCre
– 'Pinstripe' (Au)	EWoo GAbr GAgs IPen NDro NSum SPop WCre WHil
– 'Pioneer Stripe' (Au/S)	GAgs IPen SPop WCre
– 'Pippin' (Au/A)	GAgs IPen MFie NBro NDro SPop WCre WHil XBar
– 'Pixie' (Au/A)	EWoo GAgs IPen MFie NDro SPop WCre WHil
– 'Playboy' (Au/A)	NDro SPop WAln
– 'Plum Pudding' (Au/d)	SPop WAln
– 'Plums and Custard' (Au/B) **new**	XBar
– 'Poacher's Lady' (Au/d) **new**	NDro
– 'Poacher's Starlight' (Au/d)	NDro
– 'Polar Sight' (Au/B)	WAln
– 'Polestar' (Au/A)	MFie NDro NSum SPop WCre WHil
– 'Polly' (Au/B)	EBee GAgs GKev NDro NSum WCre
– 'Pollyanna' (Au/B)	WAln
– 'Pop's Blue' (Au/S/d)	NEgg SPop
– 'Portree' (Au/S)	GAbr SPop
– 'Post Master' (Au/S)	WAln
– 'Pot o' Gold' (Au/S)	EBee ECho EWoo GAgs IPen MFie NDro NEgg SPop WCre WHil XBar
– 'Powder and Paint' (Au/A)	WAln
– 'Powder Puff' (Au/B)	EWoo NDro SPop
– 'Prague' (Au/S)	EWoo GAbr IPen MFie NBir NDro SPop WCre
– 'Pretender' (Au/A)	MFie SPop
– 'Pretty Prop' (Au/St)	SPop
– 'Pretty Purple' (Au/d)	SPop WAln
– 'Pride of Poland' (Au/S)	EWoo SPop WCre
– 'Prima' (Au)	NDro
– 'Prince Bishops' (Au/S)	SPop WAln
– 'Prince Charming' (Au/S)	EWoo GAgs IPen MFie NDro SPop WCre
– 'Prince Igor' (Au/A)	SPop
– 'Prince John' (Au/A)	MFie NBro NDro SPop WCre WHil
– 'Pristine' (Au/B)	WAln
– 'Proctor's Yellow' (Au/B)	GAbr NDro
– 'Prometheus' (Au/d)	EWoo GAbr ITim LLHF MFie NDro NSum SPop WHil
– 'Prosperine' (Au/S)	SPop WAln WCre
– 'Psyche' (Au/S)	NDro SPop WAln
– 'Ptarmigan' (Au)	WAln
– 'Pumpkin' (Au)	NHpl
– 'Puppy Love' (Au/St)	SPop
– 'Purbeck' (Au/B)	SPop
– 'Purple Dusty Miller'	see *P. auricula* 'Old Purple Dusty Miller'
– 'Purple Emperor' (Au/A)	MFie
– 'Purple Frills' (Au)	MFie
– 'Purple Glow' (Au/d)	WAln
– 'Purple Haze' (Au)	SPop
– 'Purple Knight' (Au/S)	WAln
– 'Purple Lace' (Au/d)	SPop
– 'Purple Lovely' (Au)	MFie SPop
– 'Purple Orient' (Au/d)	SPop
– 'Purple Patch' (Au/d)	SPop
– 'Purple Prolific' (Au/B) **new**	NDro
– 'Purple Promise' (Au)	GAbr ITim SPop
– 'Purple Prose' (Au/St)	EWoo MFie SPop
– 'Purple Rose' (Au/d)	ITim WAln
– 'Purple Royale' (Au/B)	NDro
– 'Purple Sage' (Au/S)	EWoo ITim MFie NDro SPop WCre WHil
– 'Purple Star' (Au/d)	SPop
– 'Purple Velvet' (Au/S)	CWCL EWoo IPen NDro SPop
– 'Quatro' (Au/d)	EWoo GAgs SPop
– 'Queen Alexandra' (Au/B)	EWoo GAbr NDro WHil
– 'Queen Bee' (Au/S)	GAbr GAgs MFie SPop
– 'Queen's Bower' (Au/S)	SPop WCre
– 'Queenswood' (Au/S)	EWoo WCre
– 'Quintessence' (Au/A)	EWoo MFie WCre WHil
– 'R.L. Bowes' (Au/A)	NDro
– 'Rab C. Nesbitt' (Au/A)	SPop WAln
– 'Rabley Heath' (Au/A)	EWoo GAgs ITim MFie NDro SPop WCre WHil
– 'Rachel' (Au/A)	EWoo NDro WAln WCre
– 'Rachel de Thame' (Au/S)	WAln
– 'Rachel Labouchere' (Au/S)	WAln
– 'Radiance' (Au/A)	SPop
– 'Radiant' (Au/A)	IPen
– 'Rag Doll' (Au/S)	NDro WAln
– 'Ragnald the Magnificent' (Au/S)	WAln
– 'Rainy Days' (Au/B)	NDro
– 'Rajah' (Au/S)	ECho EWoo GAbr GAgs IPen MAsh MFie NEgg NHpl SPop WCre WHil XBar
– 'Raleigh Stripe' (Au/St)	EWoo GAbr GAgs IPen WCre
– 'Rameses' (Au/A)	IPen MFie NDro WCre
– 'Rebecca Baker' (Au/d)	SPop WHil
– 'Red Admiral' (Au)	EWoo NDro SPop WAln
– 'Red Arrows' (Au)	SPop WAln
– 'Red Baron' (Au/S)	WAln WCre
– 'Red Beret' (Au/S)	SPop
– 'Red Bordeaux' (Au/S)	GAgs NDro

- 'Red Carpet' (Au/S) SPop
- 'Red Diamond' (Au/d) WAln
- 'Red Embers' (Au/S) SPop WAln WCre
- 'Red Ensign' (Au/B) NDro
- 'Red Gauntlet' (Au/S) EWoo GAbr GAgs IPen MFie NDro SPop WCre
- 'Red King' (Au/S) WAln
- 'Red Mark' (Au/A) MFie SPop WHil XBar
- 'Red Rum' (Au/S) GAbr SPop WAln WCre
- 'Red Sonata' (Au/S) SPop
- 'Red Spin' (Au/S) SPop
- 'Red Vulcan' (Au) WCre
- 'Red Wire' (Au/St) EWoo NDro NSum SPop WCre
- 'Redcar' (Au/A) GAbr MFie NDro WCre
- 'Reddown Apricot' (Au/B) NDro
- 'Reddown Barley Meal' (Au/B) NDro
- 'Reddown Bat' (Au/d) SPop
- 'Reddown First Swallow' (Au/B) NDro
- 'Reddown Rainman' (Au/B) NDro
- 'Reddown Tickled Pink' (Au/B) NDro
- 'Redstart' (Au/S) EBee EWoo GAgs GKev IPen ITim WCre WHil
- 'Regency' (Au/A) NDro WAln
- 'Regency Carousel' (Au/St) **new** SPop
- 'Regency Dandy' (Au/St) SPop
- 'Regency Denja' (Au) IPen
- 'Regency Emperor' (Au/St) EWoo IPen SPop WCre WHil
- 'Regency Paperchase' (Au/St) SPop
- 'Regency Peppermint Tea' (Au/St) SPop
- 'Regency Saint Clements' (Au/St) NDro SPop WAln WCre
- 'Remus' (Au/S) ECho ELan EWoo GAbr GAgs IPen ITim LLHF MFie NDro NEgg SPop WCre WHil XBar
- 'Rene' (Au/A) EWoo GAbr IPen MFie SPop WCre WHil XBar
- 'Renown' (Au/A) IPen NDro WAln WCre
- 'Repton' (Au/S) **new** SPop
- 'Requiem' (Au/d) WAln
- 'Resi' (Au) GAgs WHil
- 'Respectable' (Au/A) WAln
- 'Reverie' (Au/d) SPop WAln
- 'Reynardine' (Au/d) SPop WAln
- 'Rhinegold' (Au/d) XBar
- 'Riatty' (Au/d) GAbr GAgs MFie NDro SPop
- 'Richard Shaw' (Au/A) IPen NDro SPop
- 'Ring of Bells' (Au/S) EWoo SPop WAln WCre
- 'Ring of Fire' (Au/A) WAln
- 'Risdene' (Au) IPen SPop WAln WCre
- 'Rivendell' (Au/A) WAln
- 'Robbo' (Au/B) EWoo NDro
- 'Robert Green' (Au/S) EWoo SPop WAln
- 'Robert Lee' (Au/A) WAln
- 'Roberto' (Au/S) NDro SPop WAln
- 'Robin Hood Stripe' (Au/St) EWoo GAgs NDro SPop WCre
- 'Robinette' (Au/d) EWoo IPen SPop
- 'Rock Sand' (Au/S) EWoo GAbr GAgs MFie NDro SPop WCre WHil
- 'Rockbourne' (Au/A) SPop
- 'Rodeo' (Au/A) EWoo GAgs IPen SPop
- 'Rolts' (Au/S) ECho EWoo GAbr GAgs IPen NBro NDro SPop WCre WHil
- 'Rondy' (Au/S) ITim MFie SPop WAln
- 'Ronnie Johnson' (Au) WAln
- 'Ronny Simpson' (Au) WCre
- 'Rosalie' (Au) SPop
- 'Rosalie Edwards' (Au/S) EWoo MFie NDro SPop WCre
- 'Rose Conjou' (Au/d) EWoo GAbr GAgs IPen MFie NDro SPop WCre WHil XBar
- 'Rose Kaye' (Au/A) GAbr IPen WCre
- 'Rose Petal' (Au/d) **new** XBar
- 'Rosemarket Rackler' (Au/B) NDro
- 'Rosemary' (Au/S) EWoo MFie NDro SPop WCre WHil
- 'Rosewood' (Au) SPop WAln WCre
- 'Rosie' (Au/S) NDro
- 'Rostock' (Au/B) NDro
- 'Rothesay Robin' (Au/A) WAln
- 'Rouge Gorge' (Au/B) XBar
- 'Rowena' (Au/A) IPen MFie NDro NSum SPop WCre WHil
- 'Roxborough' (Au/A) EWoo GAgs IPen
- 'Roxburgh' (Au/A) MFie NDro SPop WCre
- 'Roy Keane' (Au/A) IPen MFie NSum SPop WAln WCre
- 'Royal Mail' (Au/S) MFie NDro SPop
- 'Royal Marine' (Au/S) MFie SPop WAln
- 'Royal Scot' (Au/S) SPop
- 'Royal Velvet' (Au/S) GAbr GAgs IPen NDro WHil
- 'Ruby Hyde' (Au/B) EWoo GAbr NDro SPop WCre
- 'Ruddy Duck' (Au/S) SPop WAln WCre
- 'Rumbled' (Au/St) MAsh
- 'Runwell' (Au/B) NDro
- 'Runwell Red' (Au/B) **new** SPop
- 'Rustig' (Au/B) WAln
- 'Rusty Dusty' (Au) GAbr
- 'Ryecroft' (Au/A) WAln
- 'Sabrina' (Au/A) WAln
- 'Saginaw' (Au/A) EWoo WAln
- 'Sailor Boy' (Au/S) MFie NDro SPop WAln
- 'Saint Boswells' (Au/S) GAbr SPop
- 'Saint Elmo' (Au/A) GAbr GAgs MFie SPop WCre
- 'Saint Quentin' (Au/S) WAln
- 'Salad' (Au/S) EWoo GAbr GAgs SPop
- 'Sale Green' (Au/S) EWoo MFie NDro SPop
- 'Sally' (Au/A) MFie NDro
- 'Sam Brown' (Au/S) WAln
- 'Sam Gamgee' (Au/A) NDro SPop WAln WCre
- 'Sam Hunter' (Au/A) NDro SPop
- 'Samantha' (Au/A) EWoo MFie NDro WAln WCre
- 'Samantha' (Au/d) EWoo MFie NDro SPop WAln
- 'San Antonio' (Au/A) NDro
- 'San Gabriel' (Au/A) WAln
- 'Sanctuary Wood' (Au/d) SPop
- 'Sandhills' (Au/A) MAsh MFie SPop WCre WHil
- 'Sandmartin' (Au/S) MFie
- 'Sandpiper' (Au/d) SPop WAln
- 'Sandra' (Au/A) ELan GAgs IPen MFie NDro SPop WCre WHil
- 'Sandra's Lass' (Au/A) EWoo SPop
- 'Sandwood Bay' (Au/A) EWoo GAbr MFie NDro NEgg SPop WCre WHil
- 'Sappho' (Au/S) IPen SPop WAln
- 'Sarah Gisby' (Au/d) MAsh MFie NDro SPop WCre
- 'Sarah Grey' (Au/d) WAln
- 'Sarah Humphries' (Au/d) WAln
- 'Sarah Lodge' (Au/d) GAbr GAgs IPen NDro SPop WCre WHil
- 'Sarah Suzanne' (Au/B) NDro
- 'Saruman' (Au/A) WAln
- 'Sasha Files' (Au/A) IPen WAln
- 'Satchmo' (Au/S) SPop
- 'Satin Doll' (Au/d) MFie SPop
- 'Satsuma' (Au/d) SPop WAln

- 'Scaraben' (Au) GAbr
- 'Schaumburg' (Au/B) NDro
- 'Schicchi' (Au/d) XBar
- 'Scipio' (Au/S) NDro SPop WAln
- 'Scorcher' (Au/S) EWoo GAbr IPen LLHF MFie NDro NSum SPop
- 'Sea Lavender' (Au/d) WAln
- 'Sea Mist' (Au/d) SPop WAln
- 'Searchlight' (Au) WCre
- 'Second Victory' (Au) NDro WCre WHil XBar
- 'Seen-a-Ghost' (Au/S) SPop
- 'Serendipity' (Au/B) WAln
- 'Serenity' (Au/S) MFie SPop WCre WHil XBar
- 'Sergeant Wilson' (Au) SPop WAln
- 'Serre' (Au/d) SPop
- 'Shaheen' (Au/S) IPen
- 'Shalford' (Au/d) GAbr MFie SPop WCot WCre WHil
- 'Sharmans Cross' (Au/S) MFie SPop WAln
- 'Sharon Louise' (Au/S) IPen SPop WCre
- 'Shaun' (Au/d) ECtt GAbr GAgs GBin MHol NHpl NLar WCre WIce WTor
- 'Sheila' (Au/S) GAbr IPen NDro SPop WCre WHil
- 'Sherbet' (Au/d) **new** SPop
- 'Shere' (Au/S) EWoo MFie NDro NSum SPop WCre
- 'Shergold' (Au/A) IPen MFie SPop WCre
- 'Sherwood' (Au/S) EWoo GAbr IPen NDro NHpl SPop WCre XBar
- 'Shining Hour' (Au/St) SPop
- 'Shirley' (Au/S) NDro SPop WAln
- 'Shotley' (Au/A) MFie SPop
- 'Show Bandit' (Au/St) SPop
- 'Showtime' (Au/S) GAgs NDro SPop WCre
- 'Sibsey' (Au/d) EWoo GAgs NDro NSum SPop
- 'Sidney' (Au/A) WAln
- 'Silas' (Au/B) NDro
- 'Silbermond' (Au/B) **new** NDro
- 'Silmaril' (Au) SPop WAln
- 'Silver City' (Au/S) WAln
- 'Silver Rose' (Au) WCre
- 'Silver Surfer' (Au/St) WAln
- 'Silverway' (Au/S) EWoo NDro SPop WAln WCre WHil
- 'Simply Red' (Au) EWoo IPen MAsh MFie NDro NSum SPop XBar
- 'Sir John' (Au/A) MFie NDro WCre WHil
- 'Sir John Hall' (Au) MFie
- 'Sir Robert' (Au/d) SPop WAln
- 'Sir Titus Salt' (Au/S) WAln
- 'Sirbol' (Au/A) EWoo GAgs IPen MFie MHer NDro NSum SPop WCre WHil
- 'Sirius' (Au/A) EWoo GAbr GAgs IPen MFie MHer NDro NSum NWad SPop WCre WHil XBar
- 'Skerne Tiger' (Au/St) SPop
- 'Skylark' (Au/A) GAbr GAgs IPen ITim NDro SPop WCre WHil XBar
- 'Skyliner' (Au/A) NDro
- 'Slack Top Red' (Au) NSla
- 'Sleeping Beauty' (Au/d) SPop
- 'Slim Whitman' (Au/A) MFie NDro NSum SPop
- 'Slioch' (Au/S) EWoo GAgs IPen NSum SPop WCre WHil XBar
- 'Slip Anchor' (Au/A) WAln
- 'Smart Tar' (Au/S) WAln
- 'Smoothy' (Au/St) SPop
- 'Snips' (Au/St) SPop
- 'Snooty Fox' (Au/A) GAbr IPen MFie SPop WCre
- 'Snooty Fox II' (Au/A) MFie NDro
- 'Snow Maiden' (Au/d) SPop WAln
- 'Snowball' (Au/d) **new** SPop
- 'Snowstorm' (Au/S) IPen NDro SPop
- 'Snowy Owl' (Au/S) GAbr IPen MFie NDro SPop WCre
- 'Snowy Ridge' (Au/B) WAln
- 'Solario' (Au/F) SPop WAln
- 'Solero' (Au/St) IPen SPop
- 'Soliloquy' (Au) NDro
- 'Somersby' (Au/d) IPen
- 'Soncy Face' (Au/A) MFie SPop WCre WHil
- 'Song of India' (Au/A) SPop
- 'Sonia Nicolle' (Au/B) NDro
- 'Sonny Boy' (Au/A) SPop WAln
- 'Sooty' (Au/d) IPen NDro SPop
- 'Sophie' (Au/d) MFie SPop WAln
- 'Sophie' (Au/A) NDro SPop
- 'South Barrow' (Au/d) GAbr GAgs SPop WCre WHil
- 'Southease Jane' (Au) WAln
- 'Southport' (Au) EWoo GAbr NDro
- 'Sparky' (Au/A) NDro WAln
- 'Spartan' (Au/A) SPop WAln
- 'Spitfire' (Au/S) MFie
- 'Spokey' (Au) IPen
- 'Spring Meadows' (Au/S) EWoo GAbr MAsh MFie NDro NEgg SPop WCre WHil
- 'Springtime' (Au/A) SPop
- 'Stafford Blue' (Au/B) **new** NDro
- 'Stant's Blue' (Au/S) IPen MFie NDro SPop WCre
- 'Star Spangle' (Au/St) NDro WCre
- 'Star Wars' (Au/S) EWoo GAbr GAgs MFie SPop WAln WCre WHil
- 'Star Wars II' (Au) MAsh
- 'Stardust' (Au/S) WCre
- 'Starlight' (Au/S) SPop
- 'Starling' (Au/B) EWoo GAbr IPen NDro SPop
- 'Starry' (Au/S) NDro
- 'Starsand' (Au/S) WAln WCre
- 'Stella' (Au/S) SPop
- 'Stella Coop' (Au/d) NDro WAln
- 'Stella North' (Au/A) SPop WAln
- 'Stella South' (Au/A) IPen SPop WCre
- 'Stetson' (Au/A) WAln
- 'Stoke Poges' (Au/A) NDro
- 'Stoney Cross' (Au/S) SPop WAln
- 'Stonnal' (Au/A) MFie SPop WHil
- 'Stormin' Norman' (Au/A) EWoo MFie NDro SPop WHil
- 'Stormy Cloud' (Au/B) WAln
- 'Stormy Weather' (Au/St) SPop WCre
- 'Strawberry Fields' (Au/S) NDro SPop WCre
- 'Stripe Tease' (Au/St) SPop
- 'Striped Ace' (Au/St) NDro SPop WCre
- 'Stripey' (Au/d) IPen
- 'Stromboli' (Au/d) EWoo GAbr GAgs MFie NDro SPop WCot WCre
- 'Stuart West' (Au/A) WCre
- 'Stubb's Tartan' (Au/S) MFie WAln
- 'Subliminal' (Au/A) NDro
- 'Sue' (Au/A) MFie SPop WCre
- 'Sue Ritchie' (Au/d) EWoo SPop
- 'Suede Shoes' (Au/S) SPop
- 'Sugar Plum Fairy' (Au/S) EWoo GAgs NDro NSum SPop WCre WHil
- 'Sultan' (Au/A) WAln
- 'Summer Sky' (Au/A) NDro SPop WCre
- 'Summer Wine' (Au/A) EWoo MFie NDro SPop
- 'Sumo' (Au/A) EWoo GAbr GAgs MFie NDro SPop WCre WHil
- 'Sunflower' (Au/A/S) EWoo GAbr GAgs ITim MAsh MFie NDro SPop WCre WHil
- 'Sunlight' (Au/A) WAln
- 'Sunlit Tiger' (Au/S) EWoo WAln
- 'Sunray' (Au/St) SPop

- 'Sunrise Beauty' (Au/S)	SPop
- 'Sunsplash' (Au)	WCre
- 'Sunspot' (Au/A)	EWoo IPen WAln
- 'Sunstar' (Au/S)	NDro NSum WCre
- 'Super Para' (Au/S)	EWoo GAbr GAgs GKev IPen MFie NDro SPop WCre WHil
- 'Superb' (Au/S)	MFie SPop WAln
- 'Surething' (Au/A)	WAln
- 'Susan' (Au/A)	GAbr MFie NDro SPop WCre
- 'Susannah' (Au/d)	EWoo GAgs GMaP IPen MFie NDro NSum SPop WCre WHil XBar
- 'Sweet Chestnut' (Au/S)	WAln
- 'Sweet Georgia Brown' (Au/A)	MFie NDro SPop WAln
- 'Sweet Pastures' (Au/S)	GAbr GAgs IPen MFie NDro SPop WCre
- 'Swiss Royal Velvet' (Au/B)	NDro
- 'Sword' (Au/d)	EWoo GAbr IPen MFie NDro NSum NWad SPop WCre XBar
- 'Symphony' (Au/A)	GAgs ITim MFie NDro SPop WCre WHil XBar
- 'T.A. Hadfield' (Au/A)	EWoo GAgs MFie NDro SPop WCre WHil
- 'Tachete' (Au/d)	XBar
- 'Taffeta' (Au/S)	EBee GAbr GAgs LCro LOPS NDro NSum SPop WCre WHil
- 'Tall Purple Dusty Miller' (Au/B)	SPop
- 'Tally-ho' (Au/A)	SPop WAln
- 'Tamar Gold' (Au/d)	SPop WAln WCre
- 'Tamar Mist' (Au)	WAln WHil
- 'Tamino' (Au/S)	IPen NDro SPop WAln
- 'Tango' (Au/d)	WAln
- 'Tarantella' (Au/A)	GAbr NDro NSum SPop WCre
- 'Tawny Owl' (Au/B)	GAbr
- 'Tay Tiger' (Au/St)	EWoo GAbr GAgs MFie NDro SPop WCre WHil XBar
- 'Taylor's Grey' (Au/S)	NDro SPop
- 'Teawell Pride' (Au/d)	EWoo ITim NHpl SPop WCre WHil
- 'Ted Gibbs' (Au/A)	EWoo MFie NDro SPop WCre WHil
- 'Ted Roberts' (Au/A)	EWoo ITim MFie NDro SPop WCre WHil
- 'Teem' (Au/S)	IPen NDro SPop WCre XBar
- 'Telesto' (Au/d)	SPop
- 'Telford's Surprise' (Au/A)	WAln
- 'Temeraire' (Au/A)	MFie SPop WHil
- 'Tenby Grey' (Au/S)	SPop WCre
- 'Tender Trap' (Au/A)	IPen WAln
- 'Terpo' (Au/A)	EWoo GAgs MFie WAln WCre WHil
- 'Tess' (Au/A)	XBar
- 'The Argylls' (Au/St)	SPop
- 'The Baron' (Au/S)	GAbr GAgs GKev IPen MFie SPop WCre WHil XBar
- 'The Bishop' (Au/S)	GAgs IPen ITim MFie SPop WAln WCre WHil XBar
- 'The Bride' (Au/S)	MFie NDro SPop WCre
- 'The Cardinal' (Au/d)	EWoo WAln
- 'The Czar' (Au/A)	NDro SPop WCre
- 'The Egyptian' (Au/A)	GAgs IPen MFie NDro SPop WCre WHil
- 'The Few' (Au/St)	SPop
- 'The Hobbit' (Au/A)	WAln
- 'The Lady Galadriel' (Au/A)	NDro
- 'The Maverick' (Au/S)	MFie SPop
- 'The President' (Au/d)	WAln
- 'The Raven' (Au/S)	EWoo GAbr GAgs ITim MFie SPop WCre WHil
- 'The Sneep' (Au/A)	EWoo GAgs IPen ITim MFie NDro SPop
- 'The Snods' (Au/S)	EWoo IPen MFie NDro SPop WCre
- 'The Wrekin' (Au/S)	SPop
I - 'Theodora' (Au/S)	XBar
- 'Thetis' (Au/A)	EWoo MFie SPop WCre
- 'Thisbe' (Au/A)	NDro
- 'Thou Swell' (Au/St)	SPop
- 'Three Way Stripe' (St)	EWoo GAbr GAgs WCre WHil
- 'Thutmoses' (Au/A)	NDro WAln
- 'Tiger Tim' (Au/St)	EWoo SPop WAln
- 'Tilley' (Au/d) **new**	SPop
- 'Tim' (Au)	GAbr IPen ITim NDro NSum SPop
- 'Timpany Blues'	ITim
- 'Tim's Fancy' (Au/S)	NDro WCre
- 'Tinker' (Au/S)	WAln
- 'Tinkerbell' (Au/S)	EWoo IPen MFie SPop WCre
- 'Tiptoe' (Au/St)	SPop WCre
- 'Titania' (Au)	SPop
- 'Toddington Green' (Au/S)	WAln
- 'Toffee Apple' (Au/d) **new**	NDro
- 'Toffee Crisp' (Au/A)	EWoo GAbr GAgs IPen NDro SPop XBar
- 'Toffee Nosed' (Au/St)	SPop
- 'Tom Farmer' (Au)	SPop WCre
- 'Tomboy' (Au/S)	EWoo IPen MFie NDro SPop WCre
- 'Tony Bray' (Au/A)	SPop
- 'Toolyn' (Au/S)	EWoo GAgs NDro SPop WAln
- 'Top Cat' (Au/d)	WAln
- 'Top Style' (Au/d)	SPop WAln
- 'Tosca' (Au/S)	CWCL GAbr GAgs IPen MAsh NSum SPop WCre WHil XBar
- 'Trafalgar Square' (Au/S)	EWoo GAbr GAgs MFie NDro SPop WCre
- 'Tregor Stripe' (Au/St)	XBar
- 'Trident' (Au/d)	WAln
- 'Trish' (Au)	GAbr
- 'Trojan' (Au/S)	EBee GKev IPen WCre
- 'Tromen' (Au/d) **new**	SPop
- 'Trouble' (Au/d)	EWoo GAbr IPen MFie NDro WCre WHil
- 'Troy Aykman' (Au/A)	MFie NDro SPop WAln
- 'Trudy' (Au/S)	EWoo GAbr GAgs IPen ITim NDro SPop WCre WHil
- 'True Briton' (Au/S)	IPen MFie NDro WCre
- 'Truman' (Au/B) **new**	NDro
- 'Trumpet Blue' (Au/S)	SPop WAln WHil
- 'Tudor Rose' (Au/S)	WAln
- 'Tumbledown' (Au/A)	EWoo IPen MFie NDro SPop
- 'Tummel' (Au/A)	EWoo GAbr GAgs NDro SPop WCre WHil
- 'Tupelo Honey' (Au/d)	WAln
- 'Turnberry' (Au/S)	SPop
- 'Turnbull' (Au/A)	IPen
- 'Tut Tut' (Au/A)	SPop
- 'Tweedy' (Au/St)	SPop
- 'Twiggy' (Au/S)	NDro NSum SPop
- 'Two Steeples' (Au/A)	SPop
- 'Typhoon' (Au/A)	EWoo GAgs IPen MFie SPop WHil
- 'Uncle Arthur' (Au/A)	MFie WAln WHil
- 'Unforgettable' (Au/A)	MFie
- 'Upper Crust' (Au/St)	SPop WCre
- 'Upton Belle' (Au/S)	IPen MFie NDro SPop WCre
- 'Ursula' (Au/d)	WAln
- 'Ushba' (Au/d)	SPop
- 'V2 Green' (Au/S)	WCre
- 'Valerie' (Au/A)	IPen ITim MFie SPop WCre
- 'Valerie Clare' (Au)	MFie SPop WAln WHil
- 'Valiant' (Au/A) **new**	WAln
- 'Vee Too' (Au/A)	GAbr MFie NDro SPop WCre WHil
- 'Vega' (Au/A)	EWoo SPop WAln
- 'Velvet Moon' (Au/A)	EWoo MFie NSum SPop WAln
- 'Velvet Truffles' (Au/d)	SPop

	- 'Venetian' (Au/A)	EWoo GAgs ITim MFie NDro SPop WHil
	- 'Venus' (Au/A)	WAln
	- 'Vera' (Au/A)	NSum SPop WAln
	- 'Vera Eden' (Au)	WAln
	- 'Vera Hill' (Au/A)	WAln
	- 'Verdi' (Au/A)	EWoo SPop WAln
	- 'Verity' (Au/S) **new**	SPop
	- 'Vesuvius' (Au/d)	EWoo IPen NDro SPop WCre
	- 'Victoria' (Au/S)	SPop WAln
	- 'Victoria de Wemyss' (Au/A)	IPen MFie NDro WCre XBar
	- 'Victoria Jane' (Au/A)	WAln
	- 'Victoria Park' (Au/A)	SPop WAln
	- 'Violet Surprise' (Au/St)	NDro
	- 'Vulcan' (Au/A)	MFie NBro NDro WCre XBar
	- 'Walhampton' (Au/S)	NDro SPop
	- 'Walmar' (Au/B)	WAln
	- 'Walter Lomas' (Au/S)	WAln
	- 'Walton' (Au/A)	EWoo GAbr GAgs IPen MFie NDro SPop WCre WHil XBar
	- 'Walton Heath' (Au/d)	EWoo GAbr GAgs IPen MFie NDro SPop WCot WCre
	- 'Waltz Time' (Au/A)	MFie
	- 'Wanda's Moonlight' (Au/d)	SPop WAln WCre
	- 'Warpaint' (Au/St)	NDro NSum
	- 'Warwick' (Au/S)	MFie SPop
	- 'Watchett' (Au/S)	SPop
	- 'Wayward' (Au/S)	WAln WCre
	- 'Wedding Day' (Au/S)	EWoo GAgs MFie SPop WCre
	- 'Wentworth' (Au/A)	IPen WAln
	- 'Wheal' (Au)	EWoo SPop
	- 'Whistlejacket' (Au/S)	MFie NDro SPop
	- 'White Ensign' (Au/S)	EWoo GAbr GAgs IPen ITim MFie NDro NWad SPop WCre WHil
	- 'White Pyne' (Au/B)	NDro
	- 'White Satin' (Au/S)	SPop WAln WCre
	- 'White Water' (Au/A)	EWoo ITim MFie NDro SPop WCre WHil
	- 'White Wings' (Au/S)	IPen ITim MFie NDro NHpl NSum SPop WCre
	- 'Whitecap' (Au/S)	WAln
	- 'Whoopee' (Au/A)	EWoo NDro WAln
	- 'Whorton's Claret' (Au/S)	WAln
	- 'Wichita Falls' (Au/A)	NDro WAln
	- 'Wide Awake' (Au/A)	EWoo GAgs MFie NDro SPop
	- 'Wild and Grey' (Au/S)	NDro
	- 'Wilf Booth' (Au/A)	GAgs MFie SPop
	- 'William Gunn' (Au/d)	MFie NDro SPop WAln WCre
	- 'Willow' (Au/d) **new**	SPop
	- 'Willow Tree' (Au/S)	WAln
	- 'Wincha' (Au/S)	ITim MFie NDro NEgg SPop WCre
	- 'Windward Blue' (Au)	NDro
	- 'Windways Mystery' (Au/B)	GAbr GAgs NDro NSum
	- 'Windways Pisces' (Au/d)	WAln
	- 'Windy Goldtop' (Au/A)	WAln
	- 'Winifrid' (Au/A)	EWoo GAbr MFie NDro SPop WCre WHil
	- 'Witchcraft' (Au)	IPen SPop
	- 'Woodlands Lilac' (Au/B)	NDro
	- 'Woodmill' (Au/A)	EWoo GAgs IPen MFie NDro NSum SPop WCre WHil XBar
	- 'Wookey Hole' (Au/A)	MFie NDro SPop
	- 'Wor Jackie' (Au/S)	SPop
	- 'Wycliffe Harmony' (Au/B)	NDro
	- 'Wycliffe Midnight' (Au/B)	GAbr ITim NDro WAln
	- 'Wye Hen' (Au/St)	SPop WAln
	- 'Wye Lemon' (Au/S)	EWoo SPop
	- 'X2' (Au)	GAgs WHil
	- 'Xavier' (Au)	EBee
	- 'Yacoubi' (Au/A)	SPop
	- 'Yellow Ace' (Au)	GAbr
	- 'Yellow Border' (Au/B)	WCre
	- 'Yellow Hammer' (Au/S)	WAln
	- 'Yellow Isle' (Au/S)	WAln
	- 'Yellow Muff' (Au/S)	WAln
	- 'Yellow Ribbon'	WAln
	- 'Yes Indeed' (Au/St)	SPop
	- 'Yitzhak Rabin' (Au/A)	IPen NDro SPop WHil
	- 'Yorkshire Grey' (Au/S)	GAbr IPen NDro SPop WCre
	- 'Ypres' (Au/d)	SPop
	- 'Zambia' (Au/d)	EWoo GAbr IPen ITim NDro WCre
	- 'Ziggy' (Au/St)	SPop
	- 'Zimmer' (Au/St)	EWoo SPop WCre
	- 'Zircon' (Au/S)	SPop WAln
	- 'Zodiac' (Au/S)	WAln
	- 'Zoe' (Au/A)	SPop WAln
	- 'Zoe Ann' (Au/S)	WAln
I	- 'Zona' (Au/A)	NDro
	- 'Zorro' (Au/St)	WAln
	auriculata (Or)	EPot GKev SVic
	- subsp. ***olgae*** (Or)	GKev
	balbisii (Au)	GKev
	'Barbara Midwinter' (Pr)	CJun EBee GAbr GEdr MArt NHar NWad SHar WCot
	Barnhaven Blues Group (Pr/Prim)	MFie NCGa NSum XBar
	Barnhaven doubles (Pr/Prim/d)	XBar
	Barnhaven Gold-laced Group	see *P.* Gold-laced Group Barnhaven
	Barnhaven hybrids	NSum
	'Beatrice Wooster' (Au)	GAbr IPen LRHS MFie NRHS
	'Beeches' Pink'	GAbr GEdr NHar NSum NWad
	beesiana (Pf) Υ^{H6}	Widely available
	(Belarina Series) Belarina Amethyst Ice = 'Kerbelpicotee'^{PBR} (Pr/Prim/d)	MFie MHol NCGa WHil
	- Belarina Butter Yellow = 'Kerbelbut'^{PBR} (Pr/Prim/d)	CWCL ELon EPfP MFie NCGa NLar SPer SRot WHil WTor
	- Belarina Buttermilk = 'Kerbelmilk'^{PBR} (Pr/Prim/d)	NLar
	- Belarina Cobalt Blue = 'Kerbelcob'^{PBR} (Pr/Prim/d)	CAby ELon MFie NHpl NLar SPer SRot WHil WTor
	- Belarina Cream = 'Kerbelcrem'^{PBR} (Pr/Prim/d)	CAby CWCL ELon MFie NCGa NHpl SPer SRot WBor WHil WTor
	- Belarina Pink Ice = 'Kerbelpice'^{PBR} (Pr/Prim/d)	CWCL ELon MFie NCGa NHpl NLar SPer WBor WHil
	- Belarina Rosette Nectarine = 'Kerbelnec'^{PBR} (Pr/Prim/d)	CWCL ECtt ELon MFie MHol NCGa NLar SPer WHil WTor
	- Belarina Valentine = 'Kerbelred'^{PBR} (Pr/Prim/d)	CAby CWCL LLHF MFie MHol NCGa NLar WBor WHil WTor
	bellidifolia (Mu)	GKev IPen NGdn
	beluensis	see *P.* × *pubescens* 'Freedom'
	× ***berninae*** (Au)	WCre
§	- 'Windrush' (Au)	WAbe
	'Bewerley White'	see *P.* × *pubescens* 'Bewerley White'
	bileckii	see *P.* × *forsteri* 'Bileckii'
	'Blarney Castle Blush' **new**	NPnk

'Blarney Castle Pink' **new**	NPnk
'Blarney Castle Red' **new**	NPnk
'Blindsee' (Au)	CTal MFie NHar
blinii (Y)	EHrv EPot GKev LLHF
- SDR 7868 **new**	GKev
- SDR 7949 **new**	GKev
'Blue Ice' (Pr/Prim/d) **new**	XBar
'Blue Julianas' (Pr)	MFie NCGa NSum XBar
'Blue Riband' (Pr/Prim)	LLHF NWad SIgm
'Blue Ribbon'	WFar
'Blue Sapphire' (Pr/Prim/d)	GBin WHil XBar
'Bon Accord Cerise' (Pr/Poly/d)	GAbr
'Bon Accord Purple' (Pr/Poly/d)	WRHF
boothii subsp. ***repens*** (Pe)	GKev MNrw
'Boothman's Ruby'	see *P.* × *pubescens* 'Boothman's Variety'
bracteata (Bu)	GKev WAbe
- BOA 305 **new**	GKev
- HOLUB 2002 **new**	GKev
§ - subsp. ***dubernardiana*** (Bu)	GKev WAbe
§ ***bracteosa*** (Pe)	ITim
brevicula (Cy) SDR 4452	GKev
'Broadwell Chameleon' (Au)	ITim
'Broadwell Milkmaid' (Au) $\mathbb{Y}^{H5}$	CPBP IPen ITim MFie WAbe
'Broadwell Oliver' (Au)	IPen
'Broadwell Pink' (Au)	IPen
'Broadwell Ruby' (Au)	CPBP ITim WAbe
'Broadwell Snowstorm' (Au)	CPBP ITim
'Broadwell Violet'	IPen
'Broxbourne' $\mathbb{Y}^{H5}$	ITim MFie
'Buckland Wine' (Pr/Prim)	CElw CFis GAbr GEdr
× ***bulleesiana*** (Pf)	CAby CBot CDor CSta CWCL EPfP EWTr GBuc GKev GWyn LPot LRHS MCot MFie MWts NBro NChi NEgg NGdn NHol NLar NSum SAko SWat WFar WHar WMoo WPnP
- Moerheim hybrids (Pf)	GAbr
bulleyana (Pf) $\mathbb{Y}^{H7}$	Widely available
- ACE 2484	SWat
- SDR 4261	GKev
- hybrids (Pf)	GKev
burmanica (Pf)	CPla GBuc GKev IPen MMuc SWat WMoo
- SDR 5801	GKev
'Butter's Bronze' (Pr/Prim)	WOut
'Butterscotch' (Pr/Prim)	NCGa NSum XBar
'Caerulea Plena' (Pr/Prim)	NBid
calderiana subsp. ***calderiana*** (Pe)	GKev
- subsp. ***strumosa*** (Pe)	GKev
'Camaieu' (Pr/Prim/d) **new**	XBar
Candelabra hybrids (Pf)	CBre CHVG ECho GAbr IPen ITim LSou MFie NBir NGdn NHpl SWat WOut
'Candy Parade' (Pr)	WHil
Candy Pinks Group (Pr/Prim)	NCGa NSum XBar
capitata (Ca)	CMac ECho EMFm EPfP GKev IBoy IPen LRHS NHpl SCob SPer WCot
- CC 3843	GKev
- CC 6536B	GKev
- subsp. ***capitata*** (Ca)	IBoy
- subsp. ***mooreana*** (Ca)	CAby CHid CLAP CLet CSta CTsd ECho EDAr EPfP EWTr GKev IPen NGdn NHpl NSum SPlb SRot WAbe WHil XBar
- 'Norverna Blue' (Ca)	MHol
- 'Noverna Deep Blue' (Ca)	LRHS SHil
- 'Salvana'	EBee
- subsp. ***sphaerocephala*** (Ca) $\mathbb{Y}^{H5}$	GKev
'Captain Blood' (Pr/Prim/d)	NHpl SIgm
Carnation Victorians Group (Pr/Poly)	XBar
carniolica (Au)	GKev WCot
cernua (Mu)	GKev IPen LLHF NSum XBar
'Charlotte' (Pr/Prim)	IPen
Chartreuse Group (Pr/Poly)	MFie XBar
'Cheshire Life'	CMea
§ ***chionantha*** (Cy) $\mathbb{Y}^{H6}$	CLAP CSta ECho GBuc GCra GEdr GKev MFie NBir NCGa NGdn NLar NSum
- SDR 4426	GKev
- subsp. ***chionantha*** (Cy)	GBuc GKev IPen MHol
- subsp. ***melanops***	see *P. melanops*
§ - subsp. ***sinoplantaginea*** (Cy)	NLar
§ - subsp. ***sinopurpurea*** (Cy)	CLAP CSta EBee EPfP EWld GBuc GKev IPen NBir NCGa NSum
- - SDR 4418	GKev
chungensis (Pf)	CBod CDor CLAP CSta EBee ELon EPfP GBin GCra GKev GLog GWyn IBoy IKil IPen MHol MNrw NGdn NHol NLar NSum SWvt WMAq WMoo XBar
§ ***chungensis*** × ***pulverulenta*** (Pf)	CHid GKev SAko
× ***chunglenta***	see *P. chungensis* × *pulverulenta*
'Cisca'	GEdr WCot
'Clarence Elliott' (Au) $\mathbb{Y}^{H5}$	CPBP GKev IPen MFie MPnt NHar NRya NWad WThu
'Clarissa White' (Pr/Poly)	XBar
clarkei (Or)	WAbe
clusiana (Au)	WAbe
- 'Murray-Lyon' (Au)	NDro
cockburniana (Pf) $\mathbb{Y}^{H6}$	CPne GAbr GKev GQui IPen SWat WCot XBar
- SDR 1967	EBee
- SDR 5952	GKev
- hybrids (Pf)	SWat
- 'Kevock Sunshine' (Pf)	EBee GKev IPen
concholoba (Mu)	GEdr GKev XBar
'Corporal Baxter' (Pr/Prim/d)	ECtt EPfP EWTr LLHF
cortusoides (Co)	CLAP EPfP GCra GKev IPen
'Cottage Cream'	SVic
Cowichan Amethyst Group (Pr/Poly)	CWCL MFie NCGa XBar
Cowichan Blue Group (Pr/Poly)	MFie NCGa NSum XBar
Cowichan Garnet Group (Pr/Poly)	MFie NCGa NSum XBar
Cowichan strain (Pr/Poly)	CElw CHVG
Cowichan Venetian Group (Pr/Poly)	CHVG MFie NCGa NSum XBar
Cowichan Yellow Group (Pr/Poly)	MFie NCGa NSum XBar
'Coy' (Au)	ITim
'Craddock White' (Pr/Prim)	CFis GEdr
'Craven Gem' (Pr/Poly)	GBuc
Crescendo Series (Pr/Poly)	MMuc
'Crimson Velvet' (Au)	IPen WThu XBar
crispa	see *P. glomerata*

cuneifolia GKev
subsp. ***heterodonta*** (Cu)
daonensis (Au) GKev
darialica (Al) LLHF
'Dark Rosaleen' (Pr/Poly) Widely available
'David Valentine' (Pr) CFis GAbr GBuc GEdr WCot XBar
'Dawn Ansell' (Pr/Prim/d) CBod ECtt EPfP GAbr GBuc GMaP IBoy MBNS MHol MRav NBir NCGa NHpl NPnk NSum WCAu WHer WHil XBar
Daybreak Group (Pr/Poly) CWCL MFie NCGa XBar
deflexa (Mu) IPen
denticulata (De) ♀H5 Widely available
- CC 4629 GKev
- var. ***alba*** (De) CAby CBcs CTri EBee ECha ECho EPfP GAbr GCra GMaP GWyn LRHS LSun MBel MFie MMuc NGdn NLar NPnk NPri SCob SGbt SPer SPoG WBor WFar WGwG WMoo WWtn
- blue-flowered (De) CWCL EPfP GAbr GBin GWyn LLWG NLar NPri WBor
- 'Bressingham Beauty' (De) EBee LRHS
- var. ***cachemiriana*** hort. (De) EWTr GKev
- 'Glenroy Crimson' (De) CLAP EBee LLHF
- hybrids SCob WFar XBar
- 'Karryann' (De/v) WCot
- lavender-flowered (De) CAby
- lilac-flowered (De) ECho LRHS NHol SCob WTor
- purple-flowered (De) WMoo
- red-flowered (De) CAby ECho EPfP MFie NBir SCob WMoo
- 'Robinson's Red' (De) GBuc
- 'Rubin' (De) CWCL CWat EBee GAbr GMaP LLWG LRHS MBrN NChi NLar NRHS SPer SPoG SRms XLum
- 'Rubinball' (De) NHol WCot
deorum (Au) GKev
× ***deschmannii*** see *P.* × *vochinensis*
'Desert Sunset' (Pr/Poly) NCGa XBar
'Devon Cream' (Pr/Prim) GBuc
dickieana (Am) GKev
'Don Keefe'[PBR] CHVG CMHG EBee ECtt ELon GAbr GBin GMcL LLHF MBNS MBel MFie MHol MMuc MNrw MPie NGdn NHar NHpl NLar NPnk NWad SCob WCot WFar WMoo
'Dorothy' (Pr/Poly) MRav
'Double Lilac' see *P. vulgaris* 'Lilacina Plena'
dubernardiana see *P. bracteata* subsp. *dubernardiana*
'Duchess of York' (Pr/Poly) GAbr GEdr LLHF LLWP MHCG NLar WCot
'Duckyls Red' (Pr/Prim) WHal
'Dusky Lady' CLAP
'Early Bird' (*allionii* hybrid) (Au) EPot IPen ITim MFie XBar
'Easter Bonnet' (Pr/Prim) LRHS MMuc SEND
edgeworthii see *P. nana*
§ ***elatior*** (Pr) ♀H5 CArn CBod CDor CMac CPla ECho EWoo GKev GMaP MArt MBel MHer MHol MNHC MNrw NChi NEgg NLar SPer SPoG SWvt WBod WBrk WCot
- SDR 5439 GKev
- hose-in-hose (Pr/d) NBid
- hybrids (Pr) EPfP SPlb
- 'Magnifica' (Pr) GKev
§ - subsp. ***meyeri*** (Pr) GKev LLHF
- subsp. ***pallasii*** (Pr) GKev
- subsp. ***pseudoelatior*** (Pr) ITim WAbe
'Elizabeth Browning' GAbr WCot
'Elizabeth Killelay'[PBR] (Pr/Poly/d) CBct CBod CCVN CDor CWCL CWGN ECtt ELan GBin GBuc IBoy MMuc MNrw MPie NBir NEgg NGdn NHar NHpl NLar NPnk NSti NSum NWad SPer SPoG WCot WFar
'Ellen Page' (Au) MFie
'Elpino' CBod
erratica (De) GKev
'Ethel Barker' (Au) IPen MFie NWad
'Eugénie' (Pr/Prim/d) ECtt MRav NCGa WHil
faberi (Am) GKev
'Fairy Rose' (Au) IPen NWad
farinosa (Al) GKev IPen NGdn SIgm
fasciculata (Ar) GKev SPlb
- CLD 345 GEdr WAbe
- SDR 3092 GKev
'Feuerkönig' (Au) NDro
'Fire Dance' (Pr/Poly) MFie
'Fire Opal' LRHS
Firefly Group (Pr/Poly) CWCL MFie NCGa WCot XBar
§ ***firmipes*** (Si) GKev IPen LPot
§ ***flaccida*** (Mu) ECho GEdr GKev IPen NHar NHpl NSum WAbe XBar
- Cox 14026 GKev
- SDR 7980 **new** GKev
Flamingo Group (Pr/Poly) XBar
florindae (Si) ♀H7 Widely available
- bronze-flowered (Si) GQui NBir
- 'Dave's Red' (Si) LEdu
- hybrids (Si) CMac EHrv EShb GAbr GMaP NCGa WFar WHar WHil WWtn XBar
- Keillour hybrids (Si) CLAP IBoy NGdn NLar SWvt WBor
- 'Muadh' (Si) MMuc
- orange-flowered (Si) CSam GPSL IPen LLWG MNrw WMoo
- peach-flowered (Si) CSpe
- 'Ray's Ruby' (Si) CLAP GBuc GEdr MNrw NBir WCot WMoo
- red and copper hybrids (Si) CAby MWts SWvt WHoo
- red-flowered (Si) CSpe GBin GKev GPSL IPen LLWG MMuc NBid NLar NSum WFar
- terracotta-flowered (Si) NGdn
Footlight Parade Group (Pr/Prim) XBar
forrestii (Bu) GKev IPen WAbe
- SDR 3304 GKev
- SDR 7839 GKev
§ × ***forsteri*** (Au) NHpl NLar
§ - 'Bileckii' (Au) ECho GMaP LLHF NBir NHar NSla
- 'Dianne' (Au) ECho EDAr GAbr GCrg GKev LLHF NBro NRya WAbe WThu
- 'Dianne' hybrids (Au) NHar
'Francisca' (Pr/Poly) Widely available
'Fred Salter' ITim NRya
frondosa (Al) ♀H5 ECho GKev IPen MFie MHol MPnt
Fuchsia Victorians Group (Pr/Poly) CWCL NCGa XBar
'Gareth' (Pr/Poly) GEdr
'Garnet' (*allionii* hybrid) (Au) MFie XBar
'Garryarde Crimson' GEdr LLHF
'Garryarde Guinevere' see *P.* 'Guinevere'
gemmifera (Ar) ECho GKev LLHF
geraniifolia (Co) CLAP GCra
'Gigha' (Pr/Prim) CLAP GKev MNrw XBar
'Gilded Ginger' NCGa XBar
'Ginger Spice' (Au) NDro
§ ***glomerata*** (Ca) GKev IPen XBar
'Glowing Embers' (Pf) GKev NBir

	glutinosa All.	see *P. allionii*
	Gold-laced Group (Pr/Poly)	Widely available
§	- Barnhaven (Pr/Poly)	GBuc MFie NBir XBar
	- Beeches strain (Pr/Poly)	CWCL IPen XBar
	- red-flowered (Pr/Poly)	IPen XEll
	'Gold-laced Jack in the Green' Barnhaven	XBar
	gracilipes (Pe)	CLAP
	- 'Major'	see *P. bracteosa*
	- 'Minor'	see *P. petiolaris* Wall.
	graminifolia	see *P. chionantha*
	Grand Canyon Group (Pr/Poly)	CWCL NCGa XBar
	grandis (Sr)	GKev IPen XBar
	'Green Lace' (Pr/Poly)	ECtt NHpl
	'Groenekan's Glorie' (Pr/Prim)	CFis GAbr GBuc GEdr NBir NSum
§	'Guinevere' (Pr/Poly) ♀H6	Widely available
	'Hall Barn Blue' (Pr/Prim)	CSam CSpe ECho GEdr GMaP MHCG MMuc NHar SEND WCot
§	***halleri*** (Al)	GKev IPen MFie XBar
	- 'Longiflora'	see *P. halleri*
	- subsp. ***platyphylla*** **new**	GKev
	handeliana	GKev
	Harbinger Group (Pr/Prim)	CWCL MFie XBar
	Harbour Lights mixture (Pr/Poly)	CWCL NCGa XBar
	Harlow Car hybrids (Pf)	CRos EPfP GQui LRHS NCGa NRHS NWad SPer SPoG WMoo
	Harvest Yellows Group (Pr/Poly)	CWCL XBar
	helodoxa	see *P. prolifera*
	'Hemswell Blush' (Au)	GKev LLHF MFie NHar NHpl WCre
	'Hemswell Ember' (Au)	CPBP
	'Heritage Cream' (Pr/Prim)	CBod
	heucherifolia (Co)	IPen
	- SDR 3224	GKev
	- SDR 7877 **new**	GKev
	hidakana (R)	GEdr
	'High Point' (Au)	MFie
	hirsuta (Au)	GKev IPen MMuc SEND
	- 'Lismore Snow' (Au)	NHar NWad
	- red-flowered (Au)	EBee
	- white-flowered (Au) **new**	NRya
	- white-flowered × ***pedemontana*** 'Alba'	EPot
	hirsuta* × *minima	see *P.* × *forsteri*
	hoffmanniana	NHar NSum
	hose-in-hose (Pr/Poly/d)	MNrw
	hose-in-hose, Barnhaven (Pr/Poly)	XBar
	'Hyacinthia' (Au)	IPen MFie
	ianthina	see *P. prolifera*
	'Ilana'	IPen
	Indian Reds Group (Pr/Poly)	CWCL MFie NCGa WHil XBar
	'Ingram's Blue' (Pr/Poly)	EPfP MHol
	Inshriach hybrids (Pf)	CAby CMHG IBoy
	integrifolia (Au)	GKev
§	'Inverewe' (Pf) ♀H5	GBuc GCra GKev GQui NBir NHpl XBar
	involucrata	see *P. munroi*
	ioessa (Si)	GCra GKev IPen
	- var. ***hopeana*** (Si)	GKev
	'Iris Mainwaring' (Pr/Prim)	CFis ECtt GCra GEdr LLHF MCot
	irregularis (Pe)	ITim WAbe
	'Jackie Richards' (Au)	CTal GKev MFie
	Jack-in-the-Green Group (Pr/Poly)	CLAP CWCL MNrw WBor WMoo
	- Barnhaven (Pr/Poly)	XBar
	- red-flowered (Pr/Poly)	MMuc WHil
	- white-flowered (Pr/Poly)	IFro
	'Janet Aldrich' (Au)	CPBP
	japonica (Pf)	CMHG CSam ECha GQui IPen LRHS MSCN NBro NGdn SWat WMoo
	- 'Alba' (Pf)	CAby CBod CHVG CSta CTri ECho EPfP EShb EWoo GBuc GMcL IPen LRHS MBel MFie NGdn NWad SPer WFar
	- 'Apple Blossom' (Pf)	Widely available
*	- 'Atropurpurea' (Pf)	IPen
	- 'Carminata' (Pf)	IPen
*	- 'Carminea' (Pf)	CDor GKev IPen MFie MSCN NBro NCGa NGdn NWad WFar WRHF WWtn
	- 'Cherry Red' (Pf)	IPen
	- 'Cleo' (Pf)	IPen
	- 'Fuji' (Pf)	EBee NBro
	- 'Holly' (Pf)	IPen
	- hybrids (Pf)	CMac GCra MFie MRav WFar
	- 'Jim Saunders' (Pf)	SLon
	- 'Miller's Crimson' (Pf) ♀H6	Widely available
	- 'Oriental Sunrise' (Pf)	EHrv GBuc GKev IPen NCGa XBar
	- pale pink-flowered (Pf)	ITim NSum
	- 'Peninsula Pink' (Pf)	IPen
	- 'Pinkie' (Pf)	IPen
	- 'Postford White' (Pf) ♀H6	Widely available
	- 'Purpurascens' (Pf)	IPen
	- Redfield strain (Pf)	IPen
	- red-flowered (Pf)	IPen
	- 'Splendens' (Pf)	IPen
	- 'Valley Red' (Pf)	GKev IPen ITim
	- violet-flowered (Pf) **new**	GKev
	'Jay-Jay' (Pr)	GAbr
	jesoana (Co)	GKev LLHF
	- B&SWJ 618	WCru
	- var. ***pubescens*** (Co)	GKev
	'Jewel' (Pr)	GAbr
	'Joan Hughes' (*allionii* hybrid) (Au)	WAbe
	'Joanna'	GBuc MPnt
	'Johanna' (Pu)	GAbr GCrg GKev NGdn NHar NPnk NSum
	'John Fielding' (Pr)	CAby CBro CElw EBee NWad
	'Jo-Jo' (Au)	CTal EPot ITim MFie XBar
	'Jubilee' (Pr/Prim/d)	LCro
	juliae (Pr)	ECho EDAr GCrg LRHS NBid NHar NPnk NRHS NSum SPlb
I	- 'Millicent' (Pr)	WCot
	- white-flowered (Pr)	NSum
	'Ken Dearman' (Pr/Prim/d)	ECtt MRav NBir NHpl XBar
	kewensis (Sp) ♀H2	GKev XBar
	kialensis (Y)	WAbe
	'Kingscote' (Au) **new**	NDro
	'Kinlough Beauty' (Pr/Poly)	CFis ECtt GBuc GMaP LLHF NPnk XBar
§	***kisoana*** (Co)	CLAP GEdr GKev IPen LLHF WCru
	- var. ***alba*** (Co)	GEdr NHar XBar
	- 'Iyo-beni' (Co)	GEdr NHar XBar
	- 'Noushoku'	GEdr
	- var. ***shikokiana***	see *P. kisoana*
	'Koblenz' (Au)	NHar
	komarovii (Pr)	LEdu SPlb
	'Kusum Krishna'	CBod EBee GEdr MArt MBNS MHol MPie NHar NHpl NSti NWad WCot WFar
	'Lady Greer' (Pr/Poly) ♀H5	CBod CMac CSam CTal EBee ECtt EPfP GAbr GBuc GEdr GKev GMaP LHop LLWP MCot MHer NChi NGdn NHar NLar NSum SIgm WHea XBar

'Lambrook Mauve' (Pr/Poly)	CElw CFis
§ ***latifolia*** (Au)	GKev
latisecta (Co)	IPen
§ ***laurentiana*** (Al)	GKev
'Lea Gardens' (*allionii* hybrid) (Au)	IPen MFie NWad
'Lee Myers' (*allionii* hybrid) (Au)	IPen MFie XBar
'Lemon and Lime'	CMea
leucophylla	see *P. elatior*
'Lilac Domino' (Au)	IPen
lilacina	IPen
'Lilian Foster'	MArt WCot
limbata (Cy)	GKev
'Lindum Angelic' (Au)	NHar
'Lindum Aria' (Au)	NHar
'Lindum Buttermilk' (Au)	IPen
'Lindum Celebration' (Au)	NHar
'Lindum Crepes Suzette' (Au)	IPen ITim MFie NHar
'Lindum Finale' (Au)	IPen ITim
'Lindum First Kiss'	IPen ITim
'Lindum Frosty Moon'	IPen ITim
'Lindum Gecko' (Au)	NHar
'Lindum Lace'	IPen
'Lindum Lancelot' (Au)	NHar
'Lindum Lavender Mist'	MFie
'Lindum Limelight' **new**	ITim
'Lindum Lyric' (Au)	NHar
'Lindum Malcolm's Mate'	CPBP IPen
'Lindum Moonlight'	CPBP IPen LLHF MFie
'Lindum Morning Flight' (Au)	NHar
'Lindum Pixie'	IPen
'Lindum Rapture' (Au)	IPen
'Lindum Rhapsody'	LLHF
'Lindum Serenade' (Au)	IPen
'Lindum Smoke'	IPen NHar
'Lindum Snowball' (Au)	NHar
'Lindum Snowdrift' (Au)	IPen
'Lindum Storm Cloud' (Au)	NHar
'Lindum Wedgwood' (Au)	EPot IPen ITim MFie NHar
'Lingwood Beauty' (Pr/Prim)	CAby CElw CFis CSam GAbr
'Lipstick'	CHid
'Lismore' (Au)	NWad
'Lismore Bay' (Au)	GKev
'Lismore Peardrop' (Au)	EPot
'Lismore Pink Ice' (Au)	NWad WThu
'Lismore Sunshine'	NHar WThu
'Lismore Treasure' (Au)	CPBP MFie
'Lismore Yellow' (Au)	CPBP NHar
Lissadel hybrids (Pf)	NLar
'Little Egypt' (Pr/Poly)	CWCL NCGa XBar
littoniana	see *P. vialii*
'Lizzie Green' (Pr/Prim)	NLar
'Loisach'	NHar
× ***loiseleurii*** 'Aire Mist' (Au) 🏆H5	EPot IPen ITim NHar NHpl NRya NSla NSum NWad WAbe WThu XBar
§ – 'Aire Waves' (Au)	CWCL ITim NHar NRya NWad
– 'Pink Aire Mist' (Au)	ITim
– 'White Waves' (Au)	IPen
longiflora	see *P. halleri*
longipes (Cy)	GKev
luteola (Or)	ECho GKev LLHF NGdn NHpl NSum
macrocalyx	see *P. veris*
macrophylla (Cy)	GAbr GKev
'MacWatt's Claret' (Pr/Poly)	ECho GAbr GBuc LLWP SBch
'MacWatt's Cream' (Pr/Poly)	CFis CRos EBee EWTr GCra GEdr LLHF LRHS NHar NLar NRHS WCot WHil
magellanica (Al)	GKev SPlb WAbe
mairei (Al)	GKev
– SDR 7967 **new**	GKev
'Maisie Michael'	GEdr LLHF WAbe
marginata (Au) 🏆H5	CPne CTal ECho EWoo IPen LHop LRHS MFie MMuc NRHS NSla NSum SBch SEND WAbe
– 'Adrian Evans' (Au)	GEdr GKev SBch
– 'Alba' (Au)	LRHS MFie NBro NRHS NRya NWad XBar
– 'Ardfearn' (Au)	GEdr
– 'Arthur Branch' (Au)	MFie
– 'Baldock's Purple' (Au)	IPen NRya
– 'Barbara Clough' (Au)	GEdr IPen MFie NRya NWad XBar
– 'Beamish' (Au) 🏆H5	GEdr NBro NRya NSla NWad
– 'Beatrice Lascaris' (Au)	CTal GEdr MFie NRya WAbe
– 'Caerulea' (Au)	ITim MFie NRya NWad
– 'Clear's Variety' (Au)	IPen ITim LLHF
– 'Doctor Jenkins' (Au)	IPen ITim NRya NWad
– 'Dolomites' (Au)	NWad
– 'Drake's Form' (Au)	ECho IPen ITim NLar NRya XBar
– dwarf (Au)	ECho GEdr LRHS MFie NRHS NRya
– 'Earl L. Bolton'	see *P. marginata* 'El Bolton'
§ – 'El Bolton' (Au)	IPen NRya NWad
– 'Elizabeth Fry' (Au)	IPen MFie
– 'Grandiflora' (Au)	IPen NWad
– 'Highland Twilight' (Au)	IPen NSla
– 'Holden Variety' (Au)	IPen ITim MFie NRya NWad
– 'Holly Leaf' (Au)	GEdr
– 'Ivy Agee' (Au)	IPen NRya
– 'Janet' (Au)	ECho GEdr LLHF NWad
– 'Jenkins Variety' (Au)	ECho
– 'Johannes Holler' (Au)	ITim NRya
– 'Kesselring's Variety' (Au)	CMea ECho IPen ITim LLHF MFie NWad
– 'Laciniata' (Au)	ECho IPen LRHS NRHS
– 'Lemon Sorbet' (Au)	IPen ITim
– lilac-flowered (Au)	IPen
– 'Linda Pope' (Au) 🏆H5	ECho GEdr IPen NBir NHar NSum WAbe WThu XBar
– maritime form (Au)	IPen XBar
– 'Millard's Variety' (Au)	IPen ITim NWad
– 'Miss Fell' (Au)	IPen
– 'Mrs Carter Walmsley' (Au)	NRya NWad
– 'Mylene' (Au) **new**	NRya
– 'Napoleon' (Au)	GEdr IPen ITim MFie NRya NWad
– pale blue-flowered (Au) **new**	XBar
– 'Peggy Fell' (Au)	NWad
– 'Prichard's Variety' (Au) 🏆H5	ECho GEdr GPSL IPen ITim LLHF MFie NRya WAbe
– 'Rosea' (Au)	IPen
– 'Rubra' (Au)	ITim
– 'Sheila Denby' (Au)	IPen NRya NWad
– 'The President' (Au)	NWad
– violet-flowered (Au)	ECho
– 'Waithman's Variety' (Au)	IPen NRya NWad
– wild-collected (Au)	MFie
'Maria Talbot' (*allionii* hybrid) (Au)	CTal IPen
'Marianne Davey' (Pr/Prim/d)	WKif
Marine Blues Group (Pr/Poly)	CWCL NSum XBar
'Maris Tabard' (Au)	EPot IPen MFie XBar
'Mars' (*allionii* hybrid) (Au)	IPen MFie NWad XBar
'Marven' (Au)	IPen ITim

	'Mascara Blue' (Pr)	SVic
	Mauve Victorians Group (Pr/Poly)	MFie NCGa XBar
	maximowiczii (Cy)	ECho EDAr GBin GEdr IPen LLHF NGdn NHar NSum WHil
§	- var. ***maximowiczii*** (Cy)	GBuc GKev IPen MFie NHpl
	- Red-flowered Group	see *P. maximowiczii* var. *maximowiczii*
	megaseifolia (Pr)	GBuc GKev IPen
	melanantha (Cy)	GKev
	- 'Moonshine' (Cy) **new**	EBee GKev
	- 'Nightglow' (Cy)	GKev
I	- 'Stardust' (Cy)	GKev
§	***melanops*** (Cy)	EPot
	'Melenoc'h' (Pr/Prim/d)	XBar
§	× ***meridiana*** 'Miniera' (Au)	IPen MFie
	Midnight Group	CHVG CWCL XBar
	'Mike Smith'	IPen
	'Millstream Cream' **new**	NLar
	'Miniera'	see *P.* × *meridiana* 'Miniera'
	minima (Au)	NBro WAbe
	- var. ***alba*** (Au)	NHar
	minima × ***wulfeniana***	see *P.* × *vochinensis*
	'Miss Doris' (Pr/Prim/d)	XBar
	'Miss Indigo' (Pr/Prim/d)	CAby CTsd CWCL ECtt EPfP GMaP MBNS MFie MHol MRav NHpl NPnk NSum SPer WCAu WMoo XBar
	mistassinica (Al)	CPne GKev
	- var. ***macropoda***	see *P. laurentiana*
	miyabeana (Pf)	GKev IPen
	modesta (Al)	XBar
	- var. ***faurieae*** (Al)	IPen
	'Moerheimii'	GEdr
	monticola	GKev
	'Moorland Apricot'	WMoo
	moupinensis (Pe) Υ^{H4}	LLHF
	- subsp. ***barkamensis*** (Pe)	GKev
	'Mrs Eagland'	GAbr
	'Mrs Frank Neave' (Pr/Prim)	GAbr GEdr IPen
§	***munroi*** (Ar)	GKev IPen MFie NHar SIgm WAbe XBar
	- white-flowered (Ar)	WAbe
§	- subsp. ***yargongensis*** (Ar)	EBee GEdr GKev IPen MFie
	- - SDR 3096	GKev
	- - SDR 6121	GKev
	muscarioides (Mu)	IPen
	Muted Victorians Group (Pr/Poly)	NCGa NSum XBar
	'Myline'	WThu
§	***nana*** (Pe)	IPen
	nepalensis	see *P. tanneri* subsp. *nepalensis*
	'Netta Dennis' (Pe)	LLHF NHar
	New Pinks Group (Pr/Poly)	NCGa NSum XBar
	'Nightingale'	ITim
	nivalis Pallas	see *P. chionantha*
	nivalis ambig.	NSum
	nutans Delavay ex Franch.	see *P. flaccida*
	obconica (Ob) Υ^{H1c}	GKev
	- subsp. ***werringtonensis*** **new**	GKev
	'Oberau'	IPen
	obtusifolia (Cy)	GKev
	'Old Port' (Pr/Poly)	CAby CSam EBee GEdr NSum
	Old Rose Victorians Group (Pr/Poly)	NCGa NSum XBar
	optata (Cy)	GKev
	orbicularis (Cy)	ECho GEdr GKev LLHF NHpl
	Osiered Amber Group (Pr/Prim)	MFie NCGa NSum NWad XBar
	'Page' (Au)	IPen MFie
	palinuri (Au)	IPen
	palmata (Co)	GEdr GKev NHar
	'Paris '90' (Pr/Poly)	CWCL MFie NCGa NSum XBar
	parryi (Pa)	CSta EBee GKev LLHF
	- SDR 8184 **new**	GKev
	'Patrick'	NPnk
	pedemontana 'Alba' (Au)	MFie WThu XBar
	'Perle von Bottrop' (Pr/Prim)	ECtt GAbr GEdr NHar WCot
	petelotii (Ch)	WAbe
	'Peter Klein' (Or)	EPot GBuc GKev
	petiolaris misapplied	see *P.* 'Redpoll'
§	***petiolaris*** Wall. (Pe)	GCra NHar NSum
	- Sherriff's form	see *P.* 'Redpoll'
	'Petticoat' (Pr/Prim/d)	ECtt NWad WCot XBar
	'Pink Aire' (Au)	MFie NSum XBar
	'Pink Fairy' (Au)	IPen ITim
	'Pink Grapefruit' (Pr/Prim/d)	XBar
	'Pink Ice' (*allionii* hybrid) (Au)	GKev MFie NHar NWad XBar
	'Pink Star' (Pr/Prim/d) **new**	XBar
	pinnatifida (Mu)	GKev
	poissonii (Pf)	CDor CSta CTri CTsd CWCL EBee ELan EPfP GKev GQui IPen LRHS NGdn NHpl NRHS NSum WShi
	- SDR 4617	GKev
	- SDR 5959	GKev
	polyanthus (Pr/Poly)	CWCL
	polyneura (Co)	ECho GEdr GKev IPen MFie MHid MHol NGdn WCot
	'Port Wine' (Pr)	GCra GEdr
	'Powdery Pink'	LRHS
	prenantha (Pf) SDR 3909	GKev
	Primlet Series (Pr/Prim)	SVic
	primulina (Mi)	GKev
§	***prolifera*** (Pf) Υ^{H4}	CMHG CPne CSta EPfP GBuc GKev GMaP GQui IPen LHop LRHS NGdn NHpl NRHS SWat WMoo XBar
	- purple-flowered B&SWJ 13951 **new**	WCru
§	× ***pubescens*** (Au) Υ^{H5}	IPen LRHS MHer NGdn NRHS
	- 'A.E. Matthews' (Au)	NWad
	- 'Apple Blossom' (Au)	IPen MFie
	- 'Balfouriana' (Au)	NWad
§	- 'Bewerley White' (Au)	EBee ECho EPfP IPen NDro
	- 'Blue Wave' (Au)	IPen MFie SPop
§	- 'Boothman's Variety' (Au)	CBod CTri ECho EPfP EWoo GKev ITim MFie NHar NSla WHoo
	- 'Carmen'	see *P.* × *pubescens* 'Boothman's Variety'
	- 'Chamois' (Au)	MFie
	- 'Christine' (Au)	CMea GKev IPen MHer NBir NSum WCot
	- 'Cream Viscosa' (Au)	SPlb
	- 'Faldonside' (Au)	GCrg IPen MFie NPnk NSla NSum WThu
§	- 'Freedom' (Au)	CTal CTri ECho EWoo GKev IPen MFie NBir NHar NSla XBar
	- 'George Harrison' (Au)	MFie
	- 'Harlow Car' (Au)	CMea GQui IPen MFie MPnt NSum NWad
	- 'Hazel's White' (Au)	ITim NDro
	- 'Henry Hall' (Au)	ITim
	- 'Joan Danger' (Au)	IPen NDro
	- 'Joan Gibbs' (Au)	IPen ITim MFie NHpl XBar
	- 'Kath Dryden' (Au)	ITim
	- 'Lilac Fairy' (Au)	EPot IPen ITim NPnk NWad WThu
	- 'Moonlight' (Au)	NDro
	- 'Mrs G.F. Wilson' (Au)	ECho
	- 'Mrs J.H. Wilson' (Au)	CTal ECho GCrg MFie NRya XBar

	- 'Pat Barwick' (Au)	IPen ITim MFie NDro NRya NWad
	- 'Rufus' (Au) ♀H5	GAbr GEdr NDro WThu XBar
	- 'Sid Skelton' (Au)	IPen NRya
	- 'Slack Top Violet' (Au)	NSla
	- 'Snowcap' (Au)	IPen ITim XBar
	- 'Sonya' (Au)	IPen
	- 'The General' (Au)	CTri GEdr IPen MFie
§	- 'Wedgwood' (Au)	GAbr IPen MFie NSum XBar
	- 'Winnifred' (Au)	WHil
	- yellow-flowered (Au)	IPen
	pulchella (Pu)	GKev
	- SDR 7903 **new**	GKev
	pulverulenta (Pf) ♀H6	Widely available
	- 'Bartley' (Pf)	WWtn
	- Bartley hybrids (Pf) ♀H6	EBee GKev MMuc NHpl NSum NWad WMoo XBar
	- 'Bartley Pink' (Pf)	CPla GBuc
	purdomii	GKev
	'Purple' (Primlet Series) (Pr/Prim)	LRHS NRHS
	'Quaker's Bonnet'	see *P. vulgaris* 'Lilacina Plena'
	'Rachel Kinnen' (Au)	GAbr IPen MFie XBar
	'Ramona' (Pr/Poly)	CWCL NCGa XBar
	'Raspberry Ripple' (Pr/Prim/d)	XBar
	'Ravenglass Vermilion'	see *P.* 'Inverewe'
	'Red' (Primlet Series) (Pr/Prim)	LRHS NRHS
	'Red Ruffles' (Pr/Poly/d)	ECtt
§	'Redpoll' (Pe)	GBuc NHar
	reidii (So)	GEdr GKev
	- CC 7341	GKev
	- var. ***williamsii*** (So)	GEdr GKev IPen
*	- - ***alba*** (So)	GEdr
	reticulata (Si)	EBee GKev
	'Reverie' (Pr/Poly)	MFie XBar
	'Rheniana' (Au)	IPen MFie NRya
	'Rick Lupp'	IPen
	'Romeo' (Pr/Prim)	CLAP LLHF NWad WCot
	'Rose' (Primlet Series) (Pr/Prim)	LRHS NRHS
	rosea (Or) ♀H5	CAby CBod CElw CWCL EBee ECho EPfP GKev GLog GMaP IPen MFie MMuc NBid NBir NRya WPnP
	- CC 5260	GKev
	- 'Gigas' (Or)	CLet NRya WBor WMAq
	- 'Grandiflora' (Or)	CBod CMac ECho EPfP GCrg GMcL GPSL LHop LRHS NCGa NLar NRHS SPoG SRms SWat XLum
	'Rosemary Cottage'	GAbr WCot
§	***rotundifolia*** (Cf) SDR 7460 **new**	GKev
	'Rowallane Rose' (Pf)	GCal IPen
I	'Rowena'	GAbr GCra LLHF WCot
	roxburghii	see *P. rotundifolia*
	'Roy Cope' (Pr/Prim/d)	NBir
	'Roydon Ruby'	GEdr
	Rubens Series (Pr/Prim/d) **new**	LRHS NRHS
	rubra	see *P. firmipes*
	'Ruby Tuesday' (Au)	NDro
	rusbyi (Pa)	GKev
	- subsp. ***ellisiae*** (Pa)	GKev IPen WHil
	sachalinensis (Al)	GKev
	'Sapphire' (Au)	XBar
	'Saracen' (Au)	IPen MFie
	saxatilis ambig. (Co)	MFie
	scandinavica (Al)	GKev
§	'Schneekissen' (Pr/Prim)	CAby CBod CSam CWCL GBuc GCra LLHF MHer NBro SCob WTor
	scotica (Al)	GKev GPoy MFie NSla WAbe
	secundiflora (Pf)	CLAP CSta CWCL ECho ELan EWTr GBuc GKev LLWG MMuc NBir NSum SPlb SWat WMoo XBar
	- SDR 4401	GKev
	- SDR 4435	GKev
§	× ***sendtneri*** (Au)	MFie
	× ***serrata***	see *P.* × *vochinensis*
	serratifolia (Pf)	GKev
	- SDR 5165	GKev
	sharmae **new**	GKev
	'Shizuko Hara'	IPen
	sibthorpii	see *P. vulgaris* subsp. *sibthorpii*
	sieboldii (Co) ♀H5	ECho EWld GKev IPen MAsh MNrw NHpl NSla SBch SRms WAbe WHea
	- 'Aaimayama' (Co)	CSta WHil
	- 'Aiaigasa' (Co)	WFar
	- 'Aka Tombo' (Co) **new**	CSta
	- 'Akinoysool' (Co)	CSta WFar
	- 'Andromeda' (Co)	EBee
	- 'Aoba-no-fue' (Co)	CAby CSta
	- 'Asahi' (Co)	WFar
	- 'Asahigata' (Co)	CSta
	- 'Ayanami' (Co)	WFar
	- 'Ayasegawa' (Co)	CSta WFar WHil
	- 'Beeches Star' (Co)	EBee
	- 'Benjamin' (Co)	CSta WHil
	- 'Bide-a-Wee Blue' (Co)	NBid
	- 'Bide-a-Wee Lace' (Co)	NBid
	- 'Bijyonomai' (Co)	WFar
I	- 'Blue Lagoon' (Co)	CSta EBee EPfP LLHF LRHS NLar WFar
	- 'Blue Shades' (Co)	IPen
	- blue-flowered (Co)	CLAP CSta CWCL WHil
	- 'Blush' (Co)	CLAP CSta WHil
	- 'Boykavitch' (Co)	WHil
	- 'Bureikou' (Co)	CSta WFar
	- 'Carefree' (Co)	CLAP CSta ECtt IPen LLHF NBro NLar WHil
	- 'Carmine Pink' (Co)	WHil
	- 'Cherubim' (Co)	CLAP CSta EBee GCra LRHS WHil
	- 'Clouds Over Blighty' (Co)	EBee
	- 'Daikoshi' (Co)	CSta
	- 'Daiminnisiki' (Co)	CSta NHar
	- 'Dancing Ladies' (Co)	CLAP ECtt IPen MFie NBro NCGa NHar WFar WHil XBar
	- 'Dart Rapids' (Co)	CSta WHil WSHC
	- 'Duane's Choice' (Co)	CAby CLAP CSta WHil
	- 'Edasango' (Co)	WFar
	- 'Edomurasaki' (Co)	CSta NPnk WFar WHil
	- 'Edomurasaki' pink-feathered (Co) **new**	CSta
	- 'Essie' (Co)	CSta
	- 'Frilly Blue' (Co)	CSta EBee GEdr LRHS
	- 'Fujijishi' (Co)	WFar
	- 'Galactic' (Co)	CSta
	- 'Galaxy' (Co)	NBro
	- 'Geisha Girl' (Co)	CDor CLAP CSpe CSta EBee GEdr LRHS MRav NLar WAbe WFar WHil
	- 'Ginhukurin' (Co)	CAby CSta WFar WHil
	- 'Girl of the Limberlost' (Co) **new**	XBar
	- 'Gloaming' (Co) **new**	XBar
	- 'Gunmia Niizatia' (Co)	CSta
	- 'Hakutsuri' (Co)	WFar
	- 'Hanaguruma' (Co) **new**	CSta
	- 'Hatagarasi' (Co)	CSta WFar
	- 'Hatugoromo' (Co) **new**	CSta ETho
	- 'Hatusugato' (Co)	NHar WFar

- 'Heart's Desire' (Co)	EBee
- 'Higurasi' (Co)	WFar
- 'Hinokoromo' (Co)	WFar
- 'Hutaezuru' (Co)	WFar
- 'Inikina White' (Co)	WFar
- 'Inokima Minoura' (Co)	CSta WFar
- 'Inukina White' (Co) **new**	CSta
- 'Iso-botan' (Co) **new**	GEdr
- 'Izutu' (Co) **new**	CSta
- 'Jessica' (Co)	CSta WHil
- 'Kansenden' (Co)	WFar
- 'Karagoromo' (Co)	CSta WFar
- 'Kashima' (Co)	CAby CSta NPnk WHil
- 'Kihino Yume' (Co) **new**	CSta
- 'Kokoroiki' (Co)	CSta WFar
- 'Kotobuki' (Co) **new**	GEdr
- 'Kotonosirabe' (Co)	CSta WFar
- 'Kurama' (Co)	WFar
- 'Lacewing' (Co)	WHil
- f. ***lactiflora*** (Co)	CLAP CSta IPen LRHS NBro SRot
- 'Lilac Blue' (Co) **new**	CSta
- 'Lilac Sunbonnet' (Co)	CLAP EPfP LLHF NHar WFar
- 'Maiougi' (Co)	CSta
- 'Makazebeni' (Co)	WFar
- 'Managuruma' (Co)	WFar
- 'Manakoora' (Co)	CAby CLAP ECtt EHrv IPen MFie NBro NCGa NSum WFar XBar
- 'Mangetu' (Co)	CSta WFar
- 'Martin Nest Blue' (Co)	CSta NPnk WHil
- 'Martin Nest Pale Pink' (Co)	CSta
- 'Masasino' (Co)	WFar
- 'Matsu-no-yuki' (Co)	CSta WHil
- 'Matunoyuki' (Co)	WFar
- 'Mihonokoji' (Co)	CSta WFar
- 'Mikado' (Co)	CLAP CSta EBee ECtt GEdr IPen LRHS WFar WHil
- 'Mikininonomare' (Co)	CSta WFar
- 'Mitajiman' (Co) **new**	CSta
- 'Miyakowakare' (Co)	WFar
- 'Miyuki' (Co)	WFar
- 'Musashino' (Co)	CSta WHil
- 'Musasi' (Co)	CSta
- 'Nankin Kazakura' (Co) **new**	GEdr XBar
- 'Nirvana' (Co) **new**	XBar
- 'Noboruko' (Co)	CSta
- 'Nure Tsubane' (Co) **new**	CSta XBar
- 'Okinanotomo' (Co)	WFar
- 'Old Vienna' (Co) **new**	XBar
- 'Oshibori' (Co)	CSta GBin GWyn WHil
- 'Our White' (Co)	WFar WHil
- 'Pago-Pago' (Co)	CLAP CSta ECtt EHrv IPen MFie NBro WFar WHil XBar
- 'Pale Moon' (Co) **new**	XBar
- 'Pink Laced' (Co)	WFar
- pink-flowered (Co)	GKev NBir
- 'Purple Dusk' (Co) **new**	XBar
- 'Rasyoumon' (Co)	WFar
- 'Rock Candy' (Co)	CSta
- 'Romance' (Co) **new**	XBar
- 'Saiun' (Co)	CSta
- 'Sakuragana' (Co)	CSta WFar
- 'Sangoguko'	GBin GWyn MNrw
- 'Sekidaiko' (Co)	CSta
- 'Senyuu' (Co)	CSta WFar
- 'Seraphim' (Co)	CLAP CSta EBee LRHS MMrt NLar WFar
- 'Seto-no-ume' (Co)	CSta
- 'Shiokemuri' (Co)	CSta
- 'Shira-washi' (Co) **new**	CSta
- 'Shiro-tombo' (Co) **new**	GEdr
- 'Shirousagi' (Co)	WFar
- 'Shishifunjin' (Co)	CSta
- 'Sinakatonba' (Co) **new**	ETho
- 'Sinipukurn' (Co)	CSta WFar
- 'Sinnkirou' (Co)	WFar
- 'Sinseiu' (Co)	CSta WFar
- 'Siritonbo' (Co)	WFar
- 'Snow Flakes' (Co) **new**	CSta
- 'Snowbird' (Co) **new**	XBar
- 'Snowdrop' (Co)	CBcs CBod CDor CSta ECtt GBin GWyn LHop LSou MBel MHol MNrw MPie NCGa NCou NPnk WCot WFar WMoo
- 'Snowflake' (Co)	CLAP CSta EBee EPfP LRHS NLar WAbe WFar
- 'Sorcha's Pink' (Co)	CSta
- 'Sotodorihime' (Co)	WFar
- 'Sousiarai' (Co)	CSta WFar
- 'Spring Blush' (Co)	CSta WHil
- 'Spring Song' (Co)	CSta WHil
- 'Suibijin' (Co) **new**	ETho
- 'Sumida No Hatu' (Co)	WFar
- 'Sumizomegenji' (Co)	CSta XBar
- 'Sweetie' (Co)	CSta WFar
- 'Syosin' (Co)	CSta
- 'Syutyuka' (Co)	CSta
- 'Tagonoura' (Co)	CSta WFar WHil
- 'Tah-ni' (Co)	NBro NSum XBar
- 'Taoyami' (Co)	CSta WHil
- 'Tatutanoyuube' (Co)	CSta
- 'Tokasamesi' (Co) **new**	ETho
- 'Tokimeki' (Co)	WFar
- 'Toyonoharu' (Co)	WFar
- 'Trade Winds' (Co) **new**	XBar
- 'Tukasamesi' (Co)	CSta
- 'Turunokegoromo' (Co)	CSta WHil
- 'Usojyanohe' (Co) **new**	CSta
- 'Vilia' (Co) **new**	XBar
- 'Vivid Pink' (Co) **new**	CSta
- 'Winter Dreams' (Co)	CAby CLAP CWCL ECtt EHrv MFie NBid NBro NCGa NHar NSum WFar
- 'Yukiguruma' (Co)	WFar
- 'Yuuhibeni' (Co)	CSta
sikkimensis (Si) 🏆H6	EBee ECho EPot EWTr GKev IPen LRHS MHid MMuc NGdn NSum SPoG XBar
- CC 5730	GKev
- CC 5986	GKev
- CC 6783	GKev
- SDR 3099	GKev
- SDR 4919	GKev
- SDR 5933	GKev
- SDR 7426	GKev
- peach-flowered **new**	GKev
- var. ***pseudosikkimensis*** (Si)	GKev IPen
- - SDR 4528	GKev
- var. ***pudibunda*** (Si)	EBee GKev
- red-flowered **new**	GKev
- 'Ruby Shades' (Si)	GEdr
- 'Tilman Number 2' (Si)	GBuc
aff. ***sikkimensis*** (Si)	IPen NGdn
'Silver Lace Charlotte'	WIce
Silver-laced Group (Pr/Poly)	EPfP MMuc NLar SEND SPoG SWvt WIce
- black-flowered (Pr/Poly)	GBin XEll
simensis (Sp)	GKev
sinoplantaginea	see *P. chionantha* subsp. *sinoplantaginea*

	sinopurpurea	see *P. chionantha* subsp. *sinopurpurea*
	'Sir Bedivere' (Pr/Prim)	EBee GBuc NHar WCot
	'Siska' (Pr/Poly)	GAbr
	smithiana	see *P. prolifera*
	'Snow Carpet'	see *P.* 'Schneekissen'
	'Snow White' (Pr/Poly)	GBin GEdr MRav
	Snowcushion	see *P.* 'Schneekissen'
	'Snowruffles'	ITim
	sonchifolia (Pe)	CLAP GKev
	- subsp. ***sonchifolia***	GKev
	sorachiana	see *P. yuparensis*
	'Sorbet' (Pr/Poly)	XBar
	spectabilis (Au)	GKev
	specuicola (Al)	LLHF
	Spice Shades Group (Pr/Poly)	CHid MFie NCGa XBar
	× ***steinii***	see *P.* × *forsteri*
	stenocalyx (Pu)	XBar
	stenodonta (Pf)	GKev
	'Stradbrook Charm' (Au)	CPBP CWCL EPot MFie WThu
	'Stradbrook Dainty' (Au)	MFie NWad
	'Stradbrook Dream' (Au)	ITim MFie XBar
	'Stradbrook Lilac Lustre' (Au)	MFie
	'Stradbrook Lucy' (Au)	GEdr IPen ITim NWad
	'Stradbrook Mauve Magic' (Au)	MFie
	stricta (Al)	GKev
	Striped Victorians Group (Pr/Poly)	NCGa NSum XBar
	'Strong Beer' (d)	CHVG EBee ECtt EPfP GAbr GBin GEdr GWyn IKil MArt MHol MMuc MNrw MPie NDov NHpl NSti NSum NWad SAko SIgm WBrk WCot WFar WKif
	'Sue Jervis' (Pr/Prim/d)	EWTr MRav NBir NHpl WCAu WGwG
	suffrutescens (Su)	WAbe
	'Sundae' (Pr/Prim/d)	XBar
	'Sunrise' (Primlet Series) (Pr/Prim)	LRHS NRHS
	'Sunshine Susie' (Pr/Prim/d)	GMaP
	szechuanica (Cy)	CPne GKev IPen LLHF
	takedana (Bu)	GEdr
	'Tango' (Pr/Prim)	MFie NCGa NDro XBar
	tangutica (Cy)	GKev IPen
	tanneri (Pe)	GKev
§	- subsp. ***nepalensis*** (Pe)	GKev
	'Tantallon' (Pe)	NHar
	Tartan Reds Group (Pr/Prim)	CWCL XBar
	'Tatyana' (Pr/Prim) **new**	EBee
	'Tawny Port' (Pr/Poly)	CElw CFis
	'Theodora' (Pr)	CTal GAbr GEdr
	'Tie Dye' (Pr/Prim)	CBod ELan EPot IKil LLHF MHol MMrt MNrw MPie NHpl NLar NWad SAko WCot WFar WKif WWFP
	'Tinney's Moonlight' (Pe)	NHar
	'Tipperary Purple' (Pr/Prim)	ECtt GAbr NPnk
	'Tomato Red' (Pr/Prim)	GEdr LHop LLHF MFie NDov NHpl WCot WFar
	'Tony' (Au) Y^{H5}	CPBP IPen MFie XBar
	'Top Affair' (Au/d)	IPen WAln
	'Tortoiseshell' (Pr/d)	CHid ECtt
	Traditional Yellows Group (Pr)	XBar
	tschuktschorum (Cy)	LLHF
*	***urumiensis***	GEdr
	'Val Horncastle' (Pr/Prim/d)	ECtt EPfP EShb GAbr GMaP MFie NHpl
	Valentine Victorians Group (Pr/Poly)	XBar
	× ***venusta*** (Au)	GKev
	'Vera Maud' (Pr)	NCGa NSum XBar
§	***veris*** (Pr) Y^{H5}	Widely available
	- PAB 3777	LEdu NRHS WHar
	- subsp. ***columnae*** (Pr)	EDAr GKev
I	- 'Coronation Cowslips' (Pr)	GBuc MFie XBar
	- hose-in-hose (Pr/d)	WBrk
	- hybrids (Pr)	CRos GMcL
	- 'Katy McSparron' (Pr/d)	CBod EBee ECtt GBin MArt MAvo MHol MNrw MPie NHpl NLar NSti SAko SPer SPoG WCot WFar
	- 'Lady Agatha' (Pr)	XBar
	- subsp. ***macrocalyx*** (Pr)	WCot
	- orange-flowered (Pr)	WMoo
	- red-flowered (Pr)	NBid NGdn SBee SPer WMoo
	- 'Sunset Shades' (Pr)	CDor EAJP ECGP EPfP GBin GBuc IBoy NGdn NLar SWvt XEll
	- subsp. ***veris*** (Pr) **new**	NPnk
	vernalis	see *P. vulgaris*
	verticillata (Sp)	CPne GKev IPen
§	***vialii*** (So) Y^{H5}	Widely available
	- SDR 7894 **new**	GKev
	'Vicky' (Au)	IPen
	Violet Victorians Group (Pr/Poly)	NCGa XBar
	virginis (Am)	GKev
	viscosa All.	see *P. latifolia*
§	× ***vochinensis*** (Au)	NHar
§	***vulgaris*** (Pr/Prim) Y^{H7}	Widely available
	- var. ***alba*** (Pr/Prim)	WBrk
	- 'Alba Plena' (Pr/Prim/d)	GAbr GCal NSum
	- 'Avoca' (Pr/Prim)	GEdr NHar NPnk WCot
	- 'Avondale' (Kennedy Irish Series) (Pr/Prim)	CAby EBee GBin LLHF MHol NCGa NHar NPnk SCob WCot
	- Barnhaven Gold	XBar
	- 'Carrigdale' (Pr/Prim)	EBee GEdr NHar NPnk WCot
	- 'Claddagh' (Pr/Prim)	EBee NHar NPnk WCot
	- Cornish pink (Pr/Prim)	GKev
	- Drumcliffe = 'K74'PBR (Pr/Prim)	EBee ECtt EHoe GAbr GBin GEdr GMaP LLHF MArt MBel MFie MHol MMuc MNrw MPie NHar NHpl NLar NPnk NSti WCot WFar
	- 'Dunbeg' (Kennedy Irish Series) (Pr/Prim)	CAby EPfP GBin LLHF NCGa NHar NLar NPnk SCob WCot
	- 'Glengarriff' (Kennedy Irish Series) (Pr/Prim)	GEdr NHar NPnk SCob WCot
	- 'Golden Gem' (Pr/Prim/d)	WCot
	- green-flowered	see *P. vulgaris* 'Viridis'
	- hybrids (Pr/Prim)	CRos WFar
	- Innisfree = 'K72'PBR (Pr/Prim)	CAby CHVG EBee ECtt EPfP GAbr GBin GEdr GMaP LLHF MBel MFie MMuc MNrw MPie NCGa NDov NHar NHpl NLar NPnk NSti NWad SPad WCot WFar
§	- 'Lilacina Plena' (Pr/Prim/d)	CWCL EBee GCal IFro MRav NHpl NSum SIgm WHer
	- 'Moneygall' (Kennedy Irish Series) (Pr/Poly/d)	NHar NPnk
	- 'Mount Juliet' (Pr/Prim) **new**	NPnk
§	- subsp. ***sibthorpii*** (Pr/Prim) Y^{H5}	CDor CMHG CSam EBee ECho ELon EPfP GBuc IPen LLWP LRHS MCot MFie MHer MNrw MRav NBro NCGa NChi NWad SKHP SPtp SRms
	- - pale-flowered (Pr/Prim)	GBuc
	- 'Taigetos' (Pr/Prim)	CBro CHid
	- 'Tara' (Pr/Prim)	EBee GEdr NHar NPnk

§	- 'Viridis' (Pr/Prim/d)	MNrw
	- subsp. ***vulgaris*** (Pr/Prim/d) ♀H5	GMcL WMAq
	waltonii (Si)	CCVN CLAP CSta CWCL EPfP GKev IPen MNrw NLar NSum
	- hybrids (Si)	ELon
	'Wanda' (Pr/Prim) ♀H7	CBcs CTri ECho ESps GAbr GBin GCra GKev GMcL GWyn LRHS MBel MHer MMuc NBid NPnk SRms WBrk WCFE WCot WHea
	Wanda Group (Pr/Prim)	CHVG ECho LBMP NBro SVic
	- 'Wanda Cherry Red' (Pr/Prim) **new**	GAbr
	- 'Wanda Grace' (Pr/Prim)	NPnk
	- 'Wanda Hose-in-hose' (Pr/Prim/d)	GCra NBir WHer
	- 'Wanda Jack-in-the-Green' (Pr/Prim)	CLAP WCot
	- 'Wanda Tomato Red' (Pr/Prim) **new**	CHVG
	wardii	see *P. munroi*
	warshenewskiana (Or)	CLAP EPot EWes GBuc GCrg GJos GKev NHar NRya WGwG
	watsonii (Mu)	GKev MFie NHar
	- ACE 1402	IPen
	- maroon-flowered (Mu)	GKev
	'Wedgwood'	see *P.* × *pubescens* 'Wedgwood'
I	Westonbury Mill Hybrids **new**	WWtn
	'Wharfedale Bluebell' (Au)	CPBP IPen NBir NHar WThu
	'Wharfedale Buttercup' (Au)	IPen ITim NHar NWad WAbe
	'Wharfedale Butterfly' (Au)	NWad
	'Wharfedale Crusader' (Au)	IPen
	'Wharfedale Gem' (*allionii* hybrid) (Au)	MFie NSla NWad XBar
	'Wharfedale Ling' (*allionii* hybrid) (Au)	CTal MFie NHar NWad XBar
	'Wharfedale Sunshine' (Au)	IPen
	'Wharfedale Superb' (*allionii* hybrid) (Au)	MFie XBar
	'Wharfedale Village' (Au)	IPen MPnt NHar NSla WAbe WThu
	'White Linda Pope' (Au)	NSla NWad WThu
	'White Wanda' (Pr/Prim)	GAbr XBar
	'White Waves' (*allionii* hybrid) (Au)	ITim
	'William Genders' (Pr/Poly)	GAbr GEdr
	wilsonii (Pf)	CSta CTri CWCL EWld GAbr LLWG MMuc NBir NGdn WWtn XBar
	- SDR 7824 **new**	GKev
§	- var. ***anisodora*** (Pf)	CLAP GKev GLog IPen NGdn NWad XBar
	- var. ***wilsonii*** (Pf)	GKev
	'Windrush'	see *P.* × *berninae* 'Windrush'
	'Wisley Crimson'	see *P.* 'Wisley Red'
§	'Wisley Red' (Pr/Prim)	CElw
	wollastonii (So)	GKev
	'Woodland Walk' (Pr/Prim)	EPfP
	wulfeniana (Au)	EBee EPot GKev
	yargongensis	see *P. munroi* subsp. *yargongensis*
	'Yellow' (Primlet Series) (Pr/Prim)	LRHS NRHS
§	***yuparensis*** (Al)	CPne GBuc GKev IPen
	- white-flowered (Al)	EBee GKev
	zambalensis (Ar)	GKev IPen
	- SDR 1611	GKev
	'Zebra Blue'	NPri
	'Zenobia'	WCre

Prinsepia (*Rosaceae*)

	sinensis	MBlu NLar SLon WSHC

Pritchardia (*Arecaceae*)

	affinis	XBlo
	pacifica	XBlo

Pritzelago (*Brassicaceae*)

	alpina	GCrg NSla

Prosartes (*Liliaceae*)

§	***hookeri***	CLAP EBee ECho LLHF MNrw WCru
§	- var. ***oregana***	EBee EPPr IFoB WCru
§	***lanuginosa***	EBee EPPr LEdu LRHS WCru WPGP
§	***maculata***	CAby CLAP CTal IFoB LEdu MNrw NLar WCru
§	***smithii***	CBct EBee ECho EPfP GKev GLog LEdu MNrw NBir NLar WCot WCru WPGP WSHC
	- 'Rick' (v)	CTal

Prostanthera (*Lamiaceae*)

	aspalathoides	CBcs CCCN CTsd
	'Badja Peak'	CCCN CTsd EBee EUJe EWes MAsh MGil SLim
	baxteri 'Silver Ghost'	SLim
	cryptandroides	CBcs
	cuneata ♀H4	Widely available
	- 'Alpine Gold' (v)	LRHS MAsh
	- 'Blushing Bride'	CMac EUJe LBuc
	- Kew form	WPGP
	denticulata	CTsd
*	***digitiformis***	CTsd
	incana	CTsd
	incisa	CTsd
	lasianthos	CBcs CCCN CHll CTsd SLim SPlb SVen
	- 'Kallista Pink'	CTsd
	latifolia	CTsd
	melissifolia	CTsd
§	- var. ***parvifolia***	CCCN CTsd
	'Mint Delight'	SLim
	'Mint Royale'	CCCN EUJe LEdu SLim
	'Mint-Ice'	SLim
	ovalifolia ♀H3	CCCN CPne SEle
I	- 'Variegata' (v)	CBcs CCCN CHGN CMac CTsd LRHS LSou MGil SEle WGrn
	phylicifolia	CBcs CPne CTsd
	'Poorinda Ballerina'	CCCN CTsd EBee LRHS MAsh SEle SLim SPer SRkn WWFP
	'Poorinda Petite'	CCCN CTsd LRHS SEle
	rhombea	CTsd
	rotundifolia ♀H3	CAbb CBod CCCN CTri CTsd EBee ECho MGil MNHC MSCN SEle SPer SVen WCFE WGrn WKif
	- 'Chelsea Girl'	see *P. rotundifolia* 'Rosea'
§	- 'Rosea' ♀H3	CCCN CLet CTsd EPfP LHop LRHS SEND
	rugosa	CTsd
	sieberi misapplied	see *P. melissifolia* var. *parvifolia*
	sieberi Benth.	CTre CTsd
I	- 'Variegata' (v)	CTsd
	spinosa	CTsd
	'Starlight' (v)	CTsd
	walteri	CBcs CCCN CTsd EBee LRHS SVen

Protea (*Proteaceae*)

	aurea	SPlb
	- subsp. ***aurea***	CTre
	burchellii	SPlb
	'Clark's Red'	LRHS MPkF
	coronata	CTre SPlb

	cynaroides	CBlu CCCN CTre LRHS SBig SPlb
	- 'Little Prince'PBR **new**	CBcs CCCN
	effusa	SPlb
	eximia	CCCN CTre SPlb
	grandiceps	CCCN CTre SPlb
	lacticolor	CTre SPlb
	laurifolia	SPlb
	lepidocarpodendron	CTre
	longifolia	CTre
	nana	SPlb
	neriifolia	CCCN CTre SPlb
	- 'Snowcrest'	CTre
	obtusifolia	SPlb
	'Pink Crown'	LRHS MPkF
	'Pink Ice'	LRHS
	repens	CTre LRHS SPlb
	- 'Ruby Blush' **new**	CCCN
	scolymocephala	SPlb
	subvestita	CTre SPlb
	susannae	CTre SPlb
	'Susara' **new**	CCCN LRHS
	'Sylvia' **new**	LRHS
	'White Ice' **new**	LRHS

Prumnopitys ✿ (*Podocarpaceae*)

§	***andina***	CBcs
	elegans	see *P. andina*

Prunella (*Lamiaceae*)

§	***grandiflora***	CHby ECha ELan ESps SRms SWat WOut
	- 'Alba'	CBre EBee ECha ELan EPfP GBin GMaP NBid NLar SPer SRms WCAu WOut
	- 'Bella Deep Rose'	CWld
	- 'Blue Loveliness'	CWld SWvt
	- 'Carminea'	EBee MRav SPer
	- 'Freelander'	WHil
	- light blue-flowered	WBor
	- 'Loveliness'	CMac ECha ELan GMaP MRav NBro NGdn NSti SPer SPlb SRGP WCAu WFar
	- 'Pagoda'	CSpe NLar
	- 'Pink Loveliness'	SRms WFar
	- 'Rosea'	WFar WOut
	- 'Rubra'	NLar WOut
	- violet-flowered	EPfP
	- 'White Loveliness'	CMac
	hyssopifolia	XSen
	incisa	see *P. vulgaris*
	laciniata	EBee
	- white-flowered	EBee
	Summer Daze = 'Binsumdaz'PBR	EBee ECtt GMcL LSou SHil
§	***vulgaris***	CBod CHab CWld ENfk ESps GPoy MHer MNHC NMir SRms WHer WJek WMoo WOut
	- 'Blue Pearl'	CBod
	- f. ***leucantha***	WHer
	- 'Rose Pearl'	CBod LSRN MPie NHpl
	× ***webbiana***	see *P. grandiflora*
	- 'Gruss aus Isernhagen'	EBee GBin

Prunus ✿ (*Rosaceae*)

	'Accolade' (d) 🏆H6	Widely available
§	'Amanogawa' 🏆H6	Widely available
	amygdalus	see *P. dulcis*
	angustifolia	LPar
	Aprium Series (F)	ERea
	armeniaca	NPri
	- 'Alfred' (F)	CDul ERea GTwe SDea SKee SPer WHar
	- 'Bergeron' (F)	LRHS WMat
	- 'Blenheim' (F)	ERea
	- 'Bredase' (F)	CWib ERea SDea
	- 'De Nancy'	see *P. armeniaca* 'Gros Pêche'
	- 'Delicot' (F)	SFrt
	- 'Early Moorpark' (F)	CAgr CWib EMOT EPfP GTwe LEdu MAsh NOra SDea SEND SLon WHar WMat
	- 'Farmingdale' (F)	SDea
	- Flavorcot = 'Bayoto'PBR (F)	CAgr EPfP EPom ERea GTwe MCoo NOra SFrt SKee SPer WHar WMat
	- 'Garden Aprigold' (F)	EPom WMat
	- 'Goldcot' (F)	CAgr CDul CFGn CTho ERea LRHS MAsh MCoo NOra SDea SKee SPoG WHar WMat
	- 'Golden Glow' (F)	CAgr CFGn CTho EMOT EPfP EPom ERea MAsh MCoo NOra SKee WHar WMat
	- 'Goldrich' (F)	CAgr
§	- 'Gros Pêche' (F)	SVic WHar
	- 'Hargrand' (F)	CAgr SVic
	- 'Harogem' (F)	CAgr
	- 'Hemskirke' (F)	ERea SKee
	- 'Hongaarse' (F)	SDea
	- 'Isabella' (F)	ERea
	- 'Moniqui' (F)	ERea
	- 'Moorpark' (F)	CDul CHab CSBt CTri CWib ELan EMOT GTwe LBuc MMuc MRav NPri SDea SKee SPer
	- 'New Large Early' (F)	ERea MMuc SDea SEND
	- 'Novi Sad' (F) **new**	MRai
	- Orange Summer = 'Zaitorde'PBR (F)	EPom
	- 'Paviot' (F) **new**	MRai
	- 'Petit Muscat' (F)	EPom ERea SFrt SKee
	- 'Tomcot' (F)	CAgr CTho CTri EPfP EPom ERea GTwe LBuc LEdu LRHS LSRN MAsh MCoo NOra SFrt SKee WHar WMat
	- 'Tross Orange' (F)	CWib SDea
	- 'Vigama' (F)	MCoo WMat
	'Asano'	CLnd
	avium	Widely available
	- 'Amber Heart' (F)	NOra SBdl WMat
	- 'Archduke' (F)	SKee
	- 'August Heart' (F)	SKee
	- 'Bigarreau de Schrecken' (F)	SKee
	- 'Bigarreau Gaucher' (F)	NOra SBdl SKee WHar WMat
§	- 'Bigarreau Napoléon' (F)	CArg CSut EPom GTwe LSRN NOra SBdl SKee SVic WMat
	- 'Birchenhayes'	see *P. avium* 'Early Birchenhayes'
	- 'Black Eagle' (F)	SKee
	- 'Black Elton' (F)	SKee
	- 'Black Heart' (F)	CWib ELan MMuc SEND
	- 'Black Tartarian' (F)	SKee
	- 'Bottlers'	see *P. avium* 'Preserving'
	- 'Bradbourne Black' (F)	SKee WHar
	- 'Bullion' (F)	CEnd CTho
	- 'Burcombe' (F)	CEnd CTho
	- 'Cariad' (F) **new**	WGwG
	- Celeste = 'Sumpaca'PBR (D)	CAgr CFGn CMac CTri EMOT ERea GTwe MCoo NLar NOra SBdl SDea SLim SPoG WHar WMat
	- 'Cherokee'	see *P. avium* 'Lapins'
	- 'Colney' (F)	EPom ERea GTwe NOra SKee WHar WJas WMat
	- 'Danelia' (D)	WMat
	- 'Dun' (F)	CHab CTho WMat

§	- 'Early Birchenhayes' (F)	CEnd CTho
	- 'Early Rivers' (F)	CDul CLnd CSBt CWib EMOT GTwe IArd LSRN NOra SDea SKee SVic WHar WMat
	- 'Elton Heart' (F)	SKee
	- 'Emperor Francis' (F)	SKee
	- 'Fastigiata'	WHar
	- 'Fice' (F)	CEnd CTho
	- 'Florence' (F)	SKee
	- 'Garden Bing' (F) **new**	EPom
	- 'Giorgia' (D)	WMat
	- 'Goodnestone Black' (D)	SKee
	- 'Governor Wood' (F)	SKee
	- 'Grandiflora'	see *P. avium* 'Plena'
	- 'Greenstem Black' (F)	CTho
	- 'Hannaford' (D/C)	CHab
	- 'Hertford' (F)	NOra SKee WHar WMat
	- 'Inga' (F)	SKee
	- 'Karina' (D)	SFrt WMat
	- 'Kassins Frühe Herz' (F)	SKee
	- 'Kentish Red' (F)	SKee
	- 'Knight's Early Black' (D)	WMat
	- 'Kordia' (D) ♀H5	EPom GTwe NOra SFrt SKee WHar WMat
	- 'Kozerska' (F)	WMat
§	- 'Lapins' (F) ♀H5	CAgr CDul CFGn CLnd CTho CTri ECrN EMOT EPfP EPom GTwe LEdu MAsh MRav NLar NOra SBdl SDea SKee WHar WJas WMat WWct
	- 'May Duke'	see *P.* × *gondouinii* 'May Duke'
	- 'Merchant' (F) ♀H5	NOra SBdl SFrt SKee WMat WWct
	- 'Mermat' (F)	SKee
	- 'Merpet' (F)	SKee
	- 'Merton Bigarreau' (F)	CArg GTwe NOra SBdl SKee WHar WMat
	- 'Merton Crane' (F)	SKee
	- 'Merton Favourite' (F)	SKee
	- 'Merton Glory' (F)	CAgr CSBt EMOT EPfP GTwe IArd MAsh MMuc NOra SBdl SEND SEWo SKee SLim WHar WMat WWct
	- 'Merton Late' (F)	SKee
	- 'Merton Marvel' (F)	SKee
	- 'Merton Premier' (F)	ELan SKee SVic
	- 'Merton Reward'	see *P.* × *gondouinii* 'Merton Reward'
	- 'Mizia' (D)	WMat
	- 'Nabella' (F)	MAsh SDea WJas
	- 'Napoléon'	see *P. avium* 'Bigarreau Napoléon'
	- 'Noir de Guben' (F)	SKee WHar WMat
	- 'Noir de Meched' (D)	SKee
	- 'Octavia' (D)	WMat
	- 'Old Black Heart' (F)	SKee
	- 'Penny'PBR (F) ♀H5	CAgr EPom GTwe NOra SBdl SFrt SKee WHar WMat WWct
	- 'Petit Noir' (F)	CLnd GTwe NOra WMat
§	- 'Plena' (d) ♀H6	Widely available
§	- 'Preserving' (F)	CTho
	- 'Regina' (F)	CSut EPom NLar NOra SBdl SFrt SKee WHar WMat
	- 'Ronald's Heart' (F)	SKee
	- 'Roundel Heart' (F)	NOra SKee WHar WMat
	- 'Sasha' (F)	SFrt
	- 'Schneiders Späte Knorpel' (D)	SFrt
	- 'Skeena'PBR (F)	MCoo NOra WMat
	- 'Small Black' (F)	CHab CTho
	- 'Star Seedling' (F) **new**	WHed
	- 'Stella' (F) ♀H5	Widely available
	- 'Stella Compact' (F)	CWib ECrN LSRN SDea WHar
	- 'Strawberry Heart' (F)	SKee
	- 'Summer Sun' (D) ♀H5	CAgr CDul CLnd CMac CSut CTho CTri EMOT EPom ERea ESps GTwe LBuc LRHS MAsh MCoo MGos NLar NOra SBdl SCoo SDea SFrt SKee SLim SPoG WHar WMat WWct
	- 'Summit' (F)	CLnd SKee WMat
	- 'Sunburst' (D)	Widely available
	- 'Sweetheart' (F) ♀H5	CAgr CDul CLnd EMOT EPom GTwe LRHS LSRN MAsh NOra SBdl SKee SLim SPoG SVic WHar WMat
	- 'Sylvia' (F)	CAgr NOra WHar WMat
	- 'Turkish Black' (F)	SKee
	- 'Van' (F)	CAgr CSBt EPom NLar NOra SBdl WHar WMat
	- 'Vanda'PBR (F)	WMat
	- 'Vega' (F)	CAgr ERea GTwe NOra SFrt SKee WHar WJas WMat
	- 'Waterloo' (F)	SKee
	- 'White Heart' (F)	CHab CWib ECrN EMOT SKee
§	'Beni-tamanishiki' ♀H6	NOra WHar WMat
	'Beni-yutaka' ♀H6	CCVT CTho CTsd EMOT EWTr MAsh MRav MSwo NOra NOrn SCob SCoo SLim WHar WMat
	'Bilski'	WMat
	'Blaze'	see *P. cerasifera* 'Nigra'
	× ***blireana*** (d) ♀H6	CDul CEnd CLnd CTri ECrN EMOT EPfP ESps MGos MRav MSwo NLar NWea SCoo SPer SPoG WHar
	- 'Moseri' (d)	WTSh
	Blushing Bride	see *P.* 'Shōgetsu'
	campanulata 'Felix Jury'	EBee NOra WMat
	Candy Floss	see *P.* 'Matsumae-beni-murasaki'
	cerasifera (F)	CAgr CDul CHab CTri ECrN EPfP EPom LBuc LPar NWea SDea SKee SPer SVic WHar
	- 'Countess' (F) **new**	EPom
	- Crimson Pointe = 'Cripoizam' **new**	LRHS SPoG
	- 'Golden Sphere' (F)	CAgr CArg CFGn CLnd CTho CTri EPom NOra SBdl SDea SKee SPer WHar WMat
	- 'Gypsy' (F)	CAgr CDul CLnd CTho LRHS NOra SKee SPer WHar WMat
	- 'Hessei' (v)	EBee MHtn MMrt MRav NOrn SEle SPoG
	- 'Kentish Red' (F)	MMuc SEND
§	- Myrobalan Group (F)	ECrN MRav SDea SPre SVic WHed WMat
	- 'Myrobalan B' (F) **new**	WTSh
§	- 'Nigra' ♀H6	Widely available
	- 'Pendula'	ECrN SWvt
§	- 'Pissardii'	CWib ECrN EPfP ESps LCro LSRN NOrn NWea SCob SCoo SLon SWvt WJas WMou
*	- 'Princess'	NOrn
	- 'Ruby' (F)	CAgr CFGn EPom ERea
	- 'Woodii'	CSBt
	cerasus 'Maynard'	LSRN
	- 'Meteor Korai'	LCro LOPS LRHS MCoo WMat
	- 'Montmorency' (F)	NOra SKee
	- 'Morello' (C) ♀H6	Widely available
	- 'Nabella' (F)	SKee
	- 'Rhexii' (d)	CDul ECrN MAsh
	- 'Semperflorens'	CLnd
	'Cheal's Weeping'	EBar
	Chocolate Ice	see *P.* 'Matsumae-fuki'
§	× ***cistena*** ♀H6	CBcs CDul CLet CRos EBee ELan EPfP ESps LRHS MAsh MGos MMuc MSwo NBes SCoo SGol SHil SPoG SWvt WCFE

	– 'Crimson Dwarf'	see *P.* × *cistena*
	'Collingwood Ingram' ♀H6	EBee EBtc EPfP ESps LRHS MBlu NOrn SLim WMat
	'Cot-N-Candy' (Aprium Series)	CAgr EPom
	'Daikoku'	LRHS NOra WMat
	davidiana	SPlb
	'Delma'PBR (F)	WHar WMat
	domestica (D/C)	SPre
	– 'Allgroves Superb' (D)	ERea
	– 'Angelina Burdett' (D)	CHab SBdl SDea SKee
	– 'Anna Späth' (C/D)	SKee
	– 'Ariel' (C/D)	SDea SKee
	– 'Avalon' (D)	CAgr CCVT CLnd EMOT GTwe LBuc NOra SBdl SDea SFrt SKee WHar WMat
	– 'Beauty' (D)	CSut
	– 'Belgian Greengage' (F)	CHab SKee
	– 'Belgian Purple' (C)	SKee
	– 'Belle de Louvain' (C)	CDul CHab CLnd CTho CTri GTwe NOra SBdl SDea SKee WHar WMat WWct
	– 'Birchenhayes' (F)	CEnd
	– 'Black Diamond'	see *P. salicina* 'Black Diamond'
	– 'Blaisdon Red' (C)	CTho GTwe WHar WMat
	– 'Blue Imperatrice' (C/D)	SKee
	– 'Blue Tit' (C/D) ♀H5	CAgr CTho EPom ERea GTwe LSRN MAsh MMuc NOra SDea SEND SKee WHar WMat WWct
	– 'Bohemian' (C)	SKee
	– 'Bonne de Bry' (D)	SKee
	– 'Brandy Gage' (C/D)	SKee
	– 'Bryanston Gage' (D)	CTho SKee WMat
	– 'Burbank's Giant'	see *P. domestica* 'Giant Prune'
	– 'Burcombe' (F)	CEnd
	– 'Cambridge Gage' (D) ♀H5	Widely available
	– 'Chrislin' (F)	CTho
	– 'Coe's Golden Drop' (D)	CAgr CArg CFGn CHab CLnd ECrN EPom ERea GTwe IArd MGos MRav NOra SBdl SDea SFrt SKee SPer WHar WMat WWct
	– 'Conwy Castle' (F)	WMat
	– 'Count Althann's Gage' (D)	CHab ERea SDea SKee WWct
	– 'Cox's Emperor' (C)	SKee
	– 'Crimson Drop' (D)	SKee
	– 'Cropper'	see *P. domestica* 'Laxton's Cropper'
	– 'Curlew' (C)	SDea SKee
	– 'Czar' (C) ♀H6	Widely available
	– 'Delicious'	see *P. domestica* 'Laxton's Delicious'
	– 'Denbigh' (C)	CHab WGwG
	– 'Denniston's Superb'	see *P. domestica* 'Imperial Gage'
	– 'Des Bejonnieres' (D)	SKee
	– 'Diamond' (C)	SKee
	– 'Dittisham Black' (C)	CTho
	– 'Dittisham Ploughman' (C)	CTho SKee WMat
	– 'Drap d'Or d'Esperen' (D)	SKee
	– 'Dunster Plum' (F)	CTho CTri CWib WMat
	– 'Early Favourite' (D/C)	SKee
	– 'Early Laxton' (C/D)	CHab MMuc SDea SEND SKee
	– 'Early Prolific'	see *P. domestica* 'Early Rivers'
§	– 'Early Rivers' (C)	CAgr CDul CHab CSBt CTho CTri ELan EMOT EPom ERea ESps GTwd GTwe LRHS LSRN NOra NWea SBdl SCoo SDea SKee SPer WHar WMat WWct
	– 'Early Transparent Gage' (C/D)	CAgr CMac CSBt CTho ECrN EMOT ERea GTwe IArd LBuc LRHS MCoo NOra SBdl SCoo SDea SFrt SKee WHar WMat
	– 'Early Victoria' (C/D)	SDea
	– 'Edda' (D)	NOra WHar WMat
	– 'Edwards' (C/D)	CTri CWib SDea SKee
	– 'Excalibur' (D)	CAgr EMOT EPom GTwd GTwe IArd LBuc LSRN NOra SDea SKee WHar WMat
	– 'Finger Plum' (F)	WMat
§	– German Prune Group (C)	CFGn MCoo NOra SDea SKee WMat
§	– 'Giant Prune' (C)	CDul ECrN EMOT GTwe MMuc SBdl SDea SEND SKee WHar
I	– 'Godshill Big Sloe' (F)	SDea
	– 'Godshill Blue' (C)	SDea
	– 'Godshill Minigage' (F)	SDea
	– 'Gold Dust' (F)	WMat
	– 'Golden Transparent' (D)	MCoo SKee
	– 'Goldfinch' (D)	MCoo MMuc SEND SKee
	– 'Gordon Castle'	GQue GTwd NLar SKee WHar WMat
	– Green Gage Group	see *P. domestica* Reine-Claude Group
	– – 'Lindsey Gage' (F)	SKee
	– 'Grey Plum' (F)	CTho
	– 'Grove's Late Victoria' (D)	WWct
	– 'Guinevere' (C)	CAgr EPom LRHS MCoo NOra SBdl SFrt WHar WMat
	– 'Guthrie's Late Green' (D)	SKee
	– 'Hackman' (F)	SKee
	– 'Haganta'PBR (F) ♀H5	CAgr ERea MCoo NOra SFrt WHar WMat
	– 'Herman' (D)	CAgr CMac EMOT EPom LRHS MAsh MCoo NOra SDea SFrt SKee WHar WMat
	– 'Heron' (C)	GTwe NOra SKee WHar WMat WWct
	– 'Impérial Épineuse' (D)	SKee
§	– 'Imperial Gage' (D) ♀H5	CAgr CArg CFGn CLnd CMac CSBt CTho CTri EPom GTwe LEdu LRHS MAsh MMuc NOra SBdl SDea SEND SKee WHar WMat
	– 'Jan James' (F)	CEnd
	– 'Jefferson' (D) ♀H5	CAgr CHab CLnd EMOT GTwe NOra SBdl SDea SKee SVic WHar WMat
*	– 'Jubilaeum' (D)	CAgr CFGn CLnd CMac EPom GTwe LBuc LRHS NOra SBdl SCoo SEWo SKee WHar
	– 'Kea' (C)	CTho SKee WMat
	– 'Kirke's' (D)	CHab CTho ELan ERea GTwe NOra SDea SKee WHar WMat
	– 'Landkey Yellow' (F)	CTho WMat
	– 'Langley Gage' (D)	CAgr ERea SDea
	– 'Late Muscatelle' (D)	SKee
	– 'Late Transparent Gage' (D)	SKee
§	– 'Laxton's Cropper' (C)	CHab GTwe SKee WHar
§	– 'Laxton's Delicious' (D)	CHab
	– 'Laxton's Early Gage' (D/C)	SKee
	– 'Laxton's Gage' (D)	SDea SKee
	– 'Laxton's Jubilee' (C/D)	CSBt EMOT WMat
I	– 'Liegel's Apricot'	SKee
	– 'Madeleine Nomblot' (F)	SKee
	– 'Mallard' (D) ♀H6	NOra SKee WHar WMat
	– 'Manaccan' (C)	CTho WMat
	– 'Manns No. 1' (C/D)	SKee WMat
	– 'Marjorie's Seedling' (C) ♀H5	Widely available
	– 'Meritare' (F)	MWat NOra WMat
	– 'Merton Gage' (D)	SKee
	– 'Merton Gem' (D)	SKee
	– 'Monarch' (C)	SKee
	– 'Monsieur Jaune' (C/D)	SKee

	- 'Newark' (F)	SKee
	- Old English gage	CLnd ECrN EPom ERea SBdl
	- 'Ontario' (D)	SKee
	- 'Opal' (D) ♀H6	Widely available
	- 'Oullins Gage' (C/D) ♀H5	Widely available
	- 'Pershore' (C)	CAgr CHab CSut CWib EMOT ERea GTwe LRHS NOra SDea SKee WHar WMat WWct
	- 'Pershore Emblem' (F)	WWct
	- 'Pond's Seedling' (C)	CSBt SDea SKee
	- 'Pozegaca' (D)	SKee
	- 'President' (C)	CHab MMuc SDea SEND SKee
	- 'Primate' (D/C)	SKee
	- 'Prince Englebert' (C)	SKee
	- 'Priory Plum' (D)	SDea
	- 'Purple Pershore' (C) ♀H5	CAgr CHab CTri CWib GTwe IArd NEgg NOra SDea SKee WHar WMat WWct
	- 'Queen's Crown' (C/D)	WMat
	- 'Quetsche d'Alsace'	see *P. domestica* German Prune Group
	- 'Reeves' (C)	NOra SKee WHar
	- 'Reine Claude Reforma' (F)	SKee
	- 'Reine Claude' (RHS) (D)	SKee
	- 'Reine-Claude Dorée'	see *P. domestica* Reine-Claude Group
§	- Reine-Claude Group (D)	ELan GTwe MMuc SDea SEND SKee SLim SPer WMat
	- - 'Ingall's Grimoldby Green Gage' (D)	SKee
	- - 'Old Green Gage'	see *P. domestica* (Reine-Claude Group) 'Reine-Claude Vraie'
	- - 'Reine Claude de Brahy' (D)	SKee
	- - 'Reine-Claude de Bavais' (D)	CArg CLnd CTri GTwe NOra SDea SKee WHar WMat
	- - 'Reine-Claude de Moissac' (D)	SKee
	- - 'Reine-Claude de Vars' (D)	SKee SVic
	- - 'Reine-Claude Précoce Léon Hisse' (D)	SKee
	- - 'Reine-Claude Rosée' (D)	SKee
	- - 'Reine-Claude Tardive de Chambourcy' (D)	SKee
	- - 'Reine-Claude Violette' (D)	SKee
§	- - 'Reine-Claude Vraie' (C/D)	CAgr CMac CSBt CWib EMOT EPfP EPom LBuc LRHS LSRN MAsh NOra NPri SDea SKee SPoG WJas WMat
§	- - 'Willingham Gage' (C/D)	EMOT ERea GTwe LRHS LSRN NOra SKee WHar WMat
	- 'Royale de Vilvoorde' (D)	SKee
	- 'Sanctus Hubertus' (D)	CTri EMOT SDea WHar WWct
	- 'Seneca' (D)	EPom NOra WHar WMat
	- 'Severn Cross' (D)	SKee
	- 'Stanley' (C/D)	SVic
	- 'Stella'	CCVT ELan LOPS LSRN NEgg NPri SLim WHar
	- 'Stella's Star'	LBuc MCoo NOra WMat
	- 'Stint' (C/D)	SKee
	- 'Swan' (C)	ERea GTwe NOra SKee WHar WMat WWct
	- 'Syston White'	MGos
	- 'Thames Cross' (D)	CLnd NOra SKee
	- 'Transparent Gage' (D)	CFGn SKee
	- 'Utility' (D)	SKee
	- 'Valor' (D) ♀H5	NOra WHar
	- 'Verity' (C/D)	SKee WMat
	- 'Victoria' (D) ♀H5	Widely available
	- 'Violetta' PBR (D)	CAgr EMOT GTwe WHar
	- 'Warwickshire Drooper' (C)	CAgr CHab CTho CWib EMOT ERea ESps GTwe IArd MAsh NOra SDea SKee SLon SPer WHar WMat WWct
	- 'Washington' (D)	SDea SKee
	- 'White Magnum Bonum' (C)	SDea
	- 'Willingham'	see *P. domestica* (Reine-Claude Group) 'Willingham Gage'
	- 'Woolaston Black' (D) new	SKee
	- 'Zwetschen' new	SDea
§	***dulcis***	CDul CHab CLnd CTri CWib ELan EMOT EPfP EPom ESps EWTr LRHS MGos MMuc NWea SCoo SDea SEND SWvt WMou
	- 'Ai' (F)	CAgr
	- 'Ardéchoise' (F)	CAgr
	- 'Ferraduel' (F)	CAgr MRai
	- 'Ferragnès' (F)	CAgr MRai
*	- 'Phoebe' (F)	CAgr
	- 'Princesse' (F)	SKee
	- 'Sultane' (F) new	SKee
	- 'Supernova' (F)	CCCN MRai
	- 'Tuono' (F)	CCCN
	Easter Bonnet = 'Comet' PBR	CTri LRHS
	'Flavor King' (Pluot Series) (D)	CAgr WMat
	'Flavour Supreme' (F)	EPom
	Fragrant Cloud	see *P.* 'Shizuka'
	Frilly Frock = 'Fpmspl' (v)	EBee LPre LRHS LSRN NLar NOra SLim SPoG WMat
	'Fugenzō'	CSBt EBee WMat
	glandulosa 'Alba Plena' (d)	CDul CEnd CMac CSBt LBMP MAsh SGol SPlb SRms SWvt WCFE
	- 'Rosea Plena'	see *P. glandulosa* 'Sinensis'
§	- 'Sinensis' (d)	CDul CEnd CSBt SRms
§	× ***gondouinii*** 'May Duke' (F)	SKee WHar
§	- 'Merton Reward' (F)	SKee
	grayana B&SWJ 10903	WCru
	'Gyoikō'	CEnd CLnd EBee NOra WMat
	'Hally Jolivette'	CEnd ELan MAsh MBlu NOrn WMat
§	'Hanagasa' ♀H6	CEnd EMOT LRHS NOra NWea WMat WMou
	'Hillieri Spire'	see *P.* 'Spire'
	'Hilling's Weeping'	EBee LCro LOPS SLon
	himalaica	LRHS NLar NOra WMat
	'Hokusai' ♀H6	CDul EMOT EPfP NOra SGol WMat
	Hollywood	see *P.* 'Trailblazer'
	'Horinji'	LRHS NOra SCoo WMat
	'Howard No. 3'	WMat
	'Ichiyo' (d) ♀H6	CDul CLnd EBee ECrN EPfP ESps LRHS NOra SCoo WMat
	ilicifolia subsp. ***lyonii*** new	WPGP
	× ***incam*** 'Okamé' ♀H6	Widely available
	- 'Shosar' ♀H6	CEnd CWib ECrN MAsh SCoo SPer
	incisa	CTri NEgg
	- 'Beniomi'	MRav
	- 'February Pink'	CJun SGol
	- 'Fujimae' ♀H6	NLar
	- 'Kojo-no-mai' ♀H6	Widely available
	- 'Mikinori'	CEnd CJun CMac CSBt EBee EPfP MAsh MBlu MJak NLar NOra SCoo WMat
	- 'Oshidori' (d) ♀H6	CMac CSBt EBee ELon EPfP LRHS MMrt MRav NOra SRms WMat
	- 'Paean'	EBee NLar
	- 'Pendula' ♀H6	LCro LOPS NOra SCoo WMat
	- 'Praecox'	CHGN CSBt CTho EPfP SCoo WMat
§	- f. ***yamadei*** ♀H6	CJun LBMP MAsh NOrn

	insititia (F)	NWea
	- 'Abergwyngregin' (C)	NOra WMat
	- 'Andrierez' (F) **new**	SKee
	- 'Aylesbury Prune' (C)	WMat
	- 'Black Bullace' (F)	ERea
	- 'Blue Violet Damson' (F)	CAgr CFGn ERea GTwe MCoo NOra SKee WHar WMat
§	- 'Bradley's King Damson' (C)	MCoo NLar NOra SBdl SKee WHar WMat
	- bullace (C)	ERea LEdu SDea
	- 'Countess' (C)	CTri
	- 'Dittisham Damson' (C)	CTho WMat
	- 'Farleigh Damson' (C) 🏆H6	CAgr CArg CHab CLnd CWib ECrN EMOT EPfP EPom ERea ESps EWTr GTwe IArd LBuc LEdu MJak NOra NWea SBdl SDea SKee SPer SVic WHar WJas WMat WWct
	- 'Godshill Damson' (C)	SDea
	- 'King of Damsons'	see *P. insititia* 'Bradley's King Damson'
	- 'Langley Bullace' (C)	CAgr CDul ERea GTwe LEdu NOra SDea SKee WHar WMat
	- 'Lisna' (C)	CTri WMat
	- 'Merryweather Damson' (C)	Widely available
	- 'Mirabelle Countess' (C)	EPom WMat
	- 'Mirabelle de Nancy' (C)	CAgr CDul CLnd CTho EPom ERea GTwe NOra SBdl SDea SEWo SFrt SKee WHar WMat
	- 'Mirabelle de Nancy' red (C)	SDea
	- 'Mirabelle Ruby' (C)	CArg ERea LRHS NOra SBdl SFrt WMat
§	- 'Prune Damson' (C) 🏆H6	CAgr CArg CDul CHab CLnd CMac CTho CTri EMOT EPom ERea GTwe IArd LBuc LCro LRHS MAsh MMuc NEgg NLar NOra SBdl SDea SEND SKee SPer WHar WJas WMat WWct
	- 'Shepherd's Bullace' (C)	CTho ERea MCoo SKee
	- 'Shropshire Damson'	see *P. insititia* 'Prune Damson'
	- 'Small Bullace' (C)	SKee
	- 'Westmorland Prune' (C)	CHab NLar
	- 'Yellow Apricot' (C)	ERea SKee
	'Jō-nioi'	CDul CEnd CLnd CTho
§	'Kanzan' (d) 🏆H6	Widely available
§	'Kiku-shidare-zakura'	Widely available
	'Kobuku-zakura'	EBee EWTr NOra WMat
	Korean hill cherry	see *P. verecunda*
	'Kursar'	CDul CLnd CSBt CTri EBee EMOT EPfP ESps EUJe GKin LRHS LSRN MAsh NOrn NWea SCoo SEWo SLim SLon SPer SWvt WMat
	laurocerasus	CBcs CCVT CDul CMac EBee ECrN ELan EPfP EShb ESps GKin IBoy LPar MGos MHed MMuc MRav NPri NWea SArc SCob SEND SGol SPer WHed WMat WMoo WMou WTSh
	- 'Angustifolia'	EBee IBoy
	- 'Camelliifolia'	CMac CTri MBlu
	- 'Castlewellan' (v)	CDul CTri EBee ELan ELon EMOT EPfP EShb LHop LRHS MGos MRav MSwo NLar NWad SCob SDix SPer SPoG SSta WMoo WRHF
	- 'Caucasica'	CEnd ECrN ESps NBes NLar SCob SGol
	- 'Cherry Brandy'	SCob SGol
	- Etna = 'Anbri'PBR 🏆H5	CMac EMOT ESps GMcL LBuc LSou MAsh SCob SHil SWvt
	- Genolia = 'Mariblon'PBR	SGol
	- 'Green Marble' (v)	CTri EHoe
	- 'Greentorch'PBR	LRHS
	- 'Herbergii'	NBes
	- 'Ivory'PBR	WMoo
§	- 'Latifolia'	LRHS SHil
	- 'Magnoliifolia'	see *P. laurocerasus* 'Latifolia'
	- 'Marbled White'	see *P. laurocerasus* 'Castlewellan'
	- 'Miky'	CJun
	- 'Mount Vernon'	CTri MBlu SCob
	- 'Novita'	CBod ECrN EPfP GMcL LSRN NLar NPri WMoo
	- 'Otto Luyken' 🏆H5	Widely available
	- 'Piranha' **new**	NEoE
	- 'Reynvaanii'	CJun
	- 'Rotundifolia' 🏆H5	Widely available
	- 'Schipkaensis'	GMcL
	- 'Van Nes'	MAsh
	- 'Variegata' misapplied	see *P. laurocerasus* 'Castlewellan'
	- 'Variegata' ambig. (v)	CWib SRms
	- 'Whitespot'	SEND
	- 'Zabeliana'	CDul CMac CTri ESps GMcL MJak MSwo NEgg NWea SCob SPer SRms WHar
	litigiosa	EBee EMOT EMil NOra WMat
	'Little Pink Perfection'	CNWT NBes NOra NOrn SCoo SPoG WMat
	lusitanica 🏆H5	Widely available
	- subsp. ***azorica***	EBee LRHS WPGP
	- 'Brenelia'PBR **new**	EBee
	- 'Myrtifolia' 🏆H5	CBar CLet CRos CTri EPfP EShb ESps GMcL LRHS MRav NLar NOra SCob SGol SHil SLon SWvt WCFE WMat WMoo
	- 'Variegata' (v)	CBar CMac CTri CWib ELan ELon ESps LBMP LHop MGos MMuc MRav MSwo SCob SDix SGol SPer SPoG SSta SWvt WFar WMoo
	maackii	CLnd EMOT ESps NOrn WMou
	- 'Amber Beauty'	CBcs CDul EBee EPfP GKin MMuc MRav NOra SEND SGol SLon WMat
	mahaleb	CNWT
	maritima	LEdu
§	'Matsumae-beni-murasaki'	EMOT NLar NOra WHar WMat
	'Matsumae-beni-tamanishiki'	see *P.* 'Beni-tamanishiki'
§	'Matsumae-fuki' 🏆H6	EBee EMOT LSRN NLar NOra NOrn NWea SLim SPoG WHar WMat
	'Matsumae-hanagasa'	see *P.* 'Hanagasa'
	maximowiczii B&SWJ 10967	WCru
	'Mount Fuji'	see *P.* 'Shirotae'
	mume	CMen LPar
	- 'Alba'	LPar
	- 'Beni-chidori' 🏆H5	CBcs CDul CEnd CMac CWib EBee ELan EPfP IVic LCro LOPS LRHS MAsh MBlu NLar NOra NOrn SCob SCoo WCot WJas WMat
§	- 'Omoi-no-mama' (d)	CEnd CMen SAko
	- 'Omoi-no-wac'	see *P. mume* 'Omoi-no-mama'
	- 'Pendula'	LPar
	- var. ***rosea*** **new**	LPar
	myrobalana	see *P. cerasifera* Myrobalan Group
	nigra	WMat
	nipponica var. ***kurilensis*** 'Brillant'	CBcs CSBt LBMP LRHS MAsh MMrt NHol NLar NOrn SPoG
	- - 'Ruby'	LSRN NEgg
	'Okame Harlequin' (v)	EMOT
	'Oku-miyako' misapplied	see *P.* 'Shōgetsu'
	'Orange Beauty' **new**	LRHS
	padus	CArg CCVT CDul CHab CLnd CMac CSBt CTri ECrN ESps EWTr LBuc MGos MJak MMuc MSwo NLar NWea SCob SEND SEWo WHed WMou WTSh

- 'Albertii'	CCVT EBee LPre NOra WMat
- 'Colorata' ♀H6	CArg CDul CEnd CMac CTho EBee ECrN ELan EWTr LHop MGos MMuc MRav NLar NPri SEND SGol SPer SWvt
- 'Grandiflora'	see *P. padus* 'Watereri'
- 'Le Thoureil'	MMrt
- 'Purple Queen'	ECrN SCob SGol
§ - 'Watereri' ♀H6	CArg CCVT CDul CEnd CMCN CMac CTho CWib ECrN ELan EMOT EPfP ESps LHop MMuc NOrn NWea SEND SEWo SGol SPer SPoG WMat WMou
'Pandora' ♀H6	CCVT CDul CLnd EBee ECrN EMOT EPfP ESps LCro LHop LOPS LRHS MAsh MGos MMuc MRav MSwo NOra NOrn NWea SCob SCoo SEND SEWo SLim SPer SPoG WFar WMat WMou
§ ***pendula*** f. ***ascendens*** 'Rosea' ♀H6	MRav NOra WFar WMat
- 'Pendula Plena Rosea' (d)	NOra WFar WMat
§ - 'Pendula Rosea'	CDul CEnd CLnd CTri CWib EPfP ESps LPar MAsh SCob SPer WJas
§ - 'Pendula Rubra' ♀H6	CCVT CDul CLnd CMac CSBt CWib EBee ELan EMOT EPfP LHop LRHS MSwo NOra NOrn SCoo SLim SPer SPoG WMat WMou
§ - 'Stellata' ♀H6	EPfP NLar NOra WMat
persica	CPne ESps SPre
- 'Advance' (F) **new**	SDea
- 'Amsden June' (F)	CLnd CWib EBtc ERea GTwe LEdu NOra NRog SDea SKee WHar WMat
- 'Avalon Pride' (F)	CAgr CSut EPfP EPom ERea LBuc LRHS MCoo NRog SFrt SKee
- 'Barrington' (F)	ERea
- 'Bellegarde' (F)	CFGn ERea NOra NRog SDea WMat
- 'Black' (F)	ERea
- 'Bonanza' (F)	EPom ERea LRHS LSRN
- 'Carman' (F)	ERea WMat
- 'Champion' (F)	NRog SDea
- 'Crimson Bonfire' (F)	EPom
- 'Crimson Cascade' (F)	ELan
- 'Darling' (F)	SVic
- 'Diamond' (F)	EPom
- 'Dixi Red' (F)	CAgr ERea
- 'Doctor Hogg' (F)	ERea SDea
- 'Duke of York' (F) ♀H4	CTri ERea GTwe SDea SKee
- 'Dymond' (F)	ERea
- 'Early Alexander' (F)	ERea
- 'Foliis Rubris' (F)	CDul LRHS
- 'Francis' (F)	SKee
- 'Frost' (F)	ERea NRog WMat
- 'Garden Lady' (F)	EPom GTwe NOra SLim WHar WMat
- 'Gorgeous' (F)	SKee WMat
- 'Hale's Early' (F)	GTwe MMuc MRav NOra NRog SKee SLim SPer WHar WMat
- 'Harken' (F)	ERea
- 'Hylands' (F)	SDea
- 'Jalousia' (F)	EPom NRog
- 'Johnny Brack' (F)	ERea NRog
- 'Kestrel' (F)	ERea SKee
- 'Madison' (F)	ERea
- 'Mesembrine' PBR (F)	EPom ERea
- 'Natalia' (F)	SDea
- var. ***nectarina*** Crimson Gold (F)	SDea
- - 'Earliglo' (F)	LRHS NOra WMat
- - 'Early Blaze' (F)	LEdu
- - 'Early Gem' (F)	ERea SDea
- - 'Early Rivers' (F) ♀H4	ERea LSRN SDea WMat
- - 'Elruge' (F)	ERea SDea
- - 'Fantasia' (F)	EPfP SDea
- - 'Fire Gold' (F)	ERea SDea
- - 'Flavortop' (F)	EPfP ERea
- - 'Garden Beauty' (F/d)	WMat
- - 'Honey Kist' PBR (F)	EPom
- - 'Humboldt' (F)	CAgr CDul CFGn EMOT ERea GTwe SDea SKee WHar WMat
- - 'John Rivers' (F)	SDea SPer
- - 'Lord Napier' (F) ♀H4	CAgr CDul CSBt CTri CWib EMOT EPfP EPom ERea LRHS MAsh MGos MJak MWat NOra SDea SEND SKee SLim SPer SPoG SVic WHar WMat
- - 'Madame Blanchet' (F)	SDea
- - 'Nectared' (F)	CWib
- - 'Nectarella' (F)	EPom ERea LRHS LSRN NOra SLim WHar WMat
- - 'Pineapple' (F)	CAgr CTri ERea GTwe LRHS SDea SKee WHar WMat
- - Rubis = 'Necta Zee' PBR	EPom
- - 'Ruby Gold' (F)	SDea
- - 'Sauzee Bel'	EPom
- - 'Sauzee King' (F)	EPom
- - 'Snow Baby'	EPom
- - 'Terrace Ruby' (F)	MGos WMat
- 'Oriane' PBR (F)	NRog
- 'Pallas' (F)	ERea
- 'Peregrine' (F) ♀H4	CAgr CDul CSBt CTri CWib EMOT EPfP EPom ERea ESps EWTr GTwe LRHS LSRN MAsh MGos MJak MMuc MWat NOra NRog SDea SEND SKee SLim SPer WHar WJas WMat
- 'Raritan Rose' (F)	ERea
- 'Red Top' (F)	EPfP
- 'Redhaven' (F)	CAgr CWib EMOT ERea NRog SDea SKee SVic WHar WMat
- 'Redwing' (F)	CAgr
- 'Reliance' (F)	SDea
- 'Robin Redbreast' (F)	CAgr SDea
- 'Rochester' (F) ♀H4	CAgr CDul CFGn CSBt CTri CWib EMOT EPom ERea GTwe LRHS LSRN MGos NOra NRog SDea SKee SLim SPer SPoG WHar WMat
- 'Royal George' (F)	NRog
- 'Rubira' (F)	NRog
- 'Sanguine de Savoie' (F)	EPom LRHS NOra NRog WMat
- 'Sanguinole' (F)	CSut SKee
- 'Saturne' (F)	EMOT EPom ERea MAsh NOra NRog SDea SKee WHar WMat
- 'Springtime' (F)	SDea
- 'Terrace Amber' (F)	WMat
- 'Terrace Diamond' (F)	WMat
- 'Terrace Garnet' (F)	MGos WMat
- 'Wassenberger' (F)	SDea
× ***persicoides*** 'Ingrid' (F)	CAgr CDul CFGn EBtc ECrN EMOT ERea ESps LPre LRHS MCoo MGos NOra SCoo SKee WHar WMat
- 'Pollardii'	NWea WJas
- 'Robijn' (F)	CAgr EPom LBuc LEdu SFrt SKee SVic
- 'Spring Glow'	CCVT CDul CEnd CLnd EMOT EMil EPfP LRHS MSwo NOra NWea SCoo SEND SLim SLon WJas WMat
'Petite Noir'	CLnd LRHS
phaeosticta NJM 10.072 **new**	WPGP
Pink Parasol	see *P.* 'Hanagasa'

'Pink Perfection' ♀H6	CBcs CDul CLnd CSBt CWib ECrN ELan ELon EMOT EPfP ESps EUJe LRHS MGos MSwo NLar NOra NOrn SCob SPer WHar WJas WMat WMou
'Pink Shell'	CLnd EPfP ESps MAsh NOra SPer WMat
pissardii	see *P. cerasifera* 'Pissardii'
'Pissardii Nigra'	see *P. cerasifera* 'Nigra'
pumila var. ***depressa***	MRav SAko
'Red Dwarf' **new**	LRHS
'Royal Burgundy' (d) ♀H6	Widely available
rufa	CDul CJun CLnd EBee EBtc GKin LLHF NOra SKHP SLon WMat WPat
salicina 'Abundance' (F)	ERea
- 'Beauty'	ERea
§ - 'Black Diamond' (F)	SDea
- 'Elephant Heart' (F) **new**	MRai
- 'Golden Japan' (F) **new**	MRai
- 'Howard Miracle' (F)	ERea
- 'Lizzie' (F)	EPom
- 'Mariposa' (F)	ERea
- 'Methley' (D)	CAgr ERea MRai NLar NOra SFrt WHar WMat
- 'Ozark Premier' (F)	ERea
- 'Santa Rosa' (F)	ERea MRai
- 'Satsuma' (F)	ERea
- 'Sierra' (F)	ERea
- 'Sun Gold' (F) **new**	MRai
sargentii	Widely available
- 'Charles Sargent' ♀H6	CMCN LSRN MBlu
- 'Columnaris'	WMat
- 'Rancho'	CLnd MAsh SCoo SLim SPer SPoG WMat
× ***schmittii***	CCVT EBee ECrN ESps SPer WJas WMat
'Sekiyama'	see *P.* 'Kanzan'
§ ***serrula***	Widely available
- 'Branklyn' ♀H6	EBee MGos NLar SCob
- 'Princesse Sturdza'	MBlu
- var. ***tibetica***	see *P. serrula*
serrula × ***serrulata***	WPGP
serrulata (d)	CAco
- 'Erecta'	see *P.* 'Amanogawa'
- 'Grandiflora'	see *P.* 'Ukon'
- 'Longipes'	see *P.* 'Shōgetsu'
- 'Miyako' misapplied	see *P.* 'Shōgetsu'
- var. ***pubescens***	see *P. verecunda*
- 'Rosea'	see *P.* 'Kiku-shidare-zakura'
'Shidare-zakura'	see *P.* 'Kiku-shidare-zakura'
'Shimizu-zakura'	see *P.* 'Shōgetsu'
'Shiro' (D)	ERea SFrt
'Shirofugen' ♀H6	Widely available
§ 'Shirotae' ♀H6	Widely available
§ 'Shizuka' ♀H6	CWib ECrN ELon EMOT EWTr LRHS MSwo NLar NOra NOrn NWea SCob SCoo SLim SPer SPoG WHar WMat WMou
§ 'Shōgetsu' ♀H6	CBcs CDul CEnd CLnd CMac CSBt CTho EBee ELan EMOT EPfP ESps EWTr LRHS LSRN MAsh MMuc NEgg NLar NOra NOrn SCob SEWo SLim SPer SPoG WHar WMat WMou
× ***sieboldii*** 'Caespitosa'	see *P.* 'Takasago'
'Snow Goose'	CMac EBee ELan EMOT EPfP ESps LHop LRHS MBlu MMuc NEgg NOra SCoo SGol WHar WMat
'Snow Showers'	CCVT CEnd CMac ELan EMOT LCro LRHS LSRN MAsh MGos MMuc NOra NOrn NPri NWea SEND SLim SPer SPoG WHar WMat
spinosa	Widely available
- 'Plena' (d)	CEnd CTho MBlu
- 'Purpurea'	CDul CTho EGFP MBlu WMou
§ 'Spire' ♀H6	Widely available
Spring Snow	see *P.* 'Beni-tamanishiki'
'Spring Snow' ambig.	EMOT
'Stefania'	WMat
× ***subhirtella***	ESps LPar
- var. ***ascendens***	see *P. pendula* f. *ascendens*
- 'Autumnalis'	Widely available
- 'Autumnalis Rosea'	Widely available
- 'Falling Stars'	SLon
- 'Fukubana'	CLnd CMac EBee EMOT EPfP MAsh NLar WMat
- 'Pendula' misapplied	see *P. pendula* 'Pendula Rosea'
- 'Pendula Rosea'	see *P. pendula* 'Pendula Rosea'
- 'Pendula Rubra'	see *P. pendula* 'Pendula Rubra'
- 'Rosea'	see *P. pendula* f. *ascendens* 'Rosea'
- 'Stellata'	see *P. pendula* 'Stellata'
'Sunset Boulevard' ♀H6	CLnd ELan EMOT EPfP LSRN MGos NLar NOra WHar WMat
'Tai-haku' ♀H6	Widely available
§ 'Takasago'	EBee
'Taoyame' ♀H6	CLnd
tenella	ECha WCot
- 'Fire Hill'	CJun CSBt CWib ELan EPfP LRHS MGos NLar SKHP SPer WCot WJas
'The Bride' ♀H6	CBcs CDul CEnd CJun CTho EBee EMOT EPfP LCro LOPS LRHS MAsh SCoo SEWo WMat
tibetica	see *P. serrula*
'Tiltstone Hellfire'	EBee EMOT GBin WMat
tomentosa	SEND
§ 'Trailblazer' (C/D)	CDul CEnd CLnd CMac ECrN EMOT EMil IVic MRav MSwo SCob SKee SLon WMou
triloba	CBcs CWib ECha ESps LCro MBlu MGos NWea
- 'Multiplex' (d)	SRms WJas
§ 'Ukon' ♀H6	CBcs CDul CLnd CMCN CMac CTho CTri EBee ECrN EMOT EPfP ESps LCro LOPS LRHS MAsh MGos MRav NLar NOra NWea SGol SLim SPer WFar WHar WMat
'Umineko'	CCVT CDul CLnd CWib ECrN ESps MGos MMuc SEND SEWo SPer WHar
§ ***verecunda***	CLnd NWea WJas
- 'Autumn Glory' ♀H6	CTho
'Victoria Willis'	WMat
virginiana 'Schubert'	CDul ECrN EMOT NWea WMou
'White Cloud'	CDul
'Woodfield Cluster'	IArd
yamadae	see *P. incisa* f. *yamadei*
× ***yedoensis***	CCVT CDul CLnd EBee EMOT ESps LPar MRav NOra SEWo SLon SPer WHar WMat WMou
- 'Ivensii'	CBcs CDul CSBt CWib EMOT ESps LHop NWea SCoo SPer
- 'Pendula'	see *P.* × *yedoensis* 'Shidare-Yoshino'
- 'Perpendens'	see *P.* × *yedoensis* 'Shidare-Yoshino'
§ - 'Shidare-Yoshino'	CCVT CDul CLnd CSBt EBee ECrN EMOT ESps LRHS MAsh MGos MRav MSwo NLar NOrn NWea SLim SLon WMat
§ - 'Somei-Yoshino' ♀H6	CCVT CMCN CTho CTri EPfP NWea SLim WHar WJas
'Yoshino'	see *P.* × *yedoensis* 'Somei-Yoshino'
'Yoshino Pendula'	see *P.* × *yedoensis* 'Shidare-Yoshino'

Pseuderanthemum (*Acanthaceae*)

carruthersii	LSou
var. ***atropurpureum*** 'Rubrum'	

Pseudocydonia (*Rosaceae*)

§ ***sinensis***	CAgr CBcs CMen SSta WHil

Pseudofumaria see *Corydalis*

alba	see *Corydalis ochroleuca*

Pseudogynoxys (*Asteraceae*)

§ ***chenopodioides***	CCCN CRHN CSpe EWld SVen

Pseudolarix (*Pinaceae*)

amabilis ♀H6	CDul CMen CTho EPfP MBlu MPkF SCoo SLim SMad
kaempferi (Lamb.) Gordon	see *Larix kaempferi*

Pseudomuscari see *Muscari*

Pseudopanax ✿ (*Araliaceae*)

(Adiantifolius Group) 'Adiantifolius'	CBcs EBee ESwi SVen
- 'Cyril Watson' ♀H3	CBcs ELan SBig SVen
arboreus	see *Neopanax arboreus*
chathamicus	SArc
crassifolius	CAbb CBcs CBrP CCCN CDTJ ELon ESwi EUJe GBin IDee LRHS NLos SArc SBig WCot
- var. ***trifoliolatus***	WPGP
discolor	LEdu
ferox	CAbb CBcs CBrP CDTJ CTsd ESwi EUJe GBin IDee LTro NLos SBig SCob SPoG SVen
laetus	see *Neopanax laetus*
lessonii	CBcs CBrP
- 'Gold Splash' (v) ♀H3	CBcs EPfP IVic LRHS SBig SEND SVen
- 'Rangitira'	CBcs SBig
'Linearifolius'	LEdu
'Moa's Toes' **new**	CAbb NLos SCob
'Purpureus' ♀H3	CDTJ EBee ESwi IDee SEND SVen
'Sabre'	CBcs CDTJ EBee EPfP EUJe SEND
'Trident' ♀H3	SBig SEND SLim SVen
'Tuatara' **new**	CAbb GBin NLos SCob

Pseudosasa (*Poaceae*)

amabilis misapplied	see *Arundinaria gigantea*
§ ***japonica*** ♀H5	CAbb CBcs CBod CEnt CJng CTsd CWib ENBC EPfP ESps GBin GMcL LCro LOPS LPar LRHS MMuc MWht NLar NRHS SArc SCob SEND SEWo SPer SPoG WCFE WMoo
§ - 'Akebonosuji' (v)	CEnt CJng MWht WPGP
I - var. ***pleioblastoides***	MWht
- 'Tsutsumiana'	CJng ELon ERod EUJe GMcL MWht NLar SBig
- 'Variegata'	see *P. japonica* 'Akebonosuji'
usawai	CJng
viridula	ERod MWht

Pseudotsuga (*Pinaceae*)

§ ***menziesii***	CAco CBcs CDul CLnd EPfP MBlu MMuc NWea SEND WHed WTSh
- 'Bhiela Lhota'	CKen
- 'Blue Wonder'	CKen
- 'Densa'	CKen
- 'Fastigiata'	CKen
- 'Fletcheri'	CKen
- 'Foxy Fir'	NLar
- var. ***glauca***	CDul
- 'Glauca Pendula'	CDul CKen MBlu
I - 'Gotelli's Pendula'	CKen
- 'Graceful Grace'	CKen
- 'Hillside Pride'	NLar
- 'Idaho Gem'	CKen NLar
- 'Julie'	CKen
- 'Knaphill'	LRHS
- 'Little Jamie'	CKen
- 'Lohbrunner'	CKen
- 'McKenzie'	CKen
- 'Nana'	CKen
- 'Serpentine'	MBlu
- 'Stairii'	CKen
- 'Uwes Golden'	SLim
- 'Vladstein'	NLar
taxifolia	see *P. menziesii*

Pseudowintera (*Winteraceae*)

§ ***colorata***	CBcs CMac CPla CTsd CWib GAbr GKin IVic MPkF MRav NLar SCob SEle WPat WSHC
- 'Marjorie Congreve'	CBcs GKin IArd IDee IVic LRHS WPat
- 'Moulin Rouge'	CBcs LRHS MPkF SEle
- 'Red Glow'	CBcs
- 'Red Leopard'	CBcs LBMP LRHS NLar SEle

Psidium (*Myrtaceae*)

cattleyanum	see *P. littorale* var. *longipes*
guajava (F)	CCCN SPlb XBlo
littorale (F)	CPne
§ - var. ***longipes*** (F)	CCCN EShb XBlo

Psoralea (*Papilionaceae*)

aphylla	SVen
* ***fleta***	SPlb
glabra	SPlb
glandulosa	SBrt SPlb WSHC
* ***macrothyrsa***	EBee
oligophylla	SPlb
onobrychis	SPhx

Ptelea (*Rutaceae*)

trifoliata	CAby CBcs CDul CWib ELan EPfP MBlu NWea SChF SPer SRms WPGP
- 'Aurea' ♀H5	CAbP CBcs CBot CJun ELan EPfP LHop LRHS MBlu MMuc SMad SPer WBor WPGP

Pteracanthus see *Strobilanthes*

Pteridium (*Dennstaedtiaceae*)

aquilinum	XLum

Pteridophyllum (*Papaveraceae*)

racemosum	CTal EFEx GEdr WCru

Pteris ✿ (*Pteridaceae*)

cretica ♀H1c	CTsd
- var. ***albolineata*** ♀H1c	LCro LLWG LRHS WCot XBlo
- 'Mayi' (v)	LRHS
- 'Ouvradii'	SPlb
- 'Parkeri'	LRHS
- 'Rowei'	LRHS XBlo
- 'Wimsettii'	LRHS
* ***staminea***	XBlo
tremula	EShb

tricolor	EShb
umbrosa	LLWG NLos
wallichiana	CFil WPGP

Pterocactus (*Cactaceae*)

hickenii F&W 10240	WCot

Pterocarya ✿ (*Juglandaceae*)

fraxinifolia	CBcs CCVT CMCN CTho ECrN EPfP GQui IArd IDee MBlu MCoo MMuc MRav SAko SEND WTSh
- NJM 13.007 **new**	WPGP
- PAB 13.052 **new**	LEdu
- 'Abbotsbury Giant' **new**	WPGP
macroptera var. ***insignis***	CFil WPGP
× ***rehderiana***	CTho MBlu
rhoifolia	CDul CMCN
stenoptera	CBcs CDTJ CDul CMCN CTho NLar
- 'Fern Leaf' 🏆H6	CFil CHid EBee LRHS MBlu SHil WMou WPGP

Pterocephalus (*Caprifoliaceae*)

parnassi	see *P. perennis*
§ ***perennis***	CMea ECho MHer NBir NRya SRms WAbe WHoo
spathulatus	WAbe

Pterodiscus (*Pedaliaceae*)

aurantiacus	LToo
ngamicus	LToo

Pterostylis (*Orchidaceae*)

curta 🏆H2	CBro CTal ECho

Pterostyrax (*Styracaceae*)

corymbosa	CBcs CMCN GBin MBlu NLar SMad
- CWJ 12838 **new**	WCru
hispida 🏆H5	CAbP CAby CBcs CDul CHGN CMCN CTsd CWib EPfP EWTr GBin IDee IVic MBlu MRav NLar SAko SChF WFar WGrn WHar WHor
psilophyllus	WPGP
- trilobed **new**	WPGP

Ptilostemon (*Asteraceae*)

§ ***diacantha***	EPfP IFoB LRHS
niveus	WCot

Ptilotrichum see *Alyssum*

Ptilotus (*Amaranthaceae*)

exaltatus	SPlb
- 'Benjo'PBR	EBee

Pueraria (*Papilionaceae*)

montana var. ***lobata***	CArn

Pulicaria (*Asteraceae*)

§ ***dysenterica***	CHab LLWG NMir WHer WSFF

Pulmonaria (*Boraginaceae*)

angustifolia 🏆H7	EPfP ESps GKev GMaP MNrw NPnk SHeu SRms
- 'Azurea'	CElw ELan EPPr EPfP EWoo GAbr GBin GMaP LRHS MCot MMuc MRav NBro NLar SEND SRms
- 'Blaues Meer'	EBee ECtt GAbr LBMP LRHS MNrw NSti SGbt SHeu
- 'Munstead Blue'	CElw CLAP GBuc MCot MRav NRya SRms
'Apple Frost'	LRHS NRHS SHeu
'Barfield Regalia'	NSti
'Benediction'	EBee MAvo MNrw NSti WCot WSHC
'Beth Chatto'	CElw
'Beth's Pink'	GAbr
'Blake's Silver'	CBre CDor CMil EBee ECtt GAbr MAvo MBel MHol MNrw NEgg NSti SPoG WBrk WCot WGrn WHoo WPGP WWFP
'Blauer Hügel'	NSti
'Blauhimmel'	GCra
'Blue Crown'	CElw EWes
'Blue Ensign' 🏆H6	Widely available
'Blue Moon'	see *P. officinalis* 'Blue Mist'
'Blue Pearl'	LRHS XEll
'Blueberry Muffin'	CSpe
'Bubble Gum'PBR	CDor CWCL LRHS NRHS SHeu SHil
Caborn hybrids **new**	LLWP
'Caborn Raspberry'	LLWP
Cally hybrid	CLAP GCal
'Cedric Morris'	CElw
'Cleeton Red'	MNrw
'Coral Springs'	GBuc NLar
'Cotton Cool'	CBod CLAP CTal EAEE EBee ECha ECtt EShb EWoo GBin GBuc LRHS MAvo MBNS MBel MCot MRav MSpe NEgg NHol NPnk NSti NWad SGbt SHeu SSut WMoo WWtn
'Crawshay Chance'	CElw
'Dark Vader'	ECtt LRHS MNrw NRHS SHeu SHil SPoG
'Diana Clare' 🏆H6	Widely available
'Elworthy Rubies'	CElw
'Excalibur'	ECtt LRHS NLar NRHS SHeu
'Glacier'	EPfP MNrw WCot
'Hazel Kaye's Red'	LLWP
'High Contrast'	ECtt LRHS SHeu SHil
'Highdown'	see *P.* 'Lewis Palmer'
'Ice Ballet' (Classic Series)	CDor CLAP EBee ECtt EPfP MNrw SCob SHar SHeu WCAu
§ 'Lewis Palmer' 🏆H7	CBro CDor CSam CWCL GCal GMaP LRHS MNrw NBir SRGP SRms WHea WHoo
'Little Star'	CElw EBee ECha GBuc LRHS NSti SHeu SRGP WFar
longifolia	CBod EAEE ECha EHoe ELan EPfP GAbr GKev LRHS NBir NLar NSti SCob
§ - 'Ankum'	CElw CLAP NBir WCot
- 'Ballyrogan Blue'	LRHS
- 'Bertram Anderson'	CLet EBee ECtt GMaP IBoy LRHS NBir NLar NRHS SCob SHeu SPer SRGP SRms SWvt
- subsp. ***cevennensis***	CLAP ILea LRHS NLar SHeu WFar
- 'Coen Jansen'	see *P. longifolia* 'Ankum'
- 'Dordogne'	CLAP NBir NLar
'Mado'	ECha
'Majesté'	CBod CBot CDor CLAP CWib ECha EHrv ELan EPfP EWTr EWes GBuc GMaP IFro LRHS MRav NBir NLar NRHS NSti SCob SHeu SPer SPoG WCot
'Margery Fish'	CDor CLAP LRHS SHeu
'Mary Mottram'	ECtt NBir NSti SHeu WCot
'Mawson's Blue' 🏆H6	CLAP EWes NBir NChi SWvt WMoo WSHC
'Merlin'	CLAP SKHP
'Milky Way'	ECtt EPfP SHeu
mollis	CBod EPed GBin GCal IMou LRHS MNrw NSti WCAu

	– 'Royal Blue'	MRav
	'Monksilver'	CElw
	'Moonshine' PBR	ECtt LRHS MAsh NRHS SHeu SHil
	'Moonstone'	CElw
	'Mournful Purple'	ELon
	'Mrs Kittle'	CSam CWCL GPSL GQue IMou LRHS MRav NBir NGdn NHol NSti SHeu SSut
	'Nürnberg'	CDor
	officinalis	CHby EPed IFoB NChi SIde WBrk
§	– 'Blue Mist'	CLAP GMaP NBir WCot WMoo
	– 'Bowles's Blue'	see *P. officinalis* 'Blue Mist'
	– Cambridge Blue Group	EPfP LRHS MRav NBir NCGa NGdn NSti WCot WWtn
	– 'White Wings'	CLAP EBee NLar
	'Oliver Wyatt's White'	CLAP SRGP
	Opal = 'Ocupol'	Widely available
	'Pierre's Pure Pink'	EBee LRHS NRHS SBee SHeu
	'Pink Haze' PBR	EBee ECtt ITim LOPS LRHS MHol MPie NLar NRHS NSti SCob SWvt
	'Raspberry Splash' PBR	CLAP CWCL ECtt EShb LBMP LRHS MBel MMuc NBir NLar SCob SEND SHeu SHil SIde SPoG SWvt
*	'Rowlatt Choules'	MNrw
	'Roy Davidson'	CDor CLAP CSam ECtt EPfP LCro LHop LRHS NBir NHol NSti SRms SWvt
	rubra	CBcs CElw CWCL ECha ELan EPPr GAbr LCro LLWP LOPS MJak MMuc MNrw NBid NSti SEND SHeu SRms WCAu WHea
	– var. ***alba***	see *P. rubra* var. *albocorollata*
§	– var. ***albocorollata***	CBre GAbr GBin NBid
	– 'Ann'	GBin
	– 'Barfield Pink'	GCal IFro NBir NLar SHeu
	– 'Bowles's Red'	CAby CBod CNec EHrv EPed GMaP GPSL IFoB LRHS MNrw MRav NBir NGdn NLar SPer WFar WGwG WHoo WWtn
	– 'David Ward' (v)	CAby CPla CWCL ECha ECtt EHrv ELan EShb GMaP MBel MRav MSCN NBir NSti SHeu SPer SPoG WCFE WCot WSHC
	– 'Rachel Vernie' (v)	CLAP CMil GBin
	– 'Redstart'	CBod CDor CSam ECtt EWoo GKev LEdu LHop LLWP LRHS MNrw MRav NBir NGdn NLar SHeu SRms SWvt WFar WMoo
§	***saccharata***	ECha ELan GMaP IFro MMuc SRms
	– 'Alba'	CElw IFro MMuc SRms
	– Argentea Group ♀H7	CTri ELan EPfP GMaP LRHS MMuc MRav NGdn SEND WBrk
	– 'Dora Bielefeld'	CLAP CTal CWCL ECha EHrv EPfP GBuc GMaP LLWP LRHS MNrw MRav NBir NChi NEgg NGdn NHol NSti SHeu SPer SRGP SWvt
	– 'Frühlingshimmel'	CDor LPla MRav NSti
	– 'Glebe Cottage Blue'	CElw
	– 'Leopard'	CDor CLAP CLet CMea CSam CWCL ECha ECtt EPed GBin GBuc GMaP LRHS MBel MNrw NBir NGdn NSti SBod SHeu SWvt WCAu WCot WGwG WHoo
	– 'Mrs Moon'	CNec CTri CWib ECtt ELon EPfP GMaP IKil NLar SHeu SPer SWvt WCAu WHar
	– 'Old Rectory Silver'	NBir
	– 'Picta'	see *P. saccharata*
	– 'Reginald Kaye'	ECha EWes
	– 'Silverado' PBR	ECtt LRHS SHeu SWvt
	– 'Stanhoe'	EWes
	'Saint Ann's'	LRHS NSti
	'Samurai'	CWCL LRHS MBel NRHS NSti SHeu WFar
	'Silver Bouquet' PBR	CElw ECtt EPfP GBin LCro LSou NHpl SHeu SHil
	'Silver Lance'	SHeu
	'Silver Shimmers' PBR	SHeu
	'Sissinghurst White' ♀H7	Widely available
	'Smoky Blue'	CLAP ECtt MRav SCob SHeu
	'Spilled Milk'	SHeu
	'Stillingfleet Meg'	CLAP EAEE ECtt EPfP LRHS MBNS NGdn NSti NWad SHeu SRGP WCot WGwG WWFP WWtn
	'Tim's Silver'	GBin
	'Trevi Fountain'	CAbP CDor CHVG CHid CLAP CWCL EBee ECha ECtt EPfP EShb GKev LPla LRHS LSun MHol NDov NSti SHeu SHil SIde SPoG WCAu WCot WFar
	'Vera May' ♀H7	MNrw
	'Victorian Brooch' PBR	CBod CLAP CWCL ECtt GBin IBoy LRHS LSou MBel MHol MNrw NPri SHeu SHil SIde SPad SPoG
	'Weetwood Blue'	CBre CLAP MNrw
	'Wendy Perry'	LRHS

Pulsatilla (*Ranunculaceae*)

	alba	CBro
	albana	CBro ECho EPot LHop LLHF LRHS NPnk NRHS
	– 'Lutea'	EBee EWTr LLHF
	alpina	ECho MArt NGdn SPlb SRms
§	– subsp. ***apiifolia*** ♀H5	EBee GKev IFro NRya
	– subsp. ***sulphurea*** misapplied	see *P. alpina* subsp. *apiifolia*
	ambigua	CPBP GKev LLHF NRya
	'Blue Select' (Pr/Prim)	IBoy
	bungeana	EPot
	campanella	GEdr LLHF
	caucasica	CBro ECho LRHS NRHS
	cernua	LHop
	chinensis	GKev
	georgica	GEdr
	halleri ♀H5	EBee ECho GKev NPnk WHal
	– subsp. ***slavica*** ♀H5	GKev LLHF
	– subsp. ***taurica***	GEdr
	lutea	see *P. alpina* subsp. *apiifolia*
	montana	SPlb XEll
	occidentalis	EBee GEdr
§	***patens***	EDAr GKev NGdn WIce
	– SDR 8136 new	GKev
	– subsp. ***flavescens***	EBee
	pratensis	GPoy SIgm SRms
	– subsp. ***bohemica*** new	EPot
	– subsp. ***nigricans***	EBee GEdr LHop
	regeliana	LLHF
	rubra	GKev NGdn NPnk SPad SRot
*	***serotina***	EBee GKev
	turczaninovii	GKev LLHF MArt NSla
*	***turkestanica***	GEdr
§	***vernalis*** ♀H5	EPot GEdr NLar NSla WAbe XEll
	violacea	CBcs
§	***vulgaris*** ♀H5	Widely available
	– 'Alba'	Widely available
	– 'Barton's Pink'	CBro CRos ECho LHop LLHF LRHS NPnk NRHS SRot
	– 'Blaue Glocke'	CAby CBod GEdr IBoy LRHS MBel SHar SWvt XSen

- 'Eva Constance'	CBro CRos ECho LHop LLHF LRHS NRHS
- 'Gotlandica'	LLHF
- subsp. ***grandis***	CPBP CRos EPot GEdr LRHS NRHS NSla SIgm
- - 'Budapest Seedling'	GEdr
- - 'Carminea'	GBuc
- - 'Papageno'	CDor CSpe EAEE ECho ELon GBin GCrg IPot MBel MHol NCGa NHol NHpl NLar NSla WGwG WIce WRHF
- Heiler hybrids	CBod EAEE EShb LLHF MRav NCGa NEgg NGdn NSla SVic
- 'Perlen Glocke'	EBee EDAr GEdr LRHS MArt MHer MMrt NLar WIce
- pink-flowered	CMea GKev LLHF NSla WFar
- Red Clock	see *P. vulgaris* 'Röde Klokke'
- red-flowered	CTsd EBee GBuc IBoy SCob SGbt WFar
§ - 'Röde Klokke'	CAby CBod EAJP ECtt EPfP EWoo GBin GEdr GWyn IBoy LRHS MBel MCot MWat NWad SHar SWvt XEll XLum XSen
- Rote Glocke	see *P. vulgaris* 'Röde Klokke'
- var. ***rubra***	CMea CNec CRos ECho ELan EPfP GBin GMaP LRHS MHer NBir NLar NRHS SBod SPer SPoG SRms SRot WHoo WIce WTor
- 'Violet Bells' **new**	WHil
- violet-blue-flowered	EPfP LRHS MWat SBod SHil
§ - 'Weisse Schwan'	EBee EPfP GBin GEdr GMaP SRot
- 'White Bells'	GEdr NHol WHil
- White Swan	see *P. vulgaris* 'Weisse Schwan'

Pultenaea (*Papilionaceae*)

daphnoides	SVen
juniperina	SPlb SVen

pummelo see *Citrus maxima*

Punica (*Lythraceae*)

granatum	CArn CBcs CBod CCCN CMen CTsd ELan EPfP ESps SCob SEND SPre SVic SWvt WJek
- 'Chico' (d)	CBcs
- 'Fina Tendral' (F)	CCCN
- 'Flore Pleno'	see *P. granatum* f. *plena* 'Albescens Flore Pleno'
- 'Legrelleae' (F/d)	SEND
- 'Maxima Rubra' (d)	EShb XSen
- var. ***nana*** ♀H3	CCCN CMen EAJP EBtc EPfP EShb LEdu LRHS MHer SRms SVen SVic WPat
- f. ***plena*** (d)	CBcs LRHS MRav WCFE WPat
§ - - 'Albescens Flore Pleno' (d) **new**	LEdu
- - 'Flore Pleno Luteo' (d)	LRHS
- 'Provence' (F)	EPom XSen
- 'Wonderful' (F)	CAgr

Puschkinia (*Asparagaceae*)

scilloides	ECho NBir
- 'Aragat's Gem'	ECho GKev
- var. ***libanotica*** ♀H5	CAby ECho EPfP EPot ERCP GKev LAma LCro LEdu LOPS LRHS MMuc MPie NRHS SDeJ SEND SPer WRHF WShi
- - 'Alba'	ECho EPot GKev LAma SDeJ SPer
- 'Snowdrift'	GKev

Putoria (*Rubiaceae*)

calabrica	WHil

Puya ✿ (*Bromeliaceae*)

RH 1809	WCot
RH 2910A	WCot
RH 2961C	WCot
RH 3425B	WCot
alpestris	CCCN CFil EShb SBig SPlb WCot
§ - ***subsp. zoellneri***	CAbb CBcs CCCN CDTJ EShb SPlb SVen WCot
assurgens	LTro WCot
berteroana misapplied	see *P. alpestris* subsp. *zoellneri*
boliviensis	WCot
castellanosii	LTro NLos WCot
chilensis	CAbb CBcs CCCN CDTJ LRHS NLos SPlb SVen WCot
coerulea	CCCN CDTJ CTsd LRHS MGil NLos SPlb
- var. ***monteroana***	WCot
dyckioides	LTro WCot
- red-bracted	WCot
ferruginea	EUJe LTro NLos SPlb WCot
gilmartiniae F&W 8697	WCot
harmsii	LTro NLos WCot
hromadnikii **new**	SPlb
laxa	SPlb WCot
mirabilis	CDTJ EUJe GBin NLos
raimondii	WCot
venusta	CCCN CDTJ LRHS NLos SPlb SVen WCot
yakespala	WCot

Pycnanthemum (*Lamiaceae*)

curvipes	LEdu
incanum	SPhx
muticum	LEdu SBrt WPGP
pilosum	CArn CLau MHer SPhx XLum
tenuifolium	NLar SBrt SPhx
virginianum	EBee SPhx

Pycnostachys (*Lamiaceae*)

urticifolia	EWes SDys

Pygmea see *Chionohebe*

Pyracantha (*Rosaceae*)

Alexander Pendula = 'Renolex'	LHop MRav MSwo SRms
angustifolia	LPar WCFE
- KR 2481 **new**	WPGP
'Apache'	LPar
§ ***atalantioides***	SPlb WCFE
'Brilliant'	SCoo
coccinea 'Lalandei'	CMac
- 'Red Column'	Widely available
- 'Red Cushion'	ESps GMcL MJak MRav SArc SCob SHil SRms
crenulata	WCFE
Dart's Red = 'Interrada'	CSBt
'Fiery Cascade'	CRos EPfP LRHS SHil SPoG
gibbsii	see *P. atalantioides*
'Golden Charmer'	CMac EPfP ESps IBoy LRHS MGos MSwo NEgg NLar NWea SCob SCoo SGol SPer SPoG SRms SWvt WFar
'Golden Glow'	SGol
'Golden Paradise' **new**	SCob
'Golden Sun'	see *P.* 'Soleil d'Or'
'Harlequin' (v)	SCob SGol WFar

'Knap Hill Lemon'	MBlu
koidzumii 'Victory'	ECrN MHtn NLar
'Mohave'	CMac CRos CTri ECrN ELan ELon ESps GMcL IBoy LPar LRHS MAsh NWea SCob SCoo SGol SHil SLim SRms SWvt
'Mohave Silver' (v)	CMac ELan EShb LBMP LRHS MAsh NHol
'Navaho'	LPar SEWo
'Orange Charmer'	CDul CMac CTri ELan ESps LHop LPar LRHS MGos MJak NHol NLar NWea SCob SPer SPlb WFar WHar WHed WMoo
'Orange Glow' ♀H6	Widely available
'Red Charmer'	NHol
* 'Red Pillar'	EUJe LPar NWea
rogersiana	CDul NWea
- 'Flava' ♀H6	CDul CLet CSBt EPfP LRHS MAsh NEgg NWea SPoG SWvt
'Rosedale'	LRHS
Saphyr Jaune = 'Cadaune'PBR	CBcs CCVT CEnd CSBt EBee ECrN EPfP LCro LRHS MGos MJak MRav NHol NPri SCob SCoo SGol SPer WHar
Saphyr Orange = 'Cadange'PBR ♀H6	CBcs CCVT CEnd CMac CSBt EBee ECrN EPfP ESps LCro LPar LRHS MGos MJak MRav NEgg NPri SCob SCoo SPer WHar
Saphyr Panache = 'Cadvar'PBR (v)	MJak
Saphyr Rouge = 'Cadrou'PBR ♀H6	CBcs CCVT CChe CEnd CLet CMac CSBt EBee ECrN ELan EPfP LCro LPar LRHS MGos MJak MMuc MRav MSwo NPri SCob SCoo SEND SGol SPer SWvt WFar WHar WHed
'Shawnee'	CMac CWib MSwo
§ 'Soleil d'Or'	Widely available
'Sparkler' (v)	CMac EBee EHoe SCob SMad
'Teton' ♀H6	CMac CRos ELan EPfP GMcL LRHS MAsh MGos MJak MSwo NWea SCob SGol SHil SPoG SRms WFar
'Yellow Sun'	see *P.* 'Soleil d'Or'

× *Pyracomeles* (*Rosaceae*)

vilmorinii new	SAko

Pyrethropsis see *Rhodanthemum*

Pyrethrum see *Tanacetum*

+ *Pyrocydonia* (*Rosaceae*)

'Danielii' (F)	SAko

Pyrola (*Ericaceae*)

rotundifolia	LEdu WHer

× *Pyronia* (*Rosaceae*)

veitchii new	SAko

Pyrrocoma (*Asteraceae*)

clementis	EBee

Pyrrosia (*Polypodiaceae*)

hastata	CMen WCot
- 'Harima Jishi' new	CMen
- 'Ryujin' new	CMen
- 'Shikoku Jishi' new	CMen
- 'World Champion' new	CMen
linearifolia 'Urakoryu Jishi'	CMen
lingua	CMen WPGP
- 'Hiryu' new	CMen
- 'Tachiba Koryu' new	CMen
polydactyla	CMen
sheareri	ISha

Pyrus ✿ (*Rosaceae*)

amygdaliformis	CMCN
- W&B B-10	WCot
- var. ***cuneifolia***	CLnd
calleryana 'Chanticleer'	Widely available
- 'Chanticleer' variegated (v)	CDul MAsh
- 'Redspire'	CCVT EMOT NWea
caucasica	WMat
communis (F)	CCVT CDul CTri ECrN LBuc NWea SPer SPlb WHed WMou WTSh
- 'Abbé Fétel' (D)	SKee
- 'Bambinella' (D)	SKee
- 'Barland' (Perry)	CHab SKee
- 'Barnet' (Perry)	CHab
- 'Baronne de Mello' (D)	CTho NOra SKee WMat
- 'Beech Hill' (F)	CDul ECrN ESps SGol SPer
- 'Belle Julie' (D)	SKee
- 'Bellissime d'Hiver' (C)	SKee
- Benita = 'Rafzas' (F)	LCro LOPS LRHS MCoo WMat
- 'Bergamotte d'Automne' (D)	SKee
- 'Bergamotte Esperen' (D)	SKee
- 'Beth' (D) ♀H6	CAgr CHab CMac CSBt CTri CWib EBee ECrN EMOT EPfP EPom EWTr GTwe IArd LBuc LRHS MAsh MGos NLar NOra SBdl SCob SDea SFrt SKee SLim SPer WHar WMat
- 'Beurré Bedford' (D)	SKee
- 'Beurré Clairgeau' (C)	SKee
- 'Beurré d'Amanlis' (D)	SKee
- 'Beurré d'Anjou' (F)	SKee
- 'Beurré d'Avalon' (D)	SKee
- 'Beurré de Beugny' (D)	SKee
- 'Beurré de l'Assomption' (D)	SKee
- 'Beurré Diel' (D)	SKee
- 'Beurré Dubuisson' (D)	SKee
- 'Beurré Dumont' (D)	CAgr
- 'Beurré Giffard' (D)	CAgr
- 'Beurré Gris d'Hiver' (D)	SKee
- 'Beurré Hardy' (D) ♀H6	Widely available
§ - 'Beurré Précoce Morettini' (D)	SDea
- 'Beurré Rance' (C/D)	SKee
- 'Beurré Six' (D)	SKee
- 'Beurré Sterckmans' (D)	SKee
- 'Beurré Superfin' (D) ♀H6	CFGn GTwe SKee WHar
- 'Bishop's Thumb' (D)	SDea SKee
- 'Black Worcester' (C)	CDul CHab ESps GTwe MAsh NOra SDea SKee WHar WJas WMat WWct
- 'Blakeney Red' (Perry)	CHab NOra SDea SKee WHar WMat
- 'Blickling' (D)	SKee
- 'Brandy' (Perry)	CAgr CHab CTho NOra SDea SFrt SKee SVic WHar WMat
- 'Bristol Cross' (D)	CAgr CHab SDea SKee
- 'Butt' (Perry)	CHab SKee
- 'Calebasse Bosc' (D)	NOra SKee
- 'Canal Red' (D)	SKee
- 'Cannock' (F)	SKee WMat
- 'Catillac' (C)	CAgr CHab ECrN GTwe NOra SKee WHar WMat
- 'Chalk'	see *P. communis* 'Crawford'
- 'Chaumontel' (D)	SKee

- 'Citron des Carmes' (C) **new** — SKee
- 'Clapp's Favourite' (D) — CHab CTho ECrN NOra SKee SVic WMat
- 'Comte de Lamy' (D) — SKee
- 'Concorde'^{PBR} (D) 🏆^{H6} — Widely available
- 'Conference' (D) 🏆^{H6} — Widely available
- 'Craig's Favourite' (D) — GTwd
§ - 'Crawford' (D) — GTwd
- 'Deacon's Pear' (D) — SDea
- 'Devoe' (D) — SDea
- 'Docteur Jules Guyot' (D) — CAgr SDea SKee
- 'Doyenné d'Été' (D) — ERea MCoo
- 'Doyenné du Comice' (D) 🏆^{H6} — Widely available
- 'Duchesse d'Angoulême' (D) — SKee
- 'Durondeau' (D) — ERea GTwe NOra SBdl SDea SKee WMat
- 'Emile d'Heyst' (D) — GQue GTwe MCoo SBdl SKee WHar WMat
- 'Eva Baltet' (D) — SKee
- 'Fair Maid' (D) — GTwd
- 'Fertility' (D) — CLnd SFrt
- 'Fertility Improved' — see *P. communis* 'Improved Fertility'
- 'Fondante d'Automne' (D) — CAgr CTho NOra SBdl SKee WHar WMat
- 'Forelle' (D) — ERea SKee
- 'Gansel's Bergamot' (D) — SKee
- 'Garden Gem' (F) — WMat
- 'Gin' (Perry) — CHab WMat
- 'Glou Morceau' (D) — CAgr CArg ECrN ERea GTwe MCoo MWat NOra SBdl SDea SFrt SKee WHar WMat
- 'Gorham' (D) 🏆^{H6} — CAgr CDul CTho GTwe NOra SKee WHar WMat
- 'Green Horse' (Perry) — CHab SKee WMat
- 'Green Pear of Yair' (D) — GTwd SKee
- 'Gregoire Bordillon' (D) — SKee
- 'Hacon's Incomparable' (D) — SKee
- 'Harley Gum' (F) — WHar
- 'Harrow Delight' (D) — SDea
- 'Harvest Queen' (D/C) — CAgr SDea
- 'Harvester' (C) **new** — SKee
- 'Hellen's Early' (Perry) — CHab ERea SKee WHar WMat
- 'Hendre Huffcap' (Perry) — CAgr CHab CTho EPom NOra SFrt SKee WHar WMat
- 'Hessle' (D) — CAgr CHab GTwd NWea SDea SKee
- Humbug = 'Pysanka' (D) — EPom LBuc LPre LRHS NOra WHar WMat
§ - 'Improved Fertility' (D) — CAgr ERea SDea SKee
- Invincible = 'Delwinor' (D/C) — CAgr CArg CDul CFGn CTho EPom LBuc LRHS MAsh MCoo NLar NOra SBdl SLim WHar WMat
- 'Jargonelle' (D) — CAgr CDul CFGn CHab CTho GTwe SBdl SDea SKee WHar WMat
- 'Joséphine de Malines' (D) 🏆^{H6} — CAgr ERea GTwe IArd NOra SBdl SDea SKee WHar
- 'Judge Amphlett' (Perry) — CTho EPom NOra SKee WHar WMat
- 'Kieffer' (C) — CAgr
- 'Laird Lang' (D) — GTwd
- 'Laxton's Early Market' (C/D) — SKee
- 'Laxton's Foremost' (D) — CAgr SKee
- 'Le Lectier' (D) — SKee
- 'Légipont' (F) — CAgr
- 'Louise Bonne of Jersey' (D) 🏆^{H6} — CAgr CFGn CMac CSut CTri ECrN EPom ERea GTwe IArd MGos NOra SBdl SDea SKee WHar WMat WWct
- 'Lübecker Prinzessin Birne' (F) **new** — MRai
- 'Maggie' (D) — GTwd
- 'Magyar Kobak' (C) **new** — SKee
- 'Marguérite Marillat' (D) — SDea SKee
- 'Marie-Louise' (D) — WHar
- 'Martin Sec' (C/D) — SKee
- 'Merrylegs' (Perry) — CHab
- 'Merton Pride' (D) — CAgr CFGn CLnd CTho EPom GTwe IArd MCoo NOra SBdl SDea SKee WHar WMat
- 'Monsieur le Curé' — see *P. communis* 'Vicar of Winkfield'
- 'Moonglow' (F) — CAgr ERea NOra SDea SKee WMat
- 'Moorcroft' (Perry) — SKee
- 'Morettini' — see *P. communis* 'Beurré Précoce Morettini'
- 'Mrs Seden' (D) — SKee
- 'Nouveau Poiteau' (C/D) — CAgr
- 'Nuvar Anniversary' (D) **new** — SKee
- 'Nuvar Celebration' (F) — SKee WMat
- 'Nye Russet Bartlett' (F) — CAgr
- 'Old Home' (Perry) — WMat
- 'Oldfield' (Perry) — CHab
- 'Olivier de Serres' (D) — SKee
- 'Onward' (D) 🏆^{H6} — CAgr CArg CDul CHab CLnd CTho CTri CWib ECrN EMOT EPom ERea ESps GTwe IArd LRHS MAsh NLar NOra NWea SBdl SDea SKee WHar WMat WWct
- 'Ovid' (D) — CAgr
§ - 'Packham's Triumph' (D) — CAgr CTri CWib ECrN EMOT EPom ESps GTwe NOra SDea SKee WHar WMat
- 'Parsonage' (Perry) — CHab
- 'Passe Crassane' (D) — SKee
- 'Pear Apple' (D) — CHab SDea
- 'Penrhyn' (D) — WGwG WMat
I - 'Petite Poire' (D) — EPom
- 'Pitmaston Duchess' (C/D) 🏆^{H6} — ECrN ERea GTwe MCoo SDea SKee WHar WMat WWct
- 'Précoce de Trévoux' (D) — WHar
- 'Président Barabé' (D) — SKee
- 'Red Beurre Hardy' (C) **new** — SKee
- 'Red Comice' (D/C) — SKee
- 'Red Pear' (Perry) — CHab WMat
- 'Red Sensation Bartlett' (D/C) — EMOT EPom GTwe LBuc NOra SKee WMat
- 'Redbald' (D) — SKee
- 'Reimer Red' (C) **new** — SKee
- 'Robin' (C/D) — ERea SDea SKee WMat
- 'Roosevelt' (D) — SKee
- 'Santa Claus' (D) — SDea SKee
- 'Schweizer Hose' (F) **new** — MRai
- 'Seckel' (D) — NOra SKee
- 'Shipova' (F) — see × *Sorbopyrus auricularis* 'Shipova'
- 'Sierra' (D) — CAgr
- 'Sirrine' (C) **new** — SKee
- 'Snowdon Queen' (D) — CHab WGwG
- 'Soleil d'Automne' (F) — SKee
- 'Sommer Blutbirne' (D) **new** — SAko
- 'Souvenir du Congrès' (D) — CAgr
- 'Starkrimson' (D) — SKee

	- 'Taynton Squash' (Perry)	NOra WMat
	- 'Terrace Pearl' (D)	WMat
	- 'Tettenhall Dick' (C/D)	WHar
	- 'Thompson's' (D)	SKee
	- 'Thorn' (Perry)	CAgr CHab EPom SKee WHar WMat
	- 'Triumph'	see *P. communis* 'Packham's Triumph'
	- 'Uvedale's St Germain' (C)	SKee
	- 'Verbelu' (C)	SKee
	- 'Verdi' (F)	EPom
§	- 'Vicar of Winkfield' (C)	ECrN MRai SDea SKee
	- 'Williams' Bon Chrétien' (D/C) ♀^{H6}	Widely available
	- 'Williams' Red' (D/C)	GTwe LHop NPri SKee
	- 'Williams' Rouge Delbard' (F)	EPom
	- 'Winnal's Longdon' (Perry)	EPom WHar WMat
	- 'Winter Nelis' (D)	CAgr CHab CTri CWib ECrN EMOT GTwe NOra SDea SKee WHar WMat WWct
	- 'Woodhall' (F)	WMat
	- 'Zéphirin Grégoire' (D)	SKee
	cordata	CDul CTho
	elaeagnifolia	MAsh
	- var. ***kotschyana***	CDul SLim
	- 'Silver Sails'	CLnd CMac EBee EMOT EMil NOra SCoo WHar WMat
	× ***michauxii***	SVen
	nivalis	CDul CLnd CTho EBee ECrN EPfP LEdu NOrn NWea SPer
	- 'Catalia'	MAsh WMat
	pashia	CMCN EBee LEdu NLar WMat
	pyraster	CDul CHab WCot
	pyrifolia '20th Century'	see *P. pyrifolia* 'Nijisseiki'
	- 'Chojuro' (F)	CAgr LEdu
	- 'Hosui' (F)	CAgr LEdu SVic
	- 'Kosui' (F)	SVic
	- 'Kumoi' (F)	CAgr CFGn EPom ERea LRHS MAsh MCoo SDea SKee WHar WMat
§	- 'Nijisseiki' (F)	CDul SVic
	- 'Shinko' (F)	CAgr LEdu
	- 'Shinseiki' (F)	CAgr CFGn CLnd EMOT ERea MAsh SDea SKee WHar WMat
	- 'Shinsui' (F)	SDea SKee
*	***salicifolia*** var. ***orientalis***	CTho
	- 'Pendula' ♀^{H6}	Widely available

Q

Qiongzhuea see *Chimonobambusa*

Quercus ✿ (*Fagaceae*)

	acerifolia	EPfP
	acherdophylla	SBir
	acutifolia	SBir
	acutifolia × ***mexicana***	SBir
	acutissima	CAco CBcs CDul CMCN EPfP NLar SBir SGol
	- PAB 7957	LEdu
	- 'Gobbler'	ESwi
	- subsp. ***kingii*** NJM 13.077 new	WPGP
	aegilops	see *Q. ithaburensis* subsp. *macrolepis*
	affinis ♀^{H5}	CMCN EPfP SBir
	agrifolia	CMCN EBtc
	ajudaghiensis	see *Q. hartwissiana*
	alba	CDul CMCN WPGP
*	***alentejana***	CMCN
	aliena	CDul CMCN
	- PAB 8972	LEdu
	alnifolia	CDul WPat
	anatolica	see *Q. pubescens* subsp. *crispata*
	arkansana	CDul SBir WPat
	× ***atlantica***	SBir
	austrina	CMCN SBir
	× ***beadlei***	see *Q.* × *saulii*
	× ***benderi***	SBir
	berberidifolia	CMCN SBir
	bicolor	CAco CDul CMCN EPfP MBlu WPGP
	× ***bimundorum***	SBir
§	- 'Crimschmidt'	CDul EPfP ESwi MBlu SAko SBir SGol WPat
	borealis	see *Q. rubra*
	brantii	CMCN
	breweri	see *Q. garryana* var. *breweri*
	buckleyi	CMCN EPfP LRHS SBir
	× ***bushii***	CMCN EPfP MBlu SBir WPat
	- 'Seattle Trident'	EPfP MBlu SAko
	canariensis ♀^{H5}	CDul CMCN CTho EPfP SGol WPGP WPat
	canbyi	CMCN
	candicans	SBir WPat
	× ***capesii***	SBir WPat
	castaneifolia	CDul CMCN
	- 'Green Spire' ♀^{H6}	CMCN EBee EPfP MBlu SEND
	cerris	CArg CBcs CCVT CDul CLnd CMCN EBee ECrN EMOT EPfP ESps MGos MMuc NWea SCob SEND SGol SPer
	- 'Afyon Lace'	MBlu SBir WPat
§	- 'Argenteovariegata' (v)	CEnd CMCN EBee ELan EPfP MAsh MBlu SBir WCot WPat
	- 'Athena'	MBlu
	- 'Curly Head'^{PBR}	SMad
	- 'Variegata'	see *Q. cerris* 'Argenteovariegata'
	- 'Wodan'	MBlu
	chenii	CDul SBir
	chrysolepis	CBcs CMCN EPfP
	coccifera	CAco CLet CMCN EPfP SGol SVen WCot WPGP
	- subsp. ***calliprinos***	CMCN
	coccinea	CBcs CDul CMCN CTho CTri ECrN EPfP ESps MBlu MWht NEgg NWea SBir SEWo SPer WPat WTSh
	- 'Splendens' ♀^{H6}	CDul CEnd CHll CJun CMCN CTri ELan EPfP IArd LRHS MAsh MBlu NLar SGol SPer WPat
	aff. ***coccinea***	EMOT
	conspersa	SBir
	crassifolia	WPGP WPat
	crassipes	SBir
	Crimson Spire	see *Q.* × *bimundorum* 'Crimschmidt'
	crispipilis	SBir
	dalechampii	SBir
	dentata	CMCN
	- 'Carl Ferris Miller'	CBcs CDul CMCN EPfP ESwi LLHF MBlu MMrt SBig SBir SCob WCot WHor WPGP WPat
	- 'Pinnatifida'	CDul CMCN EPfP LLHF MBlu MPkF NLar WCot WPat
	- 'Sir Harold Hillier'	CMCN MBlu WHor WPat
	- subsp. ***yunnanensis***	SBir WPat
	dolicholepis	CMCN SBir

	'Doring's Zweizack'	SBir
	douglasii	CDul CMCN
	dumosa	WPat
	durata	CMCN EGFP
	× ***dysophylla***	CFil
	ellipsoidalis	CDul CMCN NLar SBir SGol
	- 'Hemelrijk' ♀H6	CMCN EPfP MBlu SBir WPat
	emoryi	SBir
	engleriana PAB 8183	LEdu
	× ***exacta***	SBir
	fabrei	CMCN SBir
	faginea	CDul CMCN WPGP
	- subsp. ***broteroi***	CMCN
	falcata	CMCN EBtc SBir
	- var. ***pagodifolia***	see *Q. pagoda*
	× ***fernaldii***	CMCN EPfP MBlu
	frainetto	CDul CMCN CTho EBee EPfP ESps NWea SGol SPer WMou
	- 'Düzce' **new**	WPat
	- 'Hungarian Crown' ♀H6	CMCN EPfP MBlu SBir
	- 'Trump'	CDul CMCN
	franchetii	WPGP
	fruticosa	see *Q. lusitanica* Lam.
	fusiformis	SBir
	gambelii	CAco CBcs CMCN EBtc MPkF
	garryana	CBcs CMCN EPfP
§	- var. ***breweri***	CMCN
	- var. ***fruticosa***	see *Q. garryana* var. *breweri*
	georgiana	CDul CMCN SBir
	germana	CFil WPGP
	gilva	CMCN SBir
	glabra	see *Lithocarpus glaber*
	glabrescens	WPGP
	glandulifera	see *Q. serrata.*
	glauca	CDul CMCN EPfP NLar
	graciliformis	WPat
	gravesii	CMCN EPfP SBir
	greggii	CFil WPGP
	grisea	CMCN
§	***hartwissiana***	EPfP
	× ***hastingsii***	CMCN SBir
	× ***hawkinsiae***	SBir
	× ***haynaldiana***	SBir
	hemisphaerica	CMCN EPfP SBir
	× ***heterophylla***	CMCN EPfP SBir
	× ***hickelii***	CMCN EPfP SBir
	hirtifolia	WPGP
	× ***hispanica***	EUJe
	- 'Ambrozyana'	CDul CMCN NLar
	- 'Diversifolia'	CDul CMCN EPfP MBlu WPat
	- 'Fulhamensis'	CMCN MBlu MMuc SBir SEND SGol WMou
§	- 'Lucombeana' ♀H6	CDul CMCN CSBt CTho EBee ELan EPfP MBlu MMuc SBir SPer
	- 'Suberosa'	CTho
	- 'Waasland Select'	NLar SGol WMou WPat
	- 'Wageningen'	CDul CMCN LRHS SBir
	hypoleucoides	CMCN EPfP
	ilex	Widely available
	- 'Fordii'	SBir
	ilicifolia	CMCN EPfP SBir WPGP WPat
	imbricaria	CAco CBcs CDul CMCN EPfP SBir WPat
	incana Roxb.	see *Q. leucotrichophora*
§	***incana*** Bartram	CMCN
	insignis **new**	CFil
	ithaburensis	CDul
§	- subsp. ***macrolepis***	CMCN LEdu SBir
	- - 'Hemelrijk Silver'	EPfP MBlu SBir WPGP WPat
	× ***jackiana***	SBir

	kelloggii	CBcs CDul CMCN EPfP WPGP
	× ***kewensis*** ♀H6	CMCN SBir SEND WMou
	laevis	CMCN EPfP SBir
	'Langtry'	SBir
§	***laurifolia***	CDul CMCN EPfP SBir
	laurina	SBir WPGP
	× ***leana*** **new**	CMCN
§	***leucotrichophora***	LEdu SBir WPGP
	liaotungensis	see *Q. wutaishanica*
	× ***libanerris***	SBir
	- 'Rotterdam'	CMCN SBir
	libani	CDul CMCN EPfP
	lobata	CBcs CMCN LEdu
	× ***lucombeana***	see *Q.* × *hispanica* 'Lucombeana'
	- 'William Lucombe'	see *Q.* × *hispanica* 'Lucombeana'
	× ***ludoviciana***	EPfP SBir WPat
§	***lusitanica*** Lam.	SBir
	lyrata	CMCN SGol
	- 'Arnold'	MBlu
	'Macon'	CDul
	macranthera	CDul CMCN EPfP
	- PAB 13.002 **new**	LEdu
	macrocarpa	CAco CDul CMCN EPfP WPat
	macrolepis	see *Q. ithaburensis* subsp. *macrolepis*
	marilandica	CDul CMCN EPfP MBlu SBir WPat
	'Mauri'	CDul IArd LRHS MBlu SBir
	mexicana	CMCN IArd SBir WPGP WPat
§	***michauxii***	CBcs CDul CMCN EPfP MBlu
	miquihuanensis **new**	WPat
	mohriana	SBir
	mongolica	CBcs CDul EPfP MBlu SBig
	- subsp. ***crispula***	CMCN WPat
	muhlenbergii	CDul CMCN MBlu MPkF SBir
	- 'Dallas'	EPfP
	myrsinifolia	CBcs CMCN NLar SArc
	myrtifolia	SBir WPGP
	nigra	CDul CMCN EBtc EPfP SBir
	- 'Beethoven'	MBlu SBir
I	- 'Nyewoodii'	SBir
	nuttallii	see *Q. texana*
	obtusa	see *Q. laurifolia*
	oglethorpensis	CMCN SBir WPat
§	***pagoda***	CAco CDul CMCN EGFP SBir WPat
	palustris ♀H6	CAco CArg CCVT CDul CLnd CMCN CTho EBee ELan EMOT EPfP EWTr MAsh MBlu MMuc NEgg NLar NWea SBir SCob SEWo SGol SPer WMou WTSh
	- 'Flaming Suzy'	MBlu
	- 'Green Dwarf'	CMCN LCro MBlu NLar SLim WPat
	- Green Pillar = 'Pringreen'	CTho EPfP MBlu NLar NOra SGol WMat
	- 'Isabel'	EPfP ESwi LRHS WHor WMat WPat
	- 'Pendula'	CEnd CMCN
	- 'Silhouette'	CJun SBir
	- 'Swamp Pygmy'	CMCN EBee EPfP ESwi EUJe LRHS MBlu SCob
	- 'Windischleuba'	MBlu
	pannosa	SBir
	parvula var. ***parvula***	SBir
§	× ***pauciloba***	CMCN
	pedunculata	see *Q. robur*
	pedunculiflora	see *Q. robur* subsp. *pedunculiflora*
§	***petraea***	CArg CDul CHab CLnd CTri ECrN EPfP ESps MBlu NWea SCob SGol WHed WMou WTSh
	- 'Acutiloba'	SBir
	- 'Laciniata'	see *Q. petraea* 'Laciniata Crispa'
§	- 'Laciniata Crispa'	CEnd CMCN EPfP MBlu

	- Mespilifolia Group	CDul
§	- 'Purpurea'	CMCN EPfP MBlu
	- 'Rubicunda'	see *Q. petraea* 'Purpurea'
§	***phellos***	CAco CDul CMCN EBee EBtc EPfP MBlu NLar SBir
	- Hightower = 'Qpsta'	SGol
	- var. ***latifolia***	see *Q. incana* Bartram
	aff. ***phellos***	ECrN
	phillyreoides	CBcs CDul CLet CMCN EPfP WPat
	polymorpha	CDul CMCN MPkF SBir WPGP
	Pondaim Group	CMCN EBee NOra WMou WPat
	pontica	CMCN EPfP LLHF MBlu WPat
	prinoides	CMCN
	prinus misapplied	see *Q. michauxii*
§	***prinus*** L.	CMCN
	pubescens	CDul CMCN EGFP MMuc SEND
§	- subsp. ***crispata*** NJM 12.016 new	WPGP
	pumila Michx.	see *Q. prinus* L.
	pumila Walt.	see *Q. phellos*
	pungens	CMCN
	pyrenaica	CDul CMCN EBtc MMuc SBir SEND WPat
	- 'Pendula' ♀H6	CMCN EPfP
	rhysophylla	CMCN EPfP IArd MBlu SBir WPGP
	- 'Maya' ♀H5	CJun EBee ELan EPfP EUJe LLHF MRav NLar SBir SGol SLim WHor WMat WPGP WPat
	× ***riparia***	SBir
§	***robur***	Widely available
	- 'Argenteomarginata' (v)	CMCN MBlu WPat
	- 'Atropurpurea'	MPkF NWea
	- 'Blue Gnome'	MBlu
	- 'Compacta'	MBlu WPat
	- 'Concordia'	CEnd CMCN EBtc ELan EPfP MBlu NLar SKHP
	- Cristata Group	CMCN
	- 'Dissecta'	CMCN
	- 'Facrist'	CDul SBir
	- Fastigiata Group	CAco CDul CLnd EBee EPfP ESps IArd IVic LHop MGos NWea SBir SCob SGol SLim SPer
	- - 'Koster' ♀H6	CDul CMCN CMac CNWT CTri EMOT EPfP MBlu MRav NWea SCob SPoG WMat
	- - 'Zeeland'	SBir
	- 'Filicifolia' misapplied	see *Q. robur* 'Pectinata'
	- 'Filicifolia' Hort. ex Loud.	CEnd WPat
	- var. ***haas***	CDul
	- 'Irtha'	EPfP MBlu
	- 'Menhir'	CMCN LLHF MAsh MBlu WCot WPat
§	- 'Pectinata'	EPfP MBlu WPat
§	- subsp. ***pedunculiflora***	CMCN
	- 'Pendula'	CEnd CMCN MBlu WPat
	- 'Purpurascens'	CDul CEnd CMCN
	- 'Purpurea'	MBlu
	- 'Raba'	CMCN
	- 'Rita's Gold'	WPat
§	- 'Salfast'	CDul MBlu
	- 'Salicifolia Fastigiata'	see *Q. robur* 'Salfast'
	- 'Strypemonde'	CMCN
	- 'Timuki'	MBlu WPat
	- 'Totem'	WHor
	- 'Tromp Dwarf'	MBlu
	- Variegata Group (v)	WPat
	- - 'Fürst Schwarzenburg' (v)	MBlu
	robur × ***macrocarpa*** × ***virginiana***	SBir
	× ***rosacea*** 'Columna'	WMou
	- 'Westcolumn'	WPat
	rotundifolia	CAgr CMCN EBee EPfP WPGP
§	***rubra***	Widely available
	- 'Aurea'	CEnd CMCN EBee EPfP MBlu WHor
	- 'Bolte's Gold'	MBlu NOra WHor WMat
	- 'Cyrille'	SBir
	- 'Magic Fire' ♀H6	CMCN EPfP MBlu SBir
	- 'Red Queen'	EPfP MBlu
*	- 'Sunshine'	CMCN MBlu WCot WPat
	× ***rudkinii***	EPfP
	rugosa	CFil
	× ***runcinata***	SBir WPat
	sadleriana	CMCN
	salicina	WPGP
	× ***sargentii*** 'Thomas'	CDul EPfP MBlu WPat
	sartorii	CMCN SBir
§	× ***saulii***	CMCN SBir
	× ***schochiana***	EPfP MBlu SBir WPat
	- 'Bhno' new	LRHS
	schottkyana	WPGP
	× ***schuettei***	SBir
	semecarpifolia	CMCN MBlu WPat
§	***serrata***	CDul CMCN EPfP LEdu SBir
	- 'Herkenrode'	LRHS MBlu
	sessiliflora	see *Q. petraea*
	shumardii	CDul CMCN EPfP LRHS MBlu NLar SBir SGol
	- 'Del Rio'	MBlu
	sinuata subsp. ***breviloba***	SBir
	stellata	CMCN EPfP SBir
	× ***sternbergii***	SBir
	suber	CAgr CBcs CDul CFil CMCN CTsd EBee ELan EPfP EUJe IArd LEdu LPar MBlu MGos SArc SEND SPer WPGP
	- 'Sopron'	CDul EPfP MBlu
§	***texana***	CAco CMCN EPfP NOra SBir
	- 'New Madrid'	CDul CTho EBee EPfP ESwi LLHF LRHS MBlu SBir SPer WCot WHor WMat WPat
	tomentella	SBir
	trojana	CDul CMCN SBir WPGP
	turbinella	CMCN
	× ***turneri***	CDul CLet CMCN CTho EPfP
	- 'Pseudoturneri' ♀H6	CBcs CDul EBee ELan MBlu SGol WMou
	undulata Torr.	see *Q.* × *pauciloba*
	vacciniifolia	CMCN
	variabilis	CMCN EPfP MPkF SGol WPat
	velutina	CBcs CDul CMCN CTho EPfP IVic NLar SBir WPat
	- 'Albertsii'	CJun LRHS MBlu
	- 'Habiflax'	SBig
	- 'Oakridge Walker'	MBlu
	- 'Rubrifolia'	CJun CMCN EPfP
	'Vilmoriana'	CMCN
	virginiana	CBcs CMCN SBir
	vulcanica new	WPat
	× ***warburgii***	EPfP
	× ***warei***	CMCN
	- 'Chimney Fire'	EPfP MBlu
	- Kindred Spirit	see *Q.* × *warei* 'Nadler'
§	- 'Long'	EBee EMOT EPfP MBlu MPkF NOra WMat
§	- 'Nadler'	LRHS SGol
	- Regal Prince	see *Q.* × *warei* 'Long'
	- 'Riverbank Lodge'	SBir
	- 'Windcandle'	MBlu SBir
	wislizeni	CDul CMCN NLar SBir WPat
§	***wutaishanica***	SBir
	xalapensis new	CFil

Quillaja (*Quillajaceae*)

saponaria	CBcs CCCN CLet IDee SPlb

quince see *Cydonia oblonga*

Quisqualis (*Combretaceae*)

indica	CCCN

R

Racosperma see *Acacia*

Radermachera (*Bignoniaceae*)

sinica ♀H1b	EShb

Ramonda (*Gesneriaceae*)

§ ***myconi*** ♀H5	CLAP CPBP EWes LLHF NSla SRms WAbe
- var. ***alba***	CLAP WThu
- 'Jim's Shadow'	WAbe
- 'Rosea'	LLHF
nathaliae ♀H5	SIgm WAbe WThu
- 'Alba'	CLAP NSla WAbe XEll
pyrenaica	see *R. myconi*
serbica	WThu

Ranunculus (*Ranunculaceae*)

aconitifolius	EBee ECho EHrv GCra GMaP NLar SHar SWat WFar WHal WMoo WSHC
- 'Flore Pleno' (d) ♀H7	Widely available
acris	CHab NBir NMir NPer WSFF
- subsp. ***acris*** 'Stevenii'	SDix WHal
- 'Citrinus'	CElw LLWG LSun MHol WCot WHal WHrl WMoo WPtf
- 'Flore Pleno' (d) ♀H7	Widely available
- 'Hedgehog'	ECho EPPr MMrt
- 'Sulphureus'	CBre EBee WHal
alpestris	ECho GCrg GEdr LLHF NSla
- 'Flore Pleno' (d) **new**	GEdr
amplexicaulis	GMaP NHar NSla WCot
aquatilis	CWat MSKA MWts SWat WHer WMAq WSFF
asiaticus	ERCP
- 'Aviv Orange' **new**	SDir
- 'Aviv Red'	LCro LOPS
- 'Aviv Rose'	LCro LOPS
- 'Aviv White'	GKev LCro LOPS
- 'Bloomingdale Pink Shades' (Bloomingdale Series)	SDeJ
§ ***bulbosus*** 'F.M. Burton'	CElw GBuc NRya WCot
- ***farreri***	see *R. bulbosus* 'F.M. Burton'
- 'Speciosus Plenus'	see *R. constantinopolitanus* 'Plenus'
calandrinioides ♀H4	ECho EWes IFoB NBir SBrt WAbe WThu
§ ***constantinopolitanus*** 'Plenus' (d)	GCal MNrw MRav NBid NBro NLar WCot WMoo
cortusifolius	ECre SBrt SWat
crenatus	ECho GEdr
ficaria	see *Ficaria verna* subsp. *verna*
flammula	CBen CHab CWat EWay MSKA MWts SWat
- 'Golden Tower'	EBee
- subsp. ***minimus***	EWay
giganteus ambig.	GBin
gouanii	NRya
'Gowrie'	GEdr
gramineus ♀H5	EBee ECho LRHS NRya SIgm SRms WCot XEll
- 'Pardal'	WCot
hederaceus	LLWG
illyricus	NRya WHal
kochii	CTal ECho GEdr GKev MNrw NRya WCot
lanuginosus	EPPr
lingua	SPlb WSFF
- 'Grandiflorus'	CBen MSKA NPer SWat WHal WMAq WPnP
millefoliatus	CPBP ECho GBuc WAbe
montanus double-flowered (d)	SHar WCot
- 'Miss Austria' (d) **new**	NHpl
- 'Molten Gold' ♀H5	EBee ECho GEdr GMaP MMrt MRav
nivicola	WCot
parnassiifolius	GEdr LLHF MNrw WAbe WCot
'Pauline Violet'	IFro
platanifolius	EBee LRHS
× ***prietoi*** 'Moonlight'	CElw LEdu MMrt
'Purple Heart' (d)	EPfP LCro LOPS SDeJ
repens 'Buttered Popcorn' (v)	EBee
- 'Cat's Eyes' (v)	EBee
- 'Gloria Spale'	CBre
- var. ***pleniflorus*** (d)	CBre LLWG SRot
- 'Snowdrift' (v)	EBee
- 'Timothy Clark' (d)	CBre
seguieri	ECho GEdr LHop LLHF LRHS NRHS WAbe
speciosus 'Flore Pleno'	see *R. constantinopolitanus* 'Plenus'

Ranzania (*Berberidaceae*)

japonica	GEdr WCru

Raoulia (*Asteraceae*)

australis misapplied	see *R. hookeri*
australis ambig.	GAbr GBin GMaP NHpl SMad WTor
australis Hook.f. ex Raoul	GKev ITim MAsh
§ - Lutescens Group	ECha ECho SRot
§ ***hookeri***	CMea CTal ECha EWes MAsh SIgm SPlb SRms WAbe
× ***loganii***	see × *Leucoraoulia loganii*
lutescens	see *R. australis* Lutescens Group
petriensis	WAbe
× ***petrimia*** 'Margaret Pringle'	EPot WAbe
tenuicaulis	ECha SPlb

Raphionacme (*Apocynaceae*)

lucens **new**	LToo

raspberry see *Rubus idaeus*

Ratibida (*Asteraceae*)

columnifera	ELan EPfP LRHS
- f. ***pulcherrima***	CSpe ELan EPfP LRHS XLum
- - 'Red Midget'	CBod CSpe EBee LHop LRHS SBee
mexicana **new**	CSam
pinnata	CSam CSpe EPfP NBir SBee SPhx SPlb WCot WTcb

Ravenala (*Strelitziaceae*)

madagascariensis	SPlb XBlo

Ravenea (*Arecaceae*)

rivularis	CCCN XBlo

Rechsteineria see *Sinningia*

redcurrant see *Ribes rubrum* (R)

Reevesia (*Sterculiaceae*)

pubescens CBcs

Regelia (*Myrtaceae*)

velutina SPlb

Rehderodendron (*Styracaceae*)

indochinense B&SWJ 12115 WCru
- WWJ 11869 WCru
kwangtungense WWJ 11940 WCru
kweichowense WWJ 12019 WCru
macrocarpum CBcs CFil WPGP
- B&SWJ 11841 WCru
- KWJ 12310 WCru
- WWJ 11952 WCru

Rehmannia (*Plantaginaceae*)

angulata misapplied see *R. elata*
§ **elata** ♀H2 CBod CMos CSam CSpe ELan EPfP IDee LBMP LCro LHop LLWP LRHS LSun MMuc MNHC SDys SRms XLum
glutinosa ♀H2 CSpe
'Magic Dragon' new CRos EHyd LBuc LRHS NRHS SPoG
piasezkii SMHy WPGP

Reineckea (*Asparagaceae*)

§ **carnea** CDor CHid CHll ECha ECho ELan EPPr GBin GCal GEdr GKev IMou LEdu MMuc MPie NSti SDys SEND SPlb WCot WPGP XLum
- B&SWJ 4808 ELon WCru
- SDR 330 EPPr GKev
- 'Baoxing Booty' IMou WCru
- 'Crûg's Broadleaf' WCru
- 'Variegata' (v) EShb WCot
aff. **carnea** from Sichuan WCot
incurva 'Crûg's Linearleaf' WCru

Reineckia (*Asparagaceae*)

yunnanense see *Reineckea carnea*

Reinwardtia (*Linaceae*)

§ **indica** CCCN CHll
trigyna see *R. indica*

Remusatia (*Araceae*)

hookeriana LRHS
- B&SWJ 2529 WCru
pumila EUJe LRHS
vivipara EUJe LRHS

Reseda (*Resedaceae*)

alba MHer
lutea CWld SIde SRms
luteola CBod CHab CHby GPoy MHer MNHC WHer WSFF

Restio (*Restionaceae*)

festuciformis CTre
multiflorus new LRHS
paniculatus CCCN CDTJ CTre
similis CTre LRHS
subverticillatus CTre
§ **tetraphyllus** CTre ESwi GBin LRHS SPlb SPoG
- 'Cornish Gold' (v) new CTre

Retama (*Papilionaceae*)

§ **monosperma** SBrt

Reynoutria see *Fallopia*

Rhamnus (*Rhamnaceae*)

alaternus XSen
§ - 'Argenteovariegata' (v) ♀H5 Widely available
- 'Variegata' see *R. alaternus* 'Argenteovariegata'
cathartica CCVT CDul CHab CLnd CTri ECrN EPfP EShb LBuc MCoo NLar NWea SEWo WHed WMou WSFF WTSh
davurica B&SWJ 12609 WCru
frangula see *Frangula alnus*
imeretina EBee WCot WPGP WPat
ludovici-salvatoris SBrt
lycioides subsp. **oleoides** XSen
pallasii NLar
taquetii NLar

Rhaphidophora (*Araceae*)

decursiva XBlo

× *Rhaphiobotrya* (*Rosaceae*)

§ 'Coppertone' SArc SEND WPGP

Rhaphiolepis (*Rosaceae*)

sp. LPar
× **delacourii** CWib ELan EPfP SEND SRms
- 'Coates' Crimson' CBcs CTsd EBee ELan EPfP IVic LHop LRHS MAsh MGil SEle WPat WSHC
- Enchantress = 'Moness' CCCN CTsd ELan EPfP LRHS MAsh MRav SLon
- 'Pink Cloud' EPfP LRHS
indica LPar SEND
- B&SWJ 8405 WCru
- 'Coppertone' see × *Rhaphiobotrya* 'Coppertone'
- Springtime = 'Monme' CBcs EPfP IVic LCro LOPS LRHS
integerrima CMCN
umbellata CBcs CTri CWib EBee ELan EPfP GBin LEdu LHop LRHS MAsh MGil MRav SEND SEle SLon SVen WPGP WPat WSHC
- f. **ovata** B&SWJ 4706 WCru

Rhaphithamnus (*Verbenaceae*)

cyanocarpus see *R. spinosus*
§ **spinosus** CBcs EBee EPfP LEdu MGil

Rhapidophyllum (*Arecaceae*)

hystrix CBrP

Rhapis ✿ (*Arecaceae*)

§ **excelsa** ♀H1b CCCN WCot XBlo

Rhazya (*Apocynaceae*)

orientalis see *Amsonia orientalis*

Rheum ✿ (*Polygonaceae*)

Chen Yi WCot
GWJ 9329 from Sikkim WCru
§ 'Ace of Hearts' ♀H6 Widely available
'Ace of Spades' see *R.* 'Ace of Hearts'
acuminatum HWJCM 252 WCru
- HWJK 2354 WCru

	- PAB 2487	LEdu WPGP
	alexandrae	CBct ESwi EUJe EWes GBin GCal GEdr GKev LEdu MMrt MMuc MNrw NLar SPlb WFar WPGP
	- SDR 2924	EBee
	- SDR 6031	GKev
	altaicum PAB 1055	LEdu
§	***australe***	CAgr GCal LRHS NBro NLar WCot WFar
	- CC 7492 new	GKev
	- 'Pink Marble' (v)	WCot
	'Cally Dwarf'	GCal
	'Cally Giant'	EBee EWes GCal
	× ***cultorum***	see *R.* × *hybridum*
	delavayi	GCal NLar
	- BWJ 7592	WCru WFar
	emodi	see *R. australe*
	'Great Bere'	LEdu
*	***henryi***	EBee
§	× ***hybridum***	SEND
	- 'Brandy Carr Scarlet'	LEdu MRav
	- 'Canada Red'	GTwe
	- 'Cawood Delight'	GTwe
	- 'Champagne'	CAgr EPfP EPom LBuc LCro LEdu LOPS LRHS NRHS SCob SKee SPer WMat
	- 'Fenton's Special'	CTri GTwe LEdu MCoo MRav
	- 'Fulton's Strawberry Surprise' ♀H4	GTwe
	- 'Glaskin's Perpetual'	CAgr CLet CRos CWib EPfP LBuc LRHS NRHS WHar
	- 'Grandad's Favorite' ♀H4	CRos LRHS NRHS
	- 'Hawke's Champagne' ♀H4	WCot
	- 'Holsteiner Blut'	NLar SCob SPoG
	- 'Livingstone'PBR	EPom LCro LOPS
	- 'Pink Champagne'	EPfP GQue
	- 'Prince Albert'	GTwe
	- 'Raspberry Red' ♀H4	CRos CSut EPfP EPom LBuc LCro LRHS
	- 'Red Champagne'	ELan EPfP LBuc SCob
	- 'Red Prolific'	GTwe
	- 'Reed's Early Superb' ♀H4	GTwe
	- 'Stockbridge Arrow'	CArg CMac CSut CTri EMil GTwe SFrt
	- 'Stockbridge Guardsman'	GTwe
	- 'Strawberry'	GTwe LCro LOPS NBir
	- 'Sutton's Cherry Red'	GTwe
	- 'The Sutton'	CWib EPfP GTwe
	- 'Thompson's Terrifically Tasty'	EPom
	- 'Timperley Early' ♀H4	Widely available
	- 'Timperley Early 1'	MJak
	- 'Timperley Early 2'	MJak
	- 'Timperley Early 30'	MJak
	- 'Tingley Cherry'	GTwe
	- 'Victoria'	Widely available
	- 'Victoria 1'	MJak
	- 'Victoria 2'	MJak
	- 'Victoria 9'	MJak
	- 'Vroege Engelse'	LEdu
	- 'Zwolle Seedling'	GTwe
	kialense	CBct EBee LEdu NBid NSti WPGP
	nobile	EPot GEdr GKev
	officinale	CBct GCal SIde SWat
	palmatum	CBcs CLet EBee ECha ELan EPfP GCra GKev LCro LRHS MGos MRav NGdn SCob SDix SHar SWat
	- 'Atropurpureum'	see *R. palmatum* 'Atrosanguineum'
	- 'Atropurpureum Dissectum'	IBoy
§	- 'Atrosanguineum'	CBct CBod CDor CMac ECha ELan EPfP EShb EUJe EWoo GBin GCal IFro LEdu LRHS MBel MGos MMuc MRav NBid NBro NEgg NWad SPer SPlb SPoG SPtp SWat WCru WFar
	- 'Bowles's Crimson' ♀H7	MRav NBid WCot
	- 'Ferguson's Red'	WCot
	- 'Hadspen Crimson' ♀H7	CAby CBct CGar EBee ECtt LSun MHol MNrw NBid WCot
	- 'Red Herald'	CBct WCot
	- 'Rubrum'	LRHS NBir NChi
	- 'Savill'	MRav
	- var. ***tanguticum***	Widely available
	rhaponticum	NLar
	ribes	WCot WCru
	spiciforme	WPGP
	tataricum	EBee LEdu WPGP

Rhexia (*Melastomataceae*)

	virginica	SBrt

Rhinanthus (*Orobanchaceae*)

	minor	CHab LCro

Rhodanthemum (*Asteraceae*)

	'African Eyes'	ECho ELan EPfP EWoo MBrN MGos MHol SPoG SRot SVen
	Agadir (Atlas Daisy Series)	see *R.* Moondance
§	***atlanticum***	ECho EWes
	'Casablanca'PBR (Atlas Daisy Series)	LRHS NRHS
§	***catananche***	CCCN CPBP ECho EWes MBNS SRot WAbe
§	- 'Tizi-n-Test'	ECho
	- 'Tizi-n-Tichka'	ECho EPot EWes LHop LRHS NRHS
§	***gayanum***	CCCN EWes
	- 'Flamingo'	see *R. gayanum*
§	***hosmariense*** ♀H4	CCCN ECha ECho ELan EPfP EPot GCrg GMaP LHop LRHS MCot MHol NRHS SCoo SEND SIgm SPer SRms SRot WHoo WIce
	'Marrakech' (Atlas Daisy Series)	CBod WBod
§	Moondance = 'Usrhod0701'	EPfP LRHS NRHS
	Tangier (Atlas Daisy Series)	EPfP LRHS NRHS

Rhodiola (*Crassulaceae*)

	SSSE 10	NWad
	chrysanthemifolia WJC 13669 new	WCru
	crassipes	see *R. wallichiana*
	cretinii HWJK 2283	WCru
§	***fastigiata***	CSpe GCal WCot WThu
	- BWJ 7544	SKHP WCru
§	***heterodonta***	ELan MRav WCot
	himalensis misapplied	see *R.* 'Keston'
	himalensis (D. Don) Fu	CTri GKev
	- WJC 13723 new	WCru
§	***integrifolia***	SPlb
	- subsp. ***integrifolia***	EDAr
§	***ishidae***	CTri
§	'Keston'	CTri
§	***kirilovii***	LRHS
	- var. ***rubra***	EPfP LRHS
§	***pachyclados***	CTal ECho ECtt EUJe GBin GCrg GJos GKev GMaP LRHS MHer MMuc MSCN NBir NHpl NRHS NRya NWad SEND SPlb SRot SWvt XLum
	rhodantha	NLar

§	***rosea***	CAby CArn CBod CElw EAEE EBee ECho EDAr ELan EPfP EUJe GCal GJos GKev GPoy LRHS MAvo MCot MHer MRav NBid NBir NGdn NLar NWad SPer SRms WCFE WCot WFar
	semenovii	GKev NLar
	sinuata HWJK 2318	WCru
	- HWJK 2326	WCru
§	***trollii***	ECho EPot LHop LRHS NRHS SPlb
§	***wallichiana***	NBid
	- GWJ 9263	WCru
	- HWJK 2352	WCru
§	***yunnanensis*** BWJ 7941	WCru

Rhodochiton (*Plantaginaceae*)

§	***atrosanguineus*** Υ^{H2}	CBcs CCCN CSpe CWCL ELan EPfP LBuc MPie NPri SLon SPer
	volubilis	see *R. atrosanguineus*

Rhodocoma (*Restionaceae*)

	arida	CCCN
	capensis	CAbb CBod CCCN CTre CTsd LRHS NLos
	gigantea	CCCN CTre LRHS SPlb

Rhododendron ✿ (*Ericaceae*)

	sp.	CAco GKin LPar SEWo
	'A.J. Ivens'	see *R.* 'Arthur J. Ivens'
	aberconwayi	LMil WBod
	- 'His Lordship'	GGGa LMil MHid
	acrophilum (V)	GGGa
	'Addy Wery' (EA)	GKin SPer
	adenogynum	GGGa LMil MHid
	- SDR 7850 new	GKev
	- SDR 7914 new	GKev
	adenopodum	GGGa MHid
	adenosum	GGGa
	'Admiral Piet Hein'	GGGa SReu SSta
	'Adonis' (EA/d) Υ^{H5}	CBcs CMac SLdr
	'Advance' (EA)	SLdr
	aeruginosum	see *R. campanulatum* subsp. *aeruginosum*
	aganniphum	MHid
	- var. ***flavorufum***	MHid
	- 'Rusty'	MHid
	'Aksel Olsen'	CTri GEdr
	'Aladdin' (*auriculatum* hybrid)	GGGa SSta
	'Aladdin' (EA)	SLdr
	Aladdin Group	LPar SReu
	- 'Aladdin'	LPar
	Albatross Group	SReu
	- 'Albatross'	SSta
	- 'Albatross Townhill Pink'	LMil
	'Albert Schweitzer' Υ^{H5}	CDul LMil LRHS LSRN NLar SLdr SLim SPer
	albertsenianum	MHid
	albrechtii (A)	CBcs CPne GGGa IVic LMil SLdr
	- Whitney form (A)	LMil WMoo
	'Alexander' (EA) Υ^{H4}	IVic LMil LSRN SAko SLdr
	'Alice' Υ^{H5}	CMac LMil SLdr
	Alison Johnstone Group	CBcs SLdr SReu
	- 'Alison Johnstone'	CAco GGGa LMil WThu
	'All Gold'	GGGa
	Alpine Gem Group	GQui IVic
§	***alutaceum*** var. ***alutaceum*** Globigerum Group	GGGa
§	- var. ***iodes***	MHid
§	- var. ***russotinctum***	MHid
	- - R 158	SLdr
§	- - Triplonaevium Group	GGGa
	amagianum (A)	LMil
	'Amaretto'	IVic SAko
	ambiguum	LMil MHid
	- 'Golden Summit'	GGGa
	- 'Jane Banks'	LMil
	'Ambrosia' (EA)	CSBt
	'America'	SCob
	'Amity'	LMil MHid MLea MMuc SLdr WGwG
	Amor Group	SLdr
	'Anah Kruschke'	LCro MAsh SPoG
	'Analin'	see *R.* 'Anuschka'
	'Anatta Gold' (V)	GGGa
	'Anchorite' (EA)	SLdr
	Angelo Group	LMil SReu
	- 'Angelo'	LMil SLdr SSta
	'Ann Lindsay'	SLdr WMoo
	'Anna Baldsiefen'	GKin SLim SPoG
	'Anna Rose Whitney'	CBcs CTri EPfP LPar LRHS LSRN MAsh MJak SLim
	'Annabella' (K)	SReu SSta
	annae	GGGa LMil
	'Anne Frank' (EA)	WBod WFar
	'Anne Teese'	GGGa SLdr
	'Annegret Hansmann'	GGGa
	'Anneke' (A)	GMcL LMil LRHS MGos MMuc NHol NLar SReu SSta WMoo
	anthopogon	LMil
	- 'Betty Graham'	GGGa WThu
	- subsp. ***hypenanthum*** 'Annapurna'	GGGa ITim LMil WAbe WThu
	anthosphaerum	GGGa
	'Antilope' (Vs) Υ^{H6}	CBcs LMil MMuc SReu SSta
	(Antonio Group) 'Antonio'	LMil
§	'Anuschka'	LMil MAsh
	anwheiense	GGGa
	aperantum	GGGa
	apodectum	see *R. dichroanthum* subsp. *apodectum*
	'Apple Blossom' ambig.	CMac GKin
	'Appleblossom' (EA)	see *R.* 'Ho-o'
	'Apricot Blaze' (A)	SReu SSta
	'Apricot Fantasy'	LMil
	'Apricot Surprise'	CTri MAsh
	'April Chimes'	WThu
	'April Gem'	SAko
	'April Rose'	SAko
	'April Showers' (A)	LMil
	'Aquamarin'	IVic
	'Arabesk' (EA)	GKin MAsh MGos NLar
	arborescens (A) Υ^{H6}	CTsd GGGa LMil MHid
	arboreum	GGGa IDee LMil LRHS MHid SLdr SReu
	- B&SWJ 2244	WCru
	- subsp. ***arboreum***	MHid
	- subsp. ***cinnamomeum*** Υ^{H4}	GGGa LMil MHid SLdr
	- - WJC 13821 new	WCru
	- - var. ***album***	GGGa MHid SReu
	- - 'Everest Reunion'	LMil
	- - var. ***roseum***	GGGa
	- - - 'Tony Schilling'	GKin IDee LMil LRHS SReu SSta
	- subsp. ***delavayi***	GGGa LMil MHid SLdr
	- 'Heligan'	SReu
	- 'Rubaiyat'	LMil
§	- subsp. ***zeylanicum***	GGGa
	'Arctic Fox' (EA)	GGGa
	'Arctic Regent' (K)	GQui

	'Arctic Tern' ♀H5	CSBt CTri GQui LMil MGos MLea SPer WBod WThu
	'Ardeur' (EA)	NLar
§	***argipeplum***	GGGa MHid
	(Argosy Group) 'Argosy'	LMil SReu
	argyrophyllum	MHid SLdr
	- subsp. ***argyrophyllum***	GGGa SLdr
§	- subsp. ***hypoglaucum***	GGGa MHid
	- subsp. ***nankingense***	GGGa
	- - 'Chinese Silver' ♀H6	GGGa IDee LMil LRHS MHid SLdr SReu
	'Arima' (K)	GGGa
	arizelum	CPne GCal GGGa LMil MHid
	- subsp. ***arizelum*** Rubicosum Group	GGGa LMil
	'Arkona'	IVic SAko
	armitii (V)	GGGa
	'Arneson Gem' (A) ♀H6	CBcs GGGa LMil LRHS MMuc
	'Arneson Ruby' (K)	GGGa
§	(Aronense Group) 'Fumiko' (EA)	CSBt CTsd GMcL LCro LMil MLea NLar SLdr WFar
§	- 'Hanako' (EA)	MLea WFar
§	- 'Kazuko' (EA)	GMcL
§	- 'Satschiko' (EA) ♀H5	CBcs CSBt CTsd GGGa GMcL LMil LRHS MJak MMuc NLar NPri
	'Arpège' (Vs)	LMil NLar SReu
	'Arthur Bedford'	CSBt SReu
§	'Arthur J. Ivens'	SLdr
	'Arthur Stevens'	MHid SLdr
	'Asa-gasumi' (Kurume) (EA)	SLdr
	asterochnoum	GGGa MHid
	'Astrid'	IVic LSRN SAko
	atlanticum (A)	GGGa LMil SLdr
	- 'Seaboard' (A)	LMil
	atlanticum × ***canescens***	GKev
	augustinii	CBcs GBin GGGa LMil MHid MLea NLar SLdr SSta WBod
	- 'Bowood Blue' **new**	LMil
	- 'Carolles'	LRHS
§	- subsp. ***chasmanthum***	GGGa
	- compact EGM 293	LMil
	- Electra Group	LMil SLdr
§	- - 'Electra' ♀H3	GGGa
	- Exbury form	GGGa LMil SReu
§	- subsp. ***hardyi***	GGGa
*	- 'Trewithen'	GGGa LMil
I	- 'Werrington'	SLdr SReu
	aureum	GGGa
	auriculatum	GGGa LMil MHid SLdr SSta
	- Reuthe's form	SReu
	auriculatum × ***hemsleyanum***	GGGa
	auritum	CPne SLdr
	'Aurora' (K)	SLdr
	austrinum (A)	LMil NLar
	- yellow-flowered (A)	LMil
	Autumn Magic	see *R.* 'Herbstzauber'
	(Avalanche Group) 'Avalanche'	LMil
	Avocet Group	LMil SLdr
	'Award'	LMil
	Azrie Group	SLdr
§	'Azuma-kagami' (Kurume) (EA)	CAco LMil MPkF SLdr
	'Azurika'	IVic MPkF
	'Azurro'	LMil SLdr
	'Babuschka'	LMil
	'Baden-Baden' ♀H5	CMac CTri GEdr GKin GMcL LMil MAsh MJak NEgg SLdr WBod
	baileyi	MHid SLdr
*	'Baker's Lavender' (EA)	SLdr
	balangense	GGGa
	balfourianum	GGGa
	'Baltic Amber' (A)	SPer
	'Balzac' (K)	GKin LMil MAsh NEgg
	'Bandoola'	SReu
	'Barbara Reuthe'	SSta
	'Barbarella'	IVic LMil
	barbatum	GGGa LMil MHid
	'Barbecue' (K)	LMil
	'Bariton'	GGGa
	'Barmstedt'	MAsh WMoo
	'Barnaby Sunset'	GGGa LRHS MAsh
	'Bashful' ♀H5	CBcs CSBt MJak
§	***basilicum***	GGGa LMil
	- AC 616	MHid
	'Bastion'	LMil
	× ***bathyphyllum***	GGGa
	bauhiniiflorum	see *R. triflorum* var. *bauhiniiflorum*
	beanianum	GGGa
	- APA 60	GGGa
	- KC 0122	GGGa
	- compact	see *R. piercei*
	'Beatrice Keir'	LMil MHid SReu SSta
	'Beattie' (EA)	SLdr
	(Beau Brummell Group) 'Beau Brummell'	LMil
	'Beaulieu Manor'	GQui
	beesianum	GGGa
	- AC 1528	MHid
	'Beethoven' (Vuykiana) (EA)	SLdr
	Belami = 'Hachbela'	LMil SAko
	'Belkanto'	GKin MJak MMuc NLar SLdr
	'Bellini'	LMil LRHS NLar
	'Ben Cruachan' (K)	GGGa
	'Ben Lawers' (K)	GGGa
	'Ben Lomond' (K)	GGGa
	'Ben Morrison' (EA)	LMil
	'Ben Vorlich' (K)	GGGa
	'Ben Vrackie' (K)	GGGa
	'Bengal'	GEdr LRHS LSRN MAsh NLar SCob SLdr SLim
	'Bengal Beauty' (EA)	SLdr
	'Bengal Fire' (EA)	CMac SLdr
	benhallii 'Honshu Blue'	GGGa
	- 'Plum Drops'	GGGa
	- 'Slieve Donard'	CMac
	- 'Ylva'	GGGa
	'Beni-giri' (Kurume) (EA)	CMac SLdr
	'Bergensiana'	SReu SSta
	'Bergie Larson' ♀H4	CBcs IVic LMil MMuc
	'Berg's 10'	MLea
	'Berg's Yellow'	MMuc
	'Bernard Shaw'	SSta
	'Bernstein'	CAco MAsh MJak
	'Berryrose' (K) ♀H6	CBcs CMac CSBt CTri EPfP GKin GMcL LMil LRHS MAsh MGos MHid MJak MPkF NLar SReu SSta WFar
	'Bert's Own'	CBcs
	'Beryl Taylor'	GGGa
	'Betty Anne Voss' (EA)	LCro LMil LSRN MAsh SCoo SLdr
	'Betty' (Kaempferi) (EA)	SLdr
	'Betty Wormald'	CMac MLea SLdr
	bhutanense	GGGa
	Bibiani Group	LMil
	'Bijou de Ledeberg' (Indian) (EA/v)	CMac
	'Billy Budd'	SLdr
	'Birthday Girl'	LMil LSRN MAsh MLea

	(Biskra Group) 'Biskra'	GGGa LMil
	'Blaauw's Pink' (Kurume) (EA) $\mathbb{Y}^{H4}$	CMac CSBt EPfP ESps GKin GMcL GQui LCro LMil MMuc MPkF SGol SLdr SPer SPlb SPoG SReu WBod
	'Black Hawk' (EA)	CBcs
	'Black Knight' (EA)	SLdr
	'Black Magic'	CAco GKin GMcL LMil
	'Black Sport'	MLea
	'Black Widow'	SSta
	'Blaney's Blue' **new**	MPkF
	'Blattgold' (v)	LMil
	Blaue Donau	see *R.* 'Blue Danube'
	'Blaue Jungs'	GGGa
	'Blewbury' $\mathbb{Y}^{H5}$	LMil SReu
	Bloombux = 'Microhirs3' **new**	LCro
	'Blue Boy'	LMil
§	'Blue Danube' (EA) $\mathbb{Y}^{H3}$	CBcs CMac CSBt CTri EPfP ESps GGGa GKin GMcL IVic LCro LMil LRHS MAsh MGos MJak NEgg NLar NPri SGol SLdr SLim SPer SPoG SReu SSta WFar
	Blue Diamond Group	CBcs ECho EPfP GEdr GMcL SReu
	- 'Blue Diamond'	CMac CSBt ECho LRHS LSRN MAsh MJak SLdr WGwG
	'Blue Jay'	MMuc
	'Blue Monday' (EA)	SLdr WBod
	'Blue Peter' $\mathbb{Y}^{H5}$	CBcs CSBt LMil MAsh MLea MMuc NHol SPer SReu SSta WMoo
	'Blue Pool'	LMil
	Blue Ribbon Group	SLdr
	'Blue Silver'	GGGa IVic LMil MAsh
	'Blue Star'	GMcL
	'Blue Steel'	see *R. fastigiatum* 'Blue Steel'
	Blue Tit Group	CBcs EPfP GGGa LRHS MAsh MGos SCob SLdr SLim SPer SReu SSta
	Bluebird Group	CMac CSBt SLdr
	'Blueshine Girl'	SLdr
	'Blurettia'	MMuc
	'Blutopia'	LMil
	Bohlken's Juditha	GGGa LMil
	Bohlken's Kronjewel	GGGa LMil
	Bohlken's Laura	GGGa LMil
	Bohlken's Lupinenberg	GGGa LMil
	Bohlken's Lupinenberg Laguna	LMil
	Bohlken's Snow Fire	GGGa LMil
	(Bonito Group) 'Bonito'	LMil
	boothii	GGGa
	- HECC 10077	GGGa
	Bo-peep Group	CBcs
	- 'Bo-peep'	GQui LMil SLdr
	'Boskoop Ostara'	LMil
	'Boule de Neige'	LRHS MAsh SPer
	'Bouquet de Flore' (G) $\mathbb{Y}^{H6}$	LMil
	Bow Bells Group	MLea
	- 'Bow Bells' $\mathbb{Y}^{H4}$	ECho EPfP GEdr GMcL LMil LRHS MAsh MGos NHol SLdr WBod
	'Bowjingles'	GGGa
	brachyanthum subsp. ***hypolepidotum***	GGGa
§	***brachycarpum*** subsp. ***fauriei*** B&SWJ 4326 **new**	WCru
	- 'Roseum Dwarf'	GGGa
	'Brambling'	GGGa
	'Brazier' (EA)	SLdr
	'Bremen'	LMil
	'Briane' (EA)	GGGa
	Bric-à-brac Group	CBcs
	- 'Bric-à-brac'	SLdr
	'Bright Forecast' (K)	IVic MLea
	'Brigitte'	IVic LSRN MAsh
	'Brilliant Blue' (EA)	MAsh
	'Britannia'	CSBt MJak NHol SReu SSta
	(Brocade Group) 'Brocade'	SLdr
	'Bronze Fire' (A)	NHol SLdr SReu SSta
	'Brown Eyes'	CAco GKin MMuc
	'Bruce Brechtbill'	GGGa GKin MAsh MMuc
	'Bruce Hancock' (Ad)	SLdr
§	'Bruns Gloria'	LMil
	'Bruns Schneewitchen'	SReu SSta
	'Buccaneer' (Glenn Dale) (EA)	SLdr
	'Bud Flanagan'	MMuc
	bullatum	see *R. edgeworthii*
	'Bungo-nishiki' (Wada) (EA/d)	CMac WThu
	bureavii $\mathbb{Y}^{H5}$	CBcs GGGa LMil MHid SReu SSta
	- SDR 7976 **new**	GKev
*	- ***cruentum***	GGGa
	bureavii × ***yakushimanum***	SReu
	bureavioides	LMil MHid
	'Burletta'	IVic
	burmanicum	CBcs CPne GGGa
	Bustard Group	LMil
	'Busuki'	GGGa
	'Butter Brickle'	LMil MLea SLdr
	'Buttermint'	SLdr
	'Caerhays Lavender' (EA)	CBcs
	calendulaceum (A)	GGGa LMil
	- red-flowered (A)	LMil
	- yellow-flowered (A)	LMil
	(Calfort Group) 'Calfort'	GGGa
	callimorphum	GGGa
	- var. ***myiagrum***	MHid
	calophytum $\mathbb{Y}^{H5}$	CPne GGGa LMil LRHS MHid SLdr
	calostrotum subsp. ***calostrotum*** KR 9983	MHid
	- 'Gigha' $\mathbb{Y}^{H4}$	GGGa LMil MAsh WAbe
§	- subsp. ***keleticum*** $\mathbb{Y}^{H4}$	GCal GEdr GGGa ITim NSla WThu
	- - R 58	GGGa LMil
§	- - Radicans Group	GEdr GGGa IVic NSla WAbe WThu
	- - - mound form	ITim
	- subsp. ***riparium***	ITim
§	- - Nitens Group	GGGa MMuc WThu
	caloxanthum	see *R. campylocarpum* subsp. *caloxanthum*
	'Calsap'	GGGa
	Calstocker Group	LMil
	camelliiflorum	GGGa
	campanulatum	GGGa LMil MHid SLdr SReu
	- HWJCM 195	WCru
	- HWJCM 409	WCru
§	- subsp. ***aeruginosum***	GGGa LMil MHid
	'Campfire' J.B. Gable (EA)	SLdr
	campylocarpum	GGGa LMil MHid
§	- subsp. ***caloxanthum***	GGGa
§	- - Telopeum Group	MHid
	campylogynum	GGGa LMil
	- SBEC 0519	GGGa
	- 'Album'	see *R.* 'Leucanthum'
	- black-flowered	IVic
	- Charopoeum Group	WThu
	- - 'Patricia'	ECho GEdr NSla
	- (Cremastum Group) 'Bodnant Red'	GGGa WThu
	- Myrtilloides Group $\mathbb{Y}^{H4}$	ECho GGGa GQui LMil MHid WAbe WThu

- salmon-pink-flowered	ECho
camtschaticum	GGGa IDee LMil LRHS WThu
- red-flowered	GGGa
canadense (A)	GGGa
- f. ***albiflorum*** (A)	GGGa LMil
- dark-flowered (A)	LMil
Candy Lights = 'UMinn's Candy Lights' (A) **new**	LRHS
'Candy Striped Pink'	IVic SAko
§ ***canescens*** (A)	LMil
'Cannon's Double' (K/d) ♀H6	CBcs GKin LMil LRHS MGos MLea MMuc NLar SLdr SPer WMoo
'Canzonetta' (EA/d) ♀H5	CEnd EPfP GGGa LMil LRHS MAsh SAko SLdr
'Captain Jack'	GGGa
'Caractacus'	SCob
'Carat' (A)	NLar
cardiobasis	see *R. orbiculare* subsp. *cardiobasis*
(Carita Group) 'Carita Charm'	LMil
- 'Carita Inchmery'	SLdr
- 'Golden Dream'	LMil
(Carmen Group) 'Carmen' ♀	ECho ELon GEdr GGGa GKin LMil MAsh MLea MMuc SLdr
carneum	GGGa
'Caroline Allbrook'	GGGa MAsh MLea NLar SLdr
'Caruso'	IVic
'Cary Ann'	CAco CTri LRHS MAsh
'Casablanca' (EA)	SLdr
'Cassley' (Vs)	LMil
catacosmum	GGGa
catawbiense	SLdr
'Catawbiense Album'	CAco CTri MAsh
'Catawbiense Boursault'	SLdr
'Catawbiense Grandiflorum'	CAco MAsh
'Catharine van Tol'	LMil
caucasicum	GGGa
'Caucasicum Pictum'	LMil SLdr
'Cayenne' (EA)	SLdr
'Cecile' (K) ♀H6	CBcs CMac CTri GKin GMcL LMil LSRN MMuc SReu
'Celestial' (EA)	CMac
cephalanthum	GGGa LMil
- subsp. ***cephalanthum*** SBEC 0751	WThu
- - Crebreflorum Group	GGGa LMil WAbe WThu
- - Nmaiense Group	GGGa
- subsp. ***platyphyllum***	GGGa
- - AC 1926	MHid
cerasinum	LMil MHid
- 'Cherry Brandy'	GGGa MHid
- 'Coals of Fire'	GGGa MHid
'Cetewayo'	GGGa
chaetomallum	see *R. haematodes* subsp. *chaetomallum*
chamaethomsonii	GGGa
- var. ***chamaethomsonii***	MHid
- - Rock form	GGGa
championae	GGGa
'Chanel' (Vs)	GGGa SReu SSta
changii	GGGa
'Chanticleer' (Glenn Dale) (EA)	SLdr
chapaense	see *R. maddenii* subsp. *crassum*
'Chariots of Fire' (EA)	LMil
charitopes	GCal LMil
- F 25570	GGGa LMil
- subsp. ***charitopes***	MHid
§ - subsp. ***tsangpoense***	GGGa GQui
* 'Charlotte de Rothschild' (A)	SLdr
'Charlotte Foster' **new**	GGGa
'Charlotte Megan' (A)	LMil
Charmaine Group	WBod
'Charme La'	GGGa
chasmanthum	see *R. augustinii* subsp. *chasmanthum*
'Cheer'	MAsh MMuc NEgg SPer
'Chelsea Seventy'	MHid SLdr
'Cherokee' (EA)	SLdr
'Cherry Drops' (EA)	EPfP LRHS MAsh SPoG
Cherry Kiss = 'Hachcher'PBR	GGGa LMil SAko
'Chetco' (A)	LMil MGos
'Chevalier Félix de Sauvage'	LMil
'Chikor'	CBcs ECho GGGa GKin MAsh MGos MMuc NLar
'Chinchilla' (EA)	GQui
'Chink'	MHid WBod
'Chionoides'	SLdr
'Chipmunk' (EA/d)	GGGa LRHS MAsh
'Chippewa' (Indian) (EA)	CTri IVic LMil
'Chocolate Ice' (K/d)	SLdr
Choptank River Group (A) **new**	GKev
(Choremia Group) 'Choremia' ♀H3	LMil LRHS
christi (V)	GGGa
'Christina' (Vuykiana) (EA/d)	MMuc SLdr
'Christmas Cheer' (EA/d)	see *R.* 'Ima-shojo'
'Christmas Cheer' (*caucasicum* hybrid) ♀	CBcs CSBt GGGa GKin LMil LPar MAsh MGos MLea NLar NPri SCob SLdr SPer SReu
'Christopher Loder' **new**	SLdr
chryseum	see *R. rupicola* var. *chryseum*
chrysodoron	MHid
ciliatum	CBcs GGGa SLdr
ciliipes **new**	GMcL
Cilpinense Group	CBcs GGGa
- 'Cilpinense' ♀H3	CMac CSBt ECho EPfP LMil LRHS MAsh MMuc NPri SLdr WBod
cinnabarinum	LMil MHid SLdr
- subsp. ***cinnabarinum*** BL&M 234	LMil
- - Blandfordiiflorum Group	GGGa MHid SLdr
- - 'Nepal'	LMil
- - Roylei Group	GGGa LMil
- - - 'Vin Rosé'	LMil
- Cinzan Group	LMil
§ - (Conroy Group) 'Conroy'	LMil
§ - subsp. ***tamaense*** KW 21003	MHid
§ - subsp. ***xanthocodon***	CBcs GGGa LMil MHid
§ - - Concatenans Group	CPne GGGa LMil MHid SLdr
- - - KW 5874	LMil
- - Purpurellum Group	GGGa MHid
'Cinzia' (K)	GGGa
circinnatum	GGGa
citriniflorum	LMil
- R 108	LMil
- var. ***citriniflorum***	LMil MHid
- var. ***horaeum***	GGGa MHid
'Claudine'	IVic
clementinae	GGGa MHid
- F 25705	LMil
'Cliff Garland'	GQui LMil WBod
'Coccineum Speciosum' (G) ♀H6	CMac CSBt GKin LMil SReu SSta

coeloneurum	GGGa LMil
- EGM 334	LMil
- NN 0926	MHid
collettianum	GGGa
'Colonel Coen'	GKin LMil MMuc
Colonel Rogers Group	SLdr SReu
columbianum	SLdr
'Colyer' (EA)	SLdr
Comely Group	SLdr
comisteum C 6541	GGGa
concatenans	see *R. cinnabarinum* subsp. *xanthocodon* Concatenans Group
concinnoides	GGGa
concinnum	GGGa
- Pseudoyanthinum Group ♀	GGGa GQui MHid
'Connie' (Kaempferi) (EA)	SReu SSta
'Conroy'	see *R. cinnabarinum* 'Conroy'
'Contina'	LMil
'Conversation Piece' (EA)	CEnd SLdr
'Cool Haven'	LMil
'Coral Sea' (EA)	SReu
'Coral Seas' (V)	GGGa
'Corany' (A)	LMil NLar SLdr
coriaceum	GGGa LMil MHid
'Corneille' (G/d)	CSBt LMil LRHS MPkF
'Coronation Day'	LMil
coryanum 'Chelsea Chimes'	MHid
'Cosmopolitan'	CDul GMcL MGos MMuc NLar SPer SPoG WMoo
'Cotton Candy'	LMil
'Countess of Haddington'	CBcs LMil
Cowslip Group	CTri LMil MAsh MGos MLea
- 'Cowslip' ♀H4	LRHS NLar
coxianum	GGGa
'Crane' ♀H5	EPfP GGGa GQui IVic LMil LRHS MAsh
crassum	see *R. maddenii* subsp. *crassum*
'Cream Crest'	GKin GQui SLim WMoo
'Creamy Chiffon'	MLea WGwG
crenulatum	GGGa
'Crete'	LMil
crinigerum	CPne GGGa LMil
- var. ***crinigerum***	MHid
- var. ***euadenium***	MHid
'Crinoline' (EA)	SLdr
Crossbill Group	CBcs SLdr
'Crosswater Belle'	LMil NLar
'Crosswater Red' (A)	LMil
'Csárdás'	GGGa IVic
cubittii	see *R. veitchianum* Cubittii Group
cucullatum	see *R. roxieanum* var. *cucullatum*
cumberlandense (A)	GGGa LMil
- 'Sunlight'	LMil
cuneatum	MHid
'Cunningham's Blush'	SGol
'Cunningham's White'	CAco CBcs CDul CTri ELan EPfP ESps GGGa GMcL LCro LMil LRHS MAsh MGos MMuc NHol NLar NPri SArc SCob SLdr SLim SPer SPoG SReu SSta
'Cupcake'	GGGa
'Curlew' ♀H4	CMac GEdr GKin GMcL LMil MAsh MHid MMuc NHol SLdr
cyanocarpum	GGGa MHid
'Cynthia' ♀H5	CBcs CMac CSBt GGGa LMil LSRN MHid MMuc NEgg SLdr SPer SReu SSta WMoo
'Dagmar'	IVic SAko
'Daisetsuzan' (EA) new	MPkF

dalhousiae	GGGa
- LS&T 6694	MHid
§ - var. ***rhabdotum***	GGGa
(Damozel Group) 'Damozel'	LMil
'Danuta'	IVic SAko
'Dartmoor Pixie'	WThu
'Dartmoor Shepherd's Delight'	SReu SSta
dasycladum	see *R. selense* subsp. *dasycladum*
dauricum	WBod
- 'Album'	see *R. dauricum* 'Hokkaido'
§ - 'Hokkaido'	GGGa
- 'Mid-winter' ♀H6	GGGa LMil
davidii	GGGa LMil NEgg
davidsonianum ♀H3	GGGa LMil MHid
- Bodnant form	LMil
- 'Caerhays Blotched'	GGGa
- 'Ruth Lyons'	LMil
'Daviesii' (G) ♀H6	CBcs CDul CEnd CSBt CTri ELan EPfP GKin GQui LCro LMil LRHS MAsh MHid MMuc NLar NPri SLdr SPer SPoG SReu SSta WHor WMoo
'Daybreak' (EA/d)	see *R.* 'Kirin'
'Daybreak' (K)	GQui
'Dear Barbara'	LSRN
'Dear Grandad' (EA)	CTri LMil LSRN
'Dear Grandma' (EA)	LMil LSRN
'Dearest' (EA)	LMil LRHS MAsh NPri
'Debutante'	SReu SSta
decorum ♀H4	CPne GGGa LMil MHid SLdr
- SDR 5805	GKev
- subsp. ***cordatum*** C&H 7132	GGGa
§ - subsp. ***diaprepes***	GCal MHid
- - 'Gargantua'	SLdr
- late-flowering	LMil
- pink-flowered	GGGa
decorum × ***yakushimanum***	SReu
§ ***degronianum*** subsp. ***degronianum***	LMil MHid
- subsp. ***heptamerum*** 'Ho Emma'	LMil LRHS
- - 'Oki Island'	LMil
- 'Rae's Delight'	LMil
dekatanum	GGGa
deleiense	see *R. tephropeplum*
'Delicatissimum' (O) ♀	CBcs GGGa GKin GQui LRHS MHid MPkF WGwG
'Delta'	MGos MMuc SCob SLdr SLim
dendrocharis	LMil
- Cox 5016	GGGa WAbe
- Glendoick Gem = 'Gle002'	GGGa
'Denise'	IVic SAko
* 'Denny's Rose' (A)	LMil SReu SSta
'Denny's Scarlet'	NHol SReu SSta
'Denny's White' (A)	LMil NHol SReu SSta
denudatum	LMil MHid
- EGM 294	LMil
- NN 0908	MHid
Diamant Group lilac-flowered (EA)	ECho LMil MLea
- pink-flowered (EA)	ECho MLea
§ - purple-flowered (EA)	ECho MLea
§ - red-flowered (EA)	ECho MLea SLdr WBod
- rosy red-flowered (EA)	ECho
- white-flowered (EA)	ECho
'Diamant Purpur'	see *R.* Diamant Group purple-flowered

'Diamant Rot'	see *R.* Diamant Group red-flowered
I 'Diana'	SLdr
'Diana van Herzeele'	SCob
diaprepes	see *R. decorum* subsp. *diaprepes*
dichroanthum	GGGa LMil
§ - subsp. ***apodectum***	GGGa LMil MHid
- subsp. ***dichroanthum***	MHid
- - AC 1079	MHid
§ - subsp. ***scyphocalyx***	GGGa LMil MHid
- subsp. ***scyphocalyx*** × Tally Ho Group new	SLdr
- subsp. ***septentrionale***	GGGa
didymum	see *R. sanguineum* subsp. *didymum*
'Diorama' (Vs)	SReu SSta
discolor	see *R. fortunei* subsp. *discolor*
diversipilosum 'Milky Way'	GGGa
'Doc'	CBcs CMac SLdr SReu SSta
'Doctor Arnold W. Endtz'	SReu
'Doctor M. Oosthoek' (M)	CSBt GKin SReu
'Doctor Reiger'	NLar
'Doctor Stocker'	MHid
'Dominik'	GGGa
'Don Quixote' (K)	GMcL
'Dopey' $\mathbb{Y}^{H4}$	CBcs EPfP GGGa LMil LRHS MAsh MGos MHid MJak MLea NHol NLar SCob SLdr SLim SReu SSta
'Dora Amateis' $\mathbb{Y}^{H6}$	CAco CBcs ECho GGGa IDee IVic LMil LRHS MAsh MGos MMuc SAko SLdr SLim SReu WThu
Dormouse Group	ECho LMil MAsh
'Dorothy Hayden' (EA)	SLdr
'Dörte Reich'	GGGa
'Dotella'	GGGa
'Double Beauty' (Vuykiana) (EA/d)	SReu SSta
double yellow-flowered (A/d)	SLdr
'Douglas McEwan'	SLdr
Dragonfly Group	SReu SSta
'Drake's Mountain'	GMcL
'Dreamland' $\mathbb{Y}^{H5}$	CBcs EPfP LCro LMil LPar LRHS MAsh MGos MHid MLea MMuc NLar SCob SLdr SLim SPoG SReu SSta
dryophyllum misapplied	see *R. phaeochrysum* var. *levistratum*
'Dufthecke'	see *R.* White Dufthecke
'Düsselfeuer'	IVic
'Dusty Miller'	LRHS MAsh MHid MJak MPkF SLdr
'Earl of Donoughmore'	SReu SSta
'Easter Parade' (EA)	SLdr
eastmanii (A)	GGGa
ebianense NN 904	GGGa
'Ebony Pearl'	SLdr
eclecteum	GCal GGGa LMil MHid
§ ***edgeworthii*** $\mathbb{Y}^{H3}$	CBcs GCal GGGa MPkF
'Edith Bosley'	NLar SLdr SPer
'Edna Bee' (EA)	LMil SLdr
'Egret' $\mathbb{Y}^{H4}$	ECho GEdr GGGa GMcL LMil MHid MLea NSla SLdr WBod
'Eider'	GGGa MAsh
'Eileen'	LMil
'El Camino'	MMuc SLdr
Eldorado Group	GQui
(Eleanore Group) 'Eleanore'	SLdr
'Electra'	see *R. augustinii* 'Electra'
elegantulum	CPne LMil MHid
- SDR 7864 new	GKev
(Elisabeth Hobbie Group) 'Elisabeth Hobbie' $\mathbb{Y}^{H5}$	IDee LMil NLar SLdr
'Eliska'	IVic
'Elizabeth' (EA)	CMac CSBt EPfP SLdr
Elizabeth Group	CBcs LMil MAsh SLdr SPer SReu
§ - 'Creeping Jenny'	ECho GGGa MHid SLdr WBod
- 'Elizabeth'	CDul CTri LRHS LSRN MHid NHol WBod
'Elizabeth Jenny'	see *R.* 'Creeping Jenny'
'Elizabeth Lockhart'	ECho GQui WBod
'Elizabeth Red Foliage'	CTri GGGa LMil LRHS MAsh SLdr
'Else Frye'	GGGa
'Elsie Lee' (EA/d) $\mathbb{Y}^{H5}$	CEnd CSBt EPfP LMil MAsh MMuc SLdr SReu WFar
'Emasculum'	SLdr
'Emma Williams'	CBcs
'Endsleigh Pink'	LMil
'English Roseum'	LMil
eriocarpum 'Gumpō' (EA)	CMac SLdr
eriogynum	see *R. facetum*
erosum	MHid
'Eruption'	IVic NLar
'Esmeralda'	CMac
'Esther May' (A)	SReu SSta
'Etna' (EA)	SLdr
'Etta Burrows'	GGGa SLdr
'Euan Cox'	GGGa
euchaites	see *R. neriiflorum* subsp. *neriiflorum* Euchaites Group
'Eucharis' (Glenn Dale) (EA)	SCob
euchroum	MHid
eudoxum	MHid
'Eunice Ann' (A)	SReu SSta
'Europa'	SReu SSta
'Eurydice'	LMil
eurysiphon	MHid
'Evelyn Hyde' (EA)	SLdr
'Evening Fragrance' (A)	LMil
'Everbloom' (EA)	SLdr
'Everitt Hershey' (A)	SLdr
Everred = '851C'^{PBR}	GGGa
exasperatum	GGGa
- KW 6855	LMil
Exburiense Group	MMuc
'Exbury Calstocker'	LMil
'Exbury White' (K)	GQui
excellens	CPne GGGa LMil
eximium	see *R. falconeri* subsp. *eximium*
'Explorer' (EA)	MJak
'Exquisitum' (O) $\mathbb{Y}^{H5}$	CBcs GGGa GKin LMil MMuc
exquisitum	see *R. oreotrephes* Exquisitum Group
'Extraordinaire'	GGGa LMil SReu SSta
faberi	GGGa
(Fabia Group) 'Fabia' $\mathbb{Y}^{H3}$	CBcs CMac GGGa GKin LMil MAsh SLdr
§ - 'Fabia Tangerine'	CMac MLea
- 'Fabia Waterer'	LMil
§ ***facetum***	GGGa LMil
'Faggetter's Favourite' $\mathbb{Y}^{H5}$	LMil LRHS SLdr SReu SSta
Fairy Light Group	LMil SLdr
faithae CGG 14142	GGGa
falconeri $\mathbb{Y}^{H3}$	CPne GGGa LMil MHid NEgg SLdr
§ - subsp. ***eximium***	GGGa GKev LMil MHid
'Falling Snow'	IVic
'Fanal' (K)	NLar SLdr
'Fantastica' $\mathbb{Y}^{H6}$	ELan EPfP GGGa IDee LMil LRHS MAsh MGos MJak MLea MMuc NLar NPri SLim SPoG
fargesii	see *R. oreodoxa* var. *fargesii*
farinosum NN 0904	MHid

'Fashion' (EA)	SLdr
fastigiatum	GEdr LMil MHid NSla SLdr
- SBEC 0804	GGGa WThu
- SDR 7990 **new**	GKev
§ - 'Blue Steel' ♀H6	CTri ECho GKin IVic LMil LRHS MAsh SLdr SPlb SReu WAbe
- 'Indigo Steel'	GGGa
'Fastuosum Flore Pleno' (d) ♀H6	CBcs CMac CSBt GGGa LMil MLea SLdr SPer SReu SSta
faucium	GGGa
fauriei	see *R. brachycarpum* subsp. *fauriei*
'Favorite' ambig. (EA)	SLdr
'Fawley' (K)	SLdr
'Fedora' (Kaempferi) (EA)	CBcs CTsd
Feenkissen = 'Hachkissen'PBR (EA)	IVic SAko
ferrugineum	GGGa LMil
'Feuerwerk' (K)	GMcL IVic MMuc NLar
fictolacteum	see *R. rex* subsp. *fictolacteum*
Fine Feathers Group	WBod
'Fire Bird' **new**	SLdr
'Fire Rim'	LRHS MAsh
'Fireball' (K) ♀H6	CBcs CDul CTri EPfP GGGa GKin GMcL LMil LRHS MAsh MGos MMuc NLar SLdr SPer SPoG WMoo
'Fireball' (hybrid)	MJak
'Firecracker' (A)	LRHS MAsh
'Fireglow' (EA)	GKin LMil
'Firelight' (hybrid)	GKin LMil NLar SPer
§ 'Firestorm'	NPri
'Flaming Gold'	LRHS LSRN MAsh SLdr
'Flanagan's Daughter'	LMil MAsh
'Flautando'	IVic LMil
Flava Group	see *R.* Volker Group
flavidum	GGGa MMuc
fletcherianum 'Yellow Bunting'	GGGa
floccigerum	LMil MHid
- AC 1863	MHid
- bicoloured	GGGa
'Floriade'	GMcL
floribundum	GGGa LMil SLdr
'Florida' (EA/d) ♀H4	CMac LMil SLdr SReu
'Flower Arranger' (EA)	LMil MAsh SCoo
formosanum	GGGa
formosum	CBcs GGGa
§ - var. ***formosum*** Iteaphyllum Group	GGGa
- - 'Khasia'	GGGa
- var. ***inaequale***	GGGa
forrestii	GCal
- subsp. ***forrestii***	LMil
- - Repens Group	LMil
- - - 'Seinghku'	GGGa
- Tumescens Group	GGGa WThu
Fortune Group	SLdr
fortunei ♀H6	GGGa LMil SLdr
§ - subsp. ***discolor*** ♀H5	LMil MHid
- - (Houlstonii Group) 'John R. Elcock'	LMil
- - 'Hummeltanz'	IVic
- - var. ***kwangfuense*** AC 5208	LMil
- 'Mrs Butler'	see *R.* 'Sir Charles Butler'
fragariiflorum	GGGa
'Fragrant Memories' **new**	LMil
'Fragrant Star' (A)	LRHS
'Fragrantissimum' ♀H2	CBcs CEnd CMac CSBt CTsd ECre GGGa LMil LRHS MPkF MRav NLar SKHP SLdr WBod

'Fraseri' (M)	LMil
'Fred Peste' ♀H4	GKin LMil MAsh MGos MHid MLea MMuc SLdr SLim
(Fred Wynniatt Group) 'Fred Wynniatt'	LMil MHid
'Fred Wynniatt Stanway'	see *R.* 'Stanway'
'Freya' (R/d)	LMil LSRN
'Fridoline' (EA)	IVic SAko
'Frigate' (EA)	SLdr
'Frilly Lemon' (Ad)	EPfP MPkF SLdr
'Frosted Orange' (EA)	LMil MAsh
'Frosthexe'	SAko
'Frühlingsbeginn'	IVic
'Frühlingsglühen'	IVic
'Frühlingszauber'	SLdr
'Fulbrook'	LMil
fulgens	GGGa LMil MHid
fulvum ♀H4	GCal GGGa GKin LMil MHid SReu SSta
- subsp. ***fulvoides***	MHid
'Furnivall's Daughter' ♀H5	CDul CMac CSBt GGGa LMil MHid MMuc NHol SLdr SPer SReu SSta WMoo
fuyuanense **new**	GGGa
'Gabrielle Hill' (EA)	MAsh SLdr
'Gaiety' (Glenn Dale) (EA)	LMil SLdr
galactinum	GGGa IDee LMil LRHS MHid
'Galathea' (EA)	MMuc
'Gandy Dancer'	CAco MLea SLdr
'Garden State Glow' (EA/d)	SLdr
'Gartendirektor Glocker'	ECho GGGa IVic MAsh MGos MHid SLim
'Gartendirektor Rieger' ♀H5	GGGa IVic LMil NLar SReu
'Gauche' (A)	GQui
'Gaugin'	GQui
'Geisha' (EA)	SGol
'Geisha Lilac'	see *R.* (Aronense Group) 'Hanako'
'Geisha Orange'	see *R.* (Aronense Group) 'Satschiko'
'Geisha Pink'	see *R.* 'Momoko'
'Geisha Purple'	see *R.* (Aronense Group) 'Fumiko'
'Geisha Red'	see *R.* (Aronense Group) 'Kazuko'
'Geisha White'	see *R.* 'Hisako'
'Gena Mae' (A/d)	GGGa SLdr
'General Practitioner'	SLdr
'General Wavell' (EA)	CMac SLdr
'Gene's Favourite'	SReu SSta
genestierianum	GGGa MHid
'Genoveva'	SAko
'Geoffroy Millais'	LMil
'Georg Arends' (A)	EPfP LMil LRHS MAsh NLar SLdr
'George Hyde' (EA)	EPfP LRHS LSRN MAsh SCoo
'George Johnstone'	SLdr
'George's Delight'	MHid
§ × ***geraldii***	SLdr
'Germania'	CBcs GMcL LMil LPar LRHS MAsh MGos NPri SCob SPoG SReu SSta
Gertrud Schäle Group	CTri GMcL
Gibraltar Group	LMil WFar
'Gibraltar' (K) ♀H6	CBcs CDul CSBt CTri EPfP GGGa GKin LMil MAsh MGos MJak NHol NLar SLdr SLim SPer SReu SSta WMoo
'Gilbert Mullie' (EA)	LMil NLar SLim SReu SSta
'Gillian Bramley'	SLdr
'Gill's Crimson'	SReu
'Ginger' (K)	LMil
'Ginny Gee' ♀H5	CBcs CSBt ECho EPfP GEdr GGGa GKin GMcL IVic LMil LRHS MAsh MGos MHid MLea NEgg NLar NSla NWad SReu SSta WBod

§ 'Girard's Hot Shot' (EA)	GMcL LMil LPar LRHS MPkF SReu SSta
§ 'Girard's Variegated Hot Shot' (EA/v) ♀H4	GGGa LMil LPar MAsh NEgg SLdr SPoG
'Gislinde' (A)	SAko
'Glacier' (EA)	SLdr
glanduliferum	GGGa SLdr
- EGM 347	LMil
- 'Peter the Great' **new**	LMil
glaucophyllum	CPne GGGa LMil MHid
- Borde Hill form	LMil
- 'Deer Dell'	LMil
- var. ***glaucophyllum***	MHid
§ - subsp. ***tubiforme***	GGGa
Glendoick Butterscotch = 'Gle003'	GGGa
Glendoick Crimson = 'Gle004' (EA)	GGGa
Glendoick Dove = 'Gle025' **new**	GGGa
Glendoick Dream = 'Gle005' (EA)	GGGa
Glendoick Ermine = 'Gle006' (EA)	GGGa
Glendoick Flamingo = 'Gle026' **new**	GGGa
Glendoick Frolic = 'Gle007'	GGGa
Glendoick Garnet = 'Gle008' (EA)	GGGa
Glendoick Glacier = 'Gle009' (EA)	GGGa
Glendoick Goblin = 'Gle010' (EA)	GGGa
Glendoick Gold = 'Gle011'	GGGa
Glendoick Ice Cream = 'Gle013'	GGGa
Glendoick Mystique = 'Gle014'	GGGa
Glendoick Petticoats = 'Gle015'	GGGa
Glendoick Rosebud = 'Gle022' (EA)	GGGa
Glendoick Ruby = 'Gle016'	GGGa
'Glendoick Silver'	GGGa
Glendoick Snowflakes = 'Gle001' (EA)	GGGa
§ 'Glendoick Tanager'	GGGa
Glendoick Vanilla = 'Gle017'	GGGa
Glendoick Velvet = 'Gle018'	GGGa
'Glenna'	GGGa
'Gletschernacht'	IVic SAko
glischrum	CPne GGGa
- subsp. ***glischroides***	GGGa LMil
§ - subsp. ***rude***	CPne GGGa MHid
globigerum	see *R. alutaceum* var. *alutaceum* Globigerum Group
'Gloria'	see *R.* 'Bruns Gloria'
'Glory of Littleworth' (Ad)	LMil
'Glowing Embers' (K)	CTri GKin GMcL LMil LRHS MAsh MGos MLea NHol NLar SLim SPer SReu SSta
'Goblin'	MHid SLdr
'Gog' (K)	CSBt
§ 'Goldbukett'	GGGa SAko
Golden Bouquet	see *R.* 'Goldbukett'
'Golden Coach'	CAco MHid SLdr
'Golden Eagle' (K) ♀H6	CBcs GKin GMcL LMil LRHS MGos MHid MJak MLea NLar SLdr SPer SReu WMoo
Golden Everest = 'Hachgold'PBR	GGGa SAko
'Golden Flare' (A)	CBcs GKin GMcL MMuc NEgg SLdr
'Golden Fleece'	LMil
'Golden Gate'	CSBt LRHS MGos MMuc NLar
'Golden Horn' (K)	GQui
(Golden Horn Group) 'Golden Horn'	SLdr
'Golden Lights' (A)	GKin LMil LRHS NEgg NLar
'Golden Princess'	LMil
'Golden Ruby'	CBcs SPer
'Golden Splendour'	LMil
'Golden Sunset' (K) ♀H6	EPfP LMil MAsh MLea WFar
'Golden Torch' ♀H4	CBcs CDul EPfP LMil LPar LRHS MAsh MGos MHid MJak MLea NLar NPri SLdr SLim SPer SPoG SReu
'Golden Wedding'	LMil LRHS LSRN MAsh MHid MJak SLdr SPer
'Golden Wit'	MAsh MMuc NEgg
'Golden Wonder'	MHtn
'Goldflimmer' (v)	EPfP GGGa GKin LPar LRHS MAsh MGos MJak MMuc NLar NPri SCob SLim SPoG
(Goldfort Group) 'Goldfort'	SReu
'Goldika'	LMil
'Goldinetta'	GGGa LRHS SAko
'Goldkollier'	IVic
'Goldkrone' ♀H5	ELon EPfP GGGa LCro MAsh MHtn MLea SPer SPoG SReu SSta
'Goldpracht' (K)	IVic
Goldschatz = 'Goldprinz'	CBcs IVic
'Goldsworth Orange'	CAco LMil SLdr
'Goldsworth Yellow'	CSBt
'Goldtopas' (K)	CTri EPfP GGGa GKin LMil LRHS
'Gomer Waterer' ♀H6	CBcs CDul CMac CSBt ECho EPfP GGGa GMcL LMil LPar LRHS MAsh MGos MJak MMuc NLar SCob SLdr SPer SPoG SReu SSta
'Gorbella'	SReu
Gowenianum Group (Ad)	LMil LRHS MGos
'Grace Seabrook' ♀H5	CBcs CSBt CTri GGGa MLea MMuc SLdr SPer SReu
'Graf Lennart'	GGGa
Graffito = 'Hachgraf'	GGGa IDee IVic LMil LRHS
'Graham Thomas'	LMil
'Grand Slam'	MHid
grande	GGGa LMil MHid SLdr
- KR 9483	WPGP
- pink-flowered	MHid
gratum	see *R. basilicum*
'Graziella'	GGGa LCro LRHS MGos MPkF SPoG SSta
'Greensleeves'	LMil MAsh
'Greenway' (Kurume) (EA)	CBcs SLdr
griersonianum	GGGa LMil
- F 30392 **new**	LMil
griffithianum	MHid
- B&SWJ 2425	WCru
- KR 10075	MHid
'Gristede' ♀H5	ECho LMil LRHS NLar SReu SSta
groenlandicum	MLea NLar SPer WSHC
- 'Compactum'	NLar
- 'Helma'	GBin IVic LRHS NLar
- 'Lenie'	NLar
(Grosclaude Group) 'Grosclaude'	LMil

	'Grouse' × ***keiskei*** var. ***ozawae*** 'Yaku Fairy'	ECho
	'Grumpy'	CBcs CSBt ELan EPfP LMil LRHS MAsh SCob SReu
	'Gunter Dinger'	IVic
	'Gwenda' (EA)	CTri SLdr
	'Gwendoline' (A)	SReu SSta
	(Gwillt-king Group) 'Gwillt-king'	CBcs
	habrotrichum	GGGa LMil
	'Hachmann's Brasilia'	SSta
	'Hachmann's Charmant'	EPfP GGGa SAko SPoG
	'Hachmann's Constanze'	LMil
	'Hachmann's Eskimo'	LMil SLdr
	'Hachmann's Feuerschein'	SAko
	'Hachmann's Junifeuer'	SReu SSta
	Hachmann's Kabarett = 'Hachkaba'	LMil NLar
	'Hachmann's Mamamia'	SAko
	'Hachmann's Marlis' ♀H6	LMil SReu
§	'Hachmann's Metallica'	GGGa LCro LMil
§	'Hachmann's Orakel' **new**	GGGa LMil
	Hachmann's Picobello = 'Hachpico'PBR	EPfP GGGa LMil
§	'Hachmann's Polaris' ♀H7	LMil MJak SReu
	'Hachmann's Porzellan' ♀H6	LMil
§	'Hachmann's Rokoko' (EA)	CEnd LMil SReu SSta
	'Hachmann's Sunny Boy'	LMil LRHS
§	'Hachmann's Tanaga'	GGGa
	haematodes	GGGa LMil SLdr
§	- subsp. ***chaetomallum***	GGGa LMil MHid
	- subsp. ***haematodes***	LMil
	'Halfdan Lem' ♀H4	CBcs GGGa GKin LMil MAsh MGos MLea MMuc NLar SLim SPer SReu SSta
	'Hallelujah'	IVic
	'Halopeanum'	GGGa
	'Halton'	LMil
	'Hamlet' (M)	LMil
	'Hammondii'	LMil
	'Hampshire Belle'	LMil SReu SSta WThu
	hanceanum 'Canton Consul'	GGGa
	- Nanum Group ♀H5	CBcs GGGa
	'Hanger's Flame' (A)	LMil
	'Hank Windsor'	CAco
	Hans Hachmann = 'Hachhans'	GGGa LMil
	'Hansel'	MAsh MMuc SLdr
	'Hardijzer Beauty' (Ad)	SLdr
	'Hardy Gardenia' (EA/d)	SReu SSta
	hardyi	see *R. augustinii* subsp. *hardyi*
	'Harkwood Red' (EA)	SLdr
	'Harry Tagg'	SLdr
	Harry White's hybrid (A)	SReu SSta
	'Harvest Moon' (K)	GMcL NLar SLdr SSta
	'Hatsu-giri' (EA)	CMac LMil SLdr SPer SReu SSta
	(Hawk Group) 'Crest' ♀H3	CBcs GGGa LMil SSta
	'Heather Macleod' (EA)	SLdr
	heatherae	GGGa LMil
	'Heidi'PBR (EA)	SLdr
	'Helen Close' (Glenn Dale) (EA)	SLdr
	'Helena Evelyn' (A)	LMil
	'Helene Schiffner'	SReu
	heliolepis	GGGa LMil
	- var. ***fumidum***	see *R. heliolepis* var. *heliolepis*
§	- var. ***heliolepis***	GGGa
	hemidartum	see *R. pocophorum* var. *hemidartum*
	hemsleyanum	LMil MHid SLdr
	aff. ***henanense*** **new**	GGGa
	'Herbert' (EA)	CMac MGos NLar SLdr SLim
§	'Herbstzauber'	MAsh
	'Heureuse Surprise' (G)	SLdr
	'High Sheriff' **new**	CBcs
	'High Summer'	LMil LRHS NLar
	'Hilda Margaret'	SReu
	'Himmelberg'	GGGa
	'Hinamayo'	see *R.* (Obtusum Group) 'Hinomayo'
	'Hino-crimson' (Kurume) (EA) ♀H4	CBcs CMac CSBt CTri GKin GMcL LMil LPar MAsh MGos MPkF NHol NLar SGol SLdr SPer SPoG SReu SSta
	'Hinode-giri' (EA)	CMac CSBt CTsd SLdr SPer SReu
	'Hino-red' (EA) **new**	LPar
	'Hino-scarlet' (EA)	LPar
	hippophaeoides	CBcs GKev LMil MHid SLdr
	- SDR 7919 **new**	GKev
	- 'Bei-ma-shan'	see *R. hippophaeoides* 'Haba Shan'
§	- 'Haba Shan' ♀H6	GGGa IDee LMil LRHS WThu
	hirsutum	LMil MHid
	- f. ***albiflorum***	MHid
	- 'Flore Pleno' (d)	ECho
	hirtipes	GGGa MHid
§	'Hisako' (EA)	GMcL
	hodgsonii	LMil MHid SLdr
	- B&SWJ 2195A	WCru
	'Homebush' (K/d) ♀H6	CBcs CDul CMac CTri EPfP GBin GMcL LMil MAsh MGos MJak NLar SLdr SPer SPoG SReu SSta WMoo
	'Honey Butter'	LMil MGos NLar SLim
	'Honeysuckle' (K)	NHol SReu SSta
§	'Ho-o' (Kurume) (EA)	SLdr
	'Ho-oden' (EA)	MPkF
	hookeri	CPne LMil
	- Tigh-na-Rudha form	GGGa
	'Hoppy'	CBcs LMil MAsh MGos MHid MLea MMuc NLar SLdr SLim SPer
	'Horizon Monarch' ♀H4	CBcs GGGa GKin IVic LMil LPar LRHS MGos MLea NLar SLdr SLim SPer SReu SSta WMoo
	horlickianum	GGGa
	'Hortulanus H. Witte' (M)	CSBt LRHS SReu SSta
	'Hot Shot'	see *R.* 'Girard's Hot Shot'
	'Hot Shot Variegated'	see *R.* 'Girard's Variegated Hot Shot' (EA/v)
	'Hotei'	CAco CSBt ECho EPfP GKin LMil MAsh MLea NEgg NHol SLdr SReu SSta
	(Hotspur Group) 'Hotspur' (K)	SLdr SPer
	- 'Hotspur Red' (K) ♀H6	EPfP GKin GMcL LMil MAsh NEgg WMoo
	huanum	GGGa LMil
	- EGM 316	LMil
	'Hugh Koster'	SLdr
	aff. ***huidongense***	LMil
	'Hullaballoo'	LMil LRHS
	Humming Bird Group	GEdr LMil SLdr WBod
	hunnewellianum	MHid
	'Hussar'	LMil
	'Hyde and Seek'	GQui
	'Hydon Dawn' ♀H5	CBcs LMil MHid MLea MMuc SLdr SReu SSta
	'Hydon Hunter' ♀H5	CBcs MHid SReu SSta
	'Hydon Velvet'	CBcs GGGa LMil SAko SLdr SReu WMoo

	hylaeum	MHid
	Hyperion Group	SReu
	hyperythrum	GGGa LMil MHid
	hypoglaucum	see *R. argyrophyllum* subsp. *hypoglaucum*
	'Ice Cube'	MLea MMuc SLdr
	'Iceberg'	see *R.* 'Lodauric Iceberg'
	Idaho Group **new**	LMil
	(Idealist Group) 'Idealist'	LMil
	'Ightham Yellow'	SLdr SReu
§	'Ilam Melford Lemon' (A)	LMil
§	'Ilam Ming' (A)	LMil
	'Ilam Violet'	LMil
	'Iliad' **new**	LMil
	'Imago' (K/d)	LMil
§	'Ima-shojo' (Kurume) (EA/d)	CMac LRHS SLdr
	impeditum	CBcs CSBt CWib ECho ELan GEdr GKev GQui MGos MHid MJak MLea MMuc SCob SLdr SPer SReu SSta
	- 'Blue Steel'	see *R. fastigiatum* 'Blue Steel'
	- 'Indigo'	GKin SReu WAbe
	- 'Pygmaeum'	NHar WAbe WThu
	- 'Select' **new**	MJak
	imperator	see *R. uniflorum* var. *imperator*
	(Impi Group) 'Impi'	LMil
	indicum (EA)	CTsd
§	- 'Macranthum' (EA)	SLdr
	'Ingrid Mehlquist'	GGGa
	Inkarho Lilac Dufthecke = 'Rhodunter 149'^{PBR}	LMil
	insigne ♀^{H6}	GGGa IDee LMil LRHS MHid
	- Reuthe's form	SReu
	insigne* × *yakushimanum	SReu
	Intrifast Group	GGGa
	iodes	see *R. alutaceum* var. *iodes*
	'Irene Koster' (O) ♀^{H5}	GGGa GKin LMil LRHS MGos MPkF NLar SLim SPer
	'Irohayama' (Kurume) (EA) ♀^{H3}	CBcs CEnd CMac EPfP GQui LMil LRHS MAsh NPri
	irroratum	LMil SLdr
	- subsp. ***irroratum***	MHid
	- 'Polka Dot'	GGGa LMil
	- subsp. ***yiliangense*** EGM 339	LMil
	'Isabel'	NPri
	'Isabel' (EA)	GMcL MAsh
	'Isola Bella'	GGGa
	'Issho-no-haru' (EA)	WBod
	iteaphyllum	see *R. formosum* var. *formosum* Iteaphyllum Group
	'Ivette' (Kaempferi) (EA)	CMac
	Iviza Group	LMil
	'Izumi-no-mai' (EA)	SLdr
	'J.C. Williams'	CBcs
	'J.M. de Montague'	see *R.* 'The Honourable Jean Marie de Montague'
	'Jack A. Sand' (K)	GGGa
	'Jackwill'	SAko
	(Jalisco Group) 'Jubilant'	LMil
	'James Burchett' ♀^{H6}	LMil SReu
	'James Gable' (EA)	MAsh SLdr
	Janet Group	LMil
	'Janet Rhea' (EA)	SLdr
	japonicum (A. Gray) J.V. Suringar	see *R. molle* subsp. *japonicum*
	- var. ***pentamerum***	see *R. degronianum* subsp. *degronianum*
	jasminiflorum (V)	GGGa
	'Jason'	LMil
	javanicum (V)	GGGa
	'Jean Marie Montague'	see *R.* 'The Honourable Jean Marie de Montague'
	'Jeff Hill' (EA)	SLdr
	'Jenny'	see *R.* 'Creeping Jenny'
	'Jessica Rose' (A)	LMil
	'Jim Russell' (*ciliicalyx* hybrid)	GGGa
	'Jingle Bells'	GGGa MPkF
	'Joanna'	CBcs
	'Jock'	SLdr
	Jock Group	CBcs
	'Jock Brydon' (O)	GGGa LMil
	'Johann Sebastian Bach' (EA)	SLdr
	'Johann Strauss' (EA)	WBod
	'Johanna' (EA) ♀^{H5}	CEnd CTri EPfP GMcL LMil LRHS MAsh MGos NHol NLar NPri SLdr SPer WBod
	'John Cairns' (Kaempferi) (EA)	CMac SLdr
	'John Walter'	SCob
	johnstoneanum	CBcs GGGa SLdr
	- 'Double Diamond' (d)	LMil
	'Jolie Madame' (Vs) ♀^{H6}	EPfP GKin LMil LRHS MAsh MGos MMuc NLar NPri SPer
	'Joseph Haydn' (EA)	WBod
	'Joseph Hill' (EA)	CEnd NLar
	'Jubilee'	SLdr
	'Juliette' (EA)	IVic
	'July Giant'	SLdr
	'June Fire' (A)	GGGa SReu SSta
	'Juniduft' (A)	GGGa
	kaempferi (EA)	LMil SLdr
§	- 'Mikado' (EA)	LMil SLdr SReu
	- orange-flowered (EA)	CMac
	'Kali'	GGGa
	'Kalinka'	LMil MAsh MGos SPoG
	'Karen Triplett'	LMil
	'Karin'	MJak
	'Karl Naue'	GGGa SReu
	'Kasane-kagaribi' (EA)	SLdr
	'Kate Waterer' ♀^{H5}	SReu
	'Kathleen' van Nes (EA)	SLdr
	'Katisha' (EA)	SLdr
	'Katy Watson'	SReu SSta
	'Keija' (EA)	SLdr
	keiskei compact	ITim
	- Cordifolium Group	CPne WAbe
	- var. ***ozawae*** 'Yaku Fairy' ♀^{H5}	LMil WAbe WThu
	keleticum	see *R. calostrotum* subsp. ***keleticum***
	'Kelsay's Double'	MLea
	'Ken Janeck'	GGGa
§	***kendrickii***	CPne GGGa
	'Kermesinum' (EA)	CTri MAsh MGos NWad SLdr SLim SReu
I	'Kermesinum Rosé' (EA) ♀^{H5}	CSBt LMil NLar SLdr SLim SReu
	kesangiae	GGGa LMil
	- KR 9444	GKev
	- var. ***album***	GGGa
	keysii	CPne GGGa LMil
	'Kilian' (A)	MPkF
	(Kilimanjaro Group) 'Kilimanjaro'	LMil SReu
	'Kimbeth'	GGGa
	'King George' Loder	see *R.* 'Loderi King George'
	kingianum	see *R. arboreum* subsp. *zeylanicum*
	'Kings Ride'	LMil
§	'Kirin' (Kurume) (EA/d)	LMil LPar MPkF SLdr

	'Kirsten Begeer'	IVic
	kiusianum (EA)	LMil SReu
I	- 'Album' (EA)	LMil SReu WAbe
	- 'Hillier's Pink' (EA)	LMil
	- var. ***kiusianum*** (EA)	SLdr
	'Kleiner Prinz' (EA)	SAko
	'Klondyke' (K) ♀H6	CBcs CSBt CTri EPfP GGGa GKin LCro LMil LRHS MAsh MGos NLar NPri SLdr SPer SPoG
	'Kluis Sensation' ♀H5	CBcs CMac CSBt SLdr SReu SSta
	'Kluis Triumph'	SReu
	'Knap Hill Apricot' (K)	LMil
	'Knap Hill Red' (K)	LMil
	'Kobold' (EA)	SLdr
	'Koichiro Wada'	see *R. yakushimanum* 'Koichiro Wada'
	'Kokardia'	LMil SAko
	'Kokette'	IVic
	kongboense	GGGa WAbe
	'Königstein' (EA)	IVic LMil MGos SReu SSta
§	'Koningin Emma' (M)	GKin LMil
	'Konsonanz'	IVic
	'Koromo-shikibu' (EA)	GGGa LRHS MPkF
	'Koromo-shikibu White' (EA)	GGGa
	'Koster's Brilliant Red' (M)	CSBt LCro SReu SSta
	'Kranenfee' (A)	GGGa
§	'Kure-no-yuki' (Kurume) (EA/d)	CEnd LMil
	kyawii	CPne GGGa
	'Lackblatt'	see *R.* (Volker Group) 'Flavum Lackblatt'
	(Lactcombei Group) 'Robert Keir'	SLdr
	lacteum	GGGa LMil
	'Lady Alice Fitzwilliam' ♀H3	CBcs CMHG CMac ECre GGGa GKin LMil
	(Lady Chamberlain Group) 'Salmon Trout'	LMil LSRN
	'Lady Clementine Mitford' ♀H5	CBcs CSBt LMil MLea MMuc SLdr SPer SReu
	'Lady de Rothschild' **new**	LMil
	'Lady Eleanor Cathcart'	SLdr
	'Lady Elphinstone' (EA)	SLdr
	'Lady Louise' (EA)	SLdr
	'Lady Montagu'	LMil
	'Lady Romsey'	LMil
	laetum (V)	GGGa
	Lamellen Group	LMil
	lanatoides	GGGa
	lanatum	GGGa LMil
	'Langworth'	MLea MMuc SReu
	lanigerum	LMil SReu
	'Lanzette'	IVic
	lapponicum Parviflorum Group	GGGa
	'Lapwing' (K)	NLar
	'Laramie'	GGGa
*	***laterifolium***	GGGa
	'Laura Morland' (EA)	LPar
	'Lavender Brilliant' (EA)	SLdr
	'Lavender Girl' ♀H5	CMac LMil SLdr SReu SSta
	'Lavendula'	SAko
	'Le Progrès'	LMil
	'Lea Rainbow'	MLea
	'Ledifolium'	see *R.* × ***mucronatum***
	'Ledifolium Album'	see *R.* × ***mucronatum***
	'Lee's Dark Purple'	CAco LMil MJak
	'Lee's Scarlet'	LMil
	'Lemon Dream'	LMil LRHS MAsh MGos NLar NPri SLim

*	'Lemon Drop' (A)	GGGa
	'Lemon Meringue'	LMil
	'Lemonora' (M)	CBcs GKin
	'Lem's 45'	SLdr
	'Lem's Cameo' ♀H3	GGGa LMil LRHS SReu SSta
	'Lem's Monarch' ♀H4	CBcs CDul GGGa LMil MLea MMuc MPkF SLdr SReu SSta
	'Lem's Stormcloud'	GGGa
	'Lem's Tangerine'	LMil
	'Lemur' (EA)	ECho GGGa LMil MLea NLar WThu
	'Leni'	LRHS MAsh
	'Leo' (EA)	SLdr
	'Leonardslee Giles'	SLdr
	'Leonardslee Primrose'	SLdr
	'Leonore'	LMil
	lepidostylum	CMac GGGa ITim LMil
	lepidotum	GGGa
	- var. ***album***	GGGa
	- yellow-flowered McB 110	WThu
§	***leptocarpum***	GGGa
§	'Leucanthum'	GGGa WThu
	leucaspis	CBcs SLdr
	'Leuchtpolster'	IVic
	'Lila Pedigo'	MMuc SLdr SPer
	'Lilac Time' (EA)	SLdr
	'Lilactina'	SLdr
	'Lily Marleen' (EA)	CTri MPkF
	'Linda' ♀H5	CBcs EPfP GGGa LMil LSRN MAsh MJak MLea SCob
	'Linda Stuart' (EA)	GGGa
	lindleyi	GGGa LRHS MPkF
	- 'Geordie Sherriff'	GGGa
	'Linearifolium'	see *R. stenopetalum* 'Linearifolium'
	'Lingot d'Or' (A) **new**	MPkF
	'Linnet' (K/d)	SLdr
	'Lionel's First'	LMil
	Lionel's Triumph Group	LMil
	'Little Beauty' (EA)	SLdr
	'Little Ben'	ECho ITim
	'Loch Arkaig'	GGGa
	'Loch Awe'	GGGa LMil
	'Loch Earn'	GGGa
	'Loch Faskally'	GGGa
	'Loch Laggan'	GGGa
	'Loch Leven'	GGGa
	'Loch Linnhe'	GGGa SReu
	'Loch Lomond'	GGGa
	'Loch Morar'	GGGa
	lochiae (V)	GGGa
	'Lochinch Spinbur'	GQui
	Lodauric Group	SLdr SReu
§	- 'Lodauric Iceberg'	LMil SReu
	'Lodbrit'	SReu
	Loderi Group	SLdr
	- 'Loderi Fairy Queen'	SLdr
	- 'Loderi Game Chick'	LMil SLdr
	- 'Loderi Georgette'	SLdr
	- 'Loderi Helen'	LMil SLdr
§	- 'Loderi King George' ♀H4	CBcs GGGa GKin IVic LMil MLea SLdr SPer SReu SSta
	- 'Loderi Patience'	SLdr
	- 'Loderi Pink Coral'	LMil SLdr
	- 'Loderi Pink Diamond' ♀H4	LMil SLdr
	- 'Loderi Pink Topaz'	SLdr
	- 'Loderi Pretty Polly'	SLdr
	- 'Loderi Princess Marina'	SLdr
	- 'Loderi Sir Edmund'	LMil SLdr
	- 'Loderi Sir Joseph Hooker'	SLdr
	- 'Loderi Titan'	SLdr SReu SSta

	- 'Loderi Venus' ♀H4	LMil SLdr SReu SSta
	- 'Loderi White Diamond'	SLdr
	'Loder's White' ♀H3	LMil SReu SSta
	longesquamatum	GGGa MHid
	longipes	GGGa LMil MHid SLdr
	- EGM 336	LMil
	- var. ***chienianum***	LMil MHid
	'Looking Glass'	MMuc
	'Lord Roberts' ♀H6	CAco CBcs CMac CSBt CTri EPfP GGGa LCro LMil MAsh MGos MJak MLea MMuc NHol NLar SLdr SLim SPer SReu SSta WMoo
	'Loreley'	SAko
	'Lori Eichelser'	WBod
	'Louis Pasteur'	SCob SReu
	'Louisa' (EA)	MAsh NLar
	'Louise Dowdle' (Glenn Dale) (EA)	LMil SLdr
	'Lovely William'	CMac LMil SLdr
	lowndesii	WAbe
	'Lucy Lou'	GGGa
	ludlowii	GGGa
	'Luisella'	IVic
	'Lullaby' (EA)	SLdr
	luteiflorum	GGGa
	- KW 7833	MHid
	lutescens	CBcs CTsd LMil MHid SLdr SReu
	- 'Bagshot Sands' ♀H3	GGGa LMil SLdr
	luteum (A)	Widely available
	- 'Golden Comet' (A)	GGGa
	lyi	GGGa
*	'Mac Ovata'	CMac
	macabeanum ♀H3	GGGa GKev GKin LMil MHid MLea NEgg SLdr SPer SReu SSta
	- NAPE 052	GGGa
	- Reuthe's form	SReu
	macabeanum × ***wardii***	GGGa
	'Macarena'	IVic SAko
	macgregoriae (V)	GGGa
	macranthum	see *R. indicum* 'Macranthum'
	macrophyllum B&SWJ 9561 **new**	WCru
	macrosmithii	see *R. argipeplum*
	'Macrostemon' (EA)	WBod
	maculiferum	GGGa
	'Madame Ad. van Hecke' (EA)	CTri GKin IVic LMil MAsh MGos SLim
	'Madame Albert van Hecke' (EA)	SLdr
	'Madame de Bruin'	SLdr
	'Madame Galle'	SLdr
	'Madame Masson' ♀H6	CAco CDul CTri ELan LMil LRHS LSRN MAsh MGos MLea MMuc NLar NPri SLdr SPer SReu SSta
	maddenii	CBcs IDee LMil SAko
§	- subsp. ***crassum***	CBcs CPne GGGa IVic MHid SKHP
§	- subsp. ***maddenii*** Polyandrum Group	CBcs GGGa GQui
	'Madleen'	SAko
	'Maggie'	IVic
	'Magic Flute' (EA)	LRHS MAsh
I	'Magic Flute' (V)	LMil SCoo
	magniflorum	GGGa
	- NN 0959	MHid
	'Maharani'	GGGa
	'Mai-ogi' (EA)	IVic SAko
	'Maischnee' (EA)	GGGa
	'Maja' (G)	SReu SSta
	Major Group	LMil
§	***makinoi*** ♀H5	GGGa LMil SReu SSta
	- 'Fuju-kaku-no-matsu'	MGos
	'Makiyak'	LMil SAko
	mallotum	GGGa LMil MHid
	'Mandarin Lights' (A)	NLar
	'Manderley'	LMil
	maoerense	GGGa
	'Maraschino' (EA)	GGGa IVic SAko
	'Mardi Gras'	MGos NEgg SLdr
	'Margaret Blain'	SReu
	Margaret Dunn Group	CAco
	'Maria Elena' (EA/d)	LRHS MGos NLar SLdr
	'Marie Curie'	LMil
	'Marie Fortie'	MGos NLar
	'Marie Hoffman'	LMil
	'Marilee' (EA)	EPfP IVic MAsh NLar SLdr
	(Mariloo Group) 'Mariloo' **new**	LMil
	'Marinja' (EA)	LMil
	'Marinus Koster'	SReu SSta
	'Marion Street'	LMil
	'Markeeta's Prize' ♀H4	EPfP GGGa LMil LRHS MAsh MGos MLea MMuc NLar NPri SLdr SLim SReu
	'Marlies' (A)	NLar
	'Marmot' (EA)	ECho MLea MMuc
	'Marsalla'	SAko
	'Martha Isaacson' (Ad)	LMil MLea SLdr SReu
	'Martha Wright'	EPfP GGGa LRHS MAsh NPri
	martinianum	GGGa
	'Maruschka' (EA) ♀H5	GGGa IVic LCro LMil LRHS MAsh SAko SPoG
	'Mary Desby' (EA)	CEnd
	'Mary Forte'	SCob
	'Mary Helen' (Glenn Dale) (EA)	LMil LRHS MAsh MGos NLar SCoo SLdr SLim SReu
	'Mary Poppins' (A)	GKin LMil LRHS LSRN MGos MMuc MPkF NLar SCoo SLdr SLim WMoo
	'Marylou'	LMil
	Matador Group	SReu
	- 'Matador'	GGGa LMil SLdr
	'Mathie' (A)	SReu SSta
	maximum	GGGa
§	'Maxwellii' (EA)	CMac SLdr
	May Day Group	CBcs MGos WBod
	- 'May Day' ♀H3	CMac MAsh MMuc SLdr
	'Mayor Johnstone'	CTri EPfP MAsh NPri
	'Mazurka' (K)	IVic
	meddianum var. ***atrokermesinum*** F 2649	LMil
	Medusa Group	SLdr
	megacalyx	GGGa
	'Megan' (EA)	LSRN MAsh SLdr WGwG
	megaphyllum	see *R. basilicum*
	megeratum	GGGa
	- 'Bodnant'	GGGa ITim WAbe WThu
	mekongense	GCal
	- var. ***mekongense*** Rubroluteum Group	see *R. viridescens* Rubroluteum Group
	- - Viridescens Group	see *R. viridescens*
	'Melford Lemon'	see *R.* 'Ilam Melford Lemon'
	'Melina' (EA/d)	LMil
	'Melrose Flash' **new**	GGGa MPkF
	'Melville'	MPkF SSta
	'Mendosina'	IVic
	mengtszense	MHid
§	***menziesii***	IVic
	'Merganser' ♀H4	CAco GGGa LMil SLdr
	'Merlin' (Glenn Dale) (EA)	LMil
	Metallica	see *R.* 'Hachmann's Metallica'

metternichii var. ***pentamerum***	see *R. degronianum* subsp. *degronianum*
'Mi Amor'	GGGa
'Michael Hill' (EA)	MAsh
'Michiko' (EA)	IVic SAko
micranthum	LMil LRHS
microgynum	GGGa MHid
- Gymnocarpum Group	MHid
microleucum	see *R. orthocladum* var. *microleucum*
micromeres	see *R. leptocarpum*
'Midnight Beauty'	EPfP SAko
'Midnight Mystique'	GGGa SReu SSta
'Midsummer'	IVic MMuc SLdr
'Midsummer Mermaid' (A)	LMil MAsh
'Mikado' (EA)	see *R. kaempferi* 'Mikado'
'Millennium Gold'^{PBR}	LMil LRHS
'Milton' (R)	LMil
'Mimi' (Kaempferi) (EA)	CMac
'Ming'	see *R.* 'Ilam Ming'
miniatum CER 9927	GGGa
minus	CBcs
- var. ***minus*** (Carolinianum Group) 'Epoch'	LMil
'Moerheim' ♀^{H5}	CBcs ECho LRHS MAsh MMuc NPri SLim
§ 'Moerheim's Pink'	GGGa LMil SLdr
(Mohamet Group) 'Mohamet'	LMil
'Moidart' (Vs)	LMil NLar
'Moira Salmon' (EA)	SLdr
§ ***molle*** subsp. ***japonicum*** (A)	ESps LMil LPar NEgg
- subsp. ***molle*** (A)	LMil
Mollis, orange-flowered (M)	GKin SRms
- pink-flowered (M)	GKin SRms
- red-flowered (M)	GKin
- salmon-flowered (M)	GQui
- yellow-flowered (M)	GKin GQui SRms
'Molly Ann'	ECho LSRN
'Molten Gold' (v)	GGGa LMil LRHS MAsh MJak
§ 'Momoko' (EA)	GMcL LRHS WFar
monanthum	GGGa
monosematum	see *R. pachytrichum* var. *monosematum*
'Monsieur Marcel Ménard' ♀^{H6}	CBcs CDul EPfP GGGa LMil LRHS MAsh MGos NLar NPri SCob SLdr SReu SSta
montroseanum	GGGa LMil MHid SLdr
Moonstone Group	MLea
- 'Moonstone Pink'	SLdr
- 'Moonstone Yellow'	MHid SLdr
§ 'Morgenrot'	MMuc
morii	GGGa
'Morning Cloud'	EPfP LRHS MAsh MGos NHol NLar SLim SReu SSta
Morning Red	see *R.* 'Morgenrot'
'Moser's Maroon'	CBcs GGGa LSRN MMuc SLdr
'Mother of Pearl'	SLdr
'Mother's Day' (Kurume) (EA) ♀^{H4}	CDul CMac CSBt CTri EPfP ESps GKin GQui LCro LMil LRHS LSRN MAsh MGos MJak NEgg NHol NLar NPri SCob SLdr SLim SPer SPoG SReu SSta WBod WFar
§ ***moulmainense***	CMCN
'Mount Everest'	LMil SReu SSta
'Mount Rainier' (A)	LRHS
'Mount Saint Helens' (A)	LMil NLar SLdr SLim SPer
'Mount Seven Star'	see *R. nakaharae* 'Mount Seven Star'
moupinense	GGGa MHid
- 'Fulmar'	GGGa
'Mrs A.T. de la Mare' ♀^{H6}	LMil SReu SSta
'Mrs Betty Robertson'	CMac GBin SLdr
Mrs C. Whitner Group	SLdr
'Mrs Charles E. Pearson' ♀^{H6}	CSBt LMil SLdr SReu SSta
'Mrs Davies Evans'	SReu SSta
'Mrs Emil Hager' (EA)	SLdr
'Mrs Furnivall' ♀^{H6}	GGGa MLea SReu
'Mrs G.W. Leak'	CSBt GGGa LMil SReu
'Mrs J.C. Williams' ♀^{H6}	LMil
'Mrs J.G. Millais'	LMil
'Mrs James Horlick'	CAco
'Mrs Lionel de Rothschild'	SReu
'Mrs Marks'	LMil
'Mrs P.D. Williams'	SReu
'Mrs T.H. Lowinsky' ♀^{H6}	CBcs CDul CMac GGGa GKin LMil LRHS MAsh MGos MLea MMuc NLar SLdr SLim SPer SReu
× ***mucronatum*** (EA)	CBcs MHid SLdr
mucronulatum	MHid
- B&SWJ 786	WCru
- B&SWJ 8657	WCru
- var. ***albiflorum*** **new**	SLdr
- var. ***chejuense***	see *R. mucronulatum* var. *taquetii*
- 'Cornell Pink' ♀^{H5}	GGGa
§ - var. ***taquetii***	GGGa
'Mulroy Cream'	LMil
§ ***multiflorum*** var. ***purpureum***	GGGa
'Mum'	LMil
'Muneira' (EA)	IVic
'Muriel'	SLdr
'Nabucco' (A)	EPfP GGGa MMuc NLar SLdr WMoo
nakaharae (EA) ♀^{H5}	MHid SLdr SReu
- 'Mariko' (EA)	WAbe WThu
§ - 'Mount Seven Star' (EA) ♀^{H5}	ECho GGGa ITim LMil NWad SLdr WAbe WThu
§ - orange-flowered (EA)	ECho LMil LRHS MAsh SLdr SReu
- pink-flowered (EA)	ECho MPkF SLdr SReu
- red-flowered (EA)	ECho
'Nakahari Orange'	see *R. nakaharae* orange-flowered
nakotiltum	MHid
'Nancy Evans' ♀^{H4}	CSBt EPfP GGGa GKin LMil LRHS LSRN MAsh MGos MLea NLar NPri SLdr SLim SReu SSta
'Nancy of Robinhill' (EA)	SReu
'Nancy Waterer' (G) ♀^{H6}	SReu
'Nanki Poo' (EA)	SLdr
'Naomi' (EA)	GQui SLdr
(Naomi Group) 'Exbury Naomi'	LMil
- 'Naomi Hope'	LMil
- 'Naomi Nautilus'	LMil
- 'Naomi Pink Beauty'	LMil
- 'Naomi Stella Maris'	LMil
'Narcissiflorum' (G/d) ♀^{H6}	GKin LMil LRHS MPkF NLar SReu
'Naselle'	SReu
'Ne Plus Ultra' (V)	GGGa
Negligé = 'Hachneg'^{PBR} (EA)	LMil
neriiflorum	GGGa GKev LMil MHid
- CN&W 906	LMil
- subsp. ***neriiflorum*** AC 1356	MHid
§ - - Euchaites Group	LPar
§ - - Phoenicodum Group Farrer 877	MHid
'Newcomb's Sweetheart'	LMil
'Niagara' (Glenn Dale) (EA) ♀^{H5}	CMac LMil SLdr

	'Nico' (EA)	CMac LMil LRHS MAsh WBod
	'Nicola' (EA)	LSRN
	'Nicoletta'	LMil
	'Night Sky' ♀H5	EPfP GGGa LMil LRHS MAsh MGos MHid NLar SLdr
	'Nightingale'	SReu
	nigroglandulosum	GGGa
	'Ninotschka'	IVic
	nipponicum	GGGa
	'Nishiki' (EA)	CMac
	nitens	see *R. calostrotum* subsp. *riparium* Nitens Group
	nitidulum var. ***omeiense***	GGGa WThu
	nivale subsp. ***boreale*** Ramosissimum Group	GGGa
§	- subsp. ***nivale***	ITim
	- - SDR 7887 **new**	GKev
	niveum ♀H4	CPne GGGa IDee LMil LRHS MHid SReu
	- B&SWJ 2611	WCru
	- B&SWJ 2659	WCru
	- B&SWJ 2675	WCru
	Nobleanum Group	GGGa LMil MHid SLdr SSta
	Nobleanum Album Group	GGGa LMil SReu SSta
	- 'Nobleanum Coccineum'	LMil SLdr SReu
	- 'Nobleanum Venustum'	CAco LMil SReu SSta
	(Norderney Group) 'Oudijk's Sensation'	GQui MAsh MMuc SLdr
	'Nordlicht' (EA)	SLdr
	'Noriko' (EA)	SLdr
	'Norma' (R/d)	SReu
	'Northern Hi-Lights' (A)	GKin LMil LRHS MGos NLar SLim SPer
	'Nova Zembla'	CBcs CTri EPfP GGGa LMil LRHS MAsh MGos MMuc NEgg SCob SLim SPer SReu SSta WMoo
	'Nuccio's Blue Moon' (EA)	LMil SLdr
	nudiflorum	see *R. periclymenoides*
	nudipes	MHid
	nuttallii	GGGa LMil
	nymphaeoides CGG 14027	GGGa
	'Oban'	GEdr ITim NSla
	Obtusum Group (EA)	SLdr
	- 'Amoenum' (EA/d)	CBcs CMac CSBt CTsd LMil SLdr SPer
	- 'Amoenum Coccineum' (EA/d)	SLdr SReu SSta
§	- 'Hinomayo' (EA) ♀H5	CMac CTri EPfP GKin GQui LMil LPar MPkF SLdr SPer SReu
	occidentale (A)	CDul GKin LMil
	- SIN 1830	GGGa
	ochraceum ♀H5	GGGa LMil
	'Odee Wright'	CAco CTri LRHS MAsh
	'Odoratum' (Ad)	MLea
	'Oh! Kitty'	MLea SLdr
	'Oi-no-mezame' (Kurume) (EA)	SLdr
	'Old Gold' (K)	SLdr
	'Old Port'	LMil
	oldhamii (EA)	CBcs
	- B&SWJ 3742	WCru
	'Olga' ♀H5	LMil MPkF SReu SSta
	'Olga Niblett' (EA)	SReu SSta
	oligocarpum	GGGa
	'Opossum' (EA)	GGGa
	Orakel **new**	see *R.* 'Hachmann's Orakel'
	'Orange Beauty' (Kaempferi) (EA)	CBcs GGGa MAsh SGol SLdr SReu
	'Orange King' (EA) ♀H5	LMil MGos SLdr SPoG
	'Orangeade' (K)	MPkF
	orbiculare ♀H5	GGGa LMil MHid SLdr
§	- subsp. ***cardiobasis***	GGGa MHid
	'Orchid Lights'	MAsh
	'Oregon' (EA)	SLdr
	Oregonia Group	LMil
	oreodoxa	LMil
§	- var. ***fargesii*** ♀H6	GGGa LMil MHid
	- - AC 4052	MHid
	- var. ***oreodoxa***	GGGa LMil
	oreotrephes ♀H4	LMil MHid
	- SDR 5027	GKev
	- 'Bluecalyptus'	GGGa
§	- Exquisitum Group	SLdr
	- 'Pentland'	GGGa LMil
	'Orion' ambig.	NLar
§	***orthocladum*** var. ***microleucum***	GGGa WThu
	'Osaraku Seedling' (EA)	EPfP LRHS MPkF
	'Osmar' ♀H5	GGGa
	'Ostara'	CBcs
	'Osterschnee'	IVic
	'Oudijk's Favorite'	SLdr
	'Oxydol' (K)	IVic SLdr
§	***pachypodum***	GGGa
	pachysanthum ♀H6	GGGa GKin LMil MHid SLdr SReu
	- 'Crosswater'	LMil MAsh
	pachysanthum × ***yakushimanum***	SReu
	pachytrichum	GGGa
§	- var. ***monosematum***	MHid
	'Palestrina' (Vuykiana) (EA) ♀H4	CBcs CDul CMac CSBt EPfP GKin MAsh MJak MMuc SGol SLdr SPer SReu SSta
	'Palma'	see *R. parmulatum* 'Palma'
	paludosum	see *R. nivale* subsp. *nivale*
	'Pancake'	CMac
	'Panda' (EA) ♀H5	CSBt CTri ECho EPfP GGGa LMil LRHS MAsh MLea SLdr SSta
	'Paprika Spiced'	MLea
	'Parfait' (EA)	LMil
	'Parkfeuer' (A)	GGGa IVic
	parmulatum	LMil
	- KW 5876	LMil
	- 'Ocelot'	GGGa SLdr
§	- 'Palma'	WBod
	parryae AM (*roseatum*)	GGGa
	'Patty Bee' ♀H5	CBcs CSBt CTri ECho EPfP GEdr GGGa LMil LRHS MAsh MGos MLea NPri NSla SLdr SLim SReu SSta
	'Peach Blossom'	see *R.* 'Saotome'
	'Pearl Betteridge'	LMil
	'Peep-bo' (EA)	SLdr
	'Peeping Tom'	NHol SReu SSta
	'Peggy'	LMil
	pemakoense	GGGa SLdr WThu
	'Pemakofairy'	WThu
	pendulum	GGGa
	Penelope Group	SReu
	'Penheale Blue' ♀H5	CTsd GKin LMil
	'Penjerrick'	GGGa
	'Penny Tomlin'	SReu SSta
	pentaphyllum (A)	GGGa
	'Peppermint Candy'	LMil
	'Peppina'	GGGa LMil
	'Percy Wiseman' ♀H5	CBcs CDul CSBt EPfP ESps GGGa GKin LMil LRHS MAsh MGos MHid MJak MLea MMuc NEgg NLar SCob SLdr SLim SPer SReu SSta
§	***periclymenoides*** (A)	GGGa GKev LMil

'Persil' (K) ♀H6	CBcs CSBt CTri EPfP GGGa GKin LMil LRHS MAsh MJak MMuc NEgg NHol NLar SCoo SLdr SPer SReu SSta WFar WMoo
'Peter Chapell'	GGGa
'Peter Gable' (EA)	SLdr
'Peter Koster' (hybrid)	GKin SLdr
petrocharis	GGGa
Petticoat = 'Hachpett' (EA)	LMil
'Pfauenauge'	GGGa
phaeochrysum	MHid
§ - var. ***levistratum***	MHid
- var. ***phaeochrysum*** C 12529	GGGa
'Phalarope'	GEdr MMuc
phoenicodum	see *R. neriiflorum* subsp. *neriiflorum* Phoenicodum Group
'Phyllis Korn'	IVic LMil NLar SAko
§ ***piercei***	GGGa LMil MHid
'Pine Marten' (EA)	GGGa
pingianum	GGGa
'Pink Bride'	SLdr
'Pink Cameo'	CAco
'Pink Cherub' ♀H6	LMil MAsh MLea
I 'Pink Delight' (K)	GKin MMuc
'Pink Delight' (V)	SLdr
'Pink Drift'	CSBt ECho GEdr LMil NSla SLdr WThu
'Pink Gin'	LMil
'Pink Pancake' (EA) ♀H4	EPfP GKin LMil LRHS MAsh MPkF NPri SLdr
'Pink Pearl' (EA)	see *R.* 'Azuma-kagami'
'Pink Pearl' (hybrid) ♀H4	CBcs CDul CMac CSBt CTri EPfP GGGa LCro LMil MAsh MMuc SLdr SPer SReu SSta
'Pink Pebble' ♀H5	ELon MAsh MLea
'Pink Perfection'	CMac SLdr
'Pink Polar Bear'	LMil
'Pink Ruffles' (K)	WBod
'Pintail'	GGGa LMil LRHS MAsh
'Pipit'	GGGa
'Pippa' (EA)	CMac
'PJM Regal'	IVic
'PJM Victor'	SAko
platypodum CGG 14005	GGGa
'Pleasant White' (EA)	LMil LRHS NLar
'Plover'	GGGa
pocophorum	MHid
§ - var. ***hemidartum***	MHid
- var. ***pocophorum***	GGGa
'Point Defiance'	MHid MLea SPer
'Polar Bear' (EA)	CAco SLdr
Polar Bear Group	LMil MLea
- 'Polar Bear'	CHll CSBt GGGa GKin IVic LMil SLdr SReu
'Polaris' (EA)	MJak NLar
'Polaris'	see *R.* 'Hachmann's Polaris'
'Polarnacht'	CBcs GGGa IVic LMil LRHS SAko SLdr
poluninii	GGGa
- KR 8231	LMil
polyandrum	see *R. maddenii* subsp. *maddenii* Polyandrum Group
§ ***polycladum*** Scintillans Group	GGGa
polylepis	MHid
- AC 3810	MHid
'Polyroy'	GGGa
'Pomegranate Splash'	GGGa
ponticum	CAco CDul CMac CTri ESps NHol WFar
- 'Filigran'	IVic LMil
- 'Roseum'	SGol
§ - 'Variegatum' (v)	CAco CMac EPfP ESps MAsh MGos NPri SCob SLdr SPer SPoG SRms
populare KC 0126	GGGa
'Praecox' ♀H4	CBcs CSBt ECho EPfP GGGa GKev GKin LMil LRHS MAsh MGos MJak MMuc NLar NPri SLdr SLim SPer SPoG SReu WBod
Praecox Group	MJak
praestans	GGGa GKin LMil MHid
prattii	GGGa
preptum	GGGa
'President Roosevelt' (v)	CBcs CSBt EPfP ESps GKin MAsh MJak MPkF NPri SPoG SReu SSta
'Pridenjoy'	LMil LRHS
primuliflorum ♀H5	MHid WAbe
- 'Doker-La'	GGGa LMil WAbe
'Prince Camille de Rohan'	LMil
'Princess Alice'	CBcs IDee SLdr
'Princess Anne' ♀H5	CBcs ECho ELon LMil LRHS MAsh MGos MLea NHpl NLar SLdr SLim SPoG SReu SSta WBod
'Princess Margaret of Windsor' (K)	GQui LMil
principis	GGGa LMil
- 'Lost Horizon'	LMil
prinophyllum (A)	GGGa GKin LMil
'Prins Bernhard' (EA)	MAsh SLdr
'Prinses Juliana' (Vuykiana) (EA)	SLdr SReu
'Prinses Máxima' **new**	LMil
'Professor Hugo de Vries'	SLdr
pronum	GGGa
- R.B. Cooke form	GGGa
- Towercourt form	GGGa
proteoides	GGGa
protistum	GCal GGGa
pruniflorum	GGGa
prunifolium (A)	GGGa LMil
przewalskii	GGGa MHid
pseudochrysanthum ♀H5	GGGa LMil MHid SReu
- dwarf	GGGa
- - RWJ 9807 **new**	WCru
pseudociliipes	CPne GGGa
Psyche Group	see *R.* Wega Group
'Ptarmigan' ♀H5	ECho GEdr GGGa LMil LRHS MHid SLdr WThu
pubicostatum AC 2051	MHid
pudorosum	GGGa
'Pulchrum Maxwellii'	see *R.* 'Maxwellii'
pumilum	GGGa WAbe WThu
'Pumuckl'	IVic SAko
'Purple Cushion' (EA)	EPfP LMil LRHS MAsh NPri
'Purple Diamond'	see *R.* Diamant Group purple-flowered
'Purple Gem'	MGos MMuc NLar
'Purple Passion'[PBR]	LMil LRHS LSRN NLar SLdr SPer
'Purple Queen' (EA/d)	MAsh
'Purple Splendor' (Gable) (EA)	CMac SGol SLdr
'Purple Splendour'	CBcs CSBt LMil MGos MLea MMuc NEgg NLar SPer SReu SSta WMoo
'Purple Triumph' (Vuykiana) (EA) ♀H5	LMil SLdr
'Purpureum Grandiflorum'	LMil
'Purpurtraum' (EA) ♀H5	LMil SAko
'Pyari'	GGGa

qiaojiaense NN 0903	GGGa LMil MHid
'Quail'	GGGa
'Queen Alice'	NLar
'Queen Anne's'	GGGa
Queen Emma	see *R.* 'Koningin Emma'
'Queen Mary'	SReu SSta
'Queen Souriya'	SReu
'Quentin Metsys' (R)	SLdr SReu
quinquefolium (A)	GGGa LMil SLdr
Rabatz = 'Hachraba'	GGGa IVic LMil LRHS SAko
racemosum ϒH4	LMil MHid
- BWJ 7811	WCru
- 'Rock Rose' ϒH5	EPfP LMil
'Racine' (G)	SReu
'Racoon' (EA)	GGGa
radicans	see *R. calostrotum* subsp. *keleticum* Radicans Group
'Radistrotum'	SAko
'Raimunde' (K)	IVic SAko
'Ramapo' ϒH6	ECho GGGa LMil LRHS MAsh MGos MMuc NLar SLim SPer SReu
'Raphael de Smet' (G/d)	SReu
'Raphaela'	SAko
'Rasputin'	LMil
'Razorbill' ϒH4	GGGa GKin LMil LRHS NLar SLim
recurvoides	GGGa LMil MHid SLdr SReu
- Keillour form	GGGa
'Red and Gold'	EPfP GGGa LRHS NPri
'Red Dawn'	LRHS MLea
'Red Delicious'	LMil SLdr
'Red Diamond'	see *R.* Diamant Group red-flowered
'Red Fountain' (EA)	ECho SLdr
'Red Jack'	LMil MGos SCob SPer SPoG SReu SSta
'Red Panda' (EA)	GGGa
'Red Pimpernel' (EA)	SLdr
'Red Sunset' (A)	SLdr
'Red Wood'	GGGa
'Redwing' ambig.	MAsh
'Redwings' (EA)	SLdr
'Reich's Signifikant' **new**	SAko
'Rennie' (A)	GKin MMuc
'Renoir' ϒH5	CSBt LMil SReu
reticulatum (A)	LMil MHid SReu
'Reuthe's Purple'	SReu WAbe WThu
'Rêve d'Amour' (Vs)	SReu SSta
'Rex' (EA)	MAsh
rex ϒH4	GGGa GKev GKin LMil SLdr
- EGM 295	LMil
- SDR 7924 **new**	GKev
§ - subsp. ***fictolacteum*** ϒH4	GGGa GKin LMil MHid SLdr
- - Miniforme Group	MHid
- subsp. ***rex*** ϒH4	MHid
- - NN 0904	MHid
rex × ***yakushimanum***	SReu
rhabdotum	see *R. dalhousiae* var. *rhabdotum*
'Rhododendronpark Graal-Müriz'	SReu SSta
'Ria Hardijzer' (Ad)	LMil
'Ribbon Candy' (A) **new**	LRHS
rigidum	GGGa MHid
- 'Album'	LMil
'Ring of Fire'	IVic LMil MLea
'Ripe Corn'	MHid
ririei	CPne GGGa
'Robert Croux'	SLdr
'Robert Seleger'	GGGa GKin LMil MAsh SReu
'Robert Whelan' (A)	SReu SSta
'Robin Hill Frosty' (EA)	SLdr
'Robin Hill Gillie' (EA)	SLdr

'Robinette'	MAsh SLdr
'Rocket'	CTri LMil MAsh MGos MLea MMuc SLdr SLim SPoG
'Roehr's Peggy Ann' (EA)	LMil
'Rokoko'	see *R.* 'Hachmann's Rokoko'
'Ronny'	SAko
Rosalind Group	CMac
- 'Rosalind'	WFar
'Rosalinda' (EA)	SLdr
'Rosata' (Vs) ϒH5	GGGa GKin SReu SSta
'Rose Bud'	CSBt CTri WBod WThu
'Rose Elf'	WThu
'Rose Glow' (A)	SReu SSta
'Rose Gown'	SReu
'Rose Greely' (Gable) (EA) ϒH5	NLar SLdr SLim SPer SReu
'Rose Haze' (Vs)	SReu SSta
'Rosebud' (EA/d)	CBcs CMac SLdr SReu SSta
roseum	see *R. canescens*
'Roseum Elegans'	CAco LMil LRHS MAsh SCob SLim
'Rosevallon'	MHid
Rosinetta = 'Hachrosi' (EA)	GGGa LMil
'Rosy Dream'	MAsh MMuc
'Rosy Fire' (A)	LMil SReu
'Rosy Lea'	MLea
'Rotglocke'	IVic
rothschildii	GGGa LMil MHid SLdr
'Rotkäppchen'	IVic SAko
rousei (V)	GGGa
roxieanum	GGGa LMil MHid SLdr
- AC 1753	MHid
§ - var. ***cucullatum***	GGGa GKev
- - SDR 7936 **new**	GKev
- var. ***oreonastes*** ϒH5	GGGa IVic LMil MHid
- - Nymans form	SReu
- var. ***parvum***	GGGa
'Royal Command' (K)	CBcs CTri GKin LMil
'Royal Ruby' (K)	MMuc
'Royal Windsor'	LMil
'Roza Stevenson'	SLdr
'Rubicon'	GGGa MAsh SLdr
rubiginosum ϒH4	GGGa LMil MHid
- pink-flowered	LMil
rubroluteum	see *R. viridescens* Rubroluteum Group
'Ruby Hart'	GGGa LSRN
Ruby Wedding	see *R.* 'Firestorm'
rude	see *R. glischrum* subsp. *rude*
rufum	GGGa
rugosum Sinclair 240 (V)	GGGa
§ ***rupicola*** var. ***chryseum*** SDR 7885 **new**	GKev
rushforthii	GGGa
russatum ϒH5	GGGa LMil MHid SLdr
- blue-black-flowered	LMil
* - 'Collingwood Ingram'	GGGa
Russautinii Group	SLdr
russotinctum	see *R. alutaceum* var. *russotinctum*
'Rwain' **new**	NLar
'Sabina' (EA)	SLdr
'Sacko'	GGGa LMil SLim
'Saffron Queen'	CBcs CTsd SLdr
'Saint Breward'	GQui MLea
'Saint Kew'	SLdr
'Saint Merryn' ϒH5	CBcs GEdr SLdr
'Saint Minver'	SLdr
'Saint Tudy'	SLdr
'Saint Valentine' (V)	GGGa
'Sakata Red' (EA)	SLdr WBod
'Salmon Sander' (EA)	SLdr

'Salmon's Leap' (EA/v)	CMac ELan LMil LRHS MAsh SReu SSta
saluenense	LMil SLdr WThu
'Sammetglut'	CAco
'Samuel Taylor Coleridge' (M)	GKin
sanguineum	LMil MHid
§ - subsp. ***didymum***	GGGa MHid SLdr
- subsp. ***sanguineum*** var. ***haemaleum***	GGGa LMil MHid
- - var. ***sanguineum*** F 25521	LMil
'Santa Maria' (EA) 🏆H5	GMcL LMil LSRN NLar SReu SSta
santapaui (V)	GGGa
§ 'Saotome' (EA)	SLdr
'Sapphire'	GMcL
'Sappho'	CAco CBcs CDul CMac ECho GGGa GKin LMil MLea NEgg NLar SLdr SReu SSta
sargentianum	GGGa NHar WAbe WThu
- 'Whitebait'	ITim
'Sarled' 🏆H5	GGGa ITim LMil NHar WThu
'Saskia' (K)	IVic SAko
'Satan' (K) 🏆H6	LMil LRHS NLar SReu SSta
Satsuki Group (EA)	ITim SLdr
- 'Gumpo Pink' (EA)	SLdr
- 'Gumpo Pink & White' (EA) **new**	SLdr
- 'Gumpo White' (EA)	LCro LRHS MAsh SPoG WBod
'Saturnus' (M)	GKin
§ ***scabrifolium*** var. ***spiciferum***	MHid SLdr
'Scarlet Wonder' 🏆H5	CBcs CDul CSBt EPfP GEdr GGGa GKin LMil LRHS MAsh MGos MJak MMuc NHpl NPri SLdr SPer SReu WBod
schistocalyx F 17637	MHid
schlippenbachii (A)	CBcs CMCN CPne GGGa GKev LMil MHid SLdr
'Schneekrone' 🏆H6	GGGa
Schneeperle = 'Hachschnee' (EA) 🏆H5	IVic LMil LRHS
'Schneespiegel'	GGGa
scintillans	see *R. polycladum* Scintillans Group
'Scintillation' 🏆H6	CBcs GGGa LMil MAsh MGos MLea MMuc SLdr SPer
scopulorum	GGGa SLdr
'Scotian Bells'	GGGa
scottianum	see *R. pachypodum*
'Scottish Marmalade'	GGGa
'Scout' (EA)	MAsh SLdr
scyphocalyx	see *R. dichroanthum* subsp. *scyphocalyx*
searsiae	MHid
'Seaview Sunset'	GGGa MGos
'Second Honeymoon'	MLea
seinghkuense	GGGa LMil
- CCH&H 8106	LMil
§ ***selense*** subsp. ***dasycladum***	MHid
- subsp. ***jucundum***	GGGa
semnoides	GGGa LMil
'Sennocke'	LMil
'September Red' **new**	LMil
'September Song' 🏆H4	GGGa LMil MAsh MLea NHol
'Septembercharm'	LRHS
serotinum	GGGa IDee LMil
serpyllifolium (A)	CBcs CTsd
'Sesterianum'	CMHG
Seta Group	SReu
- 'Seta'	CAbP SLdr WThu
'Shamrock' 🏆H5	ELon EPfP GEdr LRHS MAsh MGos MLea NEgg NSla SLim SPoG WThu
'Sheila' (EA)	CSBt LRHS MAsh NPri
'Shelley' (EA)	LMil LSRN
shepherdii	see *R. kendrickii*
sherriffii	GGGa MHid
'Shiko' (EA)	MAsh
'Shiko Lavender' (A)	SPoG
Shilsonii Group	LMil
'Shin-sekai' (Kurume) (EA/d)	SLdr
'Shrimp Girl'	GKin MHid
sichotense	GGGa
sidereum	CPne GCal GGGa
siderophyllum	GGGa MHid
sikangense	GGGa MHid
- SDR 7932 **new**	GKev
- var. ***exquisitum***	GGGa
'Silbervelours'	IVic
§ 'Silberwolke' 🏆H6	IVic LMil MAsh
'Silkeborg Silence'	GGGa
Silver Cloud	see *R.* 'Silberwolke'
'Silver Edge'	see *R. ponticum* 'Variegatum'
'Silver Glow' (EA)	CMac
'Silver Jubilee' 🏆H4	LMil LRHS
'Silver Moon' (Glenn Dale) (EA)	SLdr
'Silver Queen' (EA)	LPar MPkF SPoG
'Silver Sixpence'	EPfP LRHS LSRN MJak MLea MMuc SLdr
'Silver Skies'	LMil
'Silver Slipper' (K) 🏆H6	CBcs GKin LMil MLea NHol SReu SSta WFar
'Silver Sword' (EA/v)	EPfP SPoG
'Silverwood' (A)	LMil
'Silvester' (Kurume) (EA)	CTri GMcL LMil LRHS MAsh SLdr SReu WBod
'Simona'	LMil SAko
simsii (EA)	CMac SLdr
sinofalconeri	GGGa LMil MHid
- KR 7342	LMil
- SEH 229	LMil
sinogrande 🏆H3	CPne ELon GCal GGGa GKev GKin LMil NEgg
- APA 106	GGGa
- KR 4027	LMil
§ 'Sir Charles Butler'	LMil
'Sir Charles Lemon' 🏆H3	GGGa LMil MAsh
'Sir Robert' (EA)	MAsh
'Sleepy'	CBcs MAsh MHid MLea NHol SLdr
smirnowii	GGGa IDee LMil LRHS MHid
smithii	see *R. argipeplum*
'Sneezy' 🏆H5	CBcs EPfP GGGa LMil LRHS MAsh MGos MHid MJak MMuc SLdr SLim SSta
'Snipe'	CTri ECho GEdr LMil LRHS MAsh MGos MMuc NLar SLdr SLim SPer SReu WBod WThu
'Snow Crown' (*lindleyi* hybrid)	MAsh
'Snow Hill' (EA) 🏆H5	CEnd LMil
'Snow Lady'	CBcs CTsd EPfP GEdr GKin GQui MAsh MMuc SLdr SReu
'Snow Pearl'	EPfP MAsh NPri
Snow Queen Group	LMil SReu
- 'Snow Queen'	LMil
'Snowbird' (A)	CDul SLdr
'Snowbird' (EA)	CDul
'Snowflake' (EA/d)	see *R.* 'Kure-no-yuki'

	'Snowstorm'	MLea
	'Snowwhite' (EA)	MGos NLar SLdr
	'Soho' (EA)	GQui
	'Soir de Paris' (Vs) ♀H6	CEnd CSBt GGGa GKin IVic LMil LRHS NHol SReu SSta WFar WGwG
	'Soldier Sam'	SReu
	(Solent Group) 'Drury Lane' (K)	GQui LMil
	'Solidarity'	CBcs MLea SLdr SReu SSta
	'Solway' (Vs)	LMil
	'Sommerduft' (A)	IVic
	'Son de Paris' (A)	GQui
	'Sonata'	GGGa SReu
	'Sonatine'	LMil
	'Songbird'	GEdr LMil MHid SLdr WBod
	sororium (V)	LMil
	- KR 3085	LMil
	souliei	LMil
	- deep pink-flowered	GGGa
	'Souvenir de D.A. Koster'	SLdr
	'Souvenir de Doctor S. Endtz'	SReu
	'Souvenir of Anthony Waterer'	SReu SSta
	'Souvenir of W.C. Slocock'	MMuc NLar
	'Spätlese'	IVic
	'Spek's Orange' (M)	GKin
	sperabile	GGGa
	- var. ***weihsiense***	MHid
	sphaeranthum	see *R. trichostomum*
	sphaeroblastum	GGGa MHid
	- SDR 7938 **new**	GKev
	- var. ***wumengense***	GGGa
	- - KR 1481	MHid
	spiciferum	see *R. scabrifolium* var. *spiciferum*
	'Spinner's Glory'	MAsh
	spinuliferum	CBcs GGGa
	- NN 10945	MHid
	'Spitfire'	NHol SReu SSta
	'Spring Beauty' (EA)	SReu
	'Spring Morning'	CPne SReu SSta
	'Spring Pearl'	see *R.* 'Moerheim's Pink'
	'Spring Rose'	SLdr
	'Spring Sunshine'	LMil
	'Squirrel' (EA) ♀H5	ECho GGGa GKin GMcL LMil MAsh MLea SLdr SLim SReu WBod
	'Staccato'	IVic
	'Stadt Essen'	LMil SLdr
	'Stadt Westerstede'	LMil
	stamineum	GGGa
§	'Stanway'	LMil
	'Starbright Champagne'	MAsh
	'Statuette'	IVic SAko
	stenaulum	see *R. moulmainense*
§	***stenopetalum*** 'Linearifolium' (EA)	CBcs CMac GBin LMil MPkF SLdr WBod
	stenophyllum	see *R. makinoi*
	stewartianum	CPne GGGa
	'Stewartstonian' (EA)	CMac MMuc SReu
	'Stoat' (EA)	GQui NLar
	Stonefield hybrids **new**	ESps
	'Stopham Girl' (A)	LMil
	'Stopham Lad' (A)	LMil
	'Strategist'	SLdr
	'Strawberry Cream'	EPfP GGGa LRHS MAsh
	'Strawberry Ice' (K) ♀H6	CBcs CDul CSBt ELan EPfP GGGa GKin MAsh MMrt SReu WMoo
	'Strawberry Sundae'	MLea MMuc NEgg SLdr
	strigillosum	GGGa MHid
	- Reuthe's form	SReu
	subansiriense	GGGa
	suberosum	see *R. yunnanense* Suberosum Group
	'Suga-no-ito' (Kurume) (EA)	SLdr
	sulfureum JN 11062	MHid
	'Summer Dawn'	LMil LRHS
	'Summer Flame'	SReu
	'Summer Fragrance' (A) ♀H6	LMil SReu SSta
	'Summer Snow'	IVic SAko
	'Summer Sorbet'	LMil
	'Summer Wind' **new**	GGGa
	'Sun Chariot' (K)	CBcs
	'Sun Star' (EA) **new**	GGGa LMil
	Sunkist Group	SLdr
	'Sunset Pink' (K)	CDul ELan SLdr
	'Sunspray'	SReu SSta
	'Sunte Nectarine' (K) ♀H6	GKin GQui NLar
	suoilenhensis	CMCN
	- NVD 18	GGGa
	'Surprise' ambig. (EA)	CTri SLdr
	'Surprise' B.Y. Morrison (EA)	LMil
	'Surrey Heath'	CBcs EPfP LMil LRHS MAsh MGos MHid MJak MMuc SLdr SLim SPer
	'Susan' (EA)	MHid SSta
	'Susan' J.C. Williams	LMil SReu
	'Susannah Hill' (EA)	CBcs SLdr
	sutchuenense	GGGa LMil MHid
	- var. ***geraldii***	see *R.* × *geraldii*
	'Swamp Beauty'	MAsh MLea MMuc SLdr WGwG
	'Swansong' (EA)	CMac
	'Swift' ♀H4	ECho EPfP GEdr GGGa GQui LMil LRHS MAsh MMuc
	'T.S. Black' (EA)	SLdr
	taggianum	GGGa
	'Talavera'	LMil
	taliense	LMil
	- SBEC 0350	GGGa
	- 'Honigduft'	LMil LRHS NLar
	Tally Ho Group	LMil SLdr
	tamaense	see *R. cinnabarinum* subsp. *tamaense*
	Tanaga	see *R.* 'Hachmann's Tanaga'
	Tanager	see *R.* 'Glendoick Tanager'
	'Tanager' (K)	SLdr
	'Tangerine'	see *R.* 'Fabia Tangerine'
	tapetiforme	GGGa
	tatsienense SDR 7933 **new**	GKev
	'Taurus' ♀H5	CBcs GKin IVic LMil LRHS MAsh MHid MLea MMuc SAko SLdr SReu WMoo
	taxifolium (v)	GGGa
	'Teal'	ECho GEdr
	'Ted Millais'	LMil
	'Teddy Bear'	LMil MLea SReu SSta
	telopeum	see *R. campylocarpum* subsp. *caloxanthum* Telopeum Group
	Temple Belle Group	ECho GEdr SLdr WBod
	'Teniers' (R)	SReu
§	***tephropeplum***	CPne GGGa MHid
	- Deleiense Group	see *R. tephropeplum*
I	'Tequila Sunrise' USA	LMil
	'Terracotta'	LMil
	'Terra-cotta Beauty' (EA)	NWad WThu
	(Tessa Group) 'Tessa'	CBcs
	thayerianum	GGGa MHid
§	'The Honourable Jean Marie de Montague' ♀H4	GGGa GKin LMil MAsh MGos MHid MLea MMuc NLar SPer SReu SSta
	'Thomas David' (A)	LMil

thomsonii	GCal GGGa GKin LMil MHid SReu
- AC 113	MHid
- B&SWJ 2638	WCru
- TDA 073	MHid
- subsp. ***lopsangianum***	GGGa
'Thor'	GGGa SReu
'Thunderstorm'	SReu
'Tibet'	GQui LMil
'Tidbit' ♀H3	CMac GGGa LMil MLea SLdr
'Tinkerbird'	GGGa LRHS MAsh MGos NPri SLdr SPer
'Tinner's Blush'	CBcs
titapuriense	GGGa
'Titian Beauty'	CBcs CSBt ELan EPfP GGGa LMil LRHS MAsh MGos MMuc NEgg NLar SAko SLim SPer SPoG WMoo
'Titness Park'	LMil
'Tit-Willow' (EA)	LRHS MAsh SCoo
tomentosum	GPoy WThu
'Too Bee'	GEdr
'Torchlight' (EA) ♀H5	LMil MGos NLar SLdr
'Toreador' (EA)	SLdr
'Torridon' (Vs)	LMil
Tortoiseshell Group	SCob
- 'Champagne' ♀H3	CBcs CSBt LMil MAsh NLar NPri SLdr SPer SReu
- 'Tortoiseshell Orange' ♀H3	CBcs CDul CSBt LMil MGos NLar SCob SLim SPer SReu SSta
- 'Tortoiseshell Wonder' ♀H3	EPfP LMil LRHS MAsh
'Toucan' (K)	CSBt LMil MPkF
'Tower Dainty' (A)	GGGa
'Tower Daring' (A)	GGGa
'Tower Dragon' (A)	LMil
traillianum	LMil MHid
'Tree Creeper'	GGGa GKin LMil LRHS SLdr
'Tregedna Red'	SReu
'Trewithen Orange'	SLdr
trichanthum	GGGa
- 'Honey Wood'	LMil SLdr
trichocladum	CPne GKev
§ ***trichostomum***	GGGa WAbe
- Ledoides Group	LMil
triflorum	GGGa LMil
§ - var. ***bauhiniiflorum***	GGGa SLdr
- var. ***triflorum*** Mahogani Group	GGGa MHid
- - AC 3386	MHid
trilectorum	GGGa
triplonaevium	see *R. alutaceum* var. *russotinctum* Triplonaevium Group
'Tromba'	GGGa LMil SAko
tsangpoense	see *R. charitopes* subsp. *tsangpoense*
tsariense	GGGa LMil MHid
- var. ***trimoense***	GGGa LMil
- - KW 8288	LMil
- 'Yum Yum'	GGGa
tubiforme	see *R. glaucophyllum* subsp. *tubiforme*
'Tuffet' (EA)	LMil SLdr
'Tunis' (K)	EPfP MAsh NPri
'Turaço'	GGGa SLdr
'Turnstone'	GGGa
ungernii	GGGa MHid
§ ***uniflorum*** var. ***imperator***	GGGa
'Unique' (G)	CBcs EPfP GGGa MMuc SPer
'Unique' (*campylocarpum* hybrid)	MAsh MHid SLdr SReu
'Unique Marmalade'	LMil MLea MPkF SLdr
'Ursine'	IVic
uvariifolium var. ***griseum***	LMil MHid
- 'Reginald Childs'	IDee LMil LRHS
'Valencia'	IVic
valentinianum	CBcs GGGa MHid SLdr WAbe
- F 24347	MHid
- var. ***oblongilobatum***	GGGa
'Van'	LMil LRHS MGos SLim
'Van Houttei Flore Pleno' (G/d)	SReu
'Van Nes Sensation'	LMil LRHS
Vanessa Group	LMil
- 'Vanessa Pastel' ♀H3	CMac GGGa LMil SReu SSta
Varna Group	WBod
vaseyi (A) ♀H5	CBcs GGGa LMil
- 'White Find'	GGGa
- white-flowered (A)	LMil
'Vayo' (EA)	SLdr
§ ***veitchianum*** Cubittii Group	CBcs GGGa
- KNE Cox 9001	GGGa
venator	GGGa MHid
'Venetia' (K)	SReu SSta
'Venetian Chimes'	CSBt MHid MJak
vernicosum	GGGa MHid
- AC 1901	MHid
- AC 4102	MHid
- SDR 5122 **new**	GKev
vernicosum* × *wardii SDR 5026 **new**	GKev
'Vida Brown' (Kurume) (EA/d)	CMac SLdr SReu WThu
'Vinecourt Dream' (M)	GKin MMuc NLar SLdr
'Vinecourt Duke' (A/d)	GKin MMuc NEgg NLar
'Vineland Dream' (K/d)	GKin
'Vintage Rosé' ♀H5	LMil MMuc SSta
'Violetta' (Glenn Dale) (EA)	SLdr
'Violette Funken'	LMil
'Virginia Richards'	LPar SCob SLdr
Virginia Richards Group	LPar LRHS MAsh
§ ***viridescens***	MHid
- 'Doshong La'	GGGa LMil
§ - Rubroluteum Group	SLdr
viscidifolium	GGGa
viscosum (A) ♀H6	CBcs GGGa GQui LMil MGos MHid MMrt MMuc NLar SPer SReu
- 'Grey Leaf' (Vs)	LMil
- f. ***rhodanthum*** (A)	LMil
- 'Roseum' (Vs)	LMil
'Viscount Powerscourt'	SLdr
'Viscy' ♀H5	CDul GKin LMil LRHS MHid MMuc NLar SLdr
§ Volker Group	EPfP LMil LRHS MAsh
§ - 'Flavum Lackblatt'	MHid
'Vollblut'	SReu SSta
'Vulcan' ♀H4	GGGa LMil MLea SCob
'Vuyk's Rosyred' (Vuykiana) (EA) ♀H4	CBcs CDul CMac CTri GKin LMil MAsh NHol NWad SGol SLdr SPer SPoG SReu WBod WFar
'Vuyk's Scarlet' (Vuykiana) (EA) ♀H4	CBcs CMac CSBt CTri CTsd ESps GKin LRHS MAsh MMuc NHol NPri NWad SGol SLdr SPer SPlb SReu SSta
'W B I'	SReu
'W.E. Gumbleton' (M)	SReu
'W.F.H.' ♀H3	LMil MHid SLdr
'Wagtail'	GGGa
Walküre = 'Hachwalk'	LMil
wallichii	GGGa LMil MHid
- Heftii Group	GGGa
'Wallowa Red' (A)	MMuc

'Wally Miller'	MAsh
walongense	GGGa
'Walter's Pinwheel' (EA) **new**	GGGa
'Wanna Bee'	LMil
wardii	GGGa LMil MHid
- L&S 5679	GGGa MHid
- var. ***puralbum***	GGGa
- var. ***wardii*** AC 3425	MHid
- - AC 3469	MHid
'Ward's Ruby' (EA)	SLdr
wasonii	LMil MHid
- f. ***rhododactylum***	MHid
- yellow-flowered	GGGa
'Water Baby' (A)	LMil
'Water Girl' (A)	GGGa LMil
'Waterfall'	SLdr
watsonii	MHid
'Wee Bee' ♀H5	CBcs ECho EPfP GEdr GKin GMcL LMil LRHS MAsh MGos MLea NLar SAko SLim SReu SSta WBod
§ Wega Group	SLdr
'Weinlese'	SAko
'Wendy'	MAsh
'Westminster' (O)	LMil
'Weston's Pink Diamond' (d)	LMil
'What a Dane'	GGGa
'Whidbey Island'	LMil LRHS
'Whisperingrose'	GMcL LMil
'White Brocade'	SReu SSta
§ White Dufthecke = 'Rhodunter 48'PBR	LMil
'White Frills' (EA)	SLdr
'White Glory'	SLdr
'White Gold'	GGGa
'White Jade' (EA)	SLdr
'White Lady' Indian (EA)	SLdr
'White Lights' (A) ♀H7	CTri SAko
'White Pearl' (EA)	LSRN
'White Perfume' (A)	SReu SSta
'White Prince' (EA/d)	MPkF
'White Rosebud' (EA)	SReu SSta
'White Swan' (hybrid)	SReu
'White Wings'	SLdr
'Whitestone' **new**	GGGa
'Whitethroat' (K/d) ♀H6	EPfP GQui LMil LRHS MMrt MMuc SLdr SReu SSta
'Whitney's Dwarf Red'	WMoo
'Wigeon'	LMil
wightii	GGGa MHid
'Wild Ginger' **new**	GGGa
'Wilgen's Ruby'	CSBt MGos SLdr SLim SPer
'Wilgen's Surprise'	SCob
'Willbrit'	CBcs MAsh MMuc SLdr
williamsianum ♀H4	CBcs CMac ECho GGGa GMcL LMil MHid MLea SLdr SReu WBod
- 'Andrea'	IVic
'Willy' (Kaempferi) (EA)	LMil SLdr
wiltonii ♀H5	GGGa LMil
'Windsor Lad'	SReu
'Wine and Roses'PBR	CBcs GGGa LCro
Winsome Group	CMac GGGa MAsh WBod
- 'Winsome' ♀H3	CBcs GKin MGos NLar NPri SLdr SSta
'Winston Churchill' (M)	SReu SSta
'Winter Spice'	GGGa
'Winterpurpur'	IVic
'Witchery'	GGGa
'Wombat' (EA) ♀H5	CTri EPfP GGGa LMil LRHS MAsh MGos MMuc NLar NPri SLdr SReu
wongii	GGGa GQui MHid SLdr
'Woodcock'	SLdr
'Wren' ♀H5	ECho GEdr GGGa GMcL IVic LMil LRHS MAsh MLea SLdr SReu WThu
xanthocodon	see *R. cinnabarinum* subsp. *xanthocodon*
xanthostephanum	GGGa
'XXL'	SReu SSta
'Yaku Angel'	IVic LMil SAko
'Yaku Incense'	LMil MAsh MHid MLea MMuc
'Yaku Prince'	MAsh MLea MMuc SLdr
yakushimanum ♀H5	CBcs ECho ESps GKin LMil MAsh MLea MMuc NHol SArc SLdr SPer SReu SSta
- from Exbury	CMac SReu
- FCC form	see *R. yakushimanum* 'Koichiro Wada'
§ - 'Koichiro Wada' ♀H6	CMac ELan GGGa IDee IVic LMil LRHS NLar SAko SLdr SReu
- 'Schneekissen'	SAko
yaoshanense	GGGa
'Yellow Hammer' ♀H4	CAco CBcs CMac ELan GGGa GKin NLar SLdr
Yellow Hammer Group	MHid SPer SReu SSta
'Yellow Petticoats'	SReu SSta
yuefengense	GGGa LMil
yunnanense	GGGa GKev LMil MHid SLdr
- SDR 4217	GKev
- SDR 4957	GKev
- SDR 4960	GKev
- SDR 7869 **new**	GKev
- 'Openwood' ♀H3	LMil
- pink-flowered	GGGa
- 'Red Throat'	SLdr
- red-blotched	LMil
§ - Suberosum Group	SLdr
- white-flowered	GGGa
zaleucum	CBcs GGGa LMil SLdr
- Flaviflorum Group	GGGa
- var. ***zaleucum***	MHid
zeylanicum	see *R. arboreum* subsp. *zeylanicum*
ziyuanense AC 4211	MHid

Rhodohypoxis ✿ (*Hypoxidaceae*)

'1000 Cranes'	CTal IBal LEdu
'Alice'	CTal
'Andromeda'	CTal EWes IBal
'Ann Brazier'	NWad
'Annelies'	CTal
baurii ♀H4	CAvo CCCN CPne ECho IBal NBir NSla SPoG WAbe WIce
- 'Alba'	CTal ECho EWes IBal WFar
- 'Albrighton'	CTal CTri ECho EWes GEdr NBir NHol NHpl NWad WAbe WPat
- 'Apple Blossom'	CTal ECho EWes GKev IBal ITim LBee LEdu NHol NWad SRot WFar
- 'Badger'	CTal ITim NWad
- var. ***baurii***	ECho EWes LRHS
- var. ***baurii*** × ***baurii*** var. ***platypetala***	ECho
- 'Bridal Bouquet' (d)	CTal EWes GEdr IBal NHol
- 'Caro'	EWes
- 'Charlotte'	EWes
- 'Coconut Ice'	CTal EWes IBal LEdu
- var. ***confecta***	CElw CTal CTre ECho EWes GEdr GKev IBal NHol WFar WTor
- 'Daphne Mary'	EWes
- 'David Scott'	EWes
- 'Dawn'	CAby CTal ECho EWes GEdr GKev IBal SDys WAbe

– 'Douglas'	CTal ECho EPfP EWes GEdr GKev IBal LEdu NBir NHol NHpl WPGP
– 'Dulcie'	CTal ECho EWes GEdr GKev IBal
– 'Emily Peel'	CTal ECho EPot EWes GKev IBal ITim
– 'Eva-Kate'	CTal ECho EWes GKev IBal ITim WPat
– 'Fred Broome'	CTal ECho EWes GEdr GKev IBal LEdu NHol NWad WFar WPat
– 'Goliath'	CTal EWes IBal
– 'Harlequin'	CAby CTal ECho EWes GEdr GKev IBal ITim NHol NWad SRot
§ – 'Helen'	CTal ECho EWes GEdr GKev IBal LEdu NHol NHpl WAbe WPGP
– 'Jacqueline Potterton'	CTal
– 'Jeanette'	EWes IBal
– 'Kitty'	CTal EWes IBal WFar
– 'Komadori' **new**	CTal
– 'Lily Jean' (d)	CAby CMea CTal CTri ECho EPfP EWes GEdr GKev IBal ITim LRHS NHpl NWad XEll
– 'Luna'	EWes
– 'Margaret Rose'	CTal ECho EWes GKev IBal NHol
– 'Mars'	CTal EWes GKev IBal LEdu LRHS NBir NHol WFar WPGP
– 'Monique'	EWes
– 'Pearl'	CTal ECho LRHS
– 'Pearl' × ***thodiana*** **new**	CTal
– 'Perle'	ECho EWes GEdr IBal NHol NWad
– 'Picta' (v)	CTal ECho EWes GKev IBal LEdu LRHS NHol NHpl NWad WPat
– 'Pink Pearl'	CTal EWes IBal NHol WAbe
– pink-flowered	ECho
– var. ***platypetala***	CTal CWCL ECho EPfP EWes GEdr GKev IBal NHol NHpl NWad XEll
– var. ***platypetala*** × ***milloides***	IBal LLHF NHol NWad
– var. ***platypetala*** × ***milloides*** Burtt 6981	EWes
– 'Rebecca'	ECho EWes
– 'Red King'	CTal EWes IBal
– red-flowered	ECho SPlb
– 'Ruth'	ECho EWes GEdr GKev IBal NHol SDeJ
– 'Susan Garnett-Botfield'	CTal ECho EWes GEdr IBal LRHS NHpl WAbe
– 'Tetra Pink'	CAby ECho EWes GEdr IBal NHol NWad
– 'Tetra Red'	CTal ECho EWes GEdr GKev IBal NHol NWad SDeJ SRot WFar
– 'The Bride'	EWes GEdr
– white-flowered	ECho EPot LRHS
baurii × ***milloides*** **new**	SRot
'Betsy Carmine'	CCCN CTal GEdr IBal NWad WAbe WFar
'Blush'	ECho
'Bright Eyes' (d)	EWes
'Burgundy'	IBal LRHS
'Butterfly Wings'	CTal NWad
'Candy Stripe'	CTal ECho EWes GEdr LRHS NWad
'Carina'	CTal ECho EWes
'Caroline'	EWes IBal WFar
'Cathy'	CTal EWes IBal
'Cayasan'	ECho
'Confusion'	EWes LEdu NHol NHpl NWad WAbe
'Dainty Dee' (d)	EWes
deflexa	CMen CTal CTre ECho EPot EWes GKev IBal ITim LEdu LRHS NCou NHol NHpl NRHS NSla NWad WAbe WFar WPGP WTor
– 'Janette'	CTal
'Donald Mann'	CTal ECho EWes GEdr IBal ITim LLHF NHol SRot
'Drakensberg Dusk' **new**	CTal
'Dusky'	CTal ECho EWes GEdr GKev IBal
'E.A. Bowles'	CTal ECho EWes IBal NHpl NSla WFar
'Ellicks'	CTal IBal
'Flashing Ruby'	CTal GEdr IBal
'Forge Robies'	EWes
'Garnett'	ECho EWes IBal WAbe WFar
'Gemma'	EWes
'Goya' (d)	CAby ECho IBal NHpl
'Great Scot'	ECho EWes GEdr GKev IBal NHpl
'Heather'	CTal
'Hebron Farm Biscuit'	see *Hypoxis parvula* var. *albiflora* 'Hebron Farm Biscuit'
'Hebron Farm Cerise'	see × *Rhodoxis* 'Hebron Farm Cerise'
'Hebron Farm Pink'	see × *Rhodoxis hybrida* 'Hebron Farm Pink'
'Hinky Pinky'	GEdr
'Holden Rose' (d)	CTal ECho IBal NHol NWad WFar
'Hope' (d)	Tal IBal
hybrids	ELan
'Indy'	IBal
'Jap Double'	CTal
'Jupiter'	CTal GEdr NWad
'Kiwi Joy' (d)	CMen CTal EWes GEdr GKev IBal LLHF NHol NHpl NWad SDeJ
'Knockdolian Red'	GEdr IBal NHol NWad WFar
'Lily Fan'	CTal
'Lisette'	EWes
'Louise'	CTal IBal
'Midori'	CTal ECho EWes GEdr IBal NWad SDys
milloides	CAby CMen CPla CPne CTal CTre CWCL ECho EPot EWes GCrg GEdr GKev IBal ITim LBee LEdu LRHS NHol NHpl NRHS NWad WFar WPGP XEll
– 'Claret'	CAby CElw CMen CSam CTal ECho ELon EWes GEdr GKev IBal ITim LLHF LRHS NHol SDys SRot WFar WPat WTor
– 'Damask'	CTal ECho EPot EWes GKev IBal LRHS SDys SRot
– 'Donaldson'	CTal GKev SRot
– 'Drakensberg Snow'	CTal EWes
– giant	CMen ECho GKev
– pink-flowered	CMen
– 'Susan'	EWes
'Monty'	ECho EWes GEdr IBal NWad WAbe
'Mystery'	EWes IBal NHol
'Naomi'	ECho EWes
'New Look'	CTal ECho EWes GEdr GKev IBal LLHF NHpl NWad
'Ori Zuru'	CTal ECho GEdr
'Origami'	CTal IBal LEdu
'Pat Lacey'	CTal EWes IBal
'Paula'	IBal
'Pearl White'	ECho
'Pink Ice'	CTal GEdr IBal NBir NWad
'Pinkeen'	CTal ECho EWes LLHF LRHS
'Pinkie'	CTal IBal SDys
'Pintado'	CAby CTal ECho EWes GEdr GKev IBal LEdu NWad SDys
'Pretty in Pink'	CTal
'Raspberry Ice'	CTal ECho IBal NHol NWad WFar
'Roman'	CTal

'Rosalie' **new**	IBal
'Rosie Lee'	CTal EWes
'Ruby Giant' **new**	GEdr LRHS
'Shell Pink'	CTal EWes IBal NHol NWad
Slack Top hybrids	NSla
'Snow'	EWes
'Snow White'	EWes NHol NLar
'Starlett'	CTal EWes LRHS NHol
'Starry Eyes' (d)	CTal ECho EWes IBal WFar
'Stella'	CCCN CTal ECho EWes GEdr GKev IBal LRHS NHol NHpl NWad SDys
'Sunburst'	GEdr NWad
'Telios'	IBal
'Tetra Rose'	GEdr
'Tetra White'	see *R. baurii* 'Helen'
thodiana	CTal CTre ECho EWes GEdr GKev IBal NHol NHpl NWad WAbe WFar
'Twinkle Star Mixed'	ECho LRHS
'Two Tone'	EWes
'Venetia'	CMea CTal ECho GKev IBal NHol NWad
'Westacre Picotee'	EWes
'White Prince'	CTal
'White Wings'	CTal
'Wild Cherry Blossom'	CTal ECho EWes IBal

Rhodohypoxis × *Hypoxis* see × *Rhodoxis*

R. baurii* × *H. parvula	see × *Rhodoxis hybrida*

Rhodoleia (*Hamamelidaceae*)

championii B&SWJ 11603 **new**	WCru
– WWJ 11858	WCru
aff. ***henryi*** B&SWJ 11782	WCru
– DJHV 0640 **new**	WCru
parvipetala WWJ 11866 **new**	WCru
– WWJ 11943 **new**	WCru

Rhodophiala (*Amaryllidaceae*)

§ ***advena***	NRog
araucana	NRog
§ ***bifida***	NRog WCot
– pink-flowered	NRog
chilensis	NRog
montana	WCot
phycelloides	NRog
pratensis	CPne WCot
rhodolirion	SPlb

Rhodora see *Rhododendron*

Rhodothamnus (*Ericaceae*)

sessilifolius	WThu

Rhodotypos (*Rosaceae*)

kerrioides	see *R. scandens*
§ ***scandens***	CLet CTri CWib ELan EPfP IDee LEdu LHop LRHS MGil MMrt MMuc MNrw NHol NLar NQui SAko SEND SLon SPoG WCru WHar WPat WSHC

× *Rhodoxis* ✿ (*Hypoxidaceae*)

'Abigail'	EWes IBal WFar
'Anne Crock'	ECho EWes IBal
'Aurora'	CTal ECho EWes IBal WFar
'Betsy'	CTal EWes
'Bianca' **new**	CTal
'Bloodstone'	CTal ECho EWes IBal NHol NWad
'Evelien' **new**	CTal
'Fanny'	EWes
'Hebron Farm Biscuit'	see *Hypoxis parvula* var. *albiflora* 'Hebron Farm Biscuit'
§ 'Hebron Farm Cerise'	CCCN CMen CTal ECho EWes GEdr GKev IBal LEdu LRHS SDys SRot
'Hebron Farm Rose'	IBal LLHF
§ ***hybrida***	ECho EWes ITim WAbe
– 'Aya San'	CTal ECho EWes GKev IBal WFar
§ – 'Hebron Farm Pink'	CAby CElw CMen ECho EWes GEdr GKev IBal NHol SRot WAbe
– 'Hebron Farm Red Eye'	CCCN CMen CTal ECho EWes GKev IBal WAbe
– 'Hebron Farm Red Eye' seedling	CMen
– 'Pink Stars'	CTal ECho IBal
– 'Ruby Giant'	CTal ECho EWes GEdr IBal
– 'White Knight'	CTal
– 'White Stars'	CTal ECho EWes
'Irene'	ECho
'Jenny'	EWes
large red-flowered	CMen
'Little Pink Pet'	CTal EWes IBal WFar
'Nippon'	CTal
'Otterlo Ruby'	EWes WFar
'Pink Glow' **new**	IBal
'Pink Tips'	CTal IBal
'Red Flyer'	CTal EWes IBal
'Ria'	ECho EWes
'Sandra'	CTal EWes
'Sandy'	CTal ECho EWes
'Sonja'	CTal ECho
'Sue'	EWes WFar
'Summer Pink' **new**	IBal

Rhoeo see *Tradescantia*

Rhopalostylis (*Arecaceae*)

sapida	CBrP
– 'Chatham Island'	CBlu
– 'East Cape'	SBig

rhubarb see *Rheum* × *hybridum*

Rhus (*Anacardiaceae*)

ambigua	ESwi
– B&SWJ 3656	WCru
– large-leaved B&SWJ 10884	WCru
aromatica	CAgr CArn EBtc LRHS NLar
chinensis	CMCN IDee
copallinum	EBtc
coriaria	NLar
cotinus	see *Cotinus coggygria*
glabra	CBcs EBtc EPfP SPer
hirta	see *R. typhina*
incisa	SPlb
potaninii	EPfP LRHS NLar
× ***pulvinata*** (Autumn Lace Group) 'Red Autumn Lace' ♀H5	LRHS MBlu MRav SPer
punjabensis	EGFP
§ ***radicans***	GPoy WHer
succedanea	CDTJ EGFP
– NJM 10.154	WPGP
toxicodendron	see *R. radicans*
typhina	CBcs CDul CLnd CMac EBee ELan EMOT EPfP ESps GKin GMcL LCro LRHS MAsh MGos MMuc MRav NEgg NHol NLar NWea SCob SEND SGol SLim SPer SSta WFar

§ – 'Dissecta' 🏆H6	CBcs CDul CLet CLnd CMac ELan EPfP ESps GMcL MGos MJak MMuc MRav NEgg NLar NPri SArc SCob SEND SGol SLim SPer WFar
– 'Laciniata' hort.	see *R. typhina* 'Dissecta'
– Radiance = 'Sinrus' 🏆H6	LRHS MAsh MBlu SPoG
– Tiger Eyes = 'Bailtiger'[PBR] 🏆H6	ELan EPfP GKin GMcL LBuc LRHS MAsh MGos SCob SCoo SGol SHil SMad SPoG SWvt
verniciflua	EGFP NLar
virens	CFil

Rhynchospora (*Cyperaceae*)

colorata	LLWG NPer
latifolia	CKno SDix SHDw

Ribes ✿ (*Grossulariaceae*)

alpinum	ELan EPfP MRav MWht NWea SPer SRms
– 'Aureum'	CAbP EHoe NEgg
americanum 'Variegatum' (v)	EHoe NWad WPat
aureum misapplied	see *R. odoratum*
aureum ambig.	IFro
aureum Pursh. subsp. ***gracillimum***	SBrt
§ × ***beatonii***	CBcs CBot CWld EBee ECrN ELon EShb EWTr GBin LEdu LRHS MAsh MMuc NLar SBrt SDix SGol SLim SMad SPer SPoG WCot WFar WHar
'Ben Hope'[PBR] (B)	CAgr CSBt EPom MCoo SCoo SWvt WHar
'Black Velvet' (D)	CAgr MCoo
californicum	LHop SBrt
cereum	SBrt
§ × ***culverwellii*** (F)	CAgr CCCN CWib EPom GTwe LBuc LCro LEdu LOPS NLar SDea SVic SWvt WHar WMat
divaricatum	CAgr LEdu
gayanum	LEdu NLar
glaciale	WPGP
– PAB 3004	LEdu
× ***gordonianum***	see *R.* × *beatonii*
griffithii GWJ 9331	WCru
– PAB 4871	LEdu
jostaberry	see *R.* × *culverwellii*
laurifolium	CBcs CDul CEnd CHGN CPla CTho CTri EBee ELan EWTr EWes LRHS MRav NLar SChF SCob SEND SPer WBod WCFE WFar WRHF WSHC
– (f)	CMac EPfP SBrt SRms
– (m)	EPfP SBrt
– 'Mrs Amy Doncaster'	CMac EWTr LEdu SEle WBor WCot WPGP WPat
– Rosemoor form	ELan EPfP LRHS SKHP SPoG
longeracemosum	GGGa
menziesii	CHll EWes NQui WCot
× ***nidigrolaria***	CSBt SBdl
nigrum PAB 3755 (B)	LEdu
– 'Baldwin' (B)	CFGn CTri EPfP MAsh NLar SBdl SDea SKee SLim SPer SPoG WHar WMat
– 'Barchatnaja' (B)	CAgr
– 'Ben Alder' (B)	CAgr CWib EPom SBdl SCoo SDea
– 'Ben Connan'[PBR] (B) 🏆H6	Widely available
– 'Ben Gairn'[PBR] (B)	CAgr MCoo MMuc WHar
– 'Ben Lomond'[PBR] (B)	CAgr CFGn CMac CSBt CTri CWib EMOT EPfP GTwe LBuc LEdu LSRN MAsh MGos MJak MNHC MRav NEgg NLar NPri NWea SBdl SDea SKee SPer SRms SVic WHar WMat
– 'Ben More' (B)	CAgr CWib
– 'Ben Nevis' (B)	CAgr CTri CWib EMOT SDea SKee SPer
– 'Ben Sarek' (B)	Widely available
– 'Ben Tirran' (B)	CAgr CSBt CWib EPom ERea LBuc LRHS LSRN MAsh MGos NLar NPri SBdl SCoo SDea SRms SWvt WHar WMat
– 'Big Ben'[PBR] (B) 🏆H6	CArg CFGn CRos EPfP EPom ERea LBuc LCro LOPS LRHS LSRN NLar NRHS SPer SPoG WMat
– 'Black Reward' (B)	CAgr
– 'Boskoop Giant' (B)	CAgr ELan NEgg SLim WHar
– 'Byelorussian Sweet' (B)	CAgr
– 'Ebony' (B)	CArg CMac CSut EPom ERea LEdu LRHS NPri NRHS SLon SVic
– 'Hystawneznaya' (B)	CAgr
– 'Jet' (B)	CAgr NEgg
– 'Karaka Black' (B)	ERea
– 'Kosmicheskaya' (B)	CAgr
– 'Loch Ness' (B)	ERea WHar
– 'Pilot Alexander Mamkin' (B)	CAgr
– 'Ruben'[PBR] (B)	ERea
– 'Seabrook's' (B)	CAgr
– 'Titania' (B)	LRHS MCoo NLar WMat
– 'Wellington XXX' (B)	CAgr EMOT LBuc LEdu NWea SPer
§ ***odoratum***	CBcs CDul CMac CSBt CTho CWib CWld EBee ECrN ELan ELon EPfP EWTr LHop LRHS MGos MMuc MNHC MNrw MRav NLar NWea SCob SKHP SPer SPoG SRms WHar
– 'Black Pearl' **new**	SVic
– 'Crandall'	CAgr LEdu
orientale PAB 7066	LEdu
'Pink Perfection'	CMCN
praecox	CBcs MMuc SEND
roezlii	CBot
rubrum	ESps
– 'Blanka' (W)	CAgr CArg CMac CSut ERea LRHS SFrt
– 'Cascade' (R)	CAgr
– 'Cherry' (R)	CAgr
– 'Gloire de Sablons' (P)	EPom GTwe
– 'Jonkheer van Tets' (R) 🏆H6	CAgr CRos CSBt CWib EMOT EPfP EPom ESps GQue GTwe IArd LRHS LSRN MAsh MCoo NLar NRHS NWea SBdl SDea SEND SKee SLim SPer SRms WHar WMat
– 'Junifer' (R)	CAgr EPom ERea GTwe LRHS NRHS SFrt SKee
– 'Laxton's Number One' (R)	CAgr CFGn CRos CTri EPfP EPom GTwe LCro LEdu LOPS LRHS LSRN NLar NRHS NWea SBdl SDea SLim SPer SPoG SRms WHar WMat
– 'Red Lake' (R) 🏆H6	CAgr CFGn CTri CWib ECrN ELan EPfP EPom ERea GTwe LBuc LEdu MGos MJak NEgg NLar NPri SDea SKee SPer SPoG WMat
– 'Redstart' (R)	CAgr CFGn CSBt CTri CWib GTwe LBuc MAsh MMuc NLar SKee SPoG WHar WMat
– 'Rolan' (R)	CAgr EMOT
– 'Rondom' (R)	CAgr SDea SVic
– 'Rosetta' (R)	CAgr SBdl
– 'Rovada' (R)	CAgr CArg CFGn CMac CSBt CSut CWib EMOT EPom ERea GTwe LBuc LEdu LRHS LSRN MAsh NPri

	NRHS SBdl SDea SFrt SKee SVic WHar WMat
- 'Roxby Red' (R)	LEdu
- 'Stanza' (R) ♀H6	CAgr EMOT GTwe SDea SEND
§ - 'Versailles Blanche' (W/C)	CAgr CFGn CSBt CTri CWib EPfP EPom ERea GQue GTwe LBuc LCro LOPS LRHS LSRN MGos MJak MMuc NPri NRHS SDea SKee SLim SPer WHar WMat
- 'Weisse Langtraubige' (W)	CAgr
- 'White Dutch' (W)	EMOT
- 'White Grape' (W) ♀H6	LEdu
- 'White Pearl' (W)	ELan EMOT SDea SVic
- White Versailles	see *R. rubrum* 'Versailles Blanche'
- 'White Transparent' (W)	GTwe
sanguineum	CDul CNec ESps NBes NEgg WMoo
- 'Albescens'	CBot EPfP
- 'Brocklebankii'	CMac LRHS MRav NLar SChF SCob SPer SPoG SRms WCFE WSHC
- 'Carneum'	LRHS
- double-flowered	see *R. sanguineum* 'Plenum'
- 'Elkington's White'	CRos ECrN EPfP ESwi EWTr LBuc LCro LHop LRHS LSRN MGos NLar NSti SCoo SHil SLon WBor
- 'Flore Pleno'	see *R. sanguineum* 'Plenum'
- 'Icecrystal'	ESwi
- 'King Edward VII'	Widely available
- 'Koja' ♀H6	CBot CRos ELon EPfP GBin LBrs LEdu LRHS LSRN MAsh MGos MMuc NLar SCoo SEle SHil SMad SPoG WCot WPat
- 'Lombartsii'	EPfP LRHS MRav
- 'Pink Rain'	LRHS
§ - 'Plenum' (d)	EPfP
- 'Poky's Pink'	ECrN EWTr LLHF LRHS MAsh MRav SPoG
- 'Pulborough Scarlet' ♀H6	Widely available
- 'Red Bross'	EPfP LRHS SWvt
- 'Red Pimpernel'	EPfP LRHS LSRN MAsh MBNS SWvt WFar
- 'Somerset White'	LRHS
- 'Taff's Kim' (v)	LRHS
- 'Tydeman's White'	CSBt ELan EPfP NLar NWea WSHC
- var. ***variegata***	CMac
- White Icicle = 'Ubric' ♀H6	CBcs CBot CDul CTri CWib EBee ECtt EPfP GBin GMcL LBMP LRHS MAsh MBlu MHer MRav MSwo NBir NLar SCob SPer SPoG SRms SWvt WCFE WCot WFar WMoo WPat
speciosum ♀H4	Widely available
uva-crispa 'Achilles' (D)	GTwe
- 'Annelii' (F)	CAgr
- 'Blucher' (D)	GTwe
- 'Bright Venus' (D)	GTwe
- 'Broom Girl' (D)	GTwe
- 'Captivator' (C)	CFGn CRos CSBt EMOT EPom GTwe LBuc LRHS MAsh MCoo MNHC NBes NLar NRHS SBdl SDea SKee SPoG WHar WMat
- 'Careless' (C/D) ♀H6	CFGn CMac CSBt EPom GTwe LSRN MAsh MGos MJak NLar SBdl SDea SPer WHar WMat
- 'Cook's Eagle' (C)	GTwe
- 'Criterion' (D)	GTwe
- 'Crown Bob' (C/D)	GTwe
- 'Dan's Mistake' (D)	GTwe
- 'Early Sulphur' (D)	ELan GTwe SDea
- 'Firbob' (D)	GTwe
- 'Freedom' (C)	GTwe
- 'Glenton Green' (D)	GTwe
- 'Golden Drop' (D)	GTwe
- 'Green Gem' (C/D)	GTwe
- 'Green Ocean' (D)	GTwe
- 'Greenfinch' (C) ♀H6	CAgr
- 'Gunner' (C/D)	GTwe
- 'Heart of Oak' (D)	GTwe
- 'Hedgehog' (D)	GTwe
- 'Hero of the Nile' (D)	GTwe
- 'High Sheriff' (D)	GTwe
- 'Hinnonmäki' (F)	CAgr ECrN LBuc NPri SDea SPer
- 'Hinnonmäki Grön' (D)	CAgr CMac CSBt EMOT EMil EPfP LSRN MAsh MRav NPri SBdl SDea SFrt WHar
- 'Hinnonmäki Gul' (D)	CAgr CMac CSBt CSut EMil EPfP EPom ERea GBin GTwe LBuc LEdu LRHS MAsh MGos MNHC NLar NRHS SBdl SDea SKee SPer SPoG SVic WHar WMat
- 'Hinnonmäki Röd' (C/D)	CAgr CFGn CMac CRos EMOT EMil EPfP EPom ERea GTwe LBuc LCro LOPS LRHS LSRN MAsh MCoo MNHC MRav NLar NRHS SBdl SDea SFrt SKee SPer SPoG SVic WHar WMat
- 'Howard's Lancer' (C/D)	GTwe SDea
- 'Invicta' (C/D) ♀H6	Widely available
- 'Ironmonger' (D)	GTwe
- 'Jubilee' (C/D)	LBuc
- 'Jubilee Careless' (C/D)	EPom
- 'Keepsake' (C/D)	GTwe SDea
- 'King of Trumps' (D)	GTwe
- 'Lancashire Lad' (C/D)	GTwe
- 'Langley Gage' (D)	GTwe MCoo
- 'Larell' (F) **new**	CAgr
- 'Laxton's Amber' (D)	GTwe
- 'Leveller' (D) ♀H6	CTri ECrN GTwe MCoo SDea SPer WHar
- 'London' (C/D)	GTwe
- 'Martlet' (F)	GTwe MCoo SLim
- 'May Duke' (C/D)	SDea
- 'Pax'[PBR] (D)	CAgr CSut EPfP GTwe SDea SFrt SLim SVic
- 'Peru' (D)	GTwe
- 'Pitmaston Green Gage' (D)	GTwe
- 'Plunder' (C)	GTwe
- 'Queen of Trumps' (D)	GTwe
- 'Red Champagne' (D)	GTwe
- 'Redeva'[PBR] (D) **new**	CAgr
- 'Rokula'[PBR] (C/D)	ELan LRHS MCoo WMat
- 'Scotch Red Rough' (D)	GTwe
- 'Snow' (F)	EPfP
- 'Snowdrop' (D)	GTwe
- 'Spinefree' (C)	CAgr GTwe
- 'Surprise' (D)	GTwe
- 'Victoria' (C/D)	GTwe
- 'Whinham's Industry' (C/D) ♀H6	CSBt CTri ELan GTwe LBuc LHop LSRN MGos MMuc NEgg SDea SEND SPer WHar
- 'White Lion' (C/D)	GTwe
- 'White Transparent' (C)	GTwe
- 'Whitesmith' (C/D)	CTri GTwe LSRN MCoo SDea
- 'Xenia' (D)	CArg CFGn CRos EPfP EPom ERea LCro LEdu LRHS MCoo NLar NRHS SPoG WMat
- 'Yellow Champagne' (D)	GTwe
valdivianum	WCot
- 'Kathleen'	EPfP LRHS
viburnifolium	NLar SBrt SEND
'Worcesterberry' (C)	CHab IDee SDea SPer

Richea (*Ericaceae*)

scoparia	CPne

Ricinus (*Euphorbiaceae*)

communis	CDTJ SPlb
- 'Carmencita' 🏆H1c	NGBl SDys
- 'Carmencita Pink'	CDTJ
- 'Carmencita Red'	CDTJ
- 'Dominican Republic'	CDTJ
- 'Gibsonii'	CDTJ
- 'Impala'	CDTJ
- 'New Zealand Black'	CDTJ CSpe SDys
- 'Zanzibariensis' 🏆H1c	CDTJ

Ridolfia (*Apiaceae*)

segetum **new**	LRHS

Rigidella see *Tigridia*

Riocreuxia (*Apocynaceae*)

torulosa	CCCN SPlb

Robinia (*Papilionaceae*)

× ***ambigua***	EBee SKHP
§ ***hispida***	CDul CEnd CWib ELan EMOT EPfP MBlu NOrn SPer
- var. ***kelseyi***	CDul EBee EWes
- 'Macrophylla'	CEnd
§ - var. ***rosea***	LSRN
- 'Rosea' misapplied	see *R. hispida*, *R. hispida* var. rosea
- 'Rosea' ambig.	CBcs EBee
× ***margaretta*** Casque Rouge	see *R.* × *margaretta* 'Pink Cascade'
§ - 'Pink Cascade'	CEnd CLnd CMac CTri EBee ECrN ELan EMOT EPfP MAsh MGos NOra SCoo SEND SGol SLim SPer WMat
neomexicana	SIgm
pseudoacacia	CAgr CCVT CDul CNWT ELan EMOT ESps LBuc MCoo MMuc SCob SEND SGol SPlb
- 'Bessoniana'	CDul EBee ELan EMOT EPfP
- 'Frisia'	Widely available
- 'Inermis' hort.	see *R. pseudoacacia* 'Umbraculifera'
§ - 'Lace Lady'PBR	CSBt ECrN ELan EPfP LBuc MAsh MGos NLar NOrn SCoo SPoG WMat
- 'Rozynskiana'	CDul
- 'Tortuosa'	CEnd EBee EBtc SPer
- 'Twisty Baby'	see *R. pseudoacacia* 'Lace Lady'
§ - 'Umbraculifera'	CDul CLnd ECrN LSRN SArc SCob SCoo
× ***slavinii*** 'Hillieri' 🏆H5	CDul CEnd CLnd EBee ECrN ELan EMOT EPfP EUJe EWTr LSRN MAsh MBlu NLar NOrn SLon SPer SPoG

Rochea see *Crassula*

Rodgersia (*Saxifragaceae*)

aesculifolia 🏆H7	Widely available
- SSSE 306	SMHy
- green bud	IBlr
- var. ***henrici***	CLAP GCal GLog IBoy LRHS MRav NBro SGbt SPer SWat WHoo WMoo
- - KW 21015	WCru
- - 'Cherry Blush'	GBin MSCN SPad WHar
- - hybrid	CHid CLet ITim IVic NLar XLum
- 'Red Dawn'	IBlr
- 'Red Leaf'	EWoo GCal IFoB
'Badenweiter'	EBee ECha
'Blickfang' 🏆H7	EBee IBlr LRHS MMrt
'Bloody Mary'	ECtt IMou LLWG SCob SKHP WFar
'Borodin'	EBee
'Bronze Peacock'	CMos EBee ECtt GBin LLWG MHol NAst NEoE SCob WTor
Cally strain	GCal
'Dark Pokers'	EBee ECtt NLar SPoG
'Die Anmutige'	IMou
'Die Schöne'	CLAP EBee NLar
'Die Stolze'	GBin IMou LEdu LLWG MBrN
'Elfenbeinturm'	IBlr
'Fascination'	IBlr
'Herkules'	EBee ECha ECtt EHoe ELon EUJe GBin GMaP GMcL IFoB LEdu LHop LRHS LSou MBNS MMuc NLar NQui SKHP WPnP
'Irish Bronze' 🏆H7	EAEE ECtt ELan EPed EPfP EShb GPSL GQue ILea IVic LEdu LRHS LSRN MBel MWts NPnk SMad WMoo WPnP
'Koriata'	IBlr
'Kupfermond'	EBee IBlr NBir SMHy
'La Blanche'	EBee ECtt ELon LEdu LRHS MHol NLar WCot WPnP
'Maigrün'	IBlr
nepalensis	CLAP EBee LEdu LRHS WPGP
- EMAK 713	IBlr
- HWJK 2140	WCru
- 'High Flier' **new**	WCru
'Parasol'	CBro CMac IBlr NBir NHol NWad SKHP WPGP WWtn
pinnata	CAby CHid CTri EBee ECho EHrv EPau EPfP GMaP IBlr IBoy IFoB ITim IVic LEdu LRHS LSRN MBel MGos MRav NHol SCob SMad SPer WBor WMoo WPnP WWtn XLum
- B&SWJ 7741A	CBcs WCru
- L 1670	ELan IBlr WPGP
- 'Alba'	GCal IBlr LRHS
- 'Buckland Beauty' 🏆H7	EBee IBlr LRHS SMHy WMoo
- 'Cally Coral'	EBee GCal
- 'Cally Salmon'	EWes GCal IBlr IMou
- 'Candy Clouds' (d)	EBee
- 'Chocolate Wing'	Widely available
- 'Crûg Cardinal'	EBee GCal LRHS WCru
- 'Elegans'	CDor EBee EHoe ELan EPed EPfP GMaP IBlr LEdu LRHS MHol MRav NEgg NHol NWad SWvt WCFE
- 'Fireworks'PBR	CHid CLAP EBee ECtt ELan EPfP GMcL IMou NLar SPer WHil
- 'Hanna' **new**	GEdr
- hybrids	GNew LRHS
- 'Jade Dragon Mountain'	EBee GCal IBlr SKHP WPGP
- 'Maurice Mason'	CLAP EBee ECtt GKev IBlr NLar SDix SMHy
- 'Mont Blanc'	IBlr
- Mount Stewart form	IBlr
- 'Panache'	IBlr
- 'Perthshire Bronze'	IBlr
- 'Pink Beauty' **new**	EBee
- pink-flowered	WCru
- 'Rosea'	IBlr
- 'Shangri-La' **new**	WCru
- 'Snow Clouds'	EBee
- 'Superba' 🏆H7	Widely available
- white-flowered	GAbr SWat WCru
pinnata × ***sambucifolia***	IBlr
podophylla	Widely available
- B&SWJ 10818	WCru
- B&SWJ 10823	WCru

- 'Braunlaub'	CLAP EUJe GBuc GQue LLWG NBro WMoo
- 'Bronceblad'	IBlr
- 'Crûg's Colossus'	WCru
- Donard selection	IBlr
- 'Rotlaub' ♀H7	CAby CLAP EBee GBin IBlr IMou IPot IVic WBor WMoo
- 'Smaragd'	CLAP EShb GCal IBlr LRHS MRav NBir NLar
purdomii hort.	CMac GCal LRHS WCot WPGP
'Reinecke Fuchs'	IBlr
'Rosenzipfel'	IBlr
sambucifolia	CBcs CLAP CMac GCal IBoy ILea LEdu LRHS MArt MMuc NBir NEgg NLar NSti SEND SPer SWat WFar WMoo WPnP XLum
- B&SWJ 7899	WCru
- dwarf, pink-flowered	IBlr
- dwarf, white-flowered	IBlr
- large, red-stemmed	NBir
- 'Mountain Select'	EBee GCal
'Stoke Gabriel'	EBee
tabularis	see *Astilboides tabularis*

Roemeria (*Papaveraceae*)

hybrida	CSpe

Rohdea (*Asparagaceae*)

japonica	CMac WCot WPGP
- B&SWJ 4853	WCru
- B&SWJ 5091	WCru
- 'Godaishu' (v)	WCot
- 'Gunjaku' (v)	WCot
- 'Lance Leaf'	LEdu WPGP
- long-leaved	WCot
- 'Miyakonojo' (v)	WCot
- 'Talbot Manor' (v)	CBct WCot
- 'Tama-jishi' (v)	WCot
- 'Tuneshige Rokujo' (v)	WCot
tonkinensis HWJ 562	WCru
watanabei	IMou
- B&SWJ 1911	WCru

Romanzoffia (*Boraginaceae*)

californica	EBee
§ ***sitchensis***	CTri
suksdorfii Greene	see *R. sitchensis*
tracyi	GEdr
unalaschcensis	EBee SRms

Romneya (*Papaveraceae*)

coulteri ♀H5	Widely available
§ - 'White Cloud' ♀H5	EBee EPfP MRav SChF WPGP
× ***hybrida***	see *R. coulteri* 'White Cloud'

Romulea (*Iridaceae*)

atrandra	CTal NRog
§ ***autumnalis***	ECho
bulbocodium	CBro CTal ECho
- var. ***clusiana***	ECho
- var. ***crocea***	ECho EPot
- var. ***leichtliniana***	ECho GKev
diversiformis new	CTal
engleri	CTal
hirta	ECho
leipoldtii	ECho
linaresii	ECho
- subsp. ***graeca***	ECho GKev
longituba	see *R. macowanii*
§ ***macowanii***	ECho
montana	ECho
namaquensis	ECho
nivalis	CTal ECho
ramiflora	CTal ECho
rosea	ECho
- var. ***speciosa***	see *R. autumnalis*
tabularis	ECho
tempskyana	ECho EPot GKev
tetragona new	CTal
* ***zahnii***	CTal

Rorippa (*Brassicaceae*)

amphibia	LLWG MSKA
nasturtium-aquaticum	MWts WMAq

Rosa ✿ (*Rosaceae*)

NJM 11.048 from Guizhou, China	WPGP
NJM 11.077 from Guizhou, China	WPGP
NJM 11.079 from Guizhou, China	WPGP
A Shropshire Lad = 'Ausled'PBR (S) ♀H6	CKel CNec CRos EPfP ESps LBuc LRHS LSRN MAus NEgg NLar NRHS SCob SPer SSea
A Whiter Shade of Pale = 'Peafanfare'PBR (HT) ♀H6	CKel ECnt ESps ESty LSRN MAus MJak MRav SPer SSea SWCr
Abbeyfield Rose = 'Cocbrose' (HT)	MRav SPer
Abigaile = 'Tanelaigib' (F)	LSRN
Abracadabra = 'Korhocsel' (HT)	ESty
Abraham Darby = 'Auscot' (S)	CBod CKel CTri ELan EPfP EShb ESps EWTr IBoy LRHS LSRN MAus MJak MRav MWat NEgg NLar SCob SEND SLon SPer SWCr
Absent Friends = 'Dicemblem'PBR (F)	ESty IBoy SRGP SWCr WBor
Absolutely Fabulous = 'Wekvossutono'PBR (F) ♀H6	CBod CGro CSBt ECnt EPfP ESps ESty LBrs LBuc LRHS LSRN MAsh MJak MRav NPri SCoo SPad SPer SPoG SWCr
abyssinica	LEdu
'Adam' (ClT)	LSRN
Adam's Rose = 'Wekromico' (F)	LSRN
'Adélaïde d'Orléans' (Ra) ♀H6	CRHN LRHS MAus MMuc MRav NLar SEND SPer SWCr
Agatha Christie = 'Kormeita'PBR (ClF)	EPfP LBrs LRHS LSRN MAsh
'Aglaia' (Ra)	CPou MAus
'Agnes' (Ru)	EBee EPfP EWTr IArd LRHS MAus MCot MRav NLar SPer SRGP
'Aimée Vibert' (N)	CBWd EBee ELon MAus MRav NLar SPer SRGP
'Alain Blanchard' (G)	CPou EWTr MAus
Alan Titchmarsh = 'Ausjive'PBR (S)	CSBt LCro LOPS LRHS LSRN MAsh MAus NRHS SCoo SPer
× ***alba*** (A)	ESps
§ - 'Alba Maxima' (A) ♀	EBee EWTr GBin MAus MRav NLar SEND SPer WFar WHer
§ - 'Alba Semiplena' (A) ♀H7	EPfP GBin LRHS MAus NLar NRHS SPer SWCr WHer
- Celestial	see *R.* 'Céleste'
- 'Maxima'	see *R.* × *alba* 'Alba Maxima'
Alba Meidiland = 'Meiflopan'PBR (S/GC)	EAEE
'Albéric Barbier' (Ra) ♀H5	CBod CRHN CSBt CTri ECnt ELan EPfP ESps EWTr LCro LRHS MAus

	MMuc MRav MSwo MWat NLar NRHS NWea SCob SEND SMad SPer SWCr WHer
'Albertine' (Ra) ♀H6	Widely available
'Alchymist' (ClS)	CKel CPou CRHN ELon EPfP ESty LRHS MAus MRav NLar SPer
Alec's Red = 'Cored' (HT)	CBcs CKel CTri ESps IBoy LSRN MAsh MAus MJak MRav SPer SPoG SRGP SWCr
Alexander = 'Harlex' (HT) ♀H6	CGro ESps GBin IBoy LSRN MAus MRav SPer SSea SWCr
Alexander's Issie = 'Dicland'PBR (F)	IDic
'Alexandre Girault' (Ra) ♀H6	CRHN LBuc LRHS MAus NRHS SPer SWCr WHer
'Alfred de Dalmas' misapplied	see *R.* 'Mousseline'
Alfred Sisley = 'Delstrijor'PBR (S)	CBod EBee ESty MRav NLar
'Alfresco'PBR (ClHT)	MSwo
§ 'Alibaba'PBR (Cl) ♀H6	ECnt ESty EUJe LRHS LSRN MAsh MRav NPri SPer SPoG SWCr
Alice Faye = 'Seaodd' (Min) **new**	ESty
'Alida Lovett' (Ra)	LRHS MAus
Alison = 'Coclibee'PBR (F)	LSRN
Alissar, Princess of Phoenicia = 'Harsidon'PBR (S)	CPou ESty GBin NLar
§ 'Alister Stella Gray' (N) ♀H5	EBee EPfP ESty MAus MCot MMuc NEgg NLar SLon SPer SSea WBor
All American Magic = 'Meiroylear'PBR (HT)	ESty
'Allen Chandler' (ClHT)	MAus
'Allgold' (F)	SCob
Alnwick Castle	see *R.* The Alnwick Rose
'Aloha' (ClHT) ♀H7	CBcs CGro CKel CTri EBee ELon EPfP ESps ESty EWTr LRHS MAsh MAus MCot MJak MRav NLar SCob SPer SWCr
alpina	see *R. pendulina*
'Alpine Sunset' (HT)	CTri ELon ESty MRav SCob SPer SPoG SWCr
altaica Willd.	see *R. spinosissima*
Altissimo = 'Delmur' (Cl)	CKel EWTr LRHS MAsh MAus SPer SSea SWCr
Always You = 'Webalways' (HT)	ESty
'Amadis' (Bs)	MAus
Amanda = 'Beesian' (F)	ESty LSRN
Amber Queen = 'Harroony' (F) ♀H6	CKel CSBt CTri EAEE ELan ESps IArd IBoy LBuc MAsh MAus MRav MWat SPer SSea SWCr
Amber Sweet Dream = 'Fryritz' (Patio)	CKel ECnt MRav MWat
amblyotis RBS 0262	NLar
Ambridge Rose = 'Auswonder' (S)	LRHS MAus
'Amélia'	see *R.* 'Celsiana'
Amelia = 'Poulen011'PBR (Renaissance Series) (S)	ECnt LSRN SWCr
'American Pillar' (Ra)	CBod CGro CKel CRHN CSBt CTri EBee ECnt ELan EPfP IBoy LRHS MAsh MAus MMuc MRav MSwo NLar NPri SCob SPer SPoG SWCr WBor
'Amy Robsart' (RH)	MAus
Anabell = 'Korbell' (F)	LSRN
'Anaïs Ségalas' (G)	MAus
§ 'Anemone' (Cl)	CPou EWTr MAus
anemonoides	see *R.* 'Anemone'
Angela = 'Grifgela'	LSRN
Angela Rippon = 'Ocaru' (Min)	CSBt SPer
'Angela's Choice' (F)	LSRN
Anisley Dickson = 'Dickimono' (F)	SPer
Ann = 'Ausfete'PBR (S)	LSRN MAus
Ann Henderson = 'Fryhoncho' (F)	LSRN
Anna Ford = 'Harpiccolo' (Min/Patio) ♀H5	ESps SPer
Anne Boleyn = 'Ausecret'PBR (S)	EPfP IBoy LBuc LRHS MAsh MAus NEgg SCoo
'Anne Dakin' (ClHT)	MAus
Anne Harkness = 'Harkaramel' (F)	MAus SPer
Antique '89 = 'Kordalen'PBR (ClF)	LRHS MAsh
Antique = 'Antike' (F)	CPou
Aphrodite = 'Tan00847'PBR (S) ♀H6	ESty LSRN MRav SWCr
apothecary's rose	see *R. gallica* var. *officinalis*
'Apple Blossom' (Ra)	SHar
Apple Blossom = 'Noamel' (GC)	EShb
'Apricot Nectar' (F)	MAus
'Apricot Silk' (HT)	CTri SPer
Apricot Sunblaze = 'Savamark' (Min)	CSBt
'Archiduc Joseph' misapplied	see *R.* 'Général Schablikine'
'Arthur Bell' (F) ♀H7	CGro CSBt CTri EPfP ESps ESty EUJe IArd IBoy LBrs LRHS LSRN MAsh MAus MJak MRav MSwo MWat NEgg NPri SCob SPer SPoG SRGP SSea SWCr WBor
'Arthur de Sansal' (DPo)	MAus
arvensis	CCVT CHab LBuc MAus MMuc NWea SCob WHed WTSh
'Assemblage des Beautés' (G)	MAus
'Astra Desmond' (Ra)	MNrw
Audrey Wilcox = 'Frywilrey' (HT)	ESty
'Auguste Gervais' (Ra)	MAus
Austrian copper rose	see *R. foetida* 'Bicolor'
Austrian yellow	see *R. foetida*
'Autumn' (HT)	LSRN
'Autumn Delight' (HM)	NLar
Autumn Fire	see *R.* 'Herbstfeuer'
'Autumnalis'	see *R.* 'Princesse de Nassau'
Avec Amour = 'Tan04341' (HT) **new**	ESty
'Aviateur Blériot' (Ra)	CRHN
'Avon' (HT) **new**	CBod
Avon = 'Poulmulti'PBR (GC)	ELan EPfP MRav SPer
Awakening = 'Probuzení' (ClHT)	EBee MSwo NLar SWCr
'Ayrshire Splendens'	see *R.* 'Splendens'
'Baby Faurax' (Poly)	MAus
Baby Gold Star (Min)	see *R.* 'Estrellita de Oro'
Baby Love = 'Scrivluv'PBR (Min/Patio)	MAus
Baby Masquerade = 'Tanba' (Min)	CGro MRav SPer
Babyface = 'Rawril'PBR (Min)	ESty
'Ballerina' (HM/Poly) ♀H6	Widely available
'Baltimore Belle' (Ra)	CPou MAus NLar
banksiae (Ra)	CPou LPar SNig SRms
– ***alba***	see *R. banksiae* var. *banksiae*

§	- var. ***banksiae*** (Ra/d)	CBod CBot CDul CHll CKel CPou CRHN CRos CSBt CTri CWCL CWld ELan EPfP GQui LCro LOPS LPar LRHS MAus SCob SEND SLon SPer SPoG XSen
	- 'Lutea' (Ra/d) ♀H5	Widely available
	- 'Lutescens' (Ra)	CBot WPGP
	- var. ***normalis*** (Ra)	CSBt CSam EPfP MAus SKHP SLon WCot WHer WOut WPGP
I	- 'Rosea' (Ra)	CBot NLar SPer
	'Bantry Bay' (ClHT)	CSBt EBee ELan ESps LSRN SCob SLon SPer SWCr
	Barbara Austin = 'Austop'PBR (S)	MAus SCob
	Barkarole = 'Tanelorak'PBR (HT)	CSBt ESty
	'Baron Girod de l'Ain' (HP)	ELon LRHS LSRN MAus MRav NEgg NLar NRHS SPer SWCr
	'Baroness Rothschild' (HT)	see *R.* Baronne Edmond de Rothschild
	'Baroness Rothschild' ambig.	see *R.* Baronne Edmond de Rothschild, *R.* Climbing Baronne Edmond de Rothschild
§	Baronne Edmond de Rothschild = 'Meigriso' (HT)	MAus
	'Baronne Prévost' (HP)	MAus
	Baroque Floorshow = 'Harbaroque'PBR (S)	CKel MRav
	Barry Stephens = 'Horcabellero' (HT)	LSRN
	Beatrix Potter = 'Beafolly' (S)	ESty
	'Beau Narcisse' (G) ♀H7	MAus
	Beautiful Britain = 'Dicfire' (F)	ESps SCob
	'Belinda' (HM)	LSRN
§	Bella = 'Pouljill'PBR (Renaissance Series) (S)	CPou
	'Belle Amour' (A × D)	CPou GBin MAus
	'Belle de Crécy' (G)	CPou CTri LBrs LRHS MAsh MAus MNrw NLar NPri SKHP SMad SPer
	'Belle des Jardins' misapplied	see *R.* × *centifolia* 'Unique Panachée'
	Belle Epoque = 'Adasilthe'PBR (HT)	SCob
	Belle Epoque = 'Fryyaboo'PBR (HT)	ESty SCob
	Belle Happiness = 'Meileodevin'PBR (Cl)	ESty SSea
	'Belle Isis' (G)	MAus SPer
	'Belle Poitevine' (Ru)	CPou EBee
	'Belle Portugaise' (ClT)	MAus
	Belmonte = 'Harpearl'PBR (F)	ESty
§	'Belvedere' (Ra) ♀H6	CPou EBee IBoy MAus NLar SPer
	Benita = 'Dicquarrel' (HT)	IDic
	Benjamin Britten = 'Ausencart'PBR (S)	CSBt EPfP ESty IBoy LBuc LOPS LRHS MAsh MAus NEgg NRHS SCob
	Berkshire = 'Korpinka'PBR (GC) ♀H6	SCob SSea
	Beryl Joyce = 'Tan96145'PBR (HT)	CKel ESty LSRN MRav
	Best of Friends = 'Pouldunk'PBR (HT)	LSRN
	Best Wishes = 'Chessnut'PBR (ClHT/v)	ESps LSRN SRGP
	'Betty Sherriff' (Cl)	GBin
	'Betty's Smile' (HT)	LSRN
	'Bewitched' (HT)	LSRN MAsh
§	Bewitched = 'Poulbella'PBR (Castle Series) (F)	SWCr
	Bianco = 'Cocblanco' (Patio/Min)	LBrs MAus MRav MWat SPoG
	Bienvenue = 'Delrochipar' (Cl)	ESty
	Big Purple = 'Stebigpu' (HT)	ECnt ESty
	Billet Doux = 'Delrosar' (S)	ESty
	Birthday Boy = 'Tan97607'PBR (HT)	ESps ESty LSRN MRav MWat SCob SPoG SWCr
	Birthday Girl = 'Meilasso'PBR (F)	CBod CGro CKel CSBt EPfP ESps ESty LBrs LSRN MAsh MJak MRav MWat SCoo SPoG SRGP SVic SWCr
	Birthday WishesPBR (Patio)	see *R.* Shrimp Hit
	Birthday Wishes = 'Guesdelay' (HT)	CTri LRHS LSRN SSea
	Black Beauty = 'Korfleur' (HT)	MAus
	'Black Jack' (Ce)	see *R.* 'Tour de Malakoff'
	'Blairii Number Two' (ClBb)	CSam MAus MRav NEgg NLar SPer
	'Blanche Double de Coubert' (Ru) ♀H7	CBcs CBod CDul CKel CSBt CTri ECnt ELan EPfP ESps EWTr GBin LBuc LCro LSRN MAus MSwo NEgg NLar SCob SEND SPer SWCr
	'Blanche Moreau' (CeMo)	MAus SKHP SPer
	'Blanchefleur' (Ce × G)	CPou MAus
	'Blesma Soul' (HT)	CSBt
	'Blessings' (HT)	CBcs CSBt CTri ESps LBuc LSRN MAus MGos MJak MRav SCob SPer SWCr
	'Bleu Magenta' (Ra) ♀H7	CBod CRHN EBee ELan GBin IArd MAus MCot NLar SEND SWCr WKif
	Bloom of Ruth = 'Harmedley'PBR (HT)	CSBt ECnt
	'Bloomfield Abundance' (Poly)	CPou MAus MMuc NLar SPer
	'Blossomtime' (Cl)	SPer
	Blue for You = 'Pejamblu'PBR (F) ♀H6	CBod CGro CRos ECnt ELan EPfP ESty GBin LBrs LBuc LRHS MAsh MAus NPri SCob SCoo SMad SPoG SSea SWCr
	Blue Moon = 'Tannacht' (HT)	CTri ELan EPfP ESps IBoy MGos MJak MRav SCob SPer SPoG SRGP
	Blue Peter = 'Ruiblun' (Min)	ESty IBoy
	'Blush Boursault' (Bs)	MMuc
	'Blush Hip' (A)	MAus
	'Blush Noisette'	see *R.* 'Noisette Carnée'
	'Blush Rambler' (Ra)	CBod CSBt EPfP EWTr LBuc MAsh MAus MMuc SPer
	'Blushing Lucy' (Ra) ♀H6	CPou EBee EWTr MTPN SPer
	Blythe Spirit = 'Auschool'PBR (S)	MAus NEgg SCob
	'Bobbie James' (Ra) ♀H6	CRos CTri EBee EPfP EWTr LBuc LRHS MAus MRav MSwo NEgg NLar NRHS SCob SPer SSea SWCr WFar
	'Bobby Charlton' (HT)	LSRN
	Bobby Dazzler = 'Smi133-02' (F)	ESty
	Bonica = 'Meidomonac' (GC) ♀H6	Widely available
§	Bonita = 'Poulen009'PBR (Renaissance Series) (S)	ECnt
	Boogie-Woogie = 'Poulyc006'PBR (Courtyard Series) (ClHT)	ECnt LBrs LRHS MAsh SWCr
	Born Again	see *R.* Renaissance
	Boscobel = 'Auscousin'PBR (S)	CRos EPfP ESty LBuc LRHS MAus SCob

'Boule de Neige' (Bb)	CBWd CBcs CTri ECnt ELan EPfP IBoy LCro LRHS LSRN MAus MRav NLar NRHS SPer SWCr
'Bouquet d'Or' (N)	EBee MAus NLar
Bow Bells = 'Ausbells' (S)	MAus
Bowled Over = 'Tandolgnil'[PBR] (F) ♀H6	ESty SWCr
§ ***bracteata*** (S)	CRHN ECre EWes MAus SSea
'Bradley' (F) **new**	ESty
Brave Heart = 'Horbondsmile' (F)	MAus MRav
Breath of Life = 'Harquanne'[PBR] (ClHT)	ELan EPfP ESps LBuc MAus MRav SPer SWCr
Breathtaking = 'Hargalore'[PBR] (HT)	ESty
Bredon = 'Ausbred' (S)	MAus
'Brian's Star' (F)	LSRN
Bride and Groom = 'Smi10-98' (HT)	CKel ESty LSRN MRav SCoo
Bride = 'Fryyearn'[PBR] (HT)	LSRN MRav
Bridge of Sighs = 'Harglowing'[PBR] (Cl)	ECnt ESty LBrs LBuc LRHS MAsh SPoG SWCr
Bright and Breezy = 'Dicjive' (F)	ECnt LBrs
Bright as a Button = 'Chewsumsigns'[PBR] (S)	CKel CSBt CSam ESty GBin NLar SLon SPer SWCr
Bright Fire = 'Peaxi'[PBR] (ClHT)	CKel MSwo SPer SSea SWCr
Bright Future = 'Kirora'[PBR] (Cl)	ESty
Bright Ideas = 'Horcoffdrop' (Cl)	LRHS
Bright Smile = 'Dicdance' (F/Patio)	MAus
Brilliant Sweet Dream = 'Frysassy' (Patio)	ECnt LRHS SWCr
Broadlands = 'Tanmirsch'[PBR] (GC)	CBod NLar
Brother Cadfael = 'Ausglobe'[PBR] (S)	CBod CKel CNec CRos EBee ESps LRHS MAus NEgg NLar NRHS SCob SCoo SPer SSea
Brown Velvet = 'Maccultra' (F)	ESty SPer
Brownie	see *R.* Chocolate Ripples
§ ***brunonii*** (Ra)	CPne CPou EWes MAus
- CC 7290	EWld
- KR 10350 **new**	WPGP
- PAB 3083	LEdu
§ - 'La Mortola' (Ra)	MAus NLar SPer
Brush-strokes = 'Guescolour' (F)	ESty SWCr
'Buff Beauty' (HM) ♀H6	CGro CKel CSBt CTri EBee ECnt ELan EPfP ESps EWTr IBoy LCro LOPS LSRN MAsh MAus MCot MRav MSwo MWat NEgg NLar SCob SEND SPer SWCr WCFE WFar
'Bullata'	see *R.* × *centifolia* 'Bullata'
§ 'Burgundiaca' (G)	MAus
Burgundian rose	see *R.* 'Burgundiaca'
§ Burgundy Ice = 'Prose'[PBR] (F)	CGro CKel CSBt ECnt EPfP ESty LBuc LCro LRHS MRav MSwo NPri NRHS SCob SCoo SMad SPad SPer SSea SWCr
'Burgundy Iceberg'	see *R.* Burgundy Ice
'Burgundy Rose'	see *R.* 'Burgundiaca'
burnet, double pink	see *R. spinosissima* double, pink-flowered
- - white	see *R. spinosissima* double, white-flowered
Buttercup = 'Ausband'[PBR] (S)	CRos EPfP LBuc LRHS MAus
Buxom Beauty = 'Korbilant'[PBR] (HT) ♀H6	EPfP ESty LRHS LSRN SCoo SSea
'C.F. Meyer'	see *R.* 'Conrad Ferdinand Meyer'
californica (S)	MAus
- 'Plena'	see *R. nutkana* 'Plena'
'Callisto' (HM)	MAus
'Camayeux' (G)	CPou ECnt MAus NLar SPer
Cambridgeshire = 'Korhaugen'[PBR] (GC)	CTri MAus NLar SPer SSea SWCr
Camelot = 'Tan05372'[PBR] (Cl)	ESty
Camille Pisarro = 'Destricol' (F)	ESty
'Canary Bird'	see *R. xanthina* 'Canary Bird'
Candy Land = 'Wekrosopela'[PBR] (Cl)	ECnt ESty SWCr
canina (S)	Widely available
'Cantabrigiensis' (S) ♀H6	EWTr MAus NLar SPer
Canzonetta = 'Noa84497d' (F) **new**	LBrs
'Capitaine Basroger' (CeMo)	MAus
'Capitaine John Ingram' (CeMo)	MAus NLar
'Captain Christy'	see *R.* 'Climbing Captain Christy'
'Captain Scarlet' (ClMin)	ESty
'Cardinal de Richelieu' (G)	CBcs CBod CPou CSam CTri EPfP ESps IBoy LBrs LCro LRHS LSRN MAsh MAus MCot MRav MSwo NEgg NLar SCob SMad SPer SPoG
Carefree Days = 'Meirivouri' (Patio) ♀H6	EPfP ESps IBoy LBuc LRHS MAsh NPri NRHS SSea
Cariad = 'Auspanier'[PBR] (HM)	MAus
Caribbean Dawn = 'Korfeining'[PBR] (Patio)	MAsh
Caring for You ambig.	LSRN
Caritas = 'Meikolyma'[PBR] (HT)	EBee
'Carol' (F)	see *R.* 'Carol Amling'
§ 'Carol Amling' (F)	LSRN
Carol Ann = 'Peapost' (F)	LSRN
'Caroline Testout'	see *R.* 'Madame Caroline Testout'
Caroline Victoria = 'Harprior'[PBR] (HT)	LSRN
Carolyn Knight = 'Austurner' (S)	CRos LCro LOPS LRHS MAsh MAus NRHS
Carris = 'Harmanna'[PBR] (HT)	LBrs MAsh
§ Casino = 'Macca' (ClHT)	CTri ELon MRav SPer
'Castle Apricot'	see *R.* Lazy Days
'Castle Cream'	see *R.* Perfect Day
'Castle Fuchsia Pink'	see *R.* Bewitched = 'Poulbella'
'Castle Peach'	see *R.* Imagination = 'Pouldron'
'Castle Shrimp Pink'	see *R.* Fascination = 'Poulmax'
'Castle Yellow'	see *R.* Summer Gold
'Catherine Mermet' (T)	MAus
§ 'Cécile Brünner' (Poly) ♀H6	CKel CTri EBee ELan LRHS LSRN MAus MCot MMuc NLar SPer SSea
Cecily Gibson = 'Evebright' (F)	ESty
Celebration 2000 = 'Horcoffitup'[PBR] (S)	MAus
Celebration Time	see *R.* Cinco de Mayo
§ 'Céleste' (A) ♀H7	CTri EWTr GBin MAus NLar SEND SPer
'Célina' (CeMo)	GBin LSRN
'Céline Forestier' (N)	CPou EBee EWTr MAus NLar SEND SPer
§ 'Celsiana' (D) ♀H7	CPou CSam EWTr LSRN MAus NLar SPer

	Centenary = 'Koreledas'PBR (F)	MAsh SCoo
§	× ***centifolia*** (Ce)	CArn LRHS MAus SPer
§	- 'Bullata' (Ce)	MAus
§	- 'Cristata' (Ce) ♀H7	CBWd ELon LEdu LRHS MAus MMuc NLar SPer
§	- 'De Meaux' (Ce)	MAus NLar SPer
§	- 'Muscosa' (CeMo)	LEdu MAus
	- 'Parvifolia'	see *R.* 'Burgundiaca'
§	- 'Shailer's White Moss' (CeMo)	CBod MAus
	- 'Spong' (Ce)	MAus
§	- 'Unique' (Ce)	MAus NLar
§	- 'Unique Panachée' (Ce)	CPou MAus
	'Centifolia Variegata'	see *R.* × *centifolia* 'Unique Panachée'
	Centre Stage = 'Chewcreepy'PBR (S/GC) ♀H6	MAus
	'Cerise Bouquet' (S) ♀H7	MAus NLar SPer WKif
§	Champagne Moment = 'Korvanaber'PBR (F) ♀H6	CBcs CGro CRos CSBt CSam ECnt ELan ELon EPfP ESty LBrs LBuc LRHS LSRN MAsh MAus MGos MJak MRav MWat NPri NRHS SMad SPer SPoG SRGP SSea SWCr
	'Champneys Pink Cluster' (China hybrid)	MAus SCob
	Chandos Beauty = 'Harmisty'PBR (HT) ♀H6	CGro CKel CRos ECnt EPfP ESty LBrs LBuc LRHS LSRN MAsh MRav SSea SWCr
	'Chanelle' (F)	SDix SPer
	Chapeau de Napoléon	see *R.* × *centifolia* 'Cristata'
	Charles Austin = 'Ausles' (S)	MAus MRav MWat SPoG
	Charles Darwin = 'Auspeet'PBR (S)	EPfP LBuc LRHS MAus NEgg NRHS SCob SCoo SPer
	'Charles de Mills' (G) ♀H7	CBWd CBod CKel CSam CTri ECnt ELan EPfP ESps EWTr GBin GCra LCro LRHS LSRN MAus MCot MRav MSwo MWat NLar SKHP SMad SPer SWCr WHer
	Charles Rennie Mackintosh = 'Ausren' (S)	CSBt MAus NEgg
	Charlie's Rose = 'Tanellepa' (HT) ♀H6	ELan ESty LSRN
	Charlotte = 'Auspoly'PBR (S) ♀H6	CRos EBee ELan EPfP ESty LBuc LCro LOPS LRHS LSRN MAsh MAus MJak NEgg NRHS SCob SCoo SPer SWCr
	Charlotte Vieli = 'Diclooker' (F)	IDic
	Charmant = 'Korpeligo'PBR (Min)	MAsh
	Charmian = 'Ausmian' (S)	MAus
	Chartered = 'Diclingo' (F)	IDic
	Chartreuse de Parme = 'Delviola' (S)	CBod CPou ESty MRav NLar
	Chatsworth = 'Tanotax'PBR (Patio/F) ♀H6	MRav SPer
	Chaucer = 'Auscer' (S)	MAus
	Checkmate = 'Diclanky' (Cl)	IDic
§	Cheek to Cheek = 'Poulslas'PBR (Courtyard Series) (ClMin)	LRHS MAsh SWCr
	Cheerful Charlie = 'Cocquimmer'PBR (F)	LSRN MRav
	Cherie	see *R.* Songs of Praise
	Cherry Bonica = 'Meipeporia' (S) **new**	ESty
	Cherry Brandy '85 = 'Tanryrandy'PBR (HT)	CSBt
	Cheshire = 'Korkonopi'PBR (County Rose Series) (S)	MAus
	'Cheshire Life' (HT)	MAus
	'Chevy Chase' (Ra)	MCot
	Chianti = 'Auswine' (S)	MAus NLar
	Chicago Peace = 'Johnago' (HT)	SCob
	Child of Achievement	see *R.* Bella
	Chilterns = 'Kortemma'PBR (GC)	SWCr
	'Chinatown' (F/S) ♀H7	CTri ESps IBoy MAsh MAus MRav SCob SPer
	chinensis misapplied	see *R.* × *odorata*
	- 'Minima' *sensu stricto* hort.	see *R.* 'Rouletii'
	- 'Mutabilis'	see *R.* × *odorata* 'Mutabilis'
	- 'Old Blush'	see *R.* × *odorata* 'Pallida'
	- var. ***spontanea***	WPGP
	Chloe = 'Poulen003'PBR (Renaissance Series) (S)	CPou EBee ECnt EWTr LSRN SWCr
§	Chocolate Ripples = 'Simstripe' (Cl)	ESty
	Chris = 'Kirsan'PBR (ClHT)	CGro CSam ESty LBrs LSRN MAus SWCr
	Christopher = 'Cocopher' (HT)	LSRN
	Christopher Marlowe = 'Ausjump'PBR (S)	MAus SCoo
§	'Chromatella' (N)	MAus
	'Chuckles' (F) **new**	ESty
	Cider Cup = 'Dicladida' (Min/Patio)	IBoy IDic MAus
§	Cinco de Mayo = 'Wekcobeju'PBR (F)	CKel LRHS MAsh MRav SWCr
	'Cinderella' (Min)	CSBt EWTr NLar
	'Cinderella' (Ra)	MAsh
	Cinderella = 'Korfobalt' (ClS)	CPou EBee EUJe SWCr
	City Lights = 'Poulgan'PBR (Patio)	CSBt
	City Livery = 'Harhero 2000' (F)	EPfP MAsh
	City of Carlsbad	see *R.* Hanky Panky
	'City of Leeds' (F)	SPer
	City of London = 'Harukfore' (F)	CSBt SPer
	City of York = 'Direktör Benschop' (ClHT)	MCot
	Clair Matin = 'Meimont' (ClS)	CPou EWTr MAus
	Claire Austin = 'Ausprior'PBR (S)	CRos EPfP ESty LBuc LCro LRHS LSRN MAus NLar NRHS SCob SCoo SWCr
	'Claire Jacquier' (N)	MAus MMuc SPer SWCr
	Claire Marshall = 'Harunite'PBR (F)	ESty
	Claire Rose = 'Auslight'PBR (S)	LSRN MAus
	'Clarence House' (Cl)	ELan LRHS
	Claret = 'Frykristal'PBR (HT) ♀H6	ECnt ESty LRHS MRav SPoG SWCr
	Claude Monet = 'Jacdesa' (HT)	ESty
	'Clementina Carbonieri' (T)	CPou NLar
	Cleo = 'Beebop' (HT)	LSRN
	Cleopatra = 'Korverpea'PBR (HT)	MAsh SWCr
	'Cliff Richard' (F)	ESty LSRN
	'Climbing Alec's Red' (ClHT)	ELon SPer

	'Climbing Arthur Bell' (ClF)	CGro CSBt CTri ESty IBoy MAsh MSwo NPri SCob SPer SPoG SSea SWCr
	'Climbing Ballerina' (Ra)	CSBt
§	Climbing Baronne Edmond de Rothschild = 'Meigrisosar' (ClHT)	CSBt
	'Climbing Blue Moon' (ClHT)	ELan SWCr
§	'Climbing Captain Christy' (ClHT)	MAus
	'Climbing Cécile Brünner' (ClPoly) 𝕐^{H6}	CSBt CTri ECnt EPfP LSRN MAus MRav NLar SCob SEND SPer SSea SWCr
	'Climbing Christine' (ClHT)	MAus
	'Climbing Château de Clos-Vougeot' (ClHT)	MAus
§	'Climbing Columbia' (ClHT)	EShb SPer
	'Climbing Crimson Glory' (ClHT)	CPou MAus
§	'Climbing Devoniensis' (ClT)	CPou
	'Climbing Ena Harkness' (ClHT)	CRos CTri EBee MAus MRav SEND SPer SPoG SWCr
	'Climbing Étoile de Hollande' (ClHT) 𝕐^{H6}	CKel CSBt CTri EPfP IBoy LBuc LCro MAus MJak MRav NPri SMad SPer SSea SWCr WBor
	Climbing Fragrant Cloud = 'Colfragrasar' (ClHT)	CBcs ELan
	'Climbing Home Sweet Home' (ClHT)	LSRN
	'Climbing Iceberg' (ClF) 𝕐^{H7}	CGro CRos CSBt CTri EBee ELan EPfP ESps ESty EUJe IArd LBrs LCro LEdu LSRN MAsh MAus MCot MJak MRav MSwo NEgg NLar NPri SCob SPer SPoG SSea SWCr
	'Climbing Jazz'	see *R.* That's Jazz
§	'Climbing Lady Hillingdon' (ClT) 𝕐^{H4}	CKel ELan EPfP EShb ESps EUJe LBuc LRHS LSRN MAus MRav NEgg NLar SPer SWCr WBor
	'Climbing Lady Sylvia' (ClHT)	CKel CSBt EBee EPfP LRHS LSRN MAus NRHS SPer
	'Climbing Little White Pet'	see *R.* 'Félicité Perpétue'
	'Climbing Madame Abel Chatenay' (ClHT)	MAus
	'Climbing Madame Butterfly' (ClHT) 𝕐^{H6}	MAus
	'Climbing Madame Caroline Testout' (ClHT)	CPou CTri EBee EPfP MAus MRav SPer
§	'Climbing Madame Edouard Herriot' (ClHT)	MAus
	'Climbing Masquerade' (ClF)	CPou CTri MAus MRav NEgg SCob SPer SSea SWCr
	'Climbing Mrs Herbert Stevens' (ClHT)	EBee EPfP LRHS MAsh MAus MRav SEND SPer SWCr
	'Climbing Mrs Sam McGredy' (ClHT)	CSBt MAus NLar
	'Climbing Niphetos' (ClT)	MAus
	'Climbing Ophelia' (ClHT)	EBee MAus SPer
	Climbing Orange Sunblaze = 'Meiji Katarsar'^{PBR} (ClMin)	SPer
§	'Climbing Paul Lédé' (ClT)	CBod EBee EWTr LRHS MAus
	'Climbing Peace' (ClHT)	SPer
§	'Climbing Pompon de Paris' (ClMinCh)	CTri MAus MNrw MRav SEND SPer
	'Climbing Ruby Wedding' (ClHT)	LSRN
	'Climbing Shot Silk' (ClHT) 𝕐^{H6}	CKel CSam SPer
§	'Climbing Souvenir de la Malmaison' (ClBb)	CPou MAus SPer
	'Climbing White Cloud'	see *R.* White Cloud = 'Korstacha'
	'Cloth of Gold'	see *R.* 'Chromatella'
	Coco = 'Korferse' (F)	LSRN
	'Coconut Ice' (HT)	SCob
	Colchester Beauty = 'Cansend' (F)	ECnt
§	'Colonel Fabvier' (Ch)	MAus NLar
	colonial white	see *R.* 'Sombreuil'
	'Columbia' (HT)	CPou
	'Columbian'	see *R.* 'Climbing Columbia'
	'Commandant Beaurepaire' (Bb)	CPou MAus
	common moss	see *R.* × *centifolia* 'Muscosa'
	'Compassion' (ClHT) 𝕐^{H6}	Widely available
*	'Compassionate' (F)	MRav
	'Complicata' (G)	CPou CSam CTri EPfP EWTr LRHS MAus MCot MRav NLar SCob SEND SKHP SMad SPer SWCr
	'Comte de Chambord' misapplied	see *R.* 'Madame Boll'
	Comte de Champagne = 'Ausufo'^{PBR} (S)	LRHS MAus NRHS SCoo
	'Comtesse Cécile de Chabrillant' (HP)	CPou MAus
	'Comtesse de Lacépède' misapplied	see *R.* 'Du Maître d'Ecole'
§	'Comtesse de Murinais' (DMo)	MAus
§	'Comtesse du Caÿla' (Ch)	MAus
	'Conditorum' (G)	LEdu
	Congratulations = 'Korlift' (HT)	CBcs CKel CSBt ECnt IArd IBoy LSRN MAus MGos MRav MWat SCob SPer SVic SWCr
§	'Conrad Ferdinand Meyer' (Ru)	SPer
	Conservation = 'Cocdimple' (Min/Patio)	MJak
	'Constance Spry' (ClS) 𝕐^{H6}	CTri EBee EPfP ESps EWTr LCro LOPS LRHS MAus MMuc MRav MSwo MWat NEgg NLar NRHS SCob SEND SPer
§	'Cooperi' (Ra)	CAbP CRHN CSam CWib EWTr MAus SPer SSea WPGP
	Cooper's Burmese	see *R.* 'Cooperi'
	Copper Lights = 'Simhigh' (HT) **new**	ESty
	'Coral Cluster' (Poly)	MAus
	'Coral Creeper' (ClHT)	CRHN
	Coral Gem = 'Simplan' (HT) **new**	ESty
	Coral Palace	see *R.* Imagination = 'Pouldron'
	Cordelia = 'Ausbottle'^{PBR} (S)	MAus
	'Cornelia' (HM) 𝕐^{H6}	CBcs CGro CRos CTri EBee EPfP EWTr IArd LRHS LSRN MAsh MAus MCot MRav NLar SCob SDix SMad SPer SRGP SWCr
	Coronation Street = 'Wekswetrup' (F)	LSRN
	Corvedale = 'Ausnetting'^{PBR} (S)	CAbP MAus
	Cosmopolitan = 'Simgrid' (HT) **new**	ESty
	cottage maid	see *R.* × *centifolia* 'Unique Panachée'
	Cottage Maid = 'Poulspan' (S)	MAus
	Cottage Rose = 'Ausglisten'^{PBR} (S)	LSRN MAus MRav MWat SPoG

	Countess Celeste	see *R.* Imagination = 'Pouldron'
	County of Yorkshire = 'Korstarnow'PBR (GC) ♀H6	ELan ESty
	'Coupe d'Hébé' (Bb)	MAus
	Courage = 'Poulduf'PBR (HT)	ECnt
	Courvoisier = 'Macsee' (F)	CSBt
	'Cramoisi Picotée' (G)	MAus
	'Cramoisi Supérieur' (Ch)	MAus
	Crazy for You = 'Wekroalt'PBR (F) ♀H6	ESty LBrs LBuc LRHS LSRN MAsh SWCr
	Cream Abundance = 'Harflax'PBR (Abundance Series) (F)	SSea SWCr
	Crème de la Crème = 'Gancre'PBR (ClHT)	CKel CRos CSBt ECnt ELon ESty LRHS MAus MRav SPer SPoG SRGP SSea SWCr
	'Crépuscule' (N)	EWTr MAus NLar
	Cressida = 'Auscress' (S)	MAus
	crested moss	see *R.* × *centifolia* 'Cristata'
	Cricri = 'Meicri' (Min)	MAus
	Crimson Cascade = 'Fryclimbdown'PBR (ClHT) ♀H6	ESty EUJe LBuc LRHS MRav MSwo SPer SPoG SSea
	crimson damask	see *R. gallica* var. *officinalis*
	'Crimson Descant' (ClHT)	ECnt
	'Crimson Shower' (Ra)	CKel CRos CTri ELan EWTr LBuc LRHS MAus MBNS MMuc MRav MSwo NEgg NLar NRHS SEND SPer WHer
	Crimson Sweet Dream = 'Frynogo' (Patio)	CGro ECnt ESty SWCr
	'Cristata'	see *R.* × *centifolia* 'Cristata'
	Crocus Rose = 'Ausquest'PBR (S) ♀H6	CKel CRos EPfP LCro LRHS MAus MRav MWat NEgg NLar NRHS SCob SPer SWCr
	Crown Princess Margareta = 'Auswinter'PBR (S)	CRos ECnt ELan EPfP EShb ESty LBuc LRHS MAsh MAus NEgg NLar NRHS SCob SCoo SPer SWCr
	cuisse de nymphe	see *R.* 'Great Maiden's Blush'
	'Cupid' (ClHT)	EWTr MAus SPer
I	'Cutie' (Patio)	ESty
	cymosa 'Rebecca Rushforth' **new**	WPGP
	Dacapo = 'Poulcy012'PBR (Courtyard Series) (ClPatio)	ECnt
	'D'Aguesseau' (G)	MAus
	'Daily Mail'	see *R.* 'Climbing Madame Edouard Herriot'
	'Dainty Bess' (HT)	EBee MAus SSea SWCr
	× ***damascena*** var. ***bifera***	see *R.* × *damascena* var. *semperflorens*
§	- 'Professeur Émile Perrot' (D)	LEdu MAus WFar
§	- var. ***semperflorens*** (D) ♀H7	CPou EWTr MAus NLar SSea SWCr
	- 'Trigintipetala' misapplied	see *R.* × *damascena* 'Professeur Émile Perrot'
§	- 'Versicolor' (D)	MAus SPer SSea
	Dame Wendy = 'Canson' (F)	MAus
	'Danaë' (HM)	MAus
	Dancing Queen = 'Fryfeston' (ClHT) ♀H6	ECnt ESty EUJe LBuc LRHS LSRN MAsh MRav SPoG SWCr
	Daniel = 'Webwhite' (HT)	ESty
	Danny Boy = 'Dicxcon'PBR (Patio)	IDic LSRN
	'Danse du Feu' (ClF)	CBcs CKel CSBt CTri ELan ESps EUJe IBoy LRHS MAsh MAus MRav SCob SPer SWCr
	'Daphne' ambig.	LSRN
	Dapple Dawn = 'Ausapple' (S)	MAus
	Darcey Bussell = 'Ausdecorum'PBR (S) ♀H6	CGro CRos CSBt ECnt ELan EPfP ESty LBuc LCro LOPS LRHS LSRN MAus MGos NRHS SCob SPer SWCr
	'Darling Jenny' (HT)	LSRN
	David Whitfield = 'Gana'PBR (F)	LSRN
	davidii (S)	MAus
	David's Star = 'Hordadstar' (HT)	LSRN
	Dawn Chorus = 'Dicquasar'PBR (HT) ♀H6	CGro CSBt EPfP ESty IBoy MAsh MJak MRav SCob SPer SPoG SSea SWCr
	'Daybreak' (HM)	CTri MAus NLar
	'De Meaux'	see *R.* × *centifolia* 'De Meaux'
	'De Meaux, White'	see *R.* 'White de Meaux'
§	'De Resht' (DPo) ♀H7	CBod CKel CPou CTri ECnt EPfP EWTr LBuc LRHS MAsh MAus MCot MRav MWat NLar NPri SPer SWCr
	'Dear Daughter' (F)	ESty
	'Dearest' (F)	SCob SPer SWCr
	'Debbie Thomas' (HT)	LSRN
	Deb's Delight = 'Legsweet'PBR (F)	LSRN
	'Debutante' (Ra) ♀H7	CRHN EWTr LRHS MAus
	'Deep Secret' (HT)	CBcs CGro CKel CSBt CTri ECnt ELan ELon EPfP ESps ESty LBuc LRHS MAsh MJak MRav SCob SPer SRGP SSea SWCr
	'Deidre Hall' (HT)	LSRN
	'Delambre' (DPo)	MAus
	Dentelle de Malines = 'Lenfiro' (S)	CAbP MAus
	'Designer Sunset' (Patio)	MAsh
§	'Desprez à Fleur Jaune' (N)	IArd LRHS MAus MRav NEgg SPer
	'Devon Maid' (ClHT)	EBee
	'Devoniensis' (ClT)	see *R.* 'Climbing Devoniensis'
	Diamond Anniversary = 'Morsixty' (Min)	CRos LBuc LSRN
	'Diamond Celebration' (HT)	LSRN
	Diamond Days Forever = 'Fryjess'PBR (F)	ECnt LSRN
	Diamond Days = 'Hartribe' (HT)	ESty MWat
	Diamond Eyes = 'Wekwibypur' (Min) **new**	ECnt ESty
	'Diamond Jubilee' (HT)	CSBt SWCr
	Diamond = 'Korgazell'PBR (Patio) ♀H6	CGro EPfP LBrs LRHS LSRN NRHS SPoG SWCr
	'Diamond Wishes'	see *R.* Misty Hit
	Diana = 'Tananaid'PBR (HT)	LSRN
	Dick's Delight = 'Dicwhistle' (GC)	LSRN
	Dienie Stewart = 'Dicpraise' (F) **new**	IDic
	Dioressence = 'Deldiore' (F)	ESty
	Disco Queen = 'Tan08171' (Patio) **new**	ESty
	Dizzy Heights = 'Fryblissful'PBR (ClHT) ♀H6	LBrs MAus MRav SPer
	'Docteur Grill' (T)	MAus
	Doctor Jackson = 'Ausdoctor' (S)	MAus

'Doctor W. Van Fleet' (Ra/Cl)	MAus
Dolly = 'Poulvision' (F)	LSRN
'Don Charlton' (HT)	NEgg
'Doncasteri'	MAus
Donna = 'Pekcoupamaple' (HT)	LSRN
'Doreen' (HT)	LSRN
'Doris Tysterman' (HT)	CTri LBuc MAus SPer
Dorothy = 'Cocrocket'PBR (F)	LSRN MRav
'Dorothy Perkins' (Ra)	CBod CRHN CTri ESps LBuc LRHS MAsh MAus MRav NPer SCob SPer SRGP WBod WHer
'Dortmund' (S) ♀H7	MAus NLar SPer SWCr
Double Delight = 'Andeli' (HT)	ESty IBoy LSRN SPer SSea SWCr
Douglas = 'Cocfresco' (F)	LSRN
'Dream Catcher' (F)	ESty
Dream Lover = 'Peayetti'PBR (Patio)	ESty LBrs SWCr
'Dreaming Spires' (Cl)	CWld MSwo SPer
§ 'Du Maître d'Ecole' (G)	LRHS MAus WHer
Dublin Bay = 'Macdub' (ClF) ♀H6	CBod CGro CKel CSBt CSam CTri ECnt ELan ELon EPfP ESps EUJe IArd IBoy LRHS LSRN MAsh MCot MRav MSwo MWat NLar SPer SPoG SSea SWCr WBor
'Duc de Guiche' (G) ♀H7	ESps EWTr MAus MMuc NLar WHer
Duchess of Cornwall = 'Tan97157' (HT) ♀H6	CKel CSBt ELon ESty MRav SCob
'Duchess of Portland'	see *R.* 'Portlandica'
Duchess of York	see *R.* Sunseeker
'Duchesse d'Angoulême' (Ce × G) ♀H7	MAus
'Duchesse de Buccleugh' (G)	MAus MRav MWat
§ 'Duchesse de Montebello' (G) ♀H7	CPou CSam EWTr GBin LRHS MAus NLar SPer
'Duchesse de Verneuil' (CeMo)	MAus
'Duke of Edinburgh' (HP)	MAus
Duke of EdinburghPBR (Patio)	see *R.* The Gold Award Rose
'Duke of Wellington' (HP)	CPou
'Duke of Windsor' (HT)	SPer
'Dundee Rambler' (Ra)	MAus
'Dunwich Rose' (SpH)	EPfP MAus NLar SCob SKHP SPer WCot
§ 'Duplex' (S)	MAus
'Dupontii' (S) ♀H6	EWTr MAus NLar SKHP SPer
'Dusky Maiden' (F)	MAus SWCr
'Dutch Gold' (HT)	MAus SPer
Dwarf Fairy = 'Korweenu' (Min) **new**	MAsh
'E.H. Morse'	see *R.* 'Ernest H. Morse'
'Easlea's Golden Rambler' (Ra) ♀H6	ESty LRHS MAus MRav NEgg NLar
East Park = 'Harjope'PBR (HT)	ECnt ESty
'Easter Morning' (Min)	SPer
§ Easy Does It = 'Harpageant'PBR (F) ♀H6	CKel ECnt ESty LBrs MAsh MRav SWCr
Easy Going = 'Harflow'PBR (F) ♀H6	IArd LBuc MAsh SWCr
§ Ebb Tide = 'Weksmopur'PBR (F)	CSBt ECnt ESty
ecae (S)	MAus
'Éclair' (HP)	WBor
'Eddie's Crimson' (*moyesii* hybrid)	LSRN
'Eddie's Jewel' (*moyesii* hybrid)	LSRN MAus
Eden Rose '88 = 'Meiviolin' (ClHT)	CPou EBee SPer SWCr
'Edward Hyams' (*persica* hybrid)	MAus
Edward's Rose = 'Smi73/7/97' (F)	ESty LSRN MRav
eglanteria	see *R. rubiginosa*
Eglantyne = 'Ausmak'PBR (S)	CKel CRos CSBt ELan ELon EPfP LCro LOPS LRHS MAus MRav MWat NRHS SCob SPer SSea SWCr
Elaine Page = 'Poulht008'PBR (HT)	LBrs MAsh SWCr
'Eleanor' (Patio)	LSRN
Eleanor = 'Poulberin'PBR (S)	CBod CPou EBee ECnt LSRN
§ ***elegantula*** 'Persetosa' (S)	LRHS MAus NLar SKHP SPer
§ Elina = 'Dicjana' (HT) ♀H6	ECnt MAus MJak MRav SPer SWCr
'Elizabeth Harkness' (HT)	MAus SPer
Elizabeth of Glamis = 'Macel' (F)	CTri SPer
Elizabeth Stuart = 'Maselstu' (Generosa Series) (S)	LSRN
Elle = 'Meibderos'PBR (HT)	ESty LSRN
Ellen = 'Auscup' (S)	LSRN MAus
'Ellen Willmott' (HT)	EBee MAus MCot SPer
Emilia Maria	see *R.* La Rose de Molinard
Emily = 'Ausburton' (S)	LSRN
'Emily Gray' (Ra)	CPou LBuc LRHS LSRN MAsh MAus MRav NPri SCob SPer WHer
Emily Victoria = 'Boshipeacon' (F)	LSRN
'Emma Wright' (HT)	MAus
'Empereur du Maroc' (HP)	EBee IBoy MAus
'Ena Harkness' (HT)	CKel CTri ELan ESps LBuc LRHS NRHS SRGP
Enchantress = 'Tan97281'PBR (HT)	ESty
§ 'Enfant de France' (HP)	LSRN
England's Rose = 'Auslounge'PBR (S)	CGro MAus
§ England's Rose = 'Ausrace' (S)	LRHS
English Elegance = 'Ausleaf' (S)	MAus
English Garden = 'Ausbuff' (S)	CTri EPfP LSRN MAus SPer
'English Miss' (F)	CKel CPou EBee ECnt ELon ESps ESty EWTr IBoy LRHS MAsh MAus MJak MRav SPer SPoG SWCr
English Sonnet	see *R.* Samaritan
'Eos' (*moyesii* hybrid)	MAus
'Erfurt' (HM)	EBee MAus SPer
§ 'Ernest H. Morse' (HT)	CSBt CTri IBoy MRav SPer
Escapade = 'Harpade' (F) ♀H6	MAus
Especially for You = 'Fryworthy'PBR (HT) ♀H6	CKel CSBt ESps ESty LSRN SCob SCoo SSea SWCr
Essex = 'Poulnoz'PBR (GC)	CKel MRav SCob SPer SPoG
§ 'Estrellita de Oro' (Min)	SPer
'Etain' (Ra)	ECnt
§ 'Étendard' (ClHT)	CGro NLar SPer SPoG SWCr
Eternal Flame = 'Korassenet'PBR (F)	LBuc MAsh
Eternally Yours = 'Macspeego'PBR (HT)	ESty
Eternity = 'Twoetern' (HT)	MAsh

'Ethel' (Ra)	CPou EBee LSRN
'Étoile de Hollande' (HT)	EBee ELan ELon ESps EUJe LBuc LRHS MAsh MBNS MCot MJak NEgg NLar SCob
'Eugénie Guinoisseau' (Mo)	CPou
'Euphrosyne' (Ra)	MAus
'Evangeline' (Ra)	MAus
Evelyn = 'Aussaucer'PBR (S)	CBod CKel CRos CSBt EBee EPfP ESps ESty EWTr LRHS LSRN MAus MRav MWat NEgg NLar SLon SPer
§ Evelyn Fison = 'Macev' (F)	CSBt CTri ELan IBoy LSRN MAus SPer
'Evelyn May' (HT)	LRHS
'Excelsa' (Ra)	CSBt CSam CTri EPfP ESps IArd IBoy LBuc MAsh MRav NWea SCob SPoG WBor
Eye Paint = 'Maceye' (F)	MAus
Eyes for You = 'Pejbigeye' (F) ♀H6	CBod CGro CKel CSBt ESty GBin SLon SPer SWCr
'F.E. Lester'	see *R.* 'Francis E. Lester'
§ 'F.J. Grootendorst' (Ru)	CBod IBoy NEgg SPer WHer
Fab at 50 = 'Woraunt' (F)	LSRN
Fabulous at 50 = 'Rawfabsal' (F)	LSRN
Fabulous at 70	LSRN
Fabulous at 80 = 'Rawcox' (F)	LSRN
'Fabvier'	see *R.* 'Colonel Fabvier'
Fair Bianca = 'Ausca' (S)	MAus
Fair Eva = 'Seaeva' (Ra/GC) **new**	ESty
'Fairy Rose'	see *R.* 'The Fairy'
Faithful Friend = 'Beachallenge' (S)	LSRN
Falstaff = 'Ausverse'PBR (S)	CRos CSBt EPfP IBoy LCro LOPS LRHS LSRN MAsh MAus MBNS MJak MMuc MRav MSwo NEgg NRHS SCob SMad SPer SPoG SSea SWCr
'Fantin-Latour' (Ce) ♀H7	CTri ECnt ELan EWTr GCra IBoy LEdu LRHS MAus MCot MMuc MRav MWat NEgg NLar SEND SMad SPer
farreri* f. *persetosa	see *R. elegantula* 'Persetosa'
Fascination = 'Jacoyel' (Castle Series) (HT)	SCoo
§ Fascination = 'Poulmax'PBR (F) ♀H6	CBod ELon IBoy MAsh MRav SPer SWCr
Father's Favourite = 'Gandoug'PBR (F)	LSRN
fedtschenkoana misapplied	MAus SPer
Fée des Neiges	see *R.* Iceberg
'Felicia' (HM) ♀H6	CGro CKel CSBt CSam CTri EBee ECnt ELan EWTr LRHS MAsh MAus MCot MMuc MRav MSwo MWat NLar NRHS SEND SKHP SPer SSea SWCr WKif
'Félicité Parmentier' (A × D) ♀H7	CRos EPfP LRHS MAus MRav MWat NLar SPer SWCr
§ 'Félicité Perpétue' (Ra) ♀H7	CBcs CBod CRos CTri ELan EPfP EWTr IBoy LPot LRHS MAus MMuc MRav MSwo NEgg NLar SEND SPer SSea SWCr
'Fellemberg' (ClCh)	EBee MAus
Fellowship = 'Harwelcome'PBR (F) ♀H6	MAus MRav SCob SCoo SSea SWCr
'Ferdinand Pichard' (Bb) ♀H7	CKel CPou CRos CSBt CSam CTri EBee ECnt ELon EPfP ESps ESty EWTr LCro LOPS LRHS MAsh MAus MCot MRav NEgg NLar NPri SKHP SPer SPoG SSea SWCr WFar WKif
Ferdy = 'Keitoli'PBR (GC)	SPer
ferruginea	see *R. glauca* Pourr.
Festival = 'Kordialo'PBR (Patio)	IBoy MRav SPer
Festive Jewel = 'Beacost' (S)	LRHS
Fighting Temeraire = 'Austrava'PBR (S)	CRos EBee EPfP LBuc LRHS MAus NRHS SSea
§ ***filipes*** 'Kiftsgate' (Ra) ♀H6	Widely available
filipes* × *glauca	MAus
§ 'Fimbriata' (Ru)	CPou LEdu MAus NLar SPer
Financial Times Centenary = 'Ausfin' (S)	MAus
Fiona = 'Meibeluxen' (S/GC)	LSRN MSwo
Firestar	see *R.* Easy Does It
First Great Western = 'Oracharpam'PBR (HT)	ESty
'Fisher and Holmes' (HP)	MAus
Fisherman's Friend = 'Auschild' (S)	MAus
Flamingo = 'Simref' (F)	ESty SWCr
Flash Gordon = 'Simgord' (F) **new**	ESty
Flashdance = 'Poulyc004' (ClMin)	ECnt
Flirt = 'Korkopapp'PBR (F)	MAsh
'Flora' (HT)	MAus
'Florence Mary Morse' (S)	SDix
Flower Carpet Amber = 'Noa97400a'PBR (GC) ♀H6	CGro CRos CSBt ELan EUJe IBoy LBrs LBuc LRHS MAsh NPri NRHS SCoo SPoG SWCr
'Flower Carpet Coral'PBR (GC) ♀H6	CRos CSBt IBoy LBuc LRHS MAsh NPri NRHS SCoo SPer SWCr
Flower Carpet Gold = 'Noalesa'PBR (GC)	CBod CGro CRos ECnt IBoy LBuc LRHS MAsh NPri NRHS SPoG
Flower Carpet Pink	see *R.* Pink Flower Carpet
Flower Carpet Red Velvet = 'Noare'PBR (GC/S) ♀H6	CBod CGro CRos ELan EPfP IBoy LBuc LCro LOPS LRHS MAsh NPri NRHS SCoo SPer SSea
Flower Carpet Ruby (GC)	CRos EUJe LBuc LRHS MAsh NPri NRHS SCoo SPoG
Flower Carpet Scarlet = 'Noa83100b'PBR (GC) ♀H6	CRos LBuc LRHS MAsh NRHS
Flower Carpet Sunset = 'Deseo' (S)	CBod CGro CRos LBrs LRHS MAsh NPri SCoo SWCr
§ Flower Carpet Sunshine = 'Noason'PBR (GC) ♀H6	CRos EBee LCro LOPS LRHS MAsh NPri NRHS SCoo SPer SSea
Flower Carpet White = 'Noaschnee'PBR (GC) ♀H6	CBod CGro CRos CTri ECnt IBoy LBrs LCro LOPS LRHS MAsh MAus NPri NRHS SCoo SMad SPer SPoG SSea SWCr
Flower Power = 'Frycassia'PBR (Patio) ♀H6	CKel CSBt ECnt ELon ESty IBoy LRHS MAsh MAus MRav NPri SPoG SWCr
Flower Power Gold = 'Fryneon' (Patio)	ECnt ESty LRHS MAsh NPri NRHS SPoG SWCr
§ ***foetida*** (S)	MAus SPer
§ - 'Bicolor' (S)	MAus NLar SPer
§ - 'Persiana' (S)	MAus
Fond Memories = 'Kirfelix'PBR (Patio)	ESty LSRN SWCr
For You With Love = 'Fryjangle' (Patio)	LSRN
For Your Eyes Only = 'Cheweyesup' (S)	CGro CKel CPou CRos CSBt ECnt ESty GBin LBrs LBuc LCro LRHS MAsh NPri NRHS SCoo SPoG SWCr
Forget Me Not = 'Coccharm'PBR (HT)	ESty

forrestiana (S)	LRHS MAus
Fortune's double yellow	see *R.* × *odorata* 'Pseudindica'
'Fountain' (HT)	MAus
Foxy Lady = 'Simmem' (HT) **new**	ESty
Fragrant Cloud = 'Tanellis' (HT)	CBcs CGro CRos CTri ELan EPfP IBoy LBuc LRHS MAsh MAus MGos MRav SPer SPoG SWCr
'Fragrant Delight' (F) ♀H6	CKel CSBt ELan ELon ESps MAus MJak MRav SCob SPer
Fragrant Dream = 'Dicodour' (HT)	ESty IBoy MRav SSea
Fragrant Memories = 'Korpastato'PBR (HT)	CSBt SCoo SKHP
'Francesca' (HM)	EBee EWTr LRHS LSRN MAus SPer
Francine Austin = 'Ausram' (S/GC)	MAus NEgg SPer
§ 'Francis E. Lester' (HM/Ra) ♀H6	CBWd CRHN CSam EBee ELan EPfP EWTr LCro LRHS MAus MCot MMuc NLar NRHS SEND SPer SRGP SSea SWCr
× ***francofurtana*** misapplied	see *R.* 'Impératrice Joséphine'
- 'Empress Josephine'	see *R.* 'Impératrice Joséphine'
'François Juranville' (Ra) ♀H6	CHll CPou CRHN EPfP GBin IBoy LRHS MAus MMuc MRav NLar SEND SLon SPer WFar WHer WKif
§ 'Frau Karl Druschki' (HP)	MAus
'Fred Loads' (F) ♀H7	MAus
Freddie Mercury = 'Batmercury' (HT)	ESty LSRN NEgg
Free Spirit = 'Fryjeru'PBR (F) ♀H6	ECnt
Freedom = 'Dicjem' (HT) ♀H6	CKel CTri ECnt MAus MJak MRav SCob SPer
Freedom = 'Tan97544' (HT) **new**	CKel
'Frensham' (F)	CBcs SSea
Friend for Life = 'Cocnanne'PBR (F) ♀H6	LSRN MRav
Friends Forever = 'Korapriber' (F) ♀H6	EPfP LBrs MAsh SWCr
'Fritz Nobis' (S) ♀H7	CPou MAus NLar SPer
Frothy = 'Macfrothy'PBR (Patio)	ECnt ESty
'Fru Dagmar Hastrup' (Ru) ♀H7	CBcs CBod CDul CKel CSBt CTri EBee ECnt ELan EPfP ESps EWTr IBoy LBuc LRHS MAus MSwo NEgg NLar NWea SCob SEND SMad SPer SWCr
'Frühlingsgold' (SpH) ♀H7	CBcs ELan ESps LRHS MAus NLar NWea SPer
'Frühlingsmorgen' (SpH) ♀H7	EWTr MAus SMad SPer
'Fryvogue' (F) **new**	ECnt ESty
§ ***gallica*** var. ***officinalis*** (G) ♀H7	CBod CRos CTri EPfP GPoy LEdu LRHS MAsh MAus MHer MNHC MRav NLar SKHP SPer SRms SSea SWCr WHer
§ - 'Versicolor' (G) ♀H7	CArn CBod CGro CKel CSBt CTri ECnt ELan EPfP EWTr GPoy IBoy LEdu LRHS LSRN MAsh MAus MCot MHer MNHC MRav NLar NRHS NSti SPer SSea SWCr WBor WKif
Galway Bay = 'Macba' (ClHT)	CPou IBoy LBrs LBuc LRHS MAsh SPer SWCr
Garden of Roses	see *R.* Joie de Vivre
'Gardeners Glory'PBR (ClHT) ♀H6	ECnt ESty EUJe LBrs LRHS MRav NPri SPoG SWCr
'Gardenia' (Ra)	EBee LRHS MAus MMuc MSwo NLar SPer WBod
'Garnette Carol'	see *R.* 'Carol Amling'
'Garnette Pink'	see *R.* 'Carol Amling'
'Gaujard'	see *R.* Rose Gaujard
'Gelbe Dagmar Hastrup'	see *R.* Yellow Dagmar Hastrup
'Général Jacqueminot' (HP)	MAus
'Général Kléber' (CeMo) ♀H7	MAus
§ 'Général Schablikine' (T)	EWTr MAus NLar
Genesis = 'Fryjuicy'PBR (Patio)	CGro ECnt LBrs MRav SWCr
gentiliana misapplied	see *R.* 'Polyantha Grandiflora'
Gentle Hermione = 'Ausrumba'PBR (S)	CRos ELan EPfP IBoy LBuc LRHS MAus NLar NRHS SCob SPer
Gentle Touch = 'Diclulu' (Min/Patio)	CKel CSBt ESps MRav SPer
Geoff Hamilton = 'Ausham'PBR (S)	EPfP IBoy LBuc LRHS LSRN MAus MBNS NEgg NRHS SCob SCoo SPer SSea
'Geoffrey Smith' (Cl)	LSRN NDal
'Georg Arends' (HP)	MAus
George Best = 'Dichimanher'PBR (Patio) ♀H6	ESty IDic LSRN
'George Dickson' (HT)	MAus
'Georges Vibert' (G)	MAus
'Geranium' (*moyesii* hybrid) ♀H7	CBcs CBod CDul CKel CTri EBee ELan EPfP ESps IArd IBoy LRHS MAus MRav MWat NLar SCob SPer SWCr WKif
Gerbe d'Or	see *R.* Casino
'Gerbe Rose' (Ra)	MAus WHer
Gertrude Jekyll = 'Ausbord'PBR (S) ♀H6	Widely available
'Ghislaine de Féligonde' (Ra/S) ♀H6	CKel CPou CSam EBee EPfP ESty EWTr LBuc LCro LRHS MAsh MAus MCot NLar SEND SPer SWCr WBor
Ghita	see *R.* Millie
GiardinaPBR (Cl)	see *R.* L'Alhambra
gigantea	WPGP
gigantea × ***longicuspis***	WPGP
Ginger Syllabub = 'Harjolina'PBR (ClHT)	CKel CPou ECnt ELon ESty MRav SPer SPoG SRGP
Gipsy Boy	see *R.* 'Zigeunerknabe'
Glad Tidings = 'Tantide' (F)	IBoy MRav SPer SWCr
Glamis Castle = 'Auslevel'PBR (S)	CBcs CTri EBee EPfP IBoy LCro LOPS LRHS MAus NEgg NRHS SCob SCoo SPer SWCr
glauca ambig.	ESps EWTr GCra GMcL MHer MSwo MWat SCob WBod
§ ***glauca*** Pourr. (S) ♀H7	CBWd CDul CMea CSBt CTri EBee ECnt ELan EPfP GBin LCro LEdu LHop LRHS MAus MMuc MRav NEgg NLar NWea SEND SGol SKHP SPer SPoG SSea SWCr WCot WHed WMoo
'Glenfiddich' (F)	CSBt CTri ESps LSRN MAus MRav SPer
'Glenn Dale' (Cl)	CPou
Glenshane = 'Dicvood' (GC/S)	MRav
Global Beauty = 'Tan 94448' (HT)	CBod ECnt ELon MRav SWCr
'Gloire de Dijon' (ClT)	CBod CGro CKel CSBt CTri EBee ECnt ELan EPfP IBoy LCro LRHS LSRN MAus MCot MRav MWat NEgg NLar SCob SPer SRGP SSea
'Gloire de Ducher' (HP)	MAus
'Gloire de France' (G) ♀H7	MAus MRav WHer
'Gloire de Guilan' (D)	MAus

'Gloire des Mousseuses' (CeMo)	CPou LRHS MAus
'Gloire du Midi' (Poly)	MAus
'Gloire Lyonnaise' (HP)	EBee MMuc
'Gloria Mundi' (Poly)	NEgg
Gloriana = 'Chewpope'^{PBR} (ClMin)	CGro CKel ECnt ESty EUJe MAsh MAus MRav MWat SCoo SKHP SPer SPoG SSea SWCr
'Glory of Edzell' (SpH)	MAus
'Glory of Seale' (S)	SSea
Glowing Amber = 'Manglow' (Min)	ESty
Gold Charm = 'Chewalbygold' (Cl)	ESty MAsh
'Golden Anniversary' (Patio)	ESps IBoy SSea
'Golden Autumn' (HT)	LSRN
Golden Beauty = 'Clebeau' (Min)	CKel
Golden Beauty = 'Korberbeni'^{PBR} (F) ♀^{H6}	CKel CPou EBee ESty MAsh SWCr
Golden Beryl = 'Manberyl' (Min)	LSRN
Golden Celebration = 'Ausgold'^{PBR} (S) ♀^{H6}	CBod CKel CRos CSBt CTri EBee ECnt EPfP ESps ESty IBoy LCro LOPS LRHS LSRN MAsh MAus MMuc MRav MSwo MWat NLar NRHS SCob SLon SMad SPer SPoG SSea SWCr
'Golden Chersonese' (S)	MAus
'Golden Dawn' (HT)	MAsh
Golden Eureka = 'Meikanaro'^{PBR} (F)	ESty
Golden Future = 'Horanymoll'^{PBR} (ClHT) ♀^{H6}	MAus
Golden Gate = 'Korgolgat'^{PBR} (ClHT) ♀^{H6}	ECnt EPfP LRHS MAsh MAus NRHS SSea
Golden Jewel = 'Tanledolg'^{PBR} (F/Patio)	ESty
Golden Jubilee = 'Cocagold' (HT)	MRav
Golden Memories = 'Korholesea'^{PBR} (F) ♀^{H6}	CSBt ESps LBuc MAsh MGos MJak MRav NPri SCoo SPer SWCr
Golden Moment = 'Smi-99-2-04' (HT)	ESty MRav
Golden Parfum de Provence = 'Meifazedal' (HT)	ESty
'Golden Rambler'	see *R.* 'Alister Stella Gray'
'Golden Showers' (Cl)	CBcs CBod CGro CKel CSBt CTri EBee ELan EPfP ESps EUJe IBoy LCro LRHS LSRN MAsh MAus MJak MMuc MRav MWat NEgg NLar NPri SPer SPoG SSea SWCr WBor
§ Golden Smiles = 'Frykeyno'^{PBR} (F) ♀^{H6}	CKel ECnt ESty LBrs MAsh SWCr
Golden Trust = 'Hardish'^{PBR} (Patio)	CBod MWat
Golden Wedding Anniversary (F)	LSRN
Golden Wedding = 'Arokris'^{PBR} (F)	Widely available
'Golden Wedding Celebration' (F)	LSRN
'Golden Wings' (S)	CPou CTri ELan EPfP GBin IBoy LRHS MAus MRav MSwo NLar SKHP SPer SWCr
'Goldfinch' (Ra)	ELan EPfP ESps EWTr LRHS MAsh MAus MRav NEgg NLar NRHS SEND SPer SPoG WFar
Goldstar = 'Candide' (HT)	ECnt
Good as Gold = 'Chewsunbeam'^{PBR} (ClMin)	CSBt ECnt ESty SPer SWCr
Good Life = 'Cococircus'^{PBR} (HT)	SCoo SPer
Gordon Snell = 'Dicwriter' (F)	IDic
'Grace Abounding' (F)	LSRN
Grace = 'Auskeppy'^{PBR} (S) ♀^{H6}	CRos CSBt EBee EPfP EShb ESty LBuc LRHS LSRN MAsh MAus NEgg NLar NRHS SCob SMad SPer SSea SWCr
'Graciously Pink' (Min)	LBrs MAsh SPoG
Graham Thomas = 'Ausmas' (S) ♀^{H6}	Widely available
Grande Amore = 'Korcoluma'^{PBR} (HT) ♀^{H6}	CSBt LSRN
'Grandma' (F)	LSRN
'Grandpa Dickson' (HT)	IBoy MAsh MAus SPer
Granny's Favourite (Patio/F)	LSRN
Great Expectations = 'Lanican' (HT)	CBcs
Great Expectations = 'Mackalves'^{PBR} (F)	EPfP ESps IArd MRav SCoo SPer
§ 'Great Maiden's Blush' (A) ♀^{H7}	MRav NLar
'Great News' (F)	MAus
Greenall's Glory = 'Kirmac' (F/Patio)	CKel MAus MRav
Greetings = 'Jacdreco'^{PBR} (F)	ESps LBuc MAsh
'Grootendorst'	see *R.* 'F.J. Grootendorst'
Grouse 2000 = 'Korteilhab' (GC) ♀^{H6}	MAus
Grouse = 'Korimro' (S/GC)	MAus NLar SEND SPer
'Gruss an Aachen' (Poly) ♀^{H6}	EPfP MAus MJak NLar SPer
'Gruss an Teplitz' (China hybrid)	MAus NLar SPer
'Guinée' (ClHT)	CKel CSBt CTri ELan EPfP ESps EWTr MAus MRav MSwo NLar SPer SRGP SSea WCot
'Gustav Grünerwald' (HT)	MAus
Guy Savoy = 'Delstrimen'^{PBR} (F)	ESty MRav
Guy's Gold = 'Harmatch'^{PBR} (HT)	LRHS MAsh
Gwent = 'Poulurt'^{PBR} (GC)	CSBt ELan LSRN SCob SEND SPer SSea
Gypsy Boy	see *R.* 'Zigeunerknabe'
'Hakuun' (F/Patio)	MAus
Hampshire = 'Korhamp'^{PBR} (GC)	MAus
Hand in Hand = 'Haraztec'^{PBR} (Patio/Min)	LBrs
Händel = 'Macha' (ClHT)	CBcs CBod CGro CKel CSBt CTri CWld ELan EPfP ESps IBoy LBuc MAsh MRav NEgg NLar NPri SPer SPlb SSea SWCr
§ Hanky Panky = 'Wektorcent'^{PBR} (F)	CGro ESty LBrs MAsh MRav SCoo SWCr
Hannah Gordon = 'Korweiso' (F)	MAsh SPer SWCr
'Hansa' (Ru)	CBod LBuc MAus SPer SWCr

Happy 70th Birthday = 'Rawday' (F)	LSRN
Happy Anniversary ambig.	EPfP SSea
Happy Anniversary = 'Bedfranc'PBR (F)	CBod ESps LSRN MWat NPri SWCr
Happy Anniversary = 'Delpre' (F)	CTri LRHS MAsh MRav NRHS SPoG
'Happy Birthday' (Min/Patio)	ESps ESty IBoy LCro LSRN SSea SWCr
Happy Child = 'Auscomp'PBR (S)	MAus
Happy Golden Wedding	see *R.* Golden Smiles
Happy Retirement = 'Tantoras'PBR (F) ♀H6	CBcs CBod CGro EPfP ESty LBuc LSRN MAsh MRav NPri SCoo SPoG SSea SWCr
Happy Ruby Wedding = 'Frynoble'PBR (HT)	CBcs CBod LBrs MAsh
Happy Silver Wedding = 'Frysilva' (F) new	LBrs MAsh SWCr
Happy Times = 'Bedone'PBR (Patio/Min)	LBrs
§ × ***harisonii*** 'Harison's Yellow' (SpH)	MAus
§ - 'Lutea Maxima' (SpH)	MAus
§ - 'Williams' Double Yellow' (SpH)	EWTr MAus
Harlow Carr ambig.	CKel LRHS MWat SCob
Harlow Carr = 'Aushouse'PBR (S)	CGro CKel CRos EPfP IBoy LBuc LSRN MAus MRav NRHS SCob SCoo SPer SPoG
'Harry Edland' (F)	SMad SWCr
'Harry Wheatcroft' (HT)	IBoy MAus SPer
Harvest Fayre = 'Dicnorth'PBR (F)	SPer
Havana Hit = 'Poulpah032'PBR (Patio)	EPfP LBrs MAsh NPri
'Havering Rambler' (Ra)	ELon
'Hazel Le Rougetel' (Ru)	WFar
'Headleyensis' (S)	MAus SPer
Heart of Gold = 'Coctarlotte'PBR (HT) ♀H6	ECnt ESty MRav
Heathcliff = 'Ausnipper'PBR (S)	CRos CSBt EPfP ESty LBuc LRHS MAus
Heather Austin = 'Auscook'PBR (S)	MAus
Heavenly Rosalind = 'Ausmash'PBR (S)	MAus
§ 'Hebe's Lip' (D × RH)	MAus
'Helen Knight' (*ecae* hybrid) (S)	ESty MAsh MAus
Helen Robinson = 'Harlevel'PBR (HT)	ESty
helenae	CTri GBin GLog MAus NLar SPer WPGP
Helen's Trust = 'Taytrust' (HT)	LSRN
hemisphaerica (S)	MAus
§ 'Henri Martin' (CeMo) ♀	CTri IBoy LEdu LRHS MAus NEgg NLar SKHP SLon SPer
Henri Matisse = 'Delstrobla' (HT)	ESty MRav SPoG
'Henry Nevard' (HP)	MAus
§ 'Herbstfeuer' (RH)	CPou NLar
'Here's Sam' (HT)	LSRN
Heritage = 'Ausblush' (S)	CBod CGro CKel CRos CTri ELan EPfP LRHS MAus MJak MRav MWat NEgg NLar SCob SPer SPoG SSea
'Hermosa' (Ch)	MAus
Hero = 'Aushero' (S)	MAus
Hertfordshire = 'Kortenay'PBR (GC) ♀H6	ELan MAus MRav SCob SEND SPer
× ***hibernica***	MAus
'Hidcote Gold' (S)	MAus
§ 'Hidcote Yellow' (Cl)	LRHS SPer
High Hopes = 'Haryup'PBR (ClHT)	CGro EPfP EUJe IBoy LBuc MAsh MAus SPer SSea
'Highdownensis' (*moyesii* hybrid) (S)	ELan MAus
Highfield = 'Harcomp' (ClHT)	MAus
Hilda Murrell = 'Ausmurr' (S)	MAus
'Hillieri' (*moyesii* hybrid)	MAus
'Hippolyte' (G)	MAus
Hole-in-one = 'Horeagle' (F)	LSRN
holy rose	see *R.* × *richardii*
'Homère' (T)	MAus
Hommage à Barbara = 'Delchifrou'PBR (HT)	CBod EBee ESty MRav WKif
Honey Bunch = 'Cocglen'PBR (F)	CKel ELon MRav SPer SRGP
Honey Dijon = 'Weksproulses'PBR (F)	CSBt ESty
Honeybun = 'Tan98264'PBR (Patio)	ESty
'Honorine de Brabant' (Bb) ♀H6	CPou LEdu LRHS MAus MCot NLar SPer
Hope and Glory = 'Tan01360'PBR (HT)	ESty
Hot Chocolate = 'Wekpaltlez' (F) ♀H6	CGro CKel CSBt EBee ECnt ELan ELon EPfP ESps ESty GBin IBoy LBrs LBuc LRHS MAsh MJak MRav MWat SCoo SMad SPad SPer SPoG SRGP SSea SWCr WBor
House Beautiful = 'Harbingo' (Patio)	MRav
'Hugh Dickson' (HP)	CPou LSRN MAus NLar
hugonis	see *R. xanthina* f. *hugonis*
- 'Plenissima'	see *R. xanthina* f. *hugonis*
Humanity = 'Harcross'PBR (F)	MRav
Hummingbird = 'Tynpam' (F) new	ESty
Hyde Hall = 'Ausbosky'PBR (S)	CRos LBuc LRHS MAus NRHS SCob SCoo
Ice Cream = 'Korzuri'PBR (HT) ♀H6	CBod ECnt ESty IBoy MAus MRav SCob SPer SPoG SWCr
§ Iceberg = 'Korbin' (F) ♀H6	CBcs CGro CKel CNec CRos CSBt CTri EBee ECnt ELan EPfP ESps ESty IBoy LCro LEdu LRHS MAsh MAus MGos MJak MRav MWat NPri NWea SCob SPer SPoG SSea SWCr
'Illusion' (ClF)	SWCr
§ Imagination = 'Pouldron'PBR (F)	MAsh
Impératrice Farah = 'Delivour' (HT)	ESty
§ 'Impératrice Joséphine' (Gn) ♀H7	CBod EWTr IBoy LRHS NLar NRHS
In Memory Of	LSRN
In Memory of my Dog = 'Rawbark' (F)	LSRN
Indian Summer = 'Harwigwam' (ClMin)	MJak
Indian Summer = 'Peaperfume'PBR (HT) ♀H6	CKel CSBt ESps LBuc MAsh MRav SPoG SWCr
'Indigo' (DPo)	CPou MAus
Infinity = 'Frytropic' (HT)	ESty LRHS MAsh SWCr

	Ingrid Bergman = 'Poulman'PBR (HT) ♀H6	CBod CTri ECnt EPfP ESps IBoy LBrs LRHS LSRN MAsh MGos MRav MWat SPer SPoG SWCr
	'Inspiration' (ClHT)	EPfP MAsh SWCr
	Inspiration = 'Nor19597' (HT) **new**	NPri
	'Ipsilanté' (G)	MAus
	'Irène Watts' (Ch)	CPou EBee EWTr LSRN NLar SKHP SWCr
	'Irene's Delight' (HT)	ESty LSRN
	Iris = 'Coczero' (HT)	LSRN
	Iris = 'Ferecha' (HT)	LSRN
	Irish Eyes = 'Dicwitness'PBR (F) ♀H6	CBcs CGro ESps ESty IArd IBoy IDic MAsh MJak MRav SCoo SPer SWCr
	Irish Wonder	see *R.* Evelyn Fison
	Isabella = 'Poulisab'PBR (Renaissance Series) (S)	CPou CTri ECnt SWCr
	IsisPBR (HT)	see *R.* Silver Anniversary = 'Poulari'
	Isn't She Lovely = 'Diciluvit'PBR (HT) ♀H6	ELan ESty IDic LSRN SWCr
	'Ispahan' (D) ♀H7	EPfP GBin GCra LRHS MAus MCot NEgg NLar SPer WFar
	Ivor's Rose = 'Beadonald' (S)	LRHS
	Ivory Romantica = 'Meisabeyla'PBR (HT)	ESty
	'Ivory Silk' (Min)	LSRN
	'Jack Hume' (ClHT) **new**	ESty
	Jack's Wish = 'Kirsil' (HT)	LSRN
§	× *jacksonii* 'Max Graf' (GC/Ru)	LRHS MAus NLar
	- Red Max Graf	see *R.* Rote Max Graf
§	- White Max Graf = 'Korgram' (GC/Ru)	EAEE ECrN
	'Jacky's Favorite' (F)	LSRN
	Jacobite rose	see *R.* × *alba* 'Alba Maxima'
	Jacqueline du Pré = 'Harwanna' (S) ♀H6	CBod CKel ECnt EPfP ESty LSRN MAus MCot MRav MWat NLar SEND SLon SPer SSea SWCr
	Jacquenetta = 'Ausjac' (S)	MAus
	'Jacques Cartier' misapplied	see *R.* 'Marchesa Boccella'
	Jam and Jerusalem = 'Frymojo'PBR (F)	CGro CKel LBrs MRav
	James Galway = 'Auscrystal'PBR (S)	CSBt EPfP ESty IBoy LBuc LRHS LSRN MAus NEgg NRHS SCob SCoo SSea
	'James Mason' (G)	MAus
	'James Mitchell' (CeMo)	MAus
	'James Veitch' (DPoMo)	MAus
	Janet = 'Auspishus'PBR (S)	LSRN MAus
§	'Japonica' (CeMo)	EBee MAus
§	Jardins de Bagatelle = 'Meimafris' (HT)	LSRN
	Jasmina = 'Korcentex'PBR (ClHT)	CPou EBee ESty LBrs LBuc MAsh
	'Jaune Desprez'	see *R.* 'Desprez à Fleur Jaune'
	Jayne Austin = 'Ausbreak'PBR (S)	CSBt MAus SPer
	JazzPBR (ClF)	see *R.* That's Jazz
	'Jazz' (F)	LSRN
	Jean = 'Cocupland'PBR (Patio)	LSRN
	'Jean Mermoz' (Poly)	MAus
	'Jeanne de Montfort' (CeMo)	MAus
	Jeanne Moreau = 'Meidiaphaz' (HT)	CSBt ESty
	'Jenny Duval' misapplied	see *R.* 'Président de Sèze'
	Jenny's Rose = 'Cansit' (F)	EBee ECnt LSRN
	Jill's Rose = 'Ganjil'PBR (F)	LSRN
	Jilly Jewel = 'Benmfig' (Min)	LSRN
	Johann Wolfgang von Goethe Rose	see *R.* Pure Poetry
	John Clare = 'Auscent'PBR (S)	MAus
	'John Gwilliam'	MAvo MHCG
	'John Hopper' (HP)	MAus SWCr
§	Joie de Vivre = 'Korfloci 01'PBR (Patio/S) ♀H6	CGro CPou CSBt EBee ELan EPfP ESty EWTr GBin IBoy LBrs LRHS MAsh MRav MWat NLar NPri SCoo SPer SPoG SWCr
	'Josephine Bruce' (HT)	CBcs LSRN
	'Joseph's Coat' (ClS)	CBod CKel ESps GBin IArd SWCr
	Joy Vieli = 'Dickaramel' (F)	IDic
	'Jubilee Celebration' (F)	EPfP LRHS NRHS
	Jubilee Celebration = 'Aushunter'PBR (S)	CKel CRos CSBt EBee LBuc LRHS MAus NLar SPer
	Jude the Obscure = 'Ausjo'PBR (S)	CNec CSBt EPfP ESty LBuc LRHS MAus MGos NEgg NRHS SCob SWCr
	'Julia's Rose' (HT)	LSRN MAus SPer
	Julio Iglesias = 'Meistemon'PBR (F)	ESty LSRN
	'Juno' (Ch)	CPou MAus
	Just for You = 'Moryou' (Min)	LSRN
	'Just Jenny' (Min)	LSRN
	'Just Joey' (HT) ♀H6	CBcs CGro CKel CSBt CTri ECnt ELan ELon EPfP ESps IArd IBoy LSRN MAus MJak MRav MWat NEgg SCob SPer SPoG SRGP SSea SWCr
	'Just Steve'	LSRN
	'Katharina Zeimet' (Poly)	CKel CTri MAus
	'Kathleen' (HM)	LSRN
	'Kathleen Harrop' (Bb)	CBod CKel EBee ESps LRHS MAus MMuc MSwo NLar SEND SPer SRGP SWCr
	Kathleen Jane = 'Horcoed' (S/F)	LSRN
	Kathleen's Rose = 'Kirkitt' (F)	LSRN
	Kathryn Morley = 'Ausclub'PBR (F)	MAus
	'Katie' (ClF)	LSRN
	'Kazanlik' misapplied	see *R.* × *damascena* 'Professeur Émile Perrot'
	Keep Smiling = 'Fryflorida' (HT) ♀H6	CGro MAsh MRav SPoG
	'Keith Maughan' (Cl)	LRHS
§	Kent = 'Poulcov'PBR (Towne & Country Series) (S/GC) ♀H6	CBod CKel CSBt EAEE ECnt ELan EPfP ESty IBoy LCro LSRN MMuc MRav MSwo NLar SCob SEND SPer SPoG SSea SWCr
	Kew Gardens = 'Ausfence'PBR (S) ♀H6	CKel EPfP LBuc LRHS MAus NRHS SCob SSea
	'Kew Rambler' (Ra)	CBod CRHN CSam EBee MAus NLar SLon SPer
	'Kiftsgate'	see *R. filipes* 'Kiftsgate'
	'Kim' (Patio)	LSRN
	Kind Regards = 'Peatiger' (F)	LSRN
	King's Macc = 'Frydisco'PBR (HT) ♀H6	MAus
	'King's Ransom' (HT)	CSBt SPer SPoG
	Kisses of Fire = 'Chewmultiseek' (Cl)	ECnt ESty
§	'Königin von Dänemark' (A) ♀H7	EPfP IBoy LCro LRHS LSRN MRav MWat NEgg NLar SKHP SPer SWCr

	Korona = 'Kornita' (F)	SPer
	'Korresia' (F) ♀H7	CSBt CTri ECnt EPfP ESps ESty IBoy MAsh MAus MJak MRav MWat SCob SPer SPoG SWCr
	'Kronprinzessin Viktoria von Preussen' (Bb)	MAus
	L.D. Braithwaite = 'Auscrim'PBR (S)	CBcs CBod CRos CTri ELan EPfP ESps IBoy LRHS MAus MBNS MJak MRav MWat NLar NRHS SCob SPer SSea
	'La Belle Sultane'	see *R.* 'Violacea'
	'La France' (HT)	MAus
	'La Mortola'	see *R. brunonii* 'La Mortola'
	'La Perle' (Ra)	CRHN
	'La Reine Victoria'	see *R.* 'Reine Victoria'
§	La Rose de Molinard = 'Delgrarose'PBR (S) ♀H6	CPou ESty EWTr MRav NLar
	La Rose de Petit Prince = 'Delgramau' (F)	ESty MRav
	'La Rubanée'	see *R.* × *centifolia* 'Unique Panachée'
	La Sévillana = 'Meigekanu' (F/GC)	MSwo SPer WCot
	'La Ville de Bruxelles' (D) ♀H7	CSam LRHS MAus NLar SPer
	'Lady Anne' (F)	LSRN
	Lady Emma Hamilton = 'Ausbrother'PBR (S) ♀H6	CGro CNec CRos EPfP ESty IBoy LBuc LRHS MAus NRHS SCob SCoo SPer SWCr
	'Lady Gay' (Ra)	EBee WBor
	'Lady Godiva' (Ra)	MAus
	'Lady Hillingdon' (T)	MAsh MAus MWat
	'Lady Hillingdon' (ClT)	see *R.* 'Climbing Lady Hillingdon'
	Lady Marmalade = 'Hartiger' (F)	CGro CKel CSBt ECnt ESty EWTr LBrs LBuc LRHS MAsh MRav NPri SCoo SPer SPoG SWCr
	Lady Mitchell = 'Haryearn' (HT)	ECnt
	Lady of Megginch = 'Ausvolume'PBR (S)	EPfP LRHS MAus NRHS
	Lady of Shalott = 'Ausnyson'PBR (S) ♀H6	CRos LBuc LCro LOPS LRHS MAus NRHS SCob SSea
	Lady Penelope = 'Chewdor'PBR (ClHT)	CSBt
§	'Lady Penzance' (RH)	CBcs SPer
	Lady Rose = 'Korlady' (HT)	MAsh
	Lady Salisbury = 'Auscezed'PBR (S)	CRos EPfP LBuc LRHS MAsh MAus NRHS SCob SCoo
	'Lady Sylvia' (HT)	LSRN MAus NEgg SPer
	'Lady Waterlow' (ClHT)	EBee EWTr MAus
	laevigata (Ra)	MAus MMuc
	- 'Anemonoides'	see *R.* 'Anemone'
	Laguna = 'Koradigel'PBR (ClHT)	MAsh NPri
	Laguna = 'Kormulen' (HT)	LRHS
	L'Aimant = 'Harzola'PBR (F) ♀H5	CGro CSBt ESty MAus MRav SWCr
§	L'Alhambra = 'Tan97289'PBR (Cl)	ESty
	'Lamarque' (N)	CPou EBee EWTr MAus
	Lancashire = 'Korstesgli'PBR (GC) ♀H6	CKel ECnt ELan ESty LSRN MAus MRav MSwo SSea SWCr
	Lancelot = 'Tan03542'PBR (Cl)	ESty
	Laura Ford = 'Chewarvel'PBR (ClMin) ♀H5	CGro CKel CTri ESps IBoy LRHS MAsh MAus MGos MRav MWat SPer SPoG SSea
	'Laura Louisa' (Cl)	EBee EWTr
	'Laure Davoust' (Ra)	CPou EBee MMuc NLar
	Lavender Ice = 'Tan04249'PBR (F)	ESty LBrs SWCr
	'Lavender Jewel' (Min)	MAus
	'Lavender Lassie' (HM)	CPou CSam EWTr MAus NLar SPer SSea SWCr
	Lavender Symphonie = 'Meiptima' (Patio)	ESty
	Lavinia	see *R.* Lawinia
§	Lawinia = 'Tanklewi' (ClHT) ♀H6	CSBt LBuc LRHS MAsh SPer
	'Lawrence Johnston'	see *R.* 'Hidcote Yellow'
§	Lazy Days = 'Poulkalm'PBR (F)	ECnt LBrs MAsh SWCr
	'Le Rêve' (Cl)	EWTr
	Le Rouge et le Noir = 'Delcart' (HT)	ESty
	'Le Vésuve' (Ch)	CPou MAus
	Leah Tutu = 'Hornavel' (S)	ESty LRHS
	Leander = 'Auslea' (S)	MAus
	Leaping Salmon = 'Peamight'PBR (ClHT) ♀H6	CGro CSBt ELon ESps ESty EWTr LSRN MAus MRav SPer SRGP SWCr
	'Leda' (D)	EWTr MAus SPer
	'Lemon Pillar'	see *R.* 'Paul's Lemon Pillar'
	Léonardo de Vinci = 'Meideauri'PBR (F)	CSBt
	Leonidas = 'Meicofum'PBR (HT)	ESty
	'Léontine Gervais' (Ra)	CRHN LRHS MAus
	'Leo's Eye' (Ra)	CPou EPfP
	Leslie's Dream = 'Dicjoon' (HT)	IDic
	Let's Celebrate = 'Fryraffles' (F)	ECnt EPfP ESty LBuc LRHS MAsh MRav NRHS SWCr
	'Leverkusen' (ClF) ♀H7	CKel EBee EWTr LRHS MAus MRav NLar SEND SPer SWCr
	Lichfield Angel = 'Ausrelate'PBR (S) ♀H6	EPfP LBuc LRHS MAus NLar SCob SCoo
	Lichtkönigin Lucia = 'Korlillub' (S)	SSea
	Life Begins at 40! = 'Horhohoho' (F)	LSRN
	Light Fantastic = 'Dicgottago' (F) ♀H6	EPfP IDic SWCr
	Lilac Rose = 'Auslilac' (S)	MAus
	Lilac Wine = 'Dicmulti' (F) **new**	IDic
	Lilian Austin = 'Ausli' (S)	MAus
	Liliana = 'Poulsyng'PBR (S)	CBod CPou EBee ECnt LSRN SLon SWCr
	Lilli Marlene = 'Korlima' (F)	CSBt ESps IBoy SPer
	Lincoln Cathedral = 'Glanlin'PBR (HT)	MJak SPer
	Lincolnshire Poacher = 'Glareabit' (HT)	NEgg
	'Lincolnshire Yellow Belly' (F)	ESty
	Lion's Fairy Tale	see *R.* Champagne Moments
	Lisa = 'Kirdisco' (F)	LSRN
	Little Amy = 'Battamy' (Min)	LSRN
	Little Duet = 'Guesbliss' (F) **new**	ESty
	'Little Flirt' (Min)	ELan MAus
	'Little Gem' (DPMo)	MAus
	Little Jackie = 'Savor' (Min)	LSRN
	Little Miss Sunshine = 'Dicgungho' (F)	ECnt
	Little Rambler = 'Chewramb'PBR (MinRa) ♀H6	CSBt ECnt ELan ESty LBrs MAus MGos MMuc MRav SCoo SPer SSea SWCr

	'Little White Pet'	see *R.* 'White Pet'
	Lochinvar = 'Ausbilda'PBR (S)	LRHS MAus
	'Lolabelle'	CPou EBee EWTr
	'Long John Silver' (Cl)	ELan MAus SSea
	longicuspis misapplied	see *R. mulliganii*
	longicuspis Bertol. (Ra)	EBee EWTr
§	- var. ***sinowilsonii*** (Ra)	GCal MAus
	Look Good... Feel Better = 'Poulcas034'PBR (Castle Series) (Poly)	EPfP LBrs LRHS MAsh
	Lord Byron = 'Meitosier' (ClHT)	ESty
	'Lord Penzance' (RH)	EWTr NLar SPer
	Lorna = 'Cocringer' (F)	LSRN
	'L'Ouche' misapplied	see *R.* 'Louise Odier'
	'Louis Gimard' (CeMo)	MAus
	'Louis XIV' (Ch)	MCot
§	'Louise Odier' (Bb)	CBWd CKel CTri ECnt EPfP IArd LRHS LSRN MAus MRav MWat NLar SMad SPer SRGP SWCr
	Love & Peace = 'Baipeace'PBR (HT) ♀H6	ESty SWCr
	Love Knot = 'Chewglorious'PBR (ClMin) ♀H6	CRos CSBt ECnt EPfP ESps ESty LBrs LRHS MAsh MRav NPri SCoo SSea SWCr
§	Lovely Bride = 'Meiratcan'PBR (Patio)	CRos EPfP LBrs LRHS MAsh NRHS SCoo SPoG SWCr
	Lovely Lady = 'Dicjubell'PBR (HT) ♀H6	CBod CKel CSBt ECnt ESty LSRN MAus MRav SSea SWCr
	Lovely Meidiland	see *R.* Lovely Bride
	Lovely Pink = 'Meinoplius'PBR (F)	ESty
	'Lovers' Meeting' (HT)	MJak MRav SPer SWCr
	Loving Memory = 'Korgund81' (HT)	CGro CKel CSBt ECnt ESty IArd LBrs LSRN MAsh MGos MRav NPri SPer SPoG SSea SVic SWCr
	Loving Mum	see *R.* Showstar
	Lowthorpe Delight = 'Dicgoofy' (F) **new**	IDic
	Lucetta = 'Ausemi' (S)	MAus
	Lucky! = 'Frylucy' (F) ♀H6	CSBt EPfP ESty LBuc LRHS LSRN MAsh MRav NPri NRHS SCoo SPer SPoG SWCr
	Lucy = 'Kirlis' (F)	LSRN
	Ludlow Castle	see *R.* England's Rose = 'Ausrace'
	Lullaby = 'Kenfrilpin' (Cl) **new**	ESty
	Luscious Lucy = 'Tucklucy' (Patio)	LSRN
	'Lutea Maxima'	see *R.* × *harisonii* 'Lutea Maxima'
	'Lykkefund' (Ra)	CKel MAus
	'Mabel Morrison' (HP)	MAus
	Macartney rose	see *R. bracteata*, *R.* The McCartney Rose
	Macmillan Nurse = 'Beamac' (S)	ESty LRHS MCot
	'Macrantha' (Gallica hybrid)	LRHS MAus SPer
	macrophylla (S)	MAus
	- B&SWJ 2603	WCru
	- GWJ 9306	WCru
§	- 'Master Hugh' (S)	MAus
	'Madame Abel Chatenay' (HT)	MAus
	'Madame Alfred Carrière' (N) ♀H5	Widely available
	'Madame Alice Garnier' (Ra)	CPou CRHN EBee SPer
	'Madame Antoine Mari' (T)	CPou
§	'Madame Boll' (DPo)	CBWd CKel ESty EWTr LBrs LCro MSwo NLar SMad SWCr
	'Madame Bravy' (T)	MAus
	'Madame Butterfly' (HT)	LRHS MAus
§	'Madame Caroline Testout' (HT)	CTri LRHS SPoG SRGP
	'Madame de la Roche-Lambert' (DPMo)	CPou MAus
	'Madame de Sancy de Parabère' (Bs)	MAus
	'Madame Driout' (ClT)	CPou
	'Madame Ernest Calvat' (Bb)	CPou
	'Madame Eugène Résal' misapplied	see *R.* 'Comtesse du Caÿla'
§	'Madame Grégoire Staechelin' (ClHT) ♀H6	CTri ECnt ELan EPfP EWTr IBoy LCro LRHS LSRN MAsh MAus MRav MSwo NEgg NLar NRHS SCob SPer SPlb WKif
	'Madame Hardy' (D) ♀H7	CPou CSBt ECnt EPfP EWTr LRHS LSRN MAus MRav MSwo MWat NEgg NLar SCob SPer SSea SWCr WFar
	'Madame Isaac Péreire' (ClBb)	CSBt CTri ECnt EPfP ESps GBin IBoy MAus MCot MRav MSwo NLar SCob SMad SPer SPoG SSea SWCr WBor WFar
	'Madame Jules Gravereaux' (ClT)	MAus
	'Madame Knorr' (DPo) ♀H7	CPou ECnt ELon EPfP SPer SSea
	'Madame Knorr' misapplied	see *R.* 'Madame Boll'
	'Madame Laurette Messimy' (Ch)	CPou EWTr
	'Madame Lauriol de Barny' (Bb)	MAus MRav NLar
	'Madame Legras de Saint Germain' (A × N)	CPou EWTr LRHS MAus NLar SPer
	'Madame Louis Lévêque' (DPMo)	CPou EWTr
	'Madame Pierre Oger' (Bb)	CTri ECnt MAus SKHP SPer
	'Madame Plantier' (A × N)	CPou EBee EWTr LRHS MAus NLar SCob SPer WFar
	'Madame Scipion Cochet' (HP)	CPou
	'Madame Zöetmans' (D)	MAus
	'Madge' (HM)	SDix
	Magic Carpet = 'Jaclover'PBR (S/GC) ♀H6	CKel ELan ESps IBoy MAus MRav MSwo SPer SWCr
	Magic Moment = 'Forrusty' (HT) **new**	ESty
	Maid Marion = 'Austobias'PBR (HM)	EPfP MAus
	'Maid of Kent'PBR (Cl)	LSRN MAus NLar SCob SCoo SMad SPer SWCr
	'Maiden's Blush' (A)	CArn CBWd CBod CSam CTri ELan EWTr LEdu LRHS MAsh MAus SPer WHer
	'Maiden's Blush, Great'	see *R.* 'Great Maiden's Blush'
	'Maigold' (ClPiH) ♀H7	CBcs CBod CGro CTri ELan EPfP ESps LRHS MAus MCot MRav MSwo MWat NLar SCob SMad SPer SWCr WBor
	Maltese rose	see *R.* 'Cécile Brünner'
	Malvern Hills = 'Auscanary'PBR (Ra)	CGro CRos CSBt EBee EPfP ESty LRHS MAus NLar SCob SPer SWCr
	'Maman Cochet' (T)	MAus
	Mamma Mia! = 'Fryjolly'PBR (HT) ♀H6	ECnt ESty LBrs LRHS MAsh MRav NPri SPoG SWCr
	Mamy Blue = 'Delblue' (HT)	ESty

	'Mandarin' (F)	CKel SSea
	Mandarin = 'Korcelin'[PBR] (Min)	ESty IBoy MRav
	'Manning's Blush' (RH)	MAus
	'Mannington Mauve Rambler' (Ra)	ESty
	Many Happy Returns = 'Harwanted'[PBR] (F) 𝕐[H6]	CBcs CKel CRos CSBt ECnt ELan EPfP ESps IBoy LBrs LRHS LSRN MAsh MGos MJak MRav MWat NPri NRHS SCob SPer SPoG SSea SVic SWCr
	'Marbrée' (DPo)	MAus
	'Märchenland' (F)	MAus
§	'Marchesa Boccella' (DPo) 𝕐[H7]	CPou CSam CTri EBee EPfP EWTr LRHS NLar NPri SPer SSea SWCr WBor WHer
	'Maréchal Davoust' (CeMo)	LEdu MAus
	'Maréchal Niel' (N)	EShb MAus SPer SSea
	'Margaret' (HT)	LSRN
	Margaret Merril = 'Harkuly' (F)	CBcs CBod CGro CKel CSBt CTri EBee ELan EPfP ESps ESty IArd IBoy LBrs LCro LRHS LSRN MAsh MAus MJak MRav MWat SCob SPer SPoG SRGP SSea SWCr
	'Marguerite Hilling' (S)	CTri MAus MSwo NLar SPer
	'Marie Louise' (D)	EBee MAus
	'Marie Pavič' (Poly)	CPou MAus
	'Marie van Houtte' (T)	MAus
	'Marie-Jeanne' (Poly)	MAus
	Marigold Sweet Dream = 'Fryprospa' (Patio)	ECnt
	Marinette = 'Auscam'[PBR] (S)	MAus
	Marjorie Fair = 'Harhero' (Poly/S) 𝕐[H6]	ELan ESty MAus MRav SWCr
	'Marlena' (F/Patio)	MAus
	Marry Me = 'Dicwonder'[PBR] (Patio) 𝕐[H6]	ESty IDic SWCr
	'Martha' (Bb)	LSRN
	'Martin Frobisher' (Ru)	MAus
I	'Mary' (Poly)	LSRN
	Mary Magdalene = 'Ausjolly'[PBR] (S)	MAus
	Mary Rose = 'Ausmary' (S)	CBod CKel CRos CSBt CTri ELan EPfP ESps IBoy LRHS LSRN MAus MJak MRav MWat NLar NRHS SCob SLon SPer SPoG SSea SWCr WKif
	'Mary Wallace' (Cl)	MAus
	Mary Webb = 'Auswebb' (S)	MAus
	'Masquerade' (F)	CTri ELan ESps MRav SPer SWCr
	'Master Hugh'	see *R. macrophylla* 'Master Hugh'
	Matawhero Magic	see *R.* Simply the Best
	Maurice Utrillo = 'Delstavo' (HT)	ESty
	'Max Graf'	see *R. × jacksonii* 'Max Graf'
	'Maxima'	see *R. × alba* 'Alba Maxima'
	Maxima Romantica = 'Meikerira'[PBR] (HT)	ESty
	'May Queen' (Ra)	CBod CPou CRos EBee LRHS MAus MMuc MRav NLar NRHS SEND SPer SWCr
	Mayor of Casterbridge = 'Ausbrid'[PBR] (S)	MAus
	'McCartney Rose'	see *R.* The McCartney Rose
§	Medley Ruby = 'Noa140715'[PBR] (Min) **new**	LBrs MAsh
	'Meg' (ClHT)	CKel EBee EPfP EWTr LRHS LSRN MAus MCot MMuc NLar SPer SRGP
	Melody Maker = 'Dicqueen'[PBR] (F)	IBoy
	Memory Lane = 'Peavoodoo'[PBR] (F)	LSRN
	'Mermaid' (Cl) 𝕐[H5]	CBcs CDul CSBt CTri EPfP ESps LHop LRHS MAsh MAus NLar NRHS SCob SEND SPer SSea SWCr
§	'Mevrouw Nathalie Nypels' (Poly)	CTri EBee MAus MMuc MRav NLar SPer
	'Michèle Meilland' (HT)	MAus
	× ***micrugosa***	MAus
	- 'Alba'	MAus
	Middlesborough Football Club = 'Horflame' (HT)	LSRN
	Midnight Rose = 'Simdamo' (F) **new**	ESty
§	Millie = 'Poulren013'[PBR] (Renaissance Series) (S) 𝕐[H6]	CBcs CBod CGro ECnt ESty LBrs LBuc LCro LRHS LSRN MAsh NPri NRHS SPoG SWCr
	Millie Rose = 'Wekblunez'[PBR] (HT)	SWCr
	Millionaire = 'Peazara' (F)	LSRN
	Mind Games = 'Dickylie' (F)	ECnt IDic
	'Minnehaha' (Ra)	MAus SSea
	mirifica stellata	see *R. stellata* var. *mirifica*
	Mischief = 'Macmi' (HT)	LSRN SPer
	Miss Alice = 'Ausjake'[PBR] (S)	LSRN MAus
	'Miss Edith Cavell' (Poly)	MAus
	Miss Scarlet = 'Forbright' (Cl) **new**	ESty
§	'Mister Lincoln' (HT)	MJak SPer
	Mistress Quickly = 'Ausky'[PBR] (S)	MAus
§	Misty Hit = 'Poulhi011'[PBR] (PatioHit Series) (Patio)	ECnt LSRN SWCr
	Mitsouko = 'Delnat' (HT)	ESty
	Molineux = 'Ausmol'[PBR] (S) 𝕐[H6]	CRos EPfP LRHS MAus SCob SPer SWCr
	Moment in Time = 'Korcastrav'[PBR] (F) 𝕐[H6]	CBcs CGro CSBt ECnt MAsh MRav MWat NPri SCoo SPer SPoG SWCr
	Monica Bellucci = 'Meimonkeur'[PBR] (HT)	ESty
	Moody Blue = 'Fryniche' (HT)	CGro ECnt ESty IBoy LBrs LRHS MAsh MRav MWat SWCr
	Moonbeam = 'Ausbeam' (S)	MAus
	'Moonlight' (HM)	CKel CTri EWTr GBin LRHS MAus MRav MSwo MWat SPer SWCr
	Moonshine = 'Tan97123'[PBR] (HT)	LBrs
	'Morletii' (Bs)	EWTr MMuc SEND
	'Morning Jewel' (ClF) 𝕐[H7]	SPer SWCr
	Morning Mist = 'Ausfire' (S)	LBuc LRHS MAsh MAus SPer SSea
§	'Morsdag' (Poly/F)	LSRN SCob SVic
	Mortimer Sackler = 'Ausorts'[PBR] (S) 𝕐[H6]	CKel ELon EPfP LBuc LRHS MAus MMuc NRHS SCob SCoo SPer SSea SWCr
	moschata (Ra)	MAus SSea
	- 'Autumnalis'	see *R.* 'Princesse de Nassau'
	- var. ***nepalensis***	see *R. brunonii*
I	'Mother's Day'	MJak SRGP
	Mother's Day	see *R.* 'Morsdag'
	Mother's Joy = 'Horsiltrop' (F)	LSRN
	Mount Aorangi = 'Sanaran' (F) **new**	ESty
	Mountain Snow = 'Aussnow' (Ra)	LRHS MAsh MAus
	Mountbatten = 'Harmantelle' (F) 𝕐[H6]	CKel ELan ESps LBuc MAus MRav SPer SPoG SWCr
§	'Mousseline' (DPoMo)	CPou EWTr MAus MCot SPer

	'Mousseuse du Japon'	see *R.* 'Japonica'
	moyesii (S)	CTri ELan ESps EWld GCra GKev MAus MWat NEgg NWea SKHP SPer
	'Mr Bluebird' (MinCh)	MAus
	'Mr Lincoln'	see *R.* 'Mister Lincoln'
	'Mrs Anthony Waterer' (Ru)	EBee MAus SPer
	'Mrs Arthur Curtiss James' (ClHT)	MMuc
	Mrs Doreen Pike = 'Ausdor'^{PBR} (Ru)	LRHS MAus
	'Mrs Honey Dyson' (Ra)	CPou EWTr
	'Mrs John Laing' (HP)	EBee LRHS MAus NLar SWCr
	'Mrs Oakley Fisher' (HT)	MAus MCot SDix SPer SWCr
	'Mrs Paul' (Bb)	MAus
	'Mrs Sam McGredy' (HT)	CPou LRHS NEgg
§	***mulliganii*** (Ra)	EPfP GKin MAus SPer
	multibracteata (S)	CBcs GLog MAus
	multiflora (Ra)	MAus
§	- 'Grevillei' (Ra)	MAus SPer
	- 'Platyphylla'	see *R. multiflora* 'Grevillei'
	- wild-collected	GCal
	Mum in a Million	see *R.* Millie
	Mummy	see *R.* Newly Wed
	mundi	see *R. gallica* 'Versicolor'
	Munstead Wood = 'Ausbernard'^{PBR} (S) 🏆^{H6}	CGro CNec CRos EPfP EShb ESty LBuc LCro LOPS LRHS LSRN MAsh MAus NRHS SCob SPer SSea SWCr
	'Muscosa Alba'	see *R.* × *centifolia* 'Shailer's White Moss'
	'Mutabilis'	see *R.* × *odorata* 'Mutabilis'
	My Dad = 'Boselftay'^{PBR} (F)	CBcs LSRN SWCr
	'My Darling Husband' (F)	LSRN
	'My Darling Wife' (F)	LSRN
	My Girl = 'Tan00798'^{PBR} (HT)	ECnt
	'My Joy' (HT)	LSRN
	My Mum = 'Webmorrow'^{PBR} (F)	CBcs CBod CGro ESty LBrs LSRN SCob SWCr
	My Valentine = 'Mormyval' (Min)	LSRN MAsh
	Myriam = 'Cocgrand' (HT)	LSRN
	Mysterious = 'Simpansy' (F) <u>**new**</u>	ESty
	Mystery Girl = 'Dicdothis'^{PBR} (HT)	EBee ECnt
	Nancy = 'Poulninga' (Renaissance Series) (S)	CBod CPou LSRN
	'Naomi' (HT)	CPou
	'Narrow Water' (Ra) 🏆^{H6}	CPou EWTr GBin SWCr
	Natalie = 'Poulren014'^{PBR} (Renaissance Series) (S)	LSRN
	Natasha Richardson = 'Harpacket'^{PBR} (F)	CKel MRav
	'Nathalie Nypels'	see *R.* 'Mevrouw Nathalie Nypels'
	'National Trust' (HT)	CTri ESps IArd IBoy MJak MWat SPer WBod
	'Nestor' (G)	MAus
	'Nevada' (S)	CSBt CTri ECnt ELan EPfP ESps EWTr GBin IArd IBoy LEdu LRHS MAus MRav NLar SPer
	Never Forgotten = 'Gregart' (HT)	LSRN
	New Arrival	see *R.* 'Red Patio'
	New Beginnings = 'Korprofko'^{PBR} (F)	LBrs LSRN MAsh SWCr
§	'New Dawn' (Cl) 🏆^{H7}	Widely available
	'New Home'	LSRN
	New Zealand = 'Macgenev'^{PBR} (HT)	SWCr
§	Newly Wed = 'Dicwhynot'^{PBR} (Patio) 🏆^{H6}	LSRN SSea SWCr
	News = 'Legnews' (F)	MAus
	Newsflash = 'Kendutch' (F)	ESty SWCr
	Nice Day = 'Chewsea'^{PBR} (ClMin)	CGro CTri EPfP ESty IBoy MAsh MRav SPer SPoG SSea
	'Nicola' (F)	LSRN
	Night Light = 'Poullight'^{PBR} (Courtyard Series) (Cl)	ECnt
	Night Owl = 'Wekpurosot' (Cl)	ECnt ESty EWTr GBin LRHS MRav SPer SPoG
	Nina = 'Mehnina'^{PBR} (S)	LSRN
	Nina = 'Poulren018'^{PBR} (Renaissance Series) (S)	ECnt
	nitida	ESps GMcL MAus NWea SPer
	Noble Antony = 'Ausway'^{PBR} (S)	EBee EPfP LRHS MAus NRHS SCob
§	'Noisette Carnée' (N) 🏆^{H7}	CKel CPou CTri EBee EPfP EWTr GCra LEdu LRHS MBNS MRav NLar NRHS SPer SSea SWCr
	Norfolk = 'Poulfolk'^{PBR} (GC)	CKel CTri ESty MSwo SCob SPer
	'Norwich Pink' (S)	MAus
	Nostalgia = 'Savarita' (Min)	CBod CGro EPfP LBrs LBuc LRHS MAsh MAus
§	Nostalgia = 'Taneiglat'^{PBR} (HT) 🏆^{H6}	CSBt ECnt ESty MRav SPoG SSea SWCr
	Nostalgie	see *R.* Nostalgia = 'Taneiglat'
	'Nozomi' (ClMin/GC)	CAbP CBod CKel CTri ELan EPfP ESty MAus MRav NLar SPer
	'Nuits de Young' (CeMo) 🏆^{H7}	CBod EPfP LRHS MAus NLar NRHS SKHP
	'Nur Mahal' (HM)	MAus
	Nurse Tracey Davies = 'Frykookie'^{PBR} (F) 🏆^{H6}	LBrs MAsh SWCr
	nutkana (S)	MAus
§	- 'Plena' (S/D) 🏆^{H7}	MAus NLar SKHP WHer
	'Nymphenburg' (HM)	EWTr SPer
	'Nyveldt's White' (Ru)	MAus
	Octavia Hill = 'Harzeal'^{PBR} (F)	MRav NLar SPer SWCr
§	× ***odorata***	CPou
	- 'Fortune's Double Yellow'	see *R.* × *odorata* 'Pseudindica'
§	- 'Mutabilis' (Ch) 🏆^{H5}	CKel CPou CRHN CTri ECnt ECre ELan EPfP EWTr GBin LCro LRHS MAus MCot MRav NLar NRHS SEND SKHP SPer SSea SWCr WBod WCFE WCot XSen
§	- 'Ochroleuca' (Ch)	CPou EBee
§	- 'Pallida' (Ch)	CPou EPfP LRHS MAus MCot MRav NLar NRHS SPer SSea SWCr
§	- 'Pseudindica' (ClCh)	IArd MAus
§	- Sanguinea Group (Ch)	SEND XSen
	- - 'Bengal Crimson' (Ch) 🏆^{H5}	CPou ECre EPfP EWTr LRHS LSRN NRHS SDix SKHP SLon WCot WKif
	- - 'Bob's Beauty' (Ch)	WCot
§	- 'Viridiflora' (Ch)	CPou EBee LEdu LRHS MAus SLon SMad SPer SSea WCot WHer
	Odyssey = 'Franski'^{PBR} (F)	ESty
	'Oeillet Flamand'	see *R.* 'Oeillet Parfait'
§	'Oeillet Parfait' (G)	MAus
	officinalis	see *R. gallica* var. *officinalis*
	Oh Wow! = 'Wekspitrib' (Cl)	ECnt ESty
	old blush China	see *R.* × *odorata* 'Pallida'
	old cabbage	see *R.* × *centifolia*
	Old John = 'Dicwillynilly' (F)	IDic LSRN
	old pink moss rose	see *R.* × *centifolia* 'Muscosa'
	Old Port = 'Mackati'^{PBR} (F)	ESty IArd

old red moss	see *R.* 'Henri Martin'
old velvet moss	see *R.* 'William Lobb'
'Old Velvet Rose'	see *R.* 'Tuscany'
old yellow Scotch (SpH)	see *R.* × *harisonii* 'Williams' Double Yellow'
Olivia Rose Austin = 'Ausmixture' (S) **new**	ESty LCro LRHS MAus NRHS SCoo
Olivia = 'Wekquahofa' (HT)	LSRN
'Olympic Flame' (F)	EPfP MAsh
'Omar Khayyám' (D)	MAus NLar
omeiensis	see *R. sericea* subsp. *omeiensis*
Open Arms = 'Chewpixcel'PBR (ClMin) ♀H6	ESps ESty LBuc MAus SMad SPer SSea SWCr
'Ophelia' (HT)	CBod LRHS MAus
Orange Blossom Special = 'Smi52/02' (ClMin) **new**	ESty
'Orange Sensation' (F)	CTri MAus
§ Orange Sunblaze = 'Meijikatar'PBR (Min)	CSBt SPer
'Orangeade' (F)	SCob
Oranges and Lemons = 'Macoranlem'PBR (F)	CGro CSBt ESty IBoy LBrs MAus SSea SWCr
Othello = 'Auslo'PBR (S)	MAus SPer
'Our Beth' (S)	LRHS LSRN
'Our Dream' (Patio)	MAsh
Our George = 'Kirrush' (Patio)	LSRN
Our Hilda = 'Lancoro' (F)	LSRN
Our Jubilee = 'Coccages' (HT)	ESty
Our Molly = 'Dicreason' (GC/S)	IDic LSRN SPer
Oxfordshire = 'Korfullwind'PBR (GC) ♀H6	IRob MRav MWat SCob SSea
Painted Moon = 'Dicpaint' (HT)	ESty
Panache = 'Poultop'PBR (Patio/Min)	ECnt IBoy LRHS SWCr
'Papa Gontier' (T)	CPou MAus
Papa Meilland = 'Meisar' (HT)	CSBt CTri MAus SPer SSea
Paper Anniversary (Patio)	LBuc LSRN
Papi Delbard = 'Delaby' (ClHT)	EBee ESty EWTr LSRN MRav
§ 'Para Ti' (Min)	SPer
I 'Parade' (Cl) ♀H6	CKel LSRN MAus NLar SWCr
'Parkdirektor Riggers' (F)	CBod CSam EWTr GBin MAus SCob SPer
Parks's yellow China	see *R.* × *odorata* 'Ochroleuca'
Parson's pink China	see *R.* × *odorata* 'Pallida'
Partridge = 'Korweirim' (GC)	MAus SPer
parvifolia	see *R.* 'Burgundiaca'
Pascali = 'Lenip' (HT)	CBcs CTri ELon IBoy MAus MJak SCob SPer
Pat Austin = 'Ausmum'PBR (S)	CBod CRos CSBt CTri EPfP IBoy LRHS LSRN MAus MBNS MRav MWat NEgg NLar NRHS SCob SEND SPer SWCr
Paul Gauguin = 'Delstrichoc' (HT)	ESty
'Paul Lédé' (ClT)	see *R.* 'Climbing Paul Lédé'
Paul McCartneyPBR (HT)	see *R.* The McCartney Rose
'Paul Neyron' (HP)	EWTr MAus SPer
'Paul Noël' (Ra)	CRos MAus
'Paul Ricault' (Ce × HP)	MAus
Paul Shirville = 'Harqueterwife'PBR (HT)	CKel ESps MAus SPer SWCr
'Paul Transon' (Ra) ♀H6	CPou CRHN CRos EPfP LRHS MMuc NEgg NLar SEND SPer SRGP WHer
'Paula's Rose' (Patio)	LSRN
§ 'Paulii' (Ru/GC)	MAus
'Paulii Alba'	see *R.* 'Paulii'
'Paulii Rosea' (Ru/GC)	MAus
'Paul's Himalayan Musk' (Ra) ♀H6	Widely available
§ 'Paul's Lemon Pillar' (ClHT)	CKel ELon EPfP LRHS MAsh MAus NLar SPer
'Paul's Scarlet Climber' (Cl/Ra)	EBee ELan ELon ESps IBoy LBuc LRHS MAsh MAus MJak MRav MSwo NPri SPer SRGP WBor
'Paul's Single White Perpetual' (Ra)	CTri EWTr NLar
'Pax' (HM)	CPou EBee MAus WKif
Peace = 'Madame A. Meilland' (HT) ♀H6	CBcs CKel CSBt CTri EBee ECnt ELan EPfP ESty IBoy LBrs LCro LRHS LSRN MAus MRav MWat NEgg NPri NRHS SCob SPer SPoG SRGP SSea SWCr
Peacekeeper = 'Harbella'PBR (F)	CSBt
Peach Blossom = 'Ausblossom' (S)	MAus
'Peach Grootendorst' (Ru)	CPou
Peachy = 'Macrelea' (HT)	MAsh SPoG
Pearl Anniversary = 'Whitston'PBR (Min/Patio)	CKel CSBt ESps ESty LBuc LSRN MRav SSea SWCr
Pearl Drift = 'Leggab' (S)	EBee MAus MCot MSwo SPer SWCr
Pearl = 'Korterschi'PBR (F) ♀H6	MAsh MRav SWCr
Peaudouce	see *R.* Elina
Pegasus = 'Ausmoon'PBR (S)	MAus
§ ***pendulina***	MAus WOut
- 'Nana'	NWad
'Penelope' (HM) ♀H5	CKel CSBt CTri EBee ECnt ELan EPfP ESps IBoy LRHS LSRN MAsh MAus MCot MRav NLar SCob SEND SPer SRGP SSea SWCr
Penny Lane = 'Hardwell'PBR (ClHT) ♀H6	CGro CSBt ECnt ELon EPfP ESps EUJe IBoy LBuc LRHS MAsh MAus MRav NLar SCoo SPer SPoG SSea SWCr
Penny Lane = 'Talpen' (Min)	EWTr MSwo
× ***penzanceana***	see *R.* 'Lady Penzance'
Peppermint Splash	see *R.* Rachel Louise Moran
Perdita = 'Ausperd' (S)	MAus
Perennial Blue = 'Mehv9601' (Ra) ♀H6	ESty MRav SCob SSea SWCr
Perennial Blush = 'Mehbarbie'PBR (Ra) ♀H6	CKel CSam ESty MRav SSea SWCr
§ Perfect Day = 'Poulcrem' (F)	ECnt
Perfect Harmony = 'Tangustedv' (HT)	ESty SWCr
Perfect Match = 'Hartie' (F) **new**	ESty
Perfect Pet = 'Smi122-2-04' (F)	ESty
'Perle des Jardins' (T)	MAus
§ 'Perle d'Or' (Poly) ♀H6	EWTr LRHS MAus NLar SDix SLon SPer
Perle Noire = 'Delurt' (HT)	ESty
Perpetually Yours = 'Harfable'PBR (Cl)	CGro MRav SCoo

	Persian yellow	see *R. foetida* 'Persiana'
	Peter Pan = 'Chewpan'PBR (Min) ♀H6	LBrs MAus SWCr
	Peter Pan = 'Sunpete' (Patio)	MAsh
	'Petite de Hollande' (Ce)	MAus NLar SPer
	'Petite Lisette' (Ce × D)	MAus NLar
	Pheasant = 'Kordapt' (GC)	MAus SPer
	Phillipa = 'Poulheart'PBR (S)	LSRN
	Phoebe (Ru)	see *R.* 'Fimbriata'
	'Phyllis Bide' (Ra) ♀H6	CKel EBee EPfP EWTr IArd LCro LOPS LRHS MAus MCot MSwo NLar SMad SPer SRGP SSea SWCr
	Piccadilly = 'Macar' (HT)	CSBt CTri IBoy SPer SWCr
	Piccolo = 'Tanolokip' (F/Patio)	MRav SWCr
	'Picture' (HT)	MAus SPer
	Pierre Cardin = 'Meilolipo'PBR (HT)	ESty
	Pigalle '84 = 'Meicloux' (F)	SWCr
	'Pilgrim'	see *R.* The Pilgrim
	pimpinellifolia	see *R. spinosissima*
	- double yellow-flowered	see *R. × harisonii* 'Williams' Double Yellow'
	- 'Harisonii'	see *R. × harisonii* 'Harison's Yellow'
	- 'Lutea'	see *R. × harisonii* 'Lutea Maxima'
	Pink Bells = 'Poulbells' (GC)	CGro SPer
	'Pink Bouquet' (Ra)	CRHN
	'Pink Champagne' (F) **new**	LRHS
	'Pink Cloud' (ClHT) **new**	ELan
	'Pink Favorite' (HT)	SCob SPer
	Pink Fizz = 'Poulycool' (ClPatio)	ECnt
§	Pink Flower Carpet = 'Noatraum'PBR (GC) ♀H6	CBod CGro CRos CSBt CTri ECnt ELan EUJe IBoy LCro LOPS LRHS MAsh NPri NRHS SCoo SEND SPer SPoG SSea SWCr
	'Pink Garnette'	see *R.* 'Carol Amling'
	'Pink Grootendorst' (Ru)	EPfP LEdu LRHS MAus NEgg NLar SPer
§	Pink Hit = 'Poultipe'PBR (Min/Patio)	ECnt LRHS LSRN NRHS SWCr
	'Pink Leda' (D)	EBee
	Pink Martini = 'Tan04608' (HT)	ESty MWat
	pink moss	see *R. × centifolia* 'Muscosa'
	Pink Paradise = 'Delfluoro' (HT)	ESty
	'Pink Parfait' (F)	SPer
	Pink Perfection = 'Korpauvio'PBR (HT)	ECnt LRHS MAsh SSea SWCr
	'Pink Perpétué' (Cl)	CBcs CNec CSBt CTri ECnt ELan ELon EPfP ESps IBoy LBuc MAus MRav SPer SPoG SSea SWCr
	'Pink Prosperity' (HM)	MAus
	'Pink Showers' (ClHT)	MSwo
	Pirouette = 'Poulyc003'PBR (ClS)	ECnt MAsh
	Playtime = 'Morplati' (F)	MAus
	Pleine de Grâce = 'Lengra' (S)	LEdu MAus
	Polar Star = 'Tanlarpost' (HT)	CSBt ECnt ESps MRav SPer SWCr
	'Polly' (HT)	LSRN
§	'Polyantha Grandiflora' (Ra)	MAus SVic
	'Pompon Blanc Parfait' (A)	MAus
	'Pompon de Bourgogne'	see *R.* 'Burgundiaca'
	'Pompon de Paris' (ClMinCh)	see *R.* 'Climbing Pompon de Paris'
	'Pompon de Paris' (MinCh)	SCob SSea WAbe
	'Pompon Panaché' (G)	MAus
	Pomponella = 'Korpompan'PBR (F)	MAsh
	Port Sunlight = 'Auslofty'PBR (HM) ♀H6	ESty IBoy LRHS MAsh MAus
	Portland rose	see *R.* 'Portlandica'
§	'Portlandica' (Po)	CTri LRHS MAsh SPer
	Portmeirion = 'Ausguard'PBR (S)	MAus SCoo
	Pour Toi	see *R.* 'Para Ti'
	prairie rose	see *R. setigera*
	'Precious Amber' (F)	MAsh
	'Precious Gold' **new**	MAsh
	Precious Love = 'Kirlowo'PBR **new**	LBrs MAsh
	'Precious Memories' (Min)	LSRN
	Precious Memories = 'Dichello'PBR (F)	ESty
	'Precious Platinum' (HT)	MJak SPer
	Precious Time = 'Oramarpa'PBR (HT)	ESty
§	'Président de Sèze' (G) ♀H7	CPou EWTr MAus NLar SPer
	Pretty in Pink = 'Dicumpteen'PBR (GC) ♀H6	ECnt
	Pretty Jessica = 'Ausjess' (S)	CGro LSRN MAus MRav MWat SPer SPoG
	Pretty Lady = 'Scrivo'PBR (F) ♀H6	MAus
	Pretty Polly = 'Meitonje' (Min) ♀H6	CGro CKel EPfP ESps ESty IBoy LRHS MAsh MRav MWat SPer SPoG SSea SWCr
	'Prima Ballerina' (HT)	CTri EPfP ESps LRHS SPer
	primula	MAus NLar SPer
	primula × rugosa	MJak
	'Prince Camille de Rohan' (HP)	MAus
	'Prince Charles' (Bb)	MAus WKif
	Prince Jardinier = 'Meitroni'PBR (HT) ♀H6	ESty LSRN SWCr
	Princess Alexandra of Kent = 'Ausmerchant'PBR (S)	CRos EPfP EShb ESty LRHS MAus NRHS SPer
	Princess Alexandra = 'Pouldra'PBR (Renaissance Series) (S) ♀H6	CBod CTri ECnt EWTr NLar SWCr
	Princess Anne = 'Auskitchen'PBR (S) ♀H6	ECnt EPfP LBuc LOPS LRHS MAus NRHS SCob
	Princess = 'Korspobux'PBR (HT)	ECnt
	Princess of Wales = 'Hardinkum'PBR (F) ♀H6	MJak MRav SPer SWCr
§	'Princesse de Nassau' (Ra)	MAus SKHP
	'Princesse Marie' misapplied	see *R.* 'Belvedere'
	'Pristine' (HT)	MAus
	'Prolifera de Redouté' misapplied	see *R.* 'Duchesse de Montebello'
	Proper Job = 'Tan02733'PBR (HT)	ECnt ESty SWCr
	'Prosperity' (HM) ♀H6	CSam CTri EPfP GBin LRHS MAus MCot MRav NLar SPer SWCr
	Prospero = 'Auspero' (S)	MAus
	Pure Gold = 'Harhappen'PBR (F)	CSBt
§	Pure Poetry = 'Tan04179' (HT)	ESty

	'Purezza' (Ra)	NLar
	Purple Eden	see *R.* Ebb Tide
	Purple Moon = 'Dicmover' (F)	IDic
	Purple Prince = 'Simpurple' (HT) **new**	ESty
	Purple Skyliner = 'Franwekpurp'[PBR] (ClS)	MCot SPer
	Purple Tiger = 'Jacpurr'[PBR] (F)	ESty
	quatre saisons	see *R.* × *damascena* var. *semperflorens*
	'Quatre Saisons Blanche Mousseuse' (DMo)	CPou MAus NLar
	Queen Anne = 'Austruck'[PBR] (S)	CSBt EPfP ESty LRHS MAus SCoo
	Queen Elizabeth	see *R.* 'The Queen Elizabeth'
	Queen Mother = 'Korquemu'[PBR] (Patio) 🏆H6	CGro CSBt ELan EPfP ESps MAus MJak MRav SPer SWCr
	'Queen of Bourbons' (Bb)	LEdu NLar
	Queen of Denmark	see *R.* 'Königin von Dänemark'
	Queen of Sweden = 'Austiger'[PBR] (S)	CGro CNec CRos ECnt EPfP LBuc LRHS MAus NRHS SCob SPer SWCr
	'Rachel' (HT)	CPou EWTr LSRN
§	Rachel Louise Moran = 'Jacdrama'[PBR] (HT)	ESty
	Rachel = 'Tangust'[PBR] (HT) 🏆H6	CSBt ESty MRav SPoG SSea SWCr
	Rainbow Magic = 'Dicxplosion'[PBR] (Patio)	MJak
	'Rambling Rector' (Ra) 🏆H6	Widely available
	Rambling Rosie = 'Horjasper'[PBR] (Ra) 🏆H6	CGro CKel CRos CSBt EBee ECnt EPfP ESty EWTr LBrs LRHS LSRN MAus MSwo NRHS SSea SWCr
	'Raspberry Royale' (F/Patio) 🏆H6	MAsh SPoG
	'Raubritter' ('Macrantha' hybrid)	CPou MAus SPer SWCr WBod
	Raymond Blanc = 'Delnado' (HT)	EWTr LSRN MRav NLar
	Rebecca (Patio)	ESty LSRN
	'Rebecca Claire' (HT)	LSRN
	Rebecca Mary = 'Dicjury'[PBR] (F)	IDic
	Reconciliation = 'Hartillery'[PBR] (HT)	SWCr
	Red Abundance	see *R.* Songs of Praise
	Red Blanket = 'Intercell' (S/GC)	MAus SPer
	Red Coat = 'Auscoat' (F)	LRHS MAus
	Red Devil = 'Dicam' (HT)	IBoy LBrs SCoo
	Red Eden Rose = 'Meidrason'[PBR] (Cl)	ESty SSea
	Red Finesse = 'Korvillade'[PBR] (F) 🏆H6	EBee MAsh SWCr
	'Red Grootendorst'	see *R.* 'F.J. Grootendorst'
	'Red Max Graf'	see *R.* Rote Max Graf
	red moss	see *R.* 'Henri Martin'
	Red New Dawn	see *R.* 'Étendard'
	Red Parfum de Provence = 'Meiafone'[PBR] (HT)	ESty
§	'Red Patio' (F/Patio)	LSRN
	Red Perfumella = 'Meikeneza'[PBR] (HT)	ESty
	Red Rascal = 'Jacbed' (S/Patio)	CKel CSBt
	red rose of Lancaster	see *R. gallica* var. *officinalis*
	'Red Wing' (S)	MAus
	Redouté = 'Auspale'[PBR] (S)	MAus
	Regensberg = 'Macyoumis'[PBR] (F/Patio)	IBoy LEdu MAus SPer SWCr
	'Reine des Violettes' (HP) 🏆H7	CBWd CPou ELon EPfP GBin IArd LCro LRHS LSRN MAsh MAus MCot MRav NLar NPri SMad SPer SRGP SWCr
	'Reine Marie Henriette' (ClHT)	CPou
§	'Reine Victoria' (Bb)	EPfP LCro MAus MRav NLar SPer
	Remember Me = 'Cocdestin' (HT) 🏆H6	CBod CGro CSBt ECnt EPfP ESps ESty IArd IBoy LBrs LCro LRHS LSRN MAsh MAus MGos MRav NEgg NPri SCob SPer SPoG SWCr
§	Remember = 'Poulht001'[PBR] (HT) 🏆H6	ECnt EPfP LBrs LRHS NRHS SPoG SWCr
	Remembrance = 'Harxampton'[PBR] (F)	CRos EPfP ESps ESty LBrs LBuc LRHS LSRN MAsh MJak MRav MWat NPri NRHS SCob SPer SPoG SSea SWCr
§	Renaissance = 'Harzart'[PBR] (HT)	CKel CSBt ELon MJak MRav SWCr
	'René André' (Ra)	CPou CRHN EBee MAus NLar
	'René d'Anjou' (CeMo)	MAus
	'Rescht'	see *R.* 'De Resht'
	'Rêve d'Or' (N)	MAus MCot MMuc SPer
	'Réveil Dijonnais' (ClHT)	MAus
	Rhapsody in Blue = 'Frantasia'[PBR] (S) 🏆H6	Widely available
§	× ***richardii***	MAus NLar
	Rick Stein = 'Tan96205'[PBR] (HT)	LSRN
	'Rival de Paestum' (T)	MAus
	'River Gardens'	NPer
	Rob Roy = 'Cocrob' (F)	SPer
	Robbie Burns = 'Ausburn' (SpH)	MAus
	'Robert le Diable' (Ce × G)	MAus SPer
	Rock & Roll = 'Wekgobnez' (HT)	CSBt ESty
	'Roger Lambelin' (HP)	CPou MAus
	Romance = 'Tanezamor'[PBR] (S)	IBoy LSRN
	'Rosa Mundi'	see *R. gallica* 'Versicolor'
	'Rose à Parfum de l'Haÿ' (Ru)	CTri
	'Rose de Meaux'	see *R.* × *centifolia* 'De Meaux'
	'Rose de Meaux White'	see *R.* 'White de Meaux'
	'Rose de Rescht'	see *R.* 'De Resht'
	Rose des Cisterciens = 'Delarle' (HT)	ESty MRav
	'Rose des Maures' misapplied	see *R.* 'Sissinghurst Castle'
	'Rose du Maître d'Ecole'	see *R.* 'Du Maître d'Ecole'
	'Rose du Roi' (HP/DPo)	CBod ELon LRHS MAus
	'Rose du Roi à Fleurs Pourpres' (HP)	MAus
	Rose for Elaine = 'Rawdenqueen' (HT)	LSRN
§	Rose Gaujard = 'Gaumo' (HT)	LBrs MAsh
	Rose In Memory of my Cat = 'Webyum' (HT)	LSRN
	Rose of Picardy = 'Ausfudge' (S)	MAus
	'Rose-Marie Viaud' (Ra)	CPou EBee MAus MMuc
	Rosemary Harkness = 'Harrowbond' (HT)	ESps ESty MJak MRav SPer SRGP
	'Rosemary Rose' (F)	SPer

	Rosemoor = 'Austough'PBR (S) 🏆H6	CRos CSBt LBuc LRHS MAus NRHS SPer
	'Roseraie de l'Haÿ' (Ru) 🏆H7	Widely available
	Rosie = 'Benros' (Min)	LSRN
	'Rosy Cheeks' (HT)	LRHS
	Rosy Cushion = 'Interall' (S/GC)	CKel EWTr LRHS MAus MCot NLar SPer WKif
	'Rosy Mantle' (ClHT)	CSBt SPer SWCr
§	Rotary Sunrise = 'Fryglitzy' (HT)	CSBt
§	Rote Max Graf = 'Kormax' (GC/Ru)	CBod CDul CKel
§	'Rouletii' (Min) **new**	ITim
	'Roundelay' (HT)	EBee
	roxburghii	CBcs LEdu MAus SKHP
	- PAB 7331	LEdu
	- 'Plena'	see *R. roxburghii* f. *roxburghii*
§	- f. ***roxburghii*** (d)	MAus
	'Royal Air Force' (HT)	ELan
§	Royal Brompton Rose = 'Meivildo' (HT)	ESty
	Royal Copenhagen	see *R.* Remember
	'Royal Gold' (ClHT)	SSea
	Royal Jubilee = 'Auspaddle'PBR (S)	CSBt LCro LOPS MAus SCob SPer
	'Royal Occasion' (F)	SPer
	Royal William = 'Korzaun' (HT) 🏆H6	CSBt ELan ESps LBuc LRHS LSRN MAsh MAus MJak MRav MWat NPri SCob SPer SWCr
§	***rubiginosa***	CArn CCVT CDul EPfP ESps GPoy IFro LBuc MAus MRav NWea SPer WHed WMou WTSh
	rubrifolia	see *R. glauca* Pourr.
	'Rubrotincta'	see *R.* 'Hebe's Lip'
	rubus (Ra)	MAus
	Ruby Anniversary = 'Harbonny'PBR (Patio)	CGro CKel CRos CSBt ELon ESps ESty LBuc LCro LRHS LSRN MAsh MRav MSwo MWat NPri NRHS SCob SCoo SPoG SSea SVic SWCr
	Ruby Celebration = 'Peawinner'PBR (F) 🏆H6	CKel ESps ESty MRav SWCr
	Ruby Romance	see *R.* Medley Ruby
	Ruby Ruby	see *R.* Ruby Slippers
§	Ruby Slippers = 'Weksactrumi' (Min)	LRHS MAsh NRHS SPoG
	'Ruby Wedding' (HT)	CBcs CKel CNec CSBt CTri ECnt ELan EPfP ESps IArd IBoy LBrs LRHS LSRN MAsh MAus MGos MJak MRav NRHS SCob SPer SPoG SVic SWCr
	'Ruby Wedding Anniversary' (F)	LSRN
	rugosa (Ru)	CArg CBod CDul CFGn CGro CLnd CRos CTri ECrN EPfP EPom ESps LBuc LRHS MAus MHer MRav NWea SCob SGol SPlb SVic SWCr WHar WMat WMou WTSh
	- 'Alba' (Ru)	Widely available
	- 'Rubra' (Ru)	CBcs CBod CCVT CDul CGro CTri CWib ELan EPfP EPom ESps GMcL LBuc LCro LOPS NBes NWea SCob SEWo SPer SPoG SSea SVic WHar WHed
	'Rugosa Atropurpurea' (Ru)	EPom
	'Rumba' (F)	ELan
	'Rural England' (Ra)	LRHS
	Rushing Stream = 'Austream' (GC)	MAus
	'Russelliana' (Ra)	MAus NLar
	Saint Alban = 'Auschesnut'PBR (S)	MAus
	Saint Boniface = 'Kormatt' (F/Patio)	CSBt
	Saint Cecilia = 'Ausmit' (S)	MAus
	Saint Edmunds Rose	see *R.* Bonita
	Saint Ethelburga = 'Beabimbo' (S)	MCot
	Saint John's rose	see *R.* × *richardii*
	'Saint Nicholas' (D)	MAus
	Saint Swithun = 'Auswith'PBR (S)	EPfP ESty LRHS MAus NRHS SCob SPer SSea SWCr
	'Salet' (DPMo)	CPou MAus
	'Sally Holmes' (S) 🏆H7	CPou ECnt EPfP EWTr LRHS MAus MRav MWat SEND SLon SPer SWCr
	Sally Kane = 'Frygroovy'PBR (HT)	MRav
	Sally's Rose = 'Canrem' (HT)	ECnt LSRN
	Salsa	see *R.* Cheek to Cheek
	Salvation = 'Harlark'PBR (F)	ESty
§	Samaritan = 'Harverag'PBR (HT)	CSBt ESty MRav SWCr
	sancta	see *R.* × *richardii*
	'Sander's White Rambler' (Ra) 🏆H7	CRHN CRos CSam CTri EBee EPfP EWTr LRHS MAus MRav MSwo NRHS SPer SWCr WFar
	Sandra = 'Koreinek' (HT)	LSRN
	Sandra = 'Poulen055'PBR (Renaissance Series) (S)	EBee LSRN
	'Sanguinea'	see *R.* × *odorata* Sanguinea Group
	Sarah (HT)	see *R.* Jardins de Bagatelle
	'Sarah van Fleet' (Ru)	CBWd CBod CTri EBee EPfP ESps GBin IArd IBoy MAus MMuc MRav MSwo NEgg NLar SMad SPer
	Sarah, Duchess of York	see *R.* Sunseeker
	Savoy Hotel = 'Harvintage' (HT)	EPfP ESps MAus MRav SPer
	'Scabrosa' (Ru) 🏆H7	CBod EBee ECnt EPfP EWTr LBuc LRHS MAsh MAus NLar NWea SPer
	Scarborough Fair = 'Ausoran' (S) 🏆H6	LBuc LRHS MAus MMuc
	Scarlet Fire	see *R.* 'Scharlachglut'
	Scarlet Glow	see *R.* 'Scharlachglut'
	Scarlet Hit = 'Poulmo'PBR (PatioHit Series) (Min/Patio)	ECnt IBoy LRHS LSRN NRHS
	Scarlet Patio = 'Kortingle'PBR (Patio)	MAsh MWat
	Scarlet Queen Elizabeth = 'Dicel' (F)	CBcs
	Scented Carpet = 'Chewground'PBR (GC) 🏆H6	ECnt ELan MAus SWCr
	Scented Garden = 'Chewscentity' (S)	ESty
	Scented Memory = 'Poulht002'PBR (HT)	ECnt
	Scentimental = 'Wekplapep'PBR (F)	EPfP ESty MAsh MRav MWat SCoo SSea SWCr
	'Scentsation' (Min)	CKel
	Scent-sation = 'Fryromeo'PBR (HT)	CGro CKel LBrs MRav MWat SCoo SPoG SWCr
	Scepter'd Isle = 'Ausland'PBR (S)	CRos CSBt EPfP LBuc LCro LOPS LRHS MAus NRHS SCob SCoo SPer SWCr
§	'Scharlachglut' (ClS)	CPou EPfP EWTr LRHS MAus SPer
	Schloss Bad Homburg	see *R.* Alibaba
	Schneewittchen	see *R.* Iceberg
§	'Schneezwerg' (Ru) 🏆H7	CBod EBee EWTr MAus NLar SPer
	'Schoolgirl' (ClHT)	CBcs CBod CTri EBee ELan EPfP ESps EUJe IBoy LBuc LRHS MAsh

		MRav MSwo NEgg NPri SPer SSea SWCr
	'Scintillation' (S/GC)	MAus
	Scotch rose	see *R. spinosissima*
	Scotch yellow (SpH)	see *R.* × *harisonii* 'Williams' Double Yellow'
	'Seagull' (Ra) Υ^{H6}	CBWd CBod CTri ECnt EPfP ESps IBoy LEdu LRHS LSRN MRav NLar NPri NWea SCob SLon SMad SPer SWCr WHer
	'Seale Pink Diamond' (S)	SSea
	Sealed with a Kiss = 'Simwhat' (HT) **new**	ESty
	'Sealing Wax' (*moyesii* hybrid)	CPou NLar
	'Semiplena'	see *R.* × *alba* 'Alba Semiplena'
	sericea (S)	MAus
	- var. ***morrisonensis*** B&SWJ 7139	WCru
§	- subsp. ***omeiensis***	LEdu WPGP
	- - BWJ 7550	WCru
	- - PAB 2883	LEdu
	- - f. ***pteracantha*** (S)	CBcs CDul CKel CTri ELan EPfP EWTr IDee LEdu MAus MRav NLar NWea SCob SPer
§	***setigera***	MAus
	setipoda	MAus
	seven sisters rose	see *R. multiflora* 'Grevillei'
	Sexy Rexy = 'Macrexy' (F)	CBcs CSBt ESps IBoy LSRN MAsh MAus MRav MWat SCob SMad SPer SRGP SWCr
	'Shailer's White Moss'	see *R.* × *centifolia* 'Shailer's White Moss'
	Sharifa Asma = 'Ausreef'^{PBR} (S)	CBod CSBt EBee ELan LSRN MAus MRav MSwo NEgg NLar SPer SWCr
	Sheila's Perfume = 'Harsherry' (F) Υ^{H6}	CGro ECnt EPfP ESty IBoy LSRN MAsh MRav SPer SPoG SWCr
	Shine On = 'Dictalent'^{PBR} (Patio) Υ^{H6}	CSBt ECnt IBoy LBrs MWat SWCr
	Shining Light = 'Cocshimmer'^{PBR} (Patio)	SCoo
	'Shot Silk' (HT)	CKel EWTr
§	Showstar = 'Smi36-1-02' (HT)	ESty
	Showtime = 'Baitime' (ClS)	MAsh SWCr
§	Shrimp Hit = 'Poulshrimp'^{PBR} (Patio)	ECnt LBuc SPoG
	'Shropshire Lass' (S)	MAsh MAus SPer
	Shropshire Star = 'Chewsummit' (ClMin) **new**	ESty
	'Silver 25th Anniversary' (F) **new**	CGro
	Silver Anniversary ambig.	LSRN
	Silver Anniversary = 'Jaclav' (HT)	CKel MJak
	Silver Anniversary = 'Meiborfil' (HT)	ELon
§	Silver Anniversary = 'Poulari'^{PBR} (HT) Υ^{H6}	CBod CRos CSBt ECnt ELan LCro LRHS LSRN MAsh MAus MGos MRav MWat NPri NRHS SCoo SPer SPoG SSea SVic SWCr
	'Silver Jubilee' (HT)	CBcs CTri IArd IBoy LRHS MAsh MAus MRav NRHS SCob SPer SWCr
	'Silver Lining' (HT)	CKel
	Silver Shadow = 'Frystereo' (HT)	CGro ECnt ESty SWCr
	'Silver Wedding' (HT)	CBcs CGro CKel CNec ELan IArd MAus MJak MRav MSwo NEgg SCob SPer SVic SWCr
	'Silver Wedding Celebration' (F)	ESty LSRN
	Silver Wishes	see *R.* Pink Hit
	Simba = 'Korbelma' (HT)	LSRN
	'Simone' (HT) **new**	CPou EBee
	'Simplex Multiflora'	CBot CWib
	Simply Gorgeous = 'Formaui' (HT) **new**	ESty
	Simply Sally = 'Harpaint'^{PBR} (Patio)	LSRN
§	Simply the Best = 'Macamster'^{PBR} (HT) Υ^{H6}	CGro CKel CSBt ELan EPfP ESty LRHS LSRN MAsh MAus MGos MJak MRav MWat NPri NRHS SCob SCoo SPer SPoG SWCr
	sinowilsonii	see *R. longicuspis* var. *sinowilsonii*
	'Sir Cedric Morris' (Ra)	NLar SSea
	Sir Clough = 'Ausclough' (S)	MAus
	Sir Edward Elgar = 'Ausprima'^{PBR} (S)	MAus
	'Sir Galahad' deep pink-flowered (F) **new**	CKel
I	'Sir Galahad' white-flowered (F)	CKel MRav
	Sir John Betjeman = 'Ausvivid'^{PBR} (S)	EPfP LBuc LRHS MAus NRHS
	'Sir Joseph Paxton' (Bb)	CPou MAus
	Sir Paul Smith = 'Beapaul' (ClHT)	LRHS
	Sir Walter Raleigh = 'Ausspry' (S)	MAus MRav MWat
§	'Sissinghurst Castle' (G)	MAus
	Sister Elizabeth = 'Auspalette'^{PBR} (S)	LRHS LSRN MAus NRHS SCoo
	Skylark = 'Ausimple'^{PBR} (S) Υ^{H6}	LBuc LRHS MAus SCob
	'Skyrocket'	see *R.* 'Wilhelm'
	Smarty = 'Intersmart' (S/GC)	MAus SPer
	Snow Carpet = 'Maccarpe' (Min/GC)	MAus
	'Snow Dwarf'	see *R.* 'Schneezwerg'
	Snow Goose = 'Auspom'^{PBR} (ClS)	CSBt EPfP LRHS MAus NLar NRHS SPer SSea SWCr
	Snow Hit = 'Poulsnows'^{PBR} (Min/Patio)	ECnt
	'Snow Queen'	see *R.* 'Frau Karl Druschki'
	Snow Queen = 'Simseen' (HT) **new**	ESty
	Snow Sunblaze = 'Meigovin' (Min)	SPer
	Snowball = 'Macangeli' (Min/GC)	LSRN
	Snowcap = 'Harfleet'^{PBR} (Patio)	ESty
	'Snowdon' (Ru)	LRHS MAus
	Soeur Emmanuelle = 'Delamo'^{PBR} (S)	CBod ESty LSRN MRav
	'Soldier Boy' (Cl)	CBod CPou EBee
§	Solo Mio = 'Poulen002'^{PBR} (Renaissance Series) (S)	CBod CTri EBee ECnt EWTr NLar
§	'Sombreuil' (ClT)	CBod EBee EPfP IArd LRHS MAus MRav NEgg NLar SPer SWCr
	Something Different = 'Simsodiff' (HT) **new**	ESty
	Something Special = 'Macwyo'^{PBR} (HT)	ESty
	Song and Dance = 'Frydishy'^{PBR} (HT)	LBrs

§	Songs of Praise = 'Harkimono'PBR (Abundance Series) (F)	SWCr
	'Sophia'	see *R.* Solo Mio = 'Poulen002'
	'Sophie's Perpetual' (ClCh)	CPou CTri LRHS MAus SLon SPer
	Sophy's Rose = 'Auslot'PBR (S)	CRos LBuc LRHS LSRN MAus MBNS NEgg NRHS SPer SWCr
	Sorbet Fruité = 'Meihestries'PBR (ClF)	SSea
	soulieana (Ra/S)	MAus
	'Soupert et Notting' (DPoMo)	CPou LRHS MAus SPer
	'Southampton' (F) ♀H6	LSRN MAus SPer SSea SWCr
	Southern Beauty = 'Forauty' (F) **new**	ESty
	'Souvenir de Claudius Denoyel' (ClHT)	CPou SPer
	'Souvenir de Jeanne Balandreau' (HP)	CPou
	'Souvenir de la Malmaison' (Bb)	EPfP EWTr LRHS MAus MRav MWat NLar SPer
	'Souvenir de la Malmaison' (ClBb)	see *R.* 'Climbing Souvenir de la Malmaison'
	'Souvenir de Madame Léonie Viennot' (ClT)	EBee MAus MRav
	'Souvenir de Pierre Vibert' (DPMo)	CPou
	'Souvenir de Saint Anne's' (Bb)	EWTr MAus
	'Souvenir du Docteur Jamain' (ClHP)	CBWd CPou CSBt ELan ELon EPfP ESty LCro LRHS LSRN MAus MCot MRav MWat NLar SPer SPoG SSea SWCr WFar WKif
	'Spanish Beauty'	see *R.* 'Madame Grégoire Staechelin'
	Sparkle = 'Frymerlin'PBR (HT)	ECnt ESty LBrs MAsh SWCr
	Sparkler	see *R.* Kent
	Sparkling Burgundy = 'Raw1007' (F) **new**	ESty
	Sparkling Scarlet = 'Meihati' (ClF)	MAsh
	Special Anniversary = 'Whastiluc'PBR (HT) ♀H6	CBcs CBod CGro CKel CSBt EBee ECnt ELon ESty LBrs LCro LRHS LSRN MAsh MJak MRav MWat NPri NRHS SCoo SPoG SSea SWCr
	Special Child = 'Taniripsa'PBR (F/Patio) ♀H6	MRav SSea SWCr
	'Special Dad' (HT) **new**	CGro
	Special Event = 'Meibrelon' (HT)	ESty
	Special Friend = 'Kirspec'PBR (Patio)	CBod ESty LSRN SCob SWCr
	Special Occasion = 'Fryyoung'PBR (HT)	LBuc MAsh MRav MWat SNig SWCr
	Special Son (F)	ESty
	'Spectabilis' (Ra)	CPou EBee SKHP
	'Spencer' misapplied	see *R.* 'Enfant de France'
§	***spinosissima***	CArg CCCN CDul LBuc LRHS MAus MMuc NWea SCob SGol SPer WHed WTSh
	- 'Andrewsii' ♀H7	MAus MRav
§	- double, pink-flowered	SKHP WBor
§	- double, white-flowered ♀H7	ECha LEdu MAus
	- 'Falkland'	ECha GCra MAus
	- 'Marbled Pink'	MAus
	- 'Mary, Queen of Scots'	EWTr GBin MAus SRms
	- 'Mrs Colville'	MAus
	- 'Ormiston Roy'	MAus
	- 'Single Cherry'	MAus
	- 'William III'	EWes GCra MAus
	Spirit of Freedom = 'Ausbite'PBR (S)	EPfP LBuc LRHS MAsh MAus NEgg NRHS SSea
§	'Splendens' (Ra)	GBin MMuc
	Splish Splash = 'Raw1020' (F) **new**	ESty
	St Helena = 'Canlish' (F)	ECnt
	'Stanwell Perpetual' (SpH) ♀H7	CBod CTri ELan EPfP EWTr IBoy MAus MRav NLar SEND SPer SSea
	Star Dust = 'Morstar' (Min)	ELon
	'Star Performer'PBR (ClPatio)	CSBt ECnt EPfP ESty MAsh SPoG SSea SWCr
	Stardust = 'Devstar' (HT)	WBor
	Stardust = 'Peavandyke'PBR (Patio/F)	CPou ESty
	Starlight Express = 'Trobstar'PBR (Cl)	IBoy LRHS MAsh SCoo SPer
	'Stars 'n' Stripes' (Min)	MAus
	Stella (HT)	LSRN
	stellata	MAus
§	- var. ***mirifica***	MAus
	Strawberries and Cream = 'Geestraw' (Min/Patio)	ELan ESty SWCr
	Strawberry Fayre = 'Arowillip'PBR (Min/Patio)	CKel ESty MRav SPoG
	Strawberry Hill = 'Ausrimini'PBR (S) ♀H6	CSBt ESty LRHS MAus MMuc SCoo
	Strike It Rich = 'Wekbepmey'PBR (HT) ♀H6	ESty MRav SWCr
§	Sue Hipkin = 'Harzazz'PBR (HT)	ESty MRav
	'Suffolk' (HT)	SCob
	Suffolk = 'Kormixal'PBR (S/GC) ♀H6	CSBt ELan MAus MJak MRav SCob SPer SSea
	Sugar and Spice = 'Peaallure'PBR (Patio)	SPoG
	Sugar Baby = 'Tanabagus'PBR (Patio)	ESty
	Sugar 'n' Spice = 'Tinspice' (Min)	MRav
	Suma = 'Harsuma' (GC)	ESty
	Summer Beauty = 'Kororbe'PBR (F) ♀H6	ESty MAsh SWCr
	Summer Breeze = 'Korelasting'PBR (ClS)	CSam LRHS MAsh
	Summer Fragrance = 'Tanfudermos' (Castle Series) (HT)	ELon
§	Summer Gold = 'Poulreb'PBR (F)	MAsh SWCr
	'Summer Holiday' (HT)	SPer
	Summer Love = 'Franluv' (F)	CBcs
	Summer Memories = 'Koruteli'PBR (Palace Series) (F)	CKel
	Summer Snow = 'Weopop' (Patio)	WBod
	Summer Song = 'Austango'PBR (S)	CNec CRos EPfP ESty LBuc LCro LRHS LSRN MAsh MAus NRHS SCob SWCr
	Summer Wine = 'Korizont'PBR (ClHT) ♀H6	CSBt ECnt EPfP LRHS SCoo SPer SWCr
	Summertime = 'Chewlarmoll'PBR (ClPatio) ♀H6	CGro CSBt ECnt ELan EPfP IBoy LBrs LBuc LRHS MAsh MAus MRav NPri SCoo SPer SPoG

	Sun Hit = 'Poulsun'^{PBR} (PatioHit Series) (Min/Patio)	CSBt ECnt ESps MRav SWCr
	'Sunblaze'	see *R.* Orange Sunblaze
	Sunblest = 'Landora' (HT)	MAsh MRav SCob
	Sunfire = 'Jacko' (F)	ECnt
	Sunny Day = 'Savasun' (S)	EBee
	Sunny Sky = 'Koraruli'^{PBR} (HT) **new**	ECnt ESty
	Sunrise = 'Kormarter'^{PBR} (S)	CGro ESty MAsh SPoG SWCr
§	Sunseeker = 'Dicracer'^{PBR} (F/Patio) ♀^{H6}	MRav SPoG
	Sunset Boulevard = 'Harbabble'^{PBR} (F)	ESps LBrs MAsh MAus MRav SCoo SPer
	Sunset Celebration	see *R.* Warm Wishes
	Sunset Glow	see *R.* Alibaba
	Super Dorothy = 'Heldoro' (Ra) ♀^{H6}	CGro LSRN MAus SSea SWCr
	Super Elfin = 'Helkleger'^{PBR} (Ra)	CRos LBuc LRHS MAus MRav NLar SCob SPer SSea SWCr
	Super Excelsa = 'Helexa' (Ra) ♀^{H6}	ESty IBoy MAus SCob SSea SWCr
	Super Fairy = 'Helsufair'^{PBR} (Ra) ♀^{H6}	CKel EBee ECnt MAus MRav SMad SPer SSea SWCr
	Super Sparkle = 'Helfels'^{PBR} (Ra)	SCob SSea
§	Super Star = 'Tanorstar' (HT)	CKel ESps MAus MRav SWCr
	Super Trouper = 'Fryleyeca'^{PBR} (F) ♀^{H6}	CGro CSBt ECnt ESty IBoy LBrs LRHS LSRN MAsh MRav NPri SCoo SPer SWCr WBor WCot
	'Surpasse Tout' (G)	MAus
	Surrey = 'Korlanum' (GC) ♀^{H6}	CBod CKel CSBt CTri ELan ESty LCro LSRN MAus MRav MSwo NLar SCob SPer SSea SWCr
	Susan = 'Poulsue' (S)	EBee ECnt LSRN NLar SLon SWCr
	Susan Williams-Ellis = 'Ausquirk'^{PBR} (S)	CRos EPfP LBuc LRHS MAsh MAus NRHS SCob
	Sussex = 'Poulave'^{PBR} (GC)	CSBt MRav MSwo SCob SPer SSea
	Swan = 'Auswhite' (S)	MAus
	Swan Lake = 'Macmed' (Cl)	CPou EBee ECnt ELan EPfP EWTr IBoy MRav NLar SPer
	Swany = 'Meiburenac' (Min/GC)	ECrN ESps ESty EWTr LSRN MAus MJak MSwo SPer SWCr
	'Sweet Ballymaloe' (S)	IBoy
	Sweet Caroline = 'Micaroline' (Min)	LSRN
	Sweet Child of Mine (HT)	ESty
	Sweet Dream = 'Fryminicot' (Patio) ♀^{H6}	CGro CSBt CTri ELan EPfP ESps IBoy LBrs LRHS LSRN MAsh MAus MJak MRav SMad SPer SPoG SRGP SSea SWCr
	'Sweet Fairy' (Min)	CSBt
	Sweet Haze = 'Tan97274'^{PBR} (F) ♀^{H6}	CKel CSBt IBoy MRav SCoo SPer SWCr
	Sweet Juliet = 'Ausleap'^{PBR} (S)	CRos CSBt ELan IBoy LRHS MAus MSwo SPer SWCr
*	'Sweet Lemon Dream' (Patio)	CTri
	Sweet Magic = 'Dicmagic'^{PBR} (Min/Patio) ♀^{H6}	CTri ESps IBoy MRav SPoG
	Sweet Memories = 'Whamemo' (Patio)	CGro CKel CTri ECnt ELan EPfP ESps ESty IBoy LBrs LRHS MAsh MRav NPri NRHS SCoo SPer SSea SWCr
	Sweet Parfum de Provence = 'Meiclusif'^{PBR} (HT) ♀^{H6}	ESty LSRN
	Sweet Remembrance = 'Kirr' (HT)	SCoo
	'Sweet Revelation'	see *R.* Sue Hipkin
	'Sweet Wonder' (Patio)	EPfP MAsh
	'Sweetie' (Patio)	ESty
	sweginzowii	GLog MAus
	'Sydonie' (HP)	CPou
	'Sylvia Dot' (F)	LSRN
	'Sympathie' (ClHT)	MAsh SPer SSea
	Tall Story = 'Dickooky' (F) ♀^{H6}	EBee MRav SWCr
	Tam O'Shanter = 'Auscerise'^{PBR} (S)	EPfP LRHS MAus NRHS
	Tamora = 'Austamora' (S)	MAus
	Tangerine Tango = 'Cheworangemane' (Cl)	ECnt ESty
	Tango Showground = 'Chewpattens'^{PBR} (GC)	ESty SSea
	Tatton = 'Fryentice'^{PBR} (F)	ESty MAus MRav
	Tawny Tiger = 'Frygolly'^{PBR} (F)	SWCr
	Tea Clipper = 'Ausrover'^{PBR} (S)	CSBt MAus SCoo
	Tear Drop = 'Dicomo' (Min/Patio)	SCob SPer SSea SWCr
	Teasing Georgia = 'Ausbaker'^{PBR} (S) ♀^{H6}	CKel CRos ECnt EPfP ESty IBoy LBuc LRHS LSRN MAsh MAus MMuc NLar NRHS SCob SCoo SWCr
	Temptress = 'Korramal' (ClS) ♀^{H6}	CGro CPou EPfP EUJe MAsh
	Tenacious = 'Macblackpo'^{PBR} (F)	ESty SWCr
	Tequila Sunrise = 'Dicobey' (HT) ♀^{H6}	CGro CKel CTri ELan EPfP ESps ESty IBoy LBrs MAus MJak MRav SPer SSea SWCr
	Terracotta = 'Meicobuis' (HT)	ESty
	Tess of the d'Urbervilles = 'Ausmove'^{PBR} (S)	CRos EBee ELan EPfP EShb ESps ESty IBoy LCro LOPS LRHS LSRN MAus NEgg NLar NRHS SCob SCoo SPer SSea SWCr
	'Tessa' (F)	LSRN
	Thank You = 'Chesdeep'^{PBR} (Patio)	ESps ESty LBuc
§	That's Jazz = 'Poulnorm'^{PBR} (Courtyard Series) (ClF)	CSam ECnt LBrs LSRN SWCr
	The Albrighton Rambler = 'Ausmobile' (Ra)	CGro CRos EPfP LRHS MAus NRHS SWCr
	The Alexandra Rose = 'Ausday'^{PBR} (S)	EPfP LBuc LRHS MAus SPer
§	The Alnwick Rose = 'Ausgrab'^{PBR} (S)	EPfP LBuc LRHS MAus MGos NLar NRHS SCob SCoo SPer SSea
I	'The Anniversary Rose'	EPfP LBrs LBuc LRHS MAsh NPri NRHS SCoo SWCr
	The Birthday Rose (F)	CGro LBuc
	'The Bishop' (Ce × G)	MAus
	The Bosworth Rose = 'Raw1014' (F) **new**	ESty
	The Compass Rose = 'Korwisco'^{PBR} (S)	EPfP
	The Countryman = 'Ausman' (S)	IBoy MAus SCob SSea
	The Coventry Cathedral Rose = 'Smi72-02' (F)	ESty
	The Dark Lady = 'Ausbloom'^{PBR} (S)	MAus NEgg SPer
	The Diamond Wedding Rose (HT)	LSRN MAsh SWCr

§ 'The Fairy' (Poly) $\mathbb{Y}^{H7}$ — CBod CKel CSBt CTri EAEE EBee ECnt ELan ESps EWTr IBoy LEdu LRHS MAsh MAus MRav MWat NLar SCob SDix SMad SPer SSea SWCr WBor
'The Garland' (Ra) $\mathbb{Y}^{H6}$ — EPfP LBuc LRHS MAus MMuc NLar NRHS SPer SWCr
The Generous Gardener = 'Ausdrawn'PBR (S) $\mathbb{Y}^{H6}$ — CKel CRos ELan EPfP EShb ESty LBuc LRHS LSRN MAus MGos MJak NRHS SCob SCoo SPer SSea SWCr
§ The Gold Award Rose = 'Poulac008' (Palace Series) (Patio) — ECnt
The Herbalist = 'Aussemi' (S) — LRHS MAus
The Ingenious Mr Fairchild = 'Austijus'PBR (S) — EPfP LRHS MAus NRHS SCoo
The Jubilee Rose = 'Poulbrido'PBR (F) — ECnt SCoo
The Lady Gardener = 'Ausbrass' (S) — CRos EPfP LRHS MAus NRHS
The Lady of the Lake = 'Ausherbert' (Ra) **new** — LCro LRHS MAsh MAus NRHS SCob SCoo SWCr
The Lady's Blush = 'Ausoscar'PBR (S) — EPfP LRHS MAus
The Lakeland Rose = 'Harspiral' — MAsh
The Lark Ascending = 'Ausursula'PBR (S) — LBuc LCro LOPS LRHS MAus SCob SCoo SSea
The Maidstone Rose = 'Kordauerpa' (S) — SCoo
'The Margaret Coppola Rose' — see *R.* White Gold
The Mayflower = 'Austilly'PBR (S) $\mathbb{Y}^{H6}$ — CSBt ELon IBoy LBuc LRHS MAus MSwo NRHS SCob SPer
§ The McCartney Rose = 'Meizeli'PBR (HT) — SPer
'The New Dawn' — see *R.* 'New Dawn'
The Nun = 'Ausnun' (S) — LRHS MAus
'The One and Only' (HT) — LBrs LRHS MAsh NPri SWCr
The Painter = 'Mactemaik'PBR (F) — LSRN
§ The Pilgrim = 'Auswalker'PBR (S) $\mathbb{Y}^{H6}$ — CKel CRos CSBt EPfP ESps LBuc LRHS MAus MJak NLar NRHS SCob SPer SSea SWCr
The Poet's Wife = 'Auswhisper' (S) **new** — CGro CRos ESty LRHS MAsh MAus NRHS SCoo
The Prince = 'Ausvelvet'PBR (S) — LRHS MAus NLar SPer
The Prince's Trust = 'Harholding'PBR (Cl) — LBuc MAsh MAus
'The Prioress' (S) — MAus
§ 'The Queen Elizabeth' (F) — CBcs CSBt CTri ELan ESps IBoy LCro LSRN MAsh MAus MRav SCob SPer SRGP SSea SWCr WBor
The Reeve = 'Ausreeve' (S) — MAus
The Rotarian — see *R.* Rotary Sunrise
'The Royal Brompton Rose' — see *R.* Royal Brompton Rose
I 'The Rugby Rose' (HT) — LSRN
The Sheikh Khalifa Rose = 'Dickoolkid' (Patio) — IDic
The Shepherdess = 'Austwist'PBR (S) — ELan IBoy MAus
The Squire = 'Ausquire' (S) — MAus
The Times Rose = 'Korpeahn' (F) $\mathbb{Y}^{H6}$ — ECnt MAus SCob SWCr
The Wedgwood Rose = 'Ausjosiah'PBR (ClS) — EPfP LBuc LRHS MAsh MAus NRHS SCob
The Wren = 'Kormamtiza'PBR (F/Patio) — MAsh
'Thelma' (Ra) — MAus
'Thérèse Bugnet' (Ru) $\mathbb{Y}^{H7}$ — MAus
Thinking of You = 'Frydandy'PBR (HT) $\mathbb{Y}^{H6}$ — CGro ESps ESty IBoy MAsh MAus NPri SRGP SSea SWCr
'Thisbe' (HM) — CPou EBee MAus SPer
Thomas à Becket = 'Auswinston' (S) — CRos EPfP ESty LCro LOPS LRHS MAus NRHS
'Threave' (Bb) — CPou
threepenny bit rose — see *R. elegantula* 'Persetosa'
Tickled Pink = 'Fryhunky'PBR (F) $\mathbb{Y}^{H6}$ — CKel CSBt LRHS LSRN MAsh MRav MWat SCoo SPer SPoG SSea
Times Past = 'Harhilt'PBR (ClHT) — CKel EBee ESty MRav SPoG SRGP SWCr
'Tina Turner' (HT) — LSRN
Tintinara = 'Dicuptight'PBR (HT) $\mathbb{Y}^{H6}$ — ECnt
'Tipo Ideale' — see *R.* × *odorata* 'Mutabilis'
Titanic = 'Macdako'PBR (F) — ESty
Together Forever = 'Dicecho'PBR (F) — LBrs MAsh SWCr
'Tom Marshall' (Ra) — LSRN
'Tony Jacklin' (F) — LSRN
Top Marks = 'Fryministar'PBR (Min/Patio) — CGro EPfP ESps MJak MRav SCoo SWCr
Topaz Jewel — see *R.* Yellow Dagmar Hastrup
'Topsi' (F/Patio) — SPer
§ 'Tour de Malakoff' (Ce) — CPou IBoy MAus NLar SPer
Tradescant = 'Ausdir'PBR (S) — MAus SCob
Tradition — see *R.* Tradition '95
§ Tradition '95 = 'Korkeltin'PBR (ClHT) — GBin MAsh
Tranquility = 'Barout' (HT) — EPfP LRHS
Tranquillity = 'Ausnoble'PBR (S) — CRos CSBt ESty LBuc MAsh MAus SCob SCoo SPer
'Treasure Trove' (Ra) — CRHN LRHS MAus
Trevor Griffiths = 'Ausold'PBR (S) — MAus
'Tricolore de Flandre' (G) — MAus
'Trier' (Ra) — CPou EBee MAus
'Trigintipetala' misapplied — see *R.* × *damascena* 'Professeur Émile Perrot'
'Triomphe de l'Exposition' (HP) — MAus
'Triomphe du Luxembourg' (T) — MAus
'Triple Delight' (S) — LSRN
I 'Trish's Rose' — LSRN
Troika = 'Poumidor' (HT) — CSBt IBoy MAsh MAus MRav SPer SWCr
Troilus = 'Ausoil' (S) — MAus
'Tropicana' — see *R.* Super Star
Truly Scrumptious = 'Smi35-4-02' (HT) — ESty MRav
Trumpeter = 'Mactru' (F) $\mathbb{Y}^{H6}$ — CTri EBee ECnt ESps IArd IBoy LBuc MAsh MAus MRav MWat SPer SPoG SWCr
§ 'Tuscany' (G) — MAus SPer
'Tuscany Superb' (G) $\mathbb{Y}^{H7}$ — CBWd CBod CPou CRos CSBt CTri ELan EPfP EWTr LCro LEdu LOPS LRHS MAus MRav MWat NChi NLar SKHP SMad SPer SSea SWCr WBor WFar WHer WKif
Twenty-one Again! = 'Meinimo'PBR (HT) — LSRN
Twice in a Blue Moon = 'Tan96138'PBR (HT) $\mathbb{Y}^{H6}$ — CGro CKel CSBt ECnt ELon ESps ESty IBoy LBrs MRav MWat SCob SCoo SPoG SSea SWCr
Twiggy's Rose = 'Harteam'PBR (F) — LBrs LRHS MAsh

Twist = 'Poulstri'[PBR] (Courtyard Series) (ClPatio) — CGro ECnt ESty LBrs
Tynwald = 'Mattwyt' (HT) — SPer
'Ulrich Brünner' — see *R.* 'Ulrich Brünner Fils'
§ 'Ulrich Brünner Fils' (HP) — MAus
'Unique Blanche' — see *R.* × *centifolia* 'Unique'
Valencia = 'Koreklia'[PBR] (HT) — MAus SPer
Valentine Heart = 'Dicogle'[PBR] (F) ♀H6 — CSBt ELon ESps ESty IArd LBrs LSRN MAsh MAus MRav SPoG SWCr
'Vanity' (HM) — MAus
'Variegata di Bologna' (Bb) — EPfP EWTr LRHS MAus MRav SWCr
'Vatertag' (Min) — LSRN
'Veilchenblau' (Ra) ♀H7 — Widely available
Velvet Fragrance = 'Fryperdee' (HT) — CSBt ECnt ELon EPfP ESty MAus MRav SPoG SSea SWCr
Velvet Lustre = 'Simpalno' (HT) **new** — ESty
'Venusta Pendula' (Ra) — MAus
'Verschuren' (HT/v) — ESty
versicolor — see *R. gallica* 'Versicolor'
'Vick's Caprice' (HP) — MAus NLar
'Vicomtesse Pierre du Fou' (ClHT) — MAus
Victoria Joy = 'Diciwill' (F) — IDic
Viking Princess — see *R.* Imagination = 'Pouldron'
'Village Maid' — see *R.* × *centifolia* 'Unique Panachée'
villosa subsp. ***villosa*** — MAus
§ 'Violacea' (G) — MAus
Violet Cloud = 'Harquick'[PBR] (Min) — CKel ESty MRav
'Violette' (Ra) — CPou CRHN CRos ESps ESty EWTr LRHS MAus SPer WFar WHer WKif
virginea — SPer
virginiana ♀H7 — GCal MAus NWea SDix
'Viridiflora' — see *R.* × *odorata* 'Viridiflora'
Waltz = 'Poulkrid'[PBR] (Courtyard Series) (ClPatio) — ECnt
wardii var. ***culta*** — MAus
Warm Welcome = 'Chewizz'[PBR] (ClMin) ♀H6 — CGro CKel CRos ECnt ELan EPfP ESty EUJe IBoy LCro LRHS LSRN MAus MRav NRHS SMad SPer SPoG SSea SWCr
§ Warm Wishes = 'Fryxotic'[PBR] (HT) ♀H6 — CSBt ECnt ESps IBoy LBrs LBuc LRHS LSRN MAsh MAus MJak MRav MWat NPri NRHS SCob SSea SWCr
'Warrior' (F) — SPer
Warwick Castle = 'Auslian' (S) — MAus
webbiana — MAus SKHP
Wedding Bells = 'Korsteflali'[PBR] (HT) — LSRN
Wedding Celebration = 'Poulht006'[PBR] (HT) — ECnt LBuc LRHS NRHS
'Wedding Day' (Ra) — Widely available
Wee Jock = 'Cocabest' (F/Patio) — IBoy
'Weetwood' (Ra) — CRHN
Weisse Wolcke — see *R.* White Cloud = 'Korstacha'
Well-Being = 'Harjangle'[PBR] (S) — ELon
'Wendy Cussons' (HT) — CTri MRav SCob SPer
Wenlock = 'Auswen' (S) — MAus SPer
Westerland = 'Korwest' (S) ♀H6 — EWTr MRav NLar SWCr
Where the Heart Is = 'Cocoplan'[PBR] (HT) — ESty
Whisky Mac = 'Tanky' (HT) — CBcs CSBt CTri ELan ESps LBuc LSRN MRav SCob SPer SRGP
'White Bath' — see *R.* × *centifolia* 'Shailer's White Moss'
§ White Cloud = 'Korstacha'[PBR] (ClHT) — ESty SKHP SWCr
'White Cockade' (Cl) — CPou MSwo SPer SWCr
White Cover — see *R.* Kent
§ 'White de Meaux' (Ce) — MAus
White Diamond = 'Interamon'[PBR] (S) — EBee ECnt
White Eden = 'Meiviowit'[PBR] (ClHT) — ESty
§ White Gold = 'Cocquiriam'[PBR] (F) ♀H6 — CSBt
White Max Graf — see *R.* × *jacksonii* White Max Graf
White Meidiland = 'Meicoublan' (S/GC) — LRHS MAsh
white moss — see *R.* × *centifolia* 'Shailer's White Moss', *R.* 'Comtesse de Murinais'
'White Patio' (Min/Patio) — MAsh
White Perfumella = 'Meicalanq'[PBR] (HT) — ESty LSRN
§ 'White Pet' (Poly) ♀H7 — CKel CTri EBee ECnt ELan EPfP EWTr LRHS MAus MCot MRav NLar SEND SPer SSea SWCr WKif
white Provence — see *R.* × *centifolia* 'Unique'
'White Queen Elizabeth' (F) — SCob
white rose of York — see *R.* × *alba* 'Alba Semiplena'
White Star = 'Harquill' (ClHT) — ECnt MRav
'White Wings' (HT) — EWTr IBoy WKif
wichurana (Ra) — CBcs EWTr GCal MAus SDix SKHP
- 'Cally Anemone' (Ra) — MAus
- 'Variegata' (Ra/v) — EPot
'Wickwar' (Ra) ♀H6 — EWTr GCal
Wife of Bath = 'Ausbath' (S) — MAus
Wild Edric = 'Aushedge'[PBR] (Ru) ♀H6 — ECnt LBuc LRHS MAus MMuc SCob SCoo
Wild Rover = 'Dichirap'[PBR] (F) ♀H6 — ESty
Wildeve = 'Ausbonny'[PBR] (S) ♀H6 — LBuc LCro LOPS LRHS MAus NRHS
Wildfire = 'Fryessex' (Patio) — CGro ECnt ESty IBoy LRHS MAsh MAus MRav SPoG SWCr
§ 'Wilhelm' (HM) — CPou MAus SPer
'Will Scarlet' (HM) — MAus
'William Allen Richardson' (N) — MAus
William and Catherine = 'Ausrapper'[PBR] (S) — CGro CRos CSBt ESty LCro LOPS LRHS MAsh MAus NRHS SCob
'William Cobbett' (F) — SSea
§ 'William Lobb' (CeMo) ♀H7 — CGro CKel CPou EPfP IBoy LRHS MAus MNrw MRav MWat NEgg NLar NRHS SMad SPer WHer WKif
William Morris = 'Auswill'[PBR] (S) — CRos CSBt EPfP MAus NEgg SCob SPer
William Shakespeare 2000 = 'Ausromeo'[PBR] (S) — CBod CGro CKel CRos CSBt ECnt ELan EPfP EShb ESty IBoy LCro LOPS LRHS MAsh MAus MBNS MJak MSwo NEgg NLar NRHS SCob SCoo SSea SWCr
William Shakespeare = 'Ausroyal' (S) — IBoy MCot MJak SCob SPer
'William Tyndale' (Ra) — CPou
'Williams' Double Yellow' — see *R.* × *harisonii* 'Williams' Double Yellow'
willmottiae — MAus

Wiltshire = 'Kormuse'PBR (S/GC) ♀H6	CBod CSBt CTri ECnt ELan ESty IBoy LSRN MRav NLar SCob SEND SLon SSea SWCr
Winchester Cathedral = 'Auscat'PBR (S)	Widely available
Windflower = 'Auscross' (S)	LBuc MAus
Windrush = 'Ausrush' (S)	MAus SPer
Wise Portia = 'Ausport' (S)	MAus
Wisley 2008 = 'Ausbreeze'PBR (S)	CRos CSBt EPfP IBoy LBuc LRHS MAus NRHS SCob
Wisley = 'Ausintense'PBR (S)	SCoo
With All My Love = 'Coczodiac'PBR (HT)	CSBt
With Thanks = 'Fransmoov'PBR (HT)	MJak
Wizard (HT)	ESty
Wollerton Old Hall = 'Ausblanket'PBR (S)	CRos CSBt EPfP EShb ESty LBuc LRHS MAsh MAus NRHS SCob SCoo SPer SSea
'Wolley-Dod'	see *R.* 'Duplex'
Wonderful Husband = 'Raw982' (F) new	ESty
Wonderful News = 'Jonone'PBR (Patio)	CGro ESty MWat
Wonderful Wife = 'Raw1025' (HT) new	ESty
woodsii (S)	MAus
Worcestershire = 'Korlalon'PBR (GC) ♀H6	MAus MJak MRav SPer SWCr
§ ***xanthina*** 'Canary Bird' (S) ♀H7	Widely available
§ - f. ***hugonis***	CBod CTri ELan MAus NLar SKHP SPer
'Yellow Cécile Brünner'	see *R.* 'Perle d'Or'
Yellow Charles Austin = 'Ausyel' (S)	MAus
§ Yellow Dagmar Hastrup = 'Moryelrug'PBR (Ru)	CBod CPou EBee EWTr NLar SCob SPer
Yellow Flower Carpet	see *R.* Flower Carpet Sunshine
'Yellow Patio' (Min/Patio)	LRHS MAsh SPoG SWCr
yellow Scotch	see *R.* × *harisonii* 'Williams' Double Yellow'
Yellow Sunblaze = 'Meitrisical' (Min)	CSBt
'Yesterday' (Poly/F/S) ♀H6	CKel EBee EWTr MAus NLar
York and Lancaster	see *R.* × *damascena* 'Versicolor'
York Minster = 'Harquest' (F)	MRav
Yorkshire = 'Korbarkeit'PBR (GC)	ELan MRav
'Yorkshire Lady' (HT)	NEgg
Yorkshire Princess = 'Dicmouse' (Patio)	IDic
You Are My Sunshine = 'Frykwango'PBR (HT) ♀H6	SWCr
Young Lycidas = 'Ausvibrant'PBR (S)	CSBt EPfP IBoy LBuc LRHS LSRN MAus NRHS SCob
'Your Wedding Day' (F) new	CGro
You're Beautiful = 'Fryracy' (F)	CBcs CGro CKel CSBt EBee ECnt ESty LBrs LBuc LCro LRHS MRav NPri NRHS SCoo SPer SPoG SWCr
Yves Piaget	see *R.* Royal Brompton Rose
'Yvonne Rabier' (Poly) ♀H7	EWTr MAus MRav NLar SPer
'Zéphirine Drouhin' (Bb)	Widely available
§ 'Zigeunerknabe' (S)	MAus NLar SKHP SPer WFar

Roscoea ✿ (*Zingiberaceae*)

alpina	CAby CBro CLAP EBee ECho EPot GBuc GEdr GKev ILea WCru XLum
- CC 1820	IBlr
- pink-flowered	IBlr
- purple-flowered	IBlr
- short	WCru
alpina × ***cautleyoides***	IBlr
§ ***auriculata*** ♀H5	CAby CAvo CBct CBro CLAP ECho EHrv EPfP EPot GBuc GCal GEdr GKev IBlr IFoB ILea LEdu LTro MPie NHar NWad SChF SDeJ SDir SKHP SPer WCru WHar WHil
- B&SWJ 2594	WCru
- B&SWJ 2687	WCru
- GWJ 9230	WCru
- 'Anorexia'	IBlr
- brown-stemmed × ***purpurea***	IBlr
- early-flowering	IBlr WCru
- 'Floriade'	CLAP EBee GBuc GKev IBlr LPla WSHC
- green-stemmed × ***purpurea***	IBlr
- late-flowering	WCru
- 'Special'	CLAP
- 'White Cap'	EBee ECho GKev
auriculata × ***australis***	IBlr
auriculata × ***cangshanensis*** new	WCru
auriculata × ***capitata***	IBlr
auriculata × ***purpurea***	WCru
australis	CSam CTal EBee ELon GBuc GEdr LLHF MNrw WCru WThu
- pink-flowered KW 22124	IBlr
- purple-flowered KW 22124	IBlr
australis × ***humeana***	IBlr
'Ballyrogan Lavender'	IBlr
'Ballyrogan White'	IBlr
× ***beesiana*** ♀H5	CAvo CBod EPfP ILea WHil
- 'Ballyrogan Purple'	IBlr
- Cream Group	CBct CLAP CTal EBee EHrv EPfP EPot GBuc IBlr LEdu LTro MMrt NBir SKHP WCru
- Dark Group	IBlr
- Gestreept Group	CBro CLAP CMea CTal CTsd EPot EUJe EWoo GBuc GEdr GKev IBlr LAma LRHS MPie NHar SDir SKHP SPer WCru WHar
- - white-flowered new	GKev
- 'Lemon and Lavender'	IBlr
- 'Monique'	EBee EPfP IBlr NHar
- 'Moonlight'	IBlr
- 'Petite Purple'	IBlr
bhutanica PAB 3826	LEdu
Blackthorn strain	IBlr WCru WHil
brandisii misapplied	see *R. tumjensis*
brandisii (King ex Baker) K. Schum	IBlr
cangshanensis BWJ 7848	WCru
capitata	CLAP IBlr
cautleyoides	CAby CAvo CBro CWCL ECha ECho EHrv ELon ENun EPot GBuc GEdr GKev IBlr IFoB ILea LAma LHop LRHS MNrw NBid NGdn NPnk NRHS SPer SRot WCot WCru WHar XEll
- CLD 772	GEdr IBlr
I - 'Alba'	CTal
- var. ***cautleyoides*** f. ***atropurpurea***	IBlr
- - - 'Giraffe'	IBlr
- 'Crûg's Late Lemon'	WCru

- 'Doge Purple'	IBlr
- 'Early Purple'	CLAP ECho GBuc
- 'Early Yellow'	CTal EBee
- 'Himalaya' ♀H5	WHil
- 'Jeffrey Thomas' ♀H5	CLAP CSam CTal EBee ECho ELan GBuc GCal GEdr IBlr WHil
- 'Last Emperor' **new**	CTal
- late, lavender-flowered	IBlr
- - yellow-flowered	IBlr
- 'Lemon Giraffe'	IBlr
- mauve-flowered	WHil
- 'Pennine Purple'	IBlr NHar
- plum-flowered	IBlr
- var. ***pubescens***	IBlr
- 'Purple Giant'	CLAP EBee SKHP WHil
- 'Purple Queen' ♀H5	EBee GKev
- purple-flowered	CAby IBlr NHar
- 'Reinier'	CLAP CTal ECho GCal IBlr SKHP
- f. ***sinopurpurea***	GKev IBlr
- 'Vanilla'	CTal LEdu SKHP
- 'Washfield Purple'	IBlr
- 'Wine Red'	WHil
- 'Yeti'	CTal ECho SKHP
aff. ***cautleyoides***	SPlb
cautleyoides* × *humeana	CLAP IBlr LRHS WHar
cautleyoides* × *praecox	IBlr
cautleyoides* × *scillifolia* f. *atropurpurea	IBlr
debilis var. ***debilis***	IBlr
forrestii f. ***forrestii***	IBlr
- - pubescent	IBlr
- 'Ice Maiden'	IBlr
- f. ***purpurea***	IBlr
- f. ***purpurea* × *humeana***	IBlr
'Harvington Evening Star'	EBee ENun LLHF LRHS NHar
humeana	CAby CBro CLAP ECho EPot GBuc GEdr LAma LRHS NPnk WThu
- ACE 2539	IBlr
- from Cruickshank Botanic Garden	IBlr
- f. ***alba***	IBlr WHil
- Forrest's form	IBlr
- 'Guincho White Stripe'	IBlr
- 'Harvington Raw Silk' ♀H5	EBee ENun LLHF LRHS NHar WHil
- 'Harvington Royale'	EBee ENun LLHF LRHS NHar
- lavender-flowered	IBlr
- 'Long Acre Sunrise'	CLAP EBee
- f. ***lutea*** ♀H5	CLAP IBlr
- pink-flowered	IBlr
- 'Purple Streaker'	WHil
- purple-flowered	EBee ECho ENun
- 'Rosemoor Plum'	CAby CLAP WCot
- 'Snowy Owl'	GEdr
- 'Two Tone'	IBlr
- f. ***tyria*** ♀H5	IBlr WHil
- - 'Inkling'	GBuc
'Ice Maiden'	IBlr
'Kew Beauty' ♀H5	CAby CBod CLAP CMea CTal EPfP GBuc GCal LRHS NGdn SKHP SMHy WGwG WHil
'Lavender Mist'	IBlr
'McBeath's Pink'	ENun LLHF LRHS
nepalensis	WHil
'Pallid Sun'	IBlr
'Pinky'	CMea
praecox	GEdr IBlr
procera misapplied	see *R. auriculata*
procera Wall.	see *R. purpurea*
§ ***purpurea***	CAvo CBod CBro CTal ECha ELan ELon EPfP EUJe EWoo GCal GKev IBal IBlr IBoy IFoB ILea LAma LRHS MArt MAsh MMuc NBir NGdn SPer WCru WGwG WHer

- CC 1757	IBlr
- CC 3628	IBlr
- HWJK 2020	WCru
- HWJK 2169	WCru
- HWJK 2175	WCru
- HWJK 2400	WCru
- HWJK 2407	WCru
- KW 13755	IBlr
- MECC 2	IBlr
- MECC 10	IBlr
- 'Ant Marian'	EBee GKev
- Blackthorn hybrids **new**	CLAP
- 'Bronzed Albino'	IBlr
- bronze-leaved	CAby CLAP
- 'Brown Peacock'	CAvo CFil CLAP ECho GBuc GKev IBlr SDir SKHP WCot WCru
- 'Browny' **new**	GKev
- 'Butterfly' **new**	GEdr GKev
- 'Cinnamon Stick'	CAbb CLAP CWGN ECtt GEdr MMrt NHar
- 'Dalai Lama' ♀H4	EBee ECho GEdr GKev WHil
- var. ***gigantea***	WHil
- - CC 1757	IBlr
- green-stemmed	CLAP
- 'Himalayan Delight'	IBlr
- 'Julie's Glory' **new**	GKev
- 'Late Lavender'	IBlr
- 'Nico'	ECho ELan IBlr SKHP WCot
- 'Peacock'	CLAP EBee ECho EPot GKev IBlr SKHP WHil
- 'Peacock Eye'	ECho GEdr GKev IBlr SKHP
- 'Petticoat Pink' **new**	GKev
- var. ***procera***	see *R. purpurea*
- 'Purple Dwarf'	IBlr
- 'Purple Tower'	IBlr
- 'Red Foot'	EBee GKev
- 'Red Gurkha'	see *R. purpurea* f. *rubra*
- 'Red Riding Hood' **new**	GKev
- Rosemoor form	CLAP
- Royal Purple hybrids	CLAP MAsh
§ - f. ***rubra*** ♀H4	CAby CLAP CTal EBee ENun GKev IBlr LLHF LRHS NHar WPGP
- - 'Gurkha Redstem'	WCru
- 'Salt 'n' Pepper'	EBee GKev
- short	CLAP IBlr
- 'Slender Wisp'	IBlr
- 'Spice Island'	CAbb CLAP CMea CSpe CWGN EBee ECtt SPad
- 'Summer Snow' **new**	GKev
- tall	CLAP WCru
- 'Twin Towers'	EBee GKev
- 'Typico'	IBlr
- 'Vannin'	LEdu WCru
- 'Vincent'	EBee EPot GKev
- 'Wisley Amethyst'	CBro CLAP CTal EBee ENun IBlr LLHF LRHS SKHP
'Red Neck' ♀H4	EBee IBlr SKHP
schneideriana	GKev IBlr WThu
- robust form	IBlr
scillifolia	CBro ECho GBuc GEdr LAma LHop LRHS NBir NRHS SDeJ WHar
- f. ***atropurpurea***	CAby EBee EHrv EPot GBuc GCal GKev IBal IBlr WCru WThu
- black-flowered **new**	NHpl
- f. ***scillifolia***	EBee EHrv IBlr IFoB NHpl WCru WHar WHil WThu

	aff. ***scillifolia*** purple-flowered	GEdr IBlr NPnk
	'Summer Deep Purple' 🏆H5	EBee ENun LRHS
	tibetica	EBee GEdr GKev IBlr LEdu LLHF SPlb WCru WThu
	- ACE 2538	IBlr WCru
	- BWJ 7878	WCru
	- aff. f. ***albo-purpurea***	IBlr
	- f. ***atropurpurea*** BWJ 7640	WCru
	- f. ***rosea***	WCru
	aff. ***tibetica***	IBlr
§	***tumjensis***	CTal IBlr
	wardii 🏆H5	IBlr WHil

rosemary see *Rosmarinus officinalis*

Rosmarinus ✿ (*Lamiaceae*)

	corsicus 'Prostratus'	see *R. officinalis* Prostratus Group
	× ***lavandulaceus*** misapplied	see *R. officinalis* Prostratus Group
	× ***noeanus***	XSen
	officinalis	Widely available
	- 'Abraxas' <u>**new**</u>	CFGn
	- f. ***albiflorus***	CArn ENfk EPfP ESps GPoy LEdu LRHS MHer MNHC SDow SHDw SLim SPlb SRms WCFE WGwG WJek XSen
	- - 'Lady in White'	CRos CSBt ELan EPfP ESps LRHS MAsh SLim SPer SRms WGwG WJek
	- 'Alderney'	WGwG
§	- var. ***angustissimus*** 'Benenden Blue' 🏆H4	CAbP CSBt CWib ELan GPoy LRHS SDix SPer SPlb SPoG SRms WGwG WJek
	- - 'Corsican Blue'	CArn CBod EBee ELan GPoy MHer MHol MNHC SDow SGol SHDw SPer SRms WGwG
	- 'Arp'	CArn CBod ENfk EWes LHop SPad WGwG
	- 'Aureovariegatus'	see *R. officinalis* 'Aureus'
§	- 'Aureus' (v)	CBcs CPla SRms WHer WJek
	- 'Avicenna'	WGwG
	- 'Baie d'Audierne'	XSen
	- 'Barbecue'PBR	CLau ENfk LEdu SRms
	- 'Barwinnock Dwarf Blue' <u>**new**</u>	WHer
	- 'Blue Lagoon'	CBod CLau ENfk MHer MNHC SIde SPer SRms WGwG WHer WJek
	- 'Blue Rain'	CBod EPfP MHer MSwo WGwG WHer
	- 'Capercaillie'	SDow WGwG XSen
	- 'Collingwood Ingram'	see *R. officinalis* var. *angustissimus* 'Benenden Blue'
	- 'Cottage White'	WGwG WHer
	- dwarf, blue-flowered	CLau
	- 'Farinole'	CArn CLau MNHC SRms WGwG
	- 'Fota Blue'	CArn CLau CRos CWib IArd LRHS MHer MNHC SAko SDow SGol SHDw SIde SRms SVen SWvt WGwG WJek XSen
	- 'Foxtail'	CBod SRms WJek
	- 'Frimley Blue'	see *R. officinalis* 'Primley Blue'
	- 'Genges Gold' (v)	MHer WGwG
	- 'Gold Dust' (v)	CWGN ENfk
	- 'Golden Rain'	see *R. officinalis* 'Joyce DeBaggio'
	- 'Gorizia'	CArn CBcs CBod LRHS SDow SRms WPnn XSen
	- 'Green Ginger' 🏆H4	CAbP CArn CBod CLau CRos ELan ELon EPfP GBin LEdu LHop LRHS MAsh MGos MHer MNHC MRav MSCN NPer SBod SCob SDow SPer SPoG SRms SVen WGwG WJek WPnn XSen

	- 'Guilded'	see *R. officinalis* 'Aureus'
	- 'Haifa'	CBod CLau EBtc ENfk NQui SRms WGwG WJek WPnn
	- 'Heavenly Blue'	WGwG WHer
	- 'Henfield Blue'	SHDw
	- 'Huntington Carpet'	ECtt
	- 'Iden Blue Boy'	ELon
	- 'Iden Pillar'	WGwG
	- 'Jekka Blue'	WJek
§	- 'Joyce DeBaggio' (v)	MHer SDow WGwG WHer XSen
	- 'Ken Taylor'	WGwG
	- 'Knightshayes Blue'	CRos LRHS
	- 'Lady in Blue'	WGwG
	- ***lavandulaceus***	see *R. officinalis* Prostratus Group
	- 'Lilies Blue'	GPoy WGwG
	- 'Lockwood Variety'	see *R. officinalis* (Prostratus Group) 'Lockwood de Forest'
	- 'Logee Blue'	CArn
	- 'Madeline Hill'	LRHS
	- 'Majorca Pink'	CBcs CBod CLau CSBt CSpe ENfk LRHS MHer MNHC NPri SDow SPer WGwG WHer WJek XLum
	- 'Marenca'	CHll CLau MNHC SRms
	- 'Margaret of Pershore' <u>**new**</u>	WGwG
	- 'McConnell's Blue' 🏆H4	CAbP CArn CLau ELan EPfP LHop LRHS MAsh MGos MNHC SCob SDow SHDw SRms WGwG WHer WJek WPGP XSen
	- 'Miss Jessopp's Upright' 🏆H4	Widely available
	- 'Pointe du Raz'	CAbP CArn CBod CRos ELan EPfP LRHS MAsh SChF SLim SRms WGwG
§	- 'Primley Blue'	CBcs CBod CLau CSam ECtt MNHC MRav SGol SIde SRms WGwG WJek
§	- Prostratus Group	Widely available
	- - 'Capri'	CAbP CBod CDul EPfP LRHS MHer SCob SRms WFar WJek
	- - 'Freda'	WGwG
	- - 'Gethsemane'	CArn WGwG
	- - 'Jackman's Prostrate'	SDix
§	- - 'Lockwood de Forest'	WGwG WHer
	- - 'Rampant Boule'	CArn CBod CLau MHer SDow SRms WGwG WJek XLum XSen
	- - 'Sea Level'	CLau MHer WGwG
	- - 'Sheila Dore'	SPlb SVen
	- - white-flowered	GPoy
	- - 'Whitewater Silver'	LRHS
	- ***repens***	see *R. officinalis* Prostratus Group
	- 'Rex'	CLau WGwG
	- 'Roman Beauty'PBR	CAbP CBcs CSBt EHoe LHop LRHS LSRN MHol NPri SCob SLim SRms SWvt WHer
	- 'Roseus'	CArn CBot CHVG CLau CWib CWld ELan ENfk EPfP GPoy LHop LRHS MAsh MHer MNHC SDow SEND SLim SPoG SRms SVen WGwG WJek XSen
	- 'Salem'	CBod MHer
	- 'Severn Sea' 🏆H4	CArn CBod CLau CRos CSBt CSam CTri ECtt ELan ENfk EPfP ESps GPoy LRHS MAsh MGos MHer MNHC MRav MSwo SIde SLon SPer SRms SVen WCFE WGwG WJek
	- 'Shimmering Stars'	SDow WGwG XSen
	- 'Silver Sparkler'	WHer WPat
	- Silver Spires = 'Wolros'	MNHC

- 'Sissinghurst Blue' ♀H4	CArn CBod CRos CWCL EBee ECha ECrN ELan EPfP ESps LRHS MAsh MHer MHtn MNHC MRav SDow SGol SLim SPer SPlb SPoG SRms SWvt WGwG WJek XSen
- 'Sissinghurst White'	WGwG
- 'Sorcerer's Apprentice'	SDow
- 'South Downs Blue'	SHDw WGwG
- 'Spanish Snow'	WGwG
- 'Spice Island'	CBod LRHS SPer
- 'Sudbury Blue'	CBod CLau ENfk SDow SGol SHDw SRms WGwG WJek XSen
- 'Sunkissed' PBR	SRms
- 'Trusty'	WGwG
- 'Tuscan Blue'	CArn CBcs CBod CLau ECha ECrN ECtt ELan EPfP ESps LRHS MHer MNHC MSwo NEgg NPri SDow SGol SPer SRms WGwG WJek WPGP WPnn XSen
- 'Variegatus'	see *R. officinalis* 'Aureus'
- 'Vatican Blue'	WJek
- 'Vicomte de Noailles'	XSen
- 'Wisley Blue'	WGwG
repens	see *R. officinalis* Prostratus Group
Salcombe form	CHll
'Sappho'	CHll

Rostrinucula (*Lamiaceae*)

dependens	CMCN EBee ELon EPfP ESwi EWes MTPN NLar SBrt SPad WCFE

Rosularia (*Crassulaceae*)

§ ***aizoon***	CRos ECho EDAr LRHS NRHS
alba	see *R. sedoides* var. *alba*
§ ***chrysantha***	CRos ECho EDAr LRHS NHpl NRHS SPlb
crassipes	see *Rhodiola wallichiana*
libanotica RCB RL 20	WCot
§ ***muratdaghensis***	SPlb
pallida A. Berger	see *R. chrysantha*
pallida Stapf	see *R. aizoon*
pallida ambig.	EPot
platyphylla misapplied	see *R. muratdaghensis*
§ ***sedoides*** var. ***alba***	ECho EDAr EPot NHpl XLum
sempervivum	ECho ESps EWes WThu
§ - subsp. ***glaucophylla***	ECho LRHS NRHS WHal WThu
spatulata hort.	see *R. sempervivum* subsp. *glaucophylla*

Rubia (*Rubiaceae*)

peregrina	GPoy
tinctorum	CArn CHab CHby GPoy MNHC SRms SWat WSFF

Rubus ✿ (*Rosaceae*)

RCB/Eq C-1	WCot
SDR 4635	GKev
acuminatus	CBot ESwi LEdu SBrt
alceifolius Poir.	SDys
- B&SWJ 1833	WCru
arcticus	EBee ECtt EPPr LEdu NHar SHar SRot WThu XLum
- subsp. ***stellatus***	NHar
bambusarum	CBot EShb ESwi MRav WCru
'Benenden' ♀H5	CBcs CDul CLet CTri CTsd CWib EBee ECrN ELan EPfP EWTr GKin LHop LRHS LSRN MBNS MMuc MRav NEgg NLar SCob SKHP SPer SPhx WBor WCFE WHar WMoo
'Betty Ashburner'	CAgr CBcs CDul EBee EPPr EWTr GLog GMcL GQui MCoo MGos MRav SCob SPer WHar WMoo XLum
biflorus ♀H5	LEdu MBlu MMuc SEND WPGP
'Boatsberry'	SDea
'Boysenberry' (F)	CArg ERea LEdu LRHS NPri
boysenberry, thornless (F)	CMac EMil ESps GTwe LBuc LSRN NPri SDea SPer
buergeri B&SWJ 5555	WCru
caesius	WCot
calophyllus	WPGP
- PAB 13.171 **new**	LEdu
calycinoides Hayata ex Koidz.	see *R. rolfei*
calycinoides Kuntze	EBtc GKev SGol
chamaemorus	GPoy
'Clarke's Velvet Night'	SBrt
cockburnianus (F)	CBcs CRos CTri CWib EBee ELan EPfP GCra GKev GKin GMcL IFoB LBuc MMuc MRav MSwo NSti NWea SCob SPer SPlb SRms WHar
- 'Goldenvale' ♀H5	CBcs CBot CDul EHoe ELon EPfP ESps GMcL GQui IFro LHop LRHS MAsh MBlu MGos MMuc MRav MSwo NBir NEgg NLar NSti SCob SEND SLon SPer SPoG
crataegifolius	MRav
'Emerald Spreader'	WMoo
fockeanus misapplied	see *R. rolfei*
formosensis	SBrt
- B&SWJ 1798	ESwi WCru
fruticosus agg.	CArg EMOT ESps NWea WSFF
- 'Adrienne' (F)	CAgr CFGn CHab CSBt LEdu MAsh SBdl SRms WHar
- 'Apache' (F)	CHab LCro
- 'Ashton Cross' (F)	LBuc
- 'Bedford Giant' (F)	CHab CSBt LSRN MAsh MGos SBdl SEND SLim WHar
- 'Black Butte' (F)	CHab EPom SDea SLon SVic
- 'Black Satin' (F)	CAgr ECrN EMOT NLar SDea SVic
- 'Čačanska Bestrna' (F)	MCoo
- 'Chester' (F)	EPom ERea LEdu LRHS NRHS SFrt SKee SPer
- 'Godshill Goliath' (F)	SDea
- 'Helen' (F)	CAgr CSut MAsh SDea
- 'Himalayan Giant' (F)	CHab EMOT NEgg NLar SDea
- 'Karaka Black' PBR (F)	CHab CRos ERea LBuc LRHS NRHS SPoG SVic
- 'Loch Maree' PBR (F/d)	CHab CMac EPom LEdu MCoo NPri SFrt SLon
- 'Loch Ness' PBR (F) ♀H6	CAgr CArg CHab CRos CWib EMOT EPom ESps GTwe IArd LBuc LCro LOPS LRHS LSRN NPri NRHS SCoo SDea SFrt SKee SPer SVic WHar
- 'Loch Tay' PBR (F)	CArg CHab CMac EPom LRHS NRHS
- 'Merton Thornless' (F)	CSBt CWib ECrN EMOT GBin LEdu LSRN MAsh MGos SBdl SRms WHar
- 'Natchez' PBR (F)	SPer
- 'Navaho' (F)	CHab ERea LRHS NRHS
- 'No Thorn' (F)	SDea
- 'Oregon Thornless' (F)	CAgr CFGn CRos CSBt CWib ECrN EPfP ESps GTwe LCro LOPS LRHS LSRN MAsh MJak MRav NLar NRHS NWea SCoo SDea SKee SLim SPoG SRms SVic WHar WMat
- 'Ouachita' PBR (F)	CFGn LCro LOPS LRHS NRHS SKee SPer SPoG
- 'Parsley Leaved' (F)	SDea

- 'Reuben' (F)	CFGn CHab EPom GQue LBuc LCro LOPS LRHS MCoo MNHC NRHS SKee SPer WMat
- 'Thornfree' (F)	CAgr CFGn CTri EPfP LRHS NLar NPri NRHS SDea SKee SLim WMat
- 'Triple Crown' (F)	CHab CMac MCoo
- 'Variegatus' (v)	CMac MBlu WCot
- 'Waldo' (F)	CAgr CFGn CSBt CWib LBuc LSRN MAsh MGos NPri SBdl SDea SRms WHar
'Glencoe' (F)	CSut MCoo
'Golden Showers'	CWib
henryi	CBcs ESwi LRHS WCot
- var. ***henryi*** new	WCru
ichangensis	CBot CFil ESwi
idaeus	GPoy
- 'All Gold' (F) ♀H6	CFGn CMac EMOT EMil EPom ERea LBuc LRHS MAsh NLar NPri NRHS SBdl SCoo SFrt SPer SVic WHar WMat
- 'Aureus' (F)	ECha ELan LEdu MRav NBid WCot
- 'Autumn Bliss' (F) ♀H6	Widely available
- 'Autumn Treasure'PBR (F)	CSut EMil EPom ERea GTwe LRHS NPri NRHS SLon SVic
- 'Black Jewel' (F)	EPfP
- 'Cascade Delight' (F)	EPom LBuc LCro LOPS LRHS MAsh NRHS SBdl
- 'Chemainus' (F)	LCro LOPS
- 'Erika'PBR (F)	LCro LOPS LRHS MNHC NRHS SPer WMat
- 'Fallgold' (F)	CWib LSRN MMuc SKee SPoG
- 'Glen Ample'PBR (F) ♀H6	Widely available
- 'Glen Clova' (F)	CAgr CFGn CSBt CTri CWib ELan EMOT GTwe LRHS LSRN MAsh MGos NLar NPri SBdl SKee SLim SPer SPoG WHar WMat
- 'Glen Doll'PBR (F)	CAgr GQue GTwe LRHS MAsh NLar SBdl SCoo SPoG WMat
- 'Glen Fyne'PBR (F)	GTwe
- 'Glen Lyon'PBR (F)	CWib ECrN LBuc MAsh MJak NPri SBdl SCoo WHar
- 'Glen Magna'PBR (F) ♀H6	CAgr CArg CMac CSBt CWib ERea MAsh NPri SCoo SDea SKee SLim
- 'Glen Moy'PBR (F)	CAgr CArg CSBt CTri CWib EMOT GTwe LRHS LSRN MAsh MGos MJak NWea SCoo SDea SKee SLim SPer WHar
- 'Glen Prosen'PBR (F)	CAgr CSBt CWib EMOT EPfP ERea GTwe LRHS LSRN MAsh MGos NPri SBdl SCoo SDea SKee SLim SPer SPlb WHar WMat
- 'Glen Rosa' (F)	ERea SDea
- 'Heritage' (F)	CWib ELan MAsh SBdl SCoo
- Himbo Top = 'Rafzaqu'PBR (F)	CMac
- 'Joan J'PBR (F) ♀H6	CSut EPom ERea GTwe LSRN
- 'Leo'PBR (F) ♀H6	CSBt CTri CWib LSRN MAsh SBdl SCoo SKee SPer WHar
- 'Malling Admiral' (F) ♀H6	CSBt CTri CWib EMOT EPom GTwe LSRN MAsh NWea SBdl SCoo SKee WHar
- 'Malling Delight' (F)	CSBt CWib ELan SCoo SPlb
- 'Malling Jewel' (F) ♀H6	CAgr CSBt CWib EPfP EPom GTwe LBuc LSRN MAsh MJak SBdl SDea SKee
- 'Malling Promise' (F)	CWib MJak
- 'Octavia'PBR (F)	CAgr CArg CMac CSBt EMil EPom GQue LBuc LRHS MAsh MCoo NLar NWea SBdl SFrt SLim SPoG WHar WMat
- 'Polka'PBR (F) ♀H6	CRos EPfP EPom ESps LBuc LCro LOPS LRHS LSRN MAsh MCoo MRav NRHS SBdl SCoo SKee SLim WHar WMat
- 'Sugana'PBR (F)	LRHS MAsh NRHS SBdl
- 'Summer Gold' (F)	GTwe
- 'Tadmor'PBR (F)	CArg CFGn ERea LCro LOPS LRHS NRHS SKee SPer WMat
- 'Tulameen' (F) ♀H6	CAgr CSBt CWib ELan EMil EPfP EPom LBuc LCro LOPS LRHS LSRN MAsh MMuc NPri SBdl SCoo SEND SFrt SKee SLim SPer SPoG SVic WHar WMat
- 'Valentina' (F)	SFrt
- 'Zeva Herbsternte' (F)	CWib MAsh SBdl
idaeus* × *ursinus new	EMOT
illecebrosus (F)	LEdu XLum
irenaeus	CBot LEdu LRHS SEND WHal
Japanese wineberry	see *R. phoenicolasius*
'Kenneth Ashburner'	NLar
lambertianus PAB 8931	LEdu
lineatus	CBot CDTJ CWib EPfP EWes GBin LEdu LHop LRHS MCot SBrt SKHP WCru WPGP WPat
- B&SWJ 11261 from Sumatra	WCru
- HWJ 892 from Vietnam	ESwi WCru
- HWJK 2045 from Nepal	GQui WCru
- PAB 13.163 new	LEdu
- from Nepal	GCra
× ***loganobaccus*** (F)	CFGn EMOT GBin SBdl
- 'Brandywine' (F)	SDea
- 'Ly 59' (F)	ECrN EPfP MMuc SDea SEND SKee SRms
- 'Ly 654' (F) ♀H5	CSBt EPom ERea GTwe LBuc LRHS NEgg NPri NRHS SDea SPer WHar
- thornless (F)	CAgr CTri CWib EPfP EPom GTwe LEdu MJak SDea SPoG SVic WMat
ludwigii	SBrt
'Malling Minerva' (F)	CAgr CSut EPom SFrt SVic
'Margaret Gordon'	MRav
microphyllus 'Variegatus' (v)	MRav
§ ***nepalensis***	CAgr CFGn GCra GKev LEdu WPGP
nutans	see *R. nepalensis*
'Obsidian' (F)	LEdu
odoratus	CBcs ELan EPPr EPfP EWTr LEdu MBlu NBid SPer
palmatus var. ***coptophyllus***	MMuc
parkeri PAB 6891	LEdu
parviflorus	CArn IFro
- 'Bill Baker'	LEdu
- double-flowered (d)	EPPr
- 'Sunshine Spreader'	EHoe LEdu
parvus	LEdu WPGP
pectinellus var. ***trilobus***	SBrt
- - B&SWJ 1669B	WCru
peltatus	CFil NLar WPGP
pentalobus	see *R. rolfei*
§ ***phoenicolasius***	CAgr CBcs CCCN CDul CFGn CHGN ELan EMOT EPPr EPfP ERea GNew GTwe IDee LCro LEdu LHop LOPS LRHS MBlu MCoo MHer MRav SDea SPer SPoG SVic WBor WPGP
reflexus var. ***hui*** new	EShb
§ ***rolfei***	CDul CTri GEdr MCoo NWad
- B&SWJ 3546 from Taiwan	WCru
- B&SWJ 3878 from the Philippines	WCru

	- 'Emerald Carpet' ♀H5	CAgr NLar
	rosifolius NJM 10.142	WPGP
	- 'Coronarius' (d)	ECrN LSou WCot
	rubrisetulosus PAB 9532	LEdu
	'Rushbrook Redleaf'	SBrt
	saxatilis	LEdu
	- PAB 3912	LEdu
	setchuenensis	CMCN EPPr NLar
	'Silvan' (F)	MMuc SEND
	spectabilis	CBcs CWib ELan EPPr EWTr LEdu MMuc MRav WSHC
	- 'Flore Pleno'	see *R. spectabilis* 'Olympic Double'
§	- 'Olympic Double' (d)	Widely available
	- 'Olympic Gold' (d)	CLet
	splendidissimus B&SWJ 2361	WCru
	squarrosus	SMad
	'Sunberry' (F)	CCCN SDea
	swinhoei B&SWJ 1735	WCru
	taiwanicola B&SWJ 317	ESwi WCru
	- CWJ 12400	WCru
	- 'Buckingham'	NPer
	Tayberry Group (F)	CSBt CTri GTwe LRHS LSRN MGos NLar NPri NRHS SBdl SPer SRms SVic WHar
	- 'Buckingham' (F)	CArg CSut EMil EPom ERea GBin GTwe LBuc LCro LRHS NLar SVic WMat
	- 'Medana Tayberry' (F)	CAgr CRos ECrN EMOT EPfP GQue LEdu LRHS MNHC NLar NRHS NWea SDea SKee SPoG WHar WMat
§	***thibetanus*** ♀H5	Widely available
	- 'Silver Fern'	see *R. thibetanus*
	treutleri B&SWJ 2139	WCru
	tricolor	CAgr CBcs CDul CSBt CTri CWib ECrN GKev GKin GMcL MBlu MCoo MMuc MRav MSwo NLar SCob SDix SGol SPer WHar WMoo
	aff. ***tricolor***	WHar
	trilobus B&SWJ 9096	WCru
	'Tummelberry' (F)	GQue LRHS MCoo NRHS SVic
	ulmifolius 'Bellidiflorus' (d)	MRav
	ursinus	SVic
	xanthocarpus	LEdu NLar XLum
	'Youngberry' (F)	SDea

Rudbeckia ✿ (*Asteraceae*)

	alpicola	EBee
	Autumn Sun	see *R. laciniata* 'Herbstsonne'
	'Berlin'	CHVG CWGN EBee ECtt GMaP LHop LRHS LSou LSun MHol NLar SCob SPer
	californica	EBee LRHS
	deamii	see *R. fulgida* var. *deamii*
	'Dublin'	CWGN ECtt IBoy IKil LRHS LSou MBel MHol NLar SCob SPer
	fulgida	SWvt WFar
	- 'City Garden'	CKno ECtt GBin LRHS NCGa NLar SHil SRms
§	- var. ***deamii*** ♀H7	Widely available
	- 'Early Bird Gold'	CWGN EBee ECtt GBin IBoy LCro LOPS MHol NLar SAko SPoG WFar
	- var. ***fulgida***	CMea EBee EPfP LEdu SPoG WTcb
	- 'Little Goldstar' PBR	CBod CKno CRos EBee ECtt ELan EPfP LBMP LCro LOPS LRHS MAsh MPie NDov NLar NPnk NPri NRHS SCob SHil SLon SPoG WCot WFar
§	- var. ***speciosa*** ♀H7	CWCL EBee ECha ECtt ELan EPfP GBin GWyn MMuc SDix SEND SHar SPlb SPtp SRms SWvt WFar WMoo WOld WPtf XLum
I	- var. ***sullivantii*** 'Goldschirm'	EBee
	- - 'Goldsturm' ♀H7	Widely available
	- - 'Pot of Gold'	IKil
	- Viette's Little Suzy = 'Blovi'	EBee SRms
	gloriosa	see *R. hirta*
	grandiflora	LRHS MMuc
	- 'Sundance'	CHVG EBee SAko SPhx
§	***hirta***	ELan NBir SVic
	- 'Autumn Colours' (mixed)	CMea ELan LRHS SPhx
	- 'Cappuccino'	CWld ELan EPfP LRHS
	- 'Cherokee Sunset' (d)	CSpe EPfP LRHS NRHS
	- 'Cherry Brandy'	CSpe LHop LRHS SPhx
	- 'Chim Chiminee'	IKil NGBl SCob SPoG
	- 'Goldilocks'	CWCL SVic
	- 'Indian Summer' ♀H3	CRos EPfP LRHS MHol MNHC NRHS SPav SPhx
	- 'Irish Eyes'	SPav SVic
	- 'Marmalade'	EPfP LRHS NGBl NRHS SVic
	- 'Prairie Sun'	CMea CRos ELon EPfP LRHS NGBl NRHS SPhx
	- 'Sonora'	NGBl
	- 'Tiger Eye'	SPoG
	- 'Toto' ♀H3	SPav SWvt
	July Gold	see *R. laciniata* 'Juligold'
	laciniata	CHVG CKno CMac CSpe EBee ELan EPPr GCal GQue LEdu LRHS MArt MSpe NGBl NLar SMHy SPhx WCot WMoo WOld WPGP WTcb WWtn XLum
	- var. ***digitata***	IMou
	- 'Golden Glow'	see *R. laciniata* 'Hortensia'
	- 'Goldkugel' (d) ♀H7	MSpe
	- 'Goldquelle' (d)	CBod CLet CRos CWCL EBee ECha ECtt ELan ELon EPfP GMaP GWyn IVic LHop LRHS NGdn NRHS SCob SHil SMad SPer SPoG SRms SWvt WFar WGwG XLum
§	- 'Herbstsonne' ♀H7	Widely available
§	- 'Hortensia' (d)	EBee GQue MAvo MRav NGBl WBrk WCot WHoo WOld
§	- 'Juligold'	CBod EBee ECtt LRHS MBNS MPie NEgg NGdn NPnk SPoG WWFP
	- 'Starcadia Razzle Dazzle'	EWld MAvo NPnk SAko WCot WFar
	maxima	Widely available
	missouriensis	CMea EBee GBin LRHS MArt MMuc NPnk SHil
	mollis	EBee LRHS NBre
	newmannii	see *R. fulgida* var. *speciosa*
	nitida	IBoy
	occidentalis	LRHS NBre NChi
	- 'Black Beauty' PBR	EPfP
	- 'Green Wizard'	CBod CMac CWib EBee ECtt EHrv ELan EPed EPfP EShb EWTr GBin GWyn IBoy LRHS NSti SPav SPer SRms WHar WTcb
*	***paniculata***	CDor EBee LLHF NBre WCot
	'Peking' PBR	CWGN EBee ECtt IKil SCob
	purpurea	see *Echinacea purpurea*
	speciosa	see *R. fulgida* var. *speciosa*
	subtomentosa	CBWd CSam EWes GCal LEdu LRHS MSpe NDov NPnk NSti SCob SDix SMHy WCot WOld XLum
	- 'Henry Eilers'	Widely available
	- 'Little Henry' PBR	CBod CKno CSpe EBee ECGP ECtt EPed LCro LRHS MHol SCob
	Summerina Series	SCob

- Summerina Brown = 'Et Rdb 03'PBR	CHVG CMea MHol NGBl NPnk SPoG WCot
- Summerina Orange = 'Et Rdb 01'PBR	IBoy LPla LRHS MHol NPnk SPad SPoG WCot
- Summerina Yellow = 'Et Rdb 02'PBR	CMea LRHS MHol MSCN NGBl NPnk SPoG WCot
triloba ♀H7	CHVG CNec CRos CSpe ECha ELon EPfP IBoy LRHS MBel MNrw NGBl NGdn NPnk NRHS NSti SCob SDix SPhx WMoo WPGP
- 'Prairie Glow'	CBot CDor CMea CNec CSpe EAJP ELon IBoy ILea LRHS MSCN NPnk SCob SGol SPhx SRkn

rue see *Ruta graveolens*

Ruellia (*Acanthaceae*)

amoena	see *R. brevifolia*
§ ***brevifolia***	ECre EShb
humilis	EBee EShb GEdr SBrt SPhx WHil
macrantha	CCCN EShb
makoyana ♀H1a	CTsd EShb
- white-flowered	EShb
strepens	EBee
tweediana	EShb

Rumex (*Polygonaceae*)

acetosa	CAgr CArn CHab CHby CLau ENfk GPoy MCoo MHer MJak MMuc MNHC NBir SIde SRms WHer WJek WSFF WTre
- 'Abundance'	CLau LEdu
- subsp. ***acetosa*** 'Saucy' (v)	LEdu WCot
- 'Profusion'	GPoy MHer
acetosella	CAgr CHab NMir WSFF
alpinus	EBee LEdu SDix SPhx WCot WPGP
crispus	CLau
flexuosus	CSpe EPPr GCal LPot WJek
hydrolapathum	CArn CBod CHab MMuc MSKA SEND SPlb WCot WSFF
patientia	CHab CLau
sanguineus	CTri ENfk EShb LEdu MSKA NLar NQui SRms WHil XLum
- var. ***sanguineus***	CHby ELan IFoB MHer MNHC NBro WHer WJek
scutatus	CArn CBod CHby CLau ENfk GPoy MNHC SIde SPlb SRms WHer WJek
- subsp. ***induratus***	SEND
- 'Silver Shield'	EPPr LEdu MHer SRms WJek

Rumohra (*Dryopteridaceae*)

adiantiformis ♀H1c	CCCN ISha LRHS NLos SEND WFib WPGP

Ruschia (*Aizoaceae*)

putterillii	SPlb
spinosa	SPlb
tumidula	SPlb

Ruscus ✿ (*Asparagaceae*)

aculeatus	CBcs CDul CMac CTsd ELan EPfP GPoy LEdu MGil MGos MRav NLar NWea SDix SPlb SRms SWvt WRHF
- (f)	SCob
- hermaphrodite	EPfP GCal MMuc SEND SMad WPGP WThu
- var. ***aculeatus*** 'Lanceolatus' (f)	GCal
- var. ***angustifolius***	WPGP
- - PAB 254	LEdu
- 'John Redmond'PBR ♀H5	CBcs ELan ELon EPfP EShb LHop LLHF LRHS NHol NLar NWad SCob SCoo SKHP SLon SPer SWvt WBor WFar WPGP WPat
* - 'Wheeler's Variety' (f/m)	CJun MRav WPGP
hypoglossum	CMac MMuc SEND WCot
racemosus	see *Danae racemosa*

Ruspolia (*Acanthaceae*)

hypocrateriformis	CCCN

Russelia (*Plantaginaceae*)

§ ***equisetiformis*** ♀H1c	WFib
- 'Lemon Falls' ♀H1c	WFib
- 'Tangerine Falls'	WFib
juncea	see *R. equisetiformis*

Ruta (*Rutaceae*)

chalepensis	CArn XLum
corsica	CArn XLum
graveolens	CBod CDul CHab ENfk GPoy LSun MJak MNHC SIde WJek XLum
- 'Jackman's Blue'	CBcs CTri EHoe EPfP GMaP GPoy MGos MHer MNHC MRav MSwo NLar SRms SWvt XLum
- 'Variegata' (v)	MNHC MPie NPer SRms

Ruttya (*Acanthaceae*)

fruticosa	CCCN

× *Ruttyruspolia* (*Acanthaceae*)

lutea	CCCN
'Phyllis van Heerden'	CCCN

Rytidosperma (*Poaceae*)

* ***arundinaceum***	EShb

S

Sabal (*Arecaceae*)

etonia	LTro
minor	CPHo LTro NLos SBig SPlb
palmetto	LTro
uresana	LRHS LTro

Saccharum (*Poaceae*)

arundinaceum	CKno
brevibarbe var. ***contortum***	WCot
officinarum	SPlb
ravennae	SMad SPlb

sage see *Salvia officinalis*

sage, annual clary see *Salvia viridis*

sage, biennial clary see *Salvia sclarea*

sage, pineapple see *Salvia elegans*

Sageretia (*Rhamnaceae*)

§ ***thea***	CMen
theezans	see *S. thea*

Sagina (*Caryophyllaceae*)

subulata	EHoe LRHS SVic XLum
- var. ***glabrata***	MAsh

§ - - 'Aurea' CMea CTri ECha ECtt EDAr GMaP MHer NHpl SPoG

Sagittaria (*Alismataceae*)

australis EWay
'Bloomin' Babe' EWay
graminea LLWG
- 'Crushed Ice' (v) EWay
japonica see *S. sagittifolia*
lancifolia EWay LLWG
latifolia NPer
* ***leucopetala*** 'Flore Pleno' (d) NPer
§ ***sagittifolia*** CWat LLWG MSKA MWts WMAq WPnP XLum
- 'Flore Pleno' (d) CWat EWay WMAq XLum
- var. ***leucopetala*** WMAq

Saintpaulia ✿ (*Gesneriaceae*)

'Aca's Pink Delight' WDib
'Aca's Red Ember' (v) WDib
'Aca's Ronnie Redhead' **new** WDib
'Ae-Amur Elit' **new** WDib
'Ae-Armageddon' **new** WDib
'Ae-Cosmic Jaguar' **new** WDib
'Ajohn's Fruit Cocktail' WDib
'Ajohn's Shimmering Star' WDib
'Alan's White Feather' **new** WDib
'Allegro Appalachian Trail' WDib
'Always Pink' WDib
'Aly's Rosy Baby' WDib
'Amazing Grace' **new** WDib
'Amethyst' **new** WDib
'Anouk' WDib
'Anthoflores Edith' WDib
'An-Yablochnyi Spas' **new** WDib
'Apache Thunderbolt' **new** WDib
'Arctic Frost' (d) WDib
'Aussie Magic' **new** WDib
'Baby Brian' WDib
'Baby's Breath' WDib
'Ballet Snowcone' (d) WDib
'Beacon Trail' WDib
'Beatrice Trail' WDib
'Black Ace' (d) WDib
'Blackie Bryant' WDib
'Bliznecy' WDib
'Bloomlover's Cat' (d) WDib
'Bloomlover's Chimpy' **new** WDib
'Blue Dragon' (d) WDib
'Blue Tail Fly' WDib
'Blushing Ivory' WDib
'Blushing Trail' WDib
'B-Man's Taormina' **new** WDib
'Bob Serbin' (d) WDib
'Bob's Omega' WDib
'Bol's Evening Irja' WDib
brevipilosa WDib
'Buckeye Carioca' WDib
'Buffalo Hunt' (d) WDib
'Bylina' **new** WDib
'Calico Beauty' WDib
'Candy Fountain' WDib
'Candy Swirls' WDib
'Cathedral' WDib
'Chantamara' WDib
'Chantaspring' WDib
'Cherries 'n' Cream' WDib
'Chiffon Fiesta' WDib
'Chiffon Moonmoth' WDib
'Chiffon Pageant' WDib
'Chiffon Vesper' WDib
'Cirelda' **new** WDib
'Colette' WDib
'Country Romance' (d) WDib
'Crimson Ice' WDib
'Cupid's Jewel' WDib
'Deep Sky' WDib
'Deer Trail' WDib
'Delft' (d) WDib
'Desir' WDib
'Dibleys Kaarina' WDib
'Dibleys Mercedes' WDib
'Dibley's Pat' **new** WDib
'Ek Lubasha' WDib
'Ek-Vrata Raia' **new** WDib
'Electric Dreams' WDib
'Emerald Love' WDib
'Faded Denim' WDib
'Falling Raindrops' WDib
'Favorite Child' WDib
'Festive Holiday' (d) WDib
'Fire Mountain' WDib
'Flashy Angel' (v) WDib
'Flower Drum' WDib
'Gecko's Vespa Vino' WDib
'Genetic Blush' WDib
'Gillian' (d) WDib
'Golden Dawn' **new** WDib
'Golden Eye' WDib
'Golden Glow' (d) WDib
'Goluboi Tuman' WDib
'Grandmother's Halo' WDib
'Green Dragon' WDib
'Green Lace' (d) WDib
'Happy Cricket' WDib
'Heinz's Moonrays' **new** WDib
'Hot Summer Day' WDib
'In The Pink' WDib
'Indigo Ruffles' WDib
ionantha subsp. ***grotei*** WDib
- subsp. ***ionantha*** WDib
- subsp. ***rupicola*** WDib
- subsp. ***velutina*** WDib
'Irish Flirt' (d) WDib
'Irish Laughter' **new** WDib
'Island Breezes' **new** WDib
'Joli Concerto' WDib
'Jolie Madame' **new** WDib
'Jolly Cutie Pie' WDib
'Jolly Fairy' **new** WDib
'Jolly Fire' **new** WDib
'Jolly Imp' **new** WDib
'Jolly Orchid' (d) WDib
'Jolly Texan' (d) WDib
'Kamennyi Tsvetoz' **new** WDib
'Kazumi' **new** WDib
'King's Trail' (d) WDib
'Kosmicheskaia Legenda 2' **new** WDib
'Kostina Fantaziia' WDib
'Lemon Drop' (d) WDib
'Lemon Whip' (d) WDib
'Letnaya Noch' **new** WDib
'Letnie Sumerki' **new** WDib
'Lil Bit O'Irish' **new** WDib
'Lilla Blaklockan' **new** WDib
'Little Axel' WDib
'Little Seagull' **new** WDib
'Lollipop' WDib
'Looking Glass' WDib

'Louisiana Lagniappe'	WDib
'Louisiana Lullaby' (d)	WDib
'Love Spots'	WDib
'Lubimaia Dochka'	WDib
'Lucky Lee Ann' (d)	WDib
'Luminescence'	WDib
'Lyon's Minnie-HaHa' **new**	WDib
'Lyon's Paprika'	WDib
'Lyon's Plum Pudding'	WDib
'Mac's Black Jack'	WDib
'Mac's Blowing Bubbles'	WDib
'Mac's Carnival Clown'	WDib
'Mac's Cheery Cherry'	WDib
'Mac's Circus Clown'	WDib
'Mac's Coral Cutie'	WDib
'Mac's Exquisite Extravaganza'	WDib
'Mac's Glacial Grape' **new**	WDib
'Mac's Just Jeff' (d/v)	WDib
'Mac's Nocturne' (d)	WDib
'Mac's Rouge Rogue' **new**	WDib
'Mac's Southern Springtime' (d)	WDib
'Mac's Strawberry Sundae'	WDib
'Mac's Will-o'-th'-Wisp'	WDib
'Mair'	WDib
'Ma's Ching Dynasty' (d)	WDib
'Ma's Corsage'	WDib
'Ma's Easter Parade'	WDib
'Ma's Lily Pad'	WDib
'Ma's Midnight Rain' **new**	WDib
'Ma's Prince Froggie' **new**	WDib
'Masked Man'	WDib
'Midget Lilian' (v)	WDib
'Midnight Flame' (d)	WDib
'Midnight Magic' ambig.	WDib
'Midnight Rascal' (d)	WDib
'Midnight Waltz' (d)	WDib
'Milky Way Trail'	WDib
'Mindi Brooke'	WDib
'Minnie Mine'	WDib
'Minstrel's Mary Ruth'	WDib
'Munchkin Kisses' (d)	WDib
'Ness' Antique Red'	WDib
'Ness' Bangle Blue'	WDib
'Ness' Blueberry Puff'	WDib
'Ness' Cherry Smoke'	WDib
'Ness' Crinkle Blue' (d)	WDib
'Ness' Dynomite'	WDib
'Ness' Jesse' (d)	WDib
'Ness' Midnight Fantasy'	WDib
'Ness' Orange Pekoe'	WDib
'Ness' Satin Rose'	WDib
'Ness' Sheer Peach'	WDib
'Newtown Ohio'	WDib
nitida	WDib
'Nortex's Razzmatazz Haven'	WDib
'Number 32' **new**	WDib
'Ode to Beauty'	WDib
'Okie Easter Bunny'	WDib
'Oksana'	WDib
'Optimara Chico'	WDib
'Optimara Dali'	WDib
'Optimara Hiroshige'	WDib
'Optimara Little Moonstone'	WDib
'Optimara Little Ruby'	WDib
'Optimara Little Seneca'	WDib
'Otoe' (d)	WDib
'Parnikovyi Effekt'	WDib
'Pat Tracey'	WDib
'Peppermint Doll'	WDib
'Pink Wink'	WDib
'Pixie Blue'	WDib
'Pixie Pink'	WDib
'Pixie Show-off'	WDib
'Podvenechnaia' (d)	WDib
'Powder Keg' (d)	WDib
'Powwow' (d/v)	WDib
'Prancing Pony'	WDib
'Purple Passion'	WDib
'Rainbow's Limelight' (d)	WDib
'Rainbow's Quiet Riot'	WDib
'Ramblin' Amethyst'	WDib
'Ramblin' Angel' (d)	WDib
'Ramblin' Dots'	WDib
'Ramblin' Lassie'	WDib
'Ramblin' Sunshine'	WDib
'Rare Tapestry'	WDib
'Raspberry Crisp'	WDib
'Rebel's Amy' **new**	WDib
'Rebel's Splatter Kake' **new**	WDib
'Red Lantern' (d)	WDib
'Red Summit'	WDib
'Reflections of Spring' (d)	WDib
'Rhapsodie Clementine'	WDib
'Rhapsodie Rosalie'	WDib
'Robert Mayer'	WDib
'Rob's Argyle Socks' (d)	WDib
'Rob's Bamboozle' (d)	WDib
'Rob's Blue Cat'	WDib
'Rob's Blue Socks'	WDib
'Rob's Boo Hoo'	WDib
'Rob's Boogie Woogie'	WDib
'Rob's Chilly Willy' (d/v)	WDib
'Rob's Dandy Lion' (d/v)	WDib
'Rob's Dust Storm' (d)	WDib
'Rob's Fuzzy Navel'	WDib
'Rob's Hallucination'	WDib
'Rob's Heebie Jeebie'	WDib
'Rob's Hot Tamale'	WDib
'Rob's Ice Ripples' (d)	WDib
'Rob's Jitterbug'	WDib
'Rob's Love Bite' (d)	WDib
'Rob's Mad Cat' (d)	WDib
'Rob's Peedletuck'	WDib
'Rob's Pewter Bells'	WDib
'Rob's Pink Buttercups' (v)	WDib
'Rob's Rinky Dink' (d)	WDib
'Rob's Ruff Stuff'	WDib
'Rob's Sarsparilla' (d)	WDib
'Rob's Scarecrow'	WDib
'Rob's Scooter' **new**	WDib
'Rob's Scrumptious'	WDib
'Rob's Seduction' (d/v)	WDib
'Rob's Shadow Magic' (d/v)	WDib
'Rob's Smarty Pants' (d)	WDib
'Rob's Sticky Wicket' (d)	WDib
'Rob's Toorooka' (d)	WDib
'Rob's Twinkle Blue' (d)	WDib
'Rob's Twinkle Pink' (d)	WDib
'Rob's Vanilla Trail' (d)	WDib
'Rob's Wooloomooloo' (d)	WDib
'Roll Along Blue' (d)	WDib
'Rs-Boyarinya' **new**	WDib
'Rs-Gertsogninea' **new**	WDib
'Rs-Kabaret' **new**	WDib
'Rs-Korrida' **new**	WDib
'RS-Strast'	WDib
'Ruffled Skies'	WDib
'Ruffles 'n' Lace'	WDib

	'Saint Paul'	WDib
	'Santa Anita'	WDib
	'Sapphire Halo'	WDib
	'Scarlet Ribbons'	WDib
	'Senk's Arctic Fox' **new**	WDib
	'Senk's Beanstalk'	WDib
	'Shirl's Hawaiian Lei' **new**	WDib
	shumensis	WDib
	'Shy Blue' **new**	WDib
	'Silly Girl'	WDib
	'Silverglade Beads'	WDib
	'Silverglade Dolls'	WDib
	'Silverglade Dreams'	WDib
	'Silverglade Gems' **new**	WDib
	'Silverglade Jingles'	WDib
	'Silverglade Meadows' **new**	WDib
	'Sky Bells' (v)	WDib
	'Sky Trail' **new**	WDib
	'Snow Leopard'	WDib
	'Sparkleberry' **new**	WDib
	'Special Treat'	WDib
	'Sultan' (d)	WDib
	'Sun Sizzle'	WDib
	'Sunkissed Rose'	WDib
	'Sweet Amy Sue' (d)	WDib
	'Swifty Thriller' **new**	WDib
	'Taffeta Blue' (d)	WDib
	'The Madam'	WDib
	'Tiger' (v)	WDib
	'Tina's April Fantasy'	WDib
	'Toy Castle'	WDib
	'Tula'	WDib
	'Twist 'n' Shout'	WDib
	'Two-w Miss Sophie' (d) **new**	WDib
	'Vallartas Campanas Moradas' **new**	WDib
	'Warm Sunshine'	WDib
	'Whirligig Star'	WDib
	'Wild Irish Rose'	WDib
	'Winnergreen'	WDib
	'Wisteria' (d)	WDib
	'Witch Doctor' (d)	WDib
	'Wrangler's Jealous Heart'	WDib
	'Yesterday's Child'	WDib

Salicornia (*Amaranthaceae*)

	europaea	SVic

Salix ✿ (*Salicaceae*)

	acutifolia 'Blue Streak' (m) ♀H5	CEnd CWiW EPfP EWes MBlu NBir NLar SWat WMou
	- 'Pendulifolia' (m)	SGol
	'Aegma Brno' (f)	WMou
	aegyptiaca	CBot CLnd EBtc ECrN MBlu NWea WMou
	alba	CCVT CDul CHab CLnd CWiW ECrN EMOT ESps LBuc NWea SEWo SGol WHed WMou WTSh
	- f. ***argentea***	see *S. alba* var. *sericea*
	- 'Aurea'	WMou
	- var. ***caerulea***	CDul NWea WMou
	- - 'Wantage Hall' (f)	CWiW
	- 'Cardinalis' (f)	CWiW SWat
	- 'Chermesina' hort.	see *S. alba* var. *vitellina* 'Britzensis'
	- 'Golden Ness' ♀H6	CRos LRHS MAsh MBlu NOra WFar WMat
	- 'Hutchinson's Yellow'	CTho ECrN NLar NWea
	- 'Liempde' (m)	NWea
	- 'Raesfeld' (m)	CWiW
§	- var. ***sericea*** ♀H6	CDul CLnd CTho EPfP MBlu MRav NLar NWea SPer WCot WMou
	- 'Splendens'	see *S. alba* var. *sericea*
	- 'Tristis' misapplied	see *S.* × *sepulcralis* var. *chrysocoma*
§	- 'Tristis' ambig.	CLnd CTri ELan IBoy LRHS MGos MRav MSwo NLar NOra NWea SEWo SWat WHar
	- var. ***vitellina***	CDul CTri EPfP ESps LBuc MBNS MMuc NLar NWea SGol SLon SWat WHed
§	- - 'Britzensis' (m)	Widely available
	- - 'Nova'	SWat
§	- - 'Yelverton' ♀H6	CRos EPfP LRHS MAsh NOra SPoG SWat WFar WMat
	- 'Vitellina Tristis'	see *S. alba* 'Tristis' ambig.
§	***alpina***	ECho GEdr NHar
	'Americana'	CWiW
	amplexicaulis 'Pescara' (m)	CWiW
	amygdaloides	CWiW
	'Aokautere'	see *S.* × *sepulcralis* 'Aokautere'
§	***arbuscula***	ECho XEll
	arenaria	see *S. repens* var. *argentea*
	aurita	CAco NWea WHed
	babylonica	CDul CEnd LPar WMou
	- 'Annularis'	see *S. babylonica* 'Crispa'
	- 'Bijdorp'	NLar
§	- 'Crispa'	ELan GBin LHop LRHS MTPN NQui NSti SMad WFar WGrn
	- 'Pan Chih-kang'	CWiW NLar
	- var. ***pekinensis*** 'Pendula'	IArd
§	- - 'Tortuosa'	CBcs CDul CLnd CSBt CWib ECrN ELan EMOT EPfP GMcL IBoy IVic LRHS MGos MMuc NBir NOrn NPer NWea SCob SEND SGol SLon SPer SPlb SPoG SRms SWat WFar WHar
*	- 'Tortuosa Aurea'	CAco IBoy SGol SWvt
	× ***balfourii***	SDix
	'Blackskin' (f)	CWiW
	bockii	EBtc LLHF LRHS SDys SKHP
§	'Bowles's Hybrid'	WMou
	'Boydii' (f) ♀H7	CMea ECho EPot GAbr GCrg GKev GMaP ITim LEdu LRHS MGos NBir NHar NRya NSla SAko WAbe WFar WPat WThu
§	'Boyd's Pendulous' (m)	CWib
	caprea	CAco CArg CBcs CCVT CDul CHab CLnd CTri EPfP ESps LBuc MJak NBes NWea SCob SEWo SPer WHed WMou WSFF WTSh
	- 'Black Stem'	CDul
§	- 'Kilmarnock' (m)	Widely available
	- 'Mas' (m)	CNWT
	- var. ***pendula*** (m)	see *S. caprea* 'Kilmarnock' (m)
	- - (f)	see *S. caprea* 'Weeping Sally'
§	- 'Weeping Sally' (f)	WMat
	capusii	EBee WPGP
	cashmiriana	GEdr
*	***caspica rubra nana***	SWat
	chaenomeloides 'Mount Aso' **new**	EBee NLar WPGP
	'Chrysocoma'	see *S.* × *sepulcralis* var. *chrysocoma*
	cinerea	CAco CBcs CTri MJak NWea SEWo WHed WMou WTSh
	- 'Tricolor' (v)	NEoE
	'Coire Kander' **new**	GKev
	daphnoides	CBcs CCVT CDul CLnd CMac ELan EPfP ESps MGos MMuc MSwo NWea SEND SGol SPer SRms SWat WHed WMou WSFF
	- 'Aglaia' (m) ♀	CDul CTri

- 'Meikle' (f)	CWiW SWat
- 'Netta Statham' (m)	CWiW
- 'Ovaro Udine' (m)	CWiW
- 'Oxford Violet' (m)	NWea
- 'Stewartstown'	CWiW
× ***dasyclados*** 'Grandis'	NWea
§ × ***doniana*** 'Kumeti'	CWiW
'E.A. Bowles'	see *S.* 'Bowles's Hybrid'
× ***ehrhartiana***	CNat
§ ***elaeagnos***	CCVT CDul CTho CTri ECrN EPfP GMcL MBrN MMuc NWea SLon SPer SWat WHed WMou
§ - subsp. ***angustifolia*** ♀H5	CBcs CDul ELan EPfP MMuc MRav MSwo NLar NWea SCob SEND SRms
'Elegantissima'	see *S.* × *pendulina* var. *elegantissima*
eriocephala 'American Mackay' (m)	CWiW
- 'Kerksii' (m)	CWiW
- 'Mawdesley' (m)	CWiW
- 'Russelliana' (f)	CWiW
exigua ♀H5	CBcs CDul CLnd CTho ELan EPfP EWes IDee LBuc LEdu LRHS MBlu MBrN MGos MSwo NBir NLar NWea SCob SCoo SMad SPer WMou WPGP
fargesii ♀H6	CAbP CBcs CBot CDul CEnd CFil CMac EBee ELan EPfP GBin GCal LEdu LHop LRHS MBlu MGos MMuc MRav NBid SBrt SCob SKHP SMad SPer SPoG WBod WCot WCru WPat
fargesii × ***magnifica***	CFil
§ × ***finnmarchica***	WAbe
formosa	see *S. arbuscula*
fragilis	CAco CCVT CDul CHab CLnd EMOT NWea WHed WMou WTSh
§ - var. ***furcata***	CTri GCrg GKev
× ***fruticosa*** 'McElroy' (f)	CWiW
fruticulosa	see *S. fragilis* var. *furcata*
'Fuiri-koriyanagi'	see *S. integra* 'Hakuro-nishiki'
furcata	see *S. fragilis* var. *furcata*
glauca	CNat
'Golden Curls'	see *S.* × *sepulcralis* 'Erythroflexuosa'
gracilistyla	NWea WMou
§ - 'Melanostachys' (m) ♀	CBcs CBot CDul CTho ECrN ELan EPfP LHop MAsh MBNS MBlu MBrN MGos MMuc MRav NBir NEgg NLar NWea SBrt SEND SGol SPer SRms SWat WBor WPtf
× ***greyi***	NEoE
hastata (f)	SWat
- 'Wehrhahnii' (m) ♀H6	CBcs CDul CMea EBee ECho ELan EPfP ESps GCra GKev GMcL IVic LEdu MBlu MJak MMuc MRav MSwo NBir NLar NWea SPer SWat
helvetica ♀H7	CBcs CDul CLet CMac CMea EBee ECho ELan EPfP GAbr GMcL IVic MBlu MRav NBir NEgg NLar NWea SAko SPer WFar
herbacea	ECho GEdr WAbe
hibernica	see *S. phylicifolia*
hookeriana	CDul CFil ELan MBlu MBrN NLar WCFE WMou
incana	see *S. elaeagnos*
integra 'Albomaculata'	see *S. integra* 'Hakuro-nishiki'
- 'Flamingo' PBR	ELan NLar SPoG WTSh
§ - 'Hakuro-nishiki' (v) ♀H5	Widely available

- 'Pendula' (f)	CEnd MAsh
irrorata ♀H5	CDul CLnd EPfP MBlu MSwo NOra SCob SSal SWat WMat
'Jacquinii'	see *S. alpina*
kinuyanagi (m)	LHop NSti
§ ***koriyanagi***	CWiW
'Kumeti'	see *S.* × *doniana* 'Kumeti'
'Kuro-me'	see *S. gracilistyla* 'Melanostachys'
lanata ♀H7	CBcs CBot CMac ECho ELan ELon EPfP GAbr GKev GMcL MAsh MGos MJak NBir NEgg NLar NWea SBrt SWat WCFE
lapponum	LEdu MMuc NLar NWea SRms
- compact	GKev
magnifica	CBot CDul CEnd CFil EBee ELan EPfP EUJe IArd IDee LEdu LRHS MHid MMuc NLar NWea SKHP SMad SPoG SWat WFar WHer WHor WMou WPGP
'Mark Postill' (f)	CBot EBee ELon EWTr GBin LRHS MBNS MMuc MNHC NLar SAko WWFP
matsudana 'Tortuosa'	see *S. babylonica* var. *pekinensis* 'Tortuosa'
- 'Tortuosa Aureopendula'	see *S.* × *sepulcralis* 'Erythroflexuosa'
'Melanostachys'	see *S. gracilistyla* 'Melanostachys'
× ***meyeriana*** 'Lumley' (f)	CWiW
× ***mollissima***	CWiW
var. ***hippophaifolia*** 'Jefferies' (m)	
- - 'Notts Spaniard' (m)	CWiW
- - 'Trustworthy' (m)	CWiW
- var. ***undulata*** 'Kottenheider Weide' (f)	CWiW
aff. ***moupinensis*** from Vietnam	CFil
§ ***myrsinifolia***	ELan LHop MBlu MMuc NLar WGrn
- 'Black Knight'	EPfP
myrsinites var. ***jacquiniana***	see *S. alpina*
myrtilloides 'Pink Tassels' (m)	ECho GEdr NLar SBrt
myrtilloides × ***repens***	see *S.* × *finnmarchica*
nakamurana var. ***yezoalpina***	CBot EBee ELan EPot EWes GKev GQui IVic LRHS MBlu MMuc MRav NHar NLar SBrt WFar WPat
nigricans	see *S. myrsinifolia*
nivalis	see *S. reticulata* subsp. *nivalis*
§ × ***pendulina*** var. ***elegantissima***	SWat
pentandra	CBot CDul CLnd NWea WMou
- 'Patent Lumley'	CWiW
§ ***phylicifolia***	NWea WMou
- 'Malham' (m)	CWiW
§ ***purpurea***	CCVT CDul GMcL NWea SCob WHed WMou
- 'Brittany Green' (f)	CWiW
- 'Continental Reeks'	CWiW
- 'Dark Dicks' (f)	CWiW NLar WSFF
- 'Dicky Meadows' (m)	CWiW
- 'Goldstones'	CWiW NLar
- f. ***gracilis***	see *S. purpurea* 'Gracilis'
§ - 'Gracilis'	MMuc NWea SCob SEND WCot
- 'Green Dicks'	CWiW
- 'Helix'	see *S. purpurea*
- 'Howki' (m)	WMou
- 'Irette' (m)	CWiW
- 'Jagiellonka' (f)	CWiW
- var. ***japonica***	see *S. koriyanagi*

	- subsp. ***lambertiana***	CWiW
	- 'Lancashire Dicks' (m)	CWiW
	- 'Leicestershire Dicks' (m)	CWiW
	- 'Light Dicks'	CWiW
	- 'Lincolnshire Dutch' (f)	CWiW
	- 'Nancy Saunders' (f) 🏆H6	CTho CWiW EHoe EWld GLog LEdu MBNS MBlu MBrN MRav NBir NLar NSti SDix SMHy WBod WCot WGrn
	- 'Odeta'	LEdu
	- 'Pendula' 🏆H6	CCVT CEnd CMac ECrN LRHS MAsh MSwo NOrn NWea
	- 'Read' (f)	CWiW
	- 'Reeks' (f)	CWiW
	- 'Richartii' (f)	CWiW
	- 'Uralensis' (f)	CWiW
	pyrenaica	EWes
	pyrenaica* × *retusa	ECho
	repens	NWea SRms SWat WAbe
§	- var. ***argentea***	CDul ELan EWes LRHS MMuc MRav NWea SPer
	- ***pendula***	see *S.* 'Boyd's Pendulous' (m)
	- 'Voorthuizen' (f)	ECho
	reticulata 🏆H7	ECho EPot GCrg NBir NHar NSla WAbe
§	- subsp. ***nivalis***	EPot
	retusa	CTri GEdr NBir NHar
	rosmarinifolia misapplied	see *S. elaeagnos* subsp. *angustifolia*
	rosmarinifolia L.	EPfP NLar
	× ***rubens*** 'Basfordiana' (m)	CDul CLnd CTho CWiW MBNS SWat WMou
	- 'Bouton Aigu'	CWiW
	- 'Farndon'	CWiW
	- 'Flanders Red' (f)	CWiW
	- 'Fransgeel Rood' (m)	CWiW
	- 'Glaucescens' (m)	CWiW
	- 'Golden Willow'	CWiW
	- 'Jaune de Falaise'	CWiW
	- 'Jaune Hâtive'	CWiW
	- 'Laurina'	CWiW
	- 'Natural Red' (f)	CWiW
	- 'Parsons'	CWiW
	- 'Rouge Ardennais'	CWiW
	- 'Rouge Folle'	CWiW
	- 'Russet' (f)	CWiW
	× ***rubra***	CWiW
	- 'Abbey's Harrison' (f)	CWiW
	- 'Continental Osier' (f)	CWiW
	- 'Eugenei' (m)	CDul ECrN GQui MBlu SWat
	- 'Fidkin' (f)	CWiW
	- 'Harrison's' (f)	CWiW
	- 'Harrison's Seedling A' (f)	CWiW
	- 'Mawdesley'	CWiW
	- 'Mawdesley Seedling A' (f)	CWiW
	- 'Pyramidalis'	CWiW
I	'Salix Red'	WJPR
	Scarlet Curls = 'Scarcuzam'	WPat
	× ***sepulcralis***	NWea
§	- 'Aokautere'	CWiW
	- 'Caradoc'	CWiW
§	- var. ***chrysocoma*** 🏆	Widely available
	- 'Dart's Snake'	ELan EPPr EShb MAsh MBrN MRav NLar WCot
§	- 'Erythroflexuosa' 🏆H5	CAco CBcs CDul CEnd EBee ELan EMOT EPPr EPfP ESps LBMP LHop MAsh MGos MMuc MRav NOra NOrn NWea SCob SEND SGol SPer SPoG SWat WCFE WMat
	serpyllifolia	CTri GKev NHar WThu
	- 'Chamonix'	NSla
	serpyllum	see *S. fragilis* var. *furcata*
	'Setsuka'	see *S. udensis* 'Sekka'
	sitchensis	NWea
	× ***smithiana***	NWea
	× ***stipularis*** (f)	NWea
	'Stuartii'	GAbr
	subopposita	EBtc ELan MMuc SBrt WAbe
	triandra	NWea WMou
	- 'Black German' (m)	CWiW
	- 'Black Hollander' (m)	CWiW NLar
	- 'Black Maul'	CWiW
	- 'Grisette de Falaise'	CWiW
	- 'Grisette Droda' (f)	CWiW
	- 'Long Bud'	CWiW
	- 'Noir de Challans'	CWiW
	- 'Noir de Touraine'	CWiW
	- 'Noir de Villaines' (m)	CWiW WJPR
	- 'Rouge d'Orléans'	EBtc
	- 'Sarda d'Anjou'	CWiW
	- 'Whissander'	CWiW
	udensis	NWea
	- 'Golden Sunshine'	EBee EMil LRHS MPkF NEoE WCot
§	- 'Sekka' (m)	CBcs ELan MBlu MMuc NBir NWea SWat WMou
	uva-ursi	WAbe
	viminalis	CCVT CLnd CMac EPfP GMcL LBuc MJak NWea SEWo SVic WHed WJPR WMou WSFF
	- 'Green Gotz'	CWiW
	vitellina 'Pendula'	see *S. alba* 'Tristis' ambig.
	'Yelverton'	see *S. alba* var. *vitellina* 'Yelverton'

Salvia ✿ (*Lamiaceae*)

	CD&R 1141 **new**	SPin
	CD&R 1162	SPhx
	CD&R 1458	SPin
	CD&R 1495	SPin
	CD&R 3071	SPin
	PC&H 226	SPin
	from Catamarca, Argentina	SDys
	from Nur Daği, Saudi Arabia	WCot
	absconditiflora	SPin
	acerifolia	SDys
	acetabulosa	see *S. multicaulis*
	adenophora	SPin
	aethiopis	EWes SPav WCot XSen
I	'African Sky'	CElw CSpe EWoo LSou MPie SDys SMHy SPin WGrn WOut
§	***africana***	EBee SPin
	africana-caerulea	see *S. africana*
	africana-lutea	see *S. aurea*
	agnes	SDys SPin
	'Alegría'	SDys SPin
	algeriensis	SPhx
	amarissima	SPin
	'Amber'	IMou SBrt SPin
	ambigens	see *S. guaranitica* 'Blue Enigma'
	'Amistad' PBR	Widely available
	ampelophylla	SDys
	- B&SWJ 10751	SPin
§	***amplexicaulis***	CBod LPla MMuc NLar SEND SRms WHrl XSen
	amplifrons	SPin
	angustifolia Cav.	see *S. reptans*
	angustifolia Mich.	see *S. azurea*
	'Anna'	SDys
	'Anthony Parker'	WOut

apiana	EBee MHer SPin SPlb SRms SVen XSen
arenaria	SPin
argentea	CBcs CBod CDor CSpe ECha ELan EPfP EWTr EWoo GMaP LHop LRHS MSpe NSti SPer SWat WHar WJek WKif XSen
arizonica	CSam EBee EWld GCal LHop MAsh SDys SPin WSHC XSen
aspera	SPin
atrocyanea	CSam CSpe EBee ECre EWes EWld MAsh MAvo MGil SDys SPin WHal WKif
- CDPR 3071	WPGP
atropatana new	WCot
aucheri	SPin
§ ***aurea***	CHll CSpe CTre SPin SPlb SVen WBod XLum
- 'Kirstenbosch'	CAby ECtt EWld NSti SDys SPin WKif WOut
aurita	SPin
- var. ***galpinii***	SPin
austriaca	SPin
§ ***azurea***	SBrt SPhx SPin XSen
- var. ***grandiflora***	SAko SPin WCot
bacheriana	see *S. buchananii*
§ ***barrelieri***	EBee ESwi SPin XSen
'Bee's Bliss'	XSen
'Belhaven'	EBee GCal
benthamiana new	SDys
bertolonii	see *S. pratensis* Bertolonii Group
bicolor	see *S. barrelieri*
'Black Knight'	SDys SPin WOth WPGP
blancoana	see *S. lavandulifolia* subsp. *blancoana*
blepharophylla	ECtt LHop MHer MSCN SPin WHea
- 'Diablo'	ECtt
- 'Painted Lady'	CBot ECtt MAsh SDys SPin
'Bleu Armor'PBR	SPhx
'Blue Ice'	MHom
'Blue Moon'	SDys
'Blue Note'PBR	CBod CBot CMea CMos CSpe CWGN CWld EBee ECtt ELan EUJe IKil LRHS MAvo MBel MHol NDov NRHS SCob SEND SHil SPoG SRkn WCot WHil
'Blue Sky'	EWld
§ 'Blush Pink'	SDys
bogotensis new	SPin
bowleyana	SPin
brandegeei	SPin
brevilabra	SPin
brevipes	SPin
'Bright Eyes'	CWGN SCob
broussonetii	EBee SPin
§ ***buchananii*** 🏆H2	CBod CSam ECtt EWld LHop MAsh MHer MRav SDys SPin SRkn WKif
bulleyana misapplied	see *S. flava* var. *megalantha*
bulleyana Diels	CBcs EWes GPSL MMuc NQui WHea
- 'Blue Lips'	EBee LCro SCob WHil
bullulata	SPin
- pale-blue-flowered	CBot CSpe SDys SPin
cacaliifolia 🏆H2	CWCL ECtt EWld GCal MAsh MHer MPie SDys SPin SRkn
cadmica	SPin
caerulea misapplied	see *S. guaranitica*
caerulea L.	see *S. africana*
caespitosa	XSen

campanulata	SPin
- B&SWJ 9232	WCru
- DJHC C394	SPin
- GWJ 9294	SPin WCru
- var. ***hirtella*** GWJ 9397	WCru
canariensis	SEND SPin WBod
- f. ***albiflora***	EBee SVen
- f. ***candidissima***	SBrt SPin
candelabrum 🏆H3	CAbP CSpe ECre EWes MHer SPav SPhx SPin SVen WCot WKif XSen
candidissima	XSen
canescens	XSen
cardinalis	see *S. fulgens*
carnea	CSam SPin
- from Valle de Bravo, Mexico	SDys
castanea	SPin
caudata	SPin
'Cavaliero Celeste' new	SDys
§ ***chamaedryoides***	CFil ELan MAsh SBrt SPhx SPin WHea XSen
- var. ***isochroma***	EWld MAsh SDys SPin WPGP XSen
- 'Marine Blue'	MAsh MCot
- silver-leaved	CAby CSpe SPin XLum
aff. ***chamaedryoides*** B&SWJ 9032 from Guatemala	SPin
chamelaeagnea	EPPr GFai SBrt SDys SPin
'Cherry Queen'	CWGN MAsh
chiapensis	MAsh SDys SPin
chinensis	see *S. japonica*
chionophylla	CElw SPin
'Christine Yeo'	CElw EBee ECtt ELon EPri EWoo MAsh SAko SDys SEND SPin WHil WHoo WPGP WSHC WTcb XSen
'Christopher Fairweather'	ECtt
cinnabarina	SPin
cleistogama misapplied	see *S. glutinosa*
clevelandii	MHer SPav SPin WJek
- 'Winnifred Gilman'	SDys
clinopodioides	EBee SDys SPin
coahuilensis misapplied	see *S. greggii* × *serpyllifolia*
coahuilensis ambig.	EBee LSou MAsh SKHP SLon SPin SRkn WSHC WTcb XLum
coahuilensis Fernald	LHop
coccinea	SPin
- (Nymph Series) 'Coral Nymph'	SPav
- - 'Lady in Red'	SPav
- (Summer Jewel Series) 'Summer Jewel Pink' new	LRHS NRHS
- - 'Summer Jewel Red' new	EBee
concolor misapplied	see *S. guaranitica*
concolor Lamb. ex Benth.	EWld GCal MHom SDys SPin WSHC
confertiflora	CAby CBcs CBot CSam CSpe CWCL EBee ECre ECtt GCal MAsh MHer MHom MSCN SDix SDys SPin SPlb SRkn SVen WHea WKif WOth WPGP
corrugata	CBcs CElw CPne EBee ECtt GBin GCal LRHS MAsh MHer SDys SPhx SPin WPGP
'Crème Caramel'	EBee ECtt MAsh MHom SDys WHil
cruickshanksii	SPin
cryptantha	XSen
cuatrecasana	SPin
curviflora	CBot CElw CSam CSpe MAsh SBch SDys SEle SPin

	cyanescens	CFis CMea EPot LRHS SPin WPGP XSen
	cyanicalyx	SDys SPin
	daghestanica	EBee GKev SPin XSen
	'Dancing Dolls'	CWGN EWTr EWoo LRHS SCob SHil
I	***dangitalis***	SBrt SPin
	darcyi misapplied	see *S. roemeriana*
	darcyi J. Compton	CBot CHll ELan EWes MCot SDys SPin WSHC XLum XSen
	davidsonii	SPin
	'Dayglo'	ECtt
	deserta	WCot
	desoleana	EBee SPin
	dichlamys	SPin
	'Didi'	NDov
	digitaloides BWJ 7777	SPin WCru
	discolor	CBot CHll CSpe ECtt EWld GCal MAsh MHer SCob SDys SPin WOth XSen
*	- ***nigra***	CCse
	disermas	SPin SPlb XSen
	- pink-flowered	SPin
	disjuncta	CElw SPin
	- 'Chimbango'	SPin
	divinorum	LEdu
	dolichantha	CCVN CTsd NBir NLar SPin WMoo XSen
	dolomitica	SPav SPin
	dombeyi	CAby CPne CSam EWld SDys SPin
	dominica	SPin XSen
	dorisiana	MAsh MHer SDys SPin SVen
	'Dorset Wonder'	NCGa NDov
	durifolia	SPin
	'Dyson's Crimson'	CAby CSpe ELan MCot SDys WAul
	'Dyson's Gem'	SDys
	'Dyson's Joy'	CBot LHop MCot SDys WHil WKif
	eigii	SPin XSen
	eizi-matudae	SDys SPin
§	***elegans***	CBot CLau EWes GCal IDee NWad WBod WOth XLum XSen
	- 'Golden Delicious'	CAby CBod ECtt ENfk EWes MHer SPin SRms WOut
	- 'Honey Melon'	ENfk MAsh SBee SDys
	- 'Scarlet Pineapple'	CArn CBod CLau ECtt ELan ENfk EWld GPoy MCot MHer MNHC SDys SPad SPin SRms SVen WJek XSen
	- 'Sonoran Red'	SDys
	- 'Tangerine'	CArn CBod CLau ENfk EWld MHer MNHC NQui SPin SRms WJek
	'Ember's Wish'	CBot CMos ECtt NDov SDys SEle SPin WGrn WHil WTor
	'Endless Love'	EBee LSou NDov SAko
	evansiana	SPin
	'Eveline'	CKno CMac CWGN EBee ECtt EPfP LRHS NLar NRHS SHar STPC WTor
	excelsa	SPin
	exserta	EBee
	fallax	see *S. roscida*
	farinacea 'Midnight Candle' new	LRHS
	- 'Rhea'	SPoG
	- 'Strata'	SPoG
§	***flava*** var. ***megalantha***	CAby CBod EPfP EWld LRHS LSRN MSpe SPin XSen
	'Flower Child' new	SDys
	forreri	EBee MAsh NDov SDys SPin WPGP
	- 'Karen Dyson'	SDys
§	***forsskaolii***	CArn CBod CElw CSam ECtt ELan EWoo GAbr GKev LLWP MMuc MNrw MRav NLar NQui NSti SAko SEND SPav SPin SPtp WCot WHea WKif WMoo XLum XSen
	- white-flowered	EBee SPin XSen
§	***fruticosa***	CArn LRHS SLon SPin SRms XSen
§	***fulgens*** ♀H3	GCal MAsh SDys SPin SRkn WHea
	- from Mount Popocatépetl, Mexico	SPin
	gachantivana new	SPin
	'Germaine'	SPin
	gesneriiflora	ECtt EWld SPin WPGP
	- mountain form	SDys WPGP
	- 'Tequila'	SPin WOut
	gilliesii	SPin
	glabrescens B&SWJ 11152	WCru
*	- var. ***robusta*** B&SWJ 11147	WCru
	glechomifolia	SPin
§	***glutinosa***	CMac CSpe EBee EWld GCal GWyn IMou LRHS MMuc MNrw NBro NLar NSti SEND SPav SPin SPtp WCAu WCot WHea XLum XSen
	graciliramulosa	SPin
	gracilis	SPin
	grahamii	see *S. microphylla* var. *microphylla* 'Newby Hall'
	gravida	SPin
	'Great Comp'	NDov SDys
	greggii	ECtt EPfP EWes LRHS MHer SPlb SRms WTcb XLum XSen
	- CD&R 1148	MCot SDys
	- 'Alba'	CSpe WHil XLum XSen
	- 'Blush Pink'	see *S.* 'Blush Pink'
	- 'Caramba' (v)	ESwi WHil
	- 'Cream'	EAJP
	- 'Devon Cream'	see *S. greggii* 'Sungold'
	- 'Diane'	MAsh
	- 'Emperor'	LHop MAvo SEle WTcb
	- 'Flame'	CWGN ELan WHil
	- 'Icing Sugar' PBR	CBod CCVN CNor CWGN CWld EAEE EBee ECtt ELan ENfk EPfP EWoo LBMP LCro LHop LRHS MAsh MCot MSpe NDov SCob SDys SEle SRkn WBor WKif WOut WSHC
	- 'Lara'	WHil
	- 'Lipstick'	ECtt GWyn LCro LOPS MAsh
	- 'Magenta'	SPin WHil
	- 'Peach' misapplied	see *S.* × *jamensis* 'Pat Vlasto'
	- 'Peach'	CWGN EPfP MAsh SAko SDys SPin WHea WPGP XLum XSen
	- 'Pink Preference'	MAsh SDys
	- 'Raspberry Red'	XLum
	- 'Sierra San Antonio'	see *S.* × *jamensis* 'Sierra San Antonio'
	- 'Sparkler' (v)	ELan EPfP LRHS MAsh SLon
	- 'Stormy Pink'	CAby CHll CSam CSpe CWld MCot NDov SIgm WOth WPGP WTcb
§	- 'Sungold'	CWGN ECtt EPfP LRHS MAsh MPie SAko SDys SPhx XSen
	- variegated (v)	XSen
	- yellow-flowered	XLum
	greggii × ***lycioides***	see *S. greggii* × *serpyllifolia*
§	***greggii*** × ***serpyllifolia***	CAbP CSpe MAsh SDys SPin SVen
	guadalujarensis	SPin
§	***guaranitica***	ECtt MHer SPin WKif WPGP XLum XSen
	- 'Argentina Skies'	CAby CHGN ECtt EPPr SDys SPin XSen
	- 'Black and Blue'	CBcs CBod CBot CWCL CWGN EBee ECre ECtt EPfP EUJe GBin

	GCal ILea LCro LHop LRHS LSRN MSpe NCGa NRHS SDys SPin SRkn SVen WHea WHoo WPGP WSHC WTcb XSen
§ - 'Blue Enigma' Υ^{H4}	CAby CArn CBod CBot CWGN EBee ECha ECtt EHrv ELan EPfP EWoo GCal LHop LRHS MAsh MGos MRav MSpe SDix SDys SPin WHea XLum XSen
- 'Costa Rica Blue'	SDys
- 'Indigo Blue'	ECtt EPfP MAsh SPin
- 'Midnight'	CSpe SAko
- 'Purple Emperor'	CBot CWld LHop
- 'Purple Splendor'	MHer
- purple-flowered	CSam SDys
haematodes	see *S. pratensis* Haematodes Group
haenkei	CElw SPin
- 'Prawn Chorus'	MAsh
hayatae	SPin
heldreichiana	SMHy SPin XSen
henryi	SPin
hians	EWoo GCal GCra ILea MArt SRms
hierosolymitana	CHid EBee SPin XSen
hirtella	SPin
hispanica misapplied	see *S. lavandulifolia*
hispanica L.	CSam
holwayi	SDys SPin
horminum	see *S. viridis* var. *comata*
huberi	XSen
hypargeia	CPBP XSen
'I Cavalieri del Tau' **new**	SDys
inconspicua	SPin
indica	EWTr
'Indigo Spires'	CBot CHll CSam CSpe CWGN ECre ECtt EPfP IMou MAsh MCot NDov SDix SDys SEle SPhx SPin WBod WHea WKif WOth WSHC XLum
interrupta	EWld MCot SPin WHea XSen
involucrata Υ^{H3}	GCra MCot NBro SDys SPin SVen WHil WSHC
- 'Bethellii' Υ^{H3}	CArn CBod CBot CMHG EBee ECtt ELan EPfP EWld EWoo LRHS MAsh MHer NSti SDix SDys SKHP SPin SRkn WGrn WKif WOth XLum
- 'Boutin' Υ^{H3}	CTsd EBee MAsh MHom SDys SEle SPin
§ - 'Hadspen'	CBot CHll CRHN CSam CSpe EBee EWes GCal SBch SPin WOth WOut
- 'Mrs Pope'	see *S. involucrata* 'Hadspen'
- 'Pink Icicles'	SDys
involucrata* × *wagneriana	SDys
iodantha	SPin
- 'Louis Saso'	SPin
iodochroa B&SWJ 10252	SPin WCru
'Jackson's Cassis'	WTcb
'Jackson's Imperial'	WTcb
'Jackson's Kir Royale'	WTcb
'Jackson's Pink Gin'	WTcb
'Jackson's Purple'	WTcb
× ***jamensis***	EWes MAsh SPin
- 'Blue Amor'	CSpe
- 'California Sunset'	MAsh SAko SDys
- 'Dark Dancer'	MAsh SAko SDys SPhx WHil
- 'Desert Blaze' (v)	CWGN EAJP ECtt EPfP MRav SDys SPin WGrn WPGP WTcb XLum
- 'Devantville'	XLum
- 'Dysons' Orangy Pink'	CSpe NDov SDys
- 'El Durazno'	WTcb
- 'Flammenn'^{PBR}	LRHS SHil
- 'Golden Girl'	EBee EWoo WHil
§ - 'Hot Lips'	Widely available
- 'James Compton'	SIgm
- 'Javier'	CSpe MAsh SDys SPin WHil
- 'Kentish Pink'	SDys WTcb
- 'La Luna'	CSam CSpe ECtt LHop MAsh MHer MRav NDov SPin WOth WPGP WSHC WTcb XLum XSen
- 'La Siesta'	MAsh WTcb XSen
- 'La Tarde'	CTri MAsh MHom WTcb
- 'Los Lirios' Υ^{H5}	CTri SPin WHil WTcb
- 'Maraschino'	EPfP LHop LRHS MAsh SDys SPin SRms WHil WTcb XLum
- 'Melen'^{PBR}	EBee SPin
- 'Moonlight Over Ashwood' (v)	MAsh SPin WSHC
- 'Moonlight Serenade'	MAsh SDys
- 'Nachtvlinder'	Widely available
§ - 'Pat Vlasto'	SPin
- 'Peter Vidgeon'	CWGN EBee EPPr EPfP LHop LRHS MAsh MCot SAko SBee SDys SPhx SPin WSHC WTcb
- 'Pleasant Pink'	XSen
- 'Pluenn'^{PBR}	LRHS SHil
- 'Plum Wine'	WHil
- 'Raspberry Royale' Υ^{H5}	CWld ECtt EPfP LHop LRHS MAsh MHer MPie SAko SDys SPin WSHC XLum XSen
- 'Red Velvet'	EBee ECtt MAsh MCot MHom SDys SPhx WHrl WSHC WTcb
- 'Señorita Leah'	CWGN MAsh MCot NDov SDys
§ - 'Sierra San Antonio'	EPfP LRHS MAsh MHom SAko SDys WHil WPGP XLum XSen
- 'Snow White'	SPin
- 'Stormy Sunrise'	SDys
§ - 'Trebah'	CAby CBod ECre EWoo LHop MAsh MCot MHom SAko SDys SPin SRot WHea WHil WKif WSHC
- 'Trenance'	ECre ELon LHop MHer MHom SPin SRot WHil
- Violette de Loire = 'Barsal'^{PBR} **new**	LRHS
§ ***japonica***	SPin
'Jean's Jewel' **new**	SPin
'Jean's Purple Passion'	SDys SPin
'Jezebel'	EPfP LRHS SDys SPin
'Joan'	CWGN MAsh SDys SPin
judaica	CMac SPin WGrn XSen
jurisicii	CFis CWib EPfP LRHS MArt SBrt SPav WHea WJek XLum XSen
- 'Alba'	XSen
- pink-flowered	XSen
karwinskyi	SDys SPin
karwinskyi* × *univerticillata	SDys
keerlii	SPin
koyamae	SPin
- B&SWJ 10919	WCru
'Lalarsha'	CElw MCot NDov SAko SDys
lanceolata	LHop SPin
§ ***lavandulifolia***	CArn EBee ELan EPPr EPfP EWes GPoy LRHS MHer MNHC MRav SPin SRms WHoo WJek WKif XLum XSen
§ - subsp. ***blancoana***	ECha MHer SPin WHea XSen
- subsp. ***gallica***	XSen
- subsp. ***pyrenaeorum***	SPin XSen

	- 'Roquefure'	XSen
	- subsp. ***vellerea***	XSen
	lavanduloides	SPin
	lemmonii	see *S. microphylla* var. *wislizeni*
	'Lemon Pie'	SDys SPin WHlf
	leptophylla	see *S. reptans*
	leucantha ♀H2	CArn CBot CSpe ECre ELan EWld MAsh MCot MHer MRav SPin SPlb SRkn SVen WKif WOth XSen
	- Danielle's Dream = 'Ferpink'	SPin
	- 'Eder' (v)	MAsh SDys
	- 'Midnight'	CSam LHop
	- 'Purple Velvet'	CAby CSpe EBee ECtt MAsh MHer MHom SDix SDys SPin WHea
	- 'San Marcos Lavender'	SPin
	- 'Santa Barbara'	CBot CHll MAsh SDys
	- 'White Mischief'	SPin
	leucocephala	CPne SDys SPin
	leucophylla NNS 01-375	SPin
	littae	SDys SPin
	longispicata	SPin
	longistyla	CFil SDys SPin SVen WPGP
	'Love and Wishes' **new**	ECtt SDys
	lycioides misapplied	see *S. greggii* × *serpyllifolia*
	lycioides A. Gray	CAbP CHll EWld SDys SPin
	lyrata 'Burgundy Bliss'	see *S. lyrata* 'Purple Knockout'
§	- 'Purple Knockout'	CBod EPfP LRHS NRHS SPin WBor XSen
	- 'Purple Vulcano'	see *S. lyrata* 'Purple Knockout'
	macellaria misapplied	see *S. microphylla*
	- Epling	CSam
	macrophylla	GCal SDys SPin WPGP
	- Cally selection	SPin
	- purple-leaved	SDys
	macrosiphon	SPin
	'Madeline'PBR	CKno CMos CWGN EPfP EWTr GBin IBoy LCro LHop LOPS LRHS LSou MNrw NCGa SPer SPin STPC WHil
	madrensis	SDys SPin
	- 'Dunham'	EBee GCal
	'Magenta Magic'	SPin
	'Magic Potion'	CWGN
	mellifera	SPin
	mexicana	SPin
	- B&SWJ 10288	WCru
	- var. ***minor***	EWld SDys SPin
	meyeri	see *S. atrocyanea*
I	***miahuatlanensis***	SPin
§	***microphylla***	CBod CChe CLau CMHG CMac CTri EWes GMcL MHer SIgm SVen WHea WOut WTcb XLum
	- CD&R 1141	SPin
	- 'Belize'	MAsh WHil WTcb
	- 'Blue Monrovia' **new**	LRHS
	- 'Cerro Potosí'	CElw CSpe EBee ECtt ELan ELon LRHS MAsh MCot MHer MSCN SDix SDys SHar SIgm SPhx SPin WCFE WHea WHil WOth WTcb XLum
	- 'Hot Lips'	see *S.* × *jamensis* 'Hot Lips'
	- 'Huntington'	SPin
	- 'Kew Red' ♀H4	CBot MNrw SPin WHil WHoo WPGP WTcb
I	- 'Lutea'	MAsh SDys
	- 'Maroon'	SDys
	- 'Mauve'	NDov
§	- var. ***microphylla***	CRHN CTri CWib ECtt ELan ENfk EWoo LSRN MCot MHer MNHC MRav SEND SPin SRkn WJek XLum XSen
	- - 'La Foux'	SPhx XSen
§	- - 'Newby Hall' ♀H4	CBot ECtt EWes EWoo NWad SPhx WPGP WSHC
	- var. ***neurepia***	see *S. microphylla* var. *microphylla*
	- 'Norwell'	MNrw
	- 'Orange Door'	SAko SDys
	- orange-red-flowered	MRav
	- 'Oregon Peach'	EPfP LRHS
	- 'Oxford'	SPin
	- 'Pink Blush' ♀H4	CAby EAJP ECtt ELan EPfP LRHS MAsh MCot MHer MHom MNHC MSpe SDix SEND SPin SRkn WHil WHoo WKif WPGP WSHC WTcb XSen
	- 'Pleasant View' ♀H4	WHil
	- 'Ribambelle'	EAJP MAsh XLum
	- 'Robin's Pride'	SDys WHil
	- 'Rodbaston Red'	WHil
	- 'Rosy Cheeks'	WOut
	- 'San Carlos Festival'	MAsh NCGa SDys SPhx SPin WHil WPGP
	- 'Trelawny Rose Pink'	see *S.* 'Trelawney'
	- 'Trelissick Creamy Yellow'	see *S.* 'Trelissick'
	- 'Trewithen Cerise'	see *S.* 'Trewithen'
	- 'Wendy's Surprise'	SDys
	- 'Wild Watermelon'	CWGN EBee EWes GPSL LHop MAsh MAvo MCot MHer NQui SDys WGrn WHil WWFP XSen
§	- var. ***wislizeni***	CElw SPhx
	- 'Wollerton White'	MRav SDys
	- 'Zaragoza'	SPin
	microstegia	XSen
	miltiorrhiza	CSpe EBee MArt MMuc SPin WHer XLum XSen
	miniata	SPin
	misella	SPin
	mocinoi	SPin
	moorcroftiana	SPin WHea
	moschata	SPin
	muelleri misapplied	see *S. greggii* × *serpyllifolia*
	muelleri ambig.	CSpe NDov WOth
	muirii	SPin
	'Mulberry Jam'	CAby CBot CHGN CHll CSam EAJP ECtt EPfP EWes LHop MAsh MHom MSCN SDix SDys SEle SPin SRkn WKif WOth WTcb
§	***multicaulis*** ♀H3	MAsh XSen
	munzii	SDys SPin
	Mystic Spires Blue = 'Balsalmisp'PBR	CSpe CWGN EPfP NDov NPri SCob SPin SPoG
	namaensis	SPin
	nana B&SWJ 10272	SPin
	- 'Curling Waves'PBR	EBee
	napifolia	EBee LRHS MMuc NLar SPav SPin
	- 'Baby Blue'	EBee
	'Nazareth'	SPin XSen
	'Nel'	EBee EWTr LHop
	nemorosa	LSRN SPin SRms XLum XSen
	- 'Amethyst' ♀H7	CBod CRos EBee ELon EPfP GBin GQue IKil LCro LEdu LOPS LPot LRHS MBel MHol MPie MRav MSpe MTis NDov SCob SPhx SPin SRms WCot WKif XSen
	- Blue Mound	see *S.* × *sylvestris* 'Blauhügel'
	- 'Bordeau Steel Blue'	EBee ELon LRHS NRHS SRms
	- 'Caradonna' ♀H7	Widely available
	- East Friesland	see *S. nemorosa* 'Ostfriesland'

- 'Experimental Pink'	LRHS
- 'Experimental Rose Compact'	LRHS
- 'Experimental White'	LRHS
- 'Grace'	NDov
- 'Lubecca' ♀H7	CBod ECtt EHrv EPed EPfP LHop LRHS MAsh MPie NDov NEgg NGdn NLar NRHS SPer WFar XSen
- Lyrical Silvertone = 'Balyricsil' PBR	WFar
- Marcus = 'Haeumanarc' PBR	CBod EAEE EBee ECtt ELan EPed EPfP EUJe LRHS LSRN MBNS MRav NDov NLar SAko SDys SPoG WFar WHrl
- 'New Dimension Blue'	CBod EPfP WHil
- 'New Dimension Rose'	CBod EBee
§ - 'Ostfriesland' ♀H7	Widely available
- 'Pink Friesland' PBR	CAby ECtt EHoe EPfP GBin GMaP GQue LSou NDov NSti SPoG
- 'Plumosa'	see *S. nemorosa* 'Pusztaflamme'
§ - 'Pusztaflamme' ♀H7	CBod EBee ECha ECtt EPfP MRav MTis SAko SBee XSen
- 'Rose Queen'	CBod CSBt EHoe ELon GMaP GWyn LEdu MArt MSpe MTis NBir NSti SCob SPhx SWat WCot WFar XLum XSen
- 'Rosenwein'	CDor GWyn IBoy LRHS NGdn SGbt SPhx XSen
- 'Royal Distinction'	ECtt
- 'Schwellenburg'	ECtt GBuc GQue LCro LHop LSou MHol NLar SCob XSen
- (Sensation Series) Sensation Blue Improved	CRos LRHS NRHS
- - Sensation Deep Blue = 'Florsaldblue'	CBod EBee EWld GBin LRHS SHil STPC
- - Sensation Deep Rose Improved	CRos IBoy LRHS NRHS
- - Sensation Pink **new**	LRHS
- - Sensation Rose	CCVN LCro LLHF LRHS LSRN LSou MBel SHar SHil
- - Sensation White = 'Florsalwhite'	CWGN MBel MHol
§ - subsp. ***tesquicola***	CBod MMuc SPhx WFar
- 'Theodor' **new**	MTis
- 'Wesuwe'	ELon NDov XSen
'Neon'	SPin
neurepia	see *S. microphylla* var. *microphylla*
* ***nevadensis***	SPin
nilotica	SPin
nipponica	EBee
- B&SWJ 5829	SPin WCru
- 'Fuji Snow' (v)	EBee
- var. ***trisecta***	SPin
nubicola	GPoy SPin WHil XSen
- CC 4607	EBee
- CC 4762	NLar
'Nuchi'	SDys SPin
nutans	CHVG SBrt SPin XSen
officinalis	Widely available
- 'Albiflora'	MArt SPin WJek XSen
- 'Aurea' ambig.	CWib GPoy
- 'Berggarten' ♀H4	CArn CBot CLau ECha GBin GCal LEdu LHop MHer MRav SCob SDix SPhx SPin WHer WJek WKif XLum XSen
- 'Bicolor'	SPin
- 'Blackcurrant'	CBod
§ - broad-leaved	CLau ESps MHer SWat WJek
- 'Crispa'	SPin XSen
- 'Extrakta'	GCal
- 'Grete Stolze'	LHop SEND XSen
- 'Grower's Friend'	CTsd
§ - 'Icterina' (v) ♀H4	Widely available
- ***latifolia***	see *S. officinalis* broad-leaved
- narrow-leaved	see *S. lavandulifolia*
- 'Nazareth'	WJek XSen
- ***prostrata***	see *S. lavandulifolia*
- 'Purpurascens' ♀H5	Widely available
- 'Purpurascens Variegata' (v)	ESps
- 'Robin Hill'	EPed LRHS
- 'Rosea'	WJek XSen
- 'Tricolor' (v)	CBcs CBod CMea CTri CWld EBee ELan ENfk EPfP ESps GMcL GPoy LBMP MAsh MHer MNHC MRav SCob SGol SPer SPin SPoG SRms WHar WJek XSen
- 'Variegata'	see *S. officinalis* 'Icterina'
- variegated (v)	MHer
- 'Würzburg'	XSen
ombrophila	SPin
omeiana	SBrt
- BWJ 8062	SPin WCru
- 'Crûg Thundercloud'	WCru
oppositiflora misapplied	see *S. tubiflora*
oppositiflora ambig.	SDys SPin
oppositiflora Ruiz & Pav.	WPGP
'Orchid Glow' **new**	CWGN
oxyphora	CAby CSpe MPie SDys SPin WOth
pachyphylla	LRHS SPhx SPin XSen
'Pakhuis Pass'	SPin
pallida	SPin
'Pam's Purple'	MAsh
§ ***patens*** ♀H4	CAby CSpe EBee ECha ECtt ELan EPfP EWoo IFro LRHS MAsh MHer MNHC MRav NFav NGdn SDys SEND SPer SPhx SPin SPoG SRms WHea WKif WOth WPGP WSHC
- 'Alba' misapplied	see *S. patens* 'White Trophy'
- 'Blue Angel'	CCht EPfP EWTr EWes GPSL LEdu SPad WCFE
- 'Cambridge Blue' ♀H3	CAby CBod CRos CSpe CWGN EBee ECtt EHrv ELan EPfP EWoo LRHS MAsh MHer MRav MSpe NFav NLar NPer NRHS SDys SIgm SPer SPhx SPin WOth WSHC
- 'Chilcombe'	CAby SDys SPin
- 'Dot's Delight'	CBod CSpe ECtt LHop LRHS MAsh NCGa SDys SPer
- 'Guanajuato'	CBot CSBt CSam ECtt EWes EWoo MAsh MCot MHer NLar SDys SPad SPin SRot WHil WKif WOth WOut WSHC
- 'Holbrook'	CSam
- large	CSpe MPie
- light blue-flowered	LRHS NRHS
- Oceana Blue	EBee
- 'Oxford Blue'	see *S. patens*
- (Patio Series) 'Patio Deep Blue'	CAby CWGN EPfP SPoG WHil
- - 'Patio Pink' **new**	LRHS NRHS
- - 'Patio Sky Blue'	SPad
- - 'Patio White' **new**	LRHS NRHS
- 'Pink Ice'	EBee ECtt SDys WOut
- pink-flowered	SPin
- 'Royal Blue'	see *S. patens*

§	- 'White Trophy'	ECtt ELan EWld LRHS SDys SPin WOut
	pauciserrata	SPin
	'Peach Parfait'	SDys
	pennellii	SPin
	'Penny's Smile'	CAby CBot CElw CMac ELon MAsh SAko SDys SPhx SPin SPoG WGrn WHil WKif WTcb
	'Peru Blue'	EBee SDys
	'Peter Vider'	EPfP
	'Phyllis' Fancy'	CAby CBot CSam CSpe EBee MAsh MHer NDov NSti SDys SPin SPlb WOth
	pinguifolia	SPin
	'Pink Icing'	SPin
	pinnata	SPin
	pisidica	SPin XSen
	plectranthoides	SPin
	polystachya	SPin
*	'Powis Castle'	MHom
	pratensis	CArn CWib CWld ELan EPfP GJos MNHC MRav SPin WCot WOut XSen
	- W&B BGH-3	WCot
§	- Bertolonii Group	SPin XSen
	- 'Dear Anja'	see *S.* × *sylvestris* 'Dear Anja'
§	- Haematodes Group ♀H7	MNrw SPin SRms
	- 'Indigo' ♀H7	ECtt ELon EPed GMaP LRHS LSou MPie MRav NEgg NLar SPhx SPin SPoG WCot WPGP
	- 'Lapis Lazuli'	EBee EWes LPla LRHS
	- 'Pink Delight' PBR	CMos EBee ECtt EPfP LRHS MPie MSCN NCGa NDov SPoG
	- 'Rose Rhapsody' (Ballet Series)	CDor EBee EPPr EPfP MArt MMrt SPhx XSen
	- 'Rosea'	ECha SPin
	- 'Swan Lake' (Ballet Series)	CBod CDor EBee EPPr GWyn NLar SPhx SPlb XSen
	- 'Sweet Esmeralda' (Ballet Series)	CDor EBee NGdn SPhx XSen
	- 'Twilight Serenade' (Ballet Series)	CBod CDor EBee ECtt EPfP SPhx WOut XSen
	pratensis* × *transylvanica	GJos
	procurrens	EBee SPin XSen
	przewalskii	CFis EBee LRHS SPin WTcb XSen
	- ACE 1157	WCru
	- BWJ 7920	SPin WCru XLum
	pulchella	SPin
	'Purple Majesty'	CBod CHll CSam ECtt LHop NSti SDys SRkn WKif XLum
	'Purple Queen'	CAbP CAby CBod EBee LRHS LSou MCot SBee SDys SEle WHil WTcb
	purpurea	LBMP LSRN
	quitensis	SPin
	radula	EBee SPin
	ranzaniana	XSen
	'Raspberry Truffle' **new**	SPin
	raymondii subsp. ***mairanae***	SPin
	recognita	LRHS XSen
	recurva	SPin
	'Red Swing' PBR	CBod LRHS NRHS SPoG
	reflexa	SPin
	regeliana misapplied	see *S. virgata* Jacq.
	regeliana Trautv.	NBir
	regla	MAsh SDys SPin WPGP XSen
	- 'Jame'	SPin
	- 'Royal'	SPin
	repens	SPin
§	***reptans***	SBrt SPin
	- from western Texas	CAby SDys WCot
	ringens	SPin XSen
	riparia misapplied	see *S. rypara*
	roborowskii	SPin
§	***roemeriana***	CSpe IFoB WHea WPGP
	- 'Arriba' **new**	LRHS NRHS
	- 'Hot Trumpets'	CBod LRHS NRHS
	'Rolando'	SDys SPin
§	***roscida***	SPin
	'Rose Queen' ambig.	SPer
	rosifolia	XSen
	'Royal Bumble'	Widely available
	'Royal Crimson Distinction' PBR	EBee ECtt LSou
	rubescens	SPin
	rubiflora	SPin
	rubiginosa	SPin
	rufula	SPin
	runcinata	SPin
	rutilans	see *S. elegans*
§	***rypara***	SPin
	sagittata	EBee GCal SPin WOut
	'Salmon Dance'	CBod CWGN ECtt LRHS NRHS
	sanctae-luciae	SPin
	(Savannah Series) 'Savannah Purple'	SRot
	- 'Savannah Red'	EPfP
	- 'Savannah Salmon Rose'	SRot
	scabra	EBee SPin WOut
	schlechteri	EBee SPin
	sclarea	CBod CHby ECtt ENfk GPoy MHer MNHC SPin SRms WJek XLum XSen
	- var. ***turkestanica*** hort.	CBot CSpe EAJP ECha ECtt EHrv ELan EPfP EWTr EWoo LRHS LSRN LSun MRav MSpe NEgg NGdn SEND SPav SPer SPhx SPtp SRkn SWat WBrk WHar WKif XSen
	- var. ***turkestaniana*** Mottet	SPtp
	- - 'Piemont' **new**	EBee
§	- 'Vatican White'	CBot CSpe EAJP EBee ELan EWTr LPot LRHS LSun MNHC MSpe SPhx SPtp XSen
	- white-bracted	CWib SPin SWvt
	scutellarioides	SPin
	semiatrata misapplied	see *S. chamaedryoides*
	semiatrata Zucc.	SPin
	serboana	EBee WPGP
	- B&SWJ 10236	WCru
	'Serenade'	CBod ELon MHol MTis NDov SPhx WCot
	serpyllifolia	SPin XSen
	- white-flowered	SPin
	sessei	EWld SPin
	setulosa	SPin
	'Shame'	NCGa NDov
	'Shy Ruby'	SPin
	sikkimensis **new**	SPin
	'Silas Dyson'	CFil CSam ECre ECtt EPfP LRHS MAsh MHom NDov SAko SBch SDys SPhx SPin SPoG WHea WHil WPGP WSHC WTcb
	'Silke's Dream'	CFil CSam ECtt EPfP LRHS MAsh MPie SDys SHar SPin SPoG WPGP WTcb XSen
	'Silke's Red'	SDys
	sinaloensis	MAsh SPin
	smithii	SPin
	'Smoke'	SDys

	somalensis	CHVG EBee SPin SVen
	sordida **new**	SPin
	'Southern Belle'	SDys SPin
	spathacea ♀H4	SBrt SPin WOut
	- 'Avis Keedy'	SPin
	sphacelioides	SPin
	splendens 'Jimi's Good Red'	CSpe SDys WOth
	- 'Red Indian'	SDys
	- 'São Borja'	SDys
	- 'Vanguard'	NPri
§	- 'Van-Houttei' ♀H3	EBee SDys SVen
	sprucei	SPin
	squalens	SPin
	stachydifolia	SPin WPGP
§	***staminea***	SPin
	stenophylla	SPin
	'Stephanie'	SDys SPin
	stepposa	SPin
	stolonifera	CAby CSam ECre MAsh MHer SDys SPin WPGP
	striata	SDys
	- red-flowered	SPin
	styphelus	SDys SPin
	subpalmatinervis	SPin
	subpatens	SPin
	subrotunda	SDys SPin
	'Sunset Strip'	SDys
	× ***superba***	CSBt EBee ECha ECtt ELan EPfP ESps LRHS LSRN NDov NRHS SDix SRms WCAu WGwG WHar WHoo
	- 'Adora Blue'	LRHS
	- 'Adrian'	CBod EBee ECtt EPed EPfP LRHS LSRN LSou MBel SPoG WCAu WCot
	- 'Merleau'	LRHS
	- 'Merleau Blue'	SAko
	- 'Merleau Pink'	LRHS
	- 'Merleau Rose'	EBee LPot MRav NDov SRms
*	- 'Rosea'	EBee
	- 'Rubin' ♀H7	ECtt NBre
I	- 'Superba'	ECtt MRav SPhx SRkn
	× ***sylvestris***	LSRN SPin
§	- 'Blauhügel' ♀H7	CBod CGar CRos EAJP ECha ECtt ELan EPfP GBin GCal LRHS MArl MRav MSpe NDov NPri NRHS SBod SHil SPer SPhx WCAu WGwG WHoo XSen
§	- 'Blaukönigin'	CDor CNor EPfP GMaP LRHS NGBl NLar SCob SPer SPlb SPoG SRms SWvt WCot XLum XSen
	- Blue Queen	see *S.* × *sylvestris* 'Blaukönigin'
§	- 'Dear Anja'	CBWd EBee ECtt IPot LCro LHop LSou MAvo MHol NDov SAko SPhx WCot
	- 'Lye End'	MRav MWat WCot
§	- 'Mainacht' ♀H7	Widely available
	- May Night	see *S.* × *sylvestris* 'Mainacht'
	- 'Negrito'	EBee ECtt GQue NGdn NLar XSen
	- 'Rhapsody in Blue'PBR	CAbP LLWG MBNS MHol MTis NLar WCot
	- 'Rose Queen'	CBWd CBod CMac ECha ELan ELon EPed EPfP EShb ESps LCro LHop LOPS LRHS MBel MHol MJak MRav NGBl SCob SCoo SPer SPhx SPoG SWvt WHar XLum XSen
	- 'Rügen'	ELon GQue SAko XSen
	- 'Schneehügel'	CBWd CBod CMac CSBt EAJP EBee ECha ECtt EHoe ELan ELon EPPr EPfP GMaP IBoy LCro LRHS MBNS MRav MSpe MTis NLar NPri NRHS SHil SPer WCAu WHar WHil XSen
	- 'Superba'	ESps GBuc
	- 'Tänzerin' ♀H7	EBee ECtt ELon LRHS MTis NDov NLar SAko XSen
	- 'Viola Klose'	CBod EAEE EBee ECha ECtt ELan EPed EPfP EShb GBuc LCro LOPS LRHS LSRN MAvo MCot MSpe NCGa NDov NGdn NLar SPin SRms WAul XSen
	tachiei hort.	see *S. forsskaolii*
	taraxacifolia	LHop SPin XSen
	tesquicola	see *S. nemorosa* subsp. *tesquicola*
	'Theresia'	SDys
	thymoides	SPin WHil
	tianschanica	SPin
	tiliifolia	SPav SPin SRms WHea
	tingitana	SPin XSen
	tomentosa	EBee SPin XSen
	tortuosa	SPin
	transcaucasica	see *S. staminea*
	transsylvanica	IMou SPav SPhx SPin XSen
	- 'Blue Spire'	SRkn
	'Trebah Lilac White'	see *S.* × *jamensis* 'Trebah'
§	'Trelawney'	CBod EAEE ECtt LHop LRHS MAvo MHom MPie MSpe SRot WBod WHil
§	'Trelissick'	CBod CWld LHop MAsh MAvo MCot MHom MSpe SDys SEND SEle SPin SRkn SRot WHea
§	'Trewithen'	CBod ECre EWoo MAvo MHom SPin SRot WHil XLum
	trijuga	SPin
	triloba	see *S. fruticosa*
	tubifera	SPin
§	***tubiflora*** ♀H2	MAsh SPin
	uliginosa ♀H4	Widely available
	- 'African Skies'	CChe EWoo IPot SPin WOth WTcb
	- 'Ballon Azul'	CBot CSpe EWes MAsh SDys SEle SPin
	'Ultra Violet'	CWGN WTcb
	univerticillata	SPin
	urica	SPin
	- short	SDys
	'Valerie'	CAby SDys
	'Valle de Bravo'	SPin
	'Van-Houttei'	see *S. splendens* 'Van-Houttei'
	variana	SPin
	'Vatican City'	see *S. sclarea* 'Vatican White'
	vazquezii	SPin WOut
	verbenaca	CWld MHer SPin WOut XSen
	- pink-flowered	WOut
	verticillata	EPfP LEdu NLar SPin XSen
§	- 'Alba'	CAbP EBee ECtt EPed EPfP GJos GQue LRHS MRav NGdn NLar SPer SPin WAul XSen
	- 'Hannay's Blue'	EPPr GMaP LPla MAvo SBee
	- 'Hannay's Purple'	ECtt EPPr
	- 'Purple Rain'	Widely available
	- 'Smouldering Torches'	EBee LHop NDov SCob SMad SPhx
	- 'White Rain'	see *S. verticillata* 'Alba'
	villicaulis	see *S. amplexicaulis*
	'Violin Music'PBR	CBod CSpe CWGN EBee ECtt LRHS NRHS WTor
§	***virgata*** Jacq.	EBee SPin XSen
	viridis	CBod CHby MNHC SPin
	- Claryssa Series	SRms
§	- var. ***comata***	MCot WJek
	- 'Marble Arch Blue' (Marble Arch Series)	CSpe

viscosa Jacq.	SPin WHil XSen
vitifolia	CSpe SDys
- B&SWJ 10236	SDix SPin
wagneriana	SPin
'Waverly'	CBod CBot EBee EWld MAsh MHer SDys SEle SPoG
'Wendy's Wish' PBR	CAby CBod CBot CMos CSam CSpe EBee ECtt LCro LHop LRHS LSou MAsh MSCN MSpe NDov SCob SDys SPin SPoG SRkn WGrn WHil WHoo WNPC
× ***westerae***	SPin
- 'Petra'	SDys
willeana	SPin
xalapensis	SPin
yunnanensis	SPin
- BWJ 7874	WCru
aff. ***yunnanensis***	SPin

Salvinia (*Salviniaceae*)

natans	LLWG MSKA XBlo

Sambucus ✿ (*Adoxaceae*)

	adnata	SDix
	'Black Diamonds' **new**	NPri
	caerulea	see *S. nigra* subsp. *caerulea*
	coraensis	see *S. williamsii* subsp. *coreana*
	ebulus	EPPr LEdu NSti SMad WCot WWtn
	- 'Osmanli'	SDix
	formosana	WCot
*	***himalayensis***	WCot
	mexicana B&SWJ 10349	WCot WCru
	miquelii	WCot
	nigra	CArg CBcs CCVT CDul ECrN EPom ESps GMcL GPoy IBoy LBuc LPar NBes NWea SEWo SPer SVic WHed WMat WMou WSFF WTSh
	- 'Albomarginata'	see *S. nigra* 'Marginata'
	- 'Ardwall'	CAgr GBin GCal WCot
	- 'Aurea'	CBcs CDul CMac ELan EPom ESps GMcL MRav NWea SPer WCot WHed WMoo
	- 'Aureomarginata' (v)	ECrN ELan EPPr LPot MMuc MRav SEND WCot
	- 'Bont Oosterwoldë'	WCot
	- 'Bradet'	CAgr WCot WFar
	- 'Broadway' (v)	WCot
	- 'Cae Rhos Lligwy'	CAgr WCot WHer
§	- subsp. ***caerulea***	WCot WPGP
	- subsp. ***canadensis***	CDul SPhx
	- - 'Adams' (F)	WCot
	- - 'Aurea'	CWib NWea WCot WHar
	- - 'Goldfinch'	MAsh
	- - 'Johns'	CAgr WCot
	- - 'Maxima'	SDix WCot
	- - 'Rubra'	WCot
	- - 'York' (F)	CAgr WCot
	- 'Castledean'	WCot
	- 'Dart's Greenlace'	WCot
	- 'Dolomite' (v)	WCot
	- 'Donau'	CAgr WCot
	- 'Frances' (v)	EPPr WCot
	- 'Franzi'	CAgr WCot
	- 'Fructuluteo'	NLar WCot
	- 'Godshill' (F)	CAgr SDea WCot
	- 'Haidegg 17' (F) **new**	CAgr
	- 'Haschberg'	CAgr WCot
	- 'Heterophylla'	see *S. nigra* 'Linearis'
	- 'Hillier's Dwarf'	WCot
	- 'Ina'	CAgr WCot
	- 'Körsör' (F)	WCot
	- f. ***laciniata*** ♀H6	CBcs CDul CRos EBee ELan EPPr EPfP GCal LPot LRHS MBlu MMuc MRav NWea SDix SLon SPer SPoG WCFE WCot WFar WPGP WPat
§	- 'Linearis'	CWld ELan MRav NLar WCot
	- 'Long Tooth'	CDul WCot
	- 'Lutea Punctata'	WCot WFar
	- 'Madonna' (v)	CLet CMac LEdu MBlu MRav NLar NPol NQui SPer WCot
§	- 'Marginata' (v)	CDul CMac CWib EHoe GBin LBMP MHer MRav SDix WCot WFar WMoo
	- 'Marion Bull' (v)	CDul NLar WCot
I	- 'Marmorata'	NLar WCot
	- 'Mint Julep'	WCot
I	- 'Monstrosa'	WCot
	- 'Nana'	WCot
	- 'Naomi'	WCot
	- 'Norfolk Speckled' (v)	WCot
	- 'Pingo Trail'	WCot
	- 'Plena' (d)	WCot
	- f. ***porphyrophylla*** Black Beauty	see *S. nigra* f. *porphyrophylla* 'Gerda'
	- - Black Lace	see *S. nigra* f. *porphyrophylla* 'Eva'
	- - Black Tower = 'Eiffel 1' PBR	Widely available
	- - 'Blue Sheen'	CRos EPfP GBin LRHS SCoo SHil WCot
§	- - 'Eva' PBR ♀H6	Widely available
§	- - 'Gerda' PBR ♀H6	Widely available
§	- - 'Guincho Purple'	CBcs CDul CMac CTri ELan EPPr EPfP EWTr GMcL LRHS MRav NLar NWea SPlb WCot WFar WMoo
	- - 'Purple Pete'	CDul WCot
	- - 'Thundercloud' ♀H6	CDul ECrN ELon EPPr EWes GCal MAsh MMrt MNrw NChi NEoE NLar SPhx WCot WFar WMoo
	- 'Pulverulenta' (v)	CWib EPPr GCal LHop MRav NLar NQui WCot
	- 'Purpurea'	see *S. nigra* f. *porphyrophylla* 'Guincho Purple'
	- 'Pyramidalis'	MRav SMad WCot
	- 'Riese aus Vossloch'	WCot
	- 'Robert Piggin' (v)	WCot
	- var. ***rotundifolia***	WCot
	- 'Sambu' (F)	CAgr WCot
	- 'Samdal' (F)	CAgr WCot WFar
	- 'Samidan' (F)	CAgr WCot
	- 'Samnor' (F)	CAgr WCot
	- 'Sampo' (F)	CAgr WCot
	- 'Samyl' (F)	CAgr WCot
	- 'Urban Lace'	CAgr WCot
	- 'Variegata'	see *S. nigra* 'Marginata'
	- f. ***viridis***	CAgr WCot
	- Welsh Gold = 'Walfinb' PBR	LRHS SPoG
	'Ocean Depths' **new**	GBin NEoE
	palmensis	WCot
	racemosa	EPfP GBin NWea WCot
	- 'Altamont'	WCot
	- 'Aurea'	EHoe EPfP IBoy WFar
	- var. ***callicarpa***	WCot WFar
	- 'Goldenlocks'	EWes
	- subsp. ***kamtschatica***	WCot
	- var. ***melanocarpa***	WCot
	- 'Plumosa Aurea'	CBcs CDul CWib ELan EPfP ESps GCra GMcL LPar MGos MJak MRav MSwo NLar NWea SLim WCot

	- var. ***pubens***	WCot
§	- var. ***sieboldiana***	WCot
	- 'Sutherland Gold' ♀H7	Widely available
	- 'Tenuifolia'	WCot
	- 'Welsh Gold'	MAsh WCot
	sieboldiana	see *S. racemosa* var. *sieboldiana*
	'Sunny Days' **new**	GBin
	tigranii	WCot WFar
§	***williamsii*** subsp. ***coreana***	WCot

Samolus (*Primulaceae*)

valerandi	LLWG

Sandersonia (*Colchicaceae*)

aurantiaca	CAvo ECho EPot GKev LAma SDeJ SDir

Sanguinaria (*Papaveraceae*)

canadensis	CBct CBro ECho EPfP EPot EWTr GBuc GEdr GKev GPoy LAma LEdu LRHS MMuc NHol NHpl NLar NRHS NRya SDeJ SDir SEND SMHy SPer SWat WAbe WPnP
- early-flowering **new**	GEdr
- f. ***multiplex*** (d)	CLAP CTal EPot GEdr IFro LRHS NBir NRHS SPhx
- - 'Plena' (d) ♀H5	CBct CBro CWCL EBee ECha ECho ELon EPfP GBuc GCra GKev GPoy LAma LRHS NHar NHol NHpl NLar NRya NSla NSti SDeJ SKHP SPer WAbe WCot WKif WPnP

Sanguisorba ✿ (*Rosaceae*)

	from Japan	EBee MAvo
§	***albiflora***	CCVN CKno EBee ELan EPfP EShb EWTr GBuc LEdu LRHS MAvo MMuc MRav NCGa NDov NEoE NGdn SEND SPhx SWat WCAu WHil WMoo
	'All Time High'	NDov
	alpina	GLog MMuc SEND
	applanata	WCot
	armena	CElw EBee EWes IMou MNrw MPie WWtn XEll
	'Autumn Bliss'	EBee
	'Beetlewings' **new**	MAvo
	'Blacksmith's Burgundy'	LEdu MAvo
	'Blackthorn'	CKno CMos EBee ECtt GMaP IKil MAvo MTis NDov NLar SMHy SPhx WCot WHoo
	'Burr Blanc'	MAvo MSpe SMHy SPhx
	canadensis	Widely available
	- hybrid	MAvo
	'Cangshan Cranberry'	CSpe EBee GMaP IKil MAvo MHol MTis NDov SMHy WCot WWtn
*	***caucasica***	GBin LEdu SPhx
	'Ccc' **new**	MAvo
	'Chocolate Tip'	EBee ECtt IKil ILea IPot LHop LRHS MAvo
	'Coen's Cranberry'	NDov
	dodecandra	EBee IMou MAvo MTis
	'Foxtail' **new**	MAvo
	hakusanensis	CBWd CKno EBee GBin GCal GKev IBoy IFro IPot LEdu LHop LRHS MArt MAvo MMuc MNrw NBir NBro NChi NDov NEoE NLar SMad WCot WFar WHoo WSHC
	- B&SWJ 8709	WCru
	- 'Lilac Squirrel'	CMos EBee ECtt IPot LEdu MAvo MBel MSpe MTis NDov NLar WTor
	'Ivory Towers'	MAvo
	'John Coke'	EBee NLar
	'Joni' **new**	MAvo
	'Little Angel' **new**	EBee MAvo MBel MHol SPad SPoG WCot
	magnifica	EWes GCal LEdu
	- ***alba***	see *S. albiflora*
	menziesii	Widely available
	- 'Dali Marble' (v)	EBee ECtt NLar WMoo
	- 'Wake Up'	NDov
§	***minor***	CAgr CArn CHby CLau GPoy LEdu MHer MJak MNHC NMir SCob SIde SPhx SPlb SRms WHar WHer WJek WMoo WOut XLum
	- subsp. ***minor***	CHab
	'Nettlesworth Wand'	SMHy
	obtusa	Widely available
	- 'Chatto'	MAvo NLar WPGP
	- silver-leaved	MNrw
	- white-flowered	EBee EWTr GPSL MAvo MBel MTis WPGP
	officinalis	CArn CBWd CHab CKno EHoe GKev GQue MHer MSCN NEoE NMir SPer SPhx SWat WHea WMoo WOut WTre
	- CDC 262	EPPr LEdu SPhx
	- CDC 282	CSpe SPhx
	- CDC 292	MAvo WCot
	- DJHC 535	LEdu
	- from Mongolia	EBee
	- 'Arnhem'	CCse CKno EBee ECtt EHrv EPPr ILea LEdu LRHS MTis NDov SBee SMHy SPhx WCot
	- 'Crimson Queen'	EBee ECtt GQue IPot MTis
	- dark-flowered	MAvo
	- 'False Tanna'	CWib WFar
	- 'Lemon Splash' (v)	EBee ECtt LEdu MAvo MMrt WCot WFar
	- 'Lum' **new**	MAvo
	- 'Martin's Mulberry'	EBee EWes GCal GMaP LEdu MAvo MNrw NDov WPGP
	- subsp. ***microcephala*** **new**	SPer
	- 'Morning Select'	EBee ECtt EPPr GMaP MAvo NLar
	- 'Red Buttons'	MAvo NDov
	- 'Red Thunder'	CSpe CWld ECtt EPPr EWoo GMaP ILea IPot LCro LEdu LOPS LRHS MAvo MTis NDov NLar WCAu WGwG WPGP
	- 'Shiro-fukurin' (v)	CBot EBee ECtt EWes GMaP IKil LEdu LSun MAvo MBel MCot MHol MNrw MSCN MTis NLar SPer WCot WFar WHer WOut WSHC
	- 'Tsetseguun'	LEdu MAvo WPGP
	parviflora	see *S. tenuifolia* var. *parviflora*
	pimpinella	see *S. minor*
	'Pink Brushes'	ECtt GBin GQue IKil IMou IPot MAvo MTis NCGa NDov NLar
	'Pink September'	MAvo
	'Pink Tanna'	Widely available
	'Purple Tails' **new**	MAvo
	'Raspberry Coulis'	MAvo
	'Raspberry Mivvi'	SPhx
	'Rock and Roll'	ECtt EPPr MSpe MTis NLar WOut
	sitchensis	see *S. stipulata*
§	***stipulata***	CMac EBee GCal LEdu LRHS MAvo MHer MNrw
	'Tanna'	Widely available
	'Tanna' seedling	EPPr EShb

tenuifolia	EHrv GCal IFro LRHS MCot NChi NLar SDix SPhx WCot
- RBS 0266 **new**	GKev
- from Ernst Pagels **new**	MAvo
- var. ***alba***	Widely available
- - CDC	GCal MRav
- - 'Korean Snow'	CCse GMaP LEdu LRHS SMHy SPhx SSut
- 'Big Pink'	MAvo MNrw
- 'Bordeaux'	EBee ECtt EWTr MAvo MTis
- 'Henk Gerritsen'	MAvo MTis NLar
§ - var. ***parviflora***	EBee LEdu MAvo MNrw NLar WPGP
- 'Pieters' **new**	MAvo
- 'Pink Elephant'	CKno EBee ECtt EPPr GJos GQue ILea LEdu LHop LRHS MAvo MBel MSpe MTis NLar SMad WCAu WMoo WOut
- var. ***purpurea***	EBee GBin
- 'Purpurea'	CKno EBee EPPr GQue ILea LEdu MAvo MTis SPhx WCot WPGP
- 'Stand Up Comedian'	IMou LEdu MAvo NDov NLar
- 'Strawberry Frost'	MAvo
- 'Strawberry Fruli' **new**	LEdu
- 'Sturdy Guard'	LEdu
- 'The Invisible' **new**	MAvo
- 'White Elephant'	ELan
- 'White Tanna'	EBee EPPr GQue LEdu MAvo MTis

Sanicula (*Apiaceae*)

europaea	CEls GPoy IMou

Sansevieria (*Asparagaceae*)

cylindrica	ELan EShb
trifasciata	EShb
'Moonshine' ♀H1b	

Santolina (*Asteraceae*)

'Apple Court'	LRHS
benthamiana	XSen
§ ***chamaecyparissus***	Widely available
- var. ***corsica*** misapplied	see *S. chamaecyparissus* 'Nana'
- subsp. ***insularis***	XSen
- 'Lambrook Silver'	CFis CRos EBee ECtt ENfk EPfP LRHS MAsh NLar SCoo SLim XSen
- 'Lemon Queen'	CRos ENfk EPfP EWTr LRHS MAsh MNHC MSwo NBir NLar SRms SWat XSen
- subsp. ***magonica***	XSen
§ - 'Nana' ♀H5	CRos EPfP ESps LRHS MAsh MHer MRav MSwo SCob SPoG SRms SWat XSen
- 'Pretty Carroll' ♀H5	CBod CBot EBee ELan EPfP EWTr LRHS LSRN MAsh NLar SPoG WFar
- 'Small-Ness'	CSma ECho ELan ELon EPfP EWes LRHS MHer NLar SWvt WHer WTor XSen
impressa	XSen
incana	see *S. chamaecyparissus*
* ***lindavica***	XSen
pectinata	see *S. rosmarinifolia* subsp. *canescens*
pinnata	CTri MHer
§ - subsp. ***neapolitana*** ♀H5	CSBt CWib ECha ELan ENfk EPfP MMuc MRav SDix SEND
- - cream-flowered	see *S. pinnata* subsp. *neapolitana* 'Edward Bowles'
§ - - 'Edward Bowles'	Widely available
- - 'Sulphurea'	CBot EPfP LRHS MAsh SPer SPhx WKif XSen
rosmarinifolia	CDul CRos GPoy LRHS LSun MRav NRHS SBod SCob SEND SLon SPlb SRms
§ - subsp. ***canescens***	XSen
- 'Lemon Fizz' ♀H5	Widely available
§ - subsp. ***rosmarinifolia***	CLet ECha ECrN ELan ENfk EPfP MHer MRav SCob SDix SIgm SPer SRms SWvt WFar WGwG XLum XSen
- - 'Primrose Gem' ♀H5	CBcs CBod CSBt CTri EAJP ECha ELon EPfP LHop LRHS MAsh MAvo MMuc MNHC MSwo SCob SEND SGbt SPer SRms SWvt XSen
- - white-flowered	WHer XSen
Shades of Jade = 'Sant101'	ECrN
tomentosa misapplied	see *S. pinnata* subsp. *neapolitana*
villosa	XSen
virens	see *S. rosmarinifolia* subsp. *rosmarinifolia*
viridis	see *S. rosmarinifolia* subsp. *rosmarinifolia*

Sanvitalia (*Asteraceae*)

'Sunbini'PBR	CCCN LSou NPri

Sapindus (*Sapindaceae*)

saponaria	EGFP
var. ***drummondii***	

Saponaria (*Caryophyllaceae*)

× ***boissieri***	ECho EPot
'Bressingham' ♀H5	CPBP ECho ECtt EPfP EPot GCrg MHol WAbe WIce
Bressingham hybrid	MAsh
caespitosa	ECho EDAr EWes
§ ***intermedia***	NDov WCot
× ***lempergii*** 'Fritz Lemperg'	NDov WCot
- 'Max Frei'	CSam EBee ECtt ELon EPPr LCro LOPS LPla LSou MCot MRav NDov SBch SDix SPhx WCot WOld WSHC XLum
lutea	GKev
ocymoides ♀H5	CMea EBee ECha ECho ECtt EDAr ELan EPfP GAbr GMcL MAsh MMuc MNHC MSCN NFav NHpl NPnk SEND SIgm SPlb SPoG SRms SRot XLum
- 'Alba'	ECha
- 'Snow Tip'	ECho EDAr NGdn
officinalis	CArn CBod CBre CPbn CWld ENfk GBin GPoy MHer MNHC SIde SPlb SRms WHer WMoo WPtf WSFF
- W&B BGB-7	WCot
- 'Alba' **new**	CSam
- 'Alba Plena' (d)	CBre MMuc NLar SEND WFar XLum
- 'Betty Arnold' (d)	CAby EBee ECtt EPPr EWes MHer WCot WHlf
- 'Flore Pleno' (d)	CBod GAbr
- 'Rosea Plena' (d)	CAby CBre CMac ELan EPfP GCra LEdu LLWP MHer MMuc NBid NBir NGdn NPnk SCob SEND SIde SPer WFar WGwG WMoo WPtf
- 'Rubra Plena' (d)	ELan EWes MMuc SHar WHer
× ***olivana*** ♀H5	ECho ECtt EPot GCrg GMaP MAsh NLar XLum
'Rosenteppich'	CPBP
sicula subsp. ***intermedia***	see *S. intermedia*
zawadskii	see *Silene zawadskii*

Sarcandra (*Chloranthaceae*)

§ ***glabra*** f. ***flava***	SRms

Sarcococca ✿ (*Buxaceae*)

confusa ♀H5	Widely available
hookeriana	ELon GKin IFoB LPar LSRN MBlu MSwo NLar NWad SCob SGbt SWvt WFar WPGP
- B&SWJ 2585	WCru
- HWJK 2393	WCru
- HWJK 2428	WCru
- var. ***digyna***	Widely available
- - SDR 7816	GKev
- - 'Purple Stem' ♀H5	CEnd CJun CLAP CNec CTri EPfP ESps EUJe GKin LCro LOPS LRHS MGos MNrw NLar NPnk SCob SCoo SPer SPoG SRkn SWvt WCru
- - 'Schillingii'	see *S. hookeriana* var. *digyna* 'Tony Schilling'
§ - - 'Tony Schilling'	CJun WCru
- var. ***hookeriana***	CJun LSRN
- - GWJ 9222	WCru
- - GWJ 9344	WCru
- - GWJ 9369	WCru
- - HWJK 2102	WCru
- - HWJK 2366	WCru
- - HWJK 2393	WCru
- - 'Ghorepani' ♀H5	CRos LCro LRHS
- var. ***humilis***	Widely available
- Winter Gem = 'Pmoore03'PBR	CRos CSBt ELon EPfP LCro LRHS LSRN MAsh MGos MSwo NHol SHil SLon SPoG
orientalis	CBct CJun CLAP CMCN CRos ELan ELon EPfP IMou LEdu LPre LRHS MAsh NLar NWad SPoG WPGP WPat
'Roy Lancaster'	see *S. ruscifolia* var. *chinensis* 'Dragon Gate'
'Rudolph'	EPfP LLHF LRHS
ruscifolia	Widely available
- var. ***chinensis***	CJun SLon WCru WPGP WPat
§ - - 'Dragon Gate' ♀H5	CBct CJun CLAP CRos EBee ELan ELon EPfP LEdu LLHF LRHS LSRN MAsh MGos SHil SLim SLon SPoG SWvt WCru WPGP WPat
saligna	CBcs CJun EBtc ELan EPfP LRHS MRav SLon WCru WPat
- HWJK 2428	WCru
- MF P2056	WCru
- NJM 12.043 **new**	WPGP
trinervia B&SWJ 9500	WCru
vagans B&SWJ 7285	WCru
- B&SWJ 9760 from Vietnam **new**	WCru
- B&SWJ 9766 from Vietnam	WCru
aff. ***vagans*** B&SWJ 7265 from north Thailand	WCru
wallichii	CHll ELon LEdu MBlu SPoG WPGP WPat
- B&SWJ 2291	CJun WCru WSHC
- GWJ 9427	WCru
- HWJK 2425	WCru
- HWJK 2428	WCru
zeylanica B&SWJ 10199	WCru
- var. ***brevifolia*** GWJ 9480	WCru
- - GWJ 9483 **new**	WCru

Sarcopoterium (*Rosaceae*)

spinosum	SVen

Sarmienta (*Gesneriaceae*)

repens ♀H2	CFil WAbe WPGP

Sarothamnus see *Cytisus*

Sarracenia ✿ (*Sarraceniaceae*)

× ***ahlesii***	CHew NLos
alata	CHew EECP SHmp WSSs
- from Deer Park, Alabama, pubescent	NLos
- from Desoto National Forest, Mississippi	NLos
- from Robertson County, Texas	NLos
- from Stone County, Mississippi	NLos
- all green	SHmp
- 'Black Tube' ♀H3	WSSs
- heavily veined	SHmp WSSs
- var. ***nigropurpurea***	WSSs
- var. ***ornata***	WSSs
- pubescent	EECP NLos WSSs
- 'Red Lid'	EECP NLos WSSs
- 'Red Lid' × ***flava*** red pitcher	EECP
- 'Red Lid' all red clone × ***flava*** var. ***rubricorpora***	NLos
- var. ***rubrioperculata***	WSSs
- wavy lid	SHmp WSSs
- white-flowered	WSSs
alata × ***flava***	NLos
alata × ***flava*** var. ***maxima***	NLos WSSs
alata × ***leucophylla***	NLos
(***alata*** red tube × ***flava*** 'Burgundy') × (***leucophylla*** × ***purpurea***)	NLos
× ***areolata***	CHew NLos WSSs
'Barbapapa' **new**	NLos
× ***catesbaei***	CHew NLos SHmp WSSs
- 'Johnny Marr' **new**	SHmp
- RV clone × ***oreophila***	NLos
× ***catesbaei*** × ***leucophylla***	NLos
× ***catesbaei*** × ***oreophila***	NLos
× ***courtii***	SHmp
× ***courtii*** × ***minor***	NLos
'Dixie Lace' ♀H3	NLos
'Eva'	NLos SHmp WSSs
× ***excellens***	WSSs
- 'Judy'	NLos
× ***excellens*** × (***minor*** × ***rubra*** subsp. ***rubra***)	NLos
× ***excellens*** × (× ***rehdeii***)	NLos
× ***exornata***	SPlb SRms
'Fiona' **new**	SHmp
flava	WSSs
- from Bay County, Florida	NLos
- from Carteret County, North Carolina	NLos
- from Dorchester County, South Carolina	NLos
- from Jedbury, Dorchester County, Florida	NLos
- from Marston Exotics	NLos
- from McClellanville, South Carolina	NLos

	- from Santee Coastal Reserve, South Carolina	NLos
	- from SB Creek Road	NLos
	- from Shallotte, North Carolina	NLos
	- all green giant	see *S. flava* var. *maxima*
	- all red tube	NLos
	- var. ***atropurpurea***	EECP SHmp WSSs
	- - from Blackwater, Florida	NLos
	- 'Claret'	WSSs
	- var. ***cuprea***	SHmp WSSs
	- var. ***flava***	CHew EECP WSSs
	- - from Hurleyville, South Carolina	NLos
	- - very tall, from Dahlia Bog, Virginia	NLos
	- giant red tube	NLos
§	- var. ***maxima***	CHew EECP NLos SHmp WSSs
	- - from North Carolina	NLos
	- var. ***maxima*** × (× ***moorei*** Brook's hybrid)	NLos
	- var. ***ornata***	CHew EECP NLos SHmp WSSs
	- var. ***rubricorpora***	CHew EECP SHmp SPlb WSSs
	- - from Apalachicola National Forest, Florida	NLos
	- - 'Burgundy'	NLos WSSs
	- var. ***rugelii***	CHew EECP NLos SHmp WSSs
	- - from Homerville Airport, Ware County, Georgia	NLos
	- stocky, from Appalachicola National Forest, Florida	NLos
	((***flava*** × ***leucophylla***) × ***leucophylla***) × (***flava*** × ***rubra***)	NLos
	(***flava*** × ***purpurea***) × (***purpurea*** subsp. ***purpurea***)	NLos
	leucophylla	CHew NLos SHmp SPlb SRms WSSs
	- from Bens Bog, Baldwin County, Alabama	NLos
	- from Citronelle, Alabama	NLos
	- from Ctenium Fields, Perdido, Alabama	NLos
	- from gas station site, Perdido, Alabama	NLos
	- from Hosford, Liberty County, Florida	NLos
	- from Okaloosa Co., Florida	NLos SHmp
	- from Southern Eglin Reserve, Oskaloosa County, Florida	NLos
	- var. ***alba***	WSSs
	- 'Deer Park Alabama'	NLos SHmp
	- green	WSSs
	- green and white	NLos WSSs
	- pubescent	WSSs
	- pubescent from Deer Park, Alabama **new**	SHmp
	- from Perdido, Alabama	NLos
	- 'Schnell's Ghost' ♀H3	SHmp WSSs
	- 'Tarnok'	WSSs
	- f. ***viridescens***	WSSs
	leucophylla × ***oreophila***	EECP
	leucophylla × (***minor*** × ***rubra*** subsp. ***rubra***)	NLos
	leucophylla × (× ***popei***)	EECP
	(***leucophylla*** × ***purpurea***) × (***minor*** × ***oreophila***)	NLos
	leucophylla × ***rubra*** subsp. ***alabamensis***	NLos
	'Lynda Butt' ♀H3	SHmp WSSs
	'Maroon' **new**	NLos
	× ***miniata***	EECP SHmp WSSs
	minor	EECP SHmp WSSs
	- from Berkeley County, South Carolina	NLos
	- from Fitzgerald, Ben Hill County, Georgia	NLos
	- var. ***minor***	CHew
§	- 'Okee Giant'	NLos WSSs
	- 'Okefenokee Giant'	see *S. minor* 'Okee Giant'
	- var. ***okefenokeensis***	CHew WSSs
	minor × ***rubra***	NLos
	× ***mitchelliana***	NLos SHmp WSSs
	- 'Juthatip Soper' ♀H3	NLos SHmp WSSs
	× ***moorei***	CHew NLos SHmp WSSs
	- 'Brook's Hybrid' ♀H4	CHew EECP NLos WSSs
	- 'Marston Clone'	NLos
	× ***moorei*** × ***purpurea*** subsp. ***venosa***	NLos
	oreophila	CHew SHmp WSSs
	- purple throat	NLos
	oreophila × ***purpurea***	NLos
	oreophila × ***rubra*** subsp. ***wherryi*** 'Chatom Giant'	NLos
	× ***popei***	NLos WSSs
	'Pseudo-Judy'	NLos
	psittacina	CHew EECP NLos SHmp SRms WSSs
	purpurea	NLos SPlb
	- subsp. ***purpurea***	CHew SHmp WSSs
	- - f. ***heterophylla*** ♀H6	WSSs
	- subsp. ***venosa***	CHew NLos SHmp WSSs
	- - var. ***burkii***	SHmp WSSs
	× ***readei***	EECP NLos SHmp WSSs
	× ***rehderi***	SHmp
	'Rita Soper' **new**	SHmp
	rubra	EECP WSSs
	- subsp. ***alabamensis*** ♀H3	CHew SHmp WSSs
	- subsp. ***gulfensis***	CHew SHmp WSSs
*	- - f. ***heterophylla***	WSSs
*	- - - from Yellow River, North Florida	NLos
	- subsp. ***jonesii***	EECP NLos SHmp WSSs
*	- - f. ***heterophylla***	WSSs
	- subsp. ***rubra***	CHew SHmp WSSs
	- subsp. ***wherryi***	CHew EECP WSSs
	- - from near Perdido, Baldwin County, Alabama	NLos
	- - 'Chatom Giant'	NLos
	- - giant	WSSs
	- - yellow-flowered	WSSs
	× ***swaniana***	SHmp SRms
	'Velvet' **new**	NLos
	'Vogel' ♀H3	NLos SHmp WSSs
	× ***wrigleyana***	NLos SRms

Saruma (*Aristolochiaceae*)

	henryi	CAby CLAP CTal ESwi EWld GEdr GKev GLog LEdu LPla SBrt SPad WCot WCru WPGP WSHC

Sasa (*Poaceae*)

	glabra f. ***albostriata***	see *Sasaella masamuneana* 'Albostriata'
	kurilensis	CJng MWht
§	- 'Shima-shimofuri' (v)	CJng ERod EShb
	- 'Shimofuri'	see *S. kurilensis* 'Shima-shimofuri'

	nana	see *S. veitchii* f. *minor*
§	***palmata***	CWib EHoe LCro LOPS MMuc SArc WHer
	- f. ***nebulosa***	CBcs CJng ENBC MBrN MWht SArc WMoo
	tessellata	see *Indocalamus tessellatus*
	tsuboiana	CBcs LRHS MJak MWht NLar NRHS SBig SGol WMoo
§	***veitchii***	CBcs CJng EHoe ENBC MJak MMuc MRav MWht NLar SCob SGol WFar WMoo
§	- f. ***minor***	MMuc WMoo

Sasaella (*Poaceae*)

§	***masamuneana*** 'Albostriata' (v)	CEnt CJng ENBC ERod LEdu LRHS MJak MMuc MWht NRHS SBig WMoo
§	***ramosa***	GBin MWht

Sassafras (*Lauraceae*)

	albidum	CBcs CMCN ELan EPfP LRHS MAsh NLar SChF SKHP SLon SPoG

satsuma see *Citrus reticulata*

Satureja ✿ (*Lamiaceae*)

	coerulea ♀H5	EWes NBir XSen
	douglasii	CBod SHDw WJek
	- 'Indian Mint' PBR	ENfk MHer SRms
	hortensis	CBod CLau ENfk GPoy MHer MNHC SIde SRms SVic WJek
	intricata	XSen
	montana	CHby CLau EBee ENfk GPoy LEdu MHer MNHC SDix SEND SIde SRms SVic WJek XSen
*	- ***citriodora***	GPoy MHer XSen
§	- subsp. ***illyrica***	SPhx WJek XLum XSen
	- 'Purple Mountain'	GPoy MHer
	- ***subspicata***	see *S. montana* subsp. *illyrica*
	obovata	XSen
	repanda	see *S. spicigera*
§	***spicigera***	CBod ENfk EPot LEdu MHer MMuc NBir SPhx SRms WJek WTor XLum
	spinosa	XSen
	thymbra	SHDw SRms XSen

Sauromatum (*Araceae*)

	giganteum new	GKev
	guttatum	see *S. venosum*
§	***venosum***	EBee ECho EShb GKev LAma LEdu LRHS NLos SBig WCot WCru XLum

Saururus (*Saururaceae*)

	cernuus	CBen CBod CWat ELan LLWG MSKA SRms SWat WMAq WWtn XLum
	chinensis	LLWG

Saussurea (*Asteraceae*)

	costus	GPoy
	japonica B&SWJ 12672	WCru
	pseudoalpina	WCot

savory, summer see *Satureja hortensis*

savory, winter see *Satureja montana*

Saxegothaea ✿ (*Podocarpaceae*)

	conspicua	CBcs NLar

Saxifraga ✿ (*Saxifragaceae*)

	JJH 9309174	NMen
	SEP 22 (7)	CPBP
	TJR 615/01 (7) new	EPot
	acerifolia (5)	GCal GEdr
§	'Afrodite' (*sempervivum*) (7)	WAbe
	aizoides (9)	ECho GKev
	- var. ***atrorubens*** (9)	ECho
	aizoon	see *S. paniculata* subsp. *paniculata*
	× ***akinfievii*** (7)	NMen
	'Aladdin' (× *borisii*) (7)	NMen
	'Alan Hayhurst' (8)	CPBP NSla WAbe
	'Alan Martin' (× *boydilacina*) (7)	ECho EPot EWes
	'Alba' ambig.	LRHS NRHS
	'Alba' (× *apiculata*) (7) ♀H5	ECho NMen NRya SIgm SPlb
	'Alba' (*oppositifolia*) (7)	ECho ELan EWes GCrg ITim NWad WAbe
	'Albert Einstein' (× *apiculata*) (7) ♀H5	CTal NMen
	'Albertii' (*callosa*)	see *S.* 'Albida'
§	'Albida' (*callosa*) (8)	CTal ECho NWad WAbe
	'Albrecht Dürer' (Lasciva Group) (7)	EPot NMen
	'Aldo Bacci' (Milford Group) (7)	NMen NSla
	'Alfons Mucha' (7)	EPot
	'Alice Longbottom' (5)	SAko
	'Allendale Acclaim' (× *lismorensis*) (7)	NMen
	'Allendale Accord' (7)	NMen
	'Allendale Andante' (× *arco-valleyi*) (7)	NMen
	'Allendale Angel' (× *kepleri*) (7)	NMen WAbe
	'Allendale Argonaut' (7)	CPBP NMen
	'Allendale Ballad' (7)	NMen
	'Allendale Bamby' (× *lismorensis*) (7)	NHar NMen WAbe
	'Allendale Baron' (7)	NMen
	'Allendale Bauble' (7)	NMen
	'Allendale Beau' (× *lismorensis*) (7)	CTal
	'Allendale Beauty' (7)	NMen WAbe
	'Allendale Betty' (× *lismorensis*) (7)	EPot NMen
	'Allendale Billows' (7)	NHar NMen
	'Allendale Bonny' (7)	NHar NMen WAbe
	'Allendale Boon' (× *izari*) (7)	NMen
	'Allendale Bounty' (7)	NMen
	'Allendale Bravo' (× *lismorensis*) (7)	NMen WAbe
	'Allendale Cabal' (7)	CPBP NMen
	'Allendale Carol' (7)	NMen
	'Allendale Charm' (Swing Group) (7)	ITim NMen WAbe WHoo WThu
	'Allendale Chick' (7)	NHar NMen
	'Allendale Citation' (7)	NMen WAbe
	'Allendale Czech' (7)	NMen
	'Allendale Dance' (7)	NMen
	'Allendale Delight' (7)	NMen
	'Allendale Desire' (7)	NMen
	'Allendale Divine' (7)	NMen
	'Allendale Dream' (7)	EPot NMen
	'Allendale Duo' (7)	NMen
	'Allendale Eden' (7) new	NMen
	'Allendale Elegance' (7)	CPBP NMen WAbe

'Allendale Elf' (7) EPot NMen WAbe
'Allendale Elite' (7) NMen WAbe
'Allendale Envoy' (7) ITim WAbe
'Allendale Epic' (7) NHar NMen
'Allendale Fairy' (7) NHar WHoo
'Allendale Fame' (7) NMen
'Allendale Fancy' (7) NMen
'Allendale Frost' (7) NMen
'Allendale Ghost' (7) NMen
'Allendale Goblin' (7) NMen WAbe
'Allendale Grace' (7) NMen
'Allendale Gremlin' (7) NMen
'Allendale Harvest' (7) NMen
'Allendale Hobbit' (7) NHar NMen
'Allendale Host' (7) NMen
'Allendale Ice' (7) NMen
'Allendale Ina' (7) NHar NMen WAbe
'Allendale Jinn' (7) NMen
'Allendale Jo' (7) EPot NMen
'Allendale Joy' (× *wendelacina*) (7) NMen
'Allendale King' NMen
'Allendale Magic' (7) WAbe
'Allendale Noon' NMen
'Allendale Ruby' (7) NMen
'Allendale Snow' (× *rayei*) (7) NMen
'Alpenglow' (7) NMen
alpigena (7) WAbe
'Amberglow' (× *anglica*) (7) **new** NMen
'Amberine' (× *anglica*) (7) NMen
'Amedeo Modigliani' (7) NMen
'Amerigo Vespucci' (Continent Group) (7) **new** NMen
andersonii (7) GKev
'Andrea Cesalpino' (Renaissance Group) (7) EPot NMen
× ***andrewsii*** (8 × 11) XLum
angustifolia Haw. see *S. hypnoides*
'Anna' (× *fontanae*) (7) NMen
'Anne Beddall' (× *goringiana*) (7) NMen
'Anneka Hope' **new** GKev
'Antonín Dvořák' (× *arco-valleyi*) (7) **new** NMen
'Antonio Vivaldi' (7) EPot NMen
'Aphrodite' (*sempervivum*) see *S.* 'Afrodite'
× ***apiculata*** (7) ECho MAsh SIgm
× ***apiculata*** *sensu stricto* hort. see *S.* 'Gregor Mendel'
'Apple Blossom' (Mossy Group) (15) ECtt EPfP NEoE NRya
'Arabella' (× *edithae*) (7) ECho NMen
§ 'Arco' (× *arco-valleyi*) (7) ECho
× ***arco-valleyi*** *sensu stricto* hort. see *S.* 'Arco'
× ***arendsii*** purple-flowered (15) MMuc SPlb
'Ariel' (× *hornibrookii*) (7) NMen
'Arthur' (× *anglica*) (7) NMen
'Asahi' (*fortunei*) (5) IVic SAko
aspera L. (10) EDAr WAbe
'Assimilis' (× *petraschii*) (7) EPot
'Athena' (7) **new** NMen
'Atropurpurea' (*paniculata* subsp. *cartilaginea*) (8) GMaP NHar NHol WHoo WIce XLum
'Aufheiter von Eri' (*fortunei*) (5) IVic SAko
'August Hayek' (× *leyboldii*) (7) NMen
'Aurea' (*umbrosa*) see *S.* 'Aureopunctata'
'Aurea Maculata' (*cuneifolia*) see *S.* 'Aureopunctata'
§ 'Aureopunctata' (× *urbium*) (11/v) CLet CMac CTri ECha ECho ELan EPfP GKev GMaP LEdu LPot LRHS MHer MRav NRHS SPer SPlb SPoG SRms WMoo XLum
'Autumn Tribute' (*fortunei*) (5) GEdr WAbe
'Aya' (*fortunei*) (5) SAko
'Ayer's Rock' (7) WAbe
'Balcana' (*paniculata*) (8) EPot NSla WAbe
'Baldensis' see *S. paniculata* var. *minutifolia*
'Balkan' (*marginata* subsp. *marginata* var. *rocheliana*) (7) ♀H5 ITim
§ 'Beatrix Stanley' (× *angelica*) (7) CRos ECho LRHS NRHS NWad
'Bedřich Smetana' (*marginata*) (7) **new** NMen
'Beinn Eighe' (× *concinna*) (7) **new** NMen
'Beinne Alligin' (× *concinna*) (7) **new** NMen
'Ben Loyal' (× *concinna*) (7) NMen WAbe
'Benibana' (*fortunei*) (5) SAko
'Beni-komachi' (*fortunei*) (5) SAko
'Berounka' (Prominent Group) (7) **new** NMen
'Bertramka' (Holenka's Miracle Group) (× *megaseiflora*) (7) **new** NMen
'Beryl Bland' (Sugestivo Group) (7) **new** WAbe
'Bettina' (× *paulinae*) (7) NMen
× ***biasolettoi*** *sensu stricto* hort. see *S.* 'Phoenix'
× ***bilekii*** (7) ECho
'Birch Yellow' see *S.* 'Pseudoborisii'
'Black Beauty' (15) ECtt GCrg LPot MHer NWad
Black Ruby (*fortunei*) (5) CBcs CBct CLAP CSpe EBee ECha ECtt ELan GAbr GEdr GMaP GMcL IFoB IVic LLHF LRHS MNrw NHpl NLar NPnk SPer SPlb SWvt WCot WFar WGrn WMoo WPGP
'Blackberry and Apple Pie' (*fortunei*) (5) CBct CRos EBee ECho ECtt EPfP GEdr LRHS MBrN NHar NRHS SBch SWvt WMoo
'Blush' (*fortunei*) (5) LLHF
'Bob Hawkins' (Mossy Group) (15/v) NHol NWad
'Bohemia' (7) ECho EPot NSla
'Bohemian Karst' (Prominent Group) (7) **new** NMen
'Bohemian Paradise' (Region Group) (7) **new** NMen
'Bohnice' (× *megaseiflora*) (7) **new** NMen
'Bohunka' (7) **new** NMen
× ***borisii*** *sensu stricto* hort. see *S.* 'Sofia'
'Boston Spa' (× *elisabethae*) (7) ECho ECtt GCrg LRHS MHer NLar NRHS SPlb
'Brailes' (× *poluanglica*) (7) NMen
'Brian Arundel' (Magnus Group) (7) NMen
'Bridget' (× *edithae*) (7) CMea ECho LRHS NMen NRHS
'Brimstone' (7) NMen
'Brno' (× *elisabethae*) (7) EPot NMen

	'Brookside' (*burseriana*) (7)	EPot
	brunoniana	see *S. brunonis*
§	***brunonis*** (1) CC 5315	GKev
	'Bryn Llwyd' (Vanessa Group) (7)	NMen WAbe
	'Brynhyfryd's Best' new	GKev
	bryoides (10)	ECho
	'Buchholzii' (× *fleischeri*) (7)	NMen
*	'Buckland' (*fortunei*) (5)	WCot
	'Bürgel' (× *poluanglica*) (7)	EPot
	× ***burnatii*** (8)	CRos ECho LRHS NRHS NSla
	burseriana (7)	ECho NMen WAbe
	'Buster' (× *hardingii*) (7)	NMen
	× ***caesia*** misapplied (× *fritschiana*)	see *S.* 'Krain'
	caesia L. (8)	SRms WAbe
§	***callosa*** (8) ♀H5	ECho EDAr LRHS MHer MMuc NRHS SEND WAbe
	- subsp. ***callosa*** (8)	ECho
§	- - var. ***australis*** (8)	CTal
§	- subsp. ***catalaunica*** (8)	WAbe
	- var. ***lantoscana***	see *S. callosa* subsp. *callosa* var. *australis*
	- ***lingulata***	see *S. callosa*
	'Candy Floss' (7) new	NMen
	× ***canis-dalmatica***	see *S.* 'Canis-dalmatica'
§	'Canis-dalmatica' (× *gaudinii*) (8)	ECho ECtt GCrg GJos GKev LRHS NHar NRHS NWad SIgm WTor
§	'Carmen' (× *elisabethae*) (7)	WAbe
§	'Carniolica' (*paniculata*) (8)	NBro NHol WOld
	'Carniolica' (× *engleri*) (8)	WAbe
	carolinica	see *S.* 'Carniolica' (*paniculata*)
	cartilaginea	see *S. paniculata* subsp. *cartilaginea*
	'Castor' (× *bilekii*) (7)	NMen
	catalaunica	see *S. callosa* subsp. *catalaunica*
	'Caterhamensis' (*cotyledon*) (8)	NHar
	'Cathy Read' (× *polulacina*) (7)	NMen
	caucasica (7)	ECho
	cebennensis (15)	EPot NRya
	- dwarf (15)	WAbe
	'Celebration'	WAbe
	cespitosa (15)	WAbe
	'Chambers' Pink Pride'	see *S.* 'Miss Chambers'
	'Charles Chaplin' (7)	EPot NMen WAbe
	'Charles Darwin' (7)	EPot NMen
	Cheap Confections (*fortunei*) (4)	ECtt GEdr IFoB LLHF NLar SBch WBor WFar WMoo WOld WPGP
	Cherry Pie (*fortunei*) (5)	GEdr LLHF NBir NHar NHpl
	'Cherrytrees' (× *boydii*) (7)	NMen
	'Chodov' (Holenka's Miracle Group) (× *megaseiflora*) (7)	EPot NMen
	'Christian Huygens' (7)	NMen
	cinerea (7)	WAbe
	- McB 1376	NWad
	'Cio-Cio-San' (Vanessa Group) (7)	CPBP WAbe
	'Circe' (5)	SAko
	'Citronella' (7)	NMen WAbe
	'Claire Felstead' (7)	WAbe
*	'Clare' (*paniculata*) (8)	NSla
	'Clare' (× *anglica*) (7)	ECtt GPSL NHol
§	'Clarence Elliott' (London Pride Group) (*umbrosa*) (11) ♀H5	CTri ECho EWTr EWes GAbr GBin GCal GJos GKev GMaP LSun MHer NDov NLar NRya WIce WThu
	'Claude Monet' (Impressio Group) (7)	CPBP EPot NMen WAbe
	'Cloth of Gold' (*exarata* subsp. *moschata*) (15)	CRos ECha ECtt ELan EPfP GCrg GWyn LRHS MAsh NEoE NHol NHpl NRHS NRya NWad SPlb SPoG SRms WAbe WIce WTor
	cochlearis (8)	CTri LRHS MAsh NBro NRHS NSla SBch SIgm WAbe
	'Cockscomb' (*paniculata*) (8)	ECho NHar NLar NWad WAbe
	'Combrook' (× *poluanglica*) (7)	NMen
	'Conwy Snow' (*fortunei*) (5)	CLAP WAbe WFar WMoo
	'Conwy Star' (*fortunei*) (5)	GEdr WAbe WFar
	'Coolock Gem' (7)	EPot NMen WAbe
	'Coolock Jean' (7)	CPBP NMen WAbe
	'Coolock Kate' (7) ♀H5	NMen WAbe
	'Corennie Claret'	see *S.* 'Glowing Ember'
*	× ***correvensis*** new	GWyn
	'Correvoniana' misapplied	see *S.* 'Lagraveana'
	'Correvoniana' Farrer (*paniculata*) (8)	EDAr EPot MHer MMuc SEND XLum
	cortusifolia (5)	CLAP EBee ECho
	- B&SWJ 5879	WCru
	- var. ***stolonifera*** (5)	CBct ECho GCal XLum
	Cotton Crochet (*fortunei*) (5/d)	CAbP ECtt ESwi GEdr NHar SHeu WBor WFar WMoo WOld
	cotyledon (8)	CTal ECho LRHS NRHS WAbe WCFE
	cotyledon × ***cuneifolia*** (8 × 11)	NSla
§	'Cranbourne' (× *anglica*) (7) ♀H5	CMea CPBP CTal ECho EPot LRHS MAsh NMen NRHS NSla WAbe
	'Cream' (*paniculata*) (8)	ECho
	'Cream Seedling' (× *elisabethae*) (7)	ECho NMen
	'Crenata' (*burseriana*) (7) ♀H5	CMea LRHS NRHS
	'Crimscote-love' (*poluanglica*) (7)	NMen
	'Crimson Rose' (*paniculata*)	see *S.* 'Rosea' (*paniculata*)
	'Crinoline' (7)	NMen NSla WAbe
§	***crustata*** (8)	CPBP ECho NHar WAbe WThu XLum
	- var. ***vochinensis***	see *S. crustata*
	Crystal Pink (*fortunei*) (5/v)	CAbP CBct EBee ECtt GEdr GPSL IFoB MNrw NHar NHpl NLar WCot WFar
	'Crystalie' (× *biasolettoi*) (7)	LRHS NRHS
	'Cultrata' (*paniculata*) (8)	NBro
	'Cumulus' (7) ♀H5	EPot GKev NMen SIgm WAbe WThu
§	***cuneifolia*** (11)	ECho IMou MHer NWad WMoo XLum
	- var. ***capillipes***	see *S. cuneifolia* subsp. *cuneifolia*
§	- subsp. ***cuneifolia*** (11)	ECtt GJos
*	- var. ***subintegra*** (11)	ECho
	'Cuscutiformis' (*stolonifera*) (5)	CAby CElw CHid EWld GBuc GEdr MAvo MBel MSCN SBch SRms WBor WCru WPGP XLum
	dahurica	see *S. cuneifolia*
	'Dainty Dame' (× *arco-valleyi*) (7)	LRHS NRHS
	'Dana' (Prichard's Monument Group) (× *megaseiflora*) (7)	EPot NMen
	'David' (7)	NMen
	'Dawn Frost' (7)	EPot WIce
	'Delia' (× *hornibrookii*) (7)	EPot
	'Demeter' (× *petraschii*) (7)	NMen
	'Dentata' (London Pride Group) (× *polita*) (11)	EAJP ECha ECho GCal WBor WMoo
I	'Diana' (× *lincolni-fosteri*) (7)	NMen WIce
	diapensioides (7)	WAbe

dinnikii (7)	WAbe
'Dobruška' (× *irvingii*) (7)	NMen
'Doctor Clay' (*paniculata*) (8)	CRos CTal ECho EPot GCrg GKev LRHS NHar NHol NRHS NRya NSla SPlb WAbe
'Doctor Ramsey' (8)	CRos ECho EWes LRHS NRHS NWad WAbe
'Dolores Umbridge' (5)	SAko
'Donald Mann' (15)	EWes
'Donatello' (7) **new**	NMen
'Donnington Chalice'	NMen
'Donnington Gold'	NMen
'Donnington Rose' (7) **new**	CPBP
'Donnington Veil'	NMen
'Dora Ross' (× *baccii*) (7)	NMen
'Drakula' (*ferdinandi-coburgi*) (7)	ECho LRHS NMen NRHS
'Dwight Ripley' (7)	NMen
'Edgar Irmscher' (7)	NMen
'Edith' (× *edithae*) (7)	CTal ECho LRHS NRHS
'Elegance'	SAko
'Elf' (7)	see *S.* 'Beatrix Stanley'
'Elf' (*exarata* subsp. *moschata*) (15)	ECtt MAsh SIgm SRms
'Elf Rose' (15)	CRos EPfP LRHS NEoE NRHS
'Eliot Hodgkin' (× *millstreamiana*) (7)	NMen
× ***elisabethae*** *sensu stricto* hort.	see *S.* 'Carmen'
'Ellie Brinckerhoff' (× *hornibrookii*) (7)	NMen WAbe
'Elliott's Variety'	see *S.* 'Clarence Elliott' (*umbrosa*)
'Emil Holub' **new**	EPot
'Emile Burnat' (× *burnatii*) (8) 𝕐H5	CTal
× ***engleri*** (8)	CTal
epiphylla (5) BWJ 8177	WCru
§ 'Ernst Heinrich' (× *heinrichii*) (7)	NMen
'Esther' (× *burnatii*) (8)	CMea CRos ECho GKev LRHS NRHS SRGP WAbe WHoo WPnn
§ 'Eulenspiegel' (× *geuderi*) (7)	EPot NWad
'Eva Hanzliková' (× *izari*) (7)	EPot NMen
'Excellent' (Exclusive Group) (7)	CPBP EPot
'Exhibit' (Exclusive Group) (7)	NMen
fair maids of France	see *S.* 'Flore Pleno'
'Fairy Dust'	SAko
'Fairy' (*exarata* subsp. *moschata*) (15)	ECtt NBir NEoE
'Faldonside' (× *boydii*) (7)	MAsh
'Falstaff' (*burseriana*) (7)	NMen
× ***farreri*** (15)	WIce
× ***farreri*** hort.	see *S.* (Silver Farreri Group) 'Reginald Farrer'
'Favorit' (× *bilekii*) (7)	EPot NMen
§ ***federici-augusti*** subsp. ***grisebachii*** (7) 𝕐H5	ECho EPot GCrg GKev LRHS NMen NRHS NSla WAbe
'Felicity' (× *anglica*) (7)	NMen
ferdinandi-coburgi (7)	ECtt WAbe
§ - subsp. ***chrysosplenifolia*** var. ***rhodopea*** (7)	ECho EPot LRHS NRHS
- var. ***pravislavii***	see *S. ferdinandi-coburgi* subsp. *chrysosplenifolia* var. *rhodopea*
- var. ***radoslavoffii***	see *S. ferdinandi-coburgi* subsp. *chrysosplenifolia* var. *rhodopea*
'Feuerkopf' (× *biasolettoi*) (7) **new**	NMen
'Findling' (Mossy Group) (15)	EPfP GCrg NWad SPoG WAbe
'Firebrand' (× *kochii*) (7)	CPBP WAbe
Five Color (*fortunei*)	see *S.* 'Go-nishiki'
§ ***flagellaris*** (1)	WAbe
'Flavescens' misapplied	see *S.* 'Lutea' (*paniculata*)
'Fleece' (15) **new**	NHpl
§ 'Flore Pleno' (*granulata*) (15/d)	CElw EWes NBir
'Flowers of Sulphur'	see *S.* 'Schwefelblüte'
fortunei (5) 𝕐H4	CLAP CMac ECho LEdu NBir NPnk SRms WAbe WFar
- B&SWJ 6346	WCru
- from John Fielding (5)	WCot
- f. ***alpina*** from Hokkaido (5)	WCru
- var. ***koraiensis*** (5) B&SWJ 8688	WCru
- var. ***obtusocuneata*** (5)	CLAP ECho GEdr GPSL LLHF WAbe
- f. ***partita*** (5)	CLAP WCot WCru
- var. ***pilosissima*** (5) B&SWJ 8557	WCru
- pink-flowered (5)	WAbe
'Foster's Gold' (× *elisabethae*) (7)	EPot NMen
'Four Winds' (Mossy Group) (15)	EWes SPoG
'Francis Cade' (8)	GAbr WAbe
'Frank Sinatra' (× *poluanglica*) (7)	NMen
'Frantisek Holenka' (Superlatir Group) (7) **new**	NMen
'Franz Liszt' (7)	EPot NMen
'Franzii' (× *paulinae*) (7)	NMen
'Freckles'	GBin GKev NHpl
'Friesei' (× *salmonica*) (7)	CTal NMen
'Fumiko' (*fortunei*) (5)	WCru
'Funkii' (× *petraschii*) (7)	NMen
'G.W. Gould No. 1'	NMen
'Gaiety' (15)	LRHS NEoE NRHS SPoG
'Galahad' (× *elisabethae*) (7)	NMen
'Galaxie' (Holenka's Miracle Group) (× *megaseiflora*) (7)	EPot
'Ganymede' (*burseriana*) (7)	EPot NMen
× ***gaudinii*** (8)	XLum
'Gelber Findling' (7)	EPot NMen SIgm
'Gelbes Monster' (*fortunei*) (5)	IVic
'Gem' (× *irvingii*) (7)	CTal LRHS NRHS
'Gemma' (× *megaseiflora*) (7)	LRHS NRHS
genesiana (15) **new**	EWes
'Geoff Wilson' (× *biasolettoi*) (7)	EPot
'Geoffrey Gould' (7) **new**	NMen
georgei (7)	EPot WAbe
'Gerard Philipe' (7)	NMen
'Gertie Pritchard' (× *megaseiflora*)	see *S.* 'Mrs Gertie Prichard'
× ***geuderi*** *sensu stricto* hort.	see *S.* 'Eulenspiegel'
§ × ***geum*** (11)	CHid ECho MRav WFar WMoo
- Dixter form (11)	CElw ECha LEdu NDov SDix SMHy
'Gina Lollobrigida' (Blues Group) (7)	NMen
'Gleborg' (Mossy Group) (15)	SPoG

'Gloria' (*burseriana*) (7)	ECho EPot LRHS MAsh NMen NRHS WIce
§ 'Glowing Ember' (Mossy Group) (15)	EWes
'Glückliches Mädchen' (*fortunei*) (5)	IVic SAko
'Gold Dust' (× *eudoxiana*) (7)	ECho GCrg NRya
'Golden Eye' (× *poluanglica*) (7) **new**	NMen
'Golden Falls' (Mossy Group) (15/v)	EWes SPlb SPoG
Golden Prague (× *pragensis*)	see *S.* 'Zlatá Praha'
'Golem' (7)	CPBP
§ 'Go-nishiki' (*fortunei*) (5)	GEdr LLHF
'Gorges du Verdon' (8)	EWTr
'Goring White' (7)	NMen
'Gothenburg' (7)	WAbe
'Grace Farwell' (× *anglica*) (7)	ECho NLar
'Grandiflora' (*burseriana*) (7)	NMen
granulata (15)	ECho EWes GJos NMir
'Gratoides' (× *grata*) (7)	NMen
'Grébovka' (× *megaseiflora*) (7)	NMen
'Greensleeves' (*fortunei*) (5)	LLHF
§ 'Gregor Mendel' (× *apiculata*) (7) ♀H5	CMea CRos CTal ECho ECtt EPot LRHS NLar NSla NWad SIgm SRms WAbe WHoo
'Gregor' (× *poluanglica*) (7)	NMen
grisebachii	see *S. federici-augusti* subsp. *grisebachii*
'Grosser Prinz' (× *petraschii*) (7) **new**	NMen
'Haagii' (× *eudoxiana*) (7)	CTri ECho GKev
'Hare Knoll Beauty' (8)	CPBP CRos ECho EPot GKev LRHS NHar NHol NHpl NRHS NSla WAbe WIce
'Harfa' (7) **new**	NMen
'Harlow Car' (× *anglica*) (7)	EPot NSla
'Harold Bevington' (*paniculata*) (8)	CTal
'Harold Lloyd' (7)	NMen
'Harry Marshall' (× *irvingii*) (7)	NWad
'Harry Smith' (× *cimganii*) (7)	NMen
'Harvest Moon' (*stolonifera*) (5)	WBor WHer
× ***heinreichii*** *sensu stricto* hort.	see *S.* 'Ernst Heinrich'
'Heisel Kurenai' (*fortunei*) (5)	IVic SAko
'Henri Rousseau' (Conspecta Group) (7)	NMen
'Hi-Ace' (Mossy Group) (15/v)	NHpl SPlb
'Highlander Red' (Mossy Group) (15) **new**	WIce
'Highlander Red Shades' (Mossy Group) (15)	WIce
'Highlander White' (Mossy Group) (15) **new**	GWyn
'Hime' (*stolonifera*) (5)	WCru
'Hindhead Seedling' (× *boydii*) (7)	CRos ECho LRHS NMen NRHS WAbe
hirsuta (11)	EHrv ESwi EWld GEdr LEdu MMuc WCot WCru
'Hirsuta' (× *geum*)	see *S.* × *geum*
'Hirtella' Ingwersen (*paniculata*) (8)	EPot
'Hirtifolia' (*paniculata*) (8)	CTal
'His Majesty' (× *irvingii*) (7)	NMen
'Hiten' (*fortunei*) (5)	EBee GKev
'Holden Seedling' (Mossy Group) (15)	ECtt
I 'Holden Variety' (*oppositifolia*) (7)	NWad
'Honeybunch' (Safran Group) (7) **new**	NMen WAbe
'Honington' (× *poluanglica*) (7)	NMen
hostii (8)	ECho EDAr GKev NWad XLum
- subsp. ***hostii*** (8)	WAbe XLum
- - var. ***altissima*** (8)	EPot XLum
- subsp. ***rhaetica*** (8)	NBro WThu XLum
'Hradčany' (Holenka's Miracle Group) (× *megaseiflora*) (7)	NMen
'Hsitou Silver' (*stolonifera*) (5)	WCot
'Humoreska' (× *megaseiflora*) (7) **new**	NMen
'Hunscote' (× *poluanglica*) (7)	NMen
§ ***hypnoides*** (15)	NMir SPoG WAbe
hypostoma (7)	WAbe
'Iceland' (*oppositifolia*) (7)	EWes SIgm WAbe
'Ignaz Dörfler' (× *doerfleri*) (7)	NMen
imparilis (5)	EHrv GEdr WCru
'Ingeborg' (Mossy Group) (15)	CElw ECha
iranica (7)	EPot NMen
'Irena' (7)	NMen
'Irene Bacci' (× *baccii*) (7)	NMen
'Iris Prichard' (× *hardingii*) (7)	CTal NMen
× ***irvingii*** (7)	ECho
× ***irvingii*** *sensu stricto* hort.	see *S.* 'Walter Irving'
'James' (7)	EPot NMen NSla
'Jan Amos Kómenský' (× *anglica*) (7)	NMen
'Jan Neruda' (× *megaseiflora*) (7)	CPBP EPot NMen
'Jan Palach' (× *krausii*) (7)	EPot NMen WAbe
'Jan Preisler' (Conspecta Group) (7) **new**	EPot NMen
'Jaromir' (8)	NHar NMen
'Jaroslav Horný' (maginata) (7)	NMen
'Jason' (× *elisabethae*) (7)	NMen
'Jenkinsiae' (× *irvingii*) (7)	CMea CTal ECho EPot LRHS MAsh MMuc NLar NMen NRHS NSla NWad SEND WAbe WIce
'Joachim Barrande' (× *siluris*) (7)	EPot
'Jocelynne Bacci' (7)	NMen
§ 'Johann Kellerer' (× *kellereri*) (7)	EPot NMen
'Johann Wolfgang Goethe' (7)	EPot
'John Byam-Grounds' (Honor Group) (7)	NMen WAbe
'John Tomlinson' (*burseriana*) (7)	NSla
'Jorg' (× *biasolettoi*) (7)	EPot
'Josef Čapek' (Holenka's Miracle Group) (× *megaseiflora*) (7)	EPot NMen
'Joy'	see *S.* 'Kaspar Maria Sternberg'

	'Joy Bishop' (7)	NMen
	'Joyce Carruthers' (7)	NMen
	'Juliet'	see *S.* 'Riverslea'
§	***juniperifolia*** (7)	CMea ECho SIgm SRms XLum
	'Jupiter' (Holenka's Miracle Group) (× *megaseiflora*) (7)	EPot NMen
	'Kanna' (*fortunei*) (5)	IVic
	karadzicensis* × *scardica (7)	EPot
	'Karasin' (7)	NMen
	'Karel Čapek' (Prichard's Monument Group) (× *megaseiflora*) (7)	ECho EPot LRHS NMen NRHS WAbe
	'Karel Hasler' (× *megaseiflora*) (7) **new**	NMen
	'Karlštejn' (× *borisii*) (7)	EPot NMen
§	'Kaspar Maria Sternberg' (× *petraschii*) (7) ♀H5	ECho LRHS NRHS
	'Kath Dryden' (7)	ECho ECtt ITim NMen
	'Kathleen Pinsent' (8)	ECho WAbe
	'Kathleen' (× *polulacina*) (7)	EPot NMen
	'Kath's Delight' (8)	GKev
	'Kbley'	NMen
	× ***kellereri*** *sensu stricto* hort.	see *S.* 'Johann Kellerer'
	'Ken McGregor' (7)	NMen
	'Kestoniensis' (× *salmonica*) (7)	NMen
	'Kew Gem' (× *petraschii*) (7)	ECho
	'Kineton' (× *poluanglica*) (7)	NMen
	'King Lear' (× *bursiculata*) (7)	CTal ECho LRHS NRHS
	'Kinki Purple' (*stolonifera*) (5)	CBod EHrv EPri EShb EWld GBin GWyn WCru WPGP
	'Kirke' (7) **new**	EPot NMen
	'Klondike' (× *boydii*) (7)	EPot NMen
	'Knapton Pink' (Mossy Group) (15)	ECtt EDAr EPfP NEoE SPoG WAbe WIce
	'Koda' (Rezervace Group) (7) **new**	NMen
	'Kokaku' (*fortunei*) (5)	LLHF
§	'Kolbiana' (× *paulinae*) (7)	NMen
	'Kon Tiki' (7)	EPot NMen
	kotschyi (7)	NSla
	kotschyi* × *wendelboi (7)	EPot
	'Koukan' (*fortunei*) (5)	IVic
§	'Krain' (× *fritschiana*) (8)	SIgm WOld
	'Krákatit' (Prichard's Monument Group) (× *megaseiflora*) (7)	NMen
	'Krasava' (Prichard's Monument Group) (× *megaseiflora*) (7)	NMen
	'Křivoklát' (7) **new**	NMen
	'Labe' (× *arco-valleyi*) (7)	CMea CPBP ECho LRHS NMen NRHS
	'Lady Beatrix Stanley'	see *S.* 'Beatrix Stanley'
§	'Lagraveana' (*paniculata*) (8) ♀H5	ECho EDAr GCrg LRHS NRHS SIgm
	'Laka' (7)	EPot NMen
	× ***landaueri*** *sensu stricto* hort.	see *S.* 'Leonore'
	'Lantoscana' (*callosa* subsp. *callosa* var. *australis*) (8)	GKev
	'Lantoscana Superba' (*callosa* subsp. *callosa* var. *australis*) (8)	GKev WOld
	'Laura Sinclair' (× *fallsvillagensis*) (7) **new**	NMen
	'Lemon Puff'	CPBP WIce
	'Lemon Spires' (7)	EPot
	'Lenka' (× *byam-groundsii*) (7)	EPot NMen
	'Leo Gordon Godseff' (× *elisabethae*) (7)	ECho LRHS NRHS NSla
	'Leonardo da Vinci' (7)	EPot NMen WAbe
§	'Leonore' (× *landaueri*) (7)	CRos ECho LRHS NRHS SIgm
	'Leoš Janáček' **new**	NMen
	'Letchworth Gem' (London Pride Group) (× *urbium*) (11)	ECho GAbr GCal LRHS NRHS
	'Libuse' (7) **new**	NMen
	'Licht des Cerise' (*fortunei*) (5)	IVic
	'Lidice' (7)	EPot NMen WAbe WHoo
	'Lilac Time' (× *youngiana*) (7)	EPot
	lilacina (7)	NMen WAbe
	'Lily Potter' (5)	SAko
	'Limelight' (*callosa* subsp. *callosa* var. *australis*) (8)	NWad
	'Lincoln Foster' (8)	NHar
	'Lindau' (7)	NMen
	lingulata	see *S. callosa*
	'Lismore Carmine' (× *lismorensis*) (7)	EPot NMen
	'Lismore Gem' (× *lismorensis*) (7)	ECho
	'Lissadell' (*callosa*) (8)	GKev IFoB
*	'Little Piggy' (*epiphylla*) (5)	WCru
	'Lizzy' (7)	EPot NMen
	llonakhensis	WAbe
	'Lohengrin' (× *hoerhammeri*) (7)	NMen
	'Lohmuelleri' (× *biasolettoi*) (7)	GKev
	lolaensis (7)	WAbe
	longifolia (8)	ECho EPot GKev LRHS NHpl NRHS NSla
	- var. ***aitanica*** (8)	WAbe
	'Louis Armstrong' (Blues Group) (7)	NMen WAbe
	Love Me	see *S.* 'Miluj Mne'
	lowndesii (7)	WAbe
	'Loxley' (× *poluanglica*) (7)	NMen
	'Ludmila Šubrová' (× *bertolonii*) (7)	NMen
	'Lutea' (*aizoon*)	see *S.* 'Lutea' (*paniculata*)
	'Lutea' (*diapensioides*)	see *S.* 'Wilhelm Tell'
§	'Lutea' (*paniculata*) (8)	ECho EDAr EHoe EPot GMaP MMuc NBro NHol NRya NSla NWad
§	'Luteola' (× *boydii*) (7)	NMen
	'Lužníce' (× *poluluteopurpurea*) (7)	CTal
	macedonica	see *S. juniperifolia*
	'Magna' (*burseriana*) (7)	NMen
	'Maigrün' (*fortunei*) (5)	EBee
	'Major' (*cochlearis*) (8)	GKev
	'Major Lutea'	see *S.* 'Luteola'
	'Maly Trpaslík' (7)	NMen
	'Mangart' (*burseriana*) (7)	NMen
	'Marcela' (× *megaseiflora*) (7)	NMen
	marginata (7) ♀H5	WAbe
	- var. ***balcanica***	see *S. marginata* subsp. *marginata* var. *rocheliana*
	- var. ***bubakii*** (7) **new**	NSla
	- subsp. ***marginata*** var. ***boryi*** (7)	EPot LRHS NMen NRHS WAbe
	- - var. ***coriophylla*** (7)	EPot

§	- - var. ***rocheliana*** (7)	ECho LRHS NRHS
	'Maria Callas' (× *poluanglica*) (7)	CPBP WAbe
	'Maria Luisa' (× *salmonica*) (7)	NMen
	'Marianna' (× *borisii*) (7)	CMea
	'Marie' (7) **new**	NMen
	'Marilyn Monroe' (Vanessa Group) (7)	WAbe
	'Maroon Beauty' (*stolonifera*) (5)	CCVN EBee ECtt EPPr LPot MCot NBid NBre WCot
	'Mary Golds' (Swing Group) (7)	GKev ITim NLar NMen
	'Masami' (5)	SAko
	'Medea' (5)	SAko
	× ***megaseiflora*** *sensu stricto* hort.	see *S.* 'Robin Hood'
	'Merlin' (7)	SAko
	mertensiana (6)	EHrv GEdr NBir WCru WSHC
	'Meteor' (7)	NHol NRya NSla
	'Michelangelo' (Rutil Group) (7) **new**	NMen
	'Michle' (× *megaseiflora*) (7)	NMen
	micranthidifolia (4)	CLAP
	'Millstream Cream' (× *elisabethae*) (7)	ECho NMen
§	'Miluj Mne' (× *poluanglica*) (7)	CSma CTal NMen WAbe WHoo
	'Minnehaha' (× *elisabethae*) (7)	NMen
	'Minor' (*cochlearis*) (8) ♀H5	CTal ECho EPot GKev LRHS NHar NRHS NWad
§	'Miss Chambers' (London Pride Group) (11)	EWes GCal LPla SMHy WCot WMoo WSHC
	'Moai' (Multi-colored Group) (7) **new**	NMen
	'Moderne Zeit' (5)	SAko
	'Mollie Broom' (7)	NMen WAbe
	'Molly Weasley' (5)	SAko
	'Momo Sekisui' (*fortunei*) (5)	IVic SAko
	'Momo Tarou' (*fortunei*) (5)	SAko
	'Momobenkei' (*fortunei*) (5)	SAko
	'Mona Lisa' (× *borisii*) (7)	NWad
	'Monarch' (8) ♀H5	ECho EPot GAbr GCrg GKev LRHS NHpl NRHS NWad WAbe WIce
§	'Mondscheinsonate' (× *boydii*) (7)	WAbe
	'Monika' (*webrii*) (7)	NMen
	'Moon Beam' (× *boydilacina*) (7)	NMen
	'Moonlight Sonata' (× *boydii*)	see *S.* 'Mondscheinsonate'
	'Moonlight' (× *boydii*)	see *S.* 'Sulphurea'
	moorcroftiana (1) CC 6939	GKev
	'Morava' (7)	EPot NMen
	Mossy Group pink-flowered (15)	MMuc SPoG
	- red-flowered (15)	SPoG
	- white-flowered (15)	MMuc
	'Mossy Triumph'	see *S.* 'Triumph'
	'Mother of Pearl' (× *irvingii*) (7)	CMea ECho NMen WIce
	'Mother Queen' (× *irvingii*) (7)	NMen
	'Moulin Rouge' (Nobile Group) (7) **new**	NMen

	'Mount Nachi' (*fortunei*) (5)	CBct ECho EPfP EWes GAbr GEdr GMaP LRHS NBro NHpl SPlb WAbe WFar WMoo WPGP
§	'Mrs Gertie Prichard' (Prichard's Monument Group) (× *megaseiflora*) (7)	NMen
	'Mrs Helen Terry' (× *salmonica*) (7) ♀H5	LRHS NMen NRHS
	'Musgrove Pink' (*fortunei*) (5)	CLAP
	mutata (9)	GKev
	'Myra Cambria' (× *anglica*) (7)	NMen NWad
	'Myra' (× *anglica*) (7)	ECho NMen WHoo
	'Myriad' (7)	WAbe
	'Myriad Seedling' (7) **new**	NMen
	'Naarden' (7)	NMen
	'Nancye' (× *goringiana*) (7)	CPBP EPot NMen
	'Neride' (7)	NMen
	'Nicholas' (8)	GKev NHpl
	'Niobe' (× *pulvilacina*) (7)	EPot NMen
	'Nisi' (*fortunei*) (5)	IVic
	'Norvegica' (*cotyledon*) (8)	ITim
	'Nottingham Gold' (× *boydii*) (7) ♀H5	EPot NMen NWad
§	***obtusa*** (7)	EPot MHer NMen
	'Oh Yes' (*cochlearis*) (8)	WAbe
	'Olsany' (× *megaseiflora*) (7)	NMen
	'Olympus' (× *boydilacina*) (7)	NMen
	'Omar Khayyám' (7)	EPot NMen
	'Ontake-san' (5)	SAko
	'Opalescent' (7)	NMen
	'Opatov' (× *megaseiflora*) (7) **new**	NMen
	oppositifolia (7)	GCrg GKev MAsh MWat NHol NSla SPlb SRms WAbe WSHC
	- subsp. ***oppositifolia*** var. ***latina*** (7)	ECho GAbr
	- subsp. ***paradoxa*** (7)	EPot
	'Ottone Rosai' (Toscana Group) (7)	NMen
	'Pablo Picasso' (Conspecta Group) (7)	EPot NMen
	paniculata (8)	ECho EDAr EHoe EPot GKev GMaP MHer MWat NSla SPlb SRms WAbe WHoo
	- from Gorges du Verdon **new**	GKev
§	- subsp. ***cartilaginea*** (8)	GCrg
	- subsp. ***kolenatiana***	see *S. paniculata* subsp. *cartilaginea*
§	- var. ***minutifolia*** (8)	CPBP CTri ECho LRHS MSCN NBro NHar NHpl NRHS NRya NSla SIgm SPlb WAbe
§	- subsp. ***paniculata*** (8)	MAsh
	paradoxa (15)	ECho EPot LRHS NHol NRHS NWad
	'Parcevalis' (× *finnisiae*) (7 × 9)	NMen WAbe
	parnassifolia (1) CC 7509 **new**	GKev
	'Paul Gaughin' (7)	EPot NMen
	'Paul Rubens' (7)	EPot NMen WAbe
	'Peach Blossom' (7)	NMen
	'Peach Melba' (7) ♀H5	CSma CTal EPot NHpl NLar NMen WAbe WHoo
	'Peachy Head' (7)	NMen WAbe
	'Pearl Rose' (× *anglica*) (7)	EPot NMen
	'Pearly Gates' (× *irvingii*) (7)	CTal NMen
	'Pearly King' (Mossy Group) (15)	ECtt GMaP WAbe

'Pearly King' variegated (15/v)	CBod GKev
× ***pectinata*** Schott, Nyman & Kotschy	see *S.* 'Krain'
'Penelope' (× *boydilacina*) (7)	CTal ECho EPot LRHS NLar NMen NRHS NSla WHoo WThu
pensylvanica (4)	CAby EBee GCal GCra IMou
'Perikles' (7)	NMen
'Perseus' (7) **new**	NMen
'Peter Burrow' (× *poluanglica*) (7)	EPot NMen WIce
'Peter Pan' (Mossy Group) (15)	CRos EDAr EPfP GCrg GMaP LRHS MAsh MHer NHol NLar NRHS NWad SBod SPoG WSHC
'Petra' (7)	ECho
'Petřín' (× *megaseiflora*) (7) **new**	NMen
§ 'Phoenix' (× *biasolettoi*) (7)	ECho LRHS NMen NRHS
'Pierantonio Micheli' (Renaissance Group) (7)	NMen
'Pilatus' (× *boydii*) (7)	NMen
'Pink Cloud' (*fortunei*) (5)	EPri GEdr NHar WAbe
'Pink Haze' (*fortunei*) (5)	CLAP GEdr WAbe
'Pink Mist' (*fortunei*) (5)	GEdr WAbe WFar WMoo
'Pink Pagoda' (*nipponica*) (5)	CLAP EBee WCot WCru WPGP
'Pink Pearl' (7)	SBch
'Pink Ray' (*fortunei*) (5)	LLHF
'Pink Star' (× *boydilacina*) (7)	EPot NLar NMen
'Pixie' (15)	CTal CTri ECtt GCrg MAsh NHol NRya NWad SPoG SRms
'Pixie Alba'	see *S.* 'White Pixie'
'Plena' (*granulata*)	see *S.* 'Flore Pleno'
'Polar Drift'	LRHS NHar NRHS NSla SIgm WAbe
'Pollux' (× *boydii*) (7)	EPot
'Polonaise' (7) **new**	NMen
poluniniana × 'Winifred' (× *poluanglica*) (7)	ECho EPot
'Pompadour' (15)	NEoE
'Popelka' (*marginata* subsp. *marginata* var. *rocheliana*) (7)	ECho LRHS NMen NRHS
porophylla (7)	GKev
- var. ***thessalica***	see *S. sempervivum* f. *stenophylla*
'Portae' (× *fritschiana*) (8)	XLum
'Precious Piggy' (*epiphylla*) (5)	WCru
'Primrose Bee' (× *apiculata*) (7)	ITim
'Primrose Dame' (× *elisabethae*) (7)	ECho WIce
'Primulaize' (9 × 11)	GCrg
'Primulaize Salmon' (9 × 11)	NHar WHoo
'Primuloides' (*umbrosa*) (11)	ECho EDAr MMuc SRms SWvt
'Prince Hal' (*burseriana*) (7)	ECho EPot LRHS NRHS NSla
'Princess' (*burseriana*) (7)	ECho LRHS NRHS NSla
'Probynii' (*cochlearis*) (8)	CPBP EPot NWad WAbe
'Prometheus' (× *prossenii*) (7)	NMen SIgm
× ***prossenii*** *sensu stricto* hort.	see *S.* 'Regina'
§ 'Pseudoborisii' (× *borisii*) (7)	NMen
'Pseudo-paulinae' (× *paulinae*) (7)	NMen
'Pseudo-valdensis' (*cochlearis*) (8)	WAbe
pubescens (15)	WAbe
'Punctatissima' (*paniculata*) (8)	NHar
* ***punctissima***	NWad
'Pungens' (× *apiculata*) (7)	EPot
'Purple Piggy' (*epiphylla*) (5)	CLAP WCru
'Purpurea' (*fortunei*)	see *S.* 'Rubrifolia'
'Pygmalion' (× *webrii*) (7)	NMen
'Pyramidalis' (*cotyledon*) (8)	EPfP XLum
'Rachael Young' (× *borisii*) (7) **new**	NMen
'Rainsley Seedling' (8)	EPot NBro
'Ray Woodliffe' (× *dinninaris*) (7)	WAbe
'Red Poll' (× *poluanglica*) (7)	GAbr ITim NHpl NMen
* 'Regent'	WAbe
§ 'Regina' (× *prossenii*) (7)	EPot MHer NMen
§ 'Reginald Farrer' (Silver Farreri Group) (8) ♀^{H5}	WAbe
'Rembrandt van Rijn' (7)	EPot NMen WAbe
retusa (7)	WAbe
'Rex' (*paniculata*) (8)	CMac ECho NWad SIgm
rhodopetala (7)	ECho
'Risa' (5)	SAko
'River Thame' (× *polulacina*) (7)	NMen
§ 'Riverslea' (× *hornibrookii*) (7)	NMen
§ 'Robin Hood' (× *megaseiflora*) (7)	EPot NMen WHoo
'Rockrose'^{PBR} (× *arendsii*) (15) **new**	WTor
'Rokujō' (*fortunei*) (5)	CLAP IVic LHop NEoE NLar NPnk SHeu
'Rosa Tubbs' (8)	EWTr GKev
'Rosaleen' (× *salmonica*) (7)	NMen
'Rosalind' (7)	WHoo
'Rosea' (*cortusifolia*) (5)	CLAP NHar
§ 'Rosea' (*paniculata*) (8) ♀^{H5}	CBod GMaP MMuc NBro NRya NSla SEND SRms
'Rosemarie' (7)	NMen
'Rosina Sündermann' (× *rosinae*) (7)	ECho LRHS NRHS
'Rote Stadt' (*fortunei*) (5)	IVic
rotundifolia (12)	CElw EBee ECha
'Roy Clutterbuck' (7)	NMen
'Roztyly' (× *megaseiflora*) (7)	NMen
'Rubella' (× *irvingii*) (7)	NMen
'Rubin' (× *hornbrookii*) (7) **new**	NMen
'Rubra' (*aizoon*)	see *S.* 'Rosea' (*paniculata*)
§ 'Rubrifolia' (*fortunei*) (5)	CAbP CLAP CMac CSpe ECha ECtt GAbr GEdr GMcL NHpl NPnk SMad SWvt WBor WCot WCru WFar WMoo
* 'Ruby Red'	NEoE
rufescens (5) BWJ 7510	EHrv WCru
- BWJ 7684	GEdr WCru
'Rufina' (7)	NMen
'Rusalka' (× *borisii*) (7)	NMen
'Russell V. Prichard' (× *irvingii*) (7)	NMen NWad
'Ruth Draper' (*oppositifolia*) (7) ♀^{H5}	GCrg WAbe
'Ruth McConnell' (15)	CMea SBch
'Ruznyě' (× *megaseiflora*) (7)	NMen
'Saint John's' (8)	GKev WAbe
'Saint Kilda' (*oppositifolia*) (7)	GCrg ITim NWad
× ***salmonica*** *sensu stricto* hort.	see *S.* 'Salomonii'
'Salome' (× *lincolni-fosteri*) (7) **new**	NMen
§ 'Salomonii' (× *salmonica*) (7)	SRms

	sancta (7)	ECho LRHS NMen NRHS SIgm SRms
	- subsp. ***pseudosancta***	see *S. juniperifolia*
	- - var. ***macedonica***	see *S. juniperifolia*
	'Sapho' (7) **new**	NMen
	'Sara Sinclair' (× *arco-valleyi*) (7)	CMea
	'Šárka' (7)	NMen
	sarmentosa	see *S. stolonifera*
	'Satchmo' (Blues Group) (7)	EPot NMen WAbe
	'Saturn' (× *megaseiflora*) (7)	NMen
	'Saxony Red' **new**	EPfP
	'Sázava' (× *poluluteopurpurea*) (7)	CTal
§	***scardica*** (7)	NBro
	- var. ***dalmatica***	see *S. obtusa*
	- subsp. ***korabensis*** (7)	EPot
§	'Schelleri' (× *petraschii*) (7)	EPfP NMen
	'Schöne Mädchen' (*fortunei*) (5)	IVic
§	'Schwefelblüte' (15)	ECho GMaP LRHS NRHS
	'Seissera' (*burseriana*) (7)	NMen
	sempervivum (7)	NGdn WAbe
	- f. ***sempervivum*** (7) **new**	WAbe
§	- f. ***stenophylla*** (7)	ECho MHer
	sendaica (5)	WCru
	'Seren y Gwanwyn' (*oppositifolia*) (7)	WAbe
	'Setomidori' (5)	SAko
	'Sherlock Holmes' (7)	CTal NMen
	'Shimmy'	WAbe
	'Shinkunomai' (*fortunei*) (5)	IVic
§	'Silver Cushion' (15/v)	CMea CRos CTri ECho ELan LRHS NHpl NRHS SPlb SPoG WAbe WIce WTor
	'Silver Hill' (*paniculata*) (8)	NSla
	'Silver Maid' (× *engleri*) (8)	GCrg NSla
	'Silver Mound'	see *S.* 'Silver Cushion'
	'Silver Velvet' (*fortunei*) (5)	CAbP CLAP CSpe EBee ECtt GEdr GMcL IFoB MBel MNrw NHpl NPnk SDix SHeu WBor WCot
	'Simplicity' (× *ingwersenii*) (7) **new**	NMen
	'Sir Douglas Haig' (15)	NWad
	'Sissi' (7)	CPBP CTal EPot NMen WAbe
	'Slack's Ruby Southside' (Southside Seedling Group) (8) ♀H5	NSla NWad SIgm WIce
	'Slack's Supreme' (8)	NHar NSla WCot
	'Slavia' (7) **new**	NMen
	'Slzy Coventry' (× *proximae*) (7)	EPot WAbe
	'Smíchov' (× *megaseiflora*) (7) **new**	NMen
	'Sněhurka' (Fenomen Group) (7) **new**	NMen
	'Snowcap' (*pubescens*) (15)	EPot WAbe
	'Snowflake' (Silver Farreri Group) (8) ♀H5	WAbe
§	'Sofia' (× *borisii*) (7)	EPot NMen
	Southside Seedling Group (8)	Widely available
	- red-flowered (8)	EPot
	- 'Southside Star' (8) ♀H5	NHpl WAbe
	spathularis (11)	WCot WHoo
	'Spinners Snow-storm' (*fortunei*) (5)	SAko
	'Splendens' (*oppositifolia*) (7) ♀H5	ECho EPfP GAbr GKev MMuc NHar SIgm SRms WAbe WIce
	'Spotted Dog'	see *S.* 'Canis-dalmatica'
	'Sprite' (15)	SPoG
	spruneri (7)	ECho LRHS NRHS
	'Stansfieldii' (*rosacea*) (15)	GCrg SPlb SPoG
	'Star Dust' (7)	EPot
	'Starfire' (8) **new**	GKev
	'Starlight' (8) **new**	GKev
	startorii	see *S. scardica*
	'Šťásek' (*dinnikii*) (7)	WAbe
	stellaris (4)	WAbe
	stenophylla subsp. ***stenophylla***	see *S. flagellaris*
§	***stolonifera*** (5) ♀H2	CCVN CSpe CTsd ECho EShb NBro NPnk SDix SWvt WCot WMoo WPnn WWtn
	- large-flowered (5)	WCot WGrn
	'Strawberry Melba' (7)	EPot NMen
	'Sturmiana' (*paniculata*) (8)	SRms WOld
	'Sue Drew' (*fortunei*) (5)	LLHF
	'Sue Tubbs' (8)	GKev
	'Suendermannii Major' (× *kellereri*) (7)	CRos ECho LRHS NRHS
	'Suendermannii' (× *kellereri*) (7)	CRos ECho LRHS NMen NRHS
	'Sugar Plum Fairy' (*fortunei*) (5)	EBee ECtt EShb ESwi IVic
§	'Sulphurea' (× *boydii*) (7)	CMea CRos ECho EPot LRHS MAsh NRHS NSla NWad WHoo
	'Symons-Jeunei' (8)	NWad WAbe
	'Tamatsuzuri' (*fortunei*) (5)	SAko
	'Tankei' (5)	SAko
	'Tenerife' (Swirly Group) (7)	EPot ITim NMen WAbe
	'Tetín' (Teta Group) (7) **new**	NMen
	'Thalia' (7)	NMen
	'Theoden' (*oppositifolia*) (7) ♀H5	CMea ECho EWes NHar
	'Theresa Cooper' (7)	EPot
	tombeanensis (7)	NMen
	Touran Deep Red = 'Rockred' (Mossy Group) (15)	LBuc LRHS NRHS
	Touran Large White = 'Rocklarwhi'PBR (Mossy Group) (15)	EPfP LBuc LRHS NRHS WTor
	'Tricolor' (*stolonifera*) (5) ♀H2	EBak
	'Tristan' (*stribrnyi*)	WAbe
§	'Triumph' (× *arendsii*) (15)	CBod ECtt EPfP GMaP MAsh NEgg SPoG
	'Tully' (× *elisabethae*) (7)	NMen
	'Tumbling Waters' (8) ♀H5	CRos ECho EPot LHop LRHS MRav NHol NHpl NPnk NRHS NSla WAbe
§	'Tvoje Píseň' (× *poluanglica*) (7)	CTal GKev WHoo WThu
§	'Tvůj Úsměv' (× *poluanglica*) (7) ♀H5	NHpl
§	'Tvůj Úspěch' (× *poluanglica*) (7)	EPot NMen
	'Tycho Brahe' (× *doerfleri*) (7)	WAbe
	umbrosa (11)	CMac CTri ECho EDAr ESps GAbr LEdu LRHS LSun MMuc MRav NRHS SBod SCob SEND SPlb SPoG SRms SWvt WMoo XLum
*	- ***subinteger***	MMuc
	× ***urbium*** (11) ♀H5	CTri ECho ELan EPfP EWoo GMaP LEdu LPot LRHS MBel MCot SPer SRms WBor WCAu WHoo WTor
	'Vaccariana' (*oppositifolia*) (7)	EPot SHar
	'Václav Hollar' (× *gusmusii*) (7)	NMen

	'Václav Talich' (Preludium Group) (7) **new**	NMen
	'Vahlii' (× *smithii*) (7)	NMen
	'Valborg'	see *S.* 'Cranbourne'
	'Valentine'	see *S.* 'Cranbourne'
	'Valerie Keevil' (× *anglica*) (7)	NMen
I	'Variegata' (*cuneifolia*) (11/v)	CBod ECho ECtt EPfP ESps GCrg LRHS NHol NHpl NRHS NRya NWad SPlb SPoG WHoo WMoo
I	'Variegata' (*exarata* subsp. *moschata*) (15/v)	GMaP
	'Variegata' (*umbrosa*)	see *S.* 'Aureopunctata'
I	'Variegata' (× *urbium*) (11/v)	CBod EBee ECho EPfP GPSL LRHS MBel MSpe NLar SBod SCob SMad SRms WHoo WTor
	'Večerní Hvězda' (7)	NMen WAbe
	veitchiana (5)	NBro XLum
	'Vesna' (× *borisii*) (7)	NMen
	'Vikos Gold' (7) **new**	NMen
	'Vincent van Gogh' (× *borisii*) (7)	EPot NMen
	'Vitus Bering' (Revelation Group) (7) **new**	NMen
	'Vítkov' (× *megaseiflora*) (7)	NMen
	'Vladana' (× *megaseiflora*) (7)	CMea ECho EPot LRHS NMen NRHS NSla
	'Vlasta' (7)	NMen
	'Vreny' (8)	GKev
	'Wada' (*fortunei*) (5)	CAbP CAby CBod CLAP CSpe EAEE ECtt ELon EPri GBuc GMaP LRHS MNrw MSpe NBir WBor WCot WFar WOld WPGP WSHC WWtn
	'Walpole's Variety' (8)	NWad
	'Walter Ingwersen' (*umbrosa*) (11)	SRms
§	'Walter Irving' (× *irvingii*) (7) ♀^{H5}	NSla WAbe
	'Warmes Herz' (*fortunei*) (5)	IVic
	'Welsh Dragon' (15)	WAbe
	'Welsh Red' (15)	WAbe
	'Welsh Rose' (15)	WAbe
	wendelboi (7)	CTal EPot WThu
	'Wendrush' (× *wendelacina*) (7)	NMen
	'Wetterhorn' (*oppositifolia*) (7)	GCrg
	'Whatcote' (7)	NMen
	'Wheatley Lion' (× *borisii*) (7)	NMen
	'Wheatley Rose' (7)	CRos ECho LRHS NRHS
	'White Cap' (× *boydii*) (7)	NMen
	'White Delight' (× *megaseiflora*) (7) **new**	LRHS NRHS NSla
	'White Imp' (7)	NMen
§	'White Pixie' (15)	ECtt EDAr EPfP EWoo GCrg MAsh MHer NEoE NHol NRya NWad SPlb SPoG SRms WIce
	'White Star' (*fortunei*) (5)	CRos LLHF LRHS NMen NRHS
	'White Star' (× *petraschii*)	see *S.* 'Schelleri'
	'Whitehill' (8) ♀^{H5}	CMea CRos ECho ELan EPot GEdr GMaP LRHS NFav NRHS NRya NSla NWad SBch WHoo
§	'Wilhelm Tell' (× *malbyana*) (7)	NMen
	'William Boyd' (× *boydii*) (7)	WAbe
	'William Shakespeare' (Blues Group) (7)	CPBP EPot NMen WAbe
	'Winifred Bevington' (8 × 11)	CRos CSma CTal ECho EDAr EPot GCrg GMaP LHop LRHS NBro NHpl NLar NRHS NRya NWad WAbe WHoo WOld WPnn WTor
	'Winifred' (× *anglica*) (7)	CTal ECho EPot NMen WAbe
	'Winston Churchill' (15)	CRos CTri ECho LRHS NEoE NHol NRHS NWad
I	'Winston Churchill Variegata' (15/v)	NHol NWad
	'Winton' (× *paulinae*) (7)	EPot NMen
	'Wisley' (*federici-augusti* subsp. *grisebachii*) (7) ♀^{H5}	GKev
	'Wisley Primrose'	see *S.* 'Kolbiana'
	'Yellow Rock' (7)	NMen NRya
	'Youkuy' (*fortunei*) (5)	IVic
	Your Good Fortune	see *S.* 'Tvůj Úspěch'
	Your Smile	see *S.* 'Tvůj Úsměv'
	Your Song	see *S.* 'Tvoje Píseň'
	Your Success	see *S.* 'Tvůj Úspěch'
	'Yunagi' (*fortunei*) (5)	IVic SAko WOld
	'Zbraslav' (× *megaseiflora*) (7) **new**	NMen
	× ***zimmeteri*** (8 × 11)	ECho
	'Ziva' (7) **new**	NMen
§	'Zlatá Praha' (× *pragensis*) (7)	NMen WAbe
	'Zlatý Kůň' (× *laeviformis*) (7) **new**	EPot

Scabiosa (*Caprifoliaceae*)

	africana	CElw EWes SHar
	- 'Jocelyn'	EWes SHar
	alpina L.	see *Cephalaria alpina*
	argentea	EWes WPGP
	- PAB 1229	LEdu
	atropurpurea	SPav
	- 'Ace of Spades'	ELan EPfP SCob SPav SPhx
	- 'Beaujolais Bonnets'	CNor EAJP EPed EPfP LRHS SHil SPer WHar
	- 'Black Knight'	CSpe SPav
	- 'Blue Beau'	LRHS NRHS
§	- 'Chile Black'	CAby CBcs EAJP EHoe EHrv ELan EPfP EWes GWyn IBoy LRHS SCob SPav SPer SRkn SWvt WBod WHar
§	- 'Chilli Pepper'	CWCL LRHS
§	- 'Chilli Sauce'	EBee
	- 'Derry's Black'	CSpe SPtp
	- 'Fata Morgana'	SPav
	- 'Snowmaiden'	SPav
	banatica	see *S. columbaria*
	'Barocca'	CNor CSpe EBee EPfP LRHS WCot
	'Black PomPom'	CSpe CWld EBee NLar
	'Blackberry Fool' (Dessert Series)	WHlf
	'Blue Diamonds'	EBee GJos IBoy LRHS MHol WFar WHar
	'Blueberry Muffin' (Dessert Series)	WHlf
	Burgundy Bonnets = 'Scabon'^{PBR}	CBod EPfP
§	'Butterfly Blue'	Widely available
	'Cambridge Blue'	EPfP
	canescens	MSpe
	caucasica	CBod CMac EPfP GKev LEdu LRHS WHoo XSen
	- var. ***alba***	EPfP ILea NGBl WHoo
	- 'Blauer Atlas'	NDov
	- 'Blausiegel'	EHrv LRHS MRav
	- 'Clive Greaves' ♀^{H4}	EBee ECha EWTr GBuc GMaP IBoy LRHS MBNS MSpe NDov NRHS SCob SGbt SPad SPer SRms SWvt WCAu WFar WHil
	- 'Deep Waters'	CSpe EBee LRHS WPtf

- 'Fama' CSpe CWib NBir NGBl NLar SPlb SRms WFar
- 'Fama Deep Blue' LRHS SHil
- 'Fama White' LRHS SHil
- 'Goldingensis' CWCL NGdn WHil
- House's hybrids CSBt MHol NGdn SRms
- 'Isaac House' LSun XLum
- 'Kompliment' NDov WFar
- 'Miss Willmott' ♀H4 CBod CMac CSam EBee ECha ECtt EHoe EHrv GBin IBoy LHop LRHS MRav MSpe NCGa NDov SGbt SPer SPoG SWvt WCAu
- Perfecta Series CWib GBin GMcL ILea LRHS MMrt NGdn NLar NRHS SPoG SWat WHar
- - 'Perfecta Alba' CBod CDor CWib ELan ELon EPfP EWoo GBin GMaP LHop LRHS MArt MBel MHer MHol NLar NRHS SCob SPad SPer SPoG WCAu WHar XLum XSen
- - 'Perfecta Blue' CDor CMac ELan ELon EPfP EWoo GMaP MBel MHer WCot XLum
- - 'Perfecta Lilac Blue' CWib EPfP SPer
- 'Stäfa' EBee ECha LRHS NCGa NDov NEgg NLar
- 'Thorp's Variegated' (v) WCot

'Cherry Pie' (Dessert Series) LBMP SHil WHlf
'Chile Black' see *S. atropurpurea* 'Chile Black'
'Chile Pepper' see *S. atropurpurea* 'Chilli Pepper'
'Chile Sauce' see *S. atropurpurea* 'Chilli Sauce'
cinerea SPhx
§ ***columbaria*** CHab CWld EBee ECGP LRHS MArt MMuc NEgg NMir SPhx WHer WJek WSFF
* - ***alpina*** GKev
- 'Blue Note'PBR CBod EBee LRHS NPri NRHS
- blue-flowered NHpl
- 'Mariposa Blue'PBR CBod MHol NPri
- 'Misty Butterflies' CAby CCVN ECtt EPfP GBin GJos LBMP LHop MHol NCou NEgg NGdn NLar SHil WFar
- 'Nana' EBee GWyn LRHS LSun NBir NGdn NLar NRHS SBch WCFE XLum
§ - subsp. ***ochroleuca*** CKno CSpe ECha EHrv LRHS MBel MCot MSpe NBir NGBl NLar SCob SHar SPhx SPoG SRms SSut WCAu WPGP
- - MESE 344 EBee
- - 'Moon Dance' CMea CSam EAJP GBin GPSL LBMP LLHF LRHS MTis NLar SAko SGbt WHoo
- - 'Pixie Yellow' **new** LRHS NRHS
- 'Pincushion Blue' EDAr LRHS
- 'Pincushion Pink' EDAr GWyn LRHS NGdn
- 'Purple' **new** WHil

'Columbia Blue' **new** WHil
cretica SIgm XLum XSen
drakensbergensis CHid ELan EWTr EWes GBin GKev IKil ILea LRHS MTPN SLon WCot WPtf
gigantea see *Cephalaria gigantea*
graminifolia ECho GKev LRHS NBir SBch SRms XLum
- ***rosea*** EWes

'Helen Dillon' ECre EWes LSou
incisa WOut
'Irish Perpetual Flowering' see *S.* 'Butterfly Blue'
japonica var. ***acutiloba*** SPhx
- var. ***alpina*** EBee EPfP GKev MMuc NGdn SEND SPhx WHoo WWFP XLum
- - 'Blue Star' EBee NBre NCGa SGbt
- - 'Ritz Blue' CMea EPfP NCGa SPad
- - 'Ritz Rose' **new** CMea

lachnophylla GCal SPhx WCot
- 'Blue Horizon' EBee MArt

'Little Cracker' LRHS LSou SCob SLon
'Little Emily' ELon LSou
lucida CBod ECho EPfP IPot LRHS MMuc MRav SEND WPGP XLum
Magic = 'Pmoore02' EBee LOPS LSou
'Midnight' CMea
'Miss Havisham' CElw EWes MNrw
montana Mill. see *Knautia arvensis*
ochroleuca see *S. columbaria* subsp. *ochroleuca*
parnassi see *Pterocephalus perennis*
'Perpetual Flowering' see *S.* 'Butterfly Blue'
Pink Buttons = 'Walminipink' CBod EBee
'Pink Diamonds' EBee ELan EPfP MHol SBee WFar WHar
'Pink Mist'PBR CBod CRos EBee ECtt ELan EPfP GBin IBoy LCro LRHS MAsh NBir NDov NHpl NLar SCob SCoo SPer SPoG SRms WTor
pterocephala see *Pterocephalus perennis*
'Raspberry Sorbet' (Dessert Series) **new** WHlf
rhodopensis EBee
'Rhubarb Crumble' (Dessert Series) SHil
'Rosie's Pink' ECtt
rumelica see *Knautia macedonica*
'Satchmo' see *S. atropurpurea* 'Chile Black'
'Strawberry Parfait' (Dessert Series) WHlf
succisa see *Succisa pratensis*
tatarica see *Cephalaria gigantea*
ucranica WOut
'Vivid Violet' CAbb CHVG CSpe CWGN EBee ECtt LBuc LRHS LSRN LSou MBNS MHol MMuc MNrw NDov NHpl NLar SAko SHil WBrk WCot

Scadoxus ✿ (*Amaryllidaceae*)

× ***hybridus*** 'König Albert' GKev
membranaceus CLak WCot
multiflorus CCCN ECho GKev LAma SDeJ
§ - subsp. ***katherinae*** ♀H1b CLak CPne WCot
§ - subsp. ***multiflorus*** WCot
natalensis see *S. puniceus*
§ ***puniceus*** CLak CPne GKev WCot

Scaevola (*Goodeniaceae*)

aemula 'Blue Fan' see *S. aemula* 'Blue Wonder'
§ - 'Blue Wonder'PBR NPer SWvt
- 'Zig Zag'PBR CCCN

Blauer Facher = 'Saphira'PBR CCCN NLar
'Brillant'PBR LBMP LSou
crassifolia SPlb
'Mini Blue' CCCN
'Topaz Pink' LSou

Sceletium (*Aizoaceae*)

tortuosum SPlb

Schefflera ✿ (*Araliaceae*)

actinophylla 'Nova' **new** WPGP
alpina CFil IVic
- B&SWJ 8247 WCru

- B&SWJ 11827	WCru
- HWJ 936	WCru
- NJM 09.140 **new**	WPGP
- NJM 09.157 **new**	WPGP
- large-leaved WWJ 11999	WCru
arboricola 🏆H1c	SEND XBlo
- 'Gold Capella' 🏆H1c	SEND XBlo
- 'Kalahari'	XBlo
brevipedicellata HWJ 870	WCru
- KWJ 12224	WCru
§ ***chapana*** B&SWJ 11833 **new**	WCru
- B&SWJ 11848	WCru
- HWJ 983	WCru
delavayi	CFil CPne WCru
enneaphylla HWJ 1018	WCru
fantsipanensis	CFil
- B&SWJ 11666	WCru
- B&SWJ 11671	WCru
- NJM 10.137	WPGP
gracilis HWJ 622	WCru
- HWJ 878	WCru
gracilis* × *taiwaniana	WCru
hoi B&SWJ 11747	WCru
kornasii B&SWJ 11830	WCru
- HWJ 918	WCru
macrophylla B&SWJ 8210	WCru
- B&SWJ 9788	WCru
- B&SWJ 11842	WCru
- PAB 2788	LEdu
- WWJ 11681 **new**	WCru
microphylla B&SWJ 3872	WCru
multinervia B&SWJ 11727	WCru
aff. ***myriocarpa*** B&SWJ 11828	WCru
rhododendrifolia	CBct CFil CMHG EBee WPGP
- GWJ 9375	WCru
shweliensis PAB 13.216 **new**	LEdu
taiwaniana 🏆H4	CBct CFil CPne EBee IVic WPGP
- B&SWJ 3575	WCru
- B&SWJ 7096	WCru
- RWJ 10000	WCru
- RWJ 10016	WCru
vietnamensis	see *S. chapana*

Schima (*Theaceae*)

argentea	CBcs CCCN EBee EPfP WPGP
khasiana	WPGP
- NJM 13.042 **new**	WPGP
- PAB 3447	LEdu WPGP
wallichii	CBcs

Schinus (*Anacardiaceae*)

latifolius	CBcs
lentiscifolius	SPlb
molle	SPlb
montanus **new**	SPlb
polygamus	MGil SPlb

Schisandra (*Schisandraceae*)

arisanensis	MBlu NLar WPGP
- B&SWJ 3050	WCru
aff. ***bicolor***	WPGP
chinensis	CAgr CArn CBcs CRHN GKev GPoy LEdu MSwo NLar
- B&SWJ 4204	WCru
- B&SWJ 4611A	WCru
- B&SWJ 4611B	WCru
- 'Bere'	LEdu WPGP
- 'Sadova No.1' **new**	ETho
grandiflora 🏆H5	CBcs CBot CWCL EBee ELan EPfP ESwi GBin IDee IMou LRHS MBlu MGil SBrt SKHP SNig SPer WBod
- B&SWJ 2245	WCru WSHC
- PAB 3673	LEdu
- var. ***cathayensis***	see *S. sphaerandra*
- 'Jamu' (m)	WCru
- 'Lahlu' (f/F)	WCru
grandiflora* × *rubriflora	MMuc WCru
henryi subsp. ***yunnanensis*** B&SWJ 6546	WCru
incarnata BWJ 7898	WCru
incarnata* × *rubriflora	WCru
lancifolia	MBlu WPGP
nigra	see *S. repanda*
perulata FMWJ 13100	WCru
aff. ***plena*** HWJ 664	WCru
propinqua	WSHC
- subsp. ***sinensis***	CBot CMac CRHN LEdu NLar WPGP
- - BWJ 8148	WCru
§ ***repanda*** B&SWJ 5897	WCru
- B&SWJ 11455	WCru
rubriflora 🏆H5	CBcs CTri EBee EPfP ETho IMou LRHS MBlu MGos NLar NRHS SBrt SKHP SLon SMDP SPoG
- (f)	ESwi WSHC
- BWJ 7557	WCru
- 'Bodnant Redberry' (f)	WCru
§ ***sphaerandra*** BWJ 7739	WCru
- BWJ 8082	WCru
sphenanthera	EBee LRHS NLar WSHC
- BWJ 8151	WCru

Schizachyrium (*Poaceae*)

§ ***scoparium***	CKno EBee ECGP EHoe EPPr EPfP GQue LRHS XLum
- 'Blue Heaven'	ELon NDov
- 'Prairie Blues'	CSpe ELon EPfP LRHS LSun NRHS SMea SPhx WCot

Schizocarphus (*Asparagaceae*)

nervosus	WCot

Schizocodon see *Shortia*

Schizophragma (*Hydrangeaceae*)

corylifolium	NLar
- BWJ 8150	WPGP
fauriei	NLar WSHC
- B&SWJ 1701	WCru
- B&SWJ 6831	WCru
- B&SWJ 7052	WCru
- CWJ 12405	WCru
- CWJ 12433	WCru
hydrangeoides	CBcs CCCN CDul CRHN CRos EBee ELan EPfP GKin LCro LOPS LRHS MBlu MGos NRHS SGol SLim SLon SPer SWvt WCFE
- 'Brookside Littleleaf'	see *Hydrangea anomala* subsp. *petiolaris* var. *cordifolia* 'Brookside Littleleaf'
- var. ***concolor*** B&SWJ 5954	WCru
- - 'Moonlight' 🏆H5	CBcs CDul CKel CMac CWGN ELan EPfP LEdu LRHS MBlu MGil MGos MMuc NLar NRHS SKHP SLon SPer SPoG SRkn SWvt WCot WCru WPGP WSHC
- var. ***hydrangeoides*** B&SWJ 5489	WCru

- - B&SWJ 5732	WCru
- - 'Iwa Garami'	NLar
- - 'Roseum' ♀H5	CBcs CDul CMac ELan EPfP EWes GBin IArd LRHS MBlu MGil MGos NLar SGol SKHP SLon SPer SWvt WCru WPGP
* - f. ***quelpartensis***	LRHS
- 'Rose Sensation'	CCCN EBee EPfP LRHS NRHS SLon SPoG
- var. ***taquetii*** B&SWJ 8771	WCru
- - 'Cheju's Early'	WCru
- var. ***ullungdoense*** B&SWJ 8505	WCru
- - B&SWJ 8522	WCru
- var. ***yakushimense*** B&SWJ 6119	WCru
integrifolium ♀H5	CBcs CBot CCCN CDul CRHN EBee ELan EPfP LRHS MBlu MMuc SKHP SPer WKif WPGP WSHC
- BWJ 8150	WCru
molle HWJ 1011	WCru
- WWJ 11905	WCru

Schizostylis see *Hesperantha*

coccinea 'Gigantea'	see *Hesperantha coccinea* 'Major'
- 'Grandiflora'	see *Hesperantha coccinea* 'Major'
- 'Sunset'	see *Hesperantha coccinea* 'Sunrise'
'Pink Princess'	see *Hesperantha coccinea* 'Wilfred H. Bryant'

Schoenoplectus (*Cyperaceae*)

§ ***lacustris***	CWat MMuc MSKA MWLS MWts SEND
§ - subsp. ***tabernaemontani***	CSpe
- - 'Albescens' (v)	CBen CWat MMuc MNrw MSKA MWts WHal XLum
- - 'Zebrinus' (v)	CBen CWat ELan MNrw MSKA NPla SPlb SWat WMAq XLum

Schoenoxiphium (*Cyperaceae*)

lanceum new	XBlo

Schoenus (*Cyperaceae*)

pauciflorus	LLWG WMoo

Sciadopitys (*Sciadopityaceae*)

verticillata ♀H6	CAco CDul CKen CMac CPne EPfP GKin IDee LRHS MBlu MGos MMuc NHol NWea SAko SArc SCoo SEND SLim SPoG SWvt WHar
- 'Beauty Green' new	NLar
- 'Firework'	CKen
- 'Globe'	CKen
- 'Gold Star'	CKen NLar
- 'Golden Rush'	CKen MAsh NLar
- 'Goldmahne'	CKen
- 'Grüne Kugel'	CKen MAsh
- 'Jeddeloh Compact'	CKen
- 'Koja Maki'	NLar
- 'Kugelblitz'	NLar
- 'Kupferschirm'	CKen
- 'Marylin Monroe' new	NLar
- 'Mecki'	CKen
- 'Megaschirm'	CKen
- 'Moonie's Mini' new	NLar
- 'Mr Happy' new	NLar
- 'Ossorio Gold'	CKen NLar
- 'Perlenglanz'	CKen
- 'Picola'	CKen MAsh NLar
- 'Pygmy'	CKen
- 'Richie's Cream'	CKen
- 'Richie's Cushion'	CKen
- 'Shorty'	CKen
- 'Speerspitze'	CKen
- 'Star Wars'	CKen
- 'Starburst'	CKen
- 'Sternschnuppe'	CKen MAsh
- 'Tsai Cheng' new	NLar
- 'Wiels Beauty' new	NLar
- 'Wintergreen'	CKen

Scilla (*Asparagaceae*)

adlamii	see *Ledebouria cooperi*
× ***allenii***	see × *Chionoscilla allenii*
amethystina	see *S. litardierei*
amoena	ECho WCot
autumnalis	CAvo ECho EPot GKev LAma LLHF LRHS NRHS NRog WShi WThu
- white-flowered	NRog
bifolia ♀H5	CAvo CBro CTca ECho EPot GKev LAma LLWP NNys SDeJ SPhx WCot WShi
- RS 156/83	ECho
- 'Alba'	ECho GKev SPhx
- 'Rosea'	ECho GKev LAma LLWP LRHS MPie NRHS SDeJ
bithynica ♀H5	ECho EPot GKev WCot WShi
campanulata	see *Hyacinthoides hispanica*
chinensis	see *S. scilloides*
cilicica	CAvo ECho
greilhuberi	CAvo ECho EPPr LLHF WCot
hohenackeri	ECho GKev LLHF SPhx WCot WThu
- BSBE 811	WCot
§ ***hughii***	EBee ECho
hyacinthoides	EBee ECho ERCP GKev SDir SIgm WCot
ingridiae	ECho
- var. ***taurica***	ECho
italica	see *Hyacinthoides italica*
japonica	see *S. scilloides*
latifolia	GKev WCot
- from Morocco	ECho
liliohyacinthus	CAvo CBro ECho GKev IBlr WShi
- 'Alba'	CAvo
lingulata	ECho LLHF WCot
- var. ***lingulata***	ECho
§ ***litardierei*** ♀H5	ECho EPPr EPfP EPot ERCP GKev LAma MMuc SDeJ SEND SPhx WShi
lutea hort.	see *Ledebouria socialis*
madeirensis	CLak WCot
- from Madeira	CHll
melaina	ECho GKev
- JCA 0.875.000 new	WCot
mesopotamica	ECho GKev
messeniaca	GKev
- MS 38 from Greece	WCot
mischtschenkoana ♀H5	CAby CAvo CBro CHid ECho EPot IFro LAma LCro LOPS LRHS NNys NRHS SDeJ SDir WShi
§ - 'Tubergeniana' ♀H5	CMea ECho GKev SPhx
- 'Zwanenburg'	ECho
monophyllos	ECho GKev MArt WCot
morrisii	ECho GKev
natalensis	see *Merwilla plumbea*
non-scripta	see *Hyacinthoides non-scripta*
nutans	see *Hyacinthoides non-scripta*
obtusifolia	ECho
- subsp. intermedia	WCot

persica ♀H4 — ECho GKev WCot
peruviana — Widely available
- SB&L 20/1 — WCot
- 'Alba' — CBro CTal CTca CWCL ECho EPot EPri EWes GKev NHpl WCot XLum
- 'Hughii' — see *S. hughii*
- var. ***venusta*** — EBee
- - S&L 311/2 — WCot
- 'White Moon' new — GKev
pratensis — see *S. litardierei*
puschkinioides — ECho
ramburei — GKev
rosenii — ECho GBin
- 'Cloudy Sky' new — WCot
§ ***scilloides*** — ECho NRog WCot
- B&SWJ 8812 — WCru
* - 'Alba' — SDeJ
siberica ♀H5 — CAby CAvo CBro CRos CTca ECho ELan EPfP EShb GKev LAma LCro LOPS LRHS MMuc MWat NRHS SCob SDir SPer SPhx WBor WHea WShi
- 'Alba' — CAvo ECho EPfP EPot GKev LAma LRHS MArt SDeJ WShi
- 'Enem' — GKev
- 'Spring Beauty' — CMea ECho EPot ERCP GKev LAma LRHS NRHS SDeJ SPhx SRms
'Tubergeniana' — see *S. mischtschenkoana* 'Tubergeniana'
verna — ECho WShi WThu
vicentina — see *Hyacinthoides vincentina*
violacea — see *Ledebouria socialis*

Scirpoides (*Cyperaceae*)

§ ***holoschoenus*** — EBee WDra

Scirpus (*Cyperaceae*)

cernuus — see *Isolepis cernua*
'Green Mist' — WCot
holoschoenus — see *Scirpoides holoschoenus*
lacustris — see *Schoenoplectus lacustris*
- 'Spiralis' — see *Juncus effusus* f. *spiralis*
maritimus — see *Bolboschoenus maritimus*
sylvaticus — WDra
tabernaemontani — see *Schoenoplectus lacustris* subsp. *tabernaemontani*

Scleranthus (*Caryophyllaceae*)

biflorus — ECho EDAr EPot EWes GBin LEdu LRHS MAsh SPlb XLum
uniflorus — ECho EPot LEdu NHpl SMad SPlb SRot XLum
- 'Selected Bronze' new — SMad

Sclerochiton (*Acanthaceae*)

harveyanus — EShb GFai

Scoliopus (*Liliaceae*)

bigelowii — GEdr
hallii — CTal EBee GBin LEdu MNrw WCru

Scolopendrium see *Asplenium*

Scopolia (*Solanaceae*)

anomala HWJK 2252 — WCru
carniolica — CArn CAvo EBee ELan EPPr EWld GBin GPoy ILea LEdu MPhe NChi NLar NSti SPlb WCru WPGP WSHC XLum
- from Poland — LEdu
§ - var. ***brevifolia*** — EBee EHrv EPPr EPfP EWld LEdu LRHS MNrw SPhx WCot WPGP
- - WM 9811 — MPhe
- 'Zwanenburg' — ECho EHrv EPPr EWes LEdu NLar SPhx WPGP XLum
hladnikiana — see *S. carniolica* var. *brevifolia*
japonica — IMou
lurida — see *Anisodus luridus*

Scorzonera (*Asteraceae*)

hispanica — SVic

Scrophularia (*Scrophulariaceae*)

aquatica misapplied — see *S. auriculata*
§ ***auriculata*** — CHab LLWG NMir NPer WHer
§ - 'Variegata' (v) — CAby CBcs ECha EHoe ELan EPfP GCal GLog LLWG LRHS MHer NSti SHar SPer
buergeriana 'Lemon and Lime' misapplied — see *Teucrium viscidum* 'Lemon and Lime'
- 'Lemon and Lime' (v) — EBee NEgg
macrantha — SMad
nodosa — CArn GPoy NMir WHer
- ***variegata*** — see *S. auriculata* 'Variegata'
vernalis — CBgR

Scutellaria (*Lamiaceae*)

albida — EBee GJos
§ ***alpina*** — ECho GJos SPlb SRms SRot
- 'Arcobaleno' — LLHF
altissima — CFis ECha ELan GPSL MMuc MSpe NBro SPlb WHea WOut WPtf WWtn XSen
'Amazing Grace' — EWes
baicalensis — GJos GPoy IMou SIgm WPtf
barbata — GJos
biacalensis 'Oriental Blue' — GJos
canescens — see *S. incana*
chungtiensis — GEdr
costaricana — CCCN
diffusa — SBch
galericulata — CBod CHab ENfk GPoy MHer WHer
hastata — see *S. hastifolia*
§ ***hastifolia*** — CTri ECtt
§ ***incana*** — ELan EWoo GMaP LCro LHop LOPS LRHS MAvo MHol MPie NDov SPhx WCot
indica var. ***japonica*** — see *S. indica* var. *parvifolia*
§ - var. ***parvifolia*** — ECho EWes GJos ITim SRot WAbe
- - 'Alba' — ECho LLHF WAbe
lateriflora — CArn GJos GPoy SRms WJek
- PAB 3921 — LEdu
maekawae — EBee WPGP
- B&SWJ 557A — WCru
orientalis — ECtt WAbe
- subsp. ***bicolor*** — ECtt SIgm
- subsp. ***pinnatifida*** — SIgm XSen
pontica — CPBP SPhx WIce
scordiifolia — CFis CMea ECha ECho IMou LHop NRya NWad SRms WFar
- 'Seoul Sapphire' — CSpe LEdu LHop LRHS MPie NRHS SPtp WPGP WPtf
sevanensis — LHop WCot WIce
'Sherbert Lemon' — CMea CPBP SRot WTor
suffrutescens — GJos
- 'Texas Rose' — CMea CSpe ECho GJos LHop LLHF MCot NHpl SBch SRot WAbe WHoo WIce WTor
supina — see *S. alpina*

tournefortii EBee ECtt LLWP LRHS WOut XSen
* ***zhongdianensis*** WPtf

seakale see *Crambe maritima*

Sebaea (*Gentianaceae*)

rehmanii SPlb
thomasii WAbe
- 'Bychan' WAbe

Securigera (*Papilionaceae*)

§ ***varia*** LHop MMuc SEND SRms XLum

Sedastrum see *Sedum*

× *Sedeveria* (*Crassulaceae*)

'Harry Butterfield' WCot
'Letizia' SChr

Sedum ✿ (*Crassulaceae*)

'Abbey Dore' CBod ECtt ELan ELon EPfP GCal LRHS LSou MSpe MTis NBir NCGa SPhx WCAu WHar WPGP
acre CRos CTri EPfP ESps GPoy LEdu LRHS MNHC NMir NRHS SCob SPlb XLum
- 'Aureum' EDAr EHoe ELan EPfP NHpl NLar NRya SCob SPoG XLum
- 'Elegans' ECtt GCrg
- 'Golden Queen' CRos ECho LRHS MSCN NRHS SPlb SPoG
- 'Helvetica' WCot
- 'Minus' CRos ECho LRHS NRHS
§ - subsp. ***neglectum*** var. ***majus*** CChe EPfP NLar
- 'Oktoberfest' GJos
aizoon GCal NBre SPlb WFar XLum
- 'Aurantiacum' see *S. aizoon* 'Euphorbioides'
§ - 'Euphorbioides' ECha ECtt ELan LPot MHer MMuc MRav NLar SEND SHar SPer SPlb SSal
§ - subsp. ***maximowiczii*** NWad
alatum WFar
albescens see *S. forsterianum* f. *purpureum*
alboroseum see *S. erythrostictum*
§ ***album*** CRos GJos LRHS MMuc NBro NMir NRHS SEND XLum
- 'Coral Carpet' ECho ECtt EDAr EPPr EPfP EPot GAbr GCrg GJos GKev GWyn MRav NHpl NLar NRya SFgr SPoG XLum
- subsp. ***teretifolium*** var. ***micranthum*** 'Chloroticum' XLum
§ - - var. ***murale*** CTri LRHS NHpl NRHS XLum
alpestre XLum
altissimum see *S. sediforme*
* ***altum*** NBre
Amber = 'Florseamb' EBee WCot
anacampseros MHer MMuc NWad SEND XLum
'Aquarel' GBin GWyn
athoum see *S. album*
atlanticum see *S. dasyphyllum* subsp. *dasyphyllum* var. *mesatlanticum*
'Autumn Charm' see *S.* (Herbstfreude Group) 'Lajos'
Autumn Joy see *S.* 'Herbstfreude'
'Beach Party' (Party Hardy Series) LRHS
beauverdii subsp. ***vietnamense*** HWJ 824 WCru
'Bertram Anderson' Y^{H7} Widely available
beyrichianum misapplied see *S. glaucophyllum*
'Birthday Party' (Birthday Party Series) EBee LRHS SPoG
bithynicum 'Aureum' see *S. hispanicum* var. *minus* 'Aureum'
Black Beauty = 'Florseblab' ECtt LRHS MNrw NDov NLar
'Blade Runner' LRHS LSou
'Blue Pearl' (SunSparkler Series) **new** LCro LRHS
brevifolium EWes
§ - var. ***quinquefarium*** WIce
'Carl' Y^{H7} Widely available
cauticola Y^{H5} ECho EDAr EPot GBuc GCal MAvo MMuc MRav SRms SRot WAbe WIce XLum
- 'Coca-Cola' CBod CCVN CMac CWGN EAEE ECtt EHoe GBin GJos GKev GMcL GWyn LBMP LRHS MAvo MCot MRav NBir NDov NHpl SPhx SPoG SWvt WCAu WHoo
- 'Lidakense' Y^{H5} CMea CSpe CTal CWCL ECha ECho ECtt EPot GBin GBuc GCrg MHer NAst NHol NLar SBch SPlb SRot XLum
- 'Robustum' see *S.* 'Ruby Glow'
'Cherry Tart' (SunSparkler Series) ECtt
'Chocolate Drop'^{PBR} CMos CWGN EBee ECtt NLar SDys SPoG
'Chocolate Sauce' MAvo
chrysicaulum EPot
'Class Act'^{PBR} ECtt LRHS MAvo MNrw NLar SHil SPoG
'Cloud Walker'^{PBR} ECtt LRHS MNrw SPoG WFar
confusum Hemsl. SEND
crassipes see *Rhodiola wallichiana*
crassularia see *Crassula setulosa* 'Milfordiae'
'Crazy Ruffles' ECtt WCot
cryptomerioides B&SWJ 054 WCru
cyaneum 'Sakhalin' LRHS NRHS WCot
'Dark Jack' CKno ECtt ELon EPfP MTis NGdn WCot
dasyphyllum NBir NRya SPlb SRms
§ - subsp. ***dasyphyllum*** var. ***mesatlanticum*** NBir
- ***mucronatis*** see *S. dasyphyllum* subsp. *dasyphyllum* var. *mesatlanticum*
'Diamond Edge' (v) EBee ECtt IKil
divergens XLum
douglasii see *S. stenopetalum* 'Douglasii'
drymarioides NBre
'Dudley Field' MHer
'Eleanor Fisher' see *S. telephium* subsp. *ruprechtii*
ellacombeanum see *S. kamtschaticum* var. *ellacombeanum*
'Elworthy Rose' CElw
§ ***erythrostictum*** GBin XLum
- 'Frosty Morn' (v) Widely available
§ - 'Mediovariegatum' (v) CDor CNec EAEE EBee ELan LRHS MHer MNrw NLar SWvt WFar WMoo XLum
ewersii ECho ECtt EDAr EPot EWTr GCrg MMuc NBro NLar SPhx SPlb WTor
- CC 5288 GKev
- var. ***homophyllum*** 'Rosenteppich' EPPr EPfP LBuc LRHS NRHS SPoG SWvt WMoo
fabaria see *S. telephium* subsp. *fabaria*

	fastigiatum	see *Rhodiola fastigiata*
	floriferum	see *S. kamtschaticum* var. *floriferum*
	forsterianum subsp. ***elegans***	SEND SPlb XLum
	- - 'Silver Stone'	GJos MMuc
§	- f. ***purpureum***	NRya
	'Frosted Fire'	EBee LSou NSti WFar
	furfuraceum	GEdr NHpl WAbe
	Garnet Brocade = 'Garbro'PBR	CCVN
§	***glaucophyllum***	EDAr XLum
	'Gold Mound'	EUJe GWyn NHpl SWeb
	'Green Expectations'	GBin LRHS MRav NBre
	hakonense 'Chocolate Ball'	CPBP ECtt LHop LSou MHtn MSCN
	Herbstfreude Group	EHrv EPed EWTr EWoo IBoy LRHS NWsh
	- 'Autumn Fire'	EBee MAsh
	- 'Beka' (v)	LSou
	- 'Elsie's Gold' (v)	EBee ECtt EPfP LRHS MNrw NRHS SRms WHil
§	- 'Herbstfreude' ♀H7	Widely available
	- 'Jaws'PBR	CKno EBee ECtt IKil NLar WCot WFar XLum
§	- 'Lajos' (v)	LSou MAsh NEoE SPoG WCot WFar
	- 'Mini Joy'	ELon GKev LRHS MHol MNrw
	heterodontum	see *Rhodiola heterodonta*
	hidakanum	ECtt EHoe EPot GMaP NBro NHol NWad SIgm WHoo
	himalense misapplied	see *Rhodiola* 'Keston'
	hispanicum	MArt SPlb
	- 'Blue Carpet'	EPPr MSCN NHpl WGrn
	- ***glaucum***	see *S. hispanicum* var. *minus*
§	- var. ***minus***	ECho ECtt MMuc SEND SPlb WCot WMoo
§	- - 'Aureum'	ECho
	humifusum	NHpl
§	***hybridum***	XLum
	- 'Czar's Gold'	NGdn SIgm
	'Ice Ruffles' (v)	MAvo SPoG WFar
	'Indian Chief'	see *S.* (Herbstfreude Group) 'Herbstfreude'
	indicum var. ***yunnanense***	EShb
	integrifolium	see *Rhodiola integrifolia*
	ishidae	see *Rhodiola ishidae*
	'José Aubergine'PBR	CKno CMos EBee ECtt EPfP EWTr EWoo IPot LRHS MAvo MRav MTis MWat NCGa NDov NHol NLar NSti SCob SPoG WPGP
	'Joyce Henderson'	CDor CElw EAEE ELan EPfP LHop LRHS MCot MNrw MRav MTis NChi NLar SPer SRGP WBrk WCot WMoo WOld
	kamtschaticum ♀H5	ECho EDAr GJos
	- B&SWJ 10870	WCru
§	- var. ***ellacombeanum*** ♀H5	MMuc SEND WCot XLum
	- - B&SWJ 8853	WCru
§	- var. ***floriferum***	XSen
§	- - 'Weihenstephaner Gold'	CTri ECho ECtt EDAr ELan EPfP GJos GKev GMaP LPot MHer MMuc MRav NBir SPlb SPoG SRms XLum
	- var. ***kamtschaticum*** 'Variegatum' (v) ♀H5	CMea ECho EDAr EHoe ELan EPfP GCrg LRHS MHer MJak MMuc NHpl NRHS SBod SIgm SPoG SRms SRot SWvt XLum
	'Katharine's Gold' **new**	MNrw
	kirilovii	see *Rhodiola kirilovii*
	'Knight Rider'	EBee
	lanceolatum	NBre
	'Lime Zinger' (SunSparkler Series)	ECtt
	lineare 'Variegatum' (v)	SBch XLum
	'Little Dove'	SBch
§	***lydium***	CTri ECho MHer SFgr SPlb
	- 'Aureum'	see *S. hispanicum* var. *minus* 'Aureum'
	- 'Bronze Queen'	see *S. lydium*
I	'Marchants Best Red' ♀H7	ELon MNrw MRav SMHy SPhx WCot
	'Matrona' ♀H7	Widely available
	maweanum	see *S. acre* subsp. *neglectum* var. *majus*
	maximowiczii	see *S. aizoon* subsp. *maximowiczii*
	middendorffianum	ECho GCrg MBrN MHer MMuc SRms SRot WHoo XLum
§	***montanum***	MMuc
	moranense	MMuc XLum
	morganianum ♀H2	EBak EShb
	morrisonense B&SWJ 7078	WCru
	'Mr Goodbud'PBR ♀H7	CBct CBod CKno ECtt LRHS LSun MAsh MAvo MHol MNrw NBir NDov NEgg SAko SPoG WCot WTor
	'Munstead Purple' **new**	NAst
	'Munstead Red'	CBod CDor CWCL EBee ECha ECtt EHrv ELon EPfP GBin LRHS MAvo MNrw MRav MTis MWat NLar NRHS SBch SPer SPhx SPoG WHar WKif WMoo
	murale	see *S. album* subsp. *teretifolium* var. *murale*
	nevii misapplied	see *S. glaucophyllum*
	nevii ambig.	SPlb
	nicaeense	see *S. sediforme*
	obtusatum misapplied	see *S. oreganum*
§	***obtusatum*** A. Gray	NBro NSla
	obtusifolium var. ***listoniae***	EDAr
	ochroleucum	NBre WCot
	- subsp. ***montanum***	see *S. montanum*
	oppositifolium	see *S. spurium* 'Album'
§	***oreganum***	ECha ECho EDAr GAbr GCrg GKev GMaP MHer MHtn NBir SIgm SPlb SRms SRot XLum
	- 'Procumbens'	see *S. oreganum* subsp. *tenue*
§	- subsp. ***tenue***	NHol NRya NWad
§	***oregonense***	ECho LRHS MHer NRHS
	pachyclados	see *Rhodiola pachyclados*
	pachyphyllum	LAll
	palmeri	LTro MRav NBir SChr XLum
	'Parish Plum'	SBch
	pilosum	GKev WThu
	'Pink Dove'	SBch
	'Pinky'	EBee SPoG
§	***pluricaule***	ECho GCrg LRHS NRHS SPlb SRms
	'Pool Party'PBR (Party Hardy Series)	LRHS NLar
	populifolium	ECha GCal GJos IMou MHer MMuc NLar SPhx XLum
	praealtum	SChr SEND
	pulchellum	ECtt
	quinquefarium	see *S. brevifolium* var. *quinquefarium*
	'Red Cauli' ♀H7	Widely available
	'Red Rum'	GBin GWyn SPhx
	'Red Setter'	EBee WPGP
	'Red Star' **new**	MAvo
	reflexum L.	see *S. rupestre* L.
	- red-leaved **new**	NHpl
	rhodiola	see *Rhodiola rosea*

	rosea	see *Rhodiola rosea*
	rubroglaucum misapplied	see *S. oregonense*
	obtusatum Praeger	see *S. obtusatum* A. Gray
§	'Ruby Glow' ♀H5	Widely available
	'Ruby Port'	CSpe
§	***rupestre*** L.	ELan GJos MMuc MNHC SEND SPlb XLum
	- 'Angelina'	CKno CTal ECtt EPPr EWes IMou MAvo MHer NBir NDov NEoE NHol NWad SPoG SRGP WCot WGrn XLum
	- 'Blue Cushion' **new**	ESps LRHS NRHS
	- 'Green Cushion' **new**	LRHS NRHS
	- 'Monstrosum Cristatum'	NBir SMad WCot XLum
	- 'Yellow Cushion' **new**	LRHS NRHS
	ruprechtii	see *S. telephium* subsp. *ruprechtii*
	sarcocaule hort.	see *Crassula sarcocaulis*
	sarmentosum	ECho XLum
§	***sediforme***	EDAr GAbr MMuc SBrt SEND XSen
	- B&F MA 25	WCot
	- ***nicaeense***	see *S. sediforme*
	selskianum	GJos NBre NLar SBch XLum
	- 'Goldilocks'	GJos
	'September Ruby'	LRHS
	sexangulare	ELon EPot MHer MMuc NRya SEND SFgr SPlb SRms XLum
	sibiricum	see *S. hybridum*
	sieboldii	GPSL
	- 'Dragon'	MHCG
	- 'Mediovariegatum' (v) ♀H3	ECho EHoe GMcL LPot MHer MRav NWsh SPlb XLum
	'Silvermoon'	NWad
	spathulifolium	CTri ECha
	- Atropurpureum Group **new**	SRot
	- 'Aureum'	ECtt GKev WAbe
	- 'Cape Blanco' ♀H5	Widely available
	- 'Purpureum' ♀H5	CRos ECho ECtt EDAr EHoe ELan EPfP EPot ESps GAbr GKev GMaP GWyn LBee LPot LRHS MBel MHer MHtn NFav NHol NHpl NRHS NRya NWad SPlb SPoG WAbe WMoo XLum
	- subsp. ***yosemitense***	WTor
	spectabile ♀H7	CTri ELan EPfP GJos GMaP LRHS MCot MHer MRav NGdn SCob SPer SPlb SRms WBor WBrk WFar WSFF
	- Brilliant Group	CBar ESps LBMP MJak MSpe WHar
	- - 'Brilliant' ♀H7	CBcs CBod CSBt CTri EAEE ECha ECtt ELan EPfP LCro LRHS MAvo MGos MRav NFav NGdn NLar SCob SPer SPoG SWvt WFar WMoo
	- - 'Carmen'	NBir XLum
	- - 'Hot Stuff'	CAby ECtt ELan ELon EPfP LRHS LSRN NCou NPri SHil SPoG SPtp SRot WCot
	- - 'Lisa'	GBin GWyn MTPN NLar
	- - 'Meteor'	MRav MWat NLar SPhx
	- - 'Neon'	CKno EBee EPfP LRHS MAsh MAvo NDov
	- - 'Pink Fairy'	MNrw WHil
	- - 'Rosenteller'	CKno EBee GBin NBre NCGa
§	- - 'Septemberglut'	EAEE LRHS NBre XLum
	- - 'Steven Ward'	CKno EWes SRGP
	- 'Crystal Pink' PBR	LRHS MNrw NLar SBod SHil WHlf
	- 'Humile'	XLum
	- 'Iceberg'	CBod EBee ECha ECtt EHrv EPfP ESps EWTr GBin LRHS MCot MGos MRav NCGa NGdn SCob SPer SPhx SPtp SWvt WBrk WFar WMoo WSFF XLum
	- 'Nordlicht'	GWyn
	- 'Pink Chablis' (v)	WCot
	- September Glow	see *S. spectabile* (Brilliant Group) 'Septemberglut'
	- 'Stardust'	CRos CTri EBee EPfP GBin GMaP LCro LRHS LSou MRav MTis NCGa SGol SPer WFar XLum
	- 'Variegatum'	see *S. erythrostictum* 'Mediovariegatum'
	- Walberton's Pizazz	EPfP LRHS
	spinosum	see *Orostachys spinosa*
	spurium	ESps GJos MMuc SEND SRms XSen
§	- 'Album'	NRya XLum
	- 'Atropurpureum'	ECha WMoo XLum
	- 'Coccineum'	GJos MMuc SEND
	- 'Cream Split' **new**	EPot
	- Dragon's Blood	see *S. spurium* 'Schorbuser Blut'
	- 'Fuldaglut'	CTri ECho ECtt EHoe GCrg GMaP LRHS MNrw NRHS NRya WMoo WPnn
	- 'Green Mantle'	EBee ECha ECho EPfP LRHS
	- 'John Creech'	ECtt
	- Purple Carpet	see *S. spurium* 'Purpurteppich'
	- 'Purpureum'	SRms SRot
§	- 'Purpurteppich'	ECho ECtt GJos MJak MRav NBro NLar NWad SBod SRms SVen
	- 'Roseum'	SRms
	- 'Ruby Mantle'	GKev GMcL MSCN NBro NEoE SBch SPoG SRGP SWvt WMoo XLum
§	- 'Schorbuser Blut' ♀H5	CBod EAEE ECtt ELan EPau EPfP GJos GKev LRHS MCot MWat NBir NDov NRya NSla SPlb SRGP SRms WHoo WIce XLum
I	- 'Splendens Roseum'	XLum
	- 'Summer Glory'	NLar
§	- 'Tricolor' (v)	CTri EBee ECha ECho EHoe EPfP GJos GKev MHer MHtn MRav NAst NHol NRya NWad SPlb SPoG WMoo XLum
	- 'Variegatum'	see *S. spurium* 'Tricolor'
	- 'Voodoo'	ECtt EPfP EWes LRHS MBel MHer NBro NDov NGdn WTor XLum
	stefco	XLum
	stenopetalum	SPlb
§	- 'Douglasii'	MHer SRms
	'Stewed Rhubarb Mountain'	CBod CKno EAEE EBee ECha ECtt ELan EPfP LRHS MBNS MRav NLar SGbt WMoo
	stoloniferum	ECho
	stribrnyi	see *S. urvillei* Stribrnyi Group
	'Sunset Cloud'	EBee ECtt EWes GCal LPot MRav
	takesimense	XLum
	- B&SWJ 8493	WCru
	- B&SWJ 8518	WCru
	tatarinowii	WCot
	telephium	EWTr IFro NBir SRms WSFF XLum
§	- Atropurpureum Group	MRav NLar SWvt
	- - 'African Pearl'	GBin GWyn WCFE
	- - 'Arthur Branch'	EBee GBin GWyn LRHS
	- - 'Bon Bon'	LRHS MAvo MBNS MTis NLar SPoG
	- - 'Bressingham Purple'	EBee LRHS
	- - 'Chocolate'	EAEE EBee ECtt EPPr GPSL NLar
	- - 'Dark Knight'	EPfP LRHS SPoG
	- - 'El Cid'	EWes
	- - 'Karfunkelstein' ♀H7	CKno EBee ECha ECtt EPPr GBin GLog LCro MAvo MHol MTis MWat NBir NDov SPhx WCot XLum

- - 'Leonore Zuuntz'	NBre
- - 'Lynda et Rodney'	EWes
- - 'Lynda Windsor'	ECtt EPfP NLar NPnk SWvt
- - 'Möhrchen'	EHrv GMaP GMcL MHer MRav NGdn NLar NWsh SPhx WMoo
- - 'Picolette'	EAEE ECtt EPfP LRHS LSou MNrw MSCN NCGa NGdn SPoG WCot WMoo
- - 'Postman's Pride'PBR	CKno CWGN ECtt EPfP GBin LSou MNrw NGdn NQui
§ - - 'Purple Emperor' ♀H7	Widely available
- - 'Purple Moon'	SPhx
- - 'Ringmore Ruby'	EBee MHer MNrw SPhx WCot WPGP
- - 'Xenox'PBR ♀H7	CBct CWGN EAEE EBee ECtt EHoe EPfP GBin IPot LRHS MAvo MBNS MCot MNrw NLar SCob SPoG WCAu WPGP
- 'Coral Reef'PBR	EBee
- Emperor's Waves Group	ELan NGdn NWad
§ - subsp. ***fabaria***	ECtt MRav NWsh WCot
- - var. ***borderei***	CElw LPla SBch SPhx
- 'Jennifer'	EBee ECtt LLWG LSun MBel MPie NDov SBch WCot WHoo WRHF
- subsp. ***maximum*** 'Atropurpureum'	see *S. telephium* Atropurpureum Group
- - 'Gooseberry Fool'	CMea EBee ECGP ECtt ELan EPfP GMaP LRHS NAst SBch SPhx
- 'Moonlight Serenade'PBR	EBee ECtt EPfP LRHS
- 'Rainbow Xenox'PBR	LSou MAsh SCob
- 'Raspberry Truffle'	LBMP LRHS SDys
§ - subsp. ***ruprechtii***	CDor EAEE ECha ECtt EHoe EPPr EPed EPfP GMaP GMcL LRHS LSou MCot MRav NLar NSti SPer SPhx WMoo
- - 'Citrus Twist'	EBee ECtt EPed LRHS MRav NPnk
- - 'Hab Gray'	CSpe EBee ECtt EWes EWld LRHS NLar SAko SBch
- - 'Pink Dome'	ECha
- 'Strawberries and Cream'	CMac EBee ECha ECtt ELan ELon EPfP EShb EWTr GMaP LRHS MAvo MBNS MBel MMuc MRav NEoE NGdn NLar NWsh SGbt SPer SPhx WHil WMoo WPtf
- 'Sunkissed'PBR	ECtt NCGa NLar
- subsp. ***telephium***	GCra
- 'Twinkling Star'PBR	ECtt MNrw NLar
- 'Yellow Xenox'PBR	CBod EBee ECtt LRHS LSou NLar SCob
ternatum	ECho MHer
tetractinum 'Coral Reef'	CSpe MHer MHtn XLum
'Thundercloud'PBR	LBuc LRHS SCob SHil
'Thunderhead'	WHlf
trollii	see *Rhodiola trollii*
'Twinkle Stars'	EBee
urvillei Sartorianum Group	MHer XLum
§ - Stribrnyi Group	XLum
ussuriense	EPfP GBin GCal GPSL NBir SIgm
- 'Chuwangsan'	EWld WCru
valens	SPlb
'Veluwse Wakel'	ECtt GBin GWyn
'Vera Jameson' ♀H5	CMac CRos EAEE ECha ECtt EHoe ELan EPfP EShb GKev LRHS LSRN MBel MCot MRav NBir NHol NSti NWsh SBch SIgm SPer SWvt WHoo WMoo
viviparum	NLar
- B&SWJ 8662	WCru
Walberton's Pink Whisper	EPfP LRHS
'Washfield Purple'	see *S. telephium* (Atropurpureum Group) 'Purple Emperor'
'Weihenstephaner Gold'	see *S. kamtschaticum* var. *floriferum* 'Weihenstephaner Gold'
weinbergii	see *Graptopetalum paraguayense*
'Winky'	LSou
yezoense	see *S. pluricaule*
yunnanense	see *Rhodiola yunnanensis*

Seemannia see *Gloxinia*

Selaginella (*Selaginellaceae*)

apoda	CTsd LRHS NLos
braunii	CLAP WCot
erythropus var. ***sanguinea***	LRHS
helvetica	EBee IMou XLum
kraussiana ♀H2	CKel CLAP CTsd EDAr
- 'Aurea'	CBod CCCN ISha LRHS
- 'Bronsiana' **new**	NLos
- 'Brownii' ♀H2	CCCN ISha LRHS
- 'Gold Tips'	CCCN CKel ISha LRHS
lepidophylla	GKev SVic
martensii ♀H1b	CKel
- 'Jori' (v) **new**	NLos
moellendorfii	ISha LRHS
uncinata ♀H1b	CKel CLAP ISha LRHS

Selinum (*Apiaceae*)

CC 6869	EBee
KWJ 12281 from northern Vietnam	WCru
candollei HWJK 2329 **new**	WCru
carvifolium	CMac CSpe ELan GBin LEdu LHop LLWG SPhx SPtp WCAu
- PAB 2676	LEdu
cryptotaenium FMWJ 13250	WCru
- PAB 8948	LEdu
tenuifolium	see *S. wallichianum*
§ ***wallichianum*** ♀H7	Widely available
- CC 6869	GKev
- EMAK 886	EBee GPoy
- HWJK 2347	WCru
- PAB 3579	LEdu WPGP
- PAB 8969 **new**	LEdu WPGP
- WJC 13656 from Sikkim **new**	WCru

Selliera (*Goodeniaceae*)

radicans	GAbr GBin

Semele (*Asparagaceae*)

androgyna	CRHN WCot

Semiaquilegia (*Ranunculaceae*)

adoxoides double-flowered (d)	GKev
§ ***ecalcarata*** ♀H5	CSpe CWCL ECho EHrv GCal GKev MNrw NCGa NGdn NHpl SRms WHal
simulatrix	see *S. ecalcarata*
'Sugar Plum Fairy'	CSma EPfP LBuc LRHS NRHS SPoG

Semiarundinaria (*Poaceae*)

§ ***fastuosa*** ♀H4	CBcs CBod CEnt CJng CJun CTsd ENBC EPfP ERod EUJe IMou MMuc MWht SArc SEND SPlb
- var. ***viridis***	CEnt CJng ERod MWht SBig WCru
kagamiana	CJng ENBC EPfP IMou MMuc MWht SBig SEND
§ ***lubrica***	MWht
makinoi	CJng MWht

I	***maruyamana***	MWht
	nitida	see *Fargesia nitida*
§	***okuboi***	CEnt ERod MWht
	villosa	see *S. okuboi*
	yamadorii	CJng ERod MWht
	yashadake	CEnt CJng ERod MWht
	- f. ***kimmei***	CBod CEnt CJng ENBC EPfP ERod GMcL LCro LRHS MJak MMuc MWht NLar NRHS SBig SEND SPoG WMoo WPGP
I	- - 'Inversa'	CEnt

Semnanthe see *Erepsia*

Sempervivella see *Rosularia*

Sempervivum ✿ (*Crassulaceae*)

	from Picos de Europa, Spain new	LRHS NRHS
	from Sierra Nova	SFgr
	'Aalrika'	NMen
	'Aaroundina'	NMen
	'Abba'	CMea EDAr NMen WHal
	'Achalm' new	SFgr
	acuminatum	see *S. tectorum* var. *glaucum*
	'Adelaar'	NMen
	'Adelmoed'	NMen
	'Ageet'	NMen
	'Aglow'	MHom
	'Aladdin'	GEdr MSCN NMen SRms
	'Alaric'	NMen
	'Alchimist'	NMen XLum
	'Aldo Moro'	CTal EDAr LBee MHom NMen WIce XLum
	'Alenco'	NMen
	'Alesia'	NMen
	'Alfons-Roelands'	NMen
	'Alice'	MSCN
	allionii	see *Jovibarba allionii*
	'Allison'	SFgr
	'Alluring'	GAbr NMen
	'Alpha'	CMea LBee NMen SFgr SRms WHal XLum
	altum	CRos ECho LRHS MHom NMen NRHS SPlb XLum
	'Amanda'	EDAr MBrN NMen SFgr SRms WHoo
	'Ambergreen'	NMen
	andreanum	see *S. tectorum* var. *alpinum*
	'Andrenor'	NMen
	'Andrenor' sport	NMen
	'Apache' Haberer	NMen
	'Apollo'	SFgr XLum
	'Apple Blossom'	NMen
	'Apricot'	NMen
	arachnoideum ♀H5	Widely available
	- from Zermatt, Switzerland new	XLum
	- 'Ararat'	SDys
	- var. ***bryoides***	CRos ECho LLHF LRHS NRHS SRms
	- 'Clärchen'	CRos LRHS MSCN NRHS WAbe XLum
	- cristate	XLum
*	- ***densum***	EDAr EPPr WAbe
	- subsp. ***doellianum***	see *S. arachnoideum* subsp. *tomentosum* var. *glabrescens*
	- form No 1	ECho
	- 'Laggeri'	see *S. arachnoideum* subsp. *tomentosum* (C.B. Lehm. & Schnittsp.) Schinz & Thell.
	- 'Opitz'	NMen
	- 'Peña Prieta'	XLum
	- 'Red Papaver'	SFgr
	- 'Red Wings'	NMen SFgr XLum
	- 'Rheinkiesel' new	XLum
	- 'Rubin' new	CBod NHpl
	- 'Rubrum'	CRos ECho ELon EUJe GMaP LRHS NRHS SPlb XLum
	- subsp. ***tomentosum*** misapplied	see *S. × barbulatum* 'Hookeri'
	- subsp. ***tomentosum*** ambig.	ECho EPot GKev XLum
§	- subsp. ***tomentosum*** (C.B. Lehm & Schnittsp.) Schinz & Thell. ♀H5	ECho GCrg LRHS MSCN NPer NRHS NWad SFgr SPlb SRms WAbe
§	- - var. ***glabrescens***	SDys XLum
	- - 'Minus'	LRHS NRHS
§	- - 'Stansfieldii'	CRos ECho EPPr LRHS NRHS SIgm WHal
§	- 'White Christmas'	MHer NMen
	arachnoideum* × *montanum	see *S. × barbulatum*
	arachnoideum* × *nevadense	SDys
	arachnoideum* × *pittonii	NMen WAbe
	arenarium	see *Jovibarba arenaria*
	'Arlet'	EDAr
	'Arondina'	NMen
	'Aross'	CMea NMen
	'Arrowheads Red'	NMen
	'Artist'	NMen SFgr
	'Ashes of Roses'	MHom MSCN NHol NMen WAbe XLum
	'Astrid'	NMen
	'Atlantic'	SRms
	atlanticum	CTal MHom MMuc NMen NSla SFgr SRot
	- from Oukaïmeden, Morocco	NMen SRms
	- 'Edward Balls'	NMen SDys SFgr
	'Atlantis' ambig.	NMen
	'Atlantis' Adams	NWad
	'Atropurpureum' ambig.	EDAr GEdr MBrN NMen SFgr
	'Atropurpureum' Hemlich form	NMen
	'Attraction'	NMen
	'Aureum'	see *Greenovia aurea*
	'Averil'	NMen
	'Aymon Correvon'	NMen
	'Baby Skrocki'	NMen
	balcanicum	CTal EDAr NMen SRms XLum
	ballsii	ECho LLHF LRHS NMen NRHS SRms
	- from Kambeecho, Greece	MHom
	- from Smólikas, Greece	MHom NMen
	- from Tschumba Petzi, Greece	MHom SDys XLum
	'Banderi'	NMen
	'Banjo'	NMen
	'Banyan'	CRos CTal ECho LRHS NMen NRHS
§	× ***barbulatum***	LBee NMen SDys WHoo
§	- 'Hookeri'	CTri GCrg WAbe WHoo XLum
	'Baronesse' new	NMen
	'Bascour Zilver'	CMea LBee MSCN SRms WHal
	'Be Mine'	MSCN
	'Beatles Memory' new	NMen
	'Beaute'	NMen
	'Bedazzled'	NMen
	'Bedivere'	LBee NMen SRms
	'Bedivere Crested'	NMen
*	'Bedley Hi'	MHom

	'Bella Donna'	MHom
	'Bella Meade'	EDAr NMen SFgr SRms
	'Bellotts Pourpre'	NMen
	'Bennerbroek'	NMen
	'Bernstein'	EDAr MSCN NMen NWad SFgr WHal XLum
	'Beta'	MHom NMen WAbe XLum
	'Bethany'	CMea NMen NWad SFgr WHal
	'Bianca' **new**	NMen
	'Bicolor' ambig.	EPfP
	'Big Slipper'	NMen
	'Bijou'	NMen
	'Birchmaier'	NMen
	'Bitter Chocolate'	SFgr
	'Black Beauty'	NMen
	'Black Knight'	CRos ECho LRHS MHer NRHS SPlb SRms WHal
	'Black Mini'	GCrg GKev NBir NMen SRms
	'Black Mountain'	GKev LBee NMen
	'Black Rose' **new**	NMen
	'Black Velvet'	NMen
	'Blood Tip'	CMea CRos CTal ECho ELon EPfP GAbr GCra GKev LRHS LSun MHer MHtn MMuc MSCN NHol NMen NRHS NRya NWad SEND SPlb SPoG SRms WHal WHoo
	'Bloodgood'	ECho
	'Bloody Goose'	NMen
	'Bloody Mary' **new**	SFgr
	'Blue Bird' **new**	NMen
	'Blue Boy'	CTal ECho ELon EPPr GAbr LBee LRHS MSCN NMen NRHS SFgr SRms
	'Blue Knight' **new**	NMen
	'Blue Time'	EPot LLHF SFgr WHoo XLum
	'Blush'	EDAr NMen
	'Boissieri'	see *S. tectorum* subsp. *tectorum* 'Boissieri'
	'Bold Chick'	NMen
	'Bombardier'	EDAr
	'Booth's Red'	NMen
	borisii	see *S. ciliosum* var. *borisii*
	borissovae	EPot MHom NMen SDys
	'Boromir'	EDAr NMen XLum
	'Boule de Neige'	GCrg GEdr NMen NRya
	'Bowles's Variety'	NMen
	'Braune Maus'	SFgr
I	'Braunella'	NMen
	'Britta'	SDys
	'Brock'	CRos ECho LLHF LRHS MHom NMen NRHS SRms
	'Bronco' ♀H5	CRos CTal ECho ELon GAbr GBin GCrg LBee LRHS MHom MMuc NHol NMen NRHS NRya NWad SEND SRms WCot WPGP WRHF XLum
	'Bronze Beauty'	EDAr
	'Bronze Pastel'	EDAr MHom MSCN NHpl NMen NSla SFgr SRms SRot
	'Brown Owl'	ECho SRms
	'Brown Web'	NMen
	'Brownii'	NMen
	'Brunette'	ECho GAbr
	'Brunhilde'	NMen
	bungeanum hort.	NMen
	'Bunny Girl'	SFgr
	'Burgundy'	NMen
	'Burgundy Velvet'	NMen
	'Burnatii'	see *S. montanum* subsp. *burnatii*
	'Burnished Bronze'	NMen
	'Butterbur'	NMen
	'Butterfly'	NMen
	'Café'	ELon MSCN NHol NMen SFgr SRms
*	***calabricum***	NHol
	calcareum	CBod CMea CRos CTal ECho ECtt EUJe GKev LBMP LRHS MAsh MMuc NBro NHol NHpl NMen NRHS SArc SEND SPlb SPoG SRms SRot XLum
	- GDJ 92.16 from Petite Ceüse, France	SRms
	- from Cleizé, France	see *S. calcareum* 'Limelight'
	- from Col Bayard, France	GAbr NMen
	- from Colle St Michel, France	SRms
	- from Petite Ceüse, France	SRot
	- from Queyras, France	NMen
	- from Triora, Italy	NMen
	- 'Benz'	SDys
*	- 'Bicolor' **new**	SFgr
	- 'Extra' ♀H5	CRos CTal GAbr GEdr MSCN NMen SFgr SRms SRot
	- 'Greenii'	CRos ECho ECtt GKev LRHS MSCN NMen NRHS SPlb SRms
§	- 'Grigg's Surprise'	NMen SPlb
	- 'Guillaumes' ♀H5	CRos CTal LBee LRHS MSCN NMen NRHS SFgr SRms SRot WHoo
§	- 'Limelight'	CMea CRos EDAr LBee LRHS NMen NRHS WHal WHoo
	- 'Monstrosum'	see *S. calcareum* 'Grigg's Surprise'
	- 'Mrs Giuseppi'	CTal ECho GAbr GCrg GEdr LBee LSun MHer NHpl NMen SBch SFgr SRms WAbe WIce XLum
	- 'Nigricans'	NMen
	- 'Pale Face' **new**	SFgr
	- 'Pink Pearl'	MSCN NMen SDys SFgr SPlb XLum
	- 'Sir William Lawrence' ♀H5	CMea CRos ECho ECtt EDAr LBee LRHS MMuc NMen NRHS SFgr SRms WAbe WHal WHoo WThu XLum
	'Campagha' **new**	NMen
	'Canada Kate'	NMen
	'Cancer'	XLum
	'Candy Floss'	NMen
	cantabricum	MMuc NMen XLum
	- from Navafria, Spain	NMen
	- from Ticeros	XLum
	- from Valvanera, Spain	NMen
	- subsp. ***cantabricum*** from Leitariegos, Spain	GAbr MHom
I	- subsp. ***gredense*** GDJ 95.04	CTal
	- subsp. ***guadarramense***	see *S. vicentei* subsp. *paui*
	- - from Pico del Lobo, Spain, No 1	SRms SRot
	- subsp. ***urbionense***	GEdr SRms
	'Caramel'	NMen
	'Carmen'	GAbr NMen SFgr
	'Carneum'	NMen
	'Carnival'	NMen
	'Casablanca' **new**	NMen
	'Caspara' **new**	NMen
	caucasicum	CRos LRHS MHom NMen NRHS XLum
	'Cavo Doro'	NMen SFgr
	'Celon'	NMen
	'Centennial'	NMen
	charadzeae	LBee XLum
	'Chartbury'	EDAr
	'Cherry Frost'	ECho NHol NMen XLum
	'Cherry Glow'	see *Jovibarba heuffelii* 'Cherry Glow'
	'Cherry Tart'	SPlb
	'Chilli Pepper'	MSCN

'Chocolate'	NHpl WAbe
'Cholie' **new**	GKev
× *christii* 'Peter Lotter' **new**	NMen
'Christmas Time'	SFgr
ciliosum ♀H4	ECho NMen NRya SPlb
- from Alí Butús, Bulgaria	SDys
§ - var. ***borisii***	CFis EPPr EPfP GCal MHtn NMen NRya WAbe WHal
- var. ***ciliosum*** × ***ciliosum*** var. ***borisii***	CTri
- var. ***galicicum***	CTal
- - 'Mali Hat'	NMen
ciliosum × ***grandiflorum***	NMen
'Cindy'	SRms
'Circlet'	NMen
'Claey's Fluweel' **new**	NMen
'Clara Noyes'	NMen
'Clare'	MHer NMen SFgr
'Cleveland Morgan'	MHom NMen XLum
'Climax' ambig.	EPfP MHom
'Climax' Ford	NMen
'Cobweb Capers'	MHom NMen
'Cobweb Centres'	NMen
'Colchicum'	SRms
'Collecteur Anchisi'	CTal SDys SFgr
'Commander Hay' ♀H5	CTal EDAr EPfP EWes GCra GKev MHom MSCN NHpl NMen NPer NRya SRGP SRms WHal XLum
'Comte de Congae'	NMen
'Concorde'	LBee
'Congo'	NMen XLum
'Corio'	NMen
'Corona'	NMen
'Coronet'	NMen
'Corsair'	CTal ELon EPPr GEdr GKev MBrN MMuc SFgr WOld
'Cotopaxi'	NMen
'Crimson King'	SFgr
'Crimson Velvet'	CMea GCrg LBee XLum
'Cripello' **new**	NMen
§ 'Crispyn' ♀H5	CRos CTal LBee LRHS MHer MHom MMuc MSCN NMen NRHS SEND SFgr
'Croton'	NMen
'Crucify'	NMen
'Cupream'	NMen SRms
'Cyclops' **new**	NMen
'Dakota'	EDAr NMen SFgr
'Dallas'	GCrg NMen SRms
'Damask'	LBee MSCN NMen SFgr
'Dancer's Veil'	NMen
'Darjeeling'	NMen
'Dark Beauty'	CMea CRos ECho LRHS MSCN NHol NRHS SFgr WAbe WCot WHal
'Dark Cloud'	LBee WHoo XLum
'Dark Point'	MHom MSCN NMen SFgr
'Darkie'	SFgr
davisii	NMen
'De Kardijk'	NMen
'Deep Fire'	NMen SRms
× ***degenianum***	NMen SFgr XLum
'Delta' ♀H5	MHom NMen WHoo
densum	see *S. tectorum*
'Devil's Teeth'	MSCN
'Devon Glow'	MSCN
'Diane'	NMen
'Diavolo'	NMen
'Director Jacobs'	EDAr NHpl NMen SFgr
'Dolle Dina's'	NMen
dolomiticum	NMen XLum
dolomiticum × ***montanum***	NBro NMen SFgr
'Donarrose'	NMen SFgr
'Dornröschen'	NMen
'Downland Queen'	NMen
'Dr Fritz Köhlein'	NMen
'Dragoness'	NMen
'Dream Catcher'	NMen
'Dyke'	CTri EDAr GCrg NMen SFgr WHal
dzhavachischvilii	NMen XLum
'Edge of Night'	NMen
'Edwardine' **new**	NMen
'Eefje'	NMen
'El Greco'	NMen
'El Toro'	MHom MSCN NHpl NMen
'Electra' **new**	GBin
'Elva'	NMen
'Elvis'	MHom NMen SFgr
'Emerald Giant'	SFgr
'Emerson's Giant'	NMen
'Emmchen'	NMen SFgr
'Engle's'	CMea CRos CTri ECho GCrg GKev LRHS MHer MMuc MSCN NMen NRHS SEND SFgr SPlb SRms WHal
'Engle's 13-2'	NMen
'Engle's Rubrum'	CTal LBee NMen
'Eos' **new**	NMen
erythraeum	ECho LLHF LRHS MHom NHpl NMen NRHS SPlb SRms WHal
- from Mesta Valley, Bulgaria	NMen
- from Pirin, Bulgaria	NMen
- 'Red Velvet'	NMen
'Essence of Lime'	SFgr
'Eureka'	NMen
'Excalibur'	NMen
'Exhibita'	EPPr NMen SDys
'Exorna'	EDAr MHom NMen SFgr
'Fair Lady'	MHom NMen
'Fairy'	NMen
'Fame'	SPlb
'Faramir'	NMen
'Fat Jack'	NMen
× ***fauconnetii***	CTal EDAr
- 'Rubellum'	NMen
'Feldmaier'	NMen
'Fernwood'	CTal NMen
'Festival'	EDAr NMen
'Fiery Furness'	NMen
'Fiesta' ambig.	NMen WHal
fimbriatum	see *S.* × *barbulatum*
'Finerpointe'	NMen
'Fire Glint'	GCrg GEdr NMen SRms
'Firgrove Big Bronze'	SFgr
'Firgrove Early Riser' **new**	NMen
'Firgrove Silver'	SFgr
'First Try'	NMen
flagelliforme	XLum
'Flaming Heart'	EDAr MBrN NMen
'Flamingo'	NMen
'Flanders Passion'	EWes LBee NMen SRms
'Flasher'	GCrg NMen
'Fluweel'	MSCN NMen
'Forden'	MSCN NMen SFgr
'Ford's Amiability'	SDys
'Ford's Giant'	XLum
'Ford's Shadows'	SDys
'Ford's Spring'	NMen
'Freckles'	NMen
'Fronika'	NMen
'Frosty'	NMen SFgr SRms

	'Fuego' ♀H5	LRHS MHom NMen NRHS SFgr
	'Fuji'	NMen
	× ***funckii***	EDAr MBrN NMen XLum
	'Fuzzy Wuzzy'	EDAr NMen
	'Galahad'	NMen
	'Gallivarda' ♀H5	LRHS MSCN NMen NRHS SFgr SRms
	'Gambol'	NWad
	'Gamma'	LBee NMen
	'Garnet'	NMen
	'Gay Jester'	CTal CTri NMen SFgr WHoo
	'Gazelle'	XLum
	'Georgette'	NMen XLum
	'Georgia Rowan'	NMen
	'Gilosum'	EDAr
	'Ginnie's Delight'	NMen
	'Gipsy'	NMen
	giuseppii ♀H5	ECho LBee LRHS MMuc NMen NRHS SRms
	- from Coriscao, Spain	CTal LBee
	- from Peña Espigüete, Spain	SDys SRms
	'Gizmo'	NMen SFgr
	'Glaucum'	see *S. tectorum* var. *glaucum*
	globiferum	XLum
	subsp. ***globiferum*** 'Minor'	
	- subsp. ***hirtum***	SFgr
	'Gloriosum' ambig.	EDAr MSCN NMen SFgr
	'Glowing Embers'	MHom NMen SFgr WHal XLum
	'Godaert'	MMuc SEND XLum
	'Goldie'	NMen
	'Granada'	EDAr NMen
	'Granat'	GBin GWyn LBee MHer NMen SRms XLum
	'Granby'	LBee SDys
	grandiflorum	CTal NMen WThu XLum
	- 'Fasciatum'	NMen
	'Grannie's Favourite'	NMen
	'Grapetone'	MHom NMen SDys WHal
	'Graupurpur'	XLum
	'Green Apple'	GAbr MHom NMen SDys
	'Green Caro' **new**	NMen
	'Green Disk'	SRms
	'Green Dragon'	CRos CTal ECho LRHS MSCN NMen NRHS SRms
	'Green Gables'	EDAr
	'Green Ice'	NMen SFgr
	'Greenwich Time'	EDAr NMen
*	***greigii***	MSCN
	'Grey Dawn'	CRos ECho LRHS MHom NMen NRHS SRms XLum
	'Grey Ghost'	NMen
	'Grey Lady'	NMen
	'Grey Owl'	CRos ECho LRHS MSCN NMen NRHS SFgr SRms
	'Grey Velvet'	LBee NMen
	'Greyfriars'	CMea CRos CTal EDAr LBee LRHS MSCN NMen NRHS SFgr WOld
	'Greyolla'	NMen
	'Grünschnabel'	XLum
	'Gulle Dame'	CMea MHom NMen
	'Gumby' **new**	NMen
	'Gwiazda' **new**	GBin
	'Halemaumau'	NMen
I	'Hall's Hybrid'	MSCN NBro NMen
	'Happy'	CTal NMen SFgr SRms
	'Harriet' **new**	NMen
	'Hart'	NMen
	'Havana'	NMen
	'Havendijks Pride' **new**	NMen
	'Hayling'	ECho LRHS NMen NRHS NWad SRms XLum
	'Heigham Red'	CRos ECho EPPr GKev LBee LRHS NMen NRHS SRms WIce
	'Heike'	NMen
	'Helen'	EDAr GEdr
	'Heliotroop'	NMen SDys SRot
	helveticum	see *S. montanum*
	'Hermann Näpfel'	NMen
	'Hester'	ECho MBrN NBro NMen
	'Hey-hey'	CTal ECho ELon EPot LBee LRHS MBrN NMen NRHS SPlb WCot XLum
	'Hidde'	NMen SFgr SPlb
	'Hirsutum'	see *Jovibarba allionii*
	hirtum	see *Jovibarba hirta*
	'Honymoon' **new**	NMen
	'Hookeri'	see *S.* × ***barbulatum*** 'Hookeri'
	'Hopi'	NMen
	'Hortulanus Smit'	XLum
	'Hot Boyz'	NMen
	'Hot Peppermint'	NMen
	'Hullabaloo'	EDAr NMen SFgr
	'Hurricane'	GCrg NMen
	'Ice Berry'	SFgr
	'Icicle'	CMea ECho ELon LRHS MSCN NBro NHol NMen NRHS SRms
	imbricatum	see *S.* × ***barbulatum***
	'Impact' **new**	NMen
	'Imperial'	MHom NMen SPlb
	'Infinity'	SFgr
	'Inge'	see *Jovibarba heuffelii* 'Inge'
	ingwersenii	CTal MHom NMen XLum
	ingwersenii × ***pumilum***	NMen SFgr SRms
	'Iophon'	LBee
	iranicum	NMen
	'Irazu'	CTal ECho EPot GAbr GCrg LRHS MSCN NMen NRHS SDys SFgr SRms
	'Irene'	SFgr
	'Isaac Dyson'	SDys SFgr SRot
	'Isabelle'	NMen
	italicum	MHom XLum
	'Itchen'	NMen
	'Ivonne'	NMen
	'Iwo'	NMen SFgr
	'Jack Frost'	NBro NMen SFgr XLum
	'Jacquette'	NMen
	'Jadestern'	NMen
	'Janis' **new**	NMen
	'Jelly Bean'	MSCN NMen SFgr
	'Jet Stream' ♀H5	ECho ELon LRHS MHom MSCN NMen NRHS SDys SPlb SRms
	'Jewel Case'	CTal ECho LRHS NMen NRHS
I	'John Hobbs seedling No. 2'	NMen
	'John T' × 'Saffron'	NMen
	'Jolly Green Giant'	MHom NMen
	'Jo's Spark'	NMen
	'Jubilee'	CMea ECho EDAr ELan GEdr MAsh MHer NMen SFgr XLum
	'Jubilee Tricolor'	GCrg GEdr NHol NMen SFgr WAbe
	'Jungle Fires'	CMea ELon NMen SDys SRms WHoo
	'Jungle Shadows'	EDAr NMen NWad XLum
	'Jupiter'	GKev XLum
	'Jurrina'	NMen
	'Justine's Choice'	NMen SFgr SRms
	'Kalinda'	MHom
	'Kappa'	CTri NBro NMen SDys SRot
	'Katmai'	NMen SFgr

'Keiko'	NMen
'Kelly Jo'	ECho NBro SFgr
'Kelut'	NMen
'Kermit'	MHom NMen
'Kiara'	NMen
'Kibo'	NMen
'Kidlington' **new**	NMen
'Kim'	NMen
'Kimba'	NMen
'Kimble'	NMen
'Kimono'	NMen NWad
kindingeri	MHom NMen XLum
'King George'	CTal CTri GKev LBee MMuc NMen SEND SFgr SRms WHal WHoo XLum
'King Lear'	GBin
'Kip'	CMea NMen
'Kismet'	NMen
'Knight Hawk' **new**	NMen
'Koko Flanel'	CTal NMen SFgr
'Korspel Beauty' **new**	NMen
'Korspel Prince'	NMen
'Korspel Sport' **new**	NMen
'Korspelsegietje'	NMen SRms
kosaninii	NMen SFgr
- from Koprivnik, Slovenia	MSCN NMen WAbe XLum
- 'Hepworth'	SPlb
'Krakeling'	NMen
'Kramer's Spinrad'	CMea CTal EPPr GAbr GEdr GKev LBee MBel NMen SPlb SRms WHoo
'Krankii' **new**	XLum
'Krater'	NMen
'Lady Kelly'	CMea
'Lancer' **new**	NMen
'Laura Lee'	MMuc NMen SEND
'Lavender and Old Lace'	ECho EPot LBee LRHS MSCN NMen NRHS SPlb SRms WIce XLum
'Le Congai'	NMen
'Legolas'	NMen
'Leneca'	NMen
'Lennik's Glory'	see *S.* 'Crispyn'
'Lennik's Glory No.2'	NMen
'Lennik's Sport' **new**	XLum
'Lentezon'	SFgr
'Leocadia's Nephew'	NMen
leucanthum	XLum
'Lilac Queen'	NMen
'Lilac Time' ♀H5	CMea CTal ECho ELon EPPr GAbr LRHS MBrN MHer MSCN NMen NRHS SFgr SPlb SRms WHal XLum
'Limbo'	NMen
'Lion King'	CTal MSCN NMen SFgr
'Lioness'	NMen
'Lipari'	WCot XLum
'Lipstick'	NMen
'Little Coffee Cup'	SFgr
'Little Flirt'	MSCN
'Lively Bug'	ECho EDAr EPPr LBee LRHS MSCN NMen NRHS SDys SRms XLum
'Lloyd Praeger'	see *S. montanum* subsp. *stiriacum* 'Lloyd Praeger'
'Long Shanks'	MSCN
'Lonzo'	NMen SRms
'Lord Alan'	GKev NMen
'Lord Morton'	NMen
'Louisse-Marie'	NMen
'Lovely Roset'	NMen
'Lucy Liu'	NMen
'Ludmila' **new**	NMen
'Lynn's Choice'	GAbr NMen NWad SFgr WHal
macedonicum	NMen SPlb SRms XLum
'Madeleine'	SFgr
'Magic Spell'	NMen
'Magical'	NMen
'Magnificum'	NMen SFgr XLum
'Mahogany'	CTal CTri ECho EDAr GKev LBee MHer MSCN NHol NMen SFgr SRms WHal XLum
'Maigret'	GCrg NMen SFgr
'Majanka' **new**	NMen
'Majestic'	LBee NMen
'Malby's Hybrid'	see *S.* 'Reginald Malby'
'Maria Laach'	GCrg NMen
'Marijntje'	NMen
'Marjorie Newton'	NMen
'Marland Ruby'	NMen
'Marmalade'	NMen
§ ***marmoreum***	ECho EPot LBee LRHS NMen NRHS SRms WHal
- from Börzöny, Hungary **new**	XLum
- from Kanzan Gorge, Bulgaria	XLum
- from Okol, Albania	NMen
- 'Brunneifolium'	CTal LBee NMen XLum
- subsp. ***marmoreum*** var. ***dinaricum***	MHer NMen
§ - - 'Rubrifolium'	XLum
- monstrose **new**	MSCN
'Marshall'	NMen
'Mary-Beth' **new**	NMen
'Matthew's Day Dream'	GKev
'Mauna Kea'	NMen
'Mauvine'	NMen XLum
'Mayfair'	EDAr NMen
'Medallion'	NMen
'Meelah'	NMen
'Meisse'	ECho NMen
'Melanie'	MBrN NMen
'Mercury'	ECho GCrg LRHS NBro NMen NRHS SRms
'Merlin'	MSCN NMen
mettenianum	NMen
'Mickey Mouse' **new**	NMen
'Midas'	CTal ECho LRHS NMen NRHS SFgr
'Minaret'	NMen
'Mini Frost'	NMen
'Minuet'	NMen
'Mira'	GBin MHol
'Mixed Spice'	CMea NMen
'Moerkerk's Merit'	CTal LRHS NMen NRHS XLum
'Mohair'	NMen
'Mona Lisa'	NMen
'Mondstein'	GKev MSCN
'Montage'	NMen
§ ***montanum***	MHtn XLum
- from Haute-Loire, France **new**	XLum
- from Mont Aigoual, France **new**	XLum
- from Monte Tirone, Italy	LBee
- from the Pyrenees **new**	XLum
- from Vallée d'Estaing, France **new**	XLum
§ - subsp. ***burnatii***	MHom NMen
- 'Caesar'	MSCN
- subsp. ***carpaticum*** 'Cmiral's Yellow'	GKev WAbe WFar
- 'Rubrum'	see *S.* 'Red Mountain'
- subsp. ***stiriacum***	EPot NMen SFgr SRms XLum
- - from Mauterndorf, Austria	NMen

§ - - 'Lloyd Praeger' CTal LBee NMen SDys SFgr
montanum* × *tectorum NMen
var. ***boutignyanum***
'More Honey' NMen
'Morning Glow' NMen WHal
'Mount Hood' ECho ELon LRHS NMen NRHS SRms WHal
'Mount Skippet' new NMen
'Mount Usher' NMen
'Mulberry Wine' LBee NMen SFgr SRms WHoo
'Mystic' MBrN NMen
'Naemi' NMen
'Neon' NMen
'Neptune' SFgr
* ***netaginatum*** new XLum
nevadense CTal NMen SRms
'New Rose' new XLum
'Nico' NMen NWad SRms
'Night Raven' NMen
'Nigrum' see *S. tectorum* 'Nigrum'
'Niobe' NMen SFgr WHal
'Nocturno' new XLum
'Noir' EDAr GKev LRHS MSCN NBro NMen NRHS XLum
'Norbert' CTal EDAr GEdr NMen SRms XLum
'Nörtofts Beauty' NMen
'Nouveau Pastel' CFis CMea NMen WHal XLum
'Oberon' new NMen
'Octet' NMen
octopodes NBir XLum
- var. ***apetalum*** CTal EPPr MSCN NMen SRms WHoo
'Oddity' GBin MBrN MHer MHtn NMen WHal
'Ohio Burgundy' ECho LRHS MSCN NMen NRHS SRms WAbe
'Old Rose' NMen SFgr
'Olivette' NMen
'Olivine' SFgr
'Omega' NMen
'Ornatum' MHer MHom WAbe WHal
ossetiense CTal EDAr NMen XLum
'Othello' ♀H5 CTri EPfP GCra GKev NBir NMen WCot WPGP XLum
'Pachamama' new NMen
'Pacific Charm' NMen
'Pacific Devils Food' new NMen
'Pacific Hazy Embers' new NMen
'Pacific Hep' NMen
'Pacific Opal' NMen
'Pacific Purple Shadows' NMen
'Pacific Sexy' new NMen
'Pacific Spring Frost' SFgr
'Pacific Sunset' new NMen
'Pacific Thunder' new NMen
'Pacific Velveteen' SFgr
'Packardian' NMen NWad SFgr
'Painted Lady' NMen
'Palissander' EDAr NMen XLum
'Pallas' new XLum
'Pam Wain' MHom NMen
'Passionata' NMen SFgr
'Pastel' MHer SFgr
patens see *Jovibarba heuffelii*
'Patrician' LBee SRms
'Pavilion' new NMen
'Peggy' NMen
'Pekinese' CTal ECho EDAr GEdr LRHS MBrN NBro NMen NRHS SRms XLum
'Peridot' SFgr
'Peterson's Ornatum' SDys
'Petsy' NMen SFgr SRms
'Phoebe' NMen
'Pilatus' GAbr LRHS NRHS SRms XLum
'Pine Cone' NMen SFgr
'Pineapple Punch' SFgr
'Pink Astrid' NMen
'Pink Cloud' NMen
'Pink Delight' MSCN
'Pink Flamingoes' NMen
'Pink Grapefruit' new NMen
'Pink Lemonade' MHom NMen
'Pink Mist' SRms
'Pink Puff' MHom NMen SFgr
'Pippin' CMea CTal NMen SRms
pittonii ♀H5 CMea ECho NMen WHal XLum
'Pixie' NMen SFgr
'Plum Frosting' MSCN SFgr
'Plum Mist' NWad
'Plumb Rose' NMen
'Pluto' LBee NMen XLum
'Polaris' GBin MHom NMen
'Poldark' NMen
'Ponderosa' NMen
I 'Powellii' NMen
'Prairie Sunset' NMen SFgr
'President Arsac' XLum
'Probus' NMen
'Procton' GCrg NMen
'Proud Zelda' EDAr GEdr MSCN NMen
'Průhonice' NMen
'Pseudo-ornatum' LBee SRms
pulchellum new XLum
'Pumaros' SDys
pumilum ECho GKev LRHS NMen NRHS SRms
- from Techensis, Caucasus Mountains SRms
- 'Sopa' MSCN
'Purdy' MHom NHpl NMen WAbe
'Purdy's 50-6' NMen
'Purdy's 70-40' NMen
'Purdy's Big Red' NMen
'Purple Beauty' EPot GKev NMen
'Purple Dazzler' NMen
'Purple Haze' new NMen
'Purple King' CMea MHom SDys
'Purple Passion' NMen
'Purple Queen' ECho EDAr ELon EPPr LRHS NMen NRHS SFgr SRms
'Purple Shadows' new NMen
'Purple Violet' new NMen
'Pygmalion' NMen
'Quax' new NMen
'Queen Amalia' see *S. reginae-amaliae*
'Quintessence' MSCN NMen SRms
'Racey' SFgr
'Ramses' SDys
'Raspberry Ice' CMea GKev LBee MSCN NBro NHpl NMen
'Rauer Kulm' NMen
'Rauhreif' ECtt XLum
'Ravenheart' new MSCN
'Rebecca' new GKev
'Red Ace' GCrg GEdr MBel NBro NEoE NMen SFgr
'Red Beam' LRHS NMen NRHS
'Red Chief' GKev XLum
'Red Chips' EDAr MHom
'Red Delta' NBir NMen SFgr WCot WPGP

	'Red Devil'	ECho ELon LLHF LRHS NMen NRHS SFgr SPlb SRms WHoo
	'Red Knight'	NMen
	'Red Lion'	NMen SFgr
§	'Red Mountain'	LBee LSun MMuc NMen SRms
	'Red Pink'	CMea NMen
	'Red Pluche'	NMen
	'Red Robin'	EDAr NMen
	'Red Shadows'	LBee
	'Red Spider'	EPot GCrg MHom NBro NMen
	'Red West'	NMen
	'Regal'	NMen
	reginae	see *S. reginae-amaliae*
§	***reginae-amaliae***	GKev LRHS NMen NRHS SRms XLum
	- from Kambeecho, Greece, No 2	SDys
	- from Sarpun, Turkey	NMen SDys
§	'Reginald Malby'	CTri ECho LRHS NMen NRHS SFgr SRms
	'Reinhard' ♀H5	CMea CTal ECho EDAr ELon EPot GCrg GEdr GKev LRHS MAsh MBrN MHer MSCN NHpl NMen NRHS NRya SPlb SRms WHal WHoo
	'Remus'	ELan NMen SFgr
	'Rex'	NMen
	'Rhône'	LBee NMen
	'Rhubarb Crumble'	SFgr
	'Rich 'n' Fruity'	MSCN
	'Rio de Janeiro' **new**	NMen
	'Risque'	LBee
	'Rita Jane'	MHom NMen SFgr
	'Robin'	GCrg NBro NHol NMen XLum
	'Ronny'	NMen
	'Roosemaryn'	EDAr
	'Rosa Mädchen'	NMen
	× ***roseum***	NMen
	'Rosie'	CMea ECho ELon EPot GEdr GMaP LBee LRHS MAsh MMuc MSCN NHol NMen NRHS SRms WHal WHoo WIce
	'Rotkopf' ♀H5	CTal LRHS MSCN NMen NRHS NWad XLum
	'Rotmantel'	NMen
	'Rotund'	GEdr MSCN
	'Rouge'	NMen
	'Royal Opera'	EDAr NMen
	'Royal Ruby'	GCrg
	'Royale'	SFgr
	'Rubellum Mahogany'	SFgr
	'Rubikon Improved'	NMen
	'Rubin'	CBod CMea CTal CTri EPfP GKev LBMP MAsh MMuc NBir NEgg NHpl NMen SPoG SRms WAbe WIce XLum
I	'Rubra Ash'	NMen
I	'Rubra Ray'	EDAr MMuc NMen SEND
	'Rubrifolium'	see *S. marmoreum* subsp. *marmoreum* 'Rubrifolium'
*	'Ruby Glow'	EDAr
	'Ruby Heart'	EDAr
	'Rule Britannia' **new**	LRHS NRHS
	'Russian River'	WHoo
	'Rusty'	SFgr
	ruthenicum	CTal ECho EPPr LLHF LRHS MHom NRHS NRya SRms XLum
	- 'Regis-Fernandii'	XLum
	'Saga'	MHom
	'Samwise'	NMen
	'Sando'	NMen
	'Sanford's Hybrid'	NMen
	'Santis'	GKev NMen
	'Sarah'	EDAr NMen
	'Sarotte'	NMen
	'Sassy Frass'	NMen
	'Saturn'	GEdr MSCN NMen SRms
	schlehanii	see *S. marmoreum*
	schnittspahnii	XLum
	'Sea Breeze'	SFgr
	'Sea Urchin'	SFgr
	seguieri **new**	XLum
	'Seminole'	GEdr NMen
	'Seren' **new**	GBin
	'Serendipity'	EDAr
	'Sharon's Pencil'	NMen
	'Sha'uri' **new**	NMen
	'Sheila'	GAbr
	'Shirley Moore'	EDAr NMen
	'Shirley's Joy'	NMen XLum
	'Show Baby' **new**	NMen
	'Sideshow'	NMen
	'Sigma'	NMen
	'Silberkarneol' misapplied	see *S.* 'Silver Jubilee'
	'Silberkarneol' ambig.	MMuc SEND
	'Silberspitz'	CTal ECho ELon LRHS MHer MHom NBro NMen NRHS SPlb SRms
	'Silken Threads'	SFgr
	'Silver Andre'	NMen
§	'Silver Jubilee'	CMea ECho EDAr GBin LRHS NBro NMen NRHS NRya SPlb SRms XLum
	'Silver Shadow'	MSCN
	'Silver Sixpence'	SFgr
	'Silver Thaw'	EDAr GMaP LRHS NMen NRHS
	'Silverine'	EDAr
	'Simonkaianum'	see *Jovibarba hirta*
	'Sioux'	CTal GAbr LBee MBrN NMen WHal
	'Sirius'	GBin MHol NMen
	'Skrocki's Beauty'	NMen
	'Skrocki's Bronze'	LRHS NMen NRHS SRms
	'Smaragd'	LBee LRHS NRHS XLum
	'Smit's Seedling'	NMen
	'Smokey Jet'	NMen SFgr
	'Snowberger'	CTal MSCN NMen SFgr SRms WHal
	soboliferum	see *Jovibarba sobolifera*
	'Solist' **new**	NMen
	'Sombrero' **new**	NMen
	'Soothsayer'	NMen
	sosnowskyi	NMen XLum
	'Soul'	NMen
	'Space Dog' **new**	NMen
	'Spangle'	NMen
	'Spangle' sport	NMen
	'Spanish Dancer'	NMen
	'Sparkler'	CTal
	'Spherette'	EDAr MBrN MSCN NMen WAbe
	'Spice'	NMen
	'Spider's Lair' ♀H5	EDAr MHom NMen
	'Spinellii'	NMen WThu
	'Spiver's Velvet'	NMen
	'Sponnier'	XLum
	'Springmist'	EPot LRHS NMen NRHS SFgr SRms
	'Sprite'	GEdr LRHS MBel NMen NRHS SDys SRms
	'Squib'	CTal MSCN NMen
	stansfieldii	see *S. arachnoideum* subsp. *tomentosum* 'Stansfieldii'
	'Starburst'	CMea LRHS NRHS SFgr
	'Starion'	NMen
	'Starshine'	NMen SFgr
	'State Fair'	EDAr NMen

	'Steerosentern'	NMen
	'Storm Chaser' new	SFgr
	'Strawberry Sundae'	NMen
	'Strider'	NMen
	'Stuffed Olive'	NMen SDys SRms SRot
	'Sugary'	NMen
	'Sun Waves'	NMen SDys
	'Super Dome'	NMen
	'Superama'	NMen
	'Syston Flame'	NMen
	'Tamberlane'	EDAr
	'Tarita'	NMen
	'T'Boz' new	NMen
	'Teck'	NMen
§	***tectorum*** ♀H5	CArn CBod CHby CTal CTri ECho EDAr ELan EPfP EUJe GKev GPoy LBee LPot MHer MNHC SIde SPlb WJek XLum
§	- var. ***alpinum***	ECho LRHS MHom NBro NMen NRHS SRms
	- var. ***andreanum***	XLum
	- 'Atropurpureum'	ELan
	- 'Atroviolaceum'	EDAr NMen SPlb XLum
*	- 'Aureum'	NMen SFgr
	- var. ***boutignyanum***	SRms
	GDJ 94.04 from Route de Tuixén, Spain	
	- var. ***calcareum***	ECho
§	- var. ***glaucum***	NMen XLum
	- 'Marin'	NMen
	- 'Mettenianum' new	XLum
	- monstrose	SPlb
	- 'Murale'	SFgr XLum
§	- 'Nigrum'	LBee MHer NBro SDys XLum
	- 'Red Flush'	EDAr EPPr MBrN NMen SFgr
	- 'Royanum' ♀H5	MSCN
*	- subsp. ***sanguineum***	EDAr
	- 'Sunset'	CMea EDAr GCrg SDys WHal
	- subsp. ***tectorum***	GEdr NMen
§	- - 'Boissieri'	NMen
	- - 'Triste'	LBee NHpl NMen SFgr XLum
	- 'Violaceum'	MHom NMen SPlb SRms
	'Teddy Bear'	MSCN
	'Tederheid'	GCrg LRHS NMen NRHS
	'Telfan'	NMen
	'Tenburg'	NMen
	'Terlamen'	NMen
	'Terracotta Baby'	CTal ELon GCrg NMen
	'Thayne'	NMen
	'The Platters'	NMen
	× ***thompsonianum***	SFgr
	'Thunder'	NMen
	'Tiger Bay'	NMen
	'Tintenblut'	NMen
	'Tintinabulum' new	NMen
	'Tip Top'	GEdr NMen SFgr
	tissieri new	XLum
	'Titania'	NBro NMen WHal
	'Tjabine' new	NMen
	'Tommella' new	XLum
	'Topaz'	LBee NMen SRms XLum
	'Tordeur's Memory'	GCrg MMuc MSCN NMen SEND
I	'Tourmalyi'	NMen
	'T'Pol'	NMen
	'Tracy Sue'	EDAr XLum
	'Traffic Lights'	SFgr
	'Trail Walker'	LBee NMen SRms
	transcaucasicum	XLum
	'Tree Beard'	NMen
	'Trine'	NMen
	'Tristesse' ♀H5	ECtt EDAr GAbr LBee MBrN NMen SFgr
	'Troika' new	NMen
	'Truva'	NMen SFgr
	'Tumpty'	SFgr
	'Twilight Blues'	ECho LRHS NMen NRHS SFgr SRms
	'Twizzler'	MSCN SFgr
	'U4' new	NMen
	'Undine'	NMen
	'Unicorn'	NMen
	'Uralturmalin' new	NMen
	'Uranus'	XLum
	× ***vaccarii***	XLum
	'Van der Steen'	NMen
	'Vanbaelen'	GAbr NMen SDys
	'Vasi Petru'	NMen
	'Vega'	GBin MHol
	'Venus' new	XLum
	'Veughelen'	NMen
	vicentei	MHom NMen
	- from Gaton, Spain	LBee LRHS NMen NRHS
§	- subsp. ***paui***	NSla
	'Video'	MHom NMen SFgr
	'Vignola'	NMen
	'Violet Queen'	NMen
	'Virgil'	EDAr GCrg MBrN MSCN NMen NWad SDys SPlb WAbe WCot WIce
I	'Virginius'	NMen
	'Vulcano'	NMen
	'Waldalina'	NMen
	'Walnut Toffee' new	SFgr
	'Warrior'	EDAr
	'Wasti'	NMen
	'Waterlily'	NWad
	'Watermelon Rind'	NMen
	webbianum	see *S. arachnoideum* L. subsp. *tomentosum* (C.B. Lehm. & Schnittsp.) Schinz & Thell.
	'Webby Flame'	NMen
	'Webbyola'	NMen
	'Weirdo'	NMen
	'Wendy'	NMen SFgr
	'Westerlin'	NMen
	'Wheel of Fire' new	NMen
	'White Bouquet'	NMen
	'White Christmas'	see *S. arachnoideum* 'White Christmas'
	'White Ladies'	NMen
	'Whitening'	EDAr EPot GEdr
	'Whitney'	NMen
	× ***widderi***	NMen
	'Wilhelm Tell'	NMen
	'Winsome'	NWad
	'Winter Beauty'	NMen
	'Wok'	NMen
I	'Woolcott's Variety'	ECho MSCN NBir NMen SFgr SIgm
	wulfenii	NMen XLum
	- subsp. ***juvanii*** new	XLum
*	- ***roseum***	EDAr
	'Xaviera'	NMen
	'Xerxes' new	NMen
	'Yanisha'	NMen
	'Yarnton'	NMen
	'Yolanda'	NMen
	'Yvette'	NMen
	'Zaccour'	NMen
	'Zackenkrone'	NMen
	zeleborii	NMen WHal
	'Zenith'	EDAr NMen SFgr SRms
	'Zenobia'	MHom

	'Zenocrate'	NHol WHal
	'Zepherin'	NMen
	'Zilver Moon'	NMen
	'Zilver Snowflake'	NMen
	'Zilverprinsesje'	NMen
	'Zircon'	EDAr NMen
	'Zone'	NMen
	'Zorba'	NMen SFgr
	'Zulu'	NMen

Senecio (*Asteraceae*)

	aquaticus	LLWG
§	***articulatus***	EShb SEND
§	***barbertonicus***	EShb
	bidwillii	see *Brachyglottis bidwillii*
	candicans misapplied	see *S. cineraria*
	chrysanthemoides	see *Euryops chrysanthemoides*
§	***cineraria***	ESps LPot SEND
	- 'Silver Dust' ♀H4	EPfP ESps MMuc
	cinerascens	SVen
*	***coccinilifera***	SBch
	compactus	see *Brachyglottis compacta*
	confusus	see *Pseudogynoxys chenopodioides*
	crassissimus	EShb
	cristobalensis	CSpe SDix WCot
	doria	EBee EShb MMuc SAko WHrl
	elegans	SVen
	ficoides	EShb
	formosoides B&SWJ 10736	WCru
	formosus B&SWJ 10700	WCru
	gerberifolius B&SWJ 10357	WCru
	- B&SWJ 10361	WCru
	glastifolius	CPne
	'Gregynog Gold'	see *Ligularia* 'Gregynog Gold'
	greyi misapplied	see *Brachyglottis* (Dunedin Group) 'Sunshine'
	greyi Hook. f.	see *Brachyglottis greyi* (Hook. f.) B. Nord.
	haworthii ♀H1c **new**	EShb
	heritieri DC.	see *Pericallis lanata* (L'Hér.) B. Nord.
	kleiniiformis	EShb
	laxifolius hort.	see *Brachyglottis* (Dunedin Group) 'Sunshine'
	leucostachys misapplied	see *S. viravira*
	macroglossus	CHIl EShb
	mandraliscae 'Blue Finger'	WCot
	maritimus	see *S. cineraria*
	monroi	see *Brachyglottis monroi*
	petasitis	CFil SDix WCot
	polyodon	LRHS MArt SBee WHea
	- var. ***polyodon*** **new**	GBin MMuc MSCN SHil WFar WWFP
	- var. ***subglaber***	CCCN CSpe EAJP ECre EDAr EWes GLog MHol MNrw MPie MSpe NDov NLar SPhx WCFE WMoo WPGP
	- - S&SH 29	NCGa
	- - 'Harmony'	NDov
	przewalskii	see *Ligularia przewalskii*
	pulcher	CDTJ SBch SHar WPGP
	reinoldii	see *Brachyglottis rotundifolia*
	rowleyanus	EBak
	scandens	CCCN EShb IMou WPGP
	seminiveus	EBee
§	***serpens***	EShb EUJe SEND
§	***smithii***	ELan NBid WWtn
	'Sunshine'	see *Brachyglottis* (Dunedin Group) 'Sunshine'
	talinoides subsp. ***cylindricus*** 'Himalaya'	see *S. barbertonicus*
	tanguticus	see *Sinacalia tangutica*
§	***viravira***	EPri MCot WSHC

Senna (*Caesalpiniaceae*)

	alexandrina	CCCN EShb LRHS WPGP
§	***corymbosa***	CBcs CCCN CRHN CTri ECre LTro SBrt
	didymobotrya	MArt
	hebecarpa	SBrt
§	***marilandica***	EBee ELan MGil
	multiglandulosa	WPGP
	septemtrionalis	CCCN LRHS SEND

Sequoia (*Cupressaceae*)

	sempervirens ♀H6	CAco CBcs CCVT CDul CLnd CMCN CMen CTho ECrN EPfP EWTr LPar LRHS MBlu MMuc NOra NWea SArc SEND SGol WMat WMou WTSh
	- 'Adpressa'	CAco CDul MAsh MGos NWea SCoo
	- 'Glauca'	MAsh
	- 'Mount Loma Prieta Spike' **new**	NLar
	- 'Prostrata'	SEND

Sequoiadendron (*Cupressaceae*)

	giganteum ♀H6	Widely available
	- 'Barabits Requiem'	MBlu SMad
	- 'Beautiful Jop' **new**	NLar
	- 'Bultinck Yellow'	MBlu
	- 'Cannibal'	NLar
	- 'Glaucum'	CDul MBlu
*	- 'Glaucum Compactum'	MBlu
	- 'Greenpeace'	MBlu NLar
	- 'Lighting Green'	NLar
	- 'Pendulum'	CCVT CDul CKen ERod ESwi LRHS MBlu SMad
	- 'Petticoat' **new**	NLar
	- 'Powdered Blue'	WPGP

Serapias (*Orchidaceae*)

	lingua	SChF

Sericocarpus (*Asteraceae*)

	asteroides	ITim

Seriphidium see *Artemisia*

Serratula (*Asteraceae*)

	bulgarica	MAvo NDov
	coronata subsp. ***insularis*** B&SWJ 8698	WCru
	gmelinii **new**	LRHS NRHS
	lycopifolia	WCot
§	***seoanei***	CKno CMea CSam EBee ELan LEdu LHop MCot MHer MNrw MPie MRav NBid NDov SHar SPhx SRms WCot WPGP
	shawii	see *S. seoanei*
	tinctoria	CArn NLar NMir SPhx

Serruria (*Proteaceae*)

	florida	SPlb
	phylicoides	SPlb

Sesamothamnus (*Pedaliaceae*)

	lugardii **new**	LToo

Sesbania (*Papilionaceae*)

	punicea	CCCN

Seseli (*Apiaceae*)

elatum	MAvo
- PAB 9228 **new**	LEdu
gummiferum	CHid CSam CSpe EAJP MAvo SKHP SPhx
hippomarathrum	CSpe LEdu MAvo SBrt SDix SPhx WCot WHal WHrl WPGP WWtn
lehmannii RCB UA 13	WCot
§ ***libanotis***	CArn CBod CSam EBee GBin LEdu LRHS MAvo MBel NLar NPnk SDix SIgm SPhx WCot
montanum	CSam CSpe EBee IMou LHop MAvo NDov SBrt WPGP
varium	CArn

Sesleria (*Poaceae*)

§ ***albicans***	SCob
§ ***argentea***	EHoe EPPr LPla
autumnalis	CKno EBee ELon EShb EWes IMou LCro LEdu NDov SCob SPhx XLum
caerulea	CBod CKno CSam EHoe ELan ELon EPfP GQue IMou LEdu LRHS MBrN NDov SPhx SPoG WPtf XLum XSen
- subsp. ***calcarea***	see *S. albicans*
- 'Malvern Mop'	EBee WHrl
* ***candida***	EPPr
cylindrica	see *S. argentea*
glauca	EHoe NLar
'Greenlee'	CKno NDov
heufleriana	CWCL EHoe EPPr GEdr IMou LPla MBel NDov NLar SMea SPhx SPlb WCot
insularis	EBee EPPr EShb
'Morning Dew'	EBee GCal
nitida	CKno EBee EHoe IMou LEdu LRHS MBrN NDov SDix SPhx WCot XLum XSen
rigida	EHoe
sadleriana	EBee EPPr EWes

Setaria (*Poaceae*)

italica 'Red Jewel' **new**	CSpe
macrostachya	LLWP SPhx
palmifolia ♀H2	EShb EUJe MMuc MPie NLos SDix SPlb WCot
- BWJ 8132	WCru
viridis	CSpe WCot

Setcreasea see *Tradescantia*

shaddock see *Citrus maxima*

Sharon fruit see *Diospyros kaki*

Shepherdia (*Elaeagnaceae*)

argentea	CBcs NLar

Shibataea (*Poaceae*)

kumasaca ♀H5	CAbb CBcs CEnt CJng ENBC ERod GCal LEdu LRHS MBrN MWht NRHS SBig SGol
lancifolia	CJng

Shortia (*Diapensiaceae*)

galacifolia	EPot
soldanelloides var. ***magna***	EPot
uniflora	GKev NHar WAbe

Sibbaldia (*Rosaceae*)

procumbens	GKev

Sibbaldiopsis (*Rosaceae*)

§ ***tridentata***	GKev SBrt
- 'Lemon Mac'	NHar

Sidalcea (*Malvaceae*)

'Brilliant'	CBcs CNor EHrv GBin IBoy ILea MJak MNrw MSCN NBir SPer WCAu WMoo
campestris from Oregon, USA	EPPr
candida	CBod CSam EBee ECtt ELan EPfP GCra GMaP IBoy ILea LHop LRHS MBNS MMuc MRav MTis NChi NGdn NLar NSti SCob SPer WCAu WCot WPtf
- 'Bianca'	EBee EHrv EPfP NLar WFar WHal WMoo WOut
'Candy Girl'	CBod EBee NLar SCob WCot WFar
'Crimson King'	WFar
'Croftway Red'	CBod EBee ELan EWld GCra LRHS MBel NBro NGdn NHol NWad SPer SWvt WFar
'Elsie Heugh' ♀H7	Widely available
'Little Princess'PBR	CRos EBee EPfP EWes LRHS MHol MNrw NCou NGdn NLar NRHS SCob SPoG WCot
'Loveliness'	CBod EBee ECtt ELan EShb LHop LRHS MRav NBro NCGa NGdn NWad WFar WGwG WMoo WWtn
malviflora	SBrt SRms
- 'Alba'	NChi
- 'Crimson Beauty'	EBee
- subsp. ***purpurea***	LRHS
'Monarch'	WFar
'Moorland Rose Coronet'	WFar WMoo
'Mr Lindbergh'	EBee MPie NLar
'Mrs Borrodaile'	CMac MBel MRav NBro NEoE NGdn WMoo
'Mrs J. Galloway' **new**	EBee
'Mrs T. Alderson'	EBee
'My Love'	EBee NDov
'Oberon'	EBee LRHS MRav
oregana	NGdn
- subsp. ***spicata***	WFar WMoo
'Party Girl'	CMac CRos CSBt CSam ELan EPfP GJos IBoy LRHS MNHC MRav NBro NGdn NLar NRHS SPlb SPoG WBor WFar WMoo XLum
'Purpetta'	EBee ELan EPfP NEoE NGBl NLar SPad
reptans	EBee
'Reverend Page Roberts'	MRav WCot
'Rosaly'	CSam EAJP IFoB LRHS MPie NLar WFar
'Rosanna'	CSam EAJP EPfP GMaP LRHS NLar
'Rose Bud'	EBee ELan
'Rose Queen'	CBod EBee ECha EPPr LHop LRHS MRav NBro NHol SHar SPer SRms WFar
Stark's hybrids	LRHS NRHS SRms
'Sussex Beauty'	CSam EBee EWTr LRHS MBel MRav NCGa NDov NEgg NGdn SPer WCot WFar WMoo
'Wensleydale'	EBee LRHS
'William Smith' ♀H7	CBod CSam EBee ECha ECtt EPfP EWes GBin GBuc LRHS MBel MMuc

		MRav NBir NGdn NLar SEND SPer WFar WWtn
	'Wine Red'	CBod CMos EBee EShb LRHS MMrt NEgg NGdn SPoG SWvt WGwG WTor

Sideritis (*Lamiaceae*)

	RCB UA 2	WCot
	clandestina	XSen
	cypria	EBee XSen
	gomeraea	WCot
	hyssopifolia	SIgm
	- subsp. ***guillonii***	XSen
	phlomoides	SIgm XSen
	scardica	CArn XSen
	sericea	SIgm
	stachydioides	XSen
	syriaca	MHer XSen

Sieversia (*Rosaceae*)

§	***pentapetala***	GEdr WAbe
	- 'Flore Pleno' (d)	WAbe
	reptans	see *Geum reptans*

Silaum (*Apiaceae*)

	silaus	NMir

Silene (*Caryophyllaceae*)

	RBS	EPPr
	from Uzbekistan	GCal
	acaulis	ECho EDAr GCrg GJos MArt SRms WAbe
§	- subsp. ***acaulis***	ECho SPlb SRms
	- 'Alba'	ECho EWes SRms WAbe
	- 'Blush'	ECho EDAr GCrg NSla WAbe WOld
§	- subsp. ***bryoides***	NLar
	- 'Correvoniana'	NLar
	- subsp. ***elongata***	see *S. acaulis* subsp. *acaulis*
	- subsp. ***exscapa***	see *S. acaulis* subsp. *bryoides*
	- 'Frances'	CPBP ECho EDAr EPot GCrg ITim NHar NLar NRya NSla WAbe
	- 'Mount Snowdon'	ECho EPot EWes MMuc NHpl NLar SPlb SPoG SRms SRot WHoo
	- 'Pedunculata'	see *S. acaulis* subsp. *acaulis*
	alba	see *S. latifolia* subsp. *alba*
§	***alpestris***	ECho MArt SHar SRms SRot WMoo WThu
	- 'Flore Pleno' (d) ♀H5	CMea CPBP ECho EWes NSla SBch WIce
	- 'Starry Dreams'	LRHS NPnk NRHS
	araratica	WAbe
	× ***arkwrightii***	see *Lychnis* × *arkwrightii*
	armeria	SDys
	- 'Electra'	CSpe MNHC
	asterias	EBee GCal GCra MNrw SBrt SDix
	atropurpurea	see *Lychnis viscaria* subsp. *atropurpurea*
	catholica	EBee
§	***compacta***	IMou
	'Confetti'	CWld EAJP EPPr MMuc NSti SPhx
	'Country Comet'	NChi
§	***davidii***	EPot GKev
	delavayi	GEdr
§	***dioica***	CArn CBre CHab CWld GJos IKil LEdu MHer MNHC NLar NMir SPhx SPoG SRms SWat WMoo WOut WSFF WShi
	- 'Clifford Moor' (v)	ECtt MHer MSCN NSti SCoo
	- 'Compacta'	see *S. dioica* 'Minikin'
	- 'Firefly'PBR (d)	CDor CMac CSpe CWCL ECtt MBel NSti SHar SRkn SWvt
§	- 'Flore Pleno' (d)	GCra MHer MRav NBid NBro NGdn WFar WHoo WTcb
	- golden-leaved	WFar
	- 'Inane'	EBee ELon WBor WPGP WRHF WSHC
	- 'Innocence'	NChi
	- 'Kay's Winter Dream'	MAvo
§	- 'Minikin'	MAvo MSCN MTis NGdn
	- 'Purple Prince'	MAvo MMuc SEND WFar WMoo WPtf
I	- 'Ray's Golden Campion'	NWad WTou
	- 'Rollie's Favorite'PBR	EBee ECtt EPfP LBMP LRHS MAsh MHol MNrw MSCN NDov NPnk NPri NSti SPoG WBod WBor
	- 'Rubra Plena'	see *S. dioica* 'Flore Pleno'
	- 'Stella'	NChi
	- 'Thelma Kay' (d/v)	GBuc NGdn WMoo
	- 'Valley High' (v)	EBee ECtt EWes MHol MMuc
	falcata new	CPBP
§	***fimbriata***	CSpe EHrv ELan EPPr EShb ILea LEdu MArt MCot MMrt MMuc MNrw MRav NChi NLar NSti SDix WCot WKif WMoo WPGP WPtf WRHF
	aff. ***gracilicaulis*** from Mugecuo Lake, China new	SBrt
	hookeri	GBin SPlb
	- Ingramii Group	WAbe
	kantzeensis	see *S. davidii*
	keiskei	CPBP
	- var. ***akaisialpina***	NSla
	- - f. ***leucantha***	NSla
	- var. ***minor***	ECho EWes LRHS NRHS WAbe
	laciniata 'Jack Flash'	MSCN
	latifolia	CHab CWld MHer MNHC NMir WOut
§	- subsp. ***alba***	SEND
	maritima	see *S. uniflora*
	multifida	see *S. fimbriata*
	aff. ***nigrescens*** from Dali, Yunnan, China new	SBrt
	noctiflora	CHab WSFF
	nutans	SBrt SRms WSFF
	orientalis	see *S. compacta*
	plankii	CPBP
	pusilla	NHpl NLar
	quadridentata	see *S. alpestris*
	regia	EBee SBrt SPhx
	- 'Prairie Fire'	WCot
	rubra	see *S. dioica*
	schafta ♀H5	CTri ECha ECho EPfP GKev MAsh MMuc MRav NBid NFav SEND SRms WHoo XLum
	- 'Abbotswood'	see *Lychnis* × *walkeri* 'Abbotswood Rose'
	- 'Shell Pink'	CMea CPBP CSam ECha ECtt EPot EWes GJos LRHS MMuc NBid NRHS SBch SEND WHoo
	sieboldii	see *Lychnis coronata* var. *sieboldii*
	stellata	SPhx
§	***uniflora***	CHab CWld ECho EPfP MMuc NBro SPlb SRms SRot WMoo WOut
	- 'Alba Plena'	see *S. uniflora* 'Robin Whitebreast'
I	- 'Compacta'	ECho MArt SHar WMoo
§	- 'Druett's Variegated' (v)	CRos CTri ECho ECtt ELon EPot EWes GJos LHop LRHS MAsh MHer MHol MSCN NBid NHpl NRHS SPlb SPoG SRms WIce XLum

- 'Flore Pleno' — see *S. uniflora* 'Robin Whitebreast'
§ - 'Robin Whitebreast' (d) — ECha ECtt EPfP GBin NBid NBro SPhx SRms SRot WMoo WSHC XLum
- 'Rosea' — ECho GCrg GJos MMuc NHpl SEND SPlb SRot WOut
- 'Swan Lake' (d) — SIgm
- 'Variegata' — see *S. uniflora* 'Druett's Variegated'
- Weisskehlchen — see *S. uniflora* 'Robin Whitebreast'
- 'White Bells' — CTri WKif
uralensis — GEdr
viridiflora — SPhx
§ ***vulgaris*** — CAgr CHab CWld LEdu MMuc MNHC NMir SEND SRms WHer WMoo WOut
- subsp. ***maritima*** — see *S. uniflora*
wallichiana — see *S. vulgaris*
'Wisley Pink' — ECtt
yunnanensis — SPhx WSHC
§ ***zawadskii*** — GKev MMuc NWad SBrt SEND

Siler (*Umbelliferae*)

montanum — see *Laserpitium siler*

Silphium (*Asteraceae*)

integrifolium — NBre SMad SPhx WCot WOld XLum
laciniatum — CMac LEdu NBre SBrt SMad SPhx WHal XLum
perfoliatum ♀H7 — CArn CFis EBee GPoy IMou LPla LRHS MMuc NBre NDov NLar SDix SEND SPhx WCot WFar XLum
- from Great Dixter — IMou
- var. ***connatum*** — SPhx
terebinthinaceum — SBrt SPhx WCot XLum
trifoliatum — EPPr SPhx WCot

Silybum (*Asteraceae*)

marianum — ELan GPoy LRHS MArt MNHC NBir SIde SPav SRms WOut WTou

Sinacalia (*Asteraceae*)

§ ***tangutica*** — CBod CSam EPPr GQue ILea LHop MBel MSCN NBid NLar NSti SDix WCot WOld WWtn

Sinapis (*Brassicaceae*)

alba — SVic

Sinarundinaria (*Poaceae*)

anceps — see *Yushania anceps*
jaunsarensis — see *Yushania anceps*
maling — see *Yushania maling*
murielae — see *Fargesia murielae*
nitida — see *Fargesia nitida*

Sinningia (*Gesneriaceae*)

* ***caerulea*** — WDib
calcaria — WDib
canescens ♀H1c — LToo
§ ***cardinalis*** — EBak WDib
- 'Innocent' — WDib
conspicua — WDib
nivalis — WDib
speciosa 'Blanche de Méru' — SDeJ
- 'Hollywood' — SDeJ
- 'Kaiser Friedrich' — SDeJ
- 'Kaiser Wilhelm' — SDeJ
- 'Mont Blanc' — SDeJ
tubiflora — CSpe LEdu WCot WKif XLum

Sinobambusa (*Poaceae*)

tootsik — CJng

× *Sinocalycalycanthus* see *Calycanthus*

Sinocalycanthus see *Calycanthus*

Sinocrassula (*Crassulaceae*)

yunnanensis — EUJe NHpl SPlb

Sinofranchetia (*Lardizabalaceae*)

chinensis — CRHN IArd IDee SAko WPGP WSHC
- DJHS 4117 — WCru

Sinojackia (*Styracaceae*)

xylocarpa — CBcs CMCN NLar

Sinopanax (*Araliaceae*)

formosanus — CFil

Sinopodophyllum (*Berberidaceae*)

§ ***hexandrum*** — CBct CBro CWCL EBee ECho ELan EPot GBin GBuc GCra GKev GMaP GPoy ILea LPla MNrw MRav NBid NBir NChi NHar NLar SKHP SPlb WPnP WSHC
§ - var. ***chinense*** — CLAP ECho GCal GKev LEdu WCru
- - BWJ 7908 — WCru
§ - var. ***emodi*** — CArn EPfP GBuc ITim
- - 'Majus' — CLAP EWTr GBin WCot WHal

Sinowilsonia (*Hamamelidaceae*)

henryi — CBcs IArd NLar SAko

Siphocranion (*Lamiaceae*)

§ ***macranthum*** — EBee EWes WPGP

Sison (*Apiaceae*)

amomum — CBre

Sisymbrium (*Brassicaceae*)

§ ***luteum*** — EBee

Sisyrinchium (*Iridaceae*)

× ***anceps*** — see *S. angustifolium*
§ ***angustifolium*** — ECha EDAr LSun MCot NBir NChi SChF SPlb SRms WBrk
- f. ***album*** — LSun MCot NChi NLar
§ ***arenarium*** — CWCL GAbr
atlanticum — NBro
bellum hort. — see *S. idahoense* var. *bellum*
bermudiana — see *S. angustifolium*
- 'Album' — see *S. graminoides* 'Album'
'Biscutella' — CKno CTri EPfP EWoo GMaP ITim LEdu LHop MHCG NFav SPad SPlb SRot WHal WHoo WKif
'Blue France' — EPot
'Blue Ice' — GPSL ITim LRHS NLar WAbe WMoo
'Blue Skies' — ITim
boreale — see *S. californicum*
brachypus — see *S. californicum* Brachypus Group
'Californian Skies' — CAby CBro CElw CKno CRos CTri EAJP ECha ECho ECtt EWoo GMaP LHop LRHS MNrw NBir NDov NRHS NSla SRot SWvt WKif WMoo
§ ***californicum*** — CBen EDAr EWTr GWyn IMou LLWG LRHS NBro WMAq XLum

§ - Brachypus Group	ECho EPfP GAbr LPot MAsh NBir NLar SPlb SWvt WMoo
- 'Yellowstone'	CSBt EPfP GMcL MHtn
convolutum	NDov
- B&SWJ 9117	WCru
cuspidatum	see *S. arenarium*
depauperatum	MNrw
'Devon Skies'	CElw CPBP CRos CWCL ECho ECtt EWoo GCrg LRHS MNrw NLar NRHS SBch SWvt WAbe WIce
'Doctor Bailey'	EBee
douglasii	see *Olsynium douglasii*
'Dragon's Eye'	CElw CKno CMea CPBP EAJP ECtt EDAr EWes EWoo MBrN MHer SCob WIce
'E.K. Balls'	CAby CPBP CRos CTal ECho ECtt EDAr EHoe ELan EWoo GCrg GMaP LBMP LHop LRHS MAsh NHpl NRHS NRya NSla SMad SPoG SRGP SRms SRot SWvt WAbe WIce WMoo
'Emmeline'	EWoo
graminoides	GWyn IFoB NBro
§ - 'Album'	NBro
grandiflorum	see *Olsynium douglasii*
'Hemswell Sky'	ECtt EHoe EWoo NLar NRya
'Iceberg'	CAby CElw CKno EAJP ECha EWes
idahoense	ECha ECtt GAbr MHer NDov NHpl NRya SPlb SRms
§ - var. ***bellum***	CKno EPfP NFav SRms WMoo XLum
- - pale-flowered	CKno SMHy
- - 'Rocky Point'	CKno EBee EPfP EWes LRHS NRHS SPoG WFar
- var. ***macounii***	GEdr GPSL SPlb WRHF
§ - - 'Album' 🏆H5	CAby CElw CMea ECtt EWes GAbr GCrg GEdr LPot NFav WAbe WIce
'Janet Denman' (v)	ECho EWes LLHF MAvo SRot
junceum	see *Olsynium junceum*
macrocarpon misapplied	see *S. macrocarpum*
§ ***macrocarpum***	EWld
magnicapsulare	CPBP MNrw
'Marchants Seedling' **new**	SMHy
'Marion'	CMea ECtt MBrN WHoo
'May Snow'	see *S. idahoense* var. *macounii* 'Album'
'Miami'	EWoo
montanum	NHpl
montanum × ***nudicaule***	ECho GAbr SRot
'Mrs Spivey'	CSpe NBir
'North Star'	see *S.* 'Pole Star'
palmifolium	CAby CSpe EBee LEdu MHer MNrw SBch SMad SPad WSHC XLum
patagonicum	CTal ECho GKev
§ 'Pole Star'	EWoo NLar
'Quaint and Queer'	CCCN EAJP ECha EHoe EWoo MBrN MCot MNrw NBir WSHC
'Raspberry'	CKno CMea EDAr EWoo
'Sapphire'	CAby CBod CCCN CKno CWCL ECha ECtt EDAr EHoe ELan GCrg GPSL LPot LRHS MHol NHpl NLar SCob SPoG WBor WGrn WMoo
§ ***striatum***	Widely available
§ - 'Aunt May' (v)	CBod CCCN CMac ECha EHoe EPfP EWoo GMaP LRHS LSRN MGos MRav MSpe NHpl NLar NSti SCob SPer SPoG SRms SWat SWvt WCot WPGP
- 'Variegatum'	see *S. striatum* 'Aunt May'
'Stripey'^{PBR} (v) **new**	CSpe WCot
aff. ***unispathaceum*** B&SWJ 10683	WCru

Sium (*Apiaceae*)

sisarum	CAgr CArn CLau GPoy LEdu MAvo MHer NDov

Skimmia ✿ (*Rutaceae*)

anquetilia	CMac
- (f)	IVic WCru
- (m)	WCru
arborescens B&SWJ 11799	WCru
- PAB 8774 **new**	LEdu
- subsp. ***nitida*** B&SWJ 8239	WCru
arisanensis B&SWJ 7114	WCru
- CWJ 12417	WCru
black-fruited B&SWJ 8259 from northern Vietnam (f/m)	WCru
× ***confusa***	LPar
- 'Kew Green' (m) 🏆H5	Widely available
japonica	CDul CMHG CMac CWib LPar MGos NPla NWea SCob SSta WBod WFar
- (f)	CMac CTri ELan EPfP GMcL LPar SRms
- B&SWJ 5053 (f)	WCru
- B&SWJ 5053 (m)	WCru
- 'Alba'	see *S. japonica* 'Wakehurst White'
- 'Bowles's Dwarf Female' (f)	CEnd CMHG ELan MRav MWht SLim
- 'Bowles's Dwarf Male' (m)	CMHG ELan NWad SLim
- 'Bronze Knight' (m)	CMac EBee IVic MAsh MRav NLar NWad
- 'Carberry' (f)	CMac IVic
- 'Chameleon' (f)	GMcL NLar
- 'Dad's Red Dragon' (f)	CMac MAsh
- 'Emerald King' (m)	MAsh WFar
- 'Foremanii'	see *S. japonica* 'Veitchii'
§ - 'Fragrans' (m) 🏆H5	CMac CRos CSBt CTri CWib EBee EPfP LPar LRHS LSRN MAsh MGos MJak MRav NLar NPri NWea SCob SHil SLim SPer SPoG SWvt WFar WGwG
- 'Fragrant Cloud'	see *S. japonica* 'Fragrans'
- 'Fructu Albo'	see *S. japonica* 'Wakehurst White'
- 'Godrie's Dwarf' (m)	CRos EPfP LRHS NLar SHil WFar
- 'Humpty Dumpty' (f)	WFar
- var. ***intermedia*** f. ***repens*** B&SWJ 5560	WCru
- - - B&SWJ 11165	WCru
- 'John Turner' (f) **new**	GBin
- 'Kew White' (f)	CAbP CBcs CRos CWib ELan EPfP GMcL IArd LPar LRHS MAsh MGos MJak MRav NHol NWad SAko SLon SPer SSta SWvt WCFE
- Luwian = 'Wanto' (m)	CRos LRHS SHil
- 'Macpenny Dwarf' (m)	CMac
- 'Magic Marlot'^{PBR} (m/v)	CRos EBee EMil EPfP GMcL LRHS LSRN MAsh MGos MRav NHpl NLar SCob SPoG
- 'Marlot' (m)	CRos EPfP LRHS NLar NWad SPoG
- 'Nymans' (f) 🏆H5	CEnd CRos EBee ELan EPfP GBin GMcL LBrs LCro LRHS MAsh MGos MRav SCob SHil SLim SPer SPoG SRms SWvt
- Obsession = 'Obsbolwi'^{PBR} (m/f)	CRos GMcL LPar LRHS MAsh NPri SCob SHil
- 'Olympic Flame' (f)	CRos EPfP IArd LRHS MAsh MBlu MJak SHil SPoG

	- 'Pabella'PBR (f)	LPar LRHS MAsh SPoG
	- 'Red Diamonds'	CRos LRHS SHil
	- 'Red Princess' (f)	MAsh
	- 'Red Riding Hood' (f)	CRos ELan ELon LRHS MAsh NWad SBod SHil SLon SPer
	- 'Redruth' (f)	CBcs CMac CSBt CTsd ELon MAsh SEND
§	- subsp. ***reevesiana***	CBcs CDul CMHG CMac CRos CSBt CTri CWib ELan EPfP ESps GBin GMcL IVic LCro LHop LOPS LRHS MGos MRav MSwo NLar SCob SPoG SWvt WHar
	- - B&SWJ 3763	MAsh WCru
	- - 'Chilan Choice' (f/m)	LRHS WPGP
	- - 'Godries Little Ruby'PBR **new**	EPfP NLar
	- - var. ***reevesiana***	LPar MJak
	- - - B&SWJ 3544	WCru
§	- Rogersii Group	CMac CTri
	- - 'George Gardner' (m)	EPfP LRHS
	- - 'Nana Mascula' (m)	CTri
	- - 'Rogersii' (f)	CMac
	- 'Rubella' (m) ♀H5	Widely available
	- 'Rubinetta' (m)	EPfP IArd MAsh SCob
	- 'Ruby Dome' (m)	MAsh NWad
	- 'Ruby King' (m)	CSBt IArd LSRN NLar SAko
	- 'Scarlet Dwarf' (f)	MAsh NHol
	- Seduction = 'Redbolwi'PBR **new**	LRHS
	- 'Snow White'PBR (m)	MAsh
	- 'Tansley Gem' (f)	CRos LRHS MAsh MWht
	- 'Temptation'PBR (f)	CRos ELan EPfP LRHS SCob SHil
	- 'Thereza'PBR (m)	EPfP LRHS
§	- 'Veitchii' (f)	CBar CBcs CDul CMac CRos CSBt CTri ELan EPfP IArd LRHS LSRN MAsh MGos MJak MMuc MRav NLar SCob SEND SLim SPer SPoG SWvt
§	- 'Wakehurst White' (f)	CMac CSBt CTri EPfP IVic LRHS MAsh MRav SLim SPoG WFar
	- 'White Bella' (m)	CRos LRHS SHil
	- 'Winifred Crook' (f)	LRHS
	- 'Wisley Female' (f)	CTri
	laureola	MRav SRms WSHC
	- GWJ 9364	WCru
	- 'Kew Green'	CEnd NWad
	- subsp. ***laureola*** HWJK 2095	WCru
	- subsp. ***multinervia*** GWJ 9374	WCru
	reevesiana	see *S. japonica* subsp. *reevesiana*
	rogersii	see *S. japonica* Rogersii Group

Sloanea (*Elaeocarpaceae*)

sinensis **new**	WPGP

Smallanthus (*Asteraceae*)

sonchifolius	CAgr LEdu
- 'Morado'	LEdu WPGP

Smilacina see *Maianthemum*

Smilax (*Smilacaceae*)

sp.	WBor
B&SWJ 6628 from Thailand	WCru
aspera	CArn CMac LEdu WCru WPGP WSHC
china B&SWJ 4427	WCru
discotis	CBcs SEND
glaucophylla B&SWJ 2971	WCru
nipponica B&SWJ 4331	WCru
rotundifolia	LEdu
sieboldii	LEdu MRav
- B&SWJ 744	WCru

Smyrnium (*Apiaceae*)

olusatrum	CArn CHab CSpe MNHC SRms SWat WHer WSFF
perfoliatum	CHid CMea CSpe EHrv ELan ELon EWes GBin LEdu NBir SDix WCot WHal WSHC
rotundifolium	LEdu WCot
- PAB 6714 **new**	LEdu

Solandra (*Solanaceae*)

	grandiflora misapplied	see *S. maxima*
	hartwegii	see *S. maxima*
§	***maxima***	CCCN

Solanum (*Solanaceae*)

	atropurpureum	CDTJ CSpe SPlb WCot
	betaceum (F)	CCCN SVic
	- yellow-fruited (F)	SPlb
	burchellii	SPlb
	capsicastrum	SPlb
	conchifolium hort.	see *S. linearifolium*
	crispum	CBot
	- 'Autumnale'	see *S. crispum* 'Glasnevin'
§	- 'Glasnevin' ♀H4	Widely available
	dulcamara	CArn GPoy
	- 'Lucia' (v)	CNat
	- 'Variegatum' (v)	CMac EHoe MAsh
	incanum	LEdu
	jasminoides	see *S. laxum*
	- 'Blue Ice'	LSou
	laciniatum	CCCN CDTJ IDee SBig SEND SPav SPlb
§	***laxum***	CRos EBee LRHS MAsh NRHS SPer SRms SWvt WSHC
	- 'Album' ♀H4	Widely available
	- 'Album Variegatum' (v)	CWib SCob
*	- 'Aureovariegatum' (v)	CMac LBMP NEgg SPlb
	- 'Coldham'	SDix
	- 'Creche ar Pape'	ECha LRHS
§	***linearifolium***	CSpe LBMP SKHP WPGP WSHC
	muricatum (F)	CCCN CHll EShb SPlb
	pinnatum	SPlb
	pseudocapsicum variegated (v)	WCot
	pyracanthum	CDTJ SPlb WCot
	quitoense (F)	CDTJ SBig SPlb
	- 'Cannington Purple'	SPlb
	rantonnetii	see *Lycianthes rantonnetii*
	rigescentoides	SPlb
	sisymbriifolium	SPlb
	aff. ***stenophyllum*** B&SWJ 10744	WCru
	wendlandii	CCCN CHll

Solaria (*Alliaceae*)

sp.	GCal

Soldanella (*Primulaceae*)

	alpicola	GKev
	alpina	CTal EBee ECho GCra GKev LLHF SRms WAbe
	- SDR 3504	GKev
	- SDR 6332	GKev LEdu
	- SDR 6915	LEdu
I	- 'Alba'	ECho WAbe

carpatica	CTal ECho GKev LEdu LLHF SPlb WAbe
- 'Alba'	ECho GEdr LEdu NHar WAbe
carpatica* × *pusilla	CPBP ECho ITim MNrw NHar NRya NWad WAbe WSHC
carpatica* × *villosa	ECho LEdu
cyanaster	EBee ECho GBin GBuc GJos GKev GLog LEdu LLHF NHpl NQui NRya WAbe
dimoniei	CTal EBee ECho ITim LEdu WAbe
hungarica	ECho GEdr WAbe
minima	ECho GEdr GJos LEdu NHar NSla WAbe
montana	CFis ECho GBin GJos LEdu LLHF NLar SBch WKif
pindicola	CTal ECho GEdr LEdu
pusilla	NWad
'Spring Symphony'	CTal ECho GEdr GMaP ITim LEdu LLHF NHar SAko WTcb
'Sudden Spring'	CTal ECho GEdr LEdu NWad SIgm WAbe
villosa 𝕐H5	CTal EBee ECho GAbr GBin GEdr GKev GLog GPSL LEdu NRya NWad SBch WAbe WMoo WSHC

Soleirolia (*Urticaceae*)

soleirolii	CTri EUJe LLWG MMuc NLos SCob SEND SMad SPer SVic SWvt WHer XLum
- 'Argentea'	see *S. soleirolii* 'Variegata'
§ - 'Aurea'	CTri NHpl SVic SWvt
- 'Golden Queen'	see *S. soleirolii* 'Aurea'
- 'Silver Queen'	see *S. soleirolii* 'Variegata'
§ - 'Variegata' (v)	LLWG SCob SVic

Solenopsis (*Campanulaceae*)

axillaris	see *Isotoma axillaris*

Solenostemon ✿ (*Lamiaceae*)

'Autumn Rainbow'	WDib
'Beauty' (v)	WDib
'Beauty of Lyons'	EShb WDib
'Black Heart'	WDib
'Black Prince' 𝕐H1c	WDib
'Brilliant' (v)	WDib
'Bronze Pagoda'	WDib
'Buttercup'	WDib
'Chamaeleon' (v)	WDib
'City of Sunderland'	WDib
'Combat' (v) 𝕐H1c	WDib
'Crimson Ruffles' (v) 𝕐H1c	WDib
'Dazzler' (v)	WDib
'Display' (v)	WDib
'Durham Gala' 𝕐H1c	WDib
'Firelight' (v)	WDib
'Flamingo'	WDib
'Freckles' (v)	WDib
Giant Exhibition Palisandra (Giant Exhibition Series)	CSpe
Henna = 'Balcenna'PBR (v) 𝕐H1c	ECtt
'Illumination'	WDib
'Inky Fingers' (v)	WDib
'Juliet Quartermain' 𝕐H1c	EShb EUJe WDib
'Jupiter'	WDib
'Kentish Fire' (v)	WDib
'Kiwi Fern' (Stained Glassworks Series) (v)	WDib
'Kong Lime Sprite' **new**	NPri
'Lemon Chiffon'	WDib
'Lord Falmouth' (v) 𝕐H1c	WDib
'Mrs Pilkington' (v)	WDib
'Muriel Pedley' (v)	WDib
'Paisley Shawl' (v)	EShb WDib
'Peter Wonder' (v)	WDib
'Picturatus' (v) 𝕐H1c	WDib
'Pineapple Beauty' (v) 𝕐H1c	WDib
'Pineapplette' (v) 𝕐H1c	WDib
'Pink Chaos' (v) 𝕐H1c	WDib
'Red Angel' (v)	WDib
'Red Velvet' (v)	WDib
Redhead = 'Uf0646'PBR 𝕐H1c	NPri
'Rose Blush' (v)	WDib
'Roy Pedley' (v) 𝕐H1c	WDib
'Royal Scot' (v) 𝕐H1c	WDib
'Salmon Plumes' (v)	WDib
'Saturn' (v)	WDib
'The Flume'	WDib
'Timotei'	WDib
'Walter Turner' (v) 𝕐H1c	ECtt WDib
'Winsome' (v) 𝕐H1c	WDib
'Winter Sun' (v)	WDib
'Wisley Flame'	WDib
'Wisley Tapestry' (v) 𝕐H1c	WDib

Solidago (*Asteraceae*)

Babygold	see *S.* 'Goldkind'
brachystachys	see *S. cutleri*
caesia	EBee EWes LRHS NBir SMHy WFar
canadensis	CTri ELan SEND SPlb WBrk WHer WMoo WOld WWtn XLum
- var. ***salebrosa***	EBee LRHS
- var. ***scabra***	MMuc
'Citronella'	ECtt GQue
'Cloth of Gold'	CMac ECtt EPfP ESps NEoE NHol SPoG SWvt WGwG
§ 'Crown of Rays'	ECtt ELon EPfP GBin MRav SCob WFar
§ ***cutleri***	NLar SIgm SPlb SRms WFar
- 'Goldrush'	LRHS NRHS
I - ***nana***	ECho
'Ducky'	SCob
'Early Bird'	NLar WFar
flabelliformis	WCot
§ ***flexicaulis***	GMaP WCot XLum
- 'Variegata' (v)	EBee ELan EShb GMaP LRHS NLar WMoo XLum
'Foxbrook Gold'	MAvo
'Gardone' 𝕐H7	WFar
gigantea	WFar
glomerata	MMuc NLar SEND
Golden Baby	see *S.* 'Goldkind'
§ 'Golden Dwarf'	CBod CWCL WBod WPtf XLum
'Golden Fleece'	see *S. sphacelata* 'Golden Fleece'
'Golden Thumb'	see *S.* 'Queenie'
'Golden Wings'	CBre MWat
'Goldenmosa' 𝕐H7	CSBt EWes GKev GMaP SPer WFar
'Goldilocks'	SRms
§ 'Goldkind'	CAgr CBod CBre CNec CRos CSBt CTri EBee ECtt ELan EPfP ESps GAbr GMcL IBoy LRHS MMuc NEgg NRHS SWvt WBrk WFar WHar WWtn
Goldzwerg	see *S.* 'Golden Dwarf'
'Harvest Gold'	CBre
'Hiddigeigei' (v)	WCot
hybrida	see *S.* × *luteus*
latifolia	see *S. flexicaulis*

'Laurin'	NLar XLum
'Ledsham'	CBod ECtt GBin LEdu LRHS NBre NCGa SPoG
'Lena'	SRms
'Linner Gold'	NBre
litoralis **new**	GAbr
'Little Lemon'[PBR]	EBee ELan LRHS LSou MAsh NEoE SCob
§ × ***luteus***	EBee EWTr GBin SRms XLum
- 'Lemore' ♀H7	CBod CDor EBee ECha ELan EPfP GBuc GMaP GQue LHop LSou MMuc MSpe NSti SPer SPhx SPoG SRms WCot WFar XLum
* ***minutissima*** subsp. ***minuta***	MHol
ohioensis	XLum
- 'Four Seasons' **new**	GBin
§ ***ptarmicoides***	EBee XEll XLum
§ 'Queenie'	ECha MHer
riddellii	XLum
rigida	WMoo
- 'Upright Rod' **new**	GBin
rugosa	ECha MBNS MMuc SEND SPhx WCot WWtn
- 'Fireworks' ♀H7	CAby CBre CHVG CMHG CMac CMea CSam EBee ECtt ELon GBin GQue IBoy ILea LHop LRHS MAvo MSpe MWat NCGa NLar SDys SPhx WBrk WCot WFar WHoo WOld XLum
- 'Loydser Crown'	NDov
sempervirens	EBee IMou LRHS WFar WOld
'Septembergold'	CSam
shortii 'Solar Cascade'	EBee
'Sonnenschein'	NBre
speciosa	SPhx WCot
spectabilis var. ***confinis*** KM 27-01	EBee
§ ***sphacelata*** 'Golden Fleece'	CBcs ELan EPfP IMou NBre SRms
spiraeifolia	EBee
Strahlenkrone	see *S.* 'Crown of Rays'
'Super'	WCot
Sweety = 'Barseven'[PBR]	LRHS NRHS
'Tom Thumb'	MRav NBir SRms
uliginosa	EShb
ulmifolia	EBee
virgaurea	CArn GPoy MHer MMuc MNHC NLar SRms WHer
- subsp. ***alpestris*** var. ***minutissima***	GEdr
- var. ***cambrica***	see *S. virgaurea* subsp. *minuta*
§ - subsp. ***minuta***	GBin GCrg
- 'Praecox'	CSBt
§ - 'Variegata' (v)	CBre EHoe NEoE WOut
vulgaris 'Variegata'	see *S. virgaurea* 'Variegata'
'Yellow Springs'	GJos
'Yellow Stone'	EBee

× *Solidaster* see *Solidago*

hybridus	see *Solidago* × *luteus*

Sollya (*Pittosporaceae*)

sp.	WBod
fusiformis	see *S. heterophylla*
§ ***heterophylla*** ♀H3	Widely available
- 'Alba'	CBcs CCCN CFlo CKel CRos EBee ELan EPfP LPre LRHS NRHS SEle SLon SPoG SWvt WSHC
- 'Pink Charmer'	CBcs ELan LPre LRHS SEle SLon SPoG
- pink-flowered	CCCN LBMP SWvt

Sonchus (*Asteraceae*)

gomerensis **new**	WCot
pinnatus	SPlb

Sophora (*Papilionaceae*)

cassioides NJM 08.008	WPGP
- 'Goldilocks'	WPGP
- 'Goughensis'	WPGP
§ ***davidii***	CAby CBcs CWGN CWib EBee ELon EPfP LRHS MBlu MMuc SBrt SEND SPoG WGrn WPGP WSHC
- dark blue-flowered	WPGP
flavescens	SBrt
fulvida	EBee EPfP WPGP
japonica	see *Styphnolobium japonicum*
§ 'Little Baby'	CAbP CWib EBee ELan EPfP EUJe LBrs LPre LRHS LSRN MGil MGos MNHC SEle SPoG SWvt WGrn
macrocarpa	SWvt
microphylla	CTri LEdu LHop MGil WPGP
molloyi 'Dragon's Gold'	CBcs ELan ELon EPfP EUJe LRHS MAsh SCob SCoo SEND SEle SPoG SSta SWvt WPGP
- 'Early Gold'	WPGP
prostrata misapplied	see *S.* 'Little Baby'
prostrata Buchanan	CMac
Sun King = 'Hilsop'[PBR] ♀H4	CBcs CBot CDul CRos CWGN ELan EPfP EWes LRHS LSRN MGos NLar SCob SCoo SHil SLim SLon SPer SPoG SWvt WCot
tetraptera	CAbP CBcs CDul CTsd EPfP LRHS MMuc SEND SPer SWvt WCFE WPGP
viciifolia	see *S. davidii*

Sorbaria (*Rosaceae*)

aitchisonii	see *S. tomentosa* var. *angustifolia*
arborea	see *S. kirilowii*
aff. ***assurgens*** BWJ 8185	WCru
§ ***kirilowii***	CMac MRav NLar SMad WOut
- AC 3433	MHid
sorbifolia	CAbP CBcs CMCN ELan GMcL MGil MMuc SCob SEND SPer SPlb WFar
- 'Sem'[PBR] ♀H5	Widely available
- var. ***stellipila*** B&SWJ 776	WCru
§ ***tomentosa*** var. ***angustifolia*** ♀H5	CBcs CDul CTri ELan EPfP LRHS MMuc MRav NBid SCob SEND SLon SPer

× *Sorbaronia* (*Rosaceae*)

fallax	EPfP
- 'Ivan's Beauty'	ECrN

× *Sorbopyrus* (*Rosaceae*)

auricularis	MCoo
§ - 'Shipova' (F)	CAgr MAsh NOra WHar WMat

Sorbus ✿ (*Rosaceae*)

KR 5304 **new**	GKev
NJM 09.203	WPGP
SDR 7808 **new**	GKev
SDR 7822 **new**	GKev
adamii	CMCN
alnifolia	CJun CLnd CMCN EPfP MBlu
- B&SWJ 8461	WCru
- B&SWJ 10948	WCru
- 'Red Bird'	EPfP LRHS MBlu WPat
'Amber Light'	LRHS NOra WMat
americana	CLnd NWea

	anglica	CDul
	'Apricot'	CEnd
	'Apricot Queen'	CDul CLnd EBee ECrN EMOT MJak SGol WFar
	aria	CAco CCVT CDul CHab CLnd CTri ECrN EMOT ESps IBoy LBuc MGos MMuc NWea SCob SEND SEWo SGol WHar WHed WMou WTSh
	- 'Aurea'	CLnd SPer
	- 'Chrysophylla'	CDul CSBt ECrN NWea
	- 'Decaisneana'	see *S. aria* 'Majestica'
	- 'Lutescens' ♀H6	Widely available
	- 'Magnifica'	ECrN ELan EMOT ESwi NEgg NLar SEWo WJas
§	- 'Majestica' ♀H6	CCVT CDul CLnd CMac EBee ECrN EMOT ESps LHop MRav NWea SCob SPer WFar WHar WJas
	- 'Mitchellii'	see *S. thibetica* 'John Mitchell'
	- 'Quercoides' **new**	CDul
	aria × pseudovilmorinii	EBee WPGP
	arnoldiana 'Golden Wonder'	see *S.* 'Lombarts Golden Wonder'
	aronioides misapplied	see *S. caloneura*
	arranensis	CDul WPat
§	***aucuparia***	Widely available
	- 'Aspleniifolia'	CBcs CCVT CDul CLnd CMCN CMac CSBt ECrN EMOT ERea ESps EUJe IBoy LRHS MGos MJak MRav NLar NOra NOrn NWea SCob SLim SPer WFar WJas WMat WMou
§	- 'Beissneri'	CAgr CDul MRav NWea
	- Cardinal Royal = 'Michred'	CCVT CDul CLnd ECrN EMOT ESps EWTr MMuc NEgg SCoo SEWo SLon
	- 'Dirkenii'	SGol WJas WMat
§	- var. ***edulis*** (F)	CArg CBcs CDul CLnd ECrN EWTr LBuc MGos MMuc SCob SPer
	- - 'Rossica' misapplied	see *S. aucuparia* var. *edulis* 'Rossica Major'
§	- - 'Rossica Major'	CDul ECrN GQui SEWo
§	- 'Fastigiata'	CEnd CTri ELan EPfP GKin SCob
	- 'Hilling's Spire'	CBcs CTho
	- subsp. ***maderensis***	WPat
	- ***pluripinnata***	see *S. scalaris* Koehne
	- var. ***rossica*** Koehne	see *S. aucuparia* var. *edulis*
	- 'Sheerwater Seedling' ♀H6	CBcs CCVT CDul CMCN CSBt EBee ECrN ELan EMOT EPfP GKin IBoy LHop MGos MMuc MRav MSwo NOrn NWea SCob SEND SEWo SGol SPer WFar
	- var. ***xanthocarpa***	ECrN ELan EWTr
	aucuparia × scalaris	EMOT NOrn
	Autumn Spire = 'Flanrock' ♀H6	CDul CEnd CLnd CTsd EBee ELan EMOT EPfP ERea ESwi IBoy LRHS LSRN MAsh MGos MJak NLar NOra NPri NWea SCoo SEWo SLim SLon SPoG SWvt WHar WMat
	bissetii	WPat
	- Yu 14299	WCru
	brevipetiolata B&SWJ 11771	WCru
§	***caloneura***	EBee EPfP LEdu LRHS MBlu WPGP
	- Guiz 80	WCru
	carmesina B&L 12545	EBee EPfP GKev WCru
	- 'Emberglow'	EBee EPfP NOra WMat
	cashmiriana Hedl. ♀H6	Widely available
	aff. ***cashmiriana***	EMOT IBoy LCro LOPS MAsh MJak NHol NOrn WFar WTSh
	- B 751	WCru
	chamaemespilus	WThu
	'Chinese Lace'	Widely available
§	***commixta***	CBcs CDul CEnd CLnd CMCN EBee ECrN EMOT ESps IBoy LCro MBlu MGos MJak MMuc MSwo NLar SCob SEND SGol SLim SPer WJas
	- B&SWJ 10839	WCru
	- B&SWJ 11043	WCru
	- B&SWJ 12640 from Ulleungdo, South Korea	WCru
§	- 'Dodong' ♀H6	CDul CEnd CSBt EBee EMOT EPfP ERea GBin IArd LBuc LSRN MBlu NLar NOra NWea SCoo SEWo SLim SPer SPoG WHar WMat WMou
	- 'Embley' ♀H6	CBcs CCVT CDul CLnd CMCN CSBt CTho CTri EBee ECrN ELan EPfP LCro LHop LOPS MBlu MGos MMuc MRav NEgg NOrn NWea SCob SEND SGol SPer SPoG
	- Olympic Flame	see *S. commixta* 'Dodong'
	- 'Ravensbill'	EBee EPfP NLar NOra NWea SCoo WHar WMat
	- var. ***rufoferruginea***	GQui
	- - B&SWJ 11486	WCru
	- var. ***sachalinensis*** B&SWJ 8515	WCru
	aff. ***commixta***	IBoy MHid WTSh
	conradinae Koehne	see *S. esserteauana*
	'Copper Kettle' ♀H6	EBee EPfP MAsh NLar NOra SCoo WHar WMat
	'Coral Beauty'	CLnd
	corymbifera WWJ 11860	WCru
	'Covert Gold'	CEnd
	croceocarpa	CDul
	'Croft Coral'	MAsh WHar
	cuspidata	see *S. vestita*
*	***decora*** 'Grootendorst'	CDul
	- var. ***nana***	see *S. aucuparia* 'Fastigiata'
	devoniensis	CDul CTho
	- 'Devon Beauty'	CAgr
	discolor misapplied	see *S. commixta*
	discolor (Maxim.) Maxim.	EBee ESps MBlu MJak NWea WJas
	- MF 96172	MAsh
	- MF 97103	WCru
	domestica	CDul EPfP MMuc SEND WCot
	- 'Maliformis'	see *S. domestica* f. *pomifera*
§	- f. ***pomifera***	LEdu
§	- f. ***pyrifera***	LEdu
	- 'Pyriformis'	see *S. domestica* f. *pyrifera*
	- 'Rosie'	CAgr
	dunnii	EBee WPGP
	'Eastern Promise' ♀H6	CDul EBee EMOT EPfP ESps LCro MAsh MSwo NLar NOra NOrn NWea SCob SCoo SLim WHCr WHar WMat
§	***eburnea***	GKev
	- Harry Smith 12799	GQui WPGP
	eminens	CDul CNat WPat
	epidendron WWJ 11930	WCru
§	***esserteauana***	CLnd CTho WPat
	fansipanensis NJM 09.176	WPGP
	'Fastigiata'	see *S. aucuparia* 'Fastigiata', *S.* × *thuringiaca* 'Fastigiata'
	aff. ***filipes***	GKev
	- KR 5095	GKev
	- KR 6844	GKev
	folgneri	CJun
	- 'Emiel' ♀H6	EPfP MBlu NOra WMat
	- 'Lemon Drop'	CDul CEnd CJun CLnd EPfP MAsh NOra SCoo WHar WMat
	foliolosa	CLnd

	forrestii 🏆H6	CBcs CMCN EBee EPfP GKev
*	***fosteri***	EBee
§	***frutescens*** 🏆H6	NWea
	- Rock 14987	GKev
	fruticosa Crantz	NSla
	- 'Koehneana'	see *S. koehneana* C.K. Schneid.
	'Ghose'	CEnd EBee WMat
§	***glabriuscula***	EBee GKev
	'Glendoick Gleam'	GGGa
	'Glendoick Glory'	GGGa
	'Glendoick Ivory'	GGGa
	'Glendoick Pearl'	GGGa
	'Glendoick Ruby'	GGGa
	'Glendoick Spire'	EBee EMOT GGGa LRHS NLar WMat
	'Glendoick White Baby'	GGGa WMat
	glomerulata	LLHF
	'Golden Wonder'	see *S.* 'Lombarts Golden Wonder'
	gonggashanica	EBee EPfP GEdr GKev WPGP
*	***gorrodini***	CLnd
§	***graeca***	WPat
	granulosa HWJ 1041	WCru
	harrowiana	GCal LLHF WMat WPGP WPat
	- KR 21009	CDul WPGP
	hedlundii	CDul EBee EBtc EPfP NLar NWea SKHP WMat WPGP
	- GWJ 9363	WCru WPGP
	- KR 1687	WPGP
	- KR 1810	WPGP
	- WJC 13806 **new**	WCru
	helenae	WPGP
	- EN 3088	GKev WPGP
	hemsleyi	CBcs CDul CLnd EPfP WPGP WPat
	- 'John Bond' 🏆H6	EBee EMOT NLar NOra SPoG WMat
	× ***hostii***	CLnd
	hugh-mcallisteri CLD 310	EBee GKev
	hupehensis misapplied	see *S. pseudohupehensis*
	- white-berried	see *S. glabriuscula*
	aff. ***hupehensis*** misapplied	ECrN EMOT EWTr NOrn WFar WTSh
	hupehensis C.K. Schneid. 'November Pink'	see *S. pseudohupehensis* 'Pink Pagoda'
	- var. ***obtusa*** misapplied	see *S. pseudohupehensis* 'Pink Pagoda'
	- 'Rosea'	see *S. pseudohupehensis* 'Pink Pagoda'
	hybrida L.	ECrN
	- 'Gibbsii' 🏆H6	EBee ELan EPfP ESps EWTr MAsh NOra NOrn WHar WMat
	insignis	LLHF WPGP WPat
	intermedia	CAco CBcs CCVT CDul CLnd CTho CTri CWib ECrN ELan ESps MMuc NWea SEND SGol WHar WHed WMou
	- 'Brouwers'	CLnd ELan
	japonica	CDul EBee WMat
	- B&SWJ 10813	WCru
	- B&SWJ 11048	WCru
	'Joseph Rock'	Widely available
	aff. ***karchungii*** AGS/ES 347	WPGP
I	***keenanii*** KR 7746	EBee WPGP
	- NJM 12.029 **new**	WPGP
	- NJM 13.050 **new**	WPGP
	keissleri NJM 11.004 **new**	WPGP
	- NJM 11.056 **new**	WPGP
	- NJM 11.060 **new**	WPGP
	- PAB 7916 **new**	LEdu
	'Keith Rushforth' **new**	WCru
§	× ***kewensis***	CDul CLnd NWea SPlb
	khumbuensis	GKev
	'Kirsten Pink'	CWib EBee
	koehneana misapplied	see *S. frutescens*
	koehneana ambig.	GEdr
§	***koehneana*** C.K. Schneid.	CLnd CMCN ELan GKev GQui MMrt NWea WCru WMou WPat
	aff. ***koehneana*** C.K. Schneid.	see *S. eburnea*, *S. tenuis*
	lanata misapplied	see *S. vestita*
	latifolia	CLnd NWea
	- 'Henk Vink'	CCVT
	'Leonard Messel' 🏆H6	EPfP MAsh NLar NOra WHCr WMat
	'Likjornaja'	EPfP LRHS
§	'Lombarts Golden Wonder'	CBcs CDul MMuc NWea SEND
*	***maculata*** KR 5334	GKev
	matsumurana misapplied	see *S. commixta*
	matsumurana (Makino) Koehne	WPGP
	megalocarpa	CJun CMCN EBee SKHP WPGP
	- var. ***cuneata*** **new**	WPGP
	meliosmifolia B&SWJ 11709	WCru
	microphylla agg.	CMCN GKev
	- GWJ 9252	WCru
	- SICH 1009	EBee
	minima	WPat
	monbeigii (Cardot.) N.P. Balakr.	CLnd
	moravica 'Laciniata'	see *S. aucuparia* 'Beissneri'
	muliensis F 22177	EBee GKev
§	***munda***	EBee
	needhamii NJM 11.005	WPGP
	- PAB 9853	LEdu
	olivacea	EPfP
	aff. ***ovalis*** H 1948	EBee
	paniculata NJM 13.067 **new**	WPGP
	- NJM 13.092 **new**	WPGP
	- PAB 9831 **new**	LEdu
	parvifructa	GKev WPGP
	'Peaches and Cream'	LOPS
	'Pearly King'	CTho MAsh WJas
§	'Pink Pearl'	CDul EPfP
	'Pink-Ness'	EPfP MBlu NOra SCoo WMat
	pohuashanensis misapplied	see *S.* × *kewensis*
	porrigentiformis	CDul
	poteriifolia 🏆H5	EBee GEdr GKev NHar WPat
	prattii misapplied	see *S. munda*
	prattii Koehne var. ***subarachnoidea*** (Koehen) Rehder	see *S. munda*
§	***pseudohupehensis*** 🏆H6	CBcs CDul CLnd CMCN CMac CTho CTri EBee EPfP EWTr GKev GLog MHid MMuc MRav NWea SEND SGol SPer WHar WJas
§	- 'Pink Pagoda' 🏆H6	Widely available
	pseudovilmorinii	CDul GKev LRHS NLar NOra WCru WMat
	- SBEC 974 **new**	WPGP
	randaiensis	EBee GKev GQui SPlb WPGP
	- B&SWJ 156 **new**	WPGP
	- B&SWJ 3202	EPfP WCru
	'Red Robin'	IBoy
	'Red Tip'	CDul
	reducta 🏆H5	GAbr GBin GCal GKev GQui MMuc NHar NHol NLar NSla SBrt SPer WPat
	aff. ***reducta***	MHid
	reflexipetala misapplied	see *S. commixta*

rehderiana misapplied	see *S. aucuparia*
rehderiana Koehne	GKev
- AC 3459	MHid
rosea	GEdr GKev
- SEP 492	WCru WPGP
- 'Rosiness' 🏆H6	EBee EPfP LRHS WHar WMat
'Rowancroft Coral Pink'	EBee
rubescens	GKev
- Yu 1381	EBee
rupicola	NWea
rushforthii KR 5789	GKev
rutilans	GKev
'Salmon Queen'	CLnd
sambucifolia	EBee SKHP
sargentiana 🏆H6	CCVT CDul CEnd CLnd CMCN CMac CTho CTri EBee ECrN ELan EMOT EPfP ESps GQui MBlu MGos MRav MSwo NLar NOra NOrn NWea SLim SMad SPer SPoG WMat WPat
- EGM 291	WCru
'Savill Orange'	MMuc
scalaris ambig.	CBcs CMCN CNWT ELan MAsh MSwo NOra NWea WHar WMou
§ ***scalaris*** Koehne	CCVT CDul CEnd CTho CTri EBee EPfP ESps LHop MBlu SPer WJas WMat
'Schouten'	ECrN MMuc
scopulina misapplied	see *S. aucuparia* 'Fastigiata'
(sect. ***Discolores***) KR 5585	GKev WCru WPGP
- KR 6308	WCru
subulata HWJ 925	WCru
- KWJ 12272	WCru
'Sunshine'	CCVT CDul CLnd EMOT ESps EWTr MAsh MGos MMuc SEND WJas
§ ***tenuis*** new	GKev
§ ***thibetica*** 'John Mitchell' 🏆H6	CAgr CDul CEnd CLnd CMCN CWib EBee ECrN EPfP ESps MBlu MGos NLar NOra NOrn NWea SLim WMat
aff. ***thibetica*** BWJ 7757a	WCru
thomsonii GWJ 9363	WCru
- HWJ 984	WCru
- WWJ 12004	WCru
§ × ***thuringiaca*** 'Fastigiata'	CBcs CCVT CDul CLnd EBar EBee EPfP NEgg SCoo WJas WMat
tianschanica	WCru
'Titan'	EPfP
× ***tomentella***	CLnd
torminalis	CAgr CBcs CCVT CDul CHab CLnd CMCN CMac CTho CTri ELan EPfP ESps LEdu MGos MHid MMuc MRav NLar NWea SCoo SEND SEWo SPer WHar WHed WMou WTSh
umbellata var. ***cretica***	see *S. graeca*
§ ***vestita***	CLnd CMCN CTho EPfP WCru
vexans	CDul WPat
vilmorinii 🏆H6	Widely available
- 'Pink Charm'	EBee EPfP NOra WMat
- 'Robusta'	see *S.* 'Pink Pearl'
aff. ***vilmorinii***	EMOT ESps GKin IBoy LOPS MJak
- KR 6453	WCru WPGP
wardii	CDul CTho EPfP LRHS MBlu WPat
- KR 21127 new	WPGP
'White Wax'	CDul EMOT EWTr MGos NWea SPer SPoG
wilmottiana	CDul WPat
wilsoniana	CLnd GGGa GQui
- NN 0929	MHid
'Wisley Gold' 🏆H6	EBee EMOT LRHS MAsh NOra SCoo SLim WMat
yuana	EBee WPGP
- clone 1 new	WPGP
- clone 2 new	WPGP

Sorghastrum (*Poaceae*)

avenaceum	see *S. nutans*
§ ***nutans***	CBod
- 'Indian Steel'	CBod EBee LSun XLum

sorrel, common see *Rumex acetosa*

sorrel, French see *Rumex scutatus*

Souliea see *Actaea*

Sparaxis (*Iridaceae*)

'Bright Star' new	GKev
bulbifera	ECho
caryophyllacea new	NRog
elegans	SPlb
'Fire King'	GKev NRog
grandiflora subsp. ***acutiloba***	CTre ECho NRog
- subsp. ***grandiflora***	CGrW CTre ECho
mixed	NRog SDeJ
'Moonlight'	GKev LAma NRog
parviflora	ECho
'Red Reflex'	ECho GKev NRog
'Sunshine'	GKev LAma NRog
tricolor	CAby CGrW CTre ECho GKev NRog SDeJ
variegata	ECho
villosa	ECho NRog

Sparganium (*Sparganiaceae*)

§ ***erectum***	CWat NMir NPer SWat WMAq WSFF XLum
ramosum	see *S. erectum*

Sparrmannia (*Malvaceae*)

africana 🏆H1c	CCCN CHll ELan EShb SEND SPlb SVen
- 'Flore Pleno' (d)	CBcs

Spartina (*Poaceae*)

pectinata	SGol XLum
- 'Aureomarginata' (v)	CBod CWCL EBee EHoe ELan EPfP GMaP GMcL GNew LRHS MMuc NLar NRHS NWsh SEND SPer WMoo WWtn XLum

Spartium (*Papilionaceae*)

junceum 🏆H5	CAco CArn CBcs CDul CEnd CWld EBee ECrN ELan ELon EPfP ESps LRHS MGos MMuc SCob SDix SEND SPer SRms XSen
- 'Brockhill Compact'	ELan EPfP LRHS

Spartocytisus see *Cytisus*

Spathantheum (*Araceae*)

orbignyanum	GKev WCot

Spathipappus see *Tanacetum*

Spathiphyllum (*Araceae*)

wallisii	NGBl SPre

Spathodea (*Bignoniaceae*)

campanulata	SPlb

spearmint see *Mentha spicata*

Speirantha (*Asparagaceae*)

§ ***convallarioides***	CLAP CTal EBee ECho EHrv ELon EPPr EPfP LEdu MNrw WCru WHil WPGP
gardenii	see *S. convallarioides*

Sphacele see *Lepechinia*

Sphaeralcea (*Malvaceae*)

ambigua	EBee SPlb XSen
'Childerley'	CSpe CWGN EBee ECtt LHop LSun MAvo SPad SPoG WCot
coccinea	EBee SPlb
fendleri	CCCN CHll CSam
- subsp. ***venusta***	LHop
grandiflora	EBee
'Hopleys Lavender'	CCCN EWoo LHop LSou SWvt
'Hyde Hall'	MHom
incana	CCCN CSpe LHop LSou MGil
- 'Sourup'	CBod CSpe EBee ECtt ELan WCot
laxa	EBee
malviflora	CDTJ
miniata	CCCN CHll
munroana	CCCN CDTJ ECtt ELan SRkn
- pale-pink-flowered	CSam ECtt
'Newleaze Coral'	CBod CCCN CWGN ELan EWoo LBMP LHop MAsh MGil MHom MNrw SPad SPoG SRkn SWvt WBor WCot WWFP
'Newleaze Pink'	SRkn
parvifolia	EBee
remota	CMea LPla SPlb
umbellata	see *Phymosia umbellata*

Sphagneticola (*Asteraceae*)

§ ***trilobata***	LLWG

Sphenomeris (*Dennstaedtiaceae*)

chinensis B&SWJ 6108	WCru

Spigelia (*Loganiaceae*)

marilandica	EBee GKev SKHP SMad WHil
- 'Red Feather'	NLar
- 'Wisley Jester'	SKHP

Spiloxene (*Hypoxidaceae*)

capensis	NRog

Spiraea (*Rosaceae*)

alba var. ***latifolia***	MMuc SEND
albiflora	see *S. japonica* 'Albiflora'
arborea	see *Sorbaria kirilowii*
§ 'Arguta' 🏆H6	Widely available
× ***arguta*** 'Bridal Wreath'	see *S.* 'Arguta'
aff. 'Arguta'	ESps GMcL SHil
betulifolia	MRav SCob WFar
- var. ***aemiliana***	CAbP MAsh MMuc SCob
- 'Tor'	CBcs CLet EPPr
- 'Tor Gold' PBR	CBcs EBee LRHS NEoE SPoG
× ***billardii*** misapplied	see *S.* × *pseudosalicifolia*
blumei CWJ 12829	WCru
× ***bumalda*** 'Wulfenii'	see *S. japonica* 'Walluf'
callosa 'Alba'	see *S. japonica* 'Albiflora'
canescens	GKin
- AC 1354	MHid
- CC 7281	EWld
- var. ***glaucophylla***	MMuc SEND
chamaedryfolia	GKev
× ***cinerea*** 'Grefsheim' 🏆H6	CAco CBcs CSBt ELan LBuc MMuc NLar SCob SEND SGol SLim SPer SPlb
crispifolia misapplied	see *S. japonica* 'Bullata'
densiflora	GKev
- var. ***splendens*** **new**	SBrt
douglasii	CMac GKev SCob
First Editions Superstar = 'Denistar' **new**	NEoE
formosana B&SWJ 1597	WCru
fritschiana	CMac
hayatana	GKev
- RWJ 10014	WCru
hendersonii	see *Petrophytum hendersonii*
henryi	GKev
japonica	ESps
§ - 'Albiflora'	CDul CLet CMac CRos CSBt CTri ECrN ELan ELon GMcL LBrs LRHS MRav MSwo NEgg NWad SCob SGbt SGol SLim SPad SPer SRms SWvt WBor WMoo
- 'Alpina'	see *S. japonica* 'Nana'
- 'Alpine Gold'	NEoE
- 'Anthony Waterer' (v)	Widely available
- 'Blenheim'	SRms
§ - 'Bullata'	CMac GCrg NLar SRms WAbe
- 'Candlelight' 🏆H6	CSBt ELan EPfP ESps GBin GKin GMcL LRHS LSou MAsh NEgg NLar SCob SCoo SGol SLim SPer SPoG SWvt WMoo
- 'Crispa'	CAco EPfP NEoE NWad WFar WGrn WMoo
- 'Dart's Red' 🏆H6	CDul CRos ELan EPfP ESps GKin IVic LRHS WMoo
- 'Firelight'	Widely available
§ - var. ***fortunei*** 'Macrophylla'	WPat
- 'Froebelii'	GMcL
§ - 'Genpei'	CMac MAsh MJak MMuc SEND SGol SPer SPoG
- 'Gold Mound'	CBar CMac CWib EHoe ELan EPfP ESps GMcL MAsh MGos MJak MMuc MRav MSwo NLar SCoo SLim SPlb SRms WFar WHar
- Golden Princess = 'Lisp' 🏆H6	CMac CRos CTri ELan EPfP ESps GMcL IBoy LBuc LRHS MAsh MGos NEgg NLar NPri SCoo SGol SHil SPer SRms SSta WFar WMoo
- 'Goldflame'	Widely available
- 'Little Princess'	Widely available
- Magic Carpet = 'Walbuma' PBR (v) 🏆H6	CBcs CRos EPfP GMcL LBuc LRHS MAsh MMuc NLar SCob SCoo SEND SPoG
- 'Magnifica'	see *S. japonica* var. *fortunei* 'Macrophylla'
§ - 'Nana' 🏆H6	CMac CSBt ECho MAsh MRav SRms
- 'Nyewoods'	see *S. japonica* 'Nana'
- 'Shiburi'	see *S. japonica* 'Albiflora'
- 'Shirobana' misapplied	see *S. japonica* 'Genpei'
- 'Shirobana'	see *S. japonica* 'Albiflora'
- 'Snow Cap'	CWib
- 'Stanton Gold' **new**	WCFE
§ - 'Walluf'	CMac CTri CWib GBin
- 'White Cloud'	CTsd
- 'White Gold' PBR	CBod CMac CSBt ELan EPfP ESps GMcL LRHS MAsh NEoE NHol

		NWad SCoo SLim SPer SPoG SWvt WMoo
	× ***margaritae***	SPer SWvt
	nipponica	CAco CBcs
	- 'Halward's Silver'	MRav NEoE
§	- 'Snowmound' 🏆^{H6}	Widely available
	- var. ***tosaensis*** misapplied	see *S. nipponica* 'Snowmound'
	- var. ***tosaensis*** (Yatabe) Makino	LHop
	palmata 'Elegans'	see *Filipendula purpurea* 'Elegans'
	prunifolia (d)	CMac ELan EPfP ESps LRHS MRav SPer WCFE WFar WGrn WPat
	× ***pseudosalicifolia*** 'Triumphans'	MMuc SEND SPer
	'Sparkling Champagne'	CSBt LBuc LCro NEoE NWad SHil SLim SLon
	thunbergii 🏆^{H6}	CBcs CDul CMac CTri CWib EPfP MMuc MRav NWea SBrt SCob SEND SGol SLim SRms WHar
	- 'Golden Times'	LRHS SPoG
	- 'Mount Fuji'	CMac CWib MRav NEoE WFar
	trilobata	ESps
	ulmaria	see *Filipendula ulmaria*
	× ***vanhouttei***	CBcs CBod CDul CTri ELan EPfP ESps MMuc MRav MSwo SEND SLim SPer SRms WFar WMoo
	- 'Gold Fountain'	CMac ELan EMil EPfP EShb ESps LSRN MMuc NHol NLar SCoo SEND SPer SPoG WFar WMoo
	- 'Pink Ice' (v)	CWib EHoe EPfP ESps LHop LPot LRHS MAsh MMuc MRav NLar SPer SPlb SPoG SWvt
	veitchii	GLog MRav
	venusta 'Magnifica'	see *Filipendula rubra* 'Venusta'

Spiranthes (*Orchidaceae*)

	cernua	NGdn
	odorata	LSou
	- 'Chadd's Ford' 🏆^{H4}	CBcs EBee ECho EHrv GKev IKil LAma LEdu LHop LRHS MBel MNrw NBir WCot WPtf WSHC
	spiralis	WHer

Spirodela (*Araceae*)

§	***polyrrhiza***	EWay

Spodiopogon (*Poaceae*)

	sibiricus	CKno EBee EHoe EPPr GBin NDov NLos SMHy SMad WPtf XLum
	- 'West Lake'	IMou

Sporobolus (*Poaceae*)

	airoides	CBod CKno EBee EHoe EPPr EShb SMHy SMad WHrl
	heterolepis	CBWd CKno CSpe EBee EHoe GBin LRHS NDov SMHy SMea SPhx WCot
	- 'Blue Dust'	NDov
I	- 'Wisconsin Strain'	EBee EPPr IMou SPhx
	wrightii	EPPr SEND SMad SPhx

Sprekelia (*Amaryllidaceae*)

	formosissima	CGrW ECho GKev LAma LEdu SDeJ SDir SPav

Stachys (*Lamiaceae*)

	aethiopica 'Danielle'	see *S. thunbergii* 'Danielle'
§	***affinis***	CArn GPoy LEdu SPlb SVic
	albens	XSen
	alpina	EBee
	balcanica	GKev
	- MESE	EBee WPGP
	'Bello Grigio' **new**	WCot
	betonica	see *S. officinalis*
§	***byzantina***	Widely available
§	- 'Big Ears'	EBee ECha ELan EPfP ESps EWTr GMaP LCro LHop LRHS LSRN MCot MGos MMuc MRav MSCN MWat SCob SPer SPhx SPoG SRms SWvt WBor WCAu WCFE WCot WFar WHoo
§	- 'Cotton Boll'	CRos ECha GBin GCal LRHS SPer WFar
	- 'Countess Helen von Stein'	see *S. byzantina* 'Big Ears'
	- 'Fuzzy Wuzzy'	CBod WFar
	- gold-leaved	see *S. byzantina* 'Primrose Heron'
	- large-leaved	see *S. byzantina* 'Big Ears'
	- 'Limelight'	ECtt WCot WSHC XLum
§	- 'Primrose Heron'	CBod EBee ECha GBin GKev LRHS MBel MRav NLar SPer SPoG SWvt WCAu XLum
	- 'Sheila McQueen'	see *S. byzantina* 'Cotton Boll'
	- 'Silky Fleece'	CBod ECha ELan EPfP GKev GWyn LRHS MMuc NBre SRms XSen
	- 'Silver Carpet'	Widely available
	chamissonis var. ***cooleyae***	EBee GBin
	citrina	CMea GCal XSen
	coccinea	CPla ECtt EWld GEdr WMoo
	densiflora	see *S. monieri* (Gouan) P.W. Ball
§	***discolor***	CFis CMea EWes IKil LRHS NLar WCAu WCot
	germanica	NBre
	grandidentata	WPGP
	grandiflora	see *S. macrantha*
	'Hidalgo'	CSpe
	lanata Jacq.	see *S. byzantina*
	lavandulifolia	WAbe XSen
§	***macrantha***	CBod CKno CMac CTri ECha EWTr GKev GLog LEdu LRHS LSRN MArt NBir NChi NSti SPhx SRms SWat WCFE WCot
*	- 'Alba'	ECha
	- 'Ben' (v)	LEdu MAvo
	- 'Hummelo'	see *S. officinalis* 'Hummelo'
	- 'Morning Blush'	CAby GEdr SPhx WFar
*	- 'Nivea'	CSam ELan NBir
	- 'Pink Barrels' **new**	IRob
	- 'Robusta' 🏆^{H7}	ELan ELon GCal LEdu MAvo MMuc NBro NGdn WCot
	- 'Rosea'	CElw ELan GMaP LLWP LRHS MArl MAvo SCob SPlb SWat
	- 'Superba' 🏆^{H7}	CSpe ECtt EPfP ESps GCra GMaP IBoy LEdu MAvo MRav NEgg NLar SCob SPer SWvt WBor WCot WFar WMoo XLum
	- 'Violacea' 🏆^{H7}	EBee GKev MBrN NChi WCot WOut
	mexicana misapplied	see *S. thunbergii*
	monieri misapplied	see *S. officinalis*
	monieri ambig.	GKev NLar NSti WOut
§	***monieri*** (Gouan) P.W. Ball	LEdu NCGa
*	- 'Rosea'	CBre EBee LEdu NBre NDov NLar SRms
	nivea	see *S. discolor*
	obliqua	NBre WOut
§	***officinalis***	CArn CCVN CHab CWld EBee ESps GPoy ILea LEdu MHer MMuc MNHC NMir NRya SRms WCot WHer WJek WOut WTre

- 'Alba'	CArn EBee LEdu MMuc NBro SCob
- 'Cally Bicolor'	GCal
- 'Cally Pink'	GCal
- dwarf, white-flowered	CBre GCal
§ - 'Hummelo'	Widely available
- 'Marchant's Pink'	SMHy
- 'Pink Cotton Candy'	EBee STPC WNPC
- 'Powder Puff'	EBee
- 'Rosea'	CCVN EAJP GCal GQue NBro SCob WFar
- 'Rosea Superba'	ECha NBre SDix WCot
- 'Saharan Pink'	CMHG EPfP IPot LSRN NLar WOut
- 'Spitzenberg'	LPla
- 'Wisley White'	CAby CBre ECtt GQue LEdu LPot LRHS MHol NHpl NPri NRHS SRms WCot WFar WOut
olympica	see *S. byzantina*
ossetica	CFis EBee GEdr
palustris	CArn CBod CHab EBee EWay LLWG MMuc MWts NLar NMir SEND
- from Islay, Hebrides	MMuc SEND
- pale-flowered	WOut
recta	EBee
setifera	NBre XLum
spicata	see *S. macrantha*
sylvatica	CHab NMir WHer WOut WSFF
thirkei	WCot XSen
§ ***thunbergii***	LEdu MBrN WHal WHrl WPGP
§ - 'Danielle'	CBod CElw ECtt GJos LRHS NLar NRHS SDys SPhx SRkn SRms WOut
tuberifera	see *S. affinis*
tymphaea	XSen

Stachyurus (*Stachyuraceae*)

chinensis	CBcs CJun CMCN CTri CWib MGos NLar
- 'Celina' ♀H4	CJun EPfP GKin LRHS MGos NLar SHil SPoG
- 'Goldbeater'	NLar
- 'Joy Forever' (v) ♀H4	CBcs CBot CEnd CMac EBee EMil EPfP IArd IVic LLHF LRHS LSRN MGos MMuc NLar SHil SKHP SLim SPer SPoG SSta SWvt
- 'Senna'	NLar
- 'Wonderful Image'	NLar
himalaicus	CBcs NLar
- HWJCM 009	WCru
- HWJK 2035	WCru
'Magpie' (v)	CJun EPfP NLar WFar
- pink-flowered HWJK 2052 new	WCru
praecox ♀H5	Widely available
- B&SWJ 8898	WCru
- B&SWJ 10899	IDee LCro LHop WCru
- var. ***leucotrichus***	CJun NLar
- var. ***matsuzakii***	CJun NLar
- - B&SWJ 2817	WCru
- - B&SWJ 11229	WCru
- - 'Issai'	LRHS SHil
- 'Petra'	CJun
'Rubriflorus'	CJun EPfP LRHS MAsh NLar
salicifolius	CBcs CBot CFil CJun CTho EBee EPfP IDee NLar SChF SKHP WPat
sigeyosii	CBcs CFil
- B&SWJ 6915	WCru
- CWJ 12420	WCru
- RWJ 10094	WCru
aff. ***szechuanensis*** BWJ 8153	WCru
yunnanensis	CBcs CFil CJun IArd IDee NLar WSHC

Staehelina (*Asteraceae*)

dubia	SBrt

Staphylea ✿ (*Staphyleaceae*)

bolanderi	CBcs NLar
bumalda	CJun LEdu NLar
- B&SWJ 11053	WCru
- B&SWJ 12744 from Korea	WCru
colchica	CBcs CDul CHll CJun CMCN ELan EPfP ESwi EWTr EWes LEdu LRHS MGos MMrt MRav NLar SPer WKif WSHC
holocarpa	CJun EPfP
- 'Innocence'	CBcs LRHS
- var. ***rosea***	CBcs CJun EPfP MBlu NLar SAko SMad SWvt
pinnata	CAgr CBcs CJun EBtc EPfP IVic MCoo MMuc NLar SEND
- PAB 8427	LEdu
trifolia	CBcs CJun EBee ESwi

Statice see *Limonium*

Stauntonia (*Lardizabalaceae*)

sp.	CKel
FMWJ 13177 from northern Vietnam	WCru
- NJM 09.198 new	WPGP
- NJM 10.133 new	WPGP
- NJM 10.153 new	WPGP
aff. ***chinensis*** DJHV 06175	WCru
hexaphylla	CBcs CCCN CHll CTri CWGN EBee EPfP ESwi EUJe LEdu LRHS MAsh MGil NLar SAdn SKHP SNig SPer SPoG SSta WSHC
- B&SWJ 4858	WCru
aff. ***libera*** KWJ 12218	WCru
aff. ***maculata*** FMWJ 13055	WCru
obovata CWJ 12353	WCru
obovatifoliola B&SWJ 3685	WCru
purpurea B&SWJ 3690	WCru
yaoshanensis B&SWJ 8223	WCru
- HWJ 1024	WCru WPGP

Stegnogramma (*Thelypteridaceae*)

pozoi	EFer

Stellaria (*Caryophyllaceae*)

graminea	CHab
holostea	CHab CWld MMuc NBir NMir WHer WPtf WShi

Stemmacantha (*Asteraceae*)

carthamoides	CArn
§ ***centaureoides***	CAby CBWd CBod CBot CDor EBee ECGP ECha ELon EWTr GCal GQue IBoy IPot LRHS MAvo MBel MHol MSpe MTis NBid NSti SBrt WCot

Stenanthium (*Melanthiaceae*)

gramineum	CFil EWes WPGP

Stenoglottis (*Orchidaceae*)

longifolia ♀H1b	WCot

Stenomesson (*Amaryllidaceae*)

coccineum	NRog
incarnatum apricot-flowered	NRog
pearcei	ECho GKev NRog WCot
variegatum	WCot
- orange-flowered	NRog
- red-flowered	NRog
- yellow-flowered	NRog WCot

Stenotaphrum (*Poaceae*)

secundatum 'Variegatum' (v) ♀H1c	EShb LSou XLum

Stephanandra (*Rosaceae*)

incisa	CBcs SCob
§ - 'Crispa'	CDul CMac CTri EBee ELan EPfP EWTr GKin GMcL IDee LHop MBlu MJak MRav NEgg NHol SCob SPer WMoo
- 'Prostrata'	see *S. incisa* 'Crispa'
tanakae	CBcs CDul CTri EBee ELan EPfP EWTr MBlu MGil MRav NEgg SLon SPer

Stephania (*Menispermaceae*)

japonica CWJ 12823	WCru
longa KWJ 12163	WCru
sinica BWJ 8094	WCru
aff. ***tetrandra*** WWJ 11896	WCru

Stephanotis (*Apocynaceae*)

floribunda ♀H1b	CBcs CCCN

Sterculia (*Malvaceae*)

rupestris	see *Brachychiton rupestris*

Sternbergia (*Amaryllidaceae*)

'Autumn Gold'	ECho
candida	CBro NRog
colchiciflora	NRog
fischeriana	CBro NRog
greuteriana	ECho GKev NRog
lutea ♀H4	CAvo CBro CTal CTri ECha ECho EPfP EPot ERCP EWes GKev LAma LCro LHop LOPS LRHS NRHS NRog SBch SCob SDeJ SDix WHoo XLum
- Angustifolia Group	CAvo CBro CMea ECho WCot
sicula	CBro EBee ECho EPot GKev NRog
- 'Arcadian Sun'	ECho GKev NRog
- 'Dodona Gold' new	NRog
- var. ***graeca***	CTal ECho NRog
- - from Crete	ECho
- 'John Marr'	WThu

Stevia (*Asteraceae*)

rebaudiana	CArn CBod ENfk GPoy SHDw SRms WCot WJek

Stewartia ✿ (*Theaceae*)

sp.	LPar
gemmata	see *S. sinensis*
'Korean Splendor'	see *S. pseudocamellia* Koreana Group
koreana	see *S. pseudocamellia* Koreana Group
monadelpha	CBcs CJun CMen LRHS MBlu MPkF NLar
ovata	LRHS
pseudocamellia ♀H5	Widely available
- B&SWJ 11044 from North Japan	WCru
§ - Koreana Group ♀H5	CDul CEnd CJun CMCN EBee EPfP GKin LRHS NLar SLim
- 'Ogisu'	NLar
pteropetiolata	CMHG IVic
- B&SWJ 11726	WCru
- NJM 10.107	WPGP
- WWJ 11939	WCru
rostrata	CBcs CJun ELan LRHS MBlu MPkF NLar
- 'Hulsdonk Pink'	CJun
serrata	CJun CMen MPkF WCru WPGP
§ ***sinensis*** ♀H5	CBcs CCCN CJun EPfP IArd IDee IMou LRHS MBlu MPkF NLar SAko WBod WPGP

Stigmaphyllon (*Malpighiaceae*)

ciliatum	CCCN
littorale	CCCN

Stipa (*Poaceae*)

F&M 248	EBee
arundinacea	see *Anemanthele lessoniana*
- 'Sunrise'	EAEE
barbata	CKno CSpe EAJP ECha ELon EPPr ETod EWes GBin NCGa SCob WKif XSen
- 'Silver Feather'	CBot ETod WPtf
brachytricha	see *Calamagrostis brachytricha*
§ ***calamagrostis***	Widely available
- 'Allgäu'	WCot
- 'Lemperg'	CRos IMou LRHS NDov NRHS
capillata	CBod EBee EPPr GBin GCal IBoy LRHS MBel MNrw MSpe NDov NRHS SDix XSen
- 'Brautschleier'	CBod CWib
comata	SPhx
elegantissima	CKno EHoe NLos SHDw
extremiorientalis	EPPr EWoo SEND SMad
gigantea ♀H7	Widely available
- 'Gold Fontaene'	CKno CRos EPPr EPfP EWes LRHS MAvo MNrw NDov NRHS SMHy SMad WCot WMoo WPGP
- 'Pixie'	CRos LRHS NRHS
grandis	EPPr WMoo
ichu	CKno CRos LRHS MAvo NDov NLos NRHS SDix SHDw SMad
- F&M 32	CFil WPGP
joannis	EBee GCal
lasiagrostis	see *S. calamagrostis*
leptostachya	WCot
lessingiana	EBee EHoe EMFm EPPr EPed ETod LRHS NLos SEND SPhx WMoo
offneri	EPPr
papposa	SPhx
pennata	CBod EPPr ETod XSen
pseudoichu	CBod CFil CSpe EMFm EPPr ESwi ETod GBin LPla LRHS MAvo MBel MSpe SMad WCot WRHF
- RCB/Arg Y-1	EBee ELon NCGa
pulcherrima	EPPr GCal
ramosissima	CKno
robusta	SPhx
splendens misapplied	see *S. calamagrostis*
splendens Trin.	ECha GCal SAko
stenophylla	see *S. tirsa*
tenacissima	CDul GMcL IBoy MAsh
tenuifolia misapplied	see *S. tenuissima*

tenuifolia Steud.	CMea EBee EPfP ESps LRHS MRav NBir NBro NSti WHal WMoo XLum XSen
§ ***tenuissima***	Widely available
- 'Wind Whispers'	CBod CSpe LEdu LRHS MBel
§ ***tirsa***	GCal
turkestanica	NDov SWat
ucrainica	NDov

Stoebe (*Asteraceae*)

alopecuroides	SPlb

Stokesia ✿ (*Asteraceae*)

cyanea	see *S. laevis*
§ ***laevis***	ECha EPfP LRHS NLar SCob SPlb WCAu WMoo
- 'Alba'	CBod CCVN ECha EHrv ELan EPfP EPri LEdu LRHS MRav NLar WCAu
- 'Blue Star'	CAby CBcs CBod CDor CSam CWGN ELan ELon EPfP EWoo LEdu LRHS LSun MBel MHer MRav NPnk SGbt SPad SPer SPhx SPoG SRkn SWvt WGwG WHoo WHrl WMoo WSHC
- 'Color Wheel'	CMos ECtt LRHS SCob
- 'Honeysong Purple'	NLar
- 'Klaus Jelitto'	CBod CRos IPot LEdu LRHS MAvo NRHS SPoG WHrl
- 'Mary Gregory'	CAby CBod CMac CSam EBee ECtt EHrv ELan EPfP IKil LEdu LRHS LSou MBel MNrw MRav NLar NPnk SPer SPhx SRGP SWvt WGwG WHrl
- 'Mel's Blue'	ECtt LRHS NAst NPri WTor
- mixed	CPou
- 'Omega Skyrocket'	CPou
- 'Peach Melba'	ECtt NCGa WMoo
- 'Peachie's Pick'	EBee ECtt
- 'Purple Parasols'	CBod CCVN CDor CMac CWGN ECtt EPfP IKil LRHS LSou MBel NCGa NPnk SCob SPoG STPC SWvt WHrl WMoo
- 'Purple Pixie'PBR	ECtt LRHS
- 'Silver Moon'	CMos ECtt EPfP GBin LRHS MBel MTPN NPnk SPer STPC WGwG WHrl
§ - 'Träumerei'	CBod CWGN EAEE EBee ECtt EPfP LRHS NLar NPnk WHrl WMoo XLum
- 'White Star'	see *S. laevis* 'Träumerei'

Stranvaesia see *Photinia*

× *Stranvinia* see *Photinia*

Stratiotes (*Hydrocharitaceae*)

aloides	CBen CWat EWay MWts NPer SVic SWat WMAq WPnP

strawberry see *Fragaria*

Strelitzia (*Strelitziaceae*)

alba	CCCN
juncea	XBlo
nicolai	CCCN NPer SPlb XBlo
reginae 🏆H1c	CAbb CBcs CCCN CTsd ELan EShb ETod EUJe LCro NPer NPla SBig SChr SEND SPlb XBlo
- 'Kirstenbosch Gold'	XBlo

Streptocarpella see *Streptocarpus*

Streptocarpus ✿ (*Gesneriaceae*)

'Adele'	WDib
'Albatross'	CTsd WDib
'Alissa'	WDib
'Amanda' Dibley	WDib
'Ambiente' 🏆H1c	WDib
'Anne' (d)	CTsd WDib
'Awena'	WDib
baudertii	WDib
'Bella'	WDib
'Bethan' 🏆H1c	CTsd WDib
'Bianca'	WDib
'Black Gardenia'	CTsd WDib
'Black Panther'	CTsd WDib
'Blue Frills' 🏆H1c	WDib
'Blue Gem'	WDib
'Blue Leyla'	see *S.* 'Leyla'
'Blue Moon'	WDib
'Blue Nymph'	WDib
'Blushing Bride' (d)	WDib
'Boysenberry Delight'	WDib
'Branwen'	CTsd WDib
'Bristol's Black Bird'	WDib
'Bristol's Very Best'	WDib
caeruleus	WDib
'Caitlin'	CTsd WDib
candidus	WDib
'Cappuccino'	WDib
'Cariad' new	WDib
'Carol'	WDib
'Carys' 🏆H1c	CTsd WDib
caulescens	WDib
- var. ***pallescens***	WDib
'Celebration'	WDib
'Charlotte' 🏆H1c	WDib
'Chloe'	WDib
'Chorus Line'	CTsd WDib
'Concord Blue'	WDib
'Constant Nymph'	WDib
'Crystal Beauty'	WDib
'Crystal Blush'	WDib
'Crystal Charm'	WDib
'Crystal Dawn'	WDib
'Crystal Ice'PBR 🏆H1c	LCro LOPS WDib
'Crystal Snow'	WDib
'Crystal Wonder'	WDib
cyaneus	WDib
- subsp. ***polackii***	WDib
'Cynthia'	WDib
'Daphne'	WDib
'Dee'	WDib
'Delia'	WDib
'Denim'	WDib
denticulatus	WDib
'Diana'	WDib
'Dinas'	WDib
'Ds-Horus' new	WDib
dunnii	WDib
'Ellie'	WDib
'Elsi'	CTsd WDib
'Emily'	WDib
'Eve'	NWad WDib
'Falling Stars' 🏆H1c	CTsd WDib
'Festival Wales'	WDib
'Fiona'	WDib
floribundus	WDib
'Franken Alayana' new	WDib
'Franken Isabella' new	WDib
'Franken Skye' new	WDib

'Franken Strawberry Fondant' **new**	WDib
'Frosty Diamond' 🏆H1c	CTsd WDib
'Full Moon'	WDib
gardenii	WDib
glandulosissimus 🏆H1c	WDib
'Gloria' 🏆H1c	CTsd WDib
'Gwen'	WDib
'Hannah' 🏆H1c	WDib
'Harlequin Blue' PBR 🏆H1c	WDib
'Harlequin Damsel'	WDib
'Harlequin Dawn'	WDib
'Harlequin Delft'	WDib
'Harlequin Lace' 🏆H1c	WDib
'Harlequin Purple'	WDib
'Harriet'	WDib
'Hayley'	WDib
'Heidi'	CTsd WDib
'Helen'	CTsd WDib
'Hope'	WDib
'Iona'	WDib
'Isabella'	WDib
'Jacquie'	WDib
'Jennifer' 🏆H1c	WDib
'Jessica' 🏆H1c	WDib
'Joanna'	CTsd WDib
johannis	WDib
'Joy'	WDib
'Karen'	WDib
'Katie' PBR 🏆H1c	WDib
kentaniensis	WDib
'Kim' 🏆H1c	WDib
kirkii	WDib
'Laura' 🏆H1c	WDib
§ 'Leyla' PBR	WDib
'Louise'	WDib
'Lucy'	WDib
'Lyndee'	WDib
'Lynne'	WDib
'Maassen's White'	WDib
'Margaret' Gavin Brown	WDib
'Marie'	WDib
'Marion' **new**	WDib
'Megan'	WDib
'Melanie' Dibley	WDib
meyeri	WDib
'Midnight Flame'	CTsd WDib
'Mini Nymph'	WDib
modestus	WDib
'Myfanwy'	WDib
'Natalie'	WDib
'Nerys'	CTsd WDib
'Nia'	CTsd WDib
'Nicola'	CTsd WDib
'Olga'	WDib
'Olivia'	WDib
'Padarn'	WDib
'Paula'	WDib
'Pearl' 🏆H1c	WDib
pentherianus	WDib
'Pink Leyla' PBR 🏆H1c	WDib
'Pink Souffle'	WDib
'Polka-Dot Purple' **new**	WDib
polyanthus subsp. ***dracomontanus***	WDib
primulifolius	WDib
- subsp. ***formosus***	WDib
'Princesse' (Marleen Series)	WDib
prolixus	WDib
rexii	WDib
'Rhiannon'	CTsd WDib
'Rose Halo'	WDib
'Rosebud'	WDib
(Roulette Series) 'Roulette Azur' PBR 🏆H1c	WDib
- 'Roulette Cherry'	WDib
'Rubina' PBR	WDib
'Rubina Pink' 🏆H1c	WDib
'Ruby'	CTsd WDib
'Ruth'	WDib
'Sally'	WDib
'Sandra'	WDib
'Sarah'	WDib
saxorum	CCCN CTsd WDib
- compact 🏆H1c	CCCN WDib
'Scarlett'	WDib
'Seren'	WDib
'Sian'	WDib
silvaticus	WDib
'Sioned' 🏆H1c	WDib
'Snow White' 🏆H1c	WDib
'Spirit' PBR 🏆H1c	WDib
'Stella' PBR 🏆H1c	WDib
'Stephanie'	WDib
stomandrus	WDib
'Susan' 🏆H1c	CTsd WDib
'Sweet Melys'	WDib
'Tanya' **new**	WDib
'Targa' (Marleen Series)	WDib
'Teleri'	WDib
'Texas Hot Chili'	CTsd WDib
thompsonii	WDib
'Tina' 🏆H1c	WDib
'Tracey'	WDib
vandeleurii	WDib
variabilis	WDib
'Watermelon Wine'	WDib
wendlandii	WDib
'Wendy'	WDib
'White Butterfly' 🏆H1c	WDib
'Wiesmoor Red'	WDib
'Winifred'	WDib

Streptopus (*Liliaceae*)

amplexifolius	EBee ECho EHrv GAbr GBin MNrw WCru
roseus	ECho WCru
streptopoides	EBee EPPr EPfP LEdu LRHS MMrt

Streptosolen (*Solanaceae*)

jamesonii 🏆H1c	CHll EBak EShb SWvt

Strobilanthes (*Acanthaceae*)

sp.	WBor
anisophylla	EShb SDys
- Brunetthy ='Lankveld15' PBR **new**	EBee
atropurpurea misapplied	see *S. attenuata*
atropurpurea Nees	see *S. wallichii*
§ ***attenuata***	CWld EBee ECtt EPfP GCal GCra IBoy ILea ITim IVic LEdu LHop LRHS MBel MRav NChi NDov NSti SDix SPad SPoG WCru WMoo
- 'Blue Carpet'	EBee NDov
- 'Cally Bicolor'	GCal
- subsp. ***nepalensis***	CHll XLum
dyeriana 🏆H1b	EBak MPie SPlb WCot
flexicaulis	MHer
- B&SWJ 354	WCru
aff. ***inflata*** B&SWJ 7754	WCru

* ***lactea***	EShb
nutans	CPou EBee EWld NSti SBrt XLum
pentstemonoides	GCal WCot
aff. ***pentstemonoides*** HWJK 2019	WCru
rankanensis	EBee EPPr SDys SHar XLum
- B&SWJ 1771	WCru
violacea misapplied	EShb IArd LHop
§ ***wallichii***	CMac EBee EPfP EWes EWld LLWP MMuc NSti SEND WCAu WCru WMoo
- PAB 8440	LEdu

Stromanthe (*Marantaceae*)

sanguinea 'Triostar'^{PBR} (v)	XBlo

Strophanthus (*Apocynaceae*)

speciosus	CCCN CHII EShb

Strumaria (*Amaryllidaceae*)

chaplinii	NRog
discifera subsp. ***bulbifera***	NRog WCot
gemmata	NRog
karooica	NRog
salteri	NRog
tenella subsp. ***orientalis***	NRog
truncata	NRog
watermeyeri subsp. ***watermeyeri***	NRog

Stuartia see *Stewartia*

Stylidium (*Stylidiaceae*)

graminifolium	CTsd SPlb
- Little Saphire = 'St116'	SRot

Stylophorum (*Papaveraceae*)

diphyllum	CPou EWld GCal IMou LEdu MAvo MPie WCru WPGP WPnP WWtn
lasiocarpum	CSpe EBee EPPr EWes EWld GEdr MArt MMrt NBid WCot WCru WHil

Stypandra (*Phormiaceae*)

glauca	CLak

Styphelia (*Ericaceae*)

colensoi	see *Leucopogon colensoi*

Styphnolobium (*Papilionaceae*)

§ ***japonicum***	CAbP CAco CBcs CDul CHab CLet CLnd CMCN CTho CWib EPfP EWTr SCob SPlb WTSh
- 'Flavirameum'	LRHS
- 'Pendulum'	CDul NPri

Styrax ✿ (*Styracaceae*)

NJM 11.013 from Guizhou, China **new**	WPGP
NJM 11.085 from Guizhou, China **new**	WPGP
americanus	NLar
confusus	CBcs
dasyanthus	CBcs
faberi	CBcs
formosanus	CBcs CFil CJun EBee EPfP MBlu
var. ***formosanus***	WPGP
- - B&SWJ 3803	WCru
- - B&SWJ 6786	WCru
- var. ***hayatiana*** B&SWJ 6823	WCru
hemsleyanus ♀^{H5}	CBcs CTho EPfP LEdu MBlu MMuc NLar SPer
japonicus	CAco CBcs CDul CEnd CMCN CTho CTri CWib ELan EPfP ESps GKin LRHS MAsh MBlu MGos MMuc MRav NLar SPer SPoG SReu WPGP
- B&SWJ 4405	WCru
- B&SWJ 8770	WCru
- B&SWJ 11078	WCru
- Guiz 216	WPGP
- PAB 8366	LEdu
§ - Benibana Group	WPGP
- - 'Pink Chimes'	CBcs CEnd CJun CMCN CMac EBee ELan EPfP ESwi GKin IDee MBlu MMrt MPkF NLar NOra WGob WMat
- 'Carillon'	CJun
- 'Evening Light' **new**	CBcs
- 'Fargesii' ♀^{H5}	CBcs CDul CJun CTho EPfP IVic LRHS SKHP
- 'Fragrant Fountain'	MBlu NLar
- 'Pendulus'	EBee EPfP LRHS NLar SMad WPGP
I - 'Pink Snowbell' **new**	LRHS
- 'Purple Dress' ♀^{H5}	CJun MBlu NLar
- 'Roseus'	see *S. japonicus* Benibana Group
- 'Snowfall'	CJun NLar
- 'Sohuksan' ♀^{H5}	CFil CJun LRHS MBlu WPGP
limprichtii	CFil
obassia	CBcs CDul CMCN CTho EPfP IVic LRHS MBlu NLar WGob WPGP
- B&SWJ 6023	WCru
- B&SWJ 10890	WCru
officinalis	CJun
platanifolius var. ***mollis***	CFil
redivivus	SBrt
shiraianus	CFil NLar WPGP
suberifolius WWJ 11868	WCru
* ***taiwanensis***	SKHP
tonkinensis FMWJ 13134	WCru
wuyuanensis	CBcs WPGP

Succisa (*Caprifoliaceae*)

§ ***pratensis***	CAby CArn CBod CDor CHab CMac CWld EPri EWld LEdu LHop LLWG MHer MPie NLar SBch SMHy SPhx WCAu WHer WHoo WPGP WPtf WSFF WWFP XLum
- 'Alba'	EWes
- 'Cassop'	NRya
- 'Derby Purple'	CSpe WPtf
- early-flowering **new**	LEdu
- 'Peddar's Pink'	EWes LEdu LLWG SPhx

Succisella (*Caprifoliaceae*)

inflexa	EBee LEdu LRHS MSpe SPhx
- 'Frosted Pearls'	CElw CFis CMHG LEdu LLWP LRHS LSun MAvo MMuc WWFP

Sullivantia (*Saxifragaceae*)

sullivantii dwarf	WThu

sunberry see *Rubus* 'Sunberry'

Sutera (*Scrophulariaceae*)

(Abunda Series) Abunda Colossal Sky Blue = 'Balabolav'	LBMP
- Abunda Colossal Pink	LBMP
- Abunda Colossal White = 'Balabowite'^{PBR}	LBMP NPri

	cordata 'Blizzard'	LSou
	- 'Olympic Gold' (v)	SCoo
	- (Scopia Series) Scopia Golden Leaves White = 'Dancop15'	NPri
	- - Scopia Great Classic Pink = 'Dancop46'	NPri
§	- 'Snowflake'	NPer SCoo SPoG SWvt
	Great Purple = 'Dancop21'PBR (Scopia Series)	LSou
	microphylla	see *Jamesbrittenia microphylla*
	neglecta	WPGP
	Scopia Great Regal Blue = 'Dancop30' (Scopia Series) **new**	NPri
	(Secrets Series) 'Secrets Blue Delight'	LSou
	- 'Secrets Central Pink'	LSou
	- 'Secrets Silver Sky'	LSou

Sutherlandia ✿ (*Papilionaceae*)

	frutescens	CBod CSpe CTre GDun SPlb WJek
	- fine-leaved	GDun
	montana	CSpe CTre SBrt

Swainsona (*Papilionaceae*)

	galegifolia	CHll

sweet cicely see *Myrrhis odorata*

Swertia (*Gentianaceae*)

	bimaculata PAB 8845	LEdu
	perennis	GEdr
	petiolata CC 7335	GKev

Swietenia (*Meliaceae*)

	mahogani	SPlb

Syagrus (*Arecaceae*)

	botryophora	XBlo
§	***romanzoffiana***	LRHS XBlo

× *Sycoparrotia* (*Hamamelidaceae*)

	semidecidua	CBcs CJun MBlu NLar
	- 'Purple Haze'	CJun NLar WPGP
	- 'Variegata' (v) **new**	CJun

Sycopsis (*Hamamelidaceae*)

	sinensis	CAbP CBcs CWib EBee EPfP GBin GCal LEdu LRHS MGil MMuc NLar SKHP SPoG SWvt WPGP WSHC

Symphoricarpos (*Caprifoliaceae*)

	albus	CDul CMac MSwo NWea SCob WHed WTSh
	- 'Constance Spry'	SRms
§	- var. ***laevigatus***	LBuc
	× ***chenaultii*** 'Hancock'	CBar CDul CMac ELan EPfP ESps GMcL MMuc MRav MSwo SCob SEND SGol SLim SPer WCFE WHed
	× ***doorenbosii*** 'Magic Berry'	MHtn MRav NWea SGol
	- 'Mother of Pearl'	ELan EPfP ESps LCro MMuc MRav NWea SCob SPer
	- 'White Hedge'	ELan GMcL LBuc MMuc NWea SPer SPlb
	guatemalensis B&SWJ 1016	WCru
	Magical Candy = 'Kolmcan'PBR	ELan EPfP NEoE
	Magical Galaxy = 'Kolmgala'PBR	ELan EPfP
	Magical Sweet = 'Kolmaswet'PBR	SHil
	orbiculatus	SLon
	- 'Albovariegatus'	see *S. orbiculatus* 'Taff's Silver Edge'
	- 'Argenteovariegatus'	see *S. orbiculatus* 'Taff's Silver Edge'
	- 'Bowles's Golden Variegated'	see *S. orbiculatus* 'Foliis Variegatis'
§	- 'Foliis Variegatis' (v)	CMac CTri EHoe ELan MRav SGol SPer
	- 'George Gardiner'	CMac
§	- 'Taff's Silver Edge' (v)	SGol
	- 'Variegatus'	see *S. orbiculatus* 'Foliis Variegatis'
	rivularis	see *S. albus* var. *laevigatus*

Symphyandra see *Campanula*

	asiatica	see *Hanabusaya asiatica*

Symphyotrichum (*Asteraceae*)

§	× ***amethystinum***	MNrw WCot
	- 'Freiburg'	MNrw
	'Anja's Choice'	EBee LHop MSpe WOld
	'Blue Butterfly'	SPhx WOld XLum
	'Blütenregen'	MArt WCot XEll
	'Claudia'	WOld
	'Climax' misapplied	see *S. laeve* 'Arcturus', *S. laeve* 'Calliope'
	'Climax' Vicary Gibbs	MNrw WOld
	'Connecticut Snow Flurry'	see *S. ericoides* f. *prostratum* 'Snow Flurry'
§	***cordifolium***	EWoo SPhx XLum
	- from Piney Fork	EPPr
	- 'Aldebaran'	LEdu WOld
	- 'Blue Heaven'	SAko
	- 'Chieftain' ♀H7	MHCG MNrw SMHy SPhx WOld
	- 'Elegans'	CSam EBee SDix WOld
	- 'Ideal'	NLar XLum
	- 'Silver Spray'	CKno ECtt ELon GMaP GQue MWat SRGP WOld XLum
	- 'Sweet Lavender' ♀H7	EBee LRHS WOld
	- 'White Chief'	WOld
§	***dumosum*** 'Biteliness'	NLar WOld
	- 'Early Blue'	IBoy ILea
	- Sapphire = 'Kiesapphire'PBR (Autumn Jewels Series)	CChe ELon EWTr EWoo LBMP LHop LRHS LSRN MHol NCou NEgg SRGP SRkn SWvt WBod XLum
§	***ericoides***	ESps NBre WOld
	- 'Blue Star' ♀H6	LRHS NAst NLar SPer WOld
	- 'Blue Wonder'	XLum
	- 'Brimstone' ♀H6	MRav WOld
	- 'Cinderella'	EBee LRHS NSti WOld
	- 'Constance'	WOld
	- 'Deep Danziger'	SPhx
	- 'Erlkönig'	CBod EBee EPri EShb GCal GQue LEdu NGdn NLar SDix SPer SWat SWvt WCot WOld XLum
	- 'Esther'	ECha ECtt ELan SBee WOld
	- 'First Snow'	WCot WFar
	- 'Golden Spray' ♀H6	EBee ELon EPfP EWes GMaP GQue NLar SPer WOld
	- 'Herbstmyrte'	LRHS
	- 'Hon. Edith Gibbs'	WOld
	- 'Monte Cassino'	see *S. pilosum* var. *pringlei* 'Monte Cassino'
	- 'Pink Cloud' ♀H6	CBod CBot CHVG ECtt EPfP EPri EShb GBuc GCal LEdu LRHS MSpe

		NCGa NWad SAko SDix SHil SPhx SWat WCot WOld
	- f. ***prostratum***	EPot GBuc GQue MRav SAko XEll XSen
	- - 'Snow Flurry' ♀H6	CMea ECha ECtt ELon GBuc IMou LEdu MAvo MHol MNrw MWat NLar SIgm SWvt WCot WHoo WOld WOut XLum
	- 'Rosy Veil'	NBir NGdn WOld
	- 'Schneegitter'	LRHS SPhx WCot XSen
	- 'Schneetanne'	SAko
	- 'Sulphurea'	MWat
	- 'Vimmer's Delight'	MArt WCot
	- 'White Heather'	ECtt NLar WOld
	- 'Yvette Richardson'	CSam SMHy WOld
§	***falcatum***	WCot
	- var. ***commutatum***	WCot WOld
§	***foliaceum*** from Montana	EPPr
	- var. ***parryi***	EBee
§	***greatae***	EBee
	'Herfstweelde'	EBee SMad SPhx WOld
	'Hill Close Blue' new	MHCG
	'Hon. Vicary Gibbs' (*ericoides* hybrid)	WOld WOut
§	***laeve***	CDor GNew LEdu NLar SPhx
	- 'Anneke Van der Jeugd'	MNrw SAko
§	- 'Arcturus'	CElw LEdu MAvo MBel MNrw MTis NBir NCGa SDix WCot WOld XLum
	- 'Blauschleier'	EBee
	- 'Blue Bird'	WOld
§	- 'Calliope'	Widely available
	- 'Cally Compact'	GQue NLar WOld
	- 'Climax'	CElw EBee ELan GCal GQue MMuc MRav NBid NSti SDix SEND WBrk XLum
	- var. ***geyeri***	MNrw
	- 'Glow in the Dark'	EBee MAvo MSpe NLar WBrk WCot WHoo WOld
	- 'Les Moutiers'	EPPr MAvo MNrw SDix WBrk WOld
	- 'Nightshade'	MAvo MNrw MTis WOld WRHF
	- 'Orpheus'	ECGP MAvo MNrw WBrk
	- 'Vesta'	MTis WOld
§	- 'White Climax'	CSam MNrw WCot
	- white-flowered	WBrk WOld
§	***lanceolatum*** Willd.	NCGa
	- 'Edwin Beckett'	CBre MNrw SWvt WOld
§	***lateriflorum***	MAvo SWvt WOld
	- 'Bleke Bet'	WCot WFar WOld
	- 'Buck's Fizz'	ELan WOld
	- 'Chloe'	CSam NCGa SPhx WCot WFar WOld
	- 'Datschi'	XLum
	- var. ***horizontalis*** ♀H7	CBod CSam EBee ECha ECtt EHoe ELan EPPr EPfP EWoo LRHS MRav MWat NAst NBro NCGa NGdn NWad SCob SDix SPer SPlb SRms SRot SWat SWvt WCAu WOld WPtf XEll
	- 'Lady in Black'	Widely available
	- 'Lovely'	CSam MArt SRGP WCot
	- 'Prince'	Widely available
	'Little Carlow' (*cordifolium* hybrid) ♀H7	Widely available
	'Little Dorrit' (*cordifolium* hybrid)	ECtt NWsh
	'Nicholas'	ECtt WCot WOld
	'Noreen'	MAvo MHCG MTis WOld
	novae-angliae	WOld
	- 'Abendsonne'	SAko
	- 'Alex Deamon'	ELon MAvo WBrk WOld
	- 'Anabelle de Chazal'	ECtt ETho WBrk WOld
	- 'Andenken an Alma Pötschke'	Widely available
	- 'Andenken an Paul Gerber'	ECtt ELon LHop MAvo MNrw MTis NLar SRGP WOld
	- 'Augusta'	ELon MAvo NLar SPhx WBrk WOld
	- Autumn Snow	see *S. novae-angliae* 'Herbstschnee'
	- 'Badsey Pink'	WCot
	- 'Barr's Blue'	CMac EBee ECtt ELan ELon EPfP GCra MAvo MMuc MTis MWat NLar NWsh SEND SPer SRms WBrk WCAu WMoo WOld
	- 'Barr's Pink'	CBot CBre CMac EBee ECtt ELan ELon EPfP MCot MMuc MPie MTis MWat NAst NLar SEND SRGP WBrk WFar WOld WSFF
*	- 'Barr's Purple'	ECtt WBrk WCFE WOld
	- 'Barr's Violet'	CHVG ECtt MAvo NSti SRms WBrk WCot WHal WHoo WMoo WOld
	- 'Bishop Colenso'	EPPr WBrk
	- 'Blue Eyes'	MAvo WOld
	- 'Brightness' new	WCot
	- 'Brockamin'	MNrw WBrk WOld
	- 'Brunswick'	WFar WOld
	- 'Christopher Harbutt'	LEdu SRGP
	- 'Colwall Century'	MAvo WBrk WOld
	- 'Colwall Constellation'	MAvo WBrk WOld
	- 'Colwall Galaxy'	MAvo WBrk WOld
	- 'Colwall Orbit'	ECtt ELon MAvo WBrk WOld
	- 'Connie'	MNrw MSpe
	- 'Constanze'	EBee ECtt MTis
	- 'Crimson Beauty'	ECtt ELon MAvo MHCG MHer MNrw MWat SAko WBrk WOld
	- 'Dapper Tapper'	ECtt MAvo WCot WOld
	- 'Evensong'	ECtt LEdu MAvo MNrw MPie WBrk WOld
	- 'Festival'	WBrk
	- 'Foxy Emily'	ECtt MHCG WBrk WOld
	- 'Harrington's Pink' ♀H7	Widely available
	- 'Helen Picton'	CHVG CSam ECtt ELon EWld LEdu MAvo MBrN MHer MPie MWat NLar NWsh SAko WBrk WFar WHoo WOld
§	- 'Herbstschnee'	Widely available
	- 'James'	MAvo
	- 'James Ritchie'	CSam ECtt ELon WHoo WOld
	- 'John Davies'	MAvo MNrw SBch WHil WOld
	- 'John Dickinson' new	WBrk
	- 'Jon Baker'	CBot MAvo WBrk
	- 'Kate Deamon'	ECtt WOld
	- 'Kylie'	CBot ECtt EPPr LEdu LSRN MAvo MNrw MTis SPhx SRGP WBor WBrk WCot WFar WHil WOld
	- 'Lachsglut'	ELon LEdu NLar SAko WCot WOld
	- 'Ladies Day'	WOld
	- 'Little Bella'	ECtt WOld
	- 'Lou Williams'	ECtt ELon MNrw MWat NLar WFar WHil WOld
I	- 'Lucida'	MAvo SPhx WOld
	- 'Lucinda'	ECtt
	- 'Lye End Beauty'	CKno ECtt ELon LLWP MAvo MHer MNrw MPie MWat SRGP WBod WBrk WCot WFar WHoo WMoo WOld
	- 'Mabelle'	MAvo NDov
	- 'Mandie's Choice' new	WCot
	- 'Marina Wolkonsky'	CAby ECGP ECtt ELon EWes IPot LEdu LHop MAvo MMrt MNrw MTis MWat NLar SAko SPhx WBrk WCot WKif WOld

	- 'Millennium Star'	ECtt WBrk WOld
	- 'Miss K.E. Mash'	ECtt MAvo NLar SRGP WBrk WFar WOld
	- 'Mrs S.T. Wright'	CAby CTri ECtt EWes LEdu MAvo MBrN MNrw SRGP WBrk WFar WOld
	- 'Mrs S.W. Stern'	WBrk WOld
	- 'Nachtauge'	SAko
	- 'Naomi'	MAvo WBrk WOld
	- 'Pink Parfait'	CSam ECtt IKil MPie NGdn SRms WBrk WCot WFar WOld
	- 'Pink Victor'	CTri SRms WMoo
	- 'Pride of Rougham'	EWes LLWP MAvo WBrk
	- 'Primrose Upward'	CAby ECtt MNrw NDov NWsh SPhx WCot WOld
	- 'Purple Cloud'	CAby CSam ECtt ELon LHop MAvo MHer MWat NGdn WBrk WHal WOld
I	- 'Purple Dome'	Widely available
	- 'Quinton Menzies'	CAby ELon MAvo WOld
	- 'Red Cloud'	ECtt ELon LEdu MAvo MHer WBrk WOld
	- 'Rosa Sieger' ♀H7	CAby CBre CSam ECtt ELon GMaP GQue LEdu MAvo MNrw MTis NGdn NLar SPhx SRGP WBor WBrk WFar WHil WHoo WOld XLum
	- 'Rose Williams'	LEdu MAvo MPie WBrk
	- 'Röter Stern'	ECtt MAvo MPie WBrk WOld
	- 'Roter Turm'	SAko
	- 'Rougham Pink'	MAvo WBrk
	- 'Rougham Purple'	EWes
	- 'Rougham Violet'	EPPr WBrk
	- 'Rubinschatz'	EBee ECtt ELon MAvo MTis MWat NWsh SRms WOld XLum
	- 'Rudelsburg'	EBee ECtt MAvo SHar WBrk
	- 'Rudolph'	EWes
	- 'Sayer's Croft'	ECtt ELon MWat WBrk WCot WFar WHil WHoo WOld
§	- 'Septemberrubin'	CAby CMea EBee ECtt ELan ELon EPfP IFoB LEdu LHop LSou MAvo MBel MMuc MRav MTis NSti NWsh SAko SEND SPhx SRGP SRms WFar WOld XLum
	- September Ruby	see *S. novae-angliae* 'Septemberrubin'
	- 'St Michael's'	MAvo WBrk WFar WOld
	- 'Treasure'	CBre ECtt ELon EWes LRHS MAvo NBre SPhx SRGP WBrk WMoo WOld
	- 'Vibrant Dome' PBR	CRos LRHS MNrw MTis NLar NRHS
	- 'Violet Dusk'	WBrk
	- 'Violet Haze'	CMea ELon WBrk
	- 'Violetta'	CBot ECtt ELon GMaP LCro LEdu LRHS LSou MAvo MNrw MTis SCob SPhx WBrk WHil WHoo WKif WOld
	- 'W. Bowman'	ECtt MNrw WBrk WOld
	- 'Wow'	ELon WHil
	novi-belgii	ESps WHer WMoo
	- 'Ada Ballard'	CBod CFis CMac CWld EBee EHoe LHop LRHS LSRN NEgg SPer SRGP WFar WMoo WOld
	- 'Albanian'	WOld
	- 'Alderman Vokes'	WOld
	- 'Algar's Pride'	ECtt WFar WOld
	- 'Alice Haslam'	CMac CRos EBee ECtt ELan ESps LRHS MHol MJak NLar NRHS SRGP SRms WFar WOld
	- 'Angela Peel'	LRHS
	- 'Anita Ballard'	WOld
	- 'Anita Webb'	NBir WOld
	- 'Anneke'	NLar SRGP WOld
	- 'Apollo'	ILea LRHS MWat NLar WFar WOld
	- 'Apple Blossom'	WFar WOld
	- 'Aramis Rose'	EBee
	- 'Audrey'	CMac GMaP LPot LRHS LSRN MBNS NGdn SRGP SRms WFar WOld
	- 'Autumn Beauty'	WOld
	- 'Autumn Days'	WOld
	- 'Autumn Glory'	WOld
	- 'Autumn Rose'	WOld
	- 'Baby Climax'	WOld
	- Bahamas = 'Dasone' (Island Series)	CBod CNec EPfP LBMP LRHS NEgg NLar NWsh SPoG SRms SWvt WCot WHil
	- Barbados = 'Dastwo' (Island Series)	CBod EPfP LOPS NLar SPoG SWvt WCot WFar
	- 'Beauty of Colwall'	WOld
	- 'Beechwood Beacon' **new**	WFar
	- 'Beechwood Challenger'	MHCG MPie WBrk WOld
	- 'Beechwood Charm'	SDix WFar WOld
	- 'Beechwood Rival'	CTri WOld XEll
	- 'Blandie'	CTri SRGP WOld
	- 'Blauglut'	SAko WFar WOld
	- 'Blue Baby'	CMac MPie
	- 'Blue Bouquet'	CTri SRms WFar WOld
	- 'Blue Boy'	WOld
	- 'Blue Danube'	WOld
	- 'Blue Gown'	CCse GCal GQue WOld WOut
	- 'Blue Lagoon'	CBot CFis CMea ELan GMcL LSRN MMuc NPnk SRGP WBrk WOld
	- 'Blue Lapis'	EBee LRHS WFar
I	- 'Blue Moon'	WFar WOld
	- 'Blue Patrol'	WOld
	- 'Blue Radiance'	WOld
	- 'Blue Spire'	WOld
	- 'Blue Whirl'	WOld
	- 'Boningale Blue'	WOld
	- 'Boningale White'	MHCG WFar WHil WOld
	- 'Bridesmaid'	WOld
	- 'Bridgette'	NPnk
	- 'Bright Eyes'	SRGP WOld
	- 'Brightest and Best'	WOld
	- 'Brigitte'	CBod EWTr NLar
	- 'Cameo'	WOld
	- 'Cantab'	WOld
	- 'Carlingcott'	WOld
	- 'Carnival'	CMac EBee ECtt IVic LRHS SRGP WOld
	- 'Cecily'	WOld
	- 'Charles Wilson'	CFis WOld
	- 'Chatterbox'	EBee ELan EPfP LPot LRHS MRav MWat NEgg NLar SRGP SRms WFar WHar WOld
	- 'Chelwood'	WFar WOld
	- 'Chequers'	CElw EBee MBNS MHer NEgg SRGP WFar WOld
	- 'Christina'	see *S. novi-belgii* 'Kristina'
	- 'Christine Soanes'	WOld
	- 'Cliff Lewis'	WFar WOld
	- 'Climax Albus'	see *S. laeve* 'White Climax'
	- 'Cloudy Blue'	WOld
	- 'Colonel F.R. Durham'	WOld
	- 'Coombe Fishacre' ♀H7	CBot EBee ECtt ELan ELon GBuc GCal LEdu LRHS MArt MNrw NDov NLar SPhx SRGP SWvt WCAu WCot WHoo WOld
	- 'Coombe Gladys'	WOld
	- 'Coombe Margaret'	WOld

- 'Coombe Radiance'	WOld
- 'Coombe Ronald'	WOld
- 'Coombe Rosemary'	ECtt NLar WBor WOld
- 'Coombe Violet'	MWat WOld
- 'Countess of Dudley'	CFis WFar WOld
- 'Court Herald'	WOld
- 'Crimson Brocade'	CRos ECtt ELan EPfP EWTr LRHS NLar NRHS SAko SHil SPoG SRGP SRms SWvt WFar
- 'Dandy'	CMac CRos ELan EPfP LRHS NBir NGdn NRHS SRGP WFar WOld
- 'Daniela'	SRms WBrk WFar WOld
- 'Daphne Anne'	WOld
- 'Dauerblau'	EBee WOld
- 'Davey's True Blue'	CTri WFar WOld XLum
- 'David Murray'	WOld
- 'Dazzler'	ECtt WFar WOld
- 'Destiny'	WOld
- 'Diana'	ECtt NWsh
- 'Diana Watts'	WOld
- 'Dietgard'	MWat WOld
- 'Dolly'	NBir SRms WOld
- 'Dora Chiswell'	WOld
- 'Dusky Maid'	WFar WOld
- 'Elizabeth Hutton'	SRGP WFar WOld
- 'Elsie Dale'	WOld
- 'Elta'	WOld
- 'Erica'	CElw MWat WOld
- 'Ernest Ballard'	WOld
- 'Eva'	SRms WOld
- 'Eventide'	CTri LSRN WOld
- 'Fair Lady'	MWat WOld
- 'Faith'	WFar WOld
- 'Feckenham Rival' **new**	WOld
- 'Fellowship' ♀H6	CBod CBot CHVG CRos EAJP EBee ECtt ELon EPfP IKil LEdu LRHS MAvo MMuc MNrw NCGa NLar NNys NRHS SAko SHar SRGP SRms SWvt WCot WFar WOld
- 'Flamingo'	EBee LRHS WOld
- 'Freda Ballard'	CFis ECtt GMaP LRHS MWat SRGP WFar WOld
- 'Freya'	CElw LSRN WOld WSHC
- 'Fuldatal'	WFar WOld
- 'Gayborder Blue'	WFar WOld
- 'Gayborder Royal'	WOld
- 'Goliath'	WOld
- 'Grey Lady'	WFar WOld
- 'Guardsman'	WOld
- 'Gulliver'	WBrk WFar WOld
- 'Gurney Slade'	WFar WOld
- 'Guy Ballard'	WOld
- 'Harrison's Blue'	MWat WOld
- 'Heinz Richard'	CFis ECha MHer MMuc NBir NGdn SRGP SRms WOld
- 'Helen'	ELon WOld
- 'Helen Ballard'	NBid SRms WFar WOld
- 'Herbstgruss vom Bresserhof'	CRos LRHS NBre NLar NRHS SAko WOld
- 'Hilda Ballard'	WOld
- 'Ibiza'	WCot
- 'Ilse Brensell'	WOld
- 'Irene'	WOld
- 'Janet Watts'	WOld
- 'Jean'	ELon SRms WOld
- 'Jean Gyte'	WOld
- 'Jeanette'	SRms WFar WOld
- 'Jenny'	Widely available
- 'Jollity'	WOld
- 'Jugendstil'	XLum
- 'Julia'	WOld
- 'Karminkuppel'	IPot
- 'Kassel'	SRms WFar WOld
- 'King of the Belgians'	WFar WOld
- 'King's College'	WOld
§ - 'Kristina'	CRos EBee ECha GMcL ITim LRHS MMuc MNrw MRav NAst NBir NPnk NRHS WFar WOld
- 'Lady Frances'	EBee SRms WOld
- 'Lady in Blue'	Widely available
- 'Lassie'	MWat NWsh WFar WOld
- 'Lavender Dream'	WOld
- 'Lawrence Chiswell'	WOld
- 'Lederstrumpf'	NDov
- 'Lisa Dawn'	WOld
- 'Little Boy Blue'	SRms WOld XLum
- 'Little Man in Blue'	WOld
- 'Little Pink Beauty'	CNec CRos ECtt ELan EPfP ESps GMcL IBoy ITim LEdu LHop LRHS MBNS MJak NGdn NHol NRHS NWad SBod SPer SRGP SRms WBod WCAu WHar WOld
- 'Little Pink Lady'	MHCG SRms WFar WOld
- 'Little Pink Pyramid'	SRms WOld
- 'Little Red Boy'	WOld
- 'Little Treasure'	WOld
- 'Madge Cato'	SRms WOld
- 'Mammoth'	WOld
- 'Margery Bennett'	WOld
- 'Marie Ann Neil'	SRms WOld
- 'Marie Ballard'	CMac CRos CSBt GMaP LEdu LRHS MHer MRav MWat NGdn NHol NLar NPer NPnk NRHS SGol SPer SRGP SRms SWat SWvt WCAu WOld XLum
- 'Marie's Pretty Please'	WOld
- 'Marie-Theres'	SAko
- 'Marjorie'	LSRN SRGP WOld XLum
- 'Mauve Magic'	MWat SRms WFar WOld
- 'Melbourne Belle'	WOld
- 'Melbourne Magnet'	WOld
- 'Midget'	WOld
- 'Mistress Quickly'	ECtt WFar WOld
- 'Mittelmeer'	LRHS WOld XLum
- 'Mount Everest'	WOld
- 'Mrs Leo Hunter'	WOld
- 'Nachtlicht'	SAko
- 'Neron'	IMou MNrw MPie NDov
- 'Nesthäkchen'	WOld
- 'Niobe'	SAko WOld
- 'Norman's Jubilee'	EBee EPfP ESps LRHS MHer NBir SRGP WFar WOld
- 'Nursteed Charm'	WOld
- 'Oktoberschneekuppel'	WOld
- 'Pamela'	WOld
- 'Patricia Ballard' (d)	CBcs CBod CBot CMac CSBt EBee ELan EPfP GCra GMaP LCro LRHS MHer MWat NBir NLar NPer NWad SGol SPer SRGP WFar WMoo WOld
- 'Peace'	WOld
- 'Percy Thrower'	WOld
- 'Peter Chiswell'	SRms WOld
- 'Peter Harrison'	CRos EBee GMaP LRHS MHol NBir NRHS WOld XLum
- 'Peter Pan'	EWTr NLar
- 'Pink Lace'	MBNS WOld
- 'Pink Topas'	LRHS
- 'Plenty'	WOld

	- 'Porzellan'	CElw CFis CMea EBee ECtt MAvo MBNS MNrw NGdn NLar SRGP WCot WHal WOld
	- 'Pride of Colwall'	SRms WOld
	- 'Priory Blush'	CElw WOld
	- 'Professor Anton Kippenberg'	CFis CRos ELan EPfP EWTr GMaP LRHS MNrw MRav NAst NDov NLar NRHS SAko SPer SRGP SRms SWvt WFar WOld XLum
	- 'Prosperity'	WOld
	- 'Purple Dome'	CFis CNec ECha ELan EWTr LEdu LOPS LSRN MHer MWat SCob SHar SRkn WOld WOut
	- 'Ralph Picton'	WFar WOld
	- 'Red Robin'	MWat
	- 'Red Sunset'	SRms WOld
	- 'Rembrandt'	ECtt NGdn SRGP
	- 'Remembrance'	MWat SRms WFar WOld
	- 'Reverend Vincent Dale'	WOld
	- 'Richness'	WOld
	- 'Rose Bonnet'	CSBt LRHS SPlb WFar WOld
	- 'Roseanne'	WOld
	- 'Rosebud'	WOld
	- 'Rosenquartz'	NLar WFar
	- 'Rosenwichtel'	ILea NLar WHil WOld
	- 'Royal Blue'	WOld
	- 'Royal Ruby'	CFis EBee ECtt IPot LRHS NAst NLar WOld
	- 'Royal Velvet'	WOld
	- 'Rozika'	MNrw WOld
	- 'Rufus'	NWsh WFar WOld
	- 'Sailor Boy'	NCGa
	- 'Saint Egwyn'	WOld
	- 'Sam Banham'	MNrw WOld
	- Samoa = 'Dasthree' (Island Series)	CBod CNec CRos EBee EPfP EUJe LRHS LSou NEgg NLar NRHS SPoG SRms WCot
	- 'Sandford White Swan'	GBuc MHer WFar WOld
	- 'Sarah Ballard'	LRHS NAst NLar SHil SRGP WBrk WOld
§	- 'Schneekissen'	CBod ECtt ELan EPfP GMaP LRHS MBNS MHer MJak SPer SRGP SRms SWvt WHar WOld XLum
	- 'Schneezicklein'	GBin GWyn
	- 'Schöne von Dietlikon'	CKno IPot LEdu MWat WFar WOld XLum
	- 'Schoolgirl'	WOld
	- 'Sheena'	WFar WOld
	- 'Silberblaukissen'	WOld
§	- 'Silberteppich'	EBee
	- Silver Carpet	see *S. novi-belgii* 'Silberteppich'
	- Snow Cushion	see *S. novi-belgii* 'Schneekissen'
	- 'Snowsprite'	CBod CSBt ELan ESps LRHS MWat NLar SGbt SGol SRGP SRms SWat WOld
	- 'Sonata'	GMaP WOld
	- 'Sophia'	MWat WOld
	- 'Starlight'	CBod ECtt GMcL IBoy ILea NLar WFar WRHF
	- 'Steinebrück'	WOld
	- 'Sterling Silver'	WOld
	- 'Sun Queen'	WOld
	- 'Sunset'	WOld
	- 'Susan'	SRGP WOld
	- 'Sweet Briar'	WOld
	- 'Tapestry'	WOld
	- 'Terry's Pride'	SRGP WFar WOld
	- 'The Archbishop'	ECtt WOld XEll
	- 'The Bishop'	WOld
	- 'The Cardinal'	WOld

	- 'The Dean'	WOld
	- 'The Sexton'	WOld
	- 'Thundercloud'	MWat WOld
	- 'Timsbury'	SRms WOld
	- Tonga = 'Dasfour' (Island Series)	EPfP EWTr LRHS MHol NLar NWsh SPoG SRms SWvt WBod WCot
	- 'Tovarich'	WOld
	- 'Trudi Ann'	NBir WOld
	- 'Twinkle'	WOld
	- 'Victor'	WOld
	- 'Vignem'	NSti
	- 'Violet Lady'	WOld
	- 'Waterperry'	MWat WBrk WOld
	- 'White Ladies'	CBcs ECtt GCra GMaP LCro LRHS MMuc MNrw MWat NAst NLar SHil SRGP XLum
	- 'White Swan'	ECtt
	- 'White Wings'	MWat WOld
	- 'Winston S. Churchill'	CBod CRos CTri EAJP ELan EPfP GMaP IKil LEdu LRHS MHer MPie MWat NEgg NRHS SPer SPlb SPoG SRGP WOld WTor
	- 'Zwergenhimmel'	SAko
§	***oblongifolium***	NWsh WOld XSen
§	- 'Fanny's'	ECtt GCal MMuc NGdn NWad SRGP WOld
	- 'October Skies'	CSpe EBee EWes MNrw
	'Ochtendgloren' (*pilosum* var. *pringlei* hybrid) ♀H4	CSam EBee ECtt EPPr EWes GBuc MNrw NCGa NLar WCAu WHal WHoo WOld
	Octoberlight	see *S.* 'Oktoberlicht'
§	'Oktoberlicht'	EPPr LRHS MNrw NCGa WOld
§	***oolentangiense***	NLar WOld
	'Orchidee'	EPPr EPri EWTr EWes MAvo WOld
	'Pearl Star'	WOld
	'Photograph' ♀H7	CHVG CSam ECtt ELon EWes LEdu LRHS MAvo NPnk WOld WPGP
§	***pilosum***	WCot WFar
§	- var. ***pringlei*** ♀H7	ECha EWes MMuc MRav NWad WOld
§	- - 'Monte Cassino'	CBot CSBt EAEE EPfP GQue LHop LPot LRHS MBNS MRav MWat NBro SPer SPhx SRGP SRms WOld XLum
	- - 'October Glory'	CCse MMuc WFar
	- - 'Phoebe'	WOld
	'Pink Star'	CBot EBee ECtt ELon GMaP LEdu LRHS MRav MWat NSti SBch SHil SPhx WOld XLum
	'Pixie Dark Eye' (*ericoides* hybrid)	EBee ECtt SDix WCot
	'Pixie Red Eye' (*ericoides* hybrid)	EBee LEdu WCot
	'Prairie Lavender'	WOld
	'Prairie Pink'	SMHy WOld
	'Prairie Purple'	ECtt MTis SMHy WCot WOld
	'Prairie Violet'	WOld
	'Primrose Path'	LEdu MNrw NCGa SPhx WBrk WCot WOld
§	***puniceum***	CAby NLar XLum
	'Ringdove' (*ericoides* hybrid) ♀H6	MAvo NCGa NSti SRGP SWvt WCot WOld
	'Rosa Star'	WOld
§	× ***salignum***	WOld
	- Scottish form	WOld
§	***sericeum***	SBrt SPhx
	'Soft Lass'	WCot WOld
	'Star of Chesters'	WOld
	Sunplum = 'Danasplum' PBR	LEdu SRGP
	'Superstar' **new**	WHoo WOld

tradescantii	ELan MBNS MRav NSti SMad WBrk WCot WOld
'Treffpunkt'	IMou MAvo SAko
turbinellum misapplied ♀H6	CFis CKno EPfP EWes IKil LRHS MArt MMuc NGdn NWsh SDix SMHy SPhx SRkn SWvt
turbinellum Lindl.	CSam EBee EPfP EWTr MWat NCGa NLar NQui SSut WCot WOld
- 'El Fin'	EWld MNrw
- hybrid	WOld
'Vasterival'	IMou LEdu MPie MSpe MTis NCGa NDov SBee SMHy WOut XLum

Symphytum (*Boraginaceae*)

'Angela Whinfield'	CMea EBee LPla
asperum	ECha MRav NLar WMoo
* ***azureum***	LPla NChi WCAu
'Belsay'	GBuc
'Belsay Gold'	NBid NBir SDix WBor
bulbosum PAB 4886	LEdu
caucasicum	CElw EBee ECha GPoy GQue IFro LEdu NLar NSti SIde SPer WHer WMoo WOut WWtn XLum
cordatum	EPPr LEdu MNrw SKHP
§ 'Goldsmith' (v)	CBod CMea CSam EBee ECha EHrv ELan EPfP EWoo MHol MPie NBid NBir NEgg NLar NPer SPer SPoG WFar WJek
grandiflorum	CMac CTri GKev GPoy LEdu LRHS SHil SPer
- 'Sky-blue-pink'	IFro
'Hidcote Blue'	CBod CBre CLet CNec CTri ECha ECtt EPPr EPed EPfP IBoy LRHS MMuc NBro NEgg SCob SEND SPer SPoG WGwG WMoo WOut WPnP WWtn
§ 'Hidcote Pink'	CBod CNec ECha ECtt EPPr LBMP LPot LRHS MMuc MNrw NBir SEND SPer SPoG WFar WGwG WMoo WPnP WWtn XLum
'Hidcote Variegated' (v)	CMac
ibericum	CAgr CSam ECha EHrv EWTr GKev GMaP GPoy LHop LRHS MMuc NSti SEND SRms WGwG WJek WMoo WOut WWtn
- 'All Gold'	ECha LRHS MHer MNrw WMoo
- 'Blaueglocken'	ECha WMoo
- dwarf	IFro WMoo
- 'Gold in Spring'	WFar
- 'Jubilee'	see *S.* 'Goldsmith'
- 'Lilacinum'	CFis WHer
- 'Variegatum'	see *S.* 'Goldsmith'
- 'Wisley Blue'	CBcs CBod ILea IPot LRHS SCob SHil WFar WMoo
'Lambrook Gold'	LHop
'Lambrook Sunrise'	CMac LEdu NBro WCot WMoo
'Langthorns Pink'	ELan GCal
officinale	CAgr CHab ENfk GJos GPoy MHer MNHC MNrw NPer NPri SIde SPoG SRms WHea WHer WJek XLum
- var. ***ochroleucum***	WHer
orientale	EBee EPPr GCal MBel
peregrinum	see *S.* × *uplandicum*
'Romanian Red'	SDix
'Roseum'	see *S.* 'Hidcote Pink'
'Rubrum'	CBod CLet EHrv ELan EPed EPfP EWes GCra LEdu LRHS MHer MMuc NBro NLar SPer WCAu WGwG WPGP XLum
'Sera Howys'	WOut
tuberosum	CBre CElw CFis CSam EPPr GPoy LEdu LPla MHer MMuc NWad WBor WCot WHer WOut
§ × ***uplandicum***	CTri ELan GCra GPoy MMuc SEND SVic WJek
- 'Axminster Gold' (v)	CMea EWes NChi WCot
- 'Bocking 14'	CAgr CBod CFGn CHby CPbn EOHP EShb GAbr LEdu MHer MNHC SIde WSFF XLum
- 'Droitwich' (v)	WCot
- 'Moorland Heather'	EBee LPla MHer MMrt MNrw MPie WMoo
- purple-flowered	SEND
- 'Variegatum' (v)	CBot ECha ECtt ELan EWes GBuc GCal LRHS NBir NGdn NSti WMoo WWtn

Symplocos (*Symplocaceae*)

sawafutagi	NLar WPGP

Synadenium (*Euphorbiaceae*)

grantii 'Rubrum'	EShb

Syncarpha (*Asteraceae*)

vestita	SPlb

Syncolostemon (*Lamiaceae*)

'Candy Kisses'	WCot

Syneilesis (*Asteraceae*)

aconitifolia	GEdr WCot WHal
- B&SWJ 879	EHrv LEdu WCru
palmata	GEdr WCot
- B&SWJ 1003	WCru
- B&SWJ 11226	WCru
- 'Aka-fu' new	GEdr
- 'Kikkou-fu' new	GEdr
- 'Kiko'	GEdr
subglabrata B&SWJ 298	WCru
aff. ***tagawae*** B&SWJ 11191	WCot WCru

Syngonium (*Araceae*)

podophyllum ♀H1b	XBlo

Synnotia see *Sparaxis*

Synsepalum (*Sapotaceae*)

dulcificum	SCit

Synthyris (*Plantaginaceae*)

laciniata	EBee LLHF
missurica	EBee GBuc
subsp. ***missurica***	
- subsp. ***stellata***	CAby CBod CLAP EAEE EBee ECre EPfP EPri EWes GAbr GBin GBuc GCal LEdu LRHS MMrt NBir NCGa NHpl NPnk SPoG WGwG WHal WMoo WPGP WPtf WSHC
platycarpa new	EBee
reniformis	CLAP GBuc WPGP

Synurus (*Asteraceae*)

pungens	SBrt

Syringa ✿ (*Oleaceae*)

afghanica misapplied	see *S. protolaciniata*
afghanica C.K.Schneid.	IVic WSHC
Bloomerang Dark Purple ='Smsjbp7' new	LCro SPoG

Bloomerang Pink Perfume = 'Pink Perfume'PBR	LCro LRHS SPoG
Bloomerang Purple = 'Penda' **new**	LRHS NRHS
× ***chinensis***	EPfP
- 'Alba'	see *S.* 'Correlata'
- 'Bicolor'	WGob
- 'Saugeana'	MBlu MMuc SPer
§ 'Correlata' (graft-chimaera)	EBee EPfP
× ***diversifolia***	NLar
emodi 'Aurea'	NLar
- 'Aureovariegata'	see *S. emodi* 'Variegata'
- 'Elegantissima' (v)	CBcs CEnd CMac EBtc ELan EPfP GQui LRHS MAsh NEgg NLar SKHP SPoG
§ - 'Variegata' (v)	CBot EMil LRHS NLar
× ***hyacinthiflora*** 'Clarke's Giant'	NLar
- 'Esther Staley' ♀H6	EPfP MRav SKHP
- 'Pocahontas' ♀H6	LRHS
- 'Sweetheart' (d)	NOra WMat
Josée = 'Morjos 060f'	ELan ELon EPfP LSou MAsh SCob SMDP SWvt WFar WGob WPat
× ***josiflexa*** 'Agnes Smith'	EBee LRHS MMuc NLar
- 'Bellicent' ♀H6	CBot CEnd CMac ELan EPfP GMcL IFro LRHS MAsh MMuc MRav NLar NPri SEND SKHP SMad SPer SPoG SRms SWvt WCFE WFar WPat
- 'Lynette'	NEoE
- 'Redwine'	NLar SKHP
§ - 'Royalty'	NLar SKHP
josikaea	CAco CMCN CSBt EWTr NLar SPer
'Kim'	MRav
komarowii	GGGa WSHC
§ - subsp. ***reflexa***	CDul EPfP EWTr IDee MBlu NLar SLon WPGP
§ × ***laciniata*** Mill.	CJun CWCL EBee ELan EPfP LRHS MRav SPer SPoG WCFE WHar WPGP
'Lark Song'	NLar
meyeri	SVen
- 'Inge'	NLar
§ - 'Palibin' ♀H5	Widely available
'Minuet'	CBcs LBuc LRHS SKHP
'Miss Canada'	LRHS
Miss Japan	EBee LRHS
oblata	CMCN
palibiniana misapplied	see *S. meyeri* 'Palibin'
patula misapplied	see *S. meyeri* 'Palibin'
patula (Palib.) Nakai	see *S. pubescens* subsp. *patula*
pekinensis	see *S. reticulata* subsp. *pekinensis*
- Beijing Gold	see *S. reticulata* subsp. *pekinensis* 'Zhang Zhiiming'
× ***persica*** ♀H6	CJun CTri EPfP EWTr MGos MRav NLar SLon SPer WFar WGob WHar
- 'Alba' ♀H6	CJun MRav WFar WGob WPat WSHC
- var. ***laciniata***	see *S.* × *laciniata* Mill.
pinnatifolia	CBcs CBot GBin LRHS NLar SAko
× ***prestoniae*** 'Desdemona'	EBtc LRHS MMuc SEND SKHP
- 'Elinor' ♀H6	CBot CMHG ELan EMil EPfP LPre MRav SKHP
- 'Minuet' **new**	NLar
- 'Miss Poland' **new**	LRHS
- 'Nocturne'	WFar
- 'Royalty'	see *S.* × *josiflexa* 'Royalty'
§ ***protolaciniata***	IDee LRHS MMuc NLar SKHP SLim
pubescens subsp. ***julianae*** 'George Eastman'	MRav
- subsp. ***microphylla*** 'Superba' ♀H6	Widely available
§ - subsp. ***patula***	CMac EPfP LRHS MMuc MRav NWea SLim SVen
- - 'Miss Kim' ♀H6	Widely available
'Red Pixie'	CMac CRos EPfP LCro LRHS MAsh MGos MMrt SCoo SHil SKHP WGob
reflexa	see *S. komarowii* subsp. *reflexa*
reticulata	EGFP MBlu
- 'Ivory Silk'	EPfP SKHP WMat
§ - subsp. ***pekinensis***	CMCN
- - China Snow = 'Morton' ♀H6	SKHP
- - 'Yellow Fragrance'	NLar
§ - - 'Zhang Zhiiming'	EBee
× ***swegiflexa***	CDul
tomentella	EBee EWTr NWea SRms WPGP
- subsp. ***sweginzowii***	CBcs CWCL GKin LLHF MMuc SPer
- subsp. ***yunnanensis***	GGGa
velutina Kom.	see *S. pubescens* subsp. *patula*
villosa	SPlb
vulgaris	CAco CDul EPfP ESps LBuc NWea
§ - 'Andenken an Ludwig Späth' ♀H6	Widely available
- 'Aucubifolia' (d/v) **new**	SEND WGob
- 'Aurea'	MRav NEoE
- Beauty of Moscow	see *S. vulgaris* 'Krasavitsa Moskvy'
- 'Belle de Nancy' (d)	CCCN CDul CLnd CMac CWib EBee ECrN ELan ELon EMOT EWTr GMcL MAsh MMuc MRav NGdn NLar SCob SEND SGol SPoG SWvt WGob
- Carpe Diem	see *S. vulgaris* 'Evert de Gier'
- 'Charles Joly' (d) ♀H6	Widely available
- 'Comtesse d'Harcourt'	EPfP SEND WGob
- 'Congo'	LSRN
- 'Edward J. Gardner' (d) ♀H6	SEND
§ - 'Evert de Gier'PBR	CBcs
- 'Firmament' ♀H6	ELan MRav SEND SPer
- 'G. J. Baardse'	EWTr
- 'Katherine Havemeyer' (d) ♀H6	Widely available
§ - 'Krasavitsa Moskvy' (d) ♀H6	ECrN EPfP EWes GMcL LRHS MAsh NLar NOra SEND SHil WMat
- 'Lee Jewett Walker'	SSta
- 'Lila Wonder'PBR	EBee EPfP SPoG
- 'Madame Florent Stepman'	CMac ELon GMcL NGdn WGob
- 'Madame Lemoine' (d) ♀H6	Widely available
- 'Masséna'	SPer
- 'Michel Buchner' (d)	CBcs CDul CWib EBee ECrN ELan EMOT EWTr GMcL MBlu MGos NLar NOra SCob SCoo SLim SPer WHar WMat
- 'Miss Ellen Willmott' (d)	IArd NLar
- 'Mrs Edward Harding' (d) ♀H6	ECrN EMOT EPfP ESps GMcL MRav NLar NWea SPer
- 'Pat Pesata'	WGob
- 'Paul Thirion' (d)	WGob
- 'Pavlinka' (d)	IArd
- 'Président Grévy' (d)	CBar CMac EPfP MAsh SLim SPer SPoG
- 'Président Poincaré' (d) **new**	WGob
- 'Primrose' ♀H6	CBcs CCCN CMac CWib EBee ELan ELon EPfP LRHS MAsh MGos MHid MJak NLar NOra NOrn SCoo SEND SHil SKHP SPer SPoG WGob WMat

- 'Prince Wolkonsky' (d)	ELon EPfP LSRN MAsh SEND SPer WFar
- 'Princesse Sturdza'	ELon
- 'Professor Hoser'	WGob
- Rose de Moscou = 'Minkarl'^{PBR}	EPfP
- 'Sensation' ♀^{H6}	Widely available
- 'Souvenir d'Alice Harding' (d) ♀^{H6}	IBoy
- 'Souvenir de Louis Spaeth'	see *S. vulgaris* 'Andenken an Ludwig Späth'
- variegated (v)	EWes
- variegated double (d/v)	WCot
- 'Vesper'	IArd
- 'Victor Lemoine' (d)	WGob
- 'Viviand-Morel' (d)	CMac SKHP
- 'William Robinson' (d)	WGob
wolfii	EBtc

Syzygium (*Myrtaceae*)

luehmannii	EShb

T

Tabernaemontana (*Apocynaceae*)

coronaria	see *T. divaricata*
§ ***divaricata***	CCCN

Tacca (*Taccaceae*)

chantrieri	CCCN

Taccarum (*Araceae*)

weddellianum	WCot

Tacitus see *Graptopetalum*

Tagetes (*Asteraceae*)

'Cinnabar'	CSpe SDix
erecta 'Jubilee Diamond' (Jubilee Series) new	MAvo
lemmonii	SDix SHDw WJek
- 'Martin's Mutant'	WCot
'Lemon Gem'	WJek
lucida	ENfk LEdu MHer SRms WJek WTre
patula Durango Series	NPri
- - 'Durango Flame'	NPri
- - 'Durango Yellow'	NPri
- 'Harlequin'	see *T. patula* 'Old Scotch Pride'
§ - 'Old Scotch Pride'	SPav

Taiwania (*Cupressaceae*)

cryptomerioides	IArd IDee SAko

Talinum (*Portulacaceae*)

'Zoe'	CPBP

tamarillo see *Solanum betaceum*

tamarind see *Tamarindus indica*

Tamarindus (*Caesalpiniaceae*)

indica (F)	SPlb

Tamarix (*Tamaricaceae*)

gallica	NWea SEND WSHC
hampeana	SEND
§ ***parviflora*** ♀^{H5}	CDul CMac CRos EPfP IVic LRHS NLar SCob SPoG
pentandra	see *T. ramosissima* 'Rosea'
ramosissima	CCCN CLet CTri ECrN ELan EPfP MAsh NLar SCob SEWo SLim SLon SRms WHar
- 'Hulsdonk White'	CBcs SPer
- 'Pink Cascade' ♀^{H5}	CAco CBcs CCCN CDul CMac CWCL EBee ELon EPfP ESps LCro LRHS MBlu MGos MMuc MNHC MRav NEgg SCob SEND SGbt SGol SPer SPoG SWvt WBor
§ - 'Rosea'	CBcs
§ - 'Rubra'	EPfP GMcL IVic SEND SLon SPer
- 'Summer Glow'	see *T. ramosissima* 'Rubra'
tetrandra ♀^{H5}	CBcs CCVT CChe CDul CLet CTsd CWib ELan EPfP ESps LBMP LRHS MAsh MBlu MGil MGos MMuc MRav MSwo NPer SEND SGol SHil SPer SPlb SRms SWvt WHar
- var. ***purpurea***	see *T. parviflora*

Tamus (*Dioscoreaceae*)

communis	CArn

Tanacetum ✿ (*Asteraceae*)

§ ***argenteum***	ECho MRav SIde
- subsp. ***canum***	ECho LRHS MAsh SLon
aureum new	SPad
§ ***balsamita***	CArn CBod CHby CLau EBee ELan ENfk GPoy LEdu MHer MMuc MNHC SEND SRms WHer WJek WSFF XLum XSen
§ - subsp. ***balsamita***	GPoy SIde
§ - subsp. ***balsamitoides***	CBod MHer SRms WJek
- var. ***tanacetoides***	see *T. balsamita* subsp. *balsamita*
- ***tomentosum***	see *T. balsamita* subsp. *balsamitoides*
camphoratum new	SBrt
§ ***cinerariifolium***	CArn CBod GPoy MNHC
§ ***coccineum***	SVic WFar
- 'Alfred'	MNrw
- 'Bees' Pink Delight'	ECtt NEgg
- 'Duro'	LRHS NRHS
- 'Eileen May Robinson'	CBod EPfP LSRN
- 'Garden Treasure'	EBee ECtt
- 'H.M. Pike'	EBee
- 'James Kelway'	ECtt EPfP NBir
- 'Laurin'	EBee ECtt LRHS
- 'Red Dwarf' new	ECtt
- Robinson's crimson-flowered	LRHS NRHS
- Robinson's giant-flowered	CTsd LRHS NRHS SRms
- Robinson's pink-flowered	EBee EPfP GMaP MHol SCob WHar XLum
- Robinson's red-flowered	CSBt EAJP EPfP GMaP GMcL GWyn LRHS MHol SPlb SWvt WHar WTcb XLum
- Robinson's rose-flowered	CSBt EAJP
- 'Snow Cloud'	ECtt EPfP LRHS
- 'Vanessa'	MNrw
§ ***corymbosum***	EBee GCal LRHS NLar WCot
- 'Bukke'	LEdu
- 'Festtafel'	LEdu SMHy
densum	ECho EPot WCFE
- subsp. ***amani***	ECha ECho GMaP LRHS MAsh SEND XSen
- - 'Beth Chatto'	XSen
§ ***haradjanii***	ECho MCot SBch WKif
huronense	EBee
macrophyllum misapplied	see *Achillea grandifolia* Friv.

§	***macrophyllum*** (Waldst. & Kit.) Sch.Bip.	CAby EBee ECtt EPPr SPhx WBor
	- 'Cream Klenza'	WCot
	niveum	ECha SDix WCot
	- 'Jackpot'	CBot CFis CWib EPfP EWes SHar SWvt
§	***parthenium***	CArn CBod CHab CHby CLau CPbn ENfk GPoy MHer MNHC NPer SIde SRms SVic WHer WJek WTre XLum
	- 'Aureum'	CBod CHid CPbn ECha ELan ENfk EWes GPoy LEdu LPot MHer MNHC SPer SPlb SRms SWvt WCot WHer WJek WMoo XLum
	- double white-flowered (d)	NPer SRms
	- 'Golden Ball'	EPfP
	- 'Golden Moss'	XLum
	- 'Malmesbury'	WHer
	- 'Plenum' (d)	MNrw
§	- 'Rowallane' (d)	MMuc SEND WCot
	- 'Sissinghurst White'	see *T. parthenium* 'Rowallane'
	- 'Snowball' (d)	EPfP
	poteriifolium	EBee LRHS
	ptarmiciflorum 'Silver Feather'	SRms SVen
*	***tommansii***	EBee LRHS
	vulgare	CArn CHab CHby CLau CMac ECha ECtt ENfk GBin GPoy GWyn IRos LCro MHer MNHC SIde SRms SVic WFar WJek WMoo WSFF WTre XSen
	- 'All Gold'	SMad SRms
	- var. ***crispum***	CLau EBee ENfk MHer MRav SIde SMad SRms WJek
	- 'Gold Sticks'	CBod
	- 'Golden Fleece'	ECtt EWes GMcL LEdu LSou NSti WCot WGrn
	- 'Isla Gold' (v)	CDor ECtt EWes LEdu LHop MHer MMuc MRav NBid SEND WCot WFar WHil WMoo
	- 'Silver Lace' (v)	CBre EBee EWes WFar WHer WJek WMoo

Tanakaea (*Saxifragaceae*)

radicans	GEdr WCru
- B&SWJ 11407	WCru

tangelo see *Citrus* × *aurantium* Tangelo Group

tangor see *Citrus* × *aurantium* Tangor Group

Taraxacum (*Asteraceae*)

faeroense	NWad WCot
officinale agg.	CHab
- 'Nettleton'	CNat
pseudoroseum	MMuc SBee
rubrifolium	CBre EPPr

tarragon see *Artemisia dracunculus*

Tasmannia (*Winteraceae*)

§	***lanceolata***	Widely available
	- (f)	EUJe SPer
	- (m)	SPer
	- 'Mount Wellington'	GCal
	- 'Red Spice'	EPfP ESwi LSRN SEle
	- 'Suzette' (v)	LRHS MBlu SRms

Taxodium ✿ (*Cupressaceae*)

	ascendens 'Nutans'	see *T. distichum* var. *imbricarium* 'Nutans'
	distichum	Widely available
	- 'Cascade Falls'	CDul LRHS MBlu MGos NLar NOra SAko SLim
	- 'Falling Waters'	SGol SKHP
	- var. ***imbricarium***	CMCN EPfP
§	- - 'Nutans'	CBcs EPfP IArd LRHS MBlu SGol SLim WMat
	- 'Little Leaf'	SMad
	- 'Minaret'	MBlu
*	- 'Pendulum'	IDee
	- 'Peve Minaret'	CMen LRHS MGos NLar SAko SArc SCob SGol SKHP SLim SPoG
	- 'Peve Yellow'	MBlu SLim
	- 'Schloss Herten'	SLim
	- 'Secrest'	MBlu
	- Shawnee Brave = 'Mickelson'	MBlu
	mucronatum	CFil
	- NJM 09.037	WPGP

Taxus ✿ (*Taxaceae*)

	baccata 𝕐H6	Widely available
	- 'Aldenham Gold'	CKen
	- 'Amersfoort'	NLar NWad
	- 'Argentea Minor'	see *T. baccata* 'Dwarf White'
	- Aurea Group	CDul ELan LPar SRms
I	- 'Aureomarginata' (v)	CBcs MAsh NEgg SWvt
	- 'Autumn Shades'	CBcs NLar
	- 'Bridget's Gold'	CKen
	- 'Corleys Coppertip'	CKen EBtc EMOT MRav NLar SEND SLim
	- 'Cristata'	CKen MBlu NLar
	- 'David'	IArd IBoy LRHS MGos NLar SPoG SWvt
	- 'Dorothea' **new**	NLar
	- 'Dovastoniana' (m or f)	CAco CDul CMac NLar NWea
	- 'Dovastonii Aurea' (m or f/v)	CBcs GKin MBlu NLar NWea SGol SLim SMad
	- 'Drinkstone Gold' (v)	EMOT SLim
§	- 'Dwarf White' (v)	NLar
	- 'Elegantissima' (f/v)	CTho EMOT EPfP NEgg NWea SCoo SLim SPoG
§	- 'Fastigiata' (f) 𝕐H6	Widely available
	- Fastigiata Aurea Group	CLnd CMac CTho CWib EPfP ESps GMcL IArd LPar LRHS MAsh MGos MJak NLar NOrn SArc SCob SGol SRms WHar
	- 'Fastigiata Aureomarginata' (m/v) 𝕐H6	CDul CMac CSBt CTri EPfP LBee LRHS MGos MSwo NWea SCoo SLim SLon SPer SPoG SWvt WTSh
	- 'Fastigiata Robusta' (f)	CSBt EBtc ELan EMOT EPfP GMcL LRHS MAsh MGos MJak NLar SCoo SLim SPoG WMat
	- 'Goldener Zwerg'	MBlu NLar
	- 'Graciosa' **new**	NLar
	- 'Great Column'	MBlu SEND
	- 'Green Column'	CKen
	- 'Green Diamond'	CKen MBlu
	- 'Green Rocket'	CDul
	- 'Hibernica'	see *T. baccata* 'Fastigiata'
	- 'Icicle' 𝕐H6	CBcs MAsh NHol NLar NWad
	- 'Itsy Bitsy'	CKen
	- 'Ivory Tower'	CBcs CKen ELan LRHS NHol NLar NWad
	- 'Jack's Gold'	NLar
	- 'Klitzeklein'	CKen
	- 'Micro'	CKen MAsh
	- 'Nutans'	CKen

	- 'Prostrata'	CMac
	- 'Pygmaea'	CKen
	- 'Repandens' (f) ♀H6	CDul ESps GMcL IArd NWea
I	- 'Repens Aurea' (v) ♀H6	CDul CKen CMac EMOT EPfP NLar SCoo SLim
	- 'Rushmore'	NLar
	- 'Semperaurea' (m) ♀H6	CBcs CMac LBuc LRHS MAsh NLar NWea SCoo SGol SLim SPoG
	- 'Standishii' (f) ♀H6	Widely available
	- 'Stove Pipe'	CKen
	- 'Summergold' (v)	ELan EMOT ESps GMcL LRHS MAsh MRav NBir NLar SCoo SLim
	cuspidata	CAco CMen LPar
	- 'Aurescens' (v)	CKen
	- 'Minuet'	CKen
	- 'Straight Hedge'	SLim
	× ***media***	LPar
	- 'Hicksii' (f)	CDul ESps GMcL LBuc NWea SGol
	- 'Hillii'	LBuc
	wallichiana	LEdu

tayberry see *Rubus* Tayberry Group

Tecoma (*Bignoniaceae*)

	capensis ♀H1c	CHll CRHN EBee GCal SVen
	- 'Apricot'	CBcs
	- 'Lutea'	CBcs EPfP
	ricasoliana	see *Podranea ricasoliana*

Tecomanthe (*Bignoniaceae*)

speciosa	CRHN

Tecomaria see *Tecoma*

Tecophilaea (*Tecophilaeaceae*)

	cyanocrocus ♀H3	ECho EPot GKev LAma LLHF LRHS NRHS SDir
	- 'Leichtlinii' ♀H3	CAvo ECho EPot GKev LAma LLHF LRHS NRHS SDeJ SDir
	- 'Purpurea'	see *T. cyanocrocus* 'Violacea'
	- Storm Cloud Group	ECho EPot GKev LLHF SDir
§	- 'Violacea'	CAvo ECho EPot GKev LLHF LRHS NRHS SDir
	violiflora	ECho

Telekia (*Asteraceae*)

§	***speciosa***	CMac CRos CSam CSpe ELan EPfP GAbr GLog LEdu MBel MMuc NBro NChi NLar NSti SDix SEND SPlb WBrk WHer WHoo WMoo

Telesonix see *Boykinia*

Teline see *Genista*

Tellima (*Saxifragaceae*)

	grandiflora	Widely available
	- 'Bob's Choice'	WCot
	- 'Delphine' (v)	EBee EPPr EWld WCot XLum
	- 'Forest Frost'	CBod CFis CMac CMos EHoe ELan EPPr EPed EShb LRHS MBNS MPnt NLar SCob SWvt WCAu WCot WGwG WHoo WMoo WOut
	- Odorata Group	CBre ECha EHrv WCot WMoo
	- 'Purpurea'	see *T. grandiflora* Rubra Group
	- 'Purpurteppich'	CBod ECha EHrv EPPr GPSL LHop LRHS MPnt MRav SWvt WCot WMoo WPnP
§	- Rubra Group	CBod CBre CBro CMac CSam CTri ECha EHoe ELan EPfP EWoo LRHS MCot NChi NEgg NLar NPer NSti SCob SPer SPlb SRms SWvt WCAu WCot WHea WHoo WMoo WPnP
	- 'Silver Select'	EPPr

Telopea (*Proteaceae*)

'Emperor's Torch'	LRHS MPkF
oreades	SPlb
'Shady Lady Crimson' **new**	CCCN
'Shady Lady White' **new**	CCCN
'Shady Lady Yellow' **new**	CCCN
speciosissima	CCCN CTre LRHS SPlb
truncata	CCCN SPlb WCru

Temu see *Blepharocalyx*

Tephroseris (*Asteraceae*)

integrifolia subsp. ***capitata***	SPlb

Ternstroemia (*Pentaphylacaceae*)

chapaensis WWJ 11918	WCru
gymnanthera	WCru
luteoflora FMWJ 13360	WCru

Tetracentron (*Trochodendraceae*)

§	***sinense***	CBcs CMCN EPfP IArd MBlu
	- WJC 13818 **new**	WCru
	- var. ***himalense***	see *T. sinense*

Tetradium (*Rutaceae*)

	austrosinense NJM 09.215	EBee WPGP
§	***daniellii***	CBcs CDul CMCN CTho EPfP ESwi IArd LEdu SAko WGob WHar WMat WPGP
§	- Hupehense Group	CMCN CTho LRHS MCoo MHid NLar SEND WPGP
	fraxinifolium PAB 9101	LEdu
	aff. ***fraxinifolium*** WWJ 11615	WCru
	glabrifolium B&SWJ 6882	WCru
	- CWJ 12364	WCru
	ruticarpum	LEdu WPGP
	- B&SWJ 3541	WCru

Tetragonolobus see *Lotus*

Tetraneuris (*Asteraceae*)

§	***grandiflora***	GKev SPlb
	scaposa	EPot

Tetrapanax ✿ (*Araliaceae*)

	sp.	ETod
§	***papyrifer*** ♀H4	CBrP CDTJ CHGN ELan ESwi NLos SArc SBig SDix SEND SVen XBlo
	- B&SWJ 7135	WCru
	- 'Di-Sue-Shan'	WCru
	- 'Empress'	WCru
	- 'Rex'	Widely available
	- 'Steroidal Giant'	CDTJ SBig SKHP

Tetrapathaea see *Passiflora*

Tetrastigma (*Vitaceae*)

obtectum	CCCN EBee ECre ESwi EWes SEND WCFE

Teucridium (*Lamiaceae*)

parvifolium	MPie

Teucrium (*Lamiaceae*)

* ***ackermannii*** ♀H5	CMea ECho MHer SBch SIgm WAbe WHoo WIce XSen
arduinoi	XSen
aroanium	CTal ECho EPot SIgm XSen
asiaticum	XSen
aureum	XSen
botrys	MHer
chamaedrys misapplied	see *T.* × *lucidrys*
chamaedrys L.	CBar CRos CWib ELon ENfk GMaP GPoy LRHS LSRN MCot MNHC MRav MSwo NRya NWad SCob SEND SIgm SLim SPer SPlb SRms SVen SWvt WBrk WHar WJek XSen
- f. ***albiflora*** new	LPla
- 'Nanum'	ECho
- 'Rose'	SRms
- 'Spring Gold' new	LRHS
- 'Summer Sunshine'	CRos LRHS SHil
aff. ***chamaedrys***	MSCN
dunense	XSen
flavum	EBee EDAr EPPr GCal SBrt XSen
fruticans	Widely available
- 'Azureum' ♀H3	CBcs CBod CTsd EBee ELan EPfP EWTr LHop LRHS LSRN MRav SBrt SEND SMad SPer SPoG SWvt WCFE WKif XSen
I - 'Azureum Compactum'	CLet
- 'Compactum'	ELan EWTr LSRN MNHC SLim SLon SPer SPoG SWvt WCFE WPGP WPnn
- 'Drysdale'	CSBt ELan LRHS SWvt
hircanicum	CAby CElw CSam ECha ECtt ELan IFro LLWP LRHS LSRN MArt MMuc MNrw NBir NWad SEND SPhx SRkn WCFE WMoo XSen
- 'Paradise Delight'	ECtt GWyn IKil NLar
- 'Purple Tails'	CBod CSpe CTsd CWib CWld EPfP GQue LSou MCot MHol MNHC MRav NBir SPoG WGwG
lamiifolium W&B BGB-7	WCot
§ × ***lucidrys***	CArn CChe CMea CRos ECha ECrN ELan ENfk EPfP EWoo GBin LPla LRHS MHer MNHC MPie SPer SPoG SRms SWvt WCFE WFar WHar WHoo WJek WPnn XSen
- 'Lucky Gold'PBR	LRHS SPoG
lucidum	GCal SLon
marum	CArn CTri LEdu SIgm SRms WJek XSen
massiliense misapplied	see *T.* × *lucidrys*
montanum	XSen
musimonum	EPot
orientale	WAbe XSen
polium	ECho SIgm SPhx WThu XSen
pyrenaicum ♀H5	CMea CPBP ECho EPot EWes GEdr SBch SIgm XSen
- subsp. ***guarense***	XSen
scorodonia	CArn CBod CHab GPoy MCot MHer MNHC NLar NMir SRms WHer WJek XSen
- 'Binsted Gold'	NSti
- 'Crispum'	CWld LEdu LRHS MHer MMuc NBro NLar SBod SPer SRms WGrn WJek WKif WMoo WOut WSHC
- 'Crispum Marginatum' (v)	EBee ECGP ECha EHoe EPPr EPfP EWld IKil LEdu LSou MRav
- 'Winterdown' (v)	SBch
subspinosum	ECho LLHF SIgm WHoo WThu
§ ***viscidum*** 'Lemon and Lime' (v)	EBee NSti
webbianum	ECho

Thalia (*Marantaceae*)

dealbata	CBen EUJe EWay LLWG MSKA SBig SLon WMAq XLum

Thalictrum ✿ (*Ranunculaceae*)

Cox 6118	ITim
from Afghanistan	see *T. isopyroides*
actaeifolium	CLAP CWib
- B&SWJ 4664	WCru
- B&SWJ 6310	WCru
- var. ***brevistylum*** B&SWJ 8819	WCru
- - 'Twinkling Star'	ECtt
- compact B&SWJ 4946	WCru
- 'Perfume Star'	CMos CPar EBee ECtt GBin ILea IPot MMrt NDov NLar SCob
adiantifolium	see *T. minus* 'Adiantifolium'
alpinum	CTal EDAr EPPr GJos
angustifolium	see *T. lucidum*
'Anne'PBR	EBee ECtt EMFm EWTr IKil ILea IPot LRHS MBel MHol MNrw MTis NCGa NDov NGBl NLar SAko SPoG WCot
aquilegiifolium	Widely available
- SDR 5463	GKev
- 'Album'	CWCL EBee ECha ELan EPfP GBin GCra GKin LBMP LHop LRHS MArt MBel MCot MMuc NBid SEND SKHP SPer SPhx SWvt WCAu WFar
* - 'Hybridum'	WMoo
- var. ***intermedium*** B&SWJ 10965	WCru
- 'Purpureum'	NLar NQui WWtn
- var. ***sibiricum***	IMou
- - B&SWJ 11007	WCru
- 'Small Thundercloud'	GCal
- 'Thundercloud' ♀H5	Widely available
baicalense	EPPr
'Black Stockings'	Widely available
calabricum	NLar
chelidonii	EPPr
- HWJK 2216	WCru
clavatum	CAby CLAP WPGP
coreanum	see *T. ichangense*
cultratum	EBee LRHS WPGP
dasycarpum	EPPr GJos LPla WCot WPnP
§ ***delavayi*** ♀H7	Widely available
- BWJ 7800	WCru
- BWJ 7903	WCru
- var. ***acuminatum***	MBel
- - BWJ 7535	WCru
- - BWJ 7971	WCru
- 'Album'	Widely available
- 'Ankum'	CKno EBee MNrw NLar
- var. ***decorum***	CElw CLAP CWCL ECtt ELon EPPr MBel WCot WCru WPGP
- - BWJ 7770	WCru
- 'Gold Laced'	EBee NLar
- 'Hewitt's Double' (d) ♀H7	Widely available
- 'Hinkley'	NLar
- var. ***mucronatum***	MBel WCru
- - DJHC 473	WCru
- purple-stemmed BWJ 7748	WCru
- Splendide White = 'Fr21034'	CDor CMos CSpe EBee ECtt IKil IPot LCro LRHS MBel MCot NCGa NDov NLar NPnk SAko SHar SHil STPC WHil

- 'White Cloud'	GBin
aff. ***delavayi***	ESps GKin IBoy NDov
diffusiflorum	EWld IMou WAbe WCru WSHC
dipterocarpum misapplied	see *T. delavayi*
dipterocarpum Franch.	CMac EBee LRHS NRHS XLum
'Elin'	Widely available
fendleri	GBin
- var. ***polycarpum***	EBee IMou WOut
filamentosum	EPPr IMou MBel
- B&SWJ 777	WCru
- B&SWJ 4145	WCru
aff. ***finetii*** DJHC 473	CLAP
flavum	CHab CMac ELan EWld GKin LLWG NBro NMir SPhx SWat WFar WShi
- 'Chollerton'	see *T. isopyroides*
§ - subsp. ***glaucum*** ♀H7	Widely available
- - Brown's strain **new**	WCot
- - dwarf	WPGP
- - 'Silver Sparkler' (v) **new**	WCot
- - 'True Blue'	SGbt
- 'Illuminator'	CDor CElw CTri EPfP IBoy LRHS MArl MRav NLar WCot WFar
flexuosum	see *T. minus* subsp. *minus*
honanense	SKHP
- BWJ 7962	WCru
- 'Marble Leaf'	SKHP
§ ***ichangense***	CBot CHid CSpe EBee ECtt EPri GEdr IPot LEdu LRHS MBel MHol MPie MTis NWad SDix SPer WCot WRHF
- B&SWJ 8203	WCru
- Evening Star strain (v)	CAby CSpe EBee ECtt GBin MHol NCGa SCob SPad
- var. ***minus*** 'Chinese Chintz'	WCru
- 'Purple Marble'	CWGN GEdr LEdu MSCN NPnk WCot
integrilobum B&SWJ 11151 **new**	WCru
§ ***isopyroides***	EBee GBin GCal GKev GKin LRHS MBel MHol MMuc MRav NLar NPnk NWad SEND SHar WCot
javanicum	LEdu WPGP
- B&SWJ 9506	WCru
- PAB 9431	LEdu
- var. ***puberulum*** B&SWJ 6770	WCru
johnstonii B&SWJ 9127	WCru
kiusianum	Widely available
- Kew form	WSHC
koreanum	see *T. ichangense*
§ ***lucidum***	CBod CElw EBee ECtt EHoe ELan EShb GBin GCal GKin IMou LEdu LRHS MHol MMuc MPie MTis NGBl NLar NSti SDix SEND SKHP SPhx WCot WPnP
minus	GBin LEdu LRHS MMuc SEND
§ - 'Adiantifolium'	GBin GJos IPot MBel MRav NGdn SRms XLum
- var. ***hypoleucum*** B&SWJ 8634	WCru
- subsp. ***kemense***	EBee
§ - subsp. ***minus***	GJos NBre
- var. ***sipellatum*** B&SWJ 5051	WCru
morisonii	EBee LRHS NBid
'Nishiki'	GEdr
omeiense BWJ 8049	WCru
orientale	EBee LRHS
osmundifolium	WCru
petaloideum	EPPr
platycarpum B&SWJ 2261	WCru
polygamum	see *T. pubescens* Pursh
przewalskii	WCru
§ ***pubescens*** Pursh	EBee ECha GJos GMaP LRHS MAvo NDov NLar SHar SPhx WCot
punctatum B&SWJ 1272	WCru
ramosum BWJ 8126	WCru
reniforme	EBee LEdu WCot
- GWJ 9311	WCru
- HWJK 2403	WCru
- WJC 13761 **new**	WCru
rochebruneanum	Widely available
rubescens B&SWJ 10006	WCru
rugosum	EBee LRHS
sachalinense	WPGP
- RBS 0279	EBee EPPr NLar
simplex var. ***brevipes*** B&SWJ 4794	WCru
speciosissimum	see *T. flavum* subsp. *glaucum*
* ***sphaerostachyum***	CElw EBee EPPr GPSL LRHS MBel MNrw MPie WHal
'Splendide'	Widely available
squarrosum	EBee WPGP
tenuisubulatum BWJ 7929	WCru
tuberiferum var. ***yakusimense*** B&SWJ 6094	WCru
tuberosum	CElw CSpe LLHF NDov SBrt WCot
tubiferum B&SWJ 10999	WCru
'Tukker Princess'	EBee ECtt GBin IKil ILea LHop MBel MHol NDov NLar WCot
uchiyamae	EBee EWld WCot WPGP
urbainii B&SWJ 7085	WCru
'Yubari Mountains'	GEdr
yunnanense	WCru

Thamnocalamus (*Poaceae*)

crassinodus	SBig
- 'Gosainkund'	CEnt ERod MWht
- 'Kew Beauty' ♀H3	CDTJ CEnt CJng EPfP ERod MBrN MWht SBig WCot WPGP
- 'Langtang'	CEnt CJng ERod MWht WPGP
- 'Merlyn'	CEnt CJng EPfP ERod MWht WPGP
falconeri	see *Himalayacalamus falconeri*
maling	see *Yushania maling*
spathaceus misapplied	see *Fargesia murielae*
§ ***spathiflorus***	CEnt CJng
- subsp. ***nepalensis***	ERod MMuc MWht SBig
tessellatus	see *Bergbambos tessellata*

Thamnochortus (*Restionaceae*)

bachmannii	LRHS
cinereus	CTre LRHS
insignis ♀H2	CSpe CTre MPkF SPlb
lucens	SPlb
pluristachyus	LRHS
rigidus	CCCN

Thapsia (*Apiaceae*)

decipiens	see *Melanoselinum decipiens*
garganica	SBrt
maxima	SIgm
villosa	CArn

Thea see *Camellia*

Thelypteris (*Thelypteridaceae*)

kunthii	EBee ISha
limbosperma	see *Oreopteris limbosperma*

noveboracensis	see *Parathelypteris novae-boracensis*
ovata var. ***lindheimeri***	ISha
palustris	CKel EBee EShb NBro NLar SRms WFib WPnP XLum
phegopteris	see *Phegopteris connectilis*

Themeda (*Poaceae*)

triandra	SMad

Thermopsis (*Papilionaceae*)

caroliniana	see *T. villosa*
chinensis	CLet EAJP EBee ELon LPla LRHS MHer MMuc SEND WTcb
fabacea	see *T. lupinoides*
lanceolata	CMea CTri EBee ELon EPfP LRHS MMuc NQui SEND SHar SPad WCot WFar
§ ***lupinoides***	ECha EHrv
macrophylla	EBee GJos
mollis	NBid WTcb
montana	see *T. rhombifolia* var. *montana*
§ ***rhombifolia*** var. ***montana***	CBod CWCL EAEE EBee EHrv ELan EPfP GAbr GCra GMaP LHop LRHS MMuc NBir NCGa NPnk NPol NSti NWad SEND SPer SPoG WBor WTcb
§ ***villosa***	CWCL LPla LRHS MRav NGdn NLar SMHy WCot WFar WHoo

Therorhodion see *Rhododendron*

Thladiantha (*Cucurbitaceae*)

dubia	EBee SBrt SDix WCot

Thlaspi (*Brassicaceae*)

sp.	NGdn
biebersteinii	see *Pachyphragma macrophyllum*
bulbosum	WAbe
§ ***cepaeifolium*** subsp. ***rotundifolium***	GEdr WAbe
densiflorum	GEdr
rotundifolium	see *T. cepaeifolium* subsp. *rotundifolium*
zaffrani	GEdr

Thryptomene (*Myrtaceae*)

baeckeacea	CCCN

Thuja ✿ (*Cupressaceae*)

'Extra Gold'	see *T. plicata* 'Irish Gold'
§ ***koraiensis***	NLar SLim
occidentalis	ESps LPar NWea SEND
- 'Amber Glow'	CKen CSBt EMOT GMcL LRHS MAsh NHol NLar NWad SCoo SLim SPoG
- 'Anniek'PBR	CKen SPoG
- 'Bateman Broom'	CKen
- 'Beaufort' (v)	CKen
- 'Brabant' ♀H6	CDul GMcL LPar MGos MJak NLar NWea SCob SCoo SLim WHar
- 'Brobeck's Tower' ♀H6	CKen NLar SLim
- 'Caespitosa'	CKen
- 'Danica' ♀H6	CMac EMOT ESps GKin GMcL IBoy LCro MAsh MGos MJak NOrn NWea SCob SCoo SLim SPoG SRms WCFE
- 'Danica Gold'	SLim
- 'Degroot's Spire'	CKen ELan LRHS NLar SLim
- 'Douglasii Aurea' (v)	CKen
- Emerald	see *T. occidentalis* 'Smaragd'
- 'Ericoides'	ESps SRms
- 'Europa Gold' ♀H6	NLar SGol
- 'Fastigiata'	ESps
- 'Filiformis'	CKen
- 'Filips Magic Moment'PBR	SPoG
- Fire Chief = 'Congabe' **new**	CKen NLar
- 'Globosa'	ELan
I - 'Globosa Variegata' (v)	CKen
- 'Gold Drop'	CKen
- 'Golden Globe'	IBoy MJak SCoo SLim
- Golden Smaragd = 'Janed Gold'PBR	CCVT SLim SPoG
- 'Golden Tuffet' ♀H6	CKen ELan EMOT GKin LBee MPkF NLar NWad SCob SCoo SLim SPoG
- 'Hetz Midget' ♀H6	CKen EMOT ESps GKin IBoy NLar NWad SCob SCoo SLim SPlb
- 'Holmstrup' ♀H6	CDul CMac CWib ESps MAsh MGos NOrn SGol SLim SRms WHar
- 'Hoveyi'	CTri
- 'Jantar'PBR	NLar
- 'Konfettii' (v) **new**	EMOT
- 'Linesville'	CKen
- 'Little Champion'	IBoy
- 'Little Gem'	SRms
- 'Lutea Nana'	ESps
- 'Malonyana Holub'	SLim
- 'Meineke's Zwerg' (v)	CKen
- 'Miky'	LRHS
- 'Mirjam'PBR (v)	CKen SPoG
- 'Mr Bowling Ball'	NLar
- 'Ohlendorffii'	CKen
- 'Perk Vlaanderen' (v)	LRHS
I - 'Pygmaea'	CKen
- 'Pyramidalis Aurea'	ECrN GMcL
- 'Recurva Nana'	NWad
- 'Rheingold' ♀H6	Widely available
§ - 'Smaragd' ♀H6	CCVT CDul CSBt CWib ELan EMOT EPfP ESps GMcL IBoy LBuc LCro LRHS MAsh MGos MJak NLar NOrn NWea SCob SCoo SEWo SGol SLim SPoG SWvt WCFE WHar WMou
* - 'Smaragd Variegated' (v)	CKen MAsh
- 'Smokey'	CKen
- 'Spiralis'	NLar
- 'Starstruck'	SPoG
- 'Sunkist' ♀H6	CKen CMac CWib EMOT ESps GMcL MAsh MGos MJak NEgg SCoo SGol
- 'Teddy'	EMOT EPfP LBee LRHS MAsh NHol SCoo SPoG
- 'Tiny Tim'	CMac CWib IBoy SGol
- 'Trompenburg'	NLar
- 'Wansdyke Silver' (v)	CMac
- 'Wareana'	CMac
- 'Wareana Aurea'	see *T. occidentalis* 'Wareana Lutescens'
§ - 'Wareana Lutescens'	CWib
- 'Waterfield'	NLar NWad
- 'Yellow Ribbon'	CDul CKen CSBt GMcL MJak SCob SGol
orientalis	see *Platycladus orientalis*
- 'Miller's Gold'	see *Platycladus orientalis* 'Aurea Nana'
plicata	CAco CBcs CCVT CDul CMac CTho ELan EPfP ESps LPar NBes NWea SCob SPer SWeb WHar WHed WMou WTSh

- 'Atrovirens' ♀H6	CDul CLet CTri ECrN ESps GMcL LBee LBuc LCro LPar LRHS MAsh MGos MMuc NOra SCob SCoo SEND SEWo SGol SHil SRms SWvt WHar WHed WMat WMou
* - 'Atrovirens Aurea'	ESps LPar
- 'Aurea' ♀H6	MAsh SRms
- 'Can-can' (v)	ELan EMOT MAsh
I - 'Cole's Variety'	CWib MMuc
- 'Collyer's Gold'	CDul SRms
- 'Copper Kettle'	CKen GKin LRHS SLim
- 'Cuprea'	CKen
- 'Doone Valley'	CKen NWad
- 'Excelsa'	CDul LPar WMou
- 'Fastigiata'	CDul
- 'Gelderland' ♀H6	ELan EMOT EPfP NEgg SCoo SLim WHar WHed
- Goldy = '4ever' PBR	EMOT GMcL LRHS SLim SPoG
- 'Gracilis Aurea'	ESps
- 'Hillieri'	CDul
- 'Holly Turner'	SLim
§ - 'Irish Gold' (v)	CDul CMac SLim SMad
- 'Martin'	GMcL SWvt
- 'Rogersii' ♀H6	CKen CMac EMOT ESps MAsh NHol SCoo SPoG SRms WThu
- 'Semperaurescens' (v)	CMac
- 'Stoneham Gold' ♀H6	CMac ESps GKin MAsh MGos MMuc SEND SRms WCFE
- Verigold = 'Courtapli'	CCVT MMuc SEND
- 'Whipcord' ♀H6	CBcs CKen ELan EMOT EPfP EUJe GMcL LRHS MPkF NHol NLar SCoo SLim SPoG
- 'Winter Pink' (v)	CKen
- 'Zebrina' (v) ♀H6	CBcs CDul CMac CTri CWib ELan EMOT EPfP ESps LRHS MAsh MGos MMuc NLar NWea SCob SCoo SEND SLim SPoG SWvt WHar
standishii	WThu

Thujopsis (*Cupressaceae*)

dolabrata ♀H6	CBcs CDul GKin MMuc NEgg NWea SEND SWvt
- 'Aurea' (v)	CKen LRHS NLar SLim
- var. ***hondae***	IArd SLim
- 'Laetevirens'	see *T. dolabrata* 'Nana'
§ - 'Nana'	CKen CMac LRHS NLar SLim SRms
- 'Variegata' (v)	CMac GKin NLar SLim
koraiensis (Nakai) hort.	see *Thuja koraiensis*

Thunbergia ✿ (*Acanthaceae*)

alata	EPfP SPoG
- 'African Sunset'	CSpe EShb
- 'Lemon Queen'	CHll SWvt
- 'Orange Beauty'	LBuc LSou SWvt
- 'Sunny Suzy Red-Orange'	EPfP
* ***arborea***	CCCN
battiscombeii	CCCN EShb
coccinea	CCCN
erecta	CCCN
fragrans GWJ 9441	WCru
grandiflora ♀H1a	CBcs CCCN CHll WSFF
- 'Alba'	CCCN CHll
gregorii ♀H1c	CCCN CHll EShb
laurifolia B&SWJ 7166	WCru
'Lemon Star'	EPfP LBuc
'Moonglow'	CCCN
natalensis	CCCN EShb
'Orange Wonder'	CCCN

Thunia (*Orchidaceae*)

marshalliana new	GKev

thyme, caraway see *Thymus herba-barona*

thyme, garden see *Thymus vulgaris*

thyme, lemon see *Thymus citriodorus*

thyme, wild see *Thymus serpyllum*

Thymus ✿ (*Lamiaceae*)

from Albania	CArn
from Turkey	EWes LEdu SHDw
'A Touch of Frost'	SHDw
§ 'Alan Bloom'	LRHS NRHS
'Albus'	CBod ENfk
'Anderson's Gold'	see *T. pulegioides* 'Bertram Anderson'
'Aureus' ambig.	MJak
azoricus	see *T. caespititius*
'Bressingham'	CBod CMea CTri ECtt EDAr GCrg GMaP LEdu LLWP LRHS MHer MMuc MNHC NDov NRHS SPlb SRms WIce WJek
'Caborn Lilac Gem'	LLWP SHDw
'Caborn Pink Carpet'	LLWP
'Caborn Royale'	LLWP
'Caborn Wine and Roses'	ENfk LLWP SRms WJek
§ ***caespititius***	CArn GCrg GPoy MHer NRya SPlb SRms SRot WJek
caespitosus	CTri LEdu
camphoratus	ENfk ESwi EWes GCrg MHer NHpl SPhx WJek
capitatus	CArn
§ ***carnosus*** Boiss.	MHer WJek XSen
'Carol Ann' (v)	ENfk EWes MNHC SRms
cephalotos	WAbe
ciliatus	CBod XSen
cilicicus misapplied	see *T. caespititius*
cilicicus ambig.	MNHC SRms
cilicicus Boiss. & Bail.	WAbe
citriodorus misapplied	see *T.* 'Culinary Lemon'
citriodorus ambig.	CTal CTsd MMuc SRms XLum
citriodorus (Pers.) Schreb.	LEdu
- 'Archer's Gold'	see *T. pulegioides* 'Archer's Gold'
- 'Aureus'	see *T. pulegioides* 'Aureus'
- 'Bertram Anderson'	see *T. pulegioides* 'Bertram Anderson'
- 'Silver Posie'	see *T.* 'Silver Posie'
'Coccineus'	see *T.* Coccineus Group
§ Coccineus Group ♀H5	Widely available
- 'Atropurpureus' Schleipfer	see *T.* (Coccineus Group) 'Purple Beauty'
§ - 'Purple Beauty'	EPot GCrg LRHS MHer NRHS SHDw SRms XSen
§ - 'Red Elf'	CBod GAbr GCrg MHer
'Coccineus Major'	CMea EDAr LRHS MHer MNHC NRHS SCob SRms WJek
comosus misapplied	SHDw
'Creeping Lemon' misapplied	see *T. pulegioides* 'Kurt'
§ 'Culinary Lemon'	CBod CHby CLau EDAr ENfk GPoy MBrN MHer MNHC NPri WJek XLum XSen
'Dark Eyes'	SHDw
'Dartmoor'	CBod SHDw WJek
'Desboro'	see *T. serpyllum* 'Desborough'
'Dillington'	ENfk

	doerfleri	XSen
	'Doone Valley' (v)	CBod CMea CTri ECha EDAr ELan ENfk EPfP ESps EWoo GAbr GMaP LBMP LEdu LRHS MAsh MHer MJak MMuc MNHC NBir NRHS SCob SPer SPlb SPoG SRms WHoo WIce WJek
	drucei	see *T. polytrichus* A. Kern. ex Borbás subsp. *britannicus*
	'Duftkissen'PBR **new**	XSen
	'E.B.Anderson'	see *T. pulegioides* 'Bertram Anderson'
	'Eastgrove Pink'	SHDw
	'Elfin Pink Carpet'	MHol
	erectus	see *T. carnosus* Boiss.
	'Fragrantissimus'	CLau ENfk GPoy MHer MNHC SIde SPlb WJek XSen
	'Golden King' (v)	ECha EDAr ELan ENfk LHop LSRN MAsh MHer MMuc SRms XSen
	'Golden Lemon' misapplied	see *T. pulegioides* 'Aureus'
	'Golden Lemon' (v)	WJek
	'Golden Queen' (v)	CBod EDAr MHol SRms XSen
	'Gratian'	SHDw
§	'Hartington Silver' (v)	CBod ECha ECtt ENfk EPot EWes GCrg GKev LBMP LEdu LHop LRHS MAsh MHer MMuc NHpl NRHS NRya SDix SPlb SPoG SRms WHoo WJek
	herba-barona	CBod CLau CTri EDAr ENfk GPoy LEdu LLWP MHer MMuc MNHC SIde SRms WJek
	- ***citrata***	see *T. herba-barona* 'Lemon-scented'
§	- 'Lemon-scented'	CBod ECha GPoy LEdu LLWP MHer SHDw SRms WJek XSen
	'Highdown'	ECtt SHDw
	'Highdown Adur'	SHDw
	'Highdown Lemon'	SHDw
	'Highdown Red'	SHDw
	'Highdown Stretham'	SHDw
	'Highland Cream'	see *T.* 'Hartington Silver'
	hirsutus	XSen
	hyemalis	XSen
§	'Iden'	CBod WJek
	'Jekka'	CBod MHer SRms WJek
	'Kurt'	see *T. pulegioides* 'Kurt'
	'Lavender Sea'	EWes
	'Lemon Caraway'	see *T. herba-barona* 'Lemon-scented'
	'Lemon Curd'	CLau ENfk MNHC NHol SHDw SPlb SPoG SRms WJek
	'Lemon Sorbet'	SHDw
*	'Lemon Variegated' (v)	CBod CLau EDAr ENfk EPfP MNHC SPer SPoG XSen
	leucotrichus	XSen
	'Lilac Time'	ECtt ENfk EWes LEdu LLWP MHer SHDw SPlb SRms WJek
	'Lime'	LEdu
	linearis	XSen
	longicaulis	CBod CLau ECha MHer MMuc SRms
	longiflorus	XSen
	'Magic Carpet'	MArt SPhx
	marschallianus	see *T. pannonicus*
§	'Massa'	SHDw
	mastichina	SPhx XSen
	- 'Didi'	MHer
	membranaceus	WAbe
	micans	see *T. caespititius*
	minus	see *Calamintha nepeta*
	'Mountain Select'	SHDw
	neiceffii	CMea ECha SBch XSen
	nitens **new**	XSen
	'Orange'	CBod LEdu SRms
§	Orange Spice = 'Tm95'	SHDw XSen
	pallasianus	SHDw
§	***pannonicus***	MHer
	'Peter Davis'	ENfk GBin GCrg LHop LRHS LSRN MHer NBir NRHS SIde SPoG SRms WAbe WIce WTor XSen
§	'Pinewood'	CTal LEdu MHer WJek XSen
	'Pink Ripple'	CBod CLau CMea CTal ECtt ENfk EWes LEdu MHer MNHC SHDw SIgm SRms WHal WHoo WJek
	polytrichus misapplied	see *T. praecox*
§	***polytrichus*** A. Kern. ex Borbás subsp. ***britannicus***	CArn CBod CTri ECha EPot GBin GJos GMaP GPoy LEdu MBNS MHer MMuc MNHC NBir NEoE SEND SHDw SPlb SRms WHoo WJek XLum XSen
§	- - 'Thomas's White' ♀H5	CTri
	'Porlock'	CBod CLau CMea CSam CTri EPfP MHer SRms WHoo WJek
§	***praecox***	CBod CWld ESps EWoo GJos MArt MHer NMir
	- 'Albiflorus'	EWoo MRav XSen
	- subsp. ***arcticus***	see *T. polytrichus* A. Kern. ex Borbás subsp. *britannicus*
	- - 'Albus'	see *T. polytrichus* subsp. *britannicus* 'Thomas's White'
	prostrate	CBod
	'Provence'	XSen
	pulegioides	CBod CHby CLau ENfk GPoy MArt MHer MNHC NHpl SHDw SIde SRms SRot WJek
§	- 'Archer's Gold'	CTri ECtt EDAr EHoe ENfk EPfP EPot ESps GKev LEdu LHop LPot LRHS LSRN MAsh MHer MHol MNHC MRav NBir NHol NHpl NRHS SCob SRms WJek XSen
§	- 'Aureus' ♀H5	ENfk ESps GMaP LCro LLWP MAsh MHer MMuc SPer SPlb SRms WHoo WJek
§	- 'Bertram Anderson' ♀H5	CBod CMea CTal ECha ECtt ENfk EPfP GCrg GMaP LLWP MAsh MHer NBir NRya SCob SPer SPoG SRms WHoo WIce WJek XSen
	- 'Elliott's Gold'	LBMP
	- 'Foxley' (v)	CBod CLau EHoe ELon ENfk EPfP GAbr LLWP MHer MMuc MNHC SHDw SIde SPlb SPoG SRms WJek XSen
	- 'Golden Dwarf'	XSen
§	- 'Kurt'	CBod ENfk LEdu LLWP MHer SHDw SRms WJek
	- 'Sir John Lawes'	MHer
	- 'Tabor'	CBod ENfk MNHC SHDw SRms XSen
	'Rainbow Falls' (v)	EPfP SHDw SRms
	'Rasta' (v)	MHer XSen
	'Redstart'	CBod ECha ECtt ENfk LEdu LLWP MHer SHDw SRms WJek
	richardii subsp. ***nitidus*** 'Compactus Albus'	see *T. vulgaris* 'Snow White'
	'Rosa Ceeping'	SHDw
	'Rosalicht'	see *T.* 'Rosedrift'
§	'Rosedrift'	SHDw
	rotundifolius misapplied	see *T. vulgaris* 'Elsbeth'

'Ruby Glow'	ECtt EWes GCrg MHer SHDw
serpyllum ambig.	EWoo SCob SVic XLum
serpyllum L.	CArn GJos LBuc MMuc SPlb SRms WJek WRHF
- var. ***albus***	CTal ECha ELon GMaP GPoy LLWP LRHS MNHC NRHS SPer SRms WHoo WJek
- 'Albus Variegatus'	see *T.* 'Hartington Silver'
- 'Amadé' **new**	XSen
- 'Annie Hall'	CTal EDAr EPfP EPot LHop LRHS MAsh MNHC NRHS SRms WCFE WJek
- 'Atropurpureus'	see *T.* (Coccineus Group) 'Purple Beauty'
- ***coccineus*** 'Minor' misapplied	see *T.* Coccineus Group
- - 'Minor' Bloom	see *T.* 'Alan Bloom'
- 'Conwy Rose'	WAbe
§ - 'Desborough'	MHer
- 'East Lodge'	LLWP MHer MNHC SRms
- 'Elfin'	EWes EWoo GCrg MRav SPlb SRot WAbe XSen
- 'Goldstream' (v)	CBod ENfk LEdu LHop LRHS MHer NRHS SPlb SRms WJek
- 'Iden'	see *T.* 'Iden'
- 'Minimalist'	see *T. serpyllum* 'Minor'
- 'Minimus'	see *T. serpyllum* 'Minor'
§ - 'Minor'	CBod CMea CTal CTri ECha ECtt ENfk GCrg LLWP LRHS MHer MMuc MNHC NRHS NRya NSla SEND SPlb SRms SRot WAbe WHoo WJek
- 'Minus'	see *T. serpyllum* 'Minor'
- 'Pink Chintz' 🏆[H5]	CBod ECha ECtt EDAr ENfk EPfP EPot GEdr GMaP GPoy LCro LEdu LRHS MHer MNHC NRHS SPer SPlb SPoG SRms WIce WJek
- 'Posh Pinky'	CPBP
- 'Purple Beauty'	see *T.* (Coccineus Group) 'Purple Beauty'
- 'Red Carpet'	ECtt GCrg NWad SRot
- 'Red Elf'	see *T.* (Coccineus Group) 'Red Elf'
- 'Russetings'	CBod CTsd CWld ECtt ENfk EPfP EWoo LEdu MHer MNHC SCob SIde SPoG SRms WJek
- 'September'	MHer
- 'Snowdrift'	CMea ECtt EPfP LEdu LLWP MHer MNHC NWad SIde SPlb SRms WCFE WJek
- 'Variegatus'	see *T.* 'Hartington Silver'
- 'Vey'	CBod CTal EWes LHop LRHS MHer NRHS SHDw SRms WJek
- 'Wirral White' **new**	XSen
'Silver King' (v)	ENfk
§ 'Silver Posie'	Widely available
'Silver Queen' (v) 🏆[H5]	CBcs CSam ECha EDAr ELan ENfk EPfP ESps GCrg GKev GMaP MHer MNHC NHol SCob SPer SPlb SRms WJek XSen
'Spicy Orange'	see *T.* Orange Spice
striatus	LEdu
valesiacus	see *T.* 'Massa'
§ ***vulgaris***	Widely available
* - 'Compactus'	ENfk GPoy LEdu MHer MNHC MRav SPhx SRms WCAu WJek XSen
- 'Deutsche Auslese'	see *T. vulgaris*
- 'Dorcas White'	MHer
§ - 'Elsbeth'	LLWP MHer
- English, winter	SRms
- French	see *T. vulgaris*
- 'Golden Pins'	MHer
- 'Lucy'	LLWP MHer
- 'Pinewood'	see *T.* 'Pinewood'
§ - 'Snow White'	EWes WJek
- 'Tiny Tim' **new**	CSma
'Widecombe' (v)	SHDw
zygis	GJos XSen

Tiarella ✿ (*Saxifragaceae*)

'Appalachian Trail'	CBcs ECtt ELan LBMP LCro LSou MPnt NPnk NWad SHeu SPoG WNPC
'Black Snowflake'	MPnt SHeu
'Black Velvet'	MBel MPnt SHeu
'Braveheart'	EPfP LHop MPnt SHeu SPoG
'Butter and Sugar'	MPnt
'Butterfly Wings'	MPnt
'Candy Striper'	ECtt MPnt SHeu
'Cascade Creeper'[PBR]	ECtt LRHS LSou MPnt NWad SHeu WNPC
collina	see *T. wherryi*
cordifolia 🏆[H5]	CBcs CBod CMac CNec CTri ECha ELan EPed EPfP GAbr GBuc GMaP LAma LEdu LPot LRHS MCot MGos MPnt MRav NBir NDov SCob SPer SRms SWat SWvt WHoo WMoo XLum
- 'Glossy'	MPnt
- 'Milk Chocolate'	MPnt
- 'Oakleaf'	MPnt NBro SHeu
- 'Rosalie'	see × *Heucherella alba* 'Rosalie'
- 'Running Tapestry'	MPnt SHeu
- 'Slick Rock'	EPPr
'Crow Feather'[PBR]	CNec MPnt NWad SHeu
'Cygnet'	CDor CLAP ECtt GBin GMcL MPnt SHeu SRot
'Dunvegan'	MPnt
'Elizabeth Oliver'	MPnt
'Freckles'	MRav
'Happy Trails'[PBR]	EBee MPnt NPnk NWad SHeu WCot WNPC
'Hidden Carpet'	CHid
'Inkblot'	ELan LRHS MPnt NBro SHeu WMoo
'Iron Butterfly'[PBR] (v)	CAby CBod CLAP CMac EBee ECha ECtt EHoe EPfP EWoo GMaP LCro LRHS LSRN MBel MPnt MRav SCob SGbt SHeu SPer SRot
'Iron Cross'	SPlb
'Jeepers Creepers'[PBR]	CHid ECha ECtt LBMP LRHS MJak MPnt NWad SHeu WNPC
'Martha Oliver'	CLAP EBee MPnt
'Mint Chocolate'	CLAP ECtt EHoe EHrv ELan GMaP LPot LRHS MNrw MPnt MRav NBir NGdn NLar SHeu SWvt
'Moorgrün'	EPPr GCal SHeu
Morning Star = 'Tntia042'	CHid ECtt GMcL MPnt SHeu SRkn SRot WHoo
'Mystic Mist'[PBR] (v)	CDor CHid CWGN ECtt EPed LBMP LSou MPnt NPnk NWad SHeu SPad SPoG WNPC
'Neon Lights'[PBR]	CHid ECtt ELan MPnt NBir NCGa NWad SCob SHeu SWvt WNPC
§ 'Ninja'	CHid ECtt EHrv ELan GMaP GMcL LRHS MPnt NBir NLar SWvt
'Oregon Trail'	ECtt MBel MNrw MPnt NPnk NWad SHeu WCot WNPC
'Pacific Crest'[PBR]	EBee ECtt MPnt NWad SHeu WNPC
'Pink Bouquet'	CBod CLAP CMac CSpe EAEE ECtt EHrv ELan IKil LSun MBel MPie

	MPnt NBro NDov NLar SBch SBod SHeu WCot WGwG WMoo WPnP
'Pink Brushes' PBR	CLAP MPnt SHeu WPnP
'Pink Skyrocket' PBR	CDor CLAP ECtt ELan EPau LBMP LHop LLHF LSRN LSun MBel MPnt NBir NGdn NHol NWad SHeu SPad SPer SWvt WCot WPnP
'Pinwheel'	MPnt
'Pirate's Patch' PBR	LLHF MPnt SHeu
polyphylla	MPnt SHeu WCru
- 'Baoxing Pink'	CFis CLAP MPnt WCru
- 'Filigran'	ELan EPfP IBoy MPnt NHol NLar NWad SHar SHeu
- pink-flowered	EHrv
'Running Tiger'	MPnt
'Sea Foam'	MPnt SHeu
'Simsalabim'	MPnt
'Skeleton Key'	MPnt
'Skid's Variegated' (v)	ECtt MNrw MPnt SHeu SPoG SWvt WCot
'Skyrocket'	ECtt NLar
'Spanish Cross'	MPnt SHeu
'Spring Symphony' PBR	CBod CDor CLAP CNec ECtt EShb GBin GBuc GKev GMcL LCro LRHS MBel MPnt NPer NWad SHar SHil WSHC
Starburst = 'Tntia041' PBR	ECtt MPnt NWad SHeu
'Sugar and Spice' PBR	CNec CWGN EAEE EPed EPfP LRHS MBrN MPnt NCGa NDov NWad SHeu WNPC
'Sunset Ridge' PBR	EBee MPnt NWad SHeu WNPC
'Tiger Stripe'	EPfP LRHS MPnt NBro SHeu
'Timbuktu'	MAsh MPnt SHeu WNPC
trifoliata	MPnt MRav
- var. ***unifoliata***	MPnt
'Viking Ship'	see × *Heucherella* 'Viking Ship'
§ ***wherryi*** ♀H5	CBcs CBod ELan ELon EPfP ESps IBoy LPot LRHS LSun MArt MPnt NBir NBro NRya SCob SPer SPlb SWvt WHar WPnP XLum
- 'Bronze Beauty'	CLAP GBuc MPnt SBch SHeu
- bronze-leaved	SCob
- 'Green Velvet'	ECha MPnt SHeu
- 'Heronswood Mist' (v)	CAbP ECtt ELan MNrw MPnt SHeu SWvt

Tibouchina (*Melastomataceae*)

grandifolia	CCCN
heteromalla	CCCN
'Jules'	WCot
organensis	CBcs CBod CCCN CHll EUJe SEle SHeu SPoG SWvt
paratropica	CRHN GCal
semidecandra misapplied	see *T. urvilleana*
§ ***urvilleana*** ♀H1c	CBcs CBod CCCN CEnd CMan CRHN CSBt CTri CTsd EBak IDee NLos SDix SPer SRkn SWvt
- 'Compacta'	CCCN
- 'Edwardsii' ♀H1c	SAdn WCot
- 'Rich Blue Sun'	CBod
- variegated (v)	CBcs CCCN CMan SPer SWvt WCot

Tigridia (*Iridaceae*)

catarinensis	SDeJ
chiapensis new	GKev
immaculata B&SWJ 10393	WCru
lutea	ECho
orthantha 'Red-Hot Tiger'	WCot WCru WSHC
pavonia	CAby CBro ECho SDeJ WSHC
- 'Alba'	ECho
- 'Alba Grandiflora'	GKev
- 'Aurea'	ECho GKev
- 'Canariensis'	ECho GKev
- 'Lilacea'	ECho GKev SDeJ
- red-flowered	ECho
- 'Speciosa'	GKev SDeJ
- yellow-flowered	ECho
van-houttei	GKev

Tilia ✿ (*Malvaceae*)

HRS 2808	WPGP
americana	CLnd CMCN
- 'Dentata'	CDul
argentea	see *T. tomentosa*
begoniifolia	see *T. dasystyla* subsp. *caucasica*
callidonta new	WPGP
§ ***caroliniana*** subsp. ***heterophylla***	CDul CMCN ELan EPfP MBlu WPGP
chinensis	CMCN WPGP
- F 30558	WPGP
chingiana	CDul CMCN EBee SLon WPGP
cordata	Widely available
§ - 'Böhlje'	CDul ECrN
- 'Dainty Leaf'	CDul
- 'Erecta'	see *T. cordata* 'Böhlje'
- 'Greenspire' ♀H6	CArg CCVT CDul CLnd CWib EBar ECrN EPfP ESps IBoy MRav SCob SEWo WMat WMou
- 'Len Parvin'	EBee WPGP
- 'Rancho'	EMOT
- 'Roelvo'	CDul
- 'Swedish Upright'	CDul
- 'Winter Orange' ♀H6	CBod CDul CEnd CLnd EBee EPfP ESps MBlu SBir SCoo SEWo WHar WMat WPat
dasystyla	CMCN
§ - subsp. ***caucasica***	CMCN WPGP
- - A&L 16	WPGP
endochrysea	WPGP
× ***euchlora***	CArg CCVT CDul CLnd CMCN EBee ECrN EMOT EPfP ESps NWea SCob SEWo SPer WMat
§ × ***europaea***	CBcs CDul CLnd ELan ESps MMuc NWea SCob SEND
- 'Koningslinde'	CDul
- 'Pallida'	CDul CLnd MBlu NLar NWea
- 'Wratislaviensis' ♀H6	CDul EBee MBlu NLar NWea
§ 'Harold Hillier'	CMCN MBlu WPGP
henryana	CBcs CDul CEnd CLnd CMCN CWib EBee ELan EPfP ERod ESps IArd IDee MBlu MMuc NWea SBir SCoo SEND WMat WMou WPGP WPat
- 'Arnold Select'	WCot
- 'Kerdalo' new	WPGP
- large	WPGP
'Hillieri'	see *T.* 'Harold Hillier'
insularis misapplied	see *T. japonica*
intonsa	CMCN
§ ***japonica***	CDul CMCN EBee EPfP WPGP
- 'Ernest Wilson' ♀H6	CMCN MBlu
- large-leaved, from China new	WPGP
kiusiana	CDul CMCN EBee MBlu WMou WPGP WPat
mandshurica	CDul CMCN EBee WPGP
maximowicziana	CMCN EPfP WPGP
mexicana	WPGP
- CD&R 1318	EBee WPGP
miqueliana	CMCN
× ***moltkei***	CDul CMCN EBee IArd IDee WPGP

mongolica	CBcs CDul CMCN EPfP MBlu SCoo WMou WPGP
- 'Harvest Gold'	CBcs MBlu
monticola	see *T. caroliniana* subsp. *heterophylla*
nobilis KR 226	WPGP
oliveri	CDul CMCN EBee MBlu NWea WMou WPGP
paucicostata	WPGP
platyphyllos	CAco CAgr CCVT CDul CFGn CHab CLnd CMCN CSBt CTho CTri ECrN EMOT EPfP ESps EWTr LBuc MMuc NWea SCob SCoo SEND SPer WHed WMat WMou WTSh
- 'Aurea'	CDul CTho ECrN MBlu WMat
- 'Corallina'	see *T. platyphyllos* 'Rubra'
- 'Erecta'	see *T. platyphyllos* 'Fastigiata'
§ - 'Fastigiata'	CDul
- 'Laciniata'	CDul CMCN CTho MBlu
§ - 'Rubra' ♀H6	CCVT CDul CLnd CTho EBar EMOT ESps IBoy NWea SEWo
- 'Tortuosa'	MBlu
§ ***tomentosa***	CAco CDul CLnd CMCN ESps MMuc NWea SCob SCoo SEND WMou
- 'Brabant' ♀H6	CDul ELan EMOT EPfP
- 'Petiolaris' ♀H6	CArg CBcs CCVT CDul CEnd CLnd CMCN ECrN ELan EMOT EPfP ESps MBlu MSwo NWea SCob SPer WMou
tuan	WPGP
- var. ***chenmoui***	CMCN EPfP MBlu WPGP
× ***vulgaris***	see *T.* × *europaea*

Tilingia (*Apiaceae*)

ajanensis B&SWJ 11202	IMou WCru

Tillaea see *Crassula*

Tillandsia (*Bromeliaceae*)

sp.	XBlo
aeranthos	SChr
albida	SPlb
bergeri	SPlb
bulbosa	NLos SPlb
cacticola	SPlb
capitata	NLos
caput-medusae	NLos
flabellata	SPlb
fuchsii	SPlb
harrisii	NLos
ionantha	NLos
juncea	NLos
magnusiana	NLos
mooreana	SPlb
pruinosa	SPlb
seleriana	SPlb
tricolor var. ***melanocrater***	NLos
usneoides	NLos SHmp SPlb
xerographica	NLos SPlb

Tinantia (*Commelinaceae*)

pringlei	EWld GEdr LEdu MNrw MPie SBrt SDys WPGP
- AIM 77	EBee MAvo MNrw WCot
- variegated (v)	WCot

Tinnea (*Lamiaceae*)

barbata	GFai

Titanopsis (*Aizoaceae*)

calcarea ♀H2	CCCN

Titanotrichum (*Gesneriaceae*)

oldhamii	GEdr

Tithonia (*Asteraceae*)

rotundifolia 'Torch'	CSpe
'Torchlight' **new**	LRHS

Tofieldia (*Tofieldiaceae*)

coccinea	CTal GCal GEdr WCot WCru
furusei	GEdr
japonica	GEdr
- 'Rosea'	GEdr

Tolmiea (*Saxifragaceae*)

menziesii	CBod CMac EWld MCot WTou XLum
- 'Goldsplash'	see *T. menziesii* 'Taff's Gold'
- 'Maculata'	see *T. menziesii* 'Taff's Gold'
§ - 'Taff's Gold' (v)	EHoe EHrv GMaP LRHS NBid SPlb WPtf XLum
- 'Variegata'	see *T. menziesii* 'Taff's Gold'

Tolpis (*Asteraceae*)

barbata	IMou

Toona (*Meliaceae*)

§ ***sinensis***	CBcs CDul CTho CWib EBee ELan EPfP LEdu SEND WPGP
- 'Flamingo' (v)	CTho EPfP ESwi GKin IVic LCro LEdu LOPS LRHS MAsh MGos NLar SWvt WCot WMat
- 'Lisa' **new**	CMCN

Torenia (*Linderniaceae*)

Purple Moon = 'Dantopur'PBR (Moon Series)	LSou
Summer Wave Series	CCCN SCoo

Torilis (*Apiaceae*)

japonica	CBre

Townsendia (*Asteraceae*)

§ ***alpigena*** var. ***alpigena***	CPBP
condensata	WAbe
formosa	CPBP ECho NHpl
incana	WAbe
mensana	GKev
montana	see *T. alpigena* var. *alpigena*
parryi	GKev
spathulata	CPBP SPlb

Toxicodendron see *Rhus*

Trachelium (*Campanulaceae*)

§ ***asperuloides***	WAbe
caeruleum 'Black Knight'	CSpe WCot
jacquinii subsp. ***rumelianum***	SIgm
lanceolatum	WCot

Trachelospermum ✿ (*Apocynaceae*)

from Nanjing, China	EShb
§ ***asiaticum*** ♀H4	Widely available
- B&SWJ 4814	WCru
- 'Avonbank' **new**	MGil
- 'Copper Tips' **new**	MGil

	– 'Golden Memories'	CBcs CKel CWCL CWGN EBee ELan ELon EPfP LRHS LSRN NLar NRHS SKHP SLon SPoG SSta SWvt WPat
	– 'Goshiki' (v)	EShb SEle WPat
*	– 'Kiejiu Chirimen'	SKHP
	– 'Kulu Chirimen'	WCot
	– 'Nagaba' (v)	SKHP
	– 'Ōgon-nishiki' (v)	LRHS MPkF SEle SKHP SMad SPoG
	– 'Pink Showers'	SKHP
	– 'Shirofu Chirimen' (v)	SKHP
	– 'Summer Sunset'	CWCL ELan EPfP LRHS MGos MPkF WCot
	– 'Theta'	LEdu LRHS SKHP SNig WCot WPGP WPat
	'Chameleon'	ELan SKHP
	jasminoides ♀^{H4}	Widely available
	– B&SWJ 5117	LPar WCru
	– 'Major'	CMac CWCL EBee ELan EWTr MAsh SNig
§	– var. ***pubescens*** 'Japonicum'	CRHN LRHS NPri SLon SPoG WBor WSHC
	– 'Star of Toscana'	LCro LRHS NLar SCob
	– 'Tricolor' (v)	LRHS SCob SEle SGol SWvt
	– 'Variegatum' (v) ♀^{H4}	Widely available
	– 'Waterwheel'	CKel CMac CWCL EBee ELan ELon GCal LRHS NLar SCob SKHP SMad SNig SPoG SWvt WPGP WSHC
	– 'White Wings'	EBee
	– 'Wilsonii'	CHll CMac CWCL ELan ELon EPfP EUJe LRHS LSRN MRav NLar SAdn SEND SKHP SLim SNig SPer SPoG SWvt WCot WCru WPGP WPat
	majus misapplied	see *T. jasminoides* var. *pubescens* 'Japonicum'
	majus Nakai	see *T. asiaticum*

Trachycarpus ✿ (*Arecaceae*)

	from Manipur	CPHo
§	***fortunei*** ♀^{H5}	Widely available
	fortunei × ***wagnerianus***	LPar
	geminisectus	NLos
	latisectus	CBlu LTro NLos SBig
	martianus	SBig
	– from Nepal	LTro
	nanus	LPar
	oreophilus	NLos
	princeps	CBlu CBrP
	wagnerianus	CBlu CBrP CCCN CDTJ CPHo EPfP ETod EUJe LPar LRHS LTro NLos NPla SArc SBig SChr WPGP

Trachymene (*Apiaceae*)

coerulea	CSpe CWld

Trachystemon (*Boraginaceae*)

orientalis	Widely available

Tradescantia (*Commelinaceae*)

	albiflora	see *T. fluminensis*
	× ***andersoniana*** W. Ludwig & Rohw. nom. inval.	see *T.* Andersoniana Group
§	Andersoniana Group	CWib WHar WWtn
	– 'Angelic Charm' (Charm Series)	CWGN ECtt SHeu
	– 'Baby Doll'	XLum
	– 'Bilberry Ice'	CBod CMac CWCL ECtt EPfP GMaP IKil LRHS MBel NBir NBro NGBl NGdn NLar NPnk SCob SGbt SPad SWvt WHar WWtn XLum
	– 'Blue and Gold'	CBcs EBee ECtt ELon EPfP LHop LRHS MHol MRav NCou NRHS NSti WCot WFar WGrn
	– 'Blue Stone'	CCse CMea CSBt ECha ECtt IKil MAvo MRav SRkn SRms WHoo XLum
	– 'Bridal Veil'	CHll SChr WDib
	– 'Caerulea Plena'	see *T. virginiana* 'Caerulea Plena'
	– Carmine Glow	see *T.* (Andersoniana Group) 'Karminglut'
	– 'Charlotte'	ECha ECtt ELan LRHS LSRN NBro NGdn NLar WWtn XLum
	– 'Concord Grape'	Widely available
	– 'Danielle'	EPfP
	– 'Domaine de Courson'	ECtt IKil XLum
	– 'Good Luck'^{PBR}	MHol
	– 'In the Navy'	NLar
	– 'Innocence'	CAby CSBt CTri ECha ECtt ELan EPfP GCra GMaP GWyn IBoy LHop LRHS MBel MMuc NBir NGdn NPnk NRHS NSti SCob SPer SWvt XLum
	– 'Iris Prichard'	EBee ELan GCra GLog GMaP NLar
	– 'Isis'	CBWd CTri EBee ECtt ELan EPfP GCra LBMP LRHS MMuc MRav NBir NGdn NRHS SPer SWvt WGwG WKif WWtn
	– 'J.C. Weguelin'	EPfP LPot NBir SRms WCAu XLum
§	– 'Karminglut'	EBee ECtt ELan EPfP GLog GMaP IBoy NBir NGdn NPnk WHoo XLum
	– 'Leonora'	EPfP MMuc NLar SCob WHar XLum
	– 'Little Doll'	ECtt EPfP GLog LRHS MPie NBro NLar XLum
	– 'Little White Doll'	ECtt EPfP NLar
	– 'Mac's Double' (d)	CMos EBee IKil
	– 'Mariella'	EBee
	– 'Melissa'	XLum
	– 'Merlot Clusters'	LSun SCob WHlf
	– 'Mrs Loewer'	MAvo
	– 'Ocean Blue'	EPfP
	– 'Osprey'	CBWd CBcs CTri ECha ECtt ELan EWoo GCal LRHS LSun MRav NGdn NRHS NSti SPer SRms WCAu WGwG WHoo WKif WWtn XLum
	– 'Pauline'	ELon LSun MRav NBir NLar XLum
	– 'Perinne's Pink'	CWCL ECtt EPfP LRHS NSti
	– 'Pink Chablis'	CMos CWCL ECtt EPfP IKil MHol NBro NLar XLum
	– 'Purewell Giant'	CMac CTri GLog LHop LRHS NBro NLar SWvt WKif
	– 'Purple Dome'	CAby ECtt EPfP GMaP LRHS MAvo MMuc MRav NBir NBro NGdn NRHS SPoG
	– 'Red Grape'	LBMP LPot LRHS NSti SCob XLum
	– 'Regal Charm' (Charm Series)	EBee SHeu
	– 'Rosi'	EBee
	– 'Rubra'	SCob SRms XLum
	– 'Satin Doll'^{PBR}	CBcs ECtt EPfP
	– 'Snowbank'	EBee
	– 'Sunshine Charm'^{PBR} (Charm Series)	CWCL EBee LRHS NLar SHeu SHil WHil
	– 'Sweet Kate'	CMac CWCL ECtt LRHS LSRN MBNS NBro NLar SGbt SHil SPoG XLum
	– 'Sylvana'	EBee
	– 'Valour'	CSBt EBee EPfP LRHS NRHS
	– 'Zwanenburg Blue'	ECha ECtt EHrv ELan GLog LRHS NLar SPlb SPoG XLum

'Baerbel'	XLum
blossfeldiana 'Variegata'	see *T. cerinthoides* 'Variegata'
canaliculata	see *T. ohiensis*
§ ***cerinthoides*** 'Variegata' (v) ♀H1c **new**	EShb
crassifolia	CFil
- F&M 258	WPGP
§ ***fluminensis***	SChr WDib
§ - 'Aurea' ♀H1c	SChr
- 'Maiden's Blush' (v)	CSpe CWCL EShb SChr SPlb SRms SVen
- 'Quicksilver' (v) ♀H1c	EShb NGBl
- 'Variegata'	see *T. fluminensis* 'Aurea'
'Lucky Charm'	EBee NLar SHeu
§ 'Magic Bird'	LPre
§ ***ohiensis***	MAvo
pallida 'Kartuz Giant'	EShb MPie WCot
- 'Pale Puma'	EShb
§ - 'Purpurea' ♀H1c	EOHP EShb NGBl
pendula	see *T. zebrina*
'Purple Sabre'	CBcs EUJe SPlb
purpurea	see *T. pallida* 'Purpurea'
sillamontana ♀H1c	EShb MPie SChr
spathacea	EShb
- 'Versicolor'	EShb
Swallowtail	see *T.* 'Magic Bird'
tricolor	see *T. zebrina*
virginiana	ESps LPot
- 'Alba'	CMac GCal
* - 'Brevicaulis'	EBee ECha NBro
§ - 'Caerulea Plena' (d)	ELan EPfP MRav SPer SRms XLum
- 'Rubra'	SPlb
§ ***zebrina*** ♀H1c	EShb NGBl
- ***pendula***	see *T. zebrina*
- 'Purpusii' ♀H1c	SRms WDib

Tragopogon (*Asteraceae*)

crocifolius	CCVN CSpe SPhx
porrifolius	CFis GCal MCot NGBl SDix SVic WCot WTre
pratensis	CArn CWld NMir

Trautvetteria (*Ranunculaceae*)

carolinensis	IMou WSHC
- var. ***japonica***	CLAP EWld GEdr WCru
- - B&SWJ 10861	WCru
- var. ***occidentalis***	EBee EPPr LEdu WCru

Triadica (*Euphorbiaceae*)

sebifera	LEdu SBrt WCru
- CWJ 12819	WCru

Trichilia (*Meliaceae*)

hirta **new**	SMad

Trichodiadema (*Aizoaceae*)

intonsum	SPlb

Trichopetalum (*Asparagaceae*)

§ ***plumosum***	CBro

Trichostema (*Lamiaceae*)

'Blue Bonnets'	MMuc

Tricuspidaria see *Crinodendron*

Tricyrtis (*Liliaceae*)

B&SWJ 3229 from Taiwan	WCru
'Adbane'	CChe CLAP ELan EWes GBuc WGwG
affinis B&SWJ 2804	CLAP WCru
- B&SWJ 5645	WCru
- B&SWJ 6182	WCru
- B&SWJ 11169	WCru
- B&SWJ 11442	WCru
- 'Early Bird'	WCru
'Amanagowa'	GEdr
bakeri	see *T. latifolia*
'Blue Wonder'	CBod ELon IBal LBuc LRHS NNys SPad SPer WHar XLum
dilatata	see *T. macropoda*
'Empress'	CAby CBct CDor ECha ELon EPfP EThi EWTr EWes GBuc IBal LEdu LRHS LSou MJak NEgg NWad SRkn SRot WHar
flava	EBee LRHS WCru
formosana	CAby CAvo CMea CTri ECha ECho EHrv ELan EPfP EWoo GKev GLog GMaP IBoy LEdu LPot LRHS MCot MMuc MNrw SDys SEND SRms SRot WKif
- B&SWJ 355	WCru
- B&SWJ 3073	WCru
- B&SWJ 3616	WCru
- B&SWJ 3635	CLAP
- B&SWJ 3712	WCru
- B&SWJ 6741	WCru
- B&SWJ 6970	WCru
- RWJ 10109	WCru
- 'Autumn Glow' (v)	GEdr
- 'Dark Beauty'	CAby CBot CDor CLAP CWCL ECtt EHrv ELan GAbr GBuc LCro MNrw SCob WCAu WPGP WTor
- 'Daruma'	GEdr
I - 'Donkere Selectie'	EBee
- 'Emperor' (v)	EBee ESwi
- 'Gilt Edge' (v)	CBct CBod ECtt ELan EPfP EThi GBuc IBal LPot LSou MBNS NBro NEgg NLar NSti NWad SWvt
- f. ***glandosa*** B&SWJ 7084	WCru
- aff. f. ***glandosa*** 'Blu-Shing Toad'	MAvo WCru
- var. ***grandiflora*** 'W-Ho-ping Toad'	WCru
- 'Kestrel' (v)	WCot
- pale-flowered	EThi
- 'Purple Beauty'	MNrw NNys
- 'Samurai' (v)	CWCL EWes NPnk
- 'Seiryu'	EBee
- 'Shelley's'	CLAP
- 'Small Wonder'	WCru
- 'Spotted Toad'	LEdu MAvo WCru
§ - Stolonifera Group	CBcs CDor CLAP CMac EHrv ELan EPfP LEdu LRHS MCot MWat NWad SHar
- - B&SWJ 7046	WCru
- 'Taroko Toad'	WCru
- 'Tiny Toad'	WCru
- 'Variegata' (v)	LEdu NBir WCru
- 'Velvet Toad'	WCru
'Golden Leopard'	EBee LSou
'Harlequin'	LEdu
§ ***hirta***	CBcs CDor CHid CMac CTri CTsd ECho IBoy ILea LOPS LRHS LTro MCot MJak NBro NHol SEND SGbt SPlb SWvt WSHC
- B&SWJ 5971	WCru
- B&SWJ 11182	WCru
- B&SWJ 11227	WCru
- 'Alba'	CMac

- 'Albomarginata' (v)	CMac EAEE GCra LRHS NEgg NLar NSti SPoG SWvt WWtn
- 'Golden Gleam'	WCot
- var. ***masamunei***	WCru
- 'Matsukaze'	CLAP EWes
- 'Miyazaki'	CLAP CMac ECha ECtt EPfP GBuc IFoB LRHS MHer MNrw SPoG WRHF WWtn XLum
- 'Taiwan Atrianne'	CDor CLAP ECtt ELan LRHS MNrw MPie NEgg NWad SGbt SPoG WCAu WWtn
- 'Variegata' (v)	CTri EBee EWes GCra GKev GMcL LRHS WCot
Hototogisu	CLAP EAEE ECha ECtt ELan LHop LRHS MWat NHol NLar NPnk SPoG WWtn
ishiiana	CLAP CTal EBee EHrv WCru WSHC
- var. ***surugensis***	LEdu WCru
japonica	see *T. hirta*
'Kohaku'	CLAP EBee
lasiocarpa	EHrv LEdu MAvo XLum
- B&SWJ 3635	CAby WCru
- B&SWJ 6861	WCru
- B&SWJ 7013	WCru
- B&SWJ 7103	WCru
- 'Royal Toad'	WCru
§ ***latifolia***	ELan GLog GMaP GPSL LEdu LRHS WCru
- B&SWJ 10996 **new**	CBct
- 'Saffron'	WCru
- 'Yellow Sunrise'	NCGa NSti
'Lightning Strike' (v)	CDor EBee ECha ECtt LEdu WCot
'Lilac Towers'	WCru
macrantha	GAbr GLog WCru WSHC
§ - subsp. ***macranthopsis***	CAby CBct CLAP GBuc LHop WCot WCru
- - 'Juro' (d)	WCru
macranthopsis	see *T. macrantha* subsp. *macranthopsis*
* ***macrocarpa***	XLum
macropoda	ELan GLog ILea LEdu LHop LRHS MAvo WCAu
- B&SWJ 1271 from Korea	WCru
- B&SWJ 5013	WCru
- B&SWJ 5556	WCru
- B&SWJ 5847 from Japan	WCru
- B&SWJ 6209	WCru
- B&SWJ 8700	WCru
- B&SWJ 8829 from Korea	WCru
- from Yungi Temple, China	CLAP
maculata HWJCM 470	WCru
- HWJK 2010	WCru
- HWJK 2411	WCru
- PAB 3188	LEdu
'Moonlight Treasure'PBR	CLAP EBee IBoy NHol WCot
nana	WCru
- B&SWJ 11399	WCru
ohsumiensis	CAby CLAP ECha EHrv GBuc WCru
perfoliata	CLAP LEdu WCru
- 'Spring Shine' (v)	WCru
pilosa	EBee LEdu
Pink Freckles = 'Innotripf'PBR	CBct CDor CLAP CMos EBee ELon ESwi EThi GMcL LSou MPnt NCou SRot SWvt
'Raspberry Mousse'	CLAP CWCL EPfP IFoB LHop MBNS NSti
ravenii	CTal
- B&SWJ 3229	WCru
- RWJ 10012	WCru
setouchiensis	WCru
'Shimone'	CHid CLAP EBee ECha
'Sinonome'	EBee IPot MNrw
stolonifera	see *T. formosana* Stolonifera Group
suzukii RWJ 10111	WCru
'Taipei Silk'PBR	IFoB NCGa
'Tojen'	EAEE ECha ECtt ELon EPfP EWes GKev GMcL GPSL LHop LRHS MNrw NPnk SPer WCAu WHar
'Variegata' (*affinis* hybrid) (v)	CLAP
'Washfields'	EBee
'White Towers'	CBro CHid CLAP CWCL ECha EHrv EWoo GBuc IFoB LPot LRHS MRav NEgg NLar NPnk NSti SRms XLum

Trifolium (Papilionaceae)

angustifolium	CArn
arvense PAB 7952	LEdu
barnebyi **new**	CPBP
brandegeei	SPhx
dubium	SPre
incarnatum	CSpe MHer
macrocephalum	EBee SPhx
nanum	LLHF
ochroleucon	CAby EAJP ECha ECtt EHrv EWTr GBin GMaP ILea LEdu MAvo MCot MPie NPnk NSti SBch SHar SMad SPhx WAul WFar WMoo WPGP
pannonicum	CCVN CMea GCal MNrw WOut WWFP
- 'White Tiara'	GBin MMrt
pratense	CHab MHer NMir WSFF
- 'Dolly North'	see *T. pratense* 'Susan Smith'
- 'Ice Cool'	see *T. repens* 'Green Ice'
§ - 'Susan Smith' (v)	CCCN
repens	SVic WSFF
- 'Debbie'	LEdu
- 'Dragon's Blood'	CBod CMea EPPr GMcL GWyn LBMP LEdu LLWG MMuc MPie SPer WPGP WTor
- 'Gold Net'	see *T. pratense* 'Susan Smith'
§ - 'Green Ice'	LLWG NSti WHal
- 'Harlequin' (v)	WCot WMoo WOut
- 'Hullavington'	CNat
- 'Isabella'PBR	LEdu WPGP
- 'Josephine'PBR	LEdu
- 'Pentaphyllum'	see *T. repens* 'Quinquefolium'
- 'Purpurascens'	CArn CBre EPfP LLWG LRHS MBNS MHer MPie NSti SPoG WFar
§ - 'Purpurascens Quadrifolium'	CAby CBod CMea ECha EHoe EPau EWes GAbr GMcL GWyn LBMP MCot NMir NPer SPer SPlb WFar WRHF WTor
§ - 'Quinquefolium'	XLum
- 'Tetraphyllum Purpureum'	see *T. repens* 'Purpurascens Quadrifolium'
- 'Wheatfen'	CNat LEdu NDov NPer
- 'William'	CBre ECGP LEdu MMuc NDov WCot WFar WOut
rubens	Widely available
- 'Drama'	ELon MNrw
- 'Peach Pink'	ELon EPPr LHop MAvo MMrt SPhx WCot WHrl
- 'Red Feathers'	CWCL CWld ELon EPPr EWes GBin LBMP LSun MHol SHar SMad
'Spring'	LEdu
trichocephalum	EPPr

Trigonella (Papilionaceae)

foenum-graecum	WSFF

Trillidium see *Trillium*

Trillium ✿ (*Melanthiaceae*)

	albidum ♀H5	CWCL EBee ECho ENun GBuc GEdr LAma LLHF LRHS NHar SIgm SKHP
	amabile new	GEdr
	angustipetalum	EPot GEdr GKev
	apetalon	GEdr GKev LAma
	camschatcense	GEdr GKev LAma
§	***catesbyi***	CWCL EBee ECho EPot GEdr GKev LAma LLHF MNrw NWad SDir
	catesbyi* × *sulcatum new	GKev
	cernuum	CWCL ECho GCra GKev GMaP LAma
	chloropetalum	CBro CElw ENun GAbr GBuc GEdr LPla LRHS NWad SIgm
	- var. ***chloropetalum***	GBuc
	- var. ***chloropetalum* × *parviflorum***	SKHP
§	- var. ***giganteum*** ♀H5	GBin GBuc GKev SPhx WCru
	- pink-flowered	GEdr
	- var. ***rubrum***	see *T. chloropetalum* var. *giganteum*
	- white-flowered	GKev
	cuneatum	CBcs CBct CBro CWCL ECho EHrv EPot GBuc GEdr GKev GMcL LAma LEdu LRHS MNrw NBir NHol NHpl NWad SDeJ SDir SKHP WPnP
	- 'Ghost'	SKHP
	- 'Moonshine'	SKHP
	decipiens	GEdr
	decumbens	GEdr SKHP
	discolor	GEdr GKev
	erectum ♀H5	Widely available
	- f. ***albiflorum***	ECha ECho GBuc MNrw NWad SKHP WPnP
	- - Harvington clone	ENun
	- 'Beige'	GKev
	- Harvington dark form	ENun
	- f. ***luteum***	GEdr SKHP
	- red-flowered	ECho GKev
	erectum* × *flexipes	EBee ECho EHrv GBuc MNrw NBir SKHP
	flexipes	CBct CWCL ECho EHrv EPot GEdr GKev LAma LRHS MNrw NHar NHol NHpl NPnk NWad SKHP
	- 'Harvington Dusky Pink'	ENun
I	- 'Harvington Selection'	EBee ENun LRHS SKHP
	flexipes* × *simile Harvington hybrids	ENun
	foetidissimum	GEdr SKHP
	govanianum	GEdr GKev LAma LRHS
	gracile	GEdr
	grandiflorum ♀H5	Widely available
	- Gothenburg pink	GEdr
	- pale-pink-flowered new	LRHS
	- f. ***polymerum*** 'Flore Pleno' (d)	CWCL EBee ENun GEdr LLHF LRHS SDir SKHP
	- - 'Snowbunting' (d)	EWes GKev LAma LEdu LRHS MMrt NHar WThu
	- 'Quicksilver'	SKHP
	- f. ***roseum***	CWCL EBee ENun GEdr LRHS MNrw
	- white-flowered	MAvo
	kurabayashii	CPne CTal CWCL EBee ECho EHrv ENun EPot GBin GBuc GEdr LRHS MNrw SIgm SKHP WCru WPGP
	lancifolium	GEdr GKev
	ludovicianum	GEdr
	luteum ♀H5	Widely available
	maculatum	GEdr
	nivale	CBct GEdr NHar
	ovatum f. ***hibbersonii***	GBuc NHar
	parviflorum	GEdr MNrw SKHP
	pusillum	CWCL EBee ECho EPot GEdr GKev LAma LLHF MNrw NHol NHpl
*	- var. ***alabamicum***	SKHP
I	- var. ***georgianum***	SKHP
	recurvatum	CBcs CWCL EBee ECho EHrv EPot EUJe GEdr GKev LAma LEdu NHol NHpl NWad SDir SKHP WPnP
	reliquum	GEdr
	rivale ♀H4	GBuc GEdr GKev SCob
	- Purple Heart Group	GEdr
	rugelii	EBee ECho EHrv EWes GEdr GKev LAma MNrw SKHP WSHC
	- Askival hybrids	ECho GAbr GBuc MNrw SKHP
	rugelii* × *vaseyi	EBee EHrv EWes MNrw SKHP
	sessile	CWCL ECho EWTr GBuc GEdr GKev LAma MAvo MNrw NBir NPnk NWad SDeJ SKHP WCot WKif WSHC WShi
	- 'Rubrum'	see *T. chloropetalum* var. *giganteum*
	simile	EBee ECho ENun GEdr LLHF LRHS MNrw NHar SKHP
	smallii	GEdr
	stamineum	CWCL GEdr LAma
	stylosum	see *T. catesbyi*
	sulcatum	CWCL EBee ECho EHrv ENun GAbr GBuc GEdr GKev GMaP LAma LRHS MNrw NHar SKHP WSHC
	- yellow-flowered new	GKev
	taiwanense B&SWJ 3411	WCru
	texanum	SKHP
	tschonoskii	GEdr LAma
	underwoodii	GEdr
	undulatum	MNrw
	vaseyi	CWCL EBee ECho EHrv ENun EWes GEdr GKev LAma LRHS MNrw NHar SKHP
	- large-flowered	SKHP
	viridescens	GEdr LAma

Triosteum (*Caprifoliaceae*)

	erythrocarpum	EBee EWTr SMad
	himalayanum	GCal GKev WPnP WSHC
	- BWJ 7907	CLAP WCru
	pinnatifidum	CLAP EBee EWld GCal IMou

Tripleurospermum (*Asteraceae*)

§	***maritimum***	WHer

Tripolium (*Asteraceae*)

§	***pannonicum***	WHer

Tripsacum (*Poaceae*)

	dactyloides	EPPr

Tripterospermum (*Gentianaceae*)

	japonicum	GEdr
	lanceolatum RWJ 9918	WCru

Tripterygium (*Celastraceae*)

	doianum B&SWJ 11467	WCru
	aff. ***doianum*** CWJ 12852	WCru
	regelii	CBcs
	- B&SWJ 5453	WCru
	- B&SWJ 8666 from Korea	WCru
	- B&SWJ 10921	WCru
	wilfordii	EBee LEdu

- BWJ 7852 from China	WCru
- NJM 11.029 from China	WPGP
- WWJ 12009	WCru

Tristagma (*Alliaceae*)

nivale	EBee

Triteleia (*Asparagaceae*)

'4U'	CAvo EBee ECho EPfP GKev
'Aquarius' **new**	ERCP
bridgesii	ECho
californica	see *Brodiaea californica*
§ 'Corrina'	CAvo CBro EBee ECho EPot GKev
'Crystal Pink'	SDeJ
'Double Touch' (d)	EBee GKev
'Foxy'	EBee EPot GKev
grandiflora	ECho WCot
hendersonii	GKev
hyacinthina	EBee ECho GKev WCot
ixioides	ECho
- 'Splendens'	ECho GKev
- 'Starlight'	CAvo CBro CTri ECho EPfP EPot ERCP GKev SDeJ
§ ***laxa***	ECha ECho
- 'Allure'	EBee ECho
§ - 'Koningin Fabiola'	CBro CTri EBee ECho GKev LAma MNrw NBir SCob SDeJ SEND SPer WCot WRHF
- Queen Fabiola	see *T. laxa* 'Koningin Fabiola'
lemmoniae **new**	GKev
lilacina	ECho
'Ocean Queen'	EBee ERCP GKev
§ ***peduncularis***	ECho GKev WCot
'Rudy'	CAvo CBro CHid CMea CWCL EBee ECho ERCP GKev SCob SDeJ WCot
'Silver Queen'	CMea EBee ECho EPot ERCP GKev
× ***tubergenii***	ECho
'Twilight' **new**	CMea GKev
uniflora	see *Ipheion uniflorum*
'White Sweep'	EBee ECho
'www'^{PBR}	ECho

Trithrinax (*Arecaceae*)

brasiliensis	SBig
campestris	CBrP LRHS SBig

Tritoma see *Kniphofia*

Tritonia (*Iridaceae*)

crocata 🏆^{H2}	ECho GKev
- 'Baby Doll'	EBee LEdu
- 'Pink Sensation'	EBee ECho
- 'Prince of Orange'	EBee
- 'Serendipity'	EPri
deusta	EPri
disticha	SMad
§ - subsp. ***rubrolucens***	Widely available
- - tall, clear pink-flowered	WPGP
flabellifolia	ECho
laxifolia	CTca ECho EPot GKev NRog
lineata	EBee ECho EPri LEdu WPGP
- 'Parvifolia'	GKev
pallida	ECho SPlb
rosea	see *T. disticha* subsp. *rubrolucens*
securigera	CTal ECho LEdu
squalida	ECho EPri

Trixis (*Asteraceae*)

sp. **new**	NPri

Trochocarpa (*Ericaceae*)

clarkei	WThu
gunnii	WThu
thymifolia	WThu
- white-flowered	WThu

Trochodendron (*Trochodendraceae*)

aralioides	CBcs CMac CSam CTho CTsd CWib EBee ELan EPfP GBin GKin IVic LRHS MBlu MGos MMuc NLar SAko SArc SDix SKHP SLon SMad SPer SReu SSta WBor WCot WPGP
- B&SWJ 1651 from Taiwan	WCru
- B&SWJ 6080 from Japan	WCru
- CWJ 12357 from Taiwan	WCru
- RWJ 9845 from Taiwan	WCru
- from Taiwan	CFil

Trollius (*Ranunculaceae*)

SDR 2713	GKev
acaulis	ECho ELon EWes GAbr
altaicus	LRHS
buddae	CWCL EWes MRav
§ ***chinensis***	ECha GCal GKev GWyn SWat
- 'Golden Queen' 🏆^{H7}	Widely available
- 'Imperial Orange'	GWyn
- 'Morning Sun' **new**	CBct
- wild-collected **new**	GBin
× ***cultorum***	CAby
- 'Alabaster'	Widely available
- 'Baudirektor Linne'	MRav NGdn
- 'Byrne's Giant'	ECtt GBin IKil
- 'Canary Bird'	ELan GCal MJak NGdn SRms
- 'Earliest of All'	CSam CWCL NGdn NLar SPer
- 'Etna'	GMcL
§ - 'Feuertroll'	ECha ECtt MRav NEoE NGdn
- Fireglobe	see *T.* × *cultorum* 'Feuertroll'
- 'Golden Cup'	GWyn NBir NGdn
- 'Goldquelle' 🏆^{H7}	EBee GBin GBuc GWyn
- 'Goliath'	GWyn NLar
- 'Helios'	CSam GBin GBuc
- 'Lemon Queen'	CBod CMac CWCL CWat ECtt EHrv EPfP GKev GMaP LRHS MRav NLar NQui SCob SGol SPer SWat
- 'New Moon'	CAby CBct CDor CLet CWCL EBee EShb EWTr GBin GBuc IKil LRHS NPnk NQui SHil SPad WSHC
- 'Orange Crest'	EBee ECtt ELon EPfP GCal
- 'Orange Globe'	GMaP
- 'Orange Princess' 🏆^{H7}	CWat GMcL GWyn LRHS NBro NLar NRHS SPer SRms
- 'Orange Queen'	SWvt
- 'Prichard's Giant'	CMHG ECtt ELan ELon NBro NGdn WCFE
§ - 'Superbus' 🏆^{H7}	CBod CWCL ELan ELon EPfP GBin GMaP GWyn LRHS MSCN NGdn NRHS SPer WFar
- 'T. Smith'	ECtt NBro
- 'Taleggio'	CMos ECtt ELon EPfP GCal GMaP IBoy ILea LEdu LRHS LSou MBNS MBel MRav NBro NEoE NLar SKHP SWvt WFar WPnP
- 'Yellow Beauty'	GBin
'Dancing Flame'	LCro SHar
europaeus	CAby CBod CWCL ECha ELan ESps EWoo GBin GCal GMcL GWyn LEdu LHop LRHS MRav MWat NGdn NRHS SRot SWat WCFE WHar WHoo

- SDR 6306	GKev
- subsp. ***europaeus***	WFar
- 'Lemon Supreme'	GBuc GKev LRHS
- 'Superbus'	see *T.* × *cultorum* 'Superbus'
hondoensis	LLHF NEoE
ircuticus	GKev
ledebourii misapplied	see *T. chinensis*
macropetalus new	EBee GKev
pumilus	ECha ECho ELan EPfP GKev LLHF LRHS NLar NPnk NSla SPer
- ACE 1818	MHer
- 'Double Jeopardy' new	EBee
- 'Wargrave'	ECho
vaginatus	EBee
yunnanensis ♀H6	EBee GBin GKev LRHS
- orange-flowered	GKev

Tropaeolum (*Tropaeolaceae*)

azureum	CCCN CFil CPla CPne
brachyceras	CCCN CPne EBee GKev SDir
ciliatum	CCCN CFil CPla EWld GKev NBid WCot WCru WPGP
hookerianum subsp. ***austropurpureum***	CFil
- subsp. ***hookerianum***	CFil
incisum	CCCN EBee
lepidum	CPla
majus	ENfk GPoy SVic
- Alaska Series (v) ♀H3	ENfk LCro MNHC SIde WJek
- 'Black Velvet' (Tom Thumb Series)	LCro
- 'Crimson Beauty'	CSpe
§ - 'Darjeeling Double' (d) ♀H3	GCal
- 'Darjeeling Gold'	see *T. majus* 'Darjeeling Double'
- 'Empress of India'	MNHC WJek
- 'Hermine Grashoff' (d)	CSpe GCal
- Jewel Series	ENfk
- 'Margaret Long' (d)	CSpe GCal
- 'Peaches and Cream'	WJek
- 'Red Wonder'	CCCN CSpe EPfP WCot
- Tom Thumb Series	MNHC WJek
nubigenum × ***polyphyllum***	CFil
pentaphyllum	CFil CPne CRHN CSpe EBee GCal
polyphyllum ♀H3	CCCN CWCL EBee EPot GBuc LHop NBir SMHy WPGP
sessilifolium	CFil EBee
smithii	GCal
speciosum ♀H5	Widely available
sylvestre	EWld
tricolor ♀H2	CAvo CBcs CCCN CFil CRHN GKev SBrt SDir WBor XEll
tuberosum	CAgr CEnd GKev GPoy SDeJ
- var. ***lineamaculatum*** 'Ken Aslet' ♀H3	CAvo CBcs CBro CCCN CKel ECha ELan EPfP EPot GCra GKev GMcL LAma LEdu LRHS NLar NRHS SPer SPoG

Tsuga ✿ (*Pinaceae*)

canadensis	CAco CDul EPfP ESps LPar NWea
- 'Abbott's Dwarf'	CKen NHol
§ - 'Abbott's Pygmy'	CKen
- 'Bacon Cristate'	CKen
- 'Beehive'	NLar
- 'Bennett'	NLar
- 'Betty Rose' (v)	CKen
- 'Birkett's White'	CKen
- 'Brandley'	CKen
§ - 'Branklyn'	CKen WCFE
- 'Cappy's Choice'	CKen
- 'Cinnamonea'	CKen
- 'Coffin'	CKen
- 'Cole's Prostrate' ♀H7	CKen LRHS MAsh SLim
- 'Creamey' (v)	CKen
- 'Curley'	CKen
- 'Curtis Ideal'	CKen
- 'Dr Hornbeck'	see *T. canadensis* 'Hornbeck'
- 'Eisburg'	SLim
- 'Essex'	CKen
* - 'Everitt's Dense Leaf'	CKen
- 'Everitt's Golden'	CKen
- 'Fantana'	GMcL MAsh NHol
- 'Greenwood Lake'	WThu
- 'Hedgehog'	NLar
§ - 'Hornbeck'	CKen
- 'Horsford'	CKen
- 'Horstmann' No 1	CKen
- 'Hussii'	CKen NHol
- 'Jacqueline Verkade'	CKen MAsh NLar
- 'Jeddeloh' ♀H7	ESps GMcL LPar LRHS MAsh NEgg NHol NLar SCob SGol SLim
- 'Jervis'	CKen NHol NWad
- 'Julianne'	CKen
- 'Kingsville Spreader'	CKen
- 'Little Joe'	CKen
- 'Livingston'	SLim
I - 'Lutea'	CKen
- 'Many Cones'	CKen
- 'Minima'	CKen
- 'Minuta' ♀H7	CKen NHol
- 'Moon Frost'	MAsh
- 'Palomino'	CKen
- 'Pendula' ♀H7	CKen MAsh
- 'Pincushion'	CKen
- 'Prostrata'	see *T. canadensis* 'Branklyn'
- 'Pygmaea'	see *T. canadensis* 'Abbott's Pygmy'
- 'Rugg's Washington Dwarf'	CKen
- 'Snowflake'	CKen
- 'Stewart's Gem'	CKen
- 'Verkade Petite'	CKen
- 'Verkade Recurved'	CKen
- 'Von Helms' Dwarf'	CKen
- 'Warnham'	CKen MAsh
caroliniana 'La Bar Weeping'	CKen NLar
- 'Planting Fields Broom'	CKen
chinensis	CKen
diversifolia 'Gotelli'	CKen
dumosa	CKen
heterophylla ♀H6	CAco CBcs CCVT CDul EPfP ESps MMuc NWea SCob SEWo SGol WTSh
- 'Iron Springs'	CKen
- 'Laursen's Column'	CKen
- 'Thorsens Weeping'	CKen
menziesii	see *Pseudotsuga menziesii*
mertensiana 'Blue Star'	CKen MAsh
- 'Elizabeth'	CKen
- 'Glauca'	CKen
I - 'Glauca Nana'	CKen
I - 'Horstmann'	CKen
- 'Quartz Mountain'	CKen
sieboldii 'Baldwin'	CKen
- 'Green Ball'	CKen
- 'Honeywell Estate'	CKen
- 'Nana'	CKen

Tuberaria (*Cistaceae*)

lignosa	SIgm WAbe

Tulbaghia ✿ (*Alliaceae*)

	acutiloba	CTca EBee GKev LEdu MHom
	alliacea	ECho EPri GKev LEdu WCot
	alliacea* × *violacea	CAvo ECho
*	***allioides***	CBro
	'Bob Brown'	LEdu WPGP
	capensis	CPne CPou LEdu NBir
	'Cariad'	LEdu
	cernua CD&R 199	EBee LEdu
	- hybrid	EPri
§	***coddii***	CPne LEdu MHom
	cominsii	ECho EPri LEdu SBch
	cominsii* × *violacea	CAvo MHom
	'Cosmic'	CPou EBee EPPr EPri LEdu WPGP
	'Fairy Snow'	LEdu WCot
	'Fairy Star'	CKno CTca CWGN EBee EPri EShb LEdu LSou SMHy WCot
	fragrans	see *T. simmleri*
	- 'Alba'	ECho ELan EPot SDeJ
	'Hazel'	CPou EBee LEdu MHer WPGP
	'John May's Special'	CKno EShb LEdu MHom WCot WHoo WPGP
	leucantha $\mathbb{Y}^{H2}$	CTca ECho EPri LEdu MHom NWad
	- H&B 11996	LEdu
	ludwigiana	CPne MHer
	maritima	see *T. violacea* var. *maritima*
	Marwood seedling	ECho LEdu MHer MHom MTPN
	montana	EBee LEdu MHer MPie
	'Moshoeshoe'	LEdu
	natalensis $\mathbb{Y}^{H2}$	CBro CPou CPrp ECho GKev
	- B&V 421	EPri
	- B&V 421 clone 2 pink-flowered	LEdu
	- Burtt 6949	CPne
	- pink-flowered	CTca ECho LPla MHom
	- white-flowered	CTca
	poetica	see *T. coddii*
	'Purple Eye' $\mathbb{Y}^{H2}$	CBro CCht CKno CPne EBee EWoo LEdu NSti SBee SPoG WCot
§	***simmleri*** $\mathbb{Y}^{H2}$	CMos CPou EBee ECho EHrv EPri EWes GKev LAma LEdu SDeJ
	- 'Cheryl Renshaw'	WCot
	- 'Snow Queen'	CPrp
	- white-flowered	CPou CPrp ECho GKev
	'Snow White'	WCot
	verdoorniae	LEdu
	violacea $\mathbb{Y}^{H2}$	Widely available
	- from RBGE	MHom
*	- 'Alba'	CKno EBee ECho EPri EWoo GKev MHer SChF SWat WKif
I	- 'Fine Form'	CKno WKif
I	- 'Grandiflora'	CAvo
	- 'John Rider'	EPri
*	- var. ***maritima***	CPne EShb LEdu MHer MHom WCot
	- 'Pallida'	CAvo CBro CCse CPou CTca ECho LEdu WPGP
	- 'Pearl'	CPou
	- 'Peppermint Garlic'	LEdu WPGP
	- var. ***robustior***	CAby CPou ECha EWes
	- 'Seren'	LEdu
§	- 'Silver Lace' (v) $\mathbb{Y}^{H2}$	Widely available
	- 'Variegata'	see *T. violacea* 'Silver Lace'
	- 'White Goddess'	CPou

Tulipa ✿ (*Liliaceae*)

'Abba' (2)	LAma SCob SDeJ SDir
'Absalon' (9)	GKev LAma SDir
'Abu Hassan' (3)	CAvo ERCP LAma LCro SDeJ
acuminata (15)	CBro CTca ECho ERCP GKev LAma MGib SCob SDeJ SDir SPhx
'Ad Rem' (4)	SDeJ
'Addis' (14)	LAma
'Agrass White' (3)	NBri
'Aguila' **new**	SDir
'Air' (10)	ERCP
aitchisonii	see *T. clusiana*
'Akebono' (11)	GKev LAma
'Akela' (5)	LAma
'Akita' (6) **new**	GKev
'Alabaster' (5)	LAma
'Aladdin' (6)	CAby GKev LAma LCro LOPS NBri SDeJ
'Aladdin's Record' (6)	CBro LAma SDeJ
'Alba Regalis' (1)	LAma
'Albert Heijn' (13)	CBro GKev SDeJ
albertii (15)	ECho LAma
Albion Star = 'Mieke Telkamp' (13)	EPfP SDeJ
'Aleppo' (7)	SDeJ
'Alexander Pushkin'^{PBR} (3)	LAma
'Alfred Cortot' (12) $\mathbb{Y}^{H6}$	LAma SDeJ
'Ali Baba' (14) $\mathbb{Y}^{H6}$	LAma NBri
'Alibi' (3) **new**	EPfP GKev
'Alice Leclercq' (2)	LAma
'Allegretto' (11)	LAma
'Alliance' (2)	LAma
altaica (15) $\mathbb{Y}^{H6}$	ECho GKev LAma
amabilis	see *T. hoogiana*
'American Dream' (4)	LAma SDir
'American Eagle' (7)	LAma SDeJ
'Analita' (13)	LAma
'Ancilla' (12) $\mathbb{Y}^{H6}$	CAvo CBro GKev LAma NBri WShi
'André Rieu' (5)	LCro
'Angélique' (11) $\mathbb{Y}^{H6}$	CAvo CBro CTca EPfP ERCP GKev LAma LCro LOPS NBir NBri NNys SCob SDeJ SDir SPer
'Angels Wish' (5) $\mathbb{Y}^{H6}$	CAvo EPfP LAma MGib SDeJ SDir
'Annie Schilder' (3)	ERCP LAma
'Antarctica'^{PBR} (3)	LAma
'Anthony Eden' (2)	LAma SDir
'Antoinette'^{PBR} (5)	CAby EPfP LAma LCro LOPS SDir
'Antraciet' (11)	ERCP LAma LCro LOPS NNys
'Apeldoorn' (4)	GKev LAma LCro LOPS NBri SCob SDeJ
'Apeldoorn's Elite' (4) $\mathbb{Y}^{H6}$	LAma NBri SDeJ
'Apricot Beauty' (1) $\mathbb{Y}^{H6}$	CTca ERCP GKev LAma LCro NBir NBri NNys SDeJ SDir
'Apricot Delight' (4) **new**	CAvo
'Apricot Emperor' (13)	GKev MCot SDeJ
'Apricot Foxx' (3)	EPfP GKev LAma NNys
'Apricot Impression'^{PBR} (4)	GKev LAma
'Apricot Jewel'	see *T. linifolia* (Batalinii Group) 'Apricot Jewel'
'Apricot Magic' (1)	LAma
'Apricot Parrot' (10) $\mathbb{Y}^{H6}$	ERCP GKev LAma MCot NBri SDeJ
'Aquilla' (11)	LAma SDeJ
'Arabian Mystery' (3)	ERCP GKev LAma NHol SDeJ
'Aria Card' (7)	LAma SDeJ
'Artist' (8) $\mathbb{Y}^{H6}$	ERCP GKev LAma SDeJ SDir
'Atlantis' (5)	ERCP LAma NBri SDeJ
'Attila' (3)	CAvo GKev LAma
'Attila Graffiti' (3)	LAma
'Attila's Elite' (3)	LAma
aucheriana (15) $\mathbb{Y}^{H5}$	ECho EPot LAma LLHF
australis (15)	ECho GKev
'Avignon' (5)	SDeJ
aximensis (15)	ECho EPot LAma
'Bacchus' (7)	LAma

'Backpacker' (11)	MGib
bakeri	see *T. saxatilis* Bakeri Group
'Ballade' (6) ♀H6	CAvo ERCP GKev LAma LCro MCot SDeJ
Ballade Dream = 'Sonnet' (6)	LAma SDeJ
'Ballade Gold' (6)	LAma
'Ballerina' (6) ♀H6	CAby CAvo CBro CMea CTca ECho EPfP ERCP GKev LAma LCro LOPS MCot NBri NNys SCob SDeJ SDir SPer
'Banja Luka' (4)	GKev LAma NBri SDeJ
'Barbados' (7)	LAma SCob SDeJ
'Barcelona' (3) ♀H6	ERCP LAma LCro LOPS
'Baronesse' (5)	SDeJ
'Bastogne' (3)	LAma SCob
'Bastogne Parrot' (10)	LAma
batalinii	see *T. linifolia* Batalinii Group
'Bearing Point' (2) **new**	GKev
'Beau Monde' (3) ♀H6	SDeJ
'Beauty of Apeldoorn' (4)	LAma
'Beauty of Bath' (9)	LAma
'Beauty of Spring' (4)	LAma
'Beauty Queen' (1)	GKev LAma SDeJ
'Beethoven's Memory' (19) **new**	GKev
'Bel Air' PBR (2)	LAma
'Belcanto' (3)	LAma
'Belicia' (2)	GKev LAma
'Bell Song' (7) **new**	GKev
'Bellflower' (7)	LAma
'Bellona' (3)	LAma SDeJ
'Berlioz' (12)	LAma LRHS SDeJ
'Bessie' (5)	LAma
'Bestseller' (1)	SDeJ
biebersteiniana (15)	ECho
§ ***biflora*** (15)	ECho EPot ERCP GKev LAma MGib SDeJ SDir
- var. ***major*** (15) **new**	GKev
bifloriformis (15)	ECho GKev LAma LLHF
I - 'Maxima' (15)	SPhx
- 'Starlight' (15) ♀H6	GKev
'Big Chief' (4) ♀H6	LAma
'Big Smile' (5)	NNys SDir
'Black and White' (9)	LAma
'Black Charm' (3)	CAby
'Black Hero' (11)	CAby CAvo EPfP ERCP GKev LAma LCro MCot SDeJ SDir
'Black Horse' (5)	LAma
'Black Jewel' (7)	ERCP GKev LAma SDeJ SDir
'Black Parrot' (10) ♀H6	CAby CAvo CBro EPfP ERCP GKev LAma LCro LOPS NBri NNys SCob SDeJ SDir SPer
'Black Stallion' (11)	SDir
'Black Swan' (5)	SDeJ
'Blackjack' (3)	GKev LAma NNys
'Bleu Aimable' (5)	CAvo ERCP GKev LAma MCot SDeJ
'Blue Diamond' (11)	CAvo ERCP LAma NBri SDeJ SDir
'Blue Heron' (7) ♀H6	ERCP LAma LCro SDeJ
'Blue Parrot' (10)	EPfP ERCP LAma LCro NBri SCob SDeJ SPer
'Blue Ribbon' (3)	CAvo LCro LOPS
'Blue Spectacle' (11) **new**	GKev
Blueberry Ripple	see *T.* 'Zurel'
'Blumex Favourite' PBR (10)	SCob
'Blushing Apeldoorn' (4)	LAma
'Blushing Beauty' (5)	LAma SDeJ
'Blushing Bride' (5)	SDeJ
'Blushing Girl' (5)	LAma MGib SDeJ SDir
'Blushing Lady' (5)	GKev LAma MCot
'Border Legend' (13)	LAma
'Boston' (3)	ERCP LAma SDir
'Boutade' (14)	NPer
'Bridesmaid' (5)	LAma
'Bright Parrot' (10)	LAma MGib
'Brilliant Star' (1)	LAma
'Brown Sugar' (3)	EPfP ERCP
'Bruine Wimpel' (5)	GKev LAma
'Buddy' (14)	SCob
'Bulldog' (7)	CAvo SDeJ
'Burgundy' (6)	CTca ERCP GKev LAma LCro LOPS SDeJ SDir SPer
'Burgundy Lace' (7)	GKev LAma LCro LOPS SDeJ
'Burning Heart' (4) ♀H6	GKev LAma SDeJ
'Buttercup' (14)	SDeJ
'Café Noir' (5)	ERCP LAma LCro NHol NNys SDir
'Cairo' (3)	LCro LOPS
'Calgary' (3) ♀H6	CAvo GKev LAma SCob SDeJ SDir
'Calibra' (7)	LAma
'Californian Sun' (14)	LAma
'Calypso' (14) ♀H6	LAma LRHS NBri NRHS
'Canasta' (7)	GKev LAma SDeJ
'Candela' (13) ♀H6	LAma NBri SDeJ
'Candy Club' (5)	LAma
'Candy Prince' PBR (1)	LAma NBri SDeJ
'Canova' (7)	SDeJ
'Cantata' (13)	LAma
'Cape Cod' (14)	CAvo LAma NBri SDeJ
'Cardinal Mindszenty' (2)	ERCP LAma LRHS NRHS SDeJ SDir
carinata (15)	ECho
'Carlton' (2)	LAma NBri
'Carnaval de Nice' (11/v) ♀H6	CAby CBro CTca ERCP GKev LAma LCro LOPS SDeJ SPer
'Carola' (3)	LAma
'Carrousel' (7)	SDeJ
'Cartouche' (11)	LAma SDeJ
'Casablanca' (11)	GKev
'Cassini' (3)	LAma SDeJ
§ ***celsiana*** (15)	ECho LAma
'Chanson d'Amour' (14)	LAma
'Chansonnette' (3) **new**	GKev
'Charmeur' PBR (3)	SDeJ
'Charming Beauty' (11) **new**	GKev
'Charming Lady' (11) **new**	ERCP
'China Lady' (14)	SDeJ
'China Pink' (6) ♀H6	CAvo CBro CTca ERCP GKev LAma LCro LOPS SDeJ
'China Town' (8) ♀H6	CMea ERCP GKev LAma LCro MGib NNys SDeJ SDir
'Chopin' (12)	LAma NHol
'Christmas Dream' (1)	GKev LAma SDeJ
'Christmas Marvel' (1)	LAma NBri SDeJ
chrysantha Boiss. ex Baker	see *T. montana*
'Cilesta' (2)	LAma
'Cistula' (6)	SDeJ
'City Flower' (14)	LAma
'City of Vancouver' (5)	LAma
'Claudia' (6)	LAma NBri SDeJ SDir
'Clearwater' PBR (5)	CAby LAma SDeJ
§ ***clusiana*** (15)	CBro ECho EPfP ERCP GKev LAma
- f. ***cashmeriana***	GKev
- var. ***chrysantha*** (15) ♀H5	ECho GKev LAma WShi
- - 'Tubergen's Gem' (15)	ECho EPot GKev LAma
- 'Cynthia' (15) ♀H6	CAby CTca ECho EPot ERCP GKev LAma SDeJ SDir WShi
- 'Sheila' (15)	CBro ECho GKev LAma SPhx
§ - var. ***stellata*** (15)	CBro ECho GKev LAma MGib
'Colour Spectacle' PBR (5)	CAby LAma
'Columbine' (5)	ECho GKev LAma SDir
'Comedian' (14)	LAma
'Concerto' (13)	CBro LAma NPer SDeJ

'Continental' (3)	LAma
'Cool Crystal' (7)	GKev LAma
'Coquette' (1)	LAma SDeJ
'Coquette Yellow' (1)	LAma
'Corona' (12)	LAma NBri SDeJ
'Corsage' (14) Y^{H6}	LAma SDeJ
'Cortina' (9)	SDeJ
'Cottage Boy' (1)	LAma SDir
'Cotton Candy Clouds'	LAma
'Couleur Cardinal' (3)	CBro ERCP GKev LAma LCro LOPS LRHS NBri NRHS SDeJ SDir
'Cracker'^{PBR} (3)	LAma
'Cream Flag' (3) **new**	NNys
'Cream Perfection' (3)	LAma
'Creme Upstar' (11)	ERCP GKev LAma LCro LOPS SDeJ SDir
cretica (15)	ECho LAma LLHF
'Crispion Dark' (7)	ERCP
'Crystal Beauty' (7) Y^{H6}	LAma
'Cuban Night' (7)	LAma
'Cum Laude' (5)	LAma SDeJ
'Cummins' (7)	CAvo ERCP GKev LAma
'Curly Sue' (7)	ERCP LAma LCro LOPS MCot NNys SDir SPer
'Czaar Peter' (14) Y^{H6}	EPfP GKev NBri NPer SDeJ
'Dallas' (7)	LAma
'Dance' (13)	SDeJ
'Dancing Show' (8)	LAma
dasystemon (15)	ECho GKev LAma LLHF
'Davenport' (7)	ERCP
'David Teniers' (2)	ERCP LAma SDeJ
'Daydream' (4) Y^{H6}	LAma NBri NNys SCob SDeJ SDir SPer
'Daylight' (12)	LAma
'Daytona' (7)	CAvo LAma
'Deep River' (5)	LAma
'Deirdre' (8)	LAma
'Deshima' (3)	LAma
'Design Impression' (4)	LAma
'Destiny' (10)	LAma
'Diana' (1)	LAma
didieri misapplied	see *T. passeriniana*
'Dior' (2)	LCro LOPS
'Doll's Minuet' (8)	EPfP ERCP LAma LCro LOPS NBri NNys
'Dom Pedro' (5)	LAma
'Don Quichotte' (3) Y^{H6}	ERCP LAma LCro LOPS SDeJ
'Donauperle' (14)	SDeJ
'Donna Bella' (14)	SDeJ
'Dordogne' (5) Y^{H6}	LAma SDeJ
'Double Dazzle' (2)	LAma
'Double Flaming Parrot'^{PBR} (10)	LAma
'Double Price' (2)	ERCP
'Double Princess'^{PBR} (2)	LAma
'Double Red Riding Hood' (14v)	CAby GKev LAma SCob SDeJ
'Double Sugar' (11)	LAma
'Double You' (11) **new**	EPfP
'Dragon King' (3)	SDeJ
'Dream Touch' (11)	ERCP GKev LAma LCro LOPS
'Dreamboat' (14)	EPfP LAma
'Dreaming Maid' (3)	LAma
'Dreamland' (5) Y^{H6}	LAma SDeJ
dubia 'Tschimgam' **new**	GKev
- 'Beldersai' (15) **new**	GKev
'Duc van Tol' (1)	SDir
'Duc van Tol Aurora'	LAma
'Duc van Tol Max Cramoisie' (1)	LAma SDir

'Duc van Tol Primrose' (1)	LAma
'Duc van Tol Red and Yellow' (1)	GKev LAma SDir
'Duc van Tol Rose' (1)	LAma SDir
'Duc van Tol Salmon' (1)	LAma
'Duc van Tol Scarlet' (1)	LAma
'Duc van Tol Violet' (1)	LAma SDir
'Duc van Tol White' (1)	LAma
'Dyanito' (6)	LAma
'Dynasty' (3)	GKev
'Early Glory' (3)	LAma LCro
'Early Harvest' (12) Y^{H6}	CAvo GKev LAma SDeJ
'Early Star' (14)	LAma
'Easter Parade' (13)	LAma
'Easter Surprise' (14) Y^{H6}	GKev LAma SDeJ SDir
'Ego Parrot' (10)	LCro
eichleri	see *T. undulatifolia*
'El Niño' (5) **new**	SDir
'Electra' (5)	LAma NHol
'Elegans Alba' (6)	LAma
'Elegant Lady' (6)	CAvo GKev LAma NBri SDeJ
'Erna Lindgreen' (10)	LAma
'Escape'^{PBR} (3)	LAma
'Esperanto' (8/v) Y^{H6}	GKev LAma SDeJ SDir
'Esprit' (7)	LAma
'Estella Rijnveld' (10)	ERCP GKev LAma LCro LOPS SDeJ SDir
'Esther' (5)	LAma
'Eternal Flame' (2)	CAby GKev LAma LCro
'Evening Breeze' (3) Y^{H6} **new**	CAvo
'Evita'^{PBR} (2)	LAma
'Exotic Emperor' (13)	CAvo ERCP GKev LAma LCro NNys SDeJ SDir SPer
'Eye Catcher' (8)	LAma SDir
'Fabio' (7)	LAma LRHS NRHS
'Fairy Nymph' (5)	LAma
'Fancy Frills' (7) Y^{H6}	ERCP GKev LAma SDeJ SDir
'Fantasy' (10) Y^{H6}	LAma NBri
'Fashion' (12)	LAma SDeJ
ferganica (15)	ECho GKev LAma
'Fidelio' (3) Y^{H6}	SDeJ
'Fire of Love' (14)	LAma SDir
'Fire Queen' (3) Y^{H6}	ERCP LAma
'First Impression' (14)	LAma
'Flair' (1)	LAma LRHS NBri NRHS SDeJ
'Flamenco' (7)	SDeJ
'Flaming Club' (5)	CAby LAma
'Flaming Coquette'^{PBR} (1)	LAma
'Flaming Evita'^{PBR} (2)	SDeJ
'Flaming Jewel' (4)	LAma
'Flaming Parrot' (10)	CAby CAvo ERCP GKev LAma LCro LOPS SDeJ
I 'Flaming Purissima' (13)	CAvo GKev LAma SDeJ SDir
'Flaming Springgreen' (8)	CAvo ERCP GKev LAma LCro NNys SDeJ
'Flashback' (10)	ERCP LAma
'Flig Flag' (3)	ERCP
'Florette'^{PBR} (5)	LAma
'Florijn Chic' (6)	LAma
'Florosa' (8)	ERCP GKev LCro LOPS SDeJ
'Flower Power' (10) **new**	GKev
'Fontainebleau' (3)	GKev LAma SDeJ
'Formosa' (8)	EPfP LAma
'Foxtrot'^{PBR} (2)	EPfP ERCP GKev LAma SDir
'Françoise' (3)	LAma SDeJ
'Franz Léhar' (12)	SDeJ
'Freeman' (11)	LAma
'Fringed Elegance' (7) Y^{H6}	LAma LCro LOPS
'Fringed Family' (7)	SDeJ

	'Fringed Golden Apeldoorn' (7)	LAma
	'Fritz Kreisler' (12)	LAma SDeJ
	'Fulgens' (6)	LAma
	'Fulton' (5)	LAma
	'Für Elise' (14)	GKev LRHS NBri SDeJ
	'Gabriella' (3)	GKev LAma
	'Gaiety' (12)	SDeJ
	'Gander's Rhapsody' (3)	LAma
	'Garanza' (2)	GKev LAma
	'Garden Party' (3)	LAma SDeJ
	'Garden Show' (14)	LAma
	'Gavota' (3) 🏆H6	CAvo CBro GKev LAma NBri NHol SCob SDeJ
	'Generaal de Wet' (1)	LAma SDeJ
	'Georges Grappe' (5)	LAma
	'Georgette' (5)	GKev LAma
	'Gerbrand Kieft' (11) 🏆H6	ERCP GKev
	'Gipsy Love' (7)	SDeJ
	'Girlfriend' (15)	GKev
	'Giuseppe Verdi' (12)	GKev LAma LRHS NRHS
	'Glück' (12) 🏆H6	ECho EPfP LAma LRHS NRHS
	'Golden Apeldoorn' (4)	ESps GKev LAma LCro LOPS NBri SCob SDeJ
	'Golden Artist' (8)	GKev LAma SDeJ SDir
	'Golden Emperor' (13)	GKev LAma SDeJ
	'Golden Melody' (3)	SDeJ
	'Golden Nizza' (11)	LAma
	'Golden Oxford' (4)	LAma
	'Golden Parade' (4)	LAma
	'Goldwest' (14)	SDeJ
	'Gordon Cooper' (4)	LAma SDeJ
	'Gorilla' (7)	LAma
	'Goudstuk' (12)	LAma
	'Goya' (2)	LAma
	'Grand Perfection' PBR (3) 🏆H6	LCro LOPS
	'Grand Prestige' (14)	LAma
	'Grand Style' (5) 🏆H6	LAma
	'Granny Award' (11)	LAma
	'Green Eyes' (8)	SDeJ
	'Green Jay' (7) **new**	MGib
	'Green River' (8)	LAma SDeJ
	'Green Unique'	LAma
	'Green Village' (8)	LAma
	'Green Wave' (10)	ERCP GKev LAma LCro LOPS SDeJ SDir
	'Greenstar' (6)	LAma SDir
	greigii (14)	GKev LAma
	grengiolensis (15)	GKev LAma
	'Greuze' (5)	LCro LOPS
	'Groenland' (8)	CAvo CBro GKev LAma LCro MCot NBri SDeJ
	'Gudoshnik' (4)	LAma
	hageri (15)	ECho GKev LAma LLHF SDir
	- 'Splendens' (15)	GKev LAma SDeJ SPhx
	'Hakuun' (4)	ERCP LAma SDir
	'Halcro' (5) 🏆H6	LAma
	'Hamilton' (7)	GKev LAma SDeJ
	'Hans Dietrich Genscher' (3)	GKev
	'Happy Family' (3)	LAma
	'Happy Generation' (3)	GKev LAma LCro LOPS
	'Happy Hour' (7)	ERCP
	'Havran' (3)	CAvo CBro ERCP GKev LAma LCro LOPS NNys SDir
	'Heart's Delight' (12)	CAvo CBro ECho GKev LAma NBri SDeJ
	'Helmar' (3)	LAma SDeJ
	'Hemisphere' (3)	EPfP ERCP GKev LAma SDeJ SDir
	'Hermitage' (3)	ERCP LAma

	heweri (15)	EPot GKev LAma
	'Hocus Pocus' (5)	LAma SDeJ
	'Holland Baby' (2)	LAma SDeJ
	'Holland Bouquet' (3)	LAma
	'Holland Chic' (6)	LAma MCot SDeJ
	'Holland Emotions' (4)	LAma
	'Holland Happening' (10)	LAma
	'Holland Queen' PBR (3)	LAma
	'Holland Ruby' (11)	LAma
	'Holland Sun' (3)	LAma
	'Hollandia' (3)	LAma
	'Hollands Glorie' (4)	LAma SDeJ
	'Hollywood' (8)	LAma
	'Hollywood Star' (8)	LAma
	'Honeymoon' (7)	LAma
	'Hong Kong' (3) **new**	GKev
	'Honky Tonk' (15) 🏆H6	CAvo ECho GKev LAma LCro
§	***hoogiana*** (15)	ECho GKev
	'Hot Chocolate' (3)	LAma
	'Hotpants' (3)	LAma SCob
	'Huis Ten Bosch' (7)	LAma
§	***humilis*** (15)	CBro ECho GKev LAma LRHS NRHS SDeJ SDir WShi
	- 'China Carol' (15)	ECho GKev LAma SDeJ
	- 'Eastern Spice' (15)	ECho LAma
	- 'Eastern Star' (15)	ECho GKev LAma
§	- 'Lilliput' (15)	CAby CBro ECho EPot GKev LAma LRHS MGib NBri NRHS
	- 'Magenta Queen' (15)	GKev LAma
	- 'Odalisque' (15)	ECho EPot ERCP GKev LAma LRHS NRHS
	- 'Persian Pearl' (15)	CAvo ECho EPfP EPot ERCP GKev LAma LCro LOPS SCob SDeJ SDir WTor
*	- 'Pink Charm' (15)	GKev
	- var. ***pulchella*** Albocaerulea Oculata Group (15)	ECho EPot ERCP GKev SDir
	- 'Tête-à-tête' (15)	LAma SDir
§	- Violacea Group (15)	ECho LRHS NRHS
	- - black base (15)	ECho EPot ERCP GKev LAma
	- - yellow base (15)	ECho EPot GKev LAma
	'Humming Bird' (8)	LAma
	hungarica	GKev
	'Ice Age' (11) **new**	NNys
	'Ice Cream' (11)	ERCP GKev LAma SDeJ SDir
	'Ice Stick' (12)	CBro GKev SDeJ
	'Ice Wonder' (11) **new**	SDir
	'Ile de France' (5)	ERCP LAma LCro LOPS SDeJ
	iliensis (15)	CMea EPot GKev LAma LLHF
	'India' (3)	LAma
	'Indian Velvet' (5)	LCro LOPS
	ingens (15)	ECho GKev LAma
	'Innuendo' (3)	LRHS NRHS SPer
	'Insulinde' (9)	GKev LAma SDir WCot
	'Inzell' (3)	EPfP GKev LAma
	'Ivory Floradale' (4) 🏆H6	GKev LAma SDeJ SDir
	'Jaap Groot' (4)	LAma
	'Jackpot' (3)	EPfP LAma SCob
	'Jacqueline' (6)	LAma LCro LOPS
	'Jan Reus' (3)	CAvo CBro ERCP LAma LCro LOPS NNys
	'Jazz' (6)	ERCP NNys
	'Jewel of Spring' (4)	LAma
	'Jimmy' (3)	LAma
	'Jochem' (3)	LAma
	'Joffre' (1)	LAma
	'Johann Strauss' (12)	CAvo LAma NBri
	'Juan' (13) 🏆H6	GKev LAma
	'Judith Leyster' (3)	LAma SDir
	'Juliet' (5) **new**	GKev

'Juliette' (4)	LAma
'Karel Doorman' (10)	LAma
'Kathleen Truxton' (5)	LAma SDir
'Katie Melua' (7) **new**	GKev
kaufmanniana (12)	ECho EPot SDir
§ 'Kees Nelis' (3)	GKev NBri
'Keizerskroon' (1)	LAma SDeJ
'Kikomachi' (3)	LRHS NRHS
'Kingsblood' (5) ♀H6	ERCP LAma SDeJ SDir
'Kleurenpracht'	see *T.* 'Princess Margaret Rose'
kolpakowskiana (15) ♀H6	EPot ERCP GKev LAma LLHF WShi
kurdica (15)	ECho LAma SPhx
- purple-flowered (15)	ECho
'La Belle Époque' (2)	CAvo ERCP GKev LCro LOPS NNys SCob SDeJ
'La Courtine' (5)	LAma
'La Douceur' (5)	LAma SDir
'La Perla' (6) **new**	CMea GKev
'La Reine Rose' (1) **new**	GKev
'Lac van Rijn' (1)	GKev LAma SDir
* 'Lady Diana' (14)	GKev
'Lady Guna' (15) **new**	MGib
'Lady Jane' (15) ♀H6	CMea ECho GKev LAma SDir SPhx WShi
lanata (15)	GKev
'Large Copper' (14)	LAma
'Lasting Love' (3)	LAma NNys SDir
'Latvian Gold' (15)	ECho GKev
'Le Mogol' (5)	LAma
'Leen van der Mark' (3)	LAma NBri
'Libretto Parrot' (10)	LAma SDeJ
'Light and Dreamy' (4)	CAvo ERCP GKev LCro LOPS SDeJ
'Lighting Sun' (4)	LAma
'Lilac Perfection' (11)	CTca ERCP GKev LAma SDeJ
'Lilac Time' (6)	LAma SDir
'Lilac Wonder'	see *T. saxatilis* (Bakeri Group) 'Lilac Wonder'
'Lilliput'	see *T. humilis* 'Lilliput'
'Lilybeauty' (6)	LAma
'Lilyfire' (6)	GKev LAma SDeJ
'Limelight'	LAma
'Lingerie' (7)	LAma
linifolia (15) ♀H5	CAvo ECho EPot ERCP GKev LAma MGib SDeJ WShi
§ - Batalinii Group (15) ♀H5	ECho GKev SDir
§ - - 'Apricot Jewel' (15)	CBro ECho EPot ERCP GKev LAma
- - 'Bright Gem' (15) ♀H5	CBro ECho EPot GKev LAma NPer SPhx WCot WHoo
- - 'Bronze Charm' (15)	CAvo CMea ECGP ECho EPot GKev LAma SDeJ SPhx WTor
- - 'Red Gem' (15)	ECho GKev SPhx WCot
- - 'Red Hunter' (15) ♀H6	CBro ERCP GKev LAma
- - 'Red Jewel' (15)	ECho LAma
- - 'Salmon Gem' (15)	ECho
- - 'Salmon Jewel' (15) **new**	GKev
- - 'Yellow Jewel' (15)	ECho GKev LAma WShi
§ - Maximowiczii Group (15)	ECho LAma
'Lipgloss' (3)	LAma NHol
'Little Beauty' (15) ♀H6	CAby CAvo CBro ECho EPfP EPot GKev LAma LCro LOPS LRHS NBri NRHS SDeJ SPhx WCot WHoo
'Little Diamond' (12)	LRHS NRHS
'Little Girl' (14)	EPfP GKev LCro
'Little Princess' (15) ♀H6	CAvo CBro CTca ECho EPot ERCP GKev LAma LRHS NBri NRHS SDeJ SPhx
'Little Star' (15) ♀H6	GKev LAma
'London' (4)	LAma
'Long Lady' (5)	LAma
'Louvre' (7) ♀H6	LAma
'Love Song' (12)	LAma
'Lovely Surprise' (14)	SDeJ
§ 'Lustige Witwe' (3)	LAma SDeJ
'Lydia' (3)	LAma
'Mabel' (9)	LAma
§ 'Madame Lefeber' (13)	LAma LCro LOPS NBri SDeJ SDir
'Madonna' (10)	EPfP LAma
'Magic Lavender' (3) **new**	GKev
'Maja' (7)	LAma
'Makassar' (3)	LAma
'Mango Charm' (3)	LAma SDir
'March of Time' (14)	LAma
'Margaret Herbst' (14)	LAma
'Margarita' (2)	GKev LAma LCro
'Marie José' (14)	SDeJ
'Marie Louise' (5)	LAma
'Mariette' (6)	CBro GKev LAma SDeJ
'Marilyn' (6)	ERCP GKev LAma SDeJ
'Marit' (4) ♀H6	LAma
'Marjolein' (6)	LAma
marjolletii (15)	LAma
'Maroon' (7)	ERCP
'Mary Ann' (14)	GKev LAma
'Mata Hari' (3)	LAma
'Matchpoint' (7/d)	ERCP LAma SDeJ
'Maureen' (5) ♀H6	ERCP GKev LAma LCro LOPS NNys SDeJ
mauritiana 'Cindy' (15)	GKev LAma
maximowiczii	see *T. linifolia* Maximowiczii Group
'Maytime' (6)	GKev LAma LCro LOPS MCot SDeJ
'Melody d'Amour' (5)	LAma
'Melrose' (2)	LAma
'Menton' (5) ♀H6	ERCP GKev LAma LCro LOPS NNys SDeJ
'Menton Exotic' (11)	ERCP SPer
'Merlot' (6)	ERCP LAma LCro LOPS
'Merry Christmas' (1)	LAma
'Merry Christmas Design' (1)	LAma
'Merry Go Round' (3) **new**	NNys
Merry Widow	see *T.* 'Lustige Witwe'
'Mickey Mouse' (1)	LAma LCro
'Miranda' (11)	LAma
'Miskodeed' (14)	SDeJ
'Miss Elegance' (3)	LAma
'Mistress' (3)	ERCP LAma LCro NNys
'Modern Style' (5)	LAma
'Mona Lisa' (6)	LAma SDeJ
'Mondial' PBR (2)	GKev LAma
'Moneymaker' (6)	ERCP
'Monsella' (2)	GKev LAma NBri
§ ***montana*** (15)	CTca ECho EPot GKev LAma SDir
- yellow-flowered	ECho GKev LAma
'Monte Carlo' (2) ♀H6	LAma LCro NBri SDeJ SDir
'Montreux' (2)	LAma SDir
'Moonlight Girl' (6) ♀H6	MGib
'Moonshine' (6)	LAma
'Moonwalker' (4)	LAma
'Mount Tacoma' (11)	CAvo CBro ERCP GKev LAma LCro LOPS SDeJ
'Mr Van der Hoef' (2)	LAma SDeJ
'Mrs John T. Scheepers' (5)	LAma SDeJ
'Muriel' (10)	ERCP GKev
'National Velvet' (3)	LCro SDir SPer
'Negrita' (3)	ERCP GKev LAma LCro LOPS NBri SCob SDeJ SDir
neustruevae (15)	ECho EPot GKev LAma
'New Design' (3/v)	GKev LAma LCro
'Nicholas Heyek' (3)	LCro

'Night Club' (5) **new**	NNys
'Nightrider' (8)	ERCP GKev LAma LCro MCot SDeJ SDir
'Noranda' (7)	LAma
'Ollioules' (4) ♀H6	GKev LAma SDeJ
'Olympic Flame' (4) ♀H6	LAma LCro LOPS SDeJ
'Orange Angelique' (11)	GKev NNys XEll
'Orange Bouquet' (3) ♀H6	GKev LAma SDeJ
'Orange Brilliant' (13)	LAma
'Orange Cassini' (3)	LAma NBri
'Orange Emperor' (13) ♀H6	CAvo ERCP GKev LAma SDeJ SDir
'Orange Favourite' (10)	ERCP GKev LAma
'Orange Lion' (4)	LAma
'Orange Monarch' (3)	LAma
'Orange Princess' (11) ♀H6	CBro CTca ERCP GKev LAma LCro LOPS SCob SDeJ
'Orange Queen' (4)	LAma
'Orange Sun'	see *T.* 'Oranjezon'
'Orange Toronto' (14)	LAma
'Oranje Nassau' (2) ♀H6	LRHS NRHS
§ 'Oranjezon' (4) ♀H6	ERCP LAma
'Oratorio' (14) ♀H6	LAma SDeJ
'Oriental Beauty' (14) ♀H6	LAma
orithyioides	GKev
orphanidea (15)	ECho GKev LAma
- 'Flava' (15)	ECho GKev LAma
§ - Whittallii Group (15) ♀H6	ECGP EPot ERCP GKev LCro LOPS SDeJ SPhx WCot WShi
- - 'Major' (15) **new**	NNys
'Oscar' (3)	LAma NHol
ostrowskiana (15)	ECho LAma
'Oxford' (4) ♀H6	LAma
'Oxford's Elite' (4)	LAma
'Page Polka' (3)	LAma SDeJ
'Palestrina' (3)	LAma SPer
'Pandour' (14)	LAma
'Panorama' (5)	LAma
'Papillon' (9)	LAma
'Parade' (4) ♀H6	LAma
'Parrot King' (10)	SDeJ
§ ***passeriniana*** (15)	GKev
'Passionale' (3) ♀H6	EPfP LAma LCro LOPS NBri SDeJ SPer
'Paul Scherer' (3) ♀H6	CAvo ERCP LAma LCro LOPS NNys SDeJ
'Pax' (3)	LAma
'Pays Bas' (3) **new**	GKev
'Peach Blossom' (2)	ERCP GKev LAma LCro LRHS NBri NRHS SCob SDeJ SPer
Peacock Group	SDeJ SDir
'Pebble' (11) **new**	GKev
'Peppermintstick' (15) ♀H6	CAvo CBro CMea CTca ECho GKev LAma SCob SDeJ
'Perestroyka' (5)	GKev LAma SDeJ
persica	see *T. celsiana*
'Philippe de Comines' (5)	LAma SDir
'Piccolo' (15)	LAma
'Picture' (5)	ERCP LAma SDeJ
'Pieter de Leur' (6)	LAma
'Pimpernel' (8/v)	LAma SDeJ
'Pink Diamond' (5)	CAvo ERCP GKev LCro NHol SDeJ
'Pink Dwarf' (12)	SDeJ
* 'Pink Emperor' (13) **new**	GKev
'Pink Impression' (4) ♀H6	GKev LAma LCro SDeJ
'Pink Lady' (3)	LAma
'Pink Sensation' (14)	SDeJ
'Pinkeen' (13)	LAma
'Pinocchio' (14)	CAvo CBro GKev LAma LRHS NBri SDeJ
'Pirand' (13) ♀H6	SDeJ
'Pittsburg' (3)	LCro LOPS
'Plaisir' (14) ♀H6	LAma
platystigma (15)	ECho LAma
'Poco Loco' (13)	GKev SDeJ
polychroma	see *T. biflora*
'Poppie' (3) **new**	GKev
praestans (15)	ECho GKev SDir SPer WShi
- 'Bloemenlust' (15)	GKev
- 'Fusilier' (15) ♀H6	CBro EPot GKev LAma NBir NBri SDeJ SDir
- 'Moondance' (15)	GKev
- 'Shogun' (15)	ERCP GKev NBri SDeJ
- 'Unicum' (15/v)	EPot ERCP GKev LAma MGib NBri SDeJ
- 'Van Tubergen's Variety' (15)	ECho GKev LAma NPer SDir
- 'Zwanenburg Variety' (15)	ECho GKev
'Pretty Princess' (3) **new**	ERCP
'Pretty Woman' (6)	LAma SPer
'Princeps' (13)	LAma SDeJ
§ 'Princess Margaret Rose' (5)	LAma
'Princess Unique'PBR (11)	LAma
'Princesse Charmante' (14) ♀H6	LAma LCro LOPS
'Prins Carnaval' (1) ♀H6	LAma
'Prinses Irene' (3) ♀H6	CAvo CBro CMea CTca EPfP ERCP GKev LAma LCro LOPS LRHS MCot NBir NBri NHol NNys NRHS SDeJ
'Prinses Margriet' (3)	ERCP LAma
'Professor Einstein' (3)	LAma
'Professor Röntgen' (10)	ERCP GKev LAma LCro LOPS SDeJ SDir
'Professor Schotel' (15)	LAma
pulchella humilis	see *T. humilis*
'Purified' (3) **new**	GKev
§ 'Purissima' (13) ♀H6	CAvo CBro GKev LAma LCro LOPS NBri NNys SCob SDeJ SPer
'Purple Bouquet' (3)	LAma SDeJ
'Purple Dream' (6)	CBro LAma NNys SDeJ
'Purple Flag' (3)	LAma LCro LOPS
'Purple Peony' (2) **new**	NNys
'Purple Prince' (5)	LAma LCro LOPS LRHS NRHS SDeJ
'Purple Rain' (3)	LAma
'Purple Voice'	LAma
'Quebec' (14)	CAvo LAma SDeJ SDir
'Queen of Marvel' (2)	LAma SDeJ
'Queen of Night' (5)	CAvo CBro CMea CTca EPfP ERCP ESps GKev LAma LCro NBri NNys SCob SDir SPer SPhx
'Queensday' (11)	LAma SDeJ
'Queensland' (7)	CAvo LAma
'Quest' (3)	LAma
'Rai' (10)	LAma LCro
'Rainbow'	LAma
'Rajka' (6)	GKev
'Real Time' (7)	LAma SDir
'Recreado' (5)	CAvo ERCP LAma SDeJ
'Red Baby Doll' (2)	LAma
'Red Emperor'	see *T.* 'Madame Lefeber'
'Red Georgette' (5) ♀H6	CAby GKev LAma NBir
'Red Hat' (7)	LCro LOPS MGib
'Red Impression'PBR (4) ♀H6	EPfP LAma LCro LOPS
'Red Mark'PBR (3)	LAma
'Red Present' (3)	LAma
'Red Princess' (11) ♀H6	ERCP GKev LAma
'Red Revival' (1)	GKev LAma
'Red Riding Hood' (14) ♀H6	CAvo CBro EPfP ESps GKev LAma LRHS NBir NBri NRHS SCob SDeJ SPer
'Red Rover' (3)	LCro

'Red Shine' (6) 𝕐H6	CAvo CBro ERCP GKev LAma LCro SDeJ
'Red Springgreen' (8)	ERCP GKev LAma LCro LOPS SDeJ
'Red Wing' (7) 𝕐H6	LAma SDeJ
'Redwood' (14)	SDeJ
(Rembrandt Group) 'Saskia' (15)	LAma
'Rems Favourite' (3)	CAvo LCro LOPS NNys
'Renown' (5)	LAma SDeJ
'Renown Unique' (11)	LAma SDir
'Request' (3)	GKev LAma
'Rex Rubrorum' (2)	GKev LAma
rhodopea	see *T. urumoffii*
'Ringo'	see *T.* 'Kees Nelis'
'Robert Schuller' (14)	LAma
'Rockery Master' (14)	LAma
'Rococo' (10)	CBro ERCP LAma LCro LOPS NBri SDeJ
'Roi du Midi' (5)	LAma SDeJ
'Ronaldo' (3)	ERCP GKev LAma LCro LOPS NNys SDir
'Rosalie' (3)	LAma
'Rose des Dames' (5)	LAma
'Rosy Delight' (4) **new**	CAvo
'Rosy Dream' (13)	LAma SDeJ
'Roulette' (3)	LAma
'Royal Acres' (2)	LAma
'Royal Anthos' (14) **new**	SDeJ
'Royal Elegance' (7)	LAma
'Russian Princess' (4) 𝕐H6 **new**	MGib
'Ruud Lubbers' (14)	LAma
'Sahara Rally' (4)	LAma
'Salmon Impression' PBR (4)	GKev LAma NBri SDeJ
'Salmon Jewel' (3)	EPot
'Salmon Parrot' (10)	LAma
'Salut' (13)	LAma
'Sanne' (3)	CAvo ERCP LAma SDeJ
'Sapporro' (6)	ERCP GKev LAma LCro LOPS NBri
saxatilis (15)	CBro ECho EPfP GKev LAma LCro LOPS SDeJ SDir
§ - Bakeri Group (15)	MPie SCob SDir SEND
§ - - 'Lilac Wonder' (15) 𝕐H6	CAby CBro ECho EPot ERCP GKev LAma LCro LOPS NPer SCob SDir SPhx WShi WTor
'Scarlet Baby' (12)	EPfP GKev LAma NBri
'Schoonoord' (2)	LAma
schrenkii (15)	EPot ERCP GKev LAma SDir
'Seadov' (3)	LAma LCro SDir
'Seattle' (6) **new**	GKev
'Sensual Touch' (7) 𝕐H6	LAma SDeJ
'Sexy Lady' (10)	LAma
'Shakespeare' (12)	CBro ESps LAma SDeJ
'Shirley' (3)	CAvo ERCP GKev LAma LCro LOPS NBri SCob SDeJ SPer
'Shirley Dream' (3)	LAma SDeJ
'Shirley Flame' (3)	LAma
'Showtime' (14)	SDeJ
'Showwinner' (12) 𝕐H6	CAvo CBro GKev LAma NBri NHol SDeJ SDir
'Signature' (7) **new**	MGib
'Sihouette Bouquet' (3)	LAma
'Silver Dollar' (3)	LAma
'Silver Parrot' (10)	LAma LCro LOPS
'Silverado' (5)	LAma
'Silverstream' (4)	LAma
'Sinopel' (8)	LAma
'Snow Crystal' (11) **new**	SDir
'Snow Parrot' (10)	ERCP
'Snowboard' (3)	LAma
'Snowpeak' (5)	LAma
sogdiana (15)	ECho GKev LAma LLHF
'Sorbet' (5) 𝕐H6	GKev LAma SDeJ
sosnowskyi (15)	GKev
sprengeri (15) 𝕐H6	CAvo CBro CLAP CSpe CTca ECha ECho ERCP GKev LAma LLHF WHal WShi
- Trotter's form (15)	WCot
'Spring Green' (8) 𝕐H6	CAvo CBro EPfP ERCP GKev LAma LCro LOPS NBri NNys SCob SDeJ SPer SPhx
'Spryng' (3) 𝕐H6	SDeJ
'Starfighter' (7)	SDeJ
stellata	see *T. clusiana* var. *stellata*
'Stockholm' (2) 𝕐H6	LAma
'Stresa' (12) 𝕐H6	CAvo CBro GKev LAma LRHS NBri NRHS SDeJ
'Striped Sail' (3)	LAma
'Strong Gold' (3) 𝕐H6	LAma MGib SDeJ
'Stunning Apricot' (5)	LAma LCro LOPS SDir
subpraestans (15)	LAma
'Sugar Love' (3) **new**	NNys
'Sun Dance' (14)	LAma
'Sun Lover' (11)	LAma
'Sunny Prince' PBR (1)	CBro
'Super Parrot' (10)	LAma
'Survivor' (5)	NNys SDeJ
'Swan Wings' (7)	ERCP GKev LAma LCro LOPS SDeJ
'Sweet Desire' (2)	SDeJ
'Sweet Harmony' (5)	LAma
'Sweet Impression' (4) **new**	GKev
'Sweet Lady' (14)	LAma SDeJ
'Sweetheart' (13)	GKev LAma LCro LOPS NBri SDeJ
'Sweety' (3)	LAma
sylvestris (15)	CAby CAvo CBro CSpe CTca ECho EPfP EPot ERCP GKev LAma LCro MGib NBir SDeJ SDir SPhx WCot WShi
'Sylvia Warder' (14)	LAma
'Synaeda King' (6) 𝕐H6	LAma
'Synaeda Orange' (6)	LAma
systola (15)	GKev LAma
'Taco' (15)	GKev LAma
'Talisman' ambig.	LAma
'Talisman' (5)	GKev
'Talisman' (9) **new**	SDir
'Tarafa' (14)	LAma
tarda (15) 𝕐H5	CAvo CBro ECho EPfP ERCP GKev LAma LCro LOPS LPot LRHS NBri NRHS SDeJ SDir SPhx WShi
'Temple of Beauty' (5) 𝕐H6	GKev LAma NNys SDeJ
'Tennessee' (3)	LAma
'Tequila Sun' (3)	LAma
tetraphylla (15)	ECho LAma
'Texas Flame' (10)	GKev LAma NBri SDeJ
'Texas Gold' (10)	LAma SDeJ
'The First' (12)	GKev LAma NBri
'The Lizard' (9)	LAma SDir
'Theeroos' (2)	LAma SDir
'Tinka' (15) 𝕐H6	CMea ECho GKev LAma SCob SDir
'Tiny Timo' (15)	GKev LLHF
'Tom Pouce' (3)	LCro LOPS
'Ton Angustinus' (4)	LAma
'Toplips' (11)	LAma SDeJ
'Topparrot' (10)	LAma SDeJ
'Toronto' (14) 𝕐H6	CAvo LAma NBri SCob SDeJ
'Toronto Double' (2)	GKev LAma SDeJ
'Toucan' (3)	LAma

	'Toyota' (5)	SDeJ
	'Très Chic' (6)	CAvo CTca EPfP GKev LAma LCro LOPS
	'Tricolored Beauty' (8)	GKev
	'Trinket' (14) ♀H6	LAma
	'Tropical Dream' (3)	LAma
	'Tropical Lady' (3)	LAma
	tschimganica (15)	GKev LAma
	tubergeniana (15)	LAma
	- 'Keukenhof' (15)	GKev
	turkestanica (15) ♀H5	CAby CBro CHid CTca ECho EPfP EPot ERCP GKev LAma LPot NBri NPer SDeJ WHoo WShi
	'Turkish Delight' (14)	NPer
	'Twilight Princess' (8)	LAma
	'Typhoon' (3)	CMea GKev LAma
	'Uncle Tom' (11)	CAvo ERCP GKev LAma NBri SDeJ
§	***undulatifolia*** (15)	GKev
	- 'Clare Benedict' (15)	GKev
	- 'Excelsa' (15)	GKev
	'Unique de France'PBR **new**	CAvo
	'United States' (14)	LAma NPer
	'Up Rosar' (11) **new**	ERCP
	'Upstar' (11)	LAma
	urumiensis (15) ♀H5	CHid ECho EPot GKev LAma LPot SDeJ SPhx
§	***urumoffii*** (15)	ECho LAma
	'Valentine' (3)	LAma SDeJ
	'Valery Gergiev' (7)	ERCP LAma
	'Van der Neer' (1)	GKev SDeJ
	'Van Eijk'PBR (4)	LAma NBri SCob
	'Vanilla Cream' (14) **new**	CAby
	'Velvet Lily' (6)	GKev
	'Verandi' (3) **new**	GKev
	'Verona' (2)	GKev LAma NNys SDeJ
	'Véronique Sanson' (3)	ERCP LCro LOPS SDeJ
	'Victoria' (1) **new**	GKev
	'Victoria's Secret' (3)	LCro LOPS NNys
	'Viking' (2)	LAma
	'Vincent van Gogh' (7)	LAma
	violacea	see *T. humilis* Violacea Group
	'Violet Beauty' (5)	GKev LAma LCro SDeJ
	'Violet Bird' (8)	LAma LCro LOPS SDeJ
	'Virichic' (8)	ERCP GKev LAma LCro LOPS MCot SDir
	viridiflora 'Red Hue' **new**	GKev
	'Vivex' (4)	LAma
	'Vivienne Westwood' (10)	LOPS
	vvedenskyi (15)	ECho EPot GKev
	- 'Bernadette' (15)	LAma
	- 'Tangerine Beauty' (15) ♀H6	ECho GKev LAma
	'Wallflower' (5)	LAma
	'Wapen van Leiden' (1)	LAma
	'Warbler' (7)	LAma SDeJ
	'Washington' (3)	GKev LCro
	'Weber's Parrot' (10)	LAma MCot
	'Weisse Berliner' (3)	CBro GKev LAma
	'West Point' (6)	CAvo CBro CTca GKev LAma LCro LOPS SDeJ
*	'White Bouquet' (5)	LAma
	'White Dream' (3)	GKev LAma LCro LOPS NBri SDeJ
	'White Elegance' (6)	LAma
	'White Emperor'	see *T.* 'Purissima'
	'White Fire' (14) **new**	GKev
	'White Lieberstar'	ERCP
	'White Marvel' (3)	GKev LAma LRHS NRHS
	'White Parrot' (10)	CAvo ERCP GKev LAma LCro LOPS SDeJ SDir
	'White Sea' (13)	LAma
	'White Triumphator' (6) ♀H6	CAvo CBro CMea ERCP GKev LAma LCro LOPS NBir NNys SDeJ SPhx
	whittallii	see *T. orphanidea* Whittallii Group
	'Wildhof' (3) ♀H6	ERCP SDir
	'Wilja' (5) **new**	GKev
§	'Willem van Oranje' (2)	LAma LRHS NRHS SDeJ
	'Willemsoord' (2)	LAma LRHS NRHS SDeJ
	William of Orange	see *T.* 'Willem van Oranje'
	wilsoniana	see *T. montana*
	'Winterberg' (3)	LAma
	'Wirosa' (11) ♀H6	NBri
	'Wisley' (5)	LCro SCob
	'World Expression' (5) ♀H6	LAma SDeJ
	'Yellow Crown' (3)	LAma
	'Yellow Flight' (3)	LAma SDeJ
	'Yellow Pompenette'PBR (11) ♀H6	SDeJ
	'Yellow Present' (3)	LAma
I	'Yellow Purissima' (13) ♀H6	LAma SDir
	'Yellow Springgreen' (8)	CBro ERCP GKev LAma LCro LOPS SDeJ
	'Yellow Wave' (4)	LAma SDir
	'Yoko Parrot' (10)	SDeJ
	'Yokohama' (3)	GKev LAma NBri SCob SDeJ SPer
	'Yonina' (6)	LAma LCro LOPS NBri
	'Zampa' (14) ♀H6	LAma
	'Zombie' (13)	LAma
	'Zomerschoon' (5)	LAma
§	'Zurel' (3)	ERCP GKev LAma SCob SDir

tummelberry see *Rubus* 'Tummelberry'

Tunica see *Petrorhagia*

Tupistra (*Asparagaceae*)

	aurantiaca	LEdu
	- B&SWJ 2267	WCot WCru
	- B&SWJ 2401	WCru
	chinensis 'Eco China Ruffles'	WCot
	grandistigma	WCot
	- B&SWJ 11773	WCru
	jinshanensis	WCot
	urotepala HWJ 562	WCru
	wattii B&SWJ 8297	WCru

Tussilago (*Asteraceae*)

	farfara	GPoy MHer NMir WHer WSFF

Tweedia (*Apocynaceae*)

§	***coerulea*** ♀H1c	CBcs CCCN CDTJ CFlo CKel CSpe LRHS SPad SWvt

Typha (*Typhaceae*)

	angustifolia	CBen CKno CWat LLWG MMuc MSKA NPer SEND SPlb SWat WMAq WPnP
	latifolia	CBen CWat MSKA NBir NPer SVic SWat WMAq WPnP XLum
	- 'Variegata' (v)	CWat LLWG MSKA MWts NPla WMAq
§	***laxmannii***	CBen LLWG MSKA WMAq WPnP XLum
	lugdunensis	MWts
	minima	CBen CWat EHoe MSKA MWts NPer SWat WMAq WPnP XLum
	shuttleworthii	CBen LLWG
	stenophylla	see *T. laxmannii*

Typhonium (*Araceae*)

giganteum CAby SKHP WCot
horsfieldii LEdu MPie WCot
roxburghii LTro
trilobatum WCot
venosum EUJe LTro

Typhonodorum (*Araceae*)

lindleyanum XBlo

U

Uapaca (*Euphorbiaceae*)

kirkiana (F) XBlo

Uccerodendron (*Hamamelidaceae*)

* ***whartonii*** WCru
B&SWJ 11706 new

ugli see *Citrus* × *aurantium* Tangelo Group 'Ugli'

Ugni ✿ (*Myrtaceae*)

candollei SVen
§ ***molinae*** CBcs CBod CDul CHll CRos CTsd EBee ELan EPfP EShb GMcL IDee IVic LEdu LRHS MGil MGos MHer SAdn SBrt SChF SEle SWvt WGwG WHar WJek
- PAB 1347 LEdu
- 'Butterball' CBcs EBee EPfP LRHS LSou SPoG SWvt
- 'Flambeau' (v) CAgr CBcs CBod CCht CDul CMac CRos ELan EPfP EShb IVic LEdu LRHS MAsh MGil NLar SEle SLon SPoG SRkn SWvt
- 'Ka-Pow' new LCro SCob
- orange-leaved SRms WJek
- 'Variegata' (v) LEdu WJek
- 'Villarica Strawberry' new WPGP

Ulex (*Papilionaceae*)

europaeus CArn CBcs CCVT CDul CHab CMac CTri ECrN ELan EPfP ESps GMcL LBuc MCoo MGil MGos MMuc NBes NWea SCob SEWo SPer WHar
§ - 'Flore Pleno' (d) ♀H4 CBcs CBod CDul CLet CMac CSBt CTri ELan EPfP GCal IArd MBlu MGos MMuc NWea SCob SEND SPer WFar WHer
- 'Plenus' see *U. europaeus* 'Flore Pleno'
gallii NLar
- 'Mizen Head' GCal

Ullucus (*Basellaceae*)

tuberosus LEdu

Ulmus ✿ (*Ulmaceae*)

americana 'Princeton' SEWo
carpinifolia var. ***suberosa*** CDul
chenmoui IArd WPGP
'Columella' SAko
davidiana WPGP
- var. ***japonica*** new WPGP
'Dodoens' IArd MBlu SCoo
'Frontier' SGol WPGP
§ ***glabra*** CDul EGFP EPfP MJak NWea SCob SCoo WTSh
- 'Camperdownii' CMac ECrN ELan ESps WMou
- 'Exoniensis' IVic
- 'Horizontalis' see *U. glabra* 'Pendula'
- 'Lutescens' CTho CTri NOra NWea SCoo SEWo WMat
§ - 'Pendula' CMac
× ***hollandica*** EGFP
§ - 'Dampieri Aurea' ♀H6 CDul CTho EBee ELan EPfP LBuc LRHS MAsh MBlu MGos MRav NLar NWea SCob SPer SPoG WMat WPat
- 'Jacqueline Hillier' CDul CMac CSpe ECho ELan LRHS MMuc NLar SEND SGol WCFE WFar WPat
- 'Major' new EGFP
- 'Wredei' see *U.* × *hollandica* 'Dampieri Aurea'
'Homestead' new WPGP
laevis CDul WPGP
'Lobel' CCVT
Lutèce = 'Nanguen' SGol
minor CDul
- 'Dampieri Aurea' see *U.* × *hollandica* 'Dampieri Aurea'
montana see *U. glabra*
'Morfeo'PBR WMat
parvifolia CAco CMen WPGP
- 'Frosty' (v) ECho
- 'Geisha' (v) ECho ELan MAsh WPat
§ - 'Hokkaido' CMen EPot EWes SIgm WAbe WFar
- 'Pygmaea' see *U. parvifolia* 'Hokkaido'
- 'Yatsubusa' ECho GEdr MRav
plotii new EGFP
procera CDul EMOT MCoo MGos SLon WSFF
- 'Argenteovariegata' (v) NLar
pumila 'Beijing Gold' ELan NLar
'Regal'PBR WPGP
rubra CArn
'Sapporo Autumn Gold' CCVT EBee MRav SGol WCFE
szechuanica new WPGP
uyematsui WPGP
Vada = 'Wanoux'PBR SGol
villosa new WPGP

Umbellularia (*Lauraceae*)

californica IDee SAko WPGP

Umbilicus (*Crassulaceae*)

rupestris CArn SChr WHer WShi

Uncinia (*Cyperaceae*)

* ***cyparissias*** from Chile NBir
egmontiana EPfP LRHS NRHS NWad WGrn WMoo
erinacea GCal
rubra Widely available
§ - 'Belinda's Find'PBR CHid CKno EBee ELan ESwi IBoy LRHS MAsh MHol NLar NRHS SPoG
- Everflame see *U. rubra* 'Belinda's Find'
uncinata CBcs ECha SDix
* - ***rubra*** CBod CKno CTri ELon ESps IFro MAsh SCob SLim SRms SWvt

Uniola (*Poaceae*)

latifolia see *Chasmanthium latifolium*

Urginea (*Asparagaceae*)

macrocentra	ECho
maritima	EBee ECho GKev LAma WCot
ollivieri	CTal ECho
undulata	ECho GKev

Urospermum (*Asteraceae*)

dalechampii	CCCN CSam

Ursinia (*Asteraceae*)

alpina	CPBP

Urtica (*Urticaceae*)

dioica 'Bradfield Purpler'	CNat
- 'Chedglow 2' (v)	CNat
- OGG mutant	CNat
- 'Winter Yellow'	CNat

Utricularia (*Lentibulariaceae*)

sp.	EECP
alpina	SHmp
australis	EFEx
biloba	CHew
bisquamata	SHmp
- 'Betty's Bay' 🏆H2	CHew
calycifida	SHmp
dichotoma	CHew EFEx
exoleta R. Brown	see *U. gibba*
§ ***gibba***	EFEx
heterosepala	CHew
intermedia	EFEx
lateriflora	CHew EFEx
livida 🏆H2	CHew EFEx NLos SHmp
longifolia	SHmp
menziesii	EFEx
microcalyx	CHew
monanthos	CHew EFEx
nephrophylla	CHew
novae-zelandiae	CHew
ochroleuca	EFEx
paulineae	CHew
praelonga	CHew SHmp
prehensilis	CHew
reniformis	EFEx SHmp
I - ***nana***	EFEx
sandersonii 🏆H2	CHew NLos SHmp
simplex	CHew
subulata	EFEx
tricolor	CHew SHmp
uniflora	CHew
vulgaris	EFEx
warburgii	CHew
welwitschii	CHew

Uvularia (*Colchicaceae*)

§ ***caroliniana***	ECho
disporum	ECho
grandiflora 🏆H5	Widely available
- dwarf	ECho
- gold-leaved	CAby CBct MAvo
- 'Lynda Windsor'	CTal LEdu SKHP
- orange-flowered	SKHP
- var. ***pallida***	CAby CAvo CBct CLAP CTal EBee ECho EHrv EPPr EPfP EPot GBin GCal GEdr IBlr ILea LEdu LRHS MRav NCGa NHar NPnk WCru WPnP
- 'Susie Lewis'	WCru
grandiflora × ***perfoliata***	ECho NBir
perfoliata	CAby CBct CLAP CTal EBee ECha ECho EPPr EPfP EPot GBuc GKev IBlr IMou LEdu MRav NBir NHpl NPnk WCru
- tall	EPPr
pudica	see *U. caroliniana*
sessilifolia	CBct CTal ECho EPfP GEdr GKev IMou LEdu LRHS MMrt WCru
- 'Cobblewood Gold' (v)	EPPr LEdu WCru
- 'Variegata' (v) **new**	GKev

V

Vaccinium ✿ (*Ericaceae*)

arctostaphylos	SWvt
'Berkeley' (F)	CAgr CCCN CEnd CWib GKin LSRN MAsh MBlu NPla SDea SPre WHar
Blue Suede = 'Th-682' **new**	LCro
'Bluejay' (F)	CRos CWib ELan LRHS MAsh NRHS SCoo SLon SPoG WHar
'Blueray' (F)	CWib GKin SDea
'Brigitta' (F)	CEnd CTrh EMil EPom GTwe NPla SPoG SPre
chaetothrix	WAbe WThu
'Chandler' (F)	CAgr CArg CEnd CMac CTrh EMil EPom GKin LCro LOPS LRHS LSRN NPla SKee
consanguineum B&SWJ 10486	WCru
corymbosum (F)	CBcs MNHC SCoo SSta
- 'Aurora'[PBR] (F)	LCro LOPS
- 'Blauweiss-Goldtraube' (F)	CAgr CSBt CWib EPfP ESps ESwi GKin LSRN MAsh NLar NPri SDea SPoG SVic WHar WTSh
- 'Blue Duke' (F)	LSRN SFrt
- 'Blue Pearl' (F)	LBuc SFrt
- 'Bluecrop' (F)	Widely available
- 'Bluegold' (F)	CRos LRHS MAsh NRHS SFrt SPoG
- 'Bluetta' (F)	CAgr CTri CWib ELan GTwe SCoo SPoG
- 'Coville' (F)	CWib NLar
- 'Darrow' (F)	CAgr CFGn NPla SBdl WMat
- 'Dixie' (F)	CSBt NPla
- 'Duke' (F) 🏆H6	CArg CMac CTrh CWib ELan EPfP EPom IBoy LCro LOPS MGos NPla NWea SDea SPre SRkn WHar
- 'Elliott' (F)	LRHS LSRN SPer
- 'Hardyblue' (F)	CAgr
- 'Heerma' (F)	NLar
- 'Jersey' (F)	CAgr CEnd CRos CWib EPfP LRHS MAsh MGos MMuc NPla NRHS SCoo SDea SPer SPoG SVic WHar
- 'Nelson' (F)	NPla SCoo
- 'Nui' (F)	CEnd EPom LSRN MRav
- 'Patriot' (F)	CAgr CEnd CRos CSBt CTrh CWib ECrN EMOT EPom ESps GKin GQue GTwe LBuc LRHS MGos MPkF MRav NPla NPri NRHS SBdl SCoo SDea SHil SPer SPoG SPre WMat
- 'Polaris' (F)	CEnd
- 'Reka' (F)	CAgr NPer
- 'Spartan' (F) 🏆H6	CTrh CWib EPom GTwe LCro LOPS LRHS LSRN MGos NPla SKee
- 'Stanley' (F)	CRos EPfP LRHS NRHS SPoG
- 'Toro' (F)	GTwe LRHS NPla SFrt SPre

- 'Weymouth' (F)	SDea
crassifolium subsp. ***sempervirens*** 'Well's Delight' (F)	LRHS MAsh
cylindraceum ♀H5	CBcs CEnd NLar WPGP WPat
- 'Tinkerbell'	ITim
delavayi	CRos LRHS MAsh NHar NLar WThu
dunalianum	WCru
var. ***caudatifolium*** B&SWJ 1716	
- var. ***megaphyllum*** HWJ 515	WCru
'Earliblue' (F)	CAgr CFGn CMac CSBt GKin NPla SBdl SDea SFrt SPoG WMat
floribundum	CBcs CMHG GMcL LRHS MAsh WPat
glaucoalbum ♀H5	CAbP CMac EBee EPfP LRHS MAsh MBlu MRav SPoG WBod WPGP WPat
'Goldtraube 71'	EMOT MAsh NPla
griffithianum	SSta
'Herbert' (F)	CAgr CMac EPom LBuc
macrocarpon (F)	CArn ELan GTwe LRHS MAsh NHar NRHS SDea SPre SRms
- 'Centennial' (F)	NHar
- 'CN' (F)	CAgr NLar
- 'Early Black' (F)	ELan EMOT EPom GKin IDee NLar SVic WTSh
- 'Franklin' (F)	CAgr
- 'Hamilton'	WThu
- 'Howes' (F)	NHar
- 'Langlois' (F)	NLar
- 'Olson's Honkers' (F)	CAgr NLar
- 'Pilgrim' (F)	CAgr CFGn CMac EMOT GEdr GKin LCro LEdu LOPS LRHS MAsh MCoo NHar WHar WMat
- 'Red Star' (F)	CTrh
- 'Stevens' (F)	CAgr
moupinense	GEdr LRHS MAsh WThu
myrtillus	CAgr EPom GPoy SVic
'Northland' (F)	CSBt CWib EMOT EPfP EPom GQue GTwe NLar NPla NPri SBdl SCoo SDea SPoG WMat
nummularia	GEdr LRHS NHar NLar WAbe WThu
ovatum	CBcs CMHG CMac CTsd GKev GKin WPat WThu
- 'Thundercloud'	CAbP EPfP LRHS MAsh
§ ***oxycoccos*** (F)	CAgr GPoy MCoo NHar WThu
'Ozarkblue' (F)	EPom GTwe LCro LOPS LSRN
pallidum	IBlr
palustre	see *V. oxycoccos*
'Pink Lemonade'	ELan EPom LCro LOPS LRHS NPri SPer
'Pinkberry' (F) new	LRHS
retusum	WThu
'Spring Surprise'	WAbe
'Sunrise' (F)	GTwe
'Sunshine Blue' (F)	CAgr CEnd CTrh ELan EPom LBuc LRHS SDea
'Tophat' (F)	CCCN LEdu MPkF
vitis-idaea	EPfP EWes GPoy NWea SVic
- 'Aalshorst'	NLar
- 'Autumn Beauty'	NLar
- 'Compactum'	EWes
- 'Erntetraum'	NLar
- 'Ida'	LBuc
- Koralle Group ♀H5	CAgr EPot GKin GMcL NLar NWad
- 'Leucocarpa'	NLar
- subsp. ***minus***	GEdr NLar WThu
- 'Red Candy'	ELan EPfP LCro LOPS LRHS MJak MSCN NLar NRHS SCob
- 'Red Pearl'	CSBt EPom LRHS MAsh NLar
- 'Red Shank'	ITim

Vachellia (*Mimosaceae*)

§ ***karroo***	CDTJ SPlb

Valeriana (*Caprifoliaceae*)

'Alba'	see *Centranthus ruber* 'Albus'
alliariifolia	CSam GCal MSpe NBro
- PAB 3001	LEdu WPGP
'Coccinea'	see *Centranthus ruber*
dioica	LLWG
hardwickii PAB 8999	LEdu
jatamansi	GPoy SRms WJek
- PAB 6846	LEdu WPGP
montana	LEdu MMuc NBro NRya SEND SRms SWat
officinalis	Widely available
- subsp. ***sambucifolia***	EPPr GCal MNrw MSpe SHar
phu 'Aurea'	CArn CBod CDor CHby CMac EBee ECha EHoe EHrv ELan EPfP GKin LHop LRHS MCot MRav NBid NBir NBro NEgg NLar NRHS NSti NWad SDix SPer SPoG SRms WCAu WMoo
pyrenaica	EBee ECha EHrv EPPr EWTr GCal LRHS MAvo MMuc MNrw SDix SEND SHar SPhx WCot WHil WHrl WMoo
supina	CPBP
wallrothii	WCot

Valerianella (*Caprifoliaceae*)

§ ***locusta***	CBod GPoy SVic
olitoria	see *V. locusta*

Vallea (*Elaeocarpaceae*)

stipularis	CTsd

Vallisneria (*Hydrocharitaceae*)

americana new	XBlo
asiatica var. ***biwaensis***	XBlo
gigantea	XBlo
spiralis	XBlo
- 'Tortifolia'	XBlo

Vallota see *Cyrtanthus*

Vancouveria (*Berberidaceae*)

chrysantha	CFil CTal EBee EPPr EPfP GBuc GEdr GLog MRav NRya SKHP SMad WMoo WPGP
hexandra	CFil CMac CTal ECha EHrv EPPr EPfP EWld GBuc GEdr GKev GLog ILea LEdu NBir NSti SKHP SPhx WCru WMoo WPGP
planipetala	CTal IMou WCru

Vania see *Thlaspi*

veitchberry see *Rubus* 'Veitchberry'

Veltheimia ✿ (*Asparagaceae*)

§ ***bracteata*** ♀H2	CCse CLak CPne ECho EPri GKev LRHS NRog SDir
- 'Lemon Flame'	ECho GKev NRog SDir
- yellow-flowered	CPne NRog
§ ***capensis*** ♀H2	CBlu NRog
viridifolia misapplied	see *V. capensis*
viridifolia Jacq.	see *V. bracteata*

× *Venidioarctotis* see *Arctotis*

Venidium see *Arctotis*

Veratrilla (*Gentianaceae*)

baillonii	GEdr

Veratrum (*Melanthiaceae*)

album ♀H7	EBee ECha GKev GPoy ILea MAvo MNrw MRav NBid WCru WSHC
- PAB 537	LEdu
- 'Auvergne White' new	EBee MNrw
- var. ***flavum***	MNrw SPhx WCot WCru
- subsp. ***lobelianum***	GCal
- 'Lorna's Green'	EBee GCal MNrw WCot
- var. ***oxysepalum***	WCru
californicum	EBee ECha GCal MNrw NBid SMad WCru WWFP
formosanum	EBee MNrw WSHC
- B&SWJ 1575	WCru
- RWJ 9806	WCru
grandiflorum B&SWJ 4416	WCru
longebracteatum	WCru
maackii	EBee GCal MNrw
- B&SWJ 5875	WCru
- green-flowered	GCal
- var. ***japonicum***	MNrw WCru
- var. ***maackii***	MNrw
- - B&SWJ 5831	WCru
nigrum ♀H7	CBct EBee ECha GCal GEdr GMaP ILea LEdu LRHS MAvo MNrw MRav NBid NBir SMad SPhx SPlb WCot WCru WPnP WWFP
- B&SWJ 4450 from South Korea	WCru
schindleri	GEdr MNrw
- B&SWJ 4068	WCru
stamineum	WCru
viride	EBee EWes GCal MNrw NBid WCot WCru

Verbascum (*Scrophulariaceae*)

'Annie May'	LSRN
'Arctic Summer'	see *V. bombyciferum* 'Polarsommer'
arcturus	SVen
'Argentina' new	WHer
'Bill Bishop'	ECho
blattaria	GJos NBir SPav SWat WHer
- f. ***albiflorum***	CSpe IFro LLWP NDov NGBl SPlb WHer WMoo
- yellow-flowered	SPav SWat
'Blue Lagoon'	CSpe CWGN EBee EPfP SCob
'Blushing Bride'PBR	LLHF
§ ***bombyciferum***	CBod CBre ECha ELan GMaP LRHS NGBl SCob SEND
* - 'Arctic Snow'	SPav SPoG
§ - 'Polarsommer'	CSpe EPfP GJos LCro LRHS NBir SPer SWat
- 'Silver Lining'	NPer
'Broussa'	see *V. bombyciferum*
'Buttercup'	CRos LRHS NRHS SHil
'Camelot'	LRHS NRHS
'Caribbean Crush'	ECtt ELan GJos IBoy LRHS NRHS SPer SPoG WTor
chaixii	CSam ECha MMrt NBir SDix WFar WMoo
- 'Album'	Widely available
- 'Sixteen Candles'	CBod GJos MBNS WFar
- 'Wedding Candles'	CBod CWld ELan GWyn NGdn SPtp WFar
'Cherry Helen'PBR	GMcL IKil LCro LOPS LRHS LSRN NLar SCob
'Christo's Yellow Lightning' ♀H7	CBod CSpe EBee ECha ECtt GAbr MHol MPie SDix SMad WCot WRHF
'Clementine'	CBcs CMos CRos EBee ECtt ELan EPfP ILea LRHS NPnk SBee SCob SHil SPhx WHil
'Coneyhill Yellow'	EPPr
(Cotswold Group) 'Cotswold Beauty'	CSam CSpe ECtt EPfP EWoo LRHS MRav NDov NGdn SHar SPer WHoo
- 'Cotswold Queen'	CBod CSam ECtt ELan EPPr EPed EPfP IBoy LRHS MRav MWat NDov NNys SHar SPer SWvt
- 'Gainsborough' ♀H6	CSBt EAEE ECha ECtt EHrv ELan EPed EPfP EWoo GMaP GMcL IBoy LHop LRHS LSRN LSun MJak MRav NLar NSti SCob SDix SGbt SPer SPoG SWat SWvt WCAu WHil
- 'Mont Blanc'	LRHS SWat
- 'Pink Domino' ♀H6	CBod CSam ECtt ELan EPPr EPfP GMaP LCro LOPS LRHS MAvo MJak MRav NSti SPer SWvt WWFP
- 'Royal Highland'	CSam ECtt ELan EPed EPfP LRHS SWvt
'Cotswold King'	see *V. creticum*
§ ***creticum***	CSpe IKil WCot
'Dark Eyes'PBR	CWGN ECtt GMcL NHpl SCob
§ ***densiflorum***	CArn EAJP
dumulosum ♀H4	WAbe
epixanthinum ♀H5	CPla EBee
'Flower of Scotland'	MBNS
'Golden Wings' ♀H4	CPla WAbe
'Guinevere'	CRos LRHS NRHS
'Helen Johnson'	CWCL EAEE ECtt ELan GMcL LRHS LSRN MGos MRav NLar NPri SCob SCoo SPer SRkn SWvt
× ***hybridum*** 'Banana Custard'	NGBl
- 'Copper Rose'	EBee LRHS MHer
- 'Snow Maiden'	CTri CWld EPfP
'Hyde Hall Sunrise'	EPfP
'Jackie'	ECtt ELan GMcL LRHS LSRN SCob SCoo
'Jackie in Pink'	LRHS SHil
'Jackie in Yellow'PBR	LLHF
'Jester'	CBcs CWld GMcL LRHS MBNS SCob SHil
'June Johnson'	EAEE ECtt LRHS NPnk
'Kynaston'	LRHS MBNS
'Lavender Lass'	GMcL IKil LCro MHol SPer
'Letitia' ♀H4	CPla CRos ECho ECtt ELan EPot EWes GCal LRHS NRHS SWvt WAbe WCot WTor
levanticum new	GJos
'Linda'	ECtt
longifolium var. ***pannosum***	see *V. olympicum*
lychnitis	SPhx
lydium	EBee
'Megan's Mauve'	EAEE
'Merlin'PBR	EAEE ECtt EPed LRHS LSRN MBNS
nigrum	CArn CHab EBee NGdn NLar WHer WMoo
- var. ***album***	GJos MArt NChi NGdn NLar WMoo
§ ***olympicum***	CBcs CBod ELan EPfP ESps GJos IBoy LPot LRHS MBNS MMuc NGBl SCob SDix SEND SVen WCot WHar
'Petra'	LRHS SPhx
phlomoides	SPhx

phoeniceum	CBcs CSBt EBee ELan EPfP GJos NBid NBro SIgm SPlb SPoG WFar WMoo
* - 'Album'	CSpe
- 'Flush of White'	CBot EAJP EPfP EWTr GMcL GQue MArt NGBl NGdn NLar SCob WHar WHil WMoo WWFP
- hybrids	CTri GMaP NEgg NGdn SRms SWat WFar
- 'Rosetta'	CBod EAJP EPfP GWyn MArt NGBl NGdn
- 'Violetta'	CBWd CBod CBot CCVN CSpe EAJP EPPr EPfP GBin IBoy LCro LRHS MArt MHol MSpe MWat NChi NEgg NGBl NGdn SGbt SPav SPer SPhx WCFE WHlf WMoo
'Pink Kisses'	LLHF LRHS LSRN MBNS SBee
'Pink Petticoats'	EBee LBuc LRHS
(Pixie Series) 'Pixie Apricot'	SBee
- 'Pixie Blue'	EBee LRHS SHil
'Plum Smokey'PBR	ECtt IBoy LLHF
'Primrose Path'	EPfP GMcL LRHS NLar NRHS WTor
pyramidatum	EBee SPhx
'Queen of Hearts'	LRHS NRHS
'Raspberry Ripple'	LLHF MHer MRav
'Rosie'	NHpl SCob
'Sierra Sunset'	IKil LRHS NLar SPad
'Southern Charm'	EPfP GMaP NQui WHar WHil WPtf
'Spica'	CBot LRHS
'Sugar Plum'PBR	ECtt ELon GMcL LBuc LLHF NPnk
'Summer Sorbet'	CBcs ECtt MNrw SPoG
'Temptress Purple'	CBot WTor
thapsiforme	see *V. densiflorum*
thapsus	CHab ENfk GJos GPoy MNHC NBir NMir SEND SRms
'Tropic Sun' ♀H5	WHoo
'Wessex'	LRHS NRHS

Verbena (Verbenaceae)

(Aztec Series) Aztec Pearl = 'Balazpearl'PBR (G)	SCoo
- Aztec Plum Magic = 'Balazplum'PBR (G)	NPri
- Aztec Red = 'Balazred' (G)	SCoo
- Aztec Silver Magic = 'Balazsilma'PBR (G)	NPri SCoo
'Blue Prince' (G)	CSpe
§ ***bonariensis*** ♀H4	Widely available
- 'Little One'	MAsh
- 'Lollipop'PBR	Widely available
brasiliensis misapplied	see *V. bonariensis*
chamaedrifolia	see *V. peruviana*
§ 'Claret' (G)	CMac CSpe EAJP EBee ECtt EHrv ELan EPfP LRHS LSRN LSou MNrw NRHS SCoo SPhx SPoG
'Corsage Peach' (Corsage Series) (G/d)	LRHS
corymbosa	CAby CHid CHll CWld EBee ECha EWoo LRHS SPer SPhx WMoo
- 'Gravetye'	LPot
'Diamond Merci' (G)	WHoo
'Edith Eddleman' (G)	CMac CWGN EPfP LRHS NRHS SPoG
elegans	NDov
(Empress Series) Empress Flair Burgundy = 'Duefarburg'PBR (G)	LBMP
- Empress Flair Red = 'Duempflare'PBR (G)	LBMP
- Empress Flair Royal Blue = 'Duempflarobu'PBR (G)	LBMP
- Empress Flair Violet Blue = 'Duempflavibu'PBR (G)	LBMP
- Empress Flair White = 'Duempflawi'PBR (G)	LBMP
- Empress Hot Pink Charme = 'Duemphopich'PBR (G)	LBMP
- Empress Lavender Blue = 'Duemplavbu'PBR (G)	LBMP
- Empress Peach Flair (G)	LBMP
- Empress Soft Pink Charme (G)	LBMP
Estrella Voodoo Pink Star = 'Wesverepista'	LBMP
Estrella Voodoo Red Star = 'Wesverevoo'PBR	LBMP
(Fuego Series) Fuego Blues Dark Purple (G)	LBMP
- Fuego Pink = 'Kleve04334'PBR (G)	LBMP
- Fuego Red with Eye = 'Klevp10409'PBR (G)	LBMP
- Fuego Violet with Eye = 'Klevp07355'PBR (G)	LBMP
gooddingii (G)	EBee
'Hammerstein Pink'	EBee EPfP
hastata	CSpe EBee ECtt EPfP IBoy LEdu LRHS MNrw NSti SCob SPer SPhx SPlb SRms SWat SWvt WCAu WFar WMoo WOut WTcb XLum
* - 'Alba'	CTsd EBee ELan EPfP GCal IBoy NLar SCob SDix WFar WMoo XLum
- 'Blue Spires'	CNor EPfP IPot SCob WHar
- f. ***rosea***	CBre CElw CMea CSpe EHoe ELan EPfP IPot LRHS MNrw MRav NDov SDix SPer SPhx SWat WCAu WFar WHea WMoo WSHC XLum
- - 'Pink Spires'	CBWd EBee ECtt ELan EPfP LHop LRHS SCob
- 'White Spires'	CMea EPfP
'Homestead Purple' (G)	CBod CMac CRos EAJP EBee ECtt ELan ENor EPfP ESps GBin LOPS LRHS LSRN MNrw SCob SDix SRkn SWvt WHoo
'Jenny's Wine'	see *V.* 'Claret'
'La France' (G)	CHGN ECha EPfP LRHS NRHS SDix SMHy SPhx SPoG
Lanai Royal Purple with Eye = 'Lan Roypureye'PBR (Lanai Series) (G)	MCot
Lascar White = 'Kleve04340'PBR (Lascar Series) (G)	LBMP
lasiostachys	EBee
'Lois' Ruby'	see *V.* 'Claret'
macdougalii	WMoo
- 'Lavender Spires'	CSpe LRHS NDov SDix SPhx
officinalis	CArn EBee ENfk GPoy MHer MNHC SIde SRms WHer WJek WSFF WTre
- var. ***grandiflora*** 'Bampton'	CAby CBod CBre CElw CFis CSpe EBee ECha ECtt EWes GBin LEdu LHop LLWG MAvo MHer MNrw MPie NSti WCot WHoo WPGP WSHC
patagonica	see *V. bonariensis*
§ ***peruviana*** (G)	ECho LRHS NRHS SRms XLum
'Pink Bouquet'	see *V.* 'Silver Anne'
'Pink Parfait' (G)	EPfP
Quartz Series	NPri

- 'Quartz Red Polka Dot' ELan EPfP
§ ***rigida*** ♀H3 Widely available
- f. ***lilacina*** 'Lilac Haze' CMac EPfP LBMP LRHS NSti SPoG SRkn
- - 'Polaris' CBod CMea CMos CSam EAJP EBee ELan ELon EPfP EShb LHop LRHS MNrw MPie MRav NRHS SCob SDix SHar SMHy SPer SPoG
scabridoglandulosa see *Junellia succulentifolia*
Seabrook's Lavender = 'Sealav'PBR EBee EPfP ESwi LOPS LRHS NAst SCoo SHar SPer SRkn SWvt
serpyllifolia see *Junellia micrantha*
§ 'Silver Anne' (G) ♀H3 MCot SDix
§ 'Sissinghurst' (G) ♀H2 CSam ECtt SDix SRms
'Strawberry Kiss' EPfP SPoG
stricta EBee EWes NDov NLar SPhx
(Superbena Series) CAby NPri
Superbena Burgundy = 'Usbenal5'PBR (G)
- Superbena Coral Star (G) NPri
- Superbena Peach Blossom = 'Akiv691'PBR (G) **new** NPri
(Tapien Series) Tapien Compact Red = 'Suntapicore'PBR (G) LRHS NRHS
- Tapien Salmon = 'Suntapiro'PBR (G) LSou
- Tapien Sky Blue = 'Suntapilabu'PBR (G) ESps
- Tapien Violet = 'Sunvop'PBR (G) LSou
- Tapien White = 'Suntapipurew'PBR (G) ESps
(Temari Series) Temari Coral Pink = 'Sunmariripi'PBR (G) LSou
- Temari Vanilla = 'Sunmarivani'PBR (G) LSou
'Tenerife' see *V.* 'Sissinghurst'
venosa see *V. rigida*
(Vepita Series) Vepita Blue Violet = 'Invebluvio'PBR **new** NPri
- Vepita Hot Pink NPri

Verbesina (*Asteraceae*)

alternifolia CArn SDix
- 'Goldstrahl' EPPr

Vernicia (*Euphorbiaceae*)

fordii SPlb

Vernonia (*Asteraceae*)

angustifolia* × *missurica WCot
§ ***arkansana*** CHGN CSam EBee ECha ECtt EPPr EWTr EWes GLog IPot LEdu LRHS MAvo NLar SDix SPhx
- 'Alba' EBee ECtt EWTr MAvo
- 'Betty Blindeman' EBee LEdu
- 'Mammuth' CKno EBee ECtt EWTr EWes EWoo GQue ILea IPot LCro LEdu LHop LRHS MNrw MTis SBee SMad SPhx SPoG WCot WTor
baldwinii EBee MAvo SPhx
crinita see *V. arkansana*
fasciculata EWes LEdu LRHS MAvo MRav NLar SPhx WCot
gigantea ELon EWes MMuc MNrw NLar SEND SMad SPhx
glauca SPhx WCot
lettermannii 'Iron Butterfly' EBee IPot SCob
missurica LEdu SPhx
noveboracensis EBee LEdu MAvo NLar SMad XLum
- 'Albiflora' EPPr EWes
- 'White Lightning' **new** MAvo

Veronica (*Plantaginaceae*)

'Amethyst Plume' EBee MHol WFar
amethystina see *V. spuria* L.
anagallis-aquatica LLWG
'Anna'PBR MTis
armena ECho EDAr EWes MHer MMuc SBch SEND SRot WIce XSen
'Atomic Hot Pink' EBee WFar
'Atomic Lilac' LSou
'Atomic Pink' LSou
'Atomic Pink Ray'PBR EBee SHil
'Atomic Pink-White Ray' LBMP
'Atomic Red Ray' SHil
'Atomic Silvery Pink Ray' SHil
'Atomic Sky Ray'PBR LSou SHil
'Atomic Violet Ray'PBR LSou
§ ***austriaca*** EWoo NBre WMoo
- dark blue-flowered NChi
- var. ***dubia*** see *V. prostrata*
- 'Ionian Skies' CMea CTri ECha ECtt EPPr EWTr GBin MMuc NPnk NWad SEND SHar SIgm SPer WIce WKif WSHC
- 'Jacqueline' XSen
§ - subsp. ***teucrium*** CArn CSam CTri EBee ECho SRms WKif
- - 'Blue Fountain' LRHS
- - 'Crater Lake Blue' ♀H6 CDor CMos CRos EBee ECtt ELan EPfP EWld EWoo LEdu LHop LLWG LRHS MAsh MAvo MBel MHol MRav NRHS SPhx SPlb SRms WCot WFar WGwG WSHC
- - 'Kapitän' CRos ECha ECho ECtt GBuc LHop LRHS NGdn NRHS WFar
- - 'Knallblau' EAJP
- - 'Lapis Lazuli' EBee
- - 'Mammuth' IKil
- - 'Royal Blue' ♀H6 CCVN CRos EAJP EBee ECGP EPfP GMaP LRHS MArt MHol NRHS NSti SPer SRms WFar WKif WMoo XLum XSen
- subsp. ***vahlii*** LLHF
'Baby Doll'PBR MBNS
beccabunga CBen CHab CWat EWay GPoy MMuc MSKA MWLS MWts NMir NPer SEND SWat WHer WMAq WSFF
'Bergen's Blue' NLar SHar WSHC
Blue Bouquet see *V. longifolia* 'Blaubündel'
'Blue Indigo' MAvo MNrw NBre NGdn
bombycina ITim WAbe
- subsp. ***bolkardaghensis*** CPBP WAbe
bonarota see *Paederota bonarota*
caespitosa subsp. ***caespitosa*** EPot WAbe
candida see *V. spicata* subsp. *incana*
× ***cantiana*** 'Kentish Pink' WAul WCFE WMoo XLum
caucasica XSen
chamaedrys NMir XLum
'Christa Bubblegum' EPfP
Christy = 'Henslerone'PBR EPfP LBuc LRHS NEoE SCob SHil
cinerea ♀H5 SBch SBrt SIgm WHoo WSHC XSen
dabneyi WPGP

'Dark Martje'	IBoy
'Darwin's Blue'	NLar
'Ellen Mae'	CElw ECtt EWes MNrw WCot
'Eveline'[PBR]	CMea ECtt EPfP LRHS MHol NDov NHpl NLar
exaltata (d)	NChi
'Fairytale'[PBR]	LRHS MBNS MMrt NGdn WHil
'Fantasy'	NDov
filiformis	XLum
'First Love'	CMea ECtt EPfP LSou MNrw NGdn WHil
formosa	see *Parahebe formosa*
§ ***fruticans***	GJos
gentianoides	Widely available
- 'Alba'	CMea GCal LEdu NBre
- 'Barbara Sherwood' ♀[H7]	EBee EWTr LRHS NGdn
- 'Blue Streak'	EPfP XLum
- 'Nana'	EBee
- 'Pallida'	EWoo GAbr GKev MBrN MMuc MRav SCob SEND SMad SPlb WBor XLum
- 'Robusta'	CAby CBod ECtt GBin GMaP GWyn LRHS MAvo NGdn WFar WHoo
- 'Tissington White'	CBod CChe CMos CRos EAJP ECtt EPfP EWoo GMaP LEdu LRHS MCot MHol MPie MPnt MSpe MTis NBir NBro NEgg NGdn NLar NWad SHar SPoG SWat WCAu WFar WHea
- 'Variegata' (v)	EBee ECha ECtt ELan GCra GMaP GWyn LRHS MHer MRav MSCN NBir NEgg NWad SPer SPoG SWat WRHF
'Giles van Hees'	ECtt MAsh
grandis	EBee EWTr IFro LEdu MArt MMuc NChi NLar SBee SEND WHrl WMoo WPtf XLum
× ***guthrieana***	SRms
'Hocus Pocus' **new**	LRHS NRHS
incana	see *V. spicata* subsp. *incana*
* - 'Candidissima'	GCal
'Ink'	MAvo SPhx
'Inspiration'	CCse NBre
'Inspire Blue'	LPot LRHS LSou MMuc MPnt NRHS SEND SHil
'Inspire Pink'	CBod LRHS LSou MPnt SHil
kellereri	see *V. spicata*
kiusiana	CMHG EBee IFro LEdu NLar NWad SPhx
* - var. ***maxima***	CAby WPtf
kotschyana	XSen
'Lavender Plume'	CWGN EBee EPfP WHil
liwanensis	WHal XSen
longifolia	CMac CSBt ECha ELan ESps EWTr GCra MBel MSpe NSti WMoo XLum
- 'Alba'	ELan MArt MMuc SEND WMoo XEll XLum
- 'Antarctica'	EBee EWTr NNys
- 'Blaubart'	XLum
§ - 'Blaubündel'	CCse LRHS NGdn NRHS
- 'Blauer Sommer'	EBee EPfP LRHS NEgg NGdn SPer SPoG
§ - 'Blauriesin'	CTri ECtt ELan EPfP GBin GMaP NLar NPnk NSti SAko SPer XEll
- Blue Giantess	see *V. longifolia* 'Blauriesin'
- 'Blue Gown'	CAbP
- 'Blue John'	CAbP ECGP ECtt EPfP LSou MPie MTis NBre NDov NSti WCot WHoo
- blue-flowered	CBod WHar
- 'Charlotte'[PBR] (v)	EBee ECtt EHoe GBin LCro LHop LRHS MBel MHol NDov SCob SHar SHil SPoG WCot WHil WRHF
- 'Charming Pink'	LRHS NDov NPnk SAko
- 'Christa'[PBR]	EPfP
- 'Fascination'	ECtt EHoe NEoE NGdn
- 'First Glory' **new**	CMea WHil
- 'First Lady' **new**	WHil
- 'Foerster's Blue'	see *V. longifolia* 'Blauriesin'
- 'Incarnata'	EBee LRHS
- 'Joseph's Coat' (v)	NBre
- 'Lilac Fantasy'	LHop MRav NSti
- 'Marietta'	CBot ECtt MHol WCot WHil WHoo WPnP
- 'Melanie White' **new**	WHil
- 'Oxford Blue'	CBar CBod WHoo
- 'Pink Eveline'[PBR]	EBee ECtt LRHS NDov NLar SPad STPC
- pink-flowered	CBod CMac
- 'Rose Tone'	GJos WMoo
- 'Schneeriesin'	EBee ECha ECtt EPfP EWTr GBin GMaP LEdu LRHS MRav MTis NAst NBir NLar NPnk SAko SPer
lyallii	see *Parahebe lyallii*
macrostachya	SKHP
'Martje'	XLum
montana 'Corinne Tremaine' (v)	NBir SRms
officinalis	GJos XLum XSen
oltensis	CPBP ECho EPot EWld ITim MHer SIgm WAbe
orchidea	SRms
'Pacific Ocean'	ECtt NLar NNys
pectinata	ECtt
- 'Rosea'	ECho ECtt EWes XSen
peduncularis 'Oxford Blue'	see *V. umbrosa* 'Georgia Blue'
perfoliata	see *Parahebe perfoliata*
petraea 'Madame Mercier'	SRot XLum
'Pink Damask'	CSpe ECtt ELan ELon EPfP GMaP MAvo MCot MRav MSpe MTis NGdn NLar SDys SPhx WHoo
'Pink Harmony'	MHol NGBl
pinnata	SBrt
- 'Blue Feathers'	EDAr MArt WOut
piroliformis	WAbe
porphyriana	CBod EBee EDAr MMuc NLar WTor
prenja	see *V. austriaca*
§ ***prostrata*** ♀[H5]	CBod CMea CSpe CTri ECtt EDAr EPfP GCrg GJos LRHS MHol NEgg NHar NHol SRms WHoo WIce WMoo
- 'Alba'	XSen
- 'Aztec Gold'[PBR]	CMac
§ - 'Blauspiegel'	CPBP SIgm
- Blue Mirror	see *V. prostrata* 'Blauspiegel'
- 'Blue Sheen'	ECho ECtt EPfP LRHS MAsh NBir NRHS
- 'Goldwell'	EBee ECtt EPPr SRot
- 'Lavender Mist'	LRHS NRHS
- 'Lilac Time'	ECho ECtt LHop LRHS NBir NHol NRHS SBch SRms WHil WIce WRHF WTor
- 'Little Nell'	ECtt
- 'Loddon Blue'	SRms WCot
- 'Mrs Holt'	ECho ECtt GCrg LHop LRHS MHer NBir NLar NRHS NWad SRms WHoo
- 'Nana'	CPBP ECtt EPot EWes GCrg MWat WAbe
- 'Nestor'	CTri EAJP ECtt WHar WPtf XLum

	- 'Rosea'	ECho XSen
	- 'Spode Blue' 🏆^{H5}	CBod CMac CMea ECho ECtt EUJe GCrg GMaP LBMP LHop LRHS MHer MMuc NRHS SEND SPoG SRms
	- 'Trehane'	ECho ECtt EDAr EPfP GBin GCrg LEdu LHop LRHS MHer MHol NEgg NRHS NRya NWad SPlb SPoG SRms WIce
	'Purpleicious Harmony'^{PBR}	EBee EPfP GBin WFar WHil
	repens	EPfP NEoE SPlb
	'Rosalinde'	NGdn
	'Royal Pink'	LHop MRav NLar
	rupestris	see *V. prostrata*
	saturejoides	SRms
	saxatilis	see *V. fruticans*
	schmidtiana 'Nana'	GAbr GKev
	selleri	see *V. wormskjoldii*
	'Shirley Blue' 🏆^{H6}	CWib ELan EPfP ESps EWTr ILea LCro LOPS LPot LSRN MHer MJak MMuc MWat SEND SPer SPhx SRms WCAu WCFE
§	***spicata***	CSam ELan EPfP GJos LRHS MRav NBid NRHS SCob SRms WBrk WFar WMoo WShi XLum
	- 'Alba'	CBod EBee EPfP GJos LPot LRHS MRav NLar WFar XLum
	- 'Barcarolle'	NAst
§	- 'Blaufuchs'	CSam
	- 'Blue Candles'	CMos GQue MTis
	- Blue Fox	see *V. spicata* 'Blaufuchs'
§	- 'Erika'	ECtt EPfP GBin IBoy NBid NBir NGdn NLar WHil
§	- 'Glory'^{PBR}	CWGN ECtt ELan ELon GMcL LCro LOPS LRHS MMuc MPie NRHS SCob SPad SPer SPoG WCot WHoo
	- 'Heidekind'	CBod EBee ECha ECtt EDAr ELan EPot GCrg GKev LHop LPot NBir NGdn NPnk SRms SRot SWat WHil WHoo WIce XLum
	- 'High Five'^{PBR}	EBee
*	- subsp. ***hybrida***	WHer
	- - 'Elaine's Form'	WCot
§	- 'Icicle'	EBee SCob WCAu
§	- subsp. ***incana*** 🏆	ECho EHoe ELan EPfP GMcL MMuc SEND SPlb SRms SWat WCFE WMoo XSen
	- - 'Nana'	NBir SRms
	- - 'Silver Carpet'	ECtt LHop LRHS MRav SPer SPoG
	- - 'Wendy'	GCal SPhx
	- 'Nana Blauteppich'	EDAr NLar XSen
	- 'Pink Goblin'	EDAr ELan EPfP MArt
	- 'Pink Panther'^{PBR}	LSou WCot
	- Red Fox	see *V. spicata* 'Rotfuchs'
	- 'Romiley Purple'	EBee SPer
	- 'Rosalind'	NLar
	- ***rosea***	see *V. spicata* 'Erika'
§	- 'Rotfuchs'	CBod ECtt EHoe ELan ELon EPfP GMcL GWyn LPot LRHS LSou MHer MRav NAst NBid NBir NGdn NLar NPnk NRHS SCob SHil SPer SPoG SRms WCAu WCFE WMoo
	- 'Royal Candles'	see *V. spicata* 'Glory'
	- 'Sightseeing'	CWib GJos NBir SRms
	- subsp. ***spicata*** 'Nana'	XSen
	- 'Twilight'^{PBR}	ECtt EPfP LRHS NLar NRHS
	- 'Ulster Blue Dwarf'	EBee EPfP EWTr GMaP IBoy IMou LHop LRHS LSou MAvo NBid NGdn NRHS SHil WCAu XLum
	- Younique Baby Blue	CBod WCot
	- Younique Baby Red = 'Versbabyred'	WCot
§	***spuria*** L.	SEND
	stelleri	see *V. wormskjoldii*
	subsessilis 'Blaue Pyramide'	WPtf
	'Sunny Border Blue'	EPfP IKil MHol NLar
	tauricola	XSen
	teucrium	see *V. austriaca* subsp. *teucrium*
	thessalica	WHal
	thymoides new	SIgm
	- subsp. ***pseudocinerea***	SIgm
§	***umbrosa*** 'Georgia Blue' 🏆^{H5}	Widely available
	urticifolia	SBrt
	virginica	see *Veronicastrum virginicum*
	'Waterperry Blue'	ECtt
	'White Icicle'	see *V. spicata* 'Icicle'
	whitleyi	MMuc
§	***wormskjoldii***	GCrg MBrN MMuc SRms XSen

Veronicastrum ✿ (*Plantaginaceae*)

	'Adoration'	EBee ECtt GBin IPot LCro MAvo MTis NCGa NDov SMHy SPhx WCAu
	axillare	IMou
	brunonianum	GCal WSHC
	japonicum var. ***australe*** B&SWJ 11009	WCru
	latifolium	EBee WCot
	- BWJ 8158	WCru WSHC
	'Red Arrows'	CAbP CBod CBot CKno EBee ECtt ELon EPPr GMaP IKil ILea IMou IPot LSou LSun MAvo MBel MHol MNrw MTis NDov NSti SCob SHar SPer SPhx SRkn WCAu WCot WHoo
	sibiricum	CKno CSpe EBee ECha EShb GCal GQue ILea LRHS MMuc SEND SHar WMoo WWtn XLum
	- BWJ 6352	WCru WFar
	- 'Kobaltkaars'	SMHy
	- var. ***yezoense***	IMou WHoo
	- - RBS 0290	EPPr NEoE
	villosulum	EBee EWes IMou NBid NBro WSHC XLum
§	***virginicum***	CBod CKno EBee ECtt GCra GPoy MAvo NBir NLar SRms WFar WHar WMoo WWtn XLum
	- 'Album' 🏆	Widely available
	- 'Apollo'	CBct CBod CBre ECtt EHrv ELon EPPr EPfP GBin GMaP IBoy ILea LEdu LRHS MAvo NBro NLar NSti SMHy SPhx SWvt WAul WBor WHrl WMoo WPGP
	- 'Cupid'	CBot CMos EBee ECtt EPfP EWTr GMaP ILea LEdu MNrw NDov SPad
	- 'Diane'	CBod EBee ECtt EPPr GMaP IBoy ILea IPot LRHS MCot MTis NCGa NDov NLar SPhx SWvt WCAu WMoo
	- 'Erica'	Widely available
	- 'Fascination'	Widely available
	- var. ***incarnatum***	see *V. virginicum* f. *roseum*
	- 'Lavendelturm'	Widely available
	- 'Pointed Finger'	CMea GCal GMaP LEdu SPhx
§	- f. ***roseum***	CAby CBWd ECha ELan GMaP LRHS MHol MJak MRav NBro NDov

	SGbt SPer SPhx SWvt WBor WHrl WKif WMoo XLum
- - 'Pink Glow'	Widely available
- 'Spring Dew'	CBre EPPr EWTr GBin LEdu LRHS MNrw NBid NBro NEoE SPhx WCAu
- 'Temptation'	EBee EWTr GMaP IPot LEdu MRav NBro NCGa NEoE NLar SPhx

Verschaffeltia (*Arecaceae*)

splendida	XBlo

Vestia (*Solanaceae*)

§ ***foetida***	CBcs CCCN CTsd CWib EBee ELan EPfP IDee LRHS MGil MNrw MPie SBig SBrt SEND WSHC
lycioides	see *V. foetida*

Viburnum ✿ (*Adoxaceae*)

acerifolium	LLHF NWad WPat
atrocyaneum	CJun NWad SBrt SKHP WPat
- B&SWJ 7272	EPfP WCru
- HIRD 113	WPGP
betulifolium	CAbP CBcs CJun CMCN EBee ELan EPfP EWes GKin SAko WPGP
- f. ***aurantiacum***	CJun
- 'Hohuanshan'	SSta WCru
bitchiuense	CJun NLar
× ***bodnantense***	CMac CTri EBee WFar
- 'Charles Lamont' 🏆H6	Widely available
- 'Dawn' 🏆H6	Widely available
- 'Deben' 🏆H6	EPfP NLar SPer WPat
brachyandrum B&SWJ 5784	WCru
bracteatum	NLar
buddlejifolium	CMac EBee EBtc EPfP EWes LRHS MMuc SKHP WCru WPat
× ***burkwoodii***	Widely available
- 'Anika'	NLar
- 'Anne Russell'	Widely available
- 'Chenaultii'	MRav
- 'Compact Beauty'	CJun WPat
- 'Conoy'	CJun ELon LEdu LRHS MAsh
- 'Fulbrook'	CAbP CRos EPfP LEdu LRHS MAsh NLar
- 'Mohawk' 🏆H6	CAbP CEnd CJun CRos ELan ELon EPfP LCro LEdu LRHS MAsh MGos NLar SCob SCoo SHil SKHP SWvt WPat
- 'Park Farm Hybrid' 🏆H6	CAbP CJun CMac CRos CTri CWib EBee ELan ELon EPfP ESps EWoo LEdu LRHS MAsh MGos MRav NHol NLar SAko SPer SPoG SRms SWvt WKif WPat
aff. ***calvum*** WWJ 12012	WCru
× ***carlcephalum*** 🏆H6	Widely available
- 'Cayuga' 🏆H5	ELon LPar MAsh WPat
- 'Van der Maat'	NLar
carlesii	CBcs CCVT CDul CMac CTri CWib EPfP ESps GKin GMcL LPar LSRN MBlu MGos MRav MSwo SCob SEWo SGol SLim SPer WFar
- B&SWJ 8838	WCru
- 'Aurora' 🏆H6	Widely available
- 'Charis'	CJun CSBt LRHS NLar WKif
- 'Compactum'	CJun MAsh NLar SSta WPat
- 'Diana' 🏆H6	CEnd CJun CMHG CMac CRos EMil EPfP LRHS LSRN MAsh MBlu NLar SCob SPer SSta WCFE WPat
- 'Marlou'	CJun NLar WPat
cassinoides	CJun WPGP
- 'Nanum'	EPfP
- 'Sear Charm'	WPGP
'Chesapeake'	CDul CJun EWes MMuc NLar SEND
chingii	CJun WCru WPGP WPat
'Chippewa'	CJun
cinnamomifolium 🏆H5	CAbP CBcs CBot ELan EPfP EWTr LRHS MAsh NLar SArc SBrt SCob SEND SLon SPer SPoG WSHC
costaricanum B&SWJ 10477 **new**	WCru
cotinifolium	CTho
- CC 4541	NLar
cylindricum	CBot EPfP LEdu LRHS NLar SBrt SKHP WCru WPGP WPat
- B&SWJ 6479 from Thailand	WCru
- B&SWJ 7239	WCru
- B&SWJ 9719 from Vietnam	WCru
- HWJCM 434 from Nepal	WCru
- 'Chino-Crûg'	WCru
davidii 🏆H5	Widely available
- (f)	CBcs CMac CRos CSBt EBee ELan EPfP EWTr MAsh SPer SPoG SRms WCFE WHar WPat
- (m)	CBcs CMac CRos CSBt ELan EPfP SGbt SPer SPoG SRms WHar WPat
- 'Angustifolium'	CBar CJun NLar WPGP
dentatum	EBtc MAsh
- Autumn Jazz	see *V. dentatum* 'Ralph Senior'
- Blue Muffin = 'Christom'	LRHS
- 'Moonglow'	NLar
§ - 'Ralph Senior'	NLar
- 'White and Blue'	CJun NLar
dilatatum	LEdu
- B&SWJ 5844	WCru
- B&SWJ 8734	WCru
- B&SWJ 10830	WCru
- PAB 6831	LEdu
- Cardinal Candy = 'Henneke'	NLar
- 'Erie'	EPfP
- 'Sealing Wax'	NLar
'Emerald Triumph'	CJun
erosum B&SWJ 8735	WCru
- B&SWJ 8893	WCru
- B&SWJ 11083	WCru
erubescens	CAbP CJun EPfP NLar SBrt
- HWJK 2163	WCru
- var. ***gracilipes***	CJun LLHF
- 'Ward van Teylingen'	NLar
'Eskimo' 🏆H5	CAbP CBcs CCVT CJun CMac CRos CSBt EBee ELan EPfP GMcL IDee LRHS MAsh MBNS MBlu MGos SCob SCoo SKHP SLim SPoG SSta SWvt
fansipanense B&SWJ 8302	WCru
- KWJ 12239	WCru
§ ***farreri*** 🏆H6	CBcs CBod CDul CRos CSBt CTri CWib EBee ELan EPfP EWTr EWoo GMcL LBuc LEdu LRHS LSRN MGos MRav MSwo NLar NWea SCob SGol SHil SPer SWvt WBod
- 'Album'	see *V. farreri* 'Candidissimum'
§ - 'Candidissimum'	CBot CDul CMac EBee ELan EPfP LHop LRHS MAsh MRav NLar SGol SPer SWvt
- 'December Dwarf'	CJun GMcL NLar
- 'Farrer's Pink'	CAbP CJun NLar
- 'Joni'	NLar

- 'Nanum'	CJun CMac EBtc ELan ELon EPfP LRHS MAsh MBrN MRav SKHP WPat
foetens	see *V. grandiflorum* f. *foetens*
foetidum	IArd
- var. ***ceanothoides***	NLar
- var. ***rectangulatum*** B&SWJ 1888	WCru
- - B&SWJ 3451	WCru
formosanum CWJ 12460	WCru
fragrans Bunge	see *V. farreri*
'Fragrant Cloud'	ECrN SWvt
furcatum ♀H6	CBot EPfP GKin IArd IDee LRHS NLar SAko SKHP WPat
- B&SWJ 5939	WCru
- B&SWJ 10880 **new**	WCru
× ***globosum*** 'Jermyns Globe'	CAbP CJun CMHG CMac EPfP LHop MRav NLar SCob SEND SLon SPoG WFar
grandiflorum	CJun NLar
- 'De Oirsprong'	NLar
§ - f. ***foetens***	CJun LRHS
- 'Snow White'	CJun
harryanum	CAbP EBtc EWTr IArd IDee MBNS NLar WCru WPat WRHF WSHC
henryi	CAbP CJun EPfP IArd IDee NLar SBrt WPat
× ***hillieri***	CHGN
- 'Winton' ♀H5	CAbP CJun CMac CRos CWib EBee EPfP IArd IDee LCro LHop LRHS LSRN MGos MMuc NLar SHil SKHP SLon SPoG SVen WFar WPGP
hoanglienense B&SWJ 8281	WCru
- HWJ 934 **new**	WCru
- KWJ 12283	WCru
'Huron'	EPfP NLar
ichangense	CJun NLar
japonicum	EPfP SLon
- B&SWJ 5968	WCru
× ***juddii***	Widely available
kansuense BWJ 7737	WCru
koreanum	WBod
- B&SWJ 4231	WCru
lantana	CCVT CDul CHab CLnd CNWT CTho CTri CWib EAEE ECrN ELan EShb ESps EWTr LBuc NWea SCob SEND SEWo SPer SVic WHed WMat WMou WTSh
- 'Aureum'	CBot EHoe EPfP MAsh MBlu NLar
- var. ***discolor***	NLar
- 'Mohican'	NLar
- 'Variegatum' (v)	EBee
- 'Xanthocarpum'	SWvt WFar
aff. ***lautum*** B&SWJ 10290	WCru
'Le Bois Marquis'PBR	CRos EBee EPfP EShb EUJe LCro LRHS MAsh MGos SHil SPoG
lentago	CAbP CMac EPfP
lobophyllum	NLar
luzonicum	CJun
- B&SWJ 3637	WCru
- var. ***formosanum*** B&SWJ 3585	WCru
- var. ***oblongum*** B&SWJ 3549	WCru
- var. ***sinuatum*** B&SWJ 4009	WCru
macrocephalum	CJun NLar SLon WPat
mariesii	see *V. plicatum* f. *tomentosum* 'Mariesii'
mullaha B&SWJ 2251A	WCru
- GWJ 9227	WCru
aff. ***mullaha*** GWJ 9388 **new**	WCru
nervosum	EBee
- HWJK 2241	WCru
- HWJK 2373	WCru
nudum	ECrN IDee
- Brandywine = 'Bulk'	LRHS WPGP
- 'Pink Beauty'	CJun CRos EPfP LCro LOPS LRHS LSRN MMrt SHil SWvt WFar WPGP WPat
- 'Winterthur'	CJun NLar
odoratissimum misapplied	see *V. odoratissimum* var. *awabuki*
odoratissimum Ker Gawl.	EBee
- RWJ 10046	WCru
§ - var. ***awabuki***	ELon EPfP EUJe LEdu LRHS MAsh MBlu MGos NLar SEND SLim WCot
- - B&SWJ 3052 **new**	WCru
- - B&SWJ 3397	WCru
- - B&SWJ 6913	WCru
- - B&SWJ 8404	EBee WCru
- - B&SWJ 11374 from Wabuka, Japan	WCru
- - 'Emerald Lustre'	CBcs EBee LRHS WPat
aff. ***odoratissimum*** B&SWJ 3913 from the Philippines	WCru
oliganthum 'Kyo Kanzashi'	WPGP
'Oneida'	CJun
opulus	Widely available
- var. ***americanum*** 'Phillips'	CAgr
- - 'Wentworth'	CAgr
- 'Amy's Magic Gold'	NLar
- 'Apricot'	NLar
- 'Aureum'	CLet CMac CRos CWib EHoe ELan EPfP ESps EWTr LBMP LRHS MAsh MGos MMuc MRav NEgg NLar SCob WCFE WMoo
- var. ***calvescens*** B&SWJ 10544	WCru
- 'Compactum' ♀H6	Widely available
- 'Fructuluteo'	SCob SGol
* - 'Harvest Gold'	MAsh SCoo SLim SPoG
- 'Lady Marmalade'	NLar
- 'Nanum'	CAbP CBcs ELan EPfP EShb GBin GMcL MRav NLar
- 'Notcutt's Variety' ♀H6	MAsh WPat
- 'Park Harvest'	CDul EBee EBtc EPfP LRHS MAsh NLar SKHP SMad SWvt
§ - 'Roseum' ♀H6	Widely available
- 'Sterile'	see *V. opulus* 'Roseum'
* - 'Sterile Compactum'	SWvt
- 'Sylvie'	NLar
- 'Xanthocarpum' ♀H6	CBcs CDul CMac CTho EBee ELan EPfP ESps GBin LRHS MAsh MBlu MGos MMuc MRav MSwo NLar SCob SEND SKHP SLon SPer SRms SWvt WBod WFar WWtn
parvifolium	EPfP NLar WPat
- B&SWJ 3375	WCru
- B&SWJ 6768	WCru
phlebotrichum B&SWJ 11058	WCru
- B&SWJ 11470 **new**	WCru
pichinchense B&SWJ 10660	WCru
plicatum	CTri CWib ESps
- 'Janny'	IArd
- 'Nanum'	see *V. plicatum* f. *tomentosum* 'Nanum Semperflorens'

§ - f. ***plicatum***	EPfP EWTr SChF
- - 'Grandiflorum'	CAbP CMac CNec EPfP LRHS NLar NPnk SCob SPer SPoG WFar WMoo
- - 'Mary Milton'	CJun ELan NLar
- - Newport = 'Newzam'	EBee
- - 'Pink Sensation'	CJun GBin
- - 'Popcorn' 🏆H5	CAbP CJun CMac CRos EBee ELan ELon EPfP EShb LRHS LSRN MAsh NHol NLar SKHP SLim SPoG SSta WPat
- - 'Rosace'	EPfP LLHF LRHS MBlu NLar SAko
- - 'Rotundifolium'	CRos IArd LRHS MAsh MGos MRav NLar SHil WPat
- - Triumph = 'Trizam'	NLar
- 'Sterile'	see *V. plicatum* f. *plicatum*
§ - f. ***tomentosum***	IBal
- - 'Cascade' 🏆H5	CJun EWTr LRHS NLar SAko SKHP
- - 'Dart's Red Robin'	ECtt LLHF MAsh SAko
- - 'Elizabeth Bullivant'	EPfP LRHS MAsh SPoG
- - 'Igloo'	WPat
- - Kilimanjaro = 'Jww1'PBR	EBee EPfP GBin GMcL IDee LCro LOPS LRHS LSou MBlu NEoE NLar NPnk WMoo
- - 'Lanarth'	Widely available
§ - - 'Mariesii' 🏆H5	Widely available
- - 'Mariesii Great Star'	LRHS
- - 'Molly Schroeder'	CJun EBee MMrt NLar
§ - - 'Nanum Semperflorens'	CBcs CMac ECtt EShb LRHS MGos NLar SHil SPoG WFar WPat WSHC
- - 'Pink Beauty' 🏆H5	Widely available
- - 'Rowallane'	NLar
- - 'Saint Keverne'	ELan GKin
- - 'Shasta'	CJun CMCN EPfP EWTr GMcL LEdu LRHS NLar SKHP WFar
- - 'Shoshoni'	NLar
- - 'Summer Snowflake' 🏆H5	CEnd CRos CWGN EMOT EPfP EShb GMcL LBMP LRHS MAsh MSwo NLar NPnk SKHP SLim SPer SPoG WFar
- 'Watanabe'	see *V. plicatum* f. *tomentosum* 'Nanum Semperflorens'
'Pragense' 🏆H6	CAbP CBcs CBot CDul CJun CMCN EBee EPfP LRHS MGos NHol NLar SLon SPer
propinquum	CAbP WPat
- CWJ 12395 **new**	WCru
- CWJ 12426	WCru
prunifolium	EBtc SGol WCru
- 'Mrs Henry's Large'	CJun EPfP NLar
* 'Regenteum'	CWib
× ***rhytidophylloides***	IBoy
- 'Alleghany'	NLar
- Dart's Duke = 'Interduke'	WPat
- 'Willowwood'	ELan LRHS MAsh SCob SPer WPat
rhytidophyllum	CBcs CDul CMac CNWT EAEE ECrN EPfP ESps GMcL LHop LRHS MGos MJak MMuc MSwo NEgg NWea SCob SEND SGol SPer SRms SWvt WCFE WHar WMoo WSFF
- 'Roseum'	CBot SWvt
- 'Variegatum' (v)	CJun
- 'Wisley Pink'	LRHS MAsh
'Royal Guard'	CJun
sambucinum HWJ 838	WCru
- var. ***tomentosum*** HWJ 733	WCru
sargentii B&SWJ 8695	WCru
- f. ***flavum***	NLar
- 'Onondaga' 🏆H6	Widely available
- 'Susquehanna'	EPfP
semperflorens	see *V. plicatum* f. *tomentosum* 'Nanum Semperflorens'
§ ***setigerum***	EBee EPfP IDee NLar WCFE WPat
- BWJ 8409	WCru
- 'Aurantiacum'	NLar
sieboldii B&SWJ 2837	WCru
- CWJ 12808	WCru
- 'Seneca'	CJun LRHS NLar
sphaerocarpum B&SWJ 3052	WCru
subalpinum	NLar
sympodiale	CFil
taitoense CWJ 12406	WCru
taiwanianum B&SWJ 3009	WCru
- CWJ 12467 **new**	WCru
theiferum	see *V. setigerum*
tinoides B&SWJ 10612	WCru
tinus	Widely available
- 'Bewley's Variegated' (v)	EBee SCob SPer
I - 'Compactum'	SWvt
- 'Eve Price' 🏆H4	Widely available
- 'French White' 🏆H4	CDul CMac EBee ELan EMOT EPfP EWTr IBoy LBrs LCro MGos MRav NLar SAko SCob SCoo SLim SPoG SWvt WFar WHar
- 'Gwenllian' 🏆H4	Widely available
- 'Israel'	LRHS MBNS
- 'Lisarose'PBR	CRos EPfP LCro LRHS LSRN NLar SPoG SWvt
- 'Little Bognor'	NLar
- 'Lucidum'	CBcs EBee ECrN EPfP LPar NLar SGol
- 'Lucidum Variegatum' (v)	CMac SLim WFar
* - 'Macrophyllum'	EPfP LRHS NLar SPoG SWvt
- 'Peter's Purple' **new**	LRHS NRHS
- 'Pink Prelude'	SCob
- 'Purpureum'	CBcs CJun CNec CRos CSBt ECrN EHoe ELon EMOT EPfP ESps LRHS MAsh MGos MSwo NEgg NLar SCob SCoo SGol SLim SPer SPoG WMoo WPat
- Spirit = 'Anvi'PBR	CAbP CRos CSBt ELan EPfP ESps LRHS LSou MAsh MMrt NEoE NLar NWad SCob SCoo SHil SPoG SWvt
- 'Spring Bouquet'	CJun MAsh
- subsp. ***subcordatum*** B&SWJ 12544	WCru
- 'Variegatum' (v)	CBot CLet CMac CRos CTri CWib EBee EHoe ELan ELon EPfP ESps LPar LRHS MAsh MGos NEgg NLar NPol SCob SGol SLim SRms SWvt WPat
tomentosum	see *V. plicatum* f. *tomentosum*
triphyllum B&SWJ 5784	WCru
urceolatum B&SWJ 6988	WCru
utile	WThu
aff. ***venustum*** B&SWJ 10477	WCru
wrightii	EPfP IArd IDee MRav NLar
- B&SWJ 5871	WCru
- 'Hessei'	WPat
- var. ***stipellatum*** B&SWJ 5856	WCru
- - B&SWJ 8780A	WCru

Vicia (*Papilionaceae*)

americana	EBee
cracca	CHab CWld NMir WSFF
oroboides	EBee
sativa	CHab CWld
sepium	CWld

Vigna (*Papilionaceae*)

§	***caracalla***	CCCN

Villaresia see *Citronella*

Vinca (*Apocynaceae*)

	difformis	CFis CNec CTri ECha EWoo LCro LLWP LPla SDix WBod WHer XLum
	- 'Alba'	CBot CSam
	- Greystone form	EPPr MMuc SEND
	- 'Jenny Pym'	CChe CMac CRos CSam EBee EPPr EPfP EWes EWld LHop LRHS MBNS MMuc NLar SBch SEND SIde SPoG WBor WOut WRHF
	- 'Ruby Baker'	EPPr EWes NChi
	- subsp. ***sardoa***	CBod CBot EPPr EWes LRHS
	- 'Snowmound'	CBod CSBt LRHS MRav NLar SPoG SWvt
	herbacea RCB UA 21	WCot
	'Hidcote Purple'	see *V. major* var. *oxyloba*
	major	CBcs CDul CFGn CMac CSBt CWib ELan EShb ESps GMcL GPoy LBuc LCro LRHS MGos MJak MSwo NPol NPri NWea SCob SGbt SGol SHil SLim SPer SRms WMoo XLum XSen
	- 'Alba'	CMac CWib
	- subsp. ***balcanica***	IMou XLum
	- 'Elegantissima'	see *V. major* 'Variegata'
	- 'Expoflora' (v)	NLar
	- var. ***hirsuta*** misapplied	see *V. major* var. *oxyloba*
§	- subsp. ***hirsuta*** (Boiss.) Stearn	CMac WCot XLum
§	- 'Maculata' (v)	CBcs CSBt ECrN EHoe EShb ESps GMcL GWyn LRHS MMuc MRav MSwo NPri SCob SEND SGol SLim SPer SPoG SWvt WMoo WOut
§	- var. ***oxyloba***	CFis CTri ECha ELan EPfP EPri EWld LHop LPot LRHS MRav NLar SCob SRms WBor WHer XSen
	- var. ***pubescens***	see *V. major* subsp. *hirsuta* (Boiss.) Stearn
	- 'Surrey Marble'	see *V. major* 'Maculata'
§	- 'Variegata' (v) ♀H6	Widely available
	- 'Wojo's Jem' (v)	CBod CBot CMac CRos ELan EPfP EWes LRHS MGos NCou NLar NPri SCob SHil SLim SPoG SWvt WCot WMoo
	minor	CBar CBcs CDul CRos CSBt ELan ESps EWoo GAbr GBin GKin GMcL GPoy LCro LOPS LRHS MAsh MGos MJak NPri NWea SCob SLim SVic XLum
	- f. ***alba***	CBcs CBod CDul CMac ECha EPPr EPfP ESps EWTr LOPS LRHS LSRN MAsh MBel NLar NPri SCob SGol SPer WCot WHar WOut XLum
§	- - 'Alba Variegata' (v)	CBar EHoe GMcL IFro LBMP LSRN NEoE SPer SRms WCot WHoo WOut WWtn
	- - 'Gertrude Jekyll'	Widely available
	- 'Alba Aureovariegata'	see *V. minor* f. *alba* 'Alba Variegata'
§	- 'Argenteovariegata' (v) ♀H6	CBcs CDul CMac CRos CSBt CSam CTri ECha ELan ELon EPfP GMcL LBuc LRHS MGos MJak MMuc MSwo NLar NPri NWea SCob SEND SGol SLim SPer SRms
§	- 'Atropurpurea' ♀H6	Widely available
I	- 'Aureomarginata'	WMoo
§	- 'Aureovariegata' (v)	CBcs CMac CRos EBee ELan EPPr EPfP ESps GAbr LRHS MGos MRav NPri SGol SHil SLim SPer SPlb WRHF
	- 'Azurea'	CHid
§	- 'Azurea Flore Pleno' (d) ♀H6	CArn CBod CBot CMac CWib ECha EPPr EPfP GAbr GBin GCra IFro LHop LLWP LRHS MAsh MRav NLar NPri SHil SLim SPer SPoG SRms SWvt WHar WHoo WKif WMoo XLum
*	- 'Blue and Gold'	EAEE EPPr SCob
	- 'Blue Drift'	EWes MSwo
	- 'Bowles's Blue'	see *V. minor* 'La Grave'
	- 'Bowles's Purple'	CBod CTsd GMaP LBMP NCou SPer
	- 'Bowles's Variety'	see *V. minor* 'La Grave'
	- 'Burgundy'	SRms
	- 'Caerulea Plena'	see *V. minor* 'Azurea Flore Pleno'
	- 'Dartington Star'	see *V. major* var. *oxyloba*
	- 'Double Burgundy'	see *V. minor* 'Multiplex'
	- 'Flower Power'	EPPr
	- Green Carpet	see *V. minor* 'Grüner Teppich'
§	- 'Grüner Teppich'	SGol
	- 'Halstenbek'	XLum
	- 'Illumination' (v)	Widely available
	- 'Josephine'	MHol
§	- 'La Grave' ♀H6	Widely available
	- 'Marie'	EPPr
	- 'Mrs Betty James' (d)	WCot
§	- 'Multiplex' (d)	EPPr GBin MSwo SGol SLim SRms WOut
	- 'Purpurea'	see *V. minor* 'Atropurpurea'
	- 'Ralph Shugert' (v) ♀H6	CBod CBot CMac CNec CRos ECtt ELon EMOT EPPr EPfP ESps EWTr EWes EWoo GMcL LCro LHop LRHS MAsh MGos NLar NPri SCob SCoo SEle SGol SHil SPoG WMoo
	- 'Rubra'	see *V. minor* 'Atropurpurea'
	- 'Sabinka'	CHid EPPr
	- 'Silver Service' (d/v)	CHid MRav
	- 'Snowdrift'	EPPr
	- 'Variegata'	see *V. minor* 'Argenteovariegata'
	- 'Variegata Aurea'	see *V. minor* 'Aureovariegata'
	- 'White Gold'	NEoE
	- 'White Power'	EPPr

Vincetoxicum (*Apocynaceae*)

	cretaceum PAB 3432	LEdu
	fuscatum	IMou
	hirundinaria	EBee EPPr GEdr GPoy LEdu
	nigrum	CArn EBee GCal LEdu NChi WCot WTou

Viola ✿ (*Violaceae*)

	'Ada Segre' (Vt)	CGro
	'Admiral Avellan'	see *V.* 'Amiral Avellan'
	'Admiration' (Va)	WGoo
	adunca var. ***minor***	see *V. labradorica* ambig.
§	***alba***	EWes
	'Alethia' (Va)	SDys WGoo
	'Alice' (Vt)	CLAP
	'Alice Kate'	WGoo
	'Alice Witter' (Vt)	CGro LLHF
*	'Alison' (Va)	NDov WGoo
	alpina	WAbe
	'Amelia' (Va)	WGoo
§	'Amiral Avellan' (Vt)	CGro
	'Annaleisia' (Vt)	CGro
	'Annette Ross' (Va)	GWyn NDov WGoo
I	'Annie' (Vt)	CGro CLAP LLHF

	arborescens	SBrt
	'Ardross Gem' (Va)	ECho WGoo
	arenaria	see *V. rupestris*
	'Arkwright's Ruby' (Va)	MAsh NWad
	arvensis	CHab GJos
	'Ashvale Blue' (dPVt)	CGro
	'Aspasia' (Va) 🏆H5	EWoo GWyn MAsh WGoo
	'Avril Lawson' (Va)	GBin GKev SHar WGoo
	'Baby Blue'	GMcL
	'Barbara' (Va)	ECtt WGoo
	'Baroness de Rothschild' misapplied	see *V.* 'Baronne Alice de Rothschild'
	'Baroness de Rothschild' ambig. (Vt)	CGro CLAP WHer
§	'Baronne Alice de Rothschild' (Vt)	CDor WCot
	'Beatrice' (Vtta)	WGoo
	'Becky Groves' (Vt)	CGro CLAP EWTr
	'Beetroot' (Vt)	CGro
§	'Belmont Blue' (C)	CSam CTri EBee ELon EWes EWoo GAbr GBin GCal GKev GMaP IFro LCro LRHS MAsh MCot MHer MRav NBir NCGa NDov SCob SHar SPer SPhx WGoo
§	***bertolonii***	WGoo
	'Beshlie' (Va) 🏆H5	WGoo
	biflora	CMHG CPla EWld MNrw
	'Blackout'[PBR]	ECtt
	'Blue Butterfly' (C)	EWoo GWyn SPhx
	'Blue Horns' (C)	ELon
	'Blue Moon' (C)	MAsh WGoo
	Blue Moon = 'Smev1' (Va) **new**	GWyn
	'Blue Moonlight' (C)	MPie
	'Blue Tit' (Va)	ECtt
	'Boughton Blue'	see *V.* 'Belmont Blue'
	'Bournemouth Gem' (Vt)	CDor CGro
§	'Bowles's Black' (T)	CSpe EPfP LEdu MArt NBro SRms WJek
	'Boy Blue' (Vtta)	ECtt
	brevistipulata var. ***hidakana***	GEdr
	- var. ***laciniata*** **new**	GEdr
	'Bruneau' (dVt)	CBre EBee ECtt GBin LEdu WCot WFar
*	'Bryony' (Vtta)	WGoo
	bubanii	GJos GKev
	'Bullion' (Va)	WGoo
	'Burncoose Yellow'	WGoo
	'Buttercup' (Vtta)	ECtt GWyn SDys SPhx SPoG WGoo
	'Butterpat' (C)	MAsh NDov SHar SPhx WGoo
	'Buxton Blue' (Va)	WGoo
	Can Can Series	CWCL
	'Candy' (Vt)	EBee
	canina	NBro NMir
	'Carol Loxton' (Vt)	EBee
	'Catalina'	CGro CLAP
§	***chaerophylloides*** var. ***sieboldiana***	SBrt
	- - pink-flowered	SBrt
	'Charles William Groves' (Vt)	CGro CLAP ELon
	'Charles Winston Groves' (Vt)	CGro
	'Charlotte'	GWyn WGoo
	'Chloe' (Vtta)	CGro
	'Christie's Wedding' (Vt)	CGro
	'Christmas' (Vt)	CGro
	'Clementina' (Va) 🏆H5	MRav WGoo
	'Cleo' (Va)	GWyn WGoo
	'Clive Groves' (Vt)	CGro CLAP ELon
	'Coeur d'Alsace' (Vt)	CGro CLAP EBee ECtt GBin GMaP NCGa NLar SHar WHal XLum
	'Colette' (Va)	WGoo
	'Colombine' (Vt)	CAby MAsh
	'Columbine' (Va)	ECtt EPfP GMaP GWyn LRHS MHer MHol NBir NDov NRHS SPer SPoG WCot WFar WGoo WTor
§	'Conte di Brazza' (dPVt)	CGro EHrv GMaP GWyn NLar
	'Cordelia' (Vt)	CDor CLAP
	cornuta 🏆H5	CAby CElw CMea CPla ECho GKev GWyn LRHS MMuc MNrw NBir NBro SCob SEND SRms WGoo WHoo WTou
	- Alba Group (C) 🏆H5	Widely available
	- 'Alba Minor' (C)	ECho EPfP EWTr EWes EWoo NBro NChi NDov NSla SPhx
	- 'Blaue von Paris' (C) **new**	GWyn
	- blue-flowered	ECho MHer WMoo
	- 'Brimstone' (C)	GAbr SPhx
	- 'Cleopatra' (C)	EWTr MNrw MPie SPhx
	- 'Clouded Yellow' (C)	EWoo GWyn MNrw
	- 'Gypsy Moth' (C)	EWoo GWyn SPhx
	- 'Icy But Spicy' (C)	MAsh MAvo MCot MRav NDov WGoo
	- Lilacina Group (C)	ECha MRav SWat WPtf
	- 'Maiden's Blush' (C)	SPhx
	- 'Mark's Dainty' (C)	MPie
	- 'Minor' (C)	CPla CSam EPfP EWoo MAsh NBro NCGa NDov NSla WGoo
	- 'Netta Statham' (C)	EWoo MPie WGoo
	- 'Pale Apollo' (C)	SPhx
	- Purpurea Group (C)	CMea ECha WSHC
	- 'Rosea' (C)	ECha
	- 'Spider' (C)	GWyn MAsh MPie SDys WGoo
	- 'Ulla' (C)	WHer
	- 'Victoria's Blush' (C)	CElw ELon EWTr GMaP MAsh MPie NBir NDov SHar SPhx WGoo
	- 'Violacea' (C)	EWoo MAsh
	corsica	CMea CSpe EPPr SBch SPhx WHea
§	***cucullata*** 🏆H5	ECho SRms
§	- 'Alba' (Vt)	CBro ECho NBir SRms
*	- 'Striata Alba'	NBro
	'Curlylocks' **new**	ECtt
	'Czar'	see *V.* 'The Czar'
§	'Czar Bleu' (Vt)	CGro
	'Daisy Smith' (Va)	WGoo
	'Danielle Molly'	WGoo
	'Dawn' (Vtta)	CAby CBod CMea ECtt EPfP GBin GMaP NDov NLar SPoG WGoo WTor
	'Delicia' (Vtta)	GWyn NDov SPhx WGoo
	'Desdemona' (Va)	EWoo GWyn SPhx WGoo
	'Devon Cream' (Va)	WGoo
	'Diana Groves' (Vt)	CGro
	'Dick o' the Hills' (Vt)	CGro
	dissecta var. ***sieboldiana***	see *V. chaerophylloides* var. *sieboldiana*
	'Donau' (Vt)	CGro WCot
	'Double White' (dVt)	CGro
	dubyana	GJos
	'Duchesse de Parme' (dPVt)	CGro GMaP GWyn IFro NLar SRms
	'D'Udine' (dPVt)	CGro ECtt SRms WCot WHil
	'Dusk'	WGoo
	'E.A. Bowles'	see *V.* 'Bowles's Black'
	'Eastgrove Blue Scented' (C)	EWoo SDys WGoo WOut
	'Eastgrove Ice Blue' (C)	WGoo WOut
	'Elaine Quin'	ECtt GWyn MCot NDov NEgg NLar SPoG WGoo WKif

§	***elatior***	CPla EPPr MArt MNrw SBrt WPtf
	'Elizabeth' (Va)	WGoo
	'Elizabeth Lee'	WCot
	'Elliot Adam' (Va)	WGoo
	'Emperor Blue Vein'	EBee EPfP
	erecta	see *V. elatior*
	'Eris' (Va)	WGoo
	'Etain' (Va)	CAby CBod ECho ECtt ELan EPfP EWoo GBuc GMaP GWyn LRHS MAsh MHol NDov NEgg NLar NRHS SCob SPoG WFar WGoo WIce
	'Fabiola' (Vtta)	EWoo
*	'Fantasy'	WGoo
	'Fee Jalucine' (dVt)	CGro
	'Fiona' (Va)	EWoo MCot SPhx WGoo
	'Fiona Lawrenson' (Va)	WGoo
	'Florence' (Va)	GWyn NDov WGoo
	'Foxbrook Cream' (C)	MAsh WGoo
	'Francesca' (Va)	WGoo
	'Freckles'	see *V. sororia* 'Freckles'
	glabella	SBrt
	'Gladys Findlay' (Va)	WGoo
	'Glanmore'	WCot WFar
*	'Glenda'	WGoo
	'Glenholme'	EWoo GWyn MAsh
	'Governor Herrick' (Vt)	CGro CLAP EBee ECtt EHrv LLHF NLar WCot WFar
	gracilis 'Lutea'	CSam
	- 'Major'	WGoo
	'Green Goddess'PBR	EPfP GBuc WIce
	'Green Jade' (v)	CPla
	'Grey Owl' (Va)	SPhx WGoo
	'Grovemount Blue' (C)	CMea EPfP WTor
	grypoceras var. ***exilis*** 'Sylettas'	LEdu
	'Gustav Wermig' (C)	MAsh WGoo
	'Haslemere'	see *V.* 'Nellie Britton'
	'Heartthrob' (v)	EBee ECtt GEdr LSou NBir NHpl SPoG SWeb WHil WNPC
*	'Heaselands'	SMHy
§	***hederacea***	CTsd GQui GWyn IFoB MBNS SCob SRms
	- 'Putty Road' (Vt)	ECho
§	'Helen Mount' (T)	GWyn
	'Helena' (Va)	WGoo
	'Hespera' (Va)	WGoo
	heterophylla subsp. ***epirota***	see *V. bertolonii*
*	'Hetty Gatenby'	WGoo
	'Holdgate'	WGoo
	'Hudsons Blue'	CElw MNrw
	'Huntercombe Purple' (Va) ♀H5	ECho LHop LRHS MAsh NBir NRHS SCob WGoo WHal WKif
	'Iden Gem' (Va)	ECtt WGoo
	'Inverurie Beauty' (Va) ♀H5	EWoo GAbr GBin GMaP SDys WGoo WKif
	'Irish Elegance'	see *V.* 'Sulfurea'
	'Irish Molly' (Va)	CSpe ECho ECtt ELan EPfP GBuc GWyn MAsh NEgg SPer SPoG SRms WFar WGoo WIce WTor
	'Isabel'	SRms WGoo
	'Isabella' (Vt)	CGro CLAP EBee
	'Isobel'	MAsh
	'Ivory Queen' (Va)	EWoo GWyn MRav SPhx WGoo
	'Jack Sampson' (Vt)	EBee
	'Jackanapes' (Va) ♀H5	EBee ECtt ELan EPfP GWyn LRHS MAsh MAvo NRHS SPer SPoG SRms WGoo WIce WTor
	'Jane Mott' (Va)	EWoo
	'Janet' (Va)	EBee ECtt GWyn LSRN SDys SPoG
	'Janette'	NDov WGoo
	japonica	SBrt
	'Jean Arnot' (Vt)	EBee
	'Jean Jeannie'	GBuc GWyn NDov WGoo
	'Jeannie Bellew' (Va)	ECtt SPhx WGoo
	'Jennifer Andrews' (Va)	GWyn WGoo
	'Jenny Dickson' **new**	CElw
	'Joanna' (Va)	WGoo
	'Johnny Jump Up'	see *V.* 'Helen Mount'
	'Joker Violet Gold' (Joker Series)	CWCL
	jooi	ECho EPfP NBir SIgm SPhx WAbe WPtf WThu
	'Josie' (Va)	GWyn WGoo
	'Joyce Gray' (Va)	WGoo
	'Joyce Mary Paul' (Vt) **new**	CGro
	'Judy Goring' (Va)	EWoo SPhx
	'Julian' (Va)	EWoo WGoo
	'Juno' (Va)	EWoo
	'Jupiter' (Va)	GWyn WCot
	'Karpatenfrühling' (C) **new**	MArt
	'Katerina' (Va)	SPhx WGoo
	'Kerry Girl' (Vt)	CGro
	'Kim'	CGro CLAP
	'Kitten'	EWoo MAsh SDys SPhx WGoo
	'Kitty White' (Va)	EWoo GWyn SDys SPhx
§	'Königin Charlotte' (Vt)	CGro GBin GMaP LRHS MHer NLar WCot WMoo
	kosaninii **new**	GKev
	'Kurenai'	SBrt
	labradorica misapplied	see *V. riviniana* Purpurea Group
	- ***purpurea***	see *V. riviniana* Purpurea Group
§	***labradorica*** ambig.	CSBt EHrv GJos GQui GWyn NHpl SCob WCAu WHer
	'Lady Hume Campbell' (dPVt)	CGro
	'Lady Jane' (Vt)	CGro
	'Lees Peachy Pink' (Vt)	CGro CLAP
	'Letitia' (Va)	ECho MAsh MNrw MRav SDys WGoo
	'Lianne' (Vt)	CLAP LLHF WCot
	'Lindsay'	WGoo
	'Lisa Tanner' (Va)	GWyn WGoo
	'Little Angel'	ECtt
	'Little David' (Vtta) ♀H5	CSam CTri ECtt MCot NDov SPhx WGoo
	'Lizzy Wootten' (Va)	EWoo
	'Lord Plunket' (Va)	WGoo
§	'Lord Primrose'	ECtt
	'Lorna Cawthorne' (C)	MAsh SDys WGoo
	'Louisa' (Va)	EWoo GWyn WGoo
	'Lucy' (Va)	MAsh
§	***lutea***	WGoo
	- subsp. ***elegans***	see *V. lutea*
	'Luxonne' (Vt)	CGro
	'Lydia Groves' (Vt)	CGro CLAP ECtt ELon LLHF LSou SRms WCot
	'Lydia's Legacy' (Vt)	CGro
	'Madame Armandine Pagès' (Vt)	CGro
	'Maggie Mott' (Va) ♀H5	ECha ECho ECtt EWoo GWyn LHop MAsh MRav WGoo
	'Magic'	NDov WGoo
	mandshurica f. ***albiflora***	SBrt
	- 'Fuji Dawn' (v)	CPla GWyn
	- f. ***plena*** (d)	GEdr
	- - white-flowered	GEdr
	mandshurica × ***patrinii***	SBrt
	'Margaret' (Va)	ECtt WGoo

	'Marie-Louise' (dPVt)	CGro GWyn SHar
	'Mars' (Va)	LEdu
I	'Mars'	LSRN
	'Martin' (Va) ♀H5	CAby CBod CMea ECha ECtt EPfP EWoo GMaP GWyn LHop LSRN MAsh MAvo MHer MPie NDov SPer SPoG WGoo
	'Mary Mouse'	WGoo
	'Mauve Haze' (Va)	WGoo
	'Mauve Radiance' (Va)	EWoo WGoo
	'May Mott' (Va)	SPhx WGoo
	'Mayfly' (Va)	ECtt
	'Melinda' (Vtta)	WGoo
	'Mercury' (Va)	WGoo
	'Midnight' (Va)	EWoo
	'Milkmaid' (Va)	ELon EWoo NBir
	(Miracle Series) 'Miracle Bride White' (Vt)	SHar
	- 'Miracle Classy Pink' (Vt)	SHar
	- 'Miracle Ice White' (Vt)	NLar SHar
	- 'Miracle Intense Blue' (Vt)	NCGa NLar
	- 'Miracle Vanilla White' (Vt)	SHar
	'Miss Brookes' (Va)	WGoo
	'Misty Guy' (Vtta)	MAsh WGoo
	'Molly Sanderson' (Va) ♀H5	CAby EAJP ECha ECho ECtt ELan EPfP EWoo GMaP GWyn LHop LRHS MAsh MHer NEgg SCob SPer SPlb SPoG WFar WGoo WIce
	'Moonlight' (Va) ♀H5	ECho ELan LHop LRHS NRHS WGoo
	'Morwenna' (Va)	ECtt MAsh MCot NDov WGoo
	'Mrs Lancaster' (Va)	EBee ECtt ELan EWoo GMaP GWyn LHop LSRN MCot NBir NLar SDys SPoG WGoo WTor
	'Mrs Pinehurst' (Vt)	CGro EBee GMaP GWyn
	'Mrs R. Barton' (Vt)	CDor CGro CLAP SHar
	'Myfawnny' (Va)	ECho LRHS NDov NRHS SDys SRms WFar WGoo
	'Neapolitan'	see *V.* 'Pallida Plena'
§	'Nellie Britton' (Va) ♀H5	SRms
	'Netta Statham'	see *V.* 'Belmont Blue'
	'Nora'	ECtt NDov WGoo
	'Norah Church' (Vt)	CLAP
	'Norah Leigh' (Va)	WGoo
	obliqua	see *V. cucullata*
	odorata (Vt)	CArn CBcs CBod CGro CHab EPfP GPoy LCro LRHS MRav NMir SBod SEND SIde SRms SVic WJek WOut
	- 'Alba' (Vt)	CGro EBee ECho ELan EPfP GBin LEdu MHer MMuc SEND SRms WMoo
	- 'Alba Plena' (dVt)	EHrv
	- 'Albiflora' (Vt)	CLAP EPfP
	- 'Amethyst Witch' (Vt) **new**	CGro
	- apricot-flowered	see *V.* 'Sulfurea'
	- 'Bethan Davies' (d/Vt)	WCot
	- 'Christopher William Groves' (Vt) **new**	CGro
	- 'Copper Pennies' (Vt) **new**	CGro
	- 'Cyclops' (Vt) **new**	CGro
	- 'Dawnie' (Vt)	CGro EBee
	- 'Double Rose' (d)	WCot
	- var. ***dumetorum***	see *V. alba*
	- 'Elsmeer' (Vt)	ECtt LSou WCot
	- 'Explorateur Dybowski' (Vt) **new**	CGro
	- 'Hungarian Beauty' (Vt)	EBee
	- 'Katy' (Vt)	CLAP ELon
	- 'King of Violets' (dVt)	ECtt LSou SHar SPer
	- 'Lees Ivory' (Vt) **new**	CGro
	- 'Little Plum' (Vt) **new**	CGro
	- 'Melanie' (Vt)	CGro CLAP MArt WCot
	- 'Mrs R.O. Barlow' (Vt)	CLAP WCot WSHC
	- 'Piddle Pink' (Vt) **new**	CGro
	- pink-flowered	see *V. odorata* Rosea Group
	- 'Princess Thirza' (Vt) **new**	CGro
§	- Rosea Group (Vt)	CDor GBin IFoB LSou MMuc MPie MRav SEND SIde SPer SRms WCot
*	- subsp. ***subcarnea*** (Vt)	MMuc SEND
	- 'Sulphurea'	see *V.* 'Sulfurea'
	- 'Vin d'André Thorp' (Vt)	ECtt LEdu WCot
I	- 'Violett Charm' (Vt)	WCot
	- 'Wismar' (Vt)	WCot
	'Olive Edwards'	CElw WGoo
	'Opéra' (Vt)	CLAP LLHF
	'Orchid Pink' (Vt)	CGro CLAP EBee GMaP LEdu
	orientalis	GEdr
§	'Pallida Plena' (dPVt)	CGro
	palustris	EWay LLWG WHer WSFF WShi
	'Pamela Zambra' (Vt)	CLAP WSHC
	papilionacea	see *V. sororia*
	'Parchment' (Vt)	CGro EBee GWyn
	'Parme de Toulouse' (dPVt)	CGro EWTr GWyn NLar XLum
	'Pasha' (Va)	ECtt EWoo GWyn SDys SPhx
	'Pat Creasy' (Va)	NDov WGoo
	'Pat Kavanagh' (C)	MAsh WGoo
	'Patience'	WGoo
	'Patricia Lillington' (Va) **new**	GWyn
	pedata	CBro ECho EPot WAbe
	- f. ***alba***	GEdr MHer
	- 'Bicolor'	ECho WAbe
	pedatifida	IFoB
	- white-flowered	MArt
	pensylvanica	see *V. pubescens* var. *eriocarpa*
	'Peppered-palms'	EHrv
	'Perle Rose' (Vt)	CGro CLAP EHrv
	'Petra' (Vtta)	EWoo GWyn SPhx WGoo
	phalacrocarpa	SBrt
	'Phyl Dove' (Vt)	CLAP EBee WCot
	'Pickering Blue' (Va)	WGoo
	pinnata	SBrt
	'Primrose Dame' (Va)	ECtt WGoo
	'Primrose Pixie' (Va)	WGoo
	'Prince Henry' (T)	MNHC
	'Prince John' (T)	MNHC
	'Princess Diana' (Vt)	CGro EBee
	'Princess Mab' (Vtta)	WGoo
	'Princess of Prussia' (Vt)	CGro WCot
	'Princess of Wales'	see *V.* 'Princesse de Galles'
§	'Princesse de Galles' (Vt)	CGro CTri
§	***pubescens*** var. ***eriocarpa***	SRms
	'Purple Wings' (Va)	WGoo
	Queen Charlotte	see *V.* 'Königin Charlotte'
	'Raven'	LRHS SPhx WGoo
	'Rebecca' (Vtta)	Widely available
	'Red Charm' (Vt)	CGro
	'Red Giant' (Vt)	CGro EHrv LEdu MBNS
	'Red Lion' (Vt)	CGro
	'Red Queen' (Vt)	CLAP
	reichenbachiana	GJos
	'Reine des Blanches' (dVt)	EBee ECtt GBin LEdu LLWP NGdn SPer SRms WCot WOut
	'Reine des Neiges' (Vt)	CGro EBee
	reniforme	see *V. hederacea*
	riviniana	CWld GJos MHer MMuc WHer WOut WSFF WShi
	- dark pink-flowered	MMuc
§	- Purpurea Group	CBcs CBod CMac CPla CTri EBee ECha EHoe EPfP EWes EWoo GAbr

		LLWP MHer MMuc MPie MRav NBir NDov NRya NSti SPer SPhx SPlb SRms WJek WMoo
	- white-flowered	CWld EWes MMuc
	'Roem van Aalsmeer' **new**	GBin
	'Roscastle Black'	CMea EPfP EWoo GWyn MAsh NDov SBch WGoo
	'Rubra' (Vt)	EPfP MArt WOut XLum
§	***rupestris***	CTri MHer
*	- ***rosea***	CPla IFro LLWP WHer WPtf
	sagittata	LPot
	'Saint Helena' (Vt)	WCot
	'Sally' (Vtta)	CGro
	selkirkii Pursh ex Goldie	CPla WThu
	- 'Variegata' (v)	XEll
	sempervirens	SBrt
	septentrionalis	see *V. sororia*
	'Serena' (Va)	WGoo
	'Sherbet Dip'	WGoo
	'Sidborough Poppet'	EWes
	'Silver Samurai'	WCot
	'Smugglers' Moon'	GWyn WGoo
	somchetica	WCot
	'Sophie' (Vtta)	WGoo
	'Sorbet Series'	NPri
§	***sororia***	CBod ECha ECho EPPr EWoo GWyn MNrw NBir NBro SCob SPhx WGwG
*	- 'Albiflora' 🏆^{H6}	CHid ECho EPPr EPfP EWTr EWoo LEdu LRHS LSun MRav SCob SPhx WCFE WJek
	- 'Dark Freckles'	CGro EBee ECho EWTr LHop NLar NRya SPhx
§	- 'Freckles'	Widely available
	- 'Priceana'	CBod ECGP LEdu MRav NBir SPlb WCot
	- 'Sorority Sisters'	NChi
	- 'Speckles' (v)	WCot
	- 'Sweet Emma'	SPhx
*	'Spencer's Cottage'	WGoo
	Starry Night	see *V.* 'Lord Primrose'
	'Steyning' (Va)	WGoo
	stojanowii	ECho GCrg LLHF
§	'Sulfurea' (Vt)	CDor CLAP CPBP EHrv LLWP MRav WCot
	'Sundowner' **new**	ECtt
	'Susanne Lucas' (Vt)	CGro
	'Susie' (Va)	WGoo
	'Swanley White'	see *V.* 'Conte di Brazza'
	'Sybil' (SP)	WGoo
§	'The Czar' (Vt)	CBre CLAP ELon SHar WCot
	'Tiger Eyes' (Va)	CMea SPoG
	'Titania' (Va)	EBee
	'Tom Tit' (Va)	ECtt WGoo
	'Tony Venison' (C/v)	ELon EPfP GWyn NEgg NLar WFar WGoo WHer
	tricolor	CHab CWld ECho ENfk EPfP GPoy LCro MHer MNHC SIde SRms WBod WJek
	- 'Sawyer's Black'	ENfk
	vaginata	GEdr
	verecunda B&SWJ 604a	WCru
§	- var. ***yakusimana***	WThu
	'Victoria'	see *V.* 'Czar Bleu'
	'Victoria Cawthorne' (C)	EWoo GAbr GBuc MAsh MHer NDov WBod WGoo
	'Violacea' (C)	EWoo
	'Virginia' (Va)	GWyn WGoo
	'Vita' (Va)	ECtt EWoo SRms WGoo
	'Wasp' (Va)	ECtt
	'White Ladies'	see *V. cucullata* 'Alba'
	'White Pearl' (Va)	SPhx WGoo
	'White Perfection' (C)	GWyn
	'White Swan' (Va)	MAsh
	'White Witch' (Vt)	EBee
	'Winifred Jones' (Va)	GKev WGoo
	'Winona Cawthorne' (C)	EWoo
	'Wisley White'	LHop LRHS
	× ***wittrockiana*** Matrix Series	NPri
	'Woodlands Cream' (Va)	GWyn MHer WGoo
	'Woodlands Lilac' (Va)	WGoo
	yakusimana	see *V. verecunda* var. *yakusimana*
	yezoensis	SBrt
	'Zara' (Va)	WGoo
	'Zoe' (Vtta)	CBod ECtt EPfP GWyn MAsh NEgg SPoG WFar WGoo

Viscaria (*Caryophyllaceae*)

	vulgaris	see *Lychnis viscaria*

Vitaliana (*Primulaceae*)

§	***primuliflora***	ECho EDAr EPot GKev NRya NSla
	- subsp. ***assoana***	WAbe
	- subsp. ***chionantha***	WAbe
	- subsp. ***praetutiana***	EPot GCrg NHar NWad WThu

Vitex (*Lamiaceae*)

	agnus-castus	CArn CBcs CMCN EPri EShb GPoy IDee LEdu LRHS MRav NLar SEND SLon SPer SPoG WSHC XSen
	- f. ***alba***	CDul CWib MBlu NLar
	- - PAB 9281 **new**	LEdu
	- - 'Silver Spire'	CBot EBee ECre ELan EMil EPfP LRHS NLar SPoG WPGP
	- f. ***latifolia*** 🏆^{H5}	CAco CBot CWib EBee ECre ELan EPfP LRHS LSRN MGos MHer NLar SDix SPoG WPGP XSen
	chinensis	see *V. negundo* var. *heterophylla*
	incisa	see *V. negundo* var. *heterophylla*
	negundo	CArn LEdu
§	- var. ***heterophylla***	EWes XSen
	trifolia 'Purpurea' **new**	LRHS

Vitis ✿ (*Vitaceae*)

	'Abundante' (F)	WSuV
	'Alden' (O/B)	WSuV
	'Amandin' (G/W)	WSuV
	amurensis	EPfP EWoo LPre
	- B&SWJ 4138	WCru
	- B&SWJ 4299	WCru
	- B&SWJ 12568	WCru
	'Atlantis' (O/W)	WSuV
§	'Aurore' (W)	CAgr WSuV
	'Baco Noir' (O/B)	CAgr CLet SDea WSuV
	'Bata' **new**	SDea
	'Beauty Seedless' (B/S)	SDea
	betulifolia	EPfP
	'Bianca' (O/W)	WSuV
	'Birstaller Muscat' (W)	WSuV
	Black Hamburgh	see *V. vinifera* 'Schiava Grossa'
*	'Black Strawberry' (B)	CAgr SDea WSuV
	'Blanc Seedless' (W/S)	SDea
§	'Boskoop Glory' (O/B) 🏆^{H5}	CMac EMOT ERea ETod LBuc NLar SCob SCoo SDea WHar WSuV
	'Brant' (O/B) 🏆^{H5}	Widely available
	'Brilliant' (B)	WSuV
	'Buffalo' (B)	WSuV
	'Cabernet Cortis' (B) **new**	WSuV
	californica (F)	EPfP NLar

'Canadice' (O/R/S)	SDea WSuV
'Cascade'	see *V.* Seibel 13053
Castel 19637 (B)	WSuV
'Chambourcin' (B)	WSuV
Claret Cloak = 'Frovit'PBR ♀H5	CBot CLet ELan EPfP EUJe GBin LPre LRHS LSRN MAsh MBlu NLar NRHS SCoo SPer SPtp WPGP
coignetiae ♀H5	Widely available
- B&SWJ 4550 from Korea	WCru
- B&SWJ 4744	WCru
- B&SWJ 8553 from Korea	WCru
- B&SWJ 10882 from Japan	WCru
- B&SWJ 10908 from Japan	WCru
- var. ***glabrescens*** B&SWJ 8537	WCru
- 'Purple Cloak'	SCob
- Sunningdale form	NLar WGrn
'Dalkauer' (W)	WSuV
I 'Diamond' (B)	WSuV
'Dutch Black' (O/B)	WSuV
'Edwards No 1' (O/W)	WSuV
'Eger Csillaga' (O/W)	WSuV
'Einset' (B/S)	WSuV
ficifolia	see *V. thunbergii*
flexuosa B&SWJ 5568	WCru
- B&SWJ 6304 **new**	WCru
- var. ***choii*** B&SWJ 4101	WCru
- var. ***parvifolia***	NLar
- - B&SWJ 1946	WCru
'Fragola' (O/R)	CAgr CDul CFGn CMac CTri ECha EPom ERea GTwe LRHS MCoo MRav NLar SBdl SDea SLim SPoG SRms WMat WSuV
'Gagarin Blue' (O/B)	CAgr EPom GTwe SDea SVen WSuV
'Glenora' (F/B/S)	CAgr WSuV
'Hecker' (O/W)	WSuV
henryana	see *Parthenocissus henryana*
'Himrod' (O/W/S)	CCCN ELan ERea GTwe SDea WSuV
'Horizon' (O/W)	WSuV
inconstans	see *Parthenocissus tricuspidata*
'Interlaken' (O/W/S)	CAgr ERea SDea WSuV
'Johanniter' (W)	SPre WSuV
'Kempsey Black' (O/B)	CAgr WSuV
'Kozmapalme Muscatoly' (O/W)	WSuV
'Kuibishevski' (O/R)	WSuV
Landot 244 (O/B)	WSuV
Landot 3217 (O/B)	WSuV
'L'Arcadie Blanche' (W)	WSuV
'Léon Millot' (O/G/B)	CAgr CSBt LSRN SDea WSuV
'Lucy Kuhlman' (B)	WSuV
'Maréchal Foch' (O/B)	WSuV
'Maréchal Joffre' (O/R)	CAgr GTwe WSuV
'Mars' (O/B/S)	WSuV
'Merzling' (O/W)	WSuV
'Munson R.W.' (O/R)	WSuV
'Muscat Bleu' (O/B)	CCCN CFGn EPom LRHS NLar SKee SLim WMat WSuV
'Nero'PBR	CAgr
'New York Muscat' (O/B) ♀H5	WSuV
'New York Seedless' (O/W/S)	WSuV
'Niagara' (O/W)	WSuV
'Niederother Monschrebe' (O/R)	WSuV
Oberlin 595 (O/B)	WSuV
'Orion' (O/W)	LRHS MAsh NRHS WSuV
'Paletina' (O/W)	WSuV
'Perdin' (O/W)	WSuV
'Phönix' (O/W)	CAgr CCCN EPom GTwe LBuc LCro LOPS LRHS LSRN MAsh MGos NLar NPla NRHS SKee SLim SPre SVic WMat WSuV
piasezkii var. ***pagnuccii***	WCru
* 'Pink Strawberry' (O)	WSuV
'Pirovano 14' (O/B)	GTwe SDea WSuV
§ 'Plantet' (O/B)	WSuV
'Poloske Muscat' (W)	CCCN EPom ERea NLar WMat WSuV
pulchra	WCru
purpurea 'Spetchley Park' (O/B)	CAgr WSuV
quinquefolia	see *Parthenocissus quinquefolia*
'Ramdas' (O/W)	WSuV
Ravat 51 (O/W)	WSuV
'Rayon d'Or' (O/W)	WSuV
'Regent'PBR (O/B)	CAgr CCCN EPom ERea LCro LOPS LRHS MCoo MGos NLar SKee SLim SPoG SPre SVic WMat WSuV
'Reliance' (O/R/S)	CAgr ERea WSuV
'Rembrant' (R)	CAgr WSuV
riparia	NLar
'Romulus' (O/G/W/S)	WSuV
'Rondo' (O/B)	CAgr LRHS NPla SDea SPre SVic WMat WSuV
'Saturn' (O/R/S)	CAgr WSuV
'Schuyler' (O/B)	CAgr WSuV
Seibel (F)	EPfP GTwe SDea
Seibel 5279	see *V.* 'Aurore'
Seibel 5409 (W)	WSuV
Seibel 5455	see *V.* 'Plantet'
Seibel 7053	WSuV
Seibel 9549	WSuV
§ Seibel 13053 (O/B)	CMac LRHS MAsh NRHS SDea SEND WSuV
Seibel 138315 (R)	WSuV
'Seneca' (W)	WSuV
'Serena' (O/W)	WSuV
§ 'Seyval Blanc' (O/W)	CAgr GTwe MAsh SDea SEND SVic WSuV
Seyve Villard ambig.	LRHS NPer
Seyve Villard 12.375	see *V.* 'Villard Blanc'
Seyve Villard 20.473 (F)	NPer
Seyve Villard 5276	see *V.* 'Seyval Blanc'
'Sirius' (B)	WSuV
'Solaris' (O/W)	LRHS MCoo NLar SFrt WMat WSuV
'Stauffer' (O/W)	WSuV
'Suffolk Seedless' (B/S)	ERea GTwe WSuV
'Tereshkova' (O/B)	CAgr SDea WSuV
'Thornton' (O/S)	WSuV
§ ***thunbergii*** B&SWJ 4702	WCru
'Triomphe d'Alsace' (O/B)	CAgr CSBt LRHS MCoo NPer NRHS SDea WSuV
'Trollinger'	see *V. vinifera* 'Schiava Grossa'
'Vanessa' (O/R/S)	SDea WSuV
§ 'Villard Blanc' (O/W)	WSuV
vinifera	EUJe
- EM 323158B	WSuV
- 'Abouriou' (O/B)	WSuV
- 'Acolon' (O/B)	WSuV
- 'Adelheidtraube' (O/W)	WSuV
- 'Albalonga' (W)	WSuV
§ - 'Alicante' (G/B)	CBcs CMac GTwe SDea WSuV
- 'Augusta Louise' (O/W)	WSuV
- 'Auxerrois' (O/W)	WSuV
- 'Bacchus' (O/W)	CAgr ERea LRHS NLar SDea SFrt SLim SVic WMat WSuV

- 'Baresana' (G/W) EMOT NPla WSuV
- 'Beauty' CAgr
- 'Black Alicante' see *V. vinifera* 'Alicante'
- 'Black Beauty' new SDea
- 'Black Corinth' (G/B/S) ERea
- 'Black Frontignan' (G/O/B) WSuV
- Black Hamburgh see *V. vinifera* 'Schiava Grossa'
- 'Black Monukka' (G/B/S) WSuV
- 'Black Prince' (G/B) CAgr WSuV
- 'Blue Portuguese' see *V. vinifera* 'Portugieser'
- § 'Bouvier' (W) WSuV
- 'Bouviertraube' see *V. vinifera* 'Bouvier'
- 'Buckland Sweetwater' (G/W) CLet GTwe SDea SLim WSuV
- 'Cabernet Sauvignon' (O/B) EPfP EUJe LRHS MAsh MGos NPer NPri NRHS SDea SVic WSuV
- 'Cardinal' (O/R) WSuV
- 'Carla' (O/R) WSuV
- 'Centennial' (O/N/S) WSuV
- 'Chardonnay' (O/W) CAgr CCCN LRHS LSRN MAsh NPer NPri SDea SPer SPre SVic WSuV
- § 'Chasselas' (G/O/W) LRHS SDea WSuV
- 'Chasselas de Fontainebleau' (F) SVic
- 'Chasselas d'Or' see *V. vinifera* 'Chasselas'
- 'Chasselas Rosé' (G/R) CAgr WSuV
- 'Chasselas Rosé Royal' (O/R) CCCN SVic
- 'Chasselas Vibert' (G/W) WSuV
- 'Chenin Blanc' (O/W) SVic WSuV
- 'Ciotat' (F) ERea EShb MRav SDea WSuV
- 'Cot Précoce de Tours' (O/B) WSuV
- 'Crimson Seedless' (R/S) ERea WSuV
- 'Csabagyöngye' (O/W) WSuV
- 'Dattier de Beyrouth' (G/W) WSuV
- 'Dattier Saint Vallier' (O/W) SVic WSuV
- 'Dolcetto' (O/B) WSuV
- 'Dornfelder' (O/R) CCCN CFGn ERea NLar SLim SVic WMat WSuV
- 'Dunkelfelder' (O/R) WSuV
- 'Early Van der Laan' (F) CMac
- 'Ehrenfelser' (O/W) WSuV
- 'Elbling' (O/W) WSuV
- 'Exalta' (G/W/S) CCCN WSuV
- 'Excelsior' (W) SDea WSuV
- 'Faber' (O/W) WSuV
- 'Fiesta' (W/S) WSuV
- 'Findling' (W) WSuV
- 'Flame' CAgr NPla SBdl SVic WHar WMat
- 'Flame Red' (O/D) CCCN EPom
- 'Flame Seedless' (G/O/R/S) CMac EPom GTwe LRHS SFrt WSuV
- 'Forta' (O/W) WSuV
- 'Foster's Seedling' (G/W) MJak SDea SVic WSuV
- 'Freisamer' (O/W) WSuV
- 'Frühburgunder' (O/B) WSuV
- 'Gamay Hâtif des Vosges' WSuV
- 'Gamay Noir' (O/B) SVic WSuV
- Gamay Teinturier Group (O/B) WSuV
- 'Gewürztraminer' (O/R) LRHS MAsh NRHS SDea SVic WSuV
- 'Glory of Boskoop' see *V.* 'Boskoop Glory'
- 'Golden Chasselas' see *V. vinifera* 'Chasselas'
- 'Goldriesling' (O/W) WSuV
- 'Gros Colmar' (G/B) WSuV
- 'Grüner Veltliner' (O/W) WSuV
- 'Gutenborner' (O/W) WSuV
- 'Helfensteiner' (O/R) WSuV
- 'Huxelrebe' (O/W) SVic WSuV
- 'Incana' (O/B) ELon LRHS MRav SVen WCFE WCot WPGP WSHC
- 'Irsay Olive'r' (O/W) WSuV
- 'Italia' (O/W) NPla
- 'Juliaumsrebe' (O/W) WSuV
- 'Kanzler' (O/W) WSuV
- 'Kerner' (O/W) WSuV
- 'Kernling' (F) WSuV
- 'King's Ruby' (F/S) ERea WSuV
- 'Lady Hastings' (G/B) ERea
- 'Lakemont' (O/W/S) CAgr CCCN CFGn CMac ELan EMOT EPfP EPom ERea GTwe MGos NLar NPla NPri NRHS SDea SEWo SFrt SKee SLim SPoG SPre SVic WHar WMat WSuV
- 'Lival' (O/B) WSuV
- 'Madeira Frontignan' (G/R) ERea
- 'Madeleine Angevine' (O/W) CAgr GTwe LRHS LSRN MAsh NPer NPri NRHS SDea SPoG SVen SVic WSuV
- 'Madeleine Celine' (B) WSuV
- 'Madeleine Royale' (G/W) WSuV
- 'Madeleine Silvaner' (O/W) CSBt GTwe LRHS MAsh NPer NRHS SDea SPoG WSuV
- 'Madresfield Court' (G/B) GTwe WSuV
- 'Merlot' (G/B) EUJe LRHS NRHS SDea SVic WSuV
- § 'Meunier' (B) SVic WSuV
- 'Mireille' (F) SDea WSuV
- 'Morio Muscat' (O/W) WSuV
- 'Mrs Pearson' (G/W) ERea
- § 'Müller-Thurgau' (O/W) LRHS LSRN MAsh NRHS SDea SVic WSuV
- 'Muscat Blanc à Petits Grains' (O/W) SWvt WSuV
- 'Muscat Cannon Hall' (G/W) CHll
- 'Muscat de Lierval' (O/B) WSuV
- 'Muscat de Saumur' (O/W) WSuV
- 'Muscat Hamburg' (G/B) LRHS LSRN MAsh NRHS SDea SWvt WSuV
- 'Muscat of Alexandria' (G/W) CBcs CCCN CMac CRHN ERea LRHS MRav NRHS SDea SFrt SLim SPer SVic WHar WMat
- 'Muscat Ottonel' (O/W) WSuV
- 'Muscat Saint Laurent' (W) WSuV
- 'Nebbiolo' (O/B) WSuV
- 'No 69' (W) WSuV
- 'Noblessa' (W) WSuV
- 'Noir Hâtif de Marseille' (O/B) WSuV
- 'Olive Blanche' (O/W) WSuV
- 'Optima' (O/W) WSuV
- 'Ora' (O/W/S) WSuV
- 'Ortega' (O/W) CCCN WSuV
- 'Palatina' (O/W) SFrt
- 'Perle' (O/W) WSuV
- 'Perlette' (O/W/S) CCCN EPom ERea GTwe LRHS WSuV
- 'Petit Rouge' (R) WSuV
- 'Pinot Blanc' (O/W) CCCN LCro LOPS LRHS MAsh SVic WSuV
- 'Pinot Gris' (O/B) SDea SVic WSuV
- 'Pinot Noir' (O/B) CCCN SVic WSuV
- § 'Portugieser' (O/B) WSuV
- 'Précoce de Bousquet' (O/W) WSuV
- 'Précoce de Malingre' (O/W) CAgr SDea

	- 'Prima' (O/B)	WSuV
	- 'Primavis Frontignan' (G/W)	WSuV
	- 'Purpurea' (O/B) ♀H5	Widely available
	- 'Queen of Esther' (B)	SLim WSuV
	- 'Regner' (O/W)	WSuV
	- 'Reichensteiner' (O/G/W)	CAgr SDea SVic WSuV
	- 'Riesling' (O/W)	CCCN LRHS MAsh SVic WSuV
	- Riesling-Silvaner	see *V. vinifera* 'Müller-Thurgau'
	- 'Rotberger' (O/G/B)	WSuV
	- 'Royal Muscadine' (G/O/W)	GQue SBdl WMat WSuV
	- 'Saint Laurent' (G/O/W)	SVic WSuV
	- 'Sauvignon Blanc' (O/W)	CCCN LRHS NRHS SVic WSuV
	- 'Scheurebe' (O/W)	WSuV
§	- 'Schiava Grossa' (G/B/D)	Widely available
	- 'Schönburger' (O/W)	SDea SVic WSuV
	- 'Schwarzriesling'	see *V. vinifera* 'Meunier'
	- 'Sémillon'	LRHS LSRN MAsh SVic
	- 'Senator' (O/W)	WSuV
	- 'Septimer' (O/W)	WSuV
	- 'Shiraz' (B)	WSuV
	- 'Siegerrebe' (O/W/D)	CAgr LBuc LRHS MAsh NPer SDea SPoG SVic WSuV
	- 'Silvaner' (O/W)	WSuV
	- 'Spetchley Red' (O/B) ♀H5	CKel CRHN EBee NLar WAvo WCot WCru WPGP WPat
	- strawberry grape	see *V.* 'Fragola'
	- 'Suffolk Red' (G/R/S)	ERea SDea
§	- 'Sultana' (W/S)	CAgr NPla SDea WSuV
	- 'Theresa' (O/W)	SLim WSuV
	- 'Thompson Seedless'	see *V. vinifera* 'Sultana'
*	- 'Triomphe' (O/B)	SVic
	- 'Triomphrebe' (W)	WSuV
	- 'Vroege van der Laan' (O/W)	EMOT ETod MJak NLar
	- 'Wrotham Pinot' (O/B)	SDea WSuV
	- 'Würzer' (O/W)	WSuV
	- 'Zweigeltrebe' (O/B)	WSuV
*	'White Strawberry' (O/W)	WSuV
	'Zalagyöngye' (W)	CAgr WSuV

Vriesea (*Bromeliaceae*)

'Era' PBR **new**	NLos
gigantea 'Nova'	NLos
splendens ♀H1a	NLos SPlb XBlo

W

Wachendorfia (*Haemodoraceae*)

multiflora	CLak CTal SVen
paniculata	CLak CTal
thyrsiflora	CBcs CPne EBee LEdu NLos SVen WPGP

Wahlenbergia (*Campanulaceae*)

albomarginata	ECho
- 'Blue Mist'	ECho
congesta	ECho
pumilio	see *Edraianthus pumilio*
serpyllifolia	see *Edraianthus serpyllifolius*

Waldsteinia (*Rosaceae*)

fragarioides	EBee IMou
geoides	EBee EPPr MGil MMuc NEoE SHil SPer WMoo XLum
- 'Goldkäfer'	IMou
ternata	Widely available
§ - 'Mozaick' (v)	EBee EPPr EShb EWes NBir NEoE
- 'Variegata'	see *W. ternata* 'Mozaick'

walnut, black see *Juglans nigra*

walnut, common see *Juglans regia*

Wasabia (*Brassicaceae*)

wasabi	CArn GPoy LEdu

Washingtonia (*Arecaceae*)

× ***filibusta*** ♀H1c	CCCN CPHo LTro SArc SBig SEND SPlb
robusta	LTro SPlb

Watsonia (*Iridaceae*)

	aletroides	CTre EBee ECho GBin GCal GKev SDeJ SVen
	amatolae	IBlr
	angusta	CPne CPrp CTal EBee IBlr SPlb WPGP
	ardernei	see *W. borbonica* subsp. *ardernei* 'Arderne's White'
	'Ballyrogan Early Pink' **new**	IBlr
	beatricis	see *W. pillansii*
§	***borbonica***	CPne CPrp EBee
	- subsp. ***ardernei*** misapplied	see *W. borbonica* subsp. *ardernei* 'Arderne's White'
§	- subsp. ***ardernei*** 'Arderne's White'	CBre CPrp GBin GCal IBlr
	- subsp. ***borbonica***	CTal IBlr WPGP
	- 'Peach Glow'	ERCP GKev
	brevifolia	see *W. laccata*
	brick red-flowered	EBee WPGP
	coccinea Herb. ex Baker	CBlu CTre
	'Dart Sea Trout'	EBee
	densiflora	CTal
	early pink-flowered	CPne
	fourcadei	ECre GCal
	fulgens	LEdu
	galpinii lavender-flowered	IBlr
	- pink-flowered	IBlr
	galpinii × ***knysnana***	IBlr
I	'Gigantea' **new**	LRHS
§	***humilis***	EBee GCal SKHP
	knysnana	EBee IBlr
§	***laccata***	CPne CTre
	- orange-flowered	CTal
	- pink-flowered	EBee
	latifolia	IBlr
	lepida	CTre ECho SPlb
	× ***longifolia*** dark red-flowered	GCal
	marginata	CPrp CTre EBee ECho
	- ***alba***	SKHP
	meriana	CPne EBee ERCP GBin GKev IBlr MHer
	- var. ***bulbillifera***	CPne CPrp CTal EBee ECho GAbr GBin GCal GCra IBlr LTro WSHC
	'Peachy Pink Orphan'	EBee WPGP
§	***pillansii***	CCCN CPne CPrp CTal EBee ECre EPri EWld GBin IBlr ILea LEdu LRHS NCGa SVen
	- apricot-flowered **new**	LRHS
	- pink-flowered	CPrp IVic
	- red-flowered	IVic

- soft pink-flowered	EPri
pink-flowered	EBee
pyramidata	see *W. borbonica*
roseoalba	see *W. humilis*
'Stanford Scarlet'	CAby CPrp EBee ELon IBlr WPGP
tabularis	CPne CPrp IMou
transvaalensis	EBee
'Tresco Dwarf Pink'	EBee LEdu WPGP
Tresco hybrids	CAbb CBcs CTre EPri SRkn
vanderspuyae	CPne CPrp CTal EPri
wilmaniae	CPne CPrp EBee IBlr WFar WPGP
- JCA 3.955200	SKHP
- 'Ice Angel'	SKHP
wordsworthiana	GCal
zeyheri	EBee

Wattakaka see *Dregea*

Wedelia (*Asteraceae*)

trilobata	see *Sphagneticola trilobata*

Weigela ✿ (*Caprifoliaceae*)

'Abel Carrière'	CMac CTri ECtt NWea WCFE
All Summer Red = 'Slingco 1' **new**	LCro LRHS SPoG
§ 'Avalanche'	EPfP
'Avalanche' misapplied	see *W.* 'Candida'
'Avalanche' Lemoine	see *W.* 'Avalanche'
'Avant Garde'	IArd MAsh WPat
Black and White = 'Courtacad1'^{PBR}	CBot CWGN EBee EPfP LRHS LSRN NEoE NLar SCob SEle SGol SHil SPoG
'Boskoop Glory'	GQui SPer
'Bouquet Rose'	LPot
§ Briant Rubidor = 'Olympiade' (v)	CBcs CBot CMac CRos EBee ECrN EHoe ESps GMcL LRHS MAsh MGos MMuc MRav NEgg NLar SCob SGol SHil SLim SPer SPlb SPoG WHar WHil
'Bristol Ruby'	Widely available
'Bristol Snowflake'	CDul CMac EPfP EWTr MBlu MHer MSwo NBir NLar SLon
§ 'Candida'	CTri ELan MRav NLar SGol SPer
Cappuccino = 'Verweig 2'^{PBR}	MBlu MJak NLar SGol
Carnaval = 'Courtalor'^{PBR} 🏆H6	CBcs CWib GMcL LSou MRav NLar SCob
'Chameleon'	MPkF NEoE
coraeensis 🏆H6	CHll EPfP IArd MBlu MGil MMrt MNrw SBrt SPer WPat
- 'Alba'	CHll
Crimson Kisses	see All Summer Red
decora	GQui
- B&SWJ 10834	WCru
'Ebony and Ivory' **new**	CRos LCro LRHS
'Eva Rathke'	NBir NLar NWea
'Evita'	IBoy MBlu
floribunda B&SWJ 10831	WCru
florida	CDul CMac ESps NBes
- B&SWJ 8439	WCru
- f. ***alba***	CBcs
- 'Bicolor'	CMac ELan
- 'Foliis Purpureis'	Widely available
- 'Gustave Malet'	CMCN GQui
- Magical Rainbow = 'Kolmagira'^{PBR}	LBrs LBuc LCro LRHS MPkF NEoE SGol SPoG
- 'Milk and Honey'	LRHS
- Minor Black = 'Verweig 3'^{PBR}	EPfP GMcL LRHS MGos MPkF NBro NEoE NHol NLar SPoG WMoo
- Monet = 'Verweig'^{PBR} (v)	Widely available
- Moulin Rouge = 'Brigela'^{PBR}	CBcs CRos ELan EPfP LRHS MAsh MGos NQui SLim WCot
- 'Pink Princess'	EMil LRHS MSwo WHar
- Rubigold	see *W.* Briant Rubidor
§ - Sunny Fantasy = 'Kolsunn'	MPkF
'Florida Variegata' (v) 🏆H6	Widely available
florida 'Versicolor'	CMHG CWib GQui SLon
- Wine and Roses = 'Alexandra'^{PBR} 🏆H6	CAbP CBot CLet CRos CSBt EAEE EHoe ELan EMil EPfP ESps GKin IBoy LBMP LRHS LSRN MAsh MGos MRav NBro NEgg NLar SCob SEle SHil SPoG SRGP SRkn SWvt WGrn
- 'Wings of Fire'	LBuc LRHS SCob SHil
'Gold Rush'	NLar
'Golden Candy'	NEoE SCob
hortensis	WCru
B&SWJ 10808 **new**	
'Hulsdonk'	NLar
japonica 'Dart's Colourdream'	EHoe EWes MMrt MMuc SCob SEND SGol WGrn
- 'Variegated Dart's Colourdream' (v)	ELon
'Jean's Gold'	ELan MBlu MRav
'Kosteriana Variegata' (v)	CSBt EBee EPfP ESps LRHS MAsh MMuc NEgg SEle SHil
'Little Red Robin'	ELon NEoE SCob
'Looymansii Aurea'	CBot CMHG CTri ELan EPfP NLar SGol SPer WBod
maximowiczii	GQui LLHF
§ ***middendorffiana***	Widely available
- 'Mango' **new**	LCro LRHS SHil
'Minuet'	LRHS MRav MSwo NEoE
'Mont-Blanc'	MAsh MMrt
Nain Rouge = 'Courtanin'^{PBR}	CTri NLar
'Nana Variegata' (v)	ECrN ELon EPfP GMcL LCro LRHS MJak NLar SCob
Naomi Campbell = 'Bokrashine'^{PBR}	EBee EShb GKin MMrt NEgg NLar SGol WHar WMoo
'Newport Red'	see *W.* 'Vanicek'
Pink Poppet = 'Plangen'^{PBR}	CAbP CBot CLet CRos CSBt ELan EPfP ESps GBin GKin LBMP LRHS LSRN LSou MAsh MGos MPkF NLar SCob SCoo SHil SLim SPoG SRkn SWvt
praecox	ECrN
- B&SWJ 8705	WCru
'Praecox Variegata' (v) 🏆H6	CMac CTri EPfP ESps LRHS MAsh MRav NBir SDix SPer SPoG SRms WCFE WPat
'Red Prince' 🏆H6	CWCL ELan EPfP ESps GMcL LRHS MMrt MSwo NLar SCob SGol SHil SPoG WBod
Rubidor	see *W.* Briant Rubidor
Rubigold	see *W.* Briant Rubidor
'Ruby Anniversary'	CBcs LBuc LRHS SLon
'Ruby Queen'^{PBR}	CMac EPfP
Ruby Wedding	LSRN
'Rumba'	CMac MRav
sessilifolia	see *Diervilla sessilifolia*
'Snowflake'	ECrN LPot SRms
'Stelzneri'	MMuc
subsessilis B&SWJ 1056	WCru
- B&SWJ 4206	WCru
'Suzanne' (v)	EPPr
'Tango'	LRHS MAsh NEoE
§ 'Vanicek'	GMcL MBNS NWea

	'Victoria'	CDul CMac CWib ECrN EHoe ELan EPPr EPfP ESps LRHS MGos MSwo NBir NWad SCob SGol SPer WHar WMoo

Weinmannia (*Cunoniaceae*)

	racemosa	IVic

Weldenia (*Commelinaceae*)

	candida	GEdr IBlr LLHF NHar SChF

Westringia (*Lamiaceae*)

	brevifolia	SVen
	- 'Grace'	LRHS
§	***fruticosa*** ♀H1c	CBcs CCCN CHll SRms SVen WJek
	- 'Smokie' (v)	CCCN CTsd
	- 'Variegata' (v)	CCCN CTre SRms SVen WJek
	longifolia	CCCN
	rosmariniformis	see *W. fruticosa*
	'Wynyabbie Gem'	CAbb CCCN LRHS SEND SVen

whitecurrant see *Ribes rubrum* (W)

Wigandia (*Boraginaceae*)

	caracasana	CHll

Wikstroemia (*Thymelaeaceae*)

	gemmata	LRHS

wineberry see *Rubus phoenicolasius*

Wisteria ✿ (*Papilionaceae*)

	'Betty's Dwarf Blue'	NLar
§	***brachybotrys***	ERea SCob
§	- Murasaki-kapitan	CEnd CRos CTri CWGN EBtc EMil EPfP LRHS MMuc SEND SKHP
	- 'Okayama' ♀H5	EPfP ERea LRHS NOra SKHP SLau WMat
§	- 'Shiro-kapitan' ♀H5	CBcs CEnd CFlo CRHN CRos CTri CWGN EPfP LRHS LSRN MAsh MGos MMuc MRav NHol NLar SEND SHil SKHP SLau SLim SPer WPGP WPat
	- 'Showa-beni' ♀H5	CEnd CFlo CKel CRHN CRos CTri CWGN EPfP LRHS MGos MMuc NLar SCoo SEND SKHP SLau SLim SNig SPoG WPGP
*	- 'White Silk'	CBcs CKel CRos EPfP LRHS LSRN MGos NPla SLon SPoG
§	'Burford' ♀H5	CEnd CFlo CKel CWGN EBee EMil EPfP ERea LRHS LSRN MAsh NOra SCob SCoo SKHP SLau SLim WHar WMat WPGP
	'Caroline'	Widely available
	floribunda	CBcs CRHN CWib ELan ESps IBoy LPar SCob SEWo SGol WPat
	- B&SWJ 12748 from South Korea	WCru
§	- 'Alba' ♀H5	Widely available
	- 'Black Dragon'	see *W. floribunda* 'Yae-kokuryū' (d)
	- blue-flowered **new**	LPar
	- 'Burford'	see *W.* 'Burford'
	- 'Cascade'	CBcs SHil SNig
§	- 'Domino' ♀H5	Widely available
	- 'Ed's Blue Dragon' (d)	NPla SHil
	- 'Fragrantissima'	see *W. sinensis* 'Jako'
	- 'Geisha'	CBcs CEnd CFlo CKel CRos EBee ELon LRHS NRHS SEND SKHP SNig
	- 'Golden Dragon'	EPfP
	- 'Harlequin'	CBcs CFlo CRos ELon LBrs LRHS MMuc NPla SEND SKHP SNig
	- 'Hocker Edge'	SLau
	- 'Hon-beni'	see *W. floribunda* 'Rosea'
	- 'Honey Bee Pink'	see *W. floribunda* 'Rosea'
	- 'Honko'	see *W. floribunda* 'Rosea'
	- 'Issai Perfect'	CRos LRHS LSRN NLar SCoo SLon
	- 'Issai-naga'	ESps NLar SHil
	- 'Jakohn-fuji'	see *W. sinensis* 'Jako'
	- 'Kimono'	SKHP SLau
§	- 'Kuchi-beni'	CBcs CEnd CKel CRHN CRos ELan ETho GBin IBoy LCro LRHS LSRN MGos MMuc MRav NHol NLar SEND SHil SKHP SLau SMad SPer SPoG SRms WHar
	- 'Lawrence' ♀H5	CBcs CEnd CFlo CKel CRos CWGN EBtc LBrs LRHS NLar SKHP SLau
	- 'Lipstick'	see *W. floribunda* 'Kuchi-beni'
	- 'Longissima'	see *W. floribunda* 'Multijuga'
	- 'Longissima Alba'	see *W. floribunda* 'Alba'
	- 'Macrobotrys'	see *W. floribunda* 'Multijuga'
	- 'Magenta'	LRHS NPla
§	- 'Multijuga' ♀H5	Widely available
	- 'Nana Richin's Purple'	CEnd LRHS SLau
	- 'New Pink'	LRHS NRHS
	- 'Peaches and Cream'	see *W. floribunda* 'Kuchi-beni'
	- 'Pink Ice'	see *W. floribunda* 'Rosea'
	- Reindeer	see *W. sinensis* 'Jako'
§	- 'Rosea' ♀H5	Widely available
	- 'Royal Purple' ♀H5	CEnd EMil EPfP IArd NLar SGol SKHP SLau SPoG
	- 'Russelliana'	CBcs CFlo CKel GBin
	- 'Shiro-naga'	see *W. floribunda* 'Alba'
	- 'Shiro-nagi'	see *W. floribunda* 'Alba'
	- 'Shiro-noda'	see *W. floribunda* 'Alba'
	- 'Snow Showers'	see *W. floribunda* 'Alba'
	- 'Variegata' (v)	CWGN
	- 'Violacea Plena' (d) ♀H5	CBcs CMac SKHP SNig SWvt
	- 'Yae-kokuryū' (d)	Widely available
	florida Magical Fantasy	see *Weigela florida* Sunny Fantasy
	× ***formosa***	CEnd LCro LOPS SLau SLim
	- 'Black Dragon'	see *W. floribunda* 'Yae-kokuryū'
	- 'Domino'	see *W. floribunda* 'Domino'
	- 'Issai' Wada *pro parte*	see *W. floribunda* 'Domino'
	- 'Kokuryū'	see *W. floribunda* 'Yae-kokuryū'
	- 'Yae-kokuryū'	see *W. floribunda* 'Yae-kokuryū'
	frutescens	EBee EPfP
	- 'Alba'	see *W. frutescens* 'Nivea'
	- 'Amethyst Falls' PBR	CBcs CEnd CWGN EBee ELan EShb ESps IArd LCro LRHS LSRN MGos SCoo SKHP SLon SPoG WMoo
	- 'Longwood Purple'	LRHS NRHS SNig SPoG
§	- 'Nivea'	LRHS NRHS
	Kapitan-fuji	see *W. brachybotrys*
	'Lavender Lace'	CBcs CKel EPfP LRHS LSRN MAsh MJak NLar SLau
	macrostachya 'Aunt Dee'	CWGN NLar
	- 'Blue Moon'	GMcL NOra WHar
	- 'Clara Mack'	CWGN
	multijuga 'Alba'	see *W. floribunda* 'Alba'
	sinensis	Widely available
	- 'Alba'	CAco CBcs CMen CRos CWib ELan EMOT EPfP ESps ETho IBoy LCro LPar LRHS LSRN MAsh MGos MSwo NPla SCob SLau SPer SPoG SWeb
	- 'Amethyst' ♀H5	CAco CBcs CEnd CKel CRos EPfP LCro LOPS LRHS LSRN MAsh

	MGos MJak MRav NPla NRHS SHil SKHP SLau SLim SPer SPoG SWeb WPat
- 'Consequa'	see *W. sinensis* 'Prolific'
- 'Cooke's Special'	CWGN
§ - 'Jako' ♀H5	CEnd NHol
- 'Oosthoek's Variety'	see *W. sinensis* 'Prolific'
- 'Prematura'	see *W. floribunda* 'Domino'
- 'Prematura Alba'	see *W. brachybotrys* 'Shiro-kapitan'
§ - 'Prolific' ♀H5	Widely available
- 'Rosea'	CAco LSRN SCob SWvt
- 'Shiro-capital'	see *W. brachybotrys* 'Shiro-kapitan'
'Tiverton'	CBcs MJak NPla
venusta	see *W. brachybotrys* 'Shiro-kapitan'
- 'Alba'	see *W. brachybotrys* 'Shiro-kapitan'
- var. ***violacea*** misapplied	see *W. brachybotrys* Murasaki-kapitan

Withania (*Solanaceae*)

somnifera	GPoy

Wittsteinia (*Alseuosmiaceae*)

vacciniacea	SBrt WCru

Wodyetia (*Arecaceae*)

bifurcata	XBlo

Wollemia (*Araucariaceae*)

nobilis	CDTJ CDul CTho EPfP ESwi EUJe GBin LPar MGos MHtn NWea SArc WBor

Woodsia ✿ (*Woodsiaceae*)

ilvensis	NLos
obtusa	CDTJ CKel CLAP CWCL EBee EFer EPfP ISha LRHS NBro NLar SGol SPoG SRot XLum
polystichoides	SRms
pseudopolystichoides	NLos

Woodwardia ✿ (*Blechnaceae*)

areolata	SKHP
fimbriata ♀H3	CBod CCCN CLAP CTal CWCL EFer ELon EMOT EPfP ERod EWTr GCal GEdr GMcL LCro LEdu LRHS NBro NHol NLar SBig SBod SEND SPer SPlb WFib WMoo WPGP WPat
japonica new	ESps
orientalis	ESwi ISha LEdu LRHS NLos WFib WPGP
- var. ***formosana*** B&SWJ 6865	ESwi WCru
radicans ♀H3	CHid CKel CLAP EShb EWes SArc WFib XBlo
unigemmata ♀H4	CLAP EFer EShb EWes ISha LRHS NLos SArc SKHP WAbe WFib WHal
virginica	CLAP ISha LRHS

Worcesterberry see *Ribes* 'Worcesterberry'

Wulfenia (*Plantaginaceae*)

amherstiana	GEdr GKev LEdu
baldaccii	GKev
carinthiaca	CTal EBee ECho GAbr GEdr GKev LEdu NBir NLar XLum
- 'Alba'	GKev
orientalis	CTal
× ***schwarzii***	EBee IMou LEdu WPGP WSHC

Wurmbea (*Colchicaceae*)

dioica	CLak
stricta	WCot

Wyethia (*Asteraceae*)

angustifolia	SBrt

X

Xanthisma (*Asteraceae*)

§ ***coloradoense***	LLHF NSla

Xanthoceras (*Sapindaceae*)

sorbifolium ♀H5	CAgr CBcs CLnd CMCN CWib EBee ELan EPfP IArd IMou MBlu NLar SBrt

Xanthocyparis (*Cupressaceae*)

§ ***nootkatensis***	IDee
- 'Boyko's Sundown' new	NLar
- 'Glauca'	NWea
- 'Golden Waterfall' new	NLar
- 'Green Arrow' ♀H6	CKen NOra SCoo SLim WHar WMat
- 'Jubilee'	SCoo SLim WCFE WHar WMat
- 'Lutea'	NWea
- 'Pendula' ♀H6	CCVT CDul CKen CLet ELan EPfP GKin LRHS MAsh MBlu NEgg NWea WCFE
- 'Sparkling Arrow' new	NLar
- 'Strict Weeper'	CKen NLar SLim
vietnamensis new	WPGP

Xanthorhiza (*Ranunculaceae*)

simplicissima	CArn CBcs CDul EPfP IVic LEdu MGil NLar SDys WCot WPGP

Xanthorrhoea (*Xanthorrhoeaceae*)

australis	SPlb
fulva	SPlb
glauca	CCCN
johnsonii	CKel SPlb
preisii	GBin SPlb

Xerochrysum (*Asteraceae*)

§ ***bracteatum***	SVen
§ - 'Coco'	CSpe
§ - 'Dargan Hill Monarch'	CHll CSpe SRms

Xeronema (*Xeronemataceae*)

callistemon	CBcs CBrP LRHS

Xerophyllum (*Melanthiaceae*)

tenax	LRHS

Y

Youngberry see *Rubus* 'Youngberry'

Ypsilandra (*Melanthiaceae*)

cavaleriei	GEdr WCot
thibetica	CBct CHid CLAP CSpe EBee ELon EPfP GCal GEdr GKev LEdu LLHF

		LRHS MNrw NLar SChF SMad WCru WPGP WSHC
	- narrow-leaved	WCru

Yucca ✿ (*Asparagaceae*)

	SDR 3701	GKev
	aloifolia	CCCN CDTJ ETod SArc SBig SCob SPlb
§	- f. ***marginata*** (v)	SBig
	- 'Purpurea'	EBee
I	- 'Spanish Bayonet'	LPar
	- 'Variegata'	see *Y. aloifolia* f. *marginata*
	angustifolia	see *Y. glauca*
	angustissima	SIgm
	arizonica	CDTJ
	baccata	CCCN ETod LTro NLos SIgm SPlb XSen
	campestris	CDTJ
	carnerosana	CBlu CDTJ
	cernua	WCot
	constricta	CDTJ
§	***elata***	CCCN LTro WPGP XSen
§	***elephantipes*** 𝕐H2	CDTJ ETod SEND
	- 'Jewel' (v)	SEND
	- 'Puck' (v)	SEND
	- variegated (v)	SEND
	faxoniana	CDTJ SPlb
	filamentosa	Widely available
	- 'Antwerp'	GCal
	- 'Bright Edge' (v) 𝕐H3	CBcs CDul CMHG CMac CTri ELan ELon EPfP ESps LRHS LSRN MJak MRav MSwo SChr SCob SLim SPer SWvt
	- 'Color Guard' (v) 𝕐H5	EPfP EUJe LRHS SChr
	- 'Garland's Gold' (v)	CBcs CCCN MJak SBig
	- 'Variegata' (v)	CBcs ESps SCob SRms
	filifera	SPlb
	flaccida	SCob
	- 'Golden Sword' (v) 𝕐H3	CBcs CLet CMac CTsd EBee ELan EPfP ESps GMaP GMcL LRHS LSRN MAsh MGos MSwo SCob SGol SLim SPer SWvt WHar
	- 'Ivory' 𝕐H5	CEnd CTsd ELan ELon ESps GBin GCal GMaP LSRN MRav NLar SPer SRms
	× ***floribunda***	SArc
§	***glauca***	EPfP LRHS LTro SPlb WCot XSen
	gloriosa 𝕐H5	CBcs CMac CTri ESps ETod GKev LPar MMuc NPla SArc SCob SEND SPer SPlb SPoG SWvt
	- 'Aureovariegata'	see *Y. gloriosa* 'Variegata'
	- Bright Star = 'Walbristar'PBR	LBuc LHop SCob SPer SPoG WCot
§	- 'Variegata' (v) 𝕐H5	CBcs CChe CDul CMHG CMac CSBt ECrN ELan ELon EPfP ESps EUJe GMaP LEdu LRHS MMuc MRav NLos SArc SCob SEND SLim SPer SPlb SPoG SRms SWvt WCFE
	guatemalensis	see *Y. elephantipes*
	harrimaniae	SIgm
	linearifolia	WCot
	linearis	see *Y. thompsoniana*
	mexicana **new**	CDTJ
	pallida	WPGP
	queretaroensis	CDTJ
	radiosa	see *Y. elata*
	recurvifolia 𝕐H5	EPfP ETod SArc
	- Banana Split = 'Monvil' (v)	EBee EPfP LBuc MAsh SPoG
	- 'Gold Stream' (v)	WCot
	rigida	CDTJ LTro WCot WPGP XSen
	rostrata	CBlu CCCN CDTJ ETod EUJe LPar SArc SPlb WCot XSen
	- 'Sapphire Skies'	EUJe LRHS NLos WCot
	rupicola	WCot
	schottii	EShb
§	***thompsoniana***	CDTJ LTro SIgm XSen
	torreyi	CDTJ SIgm
	'Vittorio Emanuele II'	SMad
	whipplei	CBcs CCCN EBee ELan EPfP LRHS LTro SBig WPGP XSen
	- subsp. ***caespitosa*** NNS 01-412	WCot
	- subsp. ***intermedia*** NNS 01-413	WCot
	- subsp. ***whipplei*** NJM 11.001	WPGP

Yushania (*Poaceae*)

	KR 7698	ERod MWht
§	***anceps***	CAgr CBcs CDul CEnt ENBC MMuc MWht SBig SEND WMoo
	- 'Pitt White'	CEnt CJng MWht
	- 'Pitt White Rejuvenated'	ERod
	brevipaniculata	CJng ERod
	chungii	CDul CEnt CJng ERod MWht
*	***equatus***	CJng
	maculata	CDul CEnt CJng ERod MWht SBig
§	***maling***	CJng ERod
	Yunnan 5	MWht

Z

Zabelia (*Caprifoliaceae*)

§	***triflora***	CWib LHop MMuc NLar SBrt SEND SKHP WGob WSHC

Zaluzianskya (*Scrophulariaceae*)

	JCA 15665	WAbe
	elongata	SPlb
	microsiphon	SPlb
	'Orange Eye'	CTal CTre CWCL EBee EWes GKev NHpl NSla WIce
	ovata	CElw CPBP CSpe CTal CTre CWCL EPfP EWld GBin GKev LCro LOPS MHer MMuc NSla SIgm SPad SPlb SPoG SPtp WIce
	- orange-eyed	SIgm
	pulvinata	SPlb
	'Semonkong'	GCal SWvt

Zamia (*Zamiaceae*)

	furfuracea 'Super' **new**	NLos
	pumila	SPlb

Zamioculcas (*Araceae*)

	zamiifolia	CCCN

Zantedeschia (*Araceae*)

§	***aethiopica***	Widely available
	- 'Crowborough' 𝕐H4	Widely available
	- 'Glencoe'	GCal
	- 'Glow'	CMac ECtt EWoo WAvo WGwG
	- 'Green Goddess' 𝕐H2	Widely available
	- 'Little Gem'	SMad
	- 'Luzon Lovely'	WCru
	- 'Marshmallow'	CAby ECtt ELan EPfP LRHS MAsh WGwG

- 'Mr Martin'	CCCN ECtt ELon SBig SMad SWvt WCot
- 'Pershore Fantasia' (v)	WAvo WCot
- 'Pink Mist' **new**	GKev
- 'Snow White'PBR	LRHS
- 'White Gnome'	WCot
- 'White Sail'	ECtt ELan LRHS MRav NGdn WGwG
albomaculata	CTca GKev LAma SPlb
'Anneke'	CCCN GKev
'Apricot Glow'	CHll ECho GKev
'Ascari'PBR	CCCN
'Auckland'PBR	GKev SDeJ
'Barcelona'PBR	NBri
'Best Gold'	see Z. 'Florex Gold'
'Black Eyed Beauty'	GKev LAma
'Black Magic'	CCCN CMac GKev
'Black Pearl'	LAma
'Black Star'	see Z. 'Edge of Night'
'Bolero' **new**	GKev
'Cameo'	CCCN GKev LAma SDeJ
'Cantor'PBR	LRHS NBri
(Captain Series) 'Captain Florida' **new**	SDir
- 'Captain Marrero'PBR	NBri
- 'Captain Murano'PBR	SPoG
- 'Captain Prado'PBR	CRos EPfP LRHS NBri NRHS
- 'Captain Reno'PBR	EPfP SPoG
- 'Captain Romance'PBR	LOPS
- 'Captain Tendens'PBR	GKev SDeJ
'Chianti'	GKev SDeJ
'Crystal Blush'	LAma SDeJ SDir WHar
§ 'Edge of Night'	CBcs CCCN GKev NBri SDeJ
'Elegant Swan'PBR	NBri SCob
elliottiana ♀H1c	CBcs CTri EUJe LAma
'Esm Puc'PBR	ECho
'Flame'	CBcs CCCN GKev
'Flamingo'PBR	GKev WCot
'Flavo Gold'	ECho
§ 'Florex Gold'	GKev
'Galaxy'	GKev
'Garnet Glow'	SDir WHar
'Hercules'	ESwi
'Hot Chocolate'PBR **new**	GKev
'Hot Shot'	GKev
'Innocence' **new**	GKev
jucunda **new**	GKev
'Kiwi Blush'	CAby CBod CBro CCCN CLet CSpe ELan ELon EPfP LRHS SEND SKHP SPer WFar WGwG
'Lime Lady'	ECha EWay
'Mango'	EPri GKev LAma MPie
'Medusa'PBR	GKev
'Memories'PBR **new**	NBri
'Mercedes'PBR **new**	LRHS
'Mozart'	CCCN
'Odessa'PBR	LOPS SPoG
'Orange Tycoon'PBR	NBri
'Passion' **new**	GKev
'Passionfruit'PBR **new**	GKev
'Philomena'	LRHS
'Picasso'PBR	CBcs CCCN EPfP GKev NBri SDeJ SDir SPad SPoG WCot WHar
'Pink Mist'	LAma LLWG NBri SMad
'Pink Pearl' **new**	LRHS NRHS
'Pink Persuasion'	GKev LAma
'Pot of Gold'	GKev
'Purple Sensation'	MPie
'Red Alert'PBR	GKev NBri
'Red Sox'PBR	CCCN GKev SDeJ
rehmannii ♀H1c	ECho GKev LAma SDeJ SRms
'Renoir' **new**	GKev
'Samur'PBR	NBri
'San Remo'PBR **new**	GKev
'Sapporo'PBR	LRHS
'Schwarzwalder'PBR	GKev SDir
'Siberia'PBR	NBri
'Solfatare'	GKev
'Summer Sun'PBR **new**	LRHS
'Sunrise' **new**	GKev
'Treasure'	GKev
'White Giant'	EWay WPGP
'White Pixie'	EPfP

Zanthorhiza see *Xanthorhiza*

Zanthoxylum (*Rutaceae*)

acanthopodium GWJ 9287	WCru
- PAB 8760	LEdu
- WJC 13653 **new**	WCru
ailanthoides B&SWJ 11115 from Japan	WCru
- B&SWJ 11394 from Japan	WCru
- f. ***inermis*** RWJ 10048	WCru
americanum	ELan LEdu
armatum	CAgr SBrt
- B&SWJ 12753 **new**	WCru
- HWJK 2178	WCru
- NJM 11.080 **new**	WPGP
bungeanum	CArn
- BWJ 8040	WCru
clava-herculis	CFil
dissitum FMWJ 13498 **new**	WCru
fauriei B&SWJ 11080	WCru
aff. ***fauriei*** B&SWJ 11371	WCru
- B&SWJ 11523	WCru
laetum	CFil
- FMWJ 13175	WCru
- WWJ 11678	WCru
myriacanthum B&SWJ 11844	WCru
oxyphyllum	CMCN LEdu
- GWJ 9428	WCru
- HWJK 2131	WCru
piperitum	CAgr GPoy WJek
- B&SWJ 8543	WCru
- B&SWJ 11377	WCru
- B&SWJ 11433	WCru
- purple-leaved	CFil WPGP
schinifolium	CAgr LEdu
- B&SWJ 8593	WCru
- B&SWJ 11080	WCru
- B&SWJ 11391	WCru
simulans	CAgr CArn CBcs CDul IVic LEdu WPGP
stenophyllum	CMCN

Zauschneria (*Onagraceae*)

arizonica	see *Z. californica* subsp. *latifolia*
§ ***californica***	CFis CHll CTri ECho MBrN SLon SWat SWvt WBod WPnn XLum
§ - 'Dublin' ♀H4	Widely available
- 'Ed Carman'	ECha ECtt EUJe MMuc SEle
* - subsp. ***garrettii***	SDys SWat XLum
- 'Glasnevin'	see *Z. californica* 'Dublin'
§ - subsp. ***latifolia***	XLum
§ - subsp. ***mexicana***	SRms
- 'Olbrich Silver'	EBee ECha EWes LRHS WHoo WKif

- 'Western Hills' ♀H5	CFis CRos CSpe CTri ECha EPfP EWld LHop LRHS LSou MHer MMuc MRav SEND SIgm SPhx SWvt WHoo WTor XLum
§ ***cana***	ECha
- 'Sir Cedric Morris'	EPfP LRHS
- ***villosa***	see *Z. californica* subsp. *mexicana*
I 'Pumilio'	EPot MHer
§ ***septentrionalis***	WAbe

Zebrina see *Tradescantia*

Zehneria (*Cucurbitaceae*)

scabra	SVic

Zelkova ✿ (*Ulmaceae*)

abelicea	CMCN
carpinifolia	CDul CMCN NWea SPlb WPGP
- NJM 13.014 from Azerbaijan **new**	WPGP
- NJM 13.016 from Azerbaijan **new**	WPGP
- PAB 13.047 **new**	LEdu
'Kiwi Sunset'	EPfP NWea WMat
serrata ♀H6	CBcs CCVT CDul CLnd CMCN CMen EBee ECrN ELan EPfP EShb EWTr MGos MMuc NWea SEND SGol WMou
- B&SWJ 8491 from Korea	WCru
- 'Goblin'	CJun MBlu NLar
- 'Green Vase'	MBlu SCob
- 'Kiwi Sunset'PBR	CDul MGos NOra
- 'Musashino'	SGol
- 'Ogon'	EPfP SGol
- 'Variegata' (v)	CJun CMac MBlu NLar SGol SMad
sinica	CMen
× ***verschaffeltii***	CMCN EPfP IArd MBlu

Zenobia (*Ericaceae*)

pulverulenta	CAbP CBcs CDul CMac ELan EPfP IVic LRHS MAsh MBlu MGil MGos SCob SLon SSta WPat WSHC
- 'Blue Sky'	CAbP CBcs CBct CDul CMCN EBee EPfP GKin LRHS MAsh MBlu MGos MPkF NLar SCob SPer SPoG WPGP
- f. ***nitida***	CMac NLar
- 'Raspberry Ripple'	CBcs LRHS MAsh NLar SSta
- 'Viridis'	NLar

Zephyranthes (*Amaryllidaceae*)

atamasca	SKHP
'Big Dude'	SKHP
candida	CAby CBro CRos CTal EBee ECho EPot EShb EWld GKev LAma LPot LRHS NRHS NRog SChF SDeJ
- 'Lemon Drops'	GKev NRog
citrina	ECho GKev LAma SDeJ
drummondii	ECho GKev NRog
flavissima	ECho
'Ivory Crocus'	NRog
katherinae	NRog
'Krakatau'	WCot
La Bufa Rosa Group	WCot
lindleyana	NRog
mexicana	ECho
minima	ECho NRog
minuta ♀H2	ECho NRog
'Pink Beauty'	ECho
primulina	ECho GKev NRog
robusta	see *Habranthus robustus*
rosea	ECho GKev SDeJ
traubii from San Carlos	NRog
versicolor	NRog

Zigadenus (*Melanthiaceae*)

elegans	EBee ECha EPri GAbr LEdu LRHS MAvo MHer WCot WSHC
nuttallii	CTal

Zingiber ✿ (*Zingiberaceae*)

clarkei	CTsd
mioga	CAgr CFil CTsd EBee GPoy ILea IMou LEdu SChr SPlb WPGP
- 'Crûg's Zing'	CFil LEdu SBrt WCru WPGP
- 'Dancing Crane' (v)	CFil CMac EUJe LEdu
- 'White Feather'	CFil CTsd LEdu
officinale	SPre SRms

Zinnia (*Asteraceae*)

elegans	SVic
'Envy' (d)	CSpe
'Profusion Cherry'	CWCL
'Red Spider'	CSpe
'Swizzle Scarlet and Yellow'	CWCL

Zizia (*Apiaceae*)

aptera	SPhx
aurea	SBrt SDix SPhx WSHC XLum

Ziziphus (*Rhamnaceae*)

§ ***jujuba*** (F)	CAgr CBcs CDul MBlu
- 'Lang' (F)	CAgr
- 'Li' (F)	CAgr
- var. ***spinosa***	CArn
sativa	see *Z. jujuba*

BIBLIOGRAPHY

This is by no means exhaustive but lists some of the more useful works used in the preparation of the *RHS Plant Finder*. The websites of raisers of new plants (not listed here) are also an invaluable source of information.

GENERAL

Allan, H.H., et al. 2000. *Flora of New Zealand.* Wellington. http://floraseries.landcareresearch.co.nz

Armitage, J.D., et al. 2014. *The Hillier Manual of Trees and Shrubs.* London: RHS

Bean, W.J. 1988. *Trees and Shrubs Hardy in the British Isles.* (8th ed.) Sir George Taylor, D.L. Clarke (eds). Supp. D.L. Clarke (ed.). London: John Murray.

Beckett, K. (ed.). 1994. *Alpine Garden Society Encyclopaedia of Alpines.* Pershore, Worcs: Alpine Garden Society.

Boufford, D.E., et al. (eds). 2003. *Flora of Taiwan Checklist. A checklist of the vascular plants of Taiwan.* Taipei: NTU. http://tai2.ntu.edu.tw

Bramwell, D. & Bramwell, Z.I. 2001. *Wild Flowers of the Canary Islands.* (2nd ed.). Madrid: Editorial Rueda, S.L.

Brickell, C. (ed.). 2008. *The Royal Horticultural Society A-Z Encyclopedia of Garden Plants.* (3rd ed.) London: Dorling Kindersley.

Brickell, C.D. et al (eds.). 2009. *International Code of Nomenclature for Cultivated Plants* (8th ed.). ISHS.

Brummitt, R.K. (comp.). 1992. *Vascular Plant Families and Genera.* Kew: Royal Botanic Gardens. http://data.kew.org

Castroviejo, S. et al. (eds). *Flora Iberica.* 1987-2007. (Vols 1-8, 10, 14, 15, 21). Madrid: Real Jardín Botánico, C.S.I.C.

Cave, Y. & Paddison, V. 1999. *The Gardener's Encyclopaedia of New Zealand Native Plants.* Auckland: Godwit.

Cooke, I. 1998. *The Plantfinder's Guide to Tender Perennials.* Newton Abbot, Devon: David & Charles.

Cullen, J. et al. (eds). 2011. *The European Garden Flora* (2nd ed.). Cambridge: Cambridge University Press. (5 vols).

Davis, P.H., Mill, R.R. & Tan, K. (eds). 1965-88. *Flora of Turkey and the East Aegean Island.* (Vols 1-10). Edinburgh University Press.

Dirr, M.A. 1997. *Dirr's Hardy Trees & Shrubs: An Illustrated Encyclopedia.* Portland, Oregon: Timber Press.

Gardiner, J. 2012. *The Timber Press Encyclopedia of Flowering Shrubs.* Portland, Oregon: Timber Press.

Goldblatt, P. & Manning, J. 2000. *Cape Plants. A Conspectus of the Cape Flora of South Africa.* South Africa/USA: National Botanical Institute of South Africa/Missouri Botanical Garden.

Greuter, W., Brummitt, R.K., Farr, E., Kilian, N., Kirk, P.M. & Silva, P.C. (comps). 1993. *NCU-3.*

Grierson, A.J.C., Long, D.G. & Noltie, H.J. et al. (eds). 2001. *Flora of Bhutan.* Edinburgh: Royal Botanic Garden.

Grimshaw, J. & Bayton, R. 2009. *New Trees. Recent Introductions to Cultivation.* Kew: Royal Botanic Gardens.

Güner, A., Özhatay, N., Ekîm, T., Baser, K.H.C. & Hedge, I.C. 2000. *Flora of Turkey and the East Aegean Islands.* Supp. 2. Vol. 11. Edinburgh: Edinburgh University Press.

Hinkley, D.J. 2009. *The Explorer's Garden: Shrubs and Vines from the Four Corners of the World.* Portland, Oregon: Timber Press.

Hoffman, M. (ed.). 2005. *List of Woody Plants. International Standard ENA 2005-2010.* Netherlands: Applied Plant Research.

Huxley, A., Griffiths, M. & Levy, M. (eds). 1992. *The New RHS Dictionary of Gardening.* London: Macmillan.

Iwatsuki, K., et al. 1995. *Flora of Japan.* Vols I-IIIb. Tokyo, Japan: Kodansha Ltd.

Jelitto, L. & Schacht, W.R., Simon, H. 2002. *Die Freiland-Schmuchstauden.* Germany: Verlag Eugen Ulmer.

Krüssmann, G. (trans.). 1984-86. *Manual of Cultivated Broad-leaved Trees & Shrubs.* London: Batsford (3 vols).

Leslie, A.C. (trans.). *New Cultivars of Herbaceous Perennial Plants 1985-1990.* Hardy Plant Society.

Mabberley, D.J. 2008. *Mabberley's Plant Book. A Portable Dictionary of Plants, their Classification and Uses.* (3rd ed.). Cambridge: Cambridge University Press.

McNeill, J. et al. 2012. *International Code of Nomenclature for Algae, Fungi, & Plants* (Melbourne Code). Regnum Vegetabile 154. Königstein, Germany: Koeltz Scientific Books.

Metcalf, L.J. 1987. *The Cultivation of New Zealand Trees and Shrubs.* Auckland: Reed Methuen.

Nelson, E.C. 2000. *A Heritage of Beauty: The Garden Plants of Ireland: An Illustrated Encyclopaedia.* Dublin: Irish Garden Plant Society.

Ohwi, J. 1965. *Flora of Japan.* Washington DC: Smithsonian Institution.

Phillips, R. & Rix, M. 1997. *Conservatory and Indoor Plants.* London: Macmillan. (2 vols).

Press, J.R. & Short, M.J. (eds). 1994. *Flora of Madeira.* London: Natural History Museum/HMSO.

Rehder, A. 1940. *Manual of Cultivated Trees and Shrubs Hardy in North America.* (2nd ed.). New York: Macmillan.
Rice, G. (ed.), 2006. *Encyclopedia of Perennials.* London: Dorling Kindersley.
Stace, C. 2010. *New Flora of the British Isles.* (3rd ed.). Cambridge: Cambridge University Press.
Thomas, G.S. 1990. *Perennial Garden Plants. A Modern Florilegium.* (3rd ed.). London: Dent.
Trehane, P. (comp.). 1989. *Index Hortensis. Vol. 1: Perennials.* Wimborne: Quarterjack
Tutin, T.G., et al. 1964. *Flora Europaea.* Cambridge University Press. Vols 1-5.

GENERAL WEBSITES

Annotated Checklist of the Flowering Plants of Nepal. www.efloras.org/flora_page-aspx?_id=110
Australian Cultivar Registration Authority. www.anbg.gov.au/acra
Australian Plant Breeders Rights: Database Search. http://pbr.ipaustralia.optus.com.au
Australian Plant Names Index. Australian National Botanic Gardens (comp.). www.anbg.gov.au/apni/index.html
Bolivia Checklist. www.efloras.org/flora_page.aspx?flora_id=40
Botanical Expedition in Myanmar Checklist. http://botany.si-edu/myanmar/checklistNames.cfm
Canadian Ornamental Plant Foundation. www.copf.org
Canadian Plant Breeders Rights Office: Canadian Food Inspection Agency. www.inspection.gc.ca
Catalogue of the Vascular Plants of Madagascar: www.efforas.org/flora_page.aspx?flora_id+12
Darwin Checklist of Moroccan Vascular Plants www.herbarium.rdg.ac.uk/
DEFRA Plant Varieties and Seeds Gazette. www.defra.gov.uk
Flora Himalaya Database. www.leca.univ-savoie.fr
Flora Mesoamericana Internet Version (W3FM). Missouri Botanical Garden.
www.tropicos.org/Project/FM
Flora of Australia Online. Australian Biological Resources Study. www.environment.gov.au/biodiversity/abrs/online-resources/flora/index.html
Flora of Chile. www.efloras.org/flora_page.aspx?flora_id=60
Flora of China Checklist. http://flora.huh.harvard.edu/china
Flora of Pakistan. www.efloras.org/flora_page.aspd?flora_id=5
Flora of North America Website. Morin, N.R., et al. www.efloras.org-page.aspx/flora_id=1
GRIN (Germplasm Resources Information Network) Taxonomy. www.ars-grin.gov
Hatch, D. New Ornamentals Society Database. http://members.tripod.com/~Hatch_L/nos.html
International Plant Names Index. www.ipni.org
International Plant Names Index: Author Query. www.ipni.org/ipni
Manaaki Whenua: Landcare Research in New Zealand Plants Database. http://nzflora.landcareresearch.co.nz
Manual de plantas de Costa Rica. www.mobot.org/manual.plantas
Plant List, The. A working list of all plant species. www.theplantlist.org.
Plants Database. USDA, NRCS. http://plants.usda.gov
Plants of Southern Africa: an Online Checklist. http://posa.sanbi.org
PLUTO: Plant Variety Database www.upov.int/pluto/en
New Zealand Plant Variety Rights Office www.iponz.govt.nz/cms/pvr
Royal Horticultural Society. www.rhs.org.uk/plants/RHS-Publications/Plant-registers
Tropicos. www.tropicos.org
US Patent Full-Text Database. US Patent and Trademark Office, (comp.). www.uspto.gov/patft
World Checklist of Selected Families. apps.kew.org/wcsp

GENERA AND OTHER PLANT GROUPINGS

Acer

Gregory, P. & Angus, H. 2008. *World Checklist of Maple Cultivar Names.* Forestry Commission National Arboreta.
Harris, J.G.S. 2000. *The Gardener's Guide to Growing Maples.* Newton Abbot, Devon: David & Charles.
van Gelderen, C.J. & van Gelderen, D.M. 1999. *Maples for Gardens.* A Color Encyclopedia. Portland, Oregon: Timber Press.
van Gelderen, D.M., de Jong, P.C., Oterdoom, H.J. 1994. *Maples of the World.* Portland, Oregon: Timber Press.
Yano, M. 2003. *Book for Maples. Wild Maples of Japan and Maple Cultivars.* Japan: Japan Maple Publishing Group.
Vertrees, J.D. 2001. *Japanese Maples.* Momiji and Kaede. (3rd ed.). Portland, Oregon: Timber Press.

Actaea

Compton, J.A., Culham, A. & Jury, S.L. 1998. Reclassification of *Actaea* to Include *Cimicifuga* and *Souliea (Ranunculaceae). Taxon* 47:593-634.

Adiantum

Goudey, C.J. 1985. *Maidenhair Ferns in Cultivation.* Melbourne: Lothian.

Agapanthus

Snoeijer, W. 2004. *Agapanthus. A Revision of the Genus.* Portland, Oregon: Timber Press.

Agavaceae

Irish, M. & Irish, G. 2000. *Agaves, Yuccas and*

Related Plants. A Gardener's Guide. Portland, Oregon: Timber Press.

Aizoaceae

Burgoyne, P. et al. 1998. *Mesembs of the World. Illustrated Guide to a Remarkable Succulent Group*. South Africa: Briza Publications.

Allium

Davies, D. 1992. *Alliums. The Ornamental Onions*. London: Batsford

Gregory, M., et al. 1998. *Nomenclator Alliorum*. Kew: Royal Botanic Gardens.

Mathew, B. 1996. *A Review of Allium Section Allium*. Kew: Royal Botanic Gardens.

Androsace

Smith, G. & Lowe, D. 1997. *The Genus Androsace*. Pershore, Worcs: Alpine Garden Society.

Anemone, Japanese

McKendrick, M. 1990. Autumn Flowering Anemones. *The Plantsman* 12(3):140-151.

McKendrick, M. 1998. Japanese Anemones. *The Garden* (RHS) 123(9):628-633.

Anthemis

Leslie, A. 1997. Focus on Plants: *Anthemis tinctoria*. *The Garden* (RHS) 122(8):552-555.

Apiaceae

Pimenov, M.G. & Leonov, M.V. 1993. *The Genera of the Umbelliferae*. Kew: Royal Botanic Gardens.

Aquilegia

Munz, P.A. 1946. *Aquilegia:* the Cultivated and Wild Columbines. *Gentes Herb.* 7(1):1-150.

Araceae

Govaerts, R. & Frodin, D.G. 2002. *World Checklist and Bibliography of Araceae (and Acoraceae)*. Kew: Royal Botanic Gardens.

Araliaceae

Govaerts, R. & Frodin, D.G. 2002. *World Checklist and Bibliography of Araliaceae*. Kew: Royal Botanic Gardens.

***Arecaceae* (palms)**

Craft, P. & Riffle, R.L. 2003. *Encyclopedia of Cultivated Palms*. Portland, Oregon: Timber Press.

Uhl, N.W. & Dransfield, J. 1987. *Genera Palmarum*. A Classification of Palms Based on the Work of Harold E. Moore Jr. Lawrence, Kansas: Allen Press.

Argyranthemum

Humphries, C.J. 1976. A Revision of the Macaronesian Genus *Argyranthemum*. *Bull. Brit. Mus. (Nat. Hist.) Bot.* 5(4):145-240.

Arisaema

Gusman, G. & Gusman, L. 2002. *The Genus Arisaema: A Monograph for Botanists and Nature Lovers*. Ruggell, Leichtenstein: A.R. Gantner Verlag Kommanditgesellschaft.

Pradhan, U.C. 1997. *Himalayan Cobra Lilies (Arisaema). Their Botany and Culture*. (2nd ed.). Kalimpong, West Bengal, India: Primulaceae Books.

Arum

Bown, D. 2000. *Plants of the Arum Family*. (2nd ed.). Portland, Oregon: Timber Press.

Boyce, P. 1993. *The Genus Arum*. London: HMSO.

Asclepiadaceae

Eggli, U. (ed.). 2002. *Illustrated Handbook of Succulent Plants: Asclepiadaceae*. Heidelberg, Germany: Springer-Verlag.

Aster see ***Symphyotrichum***

Picton, P. 1999. *The Gardener's Guide to Growing Asters*. Newton Abbot: David & Charles.

Asteraceae

Bremer, K. et al. 1994. *Asteraceae: Cladistics and Classification*. Portland, Oregon: Timber Press.

Cubey, J.J. & Grant, M.G. 2004. *Perennial Yellow Daisies: RHS Bulletin No 6*. Wisley, Surrey: RHS.

Astilbe

Noblett, H. 2001. *Astilbe. A Guide to the Identification of Cultivars and Common Species*. Cumbria: Henry Noblett.

Aubrieta

1975. *International Registration Authority Checklist*. Weihenstephan, Germany: (Unpublished).

Bamboos

Ohrnberger, D. 1999. *The Bamboos of the World*. Amsterdam: Elsevier.

Whittaker, P. 2005. *Hardy Bamboos – Taming the Dragon*. Portland, Oregon: Timber Press.

Begonia

American Begonia Society Astro Branch Begonia Data Base. http://absastro.tripod.com

American Begonia Society Registered Begonias. http://www.begonias.org

Ingles, J. 1990. *American Begonia Society Listing of Begonia Cultivars*. Revised Edition Buxton Checklist. American Begonia Society.

Tebbitt, M.C. 2005. *Begonias: Cultivation, Identification and Natural History*. Portland, Oregon: Timber Press.

Berberidaceae

Ahrendt, L.W.A. 1961. *Berberis and Mahonia. A Taxonomic Revision*. Cambridge: Cambridge University Press.

Stearn, W.T. & Shaw, J.M.H. 2002. *The Genus Epimedium and Other Herbaceous Berberidaceae including the Genus Podophyllum*. Kew: Royal Botanic Gardens.

Betula

Ashburner, K.B. & McAllister, H. 2013. *The Genua Betula: Taxonomic Revision of Birches*. Kew: Royal Botanic Gardens.

Hunt, D. (ed.). 1993. *Betula: Proceedings of the IDS Betula Symposium 1992*. Richmond, Surrey: International Dendrology Society.

Boraginaceae

Bennett, M. 2003. *Pulmonarias and the Borage Family*. London: Batsford.

Bougainvillea

Gillis, W.T. 1976. Bougainvilleas of Cultivation (*Nyctaginaceae*). *Baileya* 20(1):34-41.

Iredell, J. 1994. *Growing Bougainvilleas.* London: Cassell.

MacDaniels, L.H. 1981. A Study of Cultivars in *Bougainvillea* (*Nyctaginaceae*). *Baileya* 21(2):77-100.

Singh, B., Panwar, R.S., Voleti, S.R., Sharma, V.K. & Thakur, S. 1999. *The New International Bougainvillea Check List.* (2nd ed.). New Delhi: Indian Agricultural Research Institute.

Bromeliaceae

Bromeliad Cultivar Registry Online Databases. Bromeliad Society International. www.bsi.org

Brugmansia

Wreggitt, L. et al. (comp.). *Register of Brugmansia Cultivars and Checklist of Names in Use.* American Brugmansia and Datura Society.

Buddleja

Stuart, D.D. 2006. *Buddlejas: Royal Horticultural Society Collector Guide.* Portland, Oregon: Timber Press.

Bulbs

Leeds, R. 2000. *The Plantfinder's Guide to Early Bulbs.* Newton Abbot, Devon: David & Charles.

KAVB Online registration pages. http://kavb.back2p.soft-orange.com

Buxus

Batdorf, L.R. 1995. *Boxwood Handbook. A Practical Guide to Knowing and Growing Boxwood.* Boyce, Virginia, USA: The American Boxwood Society.

Cactaceae

Hunt, D. et al. 2006. *New Cactus Lexicon.* (2 vols.) Sherborne, Dorset: DH Books.

Camellia

Ferrari, D. & Sfondrini, N. Web *Camellia* Register. Camellia-unipv.it/camelliadb2

Savige, T.J. (comp.). 1993. *The International Camellia Register.* (Vol 1-2). Supps. 1-2. 1997-2011. The International Camellia Society.

Trehane, J. 2007. *Camellias: The Gardener's Encyclopedia.* Portland, Oregon: Timber Press. The International Camellia Society.

Trujillo, D. J. (ed.). 2002. *Camellia Nomenclature.* (24th ed.). Southern California Camellia Society.

Campanula

Lewis, P. & Lynch, M. 1998. *Campanulas.* A Gardeners Guide. (2nd ed.). London: Batsford.

Lewis, P 2002. *Campanulas in the Garden.* Pershore, Worcs: Hardy Plant Society.

Campanulaceae

Lammers, T.G. 2007. *World Checklist and Bibliography of Campanulaceae.* Kew: Royal Botanic Gardens.

Canna

Cooke, I. 2001. *The Gardener's Guide to Growing Cannas.* Newton Abbot, Devon: David & Charles.

Gray, J. & Grant, M. 2003. *Canna: RHS Bulletin No 3.* Wisley, Surrey: RHS.

Hayward, K. www.hartcanna.com

Carnivorous Plants

Schlauer, J. (comp.). Carnivorous Plant Database. www.omnisterra.com

Ceanothus

Fross, D. & D. Wilken. 2006. *Ceanothus.* Portland, Oregon: Timber Press.

Cercidiphyllum

Dosmann, M.S. 1999. Katsura: a Review of *Cercidiphyllum* in Cultivation and in the Wild. *The New Plantsman* 6(1): 52-62.

Dosmann, M., Andrews, S., Del Tredici, P. & Li, J. 2003. Classification and Nomenclature of Weeping Katsuras. *The Plantsman* 2(1): 21-27.

Chaenomeles

Weber, C. 1963. Cultivars in the Genus *Chaenomeles. Arnoldia* 23(3):17-75.

Chrysanthemum

Brummitt, D. 1997. *Chrysanthemum* Once Again. *The Garden* (RHS) 122(9):662-663.

Chrysanthemums in Aberdeen. Directory of popular cultivars. www.chrysanthemums.info

Gosling, S.G. (ed.). 1964. *British National Register of Chrysanthemums.* Whetstone, London: National Chrysanthemum Society.

National Chrysanthemum Society. 2000. *British National Register of Names of Chrysanthemums Amalgamated Edition 1964-1999.* Tamworth, Staffordshire: National Chrysanthemum Society. Cultivar database. www.nationalchrysanthemumsociety.org.uk

Cistus

Bygrave, P. & Page, R.G. (ed.). 2001. *Cistus – A Guide to the Collection at the Chelsea Physic Garden.* London: Chelsea Physic Garden Company.

Citrus

Davies, F.S. & Albrigo, L.G. 1994. *Citrus.* Wallingford, Oxon: Cab International.

Page, M. 2008. *Growing Citrus.* London: Timber Press

Saunt, J. 1990. *Citrus Varieties of the World.* An Illustrated Guide. Norwich: Sinclair

Clematis

Donald, D., *The International Clematis Register and Checklist*, Supp. 4. 2012

Evison, R.J. 1998. *The Gardener's Guide to Growing Clematis.* Newton Abbot, Devon: David & Charles.

Grey-Wilson, C. 2000. *Clematis: the Genus.* London: Batsford

HelpMeFind Clematis. www.helpmefind.com/clematis

Johnson, M. 2001. *The Genus Clematis.* Södertälje, Sweden: Magnus Johnsons Plantskola AB & Bengt Sundström.

Matthews, V. (comp.). 2002. *The International Clematis Register and Checklist 2002* & Supps 1-3. 2004-2009. London: RHS.
Toomey, M. & Leeds, E. 2001. *An Illustrated Encyclopedia of Clematis*. Portland, Oregon: Timber Press.

Conifers

Anders, A.G. & Spicer, D.P. 2012 *RHS Encyclopedia of Conifers*. (2 vols). London: RHS & Kingsblue Publishing.
Bitner, R.L. 2007. *Conifers for Gardens. An Illustrated Encyclopedia*. Portland, Oregon: Timber Press.
Bloom, A. 2001. *Gardening with Conifers*. London: Frances Lincoln.
den Ouden, P. & Boom, B.K. 1965. *Manual of Cultivated Conifers*. The Hague: Martinus Nijhof.
Eckenwalder, J.E. 2009. *Conifers of the World*. China: Timber Press
Farjon, A. 1998. *World Checklist and Bibliography of Conifers*. Kew: Royal Botanic Gardens.
Farjon, A. 2008. *A Natural History of Conifers*. Portland, Oregon: Timber Press.
Farjon, A. 2010. *A Handbook of the World's Conifers*. (2 vols). Leiden-Boston: Brill.
Knees, S.G. & Springate, L.S. 2009. *The International Conifer Register, Pt 5*. London: RHS.
Krüssmann, G. & Epp, M.E. (trans.). 1985. *Manual of Cultivated Conifers*. London: Batsford.
Lewis, J. & Leslie, A.C. 1987-1998. *The International Conifer Register. Pts 1-4*. London: RHS.
Welch, H.J. 1979. *Manual of Dwarf Conifers*. New York: Theophrastus.
Welch, H.J. 1993. *The World Checklist of Conifers*. Bromyard, Herefordshire: Landsman's Bookshops.

Cornus

Cappiello, P. & Shadow, D. 2005. *Dogwoods*. Portland, Oregon: Timber Press.

Corydalis

Lidén, M. & Zetterlund, H. 1997. *Corydalis. A Gardener's Guide and a Monograph of the Tuberous Species*. Pershore, Worcs: Alpine Garden Society Publications.

Corylus

Crawford, M. 1995. *Hazelnuts: Production and Culture*. Dartington, Devon: Agroforestry Research Trust.

Cotoneaster

Fryer, J. & Hylmö, B. 2009. *Cotoneasters. A Comprehensive Guide to Shrubs for Flowers, Fruit and Foliage*. Portland, Oregon: Timber Press.

Crassulaceae

Rowley, G. 2003. *Crassula: A Grower's Guide*. Venegono Superiore, Italy: Cactus & Co.
Eggli, U. (ed.) 2003. *Illustrated Handbook of Succulent Plants*. Springer.

Crataegus

Phipps, J.B. 2003. *Hawthorns and Medlars. RHS Plant Collector Guide*. Portland, Oregon: Timber Press.

Crocosmia

Goldblatt, P., Manning, J.C. & Dunlop, G. 2004. *Crocosmia and Chasmanthe*. Portland, Oregon: Timber Press.

Crocus

Jacobsen, N., van Scheepen, J. & Ørgaard, M. 1997. The *Crocus chrysanthus – biflorus* Cultivars. *The New Plantsman* 4(1):6-38.
Mathew, B. 1982. *The Crocus. A Review of the Genus Crocus (Iridaceae)*. London: Batsford.
Mathew, B. 2002. *Crocus* Up-date. *The Plantsman* 1(1):44-56.

Cyclamen

Clennett, C. *Register of Cultivar Names*. www.cyclamen.org
Grey-Wilson, C. 2003. *Cyclamen. A Guide for Gardeners, Horticulturists & Botanists*. London: Batsford.

Cypripedium

Cribb, P. 1997. *The Genus Cypripedium*. Portland, Oregon: Timber Press.

Dahlia

American Dahlia Society website. www.dahlia.org
Bates, D. Dahlia Plant Finder 2007. www.dahliaworld.co.uk
McDonald, S., & Hedge, R. (comps). 1969. *Tentative Classified List and International Register of Dahlia Names 1969* & Supps 1-23. 1986-2013. London: RHS.
National Dahlia Society. 2005. *Classified Directory and Judging Rules*. (28th ed.) Aldershot, Hants: National Dahlia Society.

Daphne

Brickell, C.D. & Mathew, B. 1976. *Daphne. The Genus in the Wild and in Cultivation*. Woking, Surrey: Alpine Garden Society.
Grey-Wilson, C. (ed.). 2001. *The Smaller Daphnes. The Proceedings of 'Daphne 2000', a Conference held at the Royal Horticultural Society*. Pershore, Worcs: Alpine Garden Society.
White, R. 2006. *Daphnes: A Practical Guide for Gardeners*. Portland, Oregon: Timber Press.

Delphinium

1949. *A Tentative Check-list of Delphinium Names*. London: RHS.
1970. *A Tentative Check-list of Delphinium Names*. Addendum. London: RHS.
Bassett, D. & Wesley, W. 2004. *Delphinium: RHS Bulletin No 5*. Wisley, Surrey: RHS.
Leslie, A.C. 1996. *The International Delphinium Register Cumulative Supp. 1970-1995*. London: RHS.
Leslie, A.C. 1996-2005. The International Delphinium Register Supp. 1994-99. *The Delphinium Society Year Book 1996-2005*. London: RHS.

Dianthus
Galbally, J. & Galbally, E. 1997. *Carnations and Pinks for Garden and Greenhouse.* Portland, Oregon: Timber Press.
Leslie, A.C. *The International Dianthus Register.* 1983-2002. (2nd ed. & Supps 1-19). Supps 19-29, 2002-12. London: RHS.
Dierama
Hilliard, O.M. & Burtt, B.L. 1991. *Dierama. The Harebells of Africa.* Johannesburg; London: Acorn Books.
Dionysia
Grey-Wilson, C. 1989. *The Genus Dionysia.* Woking, Surrey: Alpine Garden Society.
Douglasia
Mitchell, B. 1999. Celebrating the Bicentenary of David Douglas: a Review of *Douglasia* in Cultivation. *The New Plantsman* 6(2):101-108.
Dracaena
Bos, J.J., Graven, P., Hetterscheid, W.L.A. & van de Wege, J.J. 1992. Wild and cultivated *Dracaena fragrans. Edinburgh J. Bot.* 49(3):311-331.
Echeveria
Schulz, L. & Kapitany, A. *Echeveria Cultivars.* Teesdale, Australia: Schulz Publishing.
Episcia
Dates, J.D. 1993. *The Gesneriad Register 1993.* Check List of Names with Descriptions of Cultivated Plants in the Genera *Episcia* & *Alsobia.* Galesburg, Illinois: American Gloxinia & Gesneriad Society, Inc.
Erodium
Clifton, R. 1994. *Geranium Family Species Checklist. Pt 1 Erodium.* (4th ed.). The Geraniaceae Group.
Toomey, N., Cubey, J.J. & Culham, A. 2002. *Erodium × variabile. The Plantsman* 1(3): 166-172
Victor, D.X. (comp.). 2000. *Erodium: Register of Cultivar Names.* The Geraniaceae Group.
Erythronium
Mathew, B. 1992. A Taxonomic and Horticultural Review of *Erythronium* L. (*Liliaceae*). *J. Linn. Soc., Bot.* 109:453-471.
Mathew, B. 1998. The Genus *Erythronium. Bull. Alpine Gard. Soc. Gr. Brit.* 66(3): 308-321.
Eupatorium sensu lato
Hind, D.J.N. 2006. Splitting *Eupatorium. The Plantsman* 5(2):185-189.
Euonymus
Brown, N. 1996. Notes on Cultivated Species of *Euonymus. The New Plantsman* 3(4):238-243.
de Jong, P. & Kolster, H. 2013. *Euonymus: Een kleurrijk geslacht.* Zeist, Netherlands: KNNV Uitgeverij.
Lancaster, C.R. 1981. An Account of *Euonymus* in Cultivation and its Availability in Commerce. *The Plantsman* 3(3):133-166.
Lancaster, C.R. 1982. *Euonymus* in Cultivation – Addendum. *The Plantsman* 4:61-64, 253-254.
Euphorbia
Govaerts, R., Frodin, D.G. & Radcliffe-Smith, A. 2000. *World Checklist and Bibliography of Euphorbiaceae.* Kew: Royal Botanic Gardens.
Turner, R. 1995. *Euphorbias. A Gardeners Guide.* London: Batsford.
Witton, D. 2000. *Euphorbias.* Pershore, Worcs: Hardy Plant Society.
Fagales
Govaerts, R. & Frodin, D.G. 1998. *World Checklist and Bibliography of Fagales.* Kew: Royal Botanic Gardens.
Fagus
Dönig, G. 1994. *Die Park-und Gartenformen der Rotbuche Fagus sylvatica L.* Erlangen, Germany: Verlag Gartenbild Heinz Hansmann.
Fascicularia
Nelson, E.C., Zizka, G., Horres, R. & Weising, K. 1999. Revision of the Genus *Fascicularia* Mez (*Bromeliaceae*). *Botanical Journal of the Linnean Society* 129(4):315-332.
Ferns
Checklist of World Ferns. http://homepages.caverock.net.nz/nbj/fern
Johns, R.J. 1996. *Index Filicum.* Supplementum Sextum pro annis 1976-1990. Kew: Royal Botanic Gardens.
Jones, D.L. 1987. *Encyclopaedia of Ferns.* Melbourne, Australia: Lothian.
Kaye, R. 1968. *Hardy Ferns.* London: Faber & Faber
Rickard, M.H. 2000. *The Plantfinder's Guide to Garden Ferns.* Newton Abbot, Devon: David & Charles.
Rush, R. 1984. *A Guide to Hardy Ferns.* London: British Pteridological Society.
Forsythia
INRA Forsythia website. www.angers.inra.fr/forsy
Fritillaria
Clark, T. & Grey-Wilson, C. 2003. Crown Imperials. *The Plantsman* 2(1):33-47.
Mathew, B., et al. 2000. *Fritillaria* Issue. *Bot. Mag.* 17(3):145-185.
Pratt, K. & Jefferson-Brown, M. 1997. *The Gardener's Guide to Growing Fritillaries.* Newton Abbot: David & Charles.
Turrill, W.B. & Sealy, J.R. 1980. *Studies in the Genus Fritillaria (Liliaceae).* Hooker's Icones Plantarum Vol. 39 (1 & 2). Kew: Royal Botanic Gardens.
Fruit
Brogdale Horticultural Trust National Fruit Collection. www.nationalfruitcollection.org.uk
Bowling, B.L. 2000. *The Berry Grower's Companion.* Portland, Oregon: Timber Press.
Hogg, R. 1884. *The Fruit Manual.* (5th ed.). London: Journal of Horticulture Office.
Fuchsia
American Fuchsia Society Registration Database. www.americanfuchsiasociety.org

Bartlett, G. 1996. *Fuchsias – A Colour Guide.* Marlborough, Wilts: Crowood Press.

Boullemier, Leo.B. (comp.). 1991. *The Checklist of Species, Hybrids and Cultivars of the Genus Fuchsia.* London, New York, Sydney: Blandford Press.

Boullemier, Leo.B. (comp.). 1995. *Addendum No 1 to the 1991 Checklist of Species, Hybrids and Cultivars of the Genus Fuchsia.* Dyfed, Wales: The British Fuchsia Society.

Goulding, E. 1995. *Fuchsias: The Complete Guide.* London: Batsford.

Johns, E.A. 1997. *Fuchsias of the 19th and Early 20th Century.* An Historical Checklist of Fuchsia Species & Cultivars, pre-1939. Kidderminster, Worcs: British Fuchsia Society

Stevens, R. Find That Fuchsia. www.findthatfuchsia.info

Galanthus

Bishop, M., Davis, A. & Grimshaw, J. 2001. *Snowdrops. A monograph of cultivated Galanthus.* Maidenhead: Griffin Press.

Davis, A.P., Mathew, B. (ed.) & King, C. (ill.). 1999. *The Genus Galanthus. A Botanical Magazine Monograph.* Oregon: Timber Press.

Gentiana

Bartlett, M. 1975. *Gentians.* Dorset: Blandford Press.

Halda, J.J. 1996. *The Genus Gentiana.* Dobré, Czech Republic: Sen.

Ho T.N. & Liu S. 2001. *Worldwide Monograph of Gentiana.* Beijing: Science Press.

Geranium

Armitage, J.D., 2005-2007. *Hardy Geraniums – Stages 1-3: RHS Bulletin Nos 10 , 14* & *18.* Wisley, Surrey: RHS.

Bath, T. & Jones, J. 1994. *The Gardener's Guide to Growing Hardy Geraniums.* Newton Abbot, Devon: David & Charles.

Bendtsen, B.H. 2005. *Gardening with Hardy Geraniums.* Portland, Oregon: Timber Press.

Clifton, R.T.F. 1995. *Geranium Family Species Check List Pt 2.* Geranium. (4th ed. issue 2). Dover: The Geraniaceae Group.

Jones, J., et al. 2001. *Hardy Geraniums for the Garden.* (3rd ed.). Pershore, Worcs: Hardy Plant Society.

Victor, D.X. 2004. *Register of Geranium Cultivar Names.* (2nd ed.). The Geraniaceae Group.

Yeo, P.F. 2002. *Hardy Geraniums.* (3rd ed.). Kent: Croom Helm.

Gesneriaceae

The Gesneriad Society. Listing of registered gesneriads. www.aggs.gesneriadsociety.org

Dates, J.D. 1986-1990. *The Gesneriad Register 1986-1987 & 1990.* Galesburg, Illinois: American Gloxinia & Gesneriad Society, Inc.

Gladiolus

British Gladiolus Society List of Cultivars Classified for Show Purposes 1994. Mayfield, Derbyshire: British Gladiolus Society.

1997-1998. British Gladiolus Society List of European, New Zealand & North American Cultivars Classified for Exhibition Purposes 1997 & 1998. Mayfield, Derbyshire: British Gladiolus Society.

Goldblatt, P. & Manning, J. 1998. *Gladiolus in Southern Africa.* Vlaeberg, South Africa: Fernwood Press.

Goldblatt, P. 1996. *Gladiolus in Tropical Africa.* Systematics Biology and Evolution. Oregon: Timber Press.

Gleditsia

Santamour, F.S. & McArdle, A.J. 1983. Checklist of Cultivars of Honeylocust (*Gleditsia triacanthos* L.). *Journal of Arboriculture.* 9:271-276.

Grevillea

Olde, P. & Marriott, N. 1995. *The Grevillea Book.* (3). Kenthurst, NSW: Kangaroo Press.

Haemanthus

Snijman, D. 1984. A Revision of the Genus *Haemanthus. Journal of South African Botany.* (Supp. Vol. 12).

Hamamelis

Lane, C. 2005. *Witch Hazels.* Portland, Oregon: Timber Press.

Heathers

Baker, H.A. & Oliver, E.G.H. 1967. *Heathers in Southern Africa.* Cape Town: Purnell.

Nelson, E.C. 2011. *Hardy Heathers from the Northern Hemisphere.* Kew: Royal Botanic Gardens.

Nelson, E.C. & Small, D.J. (eds). 2000. *International Register of Heather Names.* (Pts 1-4). The Heather Society.

Schumann, D., Kirsten, G. & Oliver, E.G.H. 1992. *Ericas of South Africa.* Vlaeberg, South Africa: Fernwood Press.

Small, D. & Wulff, E.M.T. 2008. *Gardening with Hardy Heathers.* Portland, Oregon: Timber Press.

Hebe

Hutchins, G. 1997. *Hebes: Here and There.* A Monograph on the Genus *Hebe.* Caversham, Berks: Hutchins & Davies.

Metcalf, L.J. 2001. *International Register of Hebe Cultivars.* Canterbury, New Zealand: Royal New Zealand Institute of Horticulture (Inc.).

Metcalf, L.J. 2006. *Hebes: A Guide to Species, Hybrids and Allied Genera.* Portland, Oregon: Timber Press.

Hedera

Jury, S. et al. 2006. *Hedera algeriensis*, a Fine Species of Ivy. *Sibbaldia* 4: 93-108.

McAllister, H. 1988. Canary and Algerian Ivies. *The Plantsman* 10(1):27-29.

Rose, P.Q. 1996. *The Gardener's Guide to Growing Ivies.* Newton Abbot, Devon: David & Charles.

Rutherford, A., McAllister, H. & Mill, R.R. 1993. New Ivies from the Mediterranean Area and Macaronesia. *The Plantsman* 15(2):115-128.

Heliconia

Berry, F. & Kress, W.J. 1991. *Heliconia.* An Identification Guide. Washington: Smithsonian Institution Press.

Helleborus

Burrell, C.C. & Tyler, J.K. 2006. *Hellebores: A Comprehensive Guide.* Portland, Oregon: Timber Press.

Mathew, B. 1989. *Hellebores.* Woking: Alpine Garden Society.

Rice, G. & Strangman, E. 1993. *The Gardener's Guide to Growing Hellebores.* Newton Abbot, Devon: David & Charles.

Hemerocallis

Baxter, G.J. (comp.). American Daylily Society Registry of Daylily Cultivars. www.daylilies.org

Herbs

Phillips, R. & Foy, N. 1990. *Herbs.* London: Pan Books Ltd.

Heuchera and × ***Heucherella***

Heims, D. & Ware, G. 2005. *Heucheras and Heucherellas: Coral Bells and Foamy Bells.* Portland, Oregon: Timber Press.

Hibiscus

Noble, C. Australian Hibiscus Society Database Register. www.australianhibiscus.com

Hosta

Hosta Library. www.hostalibrary.org

Grenfell, D. & Shadrack, M. 2004. *The Color Encyclopedia of Hostas.* Portland, Oregon: Timber Press.

Schmid, W.G. 1991. *The Genus Hosta.* London: Batsford.

Zilis, M.R. 2009. *The Hostapedia. An Encyclopedia of Hostas.*

Hyacinthaceae (Asparagaceae pro parte*)*

Dashwood, M. & Mathew, B. 2006. *Hyacinthaceae – little blue bulbs: RHS Bulletin No 11.* Wisley, Surrey: RHS.

Mathew, B. 2005. *Hardy Hyacinthaceae* Pt 1: *Muscari. The Plantsman* 4(1):40-53.

Mathew, B. 2005. *Hardy Hyacinthaceae* Pt 2: *Scilla, Chionodoxa* and × *Chinoscilla. The Plantsman* 4(2):110-121.

Hydrangea

Dirr, M.A. 2004. *Hydrangeas for American Gardens.* Portland, Oregon: Timber Press.

Haworth-Booth, M. 1975. *The Hydrangeas.* London: Garden Book Club.

van Gelderen, C.J. & van Gelderen, D.M. 2004. *Encyclopedia of Hydrangeas.* Portland, Oregon: Timber Press.

Hypericum

Lancaster, R. & Robson, N. 1997. Focus on Plants: Bowls of Beauty. *The Garden* (RHS) 122(8):566-571.

Ilex

Bailes, C. 2006. *Hollies for Gardeners.* Portland, Oregon: Timber Press.

Dudley, T.R. & Eisenbeiss, G.K. 1973 & 1992. *International Checklist of Cultivated Ilex, Pts 1 & 2.* Washington DC: United States Dept of Agriculture.

Galle, F.C. 1997. *Hollies: the Genus Ilex.* Portland, Oregon: Timber Press.

Impatiens

Morgan, R.J. 2007. *Impatiens: The Vibrant World of Busy Lizzies, Balsams and Touch-me-nots.* Portland, Oregon: Timber Press.

Iris

Austin, C. 2005. *Irises: A Gardener's Encyclopedia.* Oregon:Timber Press.

Hoog, M.H. 1980. Bulbous Irises . *The Plantsman* 2(3):141-64.

Lowe, A. & Lowe, M. *Iris Check List of Registered Cultivar Names 2000-2009.* Hannibal, New York.

Mathew, B. 1981. *The Iris.* London: Batsford.

Mathew, B. 1993. The Spuria Irises. *The Plantsman* 15(1):14-25.

Stebbings, G. 1997. *The Gardener's Guide to Growing Iris.* Newton Abbot: David & Charles.

The Species Group of the British Iris Society, (ed.). 1997. *A Guide to Species Irises. Their Identification and Cultivation.* Cambridge: Cambridge University Press.

Jasminum

Green, P. & Miller, D. 2009. *The Genus Jasminum in Cultivation.* Kew: Royal Botanic Gardens.

Jovibarba see under ***Sempervivum***

Kalmia

Jaynes, R.A. 2009. *Kalmia. Mountain Laurel and Related Species.* (3rd ed.). Portland, Oregon: Timber Press.

Kniphofia

Taylor, J. 1985. *Kniphofia* – a Survey. *The Plantsman* 7(3):129-160.

Whitehouse, C.M. 2012. Preliminary checklist of *Kniphofia* epithets. *Hanburyana* 6: 9-82.

Kohleria

Dates, J.D. (ed.) & Batcheller, F.N. (comp.). 1985. *The Gesneriad Register 1985. Check List of Names with Descriptions of Cultivated Plants in the Genus Kohleria.* Lincoln Acres, California: American Gloxinia and Gesneriad Society, Inc.

Lachenalia

Duncan, G.D. 1988. *The Lachenalia Hand Book.* Kirstenbosch, South Africa: National Botanic Gardens.

Duncan, G.D. 2012. *The Genus Lachenalia.* Kew: Royal Botanic Gardens.

Lantana

Howard, R.A. 1969. A Check List of Names Used in the Genus *Lantana. Arnoldia.* 29(11):73-109.

Lathyrus
Norton, S. 1996. *Lathyrus. Cousins of Sweet Pea.* Surrey: NCCPG.
Lavandula
Upson, T. & Andrews, S. 2004. *The Genus Lavandula.* Kew: Royal Botanic Garden.
Leptospermum
Check List of *Leptospermum* Cultivars. 1963. *J. Roy. New Zealand Inst. Hort.* 5(5):224-30.
Dawson, M. 1997. A History of *Leptospermum scoparium* in Cultivation: Discoveries from the Wild. *The New Plantsman* 4(1):51-59: Garden Selections. *The New Plantsman* 4(2):67-78.
Lewisia
Davidson, B.L.R. 2000. *Lewisias.* Portland, Oregon: Timber Press.
Elliott, R. 1978. *Lewisias.* Woking: Alpine Garden Society.
Mathew, B. 1989. *The Genus Lewisia.* Bromley, Kent: Christopher Helm.
Lilium
Donald, D. *The International Lily Register 1982-2002.* (4th ed.). Supp. 3, 2012. London: RHS.
Leslie, A.C. *The International Lily Register 1982-2002.* (4th ed.). Supps 1-2, 2008-2010. London: RHS.
Lonicera
Blahník, Z. 2006. *Lonicera* Cultivar Names: The First World List. *Acta Pruhoniciana* 81:59-64.
Bradshaw, D. 1996. *Lonicera. Climbing Honeysuckles.* Surrey: NCCPG.
Magnolia
Callaway, D.J. Magnolia Cultivar Checklist. www.magnoliasociety.org
Frodin, D.G. & Govaerts, R. 1996. *World Checklist and Bibliography of Magnoliaceae.* Kew: Royal Botanic Garden.
Gardiner, J. 2000. *Magnolias: A Gardener's Guide.* Portland, Oregon: Timber Press.
Hunt, D. (ed.). 1998. *Magnolias and their Allies.* London: International Dendrology Society & The Magnolia Society.
Liu, Y. 2004. *Magnolias of China.* Beijing: Beijing Science and Technology Press.
Maianthemum
Cubey, J.J. 2005 The Incorporation of *Smilacina* within *Maianthemum. The Plantsman* 4(4).
Malus
Crawford, M. 1994. *Directory of Apple Cultivars.* Devon: Agroforestry Research Trust.
Fiala, J.L. 1994. *Flowering Crabapples.* The genus *Malus.* Portland, Oregon: Timber Press.
Rouèche, A. Les Crets Fruits et Pomologie. www.pomologie.com
Spiers, V. 1996. *Burcombes, Queenies and Colloggetts.* St Dominic, Cornwall: West Brendon.
Meconopsis
Grey-Wilson, C. 1992. A Survey of the Genus *Meconopsis* in Cultivation. *The Plantsman* 14(1): 1-33.
Grey-Wilson, C. 2002. The True Identity of *Meconopsis napaulensis. Bot. Mag.* 23(2):176-209.
Meconopsis Group website. www.meconopsis.org
Stevens, E. & Brickell, C. 2001. Problems with the Big Perennial Blue Poppies. *The New Plantsman* 8(1):48-61.
Stevens, E. 2001. Further Observations on the Big Perennial Blue Poppies. *The New Plantsman* 8(2):105-111.
Miscanthus
Jones, L. 2004. *Miscanthus: RHS Bulletin No 7.* Wisley, Surrey: RHS.
Moraea
Goldblatt, P. 1986. *The Moraeas of Southern Africa.* Kirstenbosch, South Africa: National Botanic Gardens.
Musa
Banana and Plantain Section of Biodiversity International 2001. http://bananas.bioversityinternational.org
INIBAP *Musa* Germplasm Information System. www.crop-diversity.org/banana
Narcissus
Blanchard, J.W. 1990. *Narcissus – A Guide to Wild Daffodils.* Woking, Surrey: Alpine Garden Society.
Kington, S. (comp.). 2008. *The International Daffodil Register and Classified List 2008* (4th ed.)
McDonald, S. (comp.) *The International Daffodil Register and Classified List.* Supps 1-5. 2008-2012. London: RHS.
Nematanthus
Arnold, P. 1978. *The Gesneriad Register 1978.* Check List of *Nematanthus.* American Gloxinia and Gesneriad Society, Inc.
Nerium
Pagen, F.J.J. 1987. *Oleanders. Nerium L. and the Oleander Cultivars.* Wageningen, The Netherlands: Agricultural University Wageningen.
Nymphaea
Knotts, K. & Knotts, B. Victoria Adventure Website. Checklist of Waterlily Cultivars. www.victoria-adventure.org
Orchidaceae
Shaw, J.M.H. The International Orchid Register. www.rhs.org.uk/plants/plantsmanship/plant-registration/Orchid-hybrid-registration.
Origanum
White, S. 1998. *Origanum. The Herb Marjoram and its Relatives.* Surrey: NCCPG.
Paeonia
HelpMeFind Peonies. www.helpmefind.com/peony/index.php
Jakubowski, R. American Peony Society Peony Checklist. www.americanpeonysociety.org
Jakubowski, R. 2008. *Peonies 1997-2007. Registered Peony Cultivars, with a Checklist of Peony Names,*

References and Originators. Missouri: American Peony Society.
McLewin, W & Dezhong, C. 2008. *Peony rockii and the Gansu Mudan*. Massachusetts: Wellesley-Cambridge Press.
Osti, G.L. 1999. *The Book of Tree Peonies.* Turin: Umberto Allemandi.
Wang, L., et al. 1998. *Chinese Tree Peony.* Beijing: China Forestry Publishing House.

Papaver

Grey-Wilson, C. 1998. Oriental Glories. *The Garden* (RHS) 123(5):320-325.

Papaveraceae

Grey-Wilson, C. 2000. *Poppies. The Poppy Family in the Wild and in Cultivation*. London: Batsford.
Tebbitt, M. Liden, M. Zetterlund, H. 2008. *Bleeding Hearts, Corydalis and their Relatives*. Portland, Oregon: Timber Press

Passiflora

King, L.A. Passiflora online passion flower cultivar register. www.passionflow.co.uk
Ulmer, T. & MacDougal, J.M. 2004. *Passiflora – Passion Flowers of the World*. Portland, Oregon: Timber Press.

Pelargonium

Anon. 1978 & 1985. *A Checklist and Register of Pelargonium Cultivar Names.* Pts 1 & 2. Australian Pelargonium Society.
Clifton, R. 1999. *Geranium Family Species Checklist, Pt 4: Pelargonium*. The Geraniaceae Group.
Key, H. 2000. *1001 Pelargoniums.* London: Batsford.
Miller, D. 1996. *Pelargonium.* A Gardener's Guide to the Species and Cultivars and Hybrids. London: Batsford.
Pelargonium Palette: The Geranium and Pelargonium Society of Sydney Incorporated. Varieties – Alphabetical List. www.elj.com/geranium
Van der Walt, J.J.A., et al. 1977. *Pelargoniums of South Africa.* (1-3). Kirstenbosch, South Africa: National Botanic Gardens.

Penstemon

Lindgren, D.T. & Davenport, B. 1992. List and description of named cultivars in the genus *Penstemon*. University of Nebraska.
Nold, R. 1999. *Penstemons.* Portland, Oregon: Timber Press.
Way, D. & James, P. 1998. *The Gardener's Guide to Growing Penstemons.* Newton Abbott, Devon: David & Charles.
Way, D. 2006. *Penstemons*. Pershore, Worcs: Hardy Plant Society.

Phlomis

Mann Taylor, J. 1998. *Phlomis: The Neglected Genus.* Wisley: NCCPG.

Phlox

Harmer, J. & Elliott, J. 2001. *Phlox*. Pershore, Worcs: Hardy Plant Society.
Stebbings, G. 1999. Simply Charming. *The Garden* (RHS) 124(7):518-521.
Wherry, E.T. 1955. *The Genus Phlox.* Philadelphia, Pennsylvania: Morris Arboretum.

Phormium

Heenan, P.B. 1991. *Checklist of Phormium Cultivars.* Royal New Zealand Institute of Horticulture.
McBride-Whitehead, V. 1998. Phormiums of the Future. *The Garden* (RHS) 123(1):42-45.

Pieris

Bond, J. 1982. *Pieris:* a Survey. *The Plantsman* 4(2):65-75.
Wagenknecht, B.L. 1961. Registration Lists of Cultivar Names in the Genus *Pieris* D. Don. *Arnoldia* 21(8):47-50.

Pittosporum

Miller, D.M. 2006. RHS Plant Assessments: *Pittosporum tenuifolium* hybrids & cultivars.

Plectranthus

Miller, D. & Morgan, N. 2000. Focus on Plants: A New Leaf. *The Garden* (RHS) 125(11):842-845.
Shaw, J.M.H. 1999. Notes on the Identity of Swedish Ivy and Other Cultivated *Plectranthus. The New Plantsman* 6(2):71-74.
Van Jaarsveld, E.J. 2006. *South African Plectranthus.* Vlaeberg, South Africa: Fernwood Press.

Pleione

Cribb, P. & Butterfield, I. 1999. *The Genus Pleione.* (2nd ed.). Kew: Royal Botanic Gardens.
Shaw, J.M.H. (comp.). Oct 2002. *Provisional List of Pleione Cultivars*. RHS.

Poaceae

Clayton, W.D., Harman, K.T. & Williamson, H. GrassBase : The Online World Grass Flora. www.kew.org/data/grasses-syn
Darke, R. 2007. *Encyclopedia of Grasses for Livable Landscapes*. Portland, Oregon: Timber Press.
Grounds, R. 1998. *The Plantfinder's Guide to Ornamental Grasses.* Newton Abott, Devon: David & Charles.
Wood, T. 2002. *Garden Grasses, Rushes and Sedges.* (3rd ed.). Abingdon, Oxon: John Wood.

Polemonium

Nichol-Brown, D. 2000. *Polemonium.* Wisley: NCCPG.

Potentilla

Davidson, C.G., Enns, R.J. & Gobin, S. 1994. *A Checklist of Potentilla fruticosa: the Shrubby Potentillas.* Morden, Manitoba: Agriculture & Agri-Food Canada Research Centre.
Miller, D.M. 2002. *Shrubby Potentilla: RHS Bulletin No 1.* Wisley, Surrey: RHS.

Primula

Richards, J. 2002 (2nd ed.). *Primula.* London: Batsford.

Primula allionii

Archdale, B. & Richards, D. 1997. *Primula allionii Forms and Hybrids.* National Auricula & Primula Society, Midland & West Section.

Primula auricula
Baker, G. *Double Auriculas.* National Auricula & Primula Society, Midland & West Section.
Baker, G. & Ward, P. 1995. *Auriculas*. London: Batsford.
Guest, A. 2009. *The Auricula History, Cultivation and Varieties*. Woodbridge, Suffolk: Garden Art Press
Hawkes, A. 1995. Striped Auriculas. National Auricula & Primula Society, Midland & West Section.
Nicholle, G. 1996. *Border Auriculas.* National Auricula & Primula Society, Midland & West Section.
Robinson, M.A. 2000. *Auriculas for Everyone.* How to Grow and Show Perfect Plants. Lewes, Sussex: Guild of Master Craftsmen Publications.
Telford, D. 1993. *Alpine Auriculas.* National Auricula & Primula Society, Midland & West Section.
Ward, P. 1991. *Show Auriculas.* National Auricula & Primula Society, Midland & West Section.

Proteaceae
Rebelo, T. 1995. *Proteas.* A Field Guide to the Proteas of Southern Africa. Vlaeberg: Fernwood Press/National Botanical Institute.
Sadie, N. (2005). *International Proteaceae Register.* (8th ed.).

Prunus
Crawford, M. 1996. *Plums.* Dartington, Devon: Agroforestry Research Trust.
Jacobsen, A.L. 1992. *Purpleleaf Plums.* Portland, Oregon: Timber Press.
Jefferson, R.M. & Wain, K.K. 1984. *The Nomenclature of Cultivated Flowering Cherries (Prunus).* The Sato-Zakura Group. Washington DC: USDA.
Kuitert, W. 1999. *Japanese Flowering Cherries.* Portland, Oregon: Timber Press.

Pulmonaria
Bennett, M. 2003. *Pulmonarias and the borage family*. London: B.T. Batsford.
Hewitt, J. 1994. *Pulmonarias.* Pershore, Worcs: Hardy Plant Society.
Hewitt, J. 1999. Well Spotted. *The Garden* (RHS) 124(2):98-103.

Pyracantha
Egolf, D.R. & Andrick, A.O. 1995. *A Checklist of Pyracantha Cultivars.* Washington DC: Agricultural Research Service.

Pyrus
Crawford, M. 1996. *Directory of Pear Cultivars.* Totnes, Devon: Agroforestry Research Institute.
Smith, M.W.G. 1976. *Catalogue of the British Pear.* Faversham, Kent: MAFF.

Quercus
International Oak Society. Oak Name Checklist. www.oaknames.org.
Miller, H.A. & Lamb, S.H. 1985. *Oaks of North America.* Happy Camp, California: Naturegraph Publishers.
Mitchell, A. 1994. The Lucombe Oaks. *The Plantsman* 15(4):216-224.

Rhododendron
Argent, G., Fairweather, C. & Walter, K. 1996. *Accepted Names in* Rhododendron *section Vireya.* Edinburgh: Royal Botanic Garden.
Argent, G., Bond, J., Chamberlain, D., Cox, P. & Hardy, A. 1997. *The Rhododendron Handbook 1998.* Rhododendron Species in Cultivation. London: RHS.
Chamberlain, D.F. & Rae, S.J. 1990. A Revision of *Rhododendron* IV. Subgenus *Tsutsusi. Edinburgh J. Bot.* 47(2).
Chamberlain, D.F. 1982. A Revision of *Rhododendron* II. Subgenus *Hymenanthes. Notes Roy. Bot. Gard. Edinburgh* 39(2).
Chamberlain, D., Hyam, R., Argent, G., Fairweather, G. & Walter, K.S. 1996. *The Genus Rhododendron.* Edinburgh:Royal Botanic Garden.
Cox, K.N.E. 2005. *Rhododendrons and Azaleas. A Colour Guide.* Wiltshire: The Crowood Press.
Cox, P.A. & Cox, K.N.E. 1988. *Rhododendron Hybrids*. London: Batsford.
Cox, P.A. & Cox, K.N.E. 1997. *The Encyclopedia of Rhododendron Species*. Perth: Glendoick Publishing.
Cullen, J. 2005. *Hardy Rhododendron Species. A Guide to Identification.* Portland, Oregon: Timber Press.
Davidian, H.H. 1982-1992 *The Rhododendron Species* (Vols 1-4). London: Batsford.
Galle, F.C. 1985. *Azaleas.* Portland, Oregon: Timber Press.
Leslie, A.C. (comp.) 2004. *The International Rhododendron Register and Checklist* (2nd ed.) & Supps 1-6, 2004-2012. London: RHS.
McQuire, J.F.J. & Robinson, M.L.A. 2009. *Pocket Guide to Rhododendron Species*. Kew: Royal Botanic Gardens.
Tamura, T. (ed.). 1989. *Azaleas in Kurume*. Kurume, Japan: International Azalea Festival '89.
van Gelderen, D.M. & van Hoey-Smith, J.R.P. 1992. *Rhododendrons*. London: Batsford.

Ribes
Crawford, M. 1997. *Currants and Gooseberries: Production and Culture.* Dartington, Devon: Agroforestry Research Trust.

Rosa
Beales, P., Cairns, T. 1998. *Botanica's Rose: The Encyclopedia of Roses*. Hoo, Kent: Grange Books.
Cairns, T. (ed.). 2000. *Modern Roses XI. The World Encyclopedia of Roses*. London: Academic Press.
Dickerson, B.C. 1999. *The Old Rose Advisor.* Portland, Oregon: Timber Press.

Haw, S.G. 1996. Notes on Some Chinese and Himalayan Rose Species of Section *Pimpinellifoliae. The New Plantsman* 3(3):143-146.

HelpMeFind Roses. www.helpmefind.com

McCann, S. 1985. *Miniature Roses.* Newton Abbot, Devon: David & Charles.

Pawsey, Angela (ed.) 2015. *Find That Rose! 2015-2016.* (33rd ed.). Colchester, Essex. www.findthatrose.net.

Phillips, R. & Rix, M. 1993. *The Quest for the Rose.* London: BBC Books.

Phillips, R. & Rix, M. 2004. *The Ultimate Guide to Roses.* London: Macmillan.

Quest-Ritson, C. 2003. *Climbing Roses of the World.* Portland, Oregon: Timber Press.

Quest-Ritson, C. & B. 2003. *The Royal Horticultural Society Encyclopedia of Roses: The Definitive A-Z Guide.* London: Dorling Kindersley.

Thomas, G.S. 1995. *The Graham Stuart Thomas Rose Book.* London: John Murray.

Verrier, S. 1996. *Rosa Gallica.* Balmain, Australia: Florilegium.

Roscoea

Cowley, J. 2007. *The Genus Roscoea.* Kew: Royal Botanic Gardens.

Rosularia

Eggli, U. 1988. A Monographic Study of the Genus *Rosularia. Bradleya* (Supp.) 6:1-118.

Saintpaulia

Goodship, G. 1987. *Saintpaulia Variety List* (Supp.). Slough, Bucks: Saintpaulia & Houseplant Society.

Moore, H.E. 1957. *African Violets, Gloxinias and Their Relatives.* A Guide to the Cultivated Gesneriads. New York: Macmillan.

Salix

Newsholme, C. 1992. *Willows.* The Genus *Salix.* London: Batsford.

Salvia

Clebsch, B. 2003. *A Book of Salvias.* (2nd ed.). Portland, Oregon: Timber Press.

Compton, J. 1994. Mexican Salvias in Cultivation. *The Plantsman* 15(4):193-215.

Middleton, R. *Robin's Salvias.* www.robinssalvias.com

Saxifraga

Bland, B. 2000. *Silver Saxifrages.* Pershore, Worcs: Alpine Garden Society.

Dashwood, M. & Bland, B. 2005. *Silver Saxifrages: RHS Bulletin No 9.* Wisley, Surrey: RHS.

McGregor, M. Saxbase. Saxifrage Society. www.saxifraga.org

McGregor, M. 1995. *Saxifrages: The Complete Cultivars & Hybrids: International Register of Saxifrages.* (2nd ed.). Driffield, E. Yorks: Saxifrage Society.

Webb, D.A. & Gornall, R.J. 1989. *Saxifrages of Europe.* Bromley, Kent: Christopher Helm.

Sedges

Govaerts, R. & Simpson, D.A. 2007 *World Checklist of Cyperaceae: Sedges.* Kew: Royal Botanic Gardens.

Sedum

Evans, R.L. 1983. *Handbook of Cultivated Sedums.* Motcombe, Dorset: Ivory Head Press.

Lord, T. 2006. *Sedum* up for assessment. *The Plantsman* 5(4):244-252.

Stephenson, R. 1994. *Sedum.* The Cultivated Stonecrops. Portland, Oregon: Timber Press.

Sempervivum

Diehm, H. www.semperhorst.de

Miklánek, M. 2000. *List of Cultivars: Sempervivum and Jovibarba* v. 15.1. http://miklanek.tripod.com

Sinningia

Dates, J.D. 1988. *The Gesneriad Register 1988. Check List of Names with Descriptions of Cultivated Plants in the Genus Sinningia.* Galesburg, Illinois: American Gloxinia and Gesneriad Society, Inc.

Solenostemon

Addink, W. Coleus Finder. http://coleusfinder.org

Pedley, W.K. & Pedley, R. 1974. *Coleus – A Guide to Cultivation and Identification.* Edinburgh: Bartholemew.

Sorbus

McAllister, H. 2005. *The Genus Sorbus: Mountain Ash and Other Rowans.* Kew: Royal Botanical Gardens.

Snyers d'Attenhoven, C. 1999. *Sorbus* Lombarts hybrids *Belgische Dendrologie*: 76-81. Belgium.

Spiraea

Miller, D.M. 2003. *Spiraea japonica with coloured leaves: RHS Bulletin No 4.* Wisley, Surrey: RHS

Streptocarpus

Arnold, P. 1979. *The Gesneriad Register 1979: Check List of Streptocarpus.* Binghamton, New York: American Gloxinia & Gesneriad.

Succulents

Eggli, U. (ed.) 2002. *Illustrated Handbook of Succulent Plants.* Heidelberg, Germany: Springer-Verlag.

Eggli, U. & Taylor, N. 1994. *List of Names of Succulent Plants other than Cacti Published 1950-92.* Kew: Royal Botanic Gardens.

Grantham, K. & Klaassen, P. 1999. *The Plantfinder's Guide to Cacti and Other Succulents.* Newton Abbot, Devon: David & Charles.

Jacobsen, H. 1973. *Lexicon of Succulent Plants.* London: Blandford.

Syringa

Fiala, J.L. & Vrugtman, F. 2008. *A Gardener's Encyclopedia of Lilacs.* Portland, Oregon: Timber Press.

Vrugtman, F. 2000. *International Register of Cultivar Names in the Genus Syringa L. (Oleaceae).* (Contribution No 91). Hamilton, Canada: Royal Botanic Gardens.

Thymus
Easter, M. 2009. *International* Thymus *Register and Checklist*. UK: Owl Prints.
Tilia
Piggott, D. 2012. *Lime-trees and Basswoods. A Biological Monograph of the Genus Tilia.* Cambridge: Cambridge University Press.
***Tiliaceae (Malvaceae** pro parte)*
Wild, H. 1984. *Flora of Southern Africa 21 (1: Tiliaceae)*. Pretoria: Botanical Research Institute, Dept of Agriculture.
Tillandsia
Kiff, L.F. 1991. *A Distributional Checklist of the Genus Tillandsia.* Encino, California: Botanical Diversions.
Trillium
Case, F.W.J. & Case, R.B. 1997. *Trilliums.* Portland, Oregon: Timber Press.
Jacobs, D.L. & Jacobs, R.L. 1997. *American Treasures. Trilliums in Woodland Garden.* Decatur, Georgia: Eco-Gardens.
Tulipa
KAVB Online registration pages. http://kavb.back2p.soft-orange.com
Ulmus
Green, P.S. 1964. Registratration of Cultivar Names in *Ulmus. Arnoldia* 24:41-80.
Vaccinium
Trehane, J. 2004. *Blueberries, Cranberries and Other Vacciniums.* Portland, Oregon: Timber Press.
Vegetables
Official Journal of the European Communities. Common catalogue of varieties of agricultural plant species: consolidated version. http://ec.europa.eu/food
Viburnum
Dirr, M.A. 2007. *Viburnums: Flowering Shrubs for Every Season.* Portland, Oregon: Timber Press.
Kenyon, L. 2001. *Viburnum.* Surrey: NCCPG.
Viola
Coombes, R.E. 2003. *Violets.* (2nd ed.). London: Batsford.
Fuller, R. 1990. *Pansies, Violas & Violettas.* The Complete Guide. Marlborough: The Crowood Press.
Perfect, E.J. 1996. *Armand Millet and his Violets.* High Wycombe: Park Farm Press.
Robinson, P.M. & Snocken, J. 2003. Checklist of the Cultivated Forms of the Genus *Viola* including the Register of Cultivars. American Violet Society. http://americanvioletsociety.org
Vitis
Robinson, J. 1989. *Vines, Grapes and Wines.* London: Mitchell Beazley.
Watsonia
Goldblatt, P. 1989. *The Genus Watsonia. A Systematic Monograph.* South Africa: National Botanic Gardens.
Weigela
Howard, R.A. 1965. A Checklist of Cultivar Names in *Weigela. Arnoldia* 25:49-69.
Wisteria
Valder, P. 1995. *Wisterias. A Comprehensive Guide.* Balmain, Australia: Florilegium.
Yucca
Smith, C. 2004. *Yuccas: Giants among the Lilies.* NCCPG.
Zauschneria
Robinson, A. 2000. Focus on Plants: Piping Hot (*Zauschneria* Cultivars). *The Garden* (RHS) 125(9):698-699.
Zingiberaceae
Branney, T.M.E. 2005. *Hardy Gingers. Including Hedychium, Roscoea and Zingiber.* Cambridge: Timber Press.

Nurseries

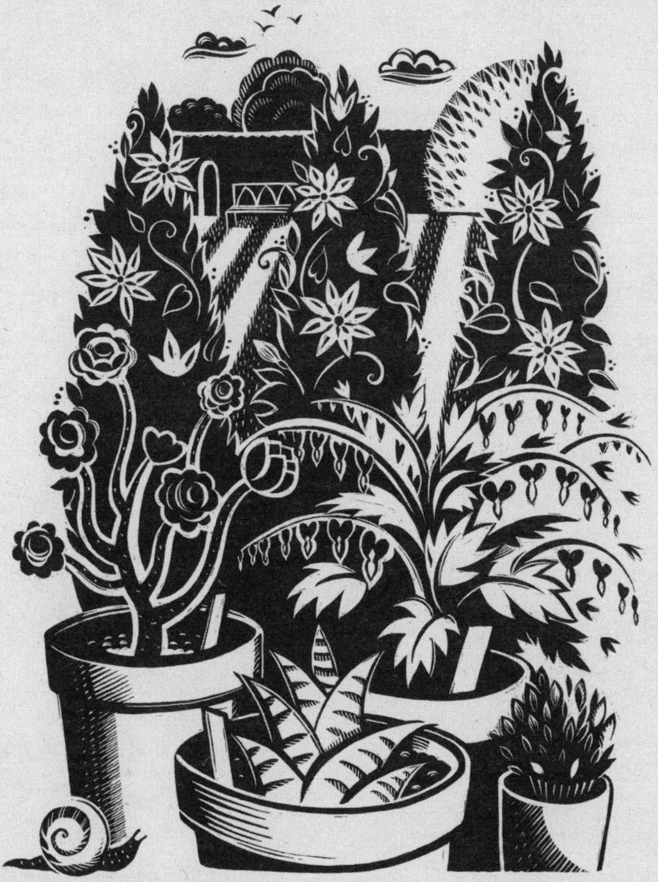

The following nurseries between them stock an unrivalled choice of plants. Before making a visit, please remember to check with the nursery that the plant you seek is currently available.

Nursery Codes and Symbols

The first letter of each nursery code represents the area of the country in which the nursery is situated.

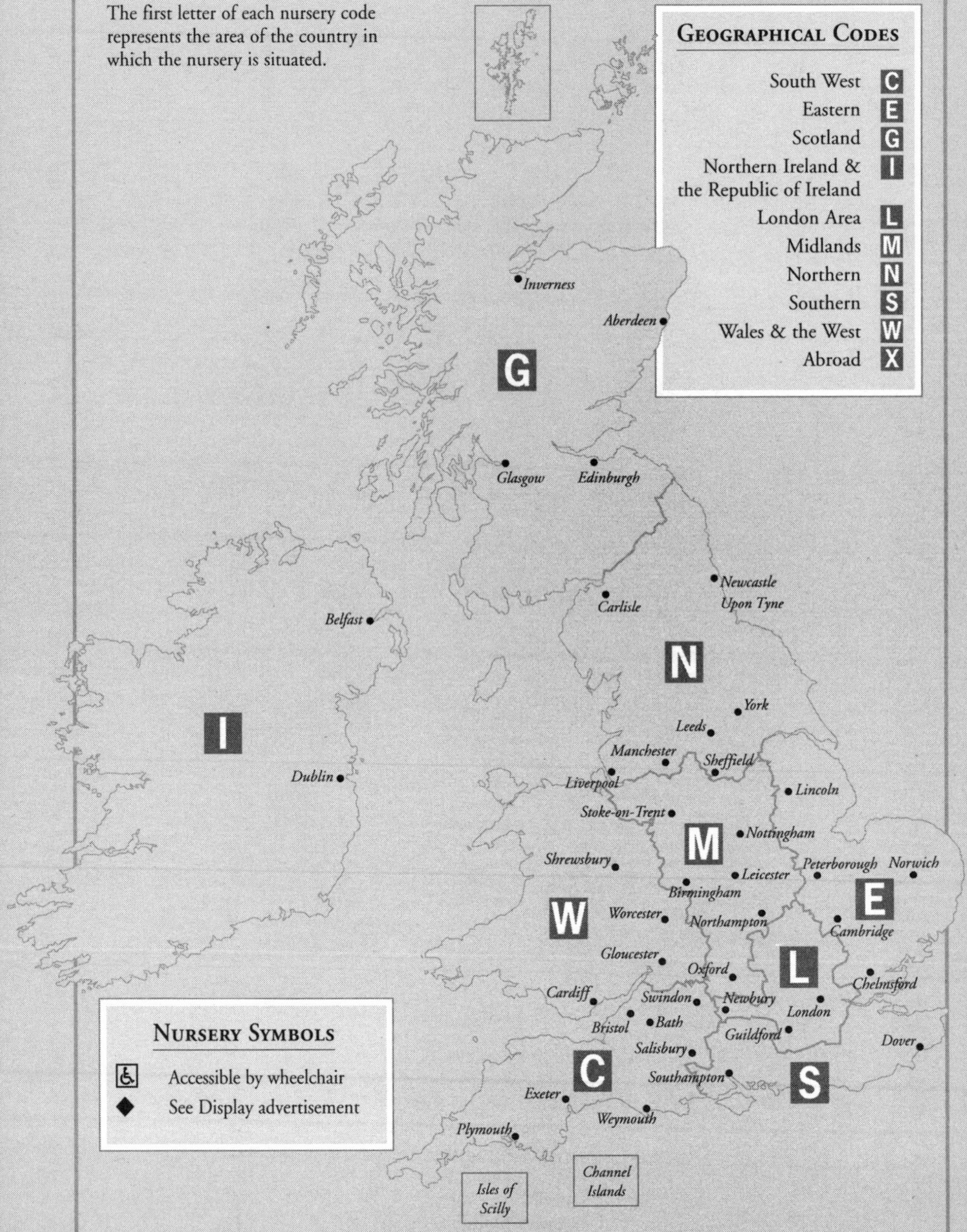

Geographical Codes

South West	C
Eastern	E
Scotland	G
Northern Ireland & the Republic of Ireland	I
London Area	L
Midlands	M
Northern	N
Southern	S
Wales & the West	W
Abroad	X

Nursery Symbols

- ♿ Accessible by wheelchair
- ◆ See Display advertisement

USING THE NURSERY LISTINGS

Your main reference from the Plant Directory is the Nursery Details by Code listing, which includes all relevant information for each nursery in order of nursery code. The Nursery Index by Name is an alphabetical list for those who know a nursery's name but not its code and wish to check its details in the main list.

1 NURSERY DETAILS BY CODE

Once you have found your plant in the Plant Directory, turn to this list to find out the name, address, opening times and other details of the nurseries whose codes accompany the plant.

KEY
♿ Accessible by wheelchair ◆ See Display advertisement

A geographical code is followed by three letters reflecting the nursery's name

SFrt **FRUIT GARDEN PLANTS** ♿ ◆
Woolton Farm, Bekesbourne, Canterbury, Kent CT4 5EA
Ⓣ (01227) 830525
Ⓜ 07710 253690
Ⓕ (01227) 831969
Ⓔ sales@fruitgardenplants.co.uk
Ⓦ www.fruitgardenplants.co.uk
Contact: Mark Mount
Opening Times: 1000-1600 Thu-Sat, 1st Nov-31st Mar. 1000-1700 Thu-Sun, 1st Apr-31st Oct.
Min Mail Order UK: £10.00
Min Mail Order EU: £35.00
Credit Cards: MasterCard, Visa
Specialities: Tree fruits & soft fruits.
Notes: Fruit display garden where visitors can see particular varieties & the methods used for growing them. Small café. Medieval tythe barn. Also sells wholesale. Delivers to shows. Wheelchair accessible.
Map Ref: S, C5 **OS Grid Ref:** TR191568

A brief summary of the plants available

Other information about the nursery

The map letter is followed by the map square in which the nursery is located

The Ordnance Survey national grid reference for use with OS maps

2 NURSERY INDEX BY NAME

If you are looking for a particular nursery, use this alphabetical index to find it, note its code and then turn to the Nursery Details by Code listing for full information.

Forest Garden, The	**CFGn**
Frogswell Nursery	IFro
Frosch Exclusive Perennials	XFro
Fruit Garden Plants	SFrt
Garden Blooms	NGBl
Garden House Nursery	NGdn
Gardeners Delight Nursery	**CGar**
George's Gorgeous Gardens	**EGeo**

How to Use the Nursery Listings

The details given for each nursery have been compiled from information supplied to us in answer to a questionnaire. In some case, because of space constraints, the entries have been abbreviated.

Nurseries are not charged for their entries and inclusion in no way implies a value judgement.

Nursery Details by Code (p.832)

Each nursery is allocated a code, for example GPoy. The first letter of each code indicates the region of the British Isles in which the nursery is situated. In this example G = Scotland. The remaining three letters reflect the nursery's name, in this case Poyntzfield Herb Nursery.

In this listing, nurseries are given in alphabetical order of code for quick referral from the Plant Directory. All of the nurseries' details, such as addresses, opening times, etc will be found in this index.

Opening Times

These are published as submitted. It is always advisable, especially if travelling a long distance, to double-check with the nursery before setting out.

Mail Order

Many nurseries offer a mail order service. This is often restricted to certain times of the year or to particular genera. Please check the **Notes** section of the nursery entry for restrictions or special conditions.

In some instances the mail order service extends throughout the European Union. Where this is the case, the minimum charge to the EU will be noted. If this is "Nmc" ("no minimum charge") please note that to send even one plant may involve the nursery in substantial postage and packaging costs. Some nurseries may not be prepared to send tender or bulky plants.

Where a nursery offers a mail order only service, this will be noted under **Opening Times** in the nursery entry. Many nurseries offer a mail order online service with some only operating in this way.

Export

This refers to mail order beyond the EU and indicates nurseries that are prepared to consider this. There is usually a substantial minimum charge and, in addition, all the costs of phytosanitary certificates and Customs have to be met by the purchaser.

Catalogue Cost

Only a shrinking number of nurseries offer a printed catalogue. Some may not charge or may ask for stamps to bear the cost of postage. If plant lists are available in an electronic format, some nurseries have indicated that they will email them to enquirers.

The majority of nurseries now publish their catalogues only on the internet as this is more cost-effective than producing a printed copy and enables them to reflect stock changes throughout the year.

Specialities

This is where nurseries list the plants or genera in which they specialise and any National Collections that they hold. Please note that some nurseries may charge an entry fee to visit a National Collection. Charges may also be levied to visit any garden to which the nursery is attached.

Nurseries also indicate here if they only have small quantities of individual plants available for sale or if they will propagate to order.

Notes

This section contains: information on restrictions to mail order or export; whether payment in euros is accepted; whether nurseries deliver to shows; details of partial wheelchair access; the nursery site address if this differs from the office address; and any other non-horticultural or general information.

Wheelchair Access ♿

Nurseries are asked to indicate if their premises are suitable for wheelchair users.

We use the wheelchair symbol for those nurseries that tell us their site is fully accessible. Where only partial or restricted access is offered, this is stated in the **Notes** section of the nursery's details and the nursery is not marked with the symbol.

Please note that wheelchair access does not necessarily relate to any gardens to which the nursery may be attached.

The assessment of ease of access is entirely the responsibility of the individual nursery.

Delivers to Shows

Many nurseries will deliver pre-ordered plants to flower shows for collection by customers. Contact the nursery for details of shows that they will be attending.

Payment in Euros

A number of UK nurseries will accept payment in euros. You should check with the nursery concerned before making such a payment, as some will only accept cash and some only cheques, whilst others will expect the purchaser to pay bank charges.

Maps

The approximate locations of nurseries are shown on the relevant maps (p.933) unless the nursery has requested not to be shown. Nurseries are also encouraged to provide their Ordnance Survey national grid reference for use with OS Land Ranger Series maps.

Nursery Index by Name

An alphabetical index of nurseries is included (p.927). Nurseries new to the book and those making a re-entry are shown in embolden type.

Deleted Nurseries

Every year some nurseries ask to be removed from the book. This may be a temporary measure because, for example, they are relocating or because their plant stocks are low due to adverse growing conditions, or it may be permanent following closure, sale, retirement or a change in the way they trade.

Some nurseries miss the deadline for submissions and may ask to re-enter the book in the following edition. Other nurseries do not respond at all and, as we have no current information on their trading status, they are not included in the book.

Please, never use an out of date edition

NURSERY DETAILS BY CODE

Please note that all these nurseries are listed in alphabetical order by their code. All nurseries are listed in alphabetical order by their name in the **Nursery Index by Name** on page 927.

SOUTH WEST

CAbb **ABBOTSBURY SUB-TROPICAL GARDENS** ♿
Abbotsbury, Nr Weymouth, Dorset DT3 4LA
Ⓣ (01305) 871344
Ⓕ (01305) 871344
Ⓔ info@abbotsburygardens.co.uk
Ⓦ www.abbotsbury-tourism.co.uk/gardens
Contact: David Sutton
Opening Times: 1000-1800 daily, mid Mar-1st Nov. 1000-1500, Nov-mid Mar.
Credit Cards: Access, Visa, MasterCard, Switch
Specialities: Less common & tender shrubs incl. palms, tree ferns, bamboos & plants from Australia, New Zealand & S. Africa.
Notes: Mail order of some plants is possible upon request, please phone/email for details & a quotation. Wheelchair accessible.

CAbP **ABBEY PLANTS** ♿
Chaffeymoor, Bourton, Gillingham, Dorset SP8 5BY
Ⓣ (01747) 840841
Contact: K Potts
Opening Times: 1000-1300 & 1400-1700 Wed-Sat Mar-Nov. Dec-Feb by appt.
Min Mail Order UK: Nmc
Cat. Cost: 2 × 2nd class.
Credit Cards: None
Specialities: Flowering trees & shrubs.
Notes: Wheelchair accessible.
Map Ref: C, B5 **OS Grid Ref:** ST762304

CAby **THE ABBEY NURSERY** ♿
Forde Abbey, Chard, Somerset TA20 4LU
Ⓣ (01460) 220088
Ⓔ theabbeynursery@hotmail.com
Contact: Paul Bygrave
Opening Times: 1000-1700 7 days, 1st Mar-31st Oct.
Cat. Cost: None issued.
Credit Cards: All major credit/debit cards
Specialities: Hardy herbaceous perennials.
Notes: Wheelchair accessible.
Map Ref: C, C4 **OS Grid Ref:** ST359052

CAco **ACORN TREES AND SHRUBS**
Hilltown Farm, Rackenford, Tiverton, Devon EX16 8DX
Ⓣ (01884) 881633
Ⓜ 07976 807510
Ⓔ goakey101@aol.com
Ⓦ www.acorntreesandshrubs.co.uk
Contact: Grahame Oakey
Opening Times: Most times but by appt. only.
Min Mail Order UK: £30.00
Cat. Cost: Full plant listing available by email only.
Credit Cards: All major credit/debit cards
Specialities: Rhododendrons, choice conifers, *Pinus montezumae*, *Cedrus atlantica* 'Glauca Pendula' & other pendulous trees.
Notes: Plant specimen procurement, incl. rare/large specimens, delivery & planting service. Also sells wholesale.

CAgr **AGROFORESTRY RESEARCH TRUST**
46 Hunters Moon, Dartington, Totnes, Devon TQ9 6JT
Ⓕ (01803) 840776
Ⓔ mail@agroforestry.co.uk
Ⓦ www.agroforestry.co.uk
Contact: Martin Crawford
Opening Times: Not open. Mail order only.
Min Mail Order UK: Nmc
Min Mail Order EU: Nmc
Cat. Cost: 4 × 1st class.
Credit Cards: All major credit/debit cards
Specialities: Top & soft fruit, nut trees including *Castanea*, *Corylus*, *Juglans*, *Pinus*. Also seeds. Some plants in small quantities only.
Notes: Euro accepted.

CAni **ANITA ALLEN**
Shapcott Barton Estate, East Knowstone, South Molton, Devon EX36 4EE
Ⓣ (01398) 341664
Contact: Anita Allen

Opening Times: By appt. only. Garden open under NGS & Plant Heritage.
Min Mail Order UK: Nmc
Cat. Cost: 5 × 1st class & state which catalogue: Shasta daisies or *Buddleja*.
Credit Cards: None
Specialities: Nat. Collections of *Leucanthemum* × *superbum* & *Buddleja davidii* & hybrids, 70+ cvs. 80+ accurately named Shasta daisies, a few in very short supply. Also many hardy perennials. Some *Buddleja* propagated to order.
Map Ref: C, B3 **OS Grid Ref:** SS846235

CArg **Ashridge Trees Ltd**
Grove Cross Barn, Castle Cary, Somerset BA7 7NJ
Ⓣ (01963) 359444
Ⓕ (01963) 359445
Ⓔ support@ashridgetrees.co.uk
Ⓦ www.ashridgetrees.co.uk
Contact: Catherine Young
Opening Times: 0900-1730, Mon-Fri.
Min Mail Order UK: £20.00
Credit Cards: MasterCard, Visa
Specialities: Trees, hedging & fruit.

CArn **Arne Herbs** ♿
Limeburn Nurseries, Limeburn Hill, Chew Magna, Bristol BS40 8QW
Ⓣ (01275) 333399
Ⓔ arneherbs@aol.com
Contact: A Lyman-Dixon & Jenny Thomas
Opening Times: By appt. only.
Cat. Cost: Sae for free plant list.
Specialities: Herbs, some very rare, largely for historical recreations & research. Also some North American, Mediterranean & UK wild flowers in limited numbers.
Notes: Euro accepted. Wheelchair accessible.
Map Ref: C, A5 **OS Grid Ref:** ST563638

CAvo **Avon Bulbs**
Burnt House Farm, Mid-Lambrook, South Petherton, Somerset TA13 5HE
Ⓣ (01460) 242177 or 249060
Ⓕ (01460) 249025
Ⓔ info@avonbulbs.co.uk
Ⓦ www.avonbulbs.co.uk
Contact: C Ireland-Jones
Opening Times: Mail order only. Collection of pre-booked orders by arrangement.
Min Mail Order UK: Nmc
Min Mail Order EU: Nmc
Cat. Cost: 4 × 2nd class.
Credit Cards: All major credit/debit cards
Specialities: Some special snowdrops are only available in small quantities.
Notes: Delivers to some shows.
Map Ref: C, B5 **OS Grid Ref:** ST422187

CBar **Barters Plant Centre & Nursery** ♿
Chapmanslade, Westbury, Wiltshire BA13 4AL
Ⓣ (01373) 832694
Ⓕ (01373) 832677
Ⓔ plantcentre@barters.co.uk
Ⓦ www.barters.co.uk
Contact: Andrew Stone
Opening Times: 0900-1700 Mon-Sat, Mar-Oct. 0900-1630 Mon-Sat, Nov-Feb. 1000-1600 Sun, except closed Sun Jul-Nov & Jan-Feb. 1000-1600 Sun, Dec only.
Cat. Cost: None issued.
Credit Cards: All, except American Express
Specialities: Wide range of shrubs. Ground cover, container trees, ferns, half-hardy perennials, grasses, herbaceous & climbers. Hedging, fruit trees, old fashioned roses & bare-root stock.
Notes: Also sells wholesale. Wheelchair accessible.

CBcs **Burncoose Nurseries** ♿
Gwennap, Redruth, Cornwall TR16 6BJ
Ⓣ (01209) 860316
Ⓔ info@burncoose.co.uk
Ⓦ www.burncoose.co.uk
Contact: C H Williams
Opening Times: 0830-1700 Mon-Sat & 1100-1700 Sun.
Min Mail Order UK: Nmc
Min Mail Order EU: Individual quotations for EU sales.
Cat. Cost: Free
Credit Cards: Visa, MasterCard, Maestro
Specialities: Extensive range of over 3500 ornamental trees & shrubs and herbaceous. Rare & unusual *Magnolia*, *Rhododendron*. Conservatory plants. 30 acre garden.
Notes: Also sells wholesale. Delivers to shows. Wheelchair accessible.
Map Ref: C, D1 **OS Grid Ref:** SW742395

CBct **Barracott Plants** ♿
Old Orchard, Calstock Road, Gunnislake, Cornwall PL18 9AA
Ⓣ (01822) 832234
Ⓜ 07811 207186
Ⓔ geoffandthelma@barracott.eclipse.co.uk
Ⓦ www.barracottplants.co.uk
Contact: Geoff & Thelma Turner
Opening Times: 0900-1700 Thu & Fri, Mar-end Sep. Other times by appt.
Min Mail Order UK: Nmc
Cat. Cost: 1st class stamp.
Credit Cards: None
Specialities: Herbaceous plants: shade-loving, foliage & form. *Acanthus*, *Aspidistra*, *Astrantia*, *Bergenia*, *Convallaria*, *Disporum*,

C

Liriope, *Maianthemum*, *Polygonatum*, *Roscoea*, *Trillium* & *Uvularia*.
Notes: Also sells wholesale. Delivers to shows. Euro accepted. Wheelchair accessible.
Map Ref: C, C3 **OS Grid Ref:** SX436702

CBen **BENNETTS WATER GARDENS** ♿
Putton Lane, Chickerell, Weymouth, Dorset DT3 4AF
Ⓣ (01305) 785150
Ⓔ info@waterlily.co.uk
Ⓦ www.waterlily.co.uk
Contact: James Bennett
Opening Times: 1000-1700 Apr-Sep, Sun-Fri.
Min Mail Order UK: Nmc
Min Mail Order EU: Nmc
Credit Cards: Visa, MasterCard, JCB, Maestro
Specialities: Nat. Collection of *Nymphaea* (hardy water lilies).
Notes: Loose plants available by mail order. Potted plants available in store. Wheelchair accessible.
Map Ref: C, C5 **OS Grid Ref:** SY650797

CBgR **BEGGAR'S ROOST PLANTS**
Lilstock, Bridgwater, Somerset TA5 1SU
Ⓣ (01278) 741519
Ⓔ ro@lilstock.eclipse.co.uk
Contact: Lady Rosemary FitzGerald
Opening Times: Not open. Mail order only.
Min Mail Order UK: £10.00
Min Mail Order EU: £15.00
Cat. Cost: 3 × large 2nd class.
Credit Cards: None
Specialities: *Hemerocallis* (incl. heritage) grown in British conditions.
Notes: Mail order for specialities *Hemerocallis*. Ask for list. Euro accepted.
Map Ref: C, B4 **OS Grid Ref:** ST168450

CBlu **BLUE NURSERIES LTD**
(Office) Brook Cottage, 2 Bleet, Steeple Ashton, Wiltshire BA14 6EA
Ⓜ 07745 067119 or 07813 894026
Ⓔ office@bluenurseries.com
Ⓦ www.bluenurseries.com
Contact: Richard Hill
Opening Times: Not open. Mail order only.
Min Mail Order UK: £4.95
Min Mail Order EU: £6.95
Cat. Cost: Online only.
Credit Cards: Paypal
Specialities: South African plants & hardy palms with slowly expanding range of plants but focussed on the architectural & rare.
Notes: Online based but displays at plant and horticultural shows. Euros accepted via Paypal only. Also sells wholesale. Euro accepted.

CBod **BODMIN NURSERY** ♿
Laveddon Mill, Laninval Hill, Bodmin, Cornwall PL30 5JU
Ⓣ (01208) 72837
Ⓕ (01208) 76491
Ⓔ bodminnursery@aol.com
Ⓦ www.bodminnursery.co.uk
Contact: Mark Lawlor
Opening Times: 0900-1700 Mon-Sat. 1000-1600 Sun.
Credit Cards: All major credit/debit cards
Specialities: Herbs, herbaceous & grasses, hardy geraniums & coastal plants. Interesting shrubs, fruit & ornamental trees.
Notes: Wheelchair accessible.
Map Ref: C, C2 **OS Grid Ref:** SX053659

CBot **THE BOTANIC NURSERY**
Coombe Lane, Atworth, Nr Melksham, Wiltshire SN12 8NU
Ⓜ 07850 328756
Ⓔ office@botanicnursery.co.uk
Ⓦ www.botanicnursery.co.uk
Contact: Terence Baker
Opening Times: 1000-1700 Tue-Sat, Mar-Oct.
Min Mail Order UK: 5 plugs or 3 plants.
Min Mail Order EU: Nmc
Cat. Cost: Online only.
Credit Cards: MasterCard, Visa
Specialities: Specialists in propagation of rare shrubs. All plants are lime-tolerant. Nat. Collection of *Digitalis*.
Notes: Mail order Oct-Mar. Plugs also available, see website or contact nursery. Delivers to shows. Only partially accessible for wheelchairs.
Map Ref: C, A5 **OS Grid Ref:** ST852655

CBre **BREGOVER PLANTS**
Middlewood, North Hill, Nr Launceston, Cornwall PL15 7NN
Ⓣ (01566) 782661
Ⓔ jenbousfield@gmail.com
Contact: Jennifer Bousfield
Opening Times: 1100-1700 Wed, Mar-mid Oct and by appt.
Min Mail Order UK: Nmc
Cat. Cost: 3 × 1st class. Plant list available as pdf download.
Credit Cards: None
Specialities: Unusual hardy perennials grown in small garden nursery. Available in small quantities only.
Notes: Mail order Oct-Mar only. Delivers to shows.
Map Ref: C, C2 **OS Grid Ref:** SX273752

CBro **BROADLEIGH GARDENS** ♿
Bishops Hull, Taunton, Somerset TA4 1AE
Ⓣ (01823) 286231

Ⓕ (01823) 323646
Ⓔ info@broadleighbulbs.co.uk
Ⓦ www.broadleighbulbs.co.uk
Contact: Christine Skelmersdale
Opening Times: 0900-1600 Mon-Fri for viewing only (charity donation). Orders may be collected if notice given.
Min Mail Order UK: Nmc
Min Mail Order EU: Nmc
Cat. Cost: 2 × 1st class.
Credit Cards: All major credit/debit cards
Specialities: Jan catalogue: bulbs in growth (*Galanthus*, *Cyclamen* etc.) & herbaceous woodland plants (trilliums, hellebores etc). Extensive list of *Agapanthus*. June catalogue: dwarf & unusual bulbs, *Iris* (DB & PC). Nat. Collection of Alec Grey hybrid daffodils.
Notes: Delivers to shows. Euro accepted as cash payment only. Wheelchair accessible.
Map Ref: C, B4 **OS Grid Ref:** ST195251

CBrP **Brooklands Plants**
25 Treves Road, Dorchester, Dorset DT1 2HE
Ⓣ (01305) 265846
Ⓔ cycads@btinternet.com
Ⓦ botanicalgardenphotography.com
Contact: Ian Watt
Opening Times: By appt. only for collection of plants.
Min Mail Order UK: £25.00 + p&p
Cat. Cost: 2 × 2nd class or by email.
Credit Cards: None
Specialities: Cycad nursery specialising in the more cold-tolerant species of *Encephalartos*, *Dioon*, *Macrozamia* & *Cycas*. Also specialist in cold-tolerant palms as well as plants from New Zealand. Some species available in small quantities only.
Notes: Euro accepted.
Map Ref: C, C5 **OS Grid Ref:** SY682897

CBur **Burnham Nurseries**
Forches Cross, Newton Abbot, Devon TQ12 6PZ
Ⓣ (01626) 352233
Ⓔ mail@orchids.uk.com
Ⓦ www.orchids.uk.com
Contact: Any member of staff
Opening Times: 1000-1600 Mon-Sun.
Min Mail Order UK: Nmc
Min Mail Order EU: £100.00 + p&p
Cat. Cost: 1 × 2nd class or online.
Credit Cards: Visa, MasterCard, Maestro
Specialities: Many types of tropical orchid species and hybrids.
Notes: Exports beyond EU, please ask for details. Delivers to shows. Euro accepted. Partial wheelchair accessiblity.
Map Ref: C, C4 **OS Grid Ref:** SX841732

CBWd **Blooming Wild** ♿
At the Oasis Plant Centre, Shaftesbury Road, Child Okeford, Dorset DT11 8EQ
Ⓜ 07525 169662
Ⓔ info@bloomingwild.co.uk
Ⓦ www.bloomingwild.co.uk
Contact: Will Holley
Opening Times: 0900-1700 Wed-Fri, 1000-1600 Sat & Sun, 1st Mar-25th Oct.
Credit Cards: All major credit/debit cards
Specialities: Small family-run nursery based in North Dorset. Specialises in growing a wide range of herbaceous perennials and ornamental grasses.
Notes: Site at bottom of Oasis Plant Centre (separate nursery).
Map Ref: C, B5 **OS Grid Ref:** ST838131

CCac **Cactus Shop** ♿
Caldicott, Winkleigh, Devon EX19 8DW
Ⓣ (01837) 83610
Ⓜ 07586 880472
Ⓕ (01837) 83610
Ⓔ ralph@cactusshop.co.uk
Ⓦ www.cactusshop.co.uk
Contact: Ralph Northcott
Opening Times: 1000-1600 daily.
Min Mail Order UK: Nmc
Min Mail Order EU: Nmc
Cat. Cost: Online only.
Credit Cards: All major credit/debit cards
Specialities: Epiphytes. Cacti hardy in the UK. Some stock in very small quantities.
Notes: Also sells wholesale. Exports beyond EU. Euro accepted. Delivers to shows. Wheelchair accessible.
Map Ref: C, C3 **OS Grid Ref:** SS618097

CCCN **Cross Common Nursery**
The Lizard, Helston, Cornwall TR12 7PD
Ⓣ (01326) 290722/290668
Ⓔ info@crosscommonnursery.co.uk
Ⓦ www.crosscommonnursery.co.uk
Contact: Kevin Bosustow
Opening Times: 1000-1700 7 days, Apr, May & Jun. Reduced hours Jul-Sep, please phone for opening times.
Min Mail Order UK: Nmc
Cat. Cost: Online only.
Credit Cards: All major credit/debit cards
Specialities: Tropical/sub-tropical, coastal plants & conservatory plants. Wide range of grapevines and citrus trees. Some plants available in small quantities only.

CChe **Cherry Tree Nursery** ♿
(Sheltered Work Opportunities Project)
off New Road Roundabout, Northbourne, Bournemouth, Dorset BH10 7DA

C

Ⓣ (01202) 593537
Ⓔ contactus@cherrytreenursery.org.uk
Ⓦ www.cherrytreenursery.org.uk
Contact: Stephen Jailler
Opening Times: 0830-1530 Mon-Fri, 0900-1500 Sat, Apr-Sep & 0900-1300 Sat, Oct-Mar. 1000-1500 Sun, Apr to Jul.
Cat. Cost: A4 sae + £2.80 stamps.
Credit Cards: All, except American Express
Specialities: Hardy shrubs, perennials, climbers, grasses & bamboos.
Notes: A registered charity providing work for adults with severe and enduring mental illness. Also sells wholesale. Wheelchair accessible.
Map Ref: C, C6 **OS Grid Ref:** SZ083965

CCht CHESTNUT NURSERY ♿
(Sheltered Work Opportunities Project)
75 Kingland Road, Poole, Dorset
BH15 1TN
Ⓣ (01202) 685999
Ⓔ info@chestnutnursery.org.uk
Ⓦ www.chestnutnursery.org.uk
Contact: Angela Mansbridge
Opening Times: 0830-1600 Mon-Fri, 1000-1600 Sat.
Credit Cards: All major credit/debit cards
Specialities: Wide variety of perennials, shrubs, ornamental grasses and seasonal crops.
Notes: A registered charity providing work for adults with severe and enduring mental illness. Wheelchair accessible.
Map Ref: C, C6 **OS Grid Ref:** SZ018909

CCse CHASE PLANTS
Hookswood Cottage, Farnham, Blandford Forum, Dorset DT11 8DQ
Ⓣ (01725) 516394
Ⓔ sales@chaseplants.co.uk
Ⓦ www.chaseplants.co.uk
Contact: Sue Lees & Eddie Wheatley
Opening Times: By appt. only.
Min Mail Order UK: £10.00
Cat. Cost: Large 1st class.
Credit Cards: None
Specialities: Hardy perennials, shrubs & some conservatory plants.
Notes: Delivers to shows.

CCVN CULM VIEW NURSERY
Waterloo Farm, Clayhidon, Devon
EX15 3TN
Ⓣ (01823) 680698
Ⓔ plants@culmviewnursery.co.uk
Ⓦ www.culmviewnursery.co.uk
Contact: Brian & Alison Jacobs
Opening Times: By appt. only for collection.
Min Mail Order UK: Nmc
Min Mail Order EU: Nmc
Credit Cards: Paypal
Specialities: Hebaceous perennials grown in peat-free compost.
Notes: Mail order seed & some plants. Exports beyond EU. Delivers to shows.

CCVT CHEW VALLEY TREES ♿
Winford Road, Chew Magna, Bristol
BS40 8HJ
Ⓣ (01275) 333752
Ⓔ info@chewvalleytrees.co.uk
Ⓦ www.chewvalleytrees.co.uk
Contact: S Scarth
Opening Times: 0800-1700 Mon-Fri all year. 0900-1600 Sat. Closed Sun. Closed B/hols & Sats Jul & Aug.
Min Mail Order UK: Nmc
Cat. Cost: Free.
Credit Cards: All major credit/debit cards
Specialities: Native British & ornamental trees, shrubs, fruit trees & hedging.
Notes: Also sells wholesale. Wheelchair accessible.
Map Ref: C, A5 **OS Grid Ref:** ST558635

CDob DOBIES OF DEVON
Long Road, Paignton, Devon TQ4 7SX
Ⓣ 0333 400 7623
Ⓕ 0844 701 7624
Ⓦ www.dobies.co.uk
Contact: Customer Services
Opening Times: Not open. Mail order only. Phone line open 0830-1700 Mon-Fri (office). Also answerphone.
Min Mail Order UK: Nmc
Min Mail Order EU: £5.00
Cat. Cost: Free.
Credit Cards: Visa, MasterCard, Switch, Delta
Specialities: Wide selection of popular flower & vegetable seeds. Also includes young plants, summer-flowering bulbs & garden sundries.
Notes: Mail order to UK & Rep. of Ireland only.

CDor DORSET PERENNIALS ◆
Berkeley Perennials, Holnest, Sherborne, Dorset DT9 5PR
Ⓣ (01963) 210643
Ⓕ (01963) 210643
Ⓔ sales@dorsetperennials.co.uk
Ⓦ www.dorsetperennials.co.uk
Contact: Dawn & Martin Preston
Opening Times: 1000-1600 Thu & Fri or by appt. during spring & summer. Please check website or contact nursery for any changes.
Min Mail Order UK: Nmc
Cat. Cost: Online only.
Credit Cards: Paypal
Specialities: We grow an eclectic mix of hardy perennials, the common alongside the unusual. Plants for herbaceous borders &

cottage gardens, with a good mix of oddities as well to tempt the discerning.
Notes: All plants available via website, with larger pot sizes available at nursery. Also sells wholesale.

CDoy **Caradoc Doy**
PO Box 28, Exeter, Devon EX3 0WY
Ⓣ (01392) 877225
Ⓕ (01392) 877225
Ⓔ info@caradocdoy.co.uk
Ⓦ www.caradocdoy.co.uk
Contact: Caradoc Doy
Opening Times: Open by appt. only.
Min Mail Order UK: Nmc
Cat. Cost: Online.
Credit Cards: All major credit/debit cards
Specialities: Olive trees.
Notes: Euro accepted.

CDTJ **Desert to Jungle** ♿
Henlade Garden Nursery, Lower Henlade, Taunton, Somerset TA3 5NB
Ⓣ (01823) 443701
Ⓔ plants@deserttojungle.com
Ⓦ www.deserttojungle.com
Contact: Rob Gudge
Opening Times: 1000-1700 Mon, Tues & Thu-Sun (closed Wed), 1st Mar-31st Oct. Thu, Fri & Sat only Nov-Feb. Opening times may vary during RHS shows, so please phone to check.
Min Mail Order UK: Nmc
Credit Cards: All major credit/debit cards
Specialities: Exotic-looking plants giving a desert or jungle effect in the garden. Incl. *Agave, Canna,* aroids, succulents, ferns, tree ferns & bamboos.
Notes: Nursery shares drive with Mount Somerset Hotel. Also sells wholesale. Delivers to shows. Wheelchair accessible.
Map Ref: C, B4 **OS Grid Ref:** ST273232

CDul **Dulford Nurseries** ♿
Cullompton, Devon EX15 2BY
Ⓣ (01884) 266361
Ⓔ dulford.nurseries@virgin.net
Ⓦ www.dulford-nurseries.co.uk
Contact: Paul Rawlings
Opening Times: 0730-1630 Mon-Fri.
Min Mail Order UK: Nmc
Min Mail Order EU: Nmc
Cat. Cost: Free.
Credit Cards: All major credit/debit cards
Specialities: Native, ornamental & unusual trees, hedging & shrubs incl. oaks, maples, beech, birch, chestnut, lime, *Malus, Sorbus* & pines.
Notes: Wheelchair accessible.
Map Ref: C, C4 **OS Grid Ref:** SY062062

CEls **Elsworth Herbs**
Farthingwood, Broadway, Sidmouth, Devon EX10 8HS
Ⓣ (01395) 578689
Ⓔ john.twibell@btinternet.com
Contact: Drs J D & J M Twibell
Opening Times: By appt. only.
Min Mail Order UK: £10.00
Cat. Cost: By email only.
Credit Cards: None
Specialities: Nat. Collection of *Artemisia.* Wide range of *Artemisia.* Stock available in small quantities only. Orders may require propagation from Collection material, for which we are the primary reference source.
Notes: Mail order only on small scale in exceptional situations. Partially accessible for wheelchairs.
Map Ref: C, C4 **OS Grid Ref:** SY119881

CElw **Elworthy Cottage Plants** ♿
Elworthy Cottage, Elworthy, Nr Lydeard St Lawrence, Taunton, Somerset TA4 3PX
Ⓣ (01984) 656427
Ⓔ mike@elworthy-cottage.co.uk
Ⓦ www.elworthy-cottage.co.uk
Contact: Mrs J M Spiller
Opening Times: 1000-1700 Thu, late Mar-end Aug. Also by appt. Feb-Oct.
Cat. Cost: 3 × 2nd class.
Credit Cards: None
Specialities: Unusual herbaceous plants esp. hardy *Geranium, Geum, Crocosmia, Monarda, Phlox, Pulmonaria* & *Epimedium.* Some varieties only available in small quantities. *Galanthus* available by mail order in Feb.
Notes: Nursery on B3188, 5 miles north of Wiveliscombe, in centre of Elworthy village. Delivers to shows. Wheelchair accessible.
Map Ref: C, B4 **OS Grid Ref:** ST084349

CEnd **Endsleigh Gardens** ♿ ◆
Milton Abbot, Tavistock, Devon PL19 0PG
Ⓣ (01822) 870235
Ⓕ (01822) 870513
Ⓔ info@endsleigh-gardens.com
Ⓦ www.endsleigh-gardens.com
Contact: Adrian Steele
Opening Times: 0800-1700 Mon-Sat. 1000-1600 Sun.
Min Mail Order UK: Nmc
Cat. Cost: 2 × 1st class.
Credit Cards: Visa, Access, Switch, MasterCard
Specialities: Choice & unusual trees & shrubs incl. *Acer* & *Cornus* cvs. Old apples & cherries. *Wisteria.* Grafting service. Modern fruit trees, soft fruit and good selection of perennials.
Notes: Wheelchair accessible (but no disabled toilets).

C

CEnt **Entwood Farm Plants**
Harcombe, Lyme Regis, Dorset DT7 3RN
Ⓣ (01297) 444034
Ⓔ jennyhlyme@hotmail.co.uk
Contact: Jenny & Ivan Harding
Opening Times: By prior arrangement only.
Credit Cards: None
Specialities: Bamboo specialist. Plus selection of shrubs & perennials. Some stock in small quantities.
Notes: Delivers to shows.
Map Ref: C, C4 **OS Grid Ref:** SY335953

CFen **Fentongollan Farm** ♿
Merther Lane, St Michael Penkivel, Tresillian, Truro, Cornwall TR2 4AQ
Ⓣ (01872) 520209
Ⓕ (01872) 520606
Ⓔ admin@flowerfarm.co.uk
Ⓦ www.flowerfarm.co.uk
Contact: James Hosking
Opening Times: 0900-1700 7 days, Aug-end Nov.
Min Mail Order UK: Nmc
Min Mail Order EU: Nmc
Cat. Cost: Free.
Credit Cards: All, except American Express
Specialities: *Narcissus*. Importers of quality Dutch bulbs.
Notes: Also sells wholesale. Delivers to shows. Euro accepted. Wheelchair accessible.
Map Ref: C, D2

CFGn **The Forest Garden**
Budock Water, Falmouth, Cornwall TR11 5ED
Ⓣ (01326) 250090
Ⓔ simonmiles@theforestgarden.co.uk
Ⓦ www.theforestgarden.co.uk
Contact: Simon Miles
Opening Times: Not open. Mail order only.
Min Mail Order UK: £10.00
Specialities: Perennial edible forest garden & agroforestry plants. Top fruit & nut trees, soft fruit, unusual & less common perennial vegetables, tubers, fruits & herbs.

CFil **Fillan's Plants**
Tuckermarsh Gardens, Yelverton, Devon PL20 7HN
Ⓣ (01822) 841551
Ⓜ 07813 161276
Ⓕ (01822) 841551
Ⓔ fillansplants@yahoo.co.uk
Ⓦ www.tuckermarshplants.co.uk
Contact: Mark Fillan
Opening Times: By appt. only. Please phone or email.
Min Mail Order UK: Nmc
Min Mail Order EU: £50.00
Cat. Cost: 4 ×1st class
Credit Cards: None
Specialities: *Aucuba, Dasylirion, Deutsia, Epimedium, Hydrangea, Mahonia, Nolina, Oreopanax, Philadelphus, Polystichum setiferum, Quercus, Schefflera* & *Yucca*. Also species *Dahlia* & *Narcissus*. Some plants available in small quanitities only.

CFis **Margery Fish Plant Nursery** ♿
East Lambrook Manor Gardens, East Lambrook, South Petherton, Somerset TA13 5HH
Ⓣ (01460) 240328
Ⓜ 07710 484745
Ⓔ enquiries@eastlambrook.com
Ⓦ www.eastlambrook.com
Contact: Tom Wild
Opening Times: 1000-1700 Tue-Sat, Feb-Oct, plus B/hol Mons & Suns Feb, May-Jul. Nov-Jan by appt.
Cat. Cost: None issued.
Credit Cards: All major credit/debit cards
Specialities: Hardy geraniums & cottage garden herbaceous plants. Stock available in small quantities only. Major collection of hardy geraniums on site.
Notes: Wheelchair accessible.
Map Ref: C, B5 **OS Grid Ref:** ST431188

CFlo **Floyds Climbers and Clematis**
36 Dowding Drive, Lower Compton, Calne, Wiltshire SN11 8QL
Ⓣ (01249) 823200
Ⓜ 07762 499416
Ⓔ sales@floydsclimbers.co.uk
Ⓦ www.floydsclimbers.co.uk
Contact: Marcel Floyd
Opening Times: Open w/ends twice a year. See website or phone for dates.
Min Mail Order UK: Nmc
Credit Cards: Paypal
Specialities: *Clematis* and climbers.
Notes: Also sells wholesale. Euro accepted. Delivers to shows.
Map Ref: C, A6

CFst **Forest Edge Nurseries**
Verwood Road, Woodlands, Wimborne, Dorset BH21 8LJ
Ⓣ (01202) 829564
Ⓕ (01202) 829564
Ⓔ heathers@forestedgenurseries.co.uk
Ⓦ www.forestedgenurseries.co.uk
Contact: David Edge
Opening Times: 0900-1630 Mon. Collection available by arrangement on other days.
Cat. Cost: £2.00
Credit Cards: Paypal
Specialities: Heathers: *Calluna, Erica, Daboecia*.

Notes: Also sells wholesale. Euro accepted.
Map Ref: C, B6

CFwr **The Flower Bower**
Woodlands, Shurton, Stogursey,
Nr Bridgwater, Somerset TA5 1QE
Ⓣ (01278) 732134
Ⓔ theflowerbower@yahoo.co.uk
Ⓦ www.theflowerbower.co.uk
Contact: Sheila Tucker
Opening Times: By appt. only. Visitors welcome during bloom times: May-Jul for *Epiphyllum* & May-Sep for daylilies.
Min Mail Order UK: Nmc
Min Mail Order EU: Nmc
Cat. Cost: Online only. For *Epiphyllum* please send email address to obtain a link to the list.
Credit Cards: None
Specialities: *Hemerocallis*, esp. newer varieties & spiders. Over 700 varieties of *Epiphyllum*. National Collection of *Epiphyllum*.
Notes: Daylilies: newer & rarer varieties mostly available in small quantities.
Map Ref: C, B4 **OS Grid Ref:** ST203442

CGar **Gardeners Delight Nursery**
Old Bideford Road, Barnstaple, Devon
EX31 2PA
Ⓣ (01271) 861461
Ⓔ g.d.n@hotmail.co.uk
Ⓦ www.gardenplantsandgifts.co.uk
Contact: Nick Wade
Opening Times: 0930-1630 Mon-Sat, 1000-1600 Sun.
Min Mail Order UK: Nmc
Credit Cards: All major credit/debit cards
Specialities: Traditional plant nursery.
Notes: Also sells wholesale. Limited wheelchair access but help available. Delivers to shows.
Map Ref: C, B3

CGro **C W Groves & Son Ltd** ♿
West Bay Road, Bridport, Dorset
DT6 4BA
Ⓣ (01308) 422654
Ⓔ garden@grovesnurseries.co.uk
Ⓦ www.grovesnurseries.co.uk
Contact: Becky Groves
Opening Times: 0830-1700 Mon-Sat, 10.00-16.00 Sun.
Min Mail Order UK: Nmc + p&p £5.99 for mainland UK
Min Mail Order EU: £15.00 + p&p
Cat. Cost: Free.
Credit Cards: Visa, Switch, MasterCard
Specialities: Established in 1866, a family run garden centre with nursery on site specialising in *Viola odorata*, Parma violets & roses.
Notes: Mainly violets by mail order. Main display at nursery in Feb, Mar & Apr. Roses when dormant (Nov-Mar). Will export violet seeds only beyond EU. Wheelchair accessible.

CGrW **The Great Western Gladiolus Nursery**
17 Valley View, Clutton, Bristol
BS39 5SN
Ⓣ (01761) 452036
Ⓔ clutton.glads@btinternet.com
Ⓦ www.greatwesterngladiolus.co.uk
Contact: G F Hazell
Opening Times: Mail order only. Open by appt. only.
Min Mail Order UK: Nmc
Min Mail Order EU: Nmc
Cat. Cost: 4 × 1st class (2 catalogues).
Credit Cards: None
Specialities: *Gladiolus* species & hybrids, corms & seeds. Other South African bulbous plants. Only available in small quantities.
Notes: Also sells wholesale. Euro accepted.

CHab **Habitat Aid Ltd.**
Hookgate Cottage, South Brewham, Somerset
BA10 0LQ
Ⓣ (01749) 812355
Ⓔ info@habitataid.co.uk
Ⓦ www.habitataid.co.uk
Contact: Nick Mann
Opening Times: Not open. Mail order only.
Min Mail Order UK: £50.00, incl. p&p.
Cat. Cost: None issued.
Credit Cards: All major credit/debit cards
Specialities: British trees, wildflowers and seeds. Local provenance seed mixes. Native aquatic plants. Cottage garden perennials. Heritage fruit trees.
Notes: Also sells wholesale. Delivers to shows.

CHby **The Herbary**
161 Chapel Street, Horningsham, Warminster,
Wiltshire BA12 7LU
Ⓣ (01985) 844442
Ⓔ info@beansandherbs.co.uk
Ⓦ www.beansandherbs.co.uk
Contact: Pippa Rosen
Opening Times: May-Sep strictly by appt. only.
Min Mail Order UK: Nmc
Min Mail Order EU: Nmc
Cat. Cost: Online only.
Credit Cards: None
Specialities: Culinary, medicinal & aromatic herbs organically grown in small quantities.
Notes: Mail order for seed only and all year for organic vegetable seed & large variety of organic bean & herb seed. Also sells wholesale. Euro accepted.

C

CHew **HEWITT-COOPER CARNIVOROUS PLANTS**
The Homestead, Glastonbury Road, West Pennard, Somerset BA6 8NN
Ⓣ (01458) 832844
Ⓕ (01458) 832712
Ⓔ sales@hccarnivorousplants.co.uk
Ⓦ www.hccarnivorousplants.co.uk
Contact: Nigel Hewitt-Cooper
Opening Times: Not open.
Min Mail Order UK: Nmc
Min Mail Order EU: Nmc
Cat. Cost: 1 × 1st class/1× IRC.
Credit Cards: All major credit/debit cards
Specialities: Carnivorous plants.
Notes: Mail order May-Nov. Euro accepted. Delivers to shows.

CHGN **HIGH GARDEN NURSERIES** ♿
Chiverstone Lane, Kenton, Exeter, Devon EX6 8NJ
Ⓣ (01626) 899106
Ⓔ highgarden@highgarden.co.uk
Ⓦ highgardenkenton.wordpress.com
Contact: Chris Britton
Opening Times: 0900-1700 Tue-Fri
Cat. Cost: None issued.
Credit Cards: All major credit/debit cards
Specialities: Quality shrubs, trees & perennials, some unusual & different.
Notes: Wheelchair accessible.
Map Ref: C, C4 **OS Grid Ref:** SX957836

CHid **HIDDEN VALLEY NURSERY**
Umberleigh, Devon EX37 9BU
Ⓣ (01769) 560567
Ⓜ 07899 788789
Ⓔ plalindley@itsosbroadband.co.uk
Contact: Linda & Peter Lindley
Opening Times: Daylight hours, but please phone first.
Cat. Cost: None issued.
Credit Cards: None
Specialities: Hardy perennials esp. shade lovers & Chatham Islands forget-me-nots (*Myosotidium hortensia*).
Notes: Nursery not easy to find using Sat Nav or Google Street Map. Delivers to shows. Euro accepted.
Map Ref: C, B3 **OS Grid Ref:** SS567205

CHII **HILL HOUSE NURSERY LTD** ♿
Landscove, Nr Ashburton, Devon TQ13 7LY
Ⓣ (01803) 762273
Ⓔ bluebird@hillhousenursery.com
Ⓦ www.hillhousenursery.com
Contact: Raymond, Sacha & Matthew Hubbard
Opening Times: 1100-1700 7 days, all year. Open all B/hols incl. Easter Sun. Closed Friday before Xmas Eve for two weeks only. Tearoom open 1st Mar-30th Sep.
Min Mail Order UK: Nmc
Cat. Cost: None issued.
Credit Cards: Delta, MasterCard, Switch, Visa, Paypal
Specialities: 3000+ varieties of plants, most propagated on premises, many rare or unusual. The garden, open to the public, was laid out by Edward Hyams. Pioneers of glasshouse pest control by beneficial insects.
Notes: Groups welcome with prior notice. Also sells wholesale. Euro accepted. Tea room & garden wheelchair accessible, access limited in nursery.
Map Ref: C, C3 **OS Grid Ref:** SX774664

CHur **HURST BROOK PLANTS** ♿
Lower Severalls, Crewkerne, Somerset TA18 7NX
Ⓣ (01458) 250666
Ⓜ 07857 645123
Ⓔ hurstbrookplants@btinternet.com
Ⓦ www.hurstbrookplants.co.uk
Contact: Sue Applegate
Opening Times: 1000-1600 Thu-Sun, Mar-Oct.
Min Mail Order UK: Nmc.
Cat. Cost: None issued.
Credit Cards: All major credit/debit cards
Specialities: *Paeonia lactiflora* & bearded iris.
Notes: Wheelchair accessible.

CHVG **HIDDEN VALLEY GARDENS** ♿
Treesmill, Nr Par, Cornwall PL24 2TU
Ⓣ (01208) 873225
Ⓔ hiddenvalleygardens@yahoo.co.uk
Ⓦ www.hiddenvalleygardens.co.uk
Contact: Mrs P Howard
Opening Times: 1000-1800 Thu-Mon (closed Tue & Wed), 20th Mar-15th Oct. Please phone for directions. Garden open as nursery.
Cat. Cost: None issued.
Credit Cards: All major credit/debit cards
Specialities: Cottage garden plants, *Dahlia* & many perennials which can be seen growing in the garden. Some stock available in small quantities. Display garden.
Notes: Award-winning Garden In Cornwall 2014. Euro accepted. Wheelchair accessible.
Map Ref: C, D2 **OS Grid Ref:** SX094567

CIri **THE IRIS GARDEN**
Yard House, Pilsdon, Bridport, Dorset DT6 5PA
Ⓣ (01308) 868797
Ⓔ info@theirisgarden.co.uk
Ⓦ www.theirisgarden.co.uk
Contact: Clive Russell

Opening Times: Show garden open by appt. only. Please email or phone for details.
Cat. Cost: None issued.
Specialities: Modern bearded & beardless *Iris* from breeders in UK, USA, France, Italy & Australia. Nat. Collection of Space Age Iris. Also Nat. Collection of 6-fall & Novelty Bearded Iris.
Notes: No mail order or sales from website. Ordering in garden only. Plants can be ordered on site with a 25% deposit but customers must be prepared to return & collect at a later date. Euro accepted.
Map Ref: C, C5 **OS Grid Ref:** SY421988

CJng **JUNGLE GIANTS** ♿
Cleave House, Sticklepath, Devon EX20 2NL
Ⓣ (01837) 840989 or (01248) 600385
Ⓔ bamboo@junglegiants.co.uk
Ⓦ www.junglegiants.co.uk
Contact: Tim Penrose
Opening Times: By appt. only 1000-1600 7 days, 1st Apr-31st Aug.
Min Mail Order UK: £35.00 + p&p
Min Mail Order EU: £60.00 + p&p
Cat. Cost: Free
Credit Cards: All, except American Express
Specialities: Bamboos.
Notes: Also sells wholesale. Exports beyond EU. Euro accepted. Wheelchair accessible.
Map Ref: C, C3 **OS Grid Ref:** SX639941

CJun **JUNKER'S NURSERY LTD.**
Higher Cobhay, Milverton, Somerset TA4 1NJ
Ⓣ (01823) 400075
Ⓔ karan@junker.co.uk
Ⓦ www.junker.co.uk
Contact: Karan Junker
Opening Times: Strictly by appt. only. Contact nursery for directions (do not rely on Sat Nav).
Min Mail Order UK: Nmc
Min Mail Order EU: Nmc
Cat. Cost: Free list available by email.
Credit Cards: None
Specialities: Choice & unusual shrubs & trees incl. grafted *Acer palmatum*, *Betula*, *Cornus*, *Daphne*, *Magnolia* cvs. Also extensive collections of *Euonymus*, *Ilex*, *Liquidambar* & *Viburnum*, all grown on own roots. Many available in larger, more mature sizes. Small quantities only of some hard to propagate plants, esp. daphnes.
Notes: Extensive planted areas showing how the plants look growing in "real world" conditions. We propagate & grow all our own plants with an increasing number grown naturally in open ground as well as younger plants in pots, incl. larger sizes. Limited wheelchair access.
Map Ref: C, B4

CKel **KELWAYS** ♿
Picts Hill, Langport, Somerset TA10 9EZ
Ⓣ (01458) 250521
Ⓔ sales@kelways.co.uk
Ⓦ www.kelways.co.uk
Contact: Dave Root, Andy Martin
Opening Times: 0900-1700 Mon-Fri & Sat, 0930-1600 Sun.
Min Mail Order UK: £3.95 + p&p
Cat. Cost: Online only.
Credit Cards: Paypal
Specialities: *Paeonia*, *Iris*, *Hemerocallis* & herbaceous perennials. Wide range of trees, shrubs & herbaceous. Hardy ferns & tree ferns.
Notes: Also sells wholesale. Delivers to shows. Euro accepted. Wheelchair accessible.
Map Ref: C, B5 **OS Grid Ref:** ST434273

CKen **KENWITH CONIFER NURSERY (GORDON HADDOW)** ♿
Blinsham, Nr Torrington, Beaford, Winkleigh, Devon EX19 8NT
Ⓣ (01805) 603274
Ⓕ (01805) 603663
Ⓔ info@kenwithconifernursery.co.uk
Ⓦ www.kenwithconifernursery.co.uk
Contact: Gordon Haddow
Opening Times: 1000-1630 Tue-Sat all year. Closed all B/hols. If travelling a long distance, please phone previous day to ensure nursery will be open.
Min Mail Order UK: £20 + p&p
Min Mail Order EU: £50 + p&p
Cat. Cost: Online only.
Credit Cards: Visa, MasterCard
Specialities: All conifer genera. Grafting a speciality.
Notes: Wheelchair accessible.
Map Ref: C, C3 **OS Grid Ref:** SS518160

CKno **KNOLL GARDENS**
Hampreston, Wimborne, Dorset BH21 7ND
Ⓣ (01202) 873931
Ⓕ (01202) 870842
Ⓔ enquiries@knollgardens.co.uk
Ⓦ www.knollgardens.co.uk
Contact: N R Lucas
Opening Times: 1000-1700 Tue-Sat, Feb-Dec. Open B/hol Mons. See website for further details.
Min Mail Order UK: Nmc
Min Mail Order EU: Nmc
Cat. Cost: None.
Credit Cards: Visa, MasterCard
Specialities: Grasses (main specialism). Flowering perennials. Nat. Collection of *Pennisetum*.
Notes: Also sells wholesale.
Map Ref: C, C6

C

CLak **Lakka Bulbs**
(Office) 127 Mill Street, Torrington, North Devon EX38 8AW
Ⓣ (01805) 625071
Ⓔ jonathan.hutchinson@talktalk.net
Contact: Jonathan Hutchinson
Opening Times: Not open. Mail order only.
Min Mail Order UK: Nmc
Min Mail Order EU: Nmc
Cat. Cost: None issued.
Credit Cards: None
Specialities: Nat. Collections of *Veltheimia bracteata* & cvs and *Scadoxus*. All available in small quantities only.

CLAP **Long Acre Plants** ♿
South Marsh, Charlton Musgrove, Nr Wincanton, Somerset BA9 8EX
Ⓣ (01963) 32802
Ⓕ (01963) 32802
Ⓔ info@plantsforshade.co.uk
Ⓦ www.plantsforshade.co.uk
Contact: Nigel & Michelle Rowland
Opening Times: 0900-1300 & 1330-1630 Thu & Fri only, Mar-Oct.
Min Mail Order UK: £10.00 + p&p
Min Mail Order EU: Nmc
Cat. Cost: 3 × 1st class.
Credit Cards: MasterCard, Visa, Maestro
Specialities: Ferns, woodland bulbs & perennials. Marginal/bog plants.
Notes: Some plants available in small numbers only and only seasonally available. Ship to EU in autumn and winter only. Delivers to shows. Wheelchair accessible.
Map Ref: C, B5

CLau **Laurel Farm Herbs**
Moorland Barn, Whiddon Down, Okehampton, Devon EX20 2QL
Ⓣ (01647) 400301
Ⓜ 07905 518666
Ⓔ laurelfarmherbs@aol.com
Ⓦ www.laurelfarmherbs.co.uk
Contact: Chris & Jenny Seagon
Opening Times: Please phone or check website for opening hours as times can vary.
Min Mail Order UK: 4 plants.
Min Mail Order EU: 6 plants.
Cat. Cost: Online only.
Credit Cards: Visa, MasterCard, Switch
Specialities: Herbs esp. rosemary, thyme, mint & sage.
Notes: Also sells wholesale. Delivers to shows (payment in advance).
Map Ref: C, C3

CLet **Letsgoplanting** ♿
Otters Reach, West Buckland, Wellington, Somerset TA21 9LD
Ⓣ (01823) 660175
Ⓕ (01823) 661107
Ⓔ mail@letsgoplanting.co.uk
Ⓦ www.letsgoplanting.co.uk
Contact: Ian Phillips
Opening Times: 0900-1700, Mon-Fri.
Min Mail Order UK: Nmc
Min Mail Order EU: Nmc
Cat. Cost: Online only.
Credit Cards: All major credit/debit cards
Specialities: Shrubs, herbaceous perennials, grasses, climbers, ferns and bamboos. Most plants propagated and grown on the nursery. All hardy stock comes with a one-year guarantee.
Notes: Payment can be taken over the phone. Euro accepted. Wheelchair accessible.
Map Ref: C, B4

CLnd **Landford Trees**
Landford Lodge, Landford, Salisbury, Wiltshire SP5 2EH
Ⓣ (01794) 390808
Ⓕ (01794) 390037
Ⓔ trees@landfordtrees.co.uk
Ⓦ www.landfordtrees.co.uk
Contact: C D Pilkington
Opening Times: 0800-1700 Mon-Thu, 0800-1530 Fri.
Cat. Cost: Free.
Credit Cards: All, except American Express
Specialities: Deciduous ornamental trees.
Notes: Also sells wholesale.
Map Ref: C, B6 **OS Grid Ref:** SU247201

CLng **Longcombe Nursery and Garden Centre** ♿
Longcombe, Totnes, Devon TQ9 6PL
Ⓣ (01803) 863098
Ⓔ info@simplyclematis.co.uk
Ⓦ www.simplyclematis.co.uk
Contact: Linda Clarke
Opening Times: 0900-1700 Mon-Sat, 1000-1600 Sun.
Min Mail Order UK: Nmc
Min Mail Order EU: Nmc
Cat. Cost: Online only.
Credit Cards: All major credit/debit cards
Specialities: *Clematis.*
Notes: Also sells wholesale. Delivers to shows. Wheelchair accessible.
Map Ref: C, C3 **OS Grid Ref:** SX834601

CLoc **C S Lockyer (Fuchsias)** ◆
Lansbury, 70 Henfield Road, Coalpit Heath, Bristol BS36 2UZ
Ⓣ (01454) 772219
Ⓕ (01454) 772219
Ⓔ Stuart@lockyerfuchsias.co.uk
Ⓦ lockyerfuchsias.co.uk

Contact: C S Lockyer
Opening Times: 1000-1300, 1430-1700 most days, please ring.
Min Mail Order UK: 6 plants + p&p
Min Mail Order EU: £12.00 + p&p
Cat. Cost: 4 × 1st class or online
Credit Cards: All major credit/debit cards
Specialities: *Fuchsia*.
Notes: Many open days & coach parties. Also sells wholesale. Exports beyond EU. Euro accepted. Delivers to shows. Partial wheelchair access.
Map Ref: C, A5

CMac **Mac Pennys Nurseries**
154 Burley Road, Bransgore, Christchurch, Dorset BH23 8DB
Ⓣ (01425) 672348
Ⓕ (01425) 673917
Ⓔ office@macpennys.co.uk
Ⓦ www.macpennys.co.uk
Contact: T & V Lowndes & S Lowndes
Opening Times: 0900-1700 Mon-Sat, 1000-1700 Sun & B/hols, except closed Xmas-New Year.
Min Mail Order UK: Nmc
Cat. Cost: A4 sae with 4 × 1st class.
Credit Cards: All, except American Express
Specialities: General. Plants available in small quantities only.
Notes: Mail order available Sep-Mar, UK only. Also sells wholesale. Nursery partially accessible for wheelchairs.
Map Ref: C, C6

CMan **Mandy Plants** ♿
(Office) 4 St Mary's Place, Ipplepen, Devon TQ12 5FF
Ⓣ (01803) 813647
Ⓜ 07432 112245
Ⓔ enquiries@mandyplants.com
Ⓦ www.mandyplants.com
Contact: Liz Spanton
Opening Times: By appt. only.
Min Mail Order UK: Nmc
Min Mail Order EU: £25.00
Cat. Cost: 2 × 1st class
Credit Cards: Paypal
Specialities: *Mandevilla* & *Dipladenia*.
Notes: Nursery is at Bishopsteignton, Devon. Also sells wholesale. Delivers to shows. Wheelchair accessible.
Map Ref: C, C3 **OS Grid Ref:** SX836667

CMCN **Mallet Court Nursery** ♿
Marshway, Curry Mallet, Taunton, Somerset TA3 6SZ
Ⓣ (01823) 481493
Ⓜ 07713 091521
Ⓕ (01823) 481493
Ⓔ malletcourtnursery@btinternet.com
Ⓦ www.malletcourt.co.uk
Contact: J G S & P M E Harris F.L.S.
Opening Times: 0930-1700 Mon-Fri summer, 0930-1600 winter. Sat & Sun by appt.
Min Mail Order UK: Nmc
Min Mail Order EU: Nmc
Cat. Cost: £1.50
Credit Cards: All major credit/debit cards
Specialities: Maples, oaks, *Magnolia*, hollies & other rare and unusual plants including those from China & South Korea.
Notes: Mail order Oct-Mar only. Also sells wholesale. Exports beyond EU. Euro accepted. Wheelchair accessible.
Map Ref: C, B4

CMea **The Mead Nursery** ♿
Brokerswood, Nr Westbury, Wiltshire BA13 4EG
Ⓣ (01373) 859990
Ⓔ info@themeadnursery.co.uk
Ⓦ www.themeadnursery.co.uk
Contact: Steve & Emma Lewis-Dale
Opening Times: 0900-1700 Wed-Sat & B/hol Mons, 1200-1700 Sun, 1st Feb-10th Oct. Closed Easter Sun.
Cat. Cost: 5 × 1st class.
Credit Cards: All major credit/debit cards
Specialities: Perennials, alpines, pot-grown bulbs and grasses.
Notes: Wheelchair accessible.
Map Ref: C, B5 **OS Grid Ref:** ST833517

CMen **Mendip Bonsai Studio**
Byways, Back Lane, Downside, Shepton Mallet, Somerset BA4 4JR
Ⓣ (01749) 344274
Ⓜ 07711 205806
Ⓔ john@mendipbonsai.co.uk
Ⓦ www.mendipbonsai.co.uk
Contact: John Trott
Opening Times: Private nursery. Visits by appt. only.
Min Mail Order UK: £15.00
Cat. Cost: Large sae for plant & workshop lists
Credit Cards: All major credit/debit cards
Specialities: Bonsai, Potensai, accent plants & garden stock. Acers, conifers, incl. many *Pinus thunbergii* species, *Aciphylla*, *Davallia* & *Pyrrosia*. Many plants available in small numbers only. Can propagate to order. Young trees for garden or bonsai culture. Many rare & unusual ferns from Japan for 'accent' use and gardens.
Notes: Education classes, lectures, demonstrations & club talks on bonsai. Stockist of most bonsai pots, related bonsai sundries & a large

C

range of bronze figures. Mail orders will normally be despatched late Mar-early Apr, late Sep-Oct. Delivers to shows by arrangement.
Map Ref: C, B5

CMHG **MARWOOD HILL GARDENS** ♿
Marwood, Barnstaple, Devon EX31 4EB
Ⓣ (01271) 342528
Ⓕ (01271) 342528
Ⓔ info@marwoodhillgarden.co.uk
Ⓦ www.marwoodhillgarden.co.uk
Contact: Malcolm Pharoah
Opening Times: 1100-1630, 7 days. Closed Nov-Feb.
Cat. Cost: 3 × 1st class.
Credit Cards: Visa, Delta, MasterCard, Switch, Solo
Specialities: Large range of unusual trees & shrubs. *Eucalyptus*, alpines, *Camellia*, *Astilbe*, bog plants & perennials. Nat. Collections of *Astilbe*, *Tulbaghia* & *Iris ensata*.
Notes: Wheelchair accessible.
Map Ref: C, B3 **OS Grid Ref:** SS545375

CMil **MILL COTTAGE PLANTS** ♿
Henley Mill, Henley Lane, Wookey, Somerset BA5 1AW
Ⓣ (01749) 676966
Ⓜ 07851 698759
Ⓔ millcottageplants@gmail.com
Ⓦ www.millcottageplants.co.uk
Contact: Sally Gregson
Opening Times: By appt. only. Phone for directions.
Min Mail Order UK: Nmc
Min Mail Order EU: £25.00 + p&p
Cat. Cost: Online only.
Credit Cards: All major credit/debit cards
Specialities: Rare *Hydrangea serrata* cvs, *H. aspera* cvs, *Epimedium*, shade & damp-loving plants.
Notes: Euro accepted. Wheelchair accessible.
Map Ref: C, B5

CMos **IAN & TERESA MOSS** ♿
(Office) 'Iona', Woolmersdon, Bridgwater, Somerset TA5 2BP
Ⓣ (01278) 661352
Ⓜ 07903 268718
Ⓔ teresa@hardyandunusualplants.co.uk
Ⓦ www.hardyandunusualplants.co.uk
Contact: Teresa Moss
Opening Times: 1000-1630, daily, 13th Mar-31st Oct 2015.
Cat. Cost: £1.50
Credit Cards: All, except American Express
Specialities: Hardy & unusual plants. Range of perennials incl. the best of recent introductions as well as more unusual varieties & reliable old favourites. Wide range of hardy geraniums.
Notes: Plant sales through Kilver Court Gardens, Kilver Street, Shepton Mallet, Somerset BA4 5NF. Delivers to shows (see website for details of which shows attended). Wheelchair accessible.
Map Ref: C, B4

CMus **MUSGROVE WILLOWS** ♿
Willowfields, Lakewall, Westonzoyland, Bridgwater, Somerset TA7 0LP
Ⓣ (01278) 691105
Ⓕ (01278) 699107
Ⓔ info@musgrovewillows.co.uk
Ⓦ www.musgrovewillows.co.uk
Contact: Ellen Musgrove
Opening Times: 0900-1700 Mon-Fri.
Min Mail Order UK: £12.50
Min Mail Order EU: Nmc
Credit Cards: All major credit/debit cards
Specialities: *Salix* (willow). A family nursery since 1928.
Notes: Exports beyond EU. Wheelchair accessible.
Map Ref: C, B4

CNat **NATURAL SELECTION**
1 Station Cottages, Hullavington, Chippenham, Wiltshire SN14 6ET
Ⓣ (01666) 837369
Ⓜ 07800 583999
Ⓔ martin@worldmutation.demon.co.uk
Ⓦ www.worldmutation.demon.co.uk
Contact: Martin Barber
Opening Times: Please phone first.
Min Mail Order UK: £9.00 + p&p
Min Mail Order EU: Nmc
Cat. Cost: 1 × 2nd class.
Credit Cards: None
Specialities: Unusual British natives & others. Also seed. Only available in small quantities.
Notes: Euro accepted.

CNec **NECTAR PLANTS GARDEN NURSERY**
646 Dorchester Road, Upwey, Weymouth, Dorset DT3 5LG
Ⓣ (01305) 814473
Ⓔ martinyoung100@btinternet.com
Ⓦ www.nectarplants.co.uk
Contact: Martin Young
Opening Times: 1000-1700 Fri, Sat, Sun only, mid-March to mid-Oct.
Cat. Cost: A5 sae for availability list.
Credit Cards: All major credit/debit cards
Specialities: Small scale nursery specialising in plants for bees & butterflies, cottage garden favourites & coastal plants. Wide selection of *Buddleja davidii*, *B. weyeriana* & hardy geraniums. Good selection of David Austin

C

roses & many flowering shrubs. Some own-propagated plants in small quantities only.
Notes: Nursery is on old Dorchester-Weymouth road. Follow signs to Upwey. Large copper beech tree next to green gate. Delivers to shows.
Map Ref: C, C5 **OS Grid Ref:** SY674838

CNMi **Newport Mills Nursery**
Wrantage, Taunton, Somerset TA3 6DJ
Ⓣ (01823) 490231
Ⓔ john@newportmillsnursery.net
Ⓦ www.newportmillsnursery.net
Contact: John Barrington
Opening Times: Not open. Mail order only.
Min Mail Order UK: Nmc free p&p
Min Mail Order EU: Nmc. EU postal rate per order.
Cat. Cost: Free.
Credit Cards: All major credit/debit cards
Specialities: *Delphinium elatum* hybrids. English scented perpetual flowering carnations. *Dianthus*. Pinks, Exhibition, Modern & Old World.
Notes: Mail order Apr-Sep for young delphiniums in 7cm pots. Euro accepted.

CNor **Northbrook Nursery** ♿
47 Northbrook Road, Broadstone, Dorset BH18 8HD
Ⓣ (01202) 695256
Ⓔ marg@northbrooknursery.co.uk
Ⓦ www.northbrooknursery.co.uk
Contact: Margaret Bailey
Opening Times: 1000-1600, Wed-Fri, Apr-Oct.
Min Mail Order UK: Nmc
Cat. Cost: None issued.
Credit Cards: Paypal
Specialities: Perennials. Plants available in small quantities only.
Notes: Delivers to shows. Wheelchair accessible.
Map Ref: C, C6 **OS Grid Ref:** SZ 001947

CNWT **New Wood Trees**
Oldwood House, Aish Road, Stoke Gabriel, Totnes, Devon TQ9 6PX
Ⓣ (01803) 782666
Ⓔ info@newwoodtrees.co.uk
Ⓦ www.newwoodtrees.co.uk
Contact: Philip Nieuwoudt
Opening Times: 0900-1700 Mon-Fri.
Credit Cards: None
Specialities: Trees. Multi-stem ornamentals; small to medium sized trees and large shrubs.
Notes: Specialises in specimen trees so when a species is sold out it takes a while to replenish stocks. Also sells wholesale. Delivers to shows.
Map Ref: C, C3 **OS Grid Ref:** SX847580

CPar **Parks Perennials**
242 Wallisdown Road, Wallisdown, Bournemouth, Dorset BH10 4HZ
Ⓣ (01202) 524464
Ⓜ 07977 878546
Ⓔ parks.perennials@ntlworld.com
Contact: S. Parks
Opening Times: Apr-Oct most days, please phone first.
Cat. Cost: None issued.
Credit Cards: None
Specialities: Hardy herbaceous perennials.
Notes: Delivers to shows.
Map Ref: C, C6

CPbn **Penborn Goat Farm** ♿
Penborn, Bounds Cross, Holsworthy, Devon EX22 6LH
Ⓣ (01288) 381569
Ⓔ penborngoats@btinternet.com
Ⓦ www.penborngoats.com
Contact: P R Oldfield
Opening Times: 1000-1600, Thu & Fri from 2nd Apr-25th Sep 2015.
Min Mail Order UK: £30.00
Min Mail Order EU: £32.50
Cat. Cost: Online.
Credit Cards: None
Specialities: *Mentha*, *Melissa*. Available in small quantities only.
Notes: Wheelchair accessible.
Map Ref: C, C2 **OS Grid Ref:** SS290021

CPBP **Parham Bungalow Plants**
Parham Lane, Market Lavington, Devizes, Wiltshire SN10 4QA
Ⓣ (01380) 812605
Ⓔ jjs@pbplants.freeserve.co.uk
Contact: Mrs D E Sample
Opening Times: Please ring first.
Min Mail Order UK: Nmc
Min Mail Order EU: Nmc
Cat. Cost: Sae.
Credit Cards: None
Specialities: Alpines.
Notes: Delivers to shows. Euro accepted.
Map Ref: C, B6

CPen **Pennard Plants**
3 The Gardens, East Pennard, Shepton Mallet, Somerset BA4 6TU
Ⓣ (01749) 860039
Ⓔ sales@pennardplants.com
Ⓦ www.pennardplants.com
Contact: Chris Smith
Opening Times: By appt. only.
Min Mail Order UK: Nmc
Min Mail Order EU: Nmc
Cat. Cost: 3 × 1st class.

C

Credit Cards: All major credit/debit cards
Specialities: *Agapanthus*.
Notes: Nursery at The Walled Garden at East Pennard. Exports beyond EU. Delivers to shows. Euro accepted.
Map Ref: C, B5

CPer **Perrie Hale Nurseries**
Northcote Hill, Honiton, Devon
EX14 9TH
Ⓣ (01404) 43344
Ⓕ (01404) 47163
Ⓔ faye@perriehale.co.uk
Ⓦ www.perriehale.co.uk
Contact: Faye Davey
Opening Times: 0800-1630 Mon-Fri, 0900-1230 Sat, Mar-Nov. Please phone first.
Min Mail Order UK: £12.50 + p&p
Cat. Cost: Sae 1 × 1st class.
Specialities: Forest trees, native hedging plants & shrubs.
Notes: Also sells wholesale.

CPhi **Alan Phipps Cacti**
62 Samuel White Road, Hanham, Bristol
BS15 3LX
Ⓣ (0117) 9607591
Ⓦ www.cactus-mall.com/alan-phipps/index.html
Contact: A Phipps
Opening Times: 1000-1700 but prior phone call essential to ensure a greeting.
Min Mail Order UK: £5.00 + p&p
Min Mail Order EU: £20.00 + p&p
Cat. Cost: Sae or 2 × IRC (EC only).
Credit Cards: None
Specialities: *Mammillaria*, *Astrophytum* & *Ariocarpus*. Species & varieties will change with times. Ample quantities exist in spring. Limited range of *Agave*.
Notes: Specimen-size plants not available by mail order. Euro accepted as cash only.
Map Ref: C, A5 **OS Grid Ref:** ST644717

CPHo **The Palm House**
8 North Street, Ottery St Mary, Devon
EX11 1DR
Ⓣ (01404) 815450
Ⓜ 07815 673397
Ⓔ george@thepalmhouse.co.uk
Ⓦ www.thepalmhouse.co.uk
Contact: George Gregory
Opening Times: Mail order only. Open by appt. only.
Min Mail Order UK: £5.00
Min Mail Order EU: £10.00
Cat. Cost: 2 × 1st class.
Credit Cards: All major credit/debit cards
Specialities: Palms.
Notes: Also sells wholesale.

CPla **Plant World Botanic Gardens** ♿
St Marychurch Road, Newton Abbot, Devon
TQ12 4SE
Ⓣ (01803) 872939
Ⓕ (01803) 875018
Ⓔ raybrown@plant-world-seeds.com
Ⓦ www.plant-world-seeds.com
Contact: Ray Brown
Opening Times: 0930-1700 7 days a week, Apr (Easter if earlier)-Oct.
Min Mail Order UK: Nmc
Min Mail Order EU: Nmc
Cat. Cost: 3 × 1st class or 2 × IRC.
Credit Cards: Visa, Access, EuroCard, MasterCard
Specialities: Alpines & unusual herbaceous plants. 4 acre garden planted as map of the world (entry charge).
Notes: Offers mail order worldwide for seed only. Also sells wholesale. Exports beyond EU. Euro accepted. Wheelchair access to nursery & café only.
Map Ref: C, C4

CPne **Pine Cottage Plants** ♿
Pine Cottage, Fourways, Eggesford,
Chulmleigh, Devon EX18 7QZ
Ⓣ (01769) 580076
Ⓜ 07718 505053
Ⓔ sales@pcplants.co.uk
Ⓦ www.pcplants.co.uk
Contact: Dick Fulcher
Opening Times: By appt. only. Please phone first.
Min Mail Order UK: £20.00
Min Mail Order EU: £20.00
Cat. Cost: 3 × 1st class.
Credit Cards: Maestro, MasterCard, Visa
Specialities: *Agapanthus* South African bulbus plants, *Rhododendron* species only & other unusual plants.
Notes: Mail order *Agapanthus* from Sep-Jun. Wheelchair accessible.
Map Ref: C, B3 **OS Grid Ref:** SS683099

CPou **Pounsley Plants** ♿
Pounsley Combe, Spriddlestone, Brixton,
Plymouth, Devon PL9 0DW
Ⓣ (01752) 402873
Ⓜ 07770 758501
Ⓕ (01752) 406682
Ⓔ pou599@aol.com
Ⓦ www.pounsleyplants.com
Contact: Mrs Jane Hollow
Opening Times: Normally 1000-1600 Mon-Sat but please phone first.
Min Mail Order UK: £10.00 + p&p
Min Mail Order EU: €20.00 + p&p
Cat. Cost: 2 × 1st class.
Credit Cards: None

Specialities: Unusual herbaceous perennials & *Clematis*. Comprehensive range of Old Roses & large selection of modern roses.
Notes: Mail order solely bare-root roses, Nov-Mar. Also sells wholesale. Delivers to shows. Euro accepted. Wheelchair accessible.
Map Ref: C, D3 **OS Grid Ref:** SX521538

CPrp **ProperPlants.com**
Penknight, Edgcumbe Road, Lostwithiel, Cornwall PL22 0JD
Ⓣ (01208) 872291
Ⓔ sarah@penknight.plus.com
Ⓦ www.ProperPlants.com
Contact: Sarah Wilks
Opening Times: By appt. only. Please phone or email first.
Min Mail Order UK: Nmc
Min Mail Order EU: Nmc
Cat. Cost: 2 × 1st class.
Credit Cards: All major credit/debit cards
Specialities: *Agapanthus*, *Crocosmia* & *Hesperantha*.
Notes: Also sells wholesale. Exports beyond EU. Delivers to shows.
Map Ref: C, C2 **OS Grid Ref:** SX093596

CQua **Quality Daffodils**
14 Roscarrack Close, Falmouth, Cornwall TR11 4PJ
Ⓣ (01326) 317959
Ⓜ 07989 243450
Ⓕ (01326) 317959
Ⓔ rascamp@daffodils.uk.com
Ⓦ www.qualitydaffodils.com
Contact: R A Scamp
Opening Times: Not open. Mail order only. Viewing by appt. only.
Min Mail Order UK: Nmc
Min Mail Order EU: Nmc
Cat. Cost: 4 × 1st class.
Credit Cards: All major credit/debit cards
Specialities: *Narcissus* hybrids & species. Some stocks are less than 100 bulbs.
Notes: Also sells wholesale. Exports beyond EU. Euro accepted.
Map Ref: C, D1

CRea **Really Wild Flowers**
H V Horticulture Ltd, Heather Cottage, 23 New Close, Bourton, Gillingham, Dorset SP8 5DL
Ⓣ (01747) 416376
Ⓔ info@reallywildflowers.co.uk
Ⓦ www.reallywildflowers.co.uk
Contact: Grahame Dixie
Opening Times: Not open. Mail order & online only.
Min Mail Order UK: £10 + p&p
Cat. Cost: 3 × 1st class.
Credit Cards: All major credit/debit cards
Specialities: Native wild flowers for grasslands, woodlands & wetlands. Seeds & bulbs. Hedge plants & trees. Advisory & soil analysis services.
Notes: Credit card payment accepted for online orders only. Also sells wholesale. Delivers to shows.

CRHN **Roseland House Nursery**
Chacewater, Truro, Cornwall TR4 8QB
Ⓣ (01872) 560451
Ⓔ clematis@roselandhouse.co.uk
Ⓦ www.roselandhouse.co.uk
Contact: C R Pridham
Opening Times: 1300-1700 Tue & Wed, Apr-Sep. Other times by appt.
Min Mail Order UK: Nmc
Min Mail Order EU: Nmc
Cat. Cost: Online only.
Credit Cards: All major credit/debit cards
Specialities: Climbing & conservatory plants. Nat. Collections of *Clematis viticella* & *Lapageria rosea*. Named *Lapageria* in short supply but occasionally available.
Notes: Garden open to the public. Credit cards accepted from mail order customers only. Delivers to shows.
Map Ref: C, D1 **OS Grid Ref:** SW752445

CRoa **Roadford Water Gardens**
Higher Goodacre Farm, Broadwoodwidger, Lifton, Devon PL16 0ER
Ⓜ 07790 779991
Ⓔ info@roadfordwatergardens.co.uk
Ⓦ www.roadfordwatergardens.co.uk
Contact: Carolyn Wixon
Opening Times: Not open. Mail order only.
Min Mail Order UK: £10.00 + p&p
Credit Cards: Paypal
Specialities: Sells Rowden Iris & other water & moisture-loving *Iris*, *Nymphaea* for small ponds, *Ranunculus*, *Caltha* & candelabra *Primula*.
Notes: Rowden Irises by mail order only (Apr-Aug 2015).

CRos **Rosemoor Plant Centre (RHS)** ♿ ◆
RHS Garden Rosemoor, Torrington, Devon EX38 8PH
Ⓣ (01805) 626842
Ⓕ (01805) 622422
Ⓔ rosemooradmin@rhs.org.uk
Ⓦ www.rhs.org.uk/rosemoor
Contact: Emma Van-Huysse or Sam Smith
Opening Times: 1000-1800 Mon-Sat, 11.30-1730 Sun, Apr-Sep (summer). 1000-1700 Mon-Sat, 1030-1630 Sun, Oct-Mar (winter). Closed Easter Sun & Xmas Day.
Cat. Cost: None issued

C

Credit Cards: All major credit/debit cards
Specialities: Wide range of shrubs, herbaceous plants, roses, climbers, alpines & seasonal lines, reflecting where possible the diversity of planting in the garden. Displays highlighting a selection of plants for sale that are looking good in the garden, AGM plants & Plants for Pollinators.
Notes: Plant centre attached to RHS Garden. Free entry to plant centre, gift shop & restaurant. Plants subject to seasonal availability but will source plants whenever possible. Wheelchair accessible.
Map Ref: C, B3 **OS Grid Ref:** SS500176

CSam **SAMPFORD SHRUBS**
Sampford Peverell, Tiverton, Devon EX16 7EN
Ⓣ (01884) 821164
Ⓔ via website
Ⓦ www.samshrub.co.uk
Contact: M Hughes-Jones & S Proud
Opening Times: 1000-1700, 1st Apr-11th Sep incl.
Min Mail Order UK: £20.00 plant value.
Cat. Cost: Online stocklist only.
Credit Cards: All major credit/debit cards
Specialities: Plants particularly suitable for naturalistic gardening.
Notes: Mail order only via dedicated ecommerce website. Despatched Oct-Mar. Euro accepted.
Map Ref: C, B4 **OS Grid Ref:** ST043153

CSBt **ST BRIDGET NURSERIES LTD** ♿
Old Rydon Lane, Exeter, Devon EX2 7JY
Ⓣ (01392) 873672
Ⓕ (01392) 876710
Ⓔ sales@stbridgetnurseries.co.uk
Ⓦ www.stbridgetnurseries.co.uk
Contact: Sales Dept
Opening Times: 0900-1700 Mon-Sat, 1030-1630 Sun. Closed Xmas Day, Boxing Day, New Year's Day & Easter Sunday.
Min Mail Order UK: Nmc
Cat. Cost: Free.
Credit Cards: All major credit/debit cards
Specialities: Large general nursery, with two retail garden centres. Celebrating 90 years in business during 2015.
Notes: Mail order available, please contact for prices & carriage charges. Also sells wholesale. Wheelchair accessible.
Map Ref: C, C4 **OS Grid Ref:** SX955905

CSgt **STRETE GATE CAMELLIAS**
(Office) 17 Seymour Drive, Torquay, Devon TQ2 8PY
Ⓣ (01803) 770710
Ⓜ 07964 824673
Ⓔ plants@stretegatecamellias.co.uk
Ⓦ www.stretegatecamellias.co.uk
Contact: Jeremy Wilson
Opening Times: Not open. Mail order only.
Min Mail Order UK: Nmc
Specialities: Over 300 varieties of *Camellia*, many in small quantities not listed.
Notes: Nursery at different site from correspondence address. Also sells wholesale.

CSma **PLANTS FOR SMALL GARDENS**
Goosegate, Bridford, Exeter, Devon EX6 7LW
Ⓜ 07845 793582
Ⓔ sales@plantsforsmallgardens.co.uk
Ⓦ www.plantsforsmallgardens.co.uk
Contact: Sue Hearnden
Opening Times: Not open. Mail order online only.
Min Mail Order UK: £12.50
Cat. Cost: Online only.
Credit Cards: Paypal
Specialities: Dwarf hardy, rockery and alpine plants, all grown on our nursery in Devon. Range to suit all types of gardeners from *Aubrieta* & *Helianthemum* to more specialist plants such as kabschia saxifrages & *Meconopsis*. Good range of hardy geraniums.

CSna **SNAPE COTTAGE**
Chaffeymoor, Bourton, Dorset SP8 5BZ
Ⓣ (01747) 840330 (evenings only).
Ⓔ ianandangela@snapecottagegarden.co.uk
Ⓦ www.snapestakes.com
Contact: Mrs Angela Whinfield
Opening Times: 1400-1700 last Sat in months Feb-Jun incl.
Min Mail Order UK: Nmc
Cat. Cost: Sae.
Credit Cards: None
Specialities: 'Old' forms of many popular garden plants. Plantsman's garden open same time as nursery. Stock available in small quantities. Snape Stakes plant supports.
Notes: Mail order *Galanthus* only. List issued in Feb. Group visits welcome all year.
Map Ref: C, B5 **OS Grid Ref:** ST762303

CSpe **SPECIAL PLANTS**
Hill Farm Barn, Greenways Lane, Cold Ashton, Chippenham, Wiltshire SN14 8LA
Ⓣ (01225) 891686
Ⓔ derry@specialplants.net
Ⓦ www.specialplants.net
Contact: Derry Watkins
Opening Times: 1000-1700 7 days Mar-Oct. Other times please ring first to check.
Min Mail Order UK: £10.00 + p&p
Cat. Cost: 2 × 1st class for seed list.
Credit Cards: All major credit/debit cards

Specialities: Tender perennials, *Pelargonium*, *Salvia*, hardy geraniums, *Anemone*, *Erysimum*, *Papaver* & grasses. Many varieties propagated in small numbers only.
Notes: Mail order Sep-Mar only. Delivers to shows. Euro accepted.
Map Ref: C, A5 **OS Grid Ref:** ST749726

CSta **STADDON FARM NURSERIES** ♿
Staddon Road, Holsworthy, Devon
EX22 6NH
Ⓜ 07547 711189
Ⓔ penny.staddonfarm@yahoo.co.uk
Ⓦ www.pennysprimulas.co.uk
Contact: Penny Jones
Opening Times: By appt. only.
Min Mail Order UK: Nmc
Cat. Cost: Online only.
Credit Cards: All major credit/debit cards
Specialities: *Primula*. National Collection of *Primula sieboldii* Japanese cvs.
Notes: Delivers to shows. Wheelchair accessible.

CSto **STONE LANE GARDENS**
Stone Farm, Chagford, Devon TQ13 8JU
Ⓣ (01647) 231311
Ⓔ paul.bartlett@stonelanegardens.com
Ⓦ www.stonelanegardens.com
Contact: Paul Bartlett
Opening Times: Open by appt. only. Not open to casual visitors. Website ordering available.
Min Mail Order UK: Nmc
Min Mail Order EU: Nmc
Cat. Cost: 6 × 1st class for colour catalogue with photos or online.
Credit Cards: All major credit/debit cards
Specialities: Comprehensive selection of wild origin *Betula* & *Alnus*, both bare-root & in pots. Choice selection of specially grafted cvs. Nat. Collection of Birch & Alder.
Notes: Arboretum open all year with summer sculpture exhibition (charges apply). Planting service available in West Country, details on request. Also sells wholesale. Credit cards accepted online only.
Map Ref: C, C3 **OS Grid Ref:** SX708908

CSut **SUTTONS SEEDS**
Woodview Road, Paignton, Devon
TQ4 7NG
Ⓣ 0333 400 2899
Ⓕ 0844 922 2265
Ⓦ www.suttons.co.uk
Contact: Customer Services
Opening Times: Office: 0830-1700 Mon-Fri. Also answerphone.
Min Mail Order UK: Nmc
Min Mail Order EU: £5.00
Cat. Cost: Free.
Credit Cards: Visa, MasterCard, Switch, Delta
Specialities: Over 1,000 varieties of flower & vegetable seed, bulbs, plants & sundries.

CTal **TALE VALLEY NURSERY**
Barratt's Cottage, Cullompton, Devon
EX15 2NQ
Ⓣ (01884) 277614
Ⓜ 07791 676162
Ⓔ contactus@talevalleynursery.co.uk
Ⓦ www.talevalleynursery.co.uk
Contact: Lorraine & Chris Birchall
Opening Times: Not open.
Min Mail Order UK: £10.00 + p&p
Min Mail Order EU: £25.00 + p&p
Credit Cards: None
Specialities: Alpines, shade/woodland herbaceous plants standard dwarf bearded *Iris* & South African bulbs. Nat. Collections of *Rhodohypoxis* & × *Rhodoxis*. Some specialist plants available in small numbers only.
Notes: Mail order for selection of Nat. Collections, other bulbs & a few select plants. Despatch of selected bare-root herbaceous plants in autumn. Delivers to shows.

CTca **TRECANNA NURSERY**
The Old Barn, Chilsworthy, Cornwall
PL18 9PB
Ⓣ (01822) 834680
Ⓜ 07785 242148
Ⓔ mark@trecanna.com
Ⓦ www.trecanna.com
Contact: Mark Wash
Opening Times: Not open. Mail order only.
Min Mail Order UK: £22.00
Min Mail Order EU: £45.00
Cat. Cost: Online only.
Credit Cards: All major credit/debit cards
Specialities: Hardy South African plants. Good collections of *Crocosmia*, *Eucomis*, *Kniphofia*, *Watsonia*, *Crinum*, *Albuca*, nerines, *Zantedeschia*, *Lachenalia* & *Moraea*. Wide range of dry bulbs from around the globe.
Notes: Talks to garden societies. Exports beyond EU. Delivers to shows.
Map Ref: C, C3 **OS Grid Ref:** SX247733

CTho **THORNHAYES NURSERY**
St Andrews Wood, Dulford, Cullompton, Devon EX15 2DF
Ⓣ (01884) 266746
Ⓕ (01884) 266739
Ⓔ trees@thornhayes-nursery.co.uk
Ⓦ www.thornhayes-nursery.co.uk
Contact: K D Croucher
Opening Times: 0800-1600 Mon-Fri. 0930-1400 Sat.
Min Mail Order UK: £30

C

Min Mail Order EU: Price on application.
Cat. Cost: Free.
Credit Cards: All major credit/debit cards
Specialities: A broad range of forms of ornamental, amenity & fruit trees incl. West Country apple varieties and choice shrubs. A particular emphasis on disease-resistant forms for the wet and windy west.
Notes: Also sells wholesale. Euro accepted. Limited wheelchair accessible.
Map Ref: C, C4

CTre **TREWIDDEN NURSERY**
Buryas Bridge, Penzance, Cornwall TR20 8TT
Ⓣ (01736) 362087
Ⓔ info@trewidden-nursery.com
Ⓦ www.trewidden-online.co.uk
Contact: Jeff Rowe
Opening Times: Not open. Mail order & RHS shows. Open w/ends, one in spring & one in autumn, contact nursery for details.
Min Mail Order UK: Nmc
Min Mail Order EU: Nmc
Cat. Cost: Online only.
Specialities: *Protea*, *Restio*, succulents and other unusual plants.
Notes: Sells at shows around the country and online. Card payments accepted at shows. Mail order through website only.

CTrh **TREHANE NURSERY** ♿
Stapehill Road, Hampreston, Wimborne, Dorset BH21 7ND
Ⓣ (01202) 873490
Ⓔ nursery@trehane.co.uk
Ⓦ www.trehane.co.uk
Contact: Lorraine Keets
Opening Times: 0830-1630 Mon-Fri all year (excl. Xmas & New Year). 1000-1600 Sat in spring & by special appt.
Min Mail Order UK: Nmc
Min Mail Order EU: Nmc
Cat. Cost: Free
Credit Cards: All major credit/debit cards
Specialities: Extensive range of *Camellia* species, cultivars & hybrids. Many new introductions. Blueberries.
Notes: Also sells wholesale. Wheelchair accessible.
Map Ref: C, C6 **OS Grid Ref:** SU059000

CTri **TRISCOMBE NURSERIES** ♿ ◆
West Bagborough, Nr Taunton, Somerset TA4 3HG
Ⓣ (01984) 618267
Ⓔ info@triscombenurseries.co.uk
Ⓦ www.triscombenurseries.co.uk
Contact: S Parkman
Opening Times: 0900-1730 Mon-Sat.
Min Mail Order UK: Nmc
Cat. Cost: 1 × 1st class.
Credit Cards: None
Specialities: Trees, shrubs, roses, fruit, *Clematis*, herbaceous & rock plants.
Notes: Wheelchair accessible.
Map Ref: C, B4

CTsd **TRESEDERS** ♿
Wallcottage Nursery, Lockengate, St. Austell, Cornwall PL26 8RU
Ⓣ (01208) 832234
Ⓔ Treseders@btconnect.com
Ⓦ www.treseders.co.uk
Contact: James Treseder
Opening Times: 0900-1700 Mon-Sat, 1000-1600 Sun. Closed Wed.
Min Mail Order UK: Nmc
Min Mail Order EU: Nmc
Cat. Cost: Plant list available on request.
Credit Cards: All major credit/debit cards
Specialities: A wide range of choice & unusual plants grown in peat-free compost. Establishing collection of *Prostanthera*.
Notes: Plants sometimes only available in small quantities. Enquiries welcome. Delivers to shows. Wheelchair accessible.
Map Ref: C, C2 **OS Grid Ref:** SX034620

CWat **THE WATER GARDEN** ♿
Hinton Parva, Swindon, Wiltshire SN4 0DH
Ⓣ (01793) 790558
Ⓕ (01793) 791298
Ⓔ mike@thewatergarden.co.uk
Ⓦ www.thewatergarden.co.uk
Contact: Mike & Anne Newman
Opening Times: 1000-1700 Wed-Sun.
Min Mail Order UK: £10.00 + p&p
Cat. Cost: 4 × 1st class.
Credit Cards: Visa, Access, Switch
Specialities: Water lilies, marginal & moisture plants, oxygenators & alpines.
Notes: Also sells wholesale. Wheelchair accessible.
Map Ref: C, A6

CWCL **WESTCOUNTRY NURSERIES**
Donkey Meadow, Woolsery, Devon EX39 5QH
Ⓣ (01237) 431111
Ⓔ info@westcountry-nurseries.co.uk
Ⓦ www.westcountry-nurseries.co.uk
Contact: Sarah Conibear
Opening Times: 1000-1600 Mar-mid Jul. Closed for lunch 1300-1330. Before travelling at a w/end, please check with nursery.
Min Mail Order UK: Nmc
Cat. Cost: 2 × 1st class + A5 sae for full colour cat.
Credit Cards: All major credit/debit cards

Specialities: *Lupinus*, *Lewisia*, *Hellebore*, *Clematis*, cyclamen, lavender, select perennials, grasses, ferns & climbers. Nat. Collection of Lupins.
Notes: Delivers to shows.
Map Ref: C, B2 **OS Grid Ref:** SS351219

CWel **WELLGARTH PLANTS**
(Office) Ravendale, St Lawrence, Bodmin, Cornwall PL30 5JL
Ⓜ 07445 240133
Ⓔ info@wellgarthplants.com
Ⓦ www.wellgarthplants.com
Contact: Cassie Corby
Opening Times: Not open, except by appt. Mail order only.
Min Mail Order UK: Nmc
Credit Cards: Paypal
Specialities: *Hemerocallis.*
Notes: Stock available in small quantities. Mail order via website only.

CWGN **WALLED GARDEN NURSERY** ♿
Brinkworth House, Brinkworth, Nr Malmesbury, Wiltshire SN15 5DF
Ⓣ (01666) 826637
Ⓜ 07921 436863
Ⓔ f.wescott@btinternet.com
Ⓦ www.clematis-nursery.co.uk
Contact: Fraser Wescott
Opening Times: 1000-1700, 7 days Mar-Oct. 1030-dusk, Mon-Fri, Nov & Feb. Closed Dec & Jan.
Min Mail Order UK: £15.00
Credit Cards: All major credit/debit cards
Specialities: *Clematis* & climbers, with a selection of unusual perennials & shrubs.
Notes: Mail order UK mainland only. Wheelchair accessible.
Map Ref: C, A6 **OS Grid Ref:** SU002849

CWGr **NATIONAL DAHLIA COLLECTION**
Varfell Farm, Long Rock, Penzance, Cornwall TR20 8AQ
Ⓣ (01736) 711271
Ⓜ 07879 337714
Ⓔ info@national-dahlia-collection.co.uk
Ⓦ www.national-dahlia-collection.co.uk
Contact: Michael Mann
Opening Times: Garden open in summer. See website or contact nursery for details.
Min Mail Order UK: Nmc
Min Mail Order EU: Nmc
Cat. Cost: Online. Contact nursery for hard copy.
Credit Cards: All, except American Express
Specialities: Nat. Collection of *Dahlia*. 1600+ *Dahlia* cultivars.
Notes: See website for plant availability. Also sells wholesale. Limited wheelchair accessible.

CWhe **WHETMAN PINKS LTD**
Houndspool, Ashcombe Road, Dawlish, Devon EX7 0QP
Ⓣ (01626) 863328
Ⓜ 07860 198238
Ⓕ (01626) 888911
Ⓔ orders@whetmanpinks.com
Ⓦ www.whetmanpinks.com
Contact: Mrs Carolyn Bourne
Opening Times: Not open. Mail order only.
Min Mail Order UK: £10.00
Min Mail Order EU: £10.00
Cat. Cost: Free.
Credit Cards: All, except American Express
Specialities: Garden pinks & hybrid *Dianthus*. Rooted cuttings available all year round.
Notes: Nursery tours for clubs & societies can be arranged by appt. Also sells wholesale. Euro accepted.

CWib **WIBBLE FARM NURSERIES** ♿
Wibble Farm, West Quantoxhead, Nr Taunton, Somerset TA4 4DD
Ⓣ (01984) 632303
Ⓕ (01984) 633168
Ⓔ sales@wibblefarmnurseries.co.uk
Ⓦ www.wibblefarmnurseries.co.uk
Contact: Mrs M L Francis
Opening Times: 0800-1700 Mon-Fri, 1000-1600 Sat. 1400-1600 Sun (open Sun Mar-Sep only). All year incl. some B/hols.
Min Mail Order UK: Nmc
Min Mail Order EU: Nmc
Cat. Cost: 3 × 1st class.
Credit Cards: All major credit/debit cards
Specialities: Growers of a wide range of hardy plants, many rare & unusual. Display gardens.
Notes: Also sells wholesale. Wheelchair accessible.

CWiW **WINDRUSH WILLOW**
Higher Barn, Sidmouth Road, Aylesbeare, Exeter, Devon EX5 2JJ
Ⓣ (01395) 233669
Ⓕ (01395) 233669
Ⓔ windrushw@aol.com
Ⓦ www.windrushwillow.com
Contact: Richard Kerwood
Opening Times: Mail order only. Open by appt.
Min Mail Order UK: Nmc
Min Mail Order EU: Nmc
Cat. Cost: 2 × 1st class.
Credit Cards: All major credit/debit cards
Specialities: *Salix*. Unrooted cuttings available Dec-Mar.
Notes: Also sells wholesale. Euro accepted.

E

CWld **Wild Thyme**
(Office) The Old Orchard, Friggle Street, Frome, Somerset BA11 5LH
Ⓣ (01373) 464417
Ⓜ 07956 888477
Ⓔ jess@wildthymeplants.co.uk
Ⓦ www.wildthymeplants.co.uk
Contact: Monica Ashman
Opening Times: Not open. Mail order only via online shop.
Min Mail Order UK: £15.00
Credit Cards: Visa, MasterCard, Maestro
Specialities: Wildflowers & fragrant plants.
Notes: Delivers to shows.

CWSG **West Somerset Garden Centre** ♿
Mart Road, Minehead, Somerset TA24 5BJ
Ⓣ (01643) 703812
Ⓕ (01643) 706476
Ⓔ wsgc@btconnect.com
Ⓦ www.westsomersetgardencentre.co.uk
Contact: Ms J K Webber
Opening Times: 0800-1700 Mon-Sat, 1000-1600 Sun.
Min Mail Order UK: Nmc
Cat. Cost: None issued.
Credit Cards: Visa, Solo, Maestro, MasterCard, American Express
Specialities: Wide general range. *Clematis* & rose varieties change throughout the season.
Notes: Wheelchair accessible.
Map Ref: C, B4

CWVF **White Veil Fuchsias** ♿
Verwood Road, Three Legged Cross, Wimborne, Dorset BH21 6RP
Ⓣ (01202) 813998
Contact: A. C. Holloway
Opening Times: 0900-1300 & 1400-1700 Mon-Sat, Jan-Jul. Closed Sun. The nursery will be closed from 1st Aug 2015 to Jan 2016.
Cat. Cost: Only available at nursery.
Credit Cards: None
Specialities: Fuchsias. Small plants grown from Jan-Apr. Available in small quantities only at the nursery.
Notes: Wheelchair accessible.

CYeo **South Yeo Nursery**
Poughill, Crediton, Devon EX17 4LF
Ⓣ (01363) 866401
Ⓜ 07971 412132
Ⓔ davidross350@btinternet.com
Ⓦ www.hesperantha.co.uk
Contact: David Ross
Opening Times: By appt. only.
Min Mail Order UK: £20
Min Mail Order EU: £50
Credit Cards: Paypal
Specialities: All plants grown are from micro-propagated plugs, virus-checked by FERA, and have been through an extensive verification programme. More cvs will become available during the year. Nat. Collection of *Hesperantha coccinea* cvs.
Notes: Also sells wholesale. Exports beyond EU. Euro accepted.

Eastern

EACa **Alpine Campanulas (Bellflower Nursery)** ♿
Langham Hall Walled Garden, Langham, Nr Bury St Edmunds, Suffolk IP31 3EE
Ⓜ 07879 644958
Ⓔ campanulas@btinternet.com
Ⓦ www.bellflowernursery.co.uk
Contact: Sue Wooster
Opening Times: 1000-1630 Thu & Fri, mid-Mar to end Oct. Other times by appt.
Min Mail Order UK: £10.00
Cat. Cost: 2 × 1st class A5 sae.
Credit Cards: None
Specialities: *Campanula*. Nat. Collection of Alpine Campanulas. Most stock in small numbers only.
Notes: Hardy plant nursery & Nat. Collection within 1.5 acre Georgian Walled Garden. Groups welcome by appt. Wheelchair accessible but nursery reached by gravel paths through walled garden.
Map Ref: E, C3 **OS Grid Ref:** TL978691

EAEE **AEE – a lover of plants**
Oak Tree Farm, Kenninghall Road (off Common Road), Bressingham, Norfolk IP22 2HG
Ⓣ (01379) 651230 (answering machine)
M: 07874 214182
Ⓔ aeesales@fsmail.net
Ⓦ www.aeesupplyingplantlovers.com
Contact: Anne Etheridge
Opening Times: 0900-1700 7 days, Mar-Sep. 1000-1600 Tue, Thu, Fri, Sun, Oct-Feb.
Min Mail Order UK: Nmc
Min Mail Order EU: Nmc
Credit Cards: All major credit/debit cards
Specialities: Perennials & grasses plus a few enticing alpines & shrubs. Alpines available in small quantities only.
Notes: Talks available Mar-Oct. For information on group & trade discounts please contact nursery. Plants delivered free within 10 miles of Roydon, Diss or Snetterton Park.

EAJP **A & J Plants**
Scenterfields, Chapel Road, Great Tey, Colchester, Essex CO6 1JR
Ⓣ (01206) 212124
Ⓕ (01206) 212124

Ⓔ mail@aandjplants.com
Ⓦ www.aandjplants.com
Contact: Jackie Rhodes
Opening Times: Not open. Mail order only. Orders can be collected from nursery by prior arrangement.
Min Mail Order UK: Nmc
Credit Cards: Visa, MasterCard
Specialities: Wide variety of choice perennials and ornamental grasses propagated on the nursery, some in small quantities.
Notes: Plant Centre at Marks Hall Garden (CO6 1TG) stocked with seasonal selection of perennials & grasses. Also sells wholesale. Delivers to shows.

EBak **B & H M Baker** ♿
Bourne Brook Nurseries, Greenstead Green, Halstead, Essex CO9 1RB
Ⓣ (01787) 476369
Contact: Clive Baker
Opening Times: 0800-1600 Mon-Fri, 0900-1200 & 1400-1600 Sat & Sun, Mar-30th Jun.
Cat. Cost: 2 × 1st class + 33p.
Credit Cards: All major credit/debit cards
Specialities: *Fuchsia* & conservatory plants.
Notes: Also sells wholesale. Wheelchair accessible.
Map Ref: E, C2

EBar **Barcham Trees PLC**
Eye Hill Drove, Ely, Cambridgeshire CB7 5XF
Ⓣ (01353) 720950
Ⓜ 07801 917566
Ⓕ (01353) 723060
Ⓔ info@barchamtrees.co.uk
Ⓦ www.barcham.co.uk
Contact: Mike Glover
Opening Times: 0900-1700 Mon-Fri. Visits to the nursery by appt. only.
Min Mail Order UK: Nmc
Min Mail Order EU: Nmc
Cat. Cost: £10.00
Credit Cards: All, except American Express
Specialities: Large grower of containerised trees. 478 varieties available, from 10-12cm to 40cm girth.
Notes: E-commerce site: www.buythetreeyousee.com. As trees range from 3-8 metres all are despatched on lorries rather than through the mailing service. Also sells wholesale. Exports beyond EU. Euro accepted.

EBee **Beeches Nursery** ♿
Crown Hill, Ashdon, Saffron Walden, Essex CB10 2HB
Ⓣ (01799) 584362
Ⓕ (01799) 584421
Ⓔ sales@beechesnursery.co.uk
Ⓦ www.beechesnursery.co.uk
Contact: Alan Bidwell/Kevin Marsh
Opening Times: 0830-1700 Mon-Sat, 1000-1700 Sun & B/hols.
Min Mail Order UK: £15.00
Min Mail Order EU: £20.00
Cat. Cost: Online.
Credit Cards: All major credit/debit cards
Specialities: Herbaceous specialists & extensive range of other garden plants. Rarieties available in limited numbers only.
Notes: Plants dispatched Oct-Feb only. Orders accepted throughout the year. No trees by mail order. Wheelchair accessible.
Map Ref: E, C2 **OS Grid Ref:** TL586420

EBtc **Botanica**
Chantry Farm, Campsea Ashe, Wickham Market, Suffolk IP13 0PZ
Ⓣ (01728) 747113
Ⓜ 07887 423964
Ⓕ (01728) 747725
Ⓔ sales@botanica.org.uk
Ⓦ www.botanicaplantnursery.co.uk
Contact: Daniel Everett
Opening Times: 0900-1700 Mon-Fri (0900-1600 in winter), 1000-1600 w/ends. Closed w/ends in Jul.
Min Mail Order UK: £30 + p&p
Cat. Cost: Online only.
Credit Cards: All, except American Express
Specialities: Range of rare & unusual hardy plants. All stock is English grown at our nursery and in non-peat based compost.
Notes: Also sells wholesale.
Map Ref: E, C3 **OS Grid Ref:** TM328550

ECGP **Cambridge Garden Plants** ♿
The Lodge, Clayhithe Road, Horningsea, Cambridgeshire CB25 9JD
Ⓣ (01223) 861370
Ⓔ kit@cambridgegardenplants.co.uk
Contact: Kit Buchdahl
Opening Times: 1100-1730 Thu-Sun mid Mar-31st Oct. Other times by appt.
Cat. Cost: 4 × 1st class.
Credit Cards: None
Specialities: Hardy perennials incl. wide range of *Geranium*, *Allium*, *Euphorbia*, *Cyclamen*, *Digitalis*.
Notes: Euro accepted. Wheelchair accessible.
Map Ref: E, C2 **OS Grid Ref:** TL497637

ECha **The Beth Chatto Gardens Ltd** ♿
Clacton Road, Elmstead Market, Colchester, Essex CO7 7DB
Ⓣ (01206) 822007
Ⓕ (01206) 825933
Ⓔ info@bethchatto.co.uk
Ⓦ www.bethchatto.co.uk
Contact: David Ward

Opening Times: 0900-1700 Mon-Sat, 1000-1700 Sun, 1st Mar-31st Oct. 0900-1600 Mon-Sat, 1000-1600 Sun, Nov-end Feb.
Min Mail Order UK: Nmc
Min Mail Order EU: Ask for details
Cat. Cost: Online only.
Credit Cards: All, except American Express
Specialities: Predominantly herbaceous perennials, grasses & ferns. Many unusual for special situations.
Notes: Wheelchair accessible.
Map Ref: E, C3 **OS Grid Ref:** TM069238

E

ECho CHOICE LANDSCAPES ♿
Priory Farm Nursery, 101 Salts Road, West Walton, Wisbech, Cambridgeshire PE14 7EF
Ⓣ (01945) 585051
Ⓔ info@choicelandscapes.org
Contact: Jillian Agg
Opening Times: By appt.
Min Mail Order UK: Nmc
Cat. Cost: 6 × 2nd class.
Specialities: Alpines, bulbs, lilies & South African bulbs.
Notes: Delivers to shows. Wheelchair accessible.
Map Ref: E, B2

ECnt CANTS OF COLCHESTER LTD
Nayland Road, Mile End, Colchester, Essex CO4 5HA
Ⓣ (01206) 844008
Ⓕ (01206) 855371
Ⓔ enquiries@cantsroses.co.uk
Ⓦ www.cantsroses.co.uk
Contact: Angela Pawsey
Opening Times: 0900-1300, 1400-1630 Mon-Fri. Sat varied, please phone first. Sun closed.
Min Mail Order UK: Nmc
Min Mail Order EU: Nmc
Cat. Cost: Free
Credit Cards: Visa, MasterCard, Delta, Maestro
Specialities: Roses. Unstaffed rose field can be viewed dawn-dusk every day from end Jun-end Sep.
Notes: Bare-root mail order end Oct-end Mar, containers Apr-Aug. Exports beyond EU. Partial wheelchair access.
Map Ref: E, C3

ECrc THE CROCOSMIA GARDENS
9 North Street, Caistor, Lincolnshire LN7 6QU
Ⓣ (01472) 859269
Ⓜ 07747 304620
Ⓔ mark@thecrocosmiagardens.net
Ⓦ www.thecrocosmiagardens.net
Contact: Mark Fox
Opening Times: 1000-1700 Mon-Sun.
Min Mail Order UK: £5.00
Min Mail Order EU: £5.00
Credit Cards: None
Specialities: *Crocosmia*. Nat. Collection of *Crocosmia*.
Notes: Exports beyond EU. Euro accepted.
Map Ref: E, A1

ECre CREAKE PLANT CENTRE ♿
Leicester Road, South Creake, Fakenham, Norfolk NR21 9PW
Ⓣ (01328) 823018
Ⓜ 07760 762499
Ⓕ (01328) 823018
Ⓔ trevor-harrison@btconnect.com
Ⓦ www.creakeplantcentre.co.uk
Contact: Mr T Harrison
Opening Times: 1000-1300 & 1400-1730 7 days excl. Xmas.
Cat. Cost: None issued
Credit Cards: All major credit/debit cards
Specialities: Unusual shrubs, herbaceous, conservatory plants, old roses. Hellebores. Some plants only available in small quantities.
Notes: Delivers to shows. Wheelchair accessible.
Map Ref: E, A2 **OS Grid Ref:** TF864353

ECrN CROWN NURSERY ♿
High Street, Ufford, Suffolk IP13 6EL
Ⓣ (01394) 460755
Ⓕ (01394) 460142
Ⓔ enquiries@crown-nursery.co.uk
Ⓦ www.crown-nursery.co.uk
Contact: Jill Proctor
Opening Times: 0900-1700 (1600 in winter) Mon-Sat.
Min Mail Order UK: Nmc
Credit Cards: All major credit/debit cards
Specialities: Mature & semi-mature native, ornamental & fruit trees. Heritage fruit varieties.
Notes: Mail order for small/young stock only. Also sells wholesale. Wheelchair accessible.
Map Ref: E, C3 **OS Grid Ref:** TM292528

ECtt COTTAGE NURSERIES ♿
Thoresthorpe, Alford, Lincolnshire LN13 0HX
Ⓣ (01507) 466968
Ⓕ (01507) 463409
Ⓔ bill@cottagenurseries.net
Ⓦ www.cottagenurseries.net
Contact: W H Denbigh
Opening Times: 0900-1700, 7 days 1st Mar-31st Oct. 1000-1500, Nov-Feb. Closed 15th Dec-6th Jan.
Min Mail Order UK: £15.00
Cat. Cost: 4 × 1st class.

Credit Cards: Visa, MasterCard, Maestro
Specialities: Hardy perennials. Wide general range.
Notes: Wheelchair accessible.
Map Ref: E, A2 **OS Grid Ref:** TF461776

EDAr **D'Arcy & Everest**
Meadowsweet Nursery, Pidley Sheep Lane, (B1040) Pidley, Cambridgeshire
PE28 3FL
Ⓣ (01480) 497672 answerphone
Ⓜ 07715 374440
Ⓕ (01480) 466042
Ⓔ angela@darcyeverest.co.uk
Ⓦ www.darcyeverest.co.uk
Contact: Angela Whiting
Opening Times: 1000-1500 Wed-Sat, Mar-end Sep. Nursery gardens open Sat only, but close at 1400 if an event on. Winter by appt. Coach parties welcome by appt.
Min Mail Order UK: £15.00 + p&p
Min Mail Order EU: £50.00 + p&p
Cat. Cost: 6 × 1st class.
Credit Cards: All major credit/debit cards
Specialities: Alpines & sempervivums.
Notes: Euro accepted. Delivers to shows. Partial wheelchair access.
Map Ref: E, C2 **OS Grid Ref:** TL338762

EDel **Delfland Nurseries Ltd** ♿
Benwick Road, Doddington, March, Cambridgeshire PE15 0TU
Ⓣ (01354) 740553
Ⓕ (01354) 741200
Ⓔ info@delfland.co.uk
Ⓦ www.organicplants.co.uk
Contact: Jill Vaughan
Opening Times: 0900-1600 Mon-Fri, 0900-1300 Sat, all year. Additionally, at peak season, 0900-1600 Sat & 1000-1600 Sun.
Min Mail Order UK: £1.95 + p&p
Cat. Cost: Free or online.
Credit Cards: All major credit/debit cards
Specialities: Vegetable, bedding & container plants.
Notes: Mail order and retail organic & peat-free from stock (mainly veg. plants) or to order (for large orders). Retail bedding & container plants not organic or peat-free. Also sells wholesale. Wheelchair accessible.
Map Ref: E, C2 **OS Grid Ref:** TL386908

EECP **Essex Carnivorous Plants**
12 Strangman Avenue, Thundersley, Essex
SS7 1RB
Ⓣ (01702) 551467
Ⓜ 07957 196391
Ⓔ Mark@essexcarnivorousplants.com
Ⓦ www.essexcarnivorousplants.com
Contact: Mark Haslett
Opening Times: By appt. only.
Min Mail Order UK: Nmc
Min Mail Order EU: Nmc
Cat. Cost: 2 × 1st class or online.
Credit Cards: Paypal
Specialities: Good range of carnivorous plants. *Sarracenia*, *Dionaea*. Some stock available in small quantities only.
Notes: Also sells wholesale. Delivers to shows.
Map Ref: E, D2 **OS Grid Ref:** TQ797875

EFer **The Fern Nursery** ♿
Grimsby Road, Binbrook, Lincolnshire
LN8 6DH
Ⓣ (01472) 398092
Ⓔ rtimm@fernnursery.co.uk
Ⓦ www.fernnursery.co.uk
Contact: R N Timm
Opening Times: 0900-1700 Fri, Sat & Sun Apr-Oct or by appt.
Min Mail Order UK: Nmc
Min Mail Order EU: Nmc
Cat. Cost: 2 × 1st class.
Credit Cards: None
Specialities: Ferns. Display garden.
Notes: Only plants in the mail order part of the catalogue can be sent mail order. Also sells wholesale. Euro accepted. Wheelchair accessible.
Map Ref: E, A1 **OS Grid Ref:** TF212942

EFEx **Flora Exotica**
Pasadena, South-Green, Fingringhoe, Colchester, Essex CO5 7DR
Ⓜ 07989 456094
Contact: J Beddoes
Opening Times: Not open. Mail order only.
Min Mail Order UK: Nmc
Min Mail Order EU: Nmc
Cat. Cost: 4 × 1st class.
Credit Cards: None
Specialities: Exotica flora incl. orchids.
Notes: Exports beyond EU. Euro accepted.

EFly **The Fly Trap Plants** ♿
Cookes Road, Thurton, Norwich, Norfolk
NR14 6AE
Ⓣ (01508) 480348
Ⓜ 07769 256556
Ⓔ sales@tftplants.co.uk
Ⓦ www.tftplants.co.uk
Contact: Pauline Steward
Opening Times: By appt. only.
Min Mail Order UK: Nmc
Cat. Cost: 1 × 1st class sae
Credit Cards: Paypal
Specialities: All kinds of carnivorous plants, from *Sarracenia*, *Drosera*, *Pinguicula*, to *Utricularia* aquatic plants.

Notes: Delivers to shows. Euro accepted. Wheelchair accessible.

E

EGeo **GEORGE'S GORGEOUS GARDENS**
Outlaws Cottage, Lugs Lane, Broome, Norfolk NR35 2HT
Ⓣ (01508) 518559
Ⓜ 07592 491234
Ⓔ georgesgorgeousgardens@gmail.com
Contact: George Gillespie
Min Mail Order UK: £20.00
Min Mail Order EU: £50.00
Cat. Cost: £2.50
Credit Cards: None
Specialities: *Plectranthus.*

EGFP **GRANGE FARM PLANTS** ♿
Grange Farm, 38 Fishergate Road, Sutton St James, Spalding, Lincolnshire PE12 0EZ
Ⓣ (01945) 440240
Ⓜ 07742 138760
Ⓕ (01945) 440355
Ⓔ ellis.family@tinyonline.co.uk
Contact: M C Ellis
Opening Times: Mail order only. Open by appt. only.
Min Mail Order UK: Nmc
Min Mail Order EU: Nmc
Cat. Cost: 1 × 1st class.
Credit Cards: None
Specialities: Rare trees & shrubs, esp. *Juglans*, *Fraxinus*. Some species available in small quantities only.
Notes: Euro accepted. Wheelchair accessible.
Map Ref: E, B2 **OS Grid Ref:** TF382186

EHoe **HOECROFT PLANTS** ♿
Severals Grange, Holt Road, Wood Norton, Norfolk NR20 5BL
Ⓣ (01362) 684206
Ⓔ hoecroft@hotmail.co.uk
Ⓦ www.hoecroft.co.uk
Contact: Jane Lister
Opening Times: 1000-1600 Thu-Sun, 1st Apr-31st Oct or by appt.
Min Mail Order UK: Nmc
Min Mail Order EU: Nmc
Cat. Cost: 5 × 2nd class.
Credit Cards: None
Specialities: An extensive range of coloured & variegated-leaved shrubs & herbaceous perennials. 260 ornamental grasses. Free entry to display gardens.
Notes: Nursery 2 miles north of Guist on B1110. Euro accepted. Wheelchair accessible.
Map Ref: E, B3 **OS Grid Ref:** TG008289

EHrv **HARVEYS GARDEN PLANTS** ♿
Great Green, Thurston, Bury St Edmunds, Suffolk IP31 3SJ
Ⓣ (01359) 233363
Ⓕ (01359) 233363 & answerphone
Ⓔ admin@harveysgardenplants.co.uk
Ⓦ www.harveysgardenplants.co.uk
Contact: Roger Harvey
Opening Times: 0930-1630 Mon-Sun, excl. Xmas & New Year's Day.
Min Mail Order UK: £20.00
Min Mail Order EU: £20.00
Cat. Cost: £3.00
Credit Cards: All major credit/debit cards
Specialities: *Helleborus*, *Anemone*, *Epimedium*, *Galanthus*, *Astrantia*, *Pulmonaria* & other herbaceous perennials, plus shade & woodland plants.
Notes: Garden design & maintenance service. Delivers to shows. Euro accepted. Wheelchair accessible.
Map Ref: E, C2 **OS Grid Ref:** TL94127

EHyd **HYDE HALL PLANT CENTRE (RHS)** ♿ ◆
RHS Garden Hyde Hall, Rettenden, Chelmsford, Essex CM3 8ET
Ⓣ (01245) 402113
Ⓕ (01245) 400013
Ⓔ lizbrown@rhs.org.uk
Ⓦ www.rhs.org.uk
Contact: Any member of staff
Opening Times: 0930-1600 Mon-Sat, 1000-1600 Sun, Nov-Feb. 0930-1800 Mon-Sat, 1100 -1700 Sun, Mar-Oct. Closed Xmas Day & Easter Sun.
Credit Cards: All major credit/debit cards

EIri **IRISESONLINE**
Slade Cottage, Petts Lane, Little Walden, Essex CB10 1XH
Ⓣ (01799) 526294
Ⓔ sales@irisesonline.co.uk
Ⓦ www.irisesonline.co.uk
Contact: Clare Kneen
Opening Times: By appt. only.
Min Mail Order UK: Nmc
Cat. Cost: 3 × 1st class or online.
Credit Cards: None
Specialities: *Iris*. Small family-run nursery. Some varieties available in small quantities only.
Map Ref: E, C2 **OS Grid Ref:** TL546416

ELad **LADYBIRD NURSERIES** ♿
Gromford Lane, Snape, Saxmundham, Suffolk IP17 1RD
Ⓣ (01728) 688289
Ⓦ www.ladybirdnurseries.co.uk
Contact: Mrs M Booker
Opening Times: 0900-1700, Mon-Sat, 1000-1600 Sun.

Credit Cards: All major credit/debit cards
Notes: Wheelchair accessible.
Map Ref: E, C3 **OS Grid Ref:** TM388589

ELan **Langthorns Plantery** ♿
High Cross Lane West, Little Canfield, Dunmow, Essex CM6 1TD
Ⓣ (01371) 872611
Ⓔ info@langthorns.com
Ⓦ www.langthorns.com
Contact: E Cannon
Opening Times: 1000-1700 or dusk (if earlier) 7 days excl. Xmas fortnight.
Min Mail Order UK: £ 20.00
Cat. Cost: Online only.
Credit Cards: Visa, Access, Switch, MasterCard, Delta
Specialities: Wide general range with many unusual plants.
Notes: Mail order any plant under 4ft tall. Mail order not available during spring & summer months. Wheelchair accessible.
Map Ref: E, D2 **OS Grid Ref:** TL592204

ELon **Long House Plants** ♿
The Long House, Church Road, Noak Hill, Romford, Essex RM4 1LD
Ⓣ (01708) 371719
Ⓔ tim@longhouse-plants.co.uk
Ⓦ www.longhouse-plants.co.uk
Contact: Tim Carter
Opening Times: 1000-1700 Fri, Sat & B/hols, 1000-1600 Sun, beginning Mar-end Sep, or by appt.
Cat. Cost: None issued.
Credit Cards: All major credit/debit cards
Specialities: Interesting range of choice trees, shrubs, climbers, roses, grasses, herbaceous perennials & ferns. Many unusual varieties. Specialities incl. *Agapanthus*, *Aster*, *Camellia*, *Hemerocallis*, *Iris sibirica*, *Kniphofia*, *Phlox* & *Symphyotrichum*. Some plants available in small quantities.
Notes: Disabled toilet. Wheelchair accessible.
Map Ref: E, D2 **OS Grid Ref:** TQ554194

EMac **Firecrest Trees & Shrubs Nursery** ♿
Hall Road, Little Bealings, Woodbridge, Suffolk IP13 6LG
Ⓣ (01473) 625937
Ⓕ (01473) 625937
Ⓔ mac@firecrest.org.uk
Ⓦ www.firecrest.org.uk
Contact: Mac McGregor
Opening Times: 0900-1600 Mon-Fri, 1230 Sat.
Min Mail Order UK: Nmc
Cat. Cost: 2 × 1st class (bare-root only).
Credit Cards: None
Specialities: Trees & shrubs. Japanese maples. Bare-root hedging.
Notes: Also sells wholesale. Euro accepted. Wheelchair accessible.

EMal **Marshall's Malmaisons** ♿
Hullwood Barn, Shelley, Ipswich, Suffolk IP7 5RE
Ⓣ (01473) 822400
Ⓜ 07768 454875
Ⓔ jim@malmaisons.plus.com
Ⓦ www.malmaisonsandiris.co.uk
Contact: J M Marshall/Sarah Cook
Opening Times: By appt. only.
Min Mail Order UK: £33.00 incl. p&p
Min Mail Order EU: £36.00 incl. p&p
Cat. Cost: 1st class sae.
Credit Cards: None
Specialities: Nat. Collections of Malmaison Carnations & Cedric Morris Irises. *Iris* stock only available in small quantities.
Notes: Also sells wholesale. Wheelchair accessible.
Map Ref: E, C3 **OS Grid Ref:** TM006394

EMFm **Mill Farm Nursery** ♿
(Office) 26 The Brambles, Middle Rasen, Lincolnshire LN8 3NS
Ⓜ 07940 302674 or 07899 905230
Ⓔ linclan@sky.com
Ⓦ www.millfarmnursery.com
Contact: Robert Parry
Opening Times: 1000-1600 Thu-Sun, Mar-Nov.
Min Mail Order UK: Nmc
Cat. Cost: Sae or email for stock list.
Credit Cards: Maestro, Visa, MasterCard, Electron
Specialities: Traditional nursery growing most plants on site. Hardy perennials & unusual types of difficult to find perennials. All perennials are British grown. Ornamental grasses, varied range of *Miscanthus* cvs, trees & specimen plants. Some stock available in small quantities only.
Notes: Nursery is at Old Gallamore Lane, Middle Rasen, LN8 3US. Two large display borders. Mail order from May 2015, please phone to check seasonal availability. Wheelchair accessible.
Map Ref: E, A1 **OS Grid Ref:** TF091891

EMic **Mickfield Hostas** ♿
The Poplars, Mickfield, Stowmarket, Suffolk IP14 5LH
Ⓣ (01449) 711576
Ⓕ (01449) 711576
Ⓔ mickfieldhostas@btconnect.com
Ⓦ www.mickfieldhostas.co.uk

E

Contact: Mr & Mrs R L C Milton
Opening Times: Nursery open every day, all season.
Min Mail Order UK: Nmc
Min Mail Order EU: Nmc
Cat. Cost: 1st class stamp.
Credit Cards: All, except American Express
Specialities: Nat. Collection of *Hosta* containing over 2000 varieties. See website for details of cvs held & latest availability. Operates a waiting list for rarities & some limited quantity plants only available at nursery. Will divide parent plants for collectors if feasible. Expect to pay more for root divisions of mature plants.
Notes: Delivers to shows. Wheelchair accessible.
Map Ref: E, C3 **OS Grid Ref:** TM136619

EMil **Mill Race Garden Centre** ♿
New Road, Aldham, Colchester, Essex CO6 3QT
Ⓣ (01206) 242521
Ⓔ plantdesk@millracegardencentre.co.uk
Ⓦ www.millracegardencentre.co.uk
Contact: Annette Bayliss
Opening Times: 0900-1730 Mon-Sat, 1000-1630 Sun.
Min Mail Order UK: £9.00
Credit Cards: All major credit/debit cards
Specialities: Stock available in small quantities only.
Notes: Trees & large shrubs not sent by mail order. Wheelchair accessible.
Map Ref: E, C2 **OS Grid Ref:** TL918268

EMOT **Mail Order Trees**
42 Station Road, Fordham, Ely, Cambridgeshire CB7 5LW
Ⓣ 0800 066 5972
Ⓔ info@mailordertrees.co.uk
Ⓦ www.mailordertrees.co.uk
Contact: Michael Simpson
Opening Times: Not open. Mail order only.
Min Mail Order UK: Nmc
Credit Cards: All major credit/debit cards
Specialities: Specialist fruit & ornamental tree growers, offering a range of home-grown evergreen & deciduous shrubs, climbing plants, conifers, soft fruit bushes & hedging plants to buy online.
Notes: Also sells wholesale.

ENBC **Norfolk Bamboo Company**
Vine Cottage, The Drift, Ingoldisthorpe, King's Lynn, Norfolk PE31 6NW
Ⓣ (01485) 543935
Ⓜ 07970 310880
Ⓔ Lewdyer@hotmail.com
Ⓦ www.norfolkbamboo.co.uk
Contact: Lewis Dyer
Opening Times: 1000-1600 Fri & 1000-1400 Sat, Apr-Sep, or by appt.
Min Mail Order UK: £10.00 + p&p
Cat. Cost: 1 × 1st class sae for price list.
Credit Cards: None
Specialities: Bamboos.
Map Ref: E, B2

ENfk **Norfolk Herbs** ♿
Blackberry Farm, Dillington, Dereham, Norfolk NR19 2QD
Ⓣ (01362) 860812
Ⓕ (01362) 860812
Ⓔ info@norfolkherbs.co.uk
Ⓦ www.norfolkherbs.co.uk
Contact: Rosemary or Oliver Clifton-Sprigg
Opening Times: 0900-1700 Mon-Sat, 1000-1600 Sun, Apr-Aug. 1000-1600 Fri & Sat, Feb, Oct & Nov. 1000-1600 Wed-Sat, Mar, Sept & Dec. Closed from Xmas to end Jan. To visit at other times, please contact nursery.
Min Mail Order UK: £6.90
Cat. Cost: 2 × 2nd class.
Credit Cards: All major credit/debit cards
Specialities: Growers & suppliers of naturally raised culinary, medicinal & aromatic herb plants. Bay trees & scented pelagoniums.
Notes: Established 1986. Sells from nursery, online & at local shows. A founding member of Norfolk Nursery Network. Also sells wholesale. Delivers to shows. Wheelchair accessible.
Map Ref: E, B2 **OS Grid Ref:** TF967150

ENor **Norfolk Lavender** ♿
Caley Mill, Heacham, King's Lynn, Norfolk PE31 7JE
Ⓣ (01485) 570384
Ⓜ 07787 550286
Ⓕ (01485) 571176
Ⓔ info@norfolk-lavender.co.uk
Ⓦ www.norfolk-lavender.co.uk
Contact: Tony Inwood
Opening Times: 0900-1700 7 days, Apr-Oct. 0900-1600 7 days, Nov-Mar.
Min Mail Order UK: Nmc
Cat. Cost: Free.
Credit Cards: All, except American Express
Specialities: Nat. Collection of *Lavandula*, sect. *L. dentata* & *L. pterostoechas*.

ENun **Twelve Nunns** ◆
16 Carisbrook Grove, Stamford, Lincolnshire PE9 2GF
Ⓣ (01778) 590455
Ⓔ penny@twelvenunns.co.uk
Ⓦ www.twelvenunns.co.uk
Contact: Penny Dawson
Opening Times: Not open. Mail order only.

Min Mail Order UK: Nmc
Min Mail Order EU: Nmc
Cat. Cost: Free.
Credit Cards: All major credit/debit cards
Specialities: *Helleborus* (incl. plants with "Harvington" prefix.), *Roscoea*, *Erythronium* & *Trillium*. Plants bred, propagated & grown on nursery.
Notes: Also sells wholesale.

EOHP **OLD HALL PLANTS**
1 The Old Hall, Barsham, Beccles, Suffolk NR34 8HB
Ⓣ (01502) 717475
Ⓔ info@oldhallplants.co.uk
Ⓦ www.oldhallplants.co.uk
Contact: Janet Elliott
Opening Times: By appt. only. Please phone first.
Min Mail Order UK: Nmc
Min Mail Order EU: Nmc
Cat. Cost: 4 × 1st class.
Credit Cards: Paypal
Specialities: A variety of rare herbs, house plants. Some plants available in small quantities.
Notes: Paypal accepted for overseas orders only. Cheques not accepted. Partial wheelchair access.
Map Ref: E, C3 **OS Grid Ref:** TM396904

EPau **PAUGERS PLANTS LTD**
Bury Road, Depden, Bury St Edmunds, Suffolk IP29 4BU
Ⓣ (01284) 850527
Ⓜ 07906 618603
Ⓔ enquiries@paugers-plants.co.uk
Ⓦ www.paugers-plants.co.uk
Contact: Geraldine Arnold
Opening Times: 0900-1730 Wed-Sat, 1000-1700 Sun & B/hols, 1st Mar-30th Nov.
Min Mail Order UK: Nmc
Cat. Cost: None issued.
Credit Cards: All major credit/debit cards
Specialities: Hardy shrubs & perennials in large or small quantities.
Notes: Also sells wholesale.
Map Ref: E, C2 **OS Grid Ref:** TL783568

EPed **PERNEWOOD PLANTS** ♿
Popes Hall, Fersfield Road, South Lopham, Diss, Norfolk IP22 2JY
Ⓜ 07870 495186
Ⓔ info@pernewoodplants.co.uk
Ⓦ www.pernewoodplants.co.uk
Contact: Kevan Milbourne
Opening Times: Please contact for appt.
Min Mail Order UK: £25.00
Credit Cards: All, except American Express
Specialities: Small family run online plant nursery, offering a wide range of hardy perennials, ornamental grasses and shade-loving plants and ferns. Plants UK sourced or raised from own nursery stock specimens.
Notes: Wheelchair accessible.
Map Ref: E, C3 **OS Grid Ref:** TM055816

EPfP **THE PLACE FOR PLANTS** ♿
East Bergholt Place, East Bergholt, Suffolk CO7 6UP
Ⓣ (01206) 299224
Ⓕ (01206) 299229
Ⓔ sales@placeforplants.co.uk
Ⓦ www.placeforplants.co.uk
Contact: Marie Pertwee
Opening Times: 1000-1700 (or dusk if earlier) 7 days. Closed Easter Sun. Garden open Mar-Oct.
Min Mail Order UK: Nmc
Cat. Cost: Online only.
Credit Cards: All major credit/debit cards
Specialities: Wide range of specialist & popular plants. Nat. Collection of Deciduous *Euonymus*. 20 acre mature garden with free access to RHS members during season (excl. Sun).
Notes: Mail order from Sep-Feb. Delivers to shows. Euro accepted. Wheelchair accessible.
Map Ref: E, C3

EPom **POMONA FRUITS LTD**
Pomona House, 12 Third Avenue, Walton-on-the-Naze, Essex CO14 8JU
Ⓣ (01255) 440410
Ⓕ (01255) 440420
Ⓔ Info@PomonaFruits.co.uk
Ⓦ www.PomonaFruits.co.uk
Contact: Ming Yang/Claire Higgins
Opening Times: Not open. Mail order only.
Min Mail Order UK: Nmc
Cat. Cost: Free.
Credit Cards: All major credit/debit cards
Specialities: Fruit stock.

EPot **POTTERTONS NURSERY** ♿
Moortown Road, Nettleton, Caistor, Lincolnshire LN7 6HX
Ⓣ (01472) 851714
Ⓕ (01472) 852580
Ⓔ sales@pottertons.co.uk
Ⓦ www.pottertons.co.uk
Contact: Robert Potterton
Opening Times: 1000-1600 Tue-Sat, Mar-Oct. By appt. only Nov-Feb.
Min Mail Order UK: Nmc
Min Mail Order EU: Nmc
Cat. Cost: £2.00 in stamps
Credit Cards: MasterCard, Visa
Specialities: Alpines, dwarf bulbs & woodland

E

plants. Hardy orchids & *Pleione*.
Notes: External talks nationally & internationally to garden clubs & societies. Group nursery tours by arrangement. Delivers to shows. Euro accepted. Wheelchair accessible.
Map Ref: E, A1 **OS Grid Ref:** TA091001

EPPr **THE PLANTSMAN'S PREFERENCE** ♿
Church Road, South Lopham, Diss, Norfolk IP22 2LW
Ⓣ (01379) 710810
Ⓜ 07799 855559
Ⓔ tim@plantpref.co.uk
Ⓦ www.plantpref.co.uk
Contact: Tim Fuller
Opening Times: 0930-1700 Fri, Sat & Sun Mar-Oct. Other times by appt.
Min Mail Order UK: Nmc
Min Mail Order EU: Nmc
Cat. Cost: Online only.
Credit Cards: All major credit/debit cards
Specialities: Hardy geraniums & ornamental grasses. Unusual & interesting perennials incl. shade/woodland. Some choice shrubs esp. *Caprifoliaceae*. Nat. Collection of *Molinia*.
Notes: Delivers to shows. Wheelchair accessible.
Map Ref: E, C3 **OS Grid Ref:** TM041819

EPri **PRIORY PLANTS** ♿
1 Covey Cottages, Hintlesham, Nr Ipswich, Suffolk IP8 3NY
Ⓣ (01473) 652656
Ⓜ 07798 627618
Ⓕ (01473) 652656
Ⓔ sue.mann3@btinternet.com
Ⓦ www.prioryplants.co.uk
Contact: Sue Mann
Opening Times: By appt. only. Please ring first to avoid disappointment.
Min Mail Order UK: £15.00 + p&p
Min Mail Order EU: £25.00
Cat. Cost: Online only.
Credit Cards: None
Specialities: Cottage garden perennials, as well as increasing range of South African plants. *Agapanthus, Astrantia, Dierama, Dietes, Geum*, Siberian *Iris, Kniphofia, Nerine, Papaver, Tritonia, Tulbaghia* & *Watsonia*.
Notes: Sells at plant fairs & agricultural shows. Also sells wholesale. Delivers to shows. Wheelchair accessible.
Map Ref: E, C3 **OS Grid Ref:** TM070448

EPts **POTASH NURSERY** ♿
Cow Green, Bacton, Stowmarket, Suffolk IP14 4HJ
Ⓣ (01449) 781671
Ⓔ enquiries@potashnursery.co.uk
Ⓦ www.potashnursery.co.uk
Contact: M W Clare
Opening Times: Pre-ordered plants can be collected by appt. only.
Min Mail Order UK: £21.00
Cat. Cost: 1 × 1st class.
Credit Cards: Visa, Delta, MasterCard
Specialities: *Fuchsia*.
Notes: Peat-free. Delivers to shows. Wheelchair accessible.
Map Ref: E, C3 **OS Grid Ref:** TM0565NE

ERCP **ROSE COTTAGE PLANTS**
Bay Tree Farm, Epping Green, Essex CM16 6PU
Ⓣ (01992) 573775
Ⓔ anne@rosecottageplants.co.uk
Ⓦ www.rosecottageplants.co.uk
Contact: Anne & Jack Barnard
Opening Times: By appt. & for special events (see website for details).
Min Mail Order UK: Nmc
Min Mail Order EU: £20.00
Cat. Cost: Online only.
Credit Cards: All, except American Express
Specialities: Bulbs.
Notes: Mail order, bulbs only. Delivers to shows.
Map Ref: E, D2 **OS Grid Ref:** TL435053

ERea **READS NURSERY**
Douglas Farm, Bungay, Suffolk NR35 2JG
Ⓣ (01986) 895555
Ⓔ plants@readsnursery.co.uk
Ⓦ www.readsnursery.co.uk
Contact: Stephen Read
Opening Times: Not open. Mail order only.
Min Mail Order UK: Nmc
Min Mail Order EU: Nmc
Cat. Cost: Free.
Credit Cards: All major credit/debit cards
Specialities: Ornamental & unusual fruit trees. Soft fruit. *Magnolia*.

ERod **THE RODINGS PLANTERY** ♿
Anchor Lane, Abbess Roding, Essex CM5 0JW
Ⓣ (01279) 876421
Ⓜ 07790 020940
Ⓔ janeandandy@therodingsplantery.co.uk
Ⓦ www.therodingsplantery.co.uk
Contact: Jane & Andy Mogridge
Opening Times: 1000-1600 Wed & Sat. By appt. only. Occasional open days, please phone for details.
Min Mail Order UK: Nmc
Min Mail Order EU: £500.00 + p&p
Cat. Cost: 3 × 1st class.
Credit Cards: None
Specialities: Bamboos. Rare & unusual trees.

Notes: Also sells wholesale. Delivers to shows. Euro accepted. Wheelchair accessible.
Map Ref: E, D2

ESgl **Seagate Irises** ♿
A17 Long Sutton By-Pass, Long Sutton, Lincolnshire PE12 9RX
Ⓣ (01406) 365138
Ⓜ 07887 856389
Ⓔ sales@irises.co.uk
Ⓦ www.irises.co.uk
Contact: Julian Browse or Wendy Browse
Opening Times: 1000-1700 daily Apr-mid Jul. Please phone for appt. mid-Jul to Mar.
Cat. Cost: £3.50 or €8.00.
Credit Cards: Maestro, Visa, MasterCard
Specialities: Different types of *Iris*, bearded, beardless & species hybrids with about 1000 varieties in all, both historic & modern. Some only available in small quantities. Many container-grown available to callers.
Notes: Wheelchair accessible.
Map Ref: E, B2 **OS Grid Ref:** TF437218

EShb **Shrubland Park Nurseries**
Maltings Farm, Whatfield Road, Elmsett, Ipswich, Suffolk IP7 6LZ
Ⓣ (01473) 657012
Ⓜ 07890 527744
Ⓔ gill@shrublandparknurseries.co.uk
Ⓦ www.shrublandparknurseries.co.uk
Contact: Gill & Catherine Stitt
Opening Times: 1000-1600 daily, 1st Mar-30th Oct. 1000-1600 Fri, Sat & Sun, 1st Nov-1st Mar. Please ring or check website for any changes if travelling a long distance.
Min Mail Order UK: Nmc
Min Mail Order EU: Nmc
Cat. Cost: 6 × 2nd class or free by email.
Credit Cards: All major credit/debit cards, Paypal
Specialities: Conservatory plants, succulents, hardy perennials, climbers, shrubs, ferns & grasses.
Notes: Delivers to shows.
Map Ref: E, C3 **OS Grid Ref:** TM052466

ESMi **Straight Mile Nursery Gardens** ♿
Ongar Road, Pilgrims Hatch, Brentwood, Essex CM15 9SA
Ⓣ (01277) 374439
Ⓔ gdlsisley@aol.com
Ⓦ www.straightmile.net
Contact: David Sisley
Opening Times: 1000-1700, 7 days (but closed some Weds, phone first.)
Min Mail Order UK: Nmc
Cat. Cost: Online only.
Credit Cards: All, except American Express
Specialities: General nursery stock. Japanese maples, *Epimedium*. Some in small quantities only.
Notes: Delivers to shows. Wheelchair accessible.
Map Ref: E, D2 **OS Grid Ref:** TQ571964

ESps **Simpson's Nurseries Ltd** ♿
42 Station Road, Fordham, Ely, Cambridgeshire CB7 5LW
Ⓣ (01638) 720194
Ⓕ (01638) 720961
Ⓔ simpstree@aol.com
Ⓦ www.simpsonsnurseries.com
Contact: Dave Simpson
Opening Times: 0900-1700.
Credit Cards: All major credit/debit cards
Specialities: Family run business. Specialist plant and tree centre with wide selection of plants. Always fully stocked with over 300 varieties of shrubs & 300 varieties of herbaceous and perennial plants, with over 90% of stock home grown.
Notes: Wheelchair accessible.
Map Ref: E, C2 **OS Grid Ref:** TL621702

EStr **Strictly Daylilies**
2 Primes Corner, Histon, Cambridgeshire CB24 9AG
Ⓣ (01223) 236239
Ⓜ 07765 236880
Ⓔ info@strictlydaylilies.com
Ⓦ www.strictlydaylilies.com
Contact: Paula & Chris Dyason
Opening Times: Mail order only. Open by appt.
Min Mail Order UK: Nmc
Min Mail Order EU: Nmc
Cat. Cost: No charge.
Credit Cards: All major credit/debit cards
Specialities: *Hemerocallis*. Some stock available in small quantities only.
Notes: Also sells wholesale. Delivers to shows.

ESty **Style Roses** ♿
(Office) Highworth, 56 Spalding Road, Holbeach, Spalding, Lincolnshire PE12 7HG
Ⓣ (01406) 424089
Ⓜ 07760 626750 or 07780 860415
Ⓕ (01406) 490006
Ⓔ mail@styleroses.co.uk
Ⓦ www.styleroses.co.uk
Contact: Margaret Styles
Opening Times: Opening times vary on workload so customers should phone to make an appt. before visiting. Nursery is at Cackle Hill Farm PE12 8AG.
Min Mail Order UK: Nmc
Min Mail Order EU: Nmc
Cat. Cost: Free in UK.
Credit Cards: MasterCard, Visa, Maestro

E

Specialities: Standard & bush roses.
Notes: Bush roses available mail order to mainland UK all year round (Highlands & Islands may be subject to additional courier charges). Standard roses mail order only Nov-Mar as bare-root plants or by collection in pots from Shows all year round. Export to EU during bare-root season Nov-Mar. Exports beyond EU subject to Plant Health Requirements (not USA). Also sells wholesale. Delivers to shows. Wheelchair accessible.
Map Ref: E, B2

ESwi **SWINES MEADOW FARM NURSERY** ♿ ◆
47 Towngate East, Market Deeping, Peterborough PE6 8LQ
Ⓣ 01778 343340
Ⓜ 07432 627766
Ⓔ ceveandsons@btconnect.com
Ⓦ www.swinesmeadowfarmnursery.co.uk
Contact: Colin Ward
Opening Times: 0900-1600 Mon-Sat, 1000-1600 Sun. Closed Jan. Open by appt. only in Jan.
Min Mail Order UK: £10.00
Min Mail Order EU: £10.00
Credit Cards: All, except American Express
Specialities: Hardy exotics, tree ferns, bamboos & phormiums. Wollemi pine stockist. Many specialities available in small quantities only.
Notes: Delivers to shows. Euro accepted. Wheelchair accessible.
Map Ref: E, B1 **OS Grid Ref:** TF150113

EThi **THISTLEFIELD PLANTS AND DESIGN**
65 Westgate Street, Shouldham, Kings Lynn, Norfolk PE33 0BL
Ⓣ (01366) 347365
Ⓜ 07899 994071
Ⓕ (01366) 347365
Ⓔ paul@thistlefieldplants.co.uk
Ⓦ www.thistlefieldplants.co.uk
Contact: Paul Welford
Opening Times: Not open. Sells at plant fairs & shows only.
Min Mail Order UK: Nmc
Cat. Cost: Online only.
Credit Cards: None
Specialities: Perennials. *Tricyrtis* available in small quantities only.
Notes: Delivers to shows.

ETho **THORNCROFT CLEMATIS LTD** ♿
The Lings, Reymerston, Norwich, Norfolk NR9 4QG
Ⓣ (01953) 850407
Ⓔ sales@thorncroftclematis.co.uk
Ⓦ www.thorncroftclematis.co.uk
Contact: Peter Skeggs-Gooch
Opening Times: Not open regularly. Mail order only but orders can be collected by prior arrangement. Telephones manned 0900-1600 Mon-Sat.
Min Mail Order UK: Nmc
Min Mail Order EU: Nmc
Cat. Cost: 6 × 2nd class.
Credit Cards: All major credit/debit cards
Specialities: *Clematis.*
Notes: Events & Open Days held throughout the year. See website or phone for details. Delivers to shows. Toilets available. Wheelchair accessible.

ETod **TODD'S BOTANICS**
West Street, Coggeshall, Colchester, Essex CO6 1NT
Ⓣ (01376) 561212
Ⓔ info@toddsbotanics.co.uk
Ⓦ www.toddsbotanics.co.uk
Contact: Mark Macdonald
Opening Times: Not open, except by appt. Mail order only.
Min Mail Order UK: Nmc
Cat. Cost: Online only.
Credit Cards: All major credit/debit cards
Specialities: Hardy exotics, herbaceous. Bamboos, palms, ferns, grasses, *Canna* & *Hedychium*. Olives, incl. named varieties. *Citrus*. Drought-resistant plants.
Notes: Not all plants available mail order, contact nursery for details. Also sells wholesale. Delivers to shows. Euro accepted. Nursery partially accessible for wheelchairs.

EUJe **URBAN JUNGLE**
Ringland Lane, Old Costessey, Norwich, Norfolk NR8 5BG
Ⓣ (01603) 744997
Ⓕ (0709) 2366869
Ⓔ lizzy@urbanjungle.uk.com
Ⓦ www.urbanjungle.uk.com
Contact: Elizabeth Browne
Opening Times: 1000-1700 1st Feb-31st Oct 7 days incl B/hols. 1000-1600 Nov-Dec Thu, Fri, Sat, Sun. Closed Jan.
Min Mail Order UK: Nmc
Min Mail Order EU: Nmc
Credit Cards: All major credit/debit cards
Specialities: Wide range of choice plants from exotic bedding to hardy evergreens.
Notes: Display gardens & living walls. Delivers to shows. Limited wheelchair access.
Map Ref: E, B3 **OS Grid Ref:** TG153127

EVic **VICTORIAN VIOLAS**
85 Fulmar Road, Lincoln, Lincolnshire LN6 0RX
Ⓣ (01522) 686343
Ⓔ victorianviolasinfo@fsmail.net

Ⓦ www.victorianviolas.co.uk
Contact: Robert Chapman
Opening Times: Not open.
Min Mail Order UK: Nmc
Cat. Cost: 2 × 1st class or online.
Credit Cards: None
Specialities: Hardy perennial violas (summer flowering).
Notes: Delivers to shows.

EWay **Wayside Water Garden Plants**
Blackmore Road, Doddinghurst, Brentwood, Essex CM15 0HU
Ⓜ 07709 791317
Ⓔ sales@watergardenplants.co.uk
Ⓦ www.watergardenplants.co.uk
Contact: Anna Robinson
Opening Times: Mail order only. With prior notice, plants may be collected during the following times: 1000-1700 Wed-Sun.
Min Mail Order UK: Nmc
Min Mail Order EU: Nmc
Cat. Cost: Online.
Credit Cards: All major credit/debit cards
Specialities: Range of water garden plants: waterlilies; floating plants; oxygenating plants; marginals; marsh plants. Some stock in small quantities.
Map Ref: E, D2 **OS Grid Ref:** TQ585995

EWes **West Acre Gardens** ♿
Tumbleyhill Road, West Acre, King's Lynn, Norfolk PE32 1UJ
Ⓣ (01760) 755562
Ⓔ info@westacregardens.co.uk
Ⓦ www.westacregardens.co.uk
Contact: J J Tuite
Opening Times: 1000-1700 7 days 1st Feb-30th Nov. Other times by appt.
Cat. Cost: None issued.
Credit Cards: Visa, MasterCard, Delta, Switch
Specialities: Very wide selection of herbaceous & other garden plants incl. *Rhodohypoxis*, *Primula auricula* & *Galanthus*.
Notes: Delivers to shows. Wheelchair accessible.
Map Ref: E, B2 **OS Grid Ref:** TF792182

EWld **Woodlands**
Peppin Lane, Fotherby, Louth, Lincolnshire LN11 0UW
Ⓣ (01507) 603586
Ⓔ annbobarmstrong@btinternet.com
Ⓦ www.woodlandsplants.co.uk
Contact: Ann Armstrong
Opening Times: Flexible, but please phone or email to avoid disappointment.
Min Mail Order UK: Nmc
Min Mail Order EU: Nmc
Cat. Cost: None issued.
Credit Cards: None
Specialities: Small but interesting range of unusual plants, esp. woodland, *Codonopsis* and *Salvia*, all grown on the nursery in limited quantity. National Collection of *Codonopsis*.
Notes: Mature garden, art gallery & refreshments. Euro accepted.
Map Ref: E, A2 **OS Grid Ref:** TF322918

EWoo **Woottens Plants** ♿
Wenhaston, Blackheath, Halesworth, Suffolk IP19 9HD
Ⓣ (01502) 478258
Ⓕ (01502) 478888
Ⓔ info@woottensplants.co.uk
Ⓦ www.woottensplants.co.uk
Contact: Elizabeth Loftus
Opening Times: 0930-1700 7 days.
Min Mail Order UK: Nmc
Min Mail Order EU: Nmc
Cat. Cost: Online only.
Credit Cards: All, except American Express
Specialities: *Pelargonium*, *Hemerocallis*, *Primula auricula*, *Iris*, *Chrysanthemum* & *Clivia*.
Notes: Also sells wholesale. Delivers to shows. Wheelchair accessible.
Map Ref: E, C3 **OS Grid Ref:** TM426749

EWTr **Walnut Tree Garden Nursery**
Flymoor Lane, Rocklands, Attleborough, Norfolk NR17 1BP
Ⓣ (01953) 488163
Ⓔ info@wtgn.co.uk
Ⓦ www.wtgn.co.uk
Contact: Jim Paine & Clare Billington
Opening Times: 0900-1800 Tue-Sun Feb-Nov & B/hols.
Min Mail Order UK: Nmc
Cat. Cost: Online.
Credit Cards: All major credit/debit cards
Map Ref: E, B2 **OS Grid Ref:** TL978973

Scotland

GAbr **Abriachan Nurseries** ♿
Loch Ness Side, Inverness, Inverness-shire IV3 8LA
Ⓣ (01463) 861232
Ⓔ info@lochnessgarden.com
Ⓦ www.lochnessgarden.com
Contact: Mr & Mrs D Davidson
Opening Times: 0900-1900 daily (dusk if earlier) Feb-Nov.
Min Mail Order UK: Nmc
Cat. Cost: 4 × 1st class.
Credit Cards: All major credit/debit cards
Specialities: Herbaceous perennials, old-fashioned *Primula*, *Helianthemum*, hardy

geraniums, *Sempervivum* & *Primula auricula*.
Notes: Delivers to shows. Wheelchair access to nursery only.
Map Ref: G, B2 **OS Grid Ref:** NH571347

G

GAgs **Angusplants**
3 Balfour Cottages, Menmuir, By Brechin, Angus DD9 7RN
Ⓣ (01356) 660280
Ⓜ 07972 026109
Ⓔ alison@angusplants.co.uk
Ⓦ www.angusplants.co.uk
Contact: Dr Alison S. Goldie & Mark A. Hutson
Opening Times: By appt. only. Please phone first.
Min Mail Order UK: Nmc
Min Mail Order EU: Nmc
Cat. Cost: 2 × 2nd large letter stamps.
Credit Cards: None
Specialities: *Primula auricula*, Nat. Collection of Alpine Auriculas.
Notes: Mail order available all year.
Map Ref: G, B3 **OS Grid Ref:** NO528643

GBin **Binny Plants** ♿
West Lodge, Binny Estate, Ecclesmachan Road, Nr Broxburn, West Lothian EH52 6NL
Ⓣ (01506) 858931
Ⓜ 07753 626117
Ⓔ contact@binnyplants.com
Ⓦ www.binnyplants.com
Contact: Billy Carruthers & David Wong
Opening Times: 1000-1700 7 days. Closed over Xmas & New Year.
Min Mail Order UK: £25.00
Min Mail Order EU: £25.00
Cat. Cost: £2.50 refundable on ordering.
Credit Cards: Visa, MasterCard, EuroCard, Maestro
Specialities: A large range of herbaceous perennials, grasses & ferns incl. *Astilbe*, *Bergenia*, *Geranium*, *Hosta*, *Molinia*, *Paeonia*, *Persicaria* & *Iris*.
Notes: Mail order Sep-Apr only. Also sells wholesale. Exports beyond the EU. Euro accepted. Wheelchair accessible.
Map Ref: G, C3 **OS Grid Ref:** NT050732

GBuc **Buckland Plants**
Whinnieliggate, Kirkcudbright, Kirkcudbrightshire DG6 4XP
Ⓣ (01557) 331323
Ⓕ (01557) 331323
Ⓔ via website
Ⓦ www.bucklandplants.co.uk
Contact: Rob Asbridge
Opening Times: 1000-1700 Thu-Sun 1st Apr-1st Oct & B/hols.
Specialities: A very wide range of scarce herbaceous, woodland plants & larger alpines incl. *Anemone*, *Cardamine*, *Erythronium*, *Helleborus*, *Lilium*, *Meconopsis*, *Nomocharis*, *Primula*, *Tricyrtis* & *Trillium*.
Notes: Euro accepted. Assisted wheelchair accessibility.
Map Ref: G, D2 **OS Grid Ref:** NX719524

GCal **Cally Gardens** ♿
Gatehouse of Fleet, Castle Douglas, Kirkcudbrightshire DG7 2DJ
Ⓣ (01557) 815029 recorded information only.
Ⓔ info@callygardens.co.uk
Ⓦ www.callygardens.co.uk
Contact: Michael Wickenden
Opening Times: 1000-1730 Sat-Sun, 1400-1730 Tue-Fri. Easter Sat-last Sun in Sept.
Min Mail Order UK: £15.00 + p&p
Cat. Cost: 3 × 1st class.
Credit Cards: None
Specialities: Unusual perennials & grasses. Some rare shrubs, climbers & conservatory plants. 3500 varieties growing in an 2.7 acre walled garden built in the 1760s.
Notes: Also sells wholesale. Wheelchair accessible.
Map Ref: G, D2 **OS Grid Ref:** NX604549

GCra **Craigieburn Garden**
Craigieburn House, by Moffat, Dumfriesshire DG10 9LF
Ⓣ (01683) 221250
Ⓜ 07824 390519
Ⓔ ajmw1@aol.com
Ⓦ www.craigieburngarden.co.uk
Contact: Janet & Andrew Wheatcroft
Opening Times: 1030-1800 daily, Easter-31st Oct. Other times by appt.
Specialities: *Meconopsis* plants for damp gardens, herbaceous perennials.
Notes: Partial wheelchair accessible.
Map Ref: G, D3

GCrg **Craigiehall Nursery**
Carnwath, Lanark, Lanarkshire ML11 8LH
Ⓣ 01555 840027 (answering machine)
Ⓕ 01555 840027
Ⓔ sales@craigiehallnursery.co.uk
Ⓦ www.craigiehallnursery.co.uk
Contact: Innes Hogg
Opening Times: Not open. Mail order only.
Min Mail Order UK: Nmc
Cat. Cost: Online only.
Credit Cards: All major credit/debit cards
Specialities: A very wide range of alpine and rock garden plants; over 500 different varieties on the nursery. Some are quite common, others much less so.
Notes: Online sales only, no telephone ordering.

GCro **Croft 16 Daffodils**
16 Midtown of Inverasdale,
Poolewe, Achnasheen, Ross-shire
IV22 2LW
Ⓣ (01445) 781717
Ⓔ sales@croft16daffodils.co.uk
Ⓦ www.croft16daffodils.co.uk
Contact: Duncan & Kate Donald
Opening Times: Not open. Mail order only.
Min Mail Order UK: Nmc
Min Mail Order EU: Nmc
Cat. Cost: Online. Customers without internet access send 4 × 1st for sales list without pictures.
Credit Cards: Paypal
Specialities: Nat. Collection of Daffodils bred pre-1930. Some stocks only available in small quantities. A waiting list for *desiderata* is in operation.
Notes: Limited availability, so please order by late Jun if possible. Orders unfulfilled in one season will take priority the following year. Customers outside the EU should contact nursery.
Map Ref: G, A1 **OS Grid Ref:** NG822851

GDun **Dunskey Gardens & Maze** ♿
Portpatrick, Stranraer, Wigtownshire
DG9 8TJ
Ⓣ (01776) 810905
Ⓜ 07899 092070
Ⓕ (01776) 810581
Ⓔ gabygardeners@btinternet.com
Ⓦ www.dunskey.com
Contact: Gabrielle Reynolds
Opening Times: 1000-1600 w/ends only Feb, 1000-1700 daily Easter-Oct. See website for details.
Credit Cards: All major credit/debit cards
Specialities: Broad range, propagated from the gardens, incl. bulbs, tender perennials, herbaceous, trees and shrubs. Available in small quantities only. National Collections of *Clianthus*, *Nicotiana* & *Sutherlandia*.
Notes: Dunskey Estate Walled Garden & Maze open to the public. Sells at local plant shows. Wheelchair accessible.
Map Ref: G, D2 **OS Grid Ref:** NX004560

GEdr **Edrom Nurseries**
Coldingham, Eyemouth, Berwickshire
TD14 5TZ
Ⓣ (01890) 771386
Ⓕ (01890) 771387
Ⓔ info@edrom-nurseries.co.uk
Ⓦ www.edrom-nurseries.co.uk
Contact: Mr Terry Hunt
Opening Times: 0900-1700 Thu, Fri, Sat & Mon (closed Tue- & Wed), 1000-1600 Sun.
Min Mail Order UK: Nmc
Min Mail Order EU: Nmc
Cat. Cost: Free.
Credit Cards: All major credit/debit cards
Specialities: *Cypripedium*, *Epimedium*, *Gentiana*, *Primula*, *Meconopsis*, *Rhodohypoxis*, *Trillium* & Japanese *Hepatica*.
Notes: Delivers to shows.
Map Ref: G, C3 **OS Grid Ref:** NT873663

GFai **Fairholm Plants**
Fairholm, Larkhall, Lanarkshire ML9 2UQ
Ⓣ (01698) 881671
Ⓕ (01698) 888135
Ⓔ fairholm.plants@stevenson-hamilton.co.uk
Contact: Mrs J M Hamilton
Opening Times: Apr-Oct by appt.
Min Mail Order UK: Nmc
Cat. Cost: 1 × 2nd class for descriptive list.
Credit Cards: None
Specialities: *Abutilon* & unusual half-hardy perennials esp. South African. Nat. Collection of *Abutilon* cvs. Plants & rooted cuttings available in small quantities only.
Notes: Mail order for young/small plants. Euro accepted.
Map Ref: G, C2 **OS Grid Ref:** NS754515

GGGa **Glendoick Gardens Ltd** ♿
Glendoick, Perth, Perthshire PH2 7NS
Ⓣ (01738) 860205
Ⓔ orders@glendoick.com
Ⓦ www.glendoick.com
Contact: Kenneth Cox
Opening Times: Nursery not open to the public. Garden centre open 0900-1730 (summer), 0900-1700 (winter) 7 days. Gardens open Apr & May, details on website.
Min Mail Order UK: £50.00
Min Mail Order EU: £100.00
Cat. Cost: £1.00.
Credit Cards: All, except American Express
Specialities: Rhododendrons, azaleas and ericaceous, *Primula* & *Meconopsis*. Plants from wild seed. Many catalogue plants available at garden centre. 3 Nat. Collections.
Notes: Exports beyond EU. Wheelchair access to Garden Centre.
Map Ref: G, C3

GJos **Jo's Garden Enterprise** ♿
Easter Balmungle Farm, Eathie Road,
by Rosemarkie, Ross-shire
IV10 8SL
Ⓣ (01381) 621006
Ⓔ jos_garden_enterprise@hotmail.co.uk
Contact: Joanna Chance
Opening Times: 1000 to dusk, 7 days.
Cat. Cost: None.
Credit Cards: None
Specialities: Alpines & herbaceous perennials. Selection of native wild flowers.

G

Notes: Wheelchair accessible.
Map Ref: G, B2 **OS Grid Ref:** NH600742

GKev **KEVOCK GARDEN PLANTS**
16 Kevock Road, Lasswade,
Midlothian EH18 1HT
Ⓣ 0131 454 0660
Ⓜ 07811 321585
Ⓕ 0131 454 0660
Ⓔ sales@kevockgarden.co.uk
Ⓦ www.kevockgarden.co.uk
Contact: Stella Rankin
Opening Times: Not open. Mail order & plant stalls only.
Min Mail Order UK: £25.00
Min Mail Order EU: £25.00
Cat. Cost: 3 × 1st class.
Credit Cards: Visa, MasterCard, Switch
Specialities: Chinese & Himalayan plants. *Androsace*, *Daphne*, *Paeonia*, *Primula*, *Meconopsis*, *Iris*, woodland plants, alpines, rock plants, marginal & bog plants, bulbs, Sino-himalayan trees & shrubs.
Notes: Also sells wholesale. Delivers to shows. Euro accepted.

GKin **KINLOCHLAICH GARDEN PLANT CENTRE**
Appin, Argyll
PA38 4BB
Ⓜ 07881 525754
Ⓔ fiona@kinlochlaich.plus.com
Ⓦ www.kinlochlaichgardencentre.co.uk
Contact: Fiona Hutchison
Opening Times: 0900-1730, 7 days.
Cat. Cost: None issued
Credit Cards: All major credit/debit cards
Specialities: Hardy shrubs, trees, azaleas, perennials. Also Gulf Stream plants such as *Tropaeolum*, *Embothrium*, *Eucryphia*, *Drymis* & more. Good selection of hardy seaside plants.
Notes: Do not offer mail order but will post where possible.
Map Ref: G, C2

GLet **LETHAM PLANTS**
11a Letham Mains Holdings,
Haddington, East Lothian
EH41 4NW
Ⓣ (01620) 822350
Ⓜ 07842 211712
Ⓔ lethamplants@hotmail.co.uk
Ⓦ www.letham-plants.co.uk
Contact: Caroline Samuel
Opening Times: By appt. only.
Min Mail Order UK: Nmc
Min Mail Order EU: Nmc
Credit Cards: All major credit/debit cards
Specialities: *Astrantia*, *Dicentra*.
Notes: Also sells wholesale. Delivers to shows. Euro accepted.
Map Ref: G, C3 **OS Grid Ref:** NT487730

GLog **LOGIE STEADING PLANTS** ♿
Forres, Moray IV36 2QN
Ⓣ (01309) 611222 or 611278
Ⓕ (01309) 611300
Ⓔ panny@logie.co.uk
Ⓦ www.logie.co.uk
Contact: Mrs Panny Laing
Opening Times: 1030-1700 hours, 7 days, April-Christmas.
Credit Cards: All major credit/debit cards
Specialities: Unusual hardy plants, grown in Scotland for Scottish gardens. Large range of hardy geraniums, bold herbaceous plants, grasses & marginal plants.
Notes: Logie House Garden open every day. Café, farm shop, art gallery, secondhand books, whisky & wine, river walk, heritage centre. Wheelchair accessible.
Map Ref: G, B2 **OS Grid Ref:** NJ006504

GMaP **MACPLANTS** ♿
Berrybank Nursery, 5 Boggs Holdings,
Pencaitland, East Lothian EH34 5BA
Ⓣ (01875) 341179
Ⓕ (01875) 340842
Ⓔ sales@macplants.co.uk
Ⓦ www.macplants.co.uk
Contact: Gavin McNaughton
Opening Times: 1030-1700 7 days, Mar-end Sep. 1030-1700 Mon-Fri, Oct. Closed Nov-end Feb.
Min Mail Order UK: Nmc
Cat. Cost: 4 × 2nd class.
Credit Cards: MasterCard, Switch, Visa
Specialities: Herbaceous perennials, alpines, hardy ferns, violas & grasses. *Meconopsis*. National Collection of *Sanguisorba*.
Notes: Also sells wholesale. Delivers to shows. Wheelchair accessible.
Map Ref: G, C3 **OS Grid Ref:** NT447703

GMcL **MCLAREN'S NURSERIES**
Lochlibo Road, Uplawmoor, Barrhead,
East Renfrewshire G78 4DN
Ⓣ (01505) 850666
Ⓕ (01505) 850706
Ⓔ mclarensplants@aol.com
Contact: Adam McGowan
Opening Times: 0800-1630 Mon-Fri, 0900-1600 Sat & Sun.
Min Mail Order UK: Nmc
Credit Cards: All major credit/debit cards
Specialities: A family-run business that is one of the largest nurseries in the UK, with over 3200 popular & rarer plants.
Notes: Also sells wholesale.

GNew **Newtonairds Hostas & Garden** ♿
Newtonairds Lodge, Newtonairds, Dumfries DG2 0JL
Ⓣ (01387) 820203
Ⓔ info@newtonairds-hostasandgarden.co.uk
Ⓦ www.newtonairds-hostasandgarden.co.uk
Contact: James & Carol Coutts
Opening Times: 1000-1800, Thu, Fri, Sat, 7th May-15th Aug (nursery & garden). Garden entry Thu for SGS charity.
Min Mail Order UK: Nmc
Cat. Cost: Free list.
Credit Cards: None
Specialities: Hostas, herbaceous perennials & grasses grown in the garden. Also some seed collected from garden. Pesticide & herbicide free plants, National Collection of Fragrant *Hosta* (*Hosta plantaginea* cultivars and hybrids). Available in small quantities only.
Notes: £4.00 entry fee applies for adults to the garden, children free. Dogs welcome on leads. Coaches by arrangement. Most of garden wheelchair accessible.
Map Ref: G, D2 **OS Grid Ref:** NX882800

GPoy **Poyntzfield Herb Nursery** ♿
Nr Balblair, Black Isle, Dingwall, Ross-shire IV7 8LX
Ⓣ (01381) 610352. Phone between 1200-1300 & 1800-1900 Mon-Sat only.
Ⓕ (01381) 610352
Ⓔ info@poyntzfieldherbs.co.uk
Ⓦ www.poyntzfieldherbs.co.uk
Contact: Duncan Ross
Opening Times: 1300-1700 Mon-Sat 1st Mar-30th Sep, 1300-1700 Sun May-Aug.
Min Mail Order UK: £10.00 + p&p
Min Mail Order EU: £20.00 + p&p
Cat. Cost: 4 × 1st class.
Credit Cards: All major credit/debit cards
Specialities: Over 400 popular, unusual & rare herbs esp. medicinal. Also seeds.
Notes: Mail order operates in the spring & autumn. Wheelchair accessible.
Map Ref: G, B2 **OS Grid Ref:** NH711642

GPPs **POGS Penstemons**
The Gatehouse, Moniaive, Dumfries & Galloway DG3 4HZ
Ⓣ (01848) 200472
Ⓜ 07905 825818
Ⓔ info@pogspenstemons.co.uk
Ⓦ www.pogspenstemons.co.uk
Contact: Allison Fitz-Earle
Opening Times: Not open. Mail order only.
Min Mail Order UK: Nmc
Cat. Cost: Free.
Credit Cards: All major credit/debit cards, Paypal
Specialities: Penstemons.
Notes: Mail order plants available all year.

GPSL **Plants, Shoots and Leaves**
Dovecot Bungalow, Haddington, East Lothian EH41 4HA
Ⓣ (01620) 823536
Ⓜ 07885 444241
Ⓔ karen.leys@btinternet.com
Ⓦ www.plantsshootsandleaves.co.uk
Contact: Karen Payne
Opening Times: 1000-1700 1st Apr-1st Oct. Closed Mon.
Min Mail Order UK: £3.50
Min Mail Order EU: £6.60
Cat. Cost: Online only.
Specialities: *Epimedium.* Perennials and some shrubs. Some available in small quantities only.
Notes: Euro accepted. Mostly accessible for wheelchairs.
Map Ref: G, C3 **OS Grid Ref:** NT5073

GQue **Quercus Garden Plants Ltd** ♿
Whitmuir Farm, Lamancha, West Linton, Scottish Borders EH46 7BB
Ⓣ (01968) 660708
Ⓔ colin@quercus.uk.net
Ⓦ www.quercuslandart.com
Contact: Colin McBeath
Opening Times: Contact nursery for details.
Cat. Cost: Online only.
Credit Cards: All major credit/debit cards
Specialities: Easy & unusual plants for contemporary Scottish gardens.
Notes: Nursery moved to new site in 2014, now co-located with Whitmuir organic farm shop, restaurant & gallery, south of Edinburgh. Delivery service available on large orders at nursery's discretion. Wheelchair accessible.
Map Ref: G, C3 **OS Grid Ref:** NT192512

GQui **Quinish Garden Nursery**
Dervaig, Isle of Mull, Argyll PA75 6QL
Ⓣ (01688) 400344
Ⓕ (01688) 400344
Ⓔ quinishplants@aol.com
Ⓦ www.Q-gardens.org
Contact: Nicholas Reed
Opening Times: By appt. only.
Min Mail Order UK: Nmc
Min Mail Order EU: Nmc
Cat. Cost: 2 × 1st class.
Credit Cards: None
Specialities: Choice garden shrubs & conservatory plants.
Map Ref: G, C1

GSPN **Spring Park Nursery**
The Gatehouse, Moniaive, Dumfries & Galloway DG3 4HZ
Ⓣ (01848) 200472
Ⓜ 07905 825818

Ⓔ info@springparknursery.co.uk
Ⓦ www.springparknursery.co.uk
Contact: Allison Fitz-Earle
Opening Times: Not open. Mail order only.
Min Mail Order UK: Nmc
Credit Cards: All major credit/debit cards, Paypal
Specialities: Heathers.
Notes: Mail order plants available all year. Also sells wholesale.

GTwd **Tweed Valley Fruit Trees Ltd**
Tighnuilt House, Innerleithen, Peeblesshire EH44 6RD
Ⓣ (01896) 831147
Ⓜ 07885 105813
Ⓔ info@tweedvalleyfruittrees.co.uk
Ⓦ www.tweedvalleyfruittrees.co.uk
Contact: Nick Edwardson
Opening Times: Not open. Mail order only. Visits may be possible by prior arrangement only.
Min Mail Order UK: Nmc
Cat. Cost: Online or phone for information.
Specialities: Wide selection of apple, pear and plum trees, all grafted & grown on a range of different rootstocks, focussing on varieties considered especially suitable for the whole UK & have a comprehensive stock of heritage Scottish cultivars.
Notes: Also sells wholesale.

GTwe **J Tweedie Fruit Trees**
Maryfield Road Nursery, Nr Terregles, Dumfriesshire DG2 9TH
Ⓣ (01387) 720880
Contact: John Tweedie
Opening Times: Please ring for times. Collections by appt.
Cat. Cost: Sae
Credit Cards: None
Specialities: Fruit trees & bushes. A wide range of old & new varieties.
Map Ref: G, D2

GWyn **Wyndford Farm Plants Ltd**
Wyndford Farm, Ecclesmachan, West Lothian EH52 6NW
Ⓜ 07871 496732
Ⓔ info@wyndfordfarmplants.com
Ⓦ www.wyndfordfarmplants.com
Contact: Adam Fleming
Opening Times: 1000-1700 Thu-Sun, Mar-Oct, or by appt.
Min Mail Order UK: Nmc
Cat. Cost: Online only.
Credit Cards: All, except American Express
Specialities: Large range of perennials & shrubs, incl. large collection of violas.
Notes: Also sells wholesale. Delivers to shows.
Map Ref: G, C2 **OS Grid Ref:** NT059731

N. Ireland & Republic

IArd **Ardcarne Garden Centre** ♿
Ardcarne, Boyle, Co. Roscommon, Rep. of Ireland
Ⓣ +353 7196 67091
Ⓕ +353 7196 67341
Ⓔ ardcarne@indigo.ie
Ⓦ www.ardcarneplantsplus.ie
Contact: James Wickham, Mary Frances Dwyer, Kirsty Ainge
Opening Times: 0900-1800 Mon-Sat, 1300-1800 Sun & B/hols.
Credit Cards: Access, Visa, American Express
Specialities: Native & unusual trees, choice perennials, roses, plants for coastal areas, fruit trees, incl. heritage Irish apple trees, vegetable plants, specimen plants & semi-mature trees. Wide general range.
Notes: Euro accepted. Wheelchair accessible.
Map Ref: I, B2

IBal **Bali-Hai Mail Order Nursery**
42 Largy Road, Carnlough, Ballymena, Co. Antrim, N. Ireland BT44 0EZ
Ⓣ 028 2888 5289
Ⓜ 07708 257164
Ⓕ 028 2888 5289
Ⓔ balihainursery@btinternet.com
Ⓦ www.mailorderplants4me.com
Contact: Mrs M E Scroggy
Opening Times: Mon-Sat by appt. only.
Min Mail Order UK: Nmc
Min Mail Order EU: Nmc
Cat. Cost: Online only.
Credit Cards: All major credit/debit cards
Specialities: Nat. Collection of *Hosta*, part planted in 1.5 acres, open to the public by appt. *Agapanthus*, *Crocosmia*, *Rhodohypoxis*, tree ferns & other perennials. Hostas grown to order.
Notes: Also sells wholesale. Export beyond EU restricted to bare-root perennials, no grasses. Euro accepted.
Map Ref: I, A3 **OS Grid Ref:** D287184

IBlr **Ballyrogan Nurseries** ♿
The Grange, Ballyrogan, Newtownards, Co. Down, N. Ireland BT23 4SD
Ⓣ 028 9181 0451 (evenings)
Ⓔ gary.dunlop@btinternet.com
Contact: Gary Dunlop
Opening Times: Only open by appt.
Min Mail Order UK: £10.00 + p&p
Min Mail Order EU: £20.00 + p&p
Cat. Cost: 2 × 2nd class.
Credit Cards: None
Specialities: Choice herbaceous. *Agapanthus*, *Crocosmia*, *Rodgersia*, *Dierama*, *Erythronium*, *Roscoea* & *Watsonia*.

Notes: Also sells wholesale. Euro accepted. Wheelchair accessible.
Map Ref: I, B3

IBoy **Boyne Garden Centre**
Ardcalf, Slane, Co. Meath, Rep. of Ireland
Ⓣ +353 419 824350
Ⓜ +353 8724 01156
Ⓔ boynegardencentre@eircom.net
Ⓦ www.boynegardencentre.com
Contact: Aileen Muldoon Byrne
Opening Times: 0930-1800 Mon-Sat (incl. B/hols), 1400-1800 Sun, Mar-Sep. W/ends only Oct-Feb, week days by appt. only.
Min Mail Order UK: Nmc
Cat. Cost: Online only.
Credit Cards: All major credit/debit cards
Specialities: Award winning growers of hardy herbaceous perennials, specialising in planting for pollinators. David Austin & Harkness roses. Trees, shrubs, climbers, grasses, bamboos & ferns.
Notes: Complimentary tea/coffee. Gift vouchers. Pre-ordered plants delivered to shows. Euro accepted.
Map Ref: I, B3

IDee **Deelish Garden Centre**
Deelish, Skibbereen, Co. Cork, Rep. of Ireland
Ⓣ +353 28 21374
Ⓕ +353 28 21374
Ⓔ deel@eircom.net
Ⓦ www.deelish.ie
Contact: Bill & Rain Chase
Opening Times: 1000-1800 Mon-Sat, 1400-1800 Sun.
Min Mail Order UK: Nmc
Min Mail Order EU: Nmc
Cat. Cost: Sae
Credit Cards: Visa, Access
Specialities: Unusual plants for the mild coastal climate of Ireland. Conservatory plants. Sole Irish agents for Chase Organic Seeds.
Notes: No mail order outside Ireland & UK. Euro accepted.
Map Ref: I, D1

IDic **Dickson Nurseries Ltd**
Milecross Road, Newtownards, Co. Down, N. Ireland BT23 4SS
Ⓣ 028 9181 2206
Ⓕ 028 9181 3366
Ⓔ mail@dickson-roses.co.uk
Ⓦ www.dickson-roses.co.uk
Contact: Colin Dickson
Opening Times: 0800-1230 & 1300-1515 Mon-Thu. 0800-1230 Fri.
Min Mail Order UK: Nmc
Min Mail Order EU: £25.00 + p&p
Cat. Cost: Free
Credit Cards: None
Specialities: Roses esp. modern Dickson varieties. Limited selection, check website. Most varieties available in small quantities only.
Notes: Also sells wholesale. Only glasshouses accessible for wheelchairs.
Map Ref: I, B3

IFoB **Field of Blooms** ♿
Ballymackey, Lisnamoe, Nenagh, Co. Tipperary, Rep. of Ireland
Ⓣ +353 67 29974
Ⓜ +353 8764 06044
Ⓔ guy2002@eircom.net
Ⓦ www.fieldofblooms.ie
Contact: Guy de Schrijver
Opening Times: Strictly by appt.
Min Mail Order UK: Nmc
Min Mail Order EU: Nmc
Cat. Cost: Online only.
Credit Cards: None
Specialities: Hellebores, herbaceous, hardy perennials, ornamental grasses, woodland plants & some alpines.
Notes: Euro accepted. Wheelchair accessible.
Map Ref: I, C2

IFro **Frogswell Nursery**
Clooncontlan, Straide, Foxford, Co. Mayo, Rep. of Ireland
Ⓜ +353 8621 06166
Ⓔ frogswell@gmail.com
Ⓦ www.frogswellhardyplants.com
Contact: Celia Graebner
Opening Times: Feb-Oct by appt. Please phone first. Also Garden Open Days & occasional workshops; see website for details.
Credit Cards: None
Specialities: A small garden-based nursery specialising in shade & woodland plants incl. hybrid hellebores & hardy geraniums, plus unusual flowering perennials, bee & wild pollinator plants for the Irish climate, all raised on site & without chemical inputs. Some in very limited quantities.
Notes: Group visits & talks by arrangement. See website for location map. Euro accepted.
Map Ref: I, B1

IKil **Kilmurry Nursery** ♿
Gorey, Co. Wexford, Rep. of Ireland
Ⓣ + 353 53 948 0223
Ⓜ + 353 8681 80623
Ⓕ + 353 53 948 0223
Ⓔ kilmurrynursery@eircom.net
Ⓦ www.kilmurrynursery.com
Contact: Paul & Orla Woods

Opening Times: 0900-1700 Mon-Fri, Mar-Sep. Wintertime by appt.
Min Mail Order UK: Nmc
Min Mail Order EU: Nmc
Cat. Cost: Online only.
Credit Cards: None
Specialities: Herbaceous perennials and grasses.
Notes: Tea rooms open during summer. Also sells wholesale. Delivers to shows. Euro accepted. Wheelchair accessible.
Map Ref: I, C3

I

ILea **Leamore Nursery**
Cronroe, Ashford, Co. Wicklow, Rep. of Ireland
Ⓣ +353 87 227 8850
Ⓕ +353 404 70126
Ⓔ info@leamorenursery.com
Ⓦ www.leamorenursery.com
Contact: Phil Havercroft
Opening Times: Not open to the public.
Min Mail Order UK: €25
Min Mail Order EU: €25
Cat. Cost: Online only.
Credit Cards: All major credit/debit cards
Specialities: *Paeonia* & other perennials. Most items in large quantities. Itoh peonies & some more unusual items only available in small quantities.
Notes: Bare-root peonies supplied in autumn, available to order from July (on website). Founding members of the Irish Specialist Nursery Association (ISNA). Also sells wholesale. Delivers to shows. Sterling & Euro accepted.
Map Ref: I, C3 **OS Grid Ref:** SG235520

IMou **Mount Venus Nursery** ♿
The Walled Garden, Mutton Lane, Dublin 16, Rep. of Ireland
Ⓣ +353 1 493 3813
Ⓜ +353 08632 18789
Ⓔ mountvenusnursery@gmail.com
Ⓦ www.mountvenusnursery.com
Contact: Oliver & Liat Schurmann
Opening Times: 1000-1800 Mon-Sat, Feb-Nov. 1300-1700 Sun, Apr-Oct.
Min Mail Order UK: €20
Min Mail Order EU: €35
Credit Cards: All major credit/debit cards
Specialities: Specialist perennials. Grasses & bamboos. Unusual woodland plants.
Notes: Also sells wholesale. Delivers to shows. Euro accepted. Wheelchair accessible.
Map Ref: I, C3

IPen **Peninsula Primulas**
72 Ballyeasborough Road, Kircubbin, Co. Down, N. Ireland BT22 1AD
Ⓣ 028 4277 2193
Ⓜ 07714 465834
Ⓔ peninsula.primulas@btinternet.com
Ⓦ www.penprimulas.com
Contact: Philip Bankhead
Opening Times: Mail order only. Not open.
Min Mail Order UK: Nmc
Min Mail Order EU: Nmc
Cat. Cost: Free
Credit Cards: Paypal
Specialities: Extensive selection of *Primula* species, plus auriculas. Also *P. allionii* cvs and European hybrid alpines.
Notes: Also sells wholesale. Delivers to shows. Euro accepted.

IPot **The Potting Shed** ♿
Bolinaspick, Camolin, Enniscorthy, Co. Wexford, Rep. of Ireland
Ⓣ +353 5393 83629
Ⓔ susan@camolinpottingshed.com
Ⓦ www.camolinpottingshed.com
Contact: Susan Carrick
Opening Times: 1100-1700, Wed-Sat (incl.), Mar-Sep 2015. Other times by appt.
Min Mail Order UK: Nmc
Min Mail Order EU: Nmc
Cat. Cost: 3 × 1st class.
Credit Cards: MasterCard, Visa
Specialities: We grow a wide range of unusual, hard to find and new introductions of herbaceous perennials, ornamental grasses and *Clematis*, many of which can be seen growing to their full potential in our many display beds.
Notes: Member of the Irish Specialist Nursery Assoc. (ISNA). Orders outside Ireland can only be delivered by courier, charges at cost. Delivers to shows. Euro accepted. Wheelchair accessible.
Map Ref: I, C3

IPPN **Perennial Plants Nursery**
Nr Ballymaloe, Barnabrow, Midleton, Co. Cork, Rep. of Ireland
Ⓣ +353 21 465 2122
Ⓔ perennialplants@eircom.net
Ⓦ www.sandysgarden.ie
Contact: Sandy McCarthy
Opening Times: Please ring for times.
Min Mail Order UK: Nmc
Min Mail Order EU: Nmc
Cat. Cost: None issued.
Credit Cards: None
Specialities: Many unusual herbaceous, ornamental grasses, tender perennials. Some available in small quantities only.
Notes: Delivers to shows. Euro accepted. Sterling accepted.
Map Ref: I, D2 **OS Grid Ref:** W9568

IRhd **Ringhaddy Daffodils**
Ringhaddy Road, Killinchy, Co. Down, N. Ireland BT23 6TU
Ⓣ 028 9754 1007
Ⓜ 07762 337534
Ⓔ info@ringhaddy-daffodils.com
Ⓦ www.ringhaddy-daffodils.com
Contact: Nial Watson
Opening Times: Mail order only. Not open.
Min Mail Order UK: £20.00 + p&p
Min Mail Order EU: £50.00 + p&p
Cat. Cost: £3.00
Credit Cards: Paypal
Specialities: Daffodil bulbs, some varieties only available in small numbers.
Notes: Exports beyond EU. Euro accepted.

IRob **Ballyrobert Cottage** ♿ ◆
154 Ballyrobert Road, Nr Templepatrick & Ballyclare, Co. Antrim, N. Ireland BT39 9RT
Ⓣ 028 9332 2952
Ⓜ 07463 793160
Ⓔ information@ballyrobertcottage.com
Ⓦ www.ballyrobertcottage.com
Contact: Paul Parkinson
Opening Times: 1000-1700 Mon-Sat, 1st Mar-1st Nov. Closed Sun.
Min Mail Order UK: £4.99
Min Mail Order EU: £4.99
Credit Cards: All major credit/debit cards
Specialities: Family run garden & nursery, in business over 25 years, selling hardy perennials that have performed successfully in our own garden.
Notes: RHSI Partner Garden. 7-acre garden containing around 4000 cvs open to the public. Euro accepted. Wheelchair accessible.
Map Ref: I, B3

IRos **Ros Ban Wildlife Garden** ♿
Common, Raphoe, Co. Donegal, Rep. of Ireland
Ⓣ +353 74 91 45336
Ⓜ +353 8608 05214
Ⓔ Rosbangarden@gmail.com
Contact: Ann Kavanagh
Opening Times: Garden open all year, morning to evening.
Credit Cards: None
Notes: Plants available in season from the garden. Please check plant availability with nursery before travelling. Euro accepted. Wheelchair accessible.
Map Ref: I, A2

ISha **Shady Plants** ♿
Coolbooa, Clashmore, Youghal, Co. Cork, Rep. of Ireland
Ⓣ +353 24 86998
Ⓜ +353 8605 42171
Ⓔ mike@shadyplants.ie
Ⓦ www.shadyplants.net
Contact: Mike Keep
Opening Times: 1300-1700, Tue-Sat, by appt. only.
Min Mail Order UK: Nmc
Min Mail Order EU: Nmc
Cat. Cost: £1.00
Credit Cards: MasterCard, Paypal, Visa
Specialities: Specialist fern nursery based near the south coast of Ireland.
Notes: Delivers to shows. Euro accepted. Wheelchair accessible.
Map Ref: I, D2

ISsi **Seaside Nursery** ♿
Claddaghduff, Co. Galway, Rep. of Ireland
Ⓣ +353 95 44687
Ⓜ +353 8633 91555
Ⓔ Tom@seasidenursery.biz
Ⓦ www.seasidenursery.biz
Contact: Tom Dyck
Opening Times: 1000-1700 Mon-Sat. Closed Sun.
Min Mail Order UK: Nmc
Min Mail Order EU: Nmc
Cat. Cost: €3.50
Credit Cards: Visa, MasterCard
Specialities: Plants & hedging suitable for seaside locations. Rare plants originating from Australia & New Zealand esp. *Phormium*, *Astelia*.
Notes: Also sells wholesale. Euro accepted. Wheelchair accessible.

ITim **Timpany Nurseries & Gardens** ♿
77 Magheratimpany Road, Ballynahinch, Co. Down, N. Ireland BT24 8PA
Ⓣ 028 9756 2812
Ⓜ 07711 428477
Ⓕ 028 9756 2812
Ⓔ s.tindall@btconnect.com
Ⓦ www.timpanynurseries.com
Contact: Susan Tindall
Opening Times: 1000-1730 Tue-Sat, Sun by appt.
Min Mail Order UK: £40.00 + p&p
Min Mail Order EU: £40.00 + p&p
Cat. Cost: £2.00
Credit Cards: All, except American Express
Specialities: *Androsace*, *Campanula*, *Cassiope*, *Celmisia*, *Cyclamen*, *Dianthus*, *Galanthus*, *Meconopsis*, *Primula*, *Primula auricula*, *Rhodohypoxis* & *Saxifraga*.
Notes: Delivers to shows. Wheelchair accessible.
Map Ref: I, B3

IVic **VICTORIA'S NURSERY & GARDEN**
Upper Kells, Kells, Cahirceveen, Co Kerry, Rep. of Ireland
Ⓣ +353 66 947 7605
Ⓜ +353 8791 11465
Ⓔ kellshouse@eircom.net
Contact: Victoria Vogel
Opening Times: 1000-1700 Wed-Sun all year except Xmas. Closed Mon & Tue, except B/hols & by arrangement.
Cat. Cost: None issued.
Credit Cards: None
Specialities: *Rhododendron*, azaleas, *Acer*, tree ferns, seaside & woodland plants, *Saxifraga fortunei* forms.
Notes: Drive along Ring of Kerry, at Kells follow signs to Kells Bay Garden towards Kells Beach, nursery to left after little bridge. Euro accepted.
Map Ref: I, D1

L

LONDON AREA

LAll **ALLWOODS** ♿
Cuddington Way, Cheam, Surrey SM2 7JB
Ⓣ 020 8393 7616
Ⓔ info@allwoods.net
Ⓦ www.allwoods.net
Contact: David & Emma James
Opening Times: Office 0900-1630 Mon-Fri. Answer machine all other times. Nursery open to visitors Mar-Jun, check website for detailed opening times.
Min Mail Order UK: Nmc
Min Mail Order EU: Nmc
Cat. Cost: 2 × 1st class.
Credit Cards: Access, Visa, MasterCard, Switch, Maestro
Specialities: Large collection of *Dianthus*, incl. hardy border carnations, pinks, perpetual flowering & spray carnations, Malmaisons & *D. allwoodii*. Unusual & collectors' geraniums & pelargoniums. *Fuchsia*, Penstemons & other garden plants. Succulents.
Notes: All listed varieties available as plugs but choice varies depending on time of year. Please phone before travelling to avoid disappointment and/or to ensure order is ready for collection. Also sells wholesale. Wheelchair accessible.

LAma **JACQUES AMAND INTERNATIONAL LTD** ♿
The Nurseries,145 Clamp Hill, Stanmore, Middlesex HA7 3JS
Ⓣ 020 8420 7110
Ⓕ 020 8954 6784
Ⓔ bulbs@jacquesamand.co.uk
Ⓦ www.jacquesamandintl.com
Contact: Stuart Chapman
Opening Times: 0900-1700 Mon-Fri, 1000-1600 Sat.
Min Mail Order UK: Nmc
Min Mail Order EU: Nmc
Cat. Cost: 1 × 1st class.
Credit Cards: All major credit/debit cards
Specialities: Rare and unusual species bulbs esp. *Arisaema*, *Trillium*, *Fritillaria*, tulips.
Notes: Also sells wholesale. Exports beyond EU. Delivers to shows. Euro accepted. Wheelchair accessible.
Map Ref: L, B3 **OS Grid Ref:** TQ149924

LAyl **AYLETT NURSERIES LTD** ♿
North Orbital Road, St Albans, Hertfordshire AL2 1DH
Ⓣ (01727) 822255
Ⓕ (01727) 823024
Ⓔ info@aylettnurseries.co.uk
Ⓦ www.aylettnurseries.co.uk
Contact: Julie Aylett
Opening Times: 0830-1730 Mon-Fri, 0830-1700 Sat, 1030-1630 Sun.
Cat. Cost: Free.
Credit Cards: All major credit/debit cards
Specialities: *Dahlia*. 2-acre trial ground adjacent to garden centre.
Notes: Wheelchair accessible.
Map Ref: L, B3 **OS Grid Ref:** TL169049

LBee **BEECHCROFT NURSERY** ♿
127 Reigate Road, Ewell, Surrey KT17 3DE
Ⓣ 020 8393 4265
Ⓕ 020 8393 4265
Ⓔ enquiries@beechcroft-nursery.co.uk
Ⓦ www.beechcroft-nursery.co.uk
Contact: C Kimber
Opening Times: 1000-1600 Mon-Sat, 1000-1400 Sun and B/hols. Closed Xmas-New Year week.
Cat. Cost: None issued.
Credit Cards: All major credit/debit cards
Specialities: Conifers.
Notes: Wheelchair accessible.
Map Ref: L, C3

LBMP **BLOOMING MARVELLOUS PLANTS**
Korketts Farm, Aylesbury Road, Winslow, Buckinghamshire, MK18 3JL
Ⓣ (01296) 714714
Ⓜ 07963 747305
Ⓔ alex@bmplants.co.uk
Ⓦ www.bmplants.co.uk
Contact: Alexia Ballance
Opening Times: 0900-1700 Tue-Sat & 1000-1600 Sun, 1st Mar-26th Oct. Closed Mon (except B/hols). Nov-Feb by appt. only.
Min Mail Order UK: Nmc
Credit Cards: All major credit/debit cards
Specialities: A wide range of unusual and

familiar perennials, shrubs, grasses, ferns & bedding plants, most in more generous sizes than usually found in nurseries. *Heuchera*, *Heucherella*, *Tiarella* & other shade-loving plants. Some more unusual plants available in small quantities only.
Notes: Located on the A413 just outside Winslow (heading in the Aylesbury direction). Cannot send large shrubs by mail order. Delivers to shows. Partial wheelchair access.
Map Ref: L, A2 **OS Grid Ref:** SP777271

LBrs **Burstow Nurseries & Garden Centre** ♿
Antlands Lane, Horley, Surrey RH6 9SR
Ⓣ (01293) 771942
Ⓕ (01293) 771942
Ⓔ enquiries@burstownurseries.co.uk
Ⓦ www.burstownurseries.co.uk
Contact: Stephen Corby
Opening Times: 0900-1700 Mon-Sat, 0930-1600 Sun.
Credit Cards: All major credit/debit cards
Specialities: Roses & shrubs as well as a good range of herbaceous perennials & seasonal bedding plants.
Notes: Please note no mail order. Wheelchair accessible.
Map Ref: L, C4

LBuc **Buckingham Nurseries** ♿ ◆
14 Tingewick Road, Buckingham MK18 4AE
Ⓣ (01280) 822133
Ⓕ (01280) 815491
Ⓔ enquiries@buckingham-nurseries.co.uk
Ⓦ www.buckingham-nurseries.co.uk
Contact: R J & P L Brown
Opening Times: 0830-1730 (1800 in summer) Mon-Sat, 1000-1600 Sun.
Min Mail Order UK: Nmc
Min Mail Order EU: Nmc
Cat. Cost: Free.
Credit Cards: American Express, Visa, MasterCard, Maestro
Specialities: Bare-rooted and container grown hedging. Fruit trees, soft fruit, trees, shrubs, herbaceous perennials, alpines, grasses & ferns.
Notes: Garden centre with restaurant. Euro accepted. Wheelchair accessible.
Map Ref: L, A2 **OS Grid Ref:** SP675333

LCla **Clay Lane Nursery**
3 Clay Lane, South Nutfield, Nr Redhill, Surrey RH1 4EG
Ⓣ (01737) 823307
Ⓔ claylane.nursery@btinternet.com
Ⓦ www.claylane-fuchsias.co.uk
Contact: K W Belton
Opening Times: Not open to general visitors. Pre-ordered plants can be collected by arrangement.
Min Mail Order UK: £10.00
Cat. Cost: 3 × 2nd class.
Credit Cards: None
Specialities: *Fuchsia*. Many varieties in small quantities only.
Notes: Mail order by telephone pre-arangement. Pre-arranged collections from the nursery. Delivers to shows.
Map Ref: L, C4

LCro **Crocus.co.uk**
Nursery Court, London Road, Windlesham, Surrey GU20 6LQ
Ⓣ (01344) 578000
Ⓕ (01344) 629600
Ⓔ customerservices@crocus.co.uk
Ⓦ www.crocus.co.uk
Contact: Customer Care Team
Opening Times: Mail order only. Order lines open 24hrs, 7 days. Nursery has four Open Days a year; see website or phone for details.
Min Mail Order UK: Nmc + delivery charges (see website or phone for details).
Cat. Cost: Free.
Credit Cards: All, except American Express
Specialities: Large general nursery.
Notes: Also sells wholesale.
Map Ref: L, C3

LEdu **Edulis** ♿
(Office) 1 Flowers Piece, Ashampstead, Reading, Berkshire RG8 8SG
Ⓣ (01635) 578113
Ⓜ 07802 812781
Ⓔ edulisnursery@gmail.com
Ⓦ www.edulis.co.uk
Contact: Paul Barney
Opening Times: Tues & by appt. Apr-Oct. Nov-Mar by appt. only. See website for Open Days.
Min Mail Order UK: £20.00 + p&p
Min Mail Order EU: £50.00 + p&p
Cat. Cost: 5 × 1st class.
Credit Cards: All, except American Express
Specialities: Unusual edibles, architectural plants, permaculture plants & many of our own collections.
Notes: Nursery is at The Walled Garden, Tidmarsh Lane, Pangbourne, RG8 8HT. Also sells wholesale. Euro accepted. Delivers to shows. Wheelchair accessible.
Map Ref: L, B2 **OS Grid Ref:** SU615747

LHel **Herts Hellebores** ♿
Green Lane Farm, Levens Green, Nr Ware, Hertfordshire SG11 1HD
Ⓣ (01920) 438458
Ⓔ lorna@herts-hellebore.co.uk
Ⓦ www.herts-hellebore.co.uk
Contact: Lorna Jones

Opening Times: 1000-1600 Wed & Sat only, 4th Feb-28th Mar 2015. Other times Jan-Apr by appt. only. Check with nursery for 2016 opening times.
Min Mail Order UK: £18
Min Mail Order EU: £18
Cat. Cost: Free.
Credit Cards: All major credit/debit cards
Specialities: Hellebore hybrids. Specialising in developments of double & anemone-centred hybrids. Seed-raised plants offered by colour. Some available in small quantities only.
Notes: Euro accepted. Wheelchair accessible.
Map Ref: L, A4 **OS Grid Ref:** TL357224

LHom **Home Farm Plants**
Home Farm, Shantock Lane, Bovingdon, Hertfordshire HP3 0NG
Ⓜ 07773 798068
Ⓔ enquiries@homefarmplants.com
Ⓦ www.homefarmplants.co.uk
Contact: Graham Austin
Opening Times: 0900-1730 Fri & Sat, 1000-1600 Sun, viewing by appointment only Mon-Thu, 1st Apr-end Oct (subject to weather conditions).
Cat. Cost: 1st class sae for list.
Specialities: *Delphinium elatum* (over 60 varieties). Also hardy perennials & seasonal cut flowers. Show area of 200+ delphiniums (contact nursery for flowering times). Some varieties only available in small quantities.
Notes: If travelling, please contact nursery to confirm plant availability. Limited wheelchair access.

LHop **Hopleys Plants Ltd** ♿
High Street, Much Hadham, Hertfordshire SG10 6BU
Ⓣ (01279) 842509
Ⓕ (01279) 843784
Ⓔ plants@hopleys.co.uk
Ⓦ www.hopleys.co.uk
Contact: Mr Aubrey Barker
Opening Times: 0900-1700 Mon & Wed-Sat, 1230-1700 Sun. Closed Jan & Feb.
Min Mail Order UK: Nmc
Credit Cards: Visa, Access, Switch
Specialities: Wide range of hardy shrubs & perennials.
Notes: Also sells wholesale. Delivers to shows. Wheelchair accessible.
Map Ref: L, A4 **OS Grid Ref:** TL428196

LLHF **Little Heath Farm (UK)** ♿
Little Heath Lane, Potten End, Berkhamsted, Hertfordshire HP4 2RY
Ⓣ (01442) 864951
Ⓜ 07835 200789
Ⓔ lhfnursery@gmail.com
Ⓦ www.littleheathfarmnursery.co.uk
Contact: John Spokes
Opening Times: 1000-1700 or dusk if earlier, 7 days.
Cat. Cost: Online only.
Credit Cards: Visa, MasterCard
Specialities: Large range of alpines, herbaceous, shrubs, many available in small quantities only.
Notes: Delivers to shows. Wheelchair accessible.
Map Ref: L, B3 **OS Grid Ref:** TL018083

LLWG **Lilies Water Gardens** ♿
Broad Lane, Newdigate, Surrey RH5 5AT
Ⓣ (01306) 631064
Ⓜ 07801 166244
Ⓔ mail@ilieswatergardens.co.uk
Ⓦ www.lilieswatergardens.co.uk
Contact: Simon Harman
Opening Times: 0900-1700 Wed-Sat, Mar-Aug. By appt. only Sep-Feb.
Min Mail Order UK: Nmc but flat rate £6.50 delivery charge.
Min Mail Order EU: Nmc
Cat. Cost: Online only.
Credit Cards: All major credit/debit cards
Specialities: Waterlilies, moist perennials, bog-garden plants, primulas, marginal plants, ferns, oxygenating plants. Pond plants, incl. submerged & free-floating, aquatic, water iris, water-garden, floating, stream & deep-water plants. Alpine, rock & creeping plants. Rushes & grasses.
Notes: Wheelchair accessible.

LLWP **LW Plants**
23 Wroxham Way, Harpenden, Hertfordshire AL5 4PP
Ⓣ (01582) 768467
Ⓔ mail@thymus.co.uk
Ⓦ www.thymus.co.uk
Contact: Mrs Margaret Easter
Opening Times: 1100-1630 most days, but please phone first.
Cat. Cost: Online only.
Credit Cards: None
Specialities: Plants from a plantsman's garden, esp. *Geranium*, grasses & *Thymus*. Some available in small quantities only. Nat. Collections of *Thymus* (Scientific), *Hyssopus* & *Satureja*. Brickell Award 2011. *Thymus* ICRA.
Map Ref: L, B3 **OS Grid Ref:** TL141153

LMea **Meadowview Nursery**
8 Bourne Way, Addlestone, Surrey KT15 2BT
Ⓣ (01932) 988631
Ⓜ 07989 474767
Ⓕ (01932) 843475
Ⓔ chris@mvnltd.co.uk
Ⓦ www.meadowviewnursery.co.uk

Contact: Chris Glazier
Opening Times: Not open. Mail order only. Online orders taken 0800-1700 Mon-Fri.
Min Mail Order UK: Nmc
Min Mail Order EU: Nmc
Cat. Cost: Online only
Credit Cards: None
Specialities: *Paeonia*: herbaceous, tree, Itou. *Iris germanica*, *Hemerocallis* & *Helleborus*.
Notes: Euro accepted. Also sells wholesale.

LMil **MILLAIS NURSERIES** ♿
Crosswater Farm, Crosswater Lane, Churt, Farnham, Surrey GU10 2JN
Ⓣ (01252) 792698
Ⓔ sales@rhododendrons.co.uk
Ⓦ www.rhododendrons.co.uk
Contact: David Millais
Opening Times: 1000-1700 Mon-Fri all year. Daily in spring. Please phone or see website for w/end opening in spring.
Min Mail Order UK: Nmc
Min Mail Order EU: Nmc
Cat. Cost: Free list on request. Full catalogue Online.
Credit Cards: All major credit/debit cards
Specialities: Rhododendrons, azaleas, magnolias, camellias & acers. Garden open in spring.
Notes: Mail order all year. Also sells wholesale. Wheelchair accessible.
Map Ref: L, C3 **OS Grid Ref:** SU856397

LOPS **RHS ONLINE PLANT SHOP** ◆
Nursery Court, London Road, Windlesham, Surrey GU20 6LQ
Ⓣ (01344) 578822
Ⓕ (01344) 629600
Ⓔ customerservices@rhsplants.co.uk
Ⓦ www.rhsplants.co.uk
Contact: Customer Care Team
Opening Times: Not open. Online mail order only.
Min Mail Order UK: Nmc
Credit Cards: All, except American Express

LPar **PARAMOUNT PLANTS & GARDENS LTD** ♿
131 Theobalds Park Road, Crews Hill, Enfield, Middlesex EN2 9BH
Ⓣ 020 8367 8809
Ⓜ 07802 952517
Ⓔ info@paramountplants.co.uk
Ⓦ www.paramountplants.co.uk
Contact: Lucas & Karen Mariconda
Opening Times: 0900-1600 7 days.
Min Mail Order UK: Nmc
Credit Cards: All major credit/debit cards
Specialities: Fully mature hardy plants including trees, large shrubs, bamboos, topiary, acers, tree ferns, palms, climbers and evergreen screening trees.
Notes: Also sells wholesale. Delivers to shows. Wheelchair accessible.
Map Ref: L, B4

LPep **PEPPERPOT NURSERY**
(Office) Stump House, Portsmouth Road, Milford, Godalming, Surrey GU8 5HX
Ⓣ (01483) 424614
Ⓜ 07979 960603
Ⓔ info@pepperpotherbplants.co.uk
Ⓦ www.pepperpotherbplants.co.uk
Contact: Catherine Wallsgrove
Opening Times: Not open, except for special Open Days.
Min Mail Order UK: £15.00 + p&p
Cat. Cost: None issued.
Credit Cards: All major credit/debit cards
Specialities: Herbs.
Notes: Nursery at Grange Road, Tilford, Farnham, GU10 2DY. Sells at farmers' markets & shows. Sells online. Also sells wholesale.

LPla **THE PLANT SPECIALIST**
7 Whitefield Lane, Great Missenden, Buckinghamshire HP16 0BH
Ⓣ (01494) 866650
Ⓕ (01494) 866650
Ⓔ enquire@theplantspecialist.co.uk
Ⓦ www.theplantspecialist.co.uk
Contact: Sean Walter
Opening Times: 1000-1700 Wed-Sat, 1000-1600 Sun, Apr-Oct.
Cat. Cost: None issued.
Credit Cards: All major credit/debit cards
Specialities: Herbaceous perennials, grasses, half-hardy perennials, bulbs.
Notes: Limited wheelchair access.

LPot **POTASH PLANTS** ♿
Potash Nursery, Drayton Parslow, Milton Keynes, Buckinghamshire MK17 0JE
Ⓣ (01296) 720578
Ⓕ (01296) 720578
Ⓔ info@potashplants.co.uk
Ⓦ www.potashplants.co.uk
Contact: Gill Gallon
Opening Times: 0900-1730 Mon-Sat. 1030-1630 Sun.
Cat. Cost: Online.
Credit Cards: All, except American Express
Specialities: Wide range of traditional and unusual hardy perennials, grasses, trees & shrubs. Some available in small quantities only.
Notes: Nursery on B4032 mid-way between Aylesbury and Milton Keynes. Also sells wholesale. Delivers to shows. Wheelchair accessible.
Map Ref: L, A3 **OS Grid Ref:** SP834279

L

LPre **PRESTON BISSETT NURSERIES** ♿
Bushey Lane, Preston Bissett,
Buckinghamshire
MK18 4ND
Ⓣ (01280) 848038
Ⓔ Sales@thenurseries.com
Ⓦ www.thenurseries.com
Contact: Peter Richardson
Opening Times: 0830-1730, 0830-1800 May & Jun, 7 days.
Min Mail Order UK: Nmc
Credit Cards: All, except American Express
Specialities: Family business offering wide general range incl. ornamental trees, alpines, cottage garden plants, shrubs, herbs, fruit bushes and fruit trees, climbers, incl. *Clematis*, roses, grasses, ferns, bamboos, topiary & architectural plants.
Map Ref: L, A2 **OS Grid Ref:** SP659300

LRHS **WISLEY PLANT CENTRE (RHS)** ♿ ◆
RHS Garden, Wisley, Woking, Surrey
GU23 6QB
Ⓣ (01483) 211113
Ⓕ (01483) 212372
Ⓔ wisleyplantcentre@rhs.org.uk
Ⓦ www.rhs.org.uk/wisleyplantcentre
Contact: Any member of staff
Opening Times: 0900-1700 Mon-Sat, Oct-Feb. 0900-1800 Mon-Sat, Mar-Sep. 1100-1700 Sun all year, browsing from 1030.
Credit Cards: All major credit/debit cards
Specialities: Over 12,000 plants, many rare or unusual, reflecting the range of the RHS flagship garden at Wisley. Also houseplants, bedding plants, bulbs & seed potatoes, plus a range of garden sundries.
Notes: Plants subject to seasonal availability. For plants not in stock, we operate a reservation service. All plants must be collected from Wisley as we do not offer mail order. Wheelchair accessible.
Map Ref: L, C3

LSou **SOUTHON PLANTS** ♿
Mutton Hill, Dormansland, Lingfield, Surrey
RH7 6NP
Ⓣ (01342) 870150
Ⓔ lyn@southon-plants.co.uk
Ⓦ www.southonplants.com
Contact: Mr Southon
Opening Times: 0900-1730 Mar-Oct. Closed Mon from Jul-Dec. For Nov, Dec, Jan & Feb times, please phone first. See website for up-to-date opening hours.
Cat. Cost: Online only.
Credit Cards: All major credit/debit cards
Specialities: New & unusual hardy & tender perennials, specialising in *Agapanthus* (over 30 varieties), & *Heuchera* (over 40 varieties). Many new varieties for tender perennials/patio plants.
Notes: Wheelchair accessible.
Map Ref: L, C4

LSRN **SPRING REACH NURSERY** ♿
Long Reach, Ockham, Guildford, Surrey
GU23 6PG
Ⓣ (01483) 284769
Ⓜ 07884 432666
Ⓕ (01483) 284769
Ⓔ info@springreachnursery.co.uk
Ⓦ www.springreachnursery.co.uk
Contact: Nick & Lissa Hourhan
Opening Times: 7 days. 1000-1700 Mon-Sat, 1030-1630 Sun. Open B/hols. Closed 23rd Dec-2nd Jan.
Min Mail Order UK: Nmc
Min Mail Order EU: Nmc
Credit Cards: All major credit/debit cards
Specialities: Shrubs, evergreen climbers, *Clematis*, perennials, roses, grasses, ferns, bamboos, trees, hedging, soft fruit & top fruit. Plants for chalk & clay. Deer & rabbit proof plants. Specimen & acid-loving plants.
Notes: Please ring for mail order details. Also sells wholesale. Delivers to shows. Wheelchair accessible.

LSun **SUNNYSIDE NURSERY**
Upper Allotments, New Road,
Northchurch, Hertfordshire
HP4 1NJ
Ⓜ 07743 552154
Ⓔ philsmith2004@yahoo.co.uk
Contact: Philip Smith
Opening Times: 0900-1700 Tue-Fri. Closed Mon. Sat, Sun & B/hols Mar-Sep at the Bridgewater Monument, National Trust Ashridge Estate.
Cat. Cost: Availability list on request.
Credit Cards: All major credit/debit cards
Specialities: Hardy perennials, alpines & ornamental grasses. Some plants available in small quantities only.
Notes: Please phone for stock availability & updates. Trade discounts available with orders of £100+.

LToo **TOOBEES EXOTICS**
20 Inglewood, St Johns, Woking, Surrey
GU21 3HX
Ⓣ (01483) 722600
Ⓜ 07836 334011
Ⓕ (01483) 751995
Ⓔ bbpotter@woking.plus.com
Ⓦ www.toobees-exotics.com
Contact: Bob Potter
Opening Times: Not open. Mail order & online shop only. Visits by appt. only.
Min Mail Order UK: Nmc

Min Mail Order EU: Nmc
Cat. Cost: Sae
Specialities: South African & Madagascan succulents, many rare & unusual species, *Euphorbia* & *Pachypodium*. Stock constantly changes.
Notes: Credit cards accepted online only. Exports beyond EU. Euro accepted.

LTop **Topiary Arts**
(Office) 224 Hospital Bridge Road, Whitton, Twickenham, Middlesex TW2 6LF
Ⓣ 020 8894 2816
Ⓜ 07775 602704
Ⓔ jcb@topiaryarts.com
Ⓦ www.topiaryarts.com
Contact: James Crebbin-Bailey
Opening Times: By appt. only.
Min Mail Order UK: £30
Cat. Cost: Online only.
Credit Cards: None
Specialities: Topiary. Small quantities of *Buxus*, *Philyrea*, *Taxus* & *Ligustrum*.
Notes: Nursery is at Copped Hall Walled Garden, Upshire, Epping, Essex CM16 5HS. Also sells wholesale. Delivers to shows.

LTro **Tropical Britain** ◆
Charwood Nurseries, 33 The Avenue, New Haw, Addlestone, Surrey KT15 3RL
Ⓔ info@tropicalbritain.co.uk
Ⓦ www.tropicalbritain.co.uk
Contact: John Edmiston
Opening Times: Not open. Mail order only.
Min Mail Order UK: Nmc
Min Mail Order EU: Nmc
Cat. Cost: Online only.
Credit Cards: All major credit/debit cards
Specialities: Hardy exotics, rare plants & perennials, incl. palms, *Agave*, *Yucca*, bananas, hardy gingers, ferns & grasses.
Notes: Mail order online only. Euro accepted.

LYaf **Yaffles** ♿
Harvest Hill, Bourne End, Buckinghamshire SL8 5JJ
Ⓣ (01628) 525455
Contact: I Butterfield
Opening Times: 0900-1300 & 1400-1700. Please phone beforehand in case we are attending shows.
Min Mail Order UK: Nmc
Min Mail Order EU: £30.00 + p&p
Cat. Cost: 2 × 2nd class.
Credit Cards: None
Specialities: *Pleione*.
Notes: Only *Pleione* by mail order. Delivers to shows. Wheelchair accessible.

Midlands

MArl **Arley Hall Nursery** ♿
Northwich, Cheshire CW9 6NA
Ⓣ (01565) 777479 or 777231
Ⓕ (01565) 777465
Ⓦ www.arleyhallandgardens.com
Contact: Jane Foster, Rob Groom
Opening Times: 0930-1730 Mon-Fri, 1100-17.30 Sat & Sun, 1st Mar-29th Sep.
Cat. Cost: 4 × 1st class.
Credit Cards: All major credit/debit cards
Specialities: Wide range of herbaceous incl. many unusual varieties, some in small quantities. Wide range of unusual pelargoniums.
Notes: Nursery is beside car park at Arley Hall Gardens. Wheelchair accessible.
Map Ref: M, A1 **OS Grid Ref:** SJ673808

MArt **Artisan Plant Nurseries** ♿
Kings Hill Nurseries, Kings Hill Lane, Finham, Coventry, Warwickshire CV3 6PS
Ⓜ 07960 340396
Ⓔ andi@artisanplantnurseries.com
Ⓦ www.artisanplantnurseries.com
Contact: Andi Strachan, Helen Lockwood
Opening Times: 1000-1600 every Tue, Wed & Thu, 1st Mar-30th Sep.
Min Mail Order UK: Nmc
Min Mail Order EU: Nmc
Cat. Cost: Online only.
Specialities: Wide range of rare & unusual hardy perennials, especially many species plants that are beneficial to wildlife. Building collections of *Primula*, *Digitalis*, *Verbascum*, *Salvia*, *Iris* & *Rudbeckia*.
Notes: Nursery in the large glasshouse on site. Cash/cheques only at nursery, credit cards accepted online. Winter talks available. Group visits welcome. Tea room at Kings Hill Nursery. Plant displays for special events. Also sells wholesale. Wheelchair accessible.
Map Ref: M, C2 **OS Grid Ref:** SP318742

MAsh **Ashwood Nurseries Ltd** ♿
Ashwood Lower Lane, Ashwood, Kingswinford, West Midlands DY6 0AE
Ⓣ (01384) 401996
Ⓕ (01384) 401108
Ⓔ mailorder@ashwoodnurseries.com
Ⓦ www.ashwoodnurseries.com
Contact: Karrina Gilbert & Steve Lampitt
Opening Times: 0900-1700 Mon-Sat & 0930-1700 Sun, excl. Xmas & Boxing Day.
Min Mail Order UK: Nmc
Min Mail Order EU: Nmc
Cat. Cost: 4 × 1st class.
Credit Cards: All major credit/debit cards
Specialities: Large range of hardy plants,

shrubs & dwarf conifers. Roses, alpines & herbaceous plants. Also specialises in *Auricula*, *Cyclamen*, *Galanthus*, hellebores, *Hepatica*, *Hydrangea* & *Salvia*. Nat. Collection of *Lewisia*.
Notes: Tea room overlooking display garden. Ample parking. Regular events. Groups by appt. to visit private garden. Wheelchair accessible.
Map Ref: M, C2 **OS Grid Ref:** SO865879

MAus **David Austin Roses Ltd** ♿ ◆
Bowling Green Lane, Albrighton, Wolverhampton, West Midlands WV7 3HB
Ⓣ (01902) 376300
Ⓕ (01902) 375177
Ⓔ retail@davidaustinroses.co.uk
Ⓦ www.davidaustinroses.com
Contact: Customer Services Dept
Opening Times: 0830-1800 Mon-Fri, 0830-1630 Sat, 1000-1400 Sun.
Min Mail Order UK: Nmc
Min Mail Order EU: Nmc
Cat. Cost: Free.
Credit Cards: All major credit/debit cards
Specialities: Roses. Nat. Collection of English Roses.
Notes: Also sells wholesale. Exports beyond EU. Euro accepted. Wheelchair accessible.

MAvo **Avondale Nursery** ♿
(Office) 3 Avondale Road, Earlsdon, Coventry, Warwickshire CV5 6DZ
Ⓣ (024) 766 73662
Ⓜ 07979 093096
Ⓔ enquiries@avondalenursery.co.uk
Ⓦ www.avondalenursery.co.uk
Contact: Brian Ellis
Opening Times: 1000-1230, 1400-1700 Mon-Sat, 1030-1630 Sun, Mar-Sep. Other times by appt.
Cat. Cost: 4 × 1st class.
Credit Cards: All major credit/debit cards
Specialities: Rare & unusual perennials esp. *Aster*, *Eryngium*, *Leucanthemum*, *Geum*, *Crocosmia*, *Sanguisorba* & grasses. Nat. Collections of *Aster novae-angliae*, *Anemone nemorosa* & *Sanguisorba*. Display garden open. Groups welcome.
Notes: Nursery is at Russell's Nursery, Mill Hill, Baginton, Nr Coventry, CV8 3AG. Delivers to shows. Wheelchair accessible.
Map Ref: M, C2 **OS Grid Ref:** SP339751

MBel **Bluebell Cottage Nursery** ♿
Lodge Lane, Dutton, Cheshire WA4 4HP
Ⓣ (01928) 713718
Ⓔ info@bluebellcottage.co.uk
Ⓦ www.bluebellcottage.co.uk
Contact: Sue Beesley
Opening Times: 1000-1700 Wed-Sun & B/hols, 1st Apr-end Sep. By appt. only outside these dates.
Min Mail Order UK: £5.95
Cat. Cost: Online only.
Credit Cards: All major credit/debit cards
Specialities: *Achillea*, *Anthemis*, *Brunnera*, *Centaurea*, *Echinacea*, *Geranium*, *Geum*, *Lychnis*, *Persicaria*, *Potentilla*, *Sanguisorba*, *Thalictrum* & ornamental grasses. Some items stocked in small quantities. Mail order plants are fully established, ready to plant out.
Notes: Mail order available all year round. Refreshments available. Delivers to shows. Wheelchair accessible.
Map Ref: M, A1 **OS Grid Ref:** SJ586779

MBlu **Bluebell Arboretum & Nursery** ♿
Annwell Lane, Smisby, Nr Ashby de la Zouch, Derbyshire LE65 2TA
Ⓣ (01530) 413700
Ⓕ (01530) 417600
Ⓔ sales@bluebellnursery.com
Ⓦ www.bluebellnursery.com
Contact: Robert & Suzette Vernon
Opening Times: 0900-1700 Mon-Sat & 1030-1630 Sun Mar-Oct, 0900-1600 Mon-Sat (not Sun) Nov-Feb. Closed 24th Dec-1st Jan incl. & Easter Sun.
Min Mail Order UK: £7.95
Min Mail Order EU: Nmc
Cat. Cost: £1.50 + 3 × 1st class.
Credit Cards: Visa, Access, Switch, MasterCard
Specialities: Uncommon trees & shrubs. Rare *Acer*, *Betula*, *Cornus*, *Fagus*, *Magnolia*, *Liquidambar*, *Quercus* & *Tilia*. Woody climbers.
Notes: Display garden & well-labelled 9-acre arboretum surrounds nursery. Guide dogs only. Working nursery, so wear appropriate clothing & sturdy footwear when visiting. Delivers to shows. Wheelchair accessible.
Map Ref: M, B2 **OS Grid Ref:** SK344187

MBNS **Barnsdale Gardens** ♿
Exton Avenue, Exton, Oakham, Rutland LE15 8AH
Ⓣ (01572) 813200
Ⓔ info@barnsdalegardens.co.uk
Ⓦ www.barnsdalegardens.co.uk
Contact: Nick Hamilton
Opening Times: 0900-1700 Mar-May & Sep-Oct, 0900-1900 Jun-Aug, 1000-1600 Nov-Feb, 7 days. Closed 24th & 25th Dec.
Min Mail Order UK: Nmc
Min Mail Order EU: Nmc
Cat. Cost: Online only.

Credit Cards: All major credit/debit cards
Specialities: Wide range of choice & unusual garden plants. *Penstemon*, *Hemerocallis*.
Notes: Mail order from website or by telephone ordering only. Delivers to shows. Wheelchair accessible.
Map Ref: M, B3 **OS Grid Ref:** SK912108

MBrN **BRIDGE NURSERY** ♿
Tomlow Road, Napton-on-the-Hill,
Nr Rugby, Warwickshire CV47 8HX
Ⓣ (01926) 812737
Ⓔ philipemartino@gmail.com
Ⓦ www.Bridge-Nursery.co.uk
Contact: Christine Dakin & Philip Martino
Opening Times: 1000-1600 Mon-Sun mid Feb-mid Nov. Other times by appt.
Min Mail Order UK: £10.00
Cat. Cost: Online only.
Credit Cards: All major credit/debit cards
Specialities: Ornamental grasses, sedges & bamboos. Also range of shrubs & perennials. Display garden.
Notes: Limited range available by mail order, please check with nursery. Also sells wholesale. Euro accepted. Wheelchair accessible.
Map Ref: M, C2 **OS Grid Ref:** SP463625

MCms **CHRYSANTHEMUMS DIRECT**
Holmes Chapel Road, Over Peover,
Knutsford, Cheshire WA16 9RA
Ⓣ 0800 046 7443
Ⓜ 07977 312 593
Ⓔ sales@chrysanthemumsdirect.co.uk
Ⓦ www.chrysanthemumsdirect.co.uk
Contact: Martyn Flint
Opening Times: Not open. Mail order only.
Min Mail Order UK: Nmc
Min Mail Order EU: Nmc
Cat. Cost: 4 × 1st class.
Credit Cards: All major credit/debit cards
Specialities: Chrysanthemums. Young plants grown to order. Delivery within 14 days.
Notes: Delivers to shows.

MCoo **COOL TEMPERATE**
(Office) 45 Stamford Street, Awsworth,
Nottinghamshire NG16 2QL
Ⓣ (0115) 916 2673
Ⓕ (0115) 916 2673
Ⓔ phil.corbett@cooltemperate.co.uk
Ⓦ www.cooltemperate.co.uk
Contact: Phil Corbett
Opening Times: 0900-1700, 7 days. Please ring/write first.
Min Mail Order UK: £30.00
Min Mail Order EU: £50.00
Cat. Cost: Online or via email.
Credit Cards: None
Specialities: Tree fruit, soft fruit, nitrogen-fixers, hedging, own-root fruit trees. Many species available in small quantities only.
Notes: Nursery at Newton's Lane, Cossall, Notts. Also sells wholesale. Exports beyond EU.
Map Ref: M, B2 **OS Grid Ref:** SK475433

MCot **COTON MANOR GARDEN**
Guilsborough, Northampton,
Northamptonshire
NN6 8RQ
Ⓣ (01604) 740219
Ⓔ nursery@cotonmanor.co.uk
Ⓦ www.cotonmanor.co.uk
Contact: Caroline Tait
Opening Times: 1200-1730 Tue-Sat, 1st Apr-27th Sep. Also Sun Apr, May & B/hol w/ends. Other times in working hours by appt.
Cat. Cost: Online only.
Credit Cards: All major credit/debit cards
Specialities: Wide-range of herbaceous perennials (1200+ varieties), some available in small quantities only. Also many tender perennials & selected shrubs.
Notes: Garden open. Tea rooms. Garden school. Partial wheelchair access.
Map Ref: M, C3 **OS Grid Ref:** SP675715

MCri **CRIN GARDENS**
79 Partons Road, Kings Heath, Birmingham
B14 6TD
Ⓜ 07805 591475
Ⓔ cringardens@tiscali.co.uk
Ⓦ www.cringardens.co.uk
Contact: M Milinkovic
Opening Times: Not open. Mail order only.
Min Mail Order UK: Nmc
Min Mail Order EU: Nmc
Cat. Cost: 2 × 1st class + 1 × 2nd.
Credit Cards: None
Specialities: Lilies. Limited stock available on first come, first served basis.
Notes: Euro accepted.

MDon **DONINGTON NURSERIES LTD** ♿
Kings Mills, Park Lane, Castle Donington,
Derbyshire DE74 2RS
Ⓣ (01332) 853004
Ⓕ (01332) 853793
Ⓔ sales@doningtonnurseries.co.uk
Ⓦ www.doningtonnurseries.co.uk
Contact: Rebecca Faulkner
Opening Times: Open daily (hours vary depending on season).
Cat. Cost: None.
Credit Cards: All major credit/debit cards
Specialities: Family-owned nursery stocking wide range of trees, shrubs, perennials & alpines. 50% of stock grown on nursery set within 4-acre former walled garden of Donington Hall. Home grown *Prunus*

laurocerasus (laurel) & *Thuja* hedging available in large quantities.
Notes: Wheelchair accessible.
Map Ref: M, B2 **OS Grid Ref:** SK421273

MEch **Echium World**
Edwinstowe House, Edwinstowe, Nottinghamshire NG21 9PR
Ⓜ 07957 602073
Ⓔ echiumworld@gmail.com
Ⓦ www.echiumworld.co.uk
Contact: Linda Heywood
Opening Times: Not open. Mail order only.
Min Mail Order UK: Nmc
Specialities: *Echium.* Nat. Collection applied for.

M

MFie **Field House Nursery** ♿
Leake Road, Gotham, Nottinghamshire NG11 0JN
Ⓣ (01159) 830278
Ⓜ 07504 125209
Ⓔ val.woolley@btinternet.com
Contact: Valerie A Woolley & Bob Taylor
Opening Times: By appt. only.
Cat. Cost: 4 × 1st class (auriculas/primulas). 2 × 1st class (astrantias).
Credit Cards: Visa, MasterCard, Electron, Maestro, Solo
Specialities: *Primula auricula* & seed, *Astrantia.* Nat. Collections of *Primula auricula* (show & alpine) & *Astrantia.*
Notes: Mail order for *Astrantia*, *Primula* & auricula seeds. Delivers to shows. Wheelchair accessible.

MGib **John Gibson Daffodils**
14 Waverley Road, Kettering, Northamptonshire NN15 6NT
Ⓣ (01536) 523350
Ⓔ gibbo.john@ntlworld.com
Ⓦ johngibson-daffodils.co.uk
Contact: John Gibson
Opening Times: Not open. Mail order only.
Min Mail Order UK: Nmc
Min Mail Order EU: Nmc
Cat. Cost: Free.
Credit Cards: None
Specialities: Small mail order business selling specialist exhibition *Narcissus* bulbs, many of own breeding, miniatures and species, plus hyacinths, tulips and other spring bulbs. Stocked in small quantities.
Notes: Euro accepted.

MGil **John Gillies** ♿
at Russell's Garden Centre, Mill Hill, Baginton, Warwickshire CV8 3AG
Ⓜ 07546 064961
Ⓔ enquiries@gilliesrareplants.com
Ⓦ www.gilliesrareplants.com
Contact: John Gillies
Opening Times: 1000-1700 Mon-Sat, 1030-1630 Sun, Mar-Sep. Closed Easter Sun. 1000-1600 Tue-Fri, Oct-15th Dec. Other times by appt.
Cat. Cost: 4 × 1st class or online.
Credit Cards: All major credit/debit cards
Specialities: A range of choice & rare plants incl., but not limited to, *Azara*, *Clethra*, *Daphne*, *Diostea*, *Embothrium*, *Ercilla*, *Iochroma*, *Lomatia* & *Rhapiolepis.* Most available in small quantities only. Contact nursery if plant not on plant list.
Notes: Nursery situated beside Avondale Nursery. Can deliver pre-purchased plants to attended plant fairs (see website for details or contact nursery). Wheelchair accessible.
Map Ref: M, C2 **OS Grid Ref:** SP337750

MGos **Goscote Nurseries Ltd** ♿
Syston Road, Cossington, Leicestershire LE7 4UZ
Ⓣ (01509) 812121
Ⓔ enquiries@goscote.co.uk
Ⓦ www.goscote.co.uk
Contact: James Toone
Opening Times: 7 days, year round, apart from between Xmas & New Year.
Cat. Cost: Online only.
Credit Cards: Visa, Access, MasterCard, Delta, Switch
Specialities: Japanese maples, rhododendrons & azaleas, *Magnolia*, *Camellia*, *Pieris* & other *Ericaceae.* Ornamental trees & shrubs, conifers, fruit, heathers, alpines, roses, *Clematis* & unusual climbers.
Notes: Design & landscaping service available. Café & show garden. Also sells wholesale. Wheelchair accessible.
Map Ref: M, B3 **OS Grid Ref:** SK602130

MHCG **Hill Close Gardens** ♿
Bread and Meat Close, Warwick, Warwickshire CV34 6HF
Ⓣ (01926) 493339
Ⓜ 07533 401934
Ⓔ gardenssupervisor@hcgt.org.uk
Ⓦ www.hillclosegardens.com
Contact: Gary Leaver
Opening Times: 1100-1700, Mon-Fri, all year. 1100-1700 Sat & Sun, Apr-Oct.
Cat. Cost: 2 × 1st class or online.
Credit Cards: All major credit/debit cards
Specialities: Small retail nursery attached to heritage garden which is open to the public. *Chrysanthemum* & *Aster.* Many other rare plants offered under Plant Heritage plant exchange.
Notes: Wheelchair accessible.
Map Ref: M, C2 **OS Grid Ref:** SP277647

MHed **Hedgexpress**
Buckland Road, Bampton, Oxfordshire
OX18 2AA
Ⓣ (01993) 850979
Ⓕ (01993) 850100
Ⓔ info@hedgexpress.co.uk
Ⓦ www.hedgexpress.co.uk
Contact: Gavin Stevens
Opening Times: 0900-1600, Mon-Fri.
Min Mail Order UK: Nmc
Cat. Cost: Online only.
Credit Cards: Paypal
Specialities: Hedging & lavenders.
Notes: Also sells wholesale.
Map Ref: M, D2 **OS Grid Ref:** SP322024

MHer **The Herb Nursery** ♿
Thistleton, Oakham, Rutland LE15 7RE
Ⓣ (01572) 767658
Ⓔ herbnursery@southwitham.net
Ⓦ www.herbnursery.co.uk
Contact: Peter Bench
Opening Times: 0900-1800 (or dusk) 7 days excl. Xmas-New Year.
Cat. Cost: Free with A5 sae.
Credit Cards: All major credit/debit cards
Specialities: Herbs, wild flowers, cottage garden plants, scented-leaf pelargoniums. *Thymus*, *Mentha*, *Lavandula*.
Notes: Wheelchair accessible.
Map Ref: M, B3

MHid **Hidden Paradise Plants (formerly Sound Garden Rhododendrons)** ♿
7 Lumber Lane, Burtonwood, Warrington, Cheshire WA5 4AS
Ⓣ (01925) 229100
Ⓜ 07931 340836
Ⓔ timothyatkinson@msn.com
Ⓦ www.sound-garden-designs.co.uk
Contact: Tim Atkinson
Opening Times: By appt. only.
Min Mail Order UK: Nmc
Cat. Cost: 2 × 1st class
Credit Cards: None
Specialities: Species *Rhododendron*. Species *Sorbus*.
Notes: Delivers to shows. Wheelchair accessible.
Map Ref: N, A1 **OS Grid Ref:** SJ948901

MHol **Hollies Farm Plant Centre** ◆
Uppertown, Bonsall, Nr Matlock, Derbyshire
DE4 2AW
Ⓣ (01629) 822734
Ⓔ rbrt.wells@gmail.com
Ⓦ www.holliesfarmplantcentre.co.uk
Contact: Robert or Linda Wells
Opening Times: 0900-1700 every day except Wed.
Credit Cards: None
Specialities: Range of rare & unusual herbaceous perennials.
Notes: Also sells wholesale.

MHom **Homestead Plants**
The Homestead, Normanton,
Bottesford, Nottingham
NG13 0EP
Ⓣ (01949) 842745
Ⓦ www.homesteadplants.com
Contact: Mrs S Palmer
Opening Times: By appt.
Min Mail Order UK: Nmc
Cat. Cost: 2 × 2nd class.
Credit Cards: None
Specialities: Unusual hardy & half-hardy perennials, esp. *Argyranthemum*, *Galanthus*, *Hosta*, *Jovibarba*, *Salvia*, *Sempervivum* & heliotrope. Most available only in small quantities. Nat. Collection of *Heliotropium* cultivars.
Notes: Mail order not offered year round. Please check with nursery for details.
Map Ref: M, B3 **OS Grid Ref:** SK812407

MHtn **Hintons Nursery** ♿
Coventry Road, Guy's Cliffe,
Warwick, Warwickshire
CV34 5FJ
Ⓣ (01926) 492273
Ⓔ info@hintonsnursery.co.uk
Ⓦ www.hintonsnursery.co.uk
Contact: S. Ridgeway
Opening Times: 0900-1700 Mon-Sat, 1000-1600 Sun. Closed Xmas Day-New Year's Day (incl.).
Min Mail Order UK: Nmc
Credit Cards: All, except American Express
Specialities: Wide selection of shrubs, herbaceous perennials, trees, alpines, herbs, acquatics, seasonal bedding, fruit and vegetables. Most grown on site.
Notes: Larger plants only available for collection. Groups welcome by prior arrangement. Wheelchair accessible.
Map Ref: M, C2 **OS Grid Ref:** SP289667

MJac **Jackson's Nurseries**
Clifton Campville, Nr Tamworth,
Staffordshire B79 0AP
Ⓣ (01827) 373307
Contact: N Jackson
Opening Times: 0900-1800 Mon & Wed-Sat, 1000-1700 Sun.
Cat. Cost: 2 × 1st class.
Credit Cards: None
Specialities: *Fuchsia*.
Notes: Also sells wholesale.
Map Ref: M, B2

MJak **Jackson's Nurseries** ♿
Thorney Edge Road, Bagnall,
Stoke-on-Trent, Staffordshire
ST9 9LE
Ⓣ (01782) 502741
Ⓕ (01782) 504932
Ⓔ sales@jacksonsnurseries.co.uk
Ⓦ www.jacksonsnurseries.co.uk
Contact: Gary Leese
Opening Times: 0800-1700 7 days, Mar-Oct. 0800-1630, Nov-Feb.
Min Mail Order UK: Nmc.
Credit Cards: MasterCard, Visa
Specialities: Good general range.
Notes: Family-run nursery, established for over 50 years, a short distance from the Peak District. Tea room. Also sells wholesale. Wheelchair accessible.
Map Ref: M, B2 **OS Grid Ref:** SJ934502

M

MLea **Lea Rhododendron Gardens Ltd** ♿
Lea, Matlock, Derbyshire DE4 5GH
Ⓣ (01629) 534380/534260
Ⓕ (01629) 534260
Ⓔ lea.gardens@hotmail.co.uk
Ⓦ www.leagarden.co.uk
Contact: Peter Tye
Opening Times: 1000-1730 7 days 20 Mar-30 Jun. Out of season by appt.
Min Mail Order UK: £15.00 + p&p
Min Mail Order EU: £15.00 + p&p
Cat. Cost: 30p + sae.
Credit Cards: All major credit/debit cards
Specialities: Rhododendrons & azaleas.
Notes: Exports beyond EU. Wheelchair accessible.
Map Ref: M, B2 **OS Grid Ref:** SK324571

MLod **Lodge Farm Plants & Wildflowers** ♿
Case Lane, Fiveways, Hatton, Warwickshire
CV35 7JD
Ⓣ (01926) 484649
Ⓜ 07977 631368
Ⓔ lodgefarmplants@btinternet.com
Ⓦ www.lodgefarm-plants.com
Contact: Janet Cook & Nick Cook
Opening Times: Open 7 days all year, except Xmas Day & Boxing Day.
Min Mail Order UK: Nmc
Cat. Cost: Availability list online.
Credit Cards: All major credit/debit cards
Specialities: All forms of fruit trees: bush; espalier; fan; stepovers; cordons. Soft fruit. Wildflower plants. Native trees & hedging.
Notes: Courier service to all UK. Offers online & phone sales as well as at nursery. Also sells wholesale. Euro accepted. Wheelchair accessible.
Map Ref: M, C2 **OS Grid Ref:** SP223700

MMrt **Morton Nurseries Ltd** ♿
Morton, Retford, Nottinghamshire
DN22 8HE
Ⓣ (01777) 702530
Ⓜ 07940 434398
Ⓔ enquiries@morton-nurseries.com
Ⓦ www.morton-nurseries.co.uk
Contact: Gill McMaster
Opening Times: 1000-1600 Mon-Fri, 1400-1700 Sat & Sun.
Min Mail Order UK: £5.00 + p&p
Cat. Cost: No longer published.
Credit Cards: All major credit/debit cards
Specialities: Shrubs & perennials.
Notes: Delivers to shows. Wheelchair accessible.
Map Ref: M, A3

MMuc **Mucklestone Nurseries**
Rock Lane, Mucklestone, Nr Market Drayton, Shropshire TF9 4FA
Ⓣ (01630) 674284
Ⓜ 07714 241668
Ⓔ info@botanyplants.co.uk
Ⓦ www.botanyplants.co.uk
Contact: William & Louise Friend
Opening Times: 0930-1700 (or dusk) Wed-Sat. Closed Sun. Mon/Tue phone for assistance. If travelling far, please phone first.
Min Mail Order UK: Nmc
Cat. Cost: Online.
Credit Cards: All major credit/debit cards
Specialities: Trees, shrubs, grasses, bamboos, rhododendrons, ferns & perennials for acid & damp soils of the north & west UK. Our nursery in Kent grows complementary range for dry, chalk & coast. Extensive grounds open where plants can be seen growing. Small numbers only of each variety available.
Notes: Any plants on website or listed under nursery code SEND (in Kent) can be collected to order or sent. Evening garden tours & talks for garden groups in Staffs, Salop or Cheshire by appt. Spring woodland trail Apr & 1st week May.
Map Ref: M, B1 **OS Grid Ref:** SJ728373

MNew **Newington Nurseries** ♿
Newington, Nr Stadhampton, Wallingford, Oxfordshire OX10 7AW
Ⓣ (01865) 400533
Ⓔ plants@newington-nurseries.co.uk
Ⓦ www.newington-nurseries.co.uk
Contact: Mrs A T Hendry
Opening Times: 0830-1700 Wed-Sun Jan-Dec.
Min Mail Order UK: Nmc
Credit Cards: Access, MasterCard, Visa, Switch
Specialities: Unusual cottage garden plants, hardy exotics, herbs, orchids, grasses, topiary

& specimen plants. Nat. Collection of *Alocasia* (*Araceae*).
Notes: Also sells wholesale. Euro accepted. Wheelchair accessible.
Map Ref: M, D3

MNHC **The National Herb Centre** ♿
Banbury Road, Warmington, Nr Banbury, Oxfordshire OX17 1DF
Ⓣ (01295) 690999
Ⓕ (01295) 690034
Ⓔ info@herbcentre.co.uk
Ⓦ www.herbcentre.co.uk
Contact: Plant Centre Staff
Opening Times: 0900-1730 Mon-Sat, 1030-1700 Sun.
Min Mail Order UK: Nmc but carriage charge of £10.00 for orders valued up to £50, more for larger orders.
Credit Cards: All major credit/debit cards
Specialities: Herbs, culinary & medicinal. Extensive selection of rosemary, thyme & lavender in particular.
Notes: Next day delivery UK mainland only, signature required. Wheelchair accessible.
Map Ref: M, C2 **OS Grid Ref:** SP413471

MNrw **Norwell Nurseries** ♿
Woodhouse Road, Norwell, Newark, Nottinghamshire NG23 6JX
Ⓣ (01636) 636337
Ⓔ wardha@aol.com
Ⓦ www.norwellnurseries.co.uk
Contact: Dr Andrew Ward
Opening Times: 1000-1700 Mon, Wed-Fri & Sun (Wed-Mon May & Jun). By appt. Aug & 20th Oct-1st Mar.
Min Mail Order UK: £20.00 + p&p
Min Mail Order EU: £40.00
Cat. Cost: 3 × 1st class or online.
Credit Cards: None
Specialities: A large collection of unusual & choice herbaceous perennials esp., hardy geraniums, *Geum*, pond & bog plants, cottage garden plants, *Hemerocallis*, grasses, *Trillium*, hardy chrysanthemums & woodland plants. Over 2500 different species & cvs grown.
Notes: One acre garden & tea room. Talks given. Also sells wholesale. Delivers to shows. Wheelchair accessible.
Map Ref: M, B3 **OS Grid Ref:** SK767616

MOld **Old Hall Nursery** ♿
Winkhill, Leek, Staffordshire ST13 7PN
Ⓣ (01538) 308257
Ⓜ 07866 175881
Ⓔ oldhallnursery@hotmail.co.uk
Ⓦ www.oldhallnursery.com
Contact: Sandra Henshall
Opening Times: 1000-1600, 7 days.
Cat. Cost: Not available.
Credit Cards: None
Specialities: Large selection of herbaceous, herbs & alpines. Also shrubs, climbers & fruit trees. All hardy.
Notes: Wheelchair accessible.
Map Ref: M, B2 **OS Grid Ref:** SK051521

MPhe **Phedar Nursery**
42 Bunkers Hill, Romiley, Stockport, Cheshire SK6 3DS
Ⓣ (0161) 430 3772
Ⓔ mclewin@phedar.com
Ⓦ www.phedar.com
Contact: Will McLewin
Opening Times: Frequent but irregular. Please phone to arrange appt.
Min Mail Order UK: Nmc
Min Mail Order EU: Nmc
Cat. Cost: Online or write for printed version.
Credit Cards: None
Specialities: *Helleborus*, *Paeonia*. Limited stock of some rare items.
Notes: Exports beyond EU subject to destination & on an ad hoc basis only. Please contact nursery for details. Also sells wholesale. Euro accepted.
Map Ref: M, A2 **OS Grid Ref:** SJ936897

MPie **Piecemeal Plants** ♿
Whatton House Gardens, Nr Kegworth, Loughborough, Leicestershire LE12 5BG
Ⓣ (01509) 672056
Ⓜ 07950 757444
Ⓔ nursery@piecemealplants.co.uk
Ⓦ www.piecemealplants.co.uk
Contact: Mary Thomas
Opening Times: 1300-1600 (1700 in summer) early Apr-mid Sep, Thu, Fri & some Sun. For up to date details please ring or see website. Also open by arrangement throughout the year.
Cat. Cost: Online only.
Credit Cards: None
Specialities: Wide range of interesting herbaceous perennials & bulbs, many unusual. Some half-hardy or tender. Majority in small quantities.
Notes: Nursery located at entrance to Whatton Gardens, off A6 between Kegworth & Hathern. Car parking in front of Whatton House at top of drive. Delivers to shows. Wheelchair accessible.
Map Ref: M, B3 **OS Grid Ref:** SK494242

MPkF **Packhorse Farm Nursery** ♿
Sandyford House, Lant Lane, Tansley, Matlock, Derbyshire DE4 5FW
Ⓣ (01629) 57206
Ⓜ 07974 095752
Ⓕ (01629) 57206

Contact: Hilton W Haynes
Opening Times: 1000-1700 Tues & Wed, 1st Mar-31st Oct. Any other time by appt. only.
Cat. Cost: 2 × 1st class for plant list.
Credit Cards: None
Specialities: *Acer*, rare stock is limited in supply. Other more unusual hardy shrubs, trees & conifers.
Notes: Delivers to shows. Wheelchair accessible.
Map Ref: M, B2 **OS Grid Ref:** SK322617

M

MPnt **PLANTAGOGO.COM**
Jubilee Cottage Nursery, Snape Lane, Englesea Brook, Crewe, Cheshire CW2 5QN
Ⓣ (01270) 820335
Ⓜ 07713 518271
Ⓔ info@plantagogo.com
Ⓦ www.plantagogo.com
Contact: Vicky & Richard Fox
Opening Times: By appt. only. Also Open Days: 1000-1600 10th, 11th & 12th Apr; 31st May; 9th, 10th & 11th Oct 2015.
Min Mail Order UK: £9.95 single payment.
Min Mail Order EU: Price on application or see website.
Cat. Cost: 4 × 1st class.
Credit Cards: All major credit/debit cards
Specialities: *Heuchera, Heucherella, Tiarella,* also large selection of perennials. Nat. Collections of *Heuchera, Heucherella* & *Tiarella.* Plants listed in the *RHS Plant Finder* are available in good quantities. Others, not listed here, are available from our collections on request.
Notes: Also sells wholesale. Delivers to shows. Limited wheelchair access.
Map Ref: M, B1 **OS Grid Ref:** SJ750516

MPtG **PLANTS2GARDENS LTD**
(Office) Ringstead Business Centre, 1-3 Spencer Street, Ringstead, Northamptonshire NN14 4BX
Ⓜ 07713 962343
Ⓔ lsatchwell@plants2gardens.com
Ⓦ www.qvuk.com
Contact: Louise Satchwell
Opening Times: Not open. Mail order only via website.
Min Mail Order UK: £3.95
Credit Cards: All major credit/debit cards
Specialities: Specialist propagator of regal, angel & species *Pelargonium.*

MRai **RAINSBROOK NURSERY**
6 Barby Lane, Rugby, Warwickshire CV22 5QJ
Ⓣ (01788) 842906
Ⓔ sales@gb-online.co.uk
Ⓦ www.gb-online.co.uk
Contact: Graeme Bale
Opening Times: Not open. Mail order only.
Min Mail Order UK: Nmc
Min Mail Order EU: Nmc
Cat. Cost: Online only.
Credit Cards: Paypal
Specialities: *Malus, Prunus, Ficus, Vitis, Mespilus, Pyrus, Diospyros, Cydonia, Juglans, Corylus, Carya* & *Castenea.*
Notes: Plant passported grower and seller of unusual fruit and nut trees, rootstock and scions via mail order. Also sells wholesale. Exports beyond EU.

MRav **RAVENSTHORPE NURSERY** ♿
6 East Haddon Road, Ravensthorpe, Northamptonshire NN6 8ES
Ⓣ (01604) 770548
Ⓕ (01604) 770548
Ⓔ ravensthorpenursery@hotmail.com
Contact: Jean & Richard Wiseman
Opening Times: 1000-1800 (or dusk if earlier) Tue-Sat. B/hol w/ends in May. Easter Mon.
Min Mail Order UK: Nmc
Min Mail Order EU: Nmc
Cat. Cost: None issued.
Credit Cards: Visa, MasterCard, Delta
Specialities: Huge range of perennials, shrubs & trees with numerous unusual varieties, many of which can be seen growing in the display garden.
Notes: Search & delivery service for large orders, winter months only. Wheelchair accessible.
Map Ref: M, C3 **OS Grid Ref:** SP665699

MSCN **STONYFORD COTTAGE NURSERY** ♿
Stonyford Lane, Cuddington, Northwich, Cheshire CW8 2TF
Ⓣ (01606) 888970/888128 (answerphone)
Ⓜ 07714 205177
Ⓔ stonyfordcottage@yahoo.co.uk
Ⓦ www.stonyfordcottagenursery.co.uk
Contact: Andrew Overland
Opening Times: 1000-1700 Tue-Sun & B/hol Mons 1st Feb-31st Oct.
Min Mail Order UK: Nmc
Min Mail Order EU: Nmc
Cat. Cost: None.
Credit Cards: All major credit/debit cards
Specialities: Wide range of herbaceous perennials, *Iris*, hardy *Geranium*, moisture-loving & bog plants. *Sempervivum, Paeonia,* candelabra *Primula.*
Notes: Also sells wholesale. Wheelchair accessible.
Map Ref: M, A1 **OS Grid Ref:** SJ580710

MSKA **Sweet Knowle Aquatics** ♿
Wimpstone-Ilmington Road, Stratford-upon-Avon, Warwickshire CV37 8NR
Ⓣ (01789) 450036
Ⓕ (01789) 450036
Ⓔ sweetknowleaquatics@hotmail.com
Ⓦ www.sweetknowleaquatics.co.uk
Contact: Zoe Harding
Opening Times: 0930-1700 Sun-Fri, closed Sat. Open B/hols.
Min Mail Order UK: Nmc
Min Mail Order EU: Nmc
Cat. Cost: By email only.
Credit Cards: All major credit/debit cards
Specialities: Aquatics. Hardy & tropical water lilies, marginals & oxygenators. 2-acre display garden open to the public (no charge).
Notes: Wheelchair accessible.
Map Ref: M, C2 **OS Grid Ref:** SP207480

MSmi **John Smith & Son** ♿
Fuchsia Centre, Thornton Nurseries, Thornton, Leicestershire LE67 1AN
Ⓣ (01530) 230331
Ⓕ (01530) 230331
Ⓔ sales@fuchsiaplants.co.uk
Ⓦ www.fuchsiaplants.co.uk
Contact: David Smith
Opening Times: 0800-1730 Mon-Fri, 1000-1600 Sat & Sun all year round.
Min Mail Order UK: Nmc
Cat. Cost: Online only.
Credit Cards: None
Specialities: Hardy, half-hardy & large American fuchsias.
Notes: Also sells wholesale. Wheelchair accessible.
Map Ref: M, B3

MSpe **SpecialPerennials.com**
Yew Tree House, Hall Lane, Hankelow, Crewe, Cheshire CW3 0JB
Ⓣ (01270) 811443
Ⓜ 07716 990695
Ⓔ plants@specialperennials.com
Ⓦ www.specialperennials.com
Contact: Janet & Martin Blow
Opening Times: Mail order only. Not open except for collection of orders by appt. only.
Min Mail Order UK: £25.00
Cat. Cost: Online or A5 sae for descriptive catalogue.
Credit Cards: Paypal
Specialities: Herbaceous perennials. *Geum*, border *Phlox*, *Hemerocallis*, *Monada* & *Persicaria*. Nat. Collections of *Helenium* cvs & *Centaurea*. All plants available in small quantities only.
Notes: All plants grown in garden nursery, most in small quantities & some sell out quickly. Orders can be delivered to Plant Hunters' Fairs. See website or phone for details.

MSwo **Swallows Nursery** ♿
Mixbury, Brackley, Northamptonshire NN13 5RR
Ⓣ (01280) 847721
Ⓔ enq@swallowsnursery.co.uk
Ⓦ www.swallowsnursery.co.uk
Contact: Chris Swallow
Opening Times: 0900-1300 & 1400-1700 (earlier in winter) Mon-Fri, 0900-1300 Sat.
Min Mail Order UK: £19.50
Cat. Cost: 3 × 1st class (plus phone number).
Credit Cards: All major credit/debit cards
Specialities: Growing a wide range, particularly shrubs, climbers, trees & roses.
Notes: Trees not for mail order unless part of larger order. Nursery transport used where possible, esp. for trees. Also sells wholesale. Wheelchair accessible.
Map Ref: M, C3 **OS Grid Ref:** SP607336

MTis **Tissington Nursery** ♿
The Old Kitchen Gardens, Tissington, Ashbourne, Derbyshire DE6 1RA
Ⓣ (01335) 390650
Ⓜ 07929 720284
Ⓔ info@tissington-nursery.co.uk
Ⓦ www.tissington-nursery.co.uk
Contact: Mairi Longdon
Opening Times: 1030-1700 daily, end Mar-end Sep.
Min Mail Order UK: Nmc
Cat. Cost: 4 × 1st class or online.
Credit Cards: All major credit/debit cards
Specialities: Choice & unusual perennials esp. *Achillea*, *Aster*, *Geranium*, *Geum*, *Helenium*, *Helianthus*, *Nepeta*, *Phlox*, *Salvia*, *Sanguisorba* & *Sedum*.
Notes: Delivers to shows. Wheelchair accessible.
Map Ref: M, B2 **OS Grid Ref:** SK176521

MTPN **Smart Plants**
Sandy Hill Lane, Moulton, Northamptonshire NN3 7JB
Ⓣ (01604) 454106
Ⓜ 07519 339508
Ⓔ smartplants@hotmail.co.uk
Contact: Stuart Smart
Opening Times: 1000-1500 Thu & Fri, 1000-1700 Sat. Other times by appt.
Min Mail Order UK: Nmc
Cat. Cost: 3 × 1st class
Credit Cards: None
Specialities: Wide range of herbaceous, alpines, shrubs, grasses, hardy *Geranium*. Some plants available in small quantities only.
Notes: Delivers to shows. Limited wheelchair access.

MWat **Waterperry Gardens Ltd** ♿
Waterperry, Nr Wheatley, Oxfordshire
OX33 1JZ
Ⓣ (01844) 339226/254
Ⓜ 07864 678864
Ⓕ (01844) 339883
Ⓔ rjacobs@waterperrygardens.co.uk
Ⓦ www.waterperrygardens.co.uk
Contact: Mr R Jacobs
Opening Times: 1000-1730 summer. 1000-1700 winter.
Min Mail Order UK: £30.00
Cat. Cost: Online only.
Credit Cards: All major credit/debit cards
Specialities: General, large range of herbaceous esp. *Aster*, also Nat. Collection of *Saxifraga* (subsect. *Kabschia* & *Engleria*).
Notes: Wheelchair accessible.
Map Ref: M, D3 **OS Grid Ref:** SP630064

MWht **Whitelea Nursery** ♿
Whitelea Lane, Tansley, Matlock, Derbyshire
DE4 5FL
Ⓣ (01629) 55010
Ⓔ sales@uk-bamboos.co.uk
Ⓦ www.uk-bamboos.co.uk
Contact: David Wilson
Opening Times: By appt.
Min Mail Order UK: Nmc
Cat. Cost: Online only. Price list available 2 × 1st class.
Credit Cards: None
Specialities: Bamboos. Substantial quantities of 45 cvs & species of bamboo, remainder stocked in small numbers only. Limited stocks of grasses, trees & shrubs.
Notes: Mail order limited by carrier restrictions, please contact nursery or see website for details. Also sells wholesale. Wheelchair accessible.
Map Ref: M, B2 **OS Grid Ref:** SK325603

MWLS **Water Line Solutions**
Lilford Lodge Farm, Barnwell, Nr Oundle,
Northamptonshire PE8 5SA
Ⓣ (01832) 272725
Ⓕ (01832) 272711
Ⓔ alex@water-lines.co.uk
Ⓦ www.water-lines.co.uk
Contact: Alexandra Budaiova
Opening Times: 0830-1700, Mon-Thu, 0830-1630, Fri.
Min Mail Order UK: Nmc
Min Mail Order EU: £50.00
Cat. Cost: Online only.
Credit Cards: All major credit/debit cards
Specialities: Wetlands nursery supplying acquatic plants.
Notes: Delivers to shows. Also sells wholesale.
Map Ref: M, C3

MWts **Waterside Nursery**
Sharnford, Leicestershire
Ⓣ (01455) 273730
Ⓜ 07931 557082
Ⓔ info@watersidenursery.co.uk
Ⓦ www.watersidenursery.co.uk
Contact: Linda Smith
Opening Times: Mail order only. Open by appt. only.
Min Mail Order UK: Nmc
Cat. Cost: Online only.
Credit Cards: All major credit/debit cards
Specialities: Aquatics, marginal pond plants, miniature waterlilies, waterlilies, bog garden plants & moisture-loving plants.

Northern

NAst **Ashcroft Perennials**
(Office) 2 Mallee Crescent, Southport,
Merseyside PR4 6XT
Ⓣ (01704) 509257
Ⓜ 07793 710350
Ⓔ sales@ashcroftperennials.co.uk
Ⓦ www.ashcroftperennials.co.uk
Contact: Chris Ashcroft
Opening Times: 0900-1600 Mon-Fri. Sat/Sun by appt. only.
Min Mail Order UK: Nmc
Min Mail Order EU: Nmc
Cat. Cost: Online only.
Credit Cards: None
Specialities: Range of herbaceous perennials.
Notes: Nursery at The Hawthornes, Marsh Road, Hesketh Bank, Preston PR4 6XT. Mail order via website. Delivers to shows.
Map Ref: N, D1

NBes **Best4Hedging**
Five Acres Nursery, Dawbers Lane, Euxton,
Lancashire PR7 6EE
Ⓣ (01257) 261243
Ⓔ enquiries@best4hedging.co.uk
Ⓦ www.best4hedging.co.uk
Contact: Kate James
Opening Times: 0800-1800 Mon-Fri, 0800-1600 Sat, 1000-1600 Sun.
Min Mail Order UK: Nmc
Cat. Cost: Online.
Specialities: Hedging.
Notes: Delivers to shows.
Map Ref: N, D1

NBid **Bide-A-Wee Cottage Gardens** ♿
Stanton, Netherwitton, Morpeth,
Northumberland NE65 8PR
Ⓣ (01670) 772238
Ⓜ 07976 559416
Ⓕ (01670) 772238
Ⓔ info@bideawee.co.uk

Ⓦ www.bideawee.co.uk
Contact: Mark Robson
Opening Times: 1330-1700 Sat & Wed, 18th Apr-29th Aug 2015. Group visits at other times, except Sun.
Min Mail Order UK: £20.00
Cat. Cost: Online only.
Credit Cards: All major credit/debit cards
Specialities: Unusual herbaceous perennials, *Agapanthus*, *Primula*, ferns, grasses. Nat. Collection of *Centaurea*.
Notes: Wheelchair accessible.
Map Ref: N, B2 **OS Grid Ref:** NZ132900

NBir **BIRKHEADS SECRET GARDENS & NURSERY** ♿
Birkheads Lane, Sunniside, Gateshead, Tyne & Wear NE16 5EL
Ⓣ (01207) 232262
Ⓜ 07778 447920
Ⓕ (01207) 232262
Ⓔ birkheadsnursery@gmail.com
Ⓦ www.birkheadssecretgardens.co.uk
Contact: Mrs Christine Liddle
Opening Times: 1000-1700 Wed-Sun (closed Mon & Tues), early Mar to late Sep. Open B/hol Mons. Coach groups by appt. See website or phone for details.
Cat. Cost: None issued.
Credit Cards: All major credit/debit cards
Specialities: Hardy herbaceous perennials, grasses, hardy bulbs. Herbs. *Allium*, *Digitalis*, *Euphorbia*, *Galanthus*, *Geranium*, *Primula*, *Sedum* & *Rodgersia*.
Notes: Nursery & Coffee Shop wheelchair accessible, please ring for special access directions.
Map Ref: N, B2 **OS Grid Ref:** NZ220569

NBre **BREEZY KNEES NURSERIES** ♿
Common Lane, Warthill, York YO19 5XS
Ⓣ (01904) 488800
Ⓦ www.breezyknees.co.uk
Contact: Any member of staff
Opening Times: 1000-1700 7 days (open 1100 Sun), 1st Apr-30th Sep.
Credit Cards: All major credit/debit cards
Specialities: Very wide range of perennials. All can be viewed in 15-acre gardens (open 21st May-30th Sep).
Notes: Wheelchair accessible.
Map Ref: N, C3 **OS Grid Ref:** SE675565

NBri **BRIGHTER BLOOMS**
Walton Flats Nursery, Gillibrand Street, Walton-le-Dale, Preston, Lancashire PR5 4AX
Ⓜ 07884 430732
Ⓔ matthew@brighterblooms.co.uk
Ⓦ www.brighterblooms.co.uk
Contact: Matthew Smith
Opening Times: By appt. only.
Min Mail Order UK: Nmc
Credit Cards: All major credit/debit cards
Specialities: *Zantedeschia*, potted & bulbs. Spring & summer bulbs (dry format). Potted bulbs available in small quantities only.
Notes: Also sells wholesale. Delivers to shows.

NBro **BROWNTHWAITE HARDY PLANTS** ♿
Fell Yeat, Casterton, Kirkby Lonsdale, Lancashire LA6 2JW
Ⓣ (01524) 271340 (after 1800 hours).
Ⓦ www.hardyplantsofcumbria.co.uk
Contact: Chris Benson
Opening Times: 1000-1700, 1st Apr-20th Sep.
Min Mail Order UK: Nmc
Cat. Cost: 5 × 1st class for *Hydrangea* list. 2 × 1st for fern list.
Credit Cards: None
Specialities: Herbaceous perennials incl. *Geranium*, *Hosta*, *Primula*, hardy ferns, *Hydrangea paniculata* & *H. serrata* varieties.
Notes: Follow brown signs from A65 between Kirkby Lonsdale & Cowan Bridge. Mail order for *Hydrangea* & hardy ferns. Delivers to shows. Wheelchair accessible.
Map Ref: N, C1 **OS Grid Ref:** SD632794

NCGa **CATHS GARDEN PLANTS** ♿
The Walled Garden, Heaves Hotel, Heaves, Levens, Cumbria LA8 8EF
Ⓣ (01539) 561126
Ⓔ cath@cathsgardenplants.co.uk
Ⓦ www.cathsgardenplants.co.uk
Contact: Bob Sanderson
Opening Times: 1030-1700 most days, Mar-Oct. Please ring to check to be certain. 1030-1600 Tue-Sat, Nov, Dec & Feb. Closed Xmas & New Year weeks & all Jan.
Min Mail Order UK: £15.00 + p&p
Min Mail Order EU: £25.00
Cat. Cost: Online only.
Credit Cards: All major credit/debit cards
Specialities: Wide variety of perennials, incl. uncommon varieties & selections of grasses, ferns, shrubs & climbing plants.
Notes: On A590 follow signs for Heaves (not in Levens village). Delivers to shows. Wheelchair accessible.
Map Ref: N, C1 **OS Grid Ref:** SD497867

NChi **CHIPCHASE CASTLE NURSERY** ♿
Chipchase Castle, Wark, Hexham, Northumberland NE48 3NT
Ⓣ (01434) 230083
Ⓜ 07575 714002
Ⓔ chipchaseplants@aim.com
Ⓦ www.chipchaseplants.com
Contact: Mark Cummings

Opening Times: 1000-1700 Thu-Sun & B/hol Mons 2nd Apr-end Sep.
Min Mail Order UK: Nmc
Min Mail Order EU: Nmc
Cat. Cost: A5 sae for list
Credit Cards: All major credit/debit cards
Specialities: Unusual herbaceous esp. *Eryngium*, *Geum* & *Geranium*. Some plants only available in small quantities.
Notes: Delivers to shows. Suitable for accompanied wheelchair users.
Map Ref: N, B2 **OS Grid Ref:** NY880758

NCou **Courtyard Planters** ♿
9 Westgate, Otley, West Yorkshire
LS21 3AT
Ⓣ (01943) 462390
Ⓔ courtyardplanters@fsmail.net
Ⓦ www.courtyardplanters.co.uk
Contact: Katie Burnett
Opening Times: 0930-1700 Tue-Sat. Closed all Jan.
Min Mail Order UK: Nmc
Cat. Cost: Online only.
Credit Cards: All, except American Express
Specialities: Perennials. Plants for heavy clay soils. Peat-free.
Notes: Gardening classes & workshops. Also sells wholesale.
Map Ref: N, C2 **OS Grid Ref:** SE201455

NCum **Cumbria Wildflowers**
The Stables, Great Orton, Carlisle, Cumbria
CA5 6NA
Ⓣ (01228) 711282
Ⓕ (01228) 711282
Ⓔ cdunt@cumbriawildflowers.co.uk
Ⓦ www.cumbriawildflowers.co.uk
Contact: Chris Dunt
Min Mail Order UK: Nmc
Min Mail Order EU: Nmc
Cat. Cost: Free.
Credit Cards: Paypal
Specialities: Native British wildflowers.
Notes: Also sells wholesale. Exports beyond EU.

NDal **Daleside Nurseries Ltd** ♿
Ripon Road, Killinghall, Harrogate,
North Yorkshire HG3 2AY
Ⓣ (01423) 506450
Ⓕ (01423) 527872
Ⓔ contact@dalesidenurseries.co.uk
Ⓦ www.dalesidenurseries.co.uk
Contact: Any Member of Staff
Opening Times: 0830-1700 Mon-Sat, 1000-1600 Sun. (Closed Sun in Jan).
Cat. Cost: Online only.
Credit Cards: All, except American Express
Specialities: Many plants & trees not generally available. Container-grown fruit trees: apples, pears & soft fruit. Container-grown trees. Conifers, *Clematis*, & hardy perennials.
Notes: Wheelchair accessible.
Map Ref: N, C2 **OS Grid Ref:** SE286592

NDav **Dave Parkinson Plants**
4 West Bank, Carlton, Goole, East Yorkshire
DN14 9PZ
Ⓣ (01405) 860693
Ⓜ 07773 564945
Ⓦ www.daveparkinsonplants.co.uk
Contact: Mary Parkinson
Opening Times: Not open. Mail order only. Sells at RHS & Orchid Shows.
Min Mail Order UK: £12 + p&p
Min Mail Order EU: Nmc
Cat. Cost: 1st class stamp.
Credit Cards: None
Specialities: Hardy orchids. Terrestrial South African *Disa* orchids, species & hybrids.
Notes: Delivers to shows.

NDov **Dove Cottage Nursery & Garden** ♿
Shibden Hall Road, Halifax, West Yorkshire
HX3 9XA
Ⓣ (01422) 203553
Ⓔ info@dovecottagenursery.co.uk
Ⓦ www.dovecottagenursery.co.uk
Contact: Stephen & Kim Rogers
Opening Times: 1000-1700 Wed-Sat, Mar-Sep. 1000-1700 Sun & B/hols Mar-Jun.
Cat. Cost: Free.
Credit Cards: All major credit/debit cards
Specialities: Herbaceous perennials & selected grasses, many displayed in adjoining naturalistic garden.
Notes: Wheelchair accessible.
Map Ref: N, D2 **OS Grid Ref:** SE115256

NDro **Drointon Nurseries** ♿
Plaster Pitts, Norton Conyers, Ripon,
North Yorkshire HG4 5EF
Ⓣ (01765) 641849
Ⓜ 07909 971529
Ⓔ info@auricula-plants.co.uk
Ⓦ www.auricula-plants.co.uk
Contact: Robin & Annabel Graham
Opening Times: Open days in spring, otherwise by appt. only.
Min Mail Order UK: Nmc
Min Mail Order EU: Nmc
Cat. Cost: 4 × 1st class.
Credit Cards: All major credit/debit cards
Specialities: *Primula auricula*. More than 900 cvs of show, alpine, double & border auriculas. Limited stock of any one cultivar. Nat. Collection of *Primula auricula* (Borders).

Notes: Also sells wholesale. Exports beyond EU. Delivers to shows. Wheelchair accessible.
Map Ref: N, C2 **OS Grid Ref:** SE315753

NEgg **EGGLESTON HALL GARDENS** ♿
Eggleston, Barnard Castle, Co. Durham DL12 0AG
Ⓣ (01833) 650230
Ⓜ 07747 620908
Ⓔ lahock@btinternet.com
Ⓦ www.egglestonhallgardens.co.uk.
Contact: Lisa Hockham
Opening Times: 1000-1700 7 days. Closed 24th Dec to 6th Jan each year.
Cat. Cost: Online only.
Credit Cards: All major credit/debit cards
Notes: Collection from nursery only. Euro accepted. Wheelchair accessible.
Map Ref: N, C2 **OS Grid Ref:** NY997233

NEoE **EAST OF EDEN NURSERY** ♿
Ainstable, Carlisle, Cumbria CA4 9QN
Ⓣ (01768) 896604
Ⓜ 07788 142969
Ⓔ roger@east-of-eden-nursery.co.uk
Ⓦ www.east-of-eden-nursery.co.uk
Contact: Roger Proud
Opening Times: Mar-Oct. Days & times variable, so please phone or email before calling.
Min Mail Order UK: £10.00
Cat. Cost: None issued
Credit Cards: All major credit/debit cards
Specialities: Interesting & unusual shrubs, perennials & alpines, esp. astilbes and geums with over 60 new *Geum* cvs, bred & raised on nursery.
Notes: Mail order available for geums & astilbes only. Also sells wholesale (geums only). Delivers to shows. Wheelchair accessible.
Map Ref: N, B1 **OS Grid Ref:** NY467504

NEqu **EQUATORIAL PLANT CO.**
The Dovecote, Newgate, Barnard Castle, Co. Durham DL12 8NW
Ⓣ (01833) 908127
Ⓕ (01833) 908127
Ⓔ Equatorial99@talktalk.net
Ⓦ www.equatorialplants.com
Contact: Dr Richard Warren
Opening Times: Mail order only. Open by appt. only.
Min Mail Order UK: Nmc
Min Mail Order EU: Nmc
Cat. Cost: Free.
Credit Cards: Visa, Access, Paypal
Specialities: Laboratory-raised orchids only.
Notes: Also sells wholesale. Exports beyond EU. Delivers to shows. Euro accepted.

NFav **PERENNIAL FAVOURITES LTD** ♿
East Park View, Blyth, Northumberland NE24 3AY
Ⓣ (01670) 540653
Ⓔ adam.greenwold@googlemail.com
Contact: Adam Greenwold
Opening Times: 0730-1700, 7 days, Apr-Oct. 0900-1600, Mon-Sat, (closed Sun) Nov-Mar.
Credit Cards: All major credit/debit cards
Specialities: Specialising in hardy herbaceous perennials, but also supplying alpines and shrubs with a bent for surviving on the north sea coast.
Notes: Also sells wholesale. Wheelchair accessible.
Map Ref: N, B2 **OS Grid Ref:** NZ320812

NGBl **GARDEN BLOOMS**
Fieldgate, Mill Field Road, Fishlake, Doncaster, Yorkshire DN7 5GH
Ⓣ (01302) 288145
Ⓔ info@gardenblooms.co.uk
Ⓦ www.gardenblooms.co.uk
Contact: Liz Webster
Opening Times: Open by appt. only.
Min Mail Order UK: Nmc
Cat. Cost: Online only.
Credit Cards: MasterCard, Visa
Specialities: Hardy & tender perennials & small range of conservatory/house plants. Some plants available in small quantities only.
Notes: Delivers to shows.
Map Ref: N, D3 **OS Grid Ref:** SE659148

NGdn **GARDEN HOUSE NURSERY** ♿
The Square, Dalston, Carlisle, Cumbria CA5 7LL
Ⓣ (01228) 710297
Ⓜ 07595 219082
Ⓔ stephickso@hotmail.co.uk
Ⓦ www.gardenhousenursery.co.uk
Contact: Stephen Hickson
Opening Times: 0900-1700 7 days Mar-Oct.
Cat. Cost: Plant list online only.
Credit Cards: None
Specialities: *Geranium*, *Hosta*, *Hemerocallis*, *Iris*, grasses, *Brunnera*, *Pulmonaria* & *Aconitum*.
Notes: Also sells wholesale. Wheelchair accessible.
Map Ref: N, B1 **OS Grid Ref:** NY369503

NHal **HALLS OF HEDDON**
West Heddon Nurseries, Heddon-on-the-Wall, Northumberland NE15 0JS
Ⓣ (01661) 852445
Ⓕ (01661) 852398
Ⓔ enquiry@hallsofheddon.co.uk
Ⓦ www.hallsofheddon.co.uk
Contact: David Hall
Opening Times: 0900-1700 Mon-Sat 1000-1700 Sun.

N

Min Mail Order UK: £10.00
Min Mail Order EU: £35.00
Cat. Cost: 3 × 2nd class
Credit Cards: MasterCard, Visa, Switch, Delta
Specialities: *Chrysanthemum* & *Dahlia*.
Notes: Also sells wholesale.
Map Ref: N, B2 **OS Grid Ref:** NZ122679

NHar **HARTSIDE NURSERY GARDEN**
Nr Alston, Cumbria CA9 3BL
Ⓣ (01434) 381372
Ⓕ (01434) 381372
Ⓔ enquiries@plantswithaltitude.co.uk
Ⓦ www.plantswithaltitude.co.uk
Contact: S L & N Huntley
Opening Times: 1130-1630 Mon-Fri, 1230-1600 w/ends & B/hols, Mar-Jun (incl.). 1130-1630 Tue-Fri, 1230-1600 B/hols, w/ends by appt., Jul-Oct (incl.). Winter months by appt. Times may vary during show season, so please phone before travelling.
Min Mail Order UK: Nmc
Min Mail Order EU: £50.00 + p&p
Cat. Cost: 4 × 1st class or 3 × IRC
Credit Cards: All major credit/debit cards
Specialities: Alpines grown at altitude of 1100ft in Pennines. *Primula*, ferns, *Gentian* & *Meconopsis*.
Notes: Delivers to shows.
Map Ref: N, B1 **OS Grid Ref:** NY708447

NHaw **THE HAWTHORNES NURSERY** ♿
Marsh Road, Hesketh Bank, Nr Preston, Lancashire PR4 6XT
Ⓣ (01772) 812379
Ⓔ richardhaw@talktalk.net
Ⓦ www.hawthornes-nursery.co.uk
Contact: Irene & Richard Hodson
Opening Times: 0900-1800 7 days, Mar-Jun & Thu-Sun, July-Oct. Gardens open for NGS. Check with nursery for National Collection Open Day 2015.
Min Mail Order UK: £10.00
Min Mail Order EU: Nmc
Cat. Cost: None issued.
Credit Cards: None
Specialities: *Clematis*. Nat. Collection of *Clematis viticella*.
Notes: Euro accepted. Wheelchair accessible.

NHer **HERTERTON HOUSE GARDEN NURSERY**
Hartington, Cambo, Morpeth, Northumberland NE61 4BN
Ⓣ (01670) 774278
Contact: Mrs M Lawley & Mr Frank Lawley
Opening Times: 1330-1730 Mon, Wed, Fri-Sun 1st Apr-end Sep. (Earlier or later in the year weather permitting.)
Cat. Cost: None issued.
Credit Cards: None
Specialities: Country garden flowers.
Notes: Not suitable for wheelchairs.
Map Ref: N, B2 **OS Grid Ref:** NZ022880

NHip **HIPPOPOTTERING NURSERY**
Orchard House, East Lound, Nr Doncaster, South Yorkshire DN9 2LR
Ⓜ 07979 764677
Ⓔ hippomaples@hotmail.co.uk
Ⓦ www.hippopottering.com
Contact: Pat Gibbons
Opening Times: By appt. only & Open Days.
Min Mail Order UK: £15.00 + p&p
Min Mail Order EU: £15.00 + p&p
Cat. Cost: Online only.
Credit Cards: Visa, MasterCard
Specialities: Japanese maples. Many available only from us.
Notes: Mail order to UK throughout year; to EU during winter. Delivers to shows. Wheelchair accessible in dry weather only.

NHol **HOLDEN CLOUGH NURSERY LTD.** ♿
Holden, Bolton-by-Bowland, Clitheroe, Lancashire BB7 4PF
Ⓣ (01200) 447615
Ⓔ info@holdencloughnursery.co.uk
Ⓦ www.holdencloughnursery.co.uk
Contact: John Foley
Opening Times: 0900-1700 Mon-Sat, 1030-1630 Sun, incl. b/hols. Closed Xmas Day & Boxing Day.
Min Mail Order UK: Nmc
Min Mail Order EU: Nmc
Cat. Cost: 2 × 1st class.
Credit Cards: All major credit/debit cards
Specialities: Large general list incl. perennials, esp. *Crocosmia*, shrubs, dwarf conifers, alpines, heathers, grasses & ferns.
Notes: Seasonal mail order on some items. Also sells wholesale on some items. Exports beyond EU. Delivers to shows. Wheelchair accessible.
Map Ref: N, C2 **OS Grid Ref:** SD773496

NHpl **HARPERLEY HALL FARM NURSERIES**
Harperley, Stanley, Co. Durham DH9 9UB
Ⓣ (01207) 233318
Ⓜ 07944 644126
Ⓔ enquiries@harperleyhallfarmnurseries.co.uk
Ⓦ www.harperleyhallfarmnurseries.co.uk
Contact: Gary McDermott
Opening Times: Nursery is only open on set days. See website or phone for details.
Min Mail Order UK: Nmc
Min Mail Order EU: Nmc
Cat. Cost: Free.
Credit Cards: All major credit/debit cards

Specialities: Alpine rock garden plants.
Notes: Euro accepted. Also sells wholesale.

NHsp **Hare Spring Cottage Plants**
Hare Spring Cottage, Finkle Street Lane, Wortley, Sheffield, Yorkshire S35 7DH
Ⓜ 07792 376805
Ⓔ harespringcottageplants@hotmail.co.uk
Ⓦ www.harespringcottageplants.co.uk
Contact: Stella Exley
Opening Times: Not open. Sells online & at plant fairs.
Min Mail Order UK: Nmc
Specialities: Hardy, mainly herbaceous perennials, especially *Camassia*, *Uvularia* & *Sidalcea*. National Collection of *Camassia* applied for. Some specialist plants available in small quantities only.
Notes: Sells at & delivers to specialist plant fairs. Talks to specialist groups & societies by arrangement.

NJRG **JRG Dahlias**
22 Summerville Road, Milnthorpe, Cumbria LA7 7DF
Ⓣ (01539) 562691
Ⓔ jack@jrg-dahlias.co.uk
Ⓦ www.jrg-dahlias.co.uk
Contact: Jack Gott
Opening Times: By appt. only.
Min Mail Order UK: £10.00 + p&p
Min Mail Order EU: Price with order.
Cat. Cost: Sae: 110mm × 220mm, 2nd class.
Credit Cards: None
Specialities: *Dahlia*.
Notes: Delivers to Shows.
Map Ref: N, C1

NLar **Larch Cottage Nurseries** ♿ ◆
Melkinthorpe, Penrith, Cumbria CA10 2DR
Ⓣ (01931) 712404
Ⓕ (01931) 712727
Ⓔ plants@larchcottage.co.uk
Ⓦ www.larchcottage.co.uk
Contact: Peter & Joanne Stott
Opening Times: Daily from 1000-1730 (or dusk in winter), all year round.
Min Mail Order UK: £20.00
Min Mail Order EU: Nmc
Cat. Cost: £7.00
Credit Cards: All major credit/debit cards
Specialities: Comprehensive plant collection in unique garden setting. Rare & unusual plants; particularly shrubs, trees, perennials, dwarf conifers & Japanese maples. *Acer*, *Hamamelis*, *Magnolia* & *Cornus kousa* cvs. Old-fashioned roses, bamboo & alpines.
Notes: Terraced restaurant & art gallery. Wheelchair accessible.
Map Ref: N, C1 **OS Grid Ref:** NY315602

NLos **The Lost World Nursery** ♿
The Hawthorns, Hesketh Bank, Nr Preston, Lancashire PR4 6XT
Ⓜ 07810 547 629
Ⓔ plants@thelostworldnursery.com
Ⓦ www.thelostworldnursery.com
Contact: Phil Ball
Opening Times: Wed afternoons, Thu, Fri, Sat & Sun. Other times by appt.
Min Mail Order UK: Nmc
Min Mail Order EU: Nmc
Cat. Cost: Online.
Credit Cards: All major credit/debit cards
Specialities: Carnivorous plants: *Sarracenia*, *Nepenthes*. Also ferns, bromeliads, bananas, palms, grasses, gingers, bamboo. Plants for exotic effect.
Notes: Plants may be pre-ordered for collection either at the nursery or at shows or plant fairs. Delivers to shows. Euro accepted. Wheelchair access in dry weather.
Map Ref: N, D1 **OS Grid Ref:** SD447239

NMat **Matthewman Sweet Peas**
14 Chariot Way, Thorpe Audlin, Pontefract, West Yorkshire WF8 3EZ
Ⓣ (01977) 621381
Ⓕ (01977) 621381
Ⓔ sales@sweetpeasonline.co.uk
Ⓦ www.sweetpeasonline.co.uk
Contact: David Matthewman
Min Mail Order UK: £1.40
Min Mail Order EU: £3.50
Cat. Cost: Free.
Credit Cards: All major credit/debit cards
Specialities: Sweet peas.
Notes: Exports beyond EU. Delivers to shows.

NMen **Mendle Nursery** ♿
Holme, Scunthorpe, North Lincolnshire DN16 3RF
Ⓣ (01724) 850864
Ⓔ annearnshaw@lineone.net
Ⓦ www.mendlenursery.co.uk
Contact: Mrs A Earnshaw
Opening Times: 1000-1600 Tue-Sun.
Min Mail Order UK: Nmc
Min Mail Order EU: Nmc
Credit Cards: Paypal
Specialities: *Jovibarba*, *Saxifraga* & *Sempervivum*.
Notes: Wheelchair accessible.

NMir **Mires Beck Nursery** ♿
Low Mill Lane, North Cave, Brough, East Riding, Yorkshire HU15 2NR
Ⓣ (01430) 421543
Ⓕ (01430) 421543
Ⓔ admin@miresbeck.co.uk

Ⓦ www.miresbeck.co.uk
Contact: Judy Burrow & Martin Rowland
Opening Times: 1000-1600 Mon-Sat 1st Mar-30th Sep. 1000-1500 Mon-Fri 1st Oct-30th Nov & by appt.
Min Mail Order UK: Nmc
Cat. Cost: 3 × 1st class.
Credit Cards: None
Specialities: Wildflower plants of Yorkshire provenance.
Notes: Mail order for wildflower plants & plugs only. Also sells wholesale. Wheelchair accessible.

NNor NORCROFT NURSERIES ♿
Roadends, Intack, Southwaite, Carlisle, Cumbria CA4 0LH
Ⓣ (01697) 473933
Ⓔ info@norcroftnurseries.co.uk
Ⓦ www.norcroftnurseries.co.uk
Contact: Keith Bell
Opening Times: Every afternoon excl. Mon (open B/hol), Apr-Jul, or ring for appt.
Min Mail Order UK: Nmc
Cat. Cost: 2 × 2nd class
Credit Cards: None
Specialities: Hardy herbaceous, *Dianthus*, *Aquilegia*, hostas, *Papaver*.
Notes: Also sells wholesale. Wheelchair accessible.
Map Ref: N, B1 **OS Grid Ref:** NY474433

NNys PETER NYSSEN LTD
124 Flixton Road, Urmston, Manchester M41 5BG
Ⓣ 0161 747 4000
Ⓕ 0161 748 6319
Ⓔ info@peternyssen.com
Ⓦ www.peternyssen.com
Contact: Karen Lynes
Opening Times: 0830-1730.
Min Mail Order UK: Nmc
Min Mail Order EU: Nmc
Cat. Cost: Free.
Credit Cards: All, except American Express
Specialities: Trading in Manchester since 1958, specialising in flower bulbs and perennial plants.
Notes: Euro accepted. Also sells wholesale.

NOra ORANGE PIPPIN LTD
(Office) 33 Algarth Rise, Pocklington, York, Yorkshire YO42 2HX
Ⓣ (01759) 392007
Ⓔ trees@orangepippin.com
Ⓦ www.orangepippintrees.co.uk
Contact: Maureen Borrie
Opening Times: Not open. Mail order online only.
Min Mail Order UK: Nmc
Min Mail Order EU: Nmc
Cat. Cost: Online only.
Credit Cards: MasterCard, Visa
Specialities: Wide range of fruit trees & ornamentals, incl. traditional & modern varieties. Wide choice of rootstocks & tree forms. Fruit tree expert available most days. Website incl. extensive tasting notes & variety comparisons.
Notes: Website for ornamental trees: www. pippintrees.co.uk. Order online all year round, deliveries from Aug-Apr. Exports to USA.

NOrn ORNAMENTAL TREES LTD
Five Acres Nursery, Dawbers Lane, Euxton, Lancashire PR7 6EE
Ⓣ (01257) 365232
Ⓔ sales@ornamental-trees.co.uk
Ⓦ www.ornamental-trees.co.uk
Contact: Any member of staff
Opening Times: Mail order only. 0800-1800, Mon-Fri, 0800-1600, Sat & 1000-1600 Sun.
Min Mail Order UK: Nmc
Specialities: Trees & hedging.
Notes: Delivers to shows.
Map Ref: N, D1

NPer PERRY'S PLANTS ♿
The River Garden, Sleights, Whitby, North Yorkshire YO21 1RR
Ⓜ 07879 498623
Ⓔ richardperry008@hotmail.co.uk
Ⓦ www.perrysplants.co.uk
Contact: Sharon & Richard Perry
Opening Times: 1000-1700 mid-March to Oct.
Cat. Cost: None published.
Credit Cards: None
Specialities: *Lavatera*, *Malva*, *Erysimum*, *Euphorbia*, *Anthemis*, *Osteospermum* & *Hebe*. Uncommon hardy & container plants & aquatic plants.
Notes: Euro accepted. Wheelchair accessible.
Map Ref: N, C3 **OS Grid Ref:** NZ869082

NPla THE PLANT DIRECTORY
Scawsby Hall Nurseries, Barnsley Road, Scawsby, Doncaster, South Yorkshire DN5 7UB
Ⓣ (01302) 783434
Ⓔ mail@the-plant-directory.co.uk
Ⓦ www.the-plant-directory.co.uk
Contact: David Lawson
Opening Times: Not open. Mail order only.
Min Mail Order UK: Nmc
Cat. Cost: None issued
Credit Cards: Visa, American Express, MasterCard, Paypal
Specialities: A wide range of herbaceous perennials, hardy trees, shrubs & indoor

plants. Some indoor & aquatic plants in small quantities only.

NPnk **PRIMROSE BANK** ♿
Redroofs, Dauby Lane, Kexby, Yorkshire
YO41 5LH
Ⓣ (01759) 380220
Ⓜ 07774 944447
Ⓔ suegoodwill@yahoo.co.uk
Ⓦ www.primrosebank.co.uk
Contact: Sue Goodwill
Opening Times: 1000-1700, Thu-Sun, 7th Mar-28 Jun. By appt. only Jul-Sep. Please ring before travelling, as occasionally closed during shows.
Min Mail Order UK: Nmc
Cat. Cost: None issued.
Credit Cards: All major credit/debit cards
Specialities: Hardy perennials.
Notes: Delivers to shows. Wheelchair accessible.
Map Ref: N, C3 **OS Grid Ref:** SE695508

NPoe **POETS COTTAGE SHRUB NURSERY** ♿
Lealholm, Whitby, North Yorkshire
YO21 2AQ
Ⓣ (01947) 897424
Ⓔ enquiries@poetscottage.co.uk
Ⓦ www.poetscottage.co.uk
Contact: Ilona J McGivern
Opening Times: 1300-1530 Feb, 0900-1700 Mar-Christmas, 7 days. Closed Jan.
Cat. Cost: None issued.
Credit Cards: All major credit/debit cards
Specialities: Dwarf conifers, *Acer* & herbaceous.
Map Ref: N, C3

NPol **POLEMONIUM PLANTERY**
28 Sunnyside, Trimdon Grange, Co. Durham
TS29 6HF
Ⓣ (01429) 881529
Ⓔ dandd@polemonium.co.uk
Ⓦ www.polemonium.co.uk
Contact: David or Dianne Nichol-Brown
Opening Times: By appt. only.
Min Mail Order UK: £10.00
Cat. Cost: 3 × 1st class
Credit Cards: None
Specialities: Nat. Collections of *Polemonium*, *Collomia*, *Gilia*, *Leptodactylon* (*Polemoniaceae*) & *Hakonechloa*.
Notes: Also sells wholesale. Delivers to shows.
Map Ref: N, B2 **OS Grid Ref:** NZ369353

NPri **PRIMROSE COTTAGE NURSERY** ♿
Ringway Road, Moss Nook, Wythenshawe, Manchester M22 5WF
Ⓣ (0161) 437 1557
Ⓜ 07798 754457
Ⓔ info@primrosecottagenursery.co.uk
Ⓦ www.primrosecottagenursery.co.uk
Contact: Caroline Dumville
Opening Times: 0830-1730 Mon-Sat, 0930-1730 Sun (summer). 0830-1700 Mon-Sat, 0930-1700 Sun (winter).
Cat. Cost: Plant lists can be sent by email.
Credit Cards: All major credit/debit cards
Specialities: Perennials, herbs, roses, patio & hanging basket plants. Shrubs, houseplants, ornamental trees, fruit trees, soft fruit bushes & vegetable plants.
Notes: Coffee shop open daily. Wheelchair accessible.
Map Ref: N, D2

NQui **QUIET CORNER PLANTS**
(Office) 20 Grove Road, Brandon, Co. Durham DH7 8AW
Ⓜ 079321 59204
Ⓔ hal@uwclub.net
Ⓦ www.quietcornerplants.co.uk
Contact: Howard Leslie
Opening Times: 1100-1700 (or sunset in winter), 7 days.
Min Mail Order UK: Nmc
Cat. Cost: Online only.
Credit Cards: All major credit/debit cards
Specialities: Hardy herbaceous & shrubby perennials, incl. small quantities of lesser known and harder to find plants.
Notes: Nursery is at Misty Blue Farm, Rock Road, Kirk Merrington, Co. Durham, DL16 7HJ. Also sells wholesale. Delivers to shows.
Map Ref: N, B2

NRHS **HARLOW CARR PLANT CENTRE (RHS)** ◆
RHS Garden, Crag Lane, Harlow Carr, Harrogate, North Yorkshire, HG3 1QB
Ⓣ (01423) 724667
Ⓕ (01423) 569521
Ⓔ nigeleaton@rhs.org.uk
Ⓦ www.rhs.org.uk
Contact: Any member of staff
Specialities: Wide general range, particularly alpines.
Notes: Programme of free plant events throughout the year. Please ring or check website for details. Customer ordering system for plants which need to be collected from the Plant Centre.

NRib **RIBBLESDALE NURSERIES** ♿
Newsham Hall Lane, Woodplumpton, Preston, Lancashire PR4 0AS
Ⓣ (01772) 863081
Ⓔ philsd@btinternet.com
Ⓦ www.ribblesdalenurseries.co.uk
Contact: Mr & Mrs Dunnett

Opening Times: 0900-1800 Mon-Sat Apr-Sep, 0900-1700 Mon-Sat Oct-Mar. 1030-1630 Sun.
Credit Cards: Visa, MasterCard, Delta, Switch
Specialities: Trees, shrubs & perennials. Conifers, hedging, alpines, fruit, climbers, herbs, aquatics, ferns & wildflowers. Own grown plants in peat-free compost.
Notes: Wheelchair accessible.

NRob **W Robinson & Son (Seeds & Plants) Ltd** ♿
Sunny Bank, Forton, Nr Preston, Lancashire PR3 0BN
Ⓣ (01524) 791210
Ⓕ (01524) 791933
Ⓔ info@mammothonion.co.uk
Ⓦ www.mammothonion.co.uk
Contact: Miss Robinson
Opening Times: 1000-1600 7 days Mar-Jun, 0800-1700 Mon-Fri Jul-Feb.
Min Mail Order UK: Nmc
Min Mail Order EU: Nmc
Cat. Cost: Free.
Credit Cards: All major credit/debit cards
Specialities: Mammoth vegetable seed. Onions, leeks, tomatoes & beans. Range of vegetable plants in the spring.
Notes: Also sells wholesale. Exports beyond EU. Delivers to shows. Wheelchair accessible.

NRog **R V Roger Ltd** ♿
The Nurseries, Pickering, North Yorkshire YO18 7JW
Ⓣ (01751) 472226
Ⓕ (01751) 476749
Ⓔ sales@rvroger.co.uk
Ⓦ www.rvroger.co.uk
Contact: Ian Roger
Opening Times: 0900-1700 Mon-Sat, 1000-1600 Sun.
Min Mail Order UK: Nmc
Min Mail Order EU: Nmc
Cat. Cost: £1.00
Credit Cards: All major credit/debit cards
Specialities: Holders of National Collection of *Erythronium*.
Notes: Also sells wholesale. Wheelchair accessible.
Map Ref: N, C3 **OS Grid Ref:** SE801827

NRya **Ryal Nursery** ♿
East Farm Cottage, Ryal, Northumberland NE20 0SA
Ⓣ (01661) 886562
Ⓔ alpines@ryal.freeserve.co.uk
Contact: R F Hadden
Opening Times: Mar-Jul by appt., please phone.
Cat. Cost: Sae.
Credit Cards: None
Specialities: Alpine & woodland plants, mainly available in small quantities only. Nat. Collection of *Primula marginata*.
Notes: Also sells wholesale. Delivers to shows. Wheelchair accessible.
Map Ref: N, B2 **OS Grid Ref:** NZ015744

NSla **Slack Top Nurseries**
Alpine House, 22A Slack Top, Hebden Bridge, West Yorkshire HX7 7HA
Ⓣ (01422) 845348
Ⓜ 07508 953804
Ⓔ enquiries@slacktopnurseries.co.uk
Ⓦ www.slacktopnurseries.co.uk
Contact: Michael & Allison Mitchell
Opening Times: 1000-1700 Fri-Sun 1st Mar-31st Aug & B/hols. Other times by appt.
Min Mail Order UK: £20.00
Min Mail Order EU: £50.00
Cat. Cost: 2 × 1st class A5 sae or online.
Credit Cards: None
Specialities: Alpine, rockery & woodland plants.
Notes: Talks given to gardening clubs & other groups by appt. Delivers to shows. Euro accepted. Some areas of garden inaccessible for wheelchairs.
Map Ref: N, D2 **OS Grid Ref:** SD977286

NSti **Stillingfleet Lodge Nurseries** ♿
Stewart Lane, Stillingfleet, York YO19 6HP
Ⓣ (01904) 728506
Ⓔ info@stillingfleetlodgenurseries.co.uk
Ⓦ www.stillingfleetlodgenurseries.co.uk
Contact: Vanessa Cook
Opening Times: 1300-1700 Wed & Fri, 1st Apr-30th Sep. 1300-1700, 1st & 3rd Sat & Sun in each month.
Cat. Cost: Online only.
Credit Cards: None
Specialities: Foliage & unusual perennials. Hardy geraniums, *Pulmonaria*, variegated plants & grasses.
Notes: Wheelchair accessible.
Map Ref: N, D2

NSue **Sue Proctor Plants**
69 Ings Mill Avenue, Clayton West, Huddersfield, West Yorkshire HD8 9QG
Ⓣ (01484) 866189
Ⓜ 07917 006636
Ⓔ hostas@sueproctorplants.co.uk
Ⓦ www.sueproctorplants.co.uk
Contact: Richard Proctor
Opening Times: By appt. only. Please phone first.
Min Mail Order UK: £3.50
Cat. Cost: Large 1st sae.

Credit Cards: All major credit/debit cards
Specialities: *Hosta*, especially miniature hostas.
Notes: Delivers to shows.
Map Ref: N, D2

NSum **SUMMERDALE GARDEN NURSERY**
Summerdale House, Cow Brow, Lupton, Carnforth, Lancashire LA6 1PE
Ⓣ (01539) 567210
Ⓔ sheals@btinternet.com
Ⓦ www.summerdalegardenplants.co.uk
Contact: Gail Sheals
Opening Times: 1000-1630 Thu, Fri & Sat, 1st Apr-31st Aug. Other times by appt. only.
Min Mail Order UK: Nmc
Cat. Cost: Online only.
Credit Cards: None
Specialities: Wide variety of perennials, large collection of *Primula*. Many moist and shade-loving plants incl. *Meconopsis* & hellebores.
Notes: Mail order for primulas only.
Map Ref: N, C1 **OS Grid Ref:** SD545819

NTay **TAYLORS CLEMATIS NURSERY** ♿
Sutton Road, Sutton, Nr Askern, Doncaster, South Yorkshire DN6 9JZ
Ⓣ (01302) 700716
Ⓔ info@taylorsclematis.co.uk
Ⓦ www.taylorsclematis.co.uk
Contact: Chris & Suzy Cocks
Opening Times: Open by appt. only. Please ring for details Mon-Fri, before 0900 or after 1500 hours. Ticket only Open Days in May & Jun. For tickets see website or contact nursery by post/ phone.
Min Mail Order UK: Nmc
Min Mail Order EU: Nmc
Cat. Cost: 4 × 2nd class.
Credit Cards: All major credit/debit cards
Specialities: *Clematis* (over 350+ varieties). 2-year old mature specimens, all grown on nursery.
Notes: Talks/presentations to clubs & societies in Feb, Mar & and Oct. Also offers next day delivery courier service. Delivers to shows. Wheelchair accessible.
Map Ref: N, D2 **OS Grid Ref:** SE552121

NTPC **TREE PEONY COMPANY**
Willow Cottage, Rillington, Malton, North Yorkshire YO17 8JU
Ⓣ (01944) 758280
Ⓔ info@treepeony.co.uk
Ⓦ www.treepeony.co.uk
Contact: Thelma Scruton, Roger Scruton
Min Mail Order UK: £12.00
Min Mail Order EU: Nmc
Cat. Cost: None.
Credit Cards: None
Specialities: Tree peonies. *Paeonia suffruticosa. P.* Gansu Group. *P. rockii.*
Notes: Also sells wholesale. Euro accepted. Delivers to shows.

NTre **TREETYME**
Prospect Hill House, Kirkoswald, Penrith, Cumbria CA10 1ER
Ⓣ (01768) 800238
Ⓕ (01768) 897138
Ⓔ sales@treetyme.co.uk
Ⓦ www.treetyme.co.uk
Contact: Hugh Povey
Opening Times: Not open. Mail order via website only. Visits by appt. only.
Min Mail Order UK: Nmc
Min Mail Order EU: Nmc
Cat. Cost: Online only.
Credit Cards: All major credit/debit cards
Specialities: *Cercis*. Stock available in small quantities only. National Collection of *Cercis*.
Notes: Also sells wholesale.

NWad **WADDOW LODGE GARDEN** ♿
Clitheroe Road, Waddington, Clitheroe, Lancashire BB7 3HQ
Ⓣ (01200) 429145
Ⓔ peterfoleyhcn@hotmail.co.uk
Ⓦ www.gardentalks.co.uk
Contact: Peter Foley
Opening Times: By appt. only all year. Also open under NGS 1300-1700 24th May & 19th Jul 2015 with plant sales for Plant Heritage NW Group.
Min Mail Order UK: Nmc
Min Mail Order EU: Nmc
Cat. Cost: Online only.
Credit Cards: None
Specialities: A developing plantsman's garden with an ever-changing & interesting plant collection. Some plants only available in small numbers.
Notes: Open for group visits by appt., incl. evenings. Wheelchair accessible.
Map Ref: N, C1 **OS Grid Ref:** SD732434

NWea **WEASDALE NURSERIES LTD.**
Newbiggin-on-Lune, Kirkby Stephen, Cumbria CA17 4LX
Ⓣ (01539) 623246
Ⓕ (01539) 623277
Ⓔ sales@weasdale.com
Ⓦ www.weasdale.com
Contact: Andrew Forsyth
Opening Times: 0830-1300 & 1400-1730 Mon-Fri. Closed w/ends, B/hols, Xmas through to the New Year.
Min Mail Order UK: Nmc
Min Mail Order EU: Nmc
Cat. Cost: Free of charge in UK or £2.00 to EU.

Credit Cards: All major credit/debit cards
Specialities: Hardy forest trees, hedging, broad-leaved & conifers. Specimen trees & shrubs grown at 850 feet (260 metres) elevation. Some rarer plants are grown in small batches, so availability can't be guaranteed. Peat-free.
Notes: Mail order a speciality. Mail order Nov-Apr only. Also sells wholesale to VAT registered customers.
Map Ref: N, C1 **OS Grid Ref:** NY690039

NWit **D S WITTON** ♿
26 Casson Drive, Harthill, Sheffield, Yorkshire S26 7WA
Ⓣ (01909) 771366
Ⓔ donshardyeuphorbias@btopenworld.com
Ⓦ www.euphorbias.co.uk
Contact: Don Witton
Opening Times: By appt. only.
Min Mail Order UK: Nmc
Cat. Cost: 1 × 1st class sae.
Credit Cards: None
Specialities: Nat. Collection of Hardy *Euphorbia*. Over 130 varieties.
Notes: Mail order seed only, Oct-June. Wheelchair accessible.
Map Ref: N, D2 **OS Grid Ref:** SK494812

NWms **WOODMOSS FUCHSIAS**
Woodmoss Lane Nursery, Woodmoss Lane, Scarisbrick, Ormskirk, Lancashire L40 9RJ
Ⓣ 01253 428 766
Ⓜ 07849 080248
Ⓔ woodmossfuchsia@yahoo.co.uk
Contact: Brian Houghton & Keith Middleton
Opening Times: 0900-1600 Mon-Fri, 0900-1230 Sat, Jan-end Jun. B/hols & w/ends by appt.
Min Mail Order UK: £12.50 for 6 plants.
Credit Cards: None
Specialities: *Fuchsia*.

NWsh **WESTSHORES NURSERIES**
82 West Street, Winterton, Lincolnshire DN15 9QF
Ⓣ (01724) 733940
Ⓜ 07875 732535
Ⓔ westshnur@aol.com
Ⓦ www.westshores.co.uk
Contact: Gail & John Summerfield
Opening Times: 1st Mar-31st Oct. Please check before visiting.
Min Mail Order UK: £15.00
Cat. Cost: Online only.
Credit Cards: All major credit/debit cards
Specialities: Ornamental grasses & autumn flowering perennials.
Notes: Wide selection of talks for gardening clubs and Hardy Plant Society groups.
Map Ref: N, D3 **OS Grid Ref:** SE927187

SOUTHERN

SAdn **ASHDOWN FOREST GARDEN CENTRE & NURSERY** ♿
Duddleswell, Ashdown Forest, East Sussex TN22 3JP
Ⓣ (01825) 712300
Ⓔ victoria@ashdownforestgardencentre.co.uk
Ⓦ www.ashdownforestgardencentre.co.uk
Contact: Victoria Falletti
Opening Times: 0900-1700 winter, 0900-1800 summer.
Min Mail Order UK: Nmc
Cat. Cost: Online only.
Credit Cards: All major credit/debit cards
Specialities: Ornamental grasses, *Lapageria*, *Fuchsia*, conservatory climbers, unusual shrubs.
Notes: Wheelchair accessible.
Map Ref: S, C4 **OS Grid Ref:** TQ468283

SAdu **ADUR VALLEY GROWERS**
(Office) 4 Newland Road, Upper Beeding, Steyning, West Sussex BN44 3JJ
Ⓣ (01903) 813780
Ⓔ clivethecannaman@gmail.com
Ⓦ www.adurvalleygrowers.co.uk
Contact: Clive Parker
Opening Times: Not open. Mail order only.
Min Mail Order UK: Nmc
Min Mail Order EU: Nmc
Cat. Cost: Online only.
Credit Cards: Paypal
Specialities: A wide range of disease-free *Canna*, many only available in very small numbers. All plants grown in own peat-free compost without the use of chemical pesticides. Will propagate to order.
Notes: Plants only available from May-Oct. Euro accepted.

SAko **AKORN AND OAKE**
18 Twyford Avenue, Southampton, Hampshire SO15 5NP
Ⓣ (02380) 344040
Ⓜ 07973 149404
Ⓔ stefan.rau@hotmail.co.uk
Contact: Stefan Rau
Opening Times: Mail order only. Open by appt. only.
Min Mail Order UK: £15.00
Specialities: *Saxifraga*.
Notes: Plants only sent out in dormant state. Delivers to shows.

SArc **ARCHITECTURAL PLANTS LTD** ♿
Stane Street, North Heath, Pulborough, West Sussex RH20 1DJ
Ⓣ (01403) 891772
Ⓕ (01403) 891056

Ⓔ enquiries@architecturalplants.com
Ⓦ www.architecturalplants.com
Contact: Cindy Hines
Opening Times: 0900-1700 Mon-Sat & B/hols. Closed Sun.
Cat. Cost: Free
Credit Cards: All, except American Express
Specialities: Architectural plants & hardy exotics esp. rare evergreen broadleaved trees & seaside exotics, spiky plants, yuccas/agaves, climbers, topiary & bamboos.
Notes: Also sells wholesale. Delivers to shows. Wheelchair accessible.
Map Ref: S, C3 **OS Grid Ref:** TQ192262

SBch **Birchwood Plants**
(Office) 10 Westering, Romsey, Hampshire
SO51 7LY
Ⓣ (01794) 502192
Ⓔ info@birchwoodplants.co.uk
Ⓦ www.birchwoodplants.co.uk
Contact: Lesley Baker
Opening Times: Not open to the public. Plants can be collected by arrangement from nursery or from sales & shows, see website or phone for details.
Min Mail Order UK: £15 + p&p
Min Mail Order EU: £15+ p&p
Cat. Cost: Online only.
Credit Cards: Paypal
Specialities: Alpines & drought-tolerant plants. Plants to attract bees & butterflies. Predominantly growing peat-free. National Collection of *Geranium nodosum*. Most stock only available in very small quantities unless ordered well in advance.
Notes: Nursery at Silverwood House, Gardener's Lane, Nr Romsey, SO51 6AD. Mail order mostly for small plants. No mail order sent Dec-Jan. Delivers to shows.
Map Ref: S, D2 **OS Grid Ref:** SU333190

SBdl **Grow at Brogdale**
Brogdale Farm, Brogdale Road,
Faversham, Kent
ME13 8XZ
Ⓣ (01795) 531888
Ⓕ (01795) 531710
Ⓔ fruit@brogdaleonline.co.uk
Ⓦ www.brogdaleonline.co.uk
Contact: Donna Cooper
Min Mail Order UK: Nmc
Min Mail Order EU: Nmc
Cat. Cost: £4.95
Credit Cards: Visa, MasterCard, Switch
Specialities: Over 5000 fruit varieties, most of which can be propagated to order. Holders of several Nat. Collections of Fruit.
Notes: Also sells wholesale. Exports beyond EU. Euro accepted.

SBee **Beechbridge Plants**
Goudhurst Road, Marden, Tonbridge, Kent
TN12 9NN
Ⓣ (01622) 832237
Ⓜ 07914 019943
Ⓔ vicusplum@yahoo.co.uk
Ⓦ www.beechbridgeplants.co.uk
Contact: Victoria Mummery
Opening Times: Open by appt. only.
Min Mail Order UK: Nmc
Cat. Cost: Online only.
Credit Cards: None
Specialities: A small family-run nursery specialising in herbaceous perennials and grasses, many of which are unusual or hard to find. Virtually all plants are grown on the nursery. Stock only available in small quantities.
Notes: Please contact nursery before travelling a long distance to check current plant availability & make an appt.
Map Ref: S, C5 **OS Grid Ref:** TQ738436

SBig **Big Plant Nursery** ♿ ◆
Hole Street, Ashington, West Sussex
RH20 3DE
Ⓣ (01903) 891466
Ⓜ 07957 262845
Ⓕ (01903) 892829
Ⓔ info@bigplantnursery.co.uk
Ⓦ www.bigplantnursery.co.uk
Contact: Bruce Jordan
Opening Times: 0900-1700 Mon-Sat, 1000-1600 Sun & B/hols.
Min Mail Order UK: Please phone for further info.
Cat. Cost: A5 sae with 2 × 1st class.
Credit Cards: All major credit/debit cards
Specialities: Bamboos, hardy exotics & palms, *Ginkgo*, *Betula*.
Notes: Programme of events & propagation tuition, see website or phone for details. Also sells wholesale. Delivers to shows. Wheelchair accessible.
Map Ref: S, D3 **OS Grid Ref:** TQ132153

SBir **Birchfleet Nurseries** ♿ ◆
Greenfields Close, Nyewood,
Petersfield, Hampshire
GU31 5JQ
Ⓣ (01730) 821636
Ⓕ (01730) 821636
Ⓔ gammoak@aol.com
Ⓦ www.birchfleetnurseries.co.uk
Contact: John & Daphne Gammon
Opening Times: By appt. only. Please phone.
Cat. Cost: 2 × 1st class.
Credit Cards: None
Specialities: Oaks. Beech. *Nyssa*. Nat. Collection of *Liquidambar*.

S

Notes: Also sells wholesale. Nursery accessible for wheelchairs in dry weather.
Map Ref: S, C3

SBod **BODIAM NURSERY**
Bodiam, Robertsbridge, East Sussex
TN32 5RA
Ⓣ (01580) 830811
Ⓜ 07971 419302
Ⓔ enquiries@bodiamnursery.co.uk
Ⓦ www.bodiamnursery.co.uk
Contact: Jill Kaye
Opening Times: 1000-1700 Tue-Sun, 1st Mar-31st Oct. Closed Nov-Feb.
Cat. Cost: None issued.
Credit Cards: All major credit/debit cards
Specialities: Wide range of *Acer palmatum*, available in small numbers of each variety. Coastal & Mediterranean plants. Many other compact & slow-growing shrubs & perennials suitable for small gardens & containers.
Notes: Between Great Dixter & Merriments Gardens, opposite Bodiam Castle, next to the level crossing for the steam railway. Delivers to shows.

SBri **BRICKWALL COTTAGE NURSERY**
1 Brickwall Cottages, Frittenden, Cranbrook, Kent TN17 2DH
Ⓣ (01580) 852425
Ⓜ 07714 529946
Ⓔ sue.martin@talktalk.net
Ⓦ www.geumcollection.co.uk
Contact: Sue Martin
Opening Times: By appt. only.
Min Mail Order UK: Nmc
Min Mail Order EU: Nmc
Credit Cards: None
Specialities: Hardy perennials. Stock available in small quantities only. Nat. Collection of *Geum*.
Notes: Limited wheelchair access.
Map Ref: S, C5 **OS Grid Ref:** TQ815410

SBrk **BROOKFIELD PLANTS**
Bigelle, Sandyhurst Lane, Ashford, Kent
TN25 4NX
Ⓣ (01233) 624934
Ⓜ 07944 213891
Ⓔ paulharris34@btinternet.com
Ⓦ www.brookfieldplants.com
Contact: Paul Harris
Opening Times: Visitors by appt. only.
Min Mail Order UK: Nmc
Min Mail Order EU: Nmc
Cat. Cost: £1.00
Credit Cards: All major credit/debit cards
Specialities: *Hemerocallis* & *Hosta*. Nat. Collection of *Hemerocallis* applied for.
Notes: Sells at shows. Euro accepted.

SBrm **BRAMBLY HEDGE**
Mill Lane, Sway, Hampshire SO41 8LN
Ⓣ (01590) 683570
Contact: Kim Williams
Opening Times: By appt. only in Jul & Aug.
Min Mail Order UK: Nmc
Cat. Cost: Sae for descriptive list.
Credit Cards: None
Specialities: Nat. Collections of *Begonia rex* cvs. Plants available in small quantities only.
Notes: Mail order Mar-Aug, small quantities only.

SBrt **BRIGHTON PLANTS** ♿
New Hall Lane, Small Dole, Sussex BN5 9YJ
Ⓜ 07955 744802
Ⓔ brighton.plants@gmail.com
Ⓦ www.brightonplants.blogspot.com/
Contact: Steve Law
Opening Times: 1000-1700 w/ends, May-Oct & B/hols. Please email/phone first.
Min Mail Order UK: Nmc
Min Mail Order EU: Nmc
Cat. Cost: 3 × 1st class.
Credit Cards: All major credit/debit cards
Specialities: Hardy herbaceous and woody plants. Drought-tolerant plants.
Notes: Exports beyond EU. Delivers to shows. Wheelchair accessible.
Map Ref: S, D3 **OS Grid Ref:** TQ208132

SCac **CACTI & SUCCULENTS**
Hammerfield, Crockham Hill, Edenbridge, Kent TN8 6RR
Ⓣ (01732) 866295
Contact: Geoff Southon
Opening Times: Flexible. Please phone first.
Min Mail Order UK: Nmc
Cat. Cost: None issued.
Credit Cards: None
Specialities: *Echeveria* & related genera & hybrids. A large range of *Aeonium*, both species & hybrids, possibly the largest collection in the country. Many available in small quantities only.

SCam **CAMELLIA GROVE NURSERY** ♿
Market Garden, Lower Beeding, West Sussex
RH13 6PP
Ⓣ (01403) 891412
Ⓔ lp@hortic.com
Ⓦ www.camellia-grove.com
Contact: Chris Loder
Opening Times: 1000-1600 Mon-Sat, please phone first so we can give you our undivided attention.
Min Mail Order UK: Nmc
Min Mail Order EU: Nmc
Cat. Cost: 2 × 1st class.
Credit Cards: All, except American Express

Specialities: *Camellia japonica*, *C. williamsii*, *C. sasanqua* & *C. reticulata*, from the purest white to richest red flowers.
Notes: Also sells wholesale. Exports beyond EU. Delivers to shows. Euro accepted. Wheelchair accessible.
Map Ref: S, C3 **OS Grid Ref:** TQ221255

SChF **CHARLESHURST FARM NURSERY**
Loxwood Road, Plaistow, Billingshurst, West Sussex RH14 0NY
Ⓣ (01403) 752273
Ⓜ 07736 522788
Ⓔ Charleshurstfarm@aol.com
Ⓦ www.charleshurstplants.co.uk
Contact: Clive Mellor
Opening Times: Normally 0900-1730 Fri, Sat, Sun, Feb-Oct, but please ring first before travelling.
Min Mail Order UK: Nmc
Min Mail Order EU: Nmc
Cat. Cost: 2 × 1st class.
Credit Cards: All major credit/debit cards
Specialities: Shrubs including some more unusual species. Good range of daphnes & Japanese maples.
Notes: Delivers to shows. Euro accepted.
Map Ref: S, C3 **OS Grid Ref:** TQ015308

SChr **JOHN CHURCHER**
47 Grove Avenue, Portchester, Fareham, Hampshire PO16 9EZ
Ⓣ (023) 9232 6740
Ⓜ 07717 495861
Ⓔ johnchurcher47@btinternet.com
Contact: John Churcher
Opening Times: By appt. only. Please phone or email.
Min Mail Order UK: Nmc
Min Mail Order EU: Nmc
Cat. Cost: None issued.
Credit Cards: None
Specialities: Hardy exotics for the Mediterranean-style garden, incl. palms, tree ferns, *Musa*, hedychiums, cycads, *Agave*, *Aloe*, *Opuntia* & echiums. Stock available in small quantities only.
Map Ref: S, D2 **OS Grid Ref:** SU614047

SCit **THE CITRUS CENTRE** ♿
West Mare Lane, Marehill, Pulborough, West Sussex RH20 2EA
Ⓣ (01798) 872786
Ⓔ enquiries@citruscentre.co.uk
Ⓦ www.citruscentre.co.uk
Contact: Amanda & Chris Dennis
Opening Times: 0930-1600 Tue-Sat. Phone for Xmas & B/hol opening times.
Min Mail Order UK: Nmc
Min Mail Order EU: Nmc
Cat. Cost: Online.
Credit Cards: Visa, MasterCard
Specialities: *Citrus* & *Citrus* relatives.
Notes: Wheelchair accessible.
Map Ref: S, D3

SCmr **CROMAR NURSERY** ♿
39 Livesey Street, North Pole, Wateringbury, Maidstone, Kent ME18 5BQ
Ⓣ (01622) 812380
Ⓔ CromarNursery@aol.com
Ⓦ www.cromarnursery.co.uk
Contact: Debra & Martin Cronk
Opening Times: 0930-1700 daily except Wed. Winter opening 0930-1630 Thu, Fri, Sat, Sun. Please check website or phone if travelling far.
Min Mail Order UK: Nmc
Min Mail Order EU: Nmc
Cat. Cost: 2 × 1st class.
Credit Cards: All major credit/debit cards
Specialities: Ornamental & fruit trees.
Notes: Wheelchair accessible.
Map Ref: S, C4 **OS Grid Ref:** TQ697547

SCob **COBLANDS NURSERIES** ♿
Trench Road, Tonbridge, Kent TN11 9NG
Ⓣ (01732) 350517
Ⓔ info@coblands.co.uk
Ⓦ www.coblands.co.uk
Contact: Lewis Normand
Opening Times: 0900-1630 Mon-Sat, all year. Closed for Xmas/New Year.
Min Mail Order UK: Nmc
Min Mail Order EU: Nmc
Cat. Cost: Online & seasonal postings to existing customers.
Credit Cards: All major credit/debit cards
Specialities: Wide range of plants esp. herbaceous perennials of garden-worthiness incl. many new varieties, *Hebe*, *Hydrangea*, *Phormium*, *Brunnera*, *Echinacea*, *Epimedium*, *Heuchera*, *Hosta*, *Rudbeckia* & ferns. Wide range of established specimen plants. New introductions may be in limited supply.
Notes: Direct online ordering service. Bare-rooted fruit trees, ornamental trees & hedging available seasonally. Also sells wholesale. Wheelchair accessible.
Map Ref: S, C4 **OS Grid Ref:** TQ586487

SCog **COGHURST CAMELLIAS** ♿
Ivy House Lane, Near Three Oaks, Hastings, East Sussex TN35 4NP
Ⓣ (01424) 756228
Ⓔ rotherview@btinternet.com
Ⓦ www.rotherview.com
Contact: R Bates & W Bates
Opening Times: 1000-1630 7 days, Mar-Sep. 1000-1530 Tue-Sun, Oct-Feb.

Min Mail Order UK: Nmc
Min Mail Order EU: Nmc
Cat. Cost: 6 × 1st class.
Credit Cards: All major credit/debit cards
Specialities: *Camellia.*
Notes: Nursery is on the same site as Rotherview Nursery. Delivers to shows. Euro accepted. Wheelchair accessible.
Map Ref: S, D5

SCoo **Cooling's Nurseries Ltd** ♿
Rushmore Hill, Knockholt, Sevenoaks, Kent TN14 7NN
Ⓣ (01959) 532269
Ⓕ (01959) 534092
Ⓔ Plantfinder@coolings.co.uk
Ⓦ www.coolings.co.uk
Contact: Mark Reeve or Gary Norris
Opening Times: 0900-1700 Mon-Sat & 0900-1630 Sun.
Min Mail Order UK: Nmc
Cat. Cost: None issued
Credit Cards: All, except American Express
Specialities: Large range of perennials, conifers & bedding plants. Many unusual shrubs & trees. Third generation family business.
Notes: Display garden. Coffee shop. Wheelchair accessible.
Map Ref: S, C4 **OS Grid Ref:** TK477610

SDay **A La Carte Daylilies**
Little Hermitage, St Catherine's Down, Ventnor, Isle of Wight PO38 2PD
Ⓣ (01983) 730512
Ⓔ andy@alacartedaylilies.co.uk
Ⓦ www.alacartedaylilies.co.uk
Contact: Jan & Andy Wyers
Opening Times: Mail order only. Open by appt. only. Difficult to find on an unmade private road, phone/email for directions.
Min Mail Order UK: Nmc
Min Mail Order EU: Nmc
Cat. Cost: 3 × 1st class.
Credit Cards: None
Specialities: *Hemerocallis*. Nat. Collections of Miniature & Small Flowered *Hemerocallis* & Large Flowered *Hemerocallis* (post-1960 award-winning cultivars).
Notes: Euro accepted.
Map Ref: S, D2 **OS Grid Ref:** SZ499787

SDea **Deacon's Nursery** ◆
Moor View, Godshill, Isle of Wight PO38 3HW
Ⓣ (01983) 840750 (24 hrs) or (01983) 522243
Ⓕ (01983) 523575
Ⓔ info@deaconsnurseryfruits.co.uk
Ⓦ www.deaconsnurseryfruits.co.uk
Contact: G D & B H W Deacon
Opening Times: 0800-1600 Mon-Fri May-Sep, 0800-1700 Mon-Fri 0800-1200 Sat Oct-Apr.
Min Mail Order UK: Nmc
Min Mail Order EU: Nmc
Cat. Cost: Free.
Credit Cards: All major credit/debit cards
Specialities: Over 300 varieties of apple, old & new, apricots, cherries, damsons, gages, nectarines, peaches, pears, plums. Modern soft fruit, grapes, hops, nuts & family trees.
Notes: Also sells wholesale. Exports beyond EU. Euro accepted.
Map Ref: S, D2

SDeJ **P. de Jager & Sons Ltd** ♿ ◆
Church Farm, Ulcombe, Maidstone, Kent ME17 1DN
Ⓣ (01622) 840229
Ⓕ (01622) 844073
Ⓔ flowerbulbs@dejager.co.uk
Ⓦ www.dejager.co.uk
Contact: George Clowes
Opening Times: Mail order only. Orders taken from 0900-1700 Mon-Fri
Min Mail Order UK: Nmc
Min Mail Order EU: Nmc
Cat. Cost: Free
Credit Cards: All major credit/debit cards
Specialities: Wide range of all flower bulbs.
Notes: Also sells wholesale. Exports beyond EU. Euro accepted. Wheelchair accessible.

SDir **Direct Bulbs**
Mault Ley, Hillside Close, Winchester, Hampshire SO22 5LW
Ⓣ (01962) 840038
Ⓔ jo@directbulbs.com
Ⓦ www.directbulbs.co.uk
Contact: Jo Woodland
Opening Times: 0900-1700 Mon-Fri.
Min Mail Order UK: £5.95
Min Mail Order EU: £20.00
Credit Cards: All major credit/debit cards
Specialities: Bulbs.

SDix **Great Dixter Nurseries** ♿
Northiam, Rye, East Sussex TN31 6PH
Ⓣ (01797) 254044
Ⓕ (01797) 252879
Ⓔ nursery@greatdixter.co.uk
Ⓦ www.greatdixter.co.uk
Contact: Michael Morphy
Opening Times: 0900-1700 7 days, Apr-Oct. 0900-1630 Mon-Fri, 0900-1230 Sat, closed Sun, Nov-Mar.
Min Mail Order UK: Nmc
Min Mail Order EU: Nmc

Cat. Cost: 5 × 1st class.
Credit Cards: All major credit/debit cards
Specialities: *Clematis*, shrubs and plants. Gardens open.
Notes: Plants dispatched Sep-Mar only. Wheelchair accessible.
Map Ref: S, C5 **OS Grid Ref:** TQ821251

SDow **Downderry Nursery** ♿
Pillar Box Lane, Hadlow, Nr Tonbridge, Kent TN11 9SW
Ⓣ (01732) 810081
Ⓕ (01732) 811398
Ⓔ info@downderry-nursery.co.uk
Ⓦ www.downderry-nursery.co.uk
Contact: Dr Simon Charlesworth
Opening Times: 1000-1700 Wed-Sun 1st May-30th Sep & B/hols. Other times by appt.
Min Mail Order UK: Nmc
Min Mail Order EU: Nmc
Cat. Cost: Free.
Credit Cards: Delta, MasterCard, Maestro, Visa
Specialities: Nat. Collections of *Lavandula* and *Rosmarinus*.
Notes: Exports beyond EU. Euro accepted. Wheelchair accessible.
Map Ref: S, C4 **OS Grid Ref:** TQ625521

SDys **Dysons Nurseries** ♿
Great Comp Garden, Platt, Sevenoaks, Kent TN15 8QS
Ⓣ (01732) 885094
Ⓜ 07887 997663
Ⓔ dysonsorders@greatcompgarden.co.uk
Ⓦ www.dysonsalvias.com
Contact: William T Dyson
Opening Times: 1100-1700 7 days 1st Apr-31st Oct. Other times by appt.
Cat. Cost: Online only.
Credit Cards: All major credit/debit cards
Specialities: Salvias & an eclectic range of choice and uncommon plants.
Notes: Delivers to shows. Wheelchair accessible.
Map Ref: S, C4

SEle **Eleplants Nursery**
32 Framfield Road, Uckfield, East Sussex TN22 5AH
Ⓣ (01825) 760356
Ⓜ 07810 660109
Ⓔ eleplantsnursery@talk21.com
Ⓦ www.eleplantsnursery.co.uk
Contact: Martin Batchelor
Opening Times: Not open but can be visited by prior appt. only.
Min Mail Order UK: Nmc
Min Mail Order EU: Nmc
Credit Cards: All major credit/debit cards, Paypal
Specialities: Shrubs.
Notes: Exports beyond EU. Delivers to shows.

SEND **East Northdown Farm & Gardens** ♿
George Hill Road (B2052), Margate, Kent CT9 3TS
Ⓣ (01843) 862060
Ⓜ 07714 241668 or 07714 241667
Ⓔ info@botanyplants.co.uk
Ⓦ www.botanyplants.co.uk
Contact: Louise & William Friend
Opening Times: 0900-1700 7 days, all year except Sun in winter. Closed Xmas week.
Min Mail Order UK: Nmc
Cat. Cost: Online only.
Credit Cards: All major credit/debit cards
Specialities: Chalk & coast-loving plants. Specimen shrubs & bamboos available. Complimentary range of plants for damp/acid conditions available to order from our Mucklestone Nursery (MMuc). Collection of rare Mediterranean plants.
Notes: Tearoom & gardens. Lectures given to gardening groups in Kent. Garden tours by appt. Free consultation/advice. Plant selection & planting service. Wheelchair accessible.
Map Ref: S, B6 **OS Grid Ref:** TR383702

SEWo **English Woodlands** ♿
Burrow Nursery, Herrings Lane, Cross-in-Hand, Heathfield, East Sussex TN21 0UG
Ⓣ (01435) 862992
Ⓕ (01435) 867742
Ⓔ sales@englishwoodlands.com
Ⓦ www.englishwoodlands.com
Contact: Joanne Carter
Opening Times: 0800-1700 Mon-Fri. 0800-1630 Sat. Closed Sun & B/hols.
Min Mail Order UK: £25.00
Cat. Cost: Free.
Credit Cards: All, except American Express
Specialities: Trees, shrubs, hedging.
Notes: Also sells wholesale. Wheelchair accessible.
Map Ref: S, C4 **OS Grid Ref:** TQ567222

SFai **Fairweather's Garden Centre** ♿
High Street, Beaulieu, Hampshire SO42 7YB
Ⓣ (01590) 612307
Ⓕ (01590) 612519
Ⓔ info@fairweathers.co.uk
Ⓦ www.fairweathers.co.uk
Contact: Sue Greaves
Opening Times: 0900-1700 7 days.
Min Mail Order UK: Nmc
Cat. Cost: None issued.
Credit Cards: Visa, MasterCard

Specialities: *Agapanthus* & *Lavandula*.
Notes: Wheelchair accessible.
Map Ref: S, D2

SFgr **FIRGROVE PLANTS**
24 Wykeham Field, Wickham, Fareham, Hampshire PO17 5AB
Ⓣ (01329) 835206 after 1900 hours.
Ⓔ jenny@firgroveplants.demon.co.uk
Ⓦ www.firgroveplants.demon.co.uk
Contact: Jenny MacKinnon
Opening Times: Not open. Mail order only.
Min Mail Order UK: £10.50
Cat. Cost: Sae.
Credit Cards: None
Specialities: Wide range of houseleeks in small quantities.
Notes: Houseleeks by mail order Apr-mid Oct.

S

SFrt **FRUIT GARDEN PLANTS** ♿ ◆
Woolton Farm, Bekesbourne, Canterbury, Kent CT4 5EA
Ⓣ (01227) 830525
Ⓜ 07710 253690
Ⓕ (01227) 831969
Ⓔ sales@fruitgardenplants.co.uk
Ⓦ www.fruitgardenplants.co.uk
Contact: Mark Mount
Opening Times: 1000-1600 Thu-Sat, 1st Nov-31st Mar. 1000-1700 Thu-Sun, 1st Apr-31st Oct.
Min Mail Order UK: £10.00
Min Mail Order EU: £35.00
Credit Cards: MasterCard, Visa
Specialities: Tree fruits & soft fruits.
Notes: Fruit display garden where visitors can see particular varieties & the methods used for growing them. Small café. Medieval tythe barn. Also sells wholesale. Delivers to shows. Wheelchair accessible.
Map Ref: S, C5 **OS Grid Ref:** TR191568

SGbt **GILBERT'S NURSERY** ♿
Dandy's Ford Lane, Sherfield English, Romsey, Hampshire SO51 6DT
Ⓣ (01794) 322566
Ⓔ gilbertsnursery@aol.com
Ⓦ www.gilbertsnursery.co.uk
Contact: Nick Gilbert
Opening Times: 0900-1700 Tue-Sat, 10.00-16.30 Sun, all year round. *Dahlia* field open from 2nd week Aug to 2nd week Oct.
Min Mail Order UK: Nmc
Min Mail Order EU: Nmc
Cat. Cost: 2 × 1st class
Credit Cards: All, except American Express
Specialities: *Dahlia*. Proper plant nursery with many unusual plants & staff happy to share their knowledge & help with plant selection.
Notes: *Dahlia* field with over 400 cvs on view (grass pathways). See above for opening times or go to www.gilbertsdahlias.co.uk. Tea room. Delivers to shows. Wheelchair accessible.
Map Ref: S, C2

SGol **GOLDEN HILL NURSERIES** ♿
Lordsfield, Goudhurst Road, Marden, Kent TN12 9LT
Ⓣ (01622) 833218
Ⓜ 07826 523655
Ⓕ (01622) 832528
Ⓔ enquiries@goldenhillplants.com
Ⓦ www.goldenhillplants.com
Contact: Roger Butler
Opening Times: 0900-1700 Mon-Sat, 1st Mar-31st Oct. 0900-1600 Mon-Sat, 1st Nov-28th Feb. 1100-1600 Sun from 3rd Sun in Feb until Xmas.
Min Mail Order UK: Nmc
Cat. Cost: Online only.
Credit Cards: All major credit/debit cards
Specialities: Specimen plants, shrubs, grasses, bamboos, Japanese maples, conifers & trees.
Notes: Also sells wholesale. Euro accepted. Wheelchair accessible.

SHaC **HART CANNA** ♿
27 Guildford Road West, Farnborough, Hampshire GU14 6PS
Ⓣ (01252) 514421
Ⓜ 07762 950000
Ⓔ sales@hartcanna.com
Ⓦ www.hartcanna.co.uk
Contact: Keith Hayward
Opening Times: By arrangement.
Min Mail Order UK: Nmc
Min Mail Order EU: Nmc
Cat. Cost: Sae.
Credit Cards: All major credit/debit cards
Specialities: *Canna*. Nat. Collection of *Canna*.
Notes: Also sells wholesale. Euro accepted. Delivers to shows. Wheelchair accessible.
Map Ref: S, C3

SHal **HALL'S COURT NURSERY** ♿
Pluckley Road, Bethersden, Ashford, Kent TN26 3ET
Ⓣ (01233) 820828
Ⓜ 07729 418275
Ⓔ info@hallscourt.co.uk
Ⓦ www.hallscourt.co.uk
Contact: Jeanette Jahnz
Opening Times: 0900-1700 every w/end, end Mar-beginning Oct. Weekdays by appt.
Cat. Cost: Online only.
Credit Cards: None
Specialities: Around 90 varieties of hardy geraniums & around 50 varieties of pelargoniums, incl. some species. Also alpines,

herbs, some succulents, perennials, hardy fuchsias & grasses. Some plants available in small quantities only.
Notes: Small nursery, situated midway between Ashford and Tenterden in rural Kent. Euro accepted. Wheelchair accessible.
Map Ref: S, C5 **OS Grid Ref:** TQ919414

SHar **HARDY'S COTTAGE GARDEN PLANTS** ♿
Priory Lane Nursery, Freefolk Priors, Whitchurch, Hampshire RG28 7NJ
Ⓣ (01256) 896533
Ⓔ info@hardys-plants.co.uk
Ⓦ www.hardys-plants.co.uk
Contact: Rosemary Hardy
Opening Times: 1000-1700 7 days, 1st Mar-30th Sep. 1000-1600 Mon-Fri, Oct, 1000-1500 Mon-Fri, 1st Nov-28th Feb. Closed 23rd Dec-4th Jan.
Min Mail Order UK: Nmc
Cat. Cost: Online only.
Credit Cards: Visa, Access, Electron, Switch, Solo
Specialities: Wide range of herbaceous perennials incl. *Achillea*, *Gaura*, *Geum*, *Geranium*, *Hemerocallis*, *Heuchera*, *Lathryus vernus*, *Paeonia*, *Penstemon* & *Salvia*.
Notes: Accepts HTA Gift Tokens. Offers trade discount. Also sells wholesale. Euro accepted. Delivers to shows. Wheelchair accessible.
Map Ref: S, C2

SHDw **HIGHDOWN NURSERY**
New Hall Lane, Small Dole, Nr Henfield, West Sussex BN5 9YH
Ⓣ (01273) 492976
Ⓜ 07900 956456
Ⓕ (01273) 492976
Ⓔ highdown.herbs@btinternet.com
Ⓦ www.highdownnursery.com
Contact: A G & J H Shearing
Opening Times: 0900-1700 7 days.
Min Mail Order UK: £10.00 + p&p
Cat. Cost: 3 × 1st class.
Credit Cards: None
Specialities: Herbs. Grasses.
Notes: Also sells wholesale. Delivers to shows. Euro accepted. Partial wheelchair access.
Map Ref: S, D3 **OS Grid Ref:** TV214134

SHeu **HEUCHERAHOLICS** ♿
Boldre Nurseries, Southampton Road, Lymington, Hampshire SO41 8ND
Ⓣ (01590) 670581
Ⓜ 07973 291062
Ⓔ jooles.heucheraholics@gmail.com
Ⓦ www.heucheraholics.co.uk
Contact: Julie Burton/Sean Atkinson
Opening Times: Visits to nursery by appt. only. Please phone first. No need to make an appt. for Open Days, see website or contact nursery for details.
Min Mail Order UK: Nmc
Cat. Cost: No charge.
Credit Cards: All major credit/debit cards
Specialities: *Heuchera*, *Heucherella*, *Pulmonaria* & *Tiarella*. Other foliage plants. *Hellebore*.
Notes: Toilet facilities. Well-behaved dogs can bring their owners. Also sells wholesale. Delivers to shows. Wheelchair accessible.
Map Ref: S, D2 **OS Grid Ref:** SZ310934

SHil **HILLIER GARDEN CENTRES**
Ampfield House, Ampfield, Romsey, Hampshire SO51 9PA
Ⓣ (01794) 368407
Ⓔ onlineshop@hillier.co.uk
Ⓦ www.hillieronline.co.uk
Opening Times: Office 0830-1700 Mon-Fri. Garden Centres: 0900-1730 Mon-Sat, 1030-1630 Sun.
Min Mail Order UK: Nmc
Cat. Cost: None issued.
Credit Cards: All major credit/debit cards
Notes: Other nursery branches in the south of England.

SHmp **HAMPSHIRE CARNIVOROUS PLANTS**
Stroudwood Nursery, Stroudwood Lane, Lower Upham, Southampton, Hampshire SO32 1HG
Ⓣ (023) 8047 3314
Ⓜ 07703 258296
Ⓕ (023) 8047 3314
Ⓔ sales@hantsflytrap.com
Ⓦ www.hantsflytrap.com
Contact: Matthew Soper
Opening Times: Mail order only. Open by appt. only.
Min Mail Order UK: Nmc
Min Mail Order EU: £50.00 + p&p
Credit Cards: All major credit/debit cards
Specialities: Carnivorous plants esp. *Cephalotus*, *Darlingtonia*, *Dionaea*, *Drosera*, *Heliamphora*, *Nepenthes*, *Pinguicula*, *Sarracenia* & *Utricularia*.
Notes: Also sells wholesale. Exports beyond the EU. Euro accepted.

SHyH **HYDRANGEA HAVEN** ♿
Market Garden, Lower Beeding, West Sussex RH13 6PP
Ⓣ (01403) 891412
Ⓔ lp@hortic.com
Ⓦ www.hydrangea-haven.com
Contact: Chris Loder
Opening Times: 1000-1600 Mon-Sat, please phone first, so we can give you our undivided attention.

Min Mail Order UK: Nmc
Min Mail Order EU: Nmc
Cat. Cost: 2 × 1st class.
Credit Cards: All, except American Express
Specialities: *Hydrangea*: mophead, lacecap & panicle. *Agapanthus*.
Notes: Also sells wholesale. Exports beyond EU. Delivers to shows. Euro accepted. Wheelchair accessible.
Map Ref: S, C3 **OS Grid Ref:** TQ221255

SIde **IDEN CROFT HERBS** ♿
Frittenden Road, Staplehurst, Kent TN12 0DH
Ⓣ (01580) 891432
Ⓔ idencroftherbs@yahoo.co.uk
Ⓦ www.uk-herbs.com
Contact: Tracey Connors-Parry
Opening Times: 1100-1700 Mon, Tue, Fri, Sat, Sun (closed Wed & Thu) Mar-Sep. Closed Oct-Feb.
Min Mail Order UK: Nmc
Min Mail Order EU: Nmc
Cat. Cost: Online only.
Credit Cards: All, except American Express
Specialities: Herbs, aromatic & wildflower plants & plants for bees & butterflies. Nat. Collections of *Mentha* & *Origanum*.
Notes: Wheelchairs available at nursery.
Map Ref: S, C5

SIgm **TIM INGRAM** ♿
Copton Ash, 105 Ashford Road, Faversham, Kent ME13 8XW
Ⓣ (01795) 535919
Ⓔ coptonash@yahoo.co.uk
Ⓦ coptonash.plus.com
Contact: Dr T J Ingram
Opening Times: 1400-1800 Fri & Sat, Mar-Oct. Other times by appt.
Credit Cards: None
Specialities: Small, specialised nursery, offering mainly alpines and spring plants. Many unusual plants available in small quantities.
Notes: Delivers to shows. Wheelchair accessible.
Map Ref: S, C5 **OS Grid Ref:** TR015598

SIri **IRIS OF SISSINGHURST**
Roughlands Farm, Goudhurst Road, Marden, Kent TN12 9NH
Ⓣ (01622) 831511
Ⓔ orders@irisofsissinghurst.com
Ⓦ www.irisofsissinghurst.com
Contact: Sue Marshall
Opening Times: Contact nursery or see website for opening times.
Min Mail Order UK: Nmc
Min Mail Order EU: Nmc
Cat. Cost: Online only.
Credit Cards: None
Specialities: *Iris*, short, intermediate & tall bearded, *ensata*, *sibirica* & many species.
Notes: Euro accepted.

SKee **KEEPERS NURSERY**
Gallants Court, Gallants Lane, East Farleigh, Maidstone, Kent ME15 0LE
Ⓣ (01622) 726465
Ⓕ 0870 705 2145
Ⓔ info@keepers-nursery.co.uk
Contact: Hamid Habibi
Opening Times: Only on a limited number of Open Days & for collection of trees & plants by arrangement.
Min Mail Order UK: Nmc
Cat. Cost: Online only.
Credit Cards: Visa, MasterCard, Switch, Maestro
Specialities: A very large range of fruit trees incl. old & rare as well as modern varieties. Soft fruit plants & nut trees.

SKHP **KEVIN HUGHES PLANTS** ♿
(Office) Heale House, Middle Woodford, Salisbury, Wiltshire SP4 6NT
Ⓣ (01722) 782504
Ⓜ 07720 718671
Ⓔ info@kevinsplants.co.uk
Ⓦ www.kevinsplants.co.uk
Contact: Kevin Hughes
Opening Times: 1100-1700 Wed-Sat, 1st Feb-31st Oct. Other times by appt. only.
Min Mail Order UK: £10.00
Min Mail Order EU: £20.00
Cat. Cost: 3 × 1st class
Credit Cards: All, except American Express
Specialities: Less common & new hardy garden plants with a particular emphasis on *Magnolia*, *Trillium*, climbers, *Philadelphus*, *Viburnum* & *Syringa*. We try to select plants that are garden-worthy & attract wildlife. Many plants are slow to propagate & will always be in short supply. None are from wild-dug sources.
Notes: Nursery at Heale Garden, SP4 5NT. Exports beyond EU. Euro accepted. Wheelchair accessible.
Map Ref: S, C1 **OS Grid Ref:** SU125363

SKin **KINGS BARN TREES**
Kings Barn Farm, Kent Street, Cowfold, West Sussex RH13 8BB
Ⓣ (01403) 865405
Ⓜ 07908 708915
Ⓔ sales@kingsbarntrees.co.uk
Ⓦ www.kingsbarntrees.co.uk
Contact: Adrian Rumble
Opening Times: Not open. Mail order via website only.

Min Mail Order UK: £9.95
Min Mail Order EU: £9.95
Cat. Cost: Not available.
Credit Cards: All major credit/debit cards
Specialities: Mainly grow containerised trees, specialising in *Eucalyptus*. Also grow willow for sale as whips & setts during the winter/ early spring. *Eucalyptus* available in small quantities only.

SLau **THE LAURELS NURSERY** ♿
Benenden, Cranbrook, Kent TN17 4JU
Ⓣ (01580) 240463
Ⓦ www.thelaurelsnursery.co.uk
Contact: Peter or Sylvia Kellett
Opening Times: 0800-1600 Wed-Fri, 0900-1200 Sat, Sun by appt. only.
Min Mail Order UK: £30
Cat. Cost: Free.
Credit Cards: All major credit/debit cards
Specialities: Open ground & container ornamental trees, shrubs & climbers especially birch, beech & *Wisteria*.
Notes: Mail order of small *Wisteria* only. Also sells wholesale. Euro accepted. Wheelchair accessible.
Map Ref: S, C5 **OS Grid Ref:** TQ815313

SLay **LAYHAM GARDEN CENTRE & NURSERY** ♿
Lower Road, Staple, Nr Canterbury, Kent CT3 1LH
Ⓣ (01304) 813267
Ⓕ (01304) 814007
Ⓔ info@layhamgardencentre.co.uk
Ⓦ www.layhamgardencentre.co.uk
Contact: Ellen Wessel
Opening Times: 0900-1700 7 days.
Min Mail Order UK: Nmc
Min Mail Order EU: £25.00 + p&p
Cat. Cost: Free.
Credit Cards: Visa, MasterCard
Specialities: Roses, herbaceous, shrubs, trees & hedging plants.
Notes: Mail order roses only. Also sells wholesale. Euro accepted. Wheelchair accessible.
Map Ref: S, C6 **OS Grid Ref:** TR276567

SLBF **LITTLE BROOK FUCHSIAS** ♿
Ash Green Lane West, Ash Green, Nr Aldershot, Hampshire GU12 6HL
Ⓣ (01252) 329731
Ⓔ carol.gubler@ntlbusiness.com
Ⓦ www.littlebrookfuchsias.co.uk
Contact: Carol Gubler
Opening Times: 1000-1700 Wed-Sun 1st Jan-28th Jun.
Cat. Cost: 50p + sae.
Credit Cards: All major credit/debit cards
Specialities: Fuchsias, old & new.
Notes: Nursery located off White Lane in Ash Green. Wheelchair accessible.
Map Ref: S, C3 **OS Grid Ref:** SU901496

SLdr **LODER PLANTS** ♿
Market Garden, Lower Beeding, West Sussex RH13 6PP
Ⓣ (01403) 891412
Ⓔ sales@rhododendrons.com
Ⓦ www.rhododendrons.com
Contact: Chris Loder
Opening Times: 1000-1600 Mon-Sat, please ring first so we can give you our undivided attention.
Min Mail Order UK: Nmc
Min Mail Order EU: Nmc
Cat. Cost: 2 × 1st class.
Credit Cards: All, except American Express
Specialities: Rhododendrons & azaleas in all sizes. Some in very limited quantities only. *Agapanthus*.
Notes: Also sells wholesale. Exports beyond EU. Delivers to shows. Euro accepted. Wheelchair accessible.
Map Ref: S, C3 **OS Grid Ref:** TQ221255

SLim **LIME CROSS NURSERY** ♿
Herstmonceux, Hailsham, East Sussex BN27 4RS
Ⓣ (01323) 833229
Ⓔ info@limecross.co.uk
Ⓦ www.limecross.co.uk
Contact: Vicky Tate, Anita Green
Opening Times: 0830-1700 Mon-Sat & 1000-1600 Sun.
Min Mail Order UK: Nmc
Min Mail Order EU: £50.00
Cat. Cost: Online only.
Credit Cards: All major credit/debit cards
Specialities: Conifers, trees & shrubs, climbers.
Notes: Wheelchair accessible.
Map Ref: S, D4 **OS Grid Ref:** TQ642125

SLon **LONGSTOCK PARK NURSERY** ♿
Longstock, Stockbridge, Hampshire SO20 6EH
Ⓣ (01264) 810894
Ⓕ (01264) 810924
Ⓔ longstocknursery@leckfordestate.co.uk
Ⓦ www.longstocknursery.co.uk
Contact: Mark Pitman
Opening Times: 0900-1730 Mon-Sat, 1000-1700 Sun. Closed 25th-27th Dec & 1st Jan.
Min Mail Order UK: £15.00
Credit Cards: All major credit/debit cards
Specialities: A wide range, over 2000 varieties, of trees, shrubs, perennials, climbers, aquatics & ferns. Extensive collection of

S

Penstemon. Nat. Collections of *Buddleja* & *Clematis viticella*.
Notes: Wheelchair accessible.
Map Ref: S, C2 **OS Grid Ref:** SU365389

SMad **MADRONA NURSERY** ♿
Pluckley Road, Bethersden, Kent TN26 3DD
Ⓣ (01233) 820100
Ⓕ (01233) 820091
Ⓔ madrona@hotmail.co.uk
Ⓦ www.madrona.co.uk
Contact: Liam Mackenzie
Opening Times: 1000-1700 Sat-Tue 15th Mar-28th Oct. Other times by appt.
Cat. Cost: Free
Credit Cards: All major credit/debit cards
Specialities: Unusual shrubs, conifers & perennials. *Eryngium*, *Colletia*.
Notes: Delivers to shows. Euro accepted. Wheelchair accessible.
Map Ref: S, C5 **OS Grid Ref:** TQ918419

S

SMDP **MARCUS DANCER PLANTS**
Kilcreggan, Alderholt Road, Sandleheath, Fordingbridge, Hampshire SP6 1PT
Ⓣ (01425) 652747
Ⓜ 07709 922730
Ⓔ marcus.dancer@btopenworld.com
Ⓦ www.clematisplants.co.uk
Contact: Marcus Dancer
Opening Times: By appointment only.
Min Mail Order UK: Nmc
Cat. Cost: 4 × 1st class.
Credit Cards: None
Specialities: Wide range of *Clematis*, smaller range of *Daphne*. Some varieties available in small quantities only.
Notes: Mail order available for all plants. Delivers to shows.
Map Ref: S, D1

SMea **MEADOWGATE NURSERY**
Street End Lane, Sidlesham, Chichester, West Sussex PO20 7RG
Ⓣ (01243) 641997
Ⓜ 07736 523262
Ⓔ meadowgatenursery@tiscali.co.uk
Ⓦ www.meadowgatenursery.co.uk
Contact: David Allen
Opening Times: 1000-1700 Sat-Wed.
Min Mail Order UK: £35.00
Credit Cards: All major credit/debit cards
Specialities: Ornamental grasses.
Notes: Also sells wholesale. Delivers to shows.

SMHy **MARCHANTS HARDY PLANTS** ♿
2 Marchants Cottages, Mill Lane, Laughton, East Sussex BN8 6AJ
Ⓣ (01323) 811737
Ⓔ graham@marchantsplants.plus.com
Ⓦ www.marchantshardyplants.co.uk
Contact: Graham Gough
Opening Times: 0930-1730 Wed-Sat, 18th Mar-24th Oct 2015.
Cat. Cost: 3 × 2nd class
Credit Cards: Visa, MasterCard
Specialities: Uncommon herbaceous perennials. *Agapanthus*, *Erodium*, choice grasses, *Galanthus*, *Miscanthus*, *Molinia*.
Notes: Euro accepted. Wheelchair accessible.
Map Ref: S, D4 **OS Grid Ref:** TQ506119

SMor **MOREHAVENS**
Stocks Lane, Meonstoke, Hampshire SO32 3NQ
Ⓣ (01489) 878501
Ⓔ morehavens@camomilelawns.co.uk
Ⓦ www.camomilelawns.co.uk
Contact: E. Clements
Opening Times: Mail order only. Open for collection only.
Min Mail Order UK: £18.00
Min Mail Order EU: £18.00 + p&p
Cat. Cost: Free.
Credit Cards: Paypal
Specialities: *Camomile nobile* 'Treneague' and *C. nobile* dwarf.
Notes: Also sells wholesale.

SNig **NIGHTINGALE NURSERY** ♿
Gardeners Lane, East Wellow, Romsey, Hampshire SO51 6AD
Ⓣ 023 8081 4350
Ⓔ gfnightingale4@gmail.com
Ⓦ www.nightingalenursery.co.uk
Contact: Graham Farmiloe
Opening Times: 0800-1700 Mon-Fri & open 7 days from mid-Mar to mid-Jun.
Cat. Cost: Free.
Credit Cards: All, except American Express
Specialities: *Clematis*. Also climbers & wall shrubs; herbaceous; seasonal bedding; hanging baskets.
Notes: Also sells wholesale. Wheelchair accessible.
Map Ref: S, D2

SPad **PADDOCK PLANTS**
The Paddock, Upper Toothill Road, Rownhams, Southampton, Hampshire SO16 8AL
Ⓣ (023) 8073 9912
Ⓜ 07763 386717
Ⓔ rob@paddockplants.co.uk
Ⓦ www.paddockplants.co.uk
Contact: Rob & Joanna Courtney
Opening Times: By appt. only. Please telephone in advance.
Min Mail Order UK: £10.00
Cat. Cost: Online only.

Credit Cards: All major credit/debit cards
Specialities: A family-run nursery offering an interesting range of perennials, grasses, ferns & shrubs, incl. some more unusual varieties or plants new to the UK market. All plants are grown in a peat-free medium. Some varieties grown in small quantities.
Notes: Local delivery by our own transport. Courier delivery throughout UK. Delivers to shows.
Map Ref: S, D2 **OS Grid Ref:** SU383177

SPav **Pavilion Plants**
18 Pavilion Road, Worthing, West Sussex BN14 7EF
Ⓣ (01903) 821338
Ⓜ 07776 409498
Ⓔ pavilionplants.worthing@yahoo.co.uk
Contact: Andrew Muggeridge
Opening Times: Please phone for details.
Min Mail Order UK: Nmc
Cat. Cost: 4 × 1st class.
Credit Cards: None
Specialities: Perennials and bulbs. *Digitalis*.
Notes: Also sells wholesale.
Map Ref: S, D3

SPer **Perryhill Nurseries Ltd** ♿
Edenbridge Road, Hartfield, East Sussex TN7 4JP
Ⓣ (01892) 770377
Ⓕ (01892) 770929
Ⓔ sales@perryhillnurseries.co.uk
Ⓦ www.perryhillnurseries.co.uk
Contact: P J Chapman
Opening Times: 0900-1700 7 days 1st Mar-31st Oct. 0900-1630 1st Nov-28th Feb.
Min Mail Order UK: Nmc
Cat. Cost: Online only.
Credit Cards: Maestro, Visa, Access, MasterCard
Specialities: Wide range of trees, shrubs, perennials, roses, fruit trees, soft fruit. Unusual & rare plants may be available in small quantities.
Notes: Mail order despatch depends on size & weight of plants. Wheelchair accessible.
Map Ref: S, C4 **OS Grid Ref:** TQ480375

SPet **Pettet's Nursery** ♿
Drainless Road, Eastry, Sandwich, Kent CT13 0EA
Ⓣ (01304) 613869
Ⓜ 07940 337520
Ⓕ (01304) 613869
Ⓔ pettets.nursery@btconnect.com
Ⓦ www.pettetsnursery.co.uk
Contact: Terry Pettet
Opening Times: 1000-1600 Tue-Sun, Apr-Oct. Closed Mon (except B/hol). Closed Nov-Mar.
Min Mail Order UK: £10.00
Cat. Cost: Online only.
Credit Cards: None
Specialities: *Pelargonium*: scented, decorative regal, unique, angel. *Fuchsia*.
Notes: Delivers to shows. Wheelchair accessible.

SPhx **Phoenix Perennial Plants** ♿
Paice Lane, Medstead, Alton, Hampshire GU34 5PR
Ⓣ (01420) 560695
Ⓜ 07909 528191
Ⓕ (01420) 563640
Ⓔ marina@phoenixperennialplants.co.uk
Ⓦ www.phoenixperennialplants.co.uk
Contact: Marina Christopher
Opening Times: Open by appt. only.
Cat. Cost: 4 × 1st class.
Credit Cards: All major credit/debit cards
Specialities: Perennials, many uncommon & hardy, selected for beneficial insects particularly pollinators. *Agastache*, *Centaurea*, *Monarda*, *Sanguisorba*, *Sedum*, *Thalictrum*, *Verbascum*, bulbs, prairie plants, grasses, especially *Molinia* & late-flowering perennials.
Notes: Co-located with Select Seeds SSss. Also sells wholesale. Delivers to shows. Wheelchair accessible.
Map Ref: S, C2 **OS Grid Ref:** SU657362

SPin **John and Lynsey's Plants** ♿
2 Hillside Cottages, Trampers Lane, North Boarhunt, Fareham, Hampshire PO17 6DA
Ⓣ (01329) 832786
Ⓔ landjpink@tiscali.co.uk
Contact: Mrs Lynsey Pink
Opening Times: By appt. only. Open under NGS.
Cat. Cost: None issued.
Credit Cards: None
Specialities: Mainly *Salvia* with a wide range of other unusual perennials. Stock is only available in small quantities but we are happy to try & propagate anything that we have. Nat. Collection of species *Salvia*.
Notes: Wheelchair accessible.
Map Ref: S, D2 **OS Grid Ref:** SU603109

SPlb **Plantbase** ♿
Sleepers Stile Road, Cousley Wood, Wadhurst, East Sussex TN5 6QX
Ⓣ (01892) 785599
Ⓜ 07967 601064
Ⓔ graham@plantbase.freeserve.co.uk
Ⓦ www.plantbase.co.uk
Contact: Graham Blunt
Opening Times: 1000-1700, 7 days all year (appt. advisable).

Min Mail Order UK: Nmc
Min Mail Order EU: Nmc
Cat. Cost: Online only.
Credit Cards: All major credit/debit cards
Specialities: Wide range of alpines, perennials, shrubs, climbers, waterside plants, herbs, Australasian, South African & South American plants in particular. Some available in small quantities only.
Notes: Delivers to shows. Euro accepted. Wheelchair accessible.
Map Ref: S, C5

SPoG **THE POTTED GARDEN NURSERY** ♿
Ashford Road, Bearsted, Maidstone, Kent ME14 4NH
Ⓣ (01622) 737801
Ⓦ www.thepottedgarden.co.uk
Contact: Any staff member
Opening Times: 0900-1730 (dusk in winter), 7 days. Xmas/New Year period opening times on website or answerphone.
Credit Cards: All major credit/debit cards
Notes: Mail order not available. Wheelchair accessible.
Map Ref: S, C5 **OS Grid Ref:** TQ810550

SPol **POLLIE'S PERENNIALS AND DAYLILY NURSERY** ♿
Lodore, Mount Pleasant Lane, Sway, Lymington, Hampshire SO41 8LS
Ⓣ (01590) 682577
Ⓜ 07712 713765
Ⓕ (01590) 682577
Ⓔ terry.maasz@btinternet.com
Ⓦ www.polliesdaylilies.co.uk
Contact: Pollie Maasz
Opening Times: 1000-1730 w/ends & 1400-1730 Mon-Fri during the daylily season, late-May to mid-Aug. Other times by appt. only.
Min Mail Order UK: Nmc
Min Mail Order EU: £20.00
Cat. Cost: 2 × 1st class.
Credit Cards: Paypal
Specialities: *Hemerocallis*, also less commonly available hardy perennials. Stock available in small quantities only. Nat. Collection of Spider & Unusual Form *Hemerocallis*. 1700+ different cvs can be viewed, mid Jun-mid Sep.
Notes: Mail order, daylilies only. Euro accepted. Wheelchair accessible.
Map Ref: S, D2

SPop **POPS PLANTS**
Pops Cottage, Barford Lane, Downton, Salisbury, Wiltshire SP5 3PZ
Ⓣ (01725) 511421
Ⓔ mail@popsplants.com
Ⓦ www.popsplants.com
Contact: Lesley Roberts
Opening Times: By appt. only, please.
Min Mail Order UK: 5 plants.
Min Mail Order EU: 5 plants.
Cat. Cost: £2.50
Credit Cards: Paypal
Specialities: *Primula auricula*. Some varieties in limited numbers. Nat. Collection of Show, Alpine, Double & Striped Auriculas.
Notes: Credit cards accepted online only. Exports beyond EU (min. mail order outside EU 10 plants). Euro accepted.

SPre **PLANTS4PRESENTS** ◆
The Glasshouses, Fletching Common, Newick, Lewes, East Sussex BN8 4JJ
Ⓣ (01825) 721162
Ⓔ plants@4presents.co.uk
Ⓦ www.plants4presents.co.uk
Contact: Emily Rae
Opening Times: Not open. Mail order only.
Min Mail Order UK: Nmc
Min Mail Order EU: Nmc
Cat. Cost: Online only.
Credit Cards: All major credit/debit cards
Specialities: Well-established nursery offering a range of unusual flowering and fruiting plants, incl. citrus trees.
Notes: Delivers to shows.

SPtp **PLANTSTOPLANT**
Fromefield Nurseries Ltd, Church Lane, Awbridge, Romsey, Hampshire SO51 0HN
Ⓣ (01794) 341123
Ⓕ (01794) 341351
Ⓔ info@plantstoplant.com
Ⓦ www.plantstoplant.com
Contact: David West
Opening Times: Not open. Mail order only.
Min Mail Order UK: £12.00
Cat. Cost: Online only.
Credit Cards: All major credit/debit cards, Paypal
Specialities: Unusual plants.
Notes: Also sells wholesale.

SReu **G REUTHE LTD**
Crown Point Nursery, Sevenoaks Road, Ightham, Nr Sevenoaks, Kent TN15 0HB
Ⓣ (01732) 865614
Ⓔ reuthe@hotmail.co.uk
Contact: Sales
Opening Times: 0900-1600 Thu-Sat. Closed Jan, Feb, Jul & Aug. Please phone before visiting as we are sometimes closed due to circumstances beyond our control. Please ask for details of special spring openings.
Credit Cards: Visa, Access
Specialities: Rhododendrons & azaleas, trees, shrubs & climbers. Some plants only available in larger sizes. Large specimen plants available

in pots & open ground.
Notes: Deliveries can be arranged at cost. Landscaping & planting service.
Map Ref: S, C4

SRGP **Rosie's Garden Plants**
Fieldview Cottage, Pratling Street, Aylesford, Kent ME20 7DG
Ⓣ (01622) 715777
Ⓜ 07740 696277
Ⓕ (01622) 715777
Ⓔ jcaviolet@aol.com
Ⓦ www.rosiesgardenplants.biz
Contact: J C Aviolet
Opening Times: Not open. Mail order only.
Min Mail Order UK: Nmc
Min Mail Order EU: Nmc
Cat. Cost: Online only.
Specialities: Hardy *Geranium*, *Buddleja* & *Aster*. Herbaceous & shrubs. Roses. Grows & sells asters, hardy geraniums, roses, plants & shrubs with people's names.
Notes: Exports beyond EU. Delivers to shows. Check web for dates of shows, talks & Farmers' Markets.

SRiF **Riverside Fuchsias** ♿
Gravel Road, Sutton-at-Hone, Dartford, Kent DA4 9HQ
Ⓣ (01322) 863891
Ⓕ (01322) 863891
Ⓔ riverside_fuchsias@btopenworld.com
Ⓦ www.riversidefuchsias.pwp.blueyonder.co.uk
Contact: George & Nellie Puddefoot
Opening Times: 0900-1700, Tue, Wed, Fri, Sat & Sun.
Min Mail Order UK: £3.00 per plant, 10 plants min. order (incl. p&p).
Min Mail Order EU: 20.00 euros
Cat. Cost: 3 × 1st class. Addendum available Mar.
Credit Cards: All major credit/debit cards
Specialities: *Fuchsia*. Nat. Collection holder.
Notes: Specimen-sized plants available Mar-Sep. Also sells wholesale. Exports beyond EU. Euro accepted.
Map Ref: S, B4

SRiv **River Garden Nurseries**
Troutbeck, Otford, Sevenoaks, Kent TN14 5PH
Ⓣ (01959) 525588
Ⓕ (01959) 525810
Ⓔ box@river-garden.co.uk
Ⓦ www.river-garden.co.uk
Contact: Jenny Alban Davies
Opening Times: By appt. only.
Min Mail Order UK: £10.00 + p&p
Min Mail Order EU: £50.00 + p&p
Cat. Cost: 2 × 1st class.
Credit Cards: None
Specialities: *Buxus* species & cultivars. *Buxus* topiary.
Notes: Also sells wholesale. Euro accepted. Delivers to shows.
Map Ref: S, C4 **OS Grid Ref:** TQ523593

SRkn **Rapkyns Nursery** ♿
Street End Lane, Broad Oak, Heathfield, East Sussex TN21 8UB
Ⓣ (01825) 830065
Ⓜ 07771 916933
Ⓔ rapkynsnursery@hotmail.com
Ⓦ www.rapkynsnursery.co.uk
Contact: Steven Moore
Opening Times: 1000-1700 Tue, Thu & Fri, Mar-Oct incl. or by appt.
Min Mail Order UK: Nmc
Min Mail Order EU: Nmc
Cat. Cost: 2 × 1st class or online.
Credit Cards: None
Specialities: Unusual shrubs, perennials & climbers. Asters, campanulas, *Ceanothus*, geraniums, lavenders, *Clematis*, penstemons & grasses. New collections of *Crocosmia*, *Anemone*, *Heuchera*, *Heucherella*, *Phlox*, *Coreopsis* & *Helleborus*. Extensive range of salvias.
Notes: Nursery next door to Scotsford Farm, TN21 8UB. Mail order Sep-Apr incl. Also sells wholesale. Delivers to shows. Wheelchair accessible.
Map Ref: S, C4 **OS Grid Ref:** TQ604248

SRms **Rumsey Gardens** ♿
117 Drift Road, Clanfield, Waterlooville, Hampshire PO8 0PD
Ⓣ (023) 9259 3367
Ⓔ info@rumsey-gardens.co.uk
Ⓦ www.rumsey-gardens.co.uk
Contact: Mrs M A Giles
Opening Times: 0900-1700 Mon-Sat & 1000-1600 Sun & B/hols. Closed Sun Nov-Feb.
Min Mail Order UK: £15.00
Cat. Cost: Online only.
Credit Cards: American Express, Visa, MasterCard
Specialities: Wide general range. Herbaceous, alpines, heathers & ferns. Nat. & International Collection of *Cotoneaster*.
Notes: Wheelchair accessible.
Map Ref: S, D2

SRot **Rotherview Nursery** ♿
Ivy House Lane, Three Oaks, Hastings, East Sussex TN35 4NP
Ⓣ (01424) 756228
Ⓔ rotherview@btinternet.com
Ⓦ www.rotherview.com

Contact: Ray & Wendy Bates
Opening Times: 1000-1700 Mar-Oct, 1000-1530 Nov-Feb, Tue to Sun.
Min Mail Order UK: Nmc
Min Mail Order EU: Nmc
Cat. Cost: 6 × 1st class.
Credit Cards: All major credit/debit cards
Specialities: Alpines. Ferns. *Camellia.*
Notes: Nursery is on same site as Coghurst Camellias. Also sells wholesale. Delivers to shows. Euro accepted. Wheelchair accessible.
Map Ref: S, D5

SSal **THE SALUTATION GARDENS AND NURSERY** ♿
The Salutation, Knightrider Street, Sandwich, Kent CT13 9EW
Ⓣ (01304) 619119
Ⓜ 07843 961813
Ⓔ thesalutationnursery@hotmail.com
Ⓦ www.the-secretgardens.co.uk
Contact: Steve Edney
Opening Times: 1000-1700 7 days, Mar-Oct &1000-1600 7 days Nov-Feb. Please note closed for 2 weeks over Xmas period.
Cat. Cost: £2.00
Credit Cards: All major credit/debit cards
Specialities: *Dahlia*, *Plectranthus*, hardy to tender perennials & annuals that are suited to light soils. Only small quantities available but can be grown to order. Plants are raised & cared for by the garden team.
Notes: Nursery attached to a Lutyens house & garden. Most plants sold can be seen in the gardens. Tea room, restaurant & hotel. Wheelchair accessible.

SSea **SEALE NURSERIES** ♿
Seale Lane, Seale, Farnham, Surrey GU10 1LD
Ⓣ (01252) 782410
Ⓔ catherine@sealenurseries.demon.co.uk
Ⓦ www.sealenurseries.co.uk
Contact: David & Catherine May
Opening Times: 1000-1600 Tue-Sat incl. Other times by appt. Closed 25th Dec-beginning of Feb.
Cat. Cost: None issued.
Credit Cards: Visa, Access, Delta, MasterCard
Specialities: Roses & *Pelargonium*. Some varieties in short supply, please phone first.
Notes: Wheelchair accessible.
Map Ref: S, C3 **OS Grid Ref:** SU887477

SSss **SELECT SEEDS** ♿
Paice Lane, Medstead, Nr Alton, Hampshire GU34 5PR
Ⓣ (01420) 560695
Ⓜ 07909 528191
Ⓕ (01420) 563640
Ⓔ marina@phoenixperennialplants.co.uk
Contact: Marina Christopher
Opening Times: Not open. Mail order only.
Min Mail Order UK: £10.00
Cat. Cost: 3 × 1st class.
Credit Cards: All major credit/debit cards
Specialities: Seeds. Unusual hardy perennial seed selection incl. many prairie plants & ornamental umbellifers. Genera incl. *Agastache, Angelica, Centaurea, Seseli, Sanguisorba* & *Silphium.*
Notes: Only sells seed by mail order. Credit cards not accepted by phone. Co-located with Phoenix Perennial Plants SPhx. Delivers to shows. Wheelchair accessible.
Map Ref: S, C2 **OS Grid Ref:** SU657362

SSta **STARBOROUGH NURSERY** ♿
Starborough Road, Marsh Green, Edenbridge, Kent TN8 5RB
Ⓣ (01732) 865614
Ⓔ starborough@hotmail.co.uk
Contact: Sales
Opening Times: 0900-1600 Thu, Fri & Sat. Closed Jan, Jul & Aug.
Credit Cards: Visa, Access
Specialities: Rare & unusual shrubs esp. *Daphne, Acer,* rhododendrons & azaleas, *Magnolia* & *Nyssa*. Some plants only available in larger sizes.
Notes: Mail order only between Oct & Apr. Deliveries can be made at cost. Planting & landscaping services available. Wheelchair accessible.
Map Ref: S, C4

SSut **DAN SUTTON** ◆
(Office) 142 Hawks Road, Hailsham, East Sussex BN27 1NA
Ⓣ (01323) 845270
Ⓜ 07772 869645
Ⓔ dansutton00@hotmail.co.uk
Contact: Dan Sutton
Opening Times: By appt. only.
Min Mail Order UK: £5.80.
Credit Cards: None
Specialities: Herbaceous perennials, bulbs/corms, incl. *Crocosima*; grasses; specimen bamboos, *Fargesia robusta, F. scabrida* & *Borinda boliana.*
Notes: Also offers landscape design. Nursery at Park Wood Farmhouse, Upper Dicker, Hailsham, BN27 3QL. Also sells wholesale.
Map Ref: S, D4

STPC **THE PLANT COMPANY** ♿
Coolham Road, West Chiltington, Pulborough, West Sussex RH20 2LH
Ⓣ (01403) 740100
Ⓔ sales@theplantco.co.uk

Ⓦ www.theplantco.co.uk
Contact: Tim Ricketts
Opening Times: 0900-1730 Mon-Sat.
Min Mail Order UK: £8.95
Min Mail Order EU: Nmc
Cat. Cost: Online only.
Credit Cards: Visa, MasterCard
Specialities: A range of herbaceous, shrubs and grasses.
Notes: Also sells wholesale. Delivers to shows. Wheelchair accessible.
Map Ref: S, C3 **OS Grid Ref:** TQ111196

STrG **TERRACE GARDENER**
(Office) Thickets, Copthall Road, Ightham, Kent TN15 9DU
Ⓣ (01732) 883776
Ⓔ info@terracegardener.com
Ⓦ www.terracegardener.co.uk
Contact: Mike McGonigle
Opening Times: Not open. Mail order only, incl. online & by phone. Telephone orders 0930-1500 Mon-Fri.
Min Mail Order UK: Nmc
Cat. Cost: Online only
Credit Cards: All, except American Express
Specialities: Patio plants & topiary trees. Container gardening. Architectural & hardy exotics.

SVen **VENTNOR BOTANIC GARDEN** ♿
Undercliff Drive, Ventnor, Isle of Wight PO38 1UL
Ⓣ (01983) 855397
Ⓔ sales@botanic.co.uk
Ⓦ www.botanic.co.uk
Contact: Jason Melia
Opening Times: 1000-1700 7 days, all year.
Min Mail Order UK: Nmc
Min Mail Order EU: Nmc
Cat. Cost: None issued
Credit Cards: All, except American Express
Specialities: Coastal, drought-tolerant, Mediterranean & southern hemisphere plants. Rare & esoteric half-hardy trees, shrubs & perennials. Nat. Collection of Hardy & Half-hardy *Puya*.
Notes: Wheelchair accessible.
Map Ref: S, D2 **OS Grid Ref:** SZ548768

SVic **VICTORIANA NURSERY GARDENS** ♿
Challock, Ashford, Kent TN25 4DG
Ⓣ (01233) 740529
Ⓔ info@victoriananursery.co.uk
Ⓦ www.victoriananursery.co.uk
Contact: Serena Shirley
Opening Times: 0930-1630 (or dusk if sooner) Mon-Fri, 1030-1500 (or dusk if sooner) Sat.
Min Mail Order UK: Nmc
Cat. Cost: Free by post or online.
Credit Cards: All major credit/debit cards
Specialities: Heritage & unusual vegetable plants, seeds, fruit trees & bushes. Specialist grower of chillies & tomatoes, with annual tasting days. Also 600+ varieties of *Fuchsia*.
Notes: Also sells wholesale. Wheelchair accessible.
Map Ref: S, C5 **OS Grid Ref:** TR018501

SWat **WATER MEADOW NURSERY** ♿
Alresford Road, Cheriton, Nr Alresford, Hampshire SO24 0QB
Ⓣ (01962) 771895
Ⓔ plantaholic101@btinternet.com
Ⓦ www.plantaholic.co.uk
Contact: Sandy Worth
Opening Times: 1000-1700 Fri & some Sat. For other times, phone for appt. only.
Min Mail Order UK: £10.00 + p&p
Min Mail Order EU: £50.00 + p&p
Cat. Cost: Online only. Phone for availability.
Credit Cards: None
Specialities: Water lilies, extensive water garden plants, unusual herbaceous perennials, aromatic herbs & wildflowers. Nat. Collection of *Papaver orientale* Group. Re-blooming *Papaver* Super Poppy Series.
Notes: Design & landscape service available. Mail order by 24 or 48 hour courier service only. Also sells wholesale. Exports beyond EU. Delivers to shows. Wheelchair accessible.
Map Ref: S, C2

SWCr **WYCH CROSS NURSERIES** ♿
Wych Cross, Forest Row, East Sussex RH18 5JW
Ⓣ (01342) 822705
Ⓕ (01342) 828246
Ⓔ jp@wychcross.co.uk
Ⓦ www.wychcross.co.uk
Contact: Stan Wyatt
Opening Times: 0900-1730 Mon-Sat.
Min Mail Order UK: Nmc
Cat. Cost: Free
Credit Cards: All major credit/debit cards
Specialities: Roses.
Notes: Wheelchair accessible.
Map Ref: S, C3 **OS Grid Ref:** TQ420320

SWeb **WEB GARDEN CENTRE**
Meadow Farm, Sway Road, Tiptoe, Nr Lymington, Hampshire SO41 6FR
Ⓜ 07523 665140
Ⓔ info@webgardencentre.com
Ⓦ www.webgardencentre.com
Contact: Stanley Jackson
Opening Times: By appt. only. Phone to arrange.
Min Mail Order UK: Nmc

Min Mail Order EU: Nmc
Cat. Cost: Online only.
Credit Cards: All major credit/debit cards
Specialities: Bespoke & traditional topiary; specimen ornamental plants; evergreen hedging (up to 6 metres tall) and 'window blockers'. Also a wide range of shrubs as well as citrus, olive, bay, *Buxus* & *Taxus*, as well as perennials, herbs & alpines.
Notes: Orders taken online. Euro accepted. Also sells wholesale.

SWhi **John Hall Plants Ltd** ♿
Whitehall Nursery, Red Lane (Off Churt Road), Headley Down, Hampshire GU35 8SR
Ⓣ (01428) 715505
Ⓜ 07714 344327
Ⓔ info@johnhallplants.com
Ⓦ www.johnhallplants.com
Contact: John Hall
Opening Times: 0900-1630 Mon-Fri, 0900-1300 Sat, by appt. only.
Min Mail Order UK: Nmc
Min Mail Order EU: Nmc
Cat. Cost: By email only.
Credit Cards: None
Specialities: *Erica*, *Calluna* & *Daboecia*.
Notes: Planting plans supplied. Also sells wholesale. Exports beyond EU. Euro accepted. Wheelchair accessible.
Map Ref: S, C3 **OS Grid Ref:** SU837371

SWvt **Wolverton Plants Ltd** ♿ ◆
Wolverton Common, Tadley, Hampshire RG26 5RU
Ⓣ (01635) 298453
Ⓕ (01635) 299075
Ⓔ Julian@wolvertonplants.co.uk
Ⓦ www.wolvertonplants.co.uk
Contact: Julian Jones
Opening Times: 0900-1800 (or dusk Nov-Feb), 7 days. Closed Xmas/New Year.
Cat. Cost: Online only.
Credit Cards: All major credit/debit cards
Specialities: Wide range of herbaceous perennials & shrubs grown on a commercial scale for the public.
Notes: Horticultural club visits welcome by prior arrangement. Also sells wholesale. Euro accepted. Wheelchair accessible.
Map Ref: S, C2 **OS Grid Ref:** SU555589

Wales and the West

WAbe **Aberconwy Nursery**
Graig, Glan Conwy, Conwy LL28 5TL
Ⓣ (01492) 580875
Contact: Keith & Tim Lever
Opening Times: 1000-1600 Tue-Sun Mar-Sep incl.
Cat. Cost: 2 × 2nd class.
Credit Cards: Visa, MasterCard
Specialities: Alpines, including specialist varieties, esp. gentians, dionysias, dwarf *Dianthus*, *Primula*, *Saxifraga* & dwarf ericaceous plants. Some choice shrubs & woodland plants incl. smaller ferns.
Notes: Delivers to shows.
Map Ref: W, A3 **OS Grid Ref:** SH799744

WAln **L. A. Allen**
Windy Ridge, Llandrindod Wells, Powys LD1 5NY
Ⓔ leslie.allen@mypostoffice.co.uk
Contact: Les Allen
Opening Times: Mail order only. Open by prior appt.
Min Mail Order UK: Nmc
Min Mail Order EU: Nmc
Cat. Cost: 6 × 1st class.
Credit Cards: None
Specialities: All sections of *Primula auricula*: alpine auricula, show-edged, show-self, doubles, show-stripe. Surplus plants from private collection so available in small quantities. Occasionally only 1 or 2 available of some cvs.
Notes: Also sells wholesale.

WAul **Aulden Farm**
Aulden, Leominster, Herefordshire HR6 0JT
Ⓣ (01568) 720129
Ⓔ pf@auldenfarm.co.uk
Ⓦ www.auldenfarm.co.uk
Contact: Alun Whitehead
Opening Times: Flexible. Individuals & groups welcome. Please contact nursery. Also open for NGS.
Min Mail Order UK: £25.00
Cat. Cost: Online only.
Credit Cards: Paypal
Specialities: Nat. Collection of Siberian *Iris*.
Notes: Three acre garden. Talks given to groups & societies.
Map Ref: W, C4 **OS Grid Ref:** SO462548

WAvo **Pershore College of Horticulture**
Avonbank, Pershore, Worcestershire WR10 3JP
Ⓣ (01386) 551149
Ⓔ plantcentre@warkscol.ac.uk
Ⓦ www.warwickshire.ac.uk/plantcentre
Contact: Jo Gildea
Opening Times: 0900-1700 Mon-Sat, 1000-1630 Sun (1600 in winter).
Cat. Cost: £1.00
Credit Cards: All major credit/debit cards
Specialities: Nat. Collections of *Penstemon* & *Philadelphus*.

W

Notes: Also sells wholesale.
Map Ref: W, C5

WBod **Bodnant Garden Nursery** ♿
Tal-y-Cafn, Conwy, Gwynedd LL28 5RE
Ⓣ (01492) 650501
Ⓜ 07971 389771
Ⓕ (01492) 650863
Ⓔ sales@bodnant-plants.co.uk
Ⓦ www.bodnant-plants.co.uk
Contact: Graham Marsh
Opening Times: 0900-1730, 7 days. Closed Xmas Day, Boxing Day & New Year's Day.
Min Mail Order UK: £12.99
Cat. Cost: None issued.
Credit Cards: Visa, MasterCard, Switch, Connect
Specialities: *Rhododendron*, *Camellia*. Wide range of unusual trees and shrubs.
Notes: Also sells wholesale. Wheelchair accessible.

WBor **Bordervale Plants** ♿
Nantyderi, Sandy Lane, Ystradowen, Cowbridge, Vale of Glamorgan CF71 7SX
Ⓣ (01446) 774036
Ⓔ bordervaleplants@gmail.com
Ⓦ www.bordervale.co.uk
Contact: Claire E Jenkins
Opening Times: 1000-1700 Fri-Sun & B/hols Mar-early Oct. Very often open Mon-Thu but please make an appt. on these days if travelling some distance.
Min Mail Order UK: £20.00 + p&p
Cat. Cost: 3 × 1st class.
Credit Cards: None
Specialities: Unusual herbaceous perennials, trees, shrubs & roses, as well as cottage garden plants, many displayed in the 2-acre garden.
Notes: Mail order available for smaller items, subject to season. Garden open mid-May to Sep when nursery open. Also open for NGS. See website for details. Delivers to shows. Nursery wheelchair accessible.
Map Ref: W, D3 **OS Grid Ref:** ST022776

WBrk **Brockamin Plants** ♿
Brockamin, Old Hills, Callow End, Worcestershire WR2 4TQ
Ⓣ (01905) 830370
Ⓔ stone.brockamin@btinternet.com
Contact: Margaret Stone
Opening Times: By appt. only.
Cat. Cost: Free.
Credit Cards: None
Specialities: Nat. Collections of *Aster novae-angliae*, *Erigeron* cvs, *Geranium sanguineum*, *G. macrorrhizum* & *G.* × *cantabrigiense*. Plants available in small quantities only.
Notes: Wheelchair accessible.
Map Ref: W, C5 **OS Grid Ref:** SO830488

WBuc **Bucknell Nurseries** ♿
Bucknell, Shropshire SY7 0EL
Ⓣ (01547) 530606
Ⓕ (01547) 530699
Ⓔ nickcoull@yahoo.co.uk
Contact: A N Coull
Opening Times: 0800-1700 Mon-Fri & 1000-1300 Sat.
Min Mail Order UK: Nmc
Cat. Cost: Free
Credit Cards: All major credit/debit cards
Specialities: Bare-rooted hedging conifers & forest trees.
Notes: Also sells wholesale. Euro accepted. Wheelchair accessible.
Map Ref: W, C4 **OS Grid Ref:** SO356736

WCAu **Claire Austin Hardy Plants**
White Hopton Farm, Wern Lane, Sarn, Newtown, Powys SY16 4EN
Ⓣ (01686) 670342
Ⓔ enquiries@claireaustin-hardyplants.co.uk
Ⓦ www.claireaustin-hardyplants.co.uk
Contact: Claire Austin
Opening Times: Mail order only. Open Day towards start of Jun. See website for details.
Min Mail Order UK: Nmc
Min Mail Order EU: Nmc
Cat. Cost: Free, UK only.
Credit Cards: MasterCard, Visa, Switch
Specialities: *Paeonia*, *Iris*, *Hemerocallis* & hardy plants. Nat. Collections of Bearded *Iris* & Hybrid Herbaceous *Paeonia*.
Notes: Euro accepted.

WCFE **Charles F Ellis**
Oak Piece Nurseries, Stanway Road, Stanton, Nr Broadway, Worcestershire WR12 7NQ
Ⓣ (01386) 584077
Ⓔ ellisplants@cooptel.net
Ⓦ www.ellisplants.co.uk
Contact: Charles Ellis
Opening Times: 1000-1600 Wed-Sun, 1st Apr-30th Sep incl.
Min Mail Order UK: £10.00
Cat. Cost: None issued.
Credit Cards: All, except American Express
Specialities: Wide range of shrubs, conifers, climbers & perennials, some unusual. Some available in small quantities only.
Notes: Euro accepted.
Map Ref: W, C5

WChG **Chennels Gate Gardens & Nursery** ♿
Eardisley, Herefordshire HR3 6LT
Ⓣ (01544) 327288
Ⓔ mark.richard.dawson60@gmail.com
Contact: Mark Dawson
Opening Times: 1000-1700 7 days Mar-Oct.

Cat. Cost: None issued.
Credit Cards: None
Specialities: Interesting & unusual cottage garden plants, grasses & shrubs.
Notes: Wheelchair accessible.
Map Ref: W, C4

WCJW **CJ WildBird Foods Ltd** ♿
The Rea, Upton Magna, Shrewbury, Shropshire SY4 4UR
Ⓣ 0800 731 2820
Ⓕ (01743) 709505
Ⓔ sales@birdfood.co.uk
Ⓦ www.birdfood.co.uk
Contact: Martin George
Opening Times: 0900-1700, Mon-Fri, 0900-1200 Sat, closed Sun.
Min Mail Order UK: Nmc
Min Mail Order EU: Nmc
Cat. Cost: Free.
Credit Cards: All major credit/debit cards
Specialities: Perennials, bulbs, fruit bushes, climbers and roses. Also garden wildlife specialists.
Notes: For EU information see www.vivara.com. Euro accepted. Wheelchair accessible.
Map Ref: W, B4 **OS Grid Ref:** SJ568121

W

WCot **Cotswold Garden Flowers**
Sands Lane, Badsey, Evesham, Worcestershire WR11 7EZ
Ⓣ Nursery: (01386) 833849 or mail order: (01386) 422829
Ⓜ 07812 833849
Ⓕ nursery: (01386) 49844
Ⓔ info@cgf.net
Ⓦ www.cgf.net
Contact: Mandie Potter, Bob Brown
Opening Times: 0900-1730 Mon-Fri &1000-1730 Sat & Sun, Mar-Sep. 0900-1630 Mon-Fri only, Oct-Feb. Closed from Xmas Eve for 10 days.
Min Mail Order UK: Nmc
Min Mail Order EU: Nmc
Cat. Cost: Free.
Credit Cards: All, except American Express
Specialities: A very wide range of easy & unusual perennials.
Notes: Delivers to shows. Euro accepted. Limited wheelchair access.
Map Ref: W, C5 **OS Grid Ref:** SP077426

WCra **Cranesbill Nursery** ◆
Greenhayes, Upper Westmancote, Tewkesbury, Gloucestershire GL20 7ES
Ⓣ (01684) 773770
Ⓜ 07970 103168
Ⓔ john@cranesbillnursery.com
Ⓦ www.cranesbillnursery.com
Contact: John Dilks
Opening Times: Mail order only. Visitors by appt. only.
Min Mail Order UK: Nmc
Min Mail Order EU: Nmc
Cat. Cost: Free.
Credit Cards: Paypal, MasterCard, Visa, Maestro, Delta
Specialities: Specialist nursery offering a wide range of hardy geraniums. Some of the more unusual cvs available in small quantities.
Map Ref: W, C5 **OS Grid Ref:** SO940378

WCre **Crescent Plants** ♿
Stoney Cross, Marden, Hereford, Herefordshire HR1 3EW
Ⓣ (01432) 880262
Ⓜ 07990 970539
Ⓔ crescent@btinternet.com
Ⓦ www.auriculas.co.uk
Contact: June Poole
Opening Times: Open Days in Apr & May (contact nursery for details). Other times by appt. only. Essential to phone first.
Min Mail Order UK: Nmc
Min Mail Order EU: Nmc
Cat. Cost: £1.50
Credit Cards: Paypal
Specialities: Named varieties of *Primula auricula* incl. selfs, alpines, double, striped, edges, fancies & border types. Help & advice freely given. Own special recipe auricula compost available for collection only.
Notes: Payment by Paypal via website or send cheque with order. Wheelchair accessible.
Map Ref: W, C4 **OS Grid Ref:** SO525477

WCru **Crûg Farm Plants** ♿
Caernarfon, Gwynedd LL55 1TU
Ⓣ (01248) 670232
Ⓜ 07774 980842
Ⓔ mailorder@crug-farm.co.uk
Ⓦ www.mailorder.crug-farm.co.uk
Contact: B and S Wynn-Jones
Opening Times: 09030-1630 Thu-Sat, last Thu in Mar to 2nd Sat in Sep, incl. Fri B/hol. Or all year Mon-Fri by appt.
Min Mail Order UK: Nmc
Min Mail Order EU: Nmc
Cat. Cost: Online only.
Credit Cards: All major credit/debit cards
Specialities: Unusual & rare inc. trees, shrubs, herbaceous & bulbous, mostly self-collected new introductions from the Far East & the Americas. Rare woody & climbers esp. *Acer, Araliaceae, Carpinus, Hydrangeaceae* & *Magnolia* with many other extraordinary introductions. Shade plants esp. *Asparagaceae, Convallariaceae, Liliaceae, Ranunculaceae* & *Saxifragaceae*. Many supplied bare-rooted. Nat. Collections of *Coriaria, Paris* & *Polygonatum*.

Notes: Delivery by overnight carrier for UK & Ireland. Courier for rest of EU. Delivers to shows. Wheelchair accessible.
Map Ref: W, A2 **OS Grid Ref:** SH509652

WDib **Dibleys Nurseries** ♿ ◆
Llanelidan, Ruthin, Denbighshire LL15 2LG
Ⓣ (01978) 790677
Ⓕ (01978) 790668
Ⓔ sales@dibleys.com
Ⓦ www.dibleys.com
Contact: R Dibley
Opening Times: 1000-1700 7 days, Apr-Aug. 1000-1700 Mon-Fri, Mar, Sep & Oct.
Min Mail Order UK: Nmc
Min Mail Order EU: Nmc
Cat. Cost: Free
Credit Cards: Visa, Access, Switch, Electron, Solo
Specialities: *Streptocarpus*, *Columnea*, *Solenostemon*, *Saintpaulia* & other gesneriads & *Begonia*. Nat. Collections of *Streptocarpus* & *Saintpaulia*.
Notes: Also sells wholesale. Euro accepted. Delivers to shows. Wheelchair accessible.
Map Ref: W, A3

WDra **Dragonfly Flora**
(Office) 7 Delfryn, Bryn, Llanelli, Carmarthenshire SA14 9AF
Ⓜ 07885 643513
Ⓔ lewises@talktalk.net
Contact: Lew Lewis
Opening Times: By appt. only.
Min Mail Order UK: Nmc
Min Mail Order EU: Nmc
Specialities: Grasses, sedges and all UK native wetland & aquatic species.
Notes: Also sells wholesale. Delivers to shows.

WFar **Farmyard Nurseries** ♿
Dol Llan Road, Llandysul, Carmarthenshire SA44 4RL
Ⓣ (01559) 363389
Ⓜ 01267 220259
Ⓕ (01559) 362200
Ⓔ sales@farmyardnurseries.co.uk
Ⓦ www.farmyardnurseries.co.uk
Contact: Richard Bramley
Opening Times: 0900-1700 7 days, excl. Xmas Day, Boxing Day & New Year's Day.
Min Mail Order UK: Nmc
Min Mail Order EU: Nmc
Cat. Cost: 4 × 1st class.
Credit Cards: Visa, Switch, MasterCard
Specialities: Large range of home grown shrubs & herbaceous perennials, incl. *Geranium*, *Helleborus* & *Primula*. Trees, shrubs, climbers, alpines, conifers & bedding plants.
Notes: Additionally sells from shop/yard in Carmarthen. Also sells wholesale. Euro accepted. Wheelchair accessible.
Map Ref: W, C2 **OS Grid Ref:** SN421406

WFib **Fibrex Nurseries Ltd** ♿
Honeybourne Road, Pebworth, Stratford-on-Avon, Warwickshire CV37 8XP
Ⓣ (01789) 720788
Ⓕ (01789) 721162
Ⓔ sales@fibrex.co.uk
Ⓦ www.fibrex.co.uk
Contact: U Key-Davis & R L Godard-Key
Opening Times: 0900-1700 Mon-Fri, 2nd Mar-28th Aug. 0900-1600 Mon-Fri, 31st Aug-26th Feb. 1030-1600 Sat & Sun, 4th Apr-28th Jun. Closed last 2 weeks Dec & 1st week Jan. Closed Easter Sun & Aug B/hol Mon.
Min Mail Order UK: £10.00 + p&p
Min Mail Order EU: £20.00 + p&p
Cat. Cost: 3 × 1st class.
Credit Cards: MasterCard, Visa, Maestro
Specialities: *Hedera*, ferns, *Pelargonium*, named tuberous begonias, *Hibiscus rosa-sinensis* cvs. Nat. Collections of *Pelargonium* & *Hedera*. Plant collections subject to time of year, please check by phone.
Notes: Also sells wholesale. Delivers to shows. Wheelchair accessible.
Map Ref: W, C5 **OS Grid Ref:** SP133458

WGob **The Gobbett Nursery**
Farlow, Kidderminster, Worcestershire DY14 8TD
Ⓣ (01746) 718647
Ⓕ (01746) 718647
Ⓔ chrislink59@gmail.com
Ⓦ www.thegobbettnursery.co.uk
Contact: C H Link
Opening Times: By appt. only.
Min Mail Order UK: £10.00
Min Mail Order EU: £50.00
Cat. Cost: None issued.
Credit Cards: None
Specialities: *Syringa*, & *Cornus*. Some varieties available in small quantities only.
Notes: Delivers to shows.

WGoo **Wildegoose Nursery home of Bouts Violas**
Yew Tree Cottage, Lower Millichope, Munslow, Craven Arms, Shropshire SY7 9HE
Ⓣ (01584) 841890
Ⓜ 07798 628762
Ⓔ flowers@boutsviolas.co.uk
Ⓦ www.boutsviolas.co.uk
Contact: Laura Willgoss
Opening Times: Mail order only. Open strictly by appt. only.

W

Min Mail Order UK: Nmc
Min Mail Order EU: Nmc
Cat. Cost: 1st class sae.
Credit Cards: All major credit/debit cards
Specialities: *Viola*. Taken over *Viola* stock from Bouts Cottage Nursery.
Notes: Delivers to shows. Euro accepted.

WGri **David J Griffiths**
(Office) Compton, Bowley Lane, Bodenham, Hereford, Herefordshire HR1 3LG
Ⓣ (01568) 797427
Ⓜ 07854 931260
Ⓔ david@compton77.freeserve.co.uk
Contact: David Griffiths
Opening Times: Not open. Sells at plant fairs only.
Credit Cards: None
Specialities: Small quantity of wide range of perennials & alpines.

W

WGrn **Green's Leaves** ♿
36 Ford House Road, Newent, Gloucestershire GL18 1LQ
Ⓣ (01531) 820154
Ⓜ 07890 413036
Ⓔ r.paul.green@hotmail.co.uk
Ⓦ www.greensleavesnursery.co.uk
Contact: Paul Green
Opening Times: By appt. only. Please phone to arrange.
Min Mail Order UK: £10.00 + p&p
Cat. Cost: 4 × 2nd class.
Credit Cards: None
Specialities: Range of rare & choice shrubs, also some perennials. Ornamental grasses, sedges & phormiums.
Notes: Also sells wholesale. Delivers to shows. Wheelchair accessible.
Map Ref: W, C4 **OS Grid Ref:** SO732273

WGwG **Gwynfor Growers**
Gwynfor, Pontgarreg, Llangrannog, Llandysul, Ceredigion SA44 6AU
Ⓣ (01239) 654151
Ⓔ info@gwynfor.co.uk
Ⓦ www.gwynfor.co.uk
Contact: Steve & Angie Hipkin
Opening Times: Usually 1000-1800 or sunset if earlier, Wed, Thu & Sun, all year round.
Min Mail Order UK: Nmc
Cat. Cost: Pdf list available by email.
Credit Cards: Paypal
Specialities: National Collection of *Rosmarinus* cvs. Specialist supplier of Welsh fruit trees. Classic & contemporary plants grown organically & peat-free. Some plants available in small quantities only. Rarities propagated to order.
Notes: Plants also available at local farmers' markets, plant fairs & some NGS Open Gardens. Delivers to shows.
Map Ref: W, C2 **OS Grid Ref:** SN331536

WHal **Hall Farm Nursery**
Vicarage Lane, Kinnerley, Nr Oswestry, Shropshire SY10 8DH
Ⓣ (01691) 682135
Ⓔ info@hallfarmnursery.co.uk
Ⓦ www.hallfarmnursery.co.uk
Contact: Christine & Nick Ffoulkes-Jones
Opening Times: 1000-1700, Tues-Sat, 1st Mar-3rd Oct 2015.
Min Mail Order UK: £20.00 + p&p
Cat. Cost: Online only.
Credit Cards: Visa, MasterCard, Electron, Maestro
Specialities: Wide range of herbaceous perennials, woodland plants, alpine & scree plants.
Notes: Partially accessible for wheelchairs.
Map Ref: W, B4 **OS Grid Ref:** SJ333209

WHar **Harley Nursery** ♿
Harley, Shrewsbury, Shropshire SY5 6LN
Ⓣ (01952) 510241
Ⓔ plants@harleynursery.co.uk
Ⓦ www.harleynursery.co.uk
Contact: Nick Murphy & Debbie Plant
Opening Times: 0900-1730 Mon-Sat, 1000-1600 Sun & B/hols. Winter hours 0830-1630 Mon-Sat, 1000-1600 Sun & B/hols.
Min Mail Order UK: £50.00
Cat. Cost: Online only.
Credit Cards: All major credit/debit cards
Specialities: Wide range of trees & shrubs. Large selection of fruit trees & bushes, many old & unusual varieties. Seasonal selection of conifers, climbing & herbaceous plants. Wide range of hedging & forestry plants, many available bare-root.
Notes: Wheelchair accessible.
Map Ref: W, B4 **OS Grid Ref:** SJ598020

WHCr **Hergest Croft Gardens**
Kington, Herefordshire HR5 3EG
Ⓣ (01544) 230160
Ⓜ 07968 435627
Ⓕ (01544) 232031
Ⓔ gardens@hergest.co.uk
Ⓦ www.hergest.co.uk
Contact: Stephen Lloyd
Opening Times: 1200-1730, 7 days, Apr-Oct.
Cat. Cost: None issued
Credit Cards: All major credit/debit cards
Specialities: *Acer*, *Betula* & unusual woody plants.
Notes: Limited wheelchair access.

WHea **HEATH GARDEN** ♿
Heath Hill, Sheriffhales, Shifnal, Shropshire TF11 8RR
Ⓣ (01952) 691341
Ⓔ 1malt@supanet.com
Contact: Gordon Malt
Opening Times: By appt. only.
Cat. Cost: None issued.
Credit Cards: None
Specialities: Interesting range of hardy & tender perennials. *Geranium*, *Salvia*, ornamental grasses & silver foliage plants. Bulbous plants.
Notes: Plants available in small quantities only. Talks & demonstrations to horticultural clubs. Garden open for groups by appt. Wheelchair accessible.
Map Ref: W, B5 **OS Grid Ref:** SJ376313

WHed **HEDGE NURSERY (CHOICE SHOPS LTD)**
Unit E, Stafford Park 18, Telford, Shropshire TF3 3BN
Ⓣ (01952) 913117
Ⓕ 08458 621651
Ⓔ hedgenursery@choiceshops.co.uk
Ⓦ www.hedgenursery.co.uk
Contact: Customer Services
Opening Times: Not open. Mail order only. Customer service phone lines open 0830-1730 Mon-Fri & 0900-1300 Sat.
Min Mail Order UK: Nmc
Cat. Cost: Online only
Credit Cards: All major credit/debit cards
Specialities: Hedging & trees, also small selection of perennials. Available in pots, bare-root, root ball, cell grown. We are the exclusive grower of RHS Licensed hedging.
Notes: Also sells wholesale.

WHer **THE HERB GARDEN & HISTORICAL PLANT NURSERY**
Frondeg, Gilfachreda, New Quay, Ceredigion SA45 9SP
Ⓣ (01545) 580893
Ⓔ corinnetremaine@gmail.com
Ⓦ www.HistoricalPlants.co.uk
Contact: Corinne Tremaine
Opening Times: By appt. only.
Min Mail Order UK: £15.00 + p&p
Min Mail Order EU: £50.00 + p&p sterling only.
Cat. Cost: Online only.
Credit Cards: None
Specialities: Rarer herbs, rare natives & wild flowers; rare & unusual & historical perennials, old roses & heritage pinks.

WHil **HILLVIEW HARDY PLANTS** ♿
(off B4176) Worfield, Nr Bridgnorth, Shropshire WV15 5NT
Ⓣ (01746) 716454
Ⓜ 07974 391608
Ⓕ (01746) 716454
Ⓔ hillview@onetel.net
Ⓦ www.hillviewhardyplants.com
Contact: Ingrid, John & Sarah Millington
Opening Times: 0930-1700 Mon-Sat, Mar-mid Oct. At other times, please phone first.
Min Mail Order UK: £10.00 + p&p
Min Mail Order EU: £10.00 + p&p
Cat. Cost: Online only.
Credit Cards: All major credit/debit cards
Specialities: Choice herbaceous perennials incl. *Acanthus*, *Albuca*, *Aquilegia*, *Primula auricula*, *Eucomis*, *Ixia*, South African bulbs. Nat. Collections of *Acanthus* & *Albuca*.
Notes: Also sells wholesale. Exports beyond EU. Delivers to shows. Euro accepted. Wheelchair accessible.
Map Ref: W, B4 **OS Grid Ref:** SO772969

WHlf **HAYLOFT PLANTS**
Manor Farm, Pensham, Pershore, Worcestershire WR10 3HB
Ⓣ (01386) 554440 or (01386) 562999
Ⓕ (01386) 553833
Ⓔ info@hayloftplants.co.uk
Ⓦ www.hayloftplants.co.uk
Contact: Yvonne Walker
Opening Times: Not open. Mail order only.
Min Mail Order UK: Nmc
Min Mail Order EU: Nmc
Cat. Cost: Free.
Credit Cards: All, except American Express

WHoo **HOO HOUSE NURSERY** ◆
Hoo House, Gloucester Road, Tewkesbury, Gloucestershire GL20 7DA
Ⓣ (01684) 293389
Ⓕ (01684) 293389
Ⓔ nursery@hoohouse.co.uk
Ⓦ www.hoohouse.co.uk
Contact: Julie & Robin Ritchie
Opening Times: 1000-1700 Mon-Sat, 1100-1700 Sun. Please ring to check Nov-Jan.
Cat. Cost: 3 × 1st class.
Credit Cards: All major credit/debit cards
Specialities: Wide range of herbaceous & alpines grown peat-free. *Aster*, *Cyclamen*, *Geranium*, *Penstemon*, *Saxifraga* & many later-flowering varieties.
Notes: Also sells wholesale. Euro accepted. Partially wheelchair accessible.
Map Ref: W, C5 **OS Grid Ref:** SO893293

WHor **HORTICULTURAL SALES**
Upper Brockington, Berrington Street, Bodenham, Herefordshire HR1 3HT
Ⓣ (01568) 797747
Ⓜ 07966 635005

Ⓕ (01568) 600484
Ⓔ pdavies@hortsales.fsnet.co.uk
Ⓦ www.hortplants.co.uk
Contact: Peter Davies
Opening Times: By appt. only.
Min Mail Order UK: Nmc
Min Mail Order EU: Nmc
Cat. Cost: Free but available by email only.
Credit Cards: Paypal
Specialities: Wide selection of less commonly grown shrubs, available in small quantities only.
Notes: Plant finding service. 39 years experience in trade. Also sells wholesale. Euro accepted.

WHrl **Harrells Hardy Plants**
(Office) 15 Coxlea Close, Evesham, Worcestershire WR11 4JS
Ⓣ (01386) 443077
Ⓜ 07799 577120 or 07733 446606
Ⓔ mail@harrellshardyplants.co.uk
Ⓦ www.harrellshardyplants.co.uk
Contact: Liz Nicklin & Kate Phillips
Opening Times: By appt. only. Please telephone.
Min Mail Order UK: Nmc
Min Mail Order EU: Nmc
Cat. Cost: Online plant list.
Credit Cards: None
Specialities: Display gardens showcase wide range of hardy perennials, esp. *Hemerocallis* & grasses.
Notes: Nursery located off Rudge Rd, Evesham. Please phone for directions or see website. Partial wheelchair access.
Map Ref: W, C5 **OS Grid Ref:** SP033443

WIce **Ice Alpines** ♿
Lyehead, Bewdley, Worcestershire DY12 2UW
Ⓣ (01299) 269219
Ⓕ (01562) 510003
Ⓔ icealpines@gmail.com
Ⓦ www.Icealpines.co.uk
Contact: Mark Lagomarsino
Opening Times: Mail order. Open by appt. only.
Min Mail Order UK: Nmc
Min Mail Order EU: £18
Credit Cards: Paypal
Specialities: British grown alpine & rockery plants.
Notes: Delivers to shows. Wheelchair accessible.

WJas **Paul Jasper Trees**
(Office) The Lighthouse, Bridge Street, Leominster, Herefordshire HR6 8DX
Ⓔ jaspertreescouk@aol.com
Ⓦ www.jaspertrees.co.uk
Contact: Paul Jasper
Opening Times: Not open. Mail order only.
Min Mail Order UK: £20.00 + p&p
Cat. Cost: Online only.
Credit Cards: All major credit/debit cards
Specialities: Full range of fruit & ornamental trees. Over 100 modern and traditional fruit tree varieties plus 100 ornamental tree varieties, all direct from the grower. Many unusual varieties of *Malus domestica* & *Prunus*.
Notes: Regular updates & notes on website. Also sells wholesale. Delivers to shows.
Map Ref: W, C4 **OS Grid Ref:** SO495595

WJek **Jekka's Herb Farm** ♿
Rose Cottage, Shellards Lane, Alveston, Bristol, South Gloucestershire BS35 3SY
Ⓣ (01454) 418878
Ⓔ sales@jekkasherbfarm.com
Ⓦ www.jekkasherbfarm.com
Contact: Jekka McVicar
Opening Times: Please check website or phone nursery for dates.
Min Mail Order UK: £10.00
Min Mail Order EU: Charges per order on application.
Cat. Cost: Online only.
Credit Cards: Visa, MasterCard, Delta, Maestro
Specialities: Possibly the largest collection of culinary herbs in the UK. The collection contains herbs from all around the world. The Herb Farm has planted the UK's first "Herbetum" which can be viewed during Open Days.
Notes: Only sell seeds via mail order. Plants are available from the farm during Open Days or can be ordered for collection with 24 hours notice. RHS Days & NGS Days. Group visits. Wheelchair accessible.
Map Ref: W, D4

WJPR **JPR Environmental**
The Malt House, Standish, Stonehouse, Gloucestershire GL10 3DL
Ⓣ (01453) 811537
Ⓔ enquiries@jprenvironmental.co.uk
Ⓦ www.jprwillow.co.uk
Contact: John Robinthwaite
Opening Times: Not open. Mail order only. 0900-1700, Mon-Fri.
Min Mail Order UK: £6.00
Credit Cards: All, except American Express
Specialities: *Salix*.
Notes: Also sells wholesale.

WKif **Kiftsgate Court Gardens** ♿
Kiftsgate Court, Chipping Camden, Gloucestershire GL55 6LN
Ⓣ (01386) 438777
Ⓕ (01386) 438777

Ⓔ anne@kiftsgate.co.uk
Ⓦ www.kiftsgate.co.uk
Contact: Mrs J Chambers
Opening Times: 1200-1800 Sat-Wed, May, Jun & Jul. 1400-1800 Sat-Wed, Aug. 1400-1800 Sun, Mon & Wed, Apr & Sep.
Cat. Cost: None issued
Credit Cards: All, except American Express
Specialities: Small range of unusual plants.
Notes: Wheelchair accessible.
Map Ref: W, C5 **OS Grid Ref:** SP170430

WLav **The Lavender Garden**
Ashcroft Nurseries, Nr Ozleworth, Kingscote, Tetbury, Gloucestershire GL8 8YF
Ⓣ (01453) 860356 or 549286
Ⓜ 07837 582943
Ⓔ Andrew007Bullock@aol.com
Ⓦ www.TheLavenderG.co.uk
Contact: Andrew Bullock
Opening Times: 1100-1700 Sat & Sun. Weekdays variable, please phone. 1st Nov-1st Mar by appt. only.
Min Mail Order UK: £10.00 + p&p
Min Mail Order EU: £20.00 + p&p
Cat. Cost: 2 × 1st class.
Credit Cards: All major credit/debit cards
Specialities: *Lavandula*, *Buddleja*, plants to attract butterflies. Herbs, wildflowers. Nat. Collection of *Buddleja*.
Notes: Also sells wholesale. Delivers to shows.
Map Ref: W, D5 **OS Grid Ref:** ST798948

WMAq **Merebrook Water Plants**
Kingfisher Barn, Merebrook Farm, Hanley Swan, Worcestershire WR8 0DX
Ⓣ (01684) 310950
Ⓜ 07876 777066
Ⓔ enquiries@pondplants.co.uk
Ⓦ www.pondplants.co.uk
Contact: Roger Kings & Biddi Kings
Opening Times: Not open. Mail order only.
Min Mail Order UK: Nmc
Min Mail Order EU: £25.00
Cat. Cost: Online only.
Credit Cards: All major credit/debit cards
Specialities: *Nymphaea*, Louisiana irises & other aquatic plants. International Waterlily & Water Gardening Soc. accredited collection.

WMat **The Tree Shop at Frank P. Matthews Ltd.** ♿
Berrington Court, Tenbury Wells, Worcestershire WR15 8TH
Ⓣ (01584) 812800
Ⓕ (01584) 811830
Ⓔ treeshop@fpmatthews.co.uk
Ⓦ www.frankpmatthews.com
Contact: Steve Grosvenor
Opening Times: 0730-1700 Mon-Fri
Cat. Cost: 4 × 1st class.
Credit Cards: All major credit/debit cards
Specialities: Fruit & deciduous ornamental Trees.
Notes: Also sells wholesale. Wheelchair accessible.
Map Ref: W, C4 **OS Grid Ref:** SO571676

WMil **Anne Milner**
Meadow House, Baunton, Cirencester, Gloucestershire GL7 7BB
Ⓣ (01285) 643731
Ⓔ anne.milner@btinternet.com
Ⓦ www.blissiris.co.uk
Contact: Anne Milner
Opening Times: By appt. only.
Min Mail Order UK: Nmc
Min Mail Order EU: Nmc
Cat. Cost: 50p (UK) £1.00 (EU) to cover postage.
Credit Cards: None
Specialities: Nat. Collection of *Iris* (A.J. Bliss introductions). Available in small quantities only.
Notes: Euro accepted. Delivers to some shows, check with nursery.

WMoo **Moorland Cottage Plants**
Rhyd-y-Groes, Brynberian, Crymych, Pembrokeshire SA41 3TT
Ⓣ (01239) 891363
Ⓦ www.moorlandcottageplants.co.uk
Contact: Jennifer Matthews
Opening Times: 1030-1700 daily excl. Wed 1st Mar-30th Sep.
Min Mail Order UK: £35.00 + carriage
Cat. Cost: 4 × 1st class.
Credit Cards: All major credit/debit cards
Specialities: Traditional & unusual hardy perennials. Many garden-worthy rarities. Cottage garden plants incl. many *Astilbe*, *Crocosmia*, *Geum*, *Geranium*, *Potentilla* & *Persicaria*. Ferns & many shade plants, moisture lovers, ornamental grasses, colourful ground cover.
Notes: Display garden open for NGS from mid-May to end Sep. Partial wheelchair access.
Map Ref: W, C2 **OS Grid Ref:** SN091343

WMou **Mount Pleasant Trees** ♿
Rockhampton, Berkeley, Gloucestershire GL13 9DU
Ⓣ (01454) 260348
Ⓔ info@mountpleasanttrees.com
Ⓦ www.mountpleasanttrees.com
Contact: Tom Locke & Elizabeth Murphy
Opening Times: 0830-1630 Mon-Fri, 0830-1230 Sat, Oct-Apr.
Min Mail Order UK: Nmc but p&p quoted on individual basis.

W

Cat. Cost: Free.
Credit Cards: All major credit/debit cards
Specialities: Wide range of trees for forestry, hedging, woodlands & gardens esp. *Populus*, *Salix*, *Tilia* & *Quercus*.
Notes: Mail order available for plants under 1m in height, quotes on request. Also sells wholesale. Wheelchair accessible.
Map Ref: W, D4 **OS Grid Ref:** ST654929

WNHG **New Hope Gardens** ♿
(Office) The Old Chapel, Cefn Einion, Nr Bishops Castle, Shropshire SY9 5LF
Ⓣ Office: (01588) 630750 or Nursery: (01584) 841222
Ⓔ Newhopegardensmz@aol.com
Ⓦ www.newhopegardens.com
Contact: Mark Zenick
Opening Times: 1300-1700 Wed-Fri, 1000-1700 Sat, 22nd Mar-28th Sep. 1300-1700 B/hol Mons during season. 1300-1700 Sun. Other times phone nursery for appt. Daylily Open Days: 27th/28th Jun, 5th/6th Jul, 11th Jul, 18th/19th Jul. (NGS Open Day: 1300-1700 12th Jul.)
Min Mail Order UK: Nmc
Min Mail Order EU: Nmc
Cat. Cost: Online only. Plant list on request.
Credit Cards: All major credit/debit cards
Specialities: American bred, British grown, *Hemerocallis*. Ships bare-rooted plants. Daylily plants are growing and for sale at Mynd Hardy Plants.
Notes: Nursery co-located with Mynd Hardy Plants (code WMnd). Wheelchair accessible.
Map Ref: W, B4 **OS Grid Ref:** SO510852

W

WNPC **Newent Plant Centre** ♿
Little Verzons Farm, Hereford Road, Ledbury, Herefordshire HR8 2PZ
Ⓣ (01531) 670121
Ⓔ markmoir999@btinternet.com
Ⓦ www.newentplantcentre.co.uk
Contact: Mark Moir
Opening Times: 0900-1700 Mon-Sat, 1000-1600 Sun. Closed Jan.
Credit Cards: All major credit/debit cards
Specialities: Extensive range of *Heuchera* & *Euphorbia*. Herbaceous perennials, climbers, shrubs, trees, alpines, herbs, roses & fruit.
Notes: Delivers to shows. Wheelchair accessible.
Map Ref: W, C4

WOld **Old Court Nurseries**
Colwall, Nr Malvern, Worcestershire WR13 6QE
Ⓣ (01684) 540416
Ⓜ 07971 522891
Ⓔ oldcourtnurseries@btinternet.com
Ⓦ www.autumnasters.co.uk
Contact: Paul, Meriel or Helen Picton
Opening Times: 1400-1700 Wed-Sat, May-Aug. 1100-1700 Wed-Sun, Aug. 1100-1700 7 days, 1st week Sep-2nd week Oct. Also by appt. May to Oct.
Min Mail Order UK: Nmc
Min Mail Order EU: Nmc
Credit Cards: None
Specialities: Nat. Collection of Michaelmas Daisies. Herbaceous perennials.
Notes: Mail order sent in spring only. Display garden open Aug-Oct.
Map Ref: W, C4 **OS Grid Ref:** SO759430

WOth **Other Fellow Fuchsias**
25 Spring Meadow Road, Lydney, Gloucestershire GL15 5LF
Ⓣ (01594) 844452
Ⓜ 07564 357637
Ⓔ info@otherfellow.co.uk
Ⓦ otherfellow.co.uk
Contact: Nick Egginton
Opening Times: Not open. Mail order only. No public access. Phones open 0830-1730 Mon-Fri, 0900-1300 Sat.
Min Mail Order UK: Nmc
Min Mail Order EU: £10.50 + p&p
Cat. Cost: Full colour £2.25. List only, free.
Credit Cards: All major credit/debit cards
Specialities: Expanding collection of *Fuchsia*, esp. unusual, single & exhibition varieties. Small selection of *Salvia* & *Brugmansia*. Some stock available in small quantities only. Can propagate to order.
Notes: Exports beyond EU. Euro accepted.

WOut **Out of the Common Way**
(Office) Penhyddgan, Boduan, Pwllheli, Gwynedd LL53 8YH
Ⓣ Office: (01758) 721577 or nursery: (01407) 720431
Ⓔ ziggymen22@hotmail.co.uk
Contact: Joanna Davidson (nursery) Margaret Mason (office & mail order)
Opening Times: By arrangement.
Min Mail Order UK: Nmc
Min Mail Order EU: Nmc
Cat. Cost: A5 sae large letter rate postage.
Credit Cards: None
Specialities: *Labiates*, esp. *Nepeta* & *Salvia*. *Symphyotrichum*, *Geranium* & *Crocosmia*. Native plants. Some plants propagated in small quantities only. Will propagate salvias to order.
Notes: Nursery is at Pandy Treban, Bryngwran, Anglesey. Delivers to shows. Euro accepted. Partially accessible for wheelchairs.
Map Ref: W, A2 **OS Grid Ref:** SH370778

WPat **Chris Pattison** ♿
Brookend, Pendock, Gloucestershire
GL19 3PL
Ⓣ (01531) 650480
Ⓕ (01531) 650480
Ⓔ cp@chris-pattison.co.uk
Ⓦ www.chris-pattison.co.uk
Contact: Chris Pattison
Opening Times: 0900-1700 Mon-Fri. W/ends by appt. only.
Min Mail Order UK: £10.00 +p&p
Cat. Cost: 3 × 1st class.
Credit Cards: None
Specialities: Choice rare shrubs & trees. Grafted stock esp. Japanese maples & *Liquidambar*. Wide range of *Viburnum* & dwarf/miniature trees & shrubs suitable for bonsai or rockery.
Notes: Mail order Nov-Feb only. Also sells wholesale. Euro accepted. Wheelchair accessible.
Map Ref: W, C5 **OS Grid Ref:** SO781327

WPGP **Pan-Global Plants** ♿
The Walled Garden, Frampton Court, Frampton-on-Severn, Gloucestershire
GL2 7EX
Ⓣ (01452) 741641
Ⓜ 07801 275138
Ⓔ info@panglobalplants.com
Ⓦ www.panglobalplants.com
Contact: Nick Macer
Opening Times: 1100-1700 Wed-Sun 1st Feb-31st Oct. Also B/hols. Closed 2nd Sun in Sep. Winter months by appt., please phone first.
Min Mail Order UK: £20.00
Min Mail Order EU: £20.00
Cat. Cost: 6 × 1st class.
Credit Cards: Maestro, MasterCard, Visa, Solo, Delta
Specialities: A plantsman's nursery offering a very wide selection of correctly named rare & desirable trees, shrubs, herbaceous, bamboos, exotics, climbers, ferns etc. Specialities incl. *Magnolia, Hydrangea, Tilia, Betula, Sorbus, Bamboo* & *Agavaceae*.
Notes: Wheelchair accessible.
Map Ref: W, D5 **OS Grid Ref:** SO750080

WPnn **The Perennial Nursery**
Rhosygilwen, St Davids, Haverfordwest, Pembrokeshire SA62 6DB
Ⓜ 07717 783492
Ⓔ theperennialnursery@tesco.net
Ⓦ www.theperennialnursery.co.uk
Contact: Mrs Philipa Symons
Opening Times: 1030-1700 Mar-Oct. Closed Tue.
Min Mail Order UK: Nmc
Min Mail Order EU: Nmc
Cat. Cost: Online only.
Credit Cards: Visa, MasterCard
Specialities: *Lampranthus*, wind & drought-tolerant plants.
Notes: Tea room.
Map Ref: W, C1 **OS Grid Ref:** SM775292

WPnP **Penlan Perennials** ♿
Wern Rhos, Newchapel, Boncath, Pembrokeshire SA37 0EN
Ⓣ (01239) 842260
Ⓜ 07857 675312
Ⓔ info@penlanperennials.co.uk
Ⓦ www.penlanperennials.co.uk
Contact: Richard Cain
Opening Times: Open for collection of orders & by appt.
Min Mail Order UK: Nmc
Min Mail Order EU: Nmc
Cat. Cost: Online PDF, or sae for CD-ROM.
Credit Cards: All major credit/debit cards
Specialities: Aquatic, marginal & bog plants. Shade-loving & woodland perennials, ferns & hardy geraniums, all grown organically in peat-free compost.
Notes: Mail order all year, next day delivery. Secure online web ordering. Also sells wholesale. Euro accepted. Delivers to shows. Wheelchair accessible.
Map Ref: W, C2 **OS Grid Ref:** SN217392

WPtf **Pantyfod Garden Nursery**
Llandewi Brefi, Tregaron, Ceredigion
SY25 6PE
Ⓣ (01570) 400564 (answering service)
Ⓔ sales@pantyfodgarden.co.uk
Ⓦ www.pantyfodgarden.co.uk
Contact: Susan Rowe
Opening Times: 1100-1700 Sat only, mid Apr-mid Sep, nursery & garden. Other times by arrangement. Garden open under the NGS with plants for sale. Please check with NGS for Open Days.
Min Mail Order UK: Nmc
Min Mail Order EU: Nmc
Cat. Cost: Online only.
Credit Cards: Paypal
Specialities: Hardy geraniums, unusual hardy perennials, grasses, plants for moist soil, black plants, woodland plants. All plants grown largely peat-free. Many plants available in small quantities.
Notes: Stock changes throughout the year. Some plants ready later in the year. Not all plants available for mail order. Mail order plants may be sent bare-rooted when dormant. See website for regular updates or phone/ email.
Map Ref: W, C3 **OS Grid Ref:** SN654540

WRHF **RED HOUSE FARM** ♿
Flying Horse Lane, Bradley Green,
Nr Redditch, Worcestershire B96 6QT
Ⓣ (01527) 821269
Ⓔ redhousenursery@googlemail.com
Ⓦ www.redhousefarmgardenandnursery.co.uk
Contact: Mrs Maureen Weaver
Opening Times: 0900-1700 Mon-Sat all year. 1000-1700 Sun & B/hols.
Cat. Cost: 2 × 1st class.
Credit Cards: None
Specialities: Cottage garden perennials.
Notes: Wheelchair accessible.
Map Ref: W, C5 **OS Grid Ref:** SO986623

WSFF **SAITH FFYNNON WILDLIFE PLANTS** ♿
Whitford, Holywell, Flintshire CH8 9EQ
Ⓣ (01352) 711198
Ⓕ (01352) 716777
Ⓔ jan@7wells.org
Ⓦ www.7wells.co.uk
Contact: Jan Miller
Opening Times: By appt. only.
Min Mail Order UK: Nmc
Min Mail Order EU: Nmc
Cat. Cost: 2 × 1st class (list only) or full catalogue online.
Credit Cards: All major credit/debit cards
Specialities: Plants and seeds to attract bees, butterflies and moths. Natural dye plants. Nat. Collection of *Eupatorium*. Stock available in small quantities unless ordered well in advance.
Notes: Percentage of profits go to conservation. Credit cards accepted via website only. Also sells wholesale. Euro accepted. Delivers to shows. Wheelchair accessible.

WSHC **STONE HOUSE COTTAGE NURSERIES** ♿
Church Lane, Stone, Nr Kidderminster, Worcestershire DY10 4BG
Ⓜ 07817 921146
Ⓔ louisa@shcn.co.uk
Ⓦ www.shcn.co.uk
Contact: L N Arbuthnott
Opening Times: 1000-1700 Wed-Sat, late Mar-early Sep only.
Cat. Cost: Sae
Credit Cards: None
Specialities: Small general range esp. wall shrubs, climbers & unusual plants.
Notes: Wheelchair accessible.
Map Ref: W, C5 **OS Grid Ref:** SO863750

WShi **SHIPTON BULBS**
Y Felin, Henllan Amgoed, Whitland, Carmarthenshire SA34 0SL
Ⓣ (01994) 240125
Ⓕ 01994 240125
Ⓔ admin@shiptonbulbs.co.uk
Ⓦ www.shiptonbulbs.co.uk
Contact: John Shipton & Astra Shipton
Opening Times: By appt. only.
Min Mail Order UK: Nmc
Min Mail Order EU: Nmc
Cat. Cost: Sae.
Credit Cards: All major credit/debit cards
Specialities: Native British bulbs. Bulbs & plants for naturalising.
Notes: Euro accepted.
Map Ref: W, D2 **OS Grid Ref:** SN188207

WSSs **SHROPSHIRE SARRACENIAS** ♿
5 Field Close, Malinslee, Telford, Shropshire TF4 2EH
Ⓣ (01952) 501598
Ⓔ mike@carnivorousplants.uk.com
Ⓦ www.carnivorousplants.uk.com
Contact: Mike King
Opening Times: By appt. only.
Min Mail Order UK: Nmc
Min Mail Order EU: Nmc
Cat. Cost: 2 × 1st class.
Credit Cards: Paypal
Specialities: *Sarracenia. Dionaea muscipula* & forms. Some stock available in small quantities only. Nat. Collections of *Sarracenia* & *Dionaea*.
Notes: Exports beyond EU. Delivers to shows. Euro accepted. Wheelchair accessible.
Map Ref: W, B4 **OS Grid Ref:** SJ689085

WSuV **SUNNYBANK VINE NURSERY (NATIONAL VINE COLLECTION)**
Cwm Barn, King Street, Ewyas Harold, Rowlestone, Herefordshire HR2 OEE
Ⓣ (01981) 240256
Ⓔ Sarah@sunnybankvines.co.uk
Ⓦ www.sunnybankvines.co.uk
Contact: Sarah Bell
Opening Times: Not open. Mail order only. Open day once a year advertised on both nursery & Plant Heritage websites.
Min Mail Order UK: £12.00 incl. p&p
Min Mail Order EU: £15.00 incl. p&p
Cat. Cost: Online only.
Credit Cards: None
Specialities: Vines. Nat. Collection of *Vitis vinifera* (hardy, incl. dessert & wine). Small quantities of 60-70 varieties available as rooted plants, the entire Collection usually available as bare wood cuttings for own propagation depending upon wood ripening this season.
Notes: EU sales by arrangement. Exports beyond EU.

WTan **TAN-Y-LLYN NURSERIES**
Meifod, Powys SY22 6YB
Ⓣ (01938) 500370
Ⓔ info@tanyllyn-nursery.co.uk

W

Ⓦ www.tanyllyn-nursery.co.uk
Contact: Callum Johnston
Opening Times: By appt. only. Please phone.
Min Mail Order UK: Nmc
Cat. Cost: 2 × 1st class or online.
Credit Cards: Paypal
Specialities: Herbs, alpines, perennials.
Map Ref: W, B3 **OS Grid Ref:** SJ167125

WTcb **T3 Plants** ♿
Wall End Nursery, Wall End Barn,
Stoke Prior, Leominster, Herefordshire
HR6 0ND
Ⓣ (01568) 760152
Ⓜ 07775 001287
Ⓔ t3plants@aol.com
Ⓦ www.t3plants.co.uk
Contact: Leila Jackson
Opening Times: 1000-1500 Mon-Wed, Apr-Sep.
Min Mail Order UK: 10 plants.
Cat. Cost: 3 × 1st class.
Specialities: Family nursery specialising in *Abutilon* & *Salvia*. *Campanula*, *Persicaria*, *Sanguisorba* & autumn-flowering plants. Some stock propagated to order. Large collection of sub-shrub *Salvia*. Nat. Collection of *Abutilon*.
Notes: Delivers to shows. Also sells wholesale. Wheelchair accessible.

WThu **Thuya Alpine Nursery**
Glebelands, Hartpury, Gloucestershire
GL19 3BW
Ⓣ (01452) 700548 (ring between 1900-2100 hours)
Contact: S W Bond
Opening Times: 1000-dusk Sat & B/hols. 1100-dusk Sun, Weekdays appt. advised.
Min Mail Order UK: £6.00 + p&p
Min Mail Order EU: £12.00 + p&p
Cat. Cost: 4 × 2nd class.
Credit Cards: None
Specialities: Wide and changing range including rarities, available in smallish numbers.
Notes: Will deliver plants to AGS shows only. Partially accessible for wheelchair users.
Map Ref: W, C5

WTor **Tortworth Plants Ltd**
Old Lodge Farm, Tortworth,
Wotton-under-Edge, Gloucestershire
GL12 8HF
Ⓣ (01454) 260020
Ⓕ (01454) 260020
Ⓔ info@tortworthplants.co.uk
Ⓦ www.tortworthplants.co.uk
Contact: Rebecca Flint or Tim Hancock
Opening Times: By appt. only.
Min Mail Order UK: Nmc
Cat. Cost: Online or 2 × 1st for plant list.
Credit Cards: All, except American Express
Specialities: Herbaceous perennials & alpines, incl. rare & unusual.
Notes: Also sells wholesale. Partial wheelchair access. Delivers to shows.

WTou **Touchwood Plants**
4 Clyne Valley Cottages, Killay, Swansea,
West Glamorgan SA2 7DU
Ⓣ (01792) 522443
Ⓔ Carrie.Thomas@ntlworld.com
Ⓦ www.touchwoodplants.co.uk
Contact: Carrie Thomas
Opening Times: Most reasonable days/times. Please phone first.
Min Mail Order UK: Nmc
Min Mail Order EU: Nmc
Cat. Cost: Online only.
Credit Cards: Paypal, All major credit/debit cards
Specialities: Seeds & plants. Nat. Collections of *Aquilegia vulgaris* cvs & *Aquilegia* hybrids. Plant stocks held in small quantities. Main stock is seed. Garden & *Aquilegia* Collection open.
Notes: Plants sent bare-rooted at relevant times of the year. Only seeds (not plants) exported outside UK. Credit cards accepted online only. Exports beyond EU.
Map Ref: W, D3 **OS Grid Ref:** SS600924

WTre **Walled Garden Treberfydd**
Llangasty, Brecon, Powys LD3 7PX
Ⓣ (01874) 730169
Ⓜ 07711 222700
Ⓔ alison@walledgardentreberfydd.com
Ⓦ www.walledgardentreberfydd.com
Contact: Alison Sparshatt
Opening Times: 1000-1700 daily, Apr-Oct. 1000-1600 daily, Nov-Mar.
Credit Cards: All, except American Express
Specialities: Old-fashioned, plant nursery in a 2-acre walled garden. Hardy plants grown in Wales which are structural, unusual, herbal or fragrant. Special emphasis on herbs & wild flowers. Display beds for all plants on sale. All plants grown peat-free.
Notes: Tea & cake available.
Map Ref: W, C4 **OS Grid Ref:** SO128255

WTSh **Tree Shop Ltd**
Unit 16, Harts Barn, Monmouth Road,
Longhope, Gloucestershire GL17 0QD
Ⓣ (01452) 832100
Ⓕ (01452) 831273
Ⓔ office@tree-shop.co.uk
Ⓦ www.tree-shop.co.uk
Contact: Helen Conneely & Lorraine Organ
Opening Times: By appt. only 0830-1600

Mon-Fri. Please phone first.
Min Mail Order UK: Nmc
Cat. Cost: Free.
Credit Cards: All, except American Express
Specialities: Trees, hedging, shrubs.

WViv **Viv Marsh Postal Plants** ♿
Walford Heath, Shrewsbury, Shropshire
SY4 2HT
Ⓣ (01939) 291475
Ⓔ mail@postalplants.co.uk
Ⓦ www.postalplants.co.uk
Contact: Mr Viv Marsh
Opening Times: Open 2 w/ends a year. Please phone or see website for details.
Min Mail Order UK: £33.00
Min Mail Order EU: £33.00
Cat. Cost: Free.
Credit Cards: All major credit/debit cards
Specialities: Specialists in *Alstroemeria* & *Lathyrus*. Nat. Collection of *Alstroemeria*, viewing by appt.
Notes: Wheelchair access to tunnels. No disabled toilet.
Map Ref: W, B4 **OS Grid Ref:** SJ445197

X

WWct **Walcot Organic Nursery**
Lower Walcot Farm, Walcot Lane, Drakes Broughton, Pershore, Worcestershire
WR10 2AL
Ⓣ (01905) 841587
Ⓜ 07780 547983
Ⓔ enquiries@walcotnursery.co.uk
Ⓦ www.walcotnursery.co.uk
Contact: Kevin O'Neill
Opening Times: 0800-1700 Mon-Fri. 1000-1300 Sat. Nov-Mar only.
Min Mail Order UK: £12.50
Cat. Cost: Free.
Credit Cards: All major credit/debit cards
Specialities: Organic fruit trees. Apples, plums, pears, cherries, quinces etc on different rootstocks.
Notes: Also sells wholesale.

WWFP **Whitehall Farmhouse Plants**
Sevenhampton, Cheltenham, Gloucestershire
GL54 5TL
Ⓣ (01242) 820772
Ⓜ 07711 021034
Ⓔ info@wfplants.co.uk
Ⓦ www.wfplants.co.uk
Contact: Victoria Logue
Opening Times: By appt. only.
Min Mail Order UK: Nmc
Credit Cards: None
Specialities: A small nursery producing a range of interesting & easy hardy perennials for the garden. Some plants held in small quantities only.
Notes: Delivers to shows.
Map Ref: W, C5 **OS Grid Ref:** SP018229

WWtn **Westonbury Mill Water Garden** ♿
Pembridge, Herefordshire HR6 9HZ
Ⓣ (01544) 388650
Ⓕ (01544) 388650
Ⓔ richardpim@btinternet.com
Ⓦ www.westonburymillwatergardens.com
Contact: Richard Pim
Opening Times: 1100-1700 daily, 1st Apr-30th Sep. By appt. only at other times & to arrange collection.
Specialities: Range of herbaceous plants suitable for a wide range of growing conditions, with special emphasis on plants for the water garden & bog areas. Some plants available in small quantities. Contact nursery to confirm availability as stock sells out quickly when in flower.
Notes: Café. Wheelchair accessible.

Abroad

XBar **Barnhaven Primroses**
11 rue du Pont Blanc, Plestin-les-grèves
22310, France
Ⓣ +33 2 9635 6841
Ⓜ +33 6 6124 7739
Ⓕ +33 2 9635 6841
Ⓔ info@barnhaven.com
Ⓦ www.barnhaven.com
Contact: Lynne & David Lawson
Opening Times: 1400-1700 Feb-Apr. For visits outside this period, please phone first.
Min Mail Order UK: Nmc
Min Mail Order EU: Nmc
Credit Cards: Visa, MasterCard
Specialities: Barnhaven strains of polyanthus, incl. gold-laced & anomalous. Also auriculas & alpines. Seeds & plants available worldwide.
Notes: Exports beyond EU. Euro accepted. Delivers to shows.

XBlo **Table Bay View Nursery**
PO Box 12123, Mill Street, Cape Town 8010, South Africa
Ⓣ +27 21 683 5108
Ⓕ +27 21 683 5108
Ⓔ info@tablebayviewnursery.co.za
Contact: Terence Bloch
Opening Times: Mail order only. No personal callers.
Min Mail Order UK: £15.00 + p&p
Min Mail Order EU: £15.00
Cat. Cost: £3.40 (postal order)
Credit Cards: None
Specialities: Tropical & sub-tropical ornamental & fruiting plants. Self-harvested

seed, predominently from our own inventory of mother stock plants.
Notes: Due to high local bank charges, can no longer accept foreign bank cheques, only undated postal orders. To comply with UK import regulations, prospective buyers must register with DEFRA before placing an order. Exports beyond EU. Euro accepted.

XEll **Ellebore**
La Chamotière, 61360 Saint-Jouin-de-Blavou, France
Ⓣ +33 2 3383 3772
Ⓜ +33 6802 28674
Ⓕ +33 2 3383 3773
Ⓔ pepiniere.ellebore@orange.fr
Ⓦ www.pepiniere-ellebore.fr
Contact: Nadine Albouy & Christian Geoffroy
Opening Times: 1000-1800 Wed-Sat, mid-Feb to late Jun & Sep-Dec. 1500-1800 Thu, Fri & Sat, Jul, Aug & Jan to mid-Feb.
Min Mail Order UK: Nmc
Min Mail Order EU: Nmc
Cat. Cost: Free.
Credit Cards: All major credit/debit cards
Specialities: *Helleborus*. Bulbs. *Clematis*.
Notes: Also sells wholesale. Euro accepted. Delivers to shows.

XFro **Frosch Exclusive Perennials**
Ziegelstadelweg 5, D-83623 Dietramszell-Lochen, Germany
Ⓣ +49 172 842 2050
Ⓕ +49 8027 904 9975
Ⓔ info@cypripedium.de
Ⓦ www.cypripedium.de
Contact: Michael Weinert
Opening Times: Not open. Mail order only. Orders taken between 0700-2200 hours.
Min Mail Order UK: £350.00 + p&p
Min Mail Order EU: £350.00 + p&p
Cat. Cost: Online only.
Credit Cards: None
Specialities: *Cypripedium* hybrids. Hardy orchids.
Notes: Also sells wholesale. Exports beyond EU. Euro accepted.

XGra **Graefswinning**
Diestersteenweg 222, 3850 Nieuwerkerken, Belgium
Ⓣ +32 1188 3611
Ⓔ info@graefswinning.be
Ⓦ www.graefswinning.be
Contact: Jeaninne Lemmens
Opening Times: Open Apr-Jun to view flower fields. Check website for further information.
Min Mail Order UK: Nmc
Min Mail Order EU: Nmc
Cat. Cost: Online only.
Credit Cards: MasterCard, Visa, Paypal
Specialities: Herbaceous, tree & Itoh peonies. Several acres of peonies in the field. Sell containerised peonies in sturdy 7L pots as well as bare-root plants. Landscape & cut-flower varieties.
Notes: Bare-root peonies are shipped in autumn to countries within the EU. Container plants available at nursery & garden shows. Exports beyond EU. Euro accepted.

XHod **SCEA Hodnik**
1 Place du 19 Mars 1962, 45700 St Maurice sur Fessard, France
Ⓣ (33) 02 3897 8459
Ⓕ (33) 02 3897 8939
Ⓔ contact@hodnik.com
Ⓦ www.hodnik.com
Contact: André Hodnik
Opening Times: Not open except by appt. Mail order only.
Min Mail Order UK: Nmc
Min Mail Order EU: Nmc
Cat. Cost: Online only.
Credit Cards: All major credit/debit cards
Specialities: A large number of tropical & Mediterreanean plants which can be grown in a conservatory. French National Collection nationale of *Bougainvillea* & *Brugmansia*.
Notes: Weekly shipments to the UK. Euro accepted.

XLum **Lumen Plantes Vivaces**
Les Coutets, 24100 Creysse-Bergerac, Occitania, France
Ⓣ +33 5 5357 6215
Ⓕ +33 5 5358 5488
Ⓔ lumenviva@aol.com
Ⓦ www.lumen.fr
Contact: Michel Lumen
Opening Times: 0900-1200 & 1300-1630 Mon-Thu, 0900-1200 & 1300-1530 Fri. Closed Sat, Sun & B/hols. 0900-1200 & 1300-1830 Mon-Sat, Mar-Jun.
Min Mail Order UK: Nmc
Min Mail Order EU: Nmc
Cat. Cost: Online only.
Credit Cards: Visa, MasterCard
Specialities: Hardy perennials. French Nat. Collection of *Miscanthus*.
Notes: Also sells wholesale. Exports beyond EU. Delivers to shows. Euro accepted.

XSen **Les Senteurs Du Quercy** Ⓛ
Mas de Fraysse, Escamps, Lot 46230, France
Ⓣ +33 5 652 10167
Ⓔ contact@senteursduquercy.com
Ⓦ www.senteursduquercy.com
Contact: Frédéric Prévot

Opening Times: 1400-1800 spring & summer (excl. Aug). Other times, incl. Aug by appt.
Min Mail Order UK: Nmc
Min Mail Order EU: Nmc
Cat. Cost: €5.00
Specialities: *Salvia*, *Iris*, *Phlomis*, *Teucrium*, *Lavandula* and drought tolerant plants. French Nat. Coll. of *Salvia* species.
Notes: Euro accepted. Delivers to shows. Wheelchair accessible.

XTur **Etablissements Pierre Turc** ♿ ◆
63 Route de Seiches, 49630 Mazé, France
Ⓣ +33 02 4180 6408
Ⓜ +33 06 4756 3327
Ⓕ +33 02 4180 2696
Ⓔ export@turcieflor.com
Ⓦ www.turcieflor.com
Contact: Mark Hodson
Opening Times: 0800-1215 & 1400-1700 Mon-Fri.
Min Mail Order UK: Nmc + p&p
Min Mail Order EU: Nmc + p&p
Specialities: *Alstroemeria*, *Agapanthus* & *Canna*. Also *Arum*, *Begonia*, *Dahlia*, *Fuchsia* & *Hippeastrum*.
Notes: Accepts payment by electronic transfer or cheques. Also sells wholesale. Exports beyond EU. Delivers to shows. Euro accepted. Wheelchair accessible.

NURSERY INDEX BY NAME

Nurseries that are included in the *RHS Plant Finder* for the first time this year (or have been reintroduced after a significant absence) are marked in **bold type**.

Full details of the nurseries will be found in **Nursery Details by Code** on page 832. For a key to the geographical codes, see the start of **Nurseries**.

Golden Hill Nurseries	SGol
Goscote Nurseries Ltd	MGos
Graefswinning	XGra
Grange Farm Plants	EGFP
Great Dixter Nurseries	SDix
Great Western Gladiolus Nursery, The	CGrW
Green's Leaves	WGrn
C W Groves & Son Ltd	**CGro**
Gwynfor Growers	WGwG
Habitat Aid Ltd.	CHab
Hall Farm Nursery	WHal
Halls of Heddon	NHal
Hall's Court Nursery	SHal
Hampshire Carnivorous Plants	**SHmp**
Hardy's Cottage Garden Plants	SHar
Hare Spring Cottage Plants	**NHsp**
Harley Nursery	WHar
Harlow Carr Plant Centre (RHS)	**NRHS**
Harperley Hall Farm Nurseries	**NHpl**
Harrells Hardy Plants	WHrl
Hart Canna	SHaC
Hartside Nursery Garden	NHar
Harveys Garden Plants	EHrv
Hawthornes Nursery, The	NHaw
Hayloft Plants	WHlf
Heath Garden	WHea
Hedge Nursery (Choice Shops Ltd)	**WHed**
Hedgexpress	MHed
Herb Garden & Historical Plant Nursery, The	WHer
Herb Nursery, The	MHer
Herbary, The	CHby
Hergest Croft Gardens	WHCr
Herterton House Garden Nursery	NHer
Herts Hellebores	LHel
Heucheraholics	SHeu
Hewitt-Cooper Carnivorous Plants	CHew
Hidden Paradise Plants (formerly Sound Garden Rhododendrons)	MHid
Hidden Valley Gardens	CHVG
Hidden Valley Nursery	CHid
High Garden Nurseries	CHGN
Highdown Nursery	SHDw
Hill Close Gardens	MHCG
Hill House Nursery Ltd	CHll
Hillier Garden Centres	SHil
Hillview Hardy Plants	WHil
Hintons Nursery	MHtn
Hippopottering Nursery	NHip
Hoecroft Plants	EHoe
Holden Clough Nursery Ltd.	NHol
Hollies Farm Plant Centre	MHol
Home Farm Plants	**LHom**
Homestead Plants	MHom
Hoo House Nursery	WHoo
Hopleys Plants Ltd	LHop
Horticultural Sales	WHor
Hurst Brook Plants	**CHur**
Hyde Hall Plant Centre (RHS)	**EHyd**
Hydrangea Haven	SHyH
Ice Alpines	WIce
Iden Croft Herbs	SIde
Ingram, Tim	SIgm
Iris Garden, The	CIri
Iris of Sissinghurst	SIri
Irisesonline	EIri
JPR Environmental	WJPR
JRG Dahlias	NJRG
Jackson's Nurseries	MJak
Jackson's Nurseries	MJac
Jacques Amand International Ltd	LAma
Jekka's Herb Farm	WJek
Jo's Garden Enterprise	GJos
John and Lynsey's Plants	SPin
John Churcher	SChr
John Gibson Daffodils	MGib
John Gillies	MGil
John Hall Plants Ltd	SWhi
John Smith & Son	MSmi
Jungle Giants	CJng
Junker's Nursery Ltd.	CJun
Keepers Nursery	SKee
Kelways	CKel
Kenwith Conifer Nursery (Gordon Haddow)	CKen
Kevin Hughes Plants	SKHP
Kevock Garden Plants	GKev
Kiftsgate Court Gardens	WKif
Kilmurry Nursery	IKil
Kings Barn Trees	SKin
Kinlochlaich Garden Plant Centre	GKin
Knoll Gardens	CKno
Ladybird Nurseries	ELad
Lakka Bulbs	CLak
Landford Trees	CLnd
Langthorns Plantery	ELan
Larch Cottage Nurseries	NLar
Laurel Farm Herbs	CLau
Laurels Nursery, The	SLau
Lavender Garden, The	WLav
Layham Garden Centre & Nursery	SLay
Lea Rhododendron Gardens Ltd	MLea
Leamore Nursery	ILea
Letham Plants	GLet
Letsgoplanting	CLet
Lilies Water Gardens	LLWG
Lime Cross Nursery	SLim
Little Brook Fuchsias	SLBF
Little Heath Farm (UK)	LLHF
C S Lockyer (Fuchsias)	CLoc
Loder Plants	SLdr
Lodge Farm Plants & Wildflowers	MLod
Logie Steading Plants	GLog
Long Acre Plants	CLAP
Long House Plants	ELon
Longcombe Nursery and Garden Centre	CLng

INDEX MAP

The maps on the following pages show the approximate location of the nurseries whose details are listed in this directory.

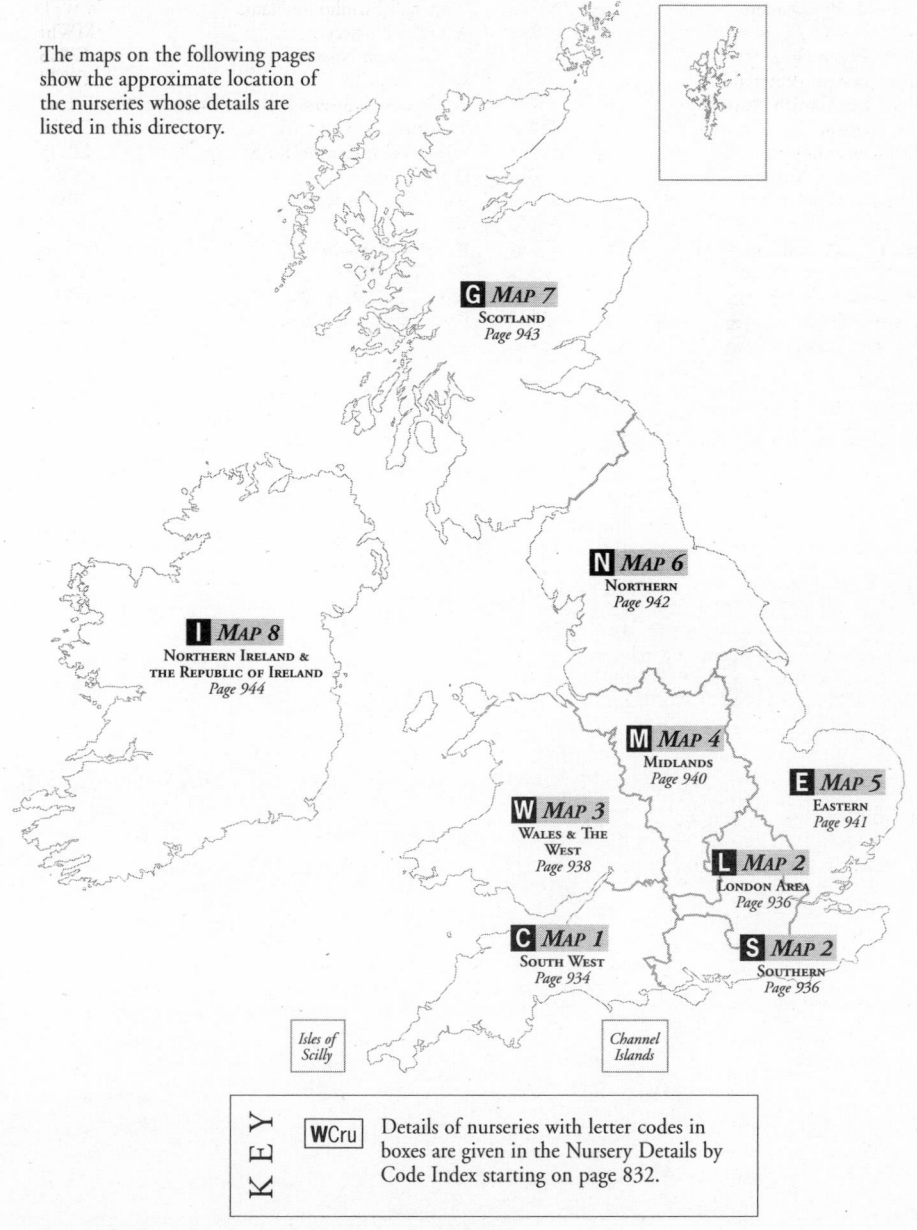

KEY

WCru Details of nurseries with letter codes in boxes are given in the Nursery Details by Code Index starting on page 832.

C
MAP ONE
SOUTH WEST
1
2
3
A
B
C
D
Llanelli
M4
Neath
Swansea
Port Talbot
Bridgend
Ilfracombe
Combe Martin
CMHG
Barnstaple
CGar
CAni
Bideford
CHid
CWCL
CRos
CKen
CPne
Bude
A39
CPbn
CCac
A377
CLau
Okehampton
CJng
CSto
Launceston
CBre
Tavistock
CBct
CMan
Newton Abbott
Wadebridge
CBod
CTca
CHll
CLng
A38
Bodmin
Liskeard
CTsd
Newquay
CPrp
Plymouth
CNWT
A30
CHVG
CPou
CRHN
St Austell
Truro
CFen
St Ives
Redruth
Camborne
CBcs
Penzance
Falmouth
Helston
CQua

4
5
6
A
B
C
D
Stroud
Cirencester
Merthyr Tydfil
Pontypool
Cwmbran
Newport
CARDIFF
M4
M5
CLoc
CWGN
Swindon
CWat
Bristol
CPhi
CSpe
Chippenham
CFlo
Calne
Marlborough
Newbury
Clevedon
CBot
Melksham
Devizes
Weston Super Mare
CArn
CCVT
Bath
Trowbridge
CMea
CPBP
Burnham on Sea
CWSG
Minehead
CFwr
CMil
Wells
CMen
Frome
Warminster
Andover
Williton
CBgR
CMus
A36
CTri
Bridgwater
Glastonbury
CSna
CElw
CBro
CMos
CPen
CAbP
Salisbury
Winche
Wincanton
CLAP
Taunton
CKel
A303
CDTJ
CFis
Shaftesbury
M3
Wellington
CLet
CMCN
CAvo
Yeovil
CLnd
CSam
CBWd
A354
CFst
Southampton
Tiverton
Chard
Ringwood
Blandford Forum
CKno
CTho
CDul
Honiton
CNor
CTrh
CMac
Lymington
Exeter
CAby
CIri
Winborne Minster
CEnt
CPar
Bridport
CChe
Lyme Regis
A35
Dorchester
Bournemouth
CSBt
CBrP
Poole
CNec
CCht
CHGN
CEls
CBen
Weymouth
Exmouth
Dawlish
CBur
Teignmouth
CPla
Torquay
Paignton
Brixham

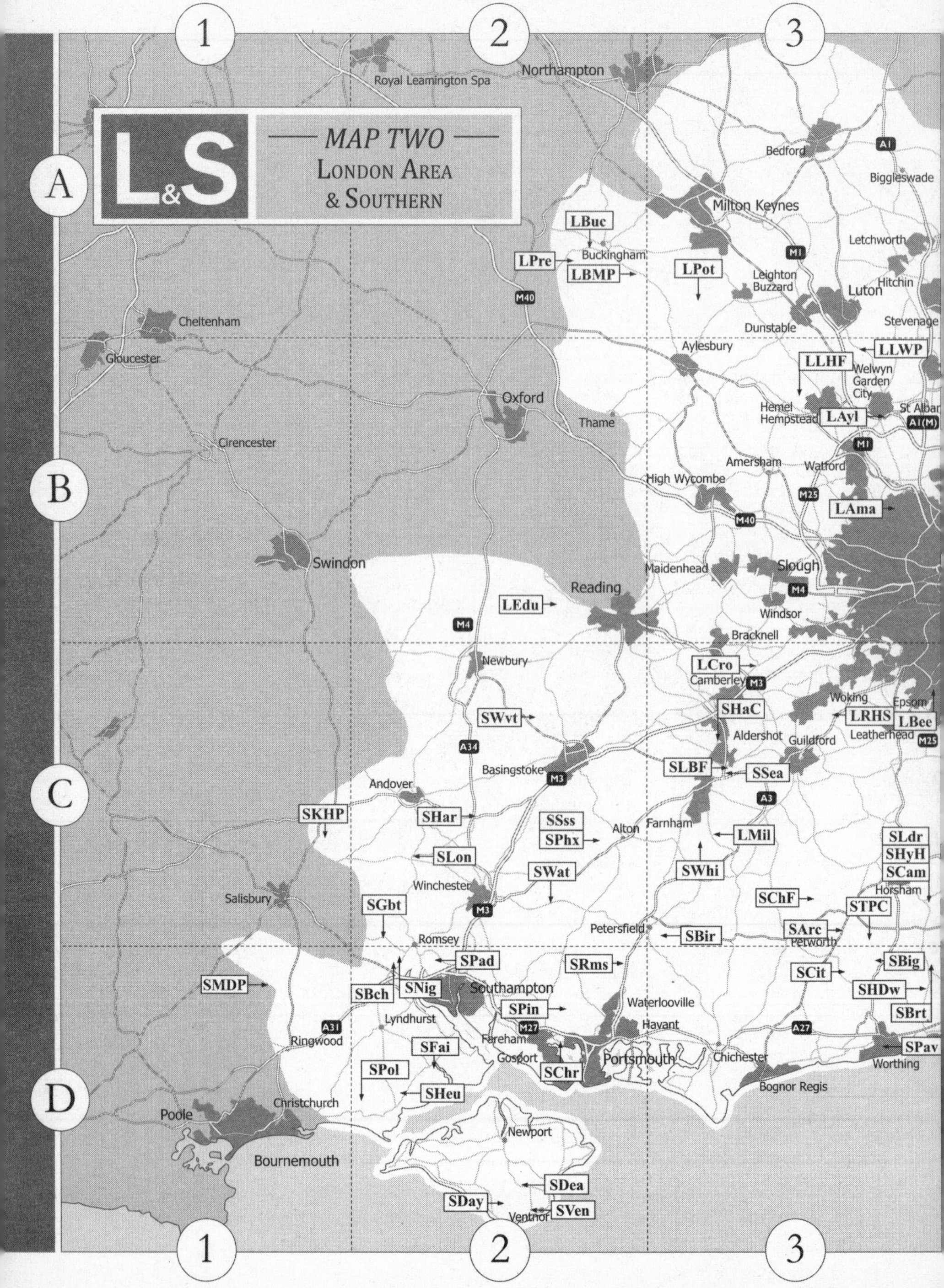
L&S
MAP TWO
LONDON AREA
& SOUTHERN
1
2
3
A
B
C
D
Northampton
Royal Leamington Spa
Bedford
Biggleswade
Milton Keynes
Letchworth
LBuc
Buckingham
LPre
LBMP
LPot
Leighton Buzzard
Hitchin
Luton
Stevenage
Dunstable
Cheltenham
Gloucester
Aylesbury
LLWP
LLHF
Welwyn Garden City
Oxford
Hemel Hempstead
LAyl
St Albar
Thame
Cirencester
Amersham
Watford
High Wycombe
LAma
Swindon
Maidenhead
Slough
Reading
LEdu
Windsor
Bracknell
Newbury
LCro
Camberley
Woking
Epsom
SHaC
SWvt
LRHS
LBee
Aldershot
Guildford
Leatherhead
Basingstoke
SLBF
SSea
Andover
SKHP
SHar
SSss
SPhx
Alton
Farnham
LMil
SLon
SLdr
SHyH
SCam
SWat
SWhi
Winchester
Horsham
Salisbury
SGbt
SChF
STPC
Petersfield
SBir
SArc
Petworth
Romsey
SPad
SRms
SBig
SMDP
SCit
SBch
SNig
Southampton
SHDw
Waterlooville
Lyndhurst
SPin
SBrt
Havant
Ringwood
Fareham
SFai
Gosport
Portsmouth
Chichester
SPav
Worthing
SPol
SChr
SHeu
Bognor Regis
Christchurch
Poole
Newport
Bournemouth
SDea
SDay
Ventnor
SVen
A1
M1
M40
A1(M)
M25
M4
M3
A34
A3
A31
M27
A27

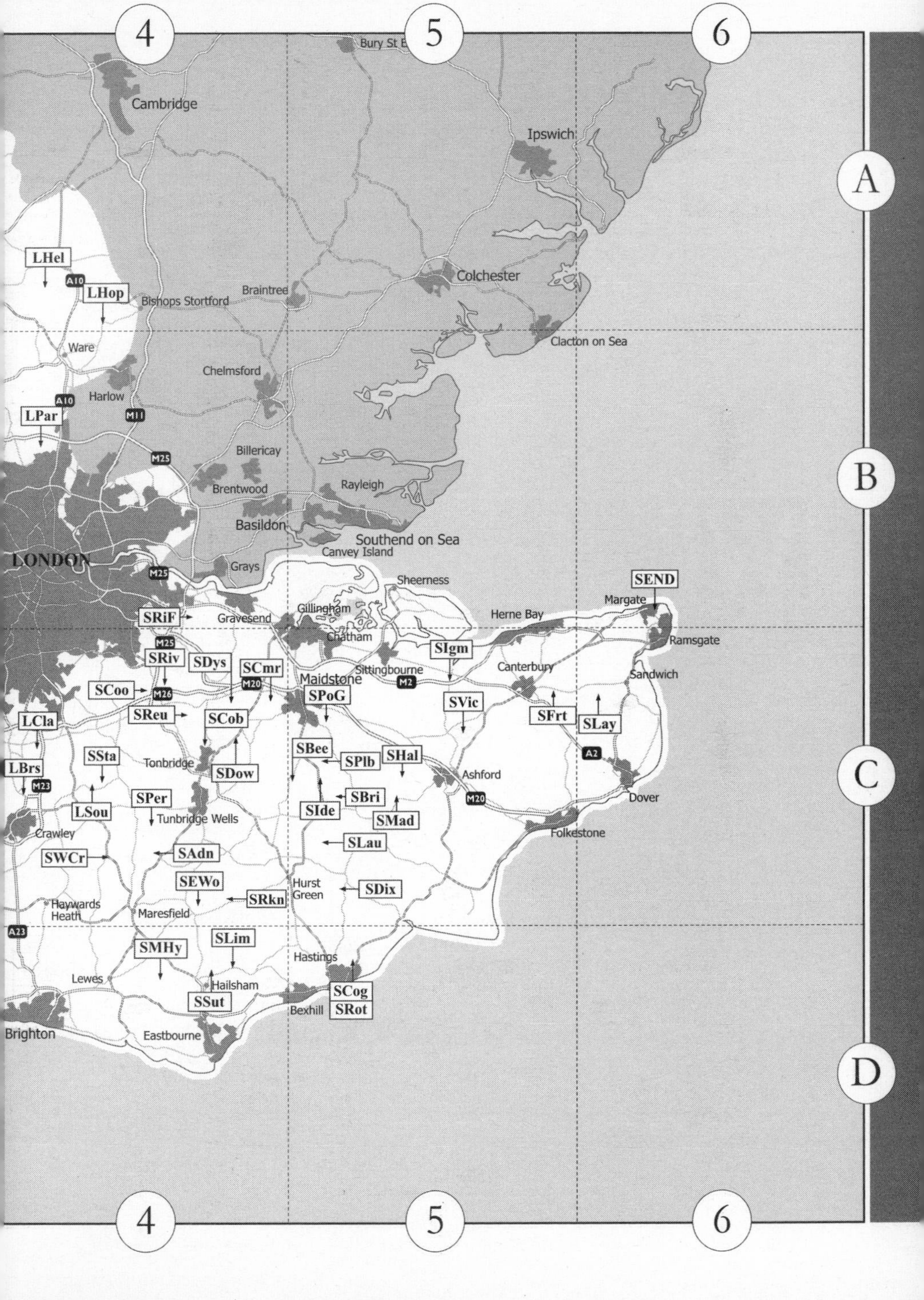
4
5
6
A
B
C
D
Bury St E
Cambridge
Ipswich
Colchester
Clacton on Sea
Braintree
Bishops Stortford
Ware
Harlow
Chelmsford
Billericay
Brentwood
Rayleigh
Basildon
Southend on Sea
Canvey Island
LONDON
Grays
Sheerness
Gravesend
Gillingham
Chatham
Herne Bay
Margate
Ramsgate
Sandwich
Canterbury
Sittingbourne
Maidstone
Tonbridge
Tunbridge Wells
Ashford
Dover
Folkestone
Crawley
Hurst Green
Haywards Heath
Maresfield
Hastings
Lewes
Hailsham
Bexhill
Brighton
Eastbourne
A10
M11
M25
M26
M20
M2
A2
M23
A23
LHel
LHop
LPar
SRiF
SRiv
SDys
SCmr
SCoo
SReu
SCob
LCla
SSta
LBrs
SDow
LSou
SPer
SPoG
SBee
SPlb
SHal
SIde
SBri
SMad
SLau
SAdn
SWCr
SEWo
SRkn
SDix
SLim
SMHy
SSut
SCog
SRot
SIgm
SVic
SFrt
SLay
SEND

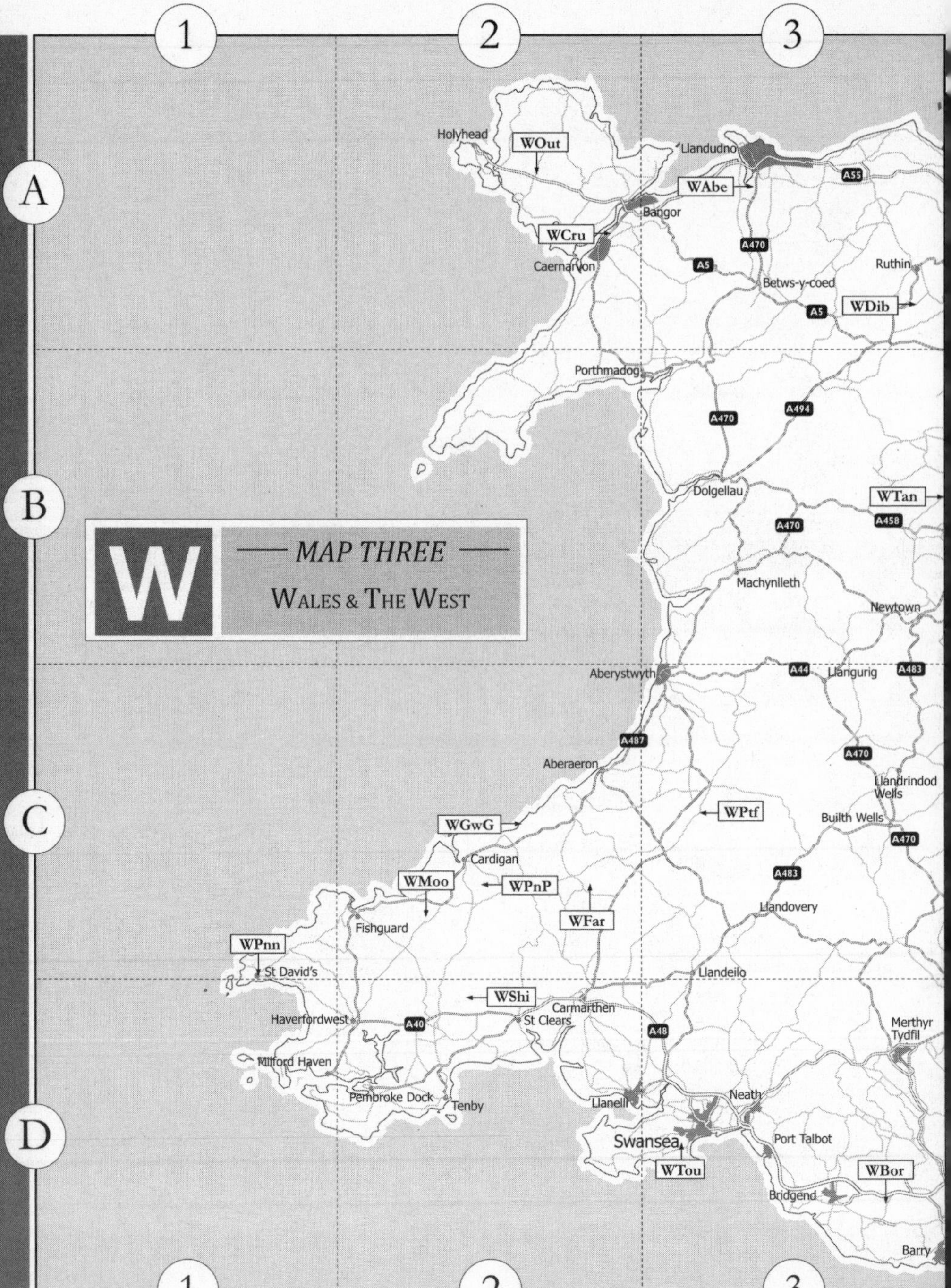
1
2
3
A
B
C
D
W
MAP THREE
WALES & THE WEST
Holyhead
WOut
Llandudno
WAbe
A55
Bangor
WCru
Caernarvon
A470
A5
Ruthin
Betws-y-coed
A5
WDib
Porthmadog
A470
A494
Dolgellau
WTan
A470
A458
Machynlleth
Newtown
Aberystwyth
A44
Llangurig
A483
A487
A470
Aberaeron
Llandrindod Wells
WPtf
WGwG
Builth Wells
A470
Cardigan
A483
WMoo
WPnP
WFar
Llandovery
Fishguard
WPnn
St David's
Llandeilo
WShi
Carmarthen
Haverfordwest
A40
St Clears
A48
Merthyr Tydfil
Milford Haven
Pembroke Dock
Tenby
Llanelli
Neath
Swansea
Port Talbot
WTou
WBor
Bridgend
Barry

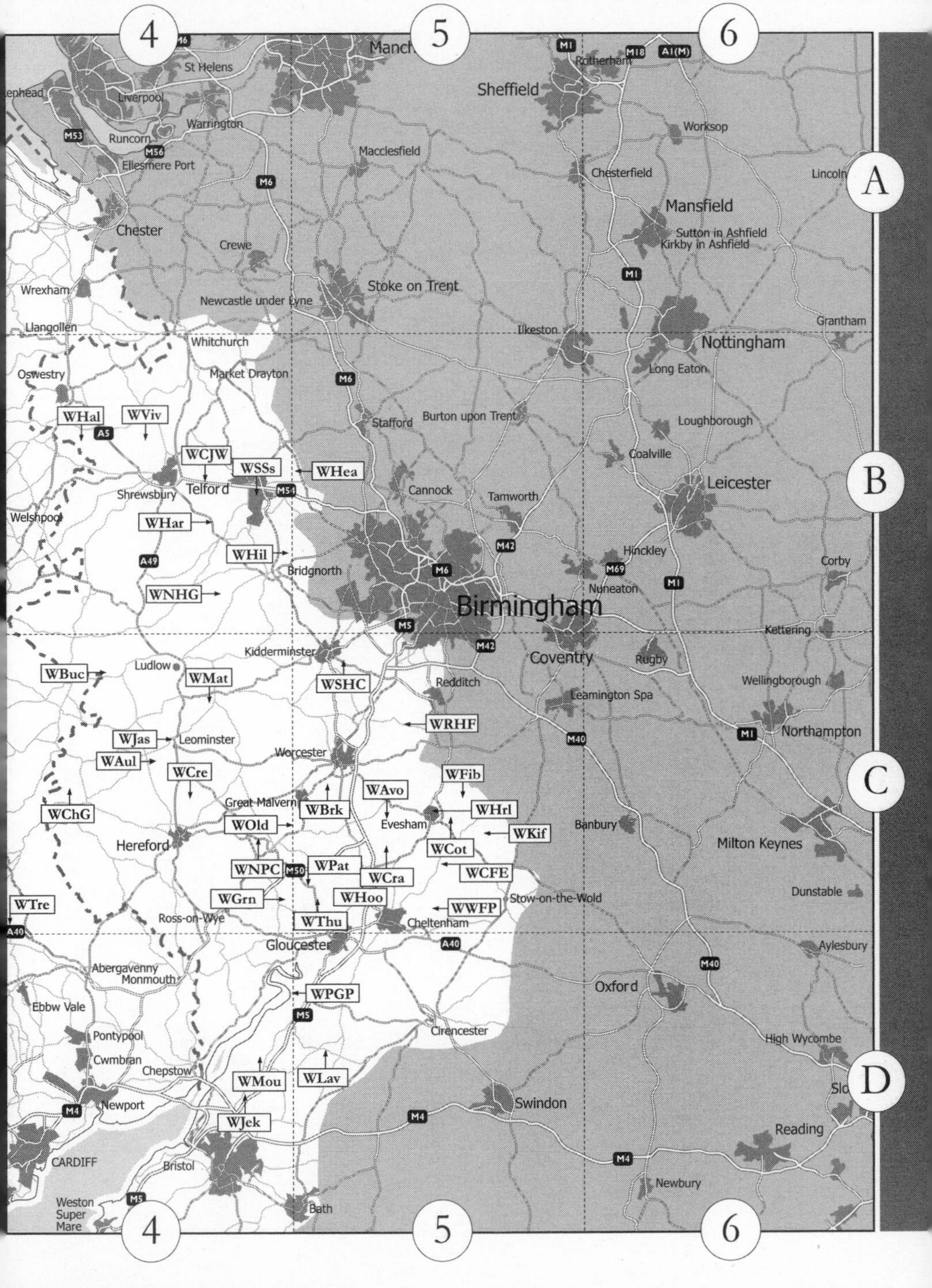
4
5
6
A
B
C
D
Manch
St Helens
enhead
Liverpool
Warrington
Runcorn
Ellesmere Port
Rotherham
Sheffield
Worksop
Macclesfield
Chesterfield
Lincoln
Mansfield
Sutton in Ashfield
Kirkby in Ashfield
Chester
Crewe
Stoke on Trent
Wrexham
Newcastle under Lyne
Llangollen
Ilkeston
Grantham
Whitchurch
Nottingham
Oswestry
Market Drayton
Long Eaton
Stafford
Burton upon Trent
Loughborough
Coalville
Shrewsbury
Telford
Leicester
Cannock
Tamworth
Welshpool
Hinckley
Bridgnorth
Corby
Nuneaton
Birmingham
Kettering
Kidderminster
Coventry
Ludlow
Rugby
Redditch
Wellingborough
Leamington Spa
Leominster
Northampton
Worcester
Great Malvern
Evesham
Banbury
Hereford
Milton Keynes
Stow-on-the-Wold
Dunstable
Ross-on-Wye
Cheltenham
Gloucester
Aylesbury
Abergavenny
Monmouth
Oxford
Ebbw Vale
Cirencester
Pontypool
High Wycombe
Cwmbran
Chepstow
Newport
Swindon
Slo
Reading
CARDIFF
Bristol
Newbury
Weston
Super
Mare
Bath
M6
M53
M56
M1
M18
A1(M)
A5
M54
A49
M42
M69
M5
M40
M50
A40
M4
WHal
WViv
WCJW
WSSs
WHea
WHar
WHil
WNHG
WBuc
WMat
WSHC
WRHF
WJas
WAul
WCre
WFib
WAvo
WChG
WBrk
WHrl
WOld
WKif
WCot
WNPC
WPat
WCra
WCFE
WGrn
WHoo
WWFP
WTre
WThu
WPGP
WMou
WLav
WJek

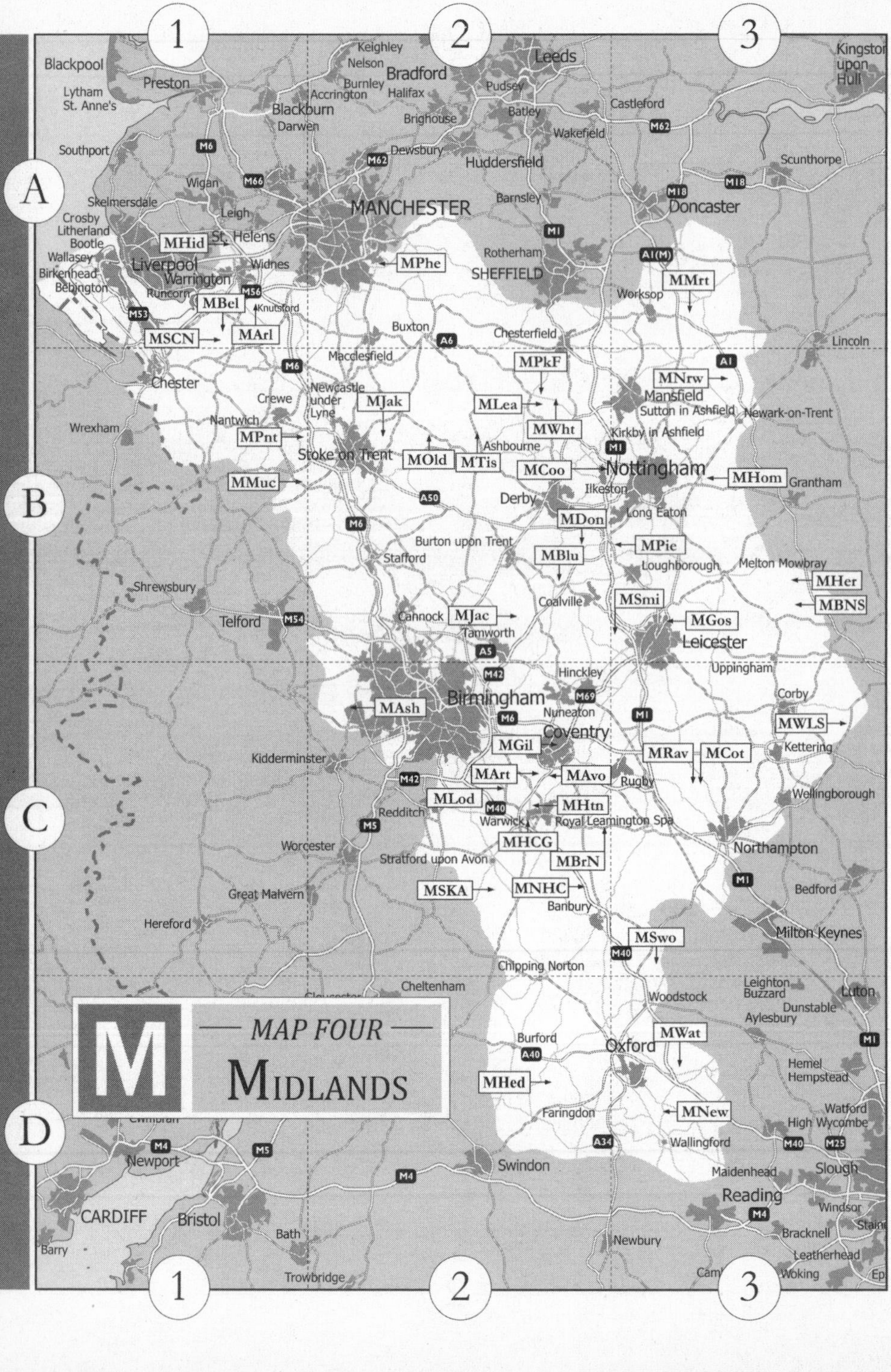
1
2
3
A
B
C
D
Blackpool
Preston
Lytham St. Anne's
Keighley
Nelson
Burnley
Bradford
Accrington
Halifax
Leeds
Pudsey
Batley
Castleford
Wakefield
Kingston upon Hull
Blackburn
Darwen
Brighouse
Southport
M6
Dewsbury
M62
Huddersfield
Scunthorpe
Wigan
M66
Skelmersdale
Leigh
MANCHESTER
Barnsley
M18
Doncaster
Crosby
Litherland
Bootle
Wallasey
Birkenhead
Bebington
MHid
St. Helens
Liverpool
Warrington
Widnes
Runcorn
M56
M53
MPhe
Rotherham
SHEFFIELD
M1
A1(M)
MMrt
Worksop
MBel
Knutsford
MSCN
MArl
Buxton
A6
Chesterfield
Lincoln
Chester
Macclesfield
MPkF
A1
MNrw
Crewe
Newcastle under Lyne
MJak
MLea
Mansfield
Sutton in Ashfield
Newark-on-Trent
Wrexham
Nantwich
MPnt
MWht
Kirkby in Ashfield
Ashbourne
Stoke on Trent
MOld
MTis
MCoo
Nottingham
MHom
Grantham
MMuc
Ilkeston
Derby
A50
MDon
Long Eaton
MPie
Burton upon Trent
Stafford
MBlu
Loughborough
Melton Mowbray
MHer
Shrewsbury
Coalville
MSmi
MBNS
Telford
M54
Cannock
MJac
MGos
Tamworth
Leicester
A5
M42
Hinckley
Uppingham
Birmingham
M69
Nuneaton
Corby
MAsh
M6
Coventry
MWLS
MGil
MRav
MCot
Kettering
Kidderminster
MArt
MAvo
Rugby
M42
MLod
M40
Wellingborough
Redditch
MHtn
Warwick
Royal Leamington Spa
M5
Worcester
MHCG
Northampton
Stratford upon Avon
MBrN
MSKA
MNHC
Bedford
Great Malvern
Banbury
Hereford
Milton Keynes
MSwo
M40
Chipping Norton
Cheltenham
Leighton Buzzard
Luton
Woodstock
Dunstable
Aylesbury
MWat
Burford
Oxford
A40
M1
Hemel Hempstead
MHed
Faringdon
MNew
Watford
High Wycombe
M4
M5
A34
Wallingford
M40
M25
Newport
Swindon
Maidenhead
Slough
M4
Reading
CARDIFF
Bristol
M4
Windsor
Bath
Bracknell
Barry
Newbury
Leatherhead
Trowbridge
Woking
M
MAP FOUR
MIDLANDS

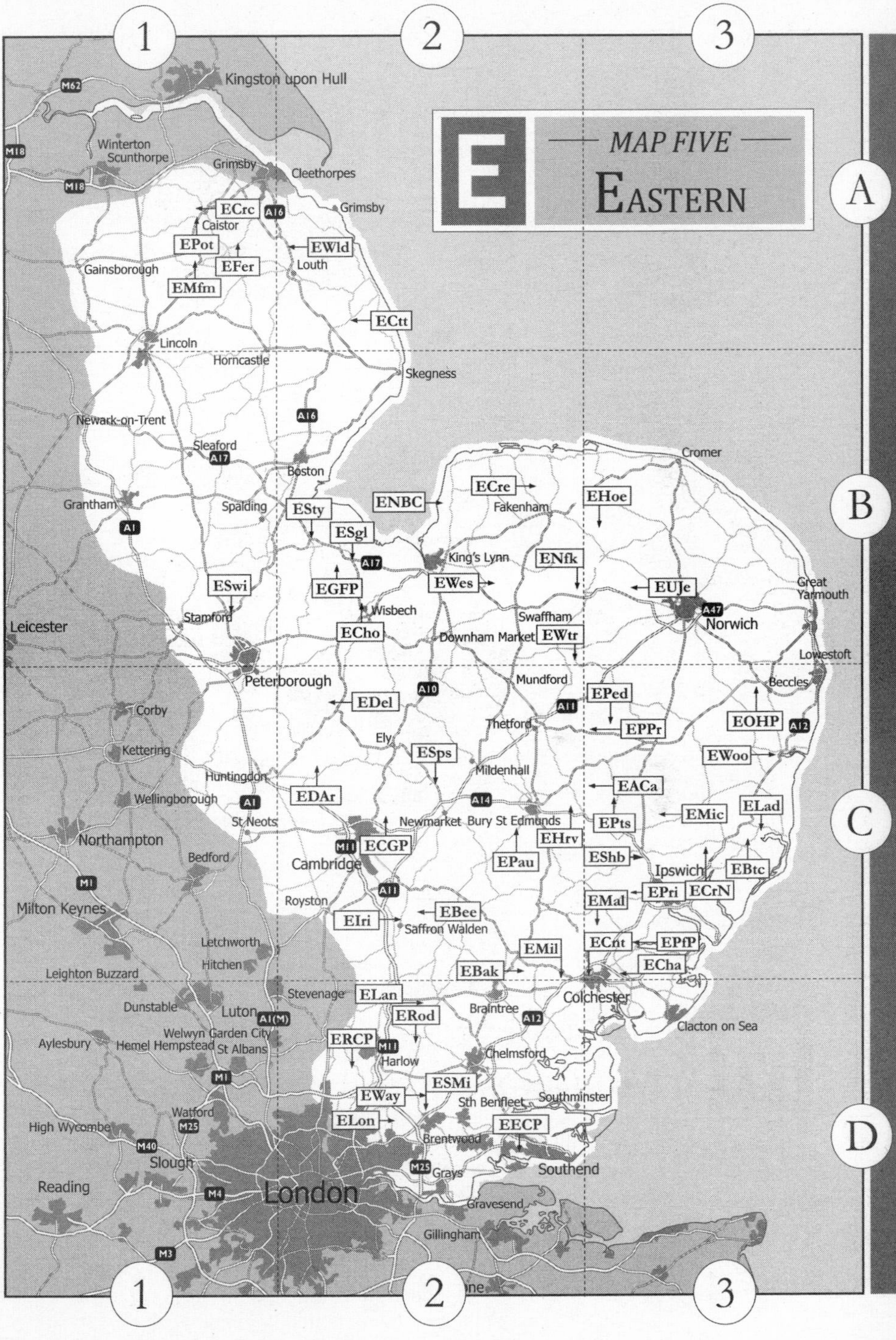
1
2
3
A
B
C
D
E
MAP FIVE
EASTERN
Kingston upon Hull
M62
M18
Winterton
Scunthorpe
Grimsby
Cleethorpes
Grimsby
ECrc
A16
Caistor
EPot
EWld
EFer
Louth
Gainsborough
EMfm
ECtt
Lincoln
Horncastle
Skegness
A16
Newark-on-Trent
Sleaford
A17
Boston
Cromer
ECre
EHoe
ENBC
Fakenham
Grantham
Spalding
ESty
A1
ESgl
A17
King's Lynn
ENfk
EGFP
EWes
EUJe
Great Yarmouth
ESwi
Wisbech
A47
Norwich
Stamford
Swaffham
Leicester
ECho
Downham Market
EWtr
Lowestoft
Mundford
Beccles
Peterborough
A10
EPed
EDel
A11
Corby
Thetford
EOHP
A12
EPPr
Ely
Kettering
ESps
EWoo
Mildenhall
Huntingdon
EACa
ELad
EDAr
A14
Wellingborough
A1
EMic
Newmarket
Bury St Edmunds
St Neots
EPts
Northampton
EHrv
Bedford
M11
ECGP
EShb
EPau
Ipswich
EBtc
Cambridge
M1
A11
EPri
ECrN
EMal
Royston
Milton Keynes
EBee
EIri
Saffron Walden
ECnt
EPfP
Letchworth
EMil
Hitchen
ECha
EBak
Leighton Buzzard
Stevenage
ELan
Colchester
Dunstable
Luton
A1(M)
Braintree
ERod
A12
Clacton on Sea
Welwyn Garden City
Aylesbury
Hemel Hempstead
St Albans
ERCP
M11
Harlow
Chelmsford
M1
ESMi
EWay
Watford
Sth Benfleet
Southminster
High Wycombe
M25
ELon
EECP
Brentwood
M40
Slough
M25
Grays
Southend
Reading
M4
London
Gravesend
Gillingham
M3

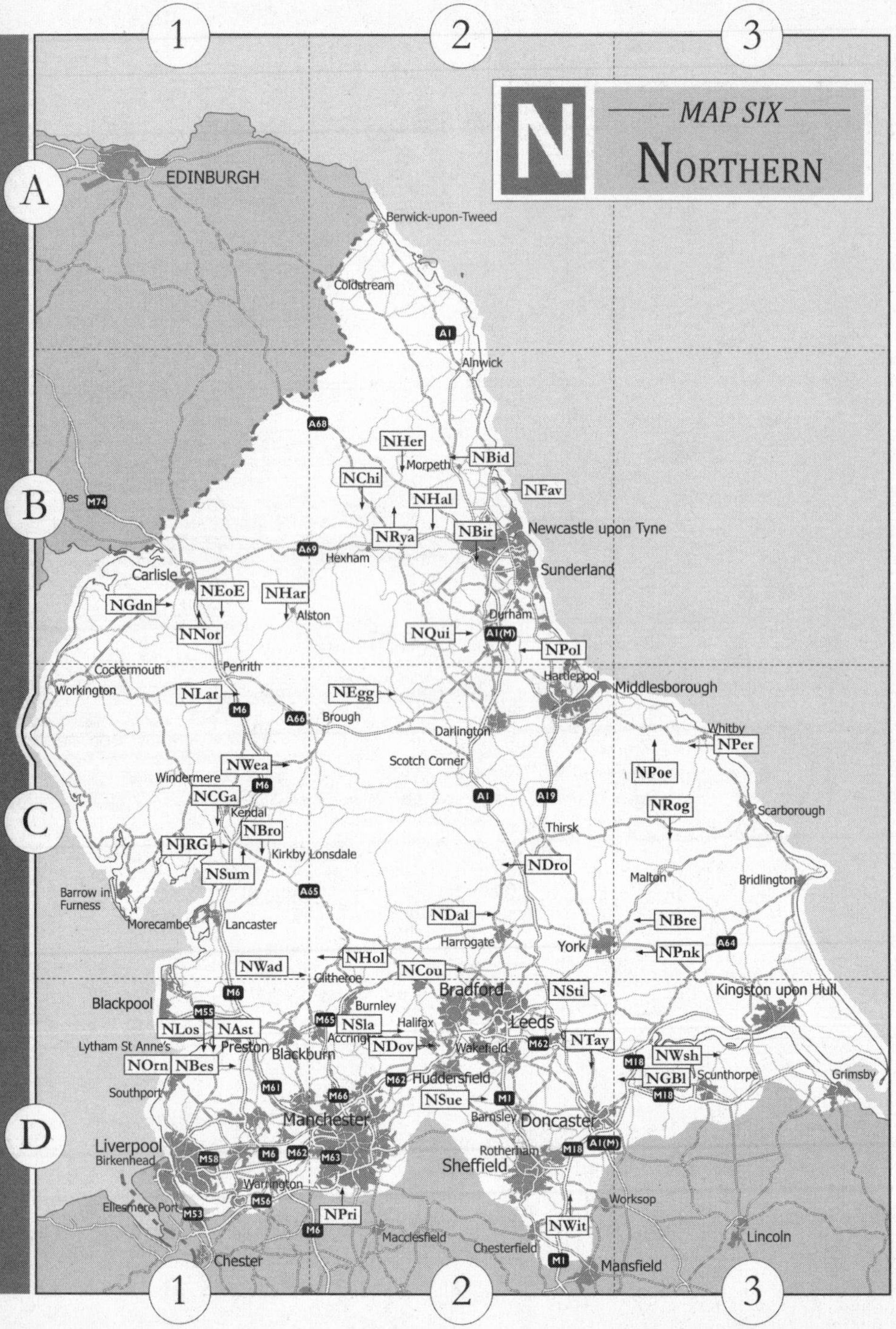
1
2
3
A
B
C
D
N
MAP SIX
NORTHERN
EDINBURGH
Berwick-upon-Tweed
Coldstream
A1
Alnwick
A68
NHer
Morpeth
NBid
NChi
NFav
NHal
M74
NRya
NBir
Newcastle upon Tyne
A69
Hexham
Sunderland
Carlisle
NEoE
NHar
NGdn
Alston
Durham
NNor
NQui
A1(M)
NPol
Cockermouth
Penrith
Hartlepool
Workington
NLar
NEgg
Middlesborough
M6
A66
Brough
Darlington
Whitby
NPer
Scotch Corner
NWea
NPoe
Windermere
M6
NCGa
A1
A19
NRog
Kendal
Scarborough
NBro
Thirsk
NJRG
Kirkby Lonsdale
NSum
NDro
Malton
Bridlington
Barrow in Furness
A65
NDal
NBre
Morecambe
Lancaster
Harrogate
York
A64
NPnk
NHol
NWad
Clitheroe
NCou
M6
Bradford
NSti
Kingston upon Hull
Blackpool
Burnley
M55
M65
NLos
NAst
NSla
Halifax
Leeds
Lytham St Anne's
Preston
Accrington
NDov
Wakefield
M62
NTay
Blackburn
M18
NWsh
NOrn
NBes
M62
Huddersfield
NGBl
Scunthorpe
Grimsby
M18
Southport
M61
M66
NSue
M1
Manchester
Barnsley
Doncaster
Liverpool
Birkenhead
M58
M6
M62
M63
Rotherham
M18
A1(M)
Sheffield
Warrington
Ellesmere Port
M53
M56
NPri
Worksop
M6
NWit
Macclesfield
Lincoln
Chesterfield
Chester
M1
Mansfield
1
2
3

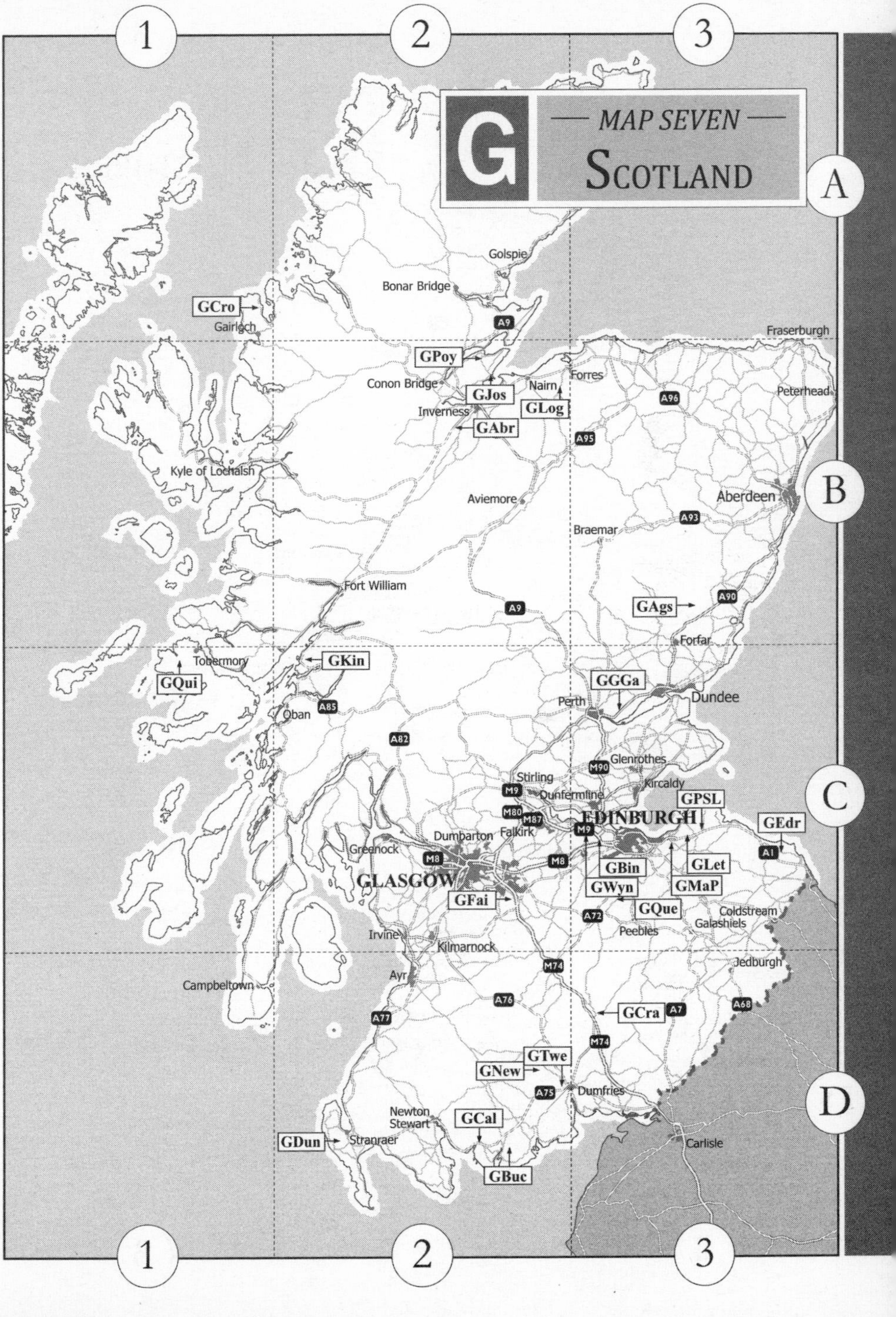
1
2
3
G
— MAP SEVEN —
SCOTLAND
A
B
C
D
Golspie
Bonar Bridge
GCro
Gairloch
A9
Fraserburgh
GPoy
Conon Bridge
GJos
Nairn
Forres
Inverness
GLog
A96
Peterhead
GAbr
A95
Kyle of Lochalsh
Aviemore
Aberdeen
A93
Braemar
Fort William
A9
GAgs
A90
Forfar
Tobermory
GKin
GQui
GGGa
Perth
Dundee
A85
Oban
A82
Glenrothes
M90
Stirling
Kircaldy
M9
Dunfermline
GPSL
M80
M87
EDINBURGH
GEdr
Dumbarton
Falkirk
M9
Greenock
A1
M8
M8
GBin
GLet
GLASGOW
GWyn
GMaP
GFai
GQue
Coldstream
A72
Galashiels
Peebles
Irvine
Kilmarnock
M74
Jedburgh
Ayr
Campbeltown
A76
GCra
A7
A68
A77
M74
GTwe
GNew
A75
Dumfries
Newton Stewart
GCal
GDun
Stranraer
Carlisle
GBuc

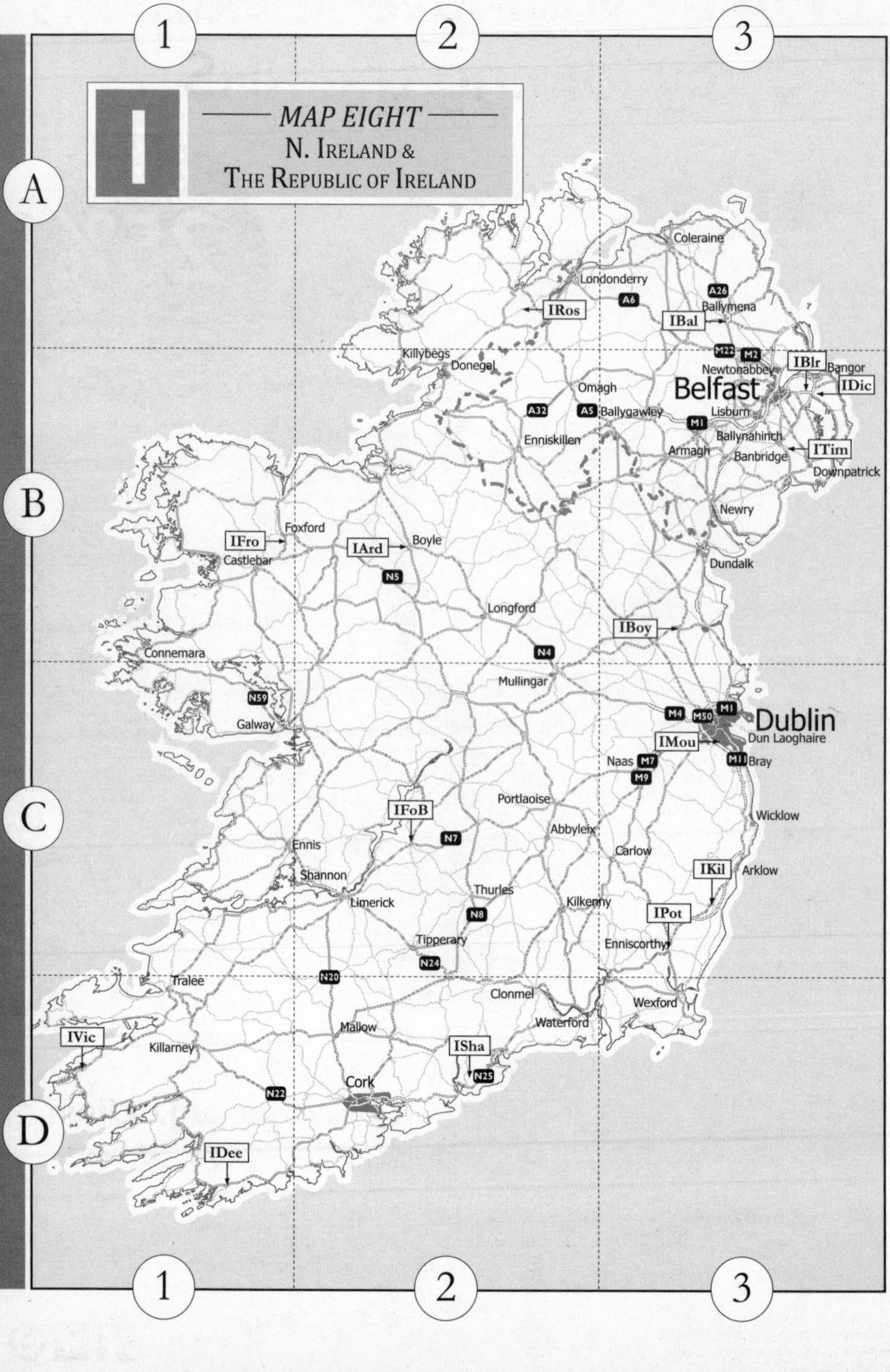
1
2
3
A
B
C
D
I
MAP EIGHT
N. IRELAND &
THE REPUBLIC OF IRELAND
Coleraine
Londonderry
A26
A6
Ballymena
IRos
IBal
Killybegs
Donegal
M22
M2
Newtonabbey
IBlr
Bangor
Belfast
IDic
Omagh
A32
A5
Ballygawley
Lisburn
M1
Enniskillen
Ballynahinch
Armagh
Banbridge
ITim
Downpatrick
Newry
Foxford
IFro
IArd
Boyle
Castlebar
Dundalk
N5
Longford
IBoy
N4
Connemara
Mullingar
N59
M4
M50
M1
Dublin
Galway
IMou
Dun Laoghaire
Naas
M7
M11
Bray
M9
Portlaoise
IFoB
Wicklow
Abbyleix
N7
Ennis
Carlow
IKil
Arklow
Shannon
Thurles
Kilkenny
Limerick
IPot
N8
Tipperary
Enniscorthy
N24
N20
Tralee
Clonmel
Wexford
Mallow
Waterford
IVic
ISha
Killarney
N25
Cork
N22
IDee

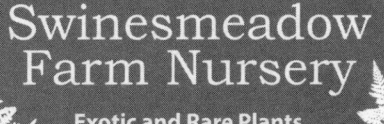

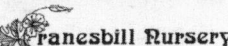

INDEX OF ADVERTISERS